List of Elements with Their Symbols and Atomic Masses

Element	Symbol	Atomic Number	Atomic Mass	Element	Symbol	Atomic Number	Atomic Mass
Actinium	Ac	89	227.03[a]	Mendelevium	Md	101	258.10[a]
Aluminum	Al	13	26.98	Mercury	Hg	80	200.59
Americium	Am	95	243.06[a]	Molybdenum	Mo	42	95.96
Antimony	Sb	51	121.76	Neodymium	Nd	60	144.24
Argon	Ar	18	39.95	Neon	Ne	10	20.18
Arsenic	As	33	74.92	Neptunium	Np	93	237.05[a]
Astatine	At	85	209.99[a]	Nickel	Ni	28	58.69
Barium	Ba	56	137.33	Niobium	Nb	41	92.91
Berkelium	Bk	97	247.07[a]	Nitrogen	N	7	14.01
Beryllium	Be	4	9.012	Nobelium	No	102	259.10[a]
Bismuth	Bi	83	208.98	Osmium	Os	76	190.23
Bohrium	Bh	107	264.12[a]	Oxygen	O	8	16.00
Boron	B	5	10.81	Palladium	Pd	46	106.42
Bromine	Br	35	79.90	Phosphorus	P	15	30.97
Cadmium	Cd	48	112.41	Platinum	Pt	78	195.08
Calcium	Ca	20	40.08	Plutonium	Pu	94	244.06[a]
Californium	Cf	98	251.08[a]	Polonium	Po	84	208.98[a]
Carbon	C	6	12.01	Potassium	K	19	39.10
Cerium	Ce	58	140.12	Praseodymium	Pr	59	140.91
Cesium	Cs	55	132.91	Promethium	Pm	61	145[a]
Chlorine	Cl	17	35.45	Protactinium	Pa	91	231.04
Chromium	Cr	24	52.00	Radium	Ra	88	226.03[a]
Cobalt	Co	27	58.93	Radon	Rn	86	222.02[a]
Copernicium	Cn	112	277[a]	Rhenium	Re	75	186.21
Copper	Cu	29	63.55	Rhodium	Rh	45	102.91
Curium	Cm	96	247.07[a]	Roentgenium	Rg	111	272[a]
Darmstadtium	Ds	110	271[a]	Rubidium	Rb	37	85.47
Dubnium	Db	105	262.11[a]	Ruthenium	Ru	44	101.07
Dysprosium	Dy	66	162.50	Rutherfordium	Rf	104	261.11[a]
Einsteinium	Es	99	252.08[a]	Samarium	Sm	62	150.36
Erbium	Er	68	167.26	Scandium	Sc	21	44.96
Europium	Eu	63	151.96	Seaborgium	Sg	106	266.12[a]
Fermium	Fm	100	257.10[a]	Selenium	Se	34	78.96
Flerovium	Fl	114	289[a]	Silicon	Si	14	28.09
Fluorine	F	9	19.00	Silver	Ag	47	107.87
Francium	Fr	87	223.02[a]	Sodium	Na	11	22.99
Gadolinium	Gd	64	157.25	Strontium	Sr	38	87.62
Gallium	Ga	31	69.72	Sulfur	S	16	32.07
Germanium	Ge	32	72.64	Tantalum	Ta	73	180.95
Gold	Au	79	196.97	Technetium	Tc	43	98[a]
Hafnium	Hf	72	178.49	Tellurium	Te	52	127.60
Hassium	Hs	108	269.13[a]	Terbium	Tb	65	158.93
Helium	He	2	4.003	Thallium	Tl	81	204.38
Holmium	Ho	67	164.93	Thorium	Th	90	232.04
Hydrogen	H	1	1.008	Thulium	Tm	69	168.93
Indium	In	49	114.82	Tin	Sn	50	118.71
Iodine	I	53	126.90	Titanium	Ti	22	47.87
Iridium	Ir	77	192.22	Tungsten	W	74	183.84
Iron	Fe	26	55.85	Uranium	U	92	238.03
Krypton	Kr	36	83.80	Ununoctium	Uuo	118	294
Lanthanum	La	57	138.91	Ununpentium	Uup	115	289
Lawrencium	Lr	103	262.11[a]	Ununseptium	Uus	117	294
Lead	Pb	82	207.2	Ununtrium	Uut	113	284
Lithium	Li	3	6.941	Vanadium	V	23	50.94
Livermorium	Lv	116	292[a]	Xenon	Xe	54	131.293
Lutetium	Lu	71	174.97	Ytterbium	Yb	70	173.05
Magnesium	Mg	12	24.31	Yttrium	Y	39	88.91
Manganese	Mn	25	54.94	Zinc	Zn	30	65.38
Meitnerium	Mt	109	268.14[a]	Zirconium	Zr	40	91.22

[a]Mass of longest-lived or most important isotope.

CHEMISTRY

A MOLECULAR APPROACH

CHEMISTRY

A MOLECULAR APPROACH

NIVALDO J. TRO
Westmont College

TRAVIS D. FRIDGEN
Memorial University of Newfoundland

LAWTON E. SHAW
Athabasca University

SECOND CANADIAN EDITION

With special contributions by
ROBERT S. BOIKESS

PEARSON

Toronto

Editorial Director: Claudine O'Donnell
Executive Acquisitions Editor: Cathleen Sullivan
Senior Marketing Manager: Kimberly Teska
Program Manager: Darryl Kamo
Project Manager: Jessica Hellen
Developmental Editor: Martina van de Velde
Media Editor: Daniella Balabuk
Media Developer: Bogdan Kosenko
Production Services: S4Carlisle Publishing Services
Permissions Project Manager: Kathryn O'Handley and Alison Derry
Photo Permissions Research: Carly Bergey
Text Permissions Research: Liz Kincaid
Cover and Interior Designer: Anthony Leung
Cover Image: Graham Johnson PhD with Megan Riel-Mehan PhD of GrahamJ Medical Media and the Mesoscope Lab at the University of California, San Francisco.

Vice-President, Cross Media and Publishing Services: Gary Bennett

Credits and acknowledgments for material borrowed from other sources and reproduced, with permission, in this textbook appear on the appropriate page within the text [or on page C-1].

5 17

Library and Archives Canada Cataloguing in Publication

Tro, Nivaldo J., author
Chemistry : a molecular approach / Nivaldo J. Tro, Travis Fridgen, Lawton E. Shaw. —Second Canadian edition.

ISBN 978-0-13-398656-3 (bound)

1. Chemistry, Physical and theoretical—Textbooks. I. Fridgen, Travis D. (Travis David), 1970-, author II. Shaw, Lawton, 1972-, author III. Title.

QD453.3.T76 2015 541 C2015-907432-0

ISBN 978-0-13-398656-3

To Michael, Ali, Kyle, and Kaden
—Nivaldo Tro

To Cailyn, Carter, Colton, and Chloe
—Travis Fridgen

To Calvin, Nathan, Alexis, and Andrew
—Lawton Shaw

About the Authors

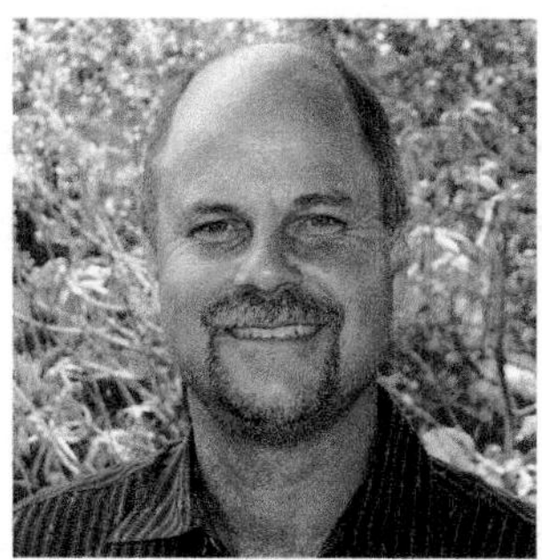

Nivaldo Tro is a Professor of Chemistry at Westmont College in Santa Barbara, California, where he has been a faculty member since 1990. He received his Ph.D. in chemistry from Stanford University for work on developing and using optical techniques to study the adsorption and desorption of molecules to and from surfaces in ultrahigh vacuum. He then went on to the University of California at Berkeley, where he did postdoctoral research on ultrafast reaction dynamics in solution. Since coming to Westmont, Professor Tro has been awarded grants from the American Chemical Society Petroleum Research Fund, from Research Corporation, and from the National Science Foundation to study the dynamics of various processes occurring in thin adlayer films adsorbed on dielectric surfaces. He has been honoured as Westmont's outstanding teacher of the year three times and has also received the college's outstanding researcher of the year award. Professor Tro lives in Santa Barbara with his wife, Ann, and their four children, Michael, Ali, Kyle, and Kaden. In his leisure time, Professor Tro enjoys mountain biking, surfing, reading to his children, and being outdoors with his family.

Travis Fridgen is currently Professor and Head in the Department of Chemistry at Memorial University of Newfoundland in St. John's, Newfoundland and Labrador. His research group studies the energetics, reactions, and structures of gaseous ion self-assembled complexes composed of metal ions and biologically relevant molecules such as DNA bases, amino acids, and peptides using a combination of mass spectrometry, tunable infrared lasers, and computational chemistry. Their research is aimed at answering fundamental questions such as why K^+ is associated with guanine quadruplexes such as telomeric DNA. He graduated with a B.Sc. (Hons) in chemistry from Trent University and a B.Ed. from Queen's University. His Ph.D. in physical chemistry is from Trent and Queen's Universities, where he studied the spectroscopy of reactive species in a cryogenic matrix environment. During his postdoctoral fellowship at the University of Waterloo, he first began conducting research using mass spectrometric methods. During a brief period as an assistant professor at Wilfrid Laurier University, he initiated a collaboration with a group of researchers from France to spectroscopically determine structures of gas phase proton-bound dimer ions. He teaches courses in physical chemistry, but he has mostly taught first-year chemistry courses (at Trent, Waterloo, Laurier, and Memorial). He lives in Mount Pearl, Newfoundland and Labrador, with his wife, Lisa, and four children, Cailyn, Carter, Colton, and Chloe. They are all avid fans of the Ottawa Senators and enjoy busy, active lives that include outdoor activities such as shovelling snow (good old Newfoundland).

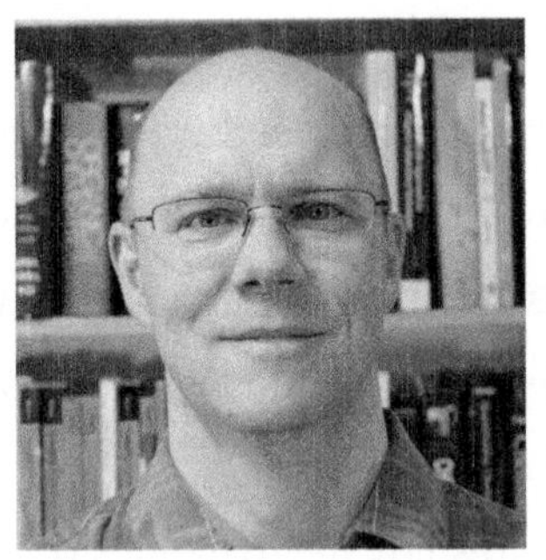

Lawton Shaw received his Ph.D. in chemistry from the University of Calgary, in the area of photochemical reaction mechanisms of organometallic complexes. Shortly after graduating, he joined the full-time teaching faculty at Mount Royal College in Calgary, where he developed one of the first science courses at Mount Royal delivered partially online. This work led to a serious interest in online and distance education. In 2005, he joined the Centre for Science at Athabasca University, where he teaches and coordinates distance-delivered chemistry courses. This experience led to the book *Accessible Elements: Teaching Science Online and at a Distance,* which he co-edited. His research interests are split between the realms of teaching/education and environmental chemistry. He studies the effects of pharmaceuticals and personal care products on biofilms in freshwater ecosystems. He is a former president of College Chemistry Canada. He lives in St. Albert, Alberta, with his wife, Tanya, and their four children. Their family leisure time is filled with activities such as cross-country skiing, swimming, and camping.

Brief Contents

Contents

4 Chemical Reactions and Stoichiometry 101

5 Gases 149

6 Thermochemistry 197

Preface

To the Student

As you begin this course, think about your reasons for enrolling in it. Why are you taking general chemistry? Why are you pursuing a university or college education at all? If you are like most students taking general chemistry, part of your answer is probably that this course is required for your major or you are pursuing your education so that you can get a job some day. Although these are both good reasons, we think there is a better one. The primary reason for an education is to prepare you to *live a good life*. You should understand chemistry—not for what it can *get* you—but for what it can *do* for you. Understanding chemistry is an important source of happiness and fulfillment.

Understanding chemistry helps you to live life to its fullest for two basic reasons. The first is *intrinsic*: through an understanding of chemistry, you gain a powerful appreciation for just how rich and extraordinary the world really is. For example, one of the most important ideas in science is that **the behaviour of matter is determined by the properties of molecules and atoms**. With this knowledge, we have been able to study the substances that compose the world around us and explain their behaviour by reference to particles so small that they can hardly be imagined. If you have never realized the remarkable sensitivity of the world we *can* see to the world we *cannot,* you have missed out on a fundamental truth about our universe. The second reason is *extrinsic*: understanding chemistry makes you a more informed citizen—it allows you to engage with many of the issues of our day. Scientific literacy helps you understand and discuss in a meaningful way important issues from the development of the oil sands in Alberta (Chapter 6) to how the production of pharmaceuticals and personal care products affects our environment and our bodies (Chapter 12). In other words, understanding chemistry makes *you* a deeper and richer person and makes your country and the world a better place to live. These reasons have been the foundation of education from the very beginnings of civilization.

So this is why we think you should take this course and why we wish you the best as you embark on the journey to understand the world around you at the molecular level. The rewards are well worth the effort.

The Strengths of *Chemistry: A Molecular Approach*

Chemistry: A Molecular Approach is first and foremost a *student-oriented book*. The main goal of the book is to motivate students and get them to achieve at the highest possible level. As we all know, many students take general chemistry because it is a requirement; they do not see the connection between chemistry and their lives or their intended careers. *Chemistry: A Molecular Approach* strives to make those connections consistently and effectively. Unlike other books, which often teach chemistry as something that happens only in the laboratory or in industry, this book teaches chemistry in the context of relevance. It shows students *why* chemistry is important to them, to their future careers, and to their world.

Second, *Chemistry: A Molecular Approach* is a *pedagogically driven book*. In seeking to develop problem-solving skills, a consistent approach is applied (Sort, Strategize, Solve, and Check), usually in a two- or three-column format. In the two-column format, the left column shows the student how to analyze the problem and devise a solution strategy. It also lists the steps of the solution and explains the rationale for each one, while the right column shows the implementation of each step. In the three-column format, the left column outlines the general procedure for solving an important category of problems that is then applied to two side-by-side examples. This strategy allows students to see both the general pattern and the slightly different ways in which the procedure may be applied in differing contexts. The aim is to help students understand both the *concept of the problem* (through the formulation of an explicit conceptual plan for each problem) and the *solution to the problem.*

Third, *Chemistry: A Molecular Approach* is a *visual book.* Wherever possible, images are used to deepen the student's insight into chemistry. In developing chemical principles, multipart images help to show the connection between everyday processes visible to the unaided eye and what atoms and molecules are actually doing. Many of these images have three parts: macroscopic, molecular, and symbolic. This combination helps students to see the relationships between the formulas they write down on paper (symbolic), the world they see around them (macroscopic), and the atoms and molecules that compose that world (molecular). In addition, most figures are designed to teach rather than just to illustrate. They include annotations and labels intended to help the student grasp the most important processes and the principles that underlie them. The resulting images are rich with information but also uncommonly clear and quickly understood.

Fourth, *Chemistry: A Molecular Approach* is a *"big picture" book.* At the beginning of each chapter, a short paragraph helps students to see the key relationships between the different topics they are learning. A focused and concise narrative helps make the basic ideas of every chapter clear to the student. Interim summaries are provided at selected spots in the narrative, making it easier to grasp (and review) the main points of important discussions. And to make sure that students never lose sight of the forest for the trees, each chapter includes several *Conceptual Connections,* which ask them to think about concepts and solve problems without doing any math. The idea is for students to learn the concepts, not just plug numbers into equations to churn out the right answer.

Finally, *Chemistry: A Molecular Approach* is a book that delivers the depth of coverage faculty want and students need. We do not have to cut corners and water down the material in order to get our students interested. We simply have to meet them where they are, challenge them to the highest level of achievement, and then support them with enough pedagogy to allow them to succeed.

The Canadian Edition

Chemistry: A Molecular Approach, by Nivaldo J. Tro, is widely used in general chemistry courses at colleges and universities across North America. So, why do we need a Canadian edition? The short answer is that general chemistry courses in Canada are different from those in the United States. First-year chemistry curricula in Canada are generally at a higher level than what is seen south of the border. There is a need for a strong chemistry textbook that serves Canadian general chemistry courses.

The Canadian adaptation of *Chemistry: A Molecular Approach* drew very heavily on feedback from professors and instructors across Canada. As the Canadian authors, we took the reviews and consultations very seriously and did our best to adapt Tro's textbook accordingly. In general terms, the adaptation involved making the following changes.

International Conventions on Units, Symbols, and Nomenclature The field of chemistry is communicated according to conventions that are determined by the broader international chemistry community, through the International Union of Pure and Applied Chemistry (IUPAC). IUPAC continually releases recommendations on chemical nomenclature, definitions, symbols, and units. IUPAC recommendations are not static; they may evolve over time as new information comes to light. Although many textbooks state that they follow the recommendations of the IUPAC, you will find that the Canadian edition of *Chemistry: A Molecular Approach* scrupulously follows IUPAC recommendations for chemical names and symbols, nomenclature, and conventions for symbols and units in measurements. In the case of chemical nomenclature, there are a number of non-IUPAC chemical names that are so common that we have to include them along with the IUPAC recommended name.

S.I. units of measurement are used exclusively. Imperial units such as the gallon, pound, and the Fahrenheit scale of temperature have not been used in modern science for over a generation. IUPAC recommended defining standard pressure as 1 bar (or 100 kPa) back in 1982. This is the standard that has been adopted by chemists worldwide and is almost exclusive in second-year physical chemistry texts. Only in first-year textbooks does the atmosphere still linger as standard pressure. In this text, standard pressure is the IUPAC-recommended bar. Students will see pressure in various units, but we make little use of the atmosphere. When dealing with ideal gases, the most common value of R is 0.08314 L bar mol^{-1} K^{-1}.

In thermodynamics, we have adopted the recommended notation for enthalpy, entropy, and Gibbs energy changes, placing subscripts for changes after the delta sign rather than after H, S, or G. For example, the standard reaction enthalpy is expressed as $\Delta_r H^\circ$ rather than ΔH°_{rxn}. This is a subtle change that matters. The type of change (Δ) is marked on the Δ symbol (reaction, Δ_r; formation, Δ_f; and so on), rather than the type of thermodynamic quantity. We understand that this notation is not used everywhere. However, we believe that students should use standard notation throughout their education. Students who continue in chemistry or other sciences will eventually come across the standard notation in physical chemistry textbooks and in places like the *CRC Handbook of Chemistry and Physics* and the NIST Chemistry Webbook (http://webbook.nist.gov/). Furthermore, thermodynamic quantities like $\Delta_r H^\circ$ are always molar quantities and have the units kJ mol^{-1}, as recommended by IUPAC. Exclusive use of IUPAC-recommended units keeps students from getting into unit troubles when doing thermodynamic calculations.

Explicitly, we have provided the distinctions and connections between the unitless thermodynamic equilibrium constant, K_{eq} or simply K, and the phenomenological equilibrium constants, K_c and K_P, which can have units in terms of concentration and pressure, respectively, again in accordance with IUPAC recommendations. This is done in the most basic of terms, assuming that gases and solutions are ideal so that their partial pressures and concentrations are assumed to be numerically equivalent to their activities, setting up for a more rigorous treatment in second-year analytical and physical chemistry courses.

Following recommendations set out by the IUPAC ensures that we speak a common language—and teach a common language. Otherwise, students who go on in chemistry have to convert from the language learned in first year as soon as the very next year, when they take their first physical chemistry course.

Current Theories We have updated the text so that the most current, consensus scientific view is described. This is most notable in the case of bonding theory and the so-called expanded octet. In this case, evidence shows that the d orbitals have a negligible contribution to bonding, which means that full sp^3d and sp^3d^2 hybridizations should no longer be included in bonding theories, even though this idea continues to appear in general chemistry textbooks. This Canadian edition reflects the most current understanding of chemical phenomenon, at the first-year level.

Organic Chemistry The coverage of organic chemistry has been expanded to two chapters, reflecting the curricula in many Canadian universities, which provide additional organic chemistry coverage in first-year chemistry. The first organic chemistry chapter covers structure and bonding, stereochemistry, and structure determination. The second chapter covers organic reactivity, and it is organized according to reaction mechanisms.

Canadian Context Naturally, a Canadian edition will include Canadian examples. In some places, the Canadian content is fun, like the hockey goalie's "Quantum mechanical five hole" in Chapter 7. In other places, Canadian chemistry examples are serious and important, like the chemistry of the oil sands. Wherever Canadian content appears in this edition, it is there to promote student engagement. This book is meant for the Canadian student.

End-of-Chapter Problems One of the first things that professors consider when choosing a chemistry textbook is the quality of end-of-chapter problems. This is because, to learn chemistry, students need to work through meaningful exercises and problems. Tro's *Chemistry: A Molecular Approach* has extensive, high-quality problems.

First-year chemistry courses are perhaps the most important courses in chemistry programs, because they lay the foundation for all higher level courses. First-year courses introduce students to the language and discipline of chemistry, and some concepts are not touched on again in the entire undergraduate curriculum. Indeed, many Ph.D. comprehensive questions fall back to ideas learned in first year. This book was prepared with the full undergraduate curriculum in mind. If you are a student, we hope that the Canadian edition of *Chemistry: A Molecular Approach* helps you succeed in chemistry. We encourage you to make use of all of the features in this book that are designed to help you learn. If you are a professor, it is our hope that this textbook provides you with the strong content you need to teach first-year chemistry in a way that is true to our discipline.

Second Canadian Edition

For the second Canadian edition, our goal was to fine-tune the content from the first Canadian edition and ensure the concepts presented are in alignment with current, accepted theories. We also replaced or updated a number of the "Chemistry in Your Day" boxes to bring them up to date and add context for students. We have also added numerous electrostatic potential maps throughout the text to give students a visual aid to better understand chemical concepts related to electrostatic forces. Some of the substantial changes are described below.

Some material has been moved. For example, balancing redox equations has been moved from Chapter 18 (Electrochemistry) to Chapter 4 (Chemical Reactions and Stoichiometry); Chapter 9 (Chemical Bonding I: Lewis Theory) has been rearranged to make the content flow better for students.

In Chapter 7 (The Quantum Mechanical Model of the Atom), we revised and expanded the section on electron configurations to bring it in line with current literature, especially in regard to the transition metals. These changes should clear up some of the misconceptions that arise when students learn the *Aufbau* principle.

Chapter 10 (Chemical Bonding II: Molecular Shapes, Valance Bond Theory, and Molecular Orbital Theory) includes a section on larger conjugated systems as well as conductors, semiconductors, and insulators, which we feel is important for students who continue in chemistry. The molecular orbital diagrams in this chapter have also been updated, providing more "realistic" visual representations.

In Chapter 17 (Gibbs Energy and Thermodynamics), we added a more rigorous and chemically-relevant description of entropy and microstates which will benefit every student who continues in chemistry and other sciences.

Supplements

For the Instructor

MasteringChemistry® is the best adaptive-learning online homework and tutorial system. Instructors can create online assignments for their students by choosing from a wide range of items, including end-of-chapter problems and research-enhanced tutorials. Assignments are automatically graded with up-to-date diagnostic information, helping instructors pinpoint where students struggle either individually or as a class as a whole.

Instructor resources are password protected and available for download from the Pearson online catalogue at http://catalogue.pearsoned.ca/.

Instructor's Solutions Manual This manual contains step-by-step solutions to all complete, end-of-chapter exercises. The Instructor's Solutions Manual to accompany the second Canadian edition has been extensively revised and checked for accuracy. The Instructor's Solutions Manual can be downloaded from the online catalogue.

Instructor's Resource Manual Organized by chapter, this useful guide includes objectives, lecture outlines, and references to figures and solved problems, as well as teaching tips. The Instructor's Resource Manual can be downloaded from the online catalogue.

Computerized Test Bank Pearson's computerized test banks allow instructors to filter and select questions to create quizzes, tests or homework. Instructors can revise questions or add their own, and may be able to choose print or online options. These questions are also available in Microsoft Word format.

PowerPoint® Presentations PowerPoint® lecture slides provide an outline to use in a lecture setting, presenting definitions, key concepts, and figures from the textbook. The textbook's worked examples and a selection of practice problems are also provided in PowerPoint® format. These PowerPoint® slides can be downloaded from the online catalogue.

Questions for Classroom Response Systems Another set of PowerPoint® slides provide sample exercises and questions to be used with Classroom Response Systems. These questions can be downloaded from the online catalogue.

Image Libraries All images, figures, and tables in the textbook are provided in PowerPoint® format. The images, figures, and tables are also available in a separate image library in jpeg or gif format. The Image Libraries are available through the online catalogue.

Learning Solutions Managers Pearson's Learning Solutions Managers work with faculty and campus course designers to ensure that Pearson technology products, assessment tools, and online course materials are tailored to meet your specific needs. This highly qualified team is dedicated to helping schools take full advantage of a wide range of educational resources, by assisting in the integration of a variety of instructional materials and media formats. Your local Pearson Sales Representative can provide you with more details on this service program.

For the Student

MasteringChemistry® provides you with two learning systems: an extensive self-study area with an interactive eBook and the most widely used chemistry homework and tutorial system (if your instructor chooses to make online assignments part of your course).

Mastering with Knewton Adaptive Learning Knewton provides personalized recommendations on what to study next—helping students work more effectively in and out of class. The Knewton award-winning Adaptive Learning Platform uses proprietary algorithms to deliver a personalized learning path for each student, each day. Knewton's technology identifies each student's strengths, weaknesses, and unique learning style. Taking into account both personal proficiencies and course requirements, the platform continuously tailors learning materials to each student's exact needs, delivering the most relevant content in the most efficient and effective form.

Learning Catalytics Learning Catalytics is a "bring your own device" student engagement, assessment, and classroom intelligence system. With Learning Catalytics, you can:

- Assess students in real time, using open-ended tasks to probe student understanding.
- Understand immediately where students are and adjust your lecture accordingly.
- Improve your students' critical-thinking skills.
- Access rich analytics to understand student performance.
- Add your own questions to make Learning Catalytics fit your course exactly.
- Manage student interactions with intelligent grouping and timing.

Learning Catalytics is a technology that has grown out of 20 years of cutting-edge research, innovation, and implementation of interactive teaching and peer instruction. Available integrated with MasteringChemistry.

Pearson eText The Pearson eText gives students access to their textbook anytime, anywhere. In addition to note taking, highlighting, and bookmarking, the Pearson eText offers interactive and sharing features. Instructors can share their comments or highlights, and students can add their own, creating a tight community of learners within the class.

NEW!

- Now available on smartphones and tablets.
- Accessible (screen-reader ready).
- Configurable reading settings, including resizable type and night reading mode.
- Instructor and student note-taking, highlighting, bookmarking, and search.

Selected Solutions Manual This manual for students contains complete, step-by-step solutions to selected odd-numbered end-of-chapter problems. The Selected Solutions Manual to accompany the second Canadian edition has been extensively revised, with all problems checked for accuracy.

During the development of this book, we obtained many helpful suggestions and comments from colleagues from across the country. We sincerely thank the following instructors who were members of our Chemistry Advisory Board for this edition:

Phil Dutton, *University of Windsor*
Noel George, *Ryerson University*
Krystyna Koczanski, *University of Manitoba*
Andrew McWilliams, *Ryerson University*
Andrew Vreugdenhil, *Trent University*

We acknowledge Prof. Dietmar Kennepohl (Athabasca University) and Dr. Nicole Sandblom (University of Calgary), Dr. Neil Anderson (Onyx Pharmaceuticals), Drs. Chris Flinn, Bob Helleur, Karen Hattenhauer, Peter Warburton, and Chris Kozak, (Memorial University), Mr. Nicholas Ryan (Memorial University), and Drs. Lucio Gelmini and Robert Hilts (MacEwan University) for helpful discussions and insightful comments.

Dr. Ian Hunt of the University of Calgary worked with us in the early development of the organic chemistry chapters. He provided sage advice on the organization of these chapters and made numerous suggestions on how to present organic chemistry in a way that is both rigorous and accessible to the first-year student.

Professor François Caron of Laurentian University provided expert advice on revisions to Chapter 19, improving the presentation of nuclear reaction energetics so that it is consistent with the field of nuclear chemistry.

We would like to thank our wives Lisa and Tanya for their encouragement and their continuing patience during all the evenings and weekends we spent working on this book when we could have been with our families.

Finally, we would also like to acknowledge the assistance of the many members of the team at Pearson Canada who were involved throughout the writing and production process: Cathleen Sullivan, Executive Acquisitions Editor; Kim Teska, Senior Marketing Manager; Darryl Kamo, Program Manager; Martina van de Velde, Developmental Editor; Jessica Hellen, Project Manager; Anthony Leung, Senior Designer.

Travis D. Fridgen
Lawton E. Shaw

Relevant examples and clear language

Chemistry is relevant to every process occurring around you, at every second. The authors help you understand this connection by weaving specific, vivid examples throughout the text that tell the story of chemistry. Every chapter begins with a brief story that illustrates how chemistry is relevant to all people, at every moment.

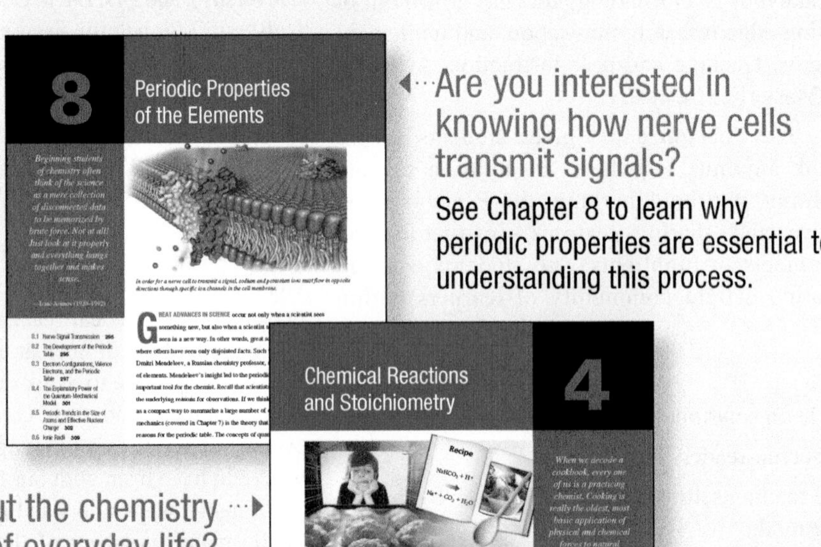

Are you interested in knowing how nerve cells transmit signals?

See Chapter 8 to learn why periodic properties are essential to understanding this process.

What about the chemistry of everyday life?

Chapter 4 illustrates the role chemistry plays in cuisine, from baking a cake to why lemons go well with fish.

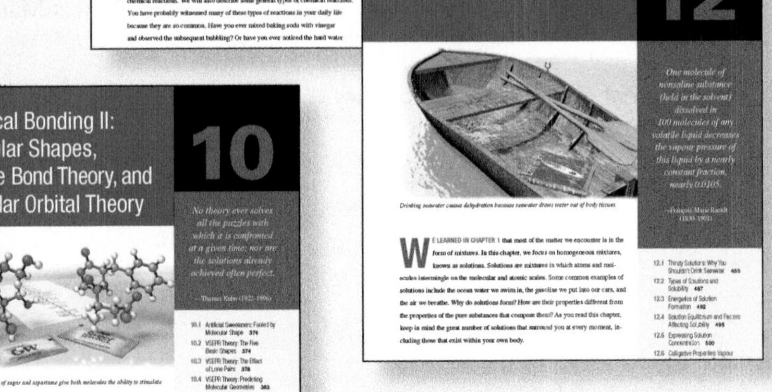

These examples make the material more accessible by contextualizing the chemistry and grounding it in the world you live in.

connect chemistry to YOUR WORLD

Student Interest

Throughout the narrative and in special boxed features, interesting descriptions of chemistry in the modern world demonstrate its importance.

CHEMISTRY AND MEDICINE Bone Density

Osteoporosis—which means *porous bone*—is a condition in which bone density becomes too low. The healthy bones of a young adult have a density of about 1.0 g cm^{-3}. Patients suffering from osteoporosis, however, can have bone densities as low as 0.22 g cm^{-3}. These low densities mean the bones have deteriorated and weakened, resulting in increased susceptibility to fractures, especially hip fractures. Patients suffering from osteoporosis can also experience height loss and disfiguration such as dowager's hump, a condition in which the patient becomes hunched over due to compression of the vertebrae. Osteoporosis is most common in postmenopausal women, but it can also occur in people (including men) who have certain diseases, such as insulin-dependent diabetes, or who take certain medications, such as prednisone. Osteoporosis is usually diagnosed and monitored with hip X-rays. Low-density bones absorb fewer of the X-rays than do high-density bones, producing characteristic differences in the X-ray image. Treatments for osteoporosis include additional calcium and vitamin D, drugs that prevent bone weakening, exercise and strength training, and, in extreme cases, hip-replacement surgery.

Question

Suppose you find a large animal bone in the woods, too large to fit in a beaker or flask. How might you approximate its density?

▲ Magnified views of the bone matrix in a normal femur (left) and one weakened by osteoporosis (right).

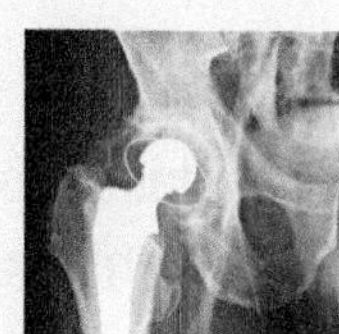

▲ Severe osteoporosis can necessitate surgery to implant an artificial hip joint, seen in this X-ray image.

CHEMISTRY IN THE ENVIRONMENT Antifreeze in Frogs

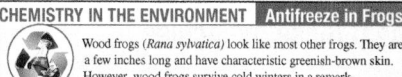

Wood frogs (*Rana sylvatica*) look like most other frogs. They are a few inches long and have characteristic greenish-brown skin. However, wood frogs survive cold winters in a remarkable way—they partially freeze. In its partially frozen state, the frog has no heartbeat, no blood circulation, no breathing, and no brain activity. Within 1–2 hours of thawing, however, these vital functions return and the frog hops off to find food. How does the wood frog do this?

Most cold-blooded animals cannot survive freezing temperatures because the water within their cells freezes. As we learned in Section 11.9, when water freezes, it expands, irreversibly damaging cells. When the wood frog hibernates for the winter, however, it produces large amounts of glucose that is secreted into its bloodstream and fills the interior of its cells. When the temperature drops below freezing, extracellular body fluids, such as those in the abdominal cavity, freeze solid. Fluids within cells, however, remain liquid because the high glucose concentration lowers their freezing point. In other words, the concentrated glucose solution within the frog's cells acts as antifreeze, preventing the water within the cells from freezing and allowing the frog to survive.

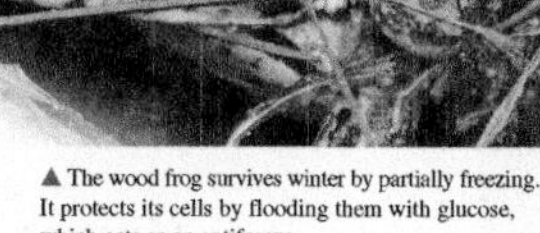

▲ The wood frog survives winter by partially freezing. It protects its cells by flooding them with glucose, which acts as an antifreeze.

Question

The wood frog can survive at body temperatures as low as −8.0 °C. Calculate the molality of a glucose solution ($C_6H_{12}O_6$) required to lower the freezing point of water to −8.0 °C.

▲ Chemistry and Medicine boxes show applications relevant to biomedical and health-related topics.

◀ Chemistry in the Environment boxes relate chapter topics to current environmental and societal issues.

▼ Chemistry In Your Day boxes demonstrate the importance of chemistry in everyday situations.

CHEMISTRY IN YOUR DAY Oxygen in Spacesuits

As is shown in Table 5.3, the air we breathe contains 78% N_2 and 21% O_2. The other 1% is a mixture of Ar, CO_2, Ne, and other trace gases. Besides oxygen, human beings can survive without any of the other gases as they fill no physiological requirements. In the low pressures of outer space, pure oxygen is exactly what astronauts breathe. For the best mobility, it is an advantage to have as low a pressure as possible in a spacesuit when astronauts go on a spacewalk. In air at a pressure of 1 bar, the partial pressure of O_2 is 207 mbar. It is not as simple as having a pressure of 207 mbar of oxygen in the spacesuit. In the alveoli of your lungs, there is a partial pressure of CO_2 (53 mbar) due to respiration and water vapour (63 mbar) from the lung tissue. This adds up to a total alveolar pressure of 116 mbar. In order to have a partial pressure of oxygen of 207 mbar, the spacesuit must be pressurized by an extra 116 mbar, to 323 mbar O_2. If the spacesuit were only pressurized to 207 mbar with pure oxygen, the partial pressure of O_2 in the lungs would be 207 – 116 = 91 mbar, about 44% of the partial pressure at sea level. This is the same as the partial pressure of oxygen at 5.5 km above sea level, which is 400 m higher than the highest permanently inhabited town in the world, Rinconada, Peru. For an astronaut, working under this low pressure of oxygen would be similar to the experience of high altitude mountain climbing.

▲ Cosmonaut Sergey Volkov dons a spacesuit during a 6 hour and 23 minute spacewalk.

Pioneering artwork makes CONCEPTS CLEAR

Annotated Molecular Art

Many illustrations have three parts:

- a macroscopic image (what you can see with your eyes)
- a molecular image (what the molecules are doing)
- a symbolic representation (how chemists represent the process with symbols and equations)

The goal is for you to connect what you see and experience (the macroscopic world) with the molecules responsible for that world, and with the way chemists represent those molecules. After all, this is what chemistry is all about.

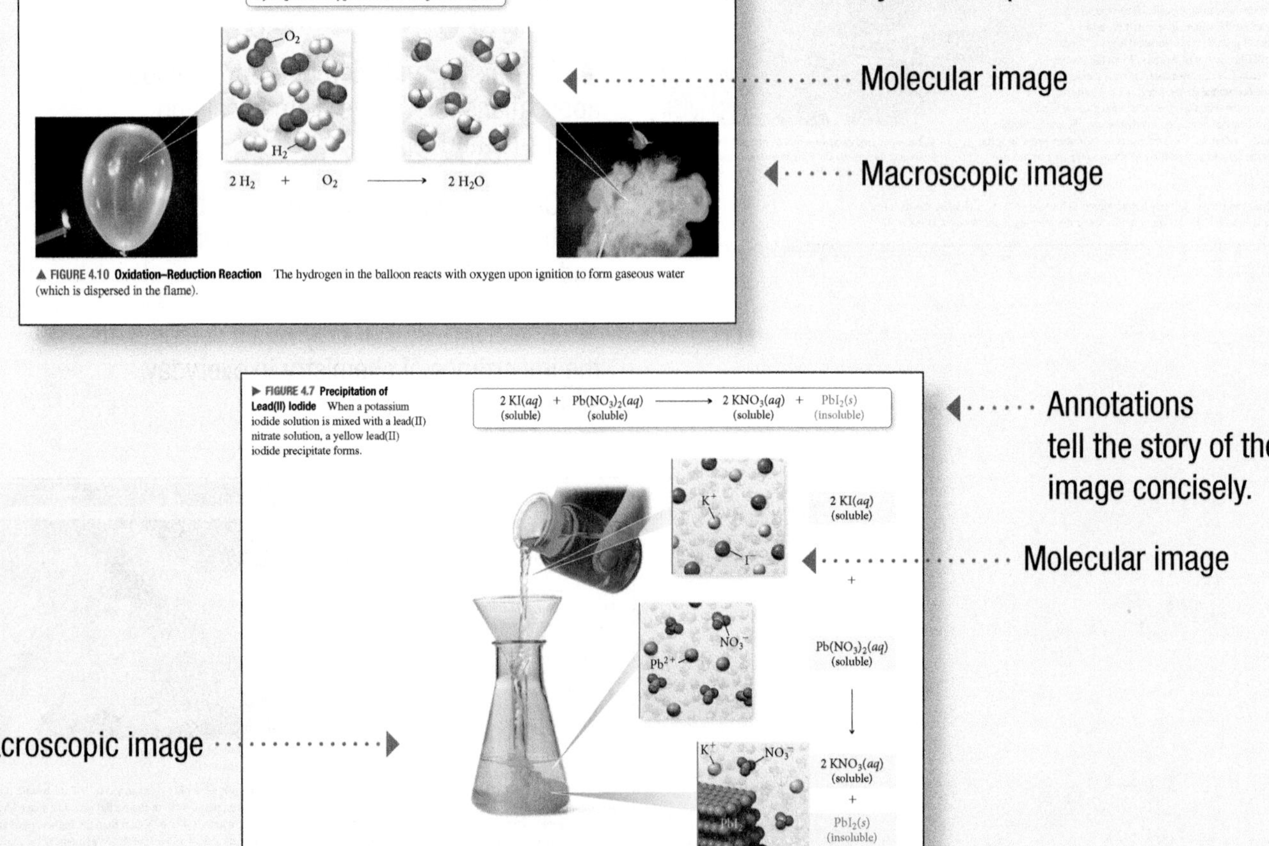

Multipart Images

Multipart images make connections among graphical representations, molecular processes, and the macroscopic world.

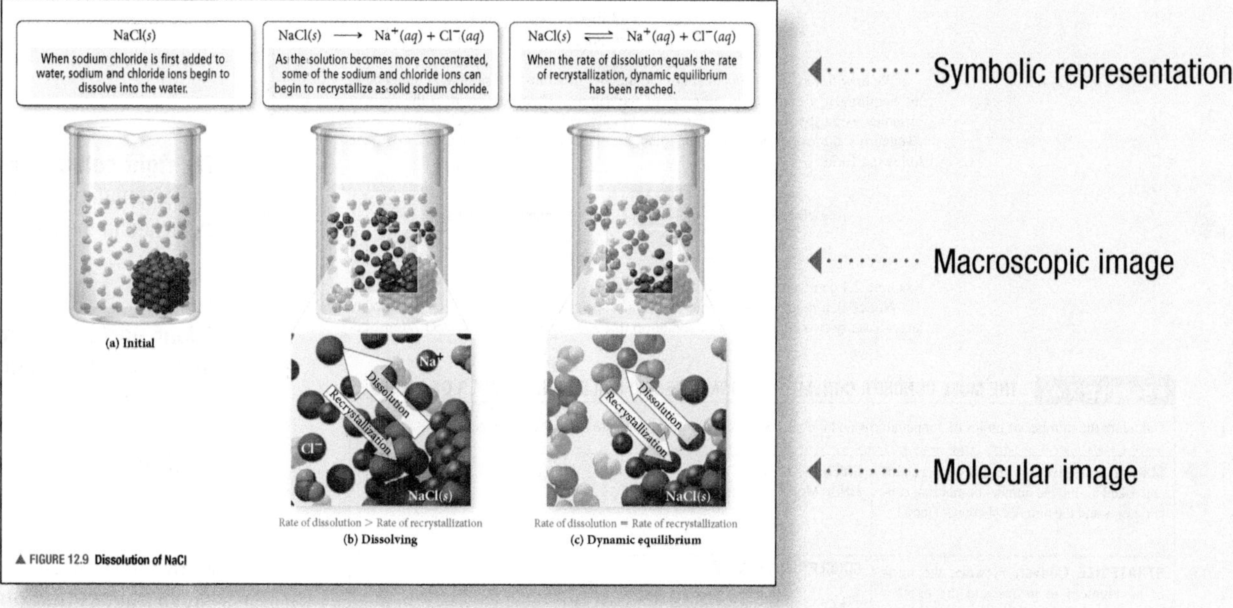

▲ FIGURE 12.9 **Dissolution of NaCl**

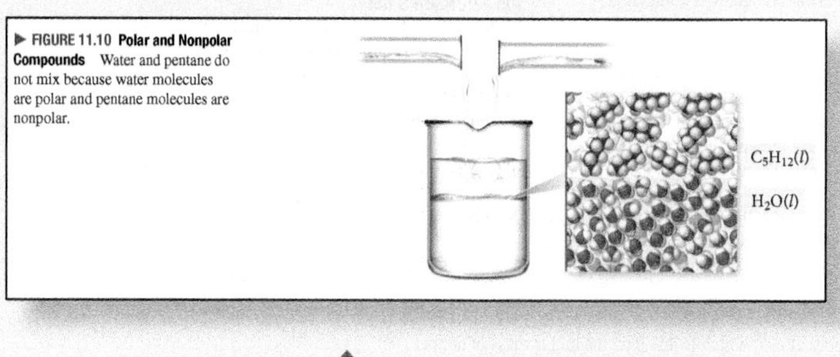

▶ FIGURE 11.10 **Polar and Nonpolar Compounds** Water and pentane do not mix because water molecules are polar and pentane molecules are nonpolar.

Graphical representation

Consistent strategies help you SOLVE PROBLEMS

Two-Column Example

A consistent approach to problem solving is used throughout the book.

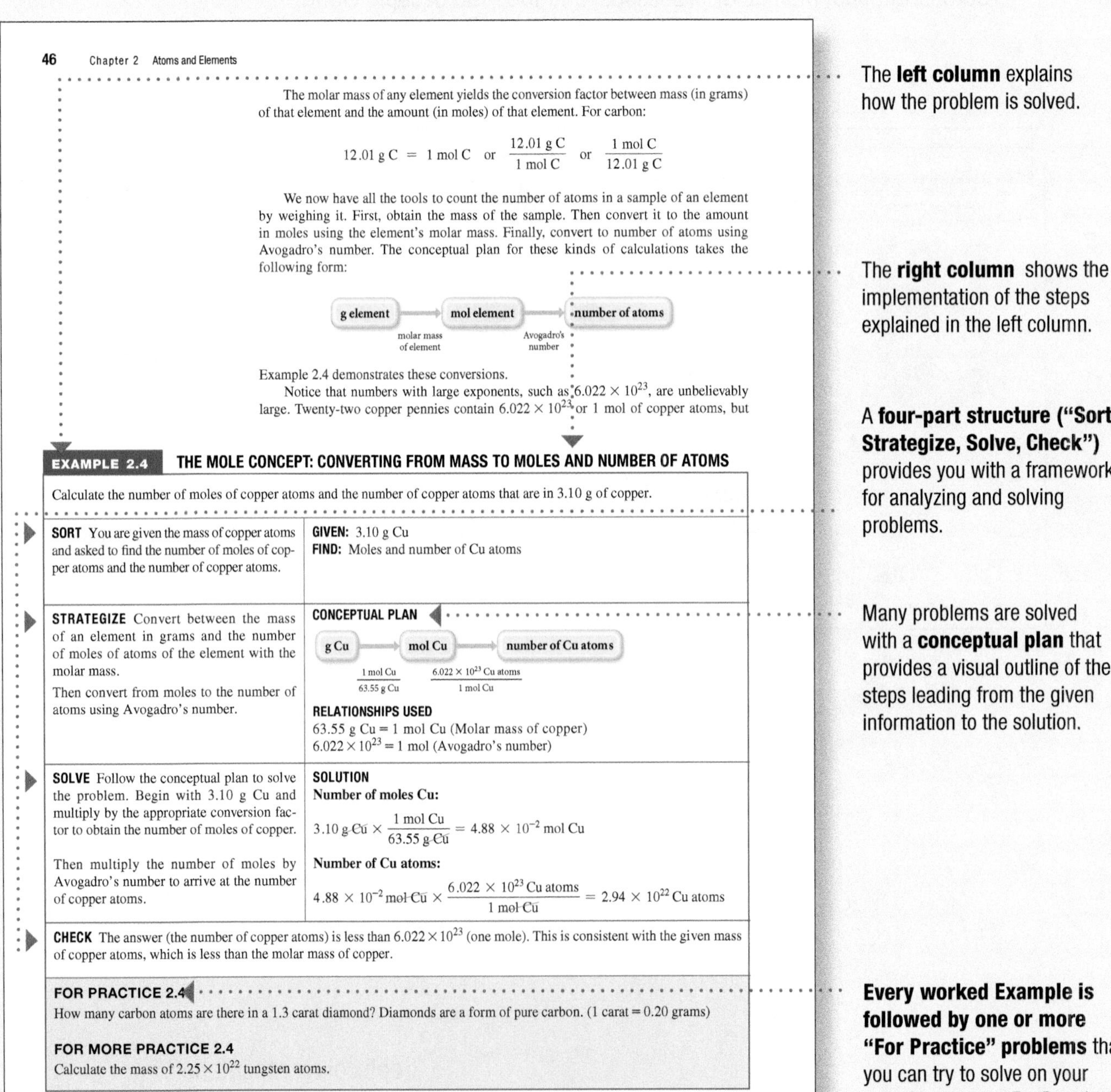

46 Chapter 2 Atoms and Elements

The molar mass of any element yields the conversion factor between mass (in grams) of that element and the amount (in moles) of that element. For carbon:

$$12.01 \text{ g C} = 1 \text{ mol C} \quad \text{or} \quad \frac{12.01 \text{ g C}}{1 \text{ mol C}} \quad \text{or} \quad \frac{1 \text{ mol C}}{12.01 \text{ g C}}$$

We now have all the tools to count the number of atoms in a sample of an element by weighing it. First, obtain the mass of the sample. Then convert it to the amount in moles using the element's molar mass. Finally, convert to number of atoms using Avogadro's number. The conceptual plan for these kinds of calculations takes the following form:

Example 2.4 demonstrates these conversions.

Notice that numbers with large exponents, such as 6.022×10^{23}, are unbelievably large. Twenty-two copper pennies contain 6.022×10^{23} or 1 mol of copper atoms, but

EXAMPLE 2.4 THE MOLE CONCEPT: CONVERTING FROM MASS TO MOLES AND NUMBER OF ATOMS

Calculate the number of moles of copper atoms and the number of copper atoms that are in 3.10 g of copper.

SORT You are given the mass of copper atoms and asked to find the number of moles of copper atoms and the number of copper atoms.	**GIVEN:** 3.10 g Cu **FIND:** Moles and number of Cu atoms
STRATEGIZE Convert between the mass of an element in grams and the number of moles of atoms of the element with the molar mass. Then convert from moles to the number of atoms using Avogadro's number.	**CONCEPTUAL PLAN** g Cu → mol Cu → number of Cu atoms $\frac{1 \text{ mol Cu}}{63.55 \text{ g Cu}}$ $\frac{6.022 \times 10^{23} \text{ Cu atoms}}{1 \text{ mol Cu}}$ **RELATIONSHIPS USED** 63.55 g Cu = 1 mol Cu (Molar mass of copper) $6.022 \times 10^{23} = 1$ mol (Avogadro's number)
SOLVE Follow the conceptual plan to solve the problem. Begin with 3.10 g Cu and multiply by the appropriate conversion factor to obtain the number of moles of copper. Then multiply the number of moles by Avogadro's number to arrive at the number of copper atoms.	**SOLUTION** **Number of moles Cu:** $3.10 \text{ g Cu} \times \frac{1 \text{ mol Cu}}{63.55 \text{ g Cu}} = 4.88 \times 10^{-2} \text{ mol Cu}$ **Number of Cu atoms:** $4.88 \times 10^{-2} \text{ mol Cu} \times \frac{6.022 \times 10^{23} \text{ Cu atoms}}{1 \text{ mol Cu}} = 2.94 \times 10^{22} \text{ Cu atoms}$

CHECK The answer (the number of copper atoms) is less than 6.022×10^{23} (one mole). This is consistent with the given mass of copper atoms, which is less than the molar mass of copper.

FOR PRACTICE 2.4
How many carbon atoms are there in a 1.3 carat diamond? Diamonds are a form of pure carbon. (1 carat = 0.20 grams)

FOR MORE PRACTICE 2.4
Calculate the mass of 2.25×10^{22} tungsten atoms.

The **left column** explains how the problem is solved.

The **right column** shows the implementation of the steps explained in the left column.

A **four-part structure ("Sort, Strategize, Solve, Check")** provides you with a framework for analyzing and solving problems.

Many problems are solved with a **conceptual plan** that provides a visual outline of the steps leading from the given information to the solution.

Every worked Example is followed by one or more "For Practice" problems that you can try to solve on your own. Answers to "For Practice" problems are in Appendix IV.

Three-Column Example

Problem-Solving Procedure Boxes for important categories of problems enable you to see how the same reasoning applies to different problems.

The formula for the ionic compound composed of *calcium* and chlorine, however, is $CaCl_2$ because Ca always forms 2+ cations and Cl always forms 1− anions in ionic compounds. In order for this compound to be charge-neutral, it must contain one Ca^{2+} cation for every two Cl^- anions.

Summarizing Ionic Compound Formulas

- Ionic compounds always contain positive and negative ions.
- In a chemical formula, the sum of the charges of the positive ions (cations) must equal the sum of the charges of the negative ions (anions).
- A formula reflects the smallest whole-number ratio of ions.

To write the formula for an ionic compound, follow the procedure in the left column in the following example. Two examples of how to apply the procedure are provided in the centre and right columns.

The general procedure is shown in the left column.

PROCEDURE FOR … Writing Formulas for Ionic Compounds	EXAMPLE 3.2 Writing Formulas for Ionic Compounds Write a formula for the ionic compound that forms between aluminum and oxygen.	EXAMPLE 3.3 Writing Formulas for Ionic Compounds Write a formula for the ionic compound that forms between calcium and oxygen.
1. Write the symbol for the metal cation and its charge followed by the symbol for the nonmetal anion and its charge. Obtain charges from the element's group number in the periodic table (refer to Figure 2.12).	Al^{3+} O^{2-}	Ca^{2+} O^{2-}
2. Adjust the subscript on each cation and anion to balance the overall charge.	Al^{3+} O^{2-} → Al_2O_3	Ca^{2+} O^{2-} → CaO
3. Check that the sum of the charges of the cations equals the sum of the charges of the anions.	cations: 2(3+) = 6+ anions: 3(2−) = 6− The charges balance.	cations: 2+ anions: 2− The charges balance.
	FOR PRACTICE 3.2 Write a formula for the compound formed between potassium and sulfur.	**FOR PRACTICE 3.3** Write a formula for the compound formed between aluminum and nitrogen.

Two worked examples, side by side, make it easy to see how differences are handled.

Every worked Example is followed by one or more "For Practice" problems that you can try to solve on your own. Answers to "For Practice" problems are in Appendix IV.

Naming Ionic Compounds The first step in naming an ionic compound is to identify it as one. Ionic compounds are often composed of metals and nonmetals; any time you see a metal and one or more nonmetals together in a chemical formula, assume that you have an ionic compound.

Table 3.2 gives names of common cations and anions. In the case of KBr, the name of the K^+ ion is potassium. For metals that form cations with only one charge, the name of the cation is the same as the metal. For metals that can form cations with different charges, the name of the cation is the name of the metal followed by the charge in roman numerals in brackets. Thus, Fe^{2+} is named *iron(II)* and Fe^{3+} is named *iron(III)*. Many transition metals give ions with different charges (Figure 3.6 ▶). Names for monoatomic anions consist of the **base name** of the element followed by the suffix *–ide*. For example, the base name for bromine is *brom*, and the name of the Br^- ion is *bromide*. The name of KBr is the name of the K^+ cation, followed by the name of the Br^- anion: *potassium bromide*.

The name of the ionic compound is simply the name of the cation followed by the name of the anion.

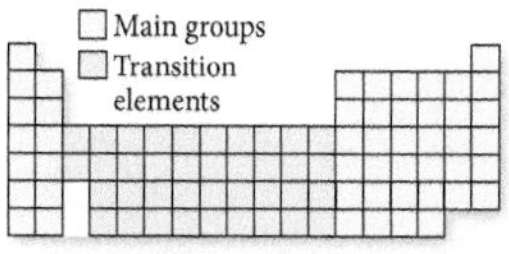

Main groups
Transition elements

▲ **FIGURE 3.6 Transition Elements** Metals that can have different charges in different compounds are usually (but not always) found in the transition elements.

End-of-chapter MATERIAL AIDS STUDY AND TEST PREP

End-of-Chapter Review Section

The end-of-chapter review section helps you study the chapter's concepts and skills in a systematic way that is ideal for test preparation.

Key Terms

Section 5.1
pressure (149)

Section 5.2
millimetre of mercury (mmHg) (151)
barometer (151)
torr (151)
pascal (Pa) (151)
atmosphere (atm) (151)
standard pressure (152)
bar (152)
millibar (mbar) (152)
manometer (152)

Section 5.3
Boyle's law (154)
Charles's law (157)
Avogadro's law (159)

Section 5.4
ideal gas law (160)
ideal gas (160)
ideal gas constant (160)

Section 5.5
molar volume (162)
standard temperature and pressure (STP) (162)

Section 5.6
partial pressure (P_n) (166)
Dalton's law of partial pressures (166)
mole fraction (χ_a) (166)
vapour pressure (169)

Section 5.8
kinetic molecular theory (174)

Section 5.9
mean free path (180)
diffusion (180)
effusion (180)
Graham's law of effusion (181)

Section 5.10
van der Waals equation (184)
real gas (184)

▲ **Key Terms** list all of the chapter's boldfaced terms, organized by section in order of appearance, with page references. Definitions are found in the Glossary.

Key Equations and Relationships

Relationship Between Pressure (P), Force (F), and Area (A) (5.2)

$$P = \frac{F}{A}$$

Boyle's Law: Relationship Between Pressure (P) and Volume (V) (5.3)

$$V \propto \frac{1}{P}$$

$$P_1V_1 = P_2V_2$$

Charles's Law: Relationship Between Volume (V) and Temperature (T) (5.3)

$$V \propto T \quad (\text{in K})$$

$$\frac{V_1}{T_1} = \frac{V_2}{T_2}$$

Avogadro's Law: Relationship Between Volume (V) and Amount in Moles (n) (5.3)

$$V \propto n$$

$$\frac{V_1}{n_1} = \frac{V_2}{n_2}$$

Ideal Gas Law: Relationship Between Volume (V), Pressure (P), Temperature (T), and Amount (n) (5.4)

$$PV = nRT$$

▲ The **Key Equations and Relationships** section lists each of the key equations and important quantitative relationships from the chapter.

Key Concepts

Pressure (5.1, 5.2)

Gas pressure is the force per unit area that results from gas particles colliding with the surfaces around them. Pressure is measured in a number of units, including bar, mbar, mmHg, torr, Pa, psi, and atm.

The Gas Laws (5.3)

The gas laws express relationships between pairs of variables when the other variables are held constant. Boyle's law states that the volume of a gas is inversely proportional to its pressure. Charles's law states that the volume of a gas is directly proportional to its temperature. Avogadro's law states that the volume of a gas is directly proportional to the amount (in moles).

The Ideal Gas Law and Its Applications (5.4, 5.5)

The ideal gas law, $PV = nRT$, gives the relationship among all four gas variables and contains the gas laws within it. We can use the ideal gas law to find one of the four variables given the other three. We can use it to calculate the molar volume of an ideal gas, which is 22.7 L at STP, and to calculate the density and molar mass of a gas.

Mixtures of Gases and Partial Pressures (5.6)

In a mixture of gases, each gas acts independently of the others so that any overall property of the mixture is the sum of the properties of the individual components. The pressure of any individual component is its partial pressure.

Gas Stoichiometry (5.7)

In reactions involving gaseous reactants and products, quantities are often reported in volumes at specified pressures and temperatures. We can convert these quantities to amounts (in moles) using the ideal gas law. Then we can use the stoichiometric coefficients from the balanced equation to determine the stoichiometric amounts of other reactants or products. The general form for these types of calculations is often as follows: volume A → amount A (in moles) → amount B (in moles) → quantity of B (in desired units). In cases where the reaction is carried out at STP, the molar volume at STP (22.7 L = 1 mol) can be used to convert between volume in litres and amount in moles.

Kinetic Molecular Theory and Its Applications (5.8, 5.9)

Kinetic molecular theory is a quantitative model for gases. The theory has three main assumptions: (1) the gas particles are negligibly small, (2) the average kinetic energy of a gas particle is proportional to the temperature in kelvin, and (3) the collision of one gas particle with another is completely elastic (the particles do not stick together). The gas laws all follow from the kinetic molecular theory.

We can also use the theory to derive the expression for the root mean square velocity of gas particles. This velocity is inversely proportional to the molar mass of the gas, and therefore—at a given temperature—smaller gas particles are (on average) moving more quickly than larger ones. The kinetic molecular theory also allows us to predict the mean free path of a gas particle (the distance it travels between collisions) and relative rates of diffusion or effusion.

Real Gases (5.10)

Real gases differ from ideal gases to the extent that they do not always fit the assumptions of kinetic molecular theory. These assumptions tend to break down at high pressures, where the volume is higher than predicted for an ideal gas because the particles are no longer negligibly small compared to the space between them. The assumptions also break down at low temperatures where the pressure is lower than predicted because the attraction between molecules combined with low kinetic energies causes partially inelastic collisions. The van der Waals equation predicts gas properties under nonideal conditions.

▲ The **Key Concepts** section summarizes the chapter's most important ideas.

Key Skills

Calculating Internal Energy from Heat and Work (6.3)
• Example 6.1 • For Practice 6.1 • Exercises 41–44, 53–54

Finding Heat from Temperature Changes (6.4)
• Example 6.2 • For Practice 6.2 • For More Practice 6.2 • Exercises 47–48

Thermal Energy Transfer (6.4)
• Example 6.3 • For Practice 6.3 • Exercises 49–50, 65–70

Finding Work from Volume Changes (6.4)
• Example 6.4 • For Practice 6.4 • Exercises 51–52

Finding Pressure–Volume Work for Chemical Reactions Involving Gases (6.4)
• Example 6.5 • For Practice 6.5 • Exercises 53–56

Using Bomb Calorimetry to Calculate $\Delta_r U$ and $\Delta_r H$ (6.5, 6.6)
• Examples 6.6, 6.7 • For Practice 6.6, 6.7 • For More Practice 6.6 • Exercises 73–74

Predicting Endothermic and Exothermic Processes (6.6)
• Example 6.6 • For Practice 6.6 • Exercises 59–60

Determining Heat from ΔH and Stoichiometry (6.6)
• Examples 6.8, 6.12 • For Practice 6.8, 6.12 • For More Practice 6.8 • Exercises 61–64

Finding $\Delta_r H$ Using Calorimetry (6.7)
• Example 6.9 • For Practice 6.9 • Exercises 75–76

Finding $\Delta_r H$ Using Hess's Law (6.8)
• Example 6.10 • For Practice 6.10 • For More Practice 6.10 • Exercises 79–82

▲ The **Key Skills** section lists the major types of problems that you should be able to solve, with the chapter examples that show the techniques needed—along with the "For Practice" problems and end-of-chapter exercises that offer practice in those skills.

End-of-Chapter Review Exercises

Answers to odd-numbered questions are in Appendix III.

Review Questions

1. Why is molecular geometry important? Give some examples.
2. According to VSEPR theory, what determines the geometry of a molecule?
3. Name and sketch the five basic electron geometries, and state the number of electron groups corresponding to each. What constitutes an *electron group*?
4. Explain the difference between electron geometry and molecular geometry. Under what circumstances are they not the same?
5. Give the correct electron and molecular geometries that correspond to each set of electron groups around the central atom of a molecule:
   a. four electron groups overall; three bonding groups and one lone pair
   c. five electron groups overall; four bonding groups and one lone pair
   d. five electron groups overall; three bonding groups and two lone pairs
   e. five electron groups overall; two bonding groups and three lone pairs
   f. six electron groups overall; five bonding groups and one lone pair
   g. six electron groups overall; four bonding groups and two lone pairs
6. How do you apply VSEPR theory to predict the shape of a molecule with more than one interior atom?
7. How do you determine whether a molecule is polar? Why is

▲ **Review Questions** can be used to review chapter content.

Cumulative Problems

79. Bromine is a highly reactive liquid, while krypton is an inert gas. Explain the difference based on their electron configurations.
80. Potassium is a highly reactive metal, while argon is an inert gas. Explain the difference based on their electron configurations.
81. Suppose you were trying to find a substitute for K^+ in nerve signal transmission. Where would you begin your search? What ions would be most like K^+? For each ion you propose, explain the ways in which it would be similar to K^+ and the ways it would be different. Refer to periodic trends in your discussion.
82. Suppose you were trying to find a substitute for Na^+ in nerve signal transmission. Where would you begin your search? What ions would be most like Na^+? For each ion you propose, explain the ways in which it would be similar to Na^+ and the ways it would be different. Use periodic trends in your discussion.
83. Life on Earth evolved around the element carbon. Based on periodic properties, what two or three elements would you expect to be most like carbon?

▲ **Cumulative Problems** combine material from different parts of the chapter, and often from previous chapters as well, allowing you to see how well you can integrate the course material.

Conceptual Problems

113. Imagine that in another universe, atoms and elements are identical to ours, except that atoms with six valence electrons have particular stability (in contrast to our universe, where atoms with eight valence electrons have particular stability). Give an example of an element in the alternative universe that corresponds to:
   a. a noble gas.
   b. a reactive nonmetal.
   c. a reactive metal.
114. According to Coulomb's law, rank the interactions between the charged particles from lowest potential energy to highest potential energy:
   a. A 1+ charge and a 1− charge separated by 100 pm.
   b. A 2+ charge and a 1− charge separated by 100 pm.
   c. A 1+ charge and a 1+ charge separated by 100 pm.
   d. A 1+ charge and a 1− charge separated by 200 pm.
115. Use the trends in ionization energy and electron affinity to explain why calcium fluoride has the formula CaF_2 and not Ca_2F or CaF.

▲ **Conceptual Problems** let you test your grasp of key chapter concepts, often through reasoning that involves little or no math.

Problems by Topic

Valence Electrons and Dot Structures

33. Write an electron configuration for N. Then write a Lewis structure for N and show which electrons from the electron configuration are included in the Lewis structure.
34. Write an electron configuration for Ne. Then write a Lewis structure for Ne and show which electrons from the electron configuration are included in the Lewis structure.
35. Write a Lewis structure for each atom or ion:
   a. Al b. Na^+ c. Cl d. Cl^-
36. Write a Lewis structure for each atom or ion:
   a. S^{2-} b. Mg c. Mg^{2+} d. P

Ionic Lewis Structures and Lattice Energy

41. Explain the trend in the lattice energies of the alkaline earth metal oxides:

Metal Oxide	Lattice Energy ($kJ\ mol^{-1}$)
MgO	−3795
CaO	−3414
SrO	−3217
BaO	−3029

42. Rubidium iodide has a lattice energy of $-617\ kJ\ mol^{-1}$, while potassium bromide has a lattice energy of $-671\ kJ\ mol^{-1}$. Why is the lattice energy of potassium bromide more exothermic than

▲ **Problems by Topic** are paired, with answers to the odd-numbered questions appearing in Appendix III.

Challenge Problems

97. Consider the densities and atomic radii of the noble gases at 1 bar and 25 °C:

Element	Atomic Radius (pm)	Density ($g\ L^{-1}$)
He	32	0.16
Ne	70	0.81
Ar	98	—
Kr	112	3.38
Xe	130	—
Rn	—	8.96

   a. Estimate the densities of argon and xenon by interpolation from the data.
   b. Provide an estimate of the density of the yet undiscovered element with atomic number 118 by extrapolation from the data.
   c. Use the molar mass of neon to estimate the mass of a neon atom. Then use the atomic radius of neon to calculate the average density of a neon atom. How does this density compare to the density of neon gas? What does this comparison suggest about the nature of neon gas?
   d. Use the densities and molar masses of krypton and neon to calculate the number of atoms of each found in a volume of 1.0 L. Use these values to estimate the number of atoms that occur in 1.0 L of Ar. Now use the molar mass of argon to estimate the density of Ar. How does this estimate compare to that in part (a)?
98. As we have seen, the periodic table is a result of empirical observation (i.e., the periodic law), but quantum theory explains *why* the table is so arranged. Suppose that, in another universe, quantum theory was such that there were one *s* orbital but only two *p* orbitals (instead of three) and only three *d* orbitals (instead of five). Draw out the first four periods of the periodic table in this alternative universe. Which elements would be the equivalent of the noble gases? Halogens? Alkali metals?
99. Consider the metals in the first transition series. Use periodic trends to predict a trend in density as you move to the right across the series.
100. Only trace amounts of the synthetic element darmstadtium, atomic number 110, have been obtained. The element is so highly unstable that no observations of its properties have been possible. Based on its position in the periodic table, propose three different plausible valence electron configurations for this element.

▲ **Challenge Problems** are designed to challenge stronger students.

MasteringChemistry® for Students

www.masteringchemistry.com

MasteringChemistry® tutorials guide students through the most challenging topics while helping them make connections between related chemical concepts. Immediate feedback and tutorial assistance help students understand and master concepts and skills in chemistry—allowing them to retain more knowledge and perform better in this course and beyond.

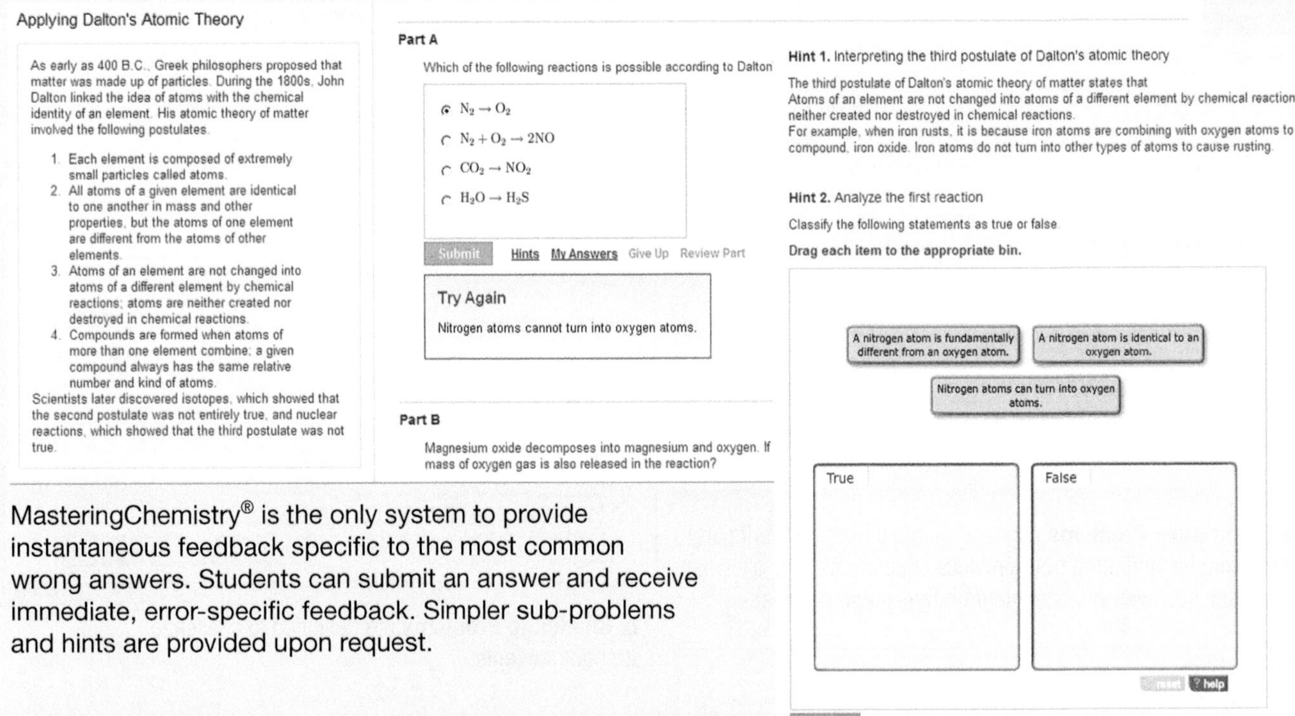

MasteringChemistry® is the only system to provide instantaneous feedback specific to the most common wrong answers. Students can submit an answer and receive immediate, error-specific feedback. Simpler sub-problems and hints are provided upon request.

Math Remediation links found in selected tutorials launch algorithmically generated math exercises that give students unlimited opportunity for practice and mastery of math skills. Math Remediation exercises provide additional practice and free up class and office-hour time to focus on the chemistry. Exercises include guided solutions, sample problems, and learning aids for extra help, and offer helpful feedback when students enter incorrect answers.

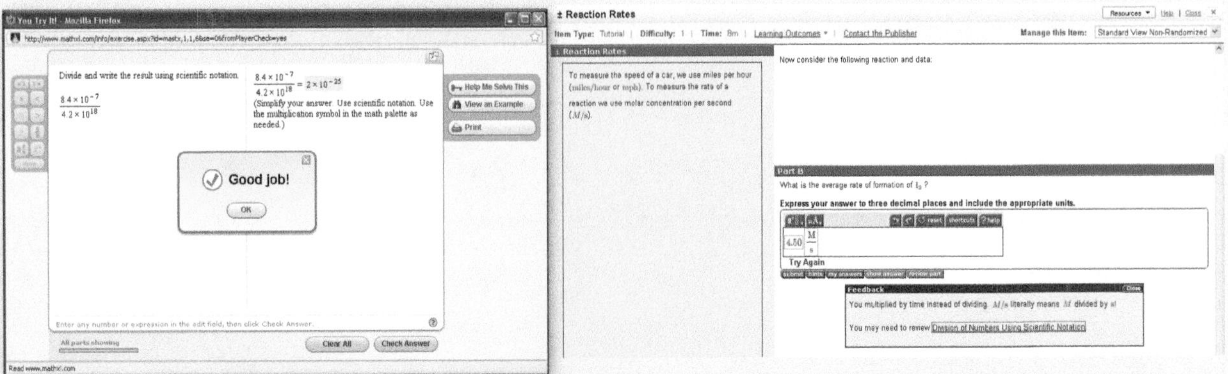

eText

Pearson eText gives students access to the text whenever and wherever they can access the Internet. The eText includes powerful interactive and customization functions.

- You can create notes, highlight text, and create bookmarks.
- You can perform a full-text search and share comments.
- Instructors can share their notes and highlights with students and can also hide chapters that they do not want their students to read.

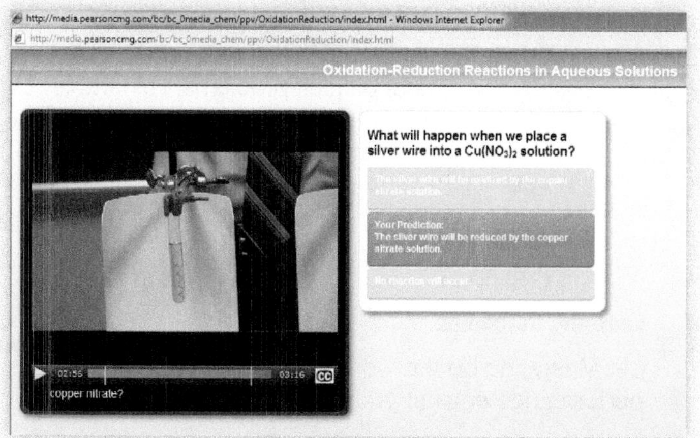

15 Pause and Predict Video Quizzes ask students to predict the outcome of experiments and demonstrations as they watch the videos; a set of multiple-choice questions challenges students to apply the concepts from the video to related scenarios. These videos are also available in web and mobile-friendly formats through the Study Area of MasteringChemistry and in the Pearson eText.

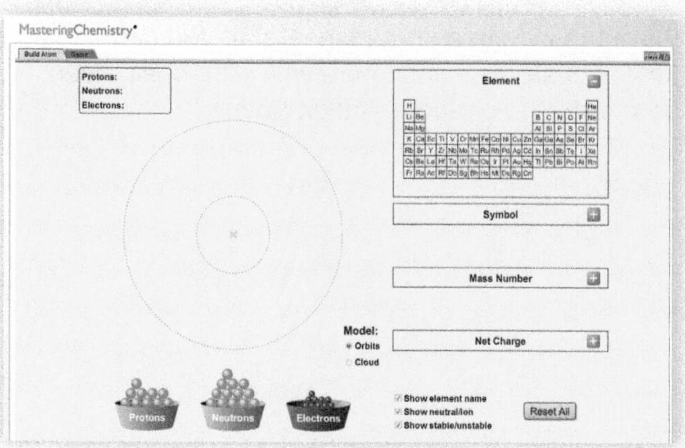

15 Simulations, assignable in MasteringChemistry®, include those developed by the PhET Chemistry Group, and the leading authors in the simulation development covering some of the most difficult chemistry concepts.

MasteringChemistry® for Instructors

www.masteringchemistry.com

The Mastering platform was developed by **scientists** for science students and instructors. Mastering has been refined from data-driven insights derived from over a decade of real-world use by faculty and students.

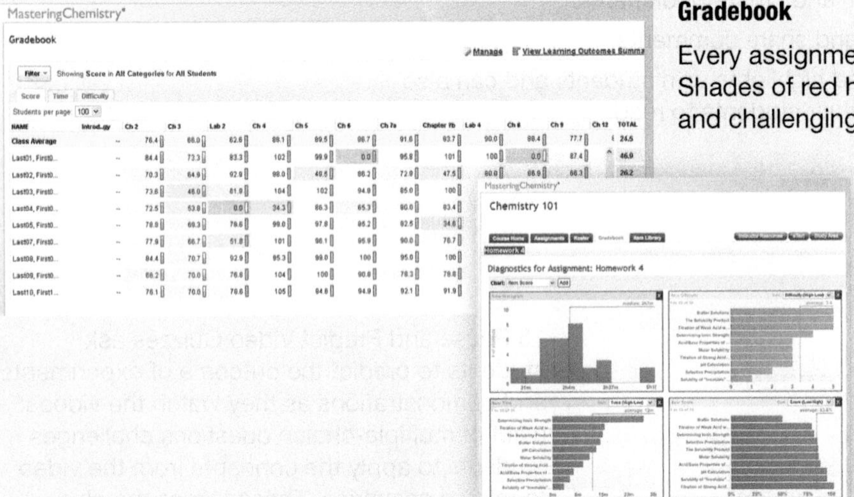

Gradebook

Every assignment is automatically graded. Shades of red highlight struggling students and challenging assignments.

Gradebook Diagnostics

This screen provides you with your favourite diagnostics. With a single click, charts summarize the most difficult problems, vulnerable students, grade distribution, and even score improvement over the course.

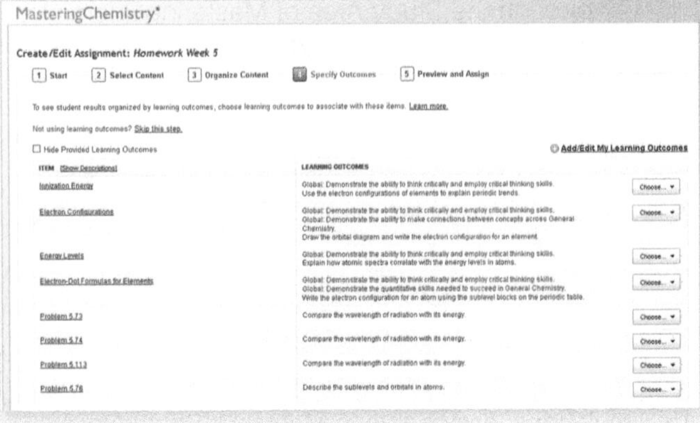

Learning Outcomes

Let Mastering do the work in tracking student performance against your learning outcomes:

- Add your own or use the publisher-provided learning outcomes.
- View class performance against the specified learning outcomes.
- Export results to a spreadsheet that you can further customize and share with your chair, dean, administrator, or accreditation board.

NEW! Dynamic Study Modules

Personalize each student's learning experience and help them study effectively on their own by continuously assessing their activity and performance in real time. Here's how it works: students complete a set of questions with a unique answer format that also asks them to indicate their confidence level. Questions repeat until the student can answer them all correctly and confidently. Once completed, Dynamic Study Modules explain the concept using materials from the text. These are available as graded assignments prior to class, and accessible on smartphones, tablets, and computers.

NEW! Learning Catalytics™

Promote student engagement, generate class discussion, guide your lecture, and promote peer-to-peer learning with real-time analytics. Mastering with eText now provides Learning Catalytics—an interactive student response tool that uses students' smartphones, tablets, or laptops to engage them in more sophisticated tasks and thinking.

Instructors, you can:

- Pose a variety of open-ended questions that help your students develop critical-thinking skills.
- Monitor responses to find out where students are struggling.
- Use real-time data to adjust your instructional strategy and try other ways of engaging your students during class.
- Manage student interactions by automatically grouping students for discussion, teamwork, and peer-to-peer learning.

NEW! Adaptive Follow-Ups

Adaptive Follow-Up Assignments are based on each student's past performance on their course work to date, including homework, tests, and quizzes. These provide additional coaching and targeted practice as needed, so students can master the material.

Units of Measurement for Physical and Chemical Change

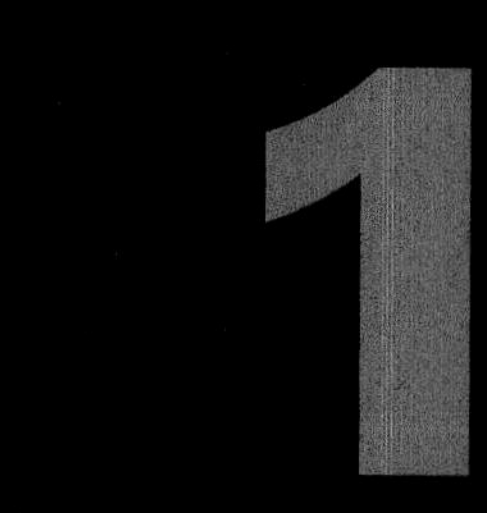

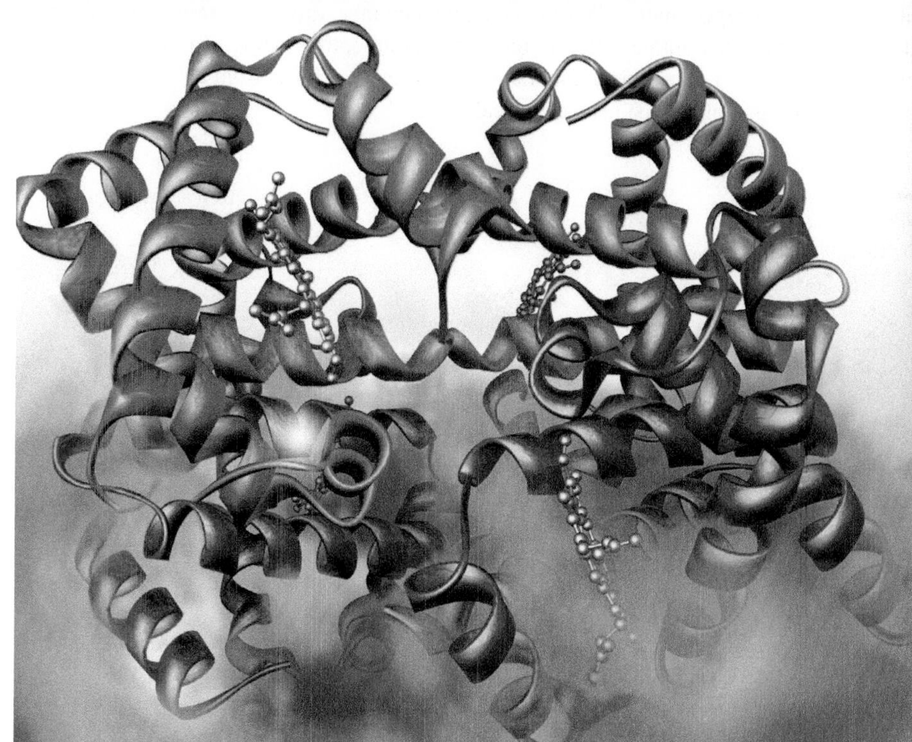

Ancient science had sought knowledge of ***what*** *things* ***are****, to be contemplated as an end in itself satisfying to the knower. In contrast, modern science seeks knowledge of* ***how*** *things* ***work****, to be used as a means for the relief and comfort of all humanity, knowers and non-knowers alike.*

—Leon R. Kass

ONE OF THE MOST fundamental ideas in chemistry, perhaps in all of science, is that **the properties of matter are determined by the properties of molecules and atoms**. The properties of atoms and molecules determine how matter behaves. The properties of water molecules determine how water behaves, the properties of sugar molecules determine how sugar behaves, and the properties of the molecules that compose our bodies determine how our bodies behave. Our understanding of matter at the molecular level gives us unprecedented control over that matter. In fact, our expanded understanding of the molecules that compose living organisms has made possible the biological revolution of the last 50 years.

1.1 Physical and Chemical Changes and Physical and Chemical Properties

Every day, whether we know it or not, we witness changes in matter that are a result of the properties of the atoms and molecules composing that matter—ice melts, iron rusts, gasoline burns, fruit ripens, water evaporates. What happens to the molecules that compose the matter during such changes? The answer depends on the type of change. **Physical changes** are those that do not alter the chemical composition. For example, when water boils, it changes state from a liquid to a gas, but both are composed of water molecules (Figure 1.1 ▼). **Chemical changes** are those that alter the composition (the chemical structure) of matter. During a chemical change, atoms rearrange, transforming the original substance into a different one. For example, the rusting of iron is a chemical change (Figure 1.1). Iron atoms combine with oxygen molecules from air to form iron(III) oxide, the orange-coloured substance we call rust.

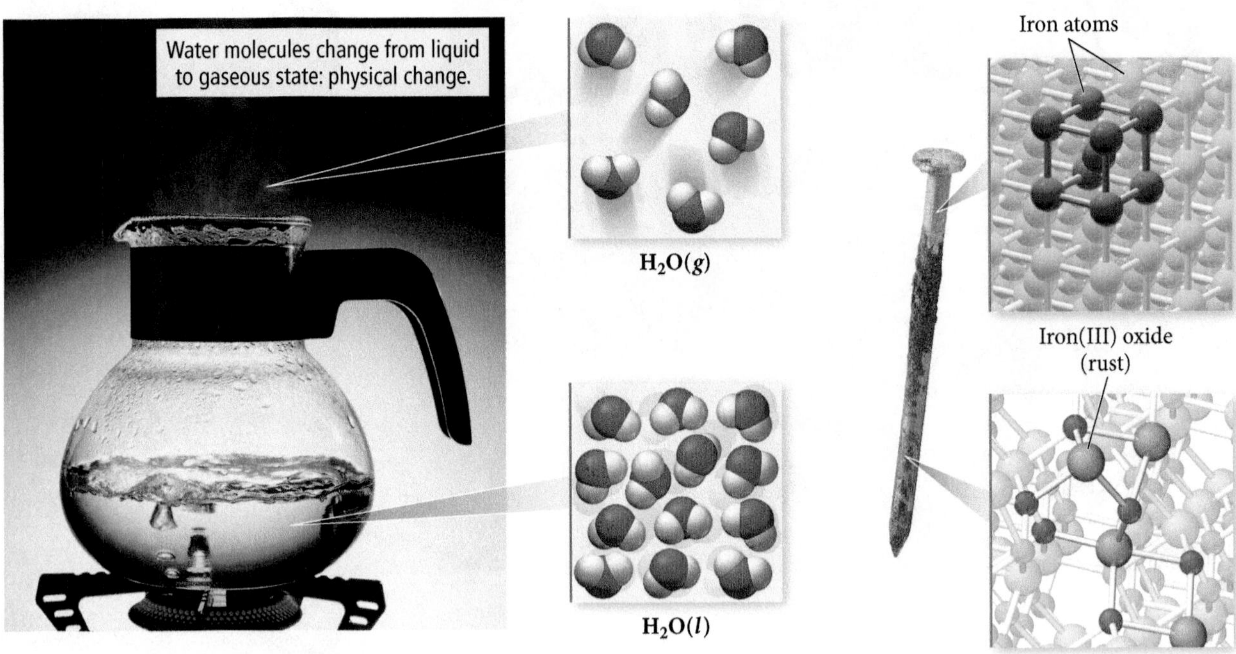

▲ FIGURE 1.1 **Boiling Is a Physical Change and Rusting Is a Chemical Change** When water boils, individual molecules leave the liquid as a gas but the chemical identity is not altered—both the liquid and the vapour are composed of water molecules. When iron rusts, the iron atoms combine with oxygen to form a different chemical substance.

Physical and chemical changes are a manifestation of physical and chemical properties. A **physical property** is one that a substance displays without changing its composition, whereas a **chemical property** is one that a substance displays only by changing its composition via a chemical change. The smell of gasoline is a physical property—gasoline does not change its composition when it exhibits its odour. The combustibility of gasoline, in contrast, is a chemical property—gasoline does change its composition when it burns, turning into completely new substances (primarily carbon dioxide and water). Physical properties include odour, taste, colour, appearance, melting point, boiling point, and density. Chemical properties include corrosiveness, flammability, acidity, toxicity, and other such characteristics.

If we want to understand the substances around us, we must understand the physical and chemical properties of the atoms and molecules that compose them—this is the central goal of chemistry. A good, simple definition of chemistry is:

Chemistry—the science that seeks to understand the properties and behaviour of matter by studying the properties and behaviour of atoms and molecules.

CONCEPTUAL CONNECTION 1.1

Chemical and Physical Changes

The diagram to the left represents liquid water molecules in a pan.
Which of the three diagrams on the right best represents the water molecules after they have been vaporized by the boiling of liquid water?

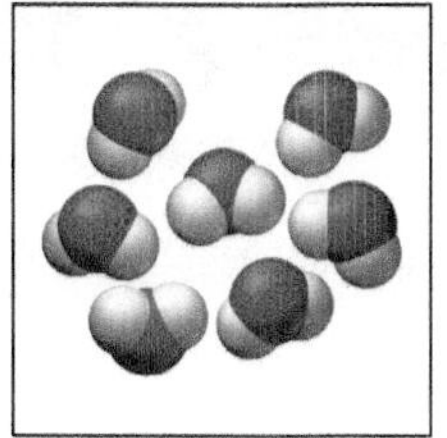

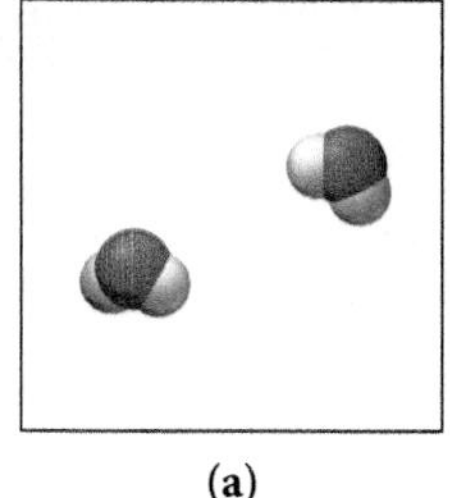

(a)

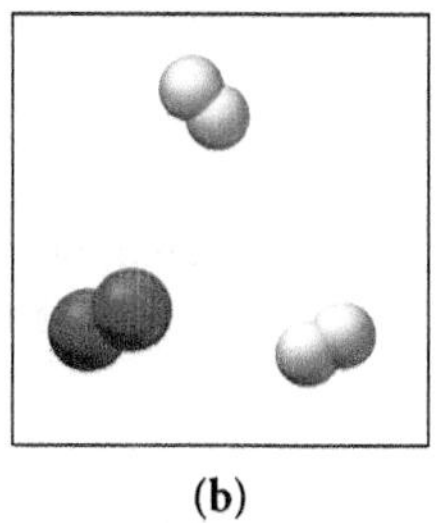

(b)

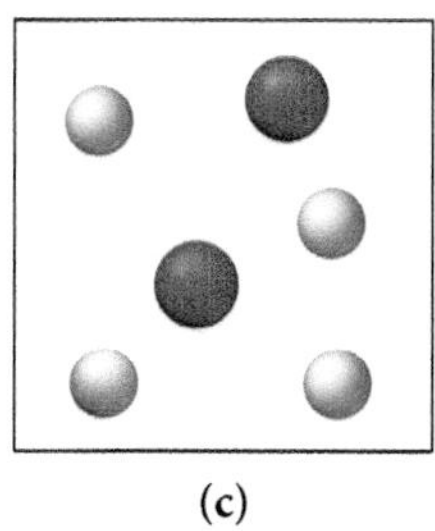

(c)

1.2 Energy: A Fundamental Part of Physical and Chemical Change

Physical and chemical changes are usually accompanied by energy changes. For example, when water evaporates from your skin (a physical change), the water molecules absorb energy from your body, making you feel cooler. When you burn natural gas on the stove (a chemical change), energy is released, heating the food you are cooking. Understanding the physical and chemical changes of matter—that is, understanding chemistry—requires that we understand energy changes and energy flow.

The *total energy* of an object is a sum of its **kinetic energy**, the energy associated with its motion, and its **potential energy**, the energy associated with its position or composition. An object held several metres from the ground has potential energy due to its position within Earth's gravitational field (Figure 1.2 ▶). If you drop the object, it accelerates, and the potential energy is converted to kinetic energy. When the object hits the ground, its kinetic energy is converted primarily to **thermal energy**, the energy associated with the temperature of an object. Thermal energy is actually a type of kinetic energy because it arises from the motion of the individual atoms or molecules that make up an object. In other words, when the object hits the ground, its kinetic energy is essentially transferred to the atoms and molecules that compose the ground, raising the temperature of the ground ever so slightly.

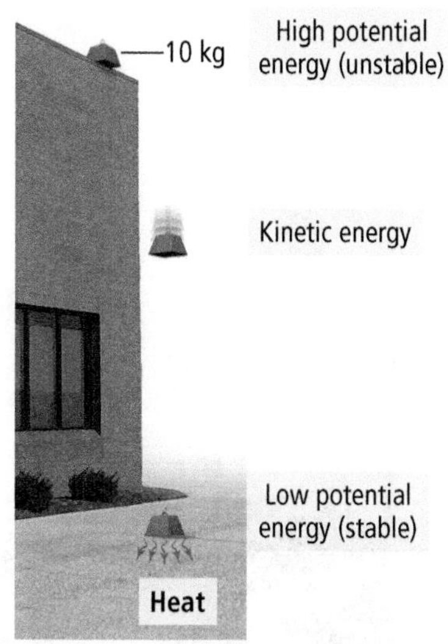

▲ **FIGURE 1.2 Energy Conversions** When the object on the roof is released, gravitational potential energy is converted into kinetic energy as the object falls. The kinetic energy is converted mostly to thermal energy when the weight strikes the ground.

According to the **law of conservation of energy**, *energy is neither created nor destroyed*. The potential energy of the object becomes kinetic energy as it accelerates toward the ground. The kinetic energy then becomes thermal energy when the object hits the ground. The total amount of thermal energy that is released through the process is exactly equal to the initial potential energy of the object.

Another principle to note is *the tendency of systems with high potential energy to change in a way that lowers their potential energy*. Objects lifted several metres from the ground, with high potential energy, tend to be *unstable* because they contain a significant amount of localized potential energy. Unless restrained, the object will naturally fall, lowering its potential energy. We can harness some of the raised object's potential energy to do work. For example, we can attach the object to a rope that turns a paddle wheel or spins a drill as it falls. After it falls to the ground, the object contains less potential energy—it has become more *stable*.

Some chemical substances are like the raised object just described. For example, the molecules that compose gasoline have a relatively high potential energy—energy is concentrated in them just as energy is concentrated in the raised object. The molecules in gasoline, therefore, tend to undergo chemical changes (specifically combustion) that will lower their potential energy. As the energy of the molecules is released, some of it can be harnessed to do work, such as moving a car down the street (Figure 1.3 ▼). The molecules that result from the chemical change have less potential energy than the original molecules in gasoline and are more stable.

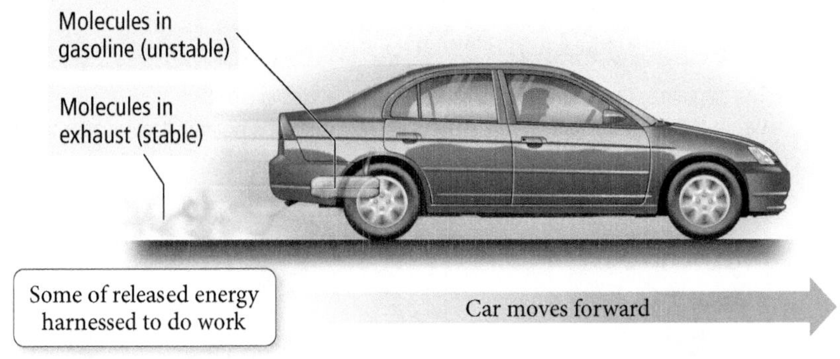

▶ **FIGURE 1.3 Using Chemical Energy to Do Work** The compounds produced when gasoline burns have less chemical potential energy than the gasoline molecules.

Chemical potential energy, such as that contained in the molecules that compose gasoline, arises primarily from electrostatic forces between the electrically charged particles (protons and electrons) that compose atoms and molecules. We will learn more about these particles, as well as the properties of charge, in Chapter 2. For now know that molecules contain specific, sometimes complex, arrangements of these charged particles. Some of these arrangements—such as the one within the molecules that compose gasoline—have a much higher potential energy than others. When gasoline undergoes combustion, the arrangement of these particles changes, creating molecules with much lower potential energy and transferring a great deal of energy (mostly in the form of heat) to the surroundings.

1.3 The Units of Measurement

On July 23, 1983, Air Canada Flight 143, a Boeing 767 jet, ran out of fuel at 7920 m altitude, halfway between its flight from Montreal, QC, to Edmonton, AB. Prior to take-off in Montreal, a fuel gauge malfunctioned, so the fuel level had to be measured manually. An investigation revealed that the ground crew had mistakenly used an incorrect conversion factor when determining how much fuel was needed to fill the plane. The jet required 22 300 kg of fuel for the flight. Unfortunately, the ground crew used the conversion factor of 1.77 lb L^{-1} to convert the number of kilograms to the number of litres required to fill the plane. The correct conversion factor is 0.803 kg L^{-1} (the density of jet fuel), so the plane had less than half the required amount of fuel for the flight. Fortunately, the pilots were able to glide the plane—with no engines running—to a safe landing at the former RCAF Station Gimli in Manitoba, AB, with no injuries to the 61 passengers or 5 crew members. In chemistry, as in aviation, **units**—the standard quantities used to specify measurement—are critical. If you get them wrong, the consequences can be disastrous.

▲ Air Canada Flight 143, nicknamed "The Gimli Glider," after landing on the tarmac at the former RCAF Station Gimli, which had been partially converted to a go-kart track.

There are many measurement systems that you may come across, such as the **imperial system**, used in the United States, and the **metric system**, used in most of the rest of the world. Scientists mainly use the **International System of Units (SI)**, which is a subsystem of the metric system. We will focus on the SI system.

TABLE 1.1 SI Base Units

Quantity	Unit	Symbol
Length	metre	m
Mass	kilogram	kg
Time	second	s
Temperature	kelvin	K
Amount of substance	mole	mol
Electric current	ampere	A
Luminous intensity	candela	cd

The Standard Units

Table 1.1 shows the standard SI base units. For now, we will focus on the first four of these units: the *metre*, the standard unit of length; the *kilogram*, the standard unit of mass; the *second*, the standard unit of time; and the *kelvin*, the standard unit of temperature.

The Metre: A Measure of Length

The **metre (m)** is defined as the distance light travels through a vacuum in precisely 1/299 792 458 s. A tall human is about 2 m tall and the CN Tower stands 553.3 m tall.

Scientists commonly deal with a wide range of lengths and distances. The separation between the sun and the closest star (Proxima Centauri) is about 3.8×10^{16} m, while many chemical bonds measure about 1.5×10^{-10} m.

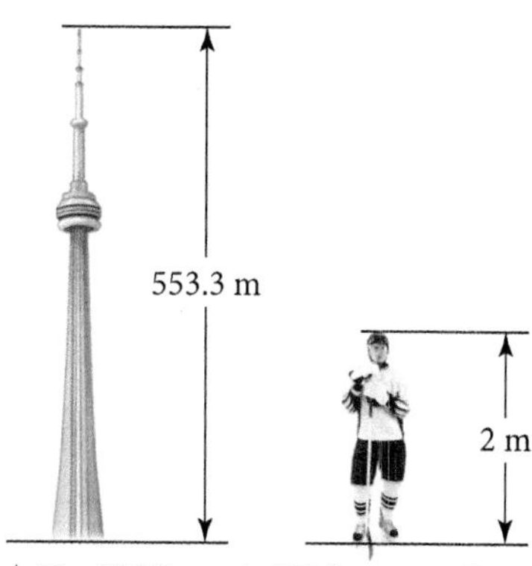

▲ The CN Tower is 553.3 metres tall. A hockey player is about 2 metres tall.

The Kilogram: A Measure of Mass

The **kilogram (kg)**, defined as the mass of a metal cylinder kept at the International Bureau of Weights and Measures at Sèvres, France, is a measure of *mass*, a quantity different from *weight*. The **mass** of an object is a measure of the quantity of matter within it, while the weight of an object is a measure of the *gravitational pull* on its matter and has the unit N, newtons. If you weigh yourself on the moon, for example, its weaker gravity pulls on you with less force than does Earth's gravity, resulting in a lower weight. A 75.0 kg person on Earth has a weight of 736 N. The same person would weigh just 122 N on the moon due to the moon's smaller gravitational field. However, the person's mass—the quantity of matter in his or her body—remains the same on every planet, 75.0 kg. This book has a mass of about 2.5 kg. A second common unit of mass is the gram (g). One gram is 1/1000 kg. A nickel has a mass of about 3.95 g.

The Second: A Measure of Time

The International Bureau of Weights and Measures originally defined the **second (s)** in terms of the day and the year, but a second is now defined more precisely as the duration of 9 192 631 770 periods of the radiation emitted from a certain transition in a cesium-133 atom. Scientists measure time on a large range of scales. The human heart beats about once every second, the age of the universe is estimated to be about 13.7 billion years, and some molecular bonds break or form in time periods as short as 1×10^{-15} s.

The Kelvin: A Measure of Temperature

The **kelvin (K)** is the SI unit of **temperature**. The temperature of a sample of matter is a measure of the average kinetic energy—the energy due to motion—of the atoms or molecules that compose the matter. The water molecules in a glass of *hot* water are, on average, moving faster than the molecules in a *cold* glass of water.

Temperature is an indirect measure of this molecular motion. Temperature also determines the direction of thermal energy transfer, or what we commonly call *heat*. Thermal energy transfers from hot objects to cold ones. For example, when you touch another person's warm hand (and yours is cold), thermal energy flows *from their hand to yours*, making your hand feel warmer. However, if you touch an ice cube, thermal energy flows *out of your hand* to the ice, cooling your hand (and possibly melting some of the ice cube).

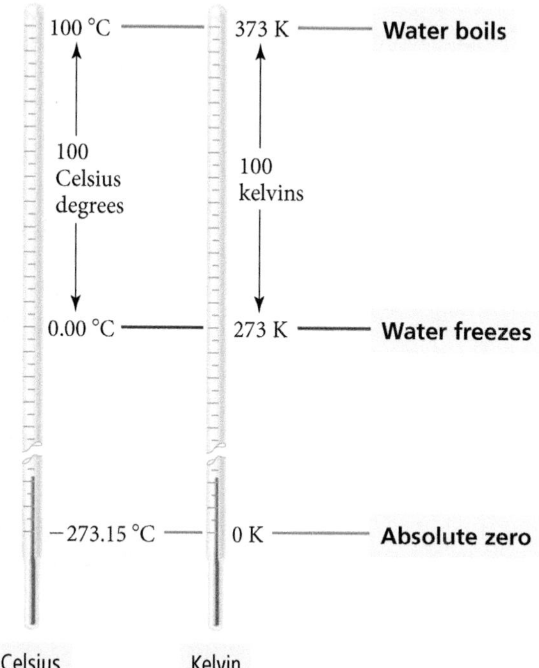

▲ **FIGURE 1.4 Comparison of the Celsius and Kelvin Temperature Scales** The zero point of the Kelvin scale is absolute zero (the lowest possible temperature), whereas the zero point of the Celsius scale is the freezing point of water.

In Figure 1.4 ▸, two common temperature scales are displayed. Most people (including scientists) use the **Celsius (°C) scale**. On this scale, pure water freezes at 0 °C and boils at 100 °C (at sea level). Room temperature is approximately 20 °C.

The SI unit for temperature, as we have seen, is the kelvin. The Kelvin scale (sometimes called the *absolute temperature scale*) avoids negative temperatures by assigning 0 K to the coldest temperature possible, absolute zero. Absolute zero (exactly −273.15 °C) is the temperature at which translational motion of molecules stops. Lower temperatures do not exist. The size of the kelvin is identical to that of the Celsius degree—the only difference is the temperature that each designates as zero. You can convert between the two temperature scales with the following formula:

Molecular motion does not *completely* stop at absolute zero because of the uncertainty principle in quantum mechanics, which we will discuss in Chapter 6.

Note that we give Kelvin temperatures in kelvins (*not* "degrees kelvin") or K (*not* °K).

$$\frac{T}{K} = \frac{T_C}{°C} + 273.15$$

Where T is the temperature in K and T_C is the temperature in °C.

Throughout this text, you will see examples worked out in formats that are designed to help you develop problem-solving skills. The most common format uses two columns to guide you through the worked example. The left column describes the thought processes and steps used in solving the problem, while the right column shows the implementation. The first example in this two-column format follows.

EXAMPLE 1.1 CONVERTING BETWEEN TEMPERATURE SCALES

A sick child has a dangerous temperature of 40.00 °C. What is the child's temperature in K?

SOLUTION

Begin by finding the equation that relates the quantity that is given (°C) and the quantity you are trying to find (K).	$\frac{T}{K} = \frac{T_C}{°C} + 273.15$
Since this equation gives the temperature in K directly, substitute in the correct value for the Celsius temperature and compute the answer.	$\frac{T}{K} = \frac{T_c}{°C} + 273.15$ $\frac{T}{K} = \frac{40.00\ \cancel{°C}}{\cancel{°C}} + 273.15$ $\frac{T}{K} = 313.15$ $T = 313.15\ K$

FOR PRACTICE 1.1

Gallium is a solid metal at room temperature, but will melt to a liquid in your hand. The melting point of gallium is 303.0 K. What is this temperature in the Celsius scale?

SI Prefixes

Scientific notation (see Appendix IA) allows us to express very large or very small quantities in a compact manner by using exponents. For example, the diameter of a proton can be written as 1.6×10^{-15} m. The International System of Units uses the **prefix multipliers**, shown in Table 1.2, with the standard units. These multipliers change the value of the unit by powers of 10. For example, the kilometre has the prefix "kilo," meaning 1000 times or 10^3 times. Therefore,

$$1 \text{ kilometre} = 1000 \text{ metres} = 10^3 \text{ metres}$$

Similarly, the millimetre has the prefix "milli," meaning 0.001 times or 10^{-3} times.

$$1 \text{ millimetre} = 0.001 \text{ metres} = 10^{-3} \text{ metres}$$

TABLE 1.2 Metric Prefixes

Prefix	Symbol	Multiplier	
exa	E	1 000 000 000 000 000 000	10^{18}
peta	P	1 000 000 000 000 000	10^{15}
tera	T	1 000 000 000 000	10^{12}
giga	G	1 000 000 000	10^{9}
mega	M	1 000 000	10^{6}
kilo	k	1000	10^{3}
hecto	h	100	10^{2}
deca	da	10	10^{1}
deci	d	0.1	10^{-1}
centi	c	0.01	10^{-2}
milli	m	0.001	10^{-3}
micro	μ	0.000 001	10^{-6}
nano	n	0.000 000 001	10^{-9}
pico	p	0.000 000 000 001	10^{-12}
femto	f	0.000 000 000 000 001	10^{-15}
atto	a	0.000 000 000 000 000 001	10^{-18}

Conversions Involving the SI Prefixes

When reporting the value of a measurement, we typically choose a prefix multiplier close to the size of the quantity being measured. For example, distances between cities are conveniently given in kilometres, but molecular dimensions such as bond length are typically reported in picometres. The distance between two singly bonded carbon atoms is 1.54×10^{-10} m, but this is sometimes more conveniently reported as 154 picometres (154 pm).

Knowing how to work with units of measurement is central to solving chemical problems. Even though many different units are used to report measured values, the SI base units of length, mass, and time are metre, kilogram, and second respectively. You will soon see that it is necessary to be able to convert between different units, and that this is a skill you must master right away.

We can use an example to illustrate how to convert between units using the metric prefixes. A hydrogen atom is 106 pm in diameter. To convert that diameter in pm to a value in m we must first find a **conversion factor**, a *value that when multiplied by a measured quantity changes it to a different unit of measure*. From Table 1.2, we find that

$$1 \text{ pm} = 10^{-12} \text{ m}$$

Another way of expressing this is as a ratio. To do this, *divide the side of the equality that has the unit you want to convert to, by the side of the equality you want to convert from.*

$\frac{\text{m}}{\text{pm}}$ and m pm^{-1} are both valid ways of expressing one unit divided by another, since $\frac{1}{\text{pm}} = \text{pm}^{-1}$. You will see both ways in science, and for the most part, the latter is the way you will see units expressed in this text.

$$\frac{10^{-12}\text{ m}}{1 \text{ pm}} = 10^{-12}\frac{\text{m}}{\text{pm}} \quad \text{or} \quad 10^{-12}\text{ m pm}^{-1}$$

Then, to convert the value from pm to m, we *multiply by this factor.*

$$106 \cancel{\text{pm}} \times 10^{-12}\text{ m }\cancel{\text{pm}^{-1}}$$
$$= 106 \times 10^{-12}\text{ m} \quad \text{or} \quad 1.06 \times 10^{-10}\text{ m}$$

Using units as a guide to solving problems is often called **dimensional analysis**. Units should always be included in calculations; they are multiplied, divided, and cancelled like any other algebraic quantity.

EXAMPLE 1.2 CONVERTING BETWEEN DIFFERENT SI PREFIXES

If DNA from a single cell were stretched out, it would have a length of about 2 m and a diameter of about 2.4 nm. What is the diameter of the stretched DNA molecule in μm?

SOLUTION

Begin by writing down the important information that is provided in the question as well as the information you are asked to find. In this case, you are told that a stretched DNA molecule is 2.4 nm in diameter and you are asked to convert this value to micrometres.	**GIVEN:** diameter = 2.4 nm **FIND:** diameter in μm
Next, we need to derive a conversion factor to convert from the unit the quantity is expressed in to the desired unit. Table 1.2 has the SI prefixes expressed in m. To convert from nm to μm, we are going to require two conversion factors—one factor to convert from nm to m, and then one factor to convert from m to μm.	From Table 1.2, we can see that 1 nm = 10^{-9} m. We first want to convert from nm to m, so we divide the side with m by the side with nm, $\frac{10^{-9}\text{ m}}{1\text{ nm}}$, to yield the conversion factor: 10^{-9} m nm^{-1} Also from Table 1.2, 1 μm = 10^{-6} m. We want to convert from m to μm, so we divide the side with μm by the side with m, $\frac{1\,\mu\text{m}}{10^{-6}\text{ m}}$, to yield the conversion factor: 10^{6} μm m^{-1}

(continued)

EXAMPLE 1.2 (CONTINUED)

Finally, we multiply the quantity given by both conversion factors to yield the quantity in the desired units.	**SOLVE:** $2.4\ \cancel{\text{nm}} \times (10^{-9}\ \cancel{\text{m}}\ \cancel{\text{nm}^{-1}}) \times (10^{6}\ \mu\text{m}\ \cancel{\text{m}^{-1}})$ $= 2.4 \times 10^{-3}\ \mu\text{m}$

CHECK You should always take a minute to make sure your answer makes sense. In this case, we wanted to convert from nm, a smaller unit to μm, a larger unit. It makes sense that the number has become smaller.

FOR PRACTICE 1.2

The world's longest carbon–carbon bond is 1.704×10^{-10} m (Schreiner *et al.*, *Nature*, 2011, **477**, 308). Convert this bond length to nm and to pm.

FOR MORE PRACTICE 1.2

A chemist requires 150 mg of a certain chemical each time she conducts an experiment. She has 11.0 g of the chemical available. How many times can she repeat the experiment?

Derived Units

Derived units are either combinations of different units or multiples of units of the same type. For example, the SI unit for speed is metres per second (m s^{-1}). Notice that this unit is formed from two other SI base units—metres and seconds—put together. You are probably more familiar with speed in kilometres per hour—also an example of a derived unit. Other common derived units in chemistry are those for volume and density. We will look at each of these individually.

Volume The measure of space is referred to as **volume**. Any unit of length, when cubed (raised to the third power), becomes a unit of volume. Thus, the cubic metre (m^3) and cubic centimetre (cm^3) are units of volume. The cubic nature of volume is not always intuitive, and we have to think abstractly in order to think about volume. For example, consider the following question: How many small cubes measuring 1 cm on each side are required to construct a large cube measuring 10 cm (or 1 dm) on each side?

The answer to this question, as you can see by carefully examining the unit cube in Figure 1.5 ◄, is 1000 small cubes. When you go from a linear, one-dimensional distance to three-dimensional volume, you must raise both the linear dimension *and* its unit to the third power. Thus, the volume of a cube is equal to the length of its edge cubed:

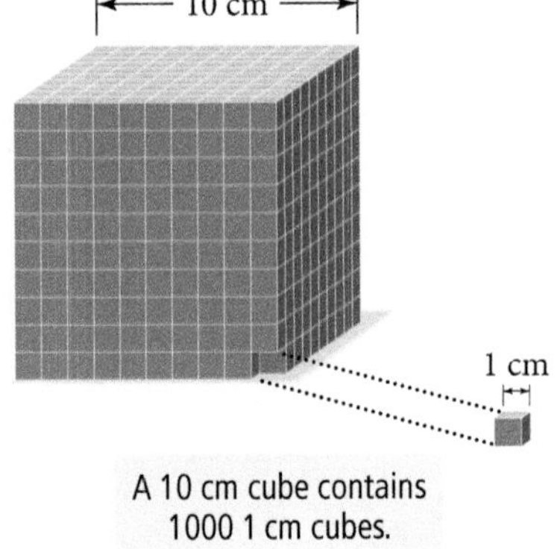

▲ **FIGURE 1.5 The Relationship Between Length and Volume**

$$\text{volume of cube} = (\text{edge length})^3$$

A cube with a 10 cm edge length has a volume of $(10\,\text{cm})^3$ (or 1000 cm^3), and a cube with a 100 cm edge length has a volume of $(100\,\text{cm})^3$ (or 1×10^6 cm^3).

To convert from m^3 to mm^3, we construct the conversion factor as follows:

$$1\ \text{m} = 1000\ \text{mm}$$
$$(1\ \text{m})^3 = (1000\ \text{mm})^3$$
$$1\ \text{m}^3 = 10^9\ \text{mm}^3$$

Then, express this equality as a ratio by dividing the side of the equality with the units you want to convert to, by the side of the equality you want to convert from:

$$1\ \text{m}^3 = 10^9\,\text{mm}^3$$
$$10^9\ \text{mm}^3\ \text{m}^{-3}$$

This is the conversion factor to convert from m^3 to mm^3. You should also realize that to convert from mm^3 to m^3, the conversion factor is just the inverse:

$$10^{-9}\ \text{m}^3\ \text{mm}^{-3}$$

Other common units of volume in chemistry are the **litre (L)**, which is equivalent to 1 dm^3; and the **millilitre (mL)**, which is equivalent to 1 cm^3. One m^3 is equivalent to a kilolitre (kL). The common units of volume are listed in Table 1.3.

TABLE 1.3 Some Common Derived Units

Quantity	Unit Name	Symbol
density	kilogram per cubic metre	kg m^{-3}
	gram per cubic centimetre	g cm^{-3}
	gram per millilitre	g mL^{-1}
speed	metre per second	m s^{-1}
	kilometre per hour	km h^{-1}
volume	cubic centimetre, millilitre	cm^3 = mL
	decimetre cubed, litre	dm^3 = L
	cubic metre, kilolitre	m^3 = kL

Density An old riddle asks, "Which weighs more, a tonne of bricks or a tonne of feathers?" The answer, of course, is neither—they both weigh the same (1 tonne). If you answered bricks, you confused weight with density. The **density (*d*)** of a substance is the ratio of its mass (m) to its volume (V):

$$\text{density} = \frac{\text{mass}}{\text{volume}} \quad \text{or} \quad d = \frac{m}{V}$$

The m in the equation for density is in italic type, meaning that it stands for mass rather than for metres. In general, the symbols for units such as metres (m), seconds (s), or kelvins (K) appear in regular type, while those for variables such as mass (m), volume (V), and time (t) appear in italics.

Density is a characteristic physical property of materials and differs from one substance to another, as you can see in Table 1.4. The density of a substance also depends on its temperature. Density is an example of an **intensive property**, one that is *independent* of the amount of the substance. The density of aluminum, for example, is the same whether you have an ounce or a tonne. Intensive properties are often used to identify substances because these properties depend only on the type of substance, not on the amount of it. For example, from Table 1.4 you can see that pure gold has a density of 19.3 g cm^{-3}. One way to determine whether a substance is pure gold is to measure its density and compare it to 19.3 g cm^{-3}. Mass, in contrast, is an **extensive property**, one that depends on the amount of the substance.

The units of density are those of mass divided by volume. Although the SI-derived unit for density is kg m^{-3}, the density of liquids and solids is most often expressed in g cm^{-3} or g mL^{-1} (cm^3 and mL are equivalent units; 1 cm^3 = 1 mL). Aluminum is one of the least dense structural metals with a density of 2.70 g cm^{-3}, while platinum is one of the densest metals with a density of 21.4 g cm^{-3}.

We calculate the density of a substance by dividing the mass of a given amount of the substance by its volume. For example, suppose a small nugget we suspect to be gold has a mass of 22.5 g and a volume of 2.38 cm^3. To find its density, we divide the mass by the volume:

$$d = \frac{m}{V} = \frac{22.5 \text{ g}}{2.38 \text{ cm}^3} = 9.45 \text{ g cm}^{-3}$$

In this case, the density reveals that the nugget is not pure gold.

TABLE 1.4 Density of Some Common Substances at 20 °C*

Substance	Density (g cm^{-3})
Charcoal (from oak)	0.57
Ethanol	0.789
Ice	0.917 (at 0 °C)
Water	1.00 (at 4 °C)
Sugar (sucrose)	1.58
Glass	2.6
Aluminum	2.70
Copper	8.96
Gold	19.3
Iron	7.86
Lead	11.4
Mercury	13.55
Platinum	21.4
Titanium	4.51

*Unless otherwise indicated.

EXAMPLE 1.3 CALCULATING DENSITY AND CONVERTING DENSITY UNITS

A student conducts an experiment to determine the density of air. He weighs an evacuated flask and one filled with air at ambient pressure, and determines the difference in mass (corresponding to the mass of air) to be 2.27 g. By displacement of water, he determines the volume of the flask to be 1.68 L. (a) Determine the density of air in g L^{-1}. (b) Convert the density to units of g cm^{-3} in order to compare it to the density of a solid like aluminum.

(*continued*)

EXAMPLE 1.3 (CONTINUED)

SOLUTION

Set up the problem by writing the important information that is given as well as the information that you are asked to find. Here, we are asked to find the density of air in the flask and then to convert the units of $g\ L^{-1}$ to $g\ cm^{-3}$ to compare to the density of aluminum metal.	**GIVEN:** $m = 2.27\ g$ $V = 1.68\ L$ **FIND:** (a) density in $g\ L^{-1}$ (b) density in $g\ cm^{-3}$
Next, write down the equation that defines density.	**EQUATION:** $d = \frac{m}{V}$
(a) Solve the problem by substituting the correct values of mass and volume into the expression for density. (b) Next, determine a conversion factor to convert L to cm^3 and apply this conversion factor to the quantity you need to convert. Since $1\ cm^3 = 1\ mL$, converting from L to mL is the same as converting from L to cm^3.	**SOLVE:** $d = \frac{2.27\ g}{1.68\ L} = 1.35\ g\ L^{-1}$ $1\ L = 10^3\ mL$ $1\ L = 10^3\ cm^3$ Thus, the conversion factor is $10^{-3}\ L\ cm^{-3}$. $1.35\ g\ \cancel{L^{-1}} \times 10^{-3}\ \cancel{L}\ cm^{-3} = 1.35 \times 10^{-3}\ g\ cm^{-3}$ The density of aluminum is $2.70\ g\ cm^{-3}$ and as such, is 2000 times as dense as air.

CHECK Ensure your answer makes sense. We know that air is not nearly as dense as a metal, so our answer, which says that air is 2000 times less dense than aluminum, makes sense.

FOR PRACTICE 1.3

The mass of a helium-4 nucleus is 6.7×10^{-27} kg and the radius is 1.9 fm (femtometres). Calculate the density of a helium nucleus in $kg\ fm^{-3}$ and in $g\ cm^{-3}$. Assume the atom is a sphere (volume $= (4/3)\pi r^3$).

FOR MORE PRACTICE 1.3

A metal cube has an edge length of 11.4 mm and a mass of 6.67 g. Calculate the density of the metal and use Table 1.4 to determine the likely identity of the metal.

CONCEPTUAL CONNECTION 1.2

Density

The density of copper decreases as temperature increases (as does the density of most substances). Which of the following will be true upon changing the temperature of a sample of copper from room temperature to 95 °C?

(a) the copper sample will become lighter

(b) the copper sample will become heavier

(c) the copper sample will expand

(d) the copper sample will contract

The units of a quantity should always be written with the number, even when performing a calculation. Let's return to the Gimli Glider example that we discussed at the beginning of the section. The correction factor that the ground crew were using to convert the mass of jet fuel to a volume was actually the density of the jet fuel, $1.77\ lb\ L^{-1}$, however, it was expressed in incorrect units. Had the ground crew kept the units with their quantities, they would have immediately realized their mistake.

$$V = \frac{m}{d} = \frac{22\,300\ kg}{1.77\ lb\ L^{-1}} = 1.26 \times 10^4\ L\ kg\ lb^{-1}$$

The units of the answer are clearly not appropriate for the quantity they were trying to obtain, which should have the units of L, not L kg lb^{-1}. The calculation with the density expressed in the correct units, 0.803 kg L^{-1}, is:

$$V = \frac{m}{d} = \frac{22\,300\ \cancel{\text{kg}}}{0.803\ \cancel{\text{kg}}\ \text{L}^{-1}} = 2.78 \times 10^4\ \text{L}$$

The volume of fuel calculated by the ground crew was less than half of the actual requirement.

Derived Units with Special Names Compiled in Table 1.5 are some common units in chemistry that are derived from the SI base units, which are also given special names. For example, the joule (J) is a derived unit and can be expressed in SI base units:

$$\text{J} = \text{kg m}^2\ \text{s}^{-2}$$

It is important to become familiar with how these derived units are expressed in the base units. For example, you know that energy or work (w) is a force (F) acting over a distance (d), or:

$$w = F \times d$$

The unit of force is the newton (N) and the unit of distance is the metre (m), so the unit of work would be N · m. If we express the newton in its SI base units, work has the units:

$$\text{kg m s}^{-2} \cdot \text{m} = \text{kg m}^2\ \text{s}^{-2} = \text{J}$$

CHEMISTRY AND MEDICINE Bone Density

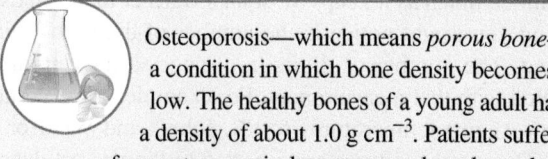

Osteoporosis—which means *porous bone*—is a condition in which bone density becomes too low. The healthy bones of a young adult have a density of about 1.0 g cm^{-3}. Patients suffering from osteoporosis, however, can have bone densities as low as 0.22 g cm^{-3}. These low densities mean the bones have deteriorated and weakened, resulting in increased susceptibility to fractures, especially hip fractures. Patients suffering from osteoporosis can also experience height loss and disfiguration such as dowager's hump, a condition in which the patient becomes hunched over due to compression of the vertebrae. Osteoporosis is most common in postmenopausal women, but it can also occur in people (including men) who have certain diseases, such as insulin-dependent diabetes, or who take certain medications, such as prednisone. Osteoporosis is usually diagnosed and monitored with hip X-rays. Low-density bones absorb fewer of the X-rays than do high-density bones, producing characteristic differences in the X-ray image. Treatments for osteoporosis include additional calcium and vitamin D, drugs that prevent bone weakening, exercise and strength training, and, in extreme cases, hip-replacement surgery.

Question

Suppose you find a large animal bone in the woods, too large to fit in a beaker or flask. How might you approximate its density?

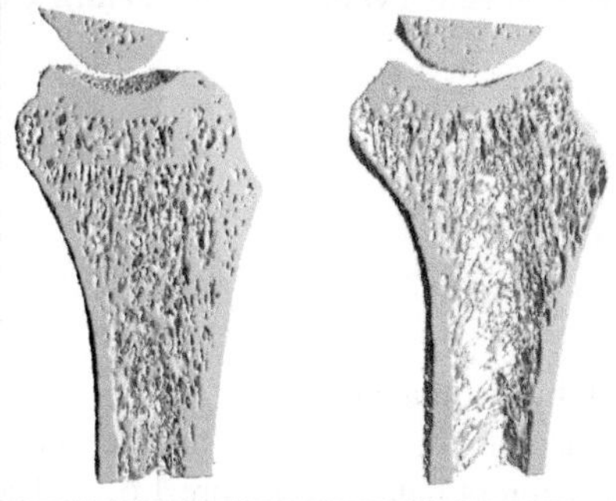

▲ Magnified views of the bone matrix in a normal femur (left) and one weakened by osteoporosis (right).

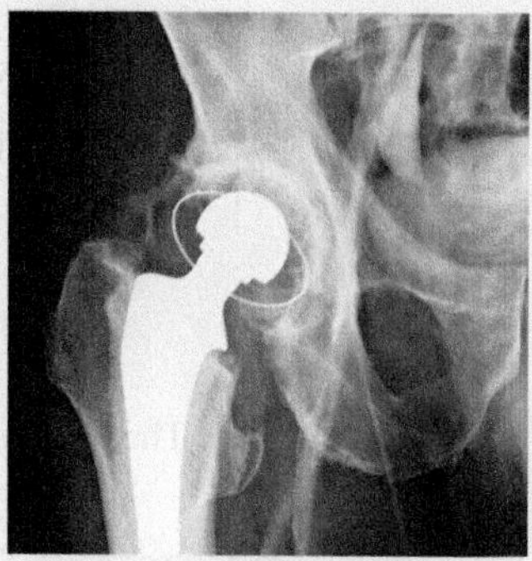

▲ Severe osteoporosis can necessitate surgery to implant an artificial hip joint, seen in this X-ray image.

TABLE 1.5 Common Derived Units with Special Names

Quantity	Unit Name	Symbol	Expression in Terms of SI Base Units
energy, work, heat	joule	J	$kg\ m^2\ s^{-2}$
pressure	pascal	Pa	$kg\ m^{-1}\ s^{-2}$
	bar	bar	$(=10^5\ Pa = 10^5\ kg\ m^{-1}\ s^{-2})$
	kilopascal	kPa	$(=10^3\ Pa = 10^3\ kg\ m^{-1}\ s^{-2})$
force	newton	N	$kg\ m\ s^{-2}$
electric charge	coulomb	C	A s
voltage, electrochemical potential	volt	V	$kg\ m^2\ s^{-2}\ C^{-1}$
frequency	hertz	Hz	s^{-1}

1.4 The Reliability of a Measurement

TABLE 1.6 Maximum August Temperatures in St. John's, NL and Windsor, ON

	Max Temp (°C)	
Year	St. John's, NL	Windsor, ON
2005	26.2	33.6
2006	24.7	35.9
2007	26.3	34.1
2008	25.6	33.5
2009	25.8	34.4
2010	26.2	33.9
2011	26.4	32.7
2012	28.4	35.1
2013	25.1	31.0
2014	27.8	30.6

One thing we spend a lot of time doing is checking the temperature. Is it cold outside, just right, or hot? In fact, we keep records of temperatures and these records date back to before the 1950s for many cities in the world. Table 1.6 lists the maximum temperatures experienced for the month of August over a one-decade time period beginning in 2005 for both St. John's, NL—a coastal city in the North Atlantic Ocean—and Windsor, ON, a city that is more centrally located in North America.

The first thing you will notice is that St. John's has a coastal climate. St. John's is considerably cooler than Windsor, mainly because the Atlantic Ocean, a vast heat sink, keeps it cooler in the summer, much as it keeps St. John's warmer than Windsor in the winter. The second thing you might notice is the number of digits to which the measurements are reported. The number of digits in a reported measurement indicates the certainty associated with that measurement. For example, a less certain measurement of the maximum August temperatures for St. John's and Windsor in 2010 might be 26 and 34 °C. These temperatures are reported to the nearest degree Celsius, while the data in Table 1.6 are reported to the nearest 0.1 °C.

Scientists agree on a standard way of reporting measured quantities in which the number of reported digits reflects the certainty in the measurement: more digits, more certainty; fewer digits, less certainty. Numbers are usually written so that the uncertainty is ± 1 in the last reported digit unless otherwise indicated. By reporting the temperature as 26.2 °C, scientists mean 26.2 $\pm$ 0.1 °C. This means that the temperature is between 26.1 and 26.3 °C—it might be 26.3 °C, for example, but it could not be 27.0 °C. In contrast, if the reported value was 26 °C, this would mean 26 $\pm$ 1 °C, or between 25 and 27 °C. In general,

Scientific measurements are reported so that every digit is certain except the last, which is estimated.

For example, consider the following reported number:

5.213

↗ ↖

certain estimated

The first three digits are certain; the last digit is estimated.

The number of digits reported in a measurement depends on the measuring device. Consider weighing a pistachio nut on two different balances (Figure 1.6 ▶). The balance on the left has marks every 1 g, while the balance on the right has marks every 0.1 g. For the balance on the left, we mentally divide the space between the 1 and 2 g marks into ten equal spaces and estimate that the pointer is at about 1.2 g. We then write the measurement as 1.2 g, indicating that we are sure of the "1" but have estimated the ".2". The

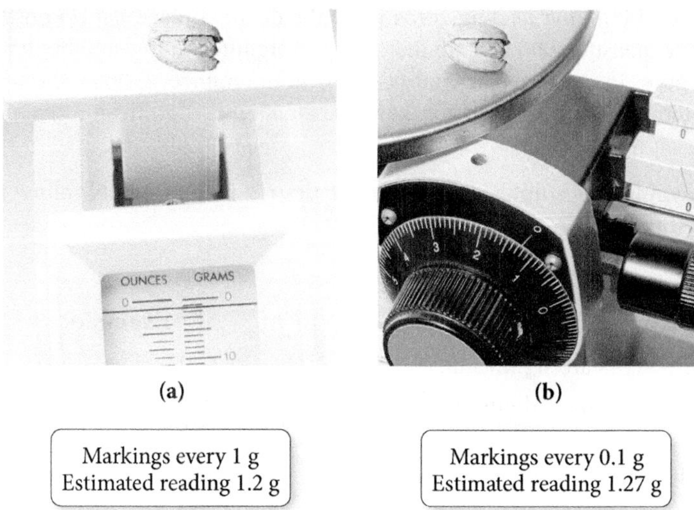

◀ **FIGURE 1.6 Estimation in Weighing** **(a)** This scale has markings every 1 g, so we estimate to the tenths place by mentally dividing the space into ten equal spaces to estimate the last digit. This reading is 1.2 g. **(b)** Because this balance has markings every 0.1 g, we estimate to the hundredths place. This reading is 1.27 g.

balance on the right, with marks every *tenth* of a gram, requires us to write the result with more digits. The pointer is between the 1.2 g mark and the 1.3 g mark. We again divide the space between the two marks into ten equal spaces and estimate the third digit. For the figure shown, we report 1.27 g.

EXAMPLE 1.4 REPORTING THE CORRECT NUMBER OF DIGITS

The graduated cylinder shown at right has markings every 0.1 mL. Report the volume (which is read at the bottom of the meniscus) to the correct number of digits. (Note: the meniscus is the crescent-shaped surface at the top of a column of liquid.)

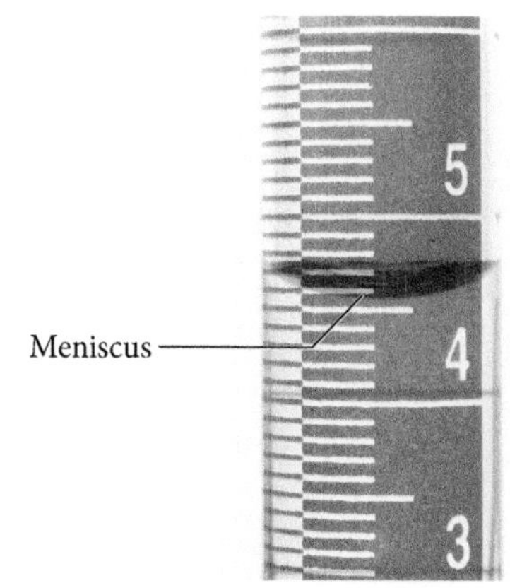

SOLUTION

Since the bottom of the meniscus is between the 4.5 and 4.6 mL markings, mentally divide the space between the markings into ten equal spaces and estimate the next digit. In this case, you should report the result as 4.57 mL.

What if you estimated a little differently and wrote 4.56 mL? In general, one unit difference in the last digit is acceptable because the last digit is estimated and different people might estimate it slightly differently. However, if you wrote 4.63 mL, you would have misreported the measurement.

FOR PRACTICE 1.4

Record the temperature on the thermometer shown at right to the correct number of digits.

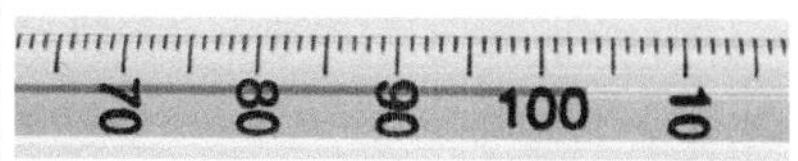

Counting Significant Figures

The certainty of a measurement—which depends on the instrument used to make the measurement—must be preserved, not only when recording the measurement, but also when performing calculations that use the measurement. We can accomplish the preservation of this certainty by using *significant figures.* In any reported measurement, the nonplaceholding digits—those that are not simply marking the decimal place—are called **significant figures** (or **significant digits**). *The greater the number of significant figures, the greater the certainty of the measurement.* For example, the number 23.5 has three significant figures, while the number 23.56 has four. To determine the number of significant figures in a number containing zeros, we must distinguish between zeros that are significant and those that simply mark the decimal place. For example, in the number 0.0008, the leading zeros mark the decimal place but *do not* add to the certainty of the measurement and are therefore not significant; this number has only one significant figure. In contrast, the trailing zeros in the number 0.000800 *do* add to the certainty of the measurement and are therefore counted as significant; this number has three significant figures.

To determine the number of significant figures in a number, follow these rules (with examples shown on the right):

Significant Figure Rules	Examples	
1. All nonzero digits are significant.	28.03	0.0540
2. Zeros between nonzero digits are significant.	408	7.0301
3. Zeros to the left of the first nonzero digit are not significant. They only serve to locate the decimal point.	0.0032	0.00006
	not significant	
4. Zeros at the end of a number are categorized as follows:		
a) Zeros after a decimal point are always significant.	45.000	3.5600
b) Zeros before a decimal point and after a nonzero number are always significant.	140.00	2500.55
c) Zeros before an implied decimal point are ambiguous and scientific notation should be used.	1200	ambiguous
	1.2×10^3	2 significant figures
	1.20×10^3	3 significant figures
	1.200×10^3	4 significant figures

When reporting temperatures, the previous rules (specifically 4c) may not be obeyed. When a temperature such as 300 K is reported, according to rule 4c, the number of significant figures is ambiguous; there could be one or three significant figures. *In chemistry*, temperature is almost always measured to an uncertainty of at least ±1 °C (or K). Therefore, if a temperature such as 100 °C, 300 K, or 420 K is reported, then there are three significant figures. Of course, if a temperature such as 300.0 K is given, then there are four significant figures.

Exact Numbers

Exact numbers have no uncertainty, and thus do not limit the number of significant figures in any calculation. We can regard an exact number as having an unlimited number of significant figures. Exact numbers originate from three sources:

- From the accurate counting of discrete objects. For example, 3 atoms means 3.00000 . . . atoms.
- From defined quantities, such as the number of centimetres in 1 m. Because 100 cm is defined as 1 m,

  $$100\,\text{cm} = 1\text{ m means } 100.000000\ldots\text{ cm} = 1.000000\ldots\text{ m}$$

  Another example is the conversion from °C to K, which is to add exactly 273.15 or 273.15000000. . . .
- From integral numbers that are part of an equation. For example, in the equation $radius = \frac{diameter}{2}$, the number 2 is exact and therefore has an unlimited number of significant figures.

EXAMPLE 1.5 **DETERMINING THE NUMBER OF SIGNIFICANT FIGURES IN A NUMBER**

How many significant figures are in each number?

(a) 0.04450 m
(b) 5.0003 km
(c) 100 cm m^{-1}
(d) 1.000×10^5 s
(e) 0.00002 mm
(f) 10 000 m
(g) 350 K

(a) 0.04450 m	*Four significant figures.* The two 4s and the 5 are significant (rule 1). The last zero is after a decimal point and is therefore significant (rule 4a). The leading zeros only mark the decimal place and are therefore not significant (rule 3).
(b) 5.0003 km	*Five significant figures.* The 5 and 3 are significant (rule 1) as are the three interior zeros (rule 2).
(c) 100 cm m^{-1}	*Unlimited significant figures.* Defined quantities have an unlimited number of significant figures.
(d) 1.000×10^5 s	*Four significant figures.* The 1 is significant (rule 1). The trailing zeros are after a decimal point and therefore significant (rule 4a).
(e) 0.00002 mm	*One significant figure.* The 2 is significant (rule 1). The leading zeros only mark the decimal place and are therefore not significant (rule 3).
(f) 10 000 m	*Ambiguous.* The 1 is significant (rule 1) but the trailing zeros occur before an implied decimal point and are therefore ambiguous (rule 4). Without more information, we would assume one significant figure. It is better to write this than to indicate a specific number of significant figures (rule 4c).
(g) 350 K	*Three significant figures.* Temperature can be assumed to be read to the nearest 1 °C at least.

FOR PRACTICE 1.5

How many significant figures are in each number?

(a) 554 km
(b) 7 pennies
(c) 1.01×10^5 m
(d) 0.00099 s
(e) 1.4500 km
(f) 21 000 m
(g) 200 °C

Significant Figures in Calculations

When you use measured quantities in calculations, the results of the calculation must reflect the precision of the measured quantities. You should not lose or gain certainty during mathematical operations. Follow these rules when carrying significant figures through calculations.

Rules for Calculations

1. In multiplication or division, the result carries the same number of significant figures as the factor with the fewest significant figures. For example:

$$\underset{\text{(4 sig. figures)}}{1.052} \times \underset{\text{(5 sig. figures)}}{12.054} \times \underset{\text{(2 sig. figures)}}{0.53} = 6.7208 = \underset{\text{(2 sig. figures)}}{6.7}$$

$$\underset{\text{(5 sig. figures)}}{2.0035} \div \underset{\text{(3 sig. figures)}}{3.20} = 0.626094 = \underset{\text{(3 sig. figures)}}{0.626}$$

2. In addition or subtraction, the result carries the same number of decimal places as the quantity with the fewest decimal places. Here are a few examples:

$$\begin{array}{l} 2.345 \\ 0.07 \\ \underline{2.9975} \\ 5.4125 = 5.41 \end{array} \qquad \begin{array}{r} 98.6122 \\ \underline{3.11} \\ 101.7222 = 101.72 \end{array} \qquad \begin{array}{r} 5.9 \\ \underline{-0.221} \\ 5.679 = 5.7 \end{array}$$

3. When computing the logarithm of a number, the result has the same number of significant figures after the decimal point (called the mantissa) as there are significant figures in the number whose logarithm is being calculated. The digits before the decimal place in the answer represent the *order of magnitude*. For example:

In this text, log means take the base 10 logarithm (i.e., $\log_{10}$) and ln means take the natural logarithm.

$\log(45.250) = \log(4.5250 \times 10^1) = 1.65562$
(5 sig. figures after the decimal)
$\log(1106.26) = \log(1.10626 \times 10^3) = 3.043857$
(6 sig. figures after the decimal)
$\log(6.2 \times 10^{10}) = 10.79$
(2 sig. figures after the decimal)

The same is true for taking the natural logarithm:

$\ln(6.89 \times 10^5) = 13.443$ (3 sig. figures after the decimal)

4. When computing the antilogarithm (the inverse of the logarithm), the number of significant figures in the result is the same as the number of significant digits after the decimal (the mantissa). The number before the decimal place represents the order of magnitude. For example:

e is a mathematical constant. To 5 significant figures, $e = 2.7183$. Natural base logarithms and antilogarithms are used quite often in chemistry, so it is useful to become familiar with them.

$10^{6.125} = 1.33 \times 10^6$ (3 sig. figures)
$10^{-10.00} = 1.0 \times 10^{-10}$ (2 sig. figures)
$e^{12.2} = 2 \times 10^5$ (1 sig. figure)

Rules for Rounding

A common rule when rounding a large number of values to be averaged is the "round to even" rule in which 5.35 would round to 5.4 and 5.45 would round to 5.4 since the last significant figure before the 5 is an even number. We will use the simpler rule in this text since it is consistent with most calculators.

When rounding to the correct number of significant figures, round down if the last (or rightmost) digit dropped is four or less; round up if the last (or rightmost) digit dropped is five or more. To two significant figures:

5.37 rounds to 5.4
5.34 rounds to 5.3
5.35 rounds to 5.4
5.349 rounds to 5.3

Notice in the last example that only the *rightmost digit being dropped* determines in which direction to round—ignore all digits to the right of it.

To avoid rounding errors in multistep calculations, round only the final answer—do not round intermediate steps. If you write down intermediate answers, keep track of significant figures by underlining the last significant digit.

$$\begin{aligned} &6.78 \times 5.903 \times (5.489 - 5.01) \\ &= 6.78 \times 5.903 \times 0.4\underline{7}9 \\ &= 19.1707 \\ &= 19 \end{aligned}$$

underline last significant digit

Notice that for multiplication or division, the quantity with the fewest *significant figures* determines the number of *significant figures* in the answer, but for addition and subtraction, the quantity with the fewest *decimal places* determines the number of *decimal places* in the answer. In multiplication and division, we focus on significant figures, but in addition and subtraction, we focus on decimal places. When a problem involves addition or subtraction, the answer may have a different number of significant figures than the initial quantities. Keep this in mind when working problems that involve both addition or subtraction and multiplication or division. For example,

$$\frac{1.002 - 0.999}{3.754} = \frac{0.003}{3.754} = 7.99 \times 10^{-4} = 8 \times 10^{-4}$$

The answer has only one significant figure, even though the initial numbers had three or four.

EXAMPLE 1.6 SIGNIFICANT FIGURES IN CALCULATIONS

Perform each calculation and report the answer to the correct number of significant figures.

(a) $1.10 \times 0.5120 \times 4.0015 \div 3.4555$

(b) $0.355 + 105.1 - 100.5820$

(c) $4.562 \times 3.99870 \div (452.6755 - 452.33)$

(d) $\log(16.45) + 2.34$

(e) $e^{8.125} \times 2.551 \times 10^{-3}$

(a) Round the intermediate result (in blue) to three significant figures to reflect the three significant figures in the least precisely known quantity (1.10).	$1.10 \times 0.5120 \times 4.0015 \div 3.4555$ $= 0.65219$ $= 0.652$
(b) Round the intermediate answer (in blue) to one decimal place to reflect the quantity with the fewest decimal places (105.1). Notice that 105.1 is *not* the quantity with the fewest significant figures, but it has the fewest decimal places and therefore determines the number of decimal places in the answer.	0.355 105.1 -100.5820 $4.8730 = 4.9$
(c) Mark the intermediate result to two decimal places to reflect the number of decimal places in the quantity within the parentheses having the fewest number of decimal places (452.33). Round the final answer to two significant figures to reflect the two significant figures in the least precisely known quantity (0.3455).	$4.562 \times 3.99870 \div (452.6755 - 452.33)$ $= 4.562 \times 3.99870 \div 0.34\underline{5}5$ $= 52.79904$ $= 53$
(d) Mark the intermediate result to the fourth digit after the decimal to reflect the number of significant figures in the result of the logarithm. Round the final answer to two decimal places to reflect the two decimal places in the least precisely known quantity (2.34).	$\log(16.45) + 2.34$ $= 1.216\underline{1}7 + 2.34$ $= 3.55617$ $= 3.56$
(e) Mark the intermediate result to three significant figures to reflect the three significant figures in the antilogarithm. Round the final answer to three significant figures to reflect the three significant figures in the least precisely known quantity (the antilogarithm).	$e^{8.125} \times 2.551 \times 10^{-3}$ $= 3.3\underline{7}79 \times 10^{3} \times 2.551 \times 10^{-3}$ $= 8.6169$ $= 8.62$

FOR PRACTICE 1.6

Perform each calculation to the correct number of significant figures.

(a) $3.10007 \times 9.441 \times 0.0301 \div 2.31$

(b) $0.881 + 132.1 - 12.02$

(c) $2.5110 \times 21.20 \div (44.11 + 1.233)$

(d) $\ln(12.5) - 0.0284$

(e) $10^{8.1325} \div 2.6 \times 10^{-3}$

Precision and Accuracy

Scientists often repeat measurements several times to increase confidence in the result. We can distinguish between two different kinds of certainty—called accuracy and precision—associated with such repeated measurements. **Accuracy** refers to how close the measured value is to the actual value. **Precision** refers to how close a series of measurements are to one another or how reproducible they are. A series of measurements can be precise (close to one another in value, and reproducible) but not accurate (not close to the true value). Consider the results of three students who repeatedly weighed a lead block known to have a true mass of 10.00 g (indicated by the solid horizontal blue line on the graphs on the next page).

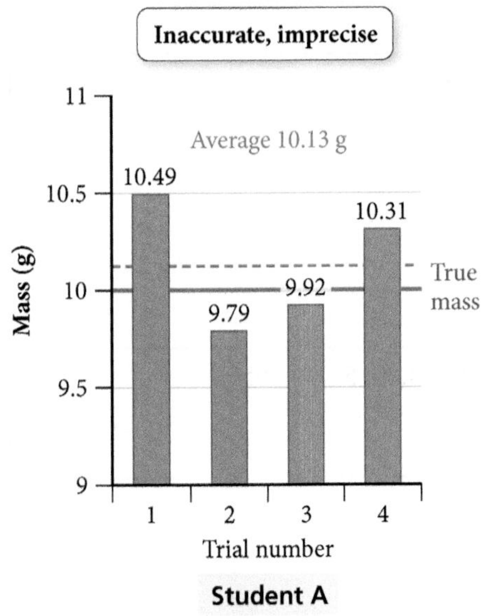

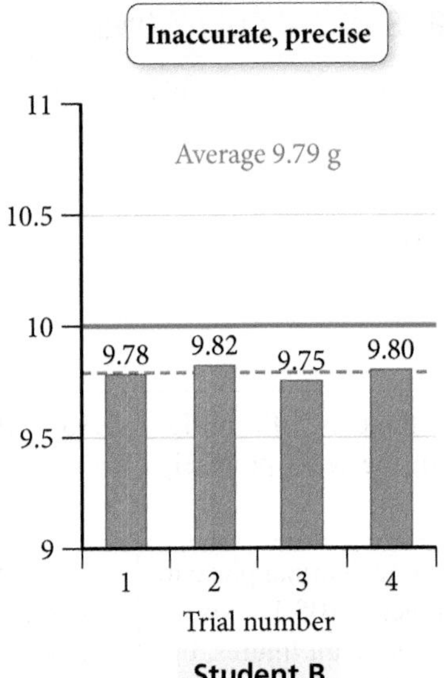

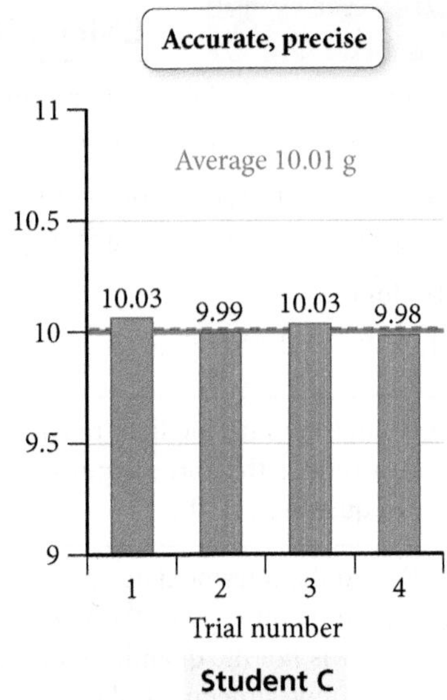

	Student A	Student B	Student C
Trial 1	10.49 g	9.78 g	10.03 g
Trial 2	9.79 g	9.82 g	9.99 g
Trial 3	9.92 g	9.75 g	10.03 g
Trial 4	10.31 g	9.80 g	9.98 g
Average	**10.13 g**	**9.79 g**	**10.01 g**

- The results of student A are both inaccurate (not close to the true value) and imprecise (not consistent with one another). The inconsistency is the result of **random error**, error that has equal probability of being too high or too low. Almost all measurements have some degree of random error. Random error can, with enough trials, average itself out.
- The results of student B are precise (close to one another in value) but inaccurate. The inaccuracy is the result of **systematic error**, error that tends toward being either too high or too low. Systematic error does not average out with repeated trials. For instance, if a balance is not properly calibrated, it may systematically read too high or too low.
- The results of student C display little systematic error or random error—they are both accurate and precise.

THE NATURE OF SCIENCE Integrity in Data Gathering

Most scientists spend many hours collecting data in the laboratory. Often, the data do not turn out exactly as the scientist had expected (or hoped). A scientist may then be tempted to "fudge" his or her results. For example, suppose you are expecting a particular set of measurements to follow a certain pattern. After working hard over several days or weeks to make the measurements, you notice that a few of them do not quite fit the pattern that you anticipated. You might find yourself wishing that you could simply change or omit the "faulty" measurements. Altering data in this way is considered highly unethical in the scientific community and, when discovered, the scientist is usually punished severely.

In 2004, Dr. Hwang Woo Suk, a stem cell researcher at the Seoul National University in Korea, published a research paper in *Science* (a highly respected research journal) claiming that he and his colleagues had cloned human embryonic stem cells. As part of his evidence, he showed photographs of the cells. The paper was hailed as an incredible breakthrough, and Dr. Hwang travelled the world lecturing on his work. *Time* magazine even listed him among their "people that matter" for 2004. Several months later, however, one of his co-workers revealed that the photographs were fraudulent. According to the co-worker, the photographs came from a computer data bank of stem cell photographs, not from a cloning experiment. A university panel investigated the results and confirmed that the photographs and other data had indeed been faked. Dr. Hwang was forced to resign his prestigious post at the university.

Although not common, incidents like this do occur from time to time. They are damaging to a community that is largely built on trust. A scientist's peers (other researchers in similar fields) review all published research papers, but usually they are judging whether the data support the conclusion—they assume that the experimental measurements are authentic. The pressure to succeed sometimes leads researchers to betray that trust. However, over time, the tendency of scientists to reproduce and build upon one another's work results in the discovery of the fraudulent data. When that happens, the researchers at fault are usually banished from the community and their careers are ruined.

1.5 Solving Chemical Problems

Learning to solve problems is one of the most important skills you will acquire in this course. No one succeeds in chemistry—or in life, really—without the ability to solve problems. Although no simple formula applies to every chemistry problem, you can learn problem-solving strategies and begin to develop some chemical intuition. Many of the problems you will solve in this course can be thought of as *unit conversion problems*, where you are given one or more quantities and asked to convert them into different units. Other problems require that you use *specific equations* to get to the information you are trying to find. In the sections that follow, you will find strategies to help you solve both of these types of problems. Of course, many problems contain both conversions and equations, requiring the combination of these strategies, and some problems may require an altogether different approach.

General Problem-Solving Strategy

In this text, we use a standard problem-solving procedure that can be adapted to many of the problems encountered in general chemistry and beyond. To solve any problem, you need to assess the information given in the problem and devise a way to get to the information asked for. In other words, you must:

- Identify the starting point (the ***given*** information).
- Identify the end point (what you must ***find***).
- Devise a way to get from the starting point to the end point using what is given as well as what you already know or can look up. (We call this the ***conceptual plan***.)

In graphic form, we can represent this progression as:

Given → Conceptual Plan → Find

One of the main difficulties students have when trying to solve problems in general chemistry is not knowing where to start. While no problem-solving procedure is applicable to all problems, the following four-step procedure can be helpful in working through many of the numerical problems you will encounter in this text.

1. **Sort.** Begin by sorting the information in the problem. *Given* information is the basic data provided by the problem—often one or more numbers with their associated units. *Find* indicates what information you will need for your answer.
2. **Strategize.** This is usually the hardest part of solving a problem. In this process, you must develop a *conceptual plan*—a series of steps that will get you from the given information to the information you are trying to find. You have already seen conceptual plans for simple unit conversion problems. Each arrow in a conceptual plan represents a computational step. On the left side of the arrow is the quantity you had before the step, on the right side of the arrow is the quantity you will have after the step, and below the arrow is the information you need to get from one to the other—the relationship between the quantities.

Often, such relationships will take the form of conversion factors or equations. These may be given in the problem, in which case you will have written them down under "Given" in step 1. Usually, however, you will need other information—which may include physical constants, formulas, or conversion factors—to help get you from what you are given to what you must find. This information comes from what you have learned or can look up in the chapter or in tables within the text. In some cases, you may get stuck at the strategize step. If you cannot figure out how to get from the given information to the information you are asked to find, you might try working backward. For example, you may want to look at the units of the quantity you are trying to find and try to find conversion factors to get to the units of the given quantity. You may even try a combination of strategies: work forward, backward, or some of both. If you persist, you will develop a strategy to solve the problem.

Most problems can be solved in more than one way. The solutions we derive in this text will tend to be the most straightforward but certainly not the only way to solve the problem.

3. **Solve.** This is the easiest part of solving a problem. Once you set up the problem properly and devise a conceptual plan, you simply follow the plan to solve the

problem. Carry out any mathematical operations (paying attention to the rules for significant figures in calculations) and cancel units as needed.

4. **Check.** This is the step beginning students most often overlook. Experienced problem solvers always ask, Does this answer make sense? Are the units correct? Is the number of significant figures correct? When solving multistep problems, errors easily creep into the solution. You can catch most of these errors by simply checking the answer, and considering the physical meaning of your result. For example, suppose you are calculating the number of atoms in a gold coin and end up with the answer of 1.1×10^{-6} atoms. Could a gold coin really be composed of one-millionth of one atom?

In the following pages, we apply this problem-solving procedure to unit conversion problems. The procedure is summarized in the left column, and two examples of applying the procedure are shown in the middle and right columns. This three-column format will be used in selected examples throughout this text. It allows you to see how you can apply a particular procedure to two different problems. Work through one problem first (from top to bottom) and then see how you can apply the same procedure to the other problem. Being able to see the commonalities and differences between problems is a key part of developing problem-solving skills.

Order-of-Magnitude Estimations

Calculation plays a major role in chemical problem solving. But precise numerical calculation is not always necessary, or even possible. Sometimes data are only approximate, so there is no point in trying to determine an extremely precise answer. At other times, you simply don't need a high degree of precision—a rough estimate or a simplified "back of the envelope" calculation is enough. Scientists often use these kinds of calculations to get an initial feel for a problem, or as a quick check to see whether a proposed solution is "in the right ballpark."

One way to make such estimates is to simplify the numbers so that they can be manipulated easily. The technique, known as *order-of-magnitude estimation*, is based on focusing only on the exponential part of numbers written in scientific notation, according to the following guidelines:

- If the decimal part of the number is less than 5, just drop it. Thus, 4.36×10^5 becomes 10^5 and 2.7×10^{-3} becomes 10^{-3}.
- If the decimal part is 5 or more, round it up to 10 and rewrite the number as a power of 10. Thus, 5.982×10^7 becomes $10 \times 10^7 = 10^8$, and 6.1101×10^{-3} becomes $10 \times 10^{-3} = 10^{-2}$.

When you make these approximations, you are left with powers of 10, which are easily multiplied and divided—often in your head. It's important to remember, however, that your answer is only as reliable as the numbers used to get it, so never assume that the results of an order-of-magnitude calculation are accurate to more than an order of magnitude.

Suppose, for example, that you want to estimate the number of years it would take an immortal being to spend 1 mole (6.022×10^{23}) of pennies at a rate of 100 million dollars per second. Since a year has 3.16×10^7 seconds, you can approximate the number of years as follows:

$$10^{24}\,\cancel{\text{pennies}} \times \frac{1\,\cancel{\text{dollar}}}{10^2\,\cancel{\text{pennies}}} \times \frac{1\,\cancel{\text{second}}}{10^8\,\cancel{\text{dollars}}} \times \frac{1\text{ year}}{10^7\,\cancel{\text{seconds}}} \approx 10^7\text{ years}$$

We have estimated that it will take about 10 million years to spend one mole of pennies at the rate of 100 million dollars per year—clearly impossible for a mere mortal.

In our general problem-solving procedure, the last step is to check whether the results seem reasonable. Order-of-magnitude estimations can often help you catch the kinds of mistakes that may happen in a detailed calculation, such as entering an incorrect exponent or sign into your calculator, or multiplying when you should have divided.

Problems Involving an Equation

Problems involving equations can be solved in much the same way as problems involving conversions. Usually, in problems involving equations, you must find one of the variables in the equation, given the others. The *conceptual plan* approach outlined previously can be used for problems involving equations. For example, suppose you are given the mass (m) and volume (V) of a sample and asked to calculate its density. The conceptual plan shows how the *equation* takes you from the *given* quantities to the *find* quantity.

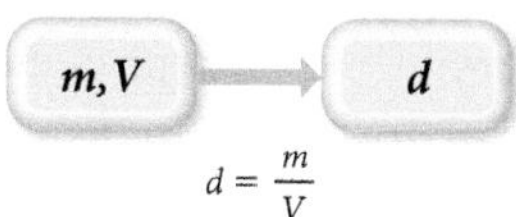

$$d = \frac{m}{V}$$

Here, instead of a conversion factor under the arrow, this conceptual plan has an equation. The equation shows the *relationship* between the quantities on the left of the arrow and the quantities on the right. Note that at this point, the equation need not be solved for the quantity on the right (although in this particular case, it is). The procedure that follows, as well as the two examples, will guide you in developing a strategy to solve problems involving equations. We will use the three-column format here. Work through one problem from top to bottom and then see how you can apply the same general procedure to the second problem.

PROCEDURE FOR ... Solving Problems Involving Equations	**EXAMPLE 1.7** Problems using Equations	**EXAMPLE 1.8** Problems using Equations
	Find the radius (r), in centimetres, of a spherical water droplet with a volume (V) of $0.058\ \text{cm}^3$. For a sphere, $V = (4/3)\pi r^3$.	Find the density, in g cm^{-3}, of a metal cylinder with a mass (m) of 8.3 g, a length (l) of 1.94 cm, and a radius (r) of 0.55 cm. For a cylinder, $V = \pi r^2 l$.
SORT Begin by sorting the information in the problem into *given* and *find* categories.	**GIVEN:** $V = 0.058\ \text{cm}^3$ **FIND:** r in cm	**GIVEN:** $m = 8.3\ \text{g}$ $l = 1.94\ \text{cm}$ $r = 0.55\ \text{cm}$ **FIND:** d in g cm^{-3}
STRATEGIZE Write a *conceptual plan* for the problem. Focus on the equation(s). The conceptual plan shows how the equation takes you from the *given* quantity (or quantities) to the *find* quantity. The conceptual plan may have several parts, involving other equations or required conversions. In these examples, you use the geometrical relationships given in the problem statements as well as the definition of density, $d = m/V$, which you learned in this chapter.	**CONCEPTUAL PLAN** 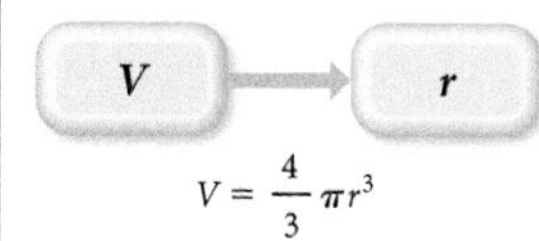 $V = \frac{4}{3}\pi r^3$ **RELATIONSHIPS USED** $V = \frac{4}{3}\pi r^3$	**CONCEPTUAL PLAN** 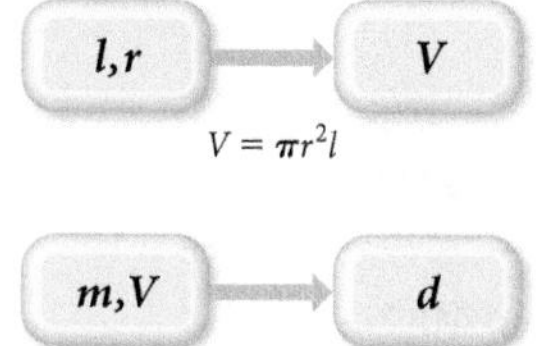 $V = \pi r^2 l$ $d = m/V$ **RELATIONSHIPS USED** $V = \pi r^2 l$ $d = \frac{m}{V}$
SOLVE Follow the conceptual plan. Solve the equation(s) for the *find* quantity (if it is not already in the proper form). Gather each of the quantities that must go into the equation in the correct units, as well as looking up any physical constants that are necessary. (Convert to the correct units if necessary.) Substitute the numerical values and their units into the equation(s) and compute the answer. Round the answer to the correct number of significant figures.	**SOLUTION** $V = \frac{4}{3}\pi r^3$ $r^3 = \frac{3}{4\pi}V$ $r = \left(\frac{3}{4\pi}V\right)^{1/3}$ $= \left(\frac{3}{4\pi}0.058\ \text{cm}^3\right)^{1/3}$ $= 0.24013\ \text{cm}$ $0.24013\ \text{cm} = 0.24\ \text{cm}$	**SOLUTION** $V = \pi r^2 l$ $= \pi(0.55\ \text{cm})^2(1.94\ \text{cm})$ $= 1.\underline{8}436\ \text{cm}^3$ $d = \frac{m}{V}$ $= \frac{8.3\ \text{g}}{1.\underline{8}436\ \text{cm}^3} = 4.50195\ \text{g cm}^{-3}$ $4.50195\ \text{g cm}^{-3} = 4.5\ \text{g cm}^{-3}$

(continued)

PROCEDURE FOR ... *(continued)*	EXAMPLE 1.7 *(continued)*	EXAMPLE 1.8 *(continued)*
CHECK Check your answer. Are the units correct? Does the answer make sense?	The units (cm) are correct and the magnitude of the result makes sense.	The units ($g\,cm^{-3}$) are correct. The magnitude of the answer seems correct for one of the lighter metals (see Table 1.4).
	FOR PRACTICE 1.7 Find the radius (r) of an aluminum cylinder that is 2.00 cm long and has a mass of 12.4 g. For a cylinder, $V = \pi r^2 l$. Density of aluminum = 2.7 $g\,cm^{-3}$.	**FOR PRACTICE 1.8** Find the density, in $g\,cm^{-3}$, of a metal cube with a mass of 50.3 g and an edge length (l) of 2.65 cm. For a cube, $V = l^3$.

CHAPTER IN REVIEW

Key Terms

Section 1.1
physical change (2)
chemical change (2)
physical property (2)
chemical property (2)

Section 1.2
kinetic energy (3)
potential energy (3)
thermal energy (3)
law of conservation of energy (3)

Section 1.3
units (4)
Imperial system (4)
metric system (4)
International System of Units (SI) (4)
metre (m) (4)
kilogram (kg) (5)
mass (5)
second (s) (5)
kelvin (K) (5)
temperature (5)
Celsius (°C) scale (5)
prefix multipliers (6)
conversion factor (7)
dimensional analysis (7)
derived unit (8)
volume (8)
litre (L) (8)
millilitre (mL) (8)
density (d) (9)
intensive property (9)
extensive property (9)

Section 1.4
significant figures (significant digits) (13)
exact numbers (14)
accuracy (17)
precision (17)
random error (18)
systematic error (18)

Key Concepts

The Properties of Matter 1.1

The properties of matter can be divided into two kinds: physical and chemical. Matter displays its physical properties without changing its composition. Matter displays its chemical properties only through changing its composition. Changes in matter in which its composition does not change are called physical changes. Changes in matter in which its composition does change are called chemical changes.

Energy 1.2

In chemical and physical changes, matter often exchanges energy with its surroundings. In these exchanges, the total energy is always conserved; energy is neither created nor destroyed. Systems with high potential energy tend to change in the direction of lower potential energy, releasing energy into the surroundings.

The Units of Measurement and Significant Figures (1.3, 1.4)

Scientists use primarily SI units, which are based on the metric system. The SI base units include the metre (m) for length, the kilogram (kg) for mass, the second (s) for time, and the kelvin (K) for temperature. Derived units are those formed from a combination of base units. Common derived units include volume (cm^3 or m^3) and density ($g\,cm^{-3}$). Measured quantities are reported so that the number of digits reflects the uncertainty in the measurement. Significant figures are the nonplaceholding digits in a reported number.

Key Equations and Relationships

Relationship between Kelvin (K) and Celsius (°C) temperature scales (1.3)

$$\frac{T}{K} = \frac{T_C}{°C} + 273.15$$

Relationship between density (d), mass (m), and volume (V) (1.3)

$$d = \frac{m}{V}$$

Key Skills

Determining Physical and Chemical Changes and Properties (1.1)
• Exercises 21–26

Converting Between Temperature Scales (1.3)
• Example 1.1 • For Practice 1.1 • Exercises 27–30

Converting Between Different SI Prefixes (1.3)
• Example 1.2 • For Practice 1.2 • For More Practice 1.2 • Exercises 31–40

Calculating Density and Converting Density Units (1.3)
• Example 1.3 • For Practice 1.3 • For More Practice 1.3 • Exercises 41–44

Reporting the Correct Number of Digits (1.4)
• Example 1.4 • For Practice 1.4 • Exercises 49, 50

Working with Significant Figures (1.4)
• Examples 1.5, 1.6 • For Practice 1.5, 1.6 • Exercises 51–66

Solving Problems Involving Equations (1.5)
• Examples 1.7, 1.8 • For Practice 1.7, 1.8 • Exercises 45–48, 83–90

EXERCISES

Review Questions

1. Explain the main goal of chemistry.

2. How do solids, liquids, and gases differ?

3. What is the difference between a physical property and a chemical property?

4. What is the difference between a physical change and a chemical change? Give some examples of each.

5. Explain the significance of the law of conservation of energy.

6. What kind of energy is chemical energy? In what way is an elevated weight similar to a tank of gasoline?

7. What are the standard SI base units of length, mass, time, and temperature?

8. What are the two common temperature scales? Does the size of a unit differ between them?

9. What are prefix multipliers? Give some examples.

10. What is a derived unit? Give an example.

11. Explain the difference between density and mass.

12. Explain the difference between intensive and extensive properties.

13. What is the meaning of the number of digits reported in a measured quantity?

14. When multiplying or dividing measured quantities, what determines the number of significant figures in the result?

15. When adding or subtracting measured quantities, what determines the number of significant figures in the result?

16. When taking the logarithm of a number, what determines the number of decimal places in the result?

17. When taking the antilogarithm of a number, what determines the number of significant figures in the result?

18. Explain the difference between precision and accuracy.

19. Explain the difference between random error and systematic error.

20. What is dimensional analysis?

Problems by Topic

Note: Answers to all odd-numbered Problems, numbered in blue, can be found in Appendix III. Exercises in the Problems by Topic section are paired, with each odd-numbered problem followed by a similar even-numbered problem. Exercises in the Cumulative Problems section are also paired, but somewhat more loosely. (Challenge Problems and Conceptual Problems, because of their nature, are unpaired.)

Physical and Chemical Changes and Properties

21. Classify each property as physical or chemical.
a. the tendency of ethanol to burn
b. the shine of silver
c. the odour of paint thinner
d. the flammability of propane gas

22. Classify each property as physical or chemical.
a. the boiling point of ethanol
b. the temperature at which dry ice evaporates
c. the tendency of iron to rust
d. the colour of gold

23. Classify each change as physical or chemical.
a. Natural gas burns in a stove.
b. The liquid propane in a gas grill evaporates because the valve was left open.
c. The liquid propane in a gas grill burns in a flame.
d. A bicycle frame rusts on repeated exposure to air and water.

24. Classify each change as physical or chemical.
   a. Sugar burns when heated on a skillet.
   b. Sugar dissolves in water.
   c. A platinum ring becomes dull because of continued abrasion.
   d. A silver surface becomes tarnished after exposure to air for a long period of time.

25. Based on the molecular diagram, classify each change as physical or chemical.

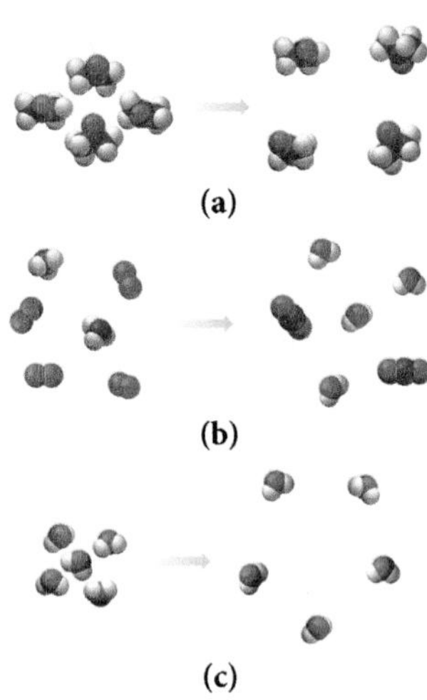

(a) (b) (c)

26. Based on the molecular diagram, classify each change as physical or chemical.

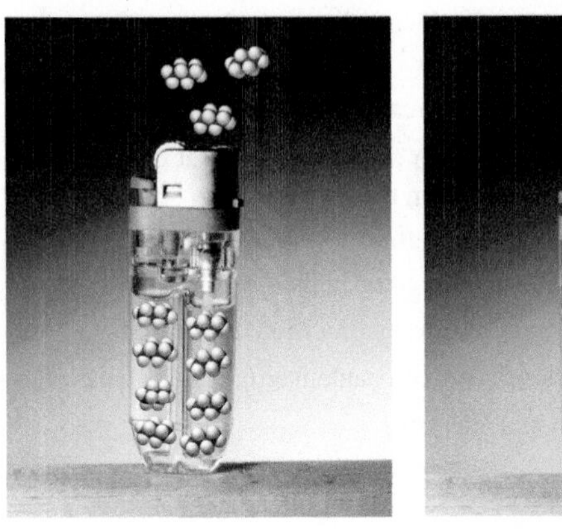

(a)

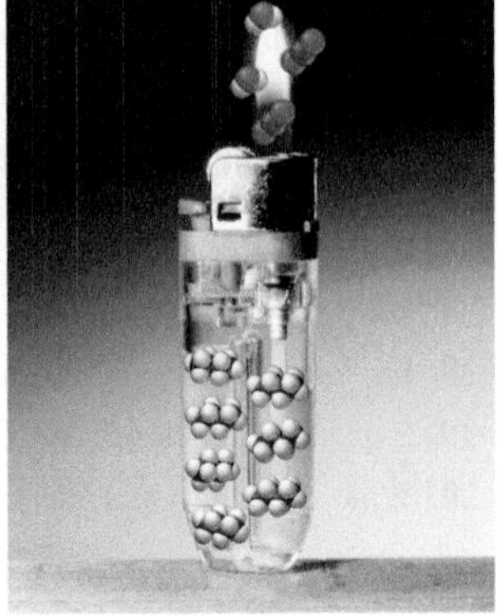

(b)

(c)

Units in Measurement

27. Convert each temperature.
   a. 0.00 °C to K (temperature at which water freezes)
   b. 77 K to °C (temperature of liquid nitrogen)
   c. 37.0 °C to K (body temperature)

28. Convert each temperature.
   a. 100.0 °C to K (temperature of boiling water at sea level)
   b. 2.735 K to °C (average temperature of the universe as measured from background blackbody radiation)
   c. 22 °C to K

29. The coldest temperature ever recorded outside of the Antarctic was on Mount Logan in the Yukon Territory on May 26, 1991, when the temperature dipped to −77.5 °C. Convert this temperature to K.

30. The warmest temperature ever measured in the world was 56.7 °C on July 10, 1913, at Furnace Creek Ranch, Death Valley, California. Convert this temperature to K.

31. Use the prefix multipliers to express each measurement without any exponents.
   a. 1.2×10^{-9} m
   b. 22×10^{-15} s
   c. 1.5×10^{9} g
   d. 3.5×10^{6} L

32. Use prefix multipliers to express each measurement without any exponents.
   a. 38.8×10^{5} g
   b. 55.2×10^{-10} s
   c. 23.4×10^{11} m
   d. 87.9×10^{-7} L

33. Use scientific notation to express each quantity with only the base units (no prefix multipliers).
   a. 4.5 ns
   b. 18 fs
   c. 128 pm
   d. 35 μm

34. Use scientific notation to express each quantity with only the base units (no prefix multipliers).
   a. 35 μL
   b. 225 Mm
   c. 133 Tg
   d. 1.5 cg

35. Complete the table:

a. 1245 kg	1.245×10^{6} g	1.245×10^{9} mg
b. 515 km	______ dm	______ cm
c. 122.355 s	______ ms	______ ks
d. 3.345 kJ	______ J	______ mJ

36. Complete the table:

a. 355 km s^{-1}	______ cm s^{-1}	______ m ms^{-1}
b. 1228 g L^{-1}	______ g mL^{-1}	______ kg ML^{-1}
c. 556 mK s^{-1}	______ K s^{-1}	______ μK ms^{-1}
d. 2.554 mg mL^{-1}	______ g L^{-1}	______ μg mL^{-1}

37. Express the quantity 254 998 m in each unit.
   a. km **b.** Mm **c.** mm **d.** cm

38. Express the quantity 556.2×10^{-12} s in each unit.
   a. ms **b.** ns **c.** ps **d.** fs

39. How many 1 cm squares would it take to construct a square that is 1 m on each side?

40. How many 1 cm cubes would it take to construct a cube that is 4 cm on its edge?

Density

41. A Canadian penny was found to have a mass of 2.35 g and a volume of 0.302 cm^3. Is the penny made of pure copper? Explain.

42. A titanium bicycle frame displaces 0.314 L of water and has a mass of 1.41 kg. What is the density of the titanium in g cm^{-3}?

43. Glycerol is a viscous liquid often used in cosmetics and soaps. A 3.25 L sample of pure glycerol has a mass of 4.10×10^3 g. What is the density of glycerol in g cm^{-3}?

44. A supposedly gold nugget is tested to determine its density. It is found to displace 19.3 mL of water and has a mass of 371 grams. Could the nugget be made of gold?

45. Ethylene glycol (antifreeze) has a density of 1.11 g cm^{-3}.
    a. What is the mass in g of 417 mL of this liquid?
    b. What is the volume in L of 4.1 kg of this liquid?

46. Acetone (nail polish remover) has a density of 0.7857 g cm^{-3}.
    a. What is the mass, in g, of 28.56 mL of acetone?
    b. What is the volume, in mL, of 6.54 g of acetone?

47. A small airplane takes on 245 L of fuel. If the density of the fuel is 0.803 g mL^{-1}, what mass of fuel has the airplane taken on?

48. Human fat has a density of 0.918 g cm^{-3}. How much volume (in cm^3) is gained by a person who gains 5.00 kg of pure fat?

The Reliability of a Measurement and Significant Figures

49. Read each measurement to the correct number of significant figures. Note: laboratory glassware should always be read from the bottom of the meniscus.

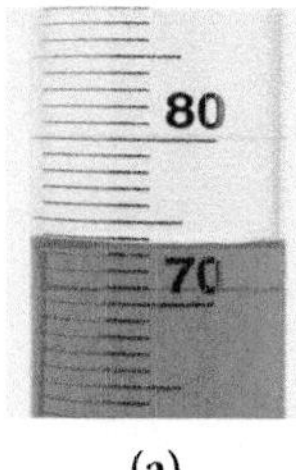

(a)

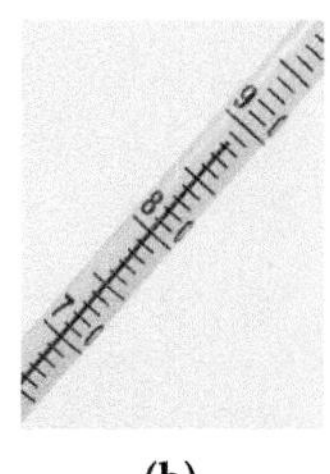
(b)

(c)

50. Read each measurement to the correct number of significant figures. Note: laboratory glassware should always be read from the bottom of the meniscus. Digital balances normally display mass to the correct number of significant figures for that particular balance.

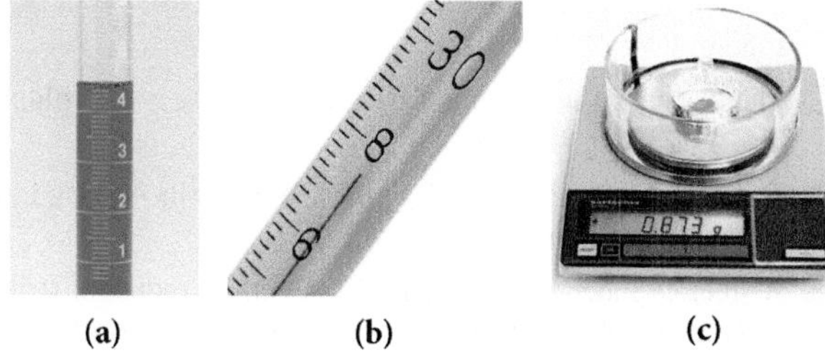

(a) (b) (c)

51. For each number, underline the zeros that are significant and draw a line through the zeros that are not:
    a. 1 050 501 km
    b. 0.0020 m
    c. 0.000000000000002 s
    d. 0.001090 cm

52. For each number, underline the zeros that are significant and draw a line through the zeros that are not:
    a. 180 701 mi
    b. 0.001040 m
    c. 0.005710 km
    d. 90 201 m

53. How many significant figures are in each number?
    a. 0.000312 m
    b. 312 000 s
    c. 3.12×10^5 km
    d. 13 127 s
    e. 2000

54. How many significant figures are in each number?
    a. 0.1111 s
    b. 0.007 m
    c. 108 700 km
    d. 1.563300×10^{11} m
    e. 30 800

55. Indicate the number of significant figures in each number. If the number is an exact number, indicate an unlimited number of significant figures.
    a. $\pi = 3.14$
    b. $1\ m^3 = 1000\ dm^3$
    c. 5683.91 km^2 (land area of Prince Edward Island)
    d. 3.0×10^8 m s^{-1} (speed of light in a vacuum)

56. Indicate the number of significant figures in each number. If the number is an exact number, indicate an unlimited number of significant figures.
    a. 12 = 1 dozen
    b. 11.4 g cm^{-3} (density of lead)
    c. 2.42×10^{19} km (distance to Andromeda galaxy)
    d. 1640 km^3 (volume of Lake Ontario)

57. Round each number to four significant figures.
    a. 156.852
    b. 156.842
    c. 156.849
    d. 156.899

58. Round each number to three significant figures.
    a. 79 845.82
    b. 1.549837×10^7
    c. 2.3499999995
    d. 0.000045389

Significant Figures in Calculations

59. Calculate to the correct number of significant figures.
    a. $9.15 \div 4.970$
    b. $1.54 \times 0.03060 \times 0.69$
    c. $27.5 \times 1.82 \div 100.04$
    d. $(2.290 \times 10^6) \div (6.7 \times 10^4)$

60. Calculate to the correct number of significant figures.
    a. $89.3 \times 77.0 \times 0.08$
    b. $(5.01 \times 10^5) \div (7.8 \times 10^2)$
    c. $4.005 \times 74 \times 0.007$
    d. $453 \div 2.031$

61. Calculate to the correct number of significant figures.
    a. $43.7 - 2.341$
    b. $17.6 + 2.838 + 2.3 + 110.77$
    c. $19.6 + 58.33 - 4.974$
    d. $5.99 - 5.572$

62. Calculate to the correct number of significant figures.
    a. $0.004 + 0.09879$
    b. $1239.3 + 9.73 + 3.42$
    c. $2.4 - 1.777$
    d. $532 + 7.3 - 48.523$

63. Acceleration is a derived unit and can be expressed in SI base units as m s^{-2}. Suppose a 1 kg mass is accelerated through 1 m at 1 m s^{-2}. Express the product of these three numbers in SI base units and a derived unit with a special name.

64. Divide a force of 1 N (1 newton) by an area of 1 m^2 and express the quotient in SI base units and a derived unit with a special name. Hint: A newton is a derived unit with a special name, so you must first express it in SI base units.

65. Calculate to the correct number of significant figures.
a. $(24.6681 \times 2.38) + 332.58$
b. $(85.3 - 21.489) \div 0.0059$
c. $(512 \div 986.7) + 5.44$
d. $[(28.7 \times 10^5) \div 48.533] + 144.99$

66. Calculate to the correct number of significant figures.
a. $[(1.7 \times 10^6) \div (2.63 \times 10^5)] + 7.33$
b. $(568.99 - 232.1) \div 5.3$
c. $(9443 + 45 - 9.9) \times 8.1 \times 10^6$
d. $(3.14 \times 2.4367) - 2.34$

Unit Conversions

67. Convert:
a. 3.25 kg to g
b. 250 μs to s
c. 0.345 L to cm^3
d. 257 dm to km

68. Convert:
a. 1405 μg to mg
b. 62 500 fs to ns
c. 1056 cm^2 to m^2
d. 25.0 mL to L

Solving Chemical Problems

69. A runner wants to run 10.0 km. She knows that her running pace is 3.5 m s^{-1}. How many minutes must she run?

70. A cyclist rides at an average speed of 8.1 m s^{-1}. If she wants to bike 212 km, how many hours must she ride?

71. A house has an area of 195 m^2. Convert its area to:
a. km^2 **b.** dm^2 **c.** cm^2

72. A bedroom has a volume of 115 m^3. Convert its volume to:
a. km^3 **b.** dm^3 **c.** cm^3

73. The average area of land burned by forest fires every year in Canada is 2.5 million hm^2 (square hectometres or hectares). What is this value in m^2 and km^2?

74. Besides Vatican City, the smallest country in the world is Monaco, which has a land area of 1.8 km^2. What is the area of Monaco in hm^2 and m^2?

75. An acetaminophen suspension for infants contains 80 mg/0.80 mL suspension. The recommended dosage is 15 mg/kg body weight. How many mL of this suspension should be given to an infant weighing 6.5 kg?

76. An ibuprofen suspension for infants contains 100 mg/5.0 mL suspension. The recommended dose is 10 mg/kg body weight. How many mL of this suspension should be given to an infant weighing 8.2 kg?

Cumulative Problems

77. There are exactly 60 seconds in a minute, there are exactly 60 minutes in an hour, there are exactly 24 hours in a mean solar day, and there are 365.24 solar days in a solar year. Find the number of seconds in a solar year. Be sure to give your answer with the correct number of significant figures.

78. Use scientific notation to indicate the number of significant figures in each statement:
a. Fifty million Frenchmen can't be wrong.
b. "For every ten jokes, thou hast got an hundred enemies" (Laurence Sterne, 1713–1768).
c. The diameter of a Ca atom is 1.8 one hundred millionths of a centimetre.
d. Sixty thousand dollars is a lot of money to pay for a car.
e. The density of platinum is 21.4 g cm^{-3}.

79. Classify each property as intensive or extensive.
a. volume
b. boiling point
c. temperature
d. electrical conductivity
e. energy

80. A temperature measurement of 25 °C has three significant figures, while a temperature measurement of −196 °C has only two significant figures. Explain.

81. Do each calculation without using your calculator and give the answers to the correct number of significant figures.
a. $1.76 \times 10^{-3}/8.0 \times 10^2$
b. $1.87 \times 10^{-2} + 2 \times 10^{-4} - 3.0 \times 10^{-3}$
c. $[(1.36 \times 10^5)(0.000322)/0.082](129.2)$

82. Using the value of the euro at C$1.37 (Canadian dollars) and the price of 1 litre of gasoline in France at 1.67 euros, calculate the price of gasoline in C$ in France.

83. A thief wants to use a can of sand to replace a solid gold cylinder that sits on a weight-sensitive, alarmed pedestal. The gold cylinder has a length of 22 cm and a radius of 3.8 cm. Given that the density of gold and sand are 19.3 g cm^{-3} and 3.00 g cm^{-3}, respectively, what volume of sand must the thief use?

84. The proton has a radius of approximately 1.0×10^{-13} cm and a mass of 1.7×10^{-24} g. Determine the density of a proton. For a sphere, $V = (4/3)\pi r^3$.

85. The density of titanium is 4.51 g cm^{-3}. What is the volume (in litres) of 3.5 kg of titanium?

86. The density of iron is 7.86 g cm^{-3}. What is its density in kilograms per cubic metre (kg m^{-3})?

87. A steel cylinder has a length of 5.49 cm, a radius of 0.56 cm, and a mass of 41 g. What is the density of the steel in g cm^{-3}?

88. A solid aluminum sphere has a mass of 85 g. Use the density of aluminum to find the radius of the sphere in decimetres.

89. A backyard swimming pool holds 185 cubic metres of water. What is the mass of the water in kilograms?

90. An iceberg has a volume of 8921 L. What is the mass of the ice (in kg) composing the iceberg?

91. The Toyota Prius, a hybrid electric vehicle, has a combined consumption rating of 3.8 L/100 km. How many kilometres can the Prius travel on 15 litres of gasoline?

92. The Ford Mustang (GT Coupe) has a consumption rating of 7.6 L/100 km on the highway or 12 L/100 km in the city. How far could you travel on a full tank of gas (61.0 L) on the highway and in the city?

93. The single proton that forms the nucleus of the hydrogen atom has a radius of approximately 1.0×10^{-13} cm. The hydrogen atom itself has a radius of approximately 52.9 pm. What fraction of the space within the atom is occupied by the nucleus?

94. A sample of gaseous neon atoms at atmospheric pressure and 0 °C contains 2.69×10^{22} atoms per litre. The atomic radius of neon is 69 pm. What fraction of the space is occupied by the atoms themselves? What does this reveal about the separation between atoms in the gaseous phase?

95. The length of a hydrogen molecule is 212 pm. Find the length in kilometres of a row of 6.02×10^{23} hydrogen molecules. The diameter of a ping pong ball is 4.0 cm. Find the length in kilometres of a row of 6.02×10^{23} ping pong balls.

96. The world's record in the 100-m dash is 9.58 s. Find the speed in km hr^{-1} of the runner who set the record.

97. Table salt contains 39.33 g of sodium per 100 g of salt. Health Canada recommends that adults consume less than 2.40 g of sodium per day. A particular snack mix contains 1.25 g of salt per 100 g of the mix. What mass of the snack mix can you consume per day and still be within the Health Canada limit?

98. Lead metal can be extracted from a mineral called galena, which contains 86.6% lead by mass. A particular ore contains 68.5% galena by mass. If the lead can be extracted with 92.5% efficiency, what mass of ore is required to make a lead sphere with a 5.00 cm radius?

99. Liquid nitrogen has a density of 0.808 g mL^{-1} and boils at 77 K. Researchers often purchase liquid nitrogen in insulated 175 L tanks. The liquid vaporizes quickly to gaseous nitrogen (which has a density of 1.15 g L^{-1} at room temperature and atmospheric pressure) when the liquid is removed from the tank. Suppose that all 175 L of liquid nitrogen in a tank accidentally vaporized in a lab that measured 10.00 m $\times$ 10.00 m $\times$ 2.50 m. What is the maximum fraction of the air in the room that could be displaced by the gaseous nitrogen?

100. Mercury is often used as an expansion medium in a thermometer. The mercury sits in a bulb on the bottom of the thermometer and rises up a thin capillary as the temperature rises. Suppose a mercury thermometer contains 3.380 g of mercury and has a capillary that is 0.200 mm in diameter. How far does the mercury rise in the capillary when the temperature changes from 0.0 °C to 25.0 °C? The density of mercury at these temperatures is 13.596 g cm^{-3} and 13.534 g cm^{-3}, respectively.

Challenge Problems

101. A force of 2.31×10^4 N is applied to a diver's face mask that has an area of 125 cm^2. Find the pressure in bar on the face mask.

102. The SI unit of force is the newton, derived from the base units by using the definition of force, $F = ma$. The dyne is a non-SI unit of force in which mass is measured in grams and time is measured in seconds. The relationship between the two units is 1 dyne $= 10^{-5}$ N. Find the unit of length used to define the dyne.

103. Kinetic energy can be defined as ½ mv^2 or as 3/2 PV. Show that the derived SI units of each of these terms are those of energy. (Pressure is force/area and force is mass $\times$ acceleration.)

104. In 1999, scientists discovered a new class of black holes with masses 100 to 10 000 times the mass of our sun, but occupying less space than our moon. Suppose that one of these black holes has a mass of 1×10^3 suns and a radius equal to one-half the radius of our moon. What is the density of the black hole in g cm^{-3}? The radius of our sun is 7.0×10^5 km and it has an average density of 1.4×10^3 kg m^{-3}. The diameter of the moon is 3.48×10^3 km.

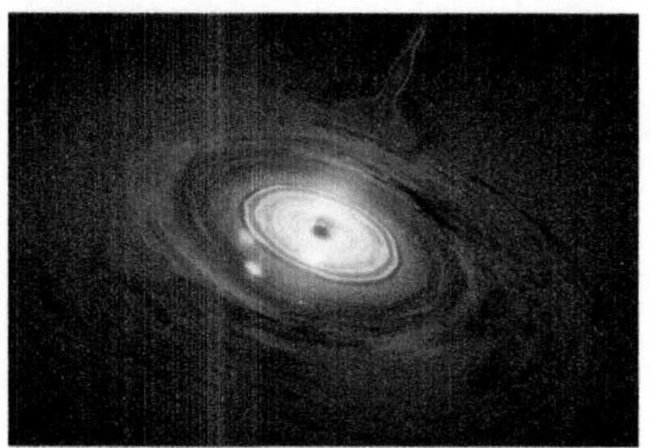

105. Nanotechnology, the field of trying to build ultrasmall structures one atom at a time, has progressed in recent years. One potential application of nanotechnology is the construction of artificial cells. The simplest cells would probably mimic red blood cells, and be used as oxygen transports within the body. For example, nanocontainers, perhaps constructed of carbon, could be pumped full of oxygen and injected into a person's bloodstream. If the person needed additional oxygen—due to a heart attack perhaps, or for the purpose of space travel—these containers could slowly release oxygen into the blood, allowing tissues that would otherwise die to remain alive. Suppose that the nanocontainers were cubic and had an edge length of 25 nm.

a. What is the volume of one nanocontainer? (Ignore the thickness of the nanocontainer's wall.)

b. Suppose that each nanocontainer could contain pure oxygen pressurized to a density of 85 g L^{-1}. How many grams of oxygen could be contained by each nanocontainer?

c. Normal air contains about 0.28 g of oxygen per litre. An average human inhales about 0.50 L of air per breath and takes about 20 breaths per minute. How many grams of oxygen does a human inhale per hour? (Assume two significant figures.)

d. What is the minimum number of nanocontainers that a person would need in their bloodstream to provide one hour's worth of oxygen?

e. What is the minimum volume occupied by the number of nanocontainers computed in part (d)? Is such a volume feasible, given that total blood volume in an adult is about 5 litres?

106. A box contains a mixture of small copper spheres and small lead spheres. The total volume of both metals, measured by the displacement of water, is 427 cm^3 and the total mass is 4.36 kg. What percentage of the spheres are copper?

Conceptual Problems

107. A volatile liquid (one that easily evaporates) is put into a jar and the jar is then sealed. Does the mass of the sealed jar and its contents change upon vaporization of the liquid?

108. The diagram represents solid carbon dioxide, also known as dry ice.

Which of the diagrams below best represents the dry ice after it has sublimed into a gas?

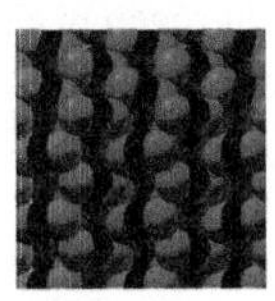

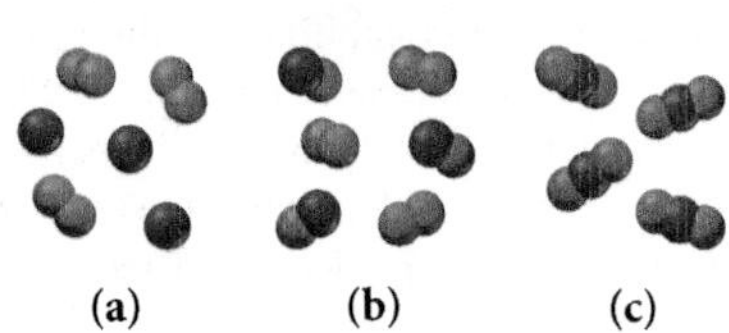

(a) (b) (c)

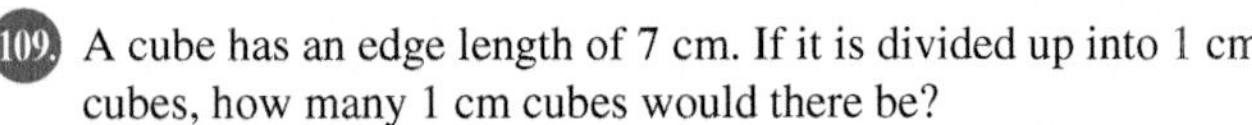

109. A cube has an edge length of 7 cm. If it is divided up into 1 cm cubes, how many 1 cm cubes would there be?

110. Substance A has a density of 1.7 g cm^{-3}. Substance B has a density of 1.7 kg m^{-3}. Without doing any calculations, determine which substance is more dense.

111. For each box, examine the blocks attached to the balances. Based on their positions and sizes, determine which block is more dense (the dark block or the lighter-coloured block), or if the relative densities cannot be determined. (Think carefully about the information being shown.)

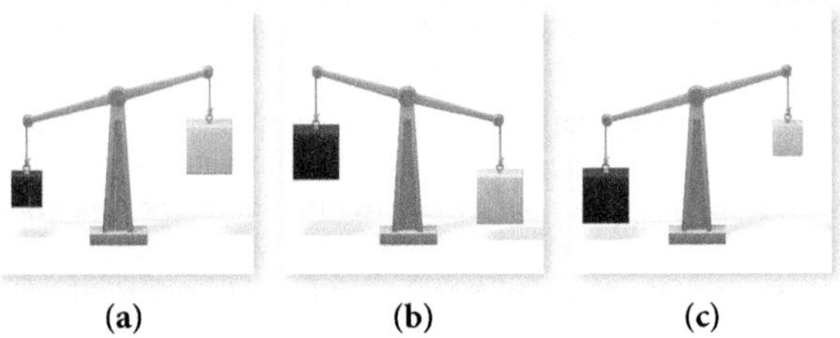

(a) (b) (c)

Atoms and Elements

2

These observations have tacitly led to the conclusion which seems universally adopted, that all bodies of sensible magnitude... are constituted of a vast number of extremely small particles, or atoms of matter...

—John Dalton (1766–1844)

IF YOU CUT A PIECE of graphite from the tip of a pencil into smaller and smaller pieces, how far could you go? Could you divide it forever? Would you eventually run into some basic particles that were no longer divisible, not because of their sheer smallness, but because of the nature of matter? This fundamental question about the nature of matter has been asked by thinkers for more than two millennia. The answers they reached, however, have varied over time. On the scale of everyday objects, matter appears continuous, or infinitely divisible. Until about 200 years ago, many scientists thought that matter was indeed continuous—but they were proven wrong. If you were to divide the graphite from your pencil tip into smaller and smaller pieces (far smaller than the eye could see), you would eventually end up with individual carbon atoms. The word *atom* comes from the Greek *atomos*, meaning "indivisible." You cannot divide a carbon atom into smaller pieces and still have carbon. Atoms compose all ordinary matter—if you want to understand matter, you must begin by understanding atoms.

2.1 Imaging and Moving Individual Atoms

On March 16, 1981, Gerd Binnig and Heinrich Rohrer worked late into the night in their laboratory at IBM in Zurich, Switzerland. They were measuring how an electrical current—flowing between a sharp metal tip and a flat metal surface—varied as the distance between the tip and the surface varied. The results of that night's experiment and subsequent results over the next several months won Binnig and Rohrer a share of the 1986 Nobel Prize in Physics. They had discovered *scanning tunnelling microscopy (STM)*, a technique that can image, and even move, individual atoms and molecules.

A scanning tunnelling microscope works by moving an extremely sharp *electrode* (an electrical conductor) over a surface and measuring the resulting *tunnelling current*, the electrical current that flows between the tip of the electrode and the surface, even though the two are not in physical contact (see Figure 2.1 ▼).

▶ **FIGURE 2.1 Scanning Tunnelling Microscopy** In this technique, an atomically sharp tip is scanned across a conducting surface. The tip is kept at a fixed distance from the surface by moving it up and down to maintain a constant tunnelling current. The motion of the tip is recorded to create an image of the surface with atomic resolution.

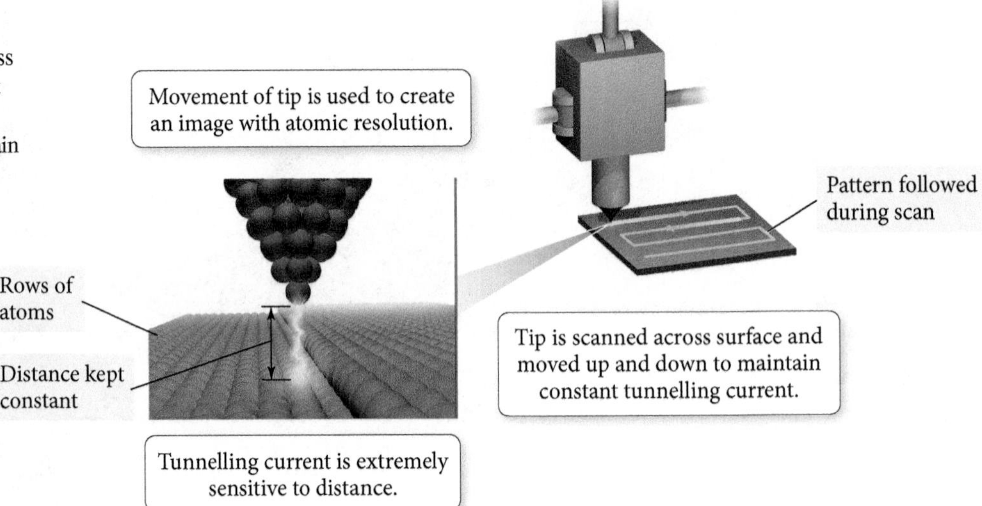
Movement of tip is used to create an image with atomic resolution.
Pattern followed during scan
Rows of atoms
Distance kept constant
Tip is scanned across surface and moved up and down to maintain constant tunnelling current.
Tunnelling current is extremely sensitive to distance.

The tunnelling current, as Binnig and Rohrer found that night in their laboratory at IBM, is extremely sensitive to the distance between the tip and the surface, making it possible to maintain a precise separation of approximately two atomic diameters between the tip and the surface simply by moving the tip so as to keep the current constant. If the current starts to drop a bit, the tip is moved down toward the surface to increase the current. If the current starts to increase a bit, the tip is moved up, away from the surface to decrease the current. As long as the current is constant, the separation between the tip and the surface is constant. As the tip goes over an atom it must move up (away from the surface) to maintain constant current. By measuring the up-and-down movement of the tip as it scans a surface, the microscope creates an image, which shows the location of individual atoms on that surface (see Figure 2.2(a) ▶).

In other words, Binnig and Rohrer discovered a type of microscope that could "see" atoms. Prior to this development in the early 1980s, scientists were certain that matter was made of atoms, but could not see them even with the most powerful microscopes (and probably never would) because they were too small. Today, with the STM, we can form incredible images of atoms and molecules. Later work by other scientists showed that the STM could also be used to *pick up and move* individual atoms or molecules, allowing structures and patterns to be made one atom at a time. Figure 2.2(b) ▶, for example, shows the Kanji characters for the word "atom" written with individual iron atoms on top of a copper surface. If all the words in Library and Archives Canada in Ottawa—20 million books—were written in letters the size of these Kanji characters, they would fit in an area of about 3.5 square millimetres.

As we will discuss later, it was only 200 years ago that John Dalton proposed his atomic theory. Now we can image atoms, move them, and are even beginning to build tiny machines out of just a few dozen atoms (an area of research called nanotechnology).

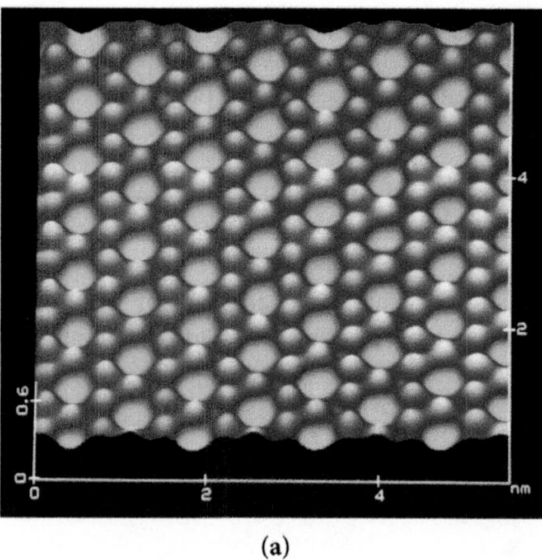
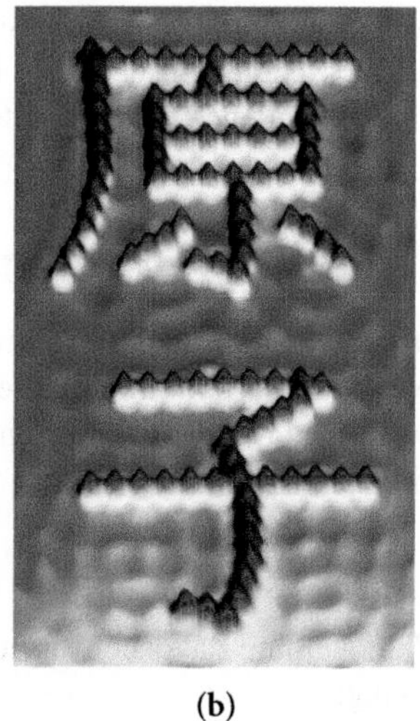

(a) (b)

▲ **FIGURE 2.2 Imaging Atoms** **(a)** A scanning tunnelling microscope image of iodine atoms (green) on a platinum surface (blue). **(b)** The Japanese Kanji characters for "atom" written with iron atoms (red) on a copper surface (blue). The copper atoms are not as distinct as the iron atoms, but they appear as blue ripples in the background.

These atomic machines, and the atoms that compose them, are almost unimaginably small. To get an idea of the size of an atom, imagine picking up a grain of sand at a beach. That grain contains more atoms than you could count in a lifetime. In fact, the number of atoms in one sand grain far exceeds the number of grains on the entire beach. If every atom within the sand grain were the size of the grain itself, the sand grain would be the size of a large mountain range.

Despite their size, atoms are the key to connecting the macroscopic and microscopic worlds. An *atom* is the smallest identifiable unit of an *element*. There are about 91 different naturally occurring elements. In addition, scientists have succeeded in making over 20 synthetic elements (not found in nature). In this chapter, we learn about atoms: what they are made of, how they differ from one another, and how they are structured. We also learn about the elements made up of these different kinds of atoms and about some of their characteristic properties. We will discover that the elements can be organized in a way that reveals patterns in their properties and helps us to understand what underlies those properties.

The exact number of naturally occurring elements is controversial because some elements that were first discovered when they were synthesized are believed to also be present in trace amounts in nature.

2.2 Early Ideas About the Building Blocks of Matter

The first people to propose that matter was composed of small, indestructible particles were Leucippus (fifth century B.C.E., exact dates unknown) and his student Democritus (460–370 B.C.E.). These Greek philosophers theorized that matter was ultimately composed of small, indivisible particles they named *atomos*. Democritus wrote, "Nothing exists except atoms and empty space; everything else is opinion." Leucippus and Democritus proposed that many different kinds of atoms existed, each different in shape and size, and that they moved randomly through empty space. Other influential Greek thinkers of the time, such as Plato and Aristotle, did not embrace the atomic ideas of Leucippus and Democritus. Instead, they held that matter had no smallest parts and that different substances were composed of various proportions of fire, air, earth, and water. Since there was no experimental way to test the relative merits of the competing ideas, Aristotle's view prevailed, largely because he was so influential. The idea that matter was composed of atoms took a back seat in intellectual thought for nearly 2000 years.

In the sixteenth century, modern science began to emerge. A greater emphasis on observation led Nicolaus Copernicus (1473–1543) to publish *On the Revolution of the Heavenly Orbs* in 1543. The publication of that book—which proposed that the sun, not Earth, was at the centre of the universe—marks the beginning of what we now call the *scientific revolution*. The next 200 years—and the work of scientists such as Francis Bacon (1561–1626), Johannes Kepler (1571–1630), Galileo Galilei (1564–1642), Robert Boyle (1627–1691), and Isaac Newton (1642–1727)—brought rapid advancement as the scientific method became the established way to learn about the physical world. By the early 1800s, certain observations led the English chemist John Dalton (1766–1844) to offer convincing evidence that supported the early atomic ideas of Leucippus and Democritus.

2.3 Modern Atomic Theory and the Laws That Led to It

The theory that all matter is composed of atoms grew out of observations and laws. The three most important laws that led to the development and acceptance of the atomic theory were the law of conservation of mass, the law of definite proportions, and the law of multiple proportions.

The Law of Conservation of Mass

In 1789, Antoine Lavoisier formulated the **law of conservation of mass**, which states the following:

In a chemical reaction, matter is neither created nor destroyed.

In other words, when a chemical reaction occurs, the total mass of the substances involved in the reaction does not change. For example, consider the reaction between sodium metal and chlorine gas to form sodium chloride.

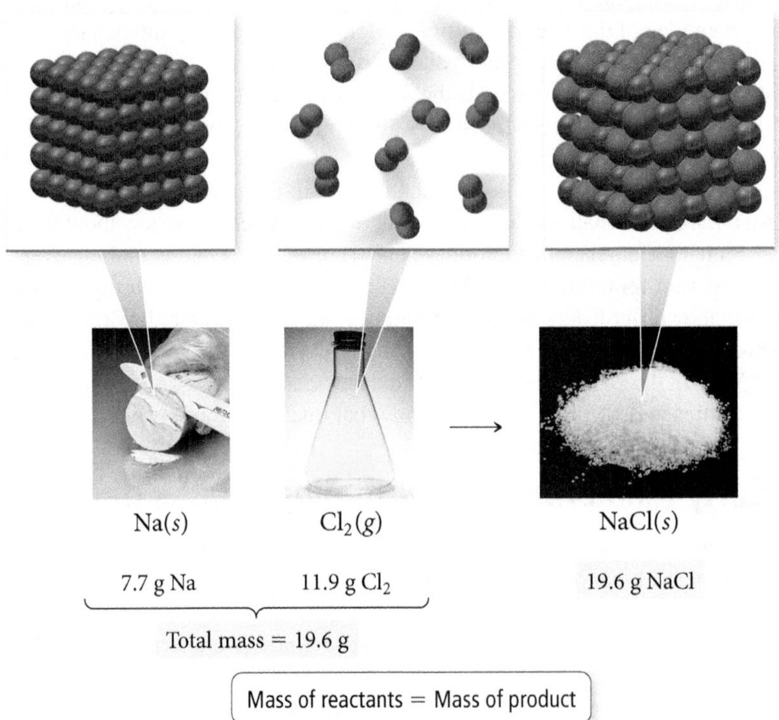

We will see in Chapter 19 that this law is a slight oversimplification. However, the changes in mass in ordinary chemical processes are so minute that they can be ignored for all practical purposes.

The combined mass of the sodium and chlorine that react (the reactants) exactly equals the mass of the sodium chloride that forms (the product). This law is consistent with the idea that matter is composed of small indestructible particles. The particles rearrange during a chemical reaction, but the amount of matter is conserved because the particles themselves are indestructible (at least by chemical means).

CONCEPTUAL CONNECTION 2.1

The Law of Conservation of Mass

When a small log completely burns in a campfire, the mass of the ash is much less than the mass of the log. What happened to the matter that composed the log?

The Law of Definite Proportions

In 1797, a French chemist named Joseph Proust (1754–1826) made observations on the composition of compounds. He found that the elements composing a given compound always occurred in fixed (or definite) proportions in all samples of the compound. In contrast, the components of a mixture could be present in any proportions whatsoever. He summarized his observations in the **law of definite proportions**:

> **All samples of a given compound, regardless of their source or how they were prepared, have the same proportions of their constituent elements.**

For example, the decomposition of 18.0 g of water results in 16.0 g of oxygen and 2.0 g of hydrogen, or an oxygen-to-hydrogen mass ratio of:

$$\text{Mass ratio} = \frac{16.0\,\text{g O}}{2.0\,\text{g H}} = 8.0 \text{ or } 8{:}1$$

This ratio holds for any sample of pure water, regardless of its origin. The law of definite proportions applies to every compound. Consider ammonia, a compound composed of nitrogen and hydrogen. Ammonia contains 14.0 g of nitrogen for every 3.0 g of hydrogen, resulting in a nitrogen-to-hydrogen mass ratio of:

$$\text{Mass ratio} = \frac{14.0\,\text{g N}}{3.0\,\text{g H}} = 4.7 \text{ or } 4.7{:}1$$

Again, this ratio is the same for every sample of ammonia. The law of definite proportions also hints at the idea that matter might be composed of atoms. Compounds have definite proportions of their constituent elements because the atoms that compose them, each with its own specific mass, occur in a definite ratio. Since the ratio of atoms is the same for all samples of a particular compound, the ratio of masses is also the same.

EXAMPLE 2.1 LAW OF DEFINITE PROPORTIONS

Two samples of carbon dioxide are decomposed into their constituent elements. One sample produces 25.6 g of oxygen and 9.60 g of carbon, and the other produces 21.6 g of oxygen and 8.10 g of carbon. Show that these results are consistent with the law of definite proportions.

SOLUTION

To show this, compute the mass ratio of one element to the other for both samples by dividing the mass of one element by the mass of the other. For convenience, divide the larger mass by the smaller one.

For the first sample:

$$\frac{\text{Mass oxygen}}{\text{Mass carbon}} = \frac{25.6\text{ g}}{9.60\text{ g}} = 2.67 \text{ or } 2.67{:}1$$

For the second sample:

$$\frac{\text{Mass oxygen}}{\text{Mass carbon}} = \frac{21.6\text{ g}}{8.10\text{ g}} = 2.67 \text{ or } 2.67{:}1$$

The ratios are the same for the two samples, so these results are consistent with the law of definite proportions.

FOR PRACTICE 2.1

Two samples of carbon monoxide are decomposed into their constituent elements. One sample produces 17.2 g of oxygen and 12.9 g of carbon, and the other sample produces 10.5 g of oxygen and 7.88 g of carbon. Show that these results are consistent with the law of definite proportions.

The Law of Multiple Proportions

In 1804, John Dalton published his **law of multiple proportions**, which asserts the following principle:

> **When two elements (call them A and B) form two different compounds, the masses of element B that combine with 1 g of element A can be expressed as a ratio of small whole numbers.**

Dalton already suspected that matter was composed of atoms, so that when two elements, A and B, combined to form more than one compound, an atom of A combined with either one, two, three, or more atoms of B (AB_1, AB_2, AB_3, etc.). Therefore, the ratio of the masses of B that reacted with a fixed mass of A would always be a small whole number. Consider the compounds carbon monoxide and carbon dioxide, which were used in Example 2.1. Carbon monoxide and carbon dioxide are two compounds composed of the same two elements: carbon and oxygen. We saw in Example 2.1 that the mass ratio of oxygen to carbon in carbon dioxide is 2.67:1; therefore, 2.67 g of oxygen would react with 1 g of carbon. In carbon monoxide, however, the mass ratio of oxygen to carbon is 1.33:1, or 1.33 g of oxygen to every 1 g of carbon.

The standard colours for atoms used throughout this text are in Appendix II A.

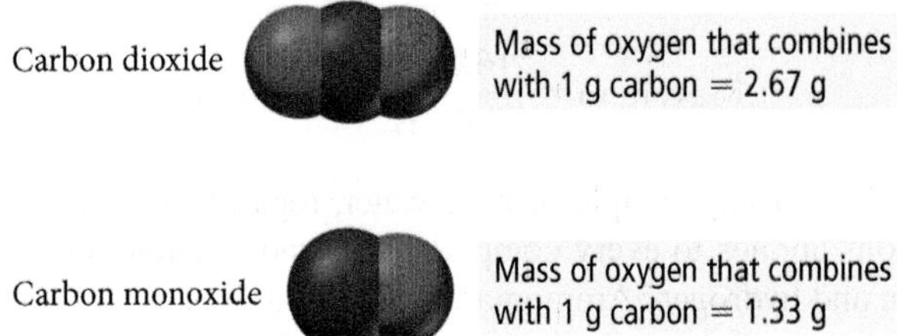

The ratio of these two masses is itself a small whole number:

$$\frac{\text{Mass of oxygen to 1 g carbon in carbon dioxide}}{\text{Mass of oxygen to 1 g carbon in carbon monoxide}} = \frac{2.67}{1.33} = 2$$

With the help of the molecular models, we can see why the ratio is 2:1—carbon dioxide contains two oxygen atoms to every carbon atom, whereas carbon monoxide contains only one oxygen atom.

John Dalton and the Atomic Theory

In 1808, John Dalton explained the laws just discussed with his **atomic theory**, which included the following concepts:

1. Each element is composed of tiny indestructible particles called atoms.
2. All atoms of a given element have the same mass and physical/chemical properties that distinguish them from the atoms of other elements.
3. Atoms combine in simple whole number ratios to form compounds.
4. Atoms of one element cannot change into atoms of another element. In a chemical reaction, atoms only change the way that they are bound together with other atoms.

In Section 2.6, we will see that contrary to Dalton's theory, for most of the elements, all atoms of a given element do not have exactly the same mass.

Today, the evidence for the atomic theory is overwhelming. Matter is indeed composed of atoms.

2.4 Atomic Structure

By the end of the nineteenth century, scientists were convinced that matter was made up of atoms—the permanent, supposedly indestructible building blocks that compose everything. However, further experiments revealed that the atom itself was composed of even smaller, more fundamental particles.

The Discovery of the Electron

In the late 1800s, an English physicist named J. J. Thomson (1856–1940), working at Cambridge University, performed experiments to probe the properties of **cathode rays**. Thomson constructed a glass tube called a **cathode ray tube**, shown in Figure 2.3 ▶. The tube was partially evacuated, which means that much of the air was pumped out of the tube

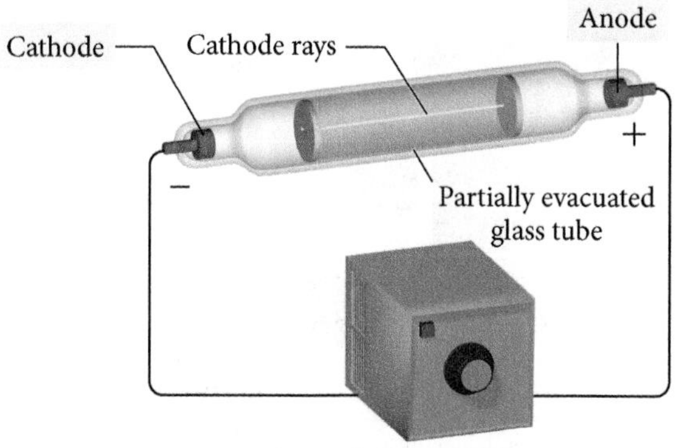

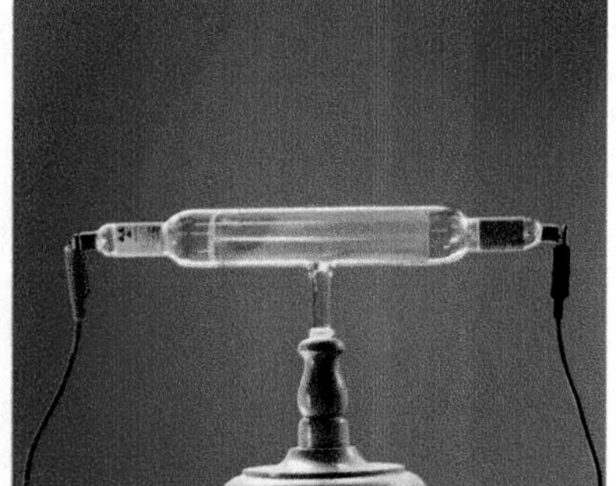

▲ **FIGURE 2.3 Cathode Ray Tube**

(because air interferes with cathode rays). Thomson then applied a high electrical voltage between two electrodes at either end of the tube. Thomson found that a beam of particles, called cathode rays, travelled from the negatively charged electrode (which is called the cathode) to the positively charged one (called the anode).

Thomson found that these particles had the following properties: they travelled in straight lines, they were independent of the composition of the material from which they originated (the cathode), and they carried a negative **electrical charge**. Electrical charge is a fundamental property of some of the particles that compose atoms, and it results in attractive and repulsive forces—called *electrostatic forces*—between those particles. The area around a charged particle where these forces exist is called an *electric field*. The characteristics of electrical charge are summarized in the figure in the margin. You have probably experienced excess electrical charge when brushing your hair on a dry day. The brushing action causes the accumulation of charged particles in your hair, which repel each other, making your hair stand on end.

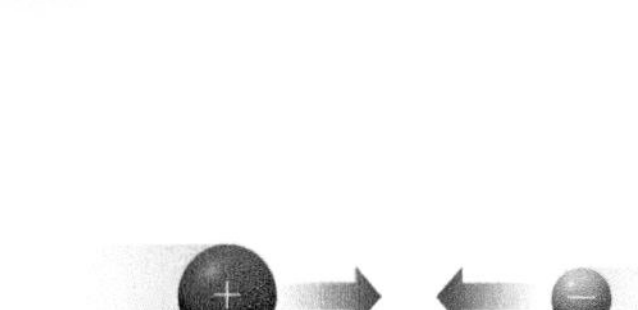

Positive (red) and negative (yellow) electrical charges attract one another.

Positive charges repel one another. Negative charges repel one another.

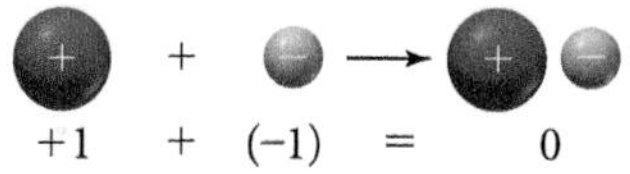

Positive and negative charges of exactly the same magnitude sum to zero when combined.

For a full explanation of electrical voltage, see Chapter 18.

The coulomb (C) is the SI unit for charge.

J. J. Thomson measured the charge-to-mass ratio of the cathode ray particles by deflecting them using electric and magnetic fields, as shown in Figure 2.4 ▼. The value he measured, -1.76×10^8 coulombs (C) per gram, implied that the cathode ray particle was about 2000 times lighter (less massive) than hydrogen, the lightest known atom. These results were incredible—the indestructible atom could apparently be chipped!

J. J. Thomson had discovered the **electron**, a negatively charged, low-mass particle present within all atoms. Thomson wrote, "We have in the cathode rays matter in a new state, a state in which the subdivision of matter is carried very much further . . . a state in which all matter . . . is of one and the same kind; this matter being the substance from which all the chemical elements are built up."

In 1909, American physicist Robert Millikan (1868–1953) performed his now famous oil drop experiment to deduce the charge of an electron. The apparatus for the oil drop experiment is shown in Figure 2.5 ▼.

In his experiment, Millikan sprayed oil into fine droplets using an atomizer. The droplets were allowed to fall under the influence of gravity through a small hole into the lower portion of the apparatus where Millikan viewed them with the aid of a light source and

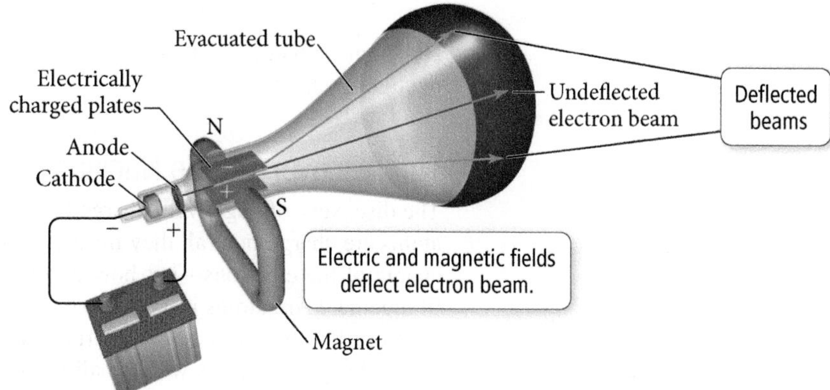

▲ **FIGURE 2.4 Thomson's Measurement of the Charge-to-Mass Ratio of the Electron**
J. J. Thomson used electric and magnetic fields to deflect the electron beam in a cathode ray tube. By measuring the strengths at which the effects of the two fields (electric and magnetic) cancelled exactly, leaving the beam undeflected, he was able to calculate the charge-to-mass ratio of the electron.

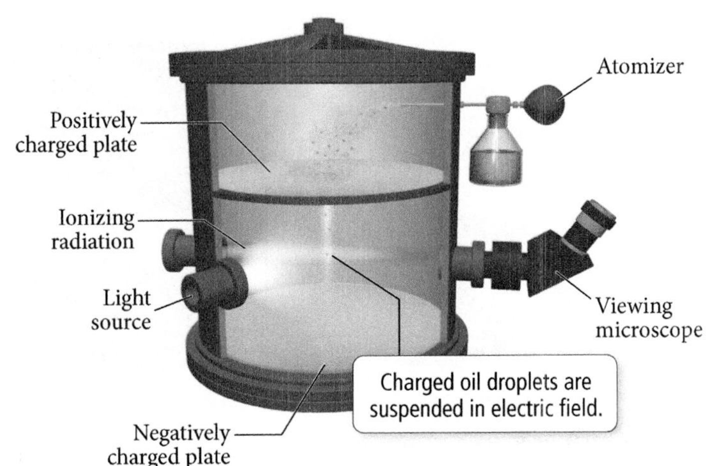

▶ **FIGURE 2.5 Millikan's Measurement of the Electron's Charge** Millikan calculated the charge on oil droplets falling in an electric field. He found that it was always a whole-number multiple of -1.60×10^{-19} C, the charge of a single electron.

a viewing microscope. During their fall, the drops acquired electrons that had been produced by bombarding the air in the chamber with ionizing radiation (a kind of energy that we will learn more about in Chapter 7). The electrons imparted a negative charge to the drops. In the lower portion of the apparatus, Millikan could create an electric field between two metal plates. Since the lower plate was negatively charged, and since Millikan could vary the strength of the electric field, the free fall of the negatively charged drops could be slowed and even reversed. (Remember that like charges repel each other.)

By measuring the size of the electric field required to halt the free fall of the drops, and determining the masses of the drops themselves (from their radii and density), Millikan calculated the charge of each drop. He then reasoned that because each drop must contain an integral (or whole) number of electrons, the charge of each drop must be a whole-number multiple of the electron's charge. Indeed, Millikan was correct: the measured charge on any drop was always a whole-number multiple of 1.60×10^{-19} C, the fundamental charge of a single electron. With this number in hand, and knowing Thomson's charge-to-mass ratio for electrons, we can calculate the mass of an electron as follows:

$$\cancel{\text{Charge}} \times \frac{\text{mass}}{\cancel{\text{charge}}} = \text{mass}$$

$$-1.60 \times 10^{-19}\,\cancel{\text{C}} \times \frac{1\text{ g}}{-1.76 \times 10^{8}\,\cancel{\text{C}}} = 9.10 \times 10^{-28}\text{ g}$$

As Thomson had correctly deduced, this mass is about 2000 times lighter than hydrogen, the lightest atom.

The Discovery of the Nucleus

The discovery of negatively charged particles within atoms raised a new question. Since atoms are charge-neutral, they must contain positive charge that neutralizes the negative charge of the electrons—but how do the positive and negative charges within the atom fit together? Are atoms just a jumble of even more fundamental particles? Are they solid spheres? Do they have some internal structure? J. J. Thomson proposed that the negatively charged electrons were small particles held within a positively charged sphere, as shown in the margin figure.

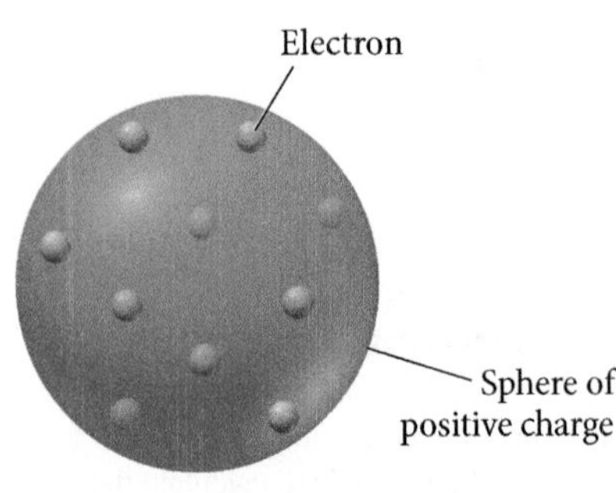

Plum-pudding model

This model, the most popular of the time, became known as the plum-pudding model. The picture suggested by Thomson, to those of us not familiar with plum pudding (an English dessert), was like a blueberry muffin, in which the blueberries are the electrons, and the muffin is the positively charged sphere.

The discovery of **radioactivity**—the emission of small energetic particles from the core of certain unstable atoms—by scientists Henri Becquerel (1852–1908) and Marie

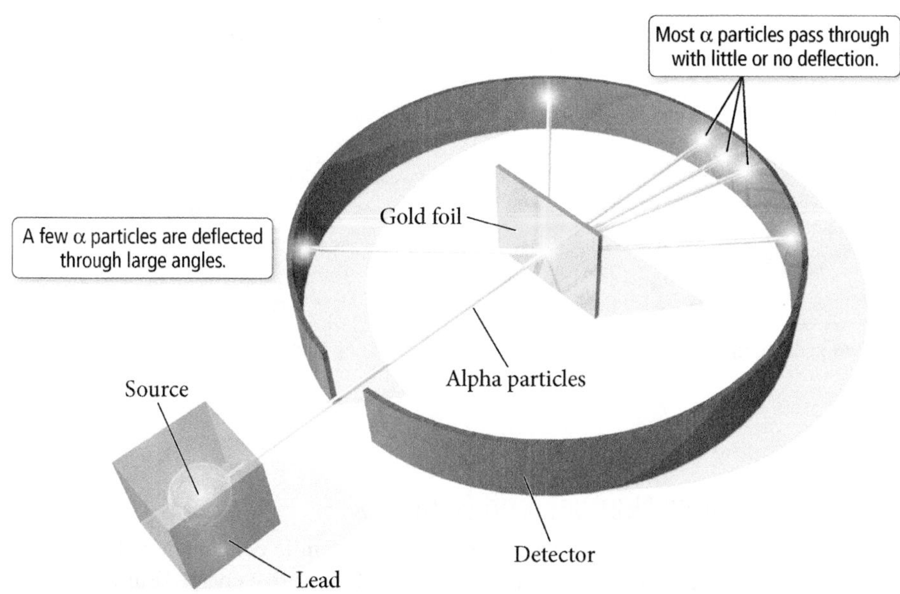
Most α particles pass through with little or no deflection.
A few α particles are deflected through large angles.
Gold foil
Alpha particles
Source
Lead
Detector

▲ **FIGURE 2.6 Rutherford's Gold Foil Experiment** Alpha (α) particles were directed at a thin sheet of gold foil. Most of the particles passed through the foil, but a small fraction were deflected, and a few even bounced backward.

Ernest Rutherford was Professor of Experimental Physics at McGill University from 1898–1907. During his time at McGill, he discovered the differences between alpha and beta radiation, and the fact that radiation was associated with the transmutation of elements, which is discussed in Chapter 19. For this work, he was awarded the Nobel Prize in 1908. In 1907, he moved to Manchester, where he discovered the nucleus. The Physics Department at McGill University is home to the Rutherford Museum, which displays Rutherford's experimental apparatus from his time there.

Curie (1867–1934) at the end of the nineteenth century—allowed researchers to experimentally probe the structure of the atom. At the time, scientists had identified three different types of radioactivity: alpha (α) particles, beta (β) particles, and gamma (γ) rays. We will discuss these and other types of radioactivity in more detail in Chapter 19. For now, just know that α particles are positively charged and they are by far the most massive of these three types of particles.

In 1909, Ernest Rutherford (1871–1937), who had worked under Thomson and subscribed to his plum-pudding model, performed an experiment in an attempt to confirm it. His experiment, which employed α particles, proved it wrong instead. In the experiment, Rutherford directed the positively charged α particles at an ultrathin sheet of gold foil, as shown in Figure 2.6 ▲.

▲ The Rutherford Museum, McGill University

These particles were to act as probes of the gold atoms' structure. If the gold atoms were indeed like blueberry muffins or plum pudding—with their mass and charge spread throughout the entire volume of the atom—these speeding probes should pass right through the gold foil with minimum deflection.

Rutherford performed the experiment, but the results were not as he expected. A majority of the particles did pass directly through the foil, but some particles were deflected, and some (approximately 1 in 20 000) even bounced back. The results puzzled Rutherford, who wrote that they were "about as credible as if you had fired a 15-inch shell at a piece of tissue paper and it came back and hit you." What sort of atomic structure could explain this odd behaviour?

Rutherford created a new model—a modern version of which is shown in Figure 2.7 ▼ alongside the plum-pudding model—to explain his results.

He realized that to account for the deflections he observed, the mass and positive charge of an atom must be concentrated in a space much smaller than the size of the atom itself. He concluded that, in contrast to the plum-pudding model, matter must not be as uniform as it appears. It must contain large regions of empty space dotted with small regions of very dense matter. Building on this idea, he proposed the **nuclear theory** of the atom, with two basic parts:

1. Most of the atom's mass and all its positive charge are contained in a small core called the **nucleus**.
2. Most of the volume of the atom is empty space, throughout which tiny, negatively charged electrons are dispersed.

▲ Ernest Rutherford

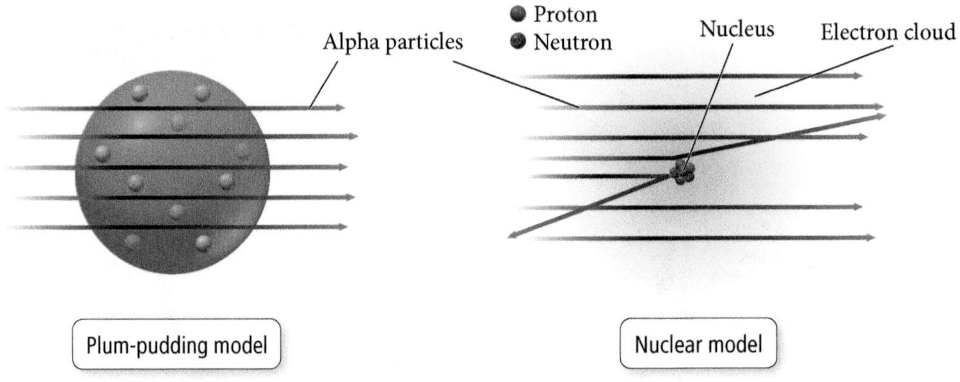

▶ **FIGURE 2.7 The Nuclear Atom** Rutherford's results could not be explained by the plum-pudding model. Instead, they suggested that the atom must have a small, dense nucleus.

Protons, the Atomic Number, and Neutrons

The nuclear model says that the positive charge in an atom is contained in the nucleus. However, the model said nothing about the nature of the positive charge. Further experiments in Rutherford's laboratory led to the knowledge that the nucleus of each element contains a different amount of charge, and that the nuclear charge is a multiple of the charge of an electron. For example, a hydrogen nucleus contains one unit of positive charge, of the same magnitude as the charge of an electron, although of opposite sign. A helium nucleus contains two units of positive charge, and so on.

Refer to the Periodic Table of Elements on the inside cover of this text and Section 2.7, later in this chapter.

The units of positive charge in a nucleus are carried by particles called **protons**, which were discovered in 1919 by Rutherford. The number of protons in a nucleus is known as the **atomic number** and is given the symbol **Z**. The atoms of any element have the same unique atomic number. For example, every hydrogen atom has one proton in its nucleus, and the atomic number is 1. Each iron atom has 26 protons in its nucleus, and the atomic number is 26. The number of protons in a nucleus is what makes atoms of one element different from those of another. The atomic number defines an element.

Each element, identified by its unique atomic number, is represented with a unique **chemical symbol**, a one- or two-letter abbreviation. The chemical symbol for helium is He; for carbon, it is C; and for uranium, it is U. The chemical symbol and the atomic number always go together. If the atomic number is 2, the chemical symbol *must be* He. If the atomic number is 6, the chemical symbol *must be* C. This is just another way of saying that the number of protons defines the element.

If a proton had the mass of a baseball, an electron would have the mass of a rice grain.

The atomic numbers of elements increase as a sequence of whole numbers. Hydrogen has an atomic number of 1, helium has an atomic number of 2, lithium has an atomic number of 3, and so on. However, the masses of atoms do not increase in a sequence of whole numbers. For example, hydrogen atoms contain one proton, and helium atoms contain two, yet a hydrogen atom has only one-fourth the mass of a helium atom. Why? The helium atom must contain some additional mass, not accounted for by protons and electrons. Later work by British scientist James Chadwick (1891–1974) demonstrated that the previously unaccounted for mass was due to **neutrons**, neutral particles in the nucleus. The mass of a neutron is similar to that of a proton, but a neutron has no electrical charge. The helium atom is four times as massive as the hydrogen atom because it contains two protons *and two neutrons* (whereas hydrogen contains only one proton and no neutrons).

Protons and neutrons have nearly identical masses. In SI units, the mass of the proton is 1.67262×10^{-27} kg, and the mass of the neutron is 1.67493×10^{-27} kg. A more common unit to express these masses, however, is the **unified atomic mass unit (u)**, defined as 1/12 the mass of a carbon atom containing 6 protons and 6 neutrons. Expressed in this unit, the mass of a proton or neutron is approximately 1 u. Electrons, by contrast, have an almost negligible mass of 9.10938×10^{-31} kg or 5.48580×10^{-4} u.

The unified atomic mass unit (u) is the SI unit for atomic mass. Sometimes, the equivalent unit dalton (Da) is used. The unit amu (atomic mass unit) is considered obsolete.

The proton and the electron both have electrical *charge*. We know from Millikan's oil drop experiment that the electron has a charge of -1.60×10^{-19} C. In atomic (or relative) units, the electron is assigned a charge of −1, and the proton is assigned a charge of +1. *The charge of the proton and the electron are equal in magnitude, but opposite in sign*, so that

TABLE 2.1 Characteristics of Subatomic Particles

	Mass (kg)	Mass (u)	Charge (relative)	Charge (C)
Proton	1.67262×10^{-27}	1.00727	+1	$+1.60218 \times 10^{-19}$
Neutron	1.67493×10^{-27}	1.00866	0	0
Electron	9.10938×10^{-31}	5.48580×10^{-4}	−1	-1.60218×10^{-19}

when the two particles are paired, the charges sum to zero. The neutron has no charge. The properties of protons, neutrons, and electrons are summarized in Table 2.1.

Isotopes: When the Number of Neutrons Varies

All atoms of a given element have the same number of protons; however, they do not necessarily have the same number of neutrons. Since a neutron has approximately the same mass as a proton (1 u), this means that—contrary to what John Dalton originally proposed in his atomic theory—for most of the elements in the periodic table, all atoms of a given element *do not* have the same mass. For example, all neon atoms contain 10 protons, but they can contain 10, 11, or 12 neutrons. All three types of neon atoms exist, and each has a slightly different mass. Atoms with the same number of protons but different numbers of neutrons are called **isotopes**. Some elements, such as beryllium (Be) and aluminum (Al), have only one naturally occurring isotope; whereas other elements, such as neon (Ne) and chlorine (Cl), have two or more. The relative amount of each different isotope in a naturally occurring sample of a given element is usually constant. For example, in any natural sample of neon atoms, 90.48% of them are the isotope with 10 neutrons, 0.27% are the isotope with 11 neutrons, and 9.25% are the isotope with 12 neutrons. These percentages are called the **natural abundance** of the isotopes. Each element has its own characteristic natural abundance of isotopes. The sum of the number of neutrons and protons in an atom is its **mass number** and is represented by the symbol A:

$$A = \text{number of protons (p)} + \text{number of neutrons (n)}$$

For neon, with 10 protons, the mass numbers of the three different naturally occurring isotopes are 20, 21, and 22, corresponding to 10, 11, and 12 neutrons, respectively. Isotopes are often symbolized in the following way:

Mass number → $^{A}_{Z}\mathrm{X}$ ← Chemical symbol
Atomic number →

where X is the chemical symbol, A is the mass number, and Z is the atomic number. Therefore, the symbols for the neon isotopes are:

$$^{20}_{10}\mathrm{Ne} \quad ^{21}_{10}\mathrm{Ne} \quad ^{22}_{10}\mathrm{Ne}$$

Notice that the chemical symbol, Ne, and the atomic number, 10, are redundant: if the atomic number is 10, the symbol must be Ne. The mass numbers, however, are different for the different isotopes, reflecting the different number of neutrons in each one. A second common notation for isotopes is the chemical symbol (or chemical name), followed by a dash and the mass number of the isotope:

Chemical symbol or name → $\mathrm{X}\text{-}A$ ← Mass number

In this notation, the neon isotopes are:

Ne-20	Ne-21	Ne-22
neon-20	neon-21	neon-22

We summarize what we have learned about the neon isotopes in the following table:

Symbol	Number of Protons	Number of Neutrons	*A* (Mass Number)	Natural Abundance (%)
Ne-20 or $^{20}_{10}Ne$	10	10	20	90.48
Ne-21 or $^{21}_{10}Ne$	10	11	21	0.27
Ne-22 or $^{22}_{10}Ne$	10	12	22	9.25

Notice that all isotopes of a given element have the same number of protons (otherwise, they would be different elements). Notice also that the mass number is the *sum* of the number of protons and the number of neutrons. The number of neutrons in an isotope is therefore the difference between the mass number and the atomic number (A–Z). The different isotopes of an element generally exhibit the same chemical behaviour—the three isotopes of neon, for example, all exhibit the same chemical inertness.

EXAMPLE 2.2 ATOMIC NUMBERS, MASS NUMBERS, AND ISOTOPE SYMBOLS

(a) What are the atomic number (Z), mass number (A), and symbol of the chlorine isotope with 18 neutrons?

(b) How many protons, electrons, and neutrons are present in an atom of $^{52}_{24}Cr$?

SOLUTION

(a) Look up the atomic number (Z) for chlorine on the periodic table. The atomic number specifies the number of protons.	$Z = 17$, so chlorine has 17 protons
The mass number (A) for an isotope is the sum of the number of protons and the number of neutrons.	A = number of protons + number of neutrons $= 17 + 18 = 35$
The symbol for an isotope is the atomic symbol with the atomic number (Z) in the lower-left corner and the mass number (A) in the upper-left corner.	$^{35}_{17}Cl$
(b) For any isotope (in this case, $^{52}_{24}Cr$) the number of protons is indicated by the atomic number located at the lower left. Since this is a neutral atom, the number of electrons equals the number of protons.	Number of protons $= Z = 24$ Number of electrons $= 24$ (neutral atom)
The number of neutrons is equal to the mass number (upper left) minus the atomic number (lower left).	Number of neutrons $= 52 - 24 = 28$

FOR PRACTICE 2.2

(a) What are the atomic number, mass number, and symbol for the carbon isotope with seven neutrons?

(b) How many protons and neutrons are present in an atom of $^{39}_{19}K$?

Ions: Losing and Gaining Electrons

The number of electrons in a neutral atom is equal to the number of protons in its nucleus (designated by its atomic number, Z). During chemical changes, however, atoms can lose or gain electrons and become charged particles called **ions**. For example, neutral lithium (Li) atoms contain three protons and three electrons; however, in many chemical reactions, lithium atoms lose one electron (e^-) to form Li^+ ions.

$$Li \longrightarrow Li^+ + 1\,e^-$$

The charge of an ion depends on the relative number of protons and electrons and is indicated in the upper-right corner of the symbol. Since the Li^+ ion contains three protons and only two electrons, its charge is 1+.

Ions can also be negatively charged. For example, neutral fluorine (F) atoms contain nine protons and nine electrons; however, in many chemical reactions, fluorine atoms gain one electron to form F^- ions.

$$F + 1\,e^- \longrightarrow F^-$$

The F^- ion contains 9 protons and 10 electrons, resulting in a charge of 1−. For many elements, such as lithium and fluorine, the ion is much more common than the neutral atom. In fact, virtually all the lithium and fluorine in nature exist as ions.

Positively charged ions, such as Li^+, are called **cations**, and negatively charged ions, such as F^-, are called **anions**. Ions react in different ways than the atoms from which they are formed. Neutral sodium atoms, for example, are highly reactive, reacting violently with most compounds that they contact. Sodium cations (Na^+), by contrast, are relatively inert; we eat them all the time in sodium chloride (table salt). In ordinary matter, cations and anions always occur together so that matter is charge-neutral overall.

CONCEPTUAL CONNECTION 2.2
The Nuclear Atom, Isotopes, and Ions

In light of the nuclear model of the atom, which statement is most likely true?

(a) The size of an isotope with more neutrons is larger than one with few neutrons.

(b) The mass of an isotope with more neutrons is greater than one with fewer neutrons.

(c) Both (a) and (b) are true.

CHEMISTRY IN YOUR DAY Where Did Elements Come From?

We find ourselves on a planet containing many different kinds of elements. If it were otherwise, we would not exist, and would not be here to reflect on why. But we are here, and so we ask, where did these elements come from? The story of element formation is as old as the universe itself, and we have to go back to the very beginning to tell the story.

The birth of the universe is described by the Big Bang theory, which asserts that the universe began as a hot, dense collection of matter and energy that expanded rapidly. As it expanded, it cooled, and within the first several hours, subatomic particles formed the first atomic nuclei: hydrogen and helium. These two elements were (and continue to be) the most abundant in the universe. As the universe continued expanding, some of the hydrogen and helium clumped together under the influence of gravity to form nebulae (clouds of gas) that eventually gave birth to stars and galaxies. These stars and galaxies became the nurseries where all other elements form.

Stars are fuelled by nuclear fusion, which we discuss in more detail in Chapter 19. Under the conditions within the core of a star, hydrogen nuclei can combine (or fuse) to form helium. Fusion gives off enormous quantities of energy; this is why stars emit so much heat and light. The fusion of hydrogen to helium can fuel a star for billions of years.

After it burns through large quantities of hydrogen, if a star is large enough, the helium that builds up in its core can, in turn, fuse to form carbon. The carbon then builds up in the core and (again, if the star is large enough) can fuse to form even heavier elements. The fusion process ends at iron, which has a highly stable nucleus. By the time iron is formed, however, the star is near the end of its existence and may enter a phase of expansion, transforming into a supernova. Within a supernova, which is in essence a large exploding star, a shower of neutrons allows the lighter elements (which formed during the lifetime of the star through the fusion processes just described) to capture extra neutrons. These neutrons can transform into protons (through processes that we discuss in Chapter 19), contributing ultimately to the formation of elements heavier than iron, all the way up to uranium. As the supernova continues to expand, the elements present within it are blown out into space, where they can incorporate into other nebulae and perhaps even form planets that orbit a star like our own sun.

▲ Stars are born in nebulae such as the Eagle Nebula (also known as M16). This image was taken by the Hubble Space Telescope and shows a gaseous pillar in a star-forming region of the Eagle Nebula.

2.5 Atomic Mass: The Average Mass of an Element's Atoms

Atomic mass is sometimes called *atomic weight, average atomic mass,* or *average atomic weight.*

17
Cl
35.45
chlorine

When percentages are used in calculations, they are converted to their decimal value by dividing by 100.

An important part of Dalton's atomic theory is that all atoms of a given element have the same mass. In Section 2.4, we learned that because of isotopes, the atoms of a given element often have different masses, so Dalton was not completely correct. We can, however, calculate an average mass—called the **atomic mass**—for each element.

The atomic mass of each element, which is listed directly beneath the element's symbol in the periodic table, represents the average mass of the isotopes that compose that element, *weighted according to the natural abundance of each isotope*. For example, the periodic table lists the atomic mass of chlorine as 35.45 u. Naturally occurring chlorine consists of 75.77% chlorine-35 atoms (mass 34.97 u) and 24.23% chlorine-37 atoms (mass 36.97 u). We can calculate its atomic mass as follows:

$$\text{Atomic mass} = 0.7577(34.97\ \text{u}) + 0.2423(36.97\ \text{u}) = 35.45\ \text{u}$$

Notice that the atomic mass of chlorine is closer to 35 than 37. Naturally occurring chlorine contains more chlorine-35 atoms than chlorine-37 atoms, so the weighted average mass of chlorine is closer to 35 u than to 37 u.

In general, the atomic mass is calculated according to the following equation, where the fractions of each isotope are the percent of natural abundances converted to their decimal values:

$$\begin{aligned}\textbf{Atomic mass} &= \sum_n \textbf{(fraction of isotope n)} \times \textbf{(mass of isotope n)}\\ &= \textbf{(fraction of isotope 1} \times \textbf{mass of isotope 1)}\\ &+ \textbf{(fraction of isotope 2} \times \textbf{mass of isotope 2)}\\ &+ \textbf{(fraction of isotope 3} \times \textbf{mass of isotope 3)} + \cdots\end{aligned}$$

The concept of atomic mass is useful because it allows us to assign a characteristic mass to each element and, as we will see shortly, it allows us to quantify the number of atoms in a sample of that element.

EXAMPLE 2.3 ATOMIC MASS

Magnesium has three naturally occurring isotopes: Mg-24 with mass 23.9850 u and a natural abundance of 78.99%, Mg-25 with mass 24.9858 u and a natural abundance of 10.00%, and Mg-26 with mass 25.9826 u and a natural abundance of 11.01%. Calculate the atomic mass of magnesium.

SOLUTION

Convert the percent of natural abundances into decimal form by dividing by 100.	$\text{Fraction Mg-24} = \frac{78.99}{100} = 0.7899$ $\text{Fraction Mg-25} = \frac{10.00}{100} = 0.1000$ $\text{Fraction Mg-26} = \frac{11.01}{100} = 0.1101$
Compute the atomic mass using the equation given in the text.	Atomic mass = 0.7899(23.9850 u) + 0.1000(24.9858 u) + 0.1101(25.9826 u) = 24.3050 u

CHECK The answer, 24.3050 u, is close to the mass of the most abundant isotope, but a little larger, which makes sense because the other two isotopes which make up about 21% are heavier.

FOR PRACTICE 2.3

Titanium has five naturally occurring isotopes with masses of 45.9526 u, 46.9518 u, 47.9479 u, 48.9479 u, and 49.9448 u; and natural abundances of 8.25%, 7.44%, 73.72%, 5.41%, and 5.18%, respectively. Calculate the atomic mass of titanium.

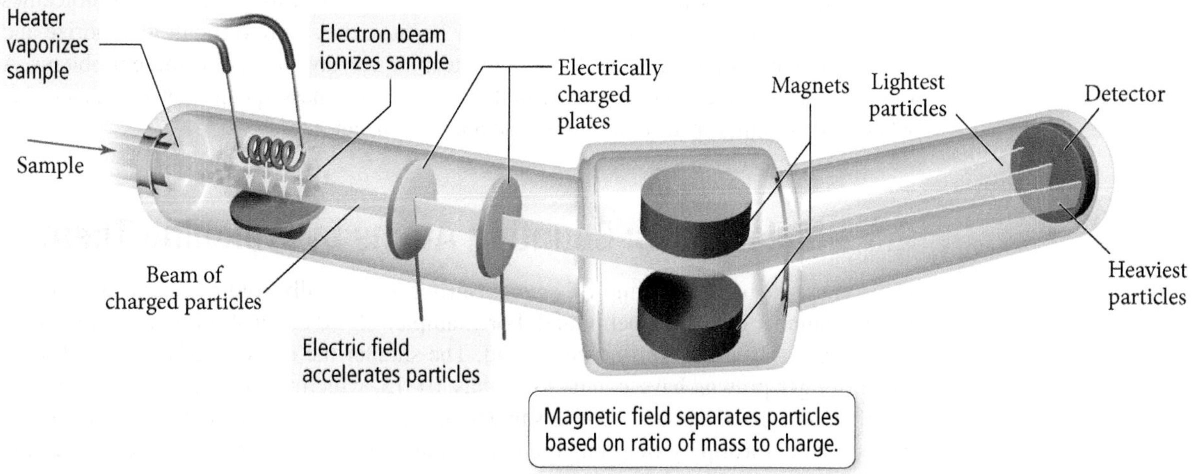

▲ **FIGURE 2.8 The Mass Spectrometer** Atoms are converted to positively charged ions, accelerated, and passed through a magnetic field that deflects their path. The heaviest ions undergo the least deflection.

Mass Spectrometry: Measuring the Mass of Atoms and Molecules

The masses of atoms and the percent abundances of isotopes are measured using **mass spectrometry**. In a mass spectrometer, such as the one in Figure 2.8 ▲, the sample (containing the atoms whose masses are to be measured) is injected into the instrument and vaporized. The vaporized atoms are then ionized with an electron beam—the fast-moving electrons in the beam knock electrons off of the neutral atoms to create positively charged ions. Charged plates with narrow slits to allow the ions to pass through are used to accelerate the ions into a magnetic field, where the ions are deflected. The amount of deflection depends on the mass of the ions—lighter ions are deflected more than heavier ones. Using this technique, even very tiny differences in mass—such as those observed between two isotopes—can be easily detected.

In the right side of the spectrometer shown in Figure 2.8, you can see three different paths, each corresponding to atoms of different mass. Finally, the ions strike a detector and produce an electrical signal that is recorded. The result is the separation of the atoms in the sample according to their mass, producing a mass spectrum such as the one in Figure 2.9 ▼. The *position* of each peak on the axis labelled *m/z* indicates the *mass of the isotope* that was ionized, and the *intensity* (indicated by the area under the peak) indicates the *relative abundance of that isotope*.

Mass spectrometry can also be used on molecules. Unlike individual atoms, molecules often fragment (break apart) after ionization, and thus the mass spectrum of a molecule usually contains many peaks. Each individual peak represents the mass of a different fragment of the molecule, as well as a peak representing the mass of the unfragmented molecule. The fragments that form following ionization, and therefore the corresponding peaks that appear in the mass spectrum, are specific to the molecule, so that a mass spectrum is like a molecular fingerprint. Mass spectrometry can therefore be used to identify an unknown molecule and to determine how much of it is present in a particular sample. For example, mass spectrometry has been used to detect organic (carbon-containing) compounds present in meteorites, a puzzling observation, which some scientists speculate might be evidence of life elsewhere in the universe. Most scientists, however, think that the compounds probably formed in the same way as the first organic molecules on Earth, indicating that the formation of organic molecules may be common in the universe.

Since the early 1990s, researchers have also successfully applied mass spectrometry to biological molecules, including proteins (the workhorse molecules in cells) and nucleic

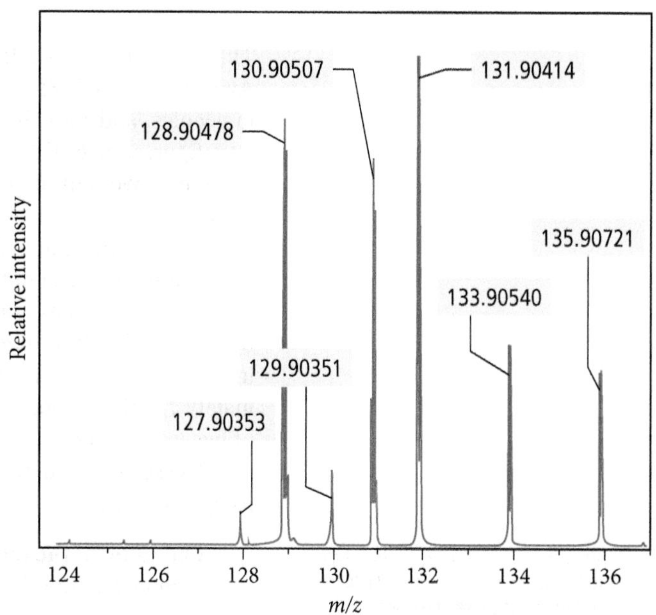

▲ **FIGURE 2.9 Mass Spectrum of Xenon** Xenon has nine stable isotopes. Two of the peaks, at *m/z* 123.90589 and 125.90428, are so small that they cannot be seen in this mass spectrum, indicating a low natural abundance for these isotopes.

acids (the molecules that carry genetic information). For a long time, these molecules could not be analyzed by mass spectrometry because they were difficult to vaporize and ionize without destroying them, but modern techniques have overcome these problems. A tumour, for example, can now be instantly analyzed by mass spectrometry to determine whether it contains specific proteins associated with cancer.

2.6 Molar Mass: Counting Atoms by Weighing Them

Have you ever bought shrimp by *count*? Shrimp is normally sold by count, which tells you the number of shrimp per pound. For example, 41–50 count shrimp means that there are between 41 and 50 shrimp per pound. The smaller the count, the larger the shrimp. The big tiger prawns have counts as low as 10–15, which means that each shrimp can weigh up to 1/10 of a pound. One advantage of categorizing shrimp in this way is that you can count the shrimp by weighing them. For example, two pounds of 41–50 count shrimp contains between 82 and 100 shrimp.

A similar (but more precise) concept exists for atoms. Counting atoms is much more difficult than counting shrimp, yet we often need to know the number of atoms in a given mass of atoms. For example, intravenous fluids—fluids that are delivered to patients by directly dripping them into their veins—are saline (salt) solutions that must have a specific number of sodium and chloride ions per litre of fluid. The result of using an intravenous fluid with the wrong number of sodium and chloride ions could be fatal.

Atoms are far too small to count by any ordinary means. As we saw earlier, even if you could somehow count atoms, and counted them 24 hours a day for as long as you lived, you would barely begin to count the number of atoms in something as small as a sand grain. Therefore, if we want to know the number of atoms in anything of ordinary size, we must count them by weighing.

The Mole: A Chemist's "Dozen"

When we count large numbers of objects, we often use units such as a dozen (12 objects) or a gross (144 objects) to organize our counting and to keep our numbers more manageable. With atoms, quadrillions of which may be in a speck of dust, we need a much larger number for this purpose. The chemist's "dozen" is the **mole** (abbreviated "**mol**"). A mole is the *amount* of material containing 6.02214×10^{23} particles:

$$1 \text{ mol} = 6.02214 \times 10^{23} \text{ particles}$$

This number is also called **Avogadro's number**, named after Italian physicist Amedeo Avogadro (1776–1856), and is a convenient number to use when working with atoms, molecules, and ions. In this text, we usually round Avogadro's number to four significant figures, or 6.022×10^{23}. Notice that the definition of the mole is an *amount* of a substance. We will often refer to the number of moles of substance as the *amount* of the substance.

The first thing to understand about the mole is that it can specify Avogadro's number of anything. For example, 1 mol of marbles corresponds to 6.022×10^{23} marbles, and 1 mol of sand grains corresponds to 6.022×10^{23} sand grains. *One mole of anything is* 6.022×10^{23} *units of that thing*. One mole of atoms, ions, or molecules, however, makes up objects of everyday sizes. Twenty-two copper pennies, for example, contain approximately 1 mol of copper atoms, and one tablespoon of water contains approximately 1 mol of water molecules.

The second, and more fundamental, thing to understand about the mole is how it gets its specific value:

It is simply by convention that carbon-12 is used to define the mole. Earlier definitions were based on the mass of oxygen.

The value of the mole is equal to the number of atoms in exactly 12 grams of carbon-12 (12 g C = 1 mol C atoms = 6.022×10^{23} C atoms).

The definition of the mole gives us a relationship between mass (grams of carbon) and number of atoms (Avogadro's number). This relationship, as we will see shortly, allows us to count atoms by weighing them.

Converting Between Number of Moles and Number of Atoms

Converting between the number of moles and number of atoms is similar to converting between dozens of eggs and number of eggs. For eggs, you use the conversion factor 1 dozen eggs = 12 eggs. For atoms, you use the conversion factor 1 mol atoms = 6.022×10^{23} atoms. The conversion factors take the following forms:

$$\frac{1 \text{ mol atoms}}{6.022 \times 10^{23} \text{ atoms}} \quad \text{or} \quad \frac{6.022 \times 10^{23} \text{ atoms}}{1 \text{ mol atoms}}$$

For example, the number of copper atoms in 2.45 mol of copper is:

$$\text{number of Cu atoms} = 2.45 \cancel{\text{mol Cu}} \times \frac{6.022 \times 10^{23} \text{ Cu atoms}}{1 \cancel{\text{mol Cu}} \text{ atoms}}$$

$$= 1.48 \times 10^{24} \text{ Cu atoms}$$

Converting Between Mass and Amount (Number of Moles)

To count atoms by weighing them, we need one other conversion factor: the mass of 1 mol of atoms. For the isotope carbon-12, we know that the mass of 1 mol of atoms is exactly 12 grams, which is numerically equivalent to carbon-12's atomic mass in unified atomic mass units. Since the masses of all other elements are defined relative to carbon-12, a similar relationship holds for all elements.

The mass of 1 mol of atoms of an element is called the **molar mass**.

The molar mass of any element, in grams per mole, is numerically equal to the element's atomic mass in unified atomic mass units.

For example, copper has an atomic mass of 63.55 u and a molar mass of 63.55 g mol^{-1}. One mole of copper atoms, therefore, has a mass of 63.55 g. The mass of 1 mol of atoms depends on the element: 1 mol of aluminum atoms (which are lighter than copper atoms) has a mass of 26.98 g, 1 mol of carbon atoms (which are even lighter than aluminum atoms) has a mass of 12.01 g, and 1 mol of helium atoms (lighter yet) has a mass of 4.003 g.

6.022×10^{23} Al atoms = 1 mol aluminum = 26.98 g aluminum (Al)

6.022×10^{23} C atoms = 1 mol carbon = 12.01 g carbon (C)

6.022×10^{23} He atoms = 1 mol helium = 4.003 g helium (He)

The lighter the atom, the less mass of 1 mol of that atom, because each individual atom has a smaller mass.

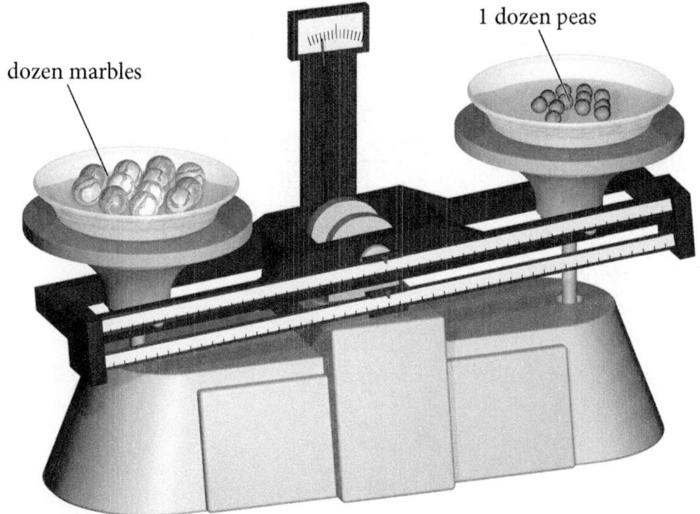

◀ The two pans each contain the same number of objects (12), but the masses in each pan are different because peas are less massive than marbles. Similarly, a mole of light atoms will have less mass than a mole of heavier atoms.

The molar mass of any element yields the conversion factor between mass (in grams) of that element and the amount (in moles) of that element. For carbon:

$$12.01 \text{ g C} = 1 \text{ mol C} \quad \text{or} \quad \frac{12.01 \text{ g C}}{1 \text{ mol C}} \quad \text{or} \quad \frac{1 \text{ mol C}}{12.01 \text{ g C}}$$

We now have all the tools to count the number of atoms in a sample of an element by weighing it. First, obtain the mass of the sample. Then convert it to the amount in moles using the element's molar mass. Finally, convert to number of atoms using Avogadro's number. The conceptual plan for these kinds of calculations takes the following form:

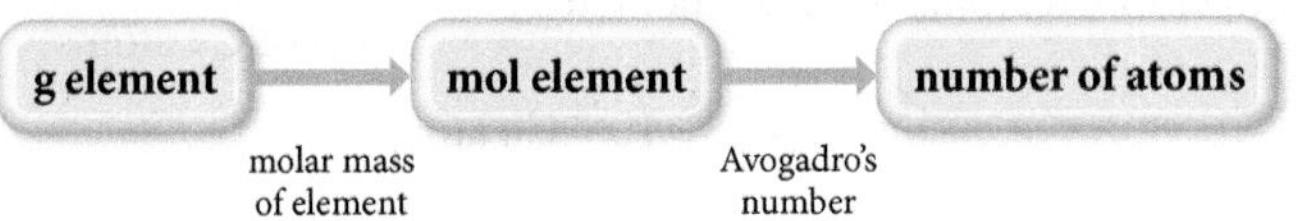

Example 2.4 demonstrates these conversions.

Notice that numbers with large exponents, such as 6.022×10^{23}, are unbelievably large. Twenty-two copper pennies contain 6.022×10^{23} or 1 mol of copper atoms, but

EXAMPLE 2.4 THE MOLE CONCEPT: CONVERTING FROM MASS TO MOLES AND NUMBER OF ATOMS

Calculate the number of moles of copper atoms and the number of copper atoms that are in 3.10 g of copper.

SORT You are given the mass of copper atoms and asked to find the number of moles of copper atoms and the number of copper atoms.

GIVEN: 3.10 g Cu
FIND: Moles and number of Cu atoms

STRATEGIZE Convert between the mass of an element in grams and the number of moles of atoms of the element with the molar mass.

Then convert from moles to the number of atoms using Avogadro's number.

CONCEPTUAL PLAN

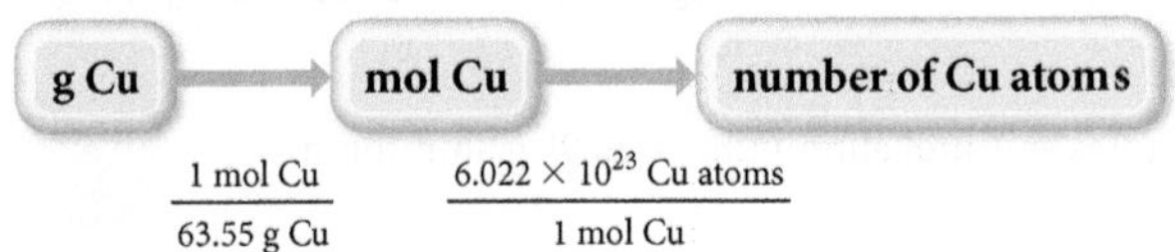

RELATIONSHIPS USED

63.55 g Cu = 1 mol Cu (Molar mass of copper)
$6.022 \times 10^{23} = 1$ mol (Avogadro's number)

SOLVE Follow the conceptual plan to solve the problem. Begin with 3.10 g Cu and multiply by the appropriate conversion factor to obtain the number of moles of copper.

SOLUTION
Number of moles Cu:

$$3.10 \text{ g } \cancel{\text{Cu}} \times \frac{1 \text{ mol Cu}}{63.55 \text{ g } \cancel{\text{Cu}}} = 4.88 \times 10^{-2} \text{ mol Cu}$$

Then multiply the number of moles by Avogadro's number to arrive at the number of copper atoms.

Number of Cu atoms:

$$4.88 \times 10^{-2} \cancel{\text{mol Cu}} \times \frac{6.022 \times 10^{23} \text{ Cu atoms}}{1 \cancel{\text{mol Cu}}} = 2.94 \times 10^{22} \text{ Cu atoms}$$

CHECK The answer (the number of copper atoms) is less than 6.022×10^{23} (one mole). This is consistent with the given mass of copper atoms, which is less than the molar mass of copper.

FOR PRACTICE 2.4
How many carbon atoms are there in a 1.3 carat diamond? Diamonds are a form of pure carbon. (1 carat = 0.20 grams)

FOR MORE PRACTICE 2.4
Calculate the mass of 2.25×10^{22} tungsten atoms.

6.022×10^{23} pennies would cover the Earth's entire surface to a depth of 300 m. Even objects small by everyday standards occupy a huge space when we have a mole of them. For example, a grain of sand has a mass of less than 1 mg and a diameter of less than 0.1 mm, yet 1 mol of sand grains would cover Atlantic Canada to a depth of several feet. For every increase of 1 in the exponent of a number, the number increases by a factor of 10, so 10^{23} is incredibly large. Of course, one mole has to be a large number if it is to have practical value because atoms are so small.

CONCEPTUAL CONNECTION 2.3

The Mole

Without doing any calculations, determine which of the following contains the most atoms.

(a) 1-g sample of copper

(b) 1-g sample of carbon

(c) 10-g sample of uranium

2.7 The Periodic Table of the Elements

The modern periodic table grew out of the work of many scientists, but most notably by Dmitri Mendeleev (1834–1907), a nineteenth-century Russian chemistry professor. In his time, scientists had discovered about 65 elements, and chemists had identified many of the properties of these elements—such as their relative masses, their chemical activity, and some of their physical properties. However, no one had developed any systematic way of organizing the elements.

Mendeleev organized the known elements in a table consisting of a series of rows in which mass increased from left to right. He arranged the rows so that elements with similar properties fell in the same vertical column. Mendeleev's periodic table contained gaps that allowed him to predict the existence (and even the properties) of yet-undiscovered elements. For example, he predicted the existence of an element he called eka-silicon, which fell below silicon on the table and between gallium and arsenic. In 1886, eka-silicon was discovered by German chemist Clemens Winkler (1838–1904), who named it germanium, after his home country.

Mendeleev's original listing evolved into the modern periodic table shown in Figures 2.10 and 2.11. In the modern table, elements are listed in order of increasing atomic number rather than increasing relative mass. The modern periodic table also contains more elements than Mendeleev's original table because more have been discovered since that time. Mendeleev's **periodic law** was based on the observation of periodic properties of the elements, but did not give the underlying reason for the observation. The theory of quantum mechanics, which we will examine in Chapters 7 and 8, offers an explanation for the periodic law.

▲ Dmitri Mendeleev, a Russian chemistry professor who proposed the periodic law and arranged early versions of the periodic table, was honoured on a Soviet postage stamp.

Eka means "the one beyond" or "the next one" in a family of elements. So, eka-silicon means the element beyond silicon in the same family as silicon.

Reihen	Gruppo I. — R^2O	Gruppo II. — RO	Gruppo III. — R^2O^3	Gruppe IV. RH^4 RO^2	Gruppe V. RH^3 R^2O^5	Gruppo VI. RH^2 RO^3	Gruppo VII. RH R^2O^7	Gruppo VIII. — RO^4
1	H=1							
2	Li=7	Be=9,4	B=11	C=12	N=14	O=16	F=19	
3	Na=23	Mg=24	Al=27,3	Si=28	P=31	S=32	Cl=35,5	
4	K=39	Ca=40	—=44	Ti=48	V=51	Cr=52	Mn=55	Fe=56, Co=59, Ni=59, Cu=63.
5	(Cu=63)	Zn=65	—=68	—=72	As=75	Se=78	Br=80	
6	Rb=85	Sr=87	?Yt=88	Zr=90	Nb=94	Mo=96	—=100	Ru=104, Rh=104, Pd=106, Ag=108.
7	(Ag=108)	Cd=112	In=113	Sn=118	Sb=122	Te=125	J=127	
8	Cs=133	Ba=137	?Di=138	?Ce=140	—	—	—	— — — —
9	(—)	—	—	—	—	—	—	
10	—	—	?Er=178	?La=180	Ta=182	W=184	—	Os=195, Ir=197, Pt=198, Au=199.
11	(Au=199)	Hg=200	Tl=204	Pb=207	Bi=208	—	—	
12	—	—	—	Th=231	—	U=240	—	— — — —

◀ Dmitri Mendeleev's periodic table from 1871. Mendeleev organized the known elements into eight groups, in order of increasing mass.

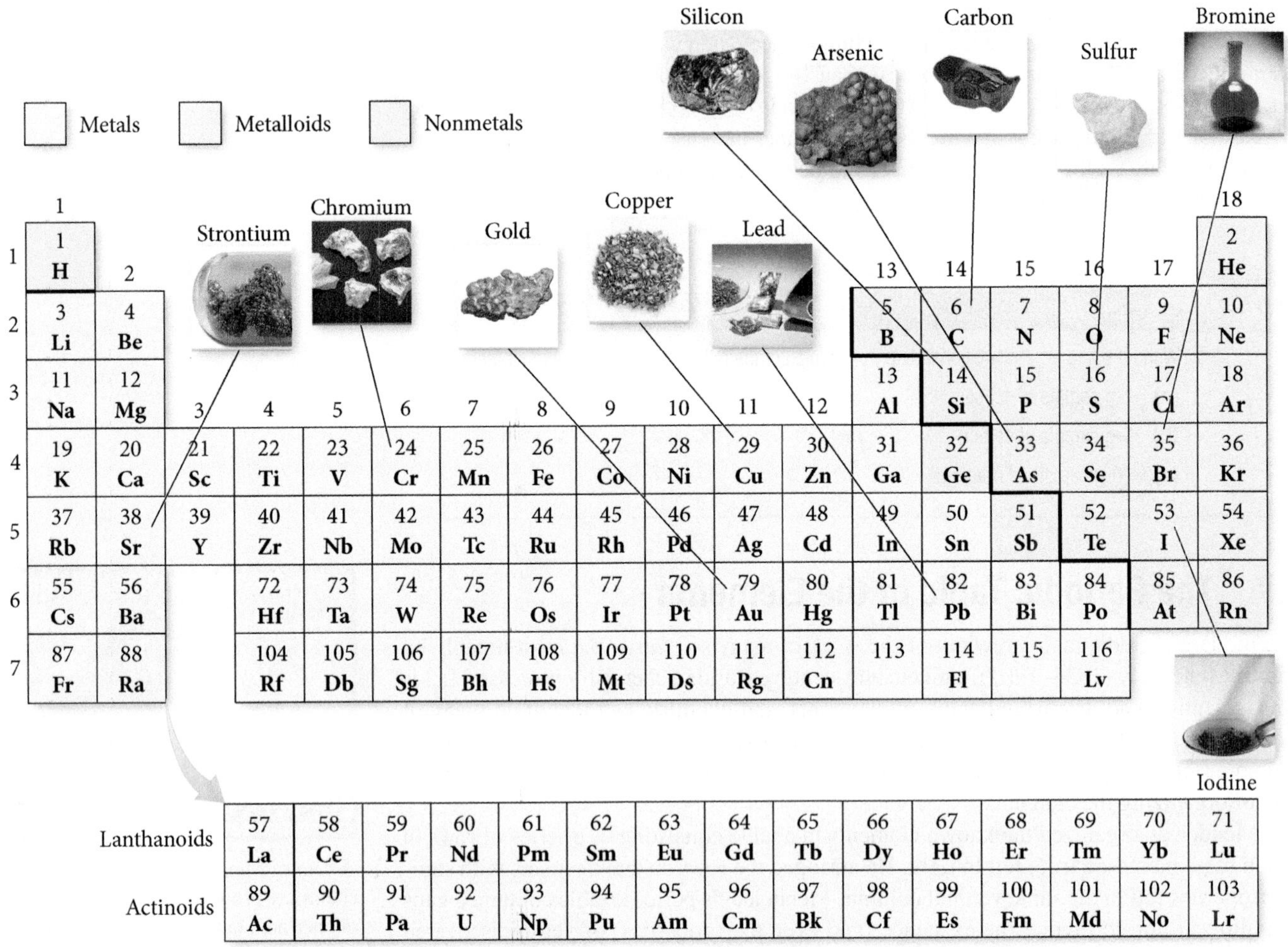

Metals | Metalloids | Nonmetals

Silicon, Arsenic, Carbon, Sulfur, Bromine, Strontium, Chromium, Gold, Copper, Lead, Iodine

	1	2	3	4	5	6	7	8	9	10	11	12	13	14	15	16	17	18
1	1 H																	2 He
2	3 Li	4 Be											5 B	6 C	7 N	8 O	9 F	10 Ne
3	11 Na	12 Mg											13 Al	14 Si	15 P	16 S	17 Cl	18 Ar
4	19 K	20 Ca	21 Sc	22 Ti	23 V	24 Cr	25 Mn	26 Fe	27 Co	28 Ni	29 Cu	30 Zn	31 Ga	32 Ge	33 As	34 Se	35 Br	36 Kr
5	37 Rb	38 Sr	39 Y	40 Zr	41 Nb	42 Mo	43 Tc	44 Ru	45 Rh	46 Pd	47 Ag	48 Cd	49 In	50 Sn	51 Sb	52 Te	53 I	54 Xe
6	55 Cs	56 Ba		72 Hf	73 Ta	74 W	75 Re	76 Os	77 Ir	78 Pt	79 Au	80 Hg	81 Tl	82 Pb	83 Bi	84 Po	85 At	86 Rn
7	87 Fr	88 Ra		104 Rf	105 Db	106 Sg	107 Bh	108 Hs	109 Mt	110 Ds	111 Rg	112 Cn	113	114 Fl	115	116 Lv		

Lanthanoids	57 La	58 Ce	59 Pr	60 Nd	61 Pm	62 Sm	63 Eu	64 Gd	65 Tb	66 Dy	67 Ho	68 Er	69 Tm	70 Yb	71 Lu
Actinoids	89 Ac	90 Th	91 Pa	92 U	93 Np	94 Pu	95 Am	96 Cm	97 Bk	98 Cf	99 Es	100 Fm	101 Md	102 No	103 Lr

▲ **FIGURE 2.10 Metals, Nonmetals, and Metalloids** The elements in the periodic table fall into these three broad classes of physical properties.

We can broadly classify the elements in the periodic table as metals, nonmetals, or metalloids, as shown in Figure 2.10 ▲. **Metals**, which are found in the lower-left side and middle of the periodic table, share some common properties: they are good conductors of heat and electricity, they can be pounded into flat sheets (malleability), they can be drawn into wires (ductility), they are often shiny, and they tend to lose electrons when they undergo chemical changes. Chromium, copper, strontium, and lead are typical metals.

Nonmetals are found on the upper-right side of the periodic table. The dividing line between metals and nonmetals is the zigzag diagonal line running from boron to astatine. Nonmetals have more varied properties—some are solids at room temperature, others are liquids or gases—but as a whole, they tend to be poor conductors of heat and electricity and they tend to gain electrons when they undergo chemical changes. Oxygen, carbon, sulfur, bromine, and iodine are nonmetals.

Many of the elements that lie along the zigzag diagonal line that divides metals and nonmetals are classified as **metalloids** and exhibit mixed metal and nonmetal properties. Several metalloids are also classified as **semiconductors** because of their intermediate (and highly temperature-dependent) electrical conductivity. The capability to change and control the conductivity of semiconductors makes metalloids useful for the manufacture of the electronic chips and circuits central to computers, mobile phones, and many other modern devices. Good examples of metalloids include silicon, arsenic, and antimony.

The periodic table, as shown in Figure 2.11 ▶, can also be divided into **main-group elements**, whose properties tend to be largely predictable based on their position in the periodic table; and **transition elements** (or **transition metals**), whose properties tend to be less predictable based simply on their position in the periodic table. Each column within the main-group regions of the periodic table is called a **family** or **group** of

Main-group elements | Transition elements | Main-group elements

Group number

Periods	1	2	3	4	5	6	7	8	9	10	11	12	13	14	15	16	17	18
1	1 H																	2 He
2	3 Li	4 Be											5 B	6 C	7 N	8 O	9 F	10 Ne
3	11 Na	12 Mg											13 Al	14 Si	15 P	16 S	17 Cl	18 Ar
4	19 K	20 Ca	21 Sc	22 Ti	23 V	24 Cr	25 Mn	26 Fe	27 Co	28 Ni	29 Cu	30 Zn	31 Ga	32 Ge	33 As	34 Se	35 Br	36 Kr
5	37 Rb	38 Sr	39 Y	40 Zr	41 Nb	42 Mo	43 Tc	44 Ru	45 Rh	46 Pd	47 Ag	48 Cd	49 In	50 Sn	51 Sb	52 Te	53 I	54 Xe
6	55 Cs	56 Ba		72 Hf	73 Ta	74 W	75 Re	76 Os	77 Ir	78 Pt	79 Au	80 Hg	81 Tl	82 Pb	83 Bi	84 Po	85 At	86 Rn
7	87 Fr	88 Ra		104 Rf	105 Db	106 Sg	107 Bh	108 Hs	109 Mt	110 Ds	111 Rg	112 Cn	113	114 Fl	115	116 Lv		

Lanthanoids	57 La	58 Ce	59 Pr	60 Nd	61 Pm	62 Sm	63 Eu	64 Gd	65 Tb	66 Dy	67 Ho	68 Er	69 Tm	70 Yb	71 Lu
Actinoids	89 Ac	90 Th	91 Pa	92 U	93 Np	94 Pu	95 Am	96 Cm	97 Bk	98 Cf	99 Es	100 Fm	101 Md	102 No	103 Lr

▲ **FIGURE 2.11 The Periodic Table Main-Group and Transition Elements** The elements in the periodic table fall into columns. The two columns at the left and the six columns at the right contain the main-group elements. Each of these eight columns is a group or family. The properties of main-group elements can generally be predicted from their relative position in the periodic table. The properties of the elements in the middle of the table, known as transition elements, are more difficult to predict, when first encountered.

elements. Groups are labelled with the numbers 1–18. Each row in the periodic table is called a **period** and is also assigned a number. The **lanthanoids** and **actinoids** are separate groups of elements that have very similar chemical and physical properties to the elements lanthanum and actinium, respectively. These elements are placed in a separate block, typically to display the periodic table in a more compact form.

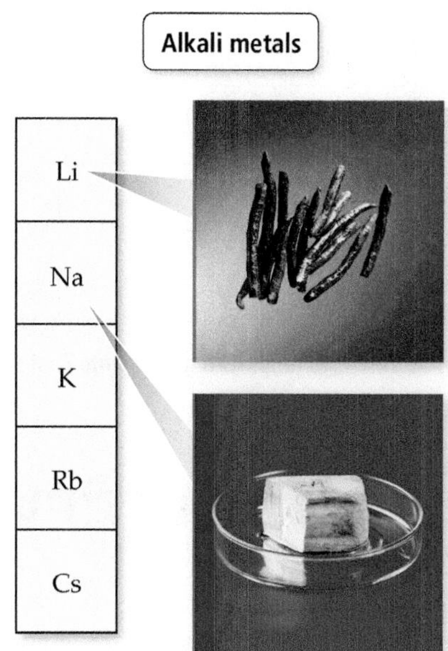

The elements within a group usually have similar properties. For example, the group 18 elements, called the **noble gases**, are mostly unreactive. The most familiar noble gas is probably helium, which is used to fill balloons. Helium is chemically stable—it does not combine with other elements to form compounds—and is therefore safe to put into balloons. Other noble gases are neon (often used in the lights of electronic signs), argon (a small component of our atmosphere), krypton, and xenon.

The group 1 elements, called the **alkali metals**, are all reactive metals. A marble-sized piece of sodium explodes violently when dropped into water. Lithium, potassium, and rubidium are also alkali metals.

The group 2 elements, called the **alkaline earth metals**, are also fairly reactive, although not quite as reactive as the alkali metals. Calcium, for example, reacts fairly vigorously when dropped into water but will not explode as dramatically as sodium. Other alkaline earth metals include magnesium (a common low-density structural metal), strontium, and barium.

The group 17 elements, called the **halogens**, are very reactive nonmetals. One of the most familiar halogens is chlorine, a greenish-yellow gas with a pungent odour. Because of its reactivity, chlorine is used as a sterilizing and disinfecting agent. Other halogens include bromine, a red-brown liquid that easily evaporates into a gas; iodine, a purple solid; and fluorine, a pale-yellow gas.

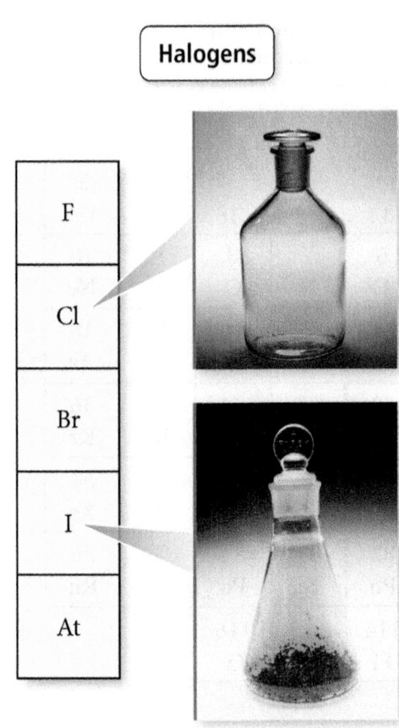

Ions and the Periodic Table

We have learned that in chemical reactions, metals tend to lose electrons (forming cations) and nonmetals tend to gain them (forming anions). The number of electrons lost or gained, and therefore the charge of the resulting ion(s), is often predictable for a given element, especially main-group elements. Main-group elements tend to form ions that have the same number of electrons as the nearest noble gas (i.e., the noble gas that is closest in atomic number to that of the element).

- ▶ **A main-group metal tends to lose electrons, forming a cation with the same number of electrons as the nearest noble gas.**
- ▶ **A main-group nonmetal tends to gain electrons, forming an anion with the same number of electrons as the nearest noble gas.**

For example, lithium, a metal with three electrons, tends to lose one electron, forming a 1+ cation that has the same number of electrons (two) as helium. Chlorine, a nonmetal with 17 electrons, tends to gain 1 electron, forming a 1– anion that has the same number of electrons (18) as argon.

In general, the alkali metals (group 1) have a tendency to lose one electron and form 1+ ions. The alkaline earth metals (group 2) tend to lose two electrons and form 2+ ions. The halogens (group 17) tend to gain one electron and form 1– ions. The oxygen family nonmetals (group 16) tend to gain two electrons and form 2– ions. More generally, for the main-group elements that form cations with predictable charge, the charge is equal to the group number. For main-group elements that form anions with predictable charge, the charge is equal to the group number minus 18. Transition elements can form various ions with different charges. Figure 2.12 ▾ shows the ions formed by the main-group elements that form ions with predictable charges. In Chapters 7 and 8, we learn about quantum theory, which more fully explains *why* these groups form ions as they do.

1	2	Transition metals	13	14	15	16	17	18
H^+							H^-	Noble Gases
Li^+					N^{3-}	O^{2-}	F^-	
Na^+	Mg^{2+}		Al^{3+}			S^{2-}	Cl^-	
K^+	Ca^{2+}					Se^{2-}	Br^-	
Rb^+	Sr^{2+}					Te^{2-}	I^-	
Cs^+	Ba^{2+}							

▲ **FIGURE 2.12 Main-Group Elements That Form Ions with Predictable Charges**

CHAPTER IN REVIEW

Key Terms

Section 2.3
law of conservation of mass (32)
law of definite proportions (33)
law of multiple proportions (33)
atomic theory (34)

Section 2.4
cathode ray (34)
cathode ray tube (34)
electrical charge (35)
electron (35)
radioactivity (36)
nuclear theory (37)
nucleus (37)
proton (38)
atomic number (*Z*) (38)
chemical symbol (38)
neutron (38)
unified atomic mass unit (u) (38)
isotope (39)
natural abundance (39)
mass number (39)
ion (40)
cation (41)
anion (41)

Section 2.5
atomic mass (42)
mass spectrometry (43)

Section 2.6
mole (mol) (44)
Avogadro's number (44)
molar mass (45)

Section 2.7
periodic law (47)
metal (48)
nonmetal (48)
metalloid (48)
semiconductor (48)
main-group elements (48)
transition elements (transition metals) (48)
family (group) (48)
period (49)
lanthanoids (49)
actinoids (49)
noble gases (49)
alkali metals (49)
alkaline earth metals (49)
halogens (49)

Key Concepts

Imaging and Moving Individual Atoms (2.1)

Although it was only 200 years ago that John Dalton proposed his atomic theory, technology has since progressed to the level where individual atoms can be imaged and moved by techniques such as *scanning tunnelling microscopy* (STM).

The Atomic Theory (2.2, 2.3)

The idea that all matter is composed of small indestructible particles, called atoms, dates back to the fifth century B.C.E.; however, at the time, the atomic idea was rejected by most Greek thinkers. At about C.E. 1800, certain observations and laws, including the law of conservation of mass, the law of constant composition, and the law of multiple proportions, led John Dalton to reformulate the atomic theory with the following postulates: (1) each element is composed of indestructible particles called atoms; (2) all atoms of a given element have the same mass and other properties; (3) atoms combine in simple, whole-number ratios to form compounds; and (4) atoms of one element cannot change into atoms of another element during a chemical reaction. In a chemical reaction, atoms change the way that they are bound together with other atoms to form new substances.

Atomic Structure (2.4)

J. J. Thomson discovered the electron in the late 1800s through experiments with cathode rays. He deduced that electrons were negatively charged and then measured their charge-to-mass ratio. Later, Robert Millikan measured the charge of the electron, which—in conjunction with Thomson's results—led to the calculation of the mass of an electron.

In 1909, Ernest Rutherford probed the inner structure of the atom by working with a form of radioactivity called alpha radiation and developed the nuclear theory of the atom. This theory states that the atom is mainly empty space, with most of its mass concentrated in a tiny region called the nucleus and most of its volume occupied by relatively light electrons.

Atoms are composed of three fundamental particles: the proton (1 u, +1 charge), the neutron (1 u, 0 charge), and the electron (~0 u, −1 charge). The number of protons in the nucleus of an atom is its atomic number (***Z***) and defines the element. The sum of the number of protons and neutrons is the mass number (***A***). Atoms of an element that have different numbers of neutrons (and therefore different mass numbers) are isotopes. Atoms that have lost or gained electrons become charged and are ions. Cations are positively charged, and anions are negatively charged.

Atomic Mass and the Mole (2.5, 2.6)

The atomic mass of an element, listed directly below its symbol in the periodic table, is a weighted average of the masses of the naturally occurring isotopes of the element.

One mole of an element is the amount of that element that contains Avogadro's number of atoms. Any sample of an element with a mass (in grams) that equals its atomic mass contains one mole of the element. For example, the atomic mass of carbon is 12.01 u; therefore, 12.01 g of carbon contains 1 mol of carbon atoms.

The Periodic Table (2.7)

The periodic table contains all known elements in order of increasing atomic number. It is arranged so that similar elements are grouped together in columns. Elements on the left side and in the centre of the periodic table are metals and tend to lose electrons in their chemical changes. Elements on the upper-right side of the periodic table are nonmetals and tend to gain electrons in their chemical reactions. Elements located on the boundary between these two classes are metalloids.

Key Equations and Relationships

Relationship between Mass Number (A), Number of Protons (p), and Number of Neutrons (n) (2.4)

$$A = \text{number of protons } (p) + \text{number of neutrons } (n)$$

Atomic Mass (2.5)

$$\text{Atomic mass} = \sum_n (\text{fraction of isotope } n) \times (\text{mass of isotope } n)$$

Avogadro's Number (2.6)

$$1 \text{ mol} = 6.022 \times 10^{23} \text{ particles}$$

Key Skills

Using the Law of Definite Proportions (2.3)
• Example 2.1 • For Practice 2.1 • Exercises 29–30

Working with Atomic Numbers, Mass Numbers, and Isotope Symbols (2.4)
• Example 2.2 • For Practice 2.2 • Exercises 43–48

Calculating Atomic Mass (2.5)
• Example 2.3 • For Practice 2.3 • Exercises 53, 54, 57–60

Converting from Mass to Moles and Number of Atoms (2.6)
• Example 2.4 • For Practice 2.4 • For More Practice 2.4 • Exercises 61–72

EXERCISES

Review Questions

1. What is scanning tunnelling microscopy? How does it work?
2. Summarize the history of the atom leading to Dalton's atomic theory. How was Dalton able to convince others to accept an idea that had been controversial for over 2000 years?
3. State the law of conservation of mass and explain what it means.
4. State the law of definite proportions and explain what it means.
5. State the law of multiple proportions and explain what it means. How is the law of multiple proportions different from the law of definite proportions?
6. What are the main ideas in Dalton's atomic theory? How do they help explain the laws of conservation of mass, of constant composition, and of definite proportions?
7. How and by whom was the electron discovered? What basic properties of the electron were reported with its discovery?
8. Explain Millikan's oil drop experiment and how it led to the measurement of the electron's charge. Why is the magnitude of the charge of the electron so important?
9. Describe Rutherford's gold foil experiment. How did the experiment show that the plum-pudding model of the atom was wrong?
10. Describe Rutherford's nuclear model of the atom. What was revolutionary about his model?
11. If matter is mostly empty space, as suggested by Rutherford, why does it appear so solid?
12. List the three subatomic particles that compose atoms and give the basic properties (mass and charge) of each.
13. What defines an element?
14. Explain the difference between Z (the atomic number) and A (the mass number).
15. What are isotopes? What is the percent natural abundance of isotopes?
16. Describe the two different notations used to specify isotopes and give an example of each.
17. What is an ion? A cation? An anion?
18. What is atomic mass? How is it computed?
19. Explain how a mass spectrometer works.
20. What kind of information can be determined from a mass spectrum?
21. What is a mole? How is the mole concept useful in chemical calculations?
22. Why is the mass corresponding to a mole of one element different from the mass corresponding to a mole of another element?
23. What is the periodic law? How did it lead to the periodic table?
24. What are the characteristic properties of metals, nonmetals, and metalloids?
25. What are the characteristic properties of each of the following groups?
    a. noble gases
    b. alkali metals
    c. alkaline earth metals
    d. halogens
26. How do you predict the charges of ions formed by main-group elements?

Problems by Topic

The Laws of Conservation of Mass, Definite Proportions, and Multiple Proportions

27. A hydrogen-filled balloon was ignited, and 1.50 g of hydrogen reacted with 11.9 g of oxygen. How many grams of water were formed? (Assume that water vapour is the only product.)
28. An automobile gasoline tank holds 21 kg of gasoline. When the gasoline burns, 84 kg of oxygen is consumed, and carbon dioxide and water are produced. What is the total combined mass of carbon dioxide and water that is produced?
29. Two samples of carbon tetrachloride were decomposed into their constituent elements. One sample produced 38.9 g of

carbon and 448 g of chlorine, and the other sample produced 14.8 g of carbon and 134 g of chlorine. Are these results consistent with the law of definite proportions? Show why or why not.

30. Two samples of sodium chloride were decomposed into their constituent elements. One sample produced 6.98 g of sodium and 10.7 g of chlorine, and the other sample produced 11.2 g of sodium and 17.3 g of chlorine. Are these results consistent with the law of definite proportions? Show why or why not.

31. The mass ratio of sodium to fluorine in sodium fluoride is 1.21:1. A sample of sodium fluoride produced 28.8 g of sodium upon decomposition. How much fluorine (in grams) was formed?

32. Upon decomposition, one sample of magnesium fluoride produced 1.65 kg of magnesium and 2.57 kg of fluorine. A second sample produced 1.32 kg of magnesium. How much fluorine (in grams) did the second sample produce?

33. Two different compounds containing osmium and oxygen have the following masses of oxygen per gram of osmium: 0.168 g and 0.3369 g, respectively. Show that these amounts are consistent with the law of multiple proportions.

34. Palladium forms three different compounds with sulfur. The mass of sulfur per gram of palladium in each compound is listed below:

Compound	Grams S per Gram Pd
A	0.603
B	0.301
C	0.151

Show that these masses are consistent with the law of multiple proportions.

35. Sulfur and oxygen form both sulfur dioxide and sulfur trioxide. When samples of these were decomposed, the sulfur dioxide produced 3.49 g oxygen and 3.50 g sulfur, and the sulfur trioxide produced 6.75 g oxygen and 4.50 g sulfur. Calculate the mass of oxygen per gram of sulfur for each sample and show that these results are consistent with the law of multiple proportions.

36. Sulfur and fluorine form several different compounds, including sulfur hexafluoride and sulfur tetrafluoride. Decomposition of a sample of sulfur hexafluoride produced 4.45 g of fluorine and 1.25 g of sulfur, and decomposition of a sample of sulfur tetrafluoride produced 4.43 g of fluorine and 1.87 g of sulfur. Calculate the mass of fluorine per gram of sulfur for each sample and show that these results are consistent with the law of multiple proportions.

Atomic Theory, Nuclear Theory, and Subatomic Particles

37. A chemist in an imaginary universe, in which electrons have a different charge than they do in our universe, performs the Millikan oil drop experiment to measure the electron's charge. The charges of several drops are recorded below. What is the charge of the electron in this imaginary universe?

Drop	Charge
A	-6.9×10^{-19} C
B	-9.2×10^{-19} C
C	-11.5×10^{-19} C
D	-4.6×10^{-19} C

38. One of the oil drops in Millikan's experiment was determined to have a mass of 5.13×10^{-15} kg. It was observed to float between two parallel plates separated by a distance of 1.0 cm with 350 V ($1\ V = 1\ kg\ m^2\ s^{-2}\ C^{-1}$; see Table 1.5) of potential difference between them. Determine how many excess electrons are on the drop. The charge, q, on a drop can be determined using the following equation, $q = mgd/V$ where m is the mass of the droplet, d is the distance between plates, V is the voltage applied across the plates and g is the acceleration due to gravity ($9.807\ m\ s^{-2}$).

39. On a dry day, your body can accumulate static charge from walking across a carpet or from brushing your hair. If your body develops a charge of $-15\mu C$ (microcoulombs), how many excess electrons has it acquired? What is their collective mass?

40. How many electrons are necessary to produce a charge of -1.0 C? What is the mass of this many electrons?

41. How many electrons would it take to equal the mass of a proton?

42. A helium nucleus has two protons and two neutrons. How many electrons would it take to equal the mass of a helium nucleus?

Isotopes and Ions

43. Write symbols of the form $^A_Z X$ for each isotope.
- **a.** the copper isotope with 34 neutrons
- **b.** the copper isotope with 36 neutrons
- **c.** the potassium isotope with 21 neutrons
- **d.** the argon isotope with 22 neutrons

44. Write symbols of the form X-*A* (e.g., C-13) for each isotope.
- **a.** the silver isotope with 60 neutrons
- **b.** the silver isotope with 62 neutrons
- **c.** the uranium isotope with 146 neutrons
- **d.** the hydrogen isotope with 1 neutron

45. Determine the number of protons and neutrons in each isotope.
a. $^{14}_{7}N$ **b.** $^{23}_{11}Na$ **c.** $^{222}_{86}Rn$ **d.** $^{208}_{82}Pb$

46. Determine the number of protons and neutrons in each isotope.
a. $^{40}_{19}K$ **b.** $^{226}_{88}Ra$ **c.** $^{99}_{43}Tc$ **d.** $^{33}_{15}P$

47. The amount of carbon-14 in ancient artifacts and fossils is often used to establish their age. Determine the number of protons and neutrons in a carbon-14 isotope and write its symbol in the form $^A_Z X$.

48. Uranium-235 is used in nuclear fission. Determine the number of protons and neutrons in uranium-235 and write its symbol in the form $^A_Z X$.

49. Determine the number of protons and electrons in each ion.
a. Ni^{2+} **b.** S^{2-} **c.** Br^{-} **d.** Cr^{3+}

50. Determine the number of protons and electrons in each ion.
a. Al^{3+} **b.** Se^{2-} **c.** Ga^{3+} **d.** Sr^{2+}

51. Fill in the blanks to complete the table.

Symbol	Ion Formed	Number of Electrons in Ion	Number of Protons in Ion
Ca	Ca^{2+}	____	____
____	Be^{2+}	2	____
Se	____	____	34
____	In^{3+}	____	____

52. Fill in the blanks to complete the table.

Symbol	Ion Formed	Number of Electrons in Ion	Number of Protons in Ion
Cl	_____	_____	17
Te	_____	54	_____
Br	Br^-	_____	_____
_____	Sr^{2+}	_____	_____

Atomic Mass

53. Gallium has two naturally occurring isotopes with the following masses and natural abundances:

Isotope	Mass (u)	Abundance (%)
Ga-69	68.92558	60.108
Ga-71	70.92470	39.892

Calculate the atomic mass of gallium and sketch its mass spectrum.

54. Sulfur has four naturally occurring isotopes with the following masses and natural abundances:

Isotope	Mass (u)	Abundance (%)
S-32	31.9721	94.99
S-33	32.9715	0.75
S-34	33.9679	4.25
S-36	35.9671	0.01

Calculate the atomic mass of sulfur and sketch its mass spectrum.

55. The atomic mass of fluorine is 18.998 u, and its mass spectrum shows a large peak at this mass. The atomic mass of chlorine is 35.45 u, yet the mass spectrum of chlorine does not show a peak at this mass. Explain the difference.

56. The atomic mass of copper is 63.546 u. Do any copper isotopes have a mass of 63.546 u? Explain.

57. An element has two naturally occurring isotopes. Isotope 1 has a mass of 120.9038 u and a relative abundance of 57.4%, and isotope 2 has a mass of 122.9042 u. Find the atomic mass of this element and identify it.

58. An element has four naturally occurring isotopes with the masses and natural abundances given here. Find the atomic mass of the element and identify it.

Isotope	Mass (u)	Abundance (%)
1	135.90714	0.19
2	137.90599	0.25
3	139.90543	88.43
4	141.90924	11.13

59. Bromine has two naturally occurring isotopes (Br-79 and Br-81) and has an atomic mass of 79.904 u. The mass of Br-81 is 80.9163 u, and its natural abundance is 49.31%. Calculate the mass and natural abundance of Br-79.

60. Silicon has three naturally occurring isotopes (Si-28, Si-29, and Si-30). The mass and natural abundance of Si-28 are 27.9769 u and 92.2%, respectively. The mass and natural abundance of Si-29 are 28.9765 u and 4.67%, respectively. Find the mass and natural abundance of Si-30.

The Mole Concept

61. How many sulfur atoms are there in 3.8 mol of sulfur?

62. How many moles of aluminum do 5.8×10^{24} aluminum atoms represent?

63. What is the amount, in moles, of each elemental sample?
a. 11.8 g Ar **b.** 3.55 g Zn
c. 26.1 g Ta **d.** 0.211 g Li

64. What is the mass, in grams, of each elemental sample?
a. 2.3×10^{-3} mol Sb **b.** 0.0355 mol Ba
c. 43.9 mol Xe **d.** 1.3 mol W

65. How many silver atoms are there in 3.78 g of silver?

66. What is the mass of 4.91×10^{21} platinum atoms?

67. Calculate the number of atoms in each sample.
a. 5.18 g P **b.** 2.26 g Hg
c. 1.87 g Bi **d.** 0.082 g Sr

68. Calculate the number of atoms in each sample.
a. 14.955 g Cr **b.** 39.733 g S
c. 12.899 g Pt **d.** 97.552 g Sn

69. Calculate the mass, in grams, of each sample.
a. 1.1×10^{23} gold atoms
b. 2.82×10^{22} helium atoms
c. 1.8×10^{23} lead atoms
d. 7.9×10^{21} uranium atoms

70. Calculate the mass, in kg, of each sample.
a. 7.55×10^{26} cadmium atoms
b. 8.15×10^{27} nickel atoms
c. 1.22×10^{27} manganese atoms
d. 5.48×10^{29} lithium atoms

71. How many carbon atoms are there in a diamond (pure carbon) with a mass of 52 mg?

72. How many helium atoms are there in a helium blimp containing 536 kg of helium?

73. Calculate the average mass, in grams, of one platinum atom.

74. Using scanning tunnelling microscopy, scientists at IBM wrote the initials of their company with 35 individual xenon atoms (as shown below). Calculate the total mass of these letters in grams.

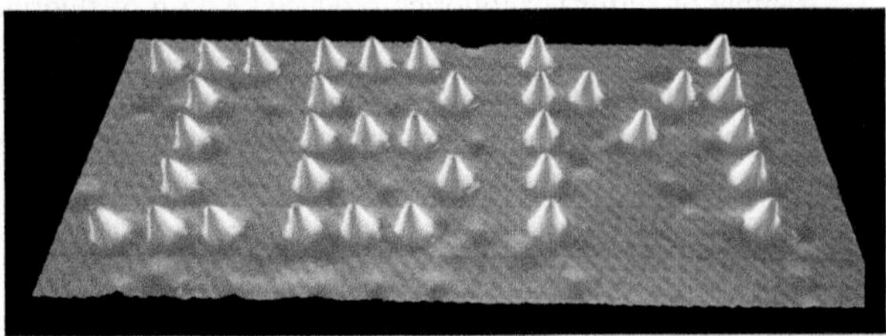

The Periodic Table and Atomic Mass

75. Write the name of each element and classify it as a metal, nonmetal, or metalloid.
a. K **b.** Ba **c.** I **d.** O **e.** Sb

76. Write the symbol for each element and classify it as a metal, nonmetal, or metalloid.
a. gold **b.** fluorine **c.** sodium
d. tin **e.** argon

77. Which elements from this list are main-group elements?
a. tellurium **b.** potassium
c. vanadium **d.** manganese

78. Which elements from this list are transition elements?
a. Cr **b.** Br **c.** Mo **d.** Cs

79. Classify each element as an alkali metal, alkaline earth metal, halogen, or noble gas.
a. sodium **b.** iodine **c.** calcium
d. barium **e.** krypton

80. Classify each element as an alkali metal, alkaline earth metal, halogen, or noble gas.
a. F **b.** Sr **c.** K **d.** Ne **e.** At

81. Which pair of elements do you expect to be most similar? Why?
a. N and Ni **b.** Mo and Sn **c.** Na and Mg
d. Cl and F **e.** Si and P

82. Which pair of elements do you expect to be most similar? Why?
a. nitrogen and oxygen **b.** titanium and gallium
c. lithium and sodium **d.** germanium and arsenic
e. argon and bromine

83. Predict the charge of the ion formed by each element.
a. O **b.** K **c.** Al **d.** Rb

84. Predict the charge of the ion formed by each element.
a. Mg **b.** N **c.** F **d.** Na

Cumulative Problems

85. A 7.83 g sample of HCN is found to contain 0.290 g of H and 4.06 g of N. Find the mass of carbon in a sample of HCN with a mass of 3.37 g.

86. The ratio of sulfur to oxygen by mass in SO_2 is 1.0:1.0.
a. Find the ratio of sulfur to oxygen by mass in SO_3.
b. Find the ratio of sulfur to oxygen by mass in S_2O.

87. The ratio of oxygen to carbon by mass in carbon monoxide is 1.33:1.00. Find the molecular formula of an oxide of carbon in which the ratio by mass of oxygen to carbon is 2.00:1.00.

88. The ratio of the mass of a nitrogen atom to the mass of an atom of ^{12}C is 7:6, and the ratio of the mass of nitrogen to oxygen in N_2O is 7:4. Find the mass of 1 mol of oxygen atoms.

89. An α particle, $^4He^{2+}$, has a mass of 4.00151 u. Find the value of its charge-to-mass ratio in C kg^{-1}.

90. Naturally occurring iodine has an atomic mass of 126.9045. A 12.3849 g sample of iodine is accidentally contaminated with an additional 1.00070 g of ^{129}I, a synthetic radioisotope of iodine used in the treatment of certain diseases of the thyroid gland. The mass of ^{129}I is 128.9050 u. Find the apparent "atomic mass" of the contaminated iodine.

91. Nuclei with the same number of *neutrons* but different mass numbers are called *isotones*. Write the symbols of four isotones of ^{236}Th.

92. Fill in the blanks to complete the table.

Symbol	Z	A	Number of p	Number of e^-	Number of n	Charge
Si	14	___	___	14	14	___
S^{2-}	___	32	___	___	___	2–
Cu^{2+}	___	___	___	___	34	2+
___	15	___	___	15	16	___

93. Fill in the blanks to complete the table.

Symbol	Z	A	Number of p	Number of e^-	Number of n	Charge
___	8	___	___	___	8	2–
Ca^{2+}	20	___	___	___	20	___
Mg^{2+}	___	25	___	___	13	2+
N^{3-}	___	14	___	10	___	___

94. Neutron stars are composed of solid nuclear matter, primarily neutrons. Assume the radius of a neutron is approximately 1.0×10^{-13} cm and calculate the density of a neutron. (*Hint*: For a sphere, $V = (4/3)\pi r^3$.) Assuming that a neutron star has the same density as a neutron, calculate the mass (in kg) of a small piece of a neutron star the size of a spherical pebble with a radius of 0.10 mm.

95. Carbon-12 contains 6 protons and 6 neutrons. The radius of the nucleus is approximately 2.7 fm (femtometres) and the radius of the atom is approximately 70. pm (picometres). Calculate the volume of the nucleus and the volume of the atom. What percentage of the carbon atom's volume is occupied by the nucleus?

96. Nitrogen is made up of two isotopes: ^{14}N and ^{15}N with atomic masses of 14.003074 and 15.000109 u, respectively. The average atomic mass for nitrogen is 14.0067 u. What are the abundances of ^{14}N and ^{15}N?

97. Suppose that atomic masses were based on the assignment of a mass of 12.000 g to 1 mol of carbon, rather than 1 mol of ^{12}C. What would the atomic mass of oxygen be?

98. A pure titanium cube has an edge length of 2.78 cm. How many titanium atoms does it contain? Titanium has a density of 4.50 g cm^{-3}.

99. A pure copper sphere has a radius of 0.935 cm. How many copper atoms does it contain? (The volume of a sphere is $(4/3)\pi r^3$ and the density of copper is 8.94 g cm^{-3}.)

100. Boron has only two naturally occurring isotopes. The mass of boron-10 is 10.01294 u, and the mass of boron-11 is 11.00931 u. Calculate the relative abundances of the two isotopes.

101. Lithium has only two naturally occurring isotopes. The mass of lithium-6 is 6.01512 u, and the mass of lithium-7 is 7.01601 u. Calculate the relative abundances of the two isotopes.

102. Common brass is a copper and zinc alloy containing 37.0% zinc by mass and having a density of 8.48 g cm^{-3}. A fitting composed of common brass has a total volume of 112.5 cm^3. How many atoms (copper and zinc) does the fitting contain?

103. A 67.2 g sample of a gold and palladium alloy contains 2.49×10^{23} atoms. What is the composition (by mass) of the alloy?

104. Naturally occurring chlorine is composed of two isotopes: 75.76% Cl-35 (mass 34.9688 u) and 24.24% Cl-37 (mass 36.9659 u). Naturally occurring oxygen is composed of three isotopes: 99.757% O-16 (mass 15.9949 u), 0.038% O-17 (mass 16.9991 u), and 0.205% O-18 (mass 17.9991 u). The compound dichloromonoxide is composed of two chlorine atoms and one oxygen atom bonded together to form the Cl_2O molecule. How many Cl_2O molecules of different masses naturally exist?

Give the masses of the three most abundant Cl_2O molecules.

105. Silver is composed of two naturally occurring isotopes: Ag-107 (51.839%) and Ag-109. The ratio of the masses of the two isotopes is 1.0187. What is the mass of Ag-107?

Challenge Problems

106. Below is a representation of 50 atoms of a fictitious element called Saskatchewanium (Sk). The red spheres represent Sk-296, the blue spheres Sk-297, and the green spheres Sk-298.

a. Assuming that the sample is statistically representative of a naturally occurring sample, calculate the percent natural abundance of each Sk isotope.

b. Draw the mass spectrum for a naturally occurring sample of Sk.

c. The mass of each Sk isotope is measured relative to C-12 and tabulated below. Use the mass of C-12 to convert each of the masses to u and calculate the atomic mass of Sk.

Isotope	Mass
Sk-296	$24.6630 \times \text{mass}\,(^{12}\text{C})$
Sk-297	$24.7490 \times \text{mass}\,(^{12}\text{C})$
Sk-298	$24.8312 \times \text{mass}\,(^{12}\text{C})$

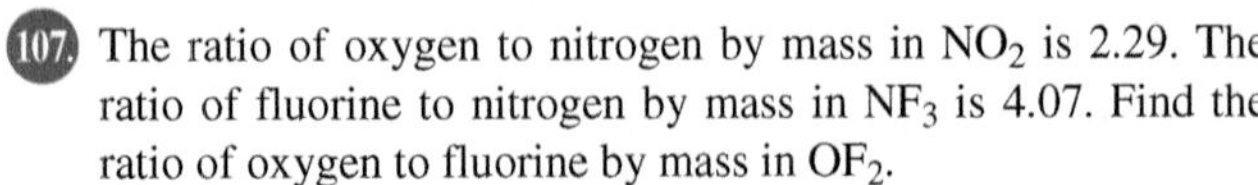

107. The ratio of oxygen to nitrogen by mass in NO_2 is 2.29. The ratio of fluorine to nitrogen by mass in NF_3 is 4.07. Find the ratio of oxygen to fluorine by mass in OF_2.

108. Naturally occurring cobalt consists of only one isotope, ^{59}Co, whose relative atomic mass is 58.9332 u. A synthetic radioactive isotope of cobalt, ^{60}Co, relative atomic mass 59.9338 u, is used in radiation therapy for cancer. A 1.5886 g sample of cobalt has an apparent "atomic mass" of 58.9901 u. Find the mass of ^{60}Co in this sample.

109. A 7.36 g sample of copper is contaminated with an additional 0.51 g of zinc. Suppose an atomic mass measurement was performed on this sample. What would the measured atomic mass be?

110. The ratio of the mass of O to the mass of N in N_2O_3 is 12:7. Another binary compound of nitrogen has a ratio of O to N of 16:7. What is its formula? What is the ratio of O to N in the next member of this series of compounds?

111. Naturally occurring magnesium has an atomic mass of 24.312 u and consists of three isotopes. The major isotope is ^{24}Mg, natural abundance 78.99%, relative atomic mass 23.98504 u. The next most abundant isotope is ^{26}Mg, relative atomic mass 25.98259 u. The third isotope is ^{25}Mg whose natural abundance is in the ratio of 0.9083 to that of ^{26}Mg. Find the relative atomic mass of ^{25}Mg.

Conceptual Problems

112. Which of the following is an example of the law of multiple proportions? Explain.

a. Two different samples of water are found to have the same ratio of hydrogen to oxygen.

b. When hydrogen and oxygen react to form water, the mass of water formed is exactly equal to the mass of hydrogen and oxygen that reacted.

c. The mass ratio of oxygen to hydrogen in water is 8:1. The mass ratio of oxygen to hydrogen in hydrogen peroxide (a compound that only contains hydrogen and oxygen) is 16:1.

113. The mole is defined as the amount of a substance containing the same number of particles as exactly 12 grams of C-12. The u is defined as 1/12 of the mass of an atom of C-12. Why is it important that both of these definitions reference the same isotope? What would be the result, for example, of defining the mole with respect to C-12, but the u with respect to Ne-20?

114. Without doing any calculations, determine which of the samples contains the greatest amount of the element in moles.

a. 55.0 g Cr **b.** 45.0 g Ti **c.** 60.0 g Zn

115. The atomic radii of the isotopes of an element are identical to one another. However, the atomic radii of the ions of an element are significantly different from the atomic radii of the neutral atom of the element. Explain.

Molecules, Compounds, and Nomenclature

3

Almost all aspects of life are engineered at the molecular level, and without understanding molecules we can only have a very sketchy understanding of life itself.

—Francis Harry Compton Crick (1916–2004)

HOW MANY DIFFERENT substances exist? We learned in Chapter 2 that about 91 different elements exist in nature, so there are at least 91 different substances. However, the world would be dull—not to mention lifeless—with only 91 different substances. Fortunately, elements combine with each other to form *compounds*. Just as combinations of only 26 letters in our English alphabet allow for an almost limitless number of words, each with its own specific meaning, combinations of the 91 naturally occurring elements allow for an almost limitless number of compounds, each with its own specific properties. The great diversity of substances that we find in nature is a direct result of the ability of elements to form compounds. Life, for example, could not exist with just 91 different elements. It takes compounds, in all their diversity, to make life possible.

3.1 Hydrogen, Oxygen, and Water

Hydrogen (H_2) is an explosive gas used as a fuel in the space shuttle. Oxygen (O_2), also a gas, is a natural component of the air on Earth. Oxygen is not itself flammable, but must be present for combustion (burning) to occur. Hydrogen and oxygen both have extremely low boiling points, as you can see from the following table. When hydrogen and oxygen combine to form the compound water (H_2O), however, a dramatically different substance results.

Selected Properties	Hydrogen	Oxygen	Water
Boiling point	−253 °C	−183 °C	100 °C
State at room temperature	Gas	Gas	Liquid
Flammability	Explosive	Necessary for combustion	Used to extinguish flame

First of all, water is a liquid rather than a gas at room temperature, and its boiling point is hundreds of degrees above the boiling points of hydrogen and oxygen. Second, instead of being flammable (like hydrogen gas) or supporting combustion (like oxygen gas), water actually smothers flames. Water is nothing like elemental hydrogen or elemental oxygen from which it was formed.

The properties of compounds are generally very different from the properties of the elements that compose them. When two elements combine to form a compound, an entirely new substance results. Common table salt, for example, is a compound composed of sodium and chlorine. Elemental sodium is a highly reactive, silvery metal that can explode on contact with water. Elemental chlorine is a corrosive, greenish-yellow gas that can be fatal if inhaled. Yet the compound formed from the combination of these two elements is sodium chloride (or table salt), a flavour enhancer that tastes great on steak.

Although some of the substances that we encounter in everyday life are elements, most are compounds. Free atoms are rare on Earth. As we learned in Chapter 2, a compound is different from a mixture of elements. In a compound, elements combine in fixed, definite proportions; in a mixture, elements can mix in any proportions whatsoever. For example, consider the difference between a hydrogen–oxygen mixture and water, as shown in Figure 3.1 ▼. A hydrogen–oxygen mixture can have any proportions of hydrogen and oxygen gas. Water, by contrast, is composed of water molecules that always contain two hydrogen atoms to every one oxygen atom. Water has a definite proportion of hydrogen to oxygen.

In this chapter, we will learn about compounds: how to represent them, how to name them, and how to distinguish between them. We will also learn how to quantify the elemental composition of a compound. This is important whenever we want to know how much of a particular element is contained within a particular compound. For example, patients with high blood pressure (hypertension) often have to reduce their sodium ion intake. Since the sodium ion is normally consumed in the form of sodium chloride, a hypertension patient needs to know how much sodium is present in a given amount of sodium chloride. Similarly, an iron-mining company needs to know how much iron it can recover from a given amount of iron ore. This chapter will give us the tools to understand and solve these kinds of problems.

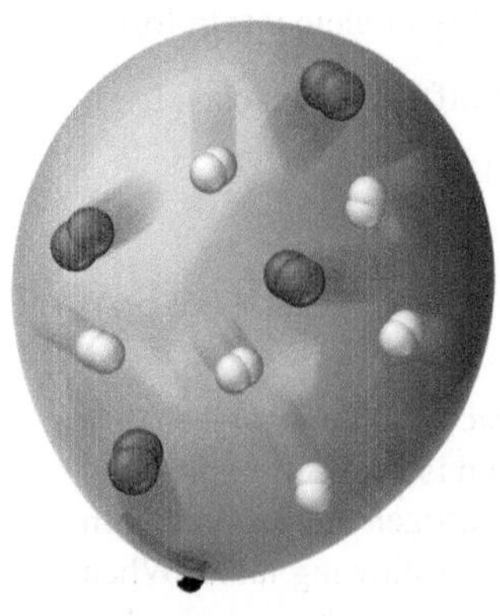

Water (A Compound)
Water molecules have a fixed ratio of hydrogen (2 atoms) to oxygen (1 atom).

▶ **FIGURE 3.1 Mixtures and Compounds** The balloon in this illustration is filled with a mixture of hydrogen gas and oxygen gas. The proportions of hydrogen and oxygen are variable. The glass is filled with water, a compound of hydrogen and oxygen. The ratio of hydrogen to oxygen in water is fixed: water molecules always have two hydrogen atoms for each oxygen atom.

3.2 Chemical Bonds

Compounds are composed of atoms held together by *chemical bonds*. Chemical bonds are the result of interactions between the charged particles—electrons and protons— that compose atoms. We discuss these interactions more thoroughly in Chapter 9 (see Section 9.2). For now, remember that, as we discussed in Section 2.4, electrostatic forces exist between charged particles; like charges repel one another and opposite charges attract one another. These electrostatic forces are responsible for chemical bonding.

We can broadly classify most chemical bonds into two types: ionic and covalent. *Ionic bonds*—which occur between metals and nonmetals—involve the *transfer* of electrons from one atom to another. *Covalent bonds*—which occur between two or more nonmetals—involve the *sharing* of electrons between two atoms.

Ionic Bonds

We learned in Chapter 2 that metals have a tendency to lose electrons, and that nonmetals have a tendency to gain them. Therefore, when a metal interacts with a nonmetal, it can transfer one or more of its electrons to the nonmetal. The metal atom then becomes a *cation* (a positively charged ion), and the nonmetal atom becomes an *anion* (a negatively charged ion), as shown in Figure 3.2 ▼. These oppositely charged ions are then attracted to one another by electrostatic forces, and they form an **ionic bond**. As multiple ion pairs form, they can group together, with the result being an ionic compound in the solid phase that is composed of a lattice—a regular three-dimensional array—of alternating cations and anions.

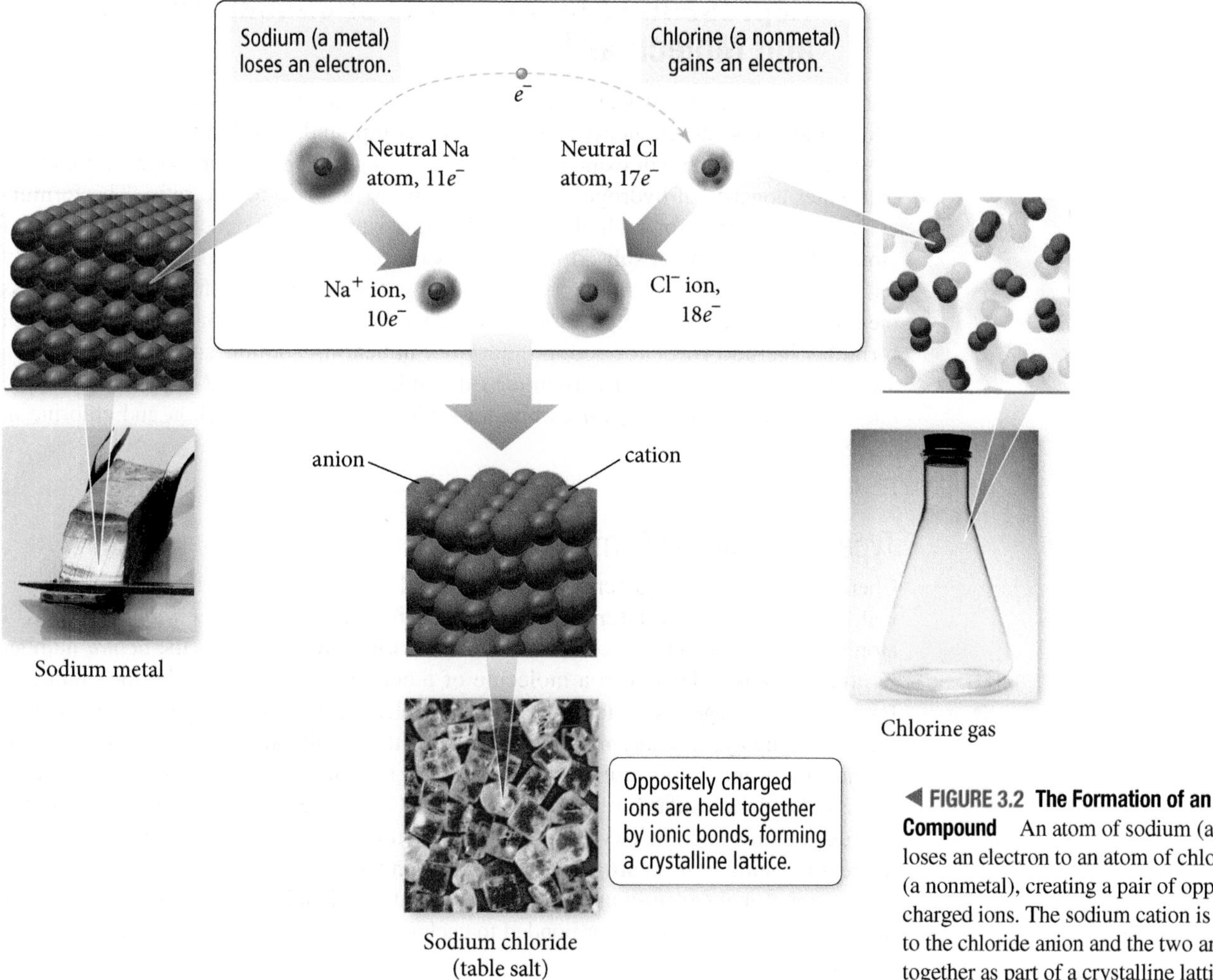

◀ **FIGURE 3.2 The Formation of an Ionic Compound** An atom of sodium (a metal) loses an electron to an atom of chlorine (a nonmetal), creating a pair of oppositely charged ions. The sodium cation is attracted to the chloride anion and the two are held together as part of a crystalline lattice.

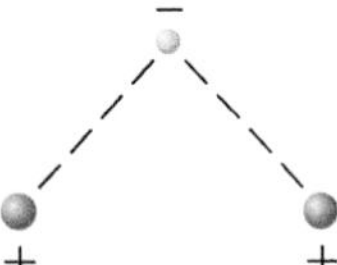

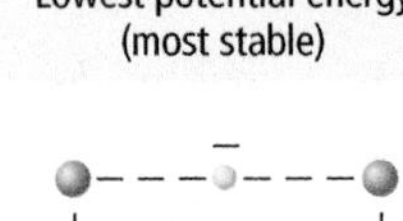

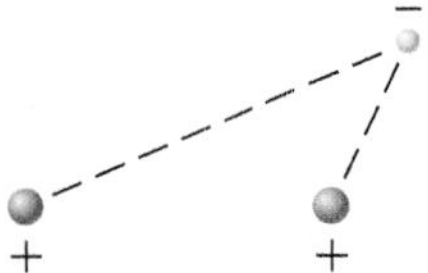

▶ **FIGURE 3.3 The Stability of a Covalent Bond** The potential energy of a negative charge interacting with two positive charges is lowest when the negative charge is between the two positive charges.

Covalent Bonds

When a nonmetal bonds with another nonmetal, neither atom transfers its electron to the other. Instead, the bonding atoms *share* some of their electrons. The shared electrons interact with the nuclei of both atoms, which lowers the potential energy (see Section 1.2) of the system through electrostatic interactions. This is called a **covalent bond**. The result is a molecular compound, which is composed of individual covalently bonded molecules. We can begin to understand the stability of a covalent bond by considering the most stable (or lowest potential energy) configuration of a negative charge interacting with two positive charges (which are separated by some small distance). As you can see from Figure 3.3 ▲, the arrangement in which the negative charge lies directly *between* the two positive charges has the lowest potential energy because the negative charge can interact with *both positive charges*. Similarly, shared electrons in a covalent chemical bond hold the bonding atoms together by attracting the positively charged nuclei of both bonding atoms.

3.3 Representing Compounds: Chemical Formulas and Molecular Models

The quickest and easiest way to represent a compound is with its **chemical formula**, which indicates the elements present in the compound and the relative number of atoms or ions of each. For example, H_2O is the chemical formula for water—it indicates that water consists of hydrogen and oxygen atoms in a two-to-one ratio. The formula contains the symbol for each element and a subscript indicating the relative number of atoms of the element. A subscript of 1 is always omitted. Chemical formulas normally list the more metallic (or more positively charged) elements first, followed by the less metallic (or more negatively charged) elements. Other examples of common chemical formulas include NaCl for sodium chloride, indicating sodium and chloride ions in a one-to-one ratio; CO_2 for carbon dioxide, indicating carbon and oxygen atoms in a one-to-two ratio; and CCl_4 for carbon tetrachloride, indicating carbon and chlorine in a one-to-four ratio.

Types of Chemical Formulas

Chemical formulas can generally be categorized as one of three different types: empirical, molecular, and structural. An **empirical formula** gives the *relative* number of atoms of each element in a compound. A **molecular formula** gives the *actual* number of atoms of each element in a molecule of a compound. For example, the empirical formula for hydrogen peroxide is HO, but its molecular formula is H_2O_2. The molecular formula is always a whole-number multiple of the empirical formula. For some compounds, the empirical formula and the molecular formula are identical. For example, the empirical and molecular formula for water is H_2O because water molecules contain two hydrogen atoms and one oxygen atom, and no simpler whole-number ratio can express the relative number of hydrogen atoms to oxygen atoms.

A **structural formula** uses lines to represent covalent bonds and shows how atoms in a molecule are connected or bonded to each other. The structural formula for H_2O_2 is shown here:

$$H—O—O—H$$

Structural formulas may also be written to give a sense of the molecule's geometry. Molecular geometry is covered in Chapter 10. The structural formula for hydrogen peroxide can be written as follows:

```
H
 \
  O—O
     \
      H
```

This version of the formula represents the approximate angles between bonds, giving a sense of the molecule's shape. Structural formulas can also depict the different types of bonds that occur between atoms within a molecule. For example, consider the structural formula for carbon dioxide:

$$O{=}C{=}O$$

These two compounds have the same empirical formula, NO_2:

NO_2 is a brown-coloured gas and has the following structural formula:

$$O{-}N{=}O$$

N_2O_4 is a colourless gas and has the following structural formula:

```
O       O
 \     /
  N—N
 /     \
O       O
```

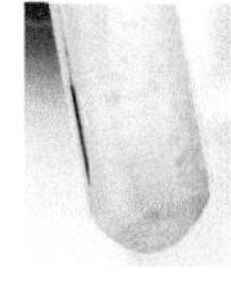

The two lines between each carbon and oxygen atom represent a double bond, which is generally stronger and shorter than a single bond (represented by a single line). A single bond corresponds to one shared electron pair, while a double bond corresponds to two shared electron pairs. We will learn more about single, double, and even triple bonds in Chapter 9.

The type of formula you use depends on how much you know about the compound and how much you want to communicate. A structural formula communicates the most detailed information, while an empirical formula communicates the least.

Throughout this text, you will see molecules represented in the following ways: empirical formulas, molecular formulas, structural formulas, **ball-and-stick models**, and **space-filling models**. These different representations of molecules are illustrated in Table 3.1. As you look at these representations, keep in mind that the details about

TABLE 3.1 Representations of Compounds

Name of Compound	Empirical Formula	Molecular Formula	Structural Formula	Ball-and-Stick Model	Space-Filling Model
Benzene	CH	C_6H_6	six-membered ring of C atoms with alternating single and double bonds, each C bonded to one H		
Ethyne	CH	C_2H_2	$H{-}C{\equiv}C{-}H$		
Glucose	CH_2O	$C_6H_{12}O_6$	O=CH H—C—OH HO—C—H H—C—OH H—C—OH H_2C—OH		
Ammonia	NH_3	NH_3	H, H, H each bonded to N		

Balls of different colours and sizes are used to represent common atoms in ball-and-stick and space-filling models.

Hydrogen
Carbon
Nitrogen
Oxygen
Fluorine
Phosphorus
Sulfur
Chlorine

a molecule—the atoms that compose it, the lengths of the bonds between atoms, the angles of the bonds between atoms, and its overall shape—determine the properties of the individual molecules and therefore any sample substance that is composed of those molecules. Change any of these details, and those properties change.

Pure substances can be categorized as either elements or compounds. We can subcategorize elements and compounds according to the basic units that compose them, as shown in Figure 3.4 ▼. Elements may be either atomic or molecular. Compounds may be either molecular or ionic.

Atomic elements are those that exist in nature with single atoms as their basic units. Most elements fall into this category. For example, helium is composed of helium atoms, aluminum is composed of aluminum atoms, and iron is composed of iron atoms.

Molecular elements do not normally exist in nature with single atoms as their basic units. Instead, these elements exist as molecules—two or more atoms of the element bonded together. Most molecular elements exist as *diatomic* molecules. For example, hydrogen is composed of H_2 molecules, nitrogen is composed of N_2 molecules, and chlorine is composed of Cl_2 molecules. A few molecular elements exist as *polyatomic molecules*. Phosphorus exists as P_4 and sulfur exists as S_8. The elements that exist primarily as diatomic or polyatomic molecules are hydrogen, nitrogen, oxygen, fluorine, phosphorus, sulfur, chlorine, selenium, bromine, and iodine.

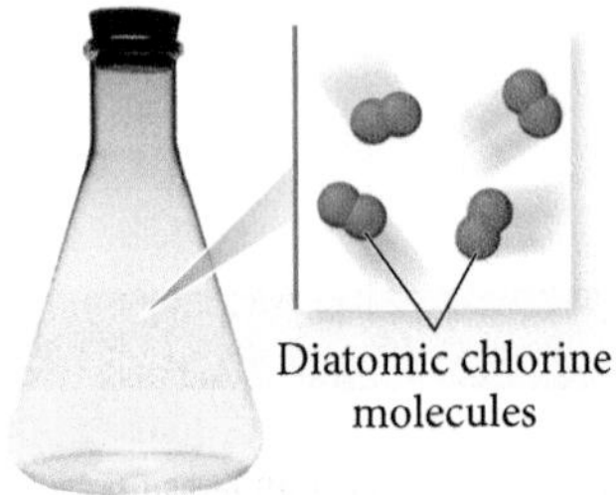

▲ The basic units that compose chlorine gas are diatomic chlorine molecules.

Molecular compounds are usually composed of two or more covalently bonded nonmetals. The basic units of molecular compounds are molecules composed of the constituent atoms. For example, water is composed of H_2O molecules, dry ice is composed of CO_2 molecules, and propane (often used as a fuel for grills) is composed of C_3H_8 molecules, as shown in Figure 3.5(a) ▶.

Ionic compounds are composed of cations (usually one type of metal) and anions (usually one or more nonmetals) bound together by ionic bonds. The basic unit of an ionic compound is the **formula unit**, the smallest, electrically neutral collection of ions. Formula units are different from molecules in that they do not exist as discrete entities, but rather only as part of a larger lattice. For example, the ionic compound table salt, with the formula unit NaCl, is composed of Na^+ and Cl^- ions in a one-to-one ratio. In table salt, Na^+ and Cl^- ions exist in a three-dimensional alternating array. Because ionic bonds are not directional, no one Na^+ ion pairs with a specific Cl^- ion. Rather, as you can see from Figure 3.5(b), any one Na^+ cation is surrounded by Cl^- anions and vice versa.

Many common ionic compounds contain ions that are composed of a group of covalently bonded atoms with an overall charge. For example, the active ingredient in household

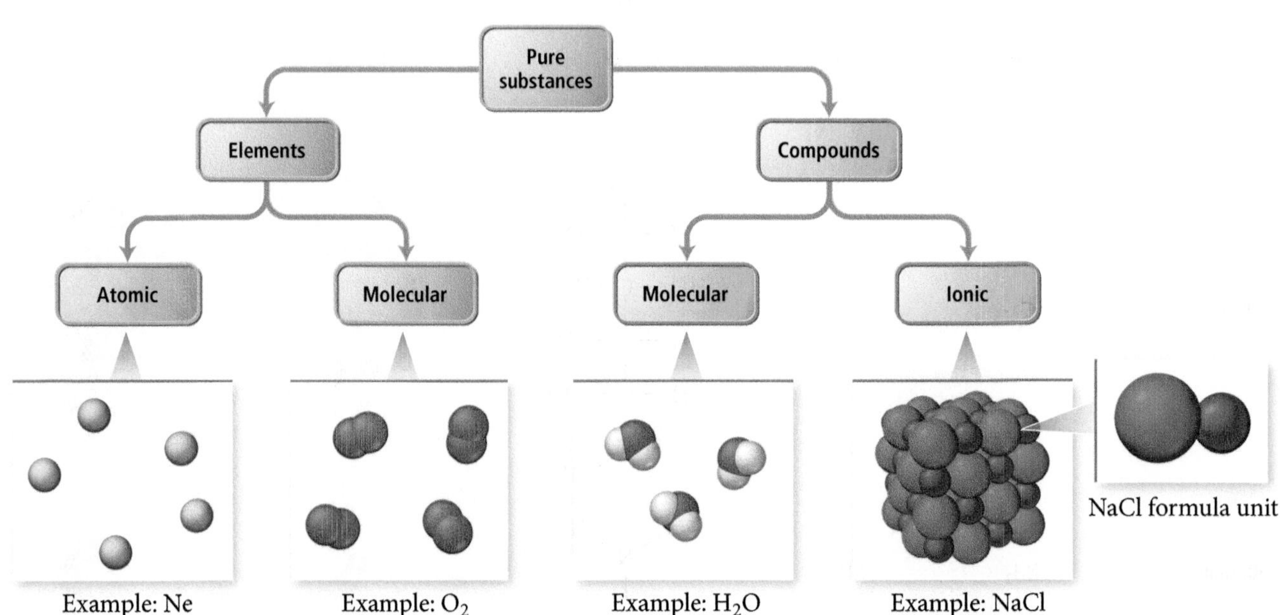

▲ **FIGURE 3.4 A Molecular View of Elements and Compounds**

A Molecular Compound

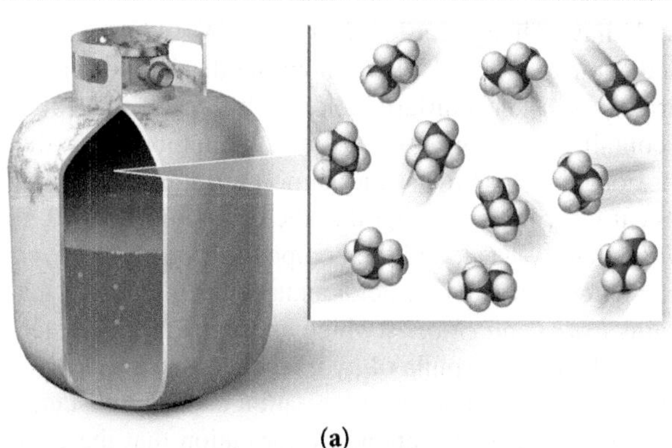

(a)

An Ionic Compound

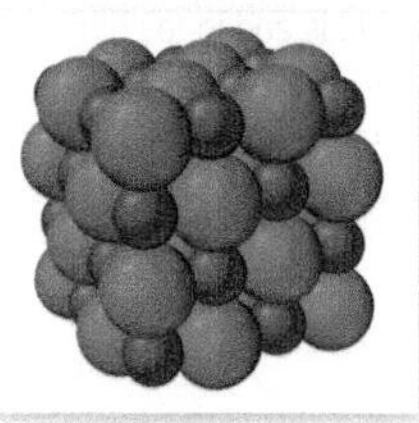

(b)

▲ **FIGURE 3.5 Molecular and Ionic Compounds** (**a**) Propane is an example of a molecular compound. The basic units that compose propane gas are propane (C_3H_8) molecules. (**b**) Table salt (NaCl) is an ionic compound. Its formula unit is the simplest charge-neutral collection of ions: one Na^+ ion and one Cl^- ion.

bleach is sodium hypochlorite, which acts to chemically alter the structure of molecules responsible for colours we can see, such as in clothes (bleaching action) and to kill bacteria (disinfection). Hypochlorite is a **polyatomic ion**—an ion composed of two or more atoms—with the formula ClO^-. (Note that the charge on the hypochlorite ion is a property of the whole ion, not just the oxygen atom; this is true for all polyatomic ions.) The hypochlorite ion is often found as a unit in other compounds as well [such as KClO and $Mg(ClO)_2$]. Other common compounds that contain polyatomic ions include sodium bicarbonate ($NaHCO_3$), also known as baking soda; sodium nitrite ($NaNO_2$), an inhibitor of bacterial growth in packaged meats; and calcium carbonate ($CaCO_3$), the active ingredient in antacids such as Tums®.

EXAMPLE 3.1 CLASSIFYING SUBSTANCES AS ATOMIC ELEMENTS, MOLECULAR ELEMENTS, MOLECULAR COMPOUNDS, OR IONIC COMPOUNDS

Classify each of the following substances as an atomic element, molecular element, molecular compound, or ionic compound.

(a) xenon
(b) $NiCl_2$
(c) bromine
(d) NO_2
(e) $NaNO_3$

SOLUTION

(a) Xenon is an element. It is not a molecular element (see Figure 3.4); therefore, it is an atomic element.

(b) $NiCl_2$ is a compound composed of a metal (left side of the periodic table) and nonmetal (right side of the periodic table); therefore, it is an ionic compound.

(c) Bromine is one of the elements that exists as a diatomic molecule (see Figure 3.4); therefore, it is a molecular element.

(d) NO_2 is a compound composed of a nonmetal and a nonmetal; therefore, it is a molecular compound.

(e) $NaNO_3$ is a compound composed of a metal and a polyatomic ion; therefore, it is an ionic compound.

FOR PRACTICE 3.1

Classify each of the following substances as an atomic element, molecular element, molecular compound, or ionic compound.

(a) fluorine
(b) N_2O
(c) silver
(d) K_2O
(e) Fe_2O_3

3.4 Formulas and Names

When sulfuric acid is added to common salt (NaCl), HCl(*g*) is evolved. This is the origin of the name "spirits of salt" for hydrochloric acid.

The names of chemical compounds have changed a lot over time. Would you know the structure of a compound called "spirits of salt"? How about another name for this compound: "muriatic acid"? Spirits of salt and muriatic acid are historical names for a common chemical that do not contain any information about the composition—that is, the formula of the compound. For many chemists, the name muriatic acid has no value because it conveys no chemical information except that the compound is an acid. Nowadays, the name *muriatic acid* is hardly used, and the compound is almost universally named *hydrochloric acid*. The name hydrochloric acid contains chemical information. The word hydrochloric contains *hydro* and *chloric*, which are parts of the element names of hydrogen and chlorine. The chemical formula of hydrochloric acid is HCl.

The purpose of chemical nomenclature is to convey information about a substance. The most useful chemical name is one that provides enough information that the composition can be inferred unambiguously. **Common names** may not convey unambiguous information about the composition of a compound. The first system of chemical nomenclature was developed by Guyton de Morveau in 1782. He saw the need for chemical names that expressed composition. His ideas were championed by Antoine Lavoisier and scientists began using the **systematic names**. As the understanding of elements and compounds grew, the corresponding names became more logical and systematized. In this section, we will see why, for example, sulfuric acid is the name for H_2SO_4. Today, the rules and standards for chemical nomenclature are determined by the International Union of Pure and Applied Chemists (IUPAC). IUPAC committees are made up of scientists from countries all over the world. Some IUPAC committees are tasked with updating and revising standards on nomenclature, symbols, and definitions. Such standards are important because they ensure a common "language" among scientists.

In this section, we will discuss the formulas and names of ionic and molecular compounds. In Section 3.5, we will cover the nomenclature of a class of molecular compounds called organic compounds.

Ionic Compounds

Ionic compounds occur throughout Earth's crust as minerals. Examples include limestone ($CaCO_3$), a type of sedimentary rock; gibbsite [$Al(OH)_3$], an aluminum-containing mineral; and soda ash (Na_2CO_3), a natural deposit. We can also find ionic compounds in the foods that we eat: table salt (NaCl); calcium carbonate ($CaCO_3$), a source of calcium necessary for bone health; and potassium chloride (KCl), a source of potassium necessary for fluid balance and muscle function. Ionic compounds are generally very stable because the attractions between cations and anions within ionic compounds are strong, and because each ion interacts with several oppositely charged ions in the crystalline lattice.

▶ Calcite (left) is the main component of limestone, marble, and other forms of calcium carbonate ($CaCO_3$) commonly found in Earth's crust. Trona (right) is a crystalline form of hydrated sodium carbonate [$Na_3(CO_3)(HCO_3) \cdot 2H_2O$].

Writing Formulas for Ionic Compounds Since ionic compounds are charge-neutral, and since many elements form only one type of ion with a predictable charge, the formulas for many ionic compounds can be deduced from their constituent elements. For example, the formula for the ionic compound composed of sodium and chlorine must be NaCl because, in ionic compounds, Na always forms 1+ cations and Cl always forms 1− anions. In order for the compound to be charge-neutral, it must contain one Na^+ cation to every one Cl^- anion.

The formula for the ionic compound composed of *calcium* and chlorine, however, is $CaCl_2$ because Ca always forms 2+ cations and Cl always forms 1− anions in ionic compounds. In order for this compound to be charge-neutral, it must contain one Ca^{2+} cation for every two Cl^- anions.

Summarizing Ionic Compound Formulas

- Ionic compounds always contain positive and negative ions.
- In a chemical formula, the sum of the charges of the positive ions (cations) must equal the sum of the charges of the negative ions (anions).
- A formula reflects the smallest whole-number ratio of ions.

To write the formula for an ionic compound, follow the procedure in the left column in the following example. Two examples of how to apply the procedure are provided in the centre and right columns.

PROCEDURE FOR ... Writing Formulas for Ionic Compounds	EXAMPLE 3.2 Writing Formulas for Ionic Compounds Write a formula for the ionic compound that forms between aluminum and oxygen.	EXAMPLE 3.3 Writing Formulas for Ionic Compounds Write a formula for the ionic compound that forms between calcium and oxygen.
1. Write the symbol for the metal cation and its charge followed by the symbol for the nonmetal anion and its charge. Obtain charges from the element's group number in the periodic table (refer to Figure 2.12).	Al^{3+} O^{2-}	Ca^{2+} O^{2-}
2. Adjust the subscript on each cation and anion to balance the overall charge.	Al^{3+} O^{2-} ↓ Al_2O_3	Ca^{2+} O^{2-} ↓ CaO
3. Check that the sum of the charges of the cations equals the sum of the charges of the anions.	cations: 2(3+) = 6+ anions: 3(2−) = 6− The charges balance.	cations: 2+ anions: 2− The charges balance.
	FOR PRACTICE 3.2 Write a formula for the compound formed between potassium and sulfur.	**FOR PRACTICE 3.3** Write a formula for the compound formed between aluminum and nitrogen.

Naming Ionic Compounds The first step in naming an ionic compound is to identify it as one. Ionic compounds are often composed of metals and nonmetals; any time you see a metal and one or more nonmetals together in a chemical formula, assume that you have an ionic compound.

The name of the ionic compound is simply the name of the cation followed by the name of the anion.

Table 3.2 gives names of common cations and anions. In the case of KBr, the name of the K^+ ion is potassium. For metals that form cations with only one charge, the name of the cation is the same as the metal. For metals that can form cations with different charges, the name of the cation is the name of the metal followed by the charge in roman numerals in brackets. Thus, Fe^{2+} is named *iron(II)* and Fe^{3+} is named *iron(III)*. Many transition metals give ions with different charges (Figure 3.6 ▶). Names for monoatomic anions consist of the **base name** of the element followed by the suffix *–ide*. For example, the base name for bromine is *brom*, and the name of the Br^- ion is *bromide*. The name of KBr is the name of the K^+ cation, followed by the name of the Br^- anion: *potassium bromide*.

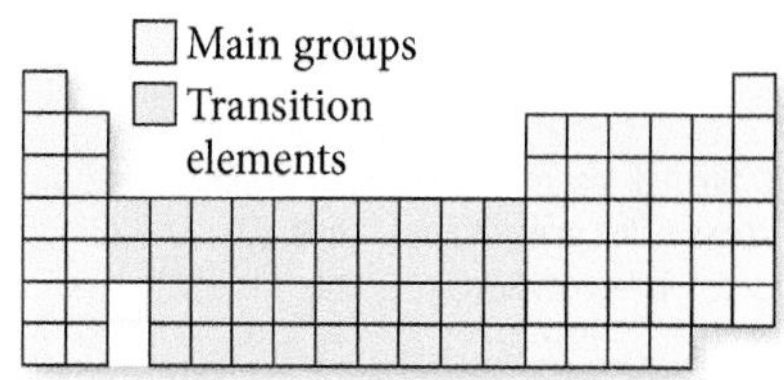

▲ **FIGURE 3.6 Transition Elements** Metals that can have different charges in different compounds are usually (but not always) found in the transition elements.

TABLE 3.2 Common Cations and Anions

Cations						Anions	
Ion	**Name**	**Ion**	**Name**	**Ion**	**Name**	**Ion**	**Name**
Li^+	Lithium	Ba^{2+}	Barium	Co^{2+}	Cobalt(II)	F^-	Fluoride
Na^+	Sodium	Al^{3+}	Aluminum	Co^{3+}	Cobalt(III)	Cl^-	Chloride
K^+	Potassium	Zn^{2+}	Zinc	Cu^+	Copper(I)	Br^-	Bromide
Rb^+	Rubidium	Sc^{3+}	Scandium	Cu^{2+}	Copper(II)	I^-	Iodide
Cs^+	Cesium	Ag^+	Silver	Sn^{2+}	Tin(II)	O^{2-}	Oxide
Be^{2+}	Beryllium	Cr^{2+}	Chromium(II)	Sn^{4+}	Tin(IV)	S^{2-}	Sulfide
Mg^{2+}	Magnesium	Cr^{3+}	Chromium(III)	Hg^{2+}	Mercury(II)	N^{3-}	Nitride
Ca^{2+}	Calcium	Fe^{2+}	Iron(II)	Pb^{2+}	Lead(II)	P^{3-}	Phosphide
Sr^{2+}	Strontium	Fe^{3+}	Iron(III)	Pb^{4+}	Lead(IV)	H^-	Hydride

Current IUPAC recommendations allow ionic charge to be expressed in brackets. For example, the Fe^{2+} ion can be named **iron(II)** or **iron(2+)**. In most cases, this makes no difference to the chemical interpretation.

Consider the compound $CrBr_3$. The charge of chromium must be 3+ in order for the compound to be charge-neutral with three Br^- ions. The cation Cr^{3+} can be named chromium(III), or chromium(3+). The roman numeral *(III)* represents the oxidation state of chromium in the ionic compound. The full name of the compound is *chromium(III) bromide.*

$CrBr_3$ chromium(III) bromide

Ionic compounds that contain a polyatomic ion are named in the same way as other ionic compounds, except that the name of the polyatomic ion is used whenever it occurs. Table 3.3 lists common polyatomic ions and their formulas. For example, $NaNO_2$ is named according to its cation, Na^+, *sodium*, and its polyatomic anions, NO_2^-, *nitrite*. Its full name is *sodium nitrite.*

$NaNO_2$ sodium nitrite

$FeSO_4$ is named according to its cation, *iron*; its oxidation state *(II)*; and its polyatomic ion, *sulfate*. Its full name is *iron(II) sulfate*.

Note that there is no space between the name of the cation and the parenthetical number indicating its charge.

$FeSO_4$ iron(II) sulfate

If the compound contains both a polyatomic cation and a polyatomic anion, use the names of both polyatomic ions. For example, NH_4NO_3 is *ammonium nitrate*.

You should be able to recognize polyatomic ions in a chemical formula, so become familiar with the ions listed in Table 3.3. Most polyatomic ions are **oxyanions**, anions containing oxygen and another element. Notice that when a series of oxyanions contains different numbers of oxygen atoms, they are named systematically according to the number of oxygen atoms in the ion. If there are only two ions in the series, the one with more oxygen atoms has the ending *–ate* and the one with fewer has the ending *–ite*. For example, NO_3^- is *nitrate* and NO_2^- is *nitrite*.

NO_3^- nitr*ate*
NO_2^- nitr*ite*

Other halides (halogen ions) form similar series with similar names. Thus, IO_3^- is called iodate and BrO_3^- is called bromate.

If there are more than two ions in the series, the prefixes *hypo-*, meaning *less than*, and *per–*, meaning *more than*, are used. So, ClO^- is hypochlorite—less oxygen than chlorite, and ClO_4^- is perchlorate—more oxygen than chlorate.

ClO^- *hypo*chlor*ite*
ClO_2^- chlor*ite*
ClO_3^- chlor*ate*
ClO_4^- *per*chlor*ate*

CONCEPTUAL CONNECTION 3.1
Unambiguous Nomenclature

Under old IUPAC nomenclature rules, the homopolyatomic cation Hg_2^{2+} was named *mercury(I)*. Explain why this name is ambiguous. The current recommended name is *dimercury(2+)*. Is the current name unambiguous?

EXAMPLE 3.4 NAMING IONIC COMPOUNDS

Name the following ionic compounds: **(a)** $PbCl_4$ **(b)** $Li_2Cr_2O_7$

SOLUTION

(a) The charge on Pb must be 4+ for the compound to be charge-neutral with 4 Cl^- anions. The name for $PbCl_4$ is the name of the cation, *lead*; followed by the charge (4+) or charge state of the cation in parentheses *(IV)*; and the base name of the anion, *chlor*, with the ending *-ide*. The full name is *lead(IV) chloride*.

$PbCl_4$ lead(IV) chloride

(b) The name for $Li_2Cr_2O_7$ is the name of the cation, *lithium*, followed by the name of the polyatomic ion, *dichromate*. Its full name is *lithium dichromate*.

$Li_2Cr_2O_7$ lithium dichromate

FOR PRACTICE 3.4

Name the following ionic compounds: **(a)** FeS **(b)** $Sn(ClO_3)_2$

FOR MORE PRACTICE 3.4

Write the formula for: **(a)** ruthenium(IV) oxide **(b)** cobalt(2+) phosphate

TABLE 3.3 Common Polyatomic Ions

Polyatomic Ion	Name
NH_4^+	Ammonium
$C_2H_3O_2^-$	Acetate
CO_3^{2-}	Carbonate
HCO_3^-	Hydrogen carbonate (or bicarbonate)
OH^-	Hydroxide
NO_2^-	Nitrite
NO_3^-	Nitrate
CrO_4^{2-}	Chromate
$Cr_2O_7^{2-}$	Dichromate
PO_4^{3-}	Phosphate
HPO_4^{2-}	Hydrogen phosphate
$H_2PO_4^-$	Dihydrogen phosphate
ClO^-	Hypochlorite
ClO_2^-	Chlorite
ClO_3^-	Chlorate
ClO_4^-	Perchlorate
MnO_4^-	Permanganate
SO_3^{2-}	Sulfite
HSO_3^-	Hydrogen sulfite
SO_4^{2-}	Sulfate
HSO_4^-	Hydrogen sulfate
CN^-	Cyanide

Hydrated Ionic Compounds Some ionic compounds—called **hydrates**—contain a specific number of water molecules associated with each formula unit. For example, the formula for Epsom salts is $MgSO_4 \cdot 7H_2O$ and its systematic name is magnesium sulfate heptahydrate. The seven H_2O molecules associated with the formula unit are *waters of hydration*. Waters of hydration can usually be removed by heating the compound. Figure 3.7 ▶, for example, shows a sample of cobalt(II) chloride hexahydrate ($CoCl_2 \cdot 6H_2O$) before and after heating. The hydrate is pink, and the **anhydrous** salt (the salt without any associated water molecules) is blue. Hydrates are named just as other ionic compounds, but they are given the additional name "*prefix*hydrate," where the prefix indicates the number of water molecules associated with each formula unit.

Other common hydrated ionic compounds and their names are as follows:

$CaSO_4 \cdot 1/2H_2O$ calcium sulfate hemihydrate
$BaCl_2 \cdot 6H_2O$ barium chloride hexahydrate
$CuSO_4 \cdot 5H_2O$ copper(II) sulfate pentahydrate

Hydrate

$CoCl_2 \cdot 6H_2O$

Anhydrous

$CoCl_2$

▲ **FIGURE 3.7 Hydrates** Cobalt(II) chloride hexahydrate is pink. Heating the compound removes the waters of hydration, leaving the blue anhydrous cobalt(II) chloride.

Common hydrate prefixes
hemi = 1/2
mono = 1
di = 2
tri = 3
tetra = 4
penta = 5
hexa = 6
hepta = 7
octa = 8

Molecular Compounds

In contrast to ionic compounds, the formula for a molecular compound *cannot* be readily determined from its constituent elements because the same combination of elements may form many different molecular compounds, each with a different formula. We learned in Chapter 2, for example, that carbon and oxygen form both CO and CO_2, and that hydrogen and oxygen form both H_2O and H_2O_2. Nitrogen and oxygen form all the following unique molecular compounds: NO, NO_2, N_2O, N_2O_3, N_2O_4, and N_2O_5. In Chapter 9, we will learn how to understand the stability of these various combinations of the same elements. For now, we focus on naming a molecular compound based on its formula and writing its formula based on its name.

Base names of common nonmetals

Element	Base Name
H	hydr
B	bor
C	carb
N	nitr
O	ox
F	fluor
Si	silic
P	phosph
S	sulf
Cl	chlor
Br	brom
I	iod

Naming Molecular Compounds Like ionic compounds, many molecular compounds have common names. For example, H_2O and NH_3 are commonly called *water* and *ammonia.* However, the sheer number of existing molecular compounds—numbering in the millions—requires a systematic approach to naming them.

The first step in naming a molecular compound is identifying it as one. Remember, *molecular compounds are composed of two or more nonmetals.* In this section, we learn how to name **binary molecular compounds**, which consist of two elements. Their names have the following form:

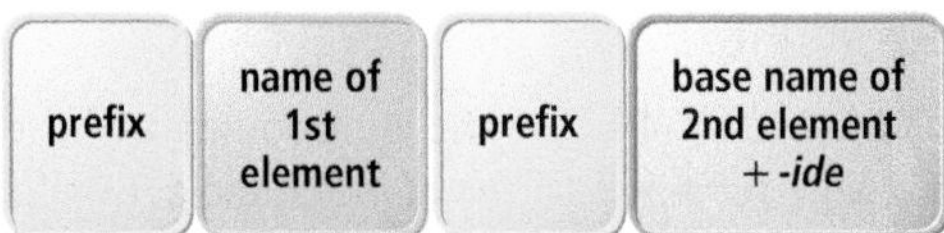

When writing the name of a molecular compound, as when writing the formula, the first element is the more metal-like one (toward the left and bottom of the periodic table). Generally, write the name of the element with the smallest group number first. If the two elements lie in the same group, write the element with the greatest row number first. The prefixes given to each element indicate the number of atoms present:

These prefixes are the same as those used in naming hydrates.

mono = 1 hexa = 6
di = 2 hepta = 7
tri = 3 octa = 8
tetra = 4 nona = 9
penta = 5 deca = 10

If there is only one atom of the *first element* in the formula, the prefix *mono-* is normally omitted. For example, NO_2 is named according to the first element, *nitrogen*, with no prefix because *mono-* is omitted for the first element, followed by the prefix *di-*, to indicate two oxygen atoms, and the base name of the second element, *ox*, with the ending *-ide*. The full name is *nitrogen dioxide.*

NO_2 nitrogen dioxide

The compound N_2O, sometimes called laughing gas, is named similarly except that we use the prefix *di-* before nitrogen to indicate two nitrogen atoms and the prefix *mono-* before oxide to indicate one oxygen atom. Its entire name is *dinitrogen monoxide.*

N_2O dinitrogen monoxide

EXAMPLE 3.5 NAMING MOLECULAR COMPOUNDS

Name each molecular compound.

(a) NI_3 **(b)** PCl_5 **(c)** P_4S_{10}

SOLUTION

(a) The name of the compound is the name of the first element, *nitrogen*, followed by the base name of the second element, *iod*, prefixed by *tri-* to indicate three, and given the suffix *-ide*.

NI_3 nitrogen triiodide

(b) The name of the compound is the name of the first element, *phosphorus*, followed by the base name of the second element, *chlor*, prefixed by *penta-* to indicate five, and given the suffix *-ide*.

PCl_5 phosphorus pentachloride

(c) The name of the compound is the name of the first element, *phosphorus*, prefixed by *tetra-* to indicate four, followed by the base name of the second element, *sulf*, prefixed by *deca-* to indicate ten, and given the suffix *-ide*.

P_4S_{10} tetraphosphorus decasulfide

FOR PRACTICE 3.5

Name the compound N_2O_5.

FOR MORE PRACTICE 3.5

Write the formula for phosphorus tribromide.

Naming Acids

Acids are molecular compounds that release hydrogen ions (H^+) when dissolved in water. They are composed of hydrogen, usually written first in their formula, and one or more nonmetals, written second. For example, HCl is a molecular compound that, when dissolved in water, forms $H^+(aq)$ and $Cl^-(aq)$ ions, where *aqueous* (*aq*) means *dissolved in water*. Therefore, HCl is an acid when dissolved in water. To distinguish between gaseous HCl (which is named hydrogen chloride because it is a molecular compound) and HCl in solution (which is named hydrochloric acid because it is an acid), we write the former as HCl(*g*) and the latter as HCl(*aq*).

▲ Many fruits are acidic and have the characteristically sour taste of acids.

Acids are characterized by their sour taste and their ability to dissolve many metals. For example, hydrochloric acid is present in stomach fluids, and its sour taste becomes painfully obvious during vomiting. Hydrochloric acid also dissolves some metals. For example, if you put a strip of zinc into a test tube of hydrochloric acid, it slowly dissolves as the $H^+(aq)$ ions convert the zinc metal into $Zn^{2+}(aq)$ cations (Figure 3.8 ▼).

Acids are present in foods such as lemons and limes and are used in household products such as toilet bowl cleaner and Lime-Away®. In this section, we learn how to name them; in Chapter 15, we will learn more about their properties. Acids can be divided into two categories: binary acids and oxyacids.

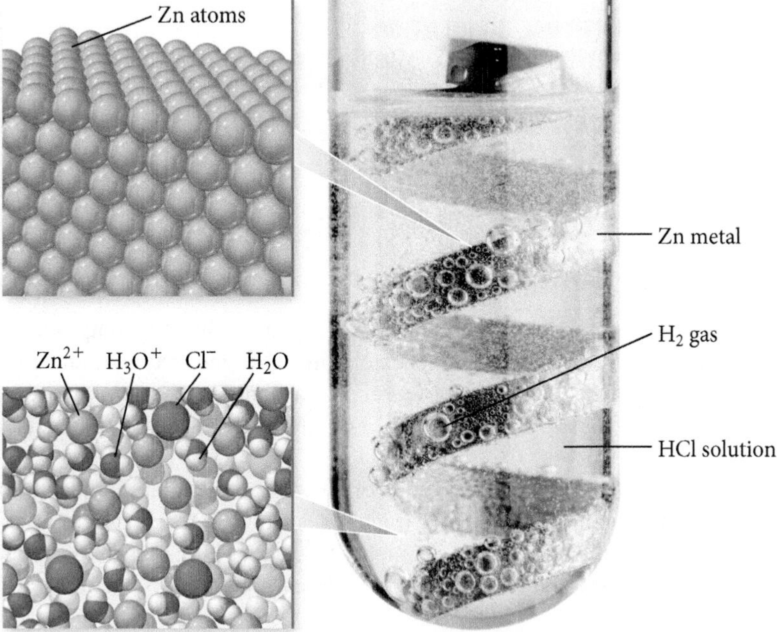

◀ **FIGURE 3.8 Hydrochloric Acid Dissolving Zinc Metal** The zinc atoms are ionized to zinc ions, which dissolve in the water. The HCl forms H_2 gas, which is responsible for the bubbles you can see in the test tube.

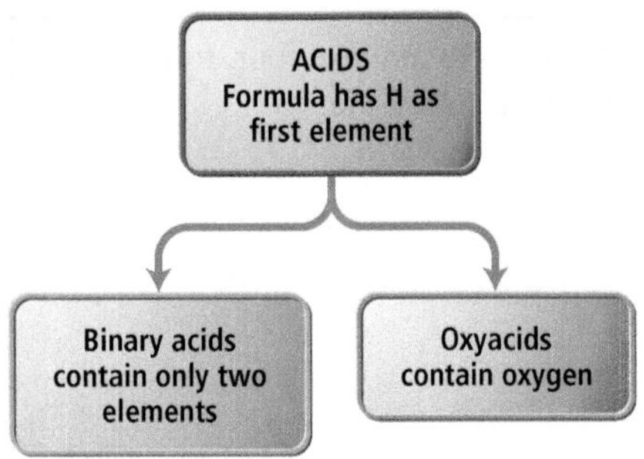

Naming Binary Acids **Binary acids** are composed of hydrogen and a nonmetal. Names for binary acids have the following form:

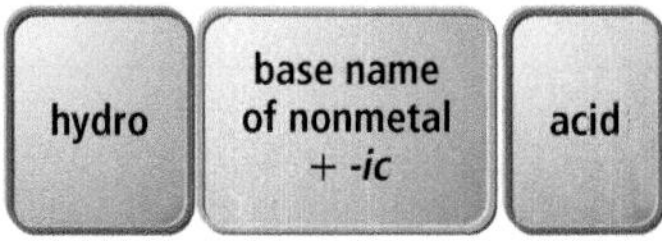

For example, HCl(*aq*) is named hydro*chloric* acid, and HBr(*aq*) is named hydro*bromic* acid.

HCl(*aq*) hydrochloric acid HBr(*aq*) hydrobromic acid

Naming Oxyacids Molecules containing hydrogen and an oxyanion (an anion containing a nonmetal and oxygen) are called **oxyacids**. The common oxyanions are listed in the table of polyatomic ions (Table 3.3). For example, $HNO_3(aq)$ contains the nitrate (NO_3^-) ion, $H_2SO_3(aq)$ contains the sulfite (SO_3^{2-}) ion, and $H_2SO_4(aq)$ contains the sulfate (SO_4^{2-}) ion. Oxyacids are a combination of one or more H^+ ions with an oxyanion (see Table 3.3). The number of H^+ ions depends on the charge of the oxyanion; the formula is always charge-neutral. The names of oxyacids depend on the ending of the oxyanion and take the following forms:

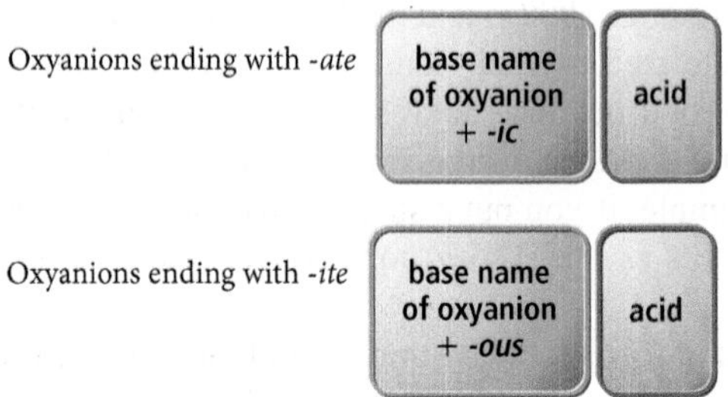

So, $HNO_3(aq)$ is nitric acid (oxyanion is nitrate), and $H_2SO_3(aq)$ is sulfurous acid (oxyanion is sulfite).

$HNO_3(aq)$ nitric acid $H_2SO_3(aq)$ sulfurous acid

CONCEPTUAL CONNECTION 3.2
Nomenclature

The compound NCl_3 is named nitrogen trichloride, but $AlCl_3$ is simply aluminum chloride. Why?

3.5 Organic Compounds

▲ Gasoline is composed mostly of hydrocarbons.

Organic compounds are a class of molecular compounds that are composed of carbon and hydrogen and a few other elements, including nitrogen, oxygen, and sulfur. The key element in organic chemistry, however, is carbon. In its compounds, with few exceptions, carbon always forms four bonds. The simplest organic compound is methane or CH_4.

The chemistry of carbon is unique and complex because carbon frequently bonds to itself to form chain, branched, and ring structures, such as the ones that follow. We can begin to scratch the surface of organic chemistry by categorizing organic compounds into two types: hydrocarbons and functionalized hydrocarbons. **Hydrocarbons** are organic compounds that contain only carbon and hydrogen. Hydrocarbons comprise common fuels such as oil, gasoline, propane, and natural gas. Hydrocarbons containing only single bonds are called **alkanes**:

```
    H  H  H
    |  |  |
 H—C—C—C—H
    |  |  |
    H  H  H
```

Propane (C_3H_8)

```
    H  H  H
    |  |  |
 H—C—C—C—H
    |  |  |
    H  |  H
    H—C—H
       |
       H
```

2-Methylpropane (C_4H_{10})

```
       H  H
    H  |  |  H
     \ C—C /
  H  /     \  H
   \/       \/
   C         C
  / \       / \
 H   \     /   H
      C—C
    / |  | \
   H  H  H  H
```

Cyclohexane (C_6H_{12})

Butane

```
    H  H  H  H
    |  |  |  |
 H—C—C—C—C—H
    |  |  |  |
    H  H  H  H
```

▲ Butane, C_4H_{10}, is a common fuel in lighters.

Carbon can also form double bonds and triple bonds with itself. Organic compounds containing double or triple bonds between carbon atoms are called **alkenes** and **alkynes**, respectively:

```
 H     H
  \   /
   C=C
  /   \
 H     H
```

Ethene (C_2H_4)
(an alkane)

H—C≡C—H

Ethyne (C_2H_2)
(an alkyne)

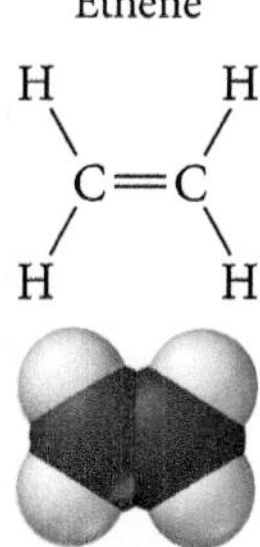

▲ Ethene, C_2H_4, is an alkene that is used for ripening fruit. It is also the raw material used to make polyethylene plastics.

This versatility allows carbon to act as the backbone of millions of different chemical compounds.

Functionalized hydrocarbons can be thought of as hydrocarbons in which a **functional group**—a characteristic atom or group of atoms—is incorporated into the hydrocarbon. For example, **alcohols** are organic compounds that have an —OH functional group. We designate the hydrocarbon portion of the molecule as "R," so the general formula for an alcohol can be written R—OH. Some examples of alcohols include methanol (also known as methyl alcohol or wood alcohol) and propan-2-ol (also known as isopropyl alcohol or rubbing alcohol):

The term *functional group* derives from the functionality or chemical character that a specific atom or group of atoms imparts to an organic compound. Even a carbon–carbon double bond can justifiably be called a "functional group as it is the most reactive site in the molecule."

Hydrocarbon (R) group → CH_3OH ← OH functional group

Methanol

```
                          CH3
Hydrocarbon (R) group →    |
                       CH3CHOH ← OH functional group
```

Propan-2-ol
(Isopropyl alcohol)

A group of organic compounds with the same functional group forms a **family**. Methanol and propan-2-ol are both members of the alcohol family of compounds.

The addition of a functional group to a hydrocarbon usually alters the properties of the compound significantly. Take *methanol*—which can be thought of as methane with an —OH group substituted for one of the hydrogen atoms: it is a liquid at room temperature, while *methane* is a gas. While each member of a family is unique, the common functional group bestows some chemical similarities on members of the same family.

Naming Hydrocarbons

As for ionic and molecular compounds, IUPAC has developed a recommended system of nomenclature for organic compounds. The system is a set of rules that allows chemists to unambiguously describe the *structure* of a compound, not just its composition, as is the case for simple binary compounds. For example, N_2O_4 is named dinitrogen tetroxide. The name does not give any information about the actual structure of the molecule. The structure must be inferred using knowledge of bonding patterns, which we will cover in Chapters 9 and 10. Considering the enormous variety of structures of organic compounds, it is the rule that for a given molecular formula, many different structures are possible. Therefore, the names of organic compounds must provide information that will allow a chemist to know the structure exactly.

TABLE 3.4 Prefixes for Base Names of Hydrocarbon Chains up to $n = 10$ carbon atoms

n	prefix
1	meth-
2	eth-
3	prop-
4	but-
5	pent-
6	hex-
7	hept-
8	oct-
9	non-
10	dec-

For many hydrocarbons, nomenclature starts with identifying the longest continuous chain of carbon atoms: the base chain. This determines the base name of the compound. The root of the base name depends on the number of carbon atoms in the base chain, as shown in Table 3.4. Base names for alkanes always have the ending *-ane*. For example:

$$CH_3—CH_2—CH_2—CH_2—CH_3$$

This molecule consists of a chain of five carbon atoms, so the base name prefix is *pent-*. It is an alkane, so the name ending is *–ane*. The name is *pentane*.

Groups of carbon atoms branching off the base chain are called alkyl groups and are named as substituents. A **substituent** is an atom or group of atoms that has been substituted for a hydrogen atom in an organic compound. Common alkyl groups are shown in Table 3.5.

TABLE 3.5 Common Alkyl Groups

Condensed Structural Formula	Name
$—CH_3$	methyl
$—CH_2CH_3$	ethyl
$—CH_2CH_2CH_3$	propyl
$—CH_2CH_2CH_2CH_3$	butyl
$—CHCH_3$ with CH_3 on the C	1-methylethyl (isopropyl)*
$—CH_2CHCH_3$ with CH_3 on the second C	2-methylpropyl (isobutyl)*
$—CHCH_2CH_3$ with CH_3 on the first C	1-methylpropyl (*sec*-butyl)*
$—CCH_3$ with two CH_3 on the C	1,1-dimethylethyl (*tert*-butyl)*

*Common names for substituents are in brackets.

The procedure shown in Examples 3.6 and 3.7 will allow you to systematically name many alkanes. The five-step procedure is presented in the left column and two examples of applying the procedure are shown in the centre and right columns.

PROCEDURE FOR ... Naming Alkanes

1. Count the number of carbon atoms in the longest continuous carbon chain to determine the base name of the compound. Locate the prefix corresponding to this number of atoms in Table 3.4 and add the ending *-ane* to form the base name.

2. Consider every branch from the base chain to be a substituent. Name each substituent according to Table 3.5.

3. Beginning with the end closest to the branching, number the base chain and assign a number to each substituent. (If two substituents occur at equal distances from each end, go to the next substituent to determine from which end to start numbering.)

4. Write the name of the compound in the following format:

(substituent number)-(substituent name)(base name)

EXAMPLE 3.6 Naming Alkanes

Name the following alkane.

$$CH_3-CH_2-\underset{\underset{CH_3}{|}}{\underset{CH_2}{\underset{|}{CH}}}-CH_2-CH_3$$

SOLUTION

This compound has five carbon atoms in its longest continuous chain.

$$CH_3-CH_2-\underset{\underset{CH_3}{|}}{\underset{CH_2}{\underset{|}{CH}}}-CH_2-CH_3$$

The correct prefix from Table 3.4 is *pent-*. The base name is pentane.

This compound has one substituent named *ethyl*.

$$CH_3-CH_2-\underset{\underset{CH_3}{|}}{\underset{CH_2}{\underset{|}{CH}}}-CH_2-CH_3$$

The base chain is numbered as follows:

$$\overset{1}{CH_3}-\overset{2}{CH_2}-\underset{\underset{CH_3}{|}}{\underset{CH_2}{\underset{|}{\overset{3}{CH}}}}-\overset{4}{CH_2}-\overset{5}{CH_3}$$

The ethyl substituent is assigned the number 3.

The name of the compound is:

3-ethylpentane

EXAMPLE 3.7 Naming Alkanes

Name the following alkane.

$$CH_3-\underset{\underset{CH_3}{|}}{CH}-CH_2-\underset{\underset{CH_3}{|}}{\underset{CH_2}{\underset{|}{CH}}}-CH_2-CH_2-\underset{\underset{CH_3}{|}}{CH}-CH_3$$

SOLUTION

This compound has eight carbon atoms in its longest continuous chain.

$$CH_3-\underset{\underset{CH_3}{|}}{CH}-CH_2-\underset{\underset{CH_3}{|}}{\underset{CH_2}{\underset{|}{CH}}}-CH_2-CH_2-\underset{\underset{CH_3}{|}}{CH}-CH_3$$

The correct prefix from Table 3.4 is *oct-*. The base name is octane.

This compound has one substituent named *ethyl* and two named *methyl.*

$$CH_3-\underset{\underset{CH_3}{|}}{CH}-CH_2-\underset{\underset{CH_3}{|}}{\underset{CH_2}{\underset{|}{CH}}}-CH_2-CH_2-\underset{\underset{CH_3}{|}}{CH}-CH_3$$

The base chain is numbered as follows:

$$\overset{1}{CH_3}-\underset{\underset{CH_3}{|}}{\overset{2}{CH}}-\overset{3}{CH_2}-\underset{\underset{CH_3}{|}}{\underset{CH_2}{\underset{|}{\overset{4}{CH}}}}-\overset{5}{CH_2}-\overset{6}{CH_2}-\underset{\underset{CH_3}{|}}{\overset{7}{CH}}-\overset{8}{CH_3}$$

The ethyl substituent is assigned the number 4 and the two methyl substituents are assigned the numbers 2 and 7.

The basic form of the name of the compound is:

4-ethyl-2,7-methyloctane

Ethyl is listed before methyl because substituents are listed in alphabetical order.

(continued)

PROCEDURE FOR ... *(continued)*	EXAMPLE 3.6 *(continued)*	EXAMPLE 3.7 *(continued)*
If there are two or more substituents, give each one a number and list them alphabetically with hyphens between words and numbers.		
5. If a compound has two or more identical substituents, indicate the number of identical substituents with the prefix *di–* (2), *tri–* (3), or *tetra–* (4) before the substituent's name. Separate the numbers indicating the positions of the substituents relative to each other with a comma. The prefixes are not taken into account when alphabetizing.	Does not apply to this compound. **FOR PRACTICE 3.6** 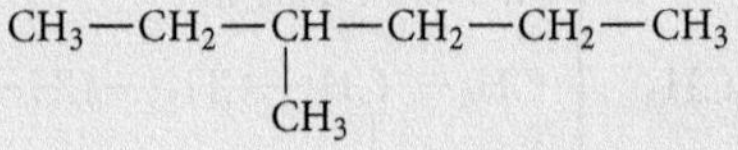 $CH_3{-}CH_2{-}\underset{\underset{\displaystyle CH_3}{\vert}}{CH}{-}CH_2{-}CH_2{-}CH_3$	This compound has two methyl substituents; therefore, the name of the compound is: 4-ethyl-2,7-dimethyloctane **FOR PRACTICE 3.7** 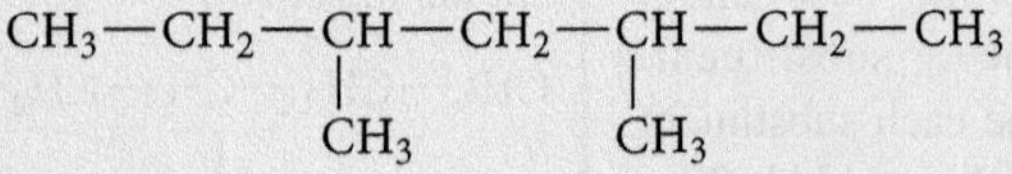 $CH_3{-}CH_2{-}\underset{\underset{\displaystyle CH_3}{\vert}}{CH}{-}CH_2{-}\underset{\underset{\displaystyle CH_3}{\vert}}{CH}{-}CH_2{-}CH_3$

Alkenes and alkynes are named the same way as alkanes with the following exceptions:

- The base chain is the longest continuous carbon chain *that contains the double or triple bond.*
- The base name has the ending *–ene* for alkenes and *–yne* for alkynes.
- The base chain is numbered to give the double and triple bond the lowest possible number.
- A number indicating the position of the double or triple bond (lowest possible number) is inserted just before the suffix *–ene* or *–yne.* Numbers that indicate a location are called **locants**.

For example, the alkene and alkyne shown here are named as follows:

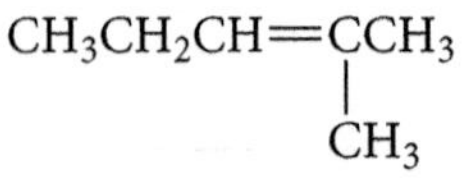

$$CH_3CH_2CH{=}\underset{\underset{\displaystyle CH_3}{\vert}}{C}CH_3 \qquad CH{\equiv}CCH_2CH_3$$

2-Methylpent-2-ene   But-1-yne

EXAMPLE 3.8 NAMING ALKENES AND ALKYNES

Name the following compounds:

(a)

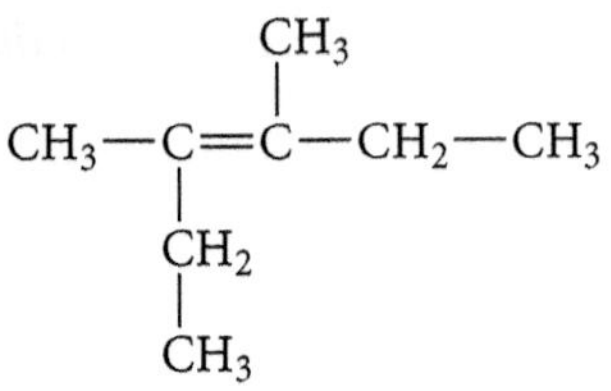

$$\begin{array}{ccccc} & & CH_3 & & \\ & & \vert & & \\ CH_3- & C= & C & -CH_2- & CH_3 \\ & \vert & & & \\ & CH_2 & & & \\ & \vert & & & \\ & CH_3 & & & \end{array}$$

(b)

$$\begin{array}{cccc} & & CH_3 & \\ & & \vert & \\ & CH_3- & CH & \\ & & \vert & \\ CH_3- & CH & -CH & -C{\equiv}CH \\ & \vert & & \\ & CH_3 & & \end{array}$$

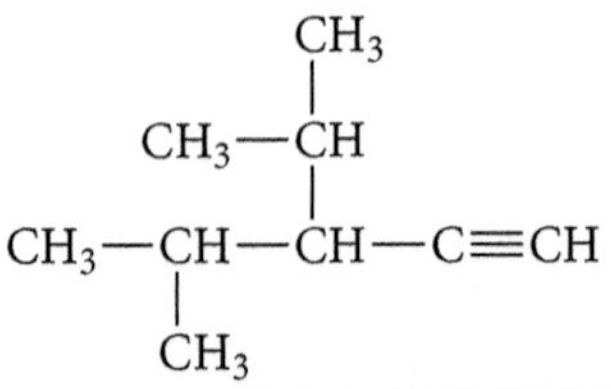

SOLUTION	
(a) 1. Since this molecule contains a double bond, it is an alkene. The longest continuous carbon chain containing the double bond has six carbon atoms. The base name is therefore *hexene*.	CH_3 | $CH_3—C{=}C—CH_2—CH_3$ | CH_2 | CH_3
2. The two substituents are both methyl.	methyl CH_3 | $CH_3—C{=}C—CH_2—CH_3$ | CH_2 | CH_3
3. When naming alkenes, number the chain so that the *double bond* has the lowest number. In this case, the double bond is equidistant from both ends of the chain. The double bond is assigned the number 3. The two methyl groups are therefore at positions 3 and 4.	CH_3 | $CH_3—C{=}C—CH_2—CH_3$ 3 4 5 6 | 2 CH_2 | CH_3 1
4. Use the general form for the name: (substituent number)-(substituent name)(base name) Since this compound contains two identical substituents, step 5 of the naming procedure applies, so use the prefix *di*-. In addition, indicate the position of each substituent with a number separated by a comma. Since this compound is an alkene, specify the position of the double bond, isolated by hyphens, just before the suffix *–ene*.	3,4-dimethylhex-3-ene
(b) 1. This molecule contains a triple bond and is therefore an alkyne. The longest continuous chain containing the triple bond is five carbons long; therefore the base name is *pentyne*.	CH_3 | $CH_3—CH$ | $CH_3—CH—CH—C{\equiv}CH$ | CH_3
2. There are two substituents: one is a methyl group and the other a 1-methylethyl, or isopropyl, group.	1-methylethyl, or isopropyl CH_3 | $CH_3—CH$ | $CH_3—CH—CH—C{\equiv}CH$ | CH_3 methyl
3. Number the base chain, giving the triple bond the lowest number (1). The 1-methylethyl and methyl groups are therefore given the numbers 3 and 4, respectively.	CH_3 | $CH_3—CH$ | $CH_3—CH—CH—C{\equiv}CH$ 5 4 3 2 1 | CH_3

(*continued*)

EXAMPLE 3.8 (CONTINUED)

4. Use the general form for the name: (substituent number)-(substituent name)(base name) Since there are two substituents, list both of them in alphabetical order. If the 1-methylethyl substituent name is used, it is surrounded by brackets. Since this compound is an alkyne, specify the position of the triple bond with a number isolated by hyphens just before the suffix *–yne*.	Two possible names: 4-methyl-3-(1-methylethyl)pent-1-yne 3-isopropyl-4-methylpent-1-yne

FOR PRACTICE 3.8

Name the following compounds:

```
                                                            CH3
                                                            |
               CH3                                          CH2
               |                                            |
(a) CH3—C≡C—C—CH3      (b) CH3—CH—CH2—CH—CH—CH=CH2
               |                    |        |
               CH3                  CH3      CH3
```

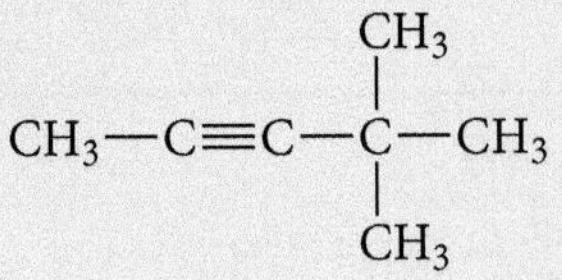

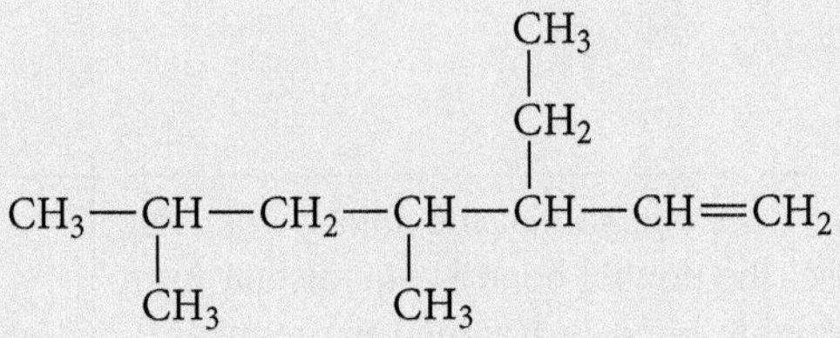

Cyclic Hydrocarbons

Many hydrocarbons contain rings of carbon chains, which are called cyclic hydrocarbons. **Cycloalkanes** are cyclic alkanes. **Cycloalkenes** are cyclic alkenes, and contain a carbon–carbon double bond in the ring structure. Cycloalkanes and cycloalkenes are named by attaching the prefix *cyclo-* to the base name of the alkane or alkene. For example:

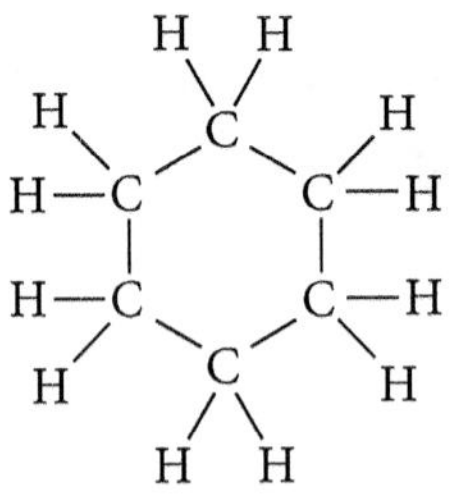

```
        H  H
         \/
  H      C      H                H   H
   \   /   \   /            H     \ /
 H—C         C—H             \   C
   |         |                C—C    H
 H—C         C—H              ||   C/
   /  \   /   \               C     \H
  H     C      H             /  \ C
       /\                   H    /\
      H  H                      H  H
   Cyclohexane               Cyclopentene
```

Cyclohexane

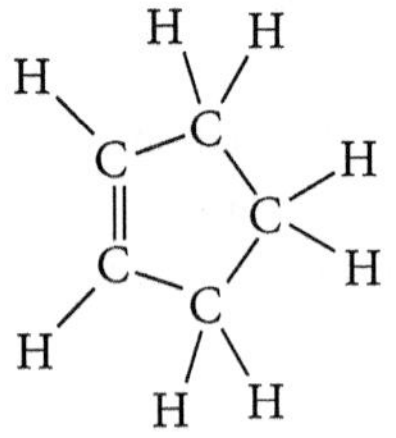

Cyclopentene

Cyclic hydrocarbons can be substituted with groups. The rules for nomenclature of substituted cyclic hydrocarbons are essentially the same as for straight-chain hydrocarbons in terms of numbering the carbon atoms in the base chain and using alphabetical order for substituents. The cyclic carbon chain is considered the base chain. In the case of cycloalkenes, the numbering of carbon atoms always begins with the alkene carbon atoms. For example, consider the following cycloalkene:

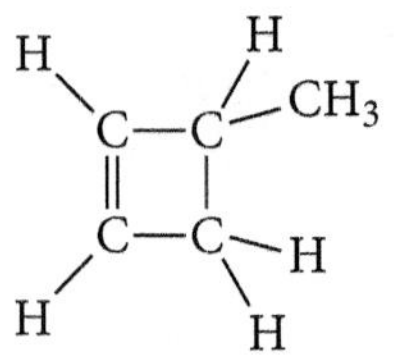

```
 H       H
  \     /
   C—C—CH3
   ‖  |
   C—C—H
  /    \
 H      H
```

There are four carbon atoms in the ring (prefix = *but–*), and the ring contains a carbon–carbon double bond (ending = *–ene*). Therefore, the base name of this compound is *cyclobutene*. There is only one substituent, a methyl group. The numbering of the ring starts with one atom in the carbon–carbon double bond and continues through the double bond, going around the ring:

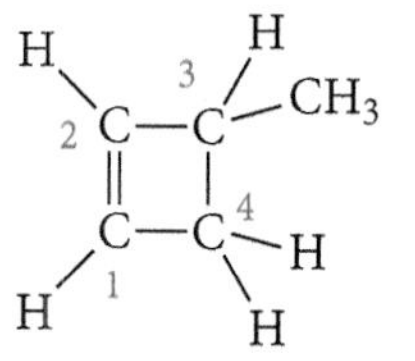

3-Methylcyclobutene

The name of the compound is 3-methylcyclobutene. It is unnecessary to give the number of the position of the double bond because it is redundant; the numbers are always chosen so that they start at the double bond and give the substituent the smallest number possible.

Aromatic Hydrocarbons

Aromatic hydrocarbons are a unique class of cyclic hydrocarbons that contain alternating single and double carbon–carbon bonds in the ring. The most common aromatic hydrocarbon is **benzene**:

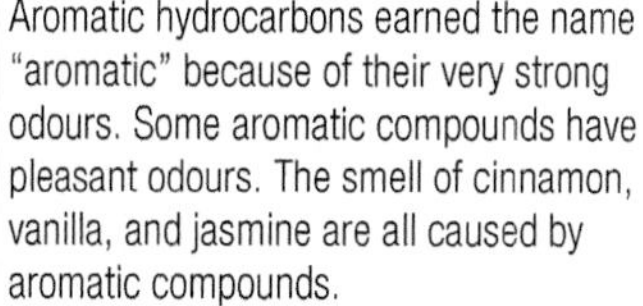
Aromatic hydrocarbons earned the name "aromatic" because of their very strong odours. Some aromatic compounds have pleasant odours. The smell of cinnamon, vanilla, and jasmine are all caused by aromatic compounds.

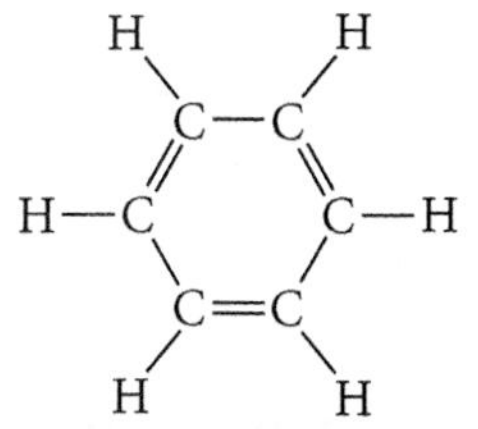

Benzene rings are commonly shown without the hydrogen atoms:

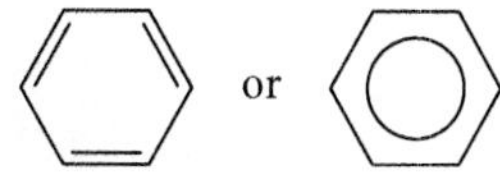

CONCEPTUAL CONNECTION 3.3

Organic Nomenclature

Write the systematic chemical name for benzene. Could someone infer the structure from the systematic name?

Substituted benzenes are benzene molecules in which one or more hydrogen has been substituted. The nomenclature of substituted benzenes follows rules similar to those of cyclic hydrocarbons. The base name of a substituted benzene is simply benzene. The position of each substituent is identified with a number. The order of numbering on the ring is determined by the alphabetical order of substituents.

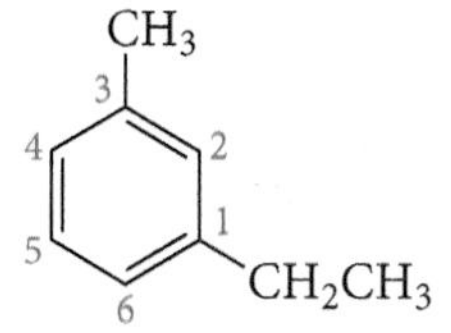

1-Ethyl-3-methylbenzene

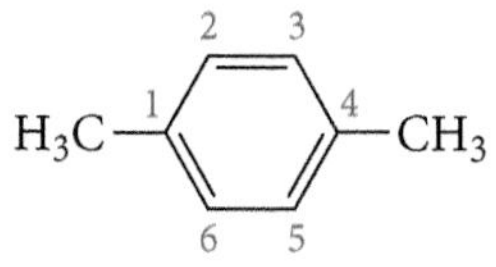

1,4-Dimethylbenzene

Some substituted benzenes, especially those with large substituents, are named by treating the benzene ring as the substituent. In these cases, the C_6H_5 substituent is called a **phenyl group**.

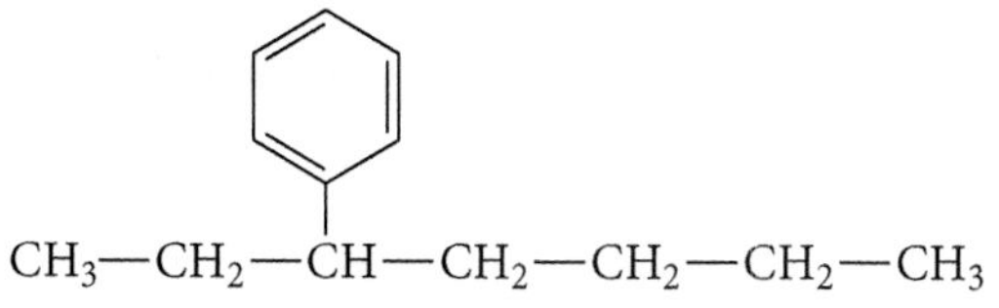

$CH_3{-}CH_2{-}CH{-}CH_2{-}CH_2{-}CH_2{-}CH_3$

3-Phenylheptane

$CH_2{=}CH{-}CH_2{-}CH{-}CH_2{-}CH_3$

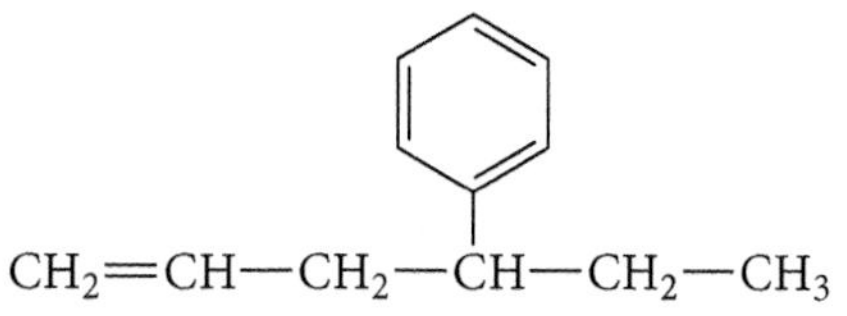

4-Phenylhex-1-ene

Functionalized Hydrocarbons

The names of functional groups have suffixes or endings unique to that functional group. Alcohols, for example, always have names that end in *-ol*. Table 3.6 provides examples of some common functional groups, their general formulas, and their characteristic suffixes or endings.

For compounds that contain a single functional group, a prefix or suffix that corresponds to the functional group is added to the hydrocarbon base name.

An example of a name with a functional group suffix is propan-2-ol. As there are three carbon atoms in the chain, the base name of the hydrocarbon is propane. The —OH group is located at carbon number 2. The suffix for alcohols is *–ol*. Notice that the *e* at the end of the base name propane is removed. Hence, the name of this alcohol is propan-2-ol.

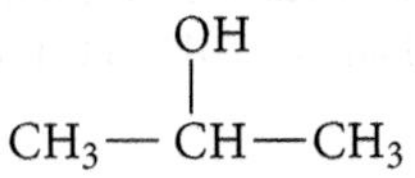

$$CH_3-\underset{}{\overset{OH}{\overset{|}{CH}}}-CH_3$$

Propan-2-ol

In the case of the halogen functional groups fluoride, chloride, bromide, and iodide, a prefix is always used. For halogenated hydrocarbons, the nomenclature follows the same form as hydrocarbons with alkyl groups. For example:

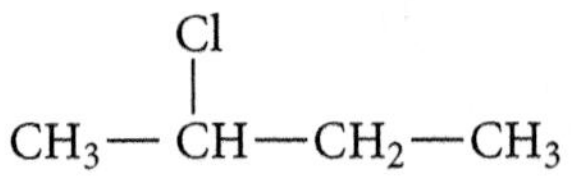

$$CH_3-\overset{Cl}{\overset{|}{CH}}-CH_2-CH_3$$

2-Chlorobutane

$$C_6H_5-Br$$

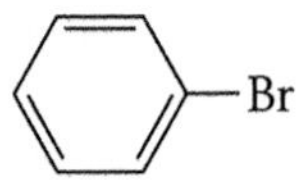

Bromobenzene

TABLE 3.6 Families of Organic Compounds

Family	General Formula	Principal Group Suffix	Substituent Group Prefix	Example	Name	Occurrence/Use
Carboxylic Acid	$R-\overset{O}{\overset{\|}{C}}-OH$	-oic acid	—	$CH_3-\overset{O}{\overset{\|}{C}}-OH$	Ethanoic acid (acetic acid)	Vinegar
Esters	$R-\overset{O}{\overset{\|}{C}}-OR'$	-oate	—	$CH_3-\overset{O}{\overset{\|}{C}}-OCH_3$	Methyl ethanoate (methyl acetate)	Laboratory solvent
Aldehydes	$R-\overset{O}{\overset{\|}{C}}-H$	-al	oxo-	$CH_3-\overset{O}{\overset{\|}{C}}-H$	Ethanal (acetaldehyde)	Perfumes, flavours
Ketones	$R-\overset{O}{\overset{\|}{C}}-R'$	-one	oxo-	$CH_3-\overset{O}{\overset{\|}{C}}-CH_3$	Propanone (acetone)	Fingernail polish remover
Alcohols	$R-OH$	-ol	hydroxy-	CH_3CH_2-OH	Ethanol	Alcohol in fermented beverages
Amines	$R-NH_2$	-amine	amino-	$CH_3CH_2-NH_2$	Ethyl amine	Smell of rotten fish
Ethers	$R-O-R'$	—	-oxy-	$CH_3CH_2-O-CH_2CH_3$	Ethoxyethane (diethyl ether)*	Anaesthetic
Halides		—		CH_3-I	Iodomethane (methyl iodide)	Soil fumigant
-F	$R-F$		fluoro-			
-Cl	$R-Cl$		chloro-			
-Br	$R-Br$		bromo-			
-I	$R-I$		iodo-			

*An alternate way to name simple ethers is to list the two alkyl groups bonded to the oxygen atom, followed by the word ether. For example, $CH_3CH_2OCH_3$ can be named *ethyl methyl ether*.

Whenever there are two or more functional groups, one suffix and one or more prefixes are used to list the groups in the name of the compound. The **principal group** is determined by an order of group priorities. Table 3.6 is listed in decreasing order of priority. The suffix for the principal group is used in the name. For the other groups, prefixes are used. For example, consider the following molecule:

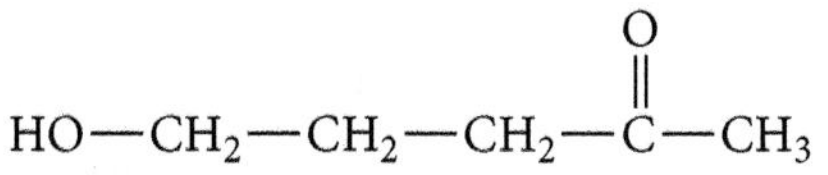

$$HO{-}CH_2{-}CH_2{-}CH_2{-}\overset{\overset{\displaystyle O}{\|}}{C}{-}CH_3$$

This molecule contains two functional groups: an alcohol and a ketone. According to Table 3.6, the principal group is the ketone. Thus, the suffix *–one* will be used. For the alcohol group, the prefix *hydroxy–* will be used. There are five carbons in the longest chain, so the base name is *pentane*. Locants are used to give the locations of the functional groups. Numbering starts from the end closest to the principal group. This compound is named 5-hydroxypentan-2-one.

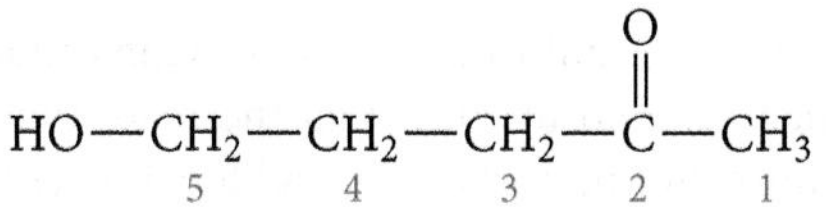

$$\underset{}{HO}{-}\underset{5}{CH_2}{-}\underset{4}{CH_2}{-}\underset{3}{CH_2}{-}\underset{2}{\overset{\overset{\displaystyle O}{\|}}{C}}{-}\underset{1}{CH_3}$$

5-Hydroxypentan-2-one

Example 3.9 illustrates how to name functionalized hydrocarbons.

EXAMPLE 3.9 NAMING FUNCTIONALIZED HYDROCARBONS

Name the following compounds:

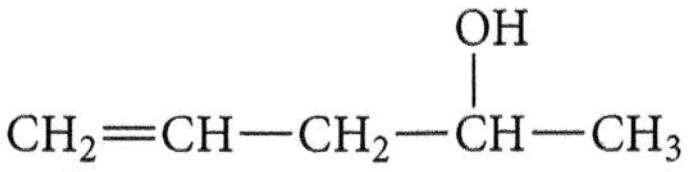

(a)

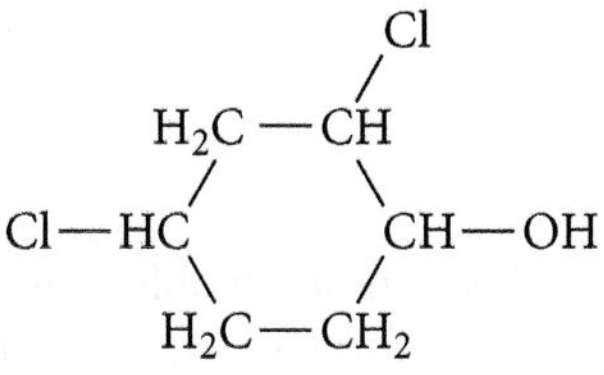

$$CH_2{=}CH{-}CH_2{-}\overset{\overset{\displaystyle OH}{|}}{C}H{-}CH_3$$

(b)

```
           Cl
          /
    H2C — CH
    /       \
Cl—HC        CH—OH
    \       /
    H2C — CH2
```

SOLUTION

(a) 1. Identify the base name of the hydrocarbon by locating the longest carbon chain.	This compound has a five-carbon chain (prefix = *pent–*). The compound contains a double bond, making it an alkene. 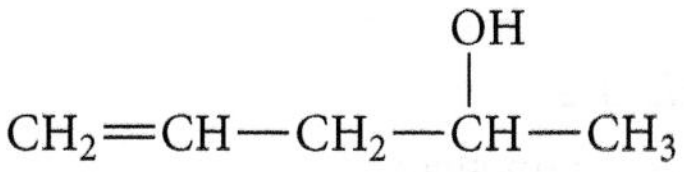 $CH_2{=}CH{-}CH_2{-}\overset{\overset{OH}{\mid}}{C}H{-}CH_3$ The base name is *pentene*. At this step, there is no locant for the double bond. This will be added in step 4.
2. Identify functional groups and select the principal group and substituent groups. Determine the suffix and/or prefixes that will appear in the name.	Not including the double bond, the only functional group is the alcohol group. This is the principal group, and the suffix is *–ol.*
3. Assign numbers to the carbon atoms in the base chain, starting from the end closest to the principal group.	Numbers start from the end closest to the alcohol group: 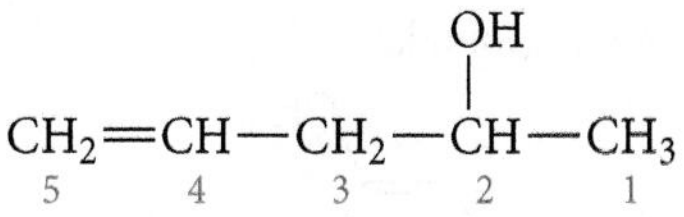 $\underset{5}{CH_2}{=}\underset{4}{CH}{-}\underset{3}{CH_2}{-}\underset{2}{\overset{\overset{OH}{\mid}}{C}H}{-}\underset{1}{CH_3}$
4. If the base chain is an alkene or alkyne, modify the base name to include the locant for the double or triple bond.	The base name from step 1 was pentene. The locant for the double bond is 4. This gives a base name of *pent-4-ene*. The last *e* of the base name will be dropped in the final name.
5. Construct the name according to this form: (locant)-(substituent prefix)-(base name)-(locant)(principal group suffix)	There are no substituent groups, so the name is: *pent-4-en-2-ol*.

(continued)

EXAMPLE 3.9 (CONTINUED)

(b) 1. Identify the base name of the hydrocarbon by locating the longest carbon chain.	The compound contains a six-membered ring. There are no double bonds. It is a cycloalkane. 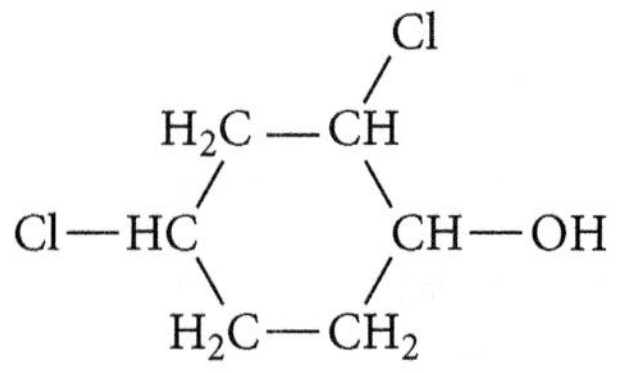 Cl / H_2C—CH / \\ Cl—HC CH—OH \\ / H_2C—CH_2 The base name is *cyclohexane*.
2. Identify functional groups and select the principal group and substituent groups. Determine the suffix and/or prefixes that will appear in the name.	There are two types of functional groups: OH (principal group, suffix = *–ol*) Cl (substituent group, prefix = *chloro–*) There are two chlorines, which means that an additional prefix *di–* must be used to show that there are two chlorine substituents. The prefix will be *dichloro–*, and locants will appear in the name.
3. Assign numbers to the carbon atoms in the base chain, starting from the end closest to the principal group.	This is a cycloalkane, and the numbering starts at the principal group and continues around the ring. Numbers are chosen so as to use the smallest numbers as locants for the substituent groups. 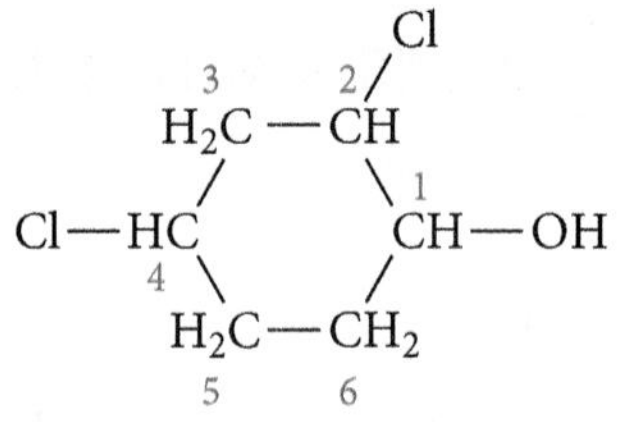 Cl 3 2/ H_2C—CH / \\ 1 Cl—HC CH—OH 4 \\ / H_2C—CH_2 5 6
4, 5. If the base chain is an alkene or alkyne, modify the base name to include the locant for the double or triple bond. Construct the name according to the form: (locant)-(substituent prefix)-(base name)-(locant)(principal group suffix)	There are no double bonds, so the base name is *cyclohexane*. The last *e* of the base name is dropped in the final name. The locants for the chlorine atoms are 2 and 4. The name is: *2,4-dichlorocyclohexanol.*

FOR PRACTICE 3.9

Name the following compounds:

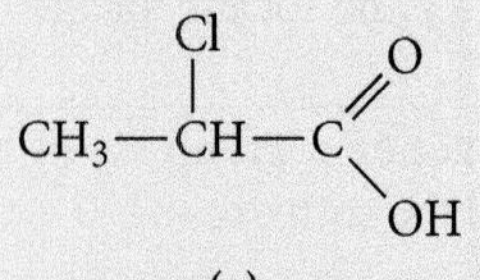

```
   Cl     O              O        O
   |    //               ||       ||
CH3—CH—C          CH3—C—CH2—C—CH3
        \
         OH
   (a)                      (b)
```

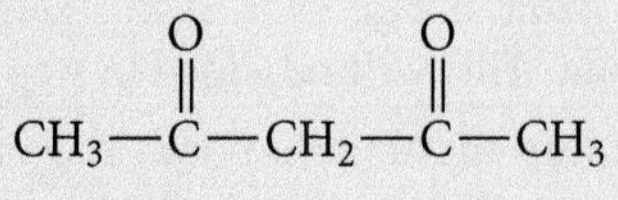

FOR MORE PRACTICE 3.9

Name the following compounds:

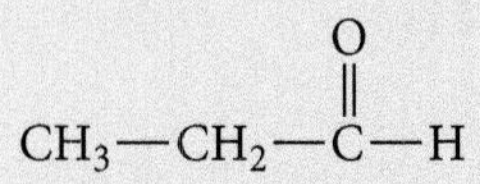

```
            O              CH3
            ||
CH3—CH2—C—H       (benzene ring)—Br
                            |
                            Br
    (a)                  (b)
```

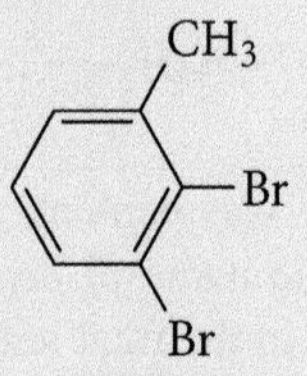

3.6 Formula Mass and the Mole Concept for Compounds

In Chapter 2, we defined the average mass of an atom of an element as its *atomic mass*. Similarly, we now define the average mass of a molecule (or a formula unit) of a compound as its **formula mass**. (The common terms *molecular mass* or *molecular weight* are synonymous with formula mass.) For any compound, the formula mass is the sum of the atomic masses of all the atoms in its chemical formula.

$$\text{Formula mass} = \left(\begin{array}{c}\text{Number of atoms}\\ \text{of 1st element in}\\ \text{chemical formula}\end{array} \times \begin{array}{c}\text{Atomic mass}\\ \text{of}\\ \text{1st element}\end{array}\right) + \left(\begin{array}{c}\text{Number of atoms}\\ \text{of 2nd element in}\\ \text{chemical formula}\end{array} \times \begin{array}{c}\text{Atomic mass}\\ \text{of}\\ \text{2nd element}\end{array}\right) + \dots$$

For example, the formula mass of carbon dioxide, CO_2, is the following:

Multiply by 2 because formula has 2 oxygen atoms.

$$\begin{aligned}\text{Formula mass} &= 12.01\text{ u} + 2(16.00\text{ u})\\ &= 44.01\text{ u}\end{aligned}$$

and that of sodium oxide, Na_2O, is this:

Multiply by 2 because formula has 2 sodium atoms.

$$\begin{aligned}\text{Formula mass} &= 2(22.99\text{ u}) + 16.00\text{ u}\\ &= 61.98\text{ u}\end{aligned}$$

EXAMPLE 3.10 CALCULATING FORMULA MASS

Calculate the formula mass of glucose, $C_6H_{12}O_6$.

SOLUTION

To find the formula mass, we add the atomic masses of each atom in the chemical formula:

$$\begin{aligned}\text{Formula mass} &= 6 \times (\text{atomic mass C}) + 12 \times (\text{atomic mass H}) + 6 \times (\text{atomic mass O})\\ &= 6(12.01\text{ u}) + 12(1.008\text{ u}) + 6(16.00\text{ u})\\ &= 180.16\text{ u}\end{aligned}$$

FOR PRACTICE 3.10

Calculate the formula mass of calcium nitrate.

Molar Mass of a Compound

In Chapter 2 (Section 2.9), we learned that an element's molar mass—the mass in grams of one mole of its atoms—is numerically equivalent to its atomic mass. We then used the molar mass in combination with Avogadro's number to determine the number of atoms in a given mass of the element. The same concept applies to compounds. The *molar mass of a compound*—the mass in grams of 1 mol of its molecules or formula units—is numerically equivalent to its formula mass. For example, we just calculated the formula mass of CO_2 to be 44.01 u. The molar mass is, therefore:

$$CO_2\text{ molar mass} = 44.01\text{ g mol}^{-1}$$

Remember, ionic compounds do not contain individual molecules. In casual language, the smallest electrically neutral collection of ions is sometimes called a molecule but is more correctly called a formula unit.

Using Molar Mass to Count Molecules by Weighing

The molar mass of CO_2 is a conversion factor between mass (in grams) and amount (in moles) of CO_2. Suppose we want to find the number of CO_2 molecules in a sample of dry ice (solid CO_2) with a mass of 10.8 g. This calculation is analogous to Example 2.4 in Chapter 2, where we found the number of moles in a sample of copper of a given mass. We begin with the mass of 10.8 g and use the molar mass to convert to the amount in moles. Then we use Avogadro's number to convert to number of molecules. The conceptual plan is as follows:

Conceptual Plan

$g\ CO_2 \xrightarrow{\frac{1\ \text{mol}\ CO_2}{44.01\ g\ CO_2}} \text{mol}\ CO_2 \xrightarrow{\frac{6.022 \times 10^{23}\ CO_2\ \text{molecules}}{1\ \text{mol}\ CO_2}} CO_2\ \text{molecules}$

To solve the problem, we follow the conceptual plan, beginning with 10.8 g CO_2, converting to moles, and then to molecules.

Solution

$$10.8\ g\ CO_2 \times \frac{1\ \text{mol}\ CO_2}{44.01\ g\ CO_2} \times \frac{6.022 \times 10^{23}\ CO_2\ \text{molecules}}{1\ \text{mol}\ CO_2} = 1.48 \times 10^{23}\ CO_2\ \text{molecules}$$

EXAMPLE 3.11 THE MOLE CONCEPT—CONVERTING BETWEEN MASS AND NUMBER OF MOLES

An aspirin tablet contains 325 mg of acetylsalicylic acid ($C_9H_8O_4$). How many moles of acetylsalicylic acid does it contain?

SORT You are given the mass of acetylsalicylic acid and asked to find the number of moles.	**GIVEN:** 325 mg $C_9H_8O_4$ **FIND:** moles of $C_9H_8O_4$
STRATEGIZE First convert to moles (using the molar mass of the compound). You will need the molar mass of acetylsalicylic acid as a conversion factor. You will also need the conversion factor between g and mg.	**CONCEPTUAL PLAN** $\text{mg}\ C_9H_8O_4 \xrightarrow{\frac{10^{-3}\ g}{1\ \text{mg}}} g\ C_9H_8O_4 \xrightarrow{\frac{1\ \text{mol}\ C_9H_8O_4}{180.15\ g\ C_9H_8O_4}} \text{mol}\ C_9H_8O_4$ **RELATIONSHIPS USED** $C_9H_8O_4$ molar mass $= 9(12.01) + 8(1.008) + 4(16.00) = 180.15\ g\ \text{mol}^{-1}$ $1\ \text{mg} = 10^{-3}\ g$
SOLVE Follow the conceptual plan to solve the problem.	**SOLUTION** $325\ \text{mg}\ C_9H_8O_4 \times \frac{10^{-3}\ g}{1\ \text{mg}} \times \frac{1\ \text{mol}\ C_9H_8O_4}{180.15\ g\ C_9H_8O_4} = 1.80 \times 10^{-3}\ \text{mol}$

CHECK The units of the answer, moles, are correct. As expected, the number of moles is smaller than the mass of the acetylsalicylic acid in the tablet, in grams (i.e., 0.325 g).

FOR PRACTICE 3.11
Find the number of moles of ibuprofen in a tablet containing 200.0 mg of ibuprofen ($C_{13}H_{18}O_2$).

FOR MORE PRACTICE 3.11
What is the mass of a sample of water containing 0.0590 mol of water?

3.7 Composition of Compounds

A chemical formula, in combination with the molar masses of its constituent elements, indicates the relative quantities of each element in a compound, which is extremely useful information. For example, about 30 years ago, scientists began to suspect that synthetic compounds known as chlorofluorocarbons (or CFCs) were destroying ozone (O_3) in Earth's upper atmosphere. Upper atmospheric ozone is important because it acts as a shield, protecting life on Earth from the sun's harmful ultraviolet light.

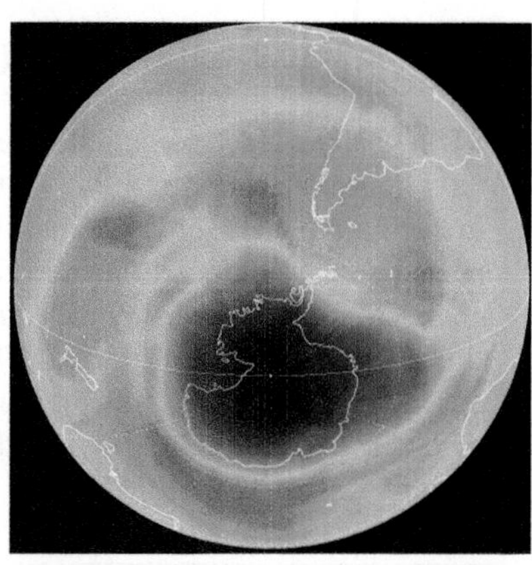

▲ The chlorine in chlorofluorocarbons caused the ozone hole over Antarctica. The dark blue colour indicates depressed ozone levels.

CFCs are chemically inert compounds that were used primarily as refrigerants and industrial solvents. Over time, CFCs began to accumulate in the atmosphere. In the upper atmosphere, sunlight breaks bonds within CFCs, releasing chlorine atoms. The chlorine atoms then react with ozone, converting it into O_2. So, the harmful part of CFCs is the chlorine atoms that they carry. How do you determine the mass of chlorine in a given mass of a CFC?

One way to express how much of an element is in a given compound is to use the element's mass percent composition for that compound. The **mass percent composition** or **mass percent** of an element is that element's percentage of the compound's total mass. The mass percent of element X in a compound can be computed from the chemical formula as follows:

$$\text{mass percent of element X} = \frac{\text{mass of element X in 1 mol of compound}}{\text{mass of 1 mol of the compound}} \times 100\%$$

Suppose, for example, that we want to calculate the mass percent composition of Cl in the chlorofluorocarbon CCl_2F_2. The mass percent Cl is given by:

CCl_2F_2

$$\text{Mass percent Cl} = \frac{2 \times \text{Molar mass Cl}}{\text{Molar mass } CCl_2F_2} \times 100\%$$

The molar mass of Cl must be multiplied by 2 because the chemical formula has a subscript of 2 for Cl, indicating that 1 mol of CCl_2F_2 contains 2 mol of Cl atoms. We calculate the molar mass of CCl_2F_2 as follows:

$$\begin{aligned}\text{Molar mass} &= 12.01\,\text{g mol}^{-1} + 2(35.45\,\text{g mol}^{-1}) + 2(19.00\,\text{g mol}^{-1})\\ &= 120.91\,\text{g mol}^{-1}\end{aligned}$$

So the mass percent of Cl in CCl_2F_2 is

$$\begin{aligned}\text{Mass percent Cl} &= \frac{2 \times \text{molar mass Cl}}{\text{molar mass } CCl_2F_2} \times 100\%\\ &= \frac{2 \times 35.45\,\cancel{\text{g mol}^{-1}}}{120.91\,\cancel{\text{g mol}^{-1}}} \times 100\%\\ &= 58.64\%\end{aligned}$$

EXAMPLE 3.12 MASS PERCENT COMPOSITION

Calculate the mass percent of Cl in Freon-112 ($C_2Cl_4F_2$), a CFC refrigerant.

SORT You are given the molecular formula of Freon-112 and asked to find the mass percent of Cl.	**GIVEN:** $C_2Cl_4F_2$ **FIND:** mass percent of Cl

(continued)

EXAMPLE 3.12 (CONTINUED)

STRATEGIZE The molecular formula tells you that there are 4 mol of Cl in each mole of Freon-112. Find the mass percent composition from the chemical formula by using the equation that defines mass percent. The conceptual plan shows how the mass of Cl in 1 mol of $C_2Cl_4F_2$ and the molar mass of $C_2Cl_4F_2$ are used to find the mass percent of Cl.

CONCEPTUAL PLAN

$$\text{Mass\% Cl} = \frac{4 \times \text{molar mass Cl}}{\text{molar mass } C_2Cl_4F_2} \times 100\%$$

RELATIONSHIPS USED

$$\text{Mass percent of element X} = \frac{\text{mass of element X in 1 mol of compound}}{\text{mass of 1 mol of compound}} \times 100\%$$

SOLVE Calculate the necessary parts of the equation and substitute the values into the equation to find the mass percent of Cl.

SOLUTION

$$4 \times \text{molar mass Cl} = 4(35.45 \text{ g mol}^{-1}) = 141.8 \text{ g mol}^{-1}$$

$$\begin{aligned}\text{Molar mass } C_2Cl_4F_2 &= 2(12.01 \text{ g mol}^{-1}) + 4(35.45 \text{ g mol}^{-1}) + 2(19.00 \text{ g mol}^{-1}) \\ &= 24.02 \text{ g mol}^{-1} + 141.8 \text{ g mol}^{-1} + 38.00 \text{ g mol}^{-1} \\ &= 203.8 \text{ g mol}^{-1}\end{aligned}$$

$$\begin{aligned}\text{Mass Cl} &= \frac{4 \times \text{molar mass Cl}}{\text{molar mass } C_2Cl_4F_2} \times 100\% \\ &= \frac{141.8 \cancel{\text{g mol}^{-1}}}{203.8 \cancel{\text{g mol}^{-1}}} \times 100\% \\ &= 69.58\%\end{aligned}$$

CHECK The units of the answer (%) are correct and the magnitude is reasonable because (a) it is between 0 and 100%, and (b) chlorine is the heaviest atom in the molecule and there are four of them.

FOR PRACTICE 3.12

Acetic acid ($C_2H_4O_2$) is the active ingredient in vinegar. Calculate the mass percent composition of oxygen in acetic acid.

FOR MORE PRACTICE 3.12

Calculate the mass percent composition of sodium in sodium oxide.

Conversion Factors in Chemical Formulas

Chemical formulas contain within them inherent relationships between atoms (or moles of atoms) and molecules (or moles of molecules). For example, the formula for CCl_2F_2 tells us that 1 mol of CCl_2F_2 contains 2 mol of Cl atoms. We write the ratio as follows:

$$1 \text{ mol } CCl_2F_2 : 2 \text{ mol Cl}$$

With ratios such as these—that come from the chemical formula—we can directly determine the amounts of the constituent elements present in a given amount of a compound without having to compute mass percent composition. For example, we calculate the number of moles of Cl in 38.5 mol of CCl_2F_2 as follows:

Conceptual Plan

$$\text{mol } CCl_2F_2 \xrightarrow{\frac{2 \text{ mol Cl}}{1 \text{ mol } CCl_2F_2}} \text{mol Cl}$$

Solution

$$38.5 \cancel{\text{mol } CCl_2F_2} \times \frac{2 \text{ mol Cl}}{1 \cancel{\text{mol } CCl_2F_2}} = 77.0 \text{ mol Cl}$$

However, we often want to know the *mass in grams* (or other units) of a constituent element in a given *mass* of the compound, not the *amount in moles* of an element in a certain number of moles of compound. Suppose we want to know the mass (in grams) of Cl contained in 25.0 g CCl_2F_2. The relationship inherent in the chemical formula (2 mol Cl : 1 mol CCl_2F_2) applies to the amount in moles, not to mass. Therefore, we first convert the mass of CCl_2F_2 to moles CCl_2F_2. *Then* we use the conversion factor from the chemical formula to convert to moles Cl. Finally, we use the molar mass of Cl to convert to grams Cl.

Conceptual Plan

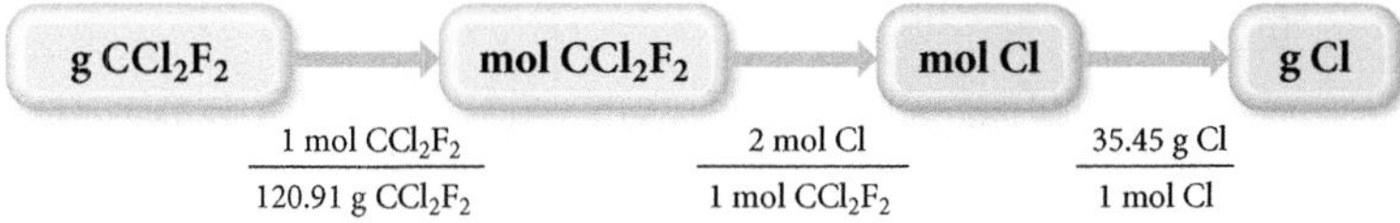

$\frac{1\text{ mol }CCl_2F_2}{120.91\text{ g }CCl_2F_2}$ $\frac{2\text{ mol Cl}}{1\text{ mol }CCl_2F_2}$ $\frac{35.45\text{ g Cl}}{1\text{ mol Cl}}$

Solution

$$25.0\text{ g }CCl_2F_2 \times \frac{1\text{ mol }CCl_2F_2}{120.91\text{ g }CCl_2F_2} \times \frac{2\text{ mol Cl}}{1\text{ mol }CCl_2F_2} \times \frac{35.45\text{ g Cl}}{1\text{ mol Cl}} = 14.7\text{ g Cl}$$

Notice that we must convert from g CCl_2F_2 to mol CCl_2F_2 *before* we can use the chemical formula as a conversion factor. *Always remember that the chemical formula gives us a relationship between the amounts (in moles) of substances, not between the masses (in grams) of them.*

The general form for solving problems where you are asked to find the mass of an element present in a given mass of a compound is:

Mass compound ⟶ moles compound ⟶ moles element ⟶ mass element

The conversions between mass and moles are accomplished using the atomic or molar mass, and the conversion between moles of an element within the formula and moles of complete molecules within that formula is accomplished using the relationships inherent in the chemical formula.

EXAMPLE 3.13 CHEMICAL FORMULAS AS CONVERSION FACTORS

Hydrogen may be used in the future to replace gasoline as a fuel. Most major automobile companies are developing vehicles that run on hydrogen. These cars are deemed environmentally friendly because their only emission is water vapour. One way to obtain hydrogen for fuel is to use an emission-free energy source such as wind power to form elemental hydrogen from water. What mass of hydrogen (in grams) is contained in 1.00 litre of water? (The density of water is 1.00 g mL^{-1}.)

SORT You are given a volume of water and asked to find the mass of hydrogen it contains. You are also given the density of water.	**GIVEN:** 1.00 L H_2O $d_{H_2O} = 1.00\text{ g mL}^{-1}$ **FIND:** g H
STRATEGIZE The first part of the conceptual plan shows how to convert the units of volume from litres to mL. It also shows how you can then use the density to convert mL to g. The second part of the conceptual plan is the basic sequence of mass → moles → moles → mass. Convert between moles and mass using the appropriate molar masses, and convert from mol H_2O to mol H using the conversion factor derived from the molecular formula.	**CONCEPTUAL PLAN** 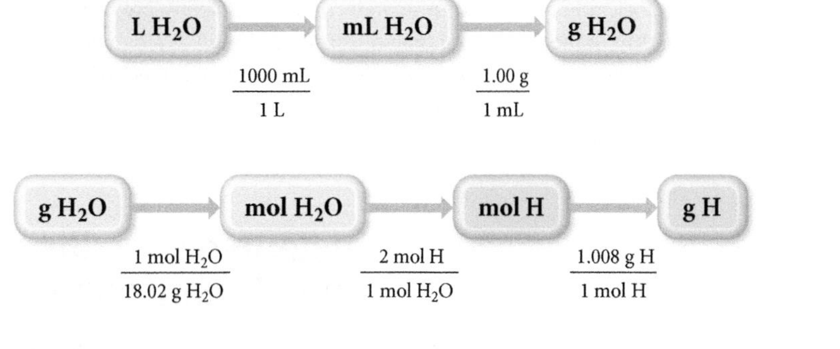

(*continued*)

EXAMPLE 3.13 (CONTINUED)

RELATIONSHIPS USED

1000 mL = 1 L
$1.00 \text{ g } H_2O = 1 \text{ mL } H_2O$ (density of H_2O)
molar mass $H_2O = 2(1.008) + 16.00 = 18.02 \text{ g mol}^{-1}$
$2 \text{ mol H} : 1 \text{ mol } H_2O$
$1.008 \text{ g H} = 1 \text{ mol H}$

SOLVE Follow the conceptual plan to solve the problem.

SOLUTION

$$1.00 \cancel{\text{L}}\, H_2O \times \frac{1000 \cancel{\text{mL}}}{1 \cancel{\text{L}}} \times \frac{1.00 \text{ g } H_2O}{1 \cancel{\text{mL}}\, H_2O} = 1.0\underline{0}0 \times 10^3 \text{ g } H_2O$$

$$1.0\underline{0}0 \times 10^3 \cancel{\text{g } H_2O} \times \frac{1 \cancel{\text{mol } H_2O}}{18.02 \cancel{\text{g } H_2O}} \times \frac{2 \cancel{\text{mol H}}}{1 \cancel{\text{mol } H_2O}} \times \frac{1.008 \text{ g H}}{1 \cancel{\text{mol H}}} = 1.12 \times 10^2 \text{ g H}$$

CHECK The units of the answer (g H) are correct, since a litre of water is about 1 kg. H is a light atom, so its mass should be significantly less than 1 kg, as it is in the answer.

FOR PRACTICE 3.13

Determine the mass of oxygen in a 7.2 g sample of $Al_2(SO_4)_3$.

FOR MORE PRACTICE 3.13

Butane (C_4H_{10}) is the liquid fuel in lighters. How many grams of carbon are present within a lighter containing 7.25 mL of butane? (The density of liquid butane is 0.601 g mL^{-1}.)

CHEMISTRY IN YOUR DAY Drug Tablets

Most of us have swallowed a pill, such as a tablet of ASA or acetaminophen to relieve a headache, a daily vitamin, or an antibiotic or some other pharmaceutical. The composition of drug tablets is probably more complex than you might realize. Tablets contain more than just the pharmaceutical. For example, the mass of the ASA tablet in the picture is 0.39920 g. However, the label on the bottle says that each ASA tablet contains 320 mg of ASA. That means that the percent of ASA in this tablet is:

$$\frac{320 \text{ mg ASA}}{0.39920 \text{ g tablet}} \times \frac{1 \text{ g}}{1000 \text{ mg}} \times 100\% = 80.2\%$$

The other 19.8% is a mixture of binders, lubricants, and a coating. Binders in tablets are compounds that hold it together in the desired shape. Starch is a common binder. Lubricants are used so that the tablet does not stick to manufacturing equipment. An example of a lubricant is magnesium stearate, which has soapy properties. Coatings are often used to keep the tablet from dissolving too quickly in the stomach. Some drugs, including ASA, can damage the stomach lining. The tablet coating slows the release of ASA and can alleviate some of the discomfort that many people get when they take ASA.

3.8 Determining a Chemical Formula from Experimental Data

In Section 3.7, we learned how to calculate mass percent composition from a chemical formula. Can we also do the reverse? Can we calculate a chemical formula from mass percent composition? This question is important because many laboratory analyses of compounds give the relative masses of each element present in the compound. For example, if we decompose water into hydrogen and oxygen in the laboratory, we can measure the masses of hydrogen and oxygen produced. Can we get a chemical formula from this kind of data? The answer is a qualified yes. We can determine a chemical formula, but it is an empirical formula (not a molecular formula). To get a molecular formula, we need additional information, such as the molar mass of the compound.

Suppose we decompose a sample of water in the laboratory and find that it produces 0.857 g of hydrogen and 6.86 g of oxygen. How do we get an empirical formula from these data? We know that an empirical formula represents a ratio of atoms or a ratio of moles of atoms, *not a ratio of masses*. So, the first thing we must do is convert our data from mass (in grams) to amount (in moles). How many moles of each element are present in the sample? To convert to moles, we divide each mass by the molar mass of that element:

$$\text{Moles H} = 0.857\,\cancel{\text{g H}} \times \frac{1\,\text{mol H}}{1.008\,\cancel{\text{g H}}} = 0.850\,\text{mol H}$$

$$\text{Moles O} = 6.86\,\cancel{\text{g O}} \times \frac{1\,\text{mol O}}{16.00\,\cancel{\text{g O}}} = 0.429\,\text{mol O}$$

From these data, we know there are 0.850 mol H for every 0.429 mol O. We can now write a pseudoformula for water:

$$H_{0.850}O_{0.429}$$

To get the smallest whole-number subscripts in our formula, we divide all the subscripts by the smallest one; in this case, 0.429:

$$H_{\frac{0.850}{0.429}}O_{\frac{0.429}{0.429}} = H_{1.98}O_1 = H_2O$$

Our empirical formula for water, which also happens to be the molecular formula, is H_2O. You can use the following procedure to obtain the empirical formula of any compound from experimental data giving the relative masses of the constituent elements. The left column outlines the procedure, and the centre and right columns show two examples of how to apply the procedure.

PROCEDURE FOR ... **Obtaining an Empirical Formula from Experimental Data**	**EXAMPLE 3.14** **Obtaining an Empirical Formula from Experimental Data** A compound containing nitrogen and oxygen is decomposed in the laboratory and produces 24.5 g nitrogen and 70.0 g oxygen. Calculate the empirical formula of the compound.	**EXAMPLE 3.15** **Obtaining an Empirical Formula from Experimental Data** A laboratory analysis of aspirin determined the following mass percent composition: C 60.00% H 4.48% O 35.52% Find the empirical formula.
1. Write down (or compute) as given the masses of each element present in a sample of the compound. If you are given mass percent composition, assume a 100 g sample and compute the masses of each element from the given percentages.	**GIVEN:** 24.5 g N, 70.0 g O **FIND:** empirical formula	**GIVEN:** In a 100 g sample: 60.00 g C, 4.48 g H, 35.52 g O **FIND:** empirical formula
2. Convert each of the masses in step 1 to moles by using the appropriate molar mass for each element as a conversion factor.	$24.5\,\cancel{\text{g N}} \times \frac{1\,\text{mol N}}{14.01\,\cancel{\text{g N}}} = 1.75\,\text{mol N}$ $70.0\,\cancel{\text{g O}} \times \frac{1\,\text{mol O}}{16.00\,\cancel{\text{g O}}} = 4.38\,\text{mol O}$	$60.00\,\cancel{\text{g C}} \times \frac{1\,\text{mol C}}{12.01\,\cancel{\text{g C}}} = 4.996\,\text{mol C}$ $4.48\,\cancel{\text{g H}} \times \frac{1\,\text{mol H}}{1.008\,\cancel{\text{g H}}} = 4.44\,\text{mol H}$ $35.52\,\cancel{\text{g O}} \times \frac{1\,\text{mol O}}{16.00\,\cancel{\text{g O}}} = 2.220\,\text{mol O}$

(continued)

PROCEDURE FOR ... *(continued)*	EXAMPLE 3.14 *(continued)*	EXAMPLE 3.15 *(continued)*
3. Write down a pseudoformula for the compound using the number of moles of each element (from step 2) as subscripts.	$N_{1.75}O_{4.38}$	$C_{4.996}H_{4.44}O_{2.220}$
4. Divide all the subscripts in the formula by the smallest subscript.	$N_{\frac{1.75}{1.75}}O_{\frac{4.38}{1.75}} \longrightarrow N_1O_{2.50}$	$C_{\frac{4.996}{2.220}}H_{\frac{4.44}{2.220}}O_{\frac{2.220}{2.220}} \longrightarrow C_{2.25}H_2O_1$
5. If the subscripts are not whole numbers, multiply all the subscripts by a small whole number (see table) to get whole-number subscripts.	$N_1O_{2.50} \times 2 \longrightarrow N_2O_5$ The correct empirical formula is N_2O_5.	$C_{2.25}H_2O_1 \times 4 \longrightarrow C_9H_8O_4$ The correct empirical formula is $C_9H_8O_4$.

Decimal Subscript	Equivalent Fraction	Multiply by
0.20	1/5	5
0.25	1/4	4
0.33	1/3	3
0.40	2/5	5
0.50	1/2	2
0.66	2/3	3
0.75	3/4	4
0.80	4/5	5

FOR PRACTICE 3.14

A sample of a compound is decomposed in the laboratory and produces 165 g carbon, 27.8 g hydrogen, and 220.2 g oxygen. Calculate the empirical formula of the compound.

FOR PRACTICE 3.15

Ibuprofen has the following mass percent composition:

C 75.69%, H 8.80%, O 15.51%

What is the empirical formula of ibuprofen?

Calculating Molecular Formulas for Compounds

We can find the molecular formula of a compound from the empirical formula if we also know the molar mass of the compound. Recall from Section 3.3 that the molecular formula is always a whole-number multiple of the empirical formula:

$$\text{Molecular formula} = \text{empirical formula} \times n, \text{where } n = 1, 2, 3, \ldots$$

Suppose we want to find the molecular formula for fructose (a sugar found in fruit) from its empirical formula, CH_2O, and its molar mass, 180.16 g mol^{-1}. We know that the molecular formula is a whole-number multiple of CH_2O:

$$\begin{aligned}\text{Molecular formula} &= (CH_2O) \times n \\ &= C_nH_{2n}O_n\end{aligned}$$

We also know that the molar mass is a whole-number multiple of the **empirical formula molar mass**, the sum of the masses of all the atoms in the empirical formula.

$$\text{Molar mass} = \text{empirical formula molar mass} \times n$$

For a particular compound, the value of n in both cases is the same. Therefore, we can find n by computing the ratio of the molar mass to the empirical formula molar mass:

$$n = \frac{\text{molar mass}}{\text{empirical formula molar mass}}$$

For fructose, the empirical formula molar mass is:

$$\begin{aligned}&\text{Empirical formula molar mass} \\ &= 12.01 \text{ g mol}^{-1} + 2(1.008 \text{ g mol}^{-1}) + 16.00 \text{ g mol}^{-1} = 30.03 \text{ g mol}^{-1}\end{aligned}$$

Therefore, n is:

$$n = \frac{180.16 \cancel{\text{g mol}^{-1}}}{30.03 \cancel{\text{g mol}^{-1}}} = 6$$

We can then use this value of n to find the molecular formula:

$$\text{Molecular formula} = (CH_2O) \times 6 = C_6H_{12}O_6$$

EXAMPLE 3.16 CALCULATING A MOLECULAR FORMULA FROM AN EMPIRICAL FORMULA AND MOLAR MASS

Butanedione—a main component responsible for the smell and taste of butter and cheese—contains the elements carbon, hydrogen, and oxygen. The empirical formula of butanedione is C_2H_3O and its molar mass is 86.09 g mol^{-1}. Find its molecular formula.

SORT You are given the empirical formula and molar mass of butanedione and asked to find the molecular formula.	**GIVEN:** empirical formula $= C_2H_3O$ molar mass $= 86.09\ \text{g mol}^{-1}$ **FIND:** molecular formula
STRATEGIZE A molecular formula is always a whole-number multiple of the empirical formula. Divide the molar mass by the empirical formula molar mass to get the whole number.	Molecular formula = empirical formula $\times\ n$ $n = \dfrac{\text{molar mass}}{\text{empirical formula molar mass}}$
SOLVE Compute the empirical formula molar mass.	Empirical formula molar mass $= 2(12.01\ \text{g mol}^{-1}) + 3(1.008\ \text{g mol}^{-1}) + 16.00\ \text{g mol}^{-1}$ $= 43.04\ \text{g mol}^{-1}$
Divide the molar mass by the empirical formula molar mass to find n.	$n = \dfrac{\text{molar mass}}{\text{empirical formula molar mass}} = \dfrac{86.09\ \cancel{\text{g mol}^{-1}}}{43.04\ \cancel{\text{g mol}^{-1}}} = 2$
Multiply the empirical formula by n to obtain the molecular formula.	Molecular formula $= C_2H_3O \times 2$ $= C_4H_6O_2$

CHECK Check the answer by computing the molar mass of the computed formula as follows:

$$4(12.01\ \text{g mol}^{-1}) + 6(1.008\ \text{g mol}^{-1}) + 2(16.00\ \text{g mol}^{-1}) = 86.09\ \text{g mol}^{-1}$$

The computed molar mass is in agreement with the given molar mass.

FOR PRACTICE 3.16

A compound has the empirical formula CH and a molar mass of 78.11 g mol^{-1}. What is its molecular formula?

FOR MORE PRACTICE 3.16

A compound with the mass percent composition shown below has a molar mass of 60.10 g mol^{-1}. Find its molecular formula.

39.97% C
13.41% H
46.62% N

CONCEPTUAL CONNECTION 3.4

Chemical Formula and Mass Percent Composition

Without doing any calculations, order the elements in the following compound in order of decreasing mass percent composition.

C_6H_6O

Combustion Analysis

In the previous section, we learned how to compute the empirical formula of a compound from the relative masses of its constituent elements. Another common (and related) way of obtaining empirical formulas for unknown compounds, especially those containing carbon and hydrogen, is **combustion analysis**. In combustion analysis, the unknown compound undergoes combustion (or burning) in the presence of pure oxygen, as shown in Figure 3.9 ▼. When the sample is burned, all of the carbon in the sample is converted to CO_2 and all of the hydrogen is converted to H_2O. The CO_2 and H_2O produced are weighed. With these masses, we can use the numerical relationships between moles inherent in the formulas for

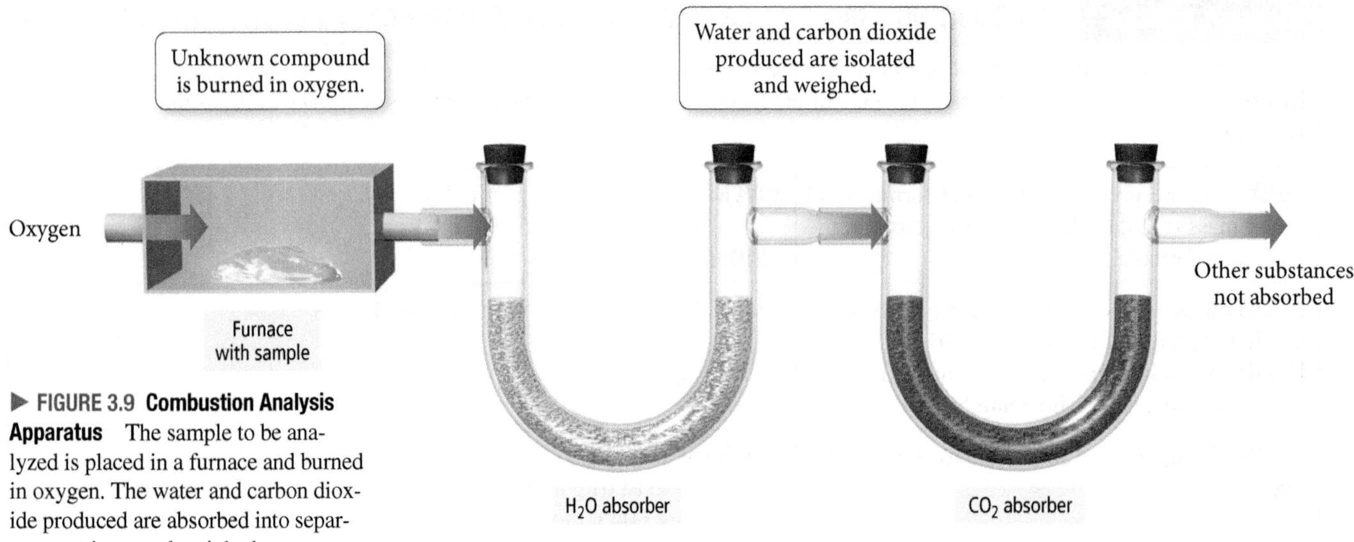
Unknown compound is burned in oxygen.
Water and carbon dioxide produced are isolated and weighed.
Oxygen
Furnace with sample
Other substances not absorbed
H_2O absorber
CO_2 absorber

▶ **FIGURE 3.9 Combustion Analysis Apparatus** The sample to be analyzed is placed in a furnace and burned in oxygen. The water and carbon dioxide produced are absorbed into separate containers and weighed.

CO_2 (1 mol CO_2 : 1 mol C) and H_2O (1 mol H_2O : 2 mol H) to determine the amounts of C and H in the original sample. Any other elemental constituents, such as O, Cl, or N, can be determined by subtracting the original mass of the sample from the sum of the masses of C and H. The following examples show how to perform these calculations for a sample containing only C and H and for a sample containing C, H, and O.

Combustion is a type of chemical reaction. We discuss chemical reactions and their representation in Chapter 4.

PROCEDURE FOR ... **Obtaining an Empirical Formula from Combustion Analysis**	EXAMPLE 3.17 **Obtaining an Empirical Formula from Combustion Analysis** Upon combustion, a compound containing only carbon and hydrogen produces 1.83 g CO_2 and 0.901 g H_2O. Find the empirical formula of the compound.	EXAMPLE 3.18 **Obtaining an Empirical Formula from Combustion Analysis** Upon combustion, a 0.8233 g sample of a compound containing only carbon, hydrogen, and oxygen produces 2.445 g CO_2 and 0.6003 g H_2O. Find the empirical formula of the compound.
1. Write down as given the masses of each combustion product and the mass of the sample (if given).	**GIVEN:** 1.83 g CO_2, 0.901 g H_2O **FIND:** empirical formula	**GIVEN:** 0.8233 g sample, 2.445 g CO_2, 0.6003 g H_2O **FIND:** empirical formula
2. Convert the masses of CO_2 and H_2O from step 1 to moles by using the appropriate molar mass for each compound as a conversion factor.	$1.83\ \text{g}\ \cancel{CO_2} \times \frac{1\ \text{mol}\ CO_2}{44.01\ \text{g}\ \cancel{CO_2}} = 0.0416\ \text{mol}\ CO_2$ $0.901\ \text{g}\ \cancel{H_2O} \times \frac{1\ \text{mol}\ H_2O}{18.02\ \text{g}\ \cancel{H_2O}} = 0.0500\ \text{mol}\ H_2O$	$2.445\ \text{g}\ \cancel{CO_2} \times \frac{1\ \text{mol}\ CO_2}{44.01\ \text{g}\ \cancel{CO_2}} = 0.05556\ \text{mol}\ CO_2$ $0.6003\ \text{g}\ \cancel{H_2O} \times \frac{1\ \text{mol}\ H_2O}{18.02\ \text{g}\ \cancel{H_2O}} = 0.03331\ \text{mol}\ H_2O$
3. Convert the moles of CO_2 and moles of H_2O from step 2 to moles of C and moles of H using the conversion factors inherent in the chemical formulas of CO_2 and H_2O.	$0.0416\ \cancel{\text{mol}\ CO_2} \times \frac{1\ \text{mol C}}{1\ \cancel{\text{mol}\ CO_2}} = 0.0416\ \text{mol C}$ $0.0500\ \cancel{\text{mol}\ H_2O} \times \frac{2\ \text{mol H}}{1\ \cancel{\text{mol}\ H_2O}} = 0.100\ \text{mol H}$	$0.05556\ \cancel{\text{mol}\ CO_2} \times \frac{1\ \text{mol C}}{1\ \cancel{\text{mol}\ CO_2}} = 0.05556\ \text{mol C}$ $0.03331\ \cancel{\text{mol}\ H_2O} \times \frac{2\ \text{mol H}}{1\ \cancel{\text{mol}\ H_2O}} = 0.06662\ \text{mol H}$

4. If the compound contains an element other than C and H, find the mass of the other element by subtracting the sum of the masses of C and H (obtained in step 3) from the mass of the sample. Finally, convert the mass of the other element to moles.	No other elements besides C and H, so proceed to next step.	Mass C $= 0.05556\ \text{mol C} \times \frac{12.01\ \text{g C}}{1\ \text{mol C}} = 0.6673\ \text{g C}$ Mass H $= 0.06662\ \text{mol H} \times \frac{1.008\ \text{g H}}{1\ \text{mol H}} = 0.06715\ \text{g H}$ Mass O $= 0.8233\ \text{g} - (0.6673\ \text{g} + 0.06715\ \text{g}) = 0.0889\ \text{g O}$ Mol O $= 0.0889\ \text{g O} \times \frac{1\ \text{mol O}}{16.00\ \text{g O}} = 0.00556\ \text{mol O}$
5. Write down a pseudoformula for the compound using the number of moles of each element (from steps 3 and 4) as subscripts.	$C_{0.0416}H_{0.100}$	$C_{0.05556}H_{0.06662}O_{0.00556}$
6. Divide all the subscripts in the formula by the smallest subscript. (Round all subscripts that are within 0.1 of a whole number, otherwise consult the table in Examples 3.14/3.15.)	$C_{\frac{0.0416}{0.0416}}H_{\frac{0.100}{0.0416}} \longrightarrow C_1H_{2.40}$	$C_{\frac{0.05556}{0.00556}}H_{\frac{0.06662}{0.00556}}O_{\frac{0.00556}{0.00556}} \longrightarrow C_{10}H_{12}O_1$
7. If the subscripts are not whole numbers, multiply all the subscripts by a small whole number to get whole-number subscripts.	$C_1H_{2.40} \times 5 \longrightarrow C_5H_{12}$ The correct empirical formula is C_5H_{12}.	The subscripts are whole numbers: no additional multiplication is needed. The correct empirical formula is $C_{10}H_{12}O$.
	FOR PRACTICE 3.17 Upon combustion, a compound containing only carbon and hydrogen produced 1.60 g CO_2 and 0.819 g H_2O. Find the empirical formula of the compound.	**FOR PRACTICE 3.18** Upon combustion, a 0.8009 g sample of a compound containing only carbon, hydrogen, and oxygen produced 1.6004 g CO_2 and 0.6551 g H_2O. Find the empirical formula of the compound.

CHAPTER IN REVIEW

Key Terms

Section 3.2
ionic bond (59)
covalent bond (60)

Section 3.3
chemical formula (60)
empirical formula (60)
molecular formula (60)
structural formula (60)
ball-and-stick model (61)
space-filling model (61)
atomic element (62)
molecular element (62)
molecular compound (62)
ionic compound (62)
formula unit (62)
polyatomic ion (63)

Section 3.4
common name (64)
systematic name (64)
base name (65)
oxyanion (66)
hydrate (67)
anhydrous (67)
binary molecular compound (68)
acid (69)
binary acid (70)
oxyacid (70)

Section 3.5
organic compound (70)
hydrocarbon (70)
alkane (71)
alkene (71)
alkyne (71)
functional group (71)
alcohol (71)
family (71)
substituent (72)
locant (74)
cycloalkane (76)
cycloalkene (76)
benzene (77)
phenyl group (77)
principal group (79)

Section 3.6
formula mass (81)

Section 3.7
mass percent composition (mass percent) (83)

Section 3.8
empirical formula molar mass (88)
combustion analysis (89)

Key Concepts

Chemical Bonds (3.2)

Chemical bonds, the forces that hold atoms together in compounds, arise from the interactions between nuclei and electrons in atoms. An ionic bond is formed when one or more electrons are *transferred* from one atom to another, forming a cation (positively charged) and an anion (negatively charged). The two ions are then drawn together by the attraction between the opposite charges. In a covalent bond, one or more electrons are *shared* between two atoms. The atoms are held together by the attraction between their nuclei and the shared electrons.

Representing Compounds: Chemical Formulas and Molecular Models (3.3)

A compound is represented with a chemical formula that indicates the elements present and the number of atoms of each. An empirical formula gives only the *relative* number of atoms, while a molecular formula gives the *actual* number of atoms present in the molecule. Structural formulas show how the atoms are bonded together, while molecular models portray the geometry of the molecule.

Compounds can be divided into two types: molecular compounds, formed between two or more covalently bonded nonmetals; and ionic compounds, usually formed between a metal ionically bonded to one or more nonmetals. The smallest identifiable unit of a molecular compound is a molecule, and the smallest identifiable unit of an ionic compound is a formula unit—the smallest electrically neutral collection of ions. Elements can also be divided into two types: molecular elements, which occur as small molecules; and atomic elements, which occur as individual atoms.

Formulas and Names (3.4)

The most useful chemical names convey unambiguous information about the formula of a compound. Accepted rules and standards for chemical nomenclature are determined by IUPAC. Ionic compound names generally consist of the cation name followed by the name of the anion. The formula of the ionic compound can be inferred from balancing the charges of the cation and anion. The names of molecular compounds are similar, but prefixes must be used to provide information about how many atoms of each type are in the chemical formula.

Organic Compounds (3.5)

Organic compounds are a class of molecular compounds composed of carbon, hydrogen, and a few other elements such as nitrogen, oxygen, and sulfur. The simplest organic compounds are hydrocarbons, compounds composed of only carbon and hydrogen. Hydrocarbons can be divided into three types based on the bonds they contain: alkanes (contain only single bonds), alkenes (contain at least one double bond), and alkynes (contain at least one triple bond). All other organic compounds can be thought of as hydrocarbons with one or more functional groups, characteristic atoms, or groups of atoms. Common functionalized hydrocarbons include alcohols, ethers, aldehydes, ketones, carboxylic acids, esters, and amines. The nomenclature of organic compounds involves the use of base names for hydrocarbon chains, with added prefixes and suffixes that identify substituent and functional groups that are present.

Formula Mass and the Mole Concept for Compounds (3.6)

The formula mass of a compound is the sum of the atomic masses of all the atoms in the chemical formula. Like the atomic masses of elements, the formula mass characterizes the average mass of a molecule (or a formula unit). The mass of one mole of a compound is called the molar mass and equals its formula mass (in grams).

Composition of Compounds (3.7, 3.8)

The mass percent composition of a compound indicates each element's percentage of the total compound's mass. The mass percent composition can be obtained from the compound's chemical formula and the molar masses of its elements. The chemical formula of a compound provides the relative number of atoms (or moles) of each element in a compound and can therefore be used to determine numerical relationships between moles of the compound and moles of its constituent elements. This relationship can be extended to mass by using the molar masses of the compound and its constituent elements. The calculation can also go the other way—if the mass percent composition and molar mass of a compound are known, the empirical and molecular formulas can be determined.

Key Equations and Relationships

Formula Mass (3.6)

$$\textbf{Formula mass} = \left(\begin{array}{c}\text{Number of atoms}\\ \text{of 1st element in}\\ \text{chemical formula}\end{array} \times \begin{array}{c}\text{Atomic mass}\\ \text{of}\\ \text{1st element}\end{array}\right) + \left(\begin{array}{c}\text{Number of atoms}\\ \text{of 2nd element in}\\ \text{chemical formula}\end{array} \times \begin{array}{c}\text{Atomic mass}\\ \text{of}\\ \text{2nd element}\end{array}\right) + \dots$$

Mass Percent Composition (3.7)

$$\text{mass percent of element X} = \frac{\text{mass of element X in 1 mol of compound}}{\text{mass of 1 mol of compound}} \times 100\%$$

Empirical Formula Molar Mass (3.8)

$$\text{molar mass} = \text{empirical formula molar mass} \times n$$

$$n = \frac{\text{molar mass}}{\text{empirical formula molar mass}}$$

Key Skills

Classifying Substances as Atomic Elements, Molecular Elements, Molecular Compounds, or Ionic Compounds (3.3)
• Example 3.1 • For Practice 3.1 • Exercises 27–32

Writing Formulas for Ionic Compounds (3.4)
• Examples 3.2, 3.3 • For Practice 3.2, 3.3 • Exercises 33–36, 43, 44

Naming Ionic Compounds (3.4)
• Example 3.4 • For Practice 3.4 • For More Practice 3.4 • Exercises 37–42

Naming Molecular Compounds (3.4)
• Example 3.5 • For Practice 3.5 • For More Practice 3.5 • Exercises 47, 48

Naming Alkanes (3.5)
• Examples 3.6, 3.7 • For Practice 3.6, 3.7 • Exercises 59, 60, 63, 64

Naming Alkenes and Alkynes (3.5)
• Example 3.8 • For Practice 3.8 • Exercises 67, 68

Naming Functionalized Hydrocarbons (3.5)
• Example 3.9 • For Practice 3.9 • For More Practice 3.9 • Exercises 77, 79, 81, 83

Calculating Formula Mass (3.6)
• Example 3.10 • For Practice 3.10 • Exercises 85, 86

Converting Between Mass and Number of Moles (3.6)
• Example 3.11 • For Practice 3.11 • For More Practice 3.11 • Exercises 87, 88

Calculating Mass Percent Composition (3.7)
• Example 3.12 • For Practice 3.12 • For More Practice 3.12 • Exercises 95–98

Using Chemical Formulas as Conversion Factors (3.7)
• Example 3.13 • For Practice 3.13 • For More Practice 3.13 • Exercises 107, 108

Obtaining an Empirical Formula from Experimental Data (3.8)
• Examples 3.14, 3.15 • For Practice 3.14, 3.15 • Exercises 109–116

Calculating a Molecular Formula from an Empirical Formula and Molar Mass (3.8)
• Example 3.16 • For Practice 3.16 • For More Practice 3.16 • Exercises 117, 118

Obtaining an Empirical Formula from Combustion Analysis (3.8)
• Examples 3.17, 3.18 • For Practice 3.17, 3.18 • Exercises 119–122

EXERCISES

Review Questions

1. How do the properties of compounds compare to the properties of the elements from which they are derived?
2. What is a chemical bond? Explain the difference between an ionic bond and a covalent bond.
3. Explain the different ways to represent compounds. Why are there so many?
4. What is the difference between an empirical formula and a molecular formula?
5. Define and provide an example for each of the following: atomic element, molecular element, ionic compound, molecular compound.
6. Explain how to write a formula for an ionic compound given the names of the metal and nonmetal (or polyatomic ion) in the compound.
7. Explain how to name binary ionic compounds. How do you name an ionic compound if it contains a polyatomic ion?
8. Why do the names of some ionic compounds include the charge of the metal ion, while others do not?
9. Explain how to name molecular inorganic compounds.
10. How many atoms are specified by these prefixes: mono, di, tri, tetra, penta, hexa?
11. Explain how to name binary acids and oxyacids.
12. What elements are normally present in organic compounds?
13. What is the difference between an alkane, an alkene, and an alkyne?
14. What are functionalized hydrocarbons? Give an example of a functionalized hydrocarbon.

15. Write a generic formula for each of the families of organic compounds.
    a. alcohols
    b. ethers
    c. aldehydes
    d. ketones
    e. carboxylic acids
    f. esters
    g. amines
16. What is the formula mass for a compound? Why is it useful?
17. Explain how the information in a chemical formula can be used to determine how much of a particular element is present in a given amount of a compound. Give some examples demonstrating why this might be important.
18. What is mass percent composition? Why is it useful?
19. What kinds of conversion factors are inherent in chemical formulas? Give an example.
20. What kind of chemical formula can be obtained from experimental data showing the relative masses of the elements in a compound?
21. How can a molecular formula be obtained from an empirical formula? What additional information is required?
22. What is combustion analysis? What is it used for?

Problems by Topic

Chemical Formulas and Molecular View of Elements and Compounds

23. Determine the number of each type of atom in each formula.
    a. $Mg_3(PO_4)_2$
    b. $BaCl_2$
    c. $Fe(NO_2)_2$
    d. $Ca(OH)_2$
24. Determine the number of each type of atom in each formula.
    a. $Ca(NO_2)_2$
    b. $CuSO_4$
    c. $Al(NO_3)_3$
    d. $Mg(HCO_3)_2$
25. Write a chemical formula for each molecular model. (See page 62 for colour codes.)

(a)

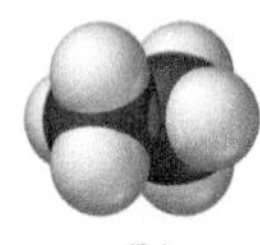
(b)

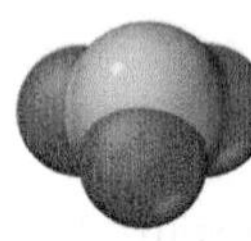
(c)

26. Write a chemical formula for each molecular model. (See page 62 for colour codes.)

(a)

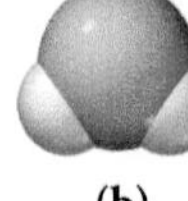
(b)

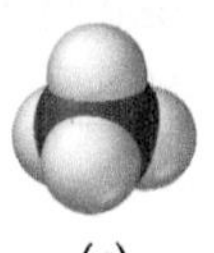
(c)

27. Classify each element as atomic or molecular.
    a. neon
    b. fluorine
    c. potassium
    d. nitrogen
28. Determine whether or not each element has molecules as its basic units.
    a. hydrogen
    b. iodine
    c. lead
    d. oxygen
29. Classify each compound as ionic or molecular.
    a. CO_2
    b. $NiCl_2$
    c. NaI
    d. PCl_3
30. Classify each compound as ionic or molecular.
    a. CF_2Cl_2
    b. CCl_4
    c. PtO_2
    d. SO_3
31. Based on the molecular views, classify each substance as an atomic element, a molecular element, an ionic compound, or a molecular compound.

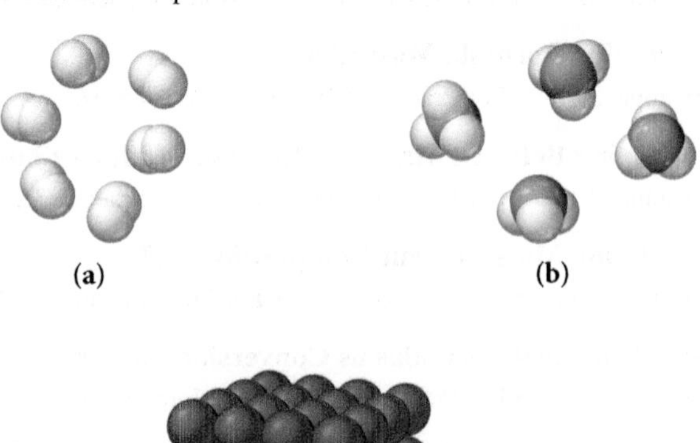
(a) (b)

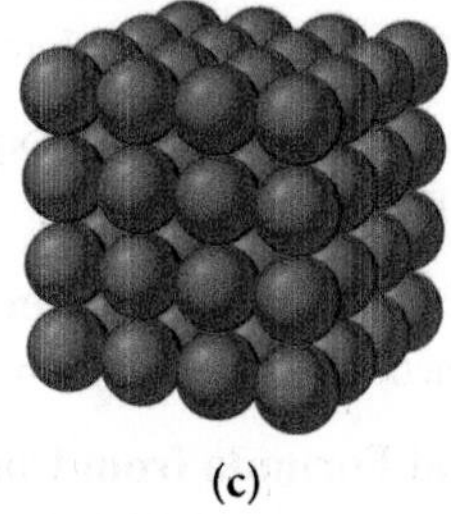
(c)

32. Based on the molecular views, classify each substance as an atomic element, a molecular element, an ionic compound, or a molecular compound.

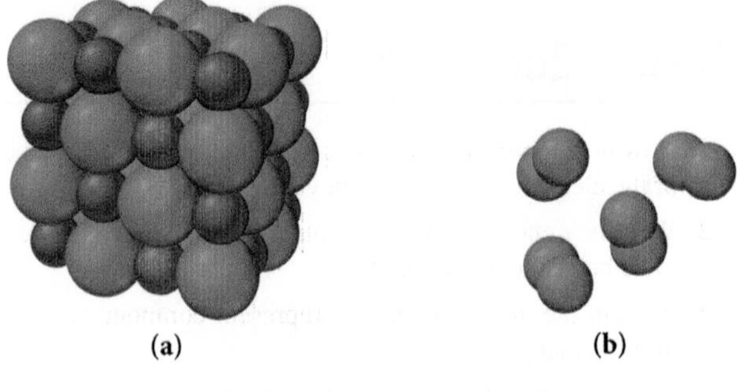
(a) (b)

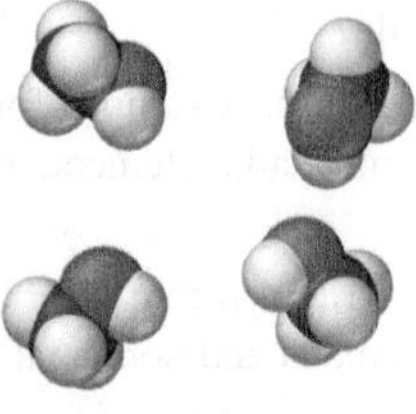
(c)

Formulas and Names for Ionic Compounds

33. Write a formula for the ionic compound that forms between each pair of elements.
a. calcium and oxygen **b.** zinc and sulfur
c. rubidium and bromine **d.** aluminum and oxygen

34. Write a formula for the ionic compound that forms between each pair of elements.
a. silver and chlorine **b.** sodium and sulfur
c. aluminum and sulfur **d.** potassium and chlorine

35. Write a formula for the compound that forms between calcium and each polyatomic ion.
a. hydroxide **b.** chromate
c. phosphate **d.** cyanide

36. Write a formula for the compound that forms between potassium and each polyatomic ion.
a. carbonate **b.** phosphate
c. hydrogen phosphate **d.** acetate

37. Name each ionic compound.
a. Mg_3N_2 **b.** KF **c.** Na_2O **d.** Li_2S
e. CsF **f.** KI **g.** $SrCl_2$ **h.** $BaCl_2$

38. Name each ionic compound.
a. $SnCl_4$ **b.** PbI_2 **c.** Fe_2O_3 **d.** CuI_2
e. SnO_2 **f.** $HgBr_2$ **g.** $CrCl_2$ **h.** $CrCl_3$

39. Give each ionic compound an appropriate name.
a. SnO **b.** Cr_2S_3 **c.** RbI **d.** $BaBr_2$

40. Give each ionic compound an appropriate name.
a. BaS **b.** $FeCl_3$ **c.** PbI_4 **d.** $SrBr_2$

41. Name each ionic compound containing a polyatomic ion.
a. $CuNO_2$ **b.** $Mg(C_2H_3O_2)_2$ **c.** $Ba(NO_3)_2$
d. $Pb(C_2H_3O_2)_2$ **e.** $KClO_3$ **f.** $PbSO_4$

42. Name each ionic compound containing a polyatomic ion.
a. $Ba(OH)_2$ **b.** NH_4I **c.** $NaBrO_4$
d. $Fe(OH)_3$ **e.** $CoSO_4$ **f.** KClO

43. Write a formula for each ionic compound.
a. sodium hydrogen sulfite
b. calcium permanganate
c. silver nitrate
d. potassium sulfate
e. rubidium hydrogen sulfate
f. potassium hydrogen carbonate

44. Write a formula for each ionic compound.
a. copper(II) chloride
b. copper(I) iodate
c. lead(II) chromate
d. calcium fluoride
e. potassium hydroxide
f. iron(II) phosphate

45. Give the name from the formula or the formula from the name for each hydrated ionic compound.
a. $CoSO_4 \cdot 7H_2O$
b. iridium(III) bromide tetrahydrate
c. $Mg(BrO_3)_2 \cdot 6H_2O$
d. potassium carbonate dihydrate

46. Give the name from the formula or the formula from the name for each hydrated ionic compound.
a. cobalt(II) phosphate octahydrate
b. $BeCl_2 \cdot 2H_2O$
c. chromium(III) phosphate trihydrate
d. $LiNO_2 \cdot H_2O$

Formulas and Names for Molecular Compounds and Acids

47. Name each molecular compound.
a. CO **b.** NI_3 **c.** $SiCl_4$
d. Se_4N_4 **e.** I_2O_5

48. Name each molecular compound.
a. SO_3 **b.** SO_2 **c.** BrF_5
d. NO **e.** XeO_3

49. Write a formula for each molecular compound.
a. phosphorus trichloride
b. chlorine monoxide
c. disulfur tetrafluoride
d. phosphorus pentafluoride
e. diphosphorus pentasulfide

50. Write a formula for each molecular compound.
a. boron tribromide **b.** dichlorine monoxide
c. xenon tetrafluoride **d.** carbon tetrabromide
e. diboron tetrachloride

51. Name each acid.
a. HI **b.** HNO_3 **c.** H_2CO_3 **d.** H_3PO_4

52. Name each acid.
a. HCl **b.** $HClO_2$ **c.** H_2SO_4 **d.** HNO_2

53. Write a formula for each acid.
a. hydrofluoric acid **b.** hydrobromic acid
c. sulfurous acid

54. Write a formula for each acid.
a. phosphoric acid **b.** hydrocyanic acid
c. chlorous acid

Organic Compounds

55. Classify each compound as organic or inorganic.
a. $CaCO_3$ **b.** C_4H_8 **c.** $C_4H_6O_6$ **d.** LiF

56. Classify each compound as organic or inorganic.
a. C_8H_{18} **b.** CH_3NH_2 **c.** CaO **d.** $FeCO_3$

57. Classify each hydrocarbon as an alkane, alkene, or alkyne.
a. $H_2C{=}CH{-}CH_3$ **b.** $H_3C{-}CH_2{-}CH_3$
c. $HC{\equiv}C{-}CH_3$ **d.** $H_3C{-}CH_2{-}CH_2{-}CH_3$

58. Classify each hydrocarbon as an alkane, alkene, or alkyne.
a. $HC{\equiv}CH$ **b.** $H_3C{-}CH{=}CH{-}CH_3$
c. $H_3C{-}CH(CH_3){-}CH_3$ **d.** $H_3C{-}C{\equiv}C{-}CH_3$

59. Write a formula based on the name, or a name based on the formula, for each hydrocarbon.
a. butane **b.** $CH_3CH_2CH_3$
c. octane **d.** $CH_3CH_2CH_2CH_2CH_3$

60. Write a formula based on the name, or a name based on the formula, for each hydrocarbon.
a. CH_3CH_3 **b.** pentane
c. $CH_3CH_2CH_2CH_2CH_2CH_3$ **d.** heptane

61. Classify each organic compound as a hydrocarbon or a functionalized hydrocarbon. For functionalized hydrocarbons, identify the family to which the compound belongs.
a. $H_3C{-}CH_2OH$ **b.** $H_3C{-}CH_3$
c. $H_3C{-}C({=}O){-}CH_2{-}CH_3$ **d.** $H_3C{-}NH_2$

62. Classify each organic compound as a hydrocarbon or a functionalized hydrocarbon. For functionalized hydrocarbons, identify the family to which the compound belongs.

a. 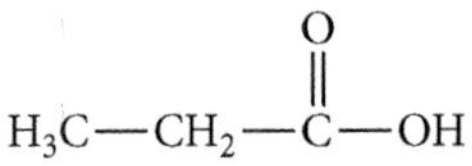 $\begin{array}{c} O \\ \| \\ H_3C-CH_2-C-OH \end{array}$

b. $\begin{array}{c} O \\ \| \\ H_3C-CH \end{array}$

c. $\begin{array}{c} CH_3 \\ | \\ H_3C-C-CH_3 \\ | \\ CH_3 \end{array}$

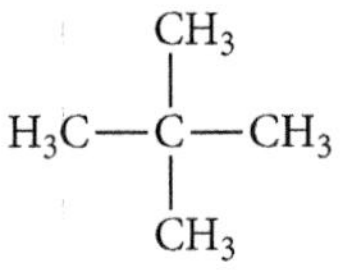

d. $H_3C-CH_2-O-CH_3$

63. Name each alkane.

a. $CH_3-CH_2-CH_2-CH_2-CH_3$

b. 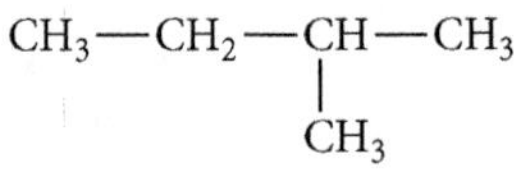 $\begin{array}{l} CH_3-CH_2-CH-CH_3 \\ | \\ CH_3 \end{array}$

c. 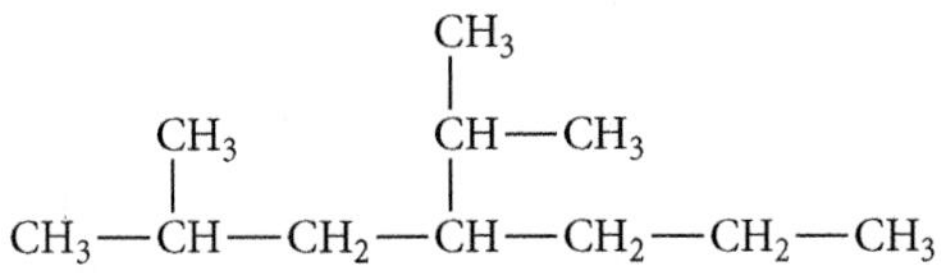 $\begin{array}{l} CH_3 \\ | \\ CH_3CH-CH_3 \\ || \\ CH_3-CH-CH_2-CH-CH_2-CH_2-CH_3 \end{array}$

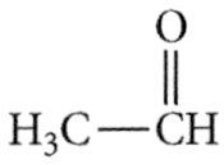

d. 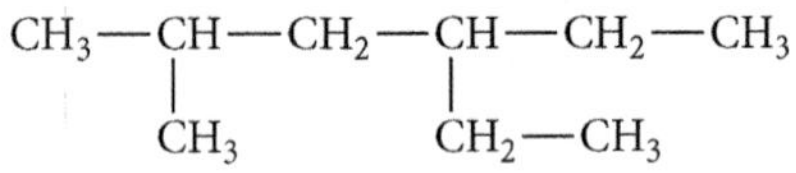 $\begin{array}{l} CH_3-CH-CH_2-CH-CH_2-CH_3 \\ || \\ CH_3CH_2-CH_3 \end{array}$

64. Name each alkane.

a. 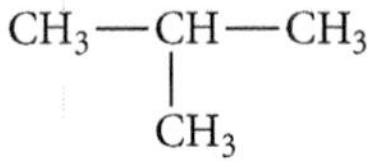 $\begin{array}{l} CH_3-CH-CH_3 \\ | \\ CH_3 \end{array}$

b. 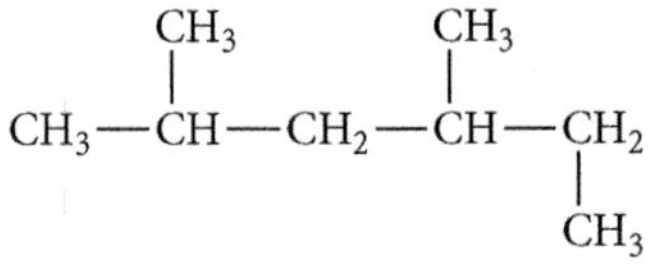 $\begin{array}{l} CH_3CH_3 \\ || \\ CH_3-CH-CH_2-CH-CH_2 \\ | \\ CH_3 \end{array}$

c. 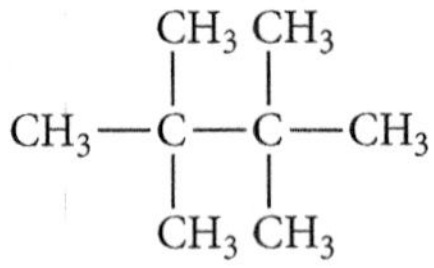 $\begin{array}{c} CH_3\ CH_3 \\ |\quad\ | \\ CH_3-C-C-CH_3 \\ |\quad\ | \\ CH_3\ CH_3 \end{array}$

d. 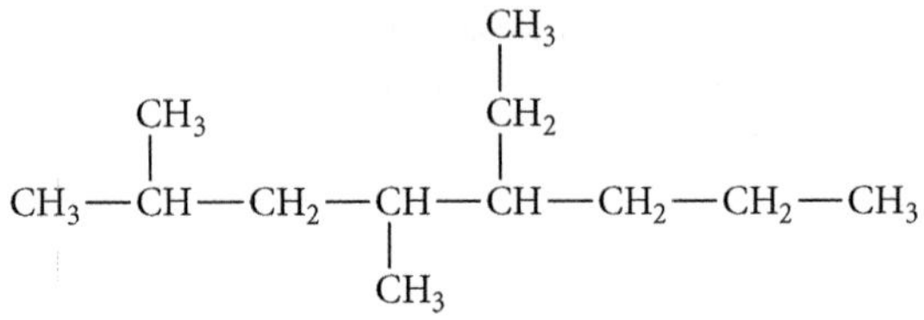 $\begin{array}{l} CH_3 \\ | \\ CH_3CH_2 \\ || \\ CH_3-CH-CH_2-CH-CH-CH_2-CH_2-CH_3 \\ | \\ CH_3 \end{array}$

65. Draw a structure for each alkane.

a. 3-ethylhexane

b. 3-ethyl-3-methylpentane

c. 2,3-dimethylbutane

d. 4,7-diethyl-2,2-dimethylnonane

66. Draw a structure for each alkane.

a. 2,2-dimethylpentane

b. 3-isopropylheptane

c. 4-ethyl-2,2-dimethylhexane

d. 4,4-diethyloctane

67. Name each alkene or alkyne.

a. $CH_2{=}CH-CH_2-CH_3$

b. 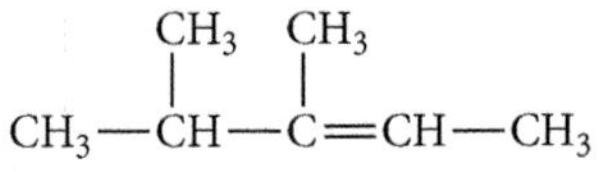 $\begin{array}{l} CH_3\ \ CH_3 \\ || \\ CH_3-CH-C{=}CH-CH_3 \end{array}$

c. $\begin{array}{l} CH{\equiv}C-CH-CH_2-CH_2-CH_3 \\ \phantom{CH{\equiv}C-}| \\ \phantom{CH{\equiv}C-}CH-CH_3 \\ \phantom{CH{\equiv}C-}| \\ \phantom{CH{\equiv}C-}CH_3 \end{array}$

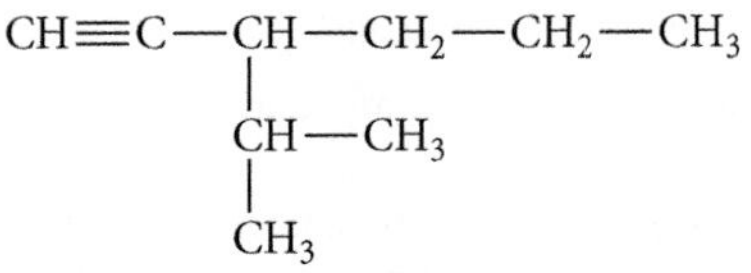

d. 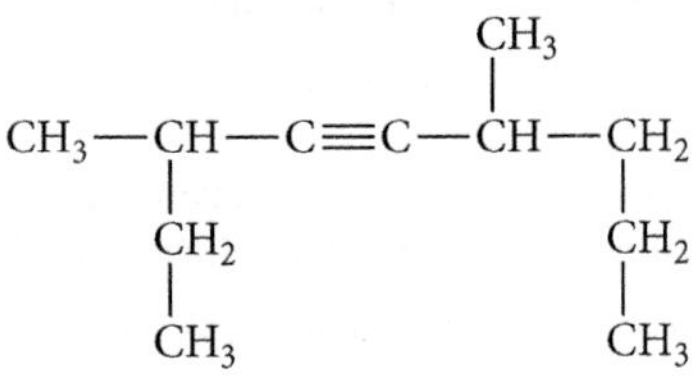 $\begin{array}{l} \phantom{CH_3-CH-C{\equiv}C-}CH_3 \\ \phantom{CH_3-CH-C{\equiv}C-}| \\ CH_3-CH-C{\equiv}C-CH-CH_2 \\ |\phantom{CH-C{\equiv}C-CH-}| \\ CH_2\phantom{-C{\equiv}C-CH-}CH_2 \\ |\phantom{CH-C{\equiv}C-CH-}| \\ CH_3\phantom{-C{\equiv}C-CH-}CH_3 \end{array}$

68. Name each alkene or alkyne.

a. $CH_3-CH_2-CH{=}CH-CH_2-CH_3$

b. 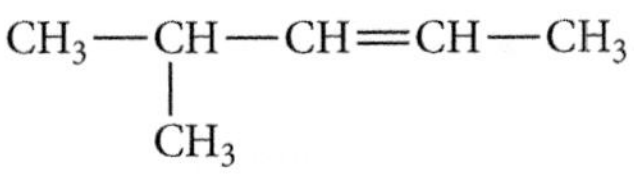 $\begin{array}{l} CH_3-CH-CH{=}CH-CH_3 \\ | \\ CH_3 \end{array}$

c. 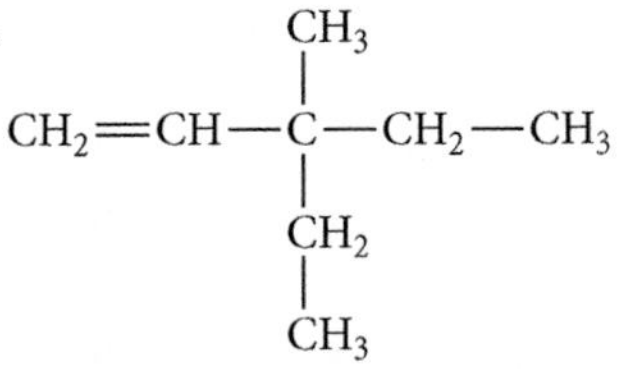 $\begin{array}{l} \phantom{CH_2{=}CH-}CH_3 \\ \phantom{CH_2{=}CH-}| \\ CH_2{=}CH-C-CH_2-CH_3 \\ \phantom{CH_2{=}CH-}| \\ \phantom{CH_2{=}CH-}CH_2 \\ \phantom{CH_2{=}CH-}| \\ \phantom{CH_2{=}CH-}CH_3 \end{array}$

d. 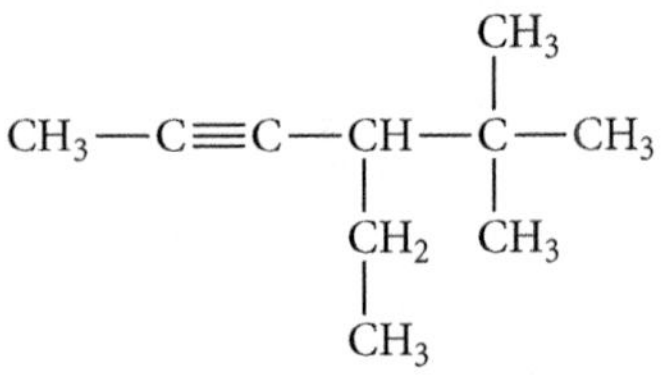 $\begin{array}{l} \phantom{CH_3-C{\equiv}C-CH-}CH_3 \\ \phantom{CH_3-C{\equiv}C-CH-}| \\ CH_3-C{\equiv}C-CH-C-CH_3 \\ \phantom{CH_3-C{\equiv}C-}|| \\ \phantom{CH_3-C{\equiv}C-}CH_2\ CH_3 \\ \phantom{CH_3-C{\equiv}C-}| \\ \phantom{CH_3-C{\equiv}C-}CH_3 \end{array}$

69. Provide a correct structure for each compound.

a. oct-4-yne

b. non-3-ene

c. 3,3-dimethylpent-1-yne

d. 5-ethyl-3,6-dimethylhept-2-ene

70. Provide a correct structure for each compound.

a. hex-2-ene

b. hept-2-yne

c. 4,4-dimethylhex-2-ene

d. 3-ethyl-4-methylpent-2-ene

71. Name each monosubstituted benzene.

a. 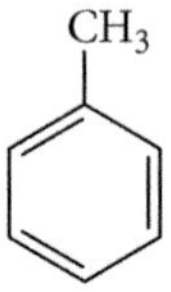 CH_3 attached to a benzene ring

b. 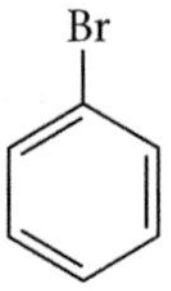 Br attached to a benzene ring

c. 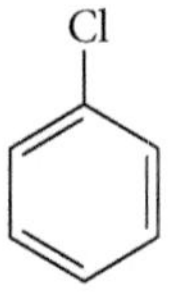 Cl attached to a benzene ring

72. Name each monosubstituted benzene.

a. 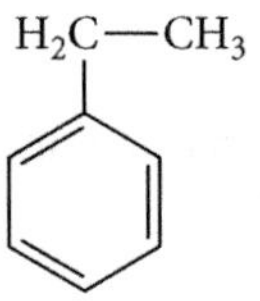 H_2C-CH_3 attached to a benzene ring

b. 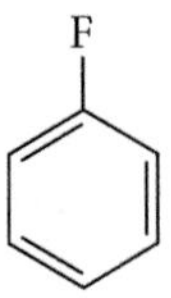 F attached to a benzene ring

c. 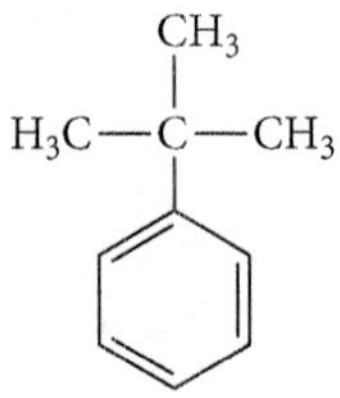 $\begin{array}{c} CH_3 \\ | \\ H_3C-C-CH_3 \end{array}$ attached to a benzene ring

73. Name each disubstituted benzene.

a. 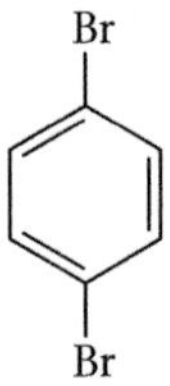 Br above and Br below on a benzene ring (para)

b. 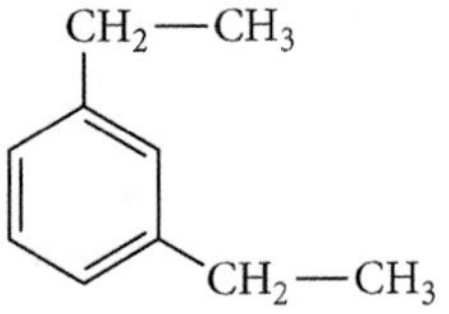 CH_2-CH_3 above and CH_2-CH_3 at lower right on a benzene ring (meta)

c. 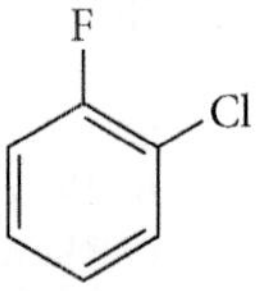 F above and Cl at upper right on a benzene ring (ortho)

74. Name each disubstituted benzene.

a. Br, Cl

b.

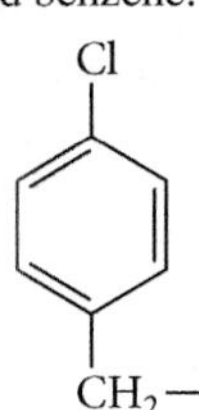

c. I, I

75. Draw a structure for each compound.
- **a.** 1-methyl-3-ethylbenzene
- **b.** 1,3-dibromobenzene
- **c.** 1-chloro-4-methylbenzene

76. Draw a structure for each compound.
- **a.** ethylbenzene
- **b.** 1-iodo-2-methylbenzene
- **c.** 1,4-diethylbenzene

77. Name each alcohol.

a. $CH_3—CH_2—CH_2—OH$

b.
$$\begin{array}{c} \quad CH_2—CH_3 \\ | \\ CH_3—CH—CH_2—CH—CH_3 \\ \qquad\qquad | \\ \qquad\qquad OH \end{array}$$

c.
$$\begin{array}{c} CH_3 \qquad\qquad\qquad CH_3 \\ | \qquad\qquad\qquad\quad | \\ CH_3—CH—CH_2—CH—CH_2—CH—CH_3 \\ | \\ OH \end{array}$$

d.
$$\begin{array}{c} HO \\ | \\ H_3C—CH_2—C—CH_2—CH_3 \\ | \\ H_3C \end{array}$$

78. Draw a structure for each alcohol.
- **a.** butan-2-ol
- **b.** 2-methylpropan-1-ol
- **c.** 3-ethylhexan-1-ol
- **d.** 2-methylpentan-1-ol

79. Name each carboxylic acid or ester.

a.
$$\begin{array}{c} O \\ \| \\ CH_3—CH_2—CH_2—C—O—CH_3 \end{array}$$

b.
$$\begin{array}{c} O \\ \| \\ CH_2—CH_2—C—OH \end{array}$$

c.
$$\begin{array}{c} \qquad\qquad\qquad\qquad O \\ \qquad\qquad\qquad\qquad \| \\ CH_3—CH—CH_2—CH_2—CH_2—C—OH \\ | \\ CH_3 \end{array}$$

d.
$$\begin{array}{c} O \\ \| \\ CH_3—CH_2—CH_2—CH_2—C—O—CH_2—CH_3 \end{array}$$

80. Draw the structure of each carboxylic acid or ester.
- **a.** pentanoic acid
- **b.** methyl hexanoate
- **c.** 3-ethylheptanoic acid
- **d.** butyl ethanoate

81. Name each ether.
- **a.** $CH_3—CH_2—CH_2—O—CH_2—CH_3$
- **b.** $CH_3—CH_2—CH_2—CH_2—CH_2—O—CH_2—CH_3$
- **c.** $CH_3—CH_2—CH_2—O—CH_2—CH_2—CH_3$
- **d.** $CH_3—CH_2—O—CH_2—CH_2—CH_2—CH_3$

82. Draw a structure for each ether.
- **a.** ethyl propyl ether
- **b.** dimethyl ether
- **c.** ethoxybenzene
- **d.** methoxyethane

83. Name each amine.

a.
$$\begin{array}{c} CH_3—CH_2—N—CH_2—CH_3 \\ | \\ H \end{array}$$

b.
$$\begin{array}{c} CH_3—CH_2—CH_2—N—CH_3 \\ | \\ H \end{array}$$

c.
$$\begin{array}{c} CH_3 \\ | \\ CH_3—CH_2—CH_2—N—CH_2—CH_2—CH_2—CH_3 \end{array}$$

84. Draw a structure for each amine.
- **a.** (1-methylethyl)amine
- **b.** triethylamine
- **c.** butylethylamine

Formula Mass and the Mole Concept for Compounds

85. Calculate the formula mass for each compound.
- **a.** NO_2
- **b.** C_4H_{10}
- **c.** $C_6H_{12}O_6$
- **d.** $Cr(NO_3)_3$

86. Calculate the formula mass for each compound.
- **a.** $MgBr_2$
- **b.** HNO_2
- **c.** CBr_4
- **d.** $Ca(NO_3)_2$

87. How many moles (of molecules or formula units) are in each sample?
- **a.** 25.5 g NO_2
- **b.** 1.25 kg CO_2
- **c.** 38.2 g KNO_3
- **d.** 155.2 kg Na_2SO_4

88. How many moles (of molecules or formula units) are in each sample?
- **a.** 55.98 g CF_2Cl_2
- **b.** 23.6 kg $Fe(NO_3)_2$
- **c.** 0.1187 g C_8H_{18}
- **d.** 195 kg CaO

89. How many molecules are in each sample?
- **a.** 6.5 g H_2O
- **b.** 389 g CBr_4
- **c.** 22.1 g O_2
- **d.** 19.3 g C_8H_{10}

90. How many molecules (or formula units) are in each sample?
- **a.** 85.26 g CCl_4
- **b.** 55.93 kg $NaHCO_3$
- **c.** 119.78 g C_4H_{10}
- **d.** 4.59×10^5 g Na_3PO_4

91. Calculate the mass (in g) of each sample.
- **a.** 5.94×10^{20} SO_3 molecules
- **b.** 2.8×10^{22} H_2O molecules
- **c.** 1 glucose molecule ($C_6H_{12}O_6$)

92. Calculate the mass (in g) of each sample.
- **a.** 4.5×10^{25} O_3 molecules
- **b.** 9.85×10^{19} CCl_2F_2 molecules
- **c.** 1 water molecule

93. A sugar crystal contains approximately 1.8×10^{17} sucrose ($C_{12}H_{22}O_{11}$) molecules. What is its mass in mg?

94. A salt crystal has a mass of 0.12 mg. How many NaCl formula units does it contain?

Composition of Compounds

95. Calculate the mass percent composition of carbon in each carbon-containing compound.
- **a.** CH_4
- **b.** C_2H_6
- **c.** C_2H_2
- **d.** C_2H_5Cl

96. Calculate the mass percent composition of nitrogen in each nitrogen-containing compound.
- **a.** N_2O
- **b.** NO
- **c.** NO_2
- **d.** HNO_3

97. Most fertilizers consist of nitrogen-containing compounds such as NH_3, $CO(NH_2)_2$, NH_4NO_3, and $(NH_4)_2SO_4$. The nitrogen content in these compounds is used for protein synthesis by plants. Calculate the mass percent composition of nitrogen in each of the fertilizers named above. Which fertilizer has the highest nitrogen content?

98. Iron from the Earth is in the form of iron ore. Common ores include Fe_2O_3 (hematite), Fe_3O_4 (magnetite), and $FeCO_3$ (siderite). Calculate the mass percent composition of iron for each of these iron ores. Which ore has the highest iron content?

99. Copper(II) fluoride contains 37.42% F by mass. Calculate the mass of fluorine (in g) contained in 55.5 g of copper(II) fluoride.

100. Silver chloride, often used in silver plating, contains 75.27% Ag by mass. Calculate the mass of silver chloride required to plate 155 mg of pure silver.

101. The iodide ion is a dietary mineral essential to good nutrition. In countries where potassium iodide is added to salt, iodine deficiency (or goiter) has been almost completely eliminated. The recommended daily allowance (RDA) for iodine is 150 μg/day. How much potassium iodide (76.45% I) should you consume if you want to meet the RDA?

102. The American Dental Association recommends that an adult female should consume 3.0 mg of fluoride (F^-) per day to prevent tooth decay. If the fluoride is consumed in the form of sodium fluoride (45.24% F), what amount of sodium fluoride contains the recommended amount of fluoride?

103. Write a ratio showing the relationship between the amounts of each element for each compound.

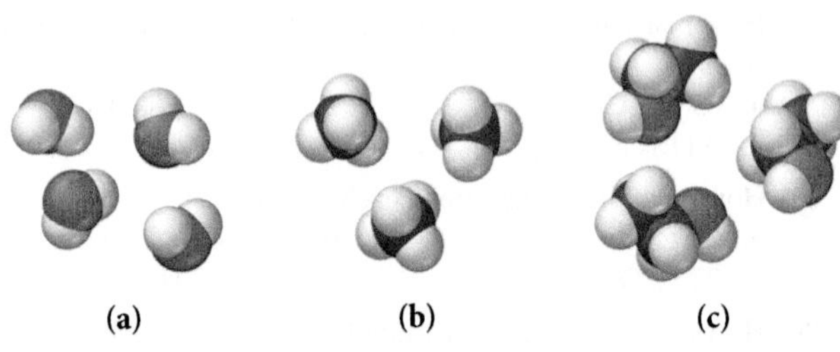

104. Write a ratio showing the relationship between the amounts of each element for each compound.

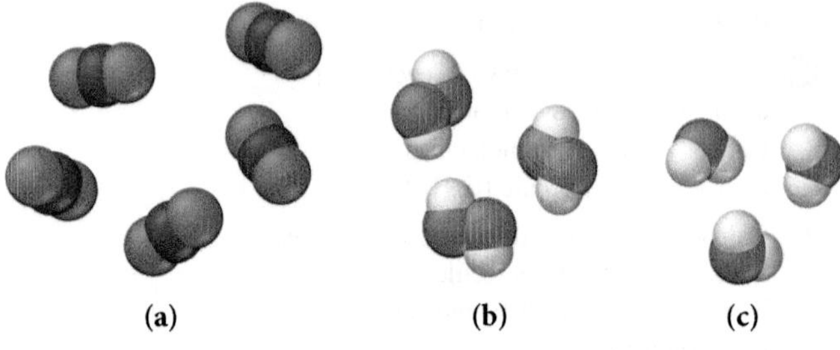

105. Determine the number of moles of hydrogen atoms in each sample.

a. 0.0885 mol C_4H_{10} **b.** 1.3 mol CH_4
c. 2.4 mol C_6H_{12} **d.** 1.87 mol C_8H_{18}

106. Determine the number of moles of oxygen atoms in each sample.

a. 4.88 mol H_2O_2 **b.** 2.15 mol N_2O
c. 0.0237 mol H_2CO_3 **d.** 24.1 mol CO_2

107. Calculate mass (in grams) of sodium in 8.5 g of each sodium-containing food additive.

a. NaCl (table salt)
b. Na_3PO_4 (sodium phosphate)
c. $NaC_7H_5O_2$ (sodium benzoate)
d. $Na_2C_6H_6O_7$ (sodium hydrogen citrate)

108. Calculate the mass (in kilograms) of chlorine in 25 kg of each chlorofluorocarbon (CFC).

a. CF_2Cl_2 **b.** $CFCl_3$ **c.** $C_2F_3Cl_3$ **d.** CF_3Cl

Chemical Formulas from Experimental Data

109. A chemist decomposes samples of several compounds; the masses of their constituent elements are shown below. Calculate the empirical formula for each compound.

a. 1.651 g Ag, 0.1224 g O
b. 0.672 g Co, 0.569 g As, 0.486 g O
c. 1.443 g Se, 5.841 g Br

110. A chemist decomposes samples of several compounds; the masses of their constituent elements are shown below. Calculate the empirical formula for each compound.

a. 1.245 g Ni, 5.381 g I
b. 2.677 g Ba, 3.115 g Br
c. 2.128 g Be, 7.557 g S, 15.107 g O

111. Calculate the empirical formula for each stimulant based on its elemental mass percent composition.

a. nicotine (found in tobacco leaves): 74.03% C, 8.70% H, 17.27% N
b. caffeine (found in coffee beans): 49.48% C, 5.19% H, 28.85% N, 16.48% O

112. Calculate the empirical formula for each natural flavour based on its elemental mass percent composition.

a. methyl butanoate (component of apple taste and smell): 58.80% C, 9.87% H, 31.33% O
b. vanillin (responsible for the taste and smell of vanilla): 63.15% C, 5.30% H, 31.55% O

113. The elemental mass percent composition of ibuprofen (an aspirin substitute) is 75.69% C, 8.80% H, and 15.51% O. Determine the empirical formula of ibuprofen.

114. The elemental mass percent composition of ascorbic acid (vitamin C) is 40.92% C, 4.58% H, and 54.50% O. Determine the empirical formula of ascorbic acid.

115. A 0.77 mg sample of nitrogen reacts with chlorine to form 6.61 mg of a nitrogen chloride. Determine the empirical formula of nitrogen chloride.

116. A 45.2 mg sample of phosphorus reacts with selenium to form 131.6 mg of a phosphorus selenide. Determine the empirical formula of phosphorus selenide.

117. The empirical formula and molar mass of several compounds are listed below. Find the molecular formula of each compound.

a. C_6H_7N, 186.24 g mol^{-1} **b.** C_2HCl, 181.44 g mol^{-1}
c. $C_5H_{10}NS_2$, 296.54 g mol^{-1}

118. The empirical formula and molar mass of several compounds are listed below. Find the molecular formula of each compound.

a. C_4H_9, 114.22 g mol^{-1} **b.** CCl, 284.77 g mol^{-1}
c. C_3H_2N, 312.29 g mol^{-1}

119. Combustion analysis of a hydrocarbon produced 33.01 g CO_2 and 13.51 g H_2O. Calculate the empirical formula of the hydrocarbon.

120. Combustion analysis of naphthalene, a hydrocarbon used in mothballs, produced 8.80 g CO_2 and 1.44 g H_2O. Calculate the empirical formula for naphthalene.

121. The foul odour of rancid butter is due largely to butanoic acid (butyric acid), a compound containing carbon, hydrogen, and oxygen. Combustion analysis of a 4.30 g sample of butyric acid produced 8.59 g CO_2 and 3.52 g H_2O. Determine the empirical formula for butyric acid.

122. Tartaric acid is the white, powdery substance that coats tart candies such as Sour Patch Kids. Combustion analysis of a 12.01 g sample of tartaric acid—which contains only carbon, hydrogen, and oxygen—produced 14.08 g CO_2 and 4.32 g H_2O. Determine the empirical formula for tartaric acid.

Cumulative Problems

123. Identify each organic compound as an alkane, alkene, alkyne, aromatic hydrocarbon, alcohol, ether, aldehyde, ketone, carboxylic acid, ester, or amine, and provide a name for the compound.

a.
```
          H3C
           |
H3C—HC—C=C—CH3
     |      |
    CH3    CH3
```

b.
```
       CH3       CH3
        |         |
CH3—C—CH2—CH—CH2—CH3
        |
       CH3
```

c.
```
               CH3          O
                |           ||
CH3—CH2—CH—CH2—C—OH
```

d.
```
             H
             |
CH3—CH—N—CH2—CH2—CH2—CH3
      |
     CH3
```

e.
```
                    CH2—OH
                     |
CH3—CH—CH2—CH—CH3
      |
     CH2—CH3
```

124. Name each compound.

a.
```
                       CH3 CH3
                        |   |
CH3—CH=CH—C—CH—CH2—CH3
                        |
                       CH2
                        |
                       CH3
```

b. (benzene ring with Br and CH_2—CH_3 substituents)
```
  Br
  |
(benzene ring)
      \
       CH2—CH3
```

c.
```
             CH3           O        CH3
              |            ||        |
CH3—CH2—CH—CH2—C—O—CH—CH3
```

d.
```
                          O
                          ||
CH3—CH—CH2—CH
      |
     CH3
```

125. How many molecules of ethanol (C_2H_5OH; the alcohol in alcoholic beverages) are present in 145 mL of ethanol? The density of ethanol is $0.789\ g\ cm^{-3}$.

126. A drop of water has a volume of approximately 0.05 mL. How many water molecules does it contain? The density of water is $1.0\ g\ cm^{-3}$.

127. Determine the chemical formula of each compound and then use it to calculate the mass percent composition of each constituent element.

a. potassium chromate **b.** lead(2+) phosphate
c. sulfurous acid **d.** cobalt(II) bromide

128. Determine the chemical formula of each compound and then use it to calculate the mass percent composition of each constituent element.

a. perchloric acid **b.** phosphorus pentachloride
c. nitrogen triiodide **d.** carbon dioxide

129. A Freon leak in the air-conditioning system of an old car releases 25 g of CF_2Cl_2 per month. What mass of chlorine is emitted into the atmosphere each year by this car?

130. A Freon leak in the air-conditioning system of a large building releases 12 kg of CHF_2Cl per month. If the leak is allowed to continue, how many kilograms of Cl will be emitted into the atmosphere each year?

131. A metal (M) forms a compound with the formula MCl_3. If the compound contains 65.57% Cl by mass, what is the identity of the metal?

132. A metal (M) forms an oxide with the formula M_2O. If the oxide contains 16.99% O by mass, what is the identity of the metal?

133. Estradiol is a female sexual hormone that causes maturation and maintenance of the female reproductive system. Elemental analysis of estradiol gives the following mass percent composition: C 79.37%, H 8.88%, O 11.75%. The molar mass of estradiol is $272.37\ g\ mol^{-1}$. Find the molecular formula of estradiol.

134. Fructose is a common sugar found in fruit. Elemental analysis of fructose gives the following mass percent composition: C 40.00%, H 6.72%, O 53.28%. The molar mass of fructose is $180.16\ g\ mol^{-1}$. Find the molecular formula of fructose.

135. Combustion analysis of a 13.42 g sample of equilin (which contains only carbon, hydrogen, and oxygen) produces 39.61 g CO_2 and 9.01 g H_2O. The molar mass of equilin is $268.34\ g\ mol^{-1}$. Find the molecular formula for equilin.

136. Estrone, which contains only carbon, hydrogen, and oxygen, is a female sexual hormone that can be measured in the urine of pregnant women. Combustion analysis of a 1.893 g sample of estrone produces 5.545 g of CO_2 and 1.388 g H_2O. The molar mass of estrone is $270.36\ g\ mol^{-1}$. Find the molecular formula for estrone.

137. Epsom salt is a hydrated ionic compound with the following formula: $MgSO_4 \cdot xH_2O$. A 4.93 g sample of Epsom salt was heated to drive off the water of hydration. The mass of the sample after complete dehydration was 2.41 g. Find the number of waters of hydration (x) in Epsom salt.

138. A hydrate of copper(II) chloride has the following formula: $CuCl_2 \cdot xH_2O$. The water in a 3.41 g sample of the hydrate was driven off by heating. The remaining sample had a mass of 2.69 g. Find the number of waters of hydration (x) in the hydrate.

139. A compound of molar mass $177\ g\ mol^{-1}$ contains only carbon, hydrogen, bromine, and oxygen. Analysis reveals that the compound contains eight times as much carbon as hydrogen by mass. Find the molecular formula.

140. Researchers obtained the following data from experiments to find the molecular formula of benzocaine, a local anesthetic, which contains only carbon, hydrogen, nitrogen, and oxygen. Complete combustion of a 3.54 g sample of benzocaine with excess O_2 formed 8.49 g CO_2 and 2.14 g H_2O. Another sample of mass 2.35 g was found to contain 0.199 g N. The molar mass of benzocaine was found to be $165\ g\ mol^{-1}$. Find the molecular formula of benzocaine.

141. Find the total number of atoms in a sample of cocaine hydrochloride, $C_{17}H_{22}ClNO_4$, of mass 23.5 mg.

142. Vanadium forms four different oxides in which the percent by mass of vanadium is respectively (a) 76%, (b) 68%, (c) 61%, and (d) 56%. Find the formula and give the name of each one of these oxides.

143. The chloride of an unknown metal is believed to have the formula MCl_3. A 2.395 g sample of the compound is found to contain 3.606×10^{-2} mol Cl. Find the molar mass of M.

144. Write the structural formulas of three different compounds that each have the molecular formula C_5H_{12}.

145. A chromium-containing compound has the formula $Fe_xCr_yO_4$ and is 28.59% oxygen by mass. Find x and y.

146. A phosphorus compound that contains 34.00% phosphorus by mass has the formula X_3P_2. Identify the element X.

147. A particular brand of beef jerky contains 0.0552% sodium nitrite by mass and is sold in a 225 g bag. What mass of sodium does the sodium nitrite contribute to the sodium content of the bag of beef jerky?

148. Phosphorus is obtained primarily from ores containing calcium phosphate. If a particular ore contains 57.8% calcium phosphate, what minimum mass of the ore must be processed to obtain 1.00 kg of phosphorus?

Challenge Problems

149. A mixture of NaCl and NaBr has a mass of 2.00 g and is found to contain 0.75 g Na. What is the mass of the NaBr in the mixture?

150. Three pure compounds form when 1.00 g samples of element X combine with 0.472 g, 0.630 g, and 0.789 g of element Z, respectively. The first compound has the formula X_2Z_3. Find the empirical formulas of the other two compounds.

151. A mixture of $CaCO_3$ and $(NH_4)_2CO_3$ is 61.9% CO_3 by mass. Find the mass percent of $CaCO_3$ in the mixture.

152. Because of increasing evidence of damage to the ozone layer, chlorofluorocarbon (CFC) production was banned in 1996. However, there are about 100 million auto air conditioners that still use CFC-12 (CF_2Cl_2). These air conditioners are recharged from stockpiled supplies of CFC-12. If each of the 100 million automobiles contains 1.1 kg of CFC-12 and leaks 25% of its CFC-12 into the atmosphere per year, how much chlorine, in kg, is added to the atmosphere each year due to auto air conditioners? (Assume two significant figures in your calculations.)

153. Lead is found in Earth's crust as several different lead ores. Suppose a certain rock is 38.0% PbS (galena), 25.0% $PbCO_3$ (cerussite), and 17.4% $PbSO_4$ (anglesite). The remainder of the rock is composed of substances containing no lead. How much of this rock (in kg) must be processed to obtain 5.0 metric tonnes of lead? (A metric tonne is 1000 kg.)

154. A 2.52 g sample of a compound containing only carbon, hydrogen, nitrogen, oxygen, and sulfur was burned in excess O_2 to yield 4.23 g of CO_2 and 1.01 g of H_2O. Another sample of the same compound, of mass 4.14 g, yielded 2.11 g of SO_3. A third sample, of mass 5.66 g, yielded 2.27 g of HNO_3. Calculate the empirical formula of the compound.

155. A compound of molar mass 229 g mol^{-1} contains only carbon, hydrogen, iodine, and sulfur. Analysis shows that a sample of the compound contains six times as much carbon as hydrogen by mass. Calculate the molecular formula of the compound.

156. The elements X and Y form a compound that is 40% X and 60% Y by mass. The atomic mass of X is twice that of Y. What is the empirical formula of the compound?

157. A compound of X and Y is $\frac{1}{3}$ X by mass. The atomic mass of element X is $\frac{1}{3}$ the atomic mass of element Y. Find the empirical formula of the compound.

158. A mixture of carbon and sulfur has a mass of 9.0 g. Complete combustion with excess O_2 gives 23.3 g of a mixture of CO_2 and SO_2. Find the mass of sulfur in the original mixture.

Conceptual Problems

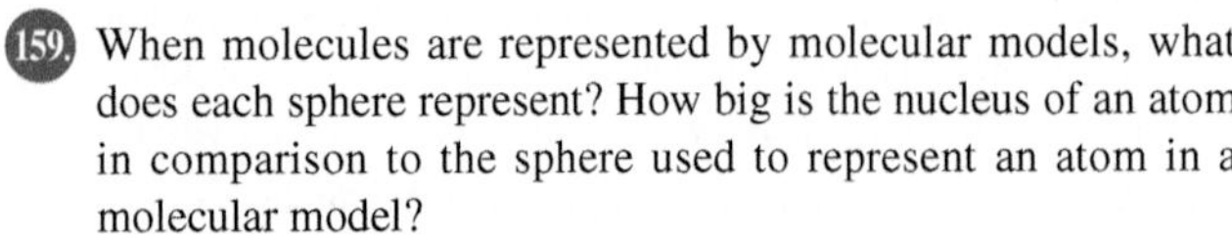

159. When molecules are represented by molecular models, what does each sphere represent? How big is the nucleus of an atom in comparison to the sphere used to represent an atom in a molecular model?

160. Without doing any calculations, determine which element in each of the compounds will have the highest mass percent.

a. CO b. N_2O c. $C_6H_{12}O_6$ d. NH_3

161. Explain the problem with the following statement and correct it: "The chemical formula for ammonia (NH_3) indicates that ammonia contains three grams of hydrogen to each gram of nitrogen."

162. Explain the problem with the following statement and correct it: "When a chemical equation is balanced, the number of molecules of each type on both sides of the equation will be equal."

163. Without doing any calculations, arrange the elements in H_2SO_4 in order of decreasing mass percent composition.

Chemical Reactions and Stoichiometry

4

When we decode a cookbook, every one of us is a practicing chemist. Cooking is really the oldest, most basic application of physical and chemical forces to natural materials.

—Arthur E. Grosser

THE AMOUNT OF PRODUCT FORMED IN A CHEMICAL REACTION is related to the amount of reactant that is consumed. This concept makes sense intuitively, but how do we describe and understand this relationship more fully? The second half of this chapter focuses on chemical stoichiometry—the numerical relationships between the amounts of reactants and products in chemical reactions. First we will learn how to write balanced chemical equations for chemical reactions. We will also describe some general types of chemical reactions. You have probably witnessed many of these types of reactions in your daily life because they are so common. Have you ever mixed baking soda with vinegar and observed the subsequent bubbling? Or have you ever noticed the hard water deposits that form on plumbing fixtures? These reactions are the subject of the first part of this chapter.

4.1 Chemistry of Cuisine

It is pretty well-known that good chemists make good cooks. Perhaps it is the techniques that are common between cooking and chemistry. Techniques such as measuring, filtering, concentrating, and distilling that chemists should be very good at may give them an edge when it comes to cooking. Maybe it is the experimental and

creative nature by which cooking is done to produce something new and tasty that is an allure for chemists to cooking. No matter the reason, one thing is for sure: cooking *is* chemistry. When we cook, from the baking of bread to the browning of meat, a chemical reaction is occurring—we are changing the chemicals in the raw ingredients to other chemical products in the final, cooked dish.

Let's consider a few practices in preparing food that are examples of chemistry occurring before your eyes. When you heat a steak on a barbeque, the meat changes from a bright red colour to the brown colour that we recognize as a steak on our plate. What is occurring is that the proteins that compose the steak are being denatured. In this particular example, the red myoglobin—the oxygen-carrying protein—is converted to metmyoglobin, which is brown. But there are many other chemical reactions that occur during the cooking of a steak as well. When you heat food that contains both protein and carbohydrates (sugars), a complex set of reactions occur—the Maillard reaction—to form many flavourful and aromatic compounds. In fact, the Maillard reaction is extremely important when cooking and is responsible for many other flavours experienced in cuisine, such as baked and toasted bread, malted barley in whisky or beer, fried onions, and countless others.

You may have been told by a parent or grandparent to walk softly when a cake is in the oven. Have you ever wondered why? To answer this, we must know a little about what chemical reaction is causing the cake to rise. Baking powder consists of sodium bicarbonate and an agent to help acidify the mixture. The sodium bicarbonate and the acid react to form carbon dioxide. In the hot oven, this reaction occurs more quickly, and the carbon dioxide gets trapped in the cake, leavening the cake, or making it expand. This reaction is much the same as when baking soda (sodium bicarbonate) reacts with vinegar (an acid). In the early stages of baking, when a crust is forming over the top of the cake, jumping can agitate the cake, break the crust, and allow the carbon dioxide gas to escape, resulting in a "fallen cake."

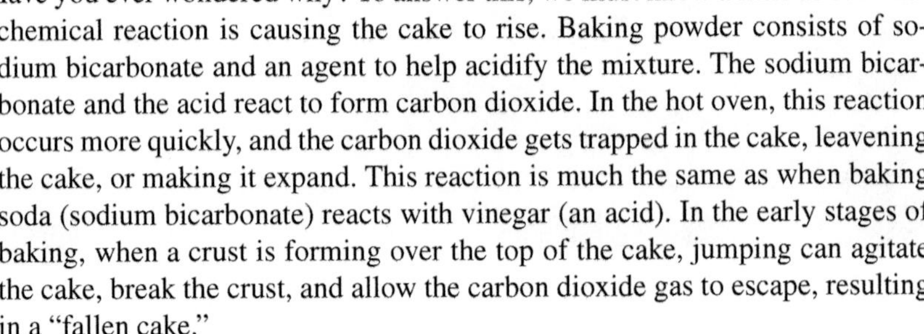

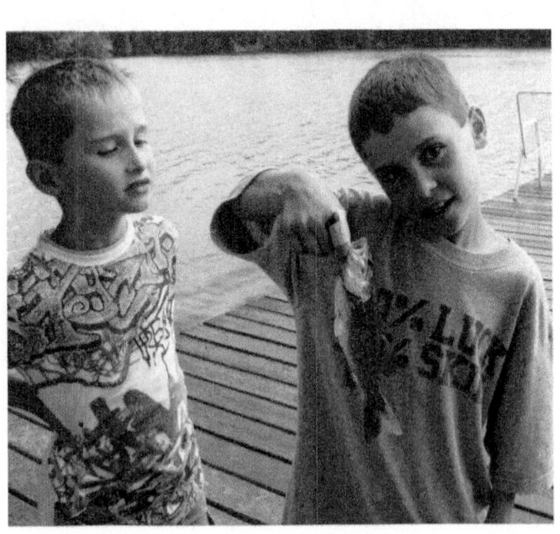

▲ Fresh fish.

A final example of the chemistry of cuisine is preparing or serving fish with lemon slices. When fish begins to decay, low molecular weight amines are produced. These compounds are volatile and produce the characteristic fishy smell. The acid from a lemon reacts with or neutralizes the amine, producing a nonvolatile and nonsmelly compound, leaving the fish smelling fresh. However, probably the best way to have fish is right out of the water, before the amines are produced; fresh fish doesn't smell.

4.2 Writing and Balancing Chemical Equations

Combustion analysis (which we saw in the previous chapter) employs a **chemical reaction**, a process in which one or more substances are converted into one or more different ones. Compounds form and change through chemical reactions. Water can be made by the reaction of hydrogen with oxygen. A **combustion reaction** is a particular type of chemical reaction in which a substance combines with oxygen to form one or more oxygen-containing compounds. Combustion reactions also emit heat. The heat produced in a number of combustion reactions is critical to supplying our society's energy needs. For example, the heat from the combustion of gasoline causes the gaseous combustion products to expand in the cylinders of a car's engine, which push the pistons and propel the car. We use the heat released by the combustion of *natural gas* to cook food and to heat our homes. In many places in the world, fossil fuels, such as coal and oil, are burned to provide electricity.

A chemical reaction is represented by a **chemical equation**. The combustion of natural gas can be represented by the following, unbalanced, equation:

$$\underbrace{CH_4 + O_2}_{\text{reactants}} \longrightarrow \underbrace{CO_2 + H_2O}_{\text{products}}$$

The substances on the left side of the equation are called the **reactants** and the substances on the right side are called the **products**. We often specify the states of each reactant or product in parentheses next to the formula as follows:

$$CH_4(g) + O_2(g) \longrightarrow CO_2(g) + H_2O(g)$$

The (*g*) indicates that these substances are gases in the reaction. The common states of reactants and products and their symbols used in chemical equations are summarized in Table 4.1.

TABLE 4.1 States of Reactants and Products in Chemical Equations

Abbreviation	State
(*g*)	Gas
(*l*)	Liquid
(*s*)	Solid
(*aq*)	Aqueous (water solution)

The equation just presented for the combustion of natural gas is not complete, however. If we look closely, we can see that the left side of the equation has two oxygen atoms and four hydrogen atoms while the right side has three oxygen atoms and two hydrogen atoms:

4 H atoms (CH₄) — 2 H atoms (H₂O)

$$CH_4(g) + O_2(g) \longrightarrow CO_2(g) + H_2O(g)$$

2 O atoms (O₂) — 2 O atoms + 1 O atom = 3 O atoms

Therefore, as written, the reaction violates the law of conservation of mass because an oxygen atom formed out of nothing and hydrogen atoms have vanished. To correct these problems—that is, to write an equation that correctly represents *what actually happens*—we must balance the equation. We need to change the coefficients (those numbers *in front of* the chemical formulas), not the subscripts (those numbers within the chemical formulas), to ensure that the number of each type of atom on the left side of the equation is equal to the number on the right side. New atoms do not form during a reaction, nor do atoms vanish—matter must be conserved.

The reason that you cannot change the subscripts when balancing a chemical equation is that changing the subscripts changes the substance itself, while changing the coefficients changes the number of molecules of the substance. For example, $2\,H_2O$ is simply two water molecules, but H_2O_2 is hydrogen peroxide, a drastically different compound.

When we add coefficients to the reactants and products to balance an equation, we change the number of molecules in the equation but not the *kind of* molecules. To balance the equation for the combustion of methane, we put the coefficient 2 before O_2 in the reactants and the coefficient 2 before H_2O in the products:

$$CH_4(g) + 2\,O_2(g) \longrightarrow CO_2(g) + 2\,H_2O(g)$$

The equation is now balanced because the numbers of each type of atom on either side of the equation are equal. The **balanced chemical equation** tells us that one CH_4 molecule reacts with two O_2 molecules to form one CO_2 molecule and two H_2O molecules. We verify that the equation is balanced by summing the number of each type of atom on each side of the equation:

$$CH_4(g) + 2\,O_2(g) \longrightarrow CO_2(g) + 2\,H_2O(g)$$

Reactants	Products
1 C atom (1 × CH_4)	1 C atom (1 × CO_2)
4 H atoms (1 × CH_4)	4 H atoms (2 × H_2O)
4 O atoms (2 × O_2)	4 O atoms (1 × CO_2 + 2 × H_2O)

The numbers of each type of atom on both sides of the equation are now equal—the equation is balanced.

How to Write Balanced Chemical Equations

We can balance many chemical equations simply by trial and error. However, some guidelines are useful. For example, balancing the atoms in the most complex substances first and the atoms in the simplest substances (such as pure elements) last often makes the process shorter. The following examples illustrate how to balance chemical equations. The general guidelines are shown on the left, with two examples of how to apply them on the right. This procedure is meant only as a flexible guide, not a rigid set of steps.

PROCEDURE FOR ... **Balancing Chemical Equations**	EXAMPLE 4.1 **Balancing Chemical Equations** Write a balanced equation for the reaction between solid cobalt(III) oxide and solid carbon to produce solid cobalt and carbon dioxide gas.	EXAMPLE 4.2 **Balancing Chemical Equations** Write a balanced equation for the combustion of gaseous butane (C_4H_{10}), a fuel used in portable stoves and grills, in which it combines with gaseous oxygen to form gaseous carbon dioxide and gaseous water.
1. Write a skeletal equation by writing chemical formulas for each of the reactants and products. (If a skeletal equation is provided, go to step 2.)	$Co_2O_3(s) + C(s) \longrightarrow Co(s) + CO_2(g)$	$C_4H_{10}(g) + O_2(g) \longrightarrow CO_2(g) + H_2O(g)$
2. Balance atoms that occur in more complex substances first. Always balance atoms in compounds before atoms in pure elements.	**Begin with O:** $Co_2O_3(s) + C(s) \longrightarrow Co(s) + CO_2(g)$ 3 O atoms ⟶ 2 O atoms To balance O, put a 2 before $Co_2O_3(s)$ and a 3 before $CO_2(g)$: $\mathbf{2}\,Co_2O_3(s) + C(s) \longrightarrow Co(s) + \mathbf{3}CO_2(g)$ 6 O atoms ⟶ 6 O atoms	**Begin with C:** $C_4H_{10}(g) + O_2(g) \longrightarrow CO_2(g) + H_2O(g)$ 4 C atoms ⟶ 1 C atom To balance C, put a 4 before $CO_2(g)$: $C_4H_{10}(g) + O_2(g) \longrightarrow \mathbf{4}\,CO_2(g) + H_2O(g)$ 4 C atoms ⟶ 4 C atoms **Balance H:** $C_4H_{10}(g) + O_2(g) \longrightarrow 4\,CO_2(g) + H_2O(g)$ 10 H atoms ⟶ 2 H atoms To balance H, put a 5 before $H_2O(g)$: $C_4H_{10}(g) + O_2(g) \longrightarrow 4\,CO_2(g) + \mathbf{5}\,H_2O(g)$ 10 H atoms ⟶ 10 H atoms
3. Balance atoms that occur as free elements on either side of the equation last. Always balance free elements by adjusting the coefficient on the free element. If the balanced equation contains a fractional coefficient, one may choose to clear these by multiplying the entire equation by the denominator of the fraction.	**Balance Co:** $2\,Co_2O_3(s) + C(s) \longrightarrow Co(s) + 3CO_2(g)$ 4 Co atoms ⟶ 1 Co atom To balance Co, put a 4 before $Co(s)$: $2\,Co_2O_3(s) + C(s) \longrightarrow \mathbf{4}\,Co(s) + 3\,CO_2(g)$ 4 Co atoms ⟶ 4 Co atoms **Balance C:** $2\,Co_2O_3(s) + C(s) \longrightarrow 4\,Co(s) + 3\,CO_2(g)$ 1 C atom ⟶ 3 C atoms To balance C, put a 3 before $C(s)$: $2\,Co_2O_3(s) + \mathbf{3}\,C(s) \longrightarrow 4\,Co(s) + 3\,CO_2(g)$	**Balance O:** $C_4H_{10}(g) + O_2(g) \longrightarrow 4\,CO_2(g) + 5\,H_2O(g)$ 2 O atoms ⟶ 8 O + 5 O = 13 O atoms To balance O, put a $\frac{13}{2}$ before $O_2(g)$: $C_4H_{10}(g) + \mathbf{\frac{13}{2}}\,O_2(g) \longrightarrow 4\,CO_2(g) + 5\,H_2O(g)$ 13 O atoms ⟶ 13 O atoms $C_4H_{10}(g) + \frac{13}{2}\,O_2(g) \longrightarrow 4\,CO_2(g) + 5\,H_2O(g)$ or $2\,C_4H_{10}(g) + 13\,O_2(g) \longrightarrow 8\,CO_2(g) + 10\,H_2O(g)$

4. Check to make certain the equation is balanced by summing the total number of each type of atom on both sides of the equation.	$2\ Co_2O_3(s) + 3\ C(s) \longrightarrow 4\ Co(s) + 3\ CO_2(g)$ Left: 4 Co atoms, 6 O atoms, 3 C atoms Right: 4 Co atoms, 6 O atoms, 3 C atoms The equation is balanced.	$C_4H_{10}(g) + \frac{13}{2}\ O_2(g) \longrightarrow 4\ CO_2(g) + 5\ H_2O(g)$ Left: 4 C atoms, 10 H atoms, 13 O atoms Right: 4 C atoms, 10 H atoms, 13 O atoms The equation is balanced.
	FOR PRACTICE 4.1 Write a balanced equation for the reaction between solid silicon dioxide and solid carbon to produce solid silicon carbide and carbon monoxide gas.	**FOR PRACTICE 4.2** Write a balanced equation for the combustion of gaseous ethane (C_2H_6), a minority component of natural gas, in which it combines with gaseous oxygen to form gaseous carbon dioxide and gaseous water.

CONCEPTUAL CONNECTION 4.1

Balanced Chemical Equations

Which quantities must always be the same on both sides of a chemical equation?

(a) the number of atoms of each kind

(b) the number of molecules of each kind

(c) the number of moles of each kind of molecule

(d) the sum of the masses of all substances involved

4.3 Solutions and Solubility

Chemical reactions involving reactants dissolved in water are among the most common and important. The reactions that occur in lakes, streams, and oceans, as well as the reactions that occur in every cell within our bodies, take place in water. A homogeneous mixture of two substances—such as salt and water—is a **solution**. The majority component of the mixture is the **solvent**, and the minority component is the **solute**. An **aqueous solution** is one in which water acts as the solvent.

Consider two familiar aqueous solutions: salt water and sugar water. Salt water is a solution of NaCl and H_2O, and sugar water is a solution of $C_{12}H_{22}O_{11}$ and H_2O. Certainly, you have made these solutions by adding table salt or sugar to water. As you stir either of these two substances into the water, it seems to disappear. However, you know that the original substance is still present because the water has a salty or a sweet taste. How do solids such as salt and sugar dissolve in water?

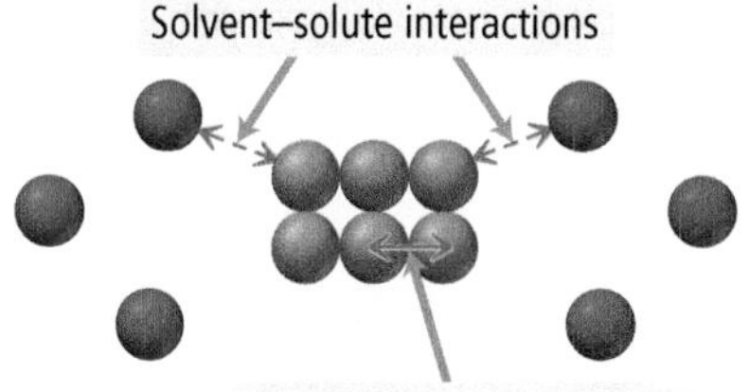

▲ **FIGURE 4.1 Solute and Solvent Interactions** When a solid is put into a solvent, the interactions between solvent and solute particles compete with the interactions among the solute particles themselves.

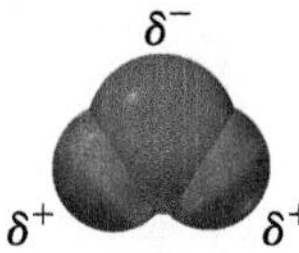

▲ **FIGURE 4.2 Charge Distribution in a Water Molecule** An uneven distribution of electrons within the water molecule causes the oxygen side of the molecule to have a partial negative charge and the hydrogen side to have a partial positive charge.

When a solid is put into a liquid solvent, the attractive forces that hold the solid together (the solute–solute interactions) come into competition with the attractive forces between the solvent molecules and the particles that compose the solid (the solvent–solute interactions), as shown in Figure 4.1 ▶. For example, when sodium chloride is put into water, there is a competition between the attraction of Na^+ cations and Cl^- anions to each other (due to their opposite charges) and the attraction of Na^+ and Cl^- to water molecules. The attraction of Na^+ and Cl^- to water is based on the *polar nature* of the water molecule. For reasons we discuss later in this text, the oxygen atom in water is electron-rich, giving it a partial negative charge (δ^-), as shown in Figure 4.2 ▶. The hydrogen atoms, in contrast, are electron-poor, giving them a partial positive charge ($\delta+$). As a result, the positively charged sodium ions are

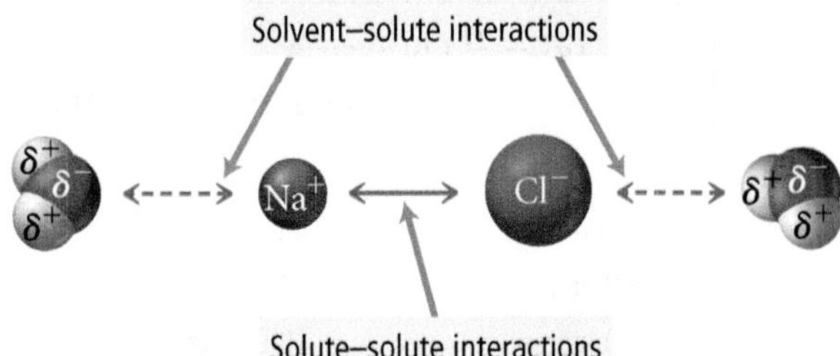

▲ **FIGURE 4.3 Solute and Solvent Interactions in a Sodium Chloride Solution** When sodium chloride is put into water, the attraction of Na^+ and Cl^- ions to water molecules competes with the attraction among the oppositely charged ions themselves.

strongly attracted to the oxygen side of the water molecule, and the negatively charged chloride ions are attracted to the hydrogen side of the water molecule, as shown in Figure 4.3 ◂. In the case of NaCl, the attraction between the separated ions and many water molecules overcomes the attraction of sodium and chloride ions to each other, and the sodium chloride dissolves in the water (Figure 4.4 ▾).

Electrolyte and Nonelectrolyte Solutions

A salt solution will conduct electricity, while a sugar solution does not. The difference between the way that salt (an ionic compound) and sugar (a molecular compound) dissolve in water illustrates a fundamental difference between types of solutions. Ionic compounds, such as sodium chloride, dissociate into their component ions when they dissolve in water. A dilute NaCl solution, represented as NaCl(*aq*), does not contain any NaCl units, but rather dissolved Na^+ and Cl^- ions. The dissolved ions act as charge carriers, allowing the solution to conduct electricity. Substances that dissolve in water to form solutions that conduct electricity are **electrolytes**. Substances such as sodium chloride that completely dissociate into ions when they dissolve in water are **strong electrolytes**, and the resulting solutions are strong electrolyte solutions.

In contrast to sodium chloride, sugar is a molecular compound. Most molecular compounds—with the important exception of acids, which we discuss shortly—dissolve in water as molecules which remain intact once dissolved. Sugar dissolves because the attraction between sugar molecules and water molecules (shown in Figure 4.5 ▾) overcomes the attraction of sugar molecules to each other. So, unlike a sodium chloride solution (which is composed of dissociated ions), a sugar solution is composed of intact $C_{12}H_{22}O_{11}$ molecules homogeneously mixed with the water molecules. Compounds such as sugar that do not dissociate into ions when dissolved in water are called **nonelectrolytes**, and the resulting solutions—called *nonelectrolyte solutions*—do not conduct electricity.

Unlike soluble ionic compounds, which contain ions and therefore *dissociate* in water, acids are molecular compounds that *ionize* in water.

Acids are molecular compounds, but they *do* ionize—form ions—when they dissolve in water. Hydrochloric acid (HCl) is a molecular compound that ionizes into H^+ and Cl^- when it dissolves in water. HCl is an example of a **strong acid**, which means that it completely ionizes in solution. Since strong acids completely ionize in solution, they

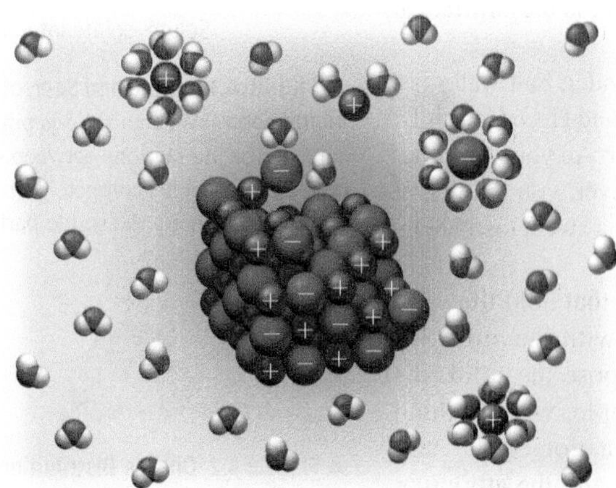

▲ **FIGURE 4.4 Sodium Chloride Dissolving in Water** The attraction between water molecules and the ions of sodium chloride causes NaCl to dissolve in water.

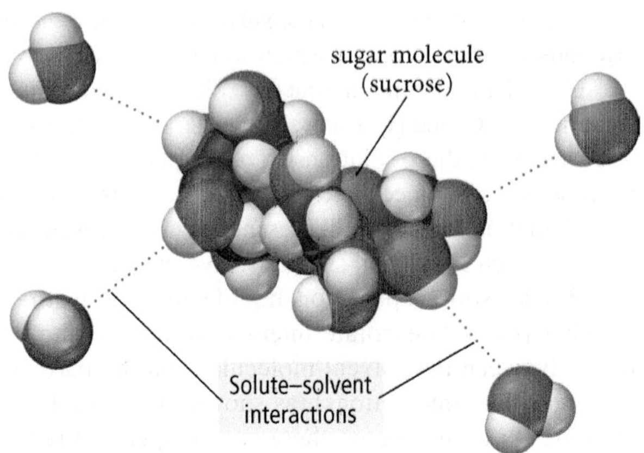

▲ **FIGURE 4.5 Sugar and Water Interactions** Partial charges on sugar molecules and water molecules (discussed more fully in Chapter 11) result in attractions between the sugar molecules and water molecules.

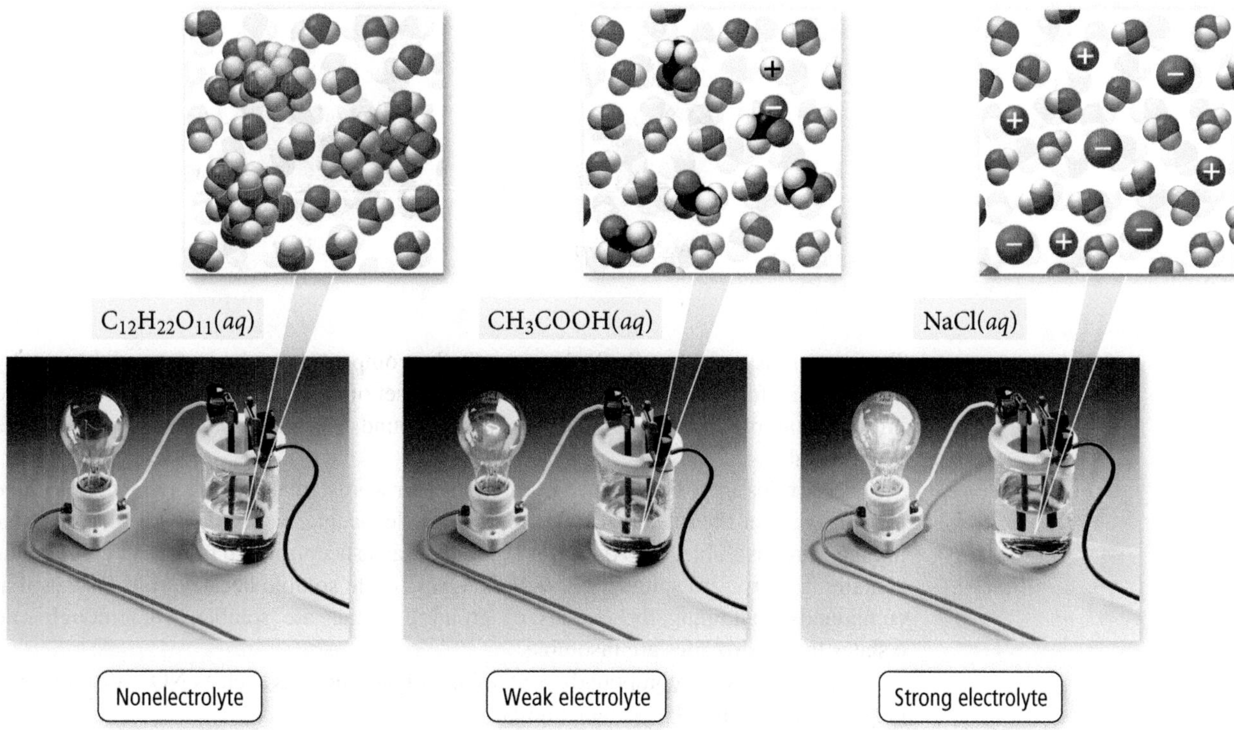

▲ **FIGURE 4.6 Properties of Electrolytes in Solutions**

are also strong electrolytes. We represent the complete ionization of a strong acid with a single reaction arrow between the acid and its ionized form:

$$HCl(aq) \longrightarrow H^+(aq) + Cl^-(aq)$$

Many acids are **weak acids**; they do not completely ionize in water. For example, acetic acid CH_3COOH, the acid present in vinegar, is a weak acid. A solution of a weak acid is composed mostly of the nonionized form of the acid molecules—only a small percentage of the acid molecules ionize. We represent the partial ionization of a weak acid with opposing half arrows between the reactants and products:

$$CH_3COOH(aq) \rightleftharpoons H^+(aq) + CH_3COO^-(aq)$$

Weak acids are classified as **weak electrolytes**, and the resulting solutions—called *weak electrolyte solutions*—conduct electricity only weakly. Figure 4.6 ▲ summarizes the properties of solutions containing electrolytes.

The Solubility of Ionic Compounds

We have just seen that when an ionic compound dissolves in water, the resulting solution contains the component ions dissolved in water. However, not all ionic compounds dissolve completely in water. If we add AgCl to water, for example, it remains solid and appears as a white powder at the bottom of the water.

In general, a compound is termed **soluble** if it dissolves in water and **insoluble** if it does not. However, these classifications are a bit of an oversimplification. In reality, solubility is a continuum, and even "insoluble" compounds dissolve to some extent, though usually orders of magnitude less than soluble compounds. For example, silver nitrate is soluble. If we mix solid $AgNO_3$ with water, it dissolves and forms a strong electrolyte solution. Silver chloride, on the other hand, is almost completely insoluble. If we mix solid AgCl with water, virtually all of it remains as an undissolved solid within the liquid water.

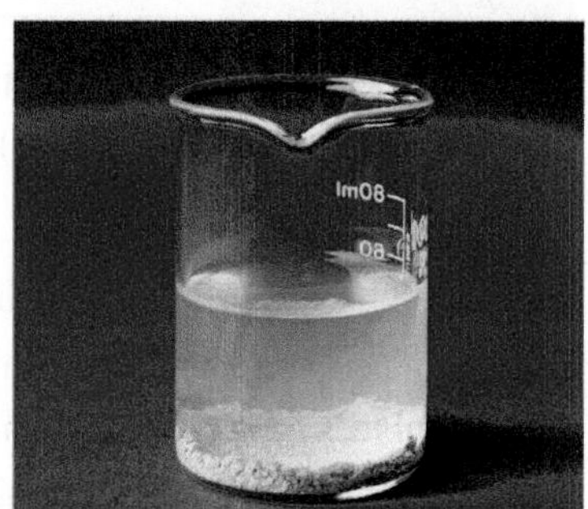

▲ AgCl does not significantly dissolve in water; it remains as a white powder at the bottom of the beaker.

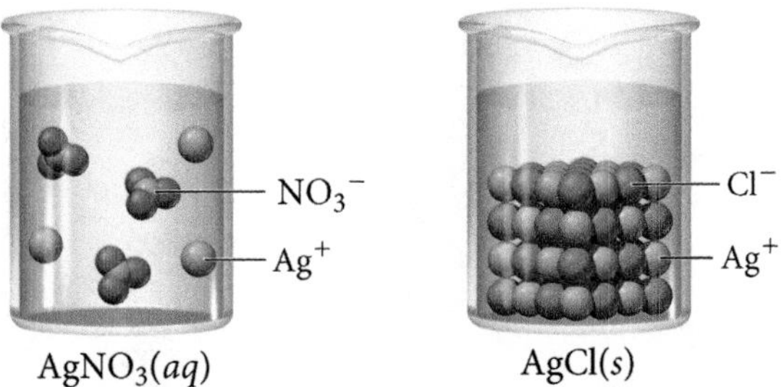

There is no easy way to tell whether a particular compound is soluble or insoluble just by looking at its formula. For now, we can follow a set of empirical rules that chemists have inferred from observations on many ionic compounds. These are *solubility rules* and are listed in Table 4.2.

These rules are to be followed in order. In other words, rules with a smaller number take precedence over the rules that follow. For example, according to rule 3, all salts containing Ag^+ are insoluble, but $AgNO_3$ is soluble because according to rule 2, all compounds containing NO_3^- are soluble. As well, NaOH is quite soluble because rule 1 states that compounds containing the cations of group 1 metals are soluble, even though rule 6 states that hydroxides are insoluble.

Notice that when compounds containing polyatomic ions such as NO_3^- dissolve, the polyatomic ions dissolve as intact units.

TABLE 4.2 General Solubility Rules for Ionic Compounds in Water

1. All salts containing cations of group 1 metals (alkali metals, Li^+, Na^+, K^+, etc.) and ammonium ions (NH_4^+) are soluble.
2. All nitrates (NO_3^-), ethanoates (acetates, CH_3COO^-), chlorates (ClO_3^-), and perchlorates (ClO_4^-) are soluble.
3. Salts containing Ag^+, Pb^{2+}, and Hg_2^{2+} are insoluble.
4. Most chlorides (Cl^-), bromides (Br^-), and iodides (I^-) are soluble.
5. Sulfates (SO_4^{2-}) are soluble, except those containing Ca^{2+}, Sr^{2+}, Ba^{2+}.
6. Carbonates (CO_3^{2-}), hydroxides (OH^-), oxides (O^{2-}), phosphates (PO_4^{3-}), and sulfides (S^{2-}) are generally insoluble.

EXAMPLE 4.3 PREDICTING WHETHER AN IONIC COMPOUND IS SOLUBLE

Predict whether each compound is soluble or insoluble:

(a) $PbCl_2$ **(b)** $CuCl_2$ **(c)** $Ca(NO_3)_2$ **(d)** $BaSO_4$

SOLUTION

(a) Insoluble. Compounds containing Cl^- are normally soluble, but Pb^{2+} is an exception.

(b) Soluble. Compounds containing Cl^- are normally soluble and Cu^{2+} is not an exception.

(c) Soluble. Compounds containing NO_3^- are always soluble.

(d) Insoluble. Compounds containing SO_4^{2-} are normally soluble, but Ba^{2+} is an exception.

FOR PRACTICE 4.3

Predict whether each compound is soluble or insoluble:

(a) NiS **(b)** $Mg_3(PO_4)_2$ **(c)** Li_2CO_3 **(d)** NH_4Cl

4.4 Precipitation Reactions

Have you ever taken a bath in hard water? Hard water contains dissolved ions such as Ca^{2+} and Mg^{2+} that diminish the effectiveness of soap. These ions react with soap to form a grey residue that may appear as a "bathtub ring" when you drain the tub. Hard water is particularly troublesome when washing clothes. Imagine how your white shirt would look covered with the grey crud from the bathtub and you can understand the problem. Consequently, most laundry detergents include substances designed to remove Ca^{2+} and Mg^{2+} from the laundry mixture. The most common substance used for this purpose is sodium carbonate, Na_2CO_3, which dissolves in water to form sodium cations and carbonate anions:

▲ The reaction of ions in hard water with soap produces a grey crud you can see after you drain the water.

$$Na_2CO_3(aq) \longrightarrow 2\,Na^+(aq) + CO_3^{2-}(aq)$$

Sodium carbonate is soluble (rule 1 in Table 4.2), but calcium carbonate and magnesium carbonate are not (rule 6 in Table 4.2). Consequently, the carbonate anions react with dissolved Ca^{2+} and Mg^{2+} ions in hard water to form solids that *precipitate* from (or come out of) solution:

$$Mg^{2+}(aq) + CO_3^{2-}(aq) \longrightarrow MgCO_3(s)$$
$$Ca^{2+}(aq) + CO_3^{2-}(aq) \longrightarrow CaCO_3(s)$$

The precipitation of these ions prevents their reaction with the soap, eliminating the grey residue and preventing white shirts from turning grey.

The reactions between Ca^{2+} or Mg^{2+} with CO_3^{2-} are examples of **precipitation reactions**, ones in which a solid or **precipitate** forms when we mix two solutions. Precipitation reactions are common in chemistry.

As another example, consider potassium iodide and lead(II) nitrate, which each form colourless, strong electrolyte solutions when dissolved in water. When the two solutions are combined, however, a brilliant yellow precipitate forms (Figure 4.7 ▼). We can describe this precipitation reaction with the following chemical equation:

$$2\,KI(aq) + Pb(NO_3)_2(aq) \longrightarrow 2\,KNO_3(aq) + PbI_2(s) \qquad [4.1]$$

The key to predicting precipitation reactions is to understand that *only insoluble compounds form precipitates*. In a precipitation reaction, two solutions containing soluble compounds combine and an insoluble compound precipitates. In the example depicted in Figure 4.7, both KI and $Pb(NO_3)_2$ are soluble and exist in their respective solutions as K^+ and I^- and as Pb^{2+} and NO_3^-. Once the two solutions are mixed, two new compounds—one or both of which might be insoluble—are possible. Specifically, the cation from either compound can pair with the anion from the other to form possibly insoluble products:

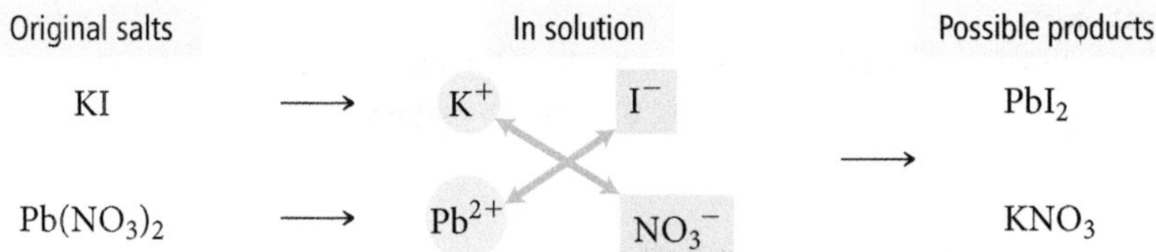

In this case, KNO_3 is soluble, but PbI_2 is essentially insoluble. Consequently, PbI_2 precipitates.

Equation 4.1 is called a **molecular equation**, an equation showing the complete neutral formulas for each compound in the reaction as if they existed as molecules. Because KI and $Pb(NO_3)_2$ are soluble, in their respective aqueous solutions, they are present only as K^+ and I^- and as Pb^{2+} and NO_3^-. We can write equations for reactions occurring in aqueous solution in a way that better shows the dissociated nature of dissolved ionic compounds. For example, Equation 4.1 could be rewritten as a **complete ionic equation**, which lists all of the ions present as either reactants or products in a chemical reaction:

$$Pb^{2+}(aq) + 2\,NO_3^-(aq) + 2\,K^+(aq) + 2\,I^-(aq) \longrightarrow$$
$$PbI_2(s) + 2\,NO_3^-(aq) + 2\,K^+(aq)$$

▶ FIGURE 4.7 Precipitation of Lead(II) Iodide When a potassium iodide solution is mixed with a lead(II) nitrate solution, a yellow lead(II) iodide precipitate forms.

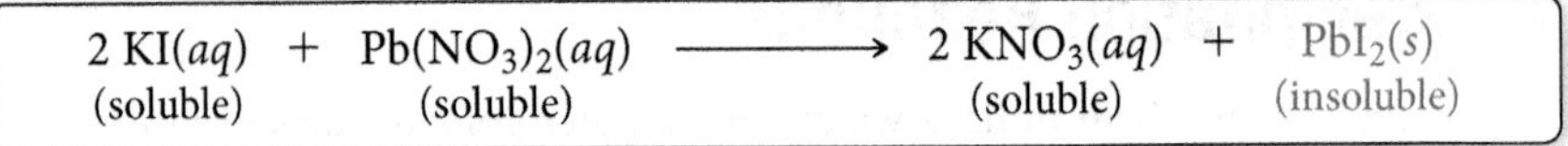

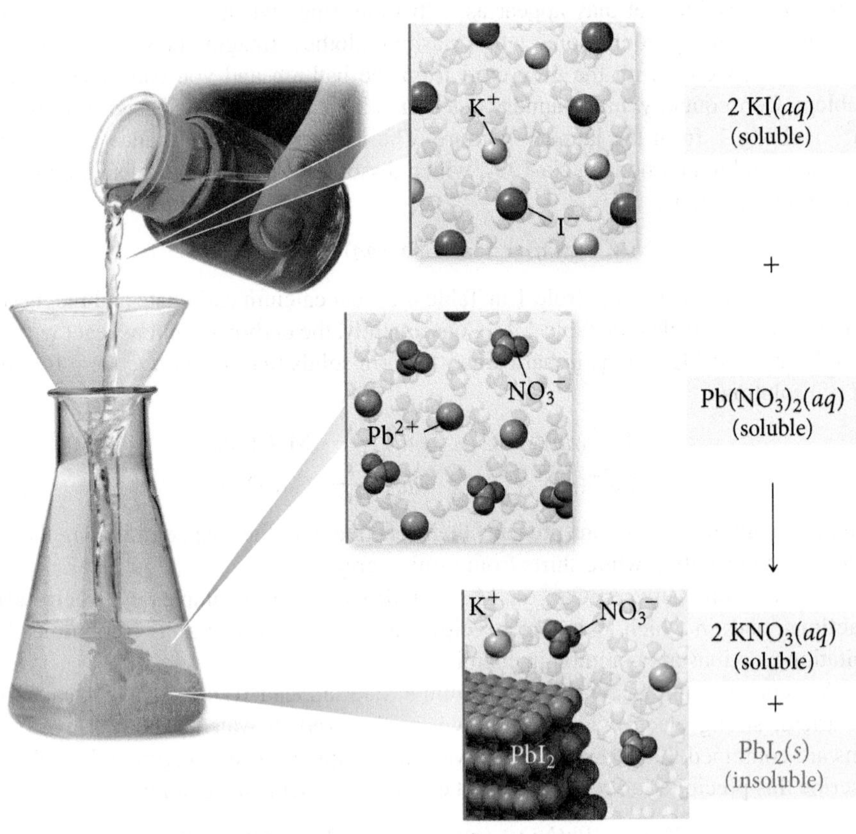

In the complete ionic equation, some ions appear on both the reactant and the product side of the equation. These ions are called **spectator ions** because they do not take part in the chemical reaction. To simplify the equation, and show more clearly what is happening, we can omit spectator ions:

$$Pb^{2+}(aq) + 2\,I^-(aq) \longrightarrow PbI_2(s)$$

This **net ionic equation** is most useful because it shows only the species that take part in the reaction.

The following example shows a procedure for predicting whether a precipitation reaction occurs or not, and how to write the net ionic equation.

EXAMPLE 4.4 WRITING EQUATIONS FOR PRECIPITATION REACTIONS

Write a net ionic equation for the precipitation reaction that occurs (if any) when solutions of potassium carbonate and nickel(II) chloride are mixed.

1. Write the formula of the two compounds being mixed as reactants.	K_2CO_3 and $NiCl_2$
2. Write the ions that are present when the two ionic compounds dissolve in water, and determine the possible products that are formed.	Original salts: K_2CO_3 ⟶ In solution: K^+, CO_3^{2-}; $NiCl_2$ ⟶ Ni^{2+}, Cl^-; ⟶ Possible products: $NiCO_3$, KCl

3. Use the solubility rules (Table 4.2) to determine whether any of the possible products are insoluble.	KCl is soluble (according to rule 1, all salts containing K^+ are soluble, and according to rule 4, all salts containing Cl^- are soluble). $NiCO_3$ is insoluble (according to rule 6, salts containing CO_3^{2-} are generally insoluble).
4. If all the possible products are soluble, there is no reaction or net ionic equation. If any of the possible products are insoluble, write the net ionic equation. It may be helpful to first write the molecular equation. Then convert the molecular equation to the complete ionic equation. Finally, cancel out the spectator ions and you will be left with the net ionic equation.	Molecular equation: $K_2CO_3(aq) + NiCl_2(aq) \longrightarrow 2\ KCl(aq) + NiCO_3(s)$ Complete ionic equation: $\cancel{2\ K^+}(aq) + CO_3^{2-}(aq) + Ni^{2+}(aq) + \cancel{2\ Cl^-}(aq) \longrightarrow \cancel{2\ K^+}(aq) + \cancel{2\ Cl^-}(aq) + NiCO_3(s)$ Net ionic equation: $Ni^{2+}(aq) + CO_3^{2-}(aq) \longrightarrow NiCO_3(s)$

FOR PRACTICE 4.4
Write a net ionic equation for the precipitation reaction that occurs (if any) when solutions of ammonium chloride and iron(III) nitrate are mixed.

FOR MORE PRACTICE 4.4
Write a net ionic equation for the precipitation reaction that occurs (if any) when solutions of sodium hydroxide and copper(II) bromide are mixed.

4.5 Acid–Base Reactions

Another important class of reactions that occur in aqueous solution are acid–base reactions. In an **acid–base reaction** (also called a **neutralization reaction**), an acid reacts with a base and the two neutralize each other, producing water (or in some cases, a weak electrolyte). As in precipitation reactions, an acid–base reaction occurs when the anion from one reactant combines with the cation of the other.

Our stomachs contain hydrochloric acid, which acts in the digestion of food. Certain foods or stress, however, can increase the stomach's acidity to uncomfortable levels, causing what has come to be known as heartburn. Antacids are over-the-counter medicines that work by reacting with and neutralizing stomach acid. Antacids employ different *bases*—substances that produce hydroxide ions (OH^-) in water—as neutralizing agents. Milk of magnesia, for example, contains magnesium hydroxide [$Mg(OH)_2$] and Mylanta® contains aluminum hydroxide [$Al(OH)_3$]. All antacids, regardless of the base they employ, have the same effect of neutralizing stomach acid and relieving heartburn through *acid–base reactions*.

The **Arrhenius definitions** (named after Swedish chemist Svante Arrhenius who lived from 1859 until 1927) of acids and bases are as follows:

- Acid: substance that produces H^+ ions in aqueous solution.
- Base: substance that produces OH^- ions in aqueous solution.

In Chapter 14, we will learn more general definitions of acids and bases, but these are sufficient to describe neutralization reactions.

According to the Arrhenius definition, HCl is an acid because it produces H^+ ions in solution:

$$HCl(aq) \longrightarrow H^+(aq) + Cl^-(aq)$$

An H^+ ion is a bare proton. In solution, bare protons associate with water molecules to form **hydronium ions**, H_3O^+ (Figure 4.8 ▶):

$$H^+(aq) + H_2O(l) \longrightarrow H_3O^+(aq)$$

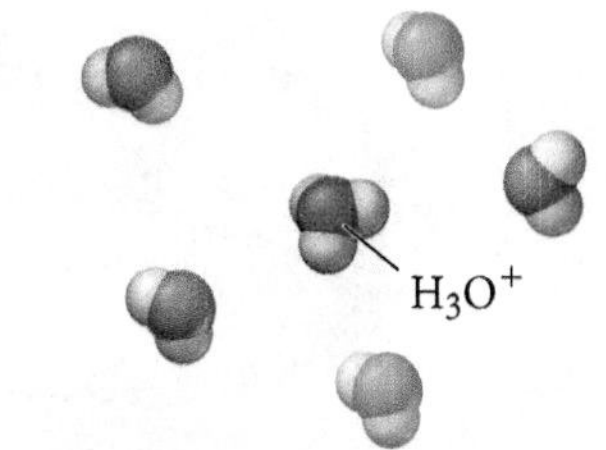

▲ **FIGURE 4.8 The Hydronium Ion** Protons associate with water molecules in solution to form H_3O^+ ions, which in turn interact with other water molecules.

▲ Lemons, limes, and vinegar contain acids. Vitamin C and aspirin are acids.

Chemists often use $H^+(aq)$ and $H_3O^+(aq)$ interchangeably. The chemical equation for the ionization of HCl is often written to show the association of the proton with a water molecule to form the hydronium ion:

$$HCl(aq) + H_2O(l) \longrightarrow H_3O^+(aq) + Cl^-(aq)$$

Some acids—called **polyprotic acids**—contain more than one ionizable proton and release them sequentially. For example, sulfuric acid, H_2SO_4, is a **diprotic acid**. It is strong in its first ionizable proton, but weak in its second:

$$H_2SO_4(aq) + H_2O(l) \longrightarrow H_3O^+(aq) + HSO_4^-(aq)$$
$$HSO_4^-(aq) + H_2O(l) \rightleftharpoons H_3O^+(aq) + SO_4^{2-}(aq)$$

According to the Arrhenius definition, NaOH is a base because it produces OH^- in solution:

$$NaOH(aq) \longrightarrow Na^+(aq) + OH^-(aq)$$

In analogy to diprotic acids, some bases such as $Sr(OH)_2$ produce two moles of OH^- per mole of the base:

$Sr(OH)_2$, and all group 2 hydroxides, are not very soluble but all of the $Sr(OH)_2$ that does dissolve dissociates. For this reason they are considered strong bases.

$$Sr(OH)_2(aq) \longrightarrow Sr^{2+}(aq) + 2\,OH^-(aq)$$

In Table 4.3, some common acids and bases are listed. You can find acids and bases in many everyday substances. Foods such as citrus fruits and vinegar contain acids. Soap, baking soda, and milk of magnesia all contain bases.

When we mix an acid and a base, the H^+ from the acid—whether it is weak or strong—combines with the OH^- from the base to form H_2O (Figure 4.9 ▶). Consider the reaction between hydrochloric acid and sodium hydroxide:

$$\underset{\text{Acid}}{HCl(aq)} + \underset{\text{Base}}{NaOH(aq)} \longrightarrow \underset{\text{Water}}{H_2O(l)} + \underset{\text{Salt}}{NaCl(aq)}$$

The word *salt* in this sense applies to any ionic compound and is therefore more general than the common usage, which refers only to table salt (NaCl).

Acid–base reactions generally form water and an ionic compound—called a **salt**—that usually remains dissolved in the solution. The net ionic equation for many acid–base reactions is:

$$H^+(aq) + OH^-(aq) \longrightarrow H_2O(l)$$

TABLE 4.3 Common Acids and Bases

Name of Acid	Formula	Name of Base	Formula
Hydrochloric acid	HCl	Sodium hydroxide	NaOH
Hydrobromic acid	HBr	Lithium hydroxide	LiOH
Hydroiodic acid	HI	Potassium hydroxide	KOH
Nitric acid	HNO_3	Calcium hydroxide	$Ca(OH)_2$
Sulfuric acid	H_2SO_4	Barium hydroxide	$Ba(OH)_2$
Perchloric acid	$HClO_4$	Ammonia*	NH_3 (weak base)
Acetic acid	CH_3COOH (weak acid)		
Hydrofluoric acid	HF (weak acid)		

*Ammonia does not contain OH^-, but it produces OH^- in a reaction with water that occurs only to a small extent: $NH_3(aq) + H_2O(l) \rightleftharpoons NH_4^+(aq) + OH^-(aq)$.

▲ Many common household products are bases.

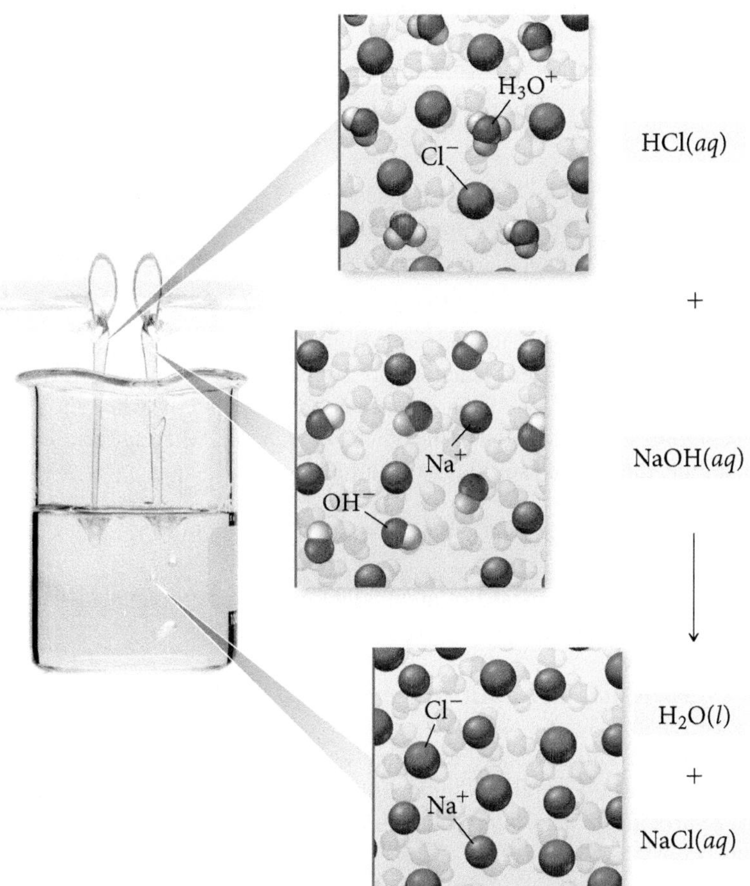

◀ **FIGURE 4.9 Acid–Base Reaction** The reaction between hydrochloric acid and sodium hydroxide forms water and a salt, sodium chloride, which remains dissolved in the solution.

EXAMPLE 4.5 **WRITING EQUATIONS FOR ACID–BASE REACTIONS**

Write a molecular and net ionic equation for the reaction between aqueous HI and aqueous $Ba(OH)_2$.

SOLUTION

You must first identify these substances as an acid and a base. Begin by writing the skeletal reaction in which the acid and the base combine to form water and a salt.	$\underset{\text{acid}}{HI(aq)} + \underset{\text{base}}{Ba(OH)_2(aq)} \longrightarrow \underset{\text{water}}{H_2O(l)} + \underset{\text{salt}}{BaI_2(aq)}$
Next, balance the equation: this is the molecular equation.	$2\,HI(aq) + Ba(OH)_2(aq) \longrightarrow 2\,H_2O(l) + BaI_2(aq)$
Write the net ionic equation by removing the spectator ions.	$2\,H^+(aq) + 2\,OH^-(aq) \longrightarrow 2\,H_2O(l)$ or simply $H^+(aq) + OH^-(aq) \longrightarrow H_2O(l)$

FOR PRACTICE 4.5

Write a molecular and net ionic equation for the reaction that occurs between aqueous H_2SO_4 and aqueous LiOH.

Another example of an acid–base reaction is the reaction between sulfuric acid and potassium hydroxide:

$$H_2SO_4(aq) + 2KOH(aq) \longrightarrow 2H_2O(l) + K_2SO_4(aq)$$

Again, notice the pattern of an acid and base reacting to form water and a salt:

$$\textit{Acid} + \textit{Base} \longrightarrow \textit{Water} + \textit{Salt}$$

When writing equations for acid–base reactions, write the formula of the salt using the procedure for writing formulas of ionic compounds given in Section 4.2.

Acid–Base Reactions Evolving a Gas

In some acid–base reactions, two aqueous solutions mix to form a gaseous product that bubbles out of solution. These reactions are sometimes called **gas-evolution reactions**. Some gas-evolution reactions form a gaseous product directly when the cation of one reactant combines with the anion of the other. For example, when sulfuric acid reacts with lithium sulfide, dihydrogen sulfide gas is formed:

$$H_2SO_4(aq) + Li_2S(aq) \longrightarrow H_2S(g) + Li_2SO_4(aq)$$

Similarly, when acids composed of ammonium cation react in an acid–base reaction in aqueous solution, ammonia gas is evolved:

$$NH_4Cl(aq) + NaOH(aq) \longrightarrow H_2O(l) + NH_3(g) + NaCl(aq)$$

Other gas-evolution reactions often form an intermediate product that then decomposes (breaks down into simpler substances) to form a gas. For example, when aqueous hydrochloric acid is mixed with aqueous sodium bicarbonate, the following reactions occur:

$$HCl(aq) + NaHCO_3(aq) \longrightarrow \underset{\text{intermediate}}{H_2CO_3(aq)} + NaCl(aq)$$

$$H_2CO_3(aq) \longrightarrow H_2O(l) + CO_2(g)$$

The intermediate product, H_2CO_3, is not stable and decomposes into H_2O and gaseous CO_2. The overall reaction can be written as follows:

$$HCl(aq) + NaHCO_3(aq) \longrightarrow H_2O(l) + CO_2(g) + NaCl(aq)$$

Like the bicarbonate example above, bases composed of carbonates, sulfites, and bisulfites also form gases in acid–base reactions occurring in aqueous solution, as is summarized in Table 4.4.

TABLE 4.4 Types of Compounds That Undergo Gas-Evolution Reactions

Reactant Type	Intermediate Product	Gas Evolved	Example
Sulfides	None	H_2S	$2\,HCl(aq) + K_2S(aq) \longrightarrow H_2S(g) + 2\,KCl(aq)$
Carbonates and bicarbonates	H_2CO_3	CO_2	$2\,HCl(aq) + K_2CO_3(aq) \longrightarrow H_2O(l) + CO_2(g) + 2\,KCl(aq)$
Sulfites and bisulfites	H_2SO_3	SO_2	$2\,HCl(aq) + K_2SO_3(aq) \longrightarrow H_2O(l) + SO_2(g) + 2\,KCl(aq)$
Ammonium	NH_4OH	NH_3	$NH_4Cl(aq) + KOH(aq) \longrightarrow H_2O(l) + NH_3(g) + KCl(aq)$

EXAMPLE 4.6 **WRITING EQUATIONS FOR GAS-EVOLUTION REACTIONS**

Write a molecular equation for the gas-evolution reaction that occurs when you mix aqueous nitric acid and aqueous sodium carbonate.

Begin by writing a skeletal equation in which the cation of each reactant combines with the anion of the other.	$HNO_3(aq) + Na_2CO_3(aq) \longrightarrow H_2CO_3(aq) + NaNO_3(aq)$
You must then recognize that $H_2CO_3(aq)$ decomposes into $H_2O(l)$ and $CO_2(g)$, and write these products into the equation.	$HNO_3(aq) + Na_2CO_3(aq) \longrightarrow H_2O(l) + CO_2(g) + NaNO_3(aq)$
Finally, balance the equation.	$2\,HNO_3(aq) + Na_2CO_3(aq) \longrightarrow H_2O(l) + CO_2(g) + 2\,NaNO_3(aq)$

FOR PRACTICE 4.6

Write a molecular equation for the gas-evolution reaction that occurs when you mix aqueous hydrobromic acid and aqueous potassium sulfite.

FOR MORE PRACTICE 4.6

Write a net ionic equation for the reaction that occurs when you mix hydroiodic acid with calcium sulfide.

4.6 Oxidation–Reduction Reactions

Oxidation–reduction reactions or **redox reactions** are reactions in which electrons transfer from one reactant to the other. The rusting of iron, the bleaching of hair, and the production of electricity in batteries involve redox reactions. Many redox reactions (for example, combustion reactions) involve the reaction of a substance with oxygen (Figure 4.10 ▼):

Applications of oxidation–reduction reactions are covered in Chapter 18.

$$4\,Fe(s) + 3\,O_2(g) \longrightarrow 2\,Fe_2O_3(s)$$
$$C_8H_{18}(l) + \tfrac{25}{2}\,O_2(g) \longrightarrow 8\,CO_2(g) + 9\,H_2O(g)$$
$$2\,H_2(g) + O_2(g) \longrightarrow 2\,H_2O(l)$$

$2\,H_2(g) + O_2(g) \longrightarrow 2\,H_2O(g)$

Hydrogen and oxygen react to form gaseous water.

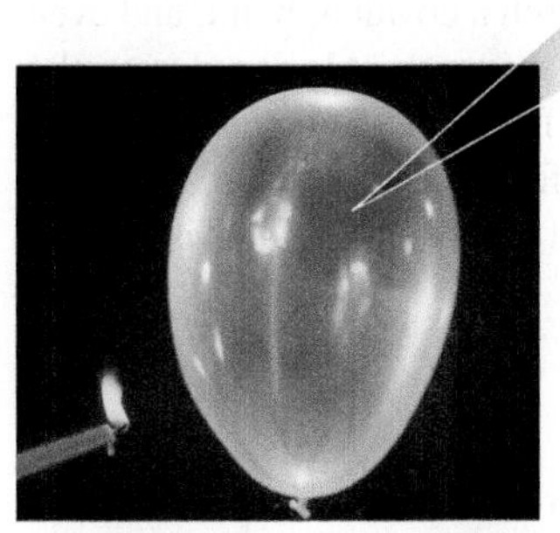

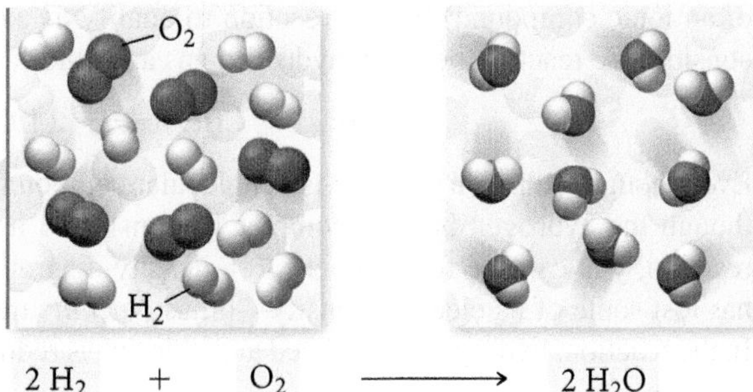

$2\,H_2 + O_2 \longrightarrow 2\,H_2O$

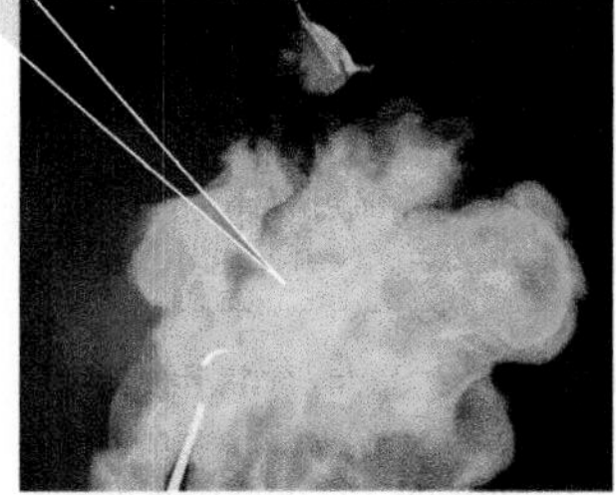

▲ **FIGURE 4.10 Oxidation–Reduction Reaction** The hydrogen in the balloon reacts with oxygen upon ignition to form gaseous water (which is dispersed in the flame).

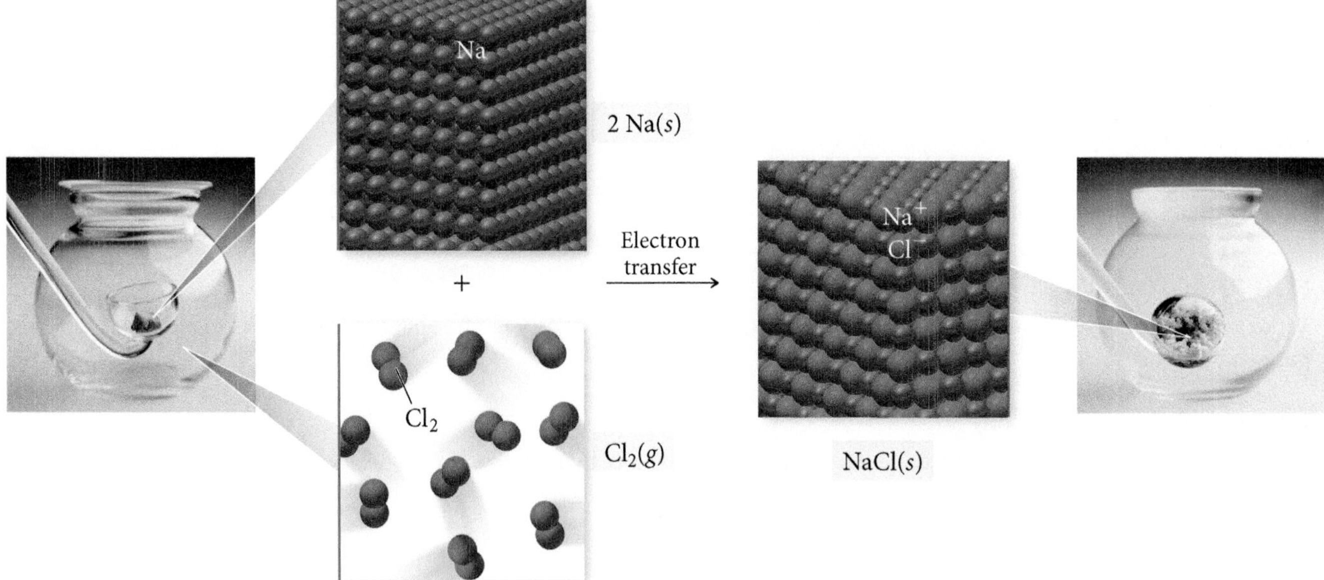

▲ **FIGURE 4.11 Oxidation–Reduction Without Oxygen** When sodium reacts with chlorine, electrons transfer from the sodium to the chlorine, resulting in the formation of sodium chloride. In this redox reaction, sodium is oxidized and chlorine is reduced.

The ability of an element to attract electrons in a chemical bond is called electronegativity. We cover electronegativity in more detail in Section 9.7.

However, redox reactions need not involve oxygen. Consider, for example, the reaction between sodium and chlorine to form sodium chloride (NaCl), depicted in Figure 4.11 ▲:

$$2\ Na(s) + Cl_2(g) \longrightarrow 2\ NaCl(s)$$

This reaction is similar to the reaction between sodium and oxygen, which forms sodium oxide:

$$4\ Na(s) + O_2(g) \longrightarrow 2\ Na_2O(s)$$

In both cases, a metal (which has a tendency to lose electrons) reacts with a nonmetal (which has a tendency to gain electrons). In both cases, metal atoms lose electrons to nonmetal atoms. A fundamental definition of **oxidation** is the loss of electrons, and a fundamental definition of **reduction** is the gain of electrons.

The transfer of electrons need not be a *complete* transfer (as occurs in the formation of an ionic compound) for the reaction to qualify as oxidation–reduction. For example, consider the reaction between hydrogen gas and chlorine gas:

$$H_2(g) + Cl_2(g) \longrightarrow 2\ HCl(g)$$

Even though hydrogen chloride is a molecular compound with a covalent bond, and even though the hydrogen has not completely transferred its electron to chlorine during the reaction, you can see from the electron density diagrams (Figure 4.12 ◄) that hydrogen has lost some of its electron density—it has *partially* transferred its electron to chlorine. In the reaction, hydrogen is oxidized and chlorine is reduced and, therefore, this is a redox reaction.

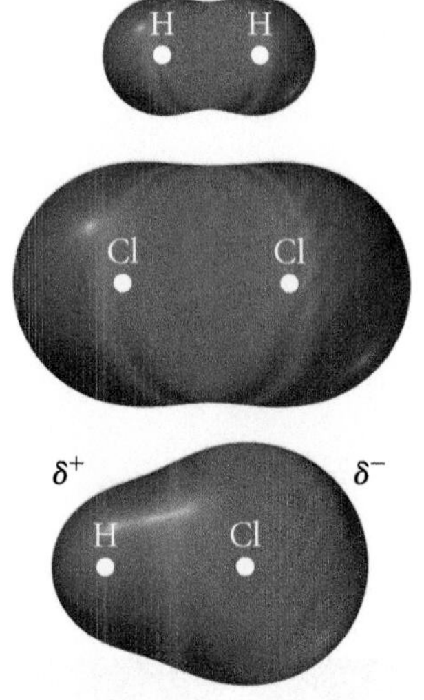

▲ **FIGURE 4.12 Redox with Partial Electron Transfer** When hydrogen bonds to chlorine, the electrons are unevenly shared, resulting in an increase of electron density (reduction) for chlorine and a decrease in electron density (oxidation) for hydrogen.

Oxidation States

Identifying whether or not a reaction between a metal and a nonmetal is a redox reaction is fairly straightforward because of ion formation. But how do we identify redox reactions that occur between nonmetals? Chemists have devised a scheme to track electrons before and after a chemical reaction. In this scheme—which is like bookkeeping for electrons—each shared electron is assigned to the atom that attracts the electrons most strongly. Then a number, called the **oxidation state** or oxidation number, is given to each atom based on the electron assignments. In other words, the oxidation number of an atom in a compound is the "charge" it would have if all shared electrons were assigned to the atom with the greatest attraction for those electrons.

For example, consider HCl. Since chlorine attracts electrons more strongly than hydrogen, we assign the two shared electrons in the bond to chlorine; then H (which has lost an electron in our assignment) has an oxidation state of +1, and Cl (which has gained one electron in our assignment) has an oxidation state of −1. You can use the following rules to assign oxidation states to atoms in elements and compounds.

Do not confuse oxidation state with ionic charge. Unlike ionic charge—which is a real property of an ion—the oxidation state of an atom is merely a theoretical (but useful) construct.

Rules for Assigning Oxidation States These rules are hierarchical. If any two rules conflict, follow the rule with the smaller number (i.e., rule 1 takes precedence over rule 2):

1. The oxidation state of each atom in an element is 0.
2. The oxidation state of the atom in a monoatomic ion is equal to the ion's charge.
3. The sum of the oxidation states of all atoms in:
   - a neutral molecule is always 0.
   - a polyatomic ion is always equal to the charge of the ion.
4. In their compounds, metals have positive oxidation states:
   - Group 1 metals always have an oxidation state of +1.
   - Group 2 metals always have an oxidation state of +2.
5. The oxidation state of hydrogen in a compound is usually +1.
6. In their compounds, the nonmetals typically have negative oxidation states:
   - Fluorine always has an oxidation state of −1.
   - The other group 17 elements usually have an oxidation state of −1.
   - Oxygen usually has an oxidation state of −2.
   - The other group 16 elements usually have an oxidation state of −2.
   - Group 15 elements usually have an oxidation number of −3.

Another point to keep in mind is that when assigning oxidation states to elements that are not covered by the rules, such as carbon, use rule 3 to deduce their oxidation state once all other oxidation states have been assigned. For example, when assigning oxidation states to C and H in methane, CH_4, rule 5 says that the oxidation state of hydrogen is +1. According to rule 3, the sum of all oxidation states for methane must be 0, so the oxidation state of carbon must be −4.

EXAMPLE 4.7 ASSIGNING OXIDATION STATES

Assign an oxidation state to each atom in each element, ion, or compound:

(a) Cl_2 **(b)** Na^+ **(c)** KF **(d)** CO_2 **(e)** SO_4^{2-} **(f)** K_2O_2

SOLUTION

(a) Since Cl_2 is an element, the oxidation state of both Cl atoms is 0 (rule 1).	Cl_2 ClCl 0 0
(b) Since Na^+ is a monoatomic ion, its oxidation state is equal to its charge, 1+ (rule 2).	Na^+ Na^+ +1
(c) The oxidation state of K is +1 (rule 4). Since there are only two atoms in this compound, we can use rule 3 to assign an oxidation number to F. The sum of the oxidation numbers must be 0, so the oxidation number of F is −1, which agrees with rule 6.	KF KF +1 −1 sum: +1−1 = 0

(continued)

EXAMPLE 4.7 (CONTINUED)

(d) The oxidation state of each oxygen is −2 (rule 6). The sum of the oxidation states must be 0 (rule 3), so the oxidation state of carbon is +4.	CO_2 (C ox state) + 2(O ox state) = 0 (C ox state) + 2(−2) = 0 C ox state = +4 CO_2 +4 −2 sum: +4+2(−2) = 0
(e) The oxidation state of each oxygen is −2 (rule 6). We might expect the oxidation state of sulfur to be −2. However, if that were the case, the sum of the oxidation states would not equal the charge on the ion. Since O is mentioned higher on the list of rules than S, it takes priority and we compute the oxidation state of sulfur by setting the sum of all the oxidation states equal to −2 (the charge of the ion, rule 3).	SO_4^{2-} (S ox state) + 4(O ox state) = −2 (S ox state) + 4(−2) = −2 S ox state = +6 SO_4^{2-} +6 −2 sum: +6+4(−2) = −2
(f) The oxidation state of potassium is +1 (rule 4). We might ordinarily expect the oxidation state of O to be −2 (rule 6), but group 1 metals are mentioned higher on the list of rules (rule 4), so we deduce the oxidation state of O by setting the sum of all the oxidation states equal to 0 (rule 3).	K_2O_2 2(K ox state) + 2(O ox state) = 0 2(+1) + 2(O ox state) = 0 O ox state = −1 K_2O_2 +1 −1 sum: 2(+1) + 2(−1) = 0

FOR PRACTICE 4.7

Assign an oxidation state to each atom in each element, ion, or compound:

(a) Cr **(b)** Cr^{3+} **(c)** CCl_4 **(d)** $SrBr_2$ **(e)** SO_3 **(f)** NO_3^-

In most cases, oxidation states are positive or negative integers; on occasion, an atom within a compound can have a fractional oxidation state. Consider KO_2. The oxidation states are assigned as follows:

$$\underset{+1\ -\frac{1}{2}}{KO_2}$$

$$\text{sum: } +1+2(-\tfrac{1}{2}) = 0$$

In KO_2, oxygen has a $-\frac{1}{2}$ oxidation state. Although this seems unusual, it is acceptable because oxidation states are merely an imposed electron bookkeeping scheme, not an actual physical quantity.

Identifying Redox Reactions

We can use oxidation states to identify redox reactions, even between nonmetals. For example, is the following reaction between carbon and sulfur a redox reaction?

$$C + 2S \longrightarrow CS_2$$

If so, what element is oxidized? What element is reduced? We can use the oxidation state rules to assign oxidation states to all elements on both sides of the equation.

$$C + 2\,S \longrightarrow CS_2$$

Oxidation states: 0 0 +4 −2

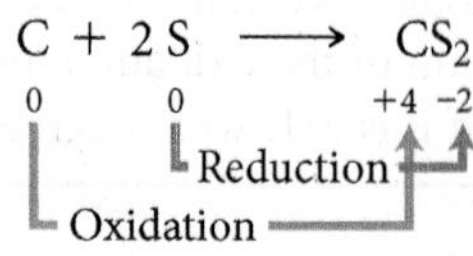

Carbon changes from an oxidation state of 0 to an oxidation state of +4. In terms of our electron bookkeeping scheme (the assigned oxidation state), carbon *loses electrons* during the conversion of reactants to products and is *oxidized.* During the conversion of reactants to products, sulfur changes from an oxidation state of 0 to an oxidation state of −2. In terms of our electron bookkeeping scheme, sulfur *gains electrons* and is *reduced.* In terms of oxidation states, oxidation and reduction are defined as follows:

- Oxidation: an increase in oxidation state.
- Reduction: a decrease in oxidation state.

Notice that oxidation and reduction must occur together. If one substance loses electrons (oxidation), then another substance must gain electrons (reduction). A substance that causes the oxidation of another substance is called an **oxidizing agent**. Oxygen, for example, is an excellent oxidizing agent because it causes the oxidation of many substances. In a redox reaction, *the oxidizing agent is always reduced.* A substance that causes the reduction of another substance is called a **reducing agent**. Hydrogen, for example, as well as the group 1 and group 2 metals (because of their tendency to lose electrons) are excellent reducing agents. In a redox reaction, *the reducing agent is always oxidized.*

Remember that a reduction is a *reduction* in oxidation state.

You will learn more about redox reactions below, including how to balance them. For now, you need to be able to identify redox reactions, as well as oxidizing and reducing agents, according to the following guidelines:

Redox reactions:

- Any reaction in which there is a change in the oxidation states of atoms in going from reactants to products.

In a redox reaction:

- The oxidizing agent oxidizes another substance (and is itself reduced).
- The reducing agent reduces another substance (and is itself oxidized).

EXAMPLE 4.8 IDENTIFYING REDOX REACTIONS, OXIDIZING AGENTS, AND REDUCING AGENTS

Determine whether each reaction is an oxidation–reduction reaction. For each oxidation–reduction reaction, identify the oxidizing agent and the reducing agent.

(a) $2\,Mg(s) + O_2(g) \longrightarrow 2\,MgO(s)$

(b) $2\,HBr(aq) + Ca(OH)_2(aq) \longrightarrow 2\,H_2O(l) + CaBr_2(aq)$

(c) $Zn(s) + 2\,Fe^{2+}(aq) \longrightarrow Zn^{2+}(aq) + 2\,Fe(s)$

(d) $C_2H_6(g) + \frac{7}{2}O_2(g) \longrightarrow 2\,CO_2(g) + 3\,H_2O(l)$

SOLUTION

(a) This is a redox reaction because magnesium increases in oxidation number (oxidation) and oxygen decreases in oxidation number (reduction).	$2\,Mg(s) + O_2(g) \longrightarrow 2\,MgO(s)$ Oxidation states: Mg 0; O_2 0; MgO +2 −2 Mg → Mg: Oxidation; O → O: Reduction Oxidizing agent: O_2 Reducing agent: Mg
(b) This is not a redox reaction because none of the atoms undergoes a change in oxidation number. This is an acid–base or neutralization reaction.	$2\,HBr(aq) + Ca(OH)_2(aq) \longrightarrow 2\,H_2O(l) + CaBr_2(aq)$ HBr: +1 −1; $Ca(OH)_2$: +2 −2 +1; H_2O: +1 −2; $CaBr_2$: +2 −1
(c) This is a redox reaction because zinc increases in oxidation number (oxidation) and iron decreases in oxidation number (reduction).	$Zn(s) + Fe^{2+}(aq) \longrightarrow Zn^{2+}(aq) + Fe(s)$ Oxidation states: Zn 0; Fe^{2+} +2; Zn^{2+} +2; Fe 0 Zn → Zn^{2+}: Oxidation; Fe^{2+} → Fe: Reduction Oxidizing agent: Fe^{2+} Reducing agent: Zn

(continued)

EXAMPLE 4.8 (CONTINUED)

(d) This is a redox reaction because carbon increases in oxidation number (oxidation) and oxygen decreases in oxidation number (reduction). Combustion reactions are redox reactions.

$$\underset{-3\ +1}{C_2H_6(g)} + \underset{0}{\tfrac{7}{2}O_2(g)} \rightarrow \underset{+4\ -2}{2\,CO_2(g)} + \underset{+1\ -2}{3\,H_2O(l)}$$

Reduction; Oxidation

Oxidizing agent: O_2
Reducing agent: C_2H_6

FOR PRACTICE 4.8

Determine whether each reaction is an oxidation–reduction reaction. For all redox reactions, identify the oxidizing agent and the reducing agent.

(a) $2\,Li(s) + Cl_2(g) \longrightarrow 2\,LiCl(s)$
(b) $2\,Al(s) + 3\,Sn^{2+}(aq) \longrightarrow 2\,Al^{3+}(aq) + 3\,Sn(s)$
(c) $Pb(NO_3)_2(aq) + 2\,LiCl(aq) \longrightarrow PbCl_2(s) + 2\,LiNO_3(aq)$
(d) $C(s) + O_2(g) \longrightarrow CO_2(g)$

CONCEPTUAL CONNECTION 4.2
Oxidation and Reduction

Which statement is true?

(a) A redox reaction involves *either* the transfer of an electron *or* a change in the oxidation state of an element.

(b) If any of the reactants or products in a reaction contain oxygen, the reaction is a redox reaction.

(c) In a reaction, oxidation can occur independently of reduction.

(d) In a redox reaction, any increase in the oxidation state of a reactant must be accompanied by a decrease in the oxidation state of a reactant.

CHEMISTRY IN YOUR DAY Bleached Blonde

Have you ever bleached your hair? Most home kits for hair bleaching contain hydrogen peroxide (H_2O_2), an excellent oxidizing agent. When applied to hair, hydrogen peroxide oxidizes melanin, the dark pigment that gives hair its colour. Once melanin is oxidized, it no longer imparts a dark colour to hair, leaving the hair with the familiar bleached look. Hydrogen peroxide also oxidizes other components of hair. For example, protein molecules in hair contain —SH groups called thiols. Hydrogen peroxide oxidizes these thiol groups to sulfonic acid groups, $—SO_3H$. The oxidation of thiol groups to sulfonic acid groups causes changes in the proteins that compose hair, making the hair more brittle and more likely to tangle. Consequently, people with heavily bleached hair generally use conditioners, which contain compounds that form thin, lubricating coatings on individual hair shafts. These coatings prevent tangling and make hair softer and more manageable.

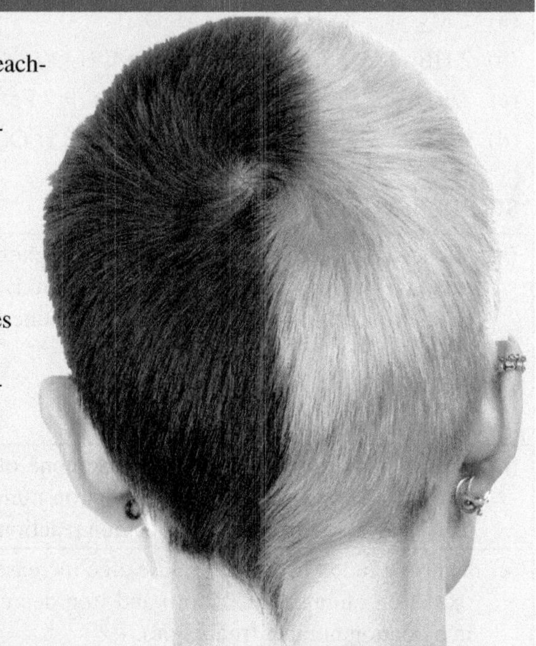

Question

The following is a reaction of hydrogen peroxide with an alkene:

$$H_2O_2 + C_2H_4 \longrightarrow C_2H_4O + H_2O$$

Can you see why this reaction is a redox reaction? Can you identify the oxidizing and reducing agents?

▶ The bleaching of hair involves a redox reaction in which melanin—the main pigment in hair—is oxidized.

Balancing Oxidation–Reduction Equations

Consider the following reaction between calcium and water:

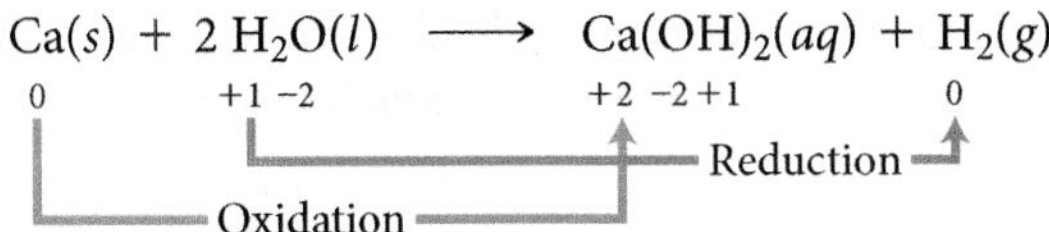

Since calcium increases in oxidation state from 0 to +2, it is oxidized. Since hydrogen decreases in oxidation state from +1 to 0, it is reduced.

Balancing redox reactions can be more complicated than balancing other types of reactions because both the mass (or number of each type of atom) and the *charge* must be balanced. Redox reactions occurring in aqueous solutions can be balanced by using a special procedure called the *half-reaction method of balancing.* In this procedure, the overall equation is broken down into two half-reactions: one for oxidation and one for reduction. The half-reactions are balanced individually and then added together. The steps differ slightly for reactions occurring in acidic and in basic solution. The following example demonstrates the method used for an acidic solution, and Example 4.10 demonstrates the method used for a basic solution.

EXAMPLE 4.9 **HALF-REACTION METHOD OF BALANCING AQUEOUS REDOX REACTIONS IN ACIDIC SOLUTION**

Balance the following redox reaction in acidic solution:

$$Fe^{2+}(aq) + MnO_4^-(aq) \longrightarrow Fe^{3+}(aq) + Mn^{2+}(aq)$$

1. *Assign oxidation states* to all atoms and identify the substances being oxidized and reduced. This step simply allows you to categorize, with confidence, the half-reactions as oxidation or reduction in the next step.	$Fe^{2+}(aq) + MnO_4^-(aq) \longrightarrow Fe^{3+}(aq) + Mn^{2+}(aq)$ +2 +7 −2 +3 +2 Reduction Oxidation Fe^{2+} is being oxidized by MnO_4^- to Fe^{3+}. MnO_4^- is the oxidizing agent. The reducing agent, Fe^{2+}, reduces MnO_4^- to Mn^{2+}.
2. *Separate the overall reaction into two half-reactions*: one for oxidation and one for reduction.	**Oxidation:** $Fe^{2+}(aq) \longrightarrow Fe^{3+}(aq)$ **Reduction:** $MnO_4^-(aq) \longrightarrow Mn^{2+}(aq)$
3. *Balance each half-reaction with respect to mass* in the following order: • Balance all elements other than H and O. • Balance O by adding H_2O. • Balance H by adding H^+.	All elements other than O and H are balanced, so proceed to balance O and then H. The oxidation half-reaction does not contain O or H, so it remains the same for this step. $Fe^{2+}(aq) \longrightarrow Fe^{3+}(aq)$ Since the left side of the reaction contains 4 O, we add 4 H_2O to the right side. This results in 8 H on the right side, so we add 8 H^+ to the left side. All elements should now be balanced. $8\,H^+(aq) + MnO_4^-(aq) \longrightarrow Mn^{2+}(aq) + 4\,H_2O(l)$
4. *Balance each half-reaction with respect to charge* by adding electrons. (Make the sum of the charges on both sides of the equation equal by adding as many electrons as necessary.)	For the oxidation reaction, there is a net positive charge on the right side, so we add one electron to the right to balance this charge: $Fe^{2+}(aq) \longrightarrow Fe^{3+}(aq) + e^-$ The reduction reaction has a net 7+ on the left side and 2+ on the right side. To balance the charge, we add five electrons to the left side: $5e^- + 8\,H^+(aq) + MnO_4^-(aq) \longrightarrow Mn^{2+}(aq) + 4\,H_2O(l)$

(continued)

EXAMPLE 4.9 (CONTINUED)

5. *Make the number of electrons in both half-reactions equal* by multiplying one or both half-reactions by a small whole number.	Multiply the oxidation reaction by 5 so that there are an equal number of electrons on the left side of the oxidation half-reaction as there are electrons on the right side of the reduction half-reaction. $$5\,Fe^{2+}(aq) \longrightarrow 5\,Fe^{3+}(aq) + 5e^-$$ $$5\,e^- + 8\,H^+(aq) + MnO_4^-(aq) \longrightarrow Mn^{2+}(aq) + 4\,H_2O(l)$$
6. *Add the two half-reactions together,* cancelling electrons and other species as necessary.	$$5\,Fe^{2+}(aq) \longrightarrow 5\,Fe^{3+}(aq) + 5e^-$$ $$5e^- + 8\,H^+(aq) + MnO_4^-(aq) \longrightarrow Mn^{2+}(aq) + 4\,H_2O(l)$$ $$5\,Fe^{2+}(aq) + 8\,H^+(aq) + MnO_4^-(aq) \longrightarrow 5\,Fe^{3+}(aq) + Mn^{2+}(aq) + 4\,H_2O(l)$$
7. *Verify that the reaction is balanced* both with respect to mass and with respect to charge.	**Reactants** / **Products**: 5 Fe / 5 Fe; 8 H / 8 H; 1 Mn / 1 Mn; 4 O / 4 O; +17 charge / +17 charge

FOR PRACTICE 4.9

Balance the following redox reaction in acidic solution:

$$H^+(aq) + Cr(s) \longrightarrow H_2(g) + Cr^{2+}(aq)$$

FOR MORE PRACTICE 4.9

Balance the following redox reaction in acidic solution:

$$Cu(s) + NO_3^-(aq) \longrightarrow Cu^{2+}(aq) + NO_2(g)$$

When a redox reaction occurs in basic solution, you can balance the reaction in exactly the same way, except that you must add an additional step to neutralize any H^+ with OH^-. The H^+ and the OH^- combine to form H_2O as shown in the following example.

EXAMPLE 4.10 BALANCING REDOX REACTIONS OCCURRING IN BASIC SOLUTION

In Example 4.9, we balanced the reaction between iron(II) and the permanganate ion in acidic solution:

$$5\,Fe^{2+}(aq) + 8\,H^+(aq) + MnO_4^-(aq) \longrightarrow 5\,Fe^{3+}(aq) + Mn^{2+}(aq) + 4\,H_2O(l)$$

Balance this reaction in basic solution.

SOLUTION

To balance redox reactions occurring in basic solution, follow the half-reaction method outlined above for acidic solutions, but add an extra step to neutralize the H^+ with OH^- as shown in step 1 below.

1. Starting with the balanced redox reaction in acidic solution, neutralize H^+ by adding the same number of OH^- ions to both sides of the equation.	$$5\,Fe^{2+}(aq) + 8\,H^+(aq) + 8\,OH^-(aq) + MnO_4^-(aq) \longrightarrow 5\,Fe^{3+}(aq) + Mn^{2+}(aq) + 4\,H_2O(l) + 8\,OH^-(aq)$$

2. The side with both H^+ and OH^- will combine to form water.	$5\,Fe^{2+}(aq) + \cancel{8}^{4}\,H_2O(l) + MnO_4^-(aq)$ $\longrightarrow 5\,Fe^{3+}(aq) + Mn^{2+}(aq) + \cancel{4H_2O(l)} + 8\,OH^-(aq)$
Then cancel as much water as possible from both sides of the equation.	$5\,Fe^{2+}(aq) + 4\,H_2O(l) + MnO_4^-(aq)$ $\longrightarrow 5\,Fe^{3+}(aq) + Mn^{2+}(aq) + 8\,OH^-(aq)$
3. Verify that the reaction is balanced.	**Reactants** / **Products**: 5 Fe / 5 Fe; 8 H / 8 H; 5 O / 5 O; 1 Mn / 1 Mn; −9 charge / −9 charge

Reactants	Products
5 Fe	5 Fe
8 H	8 H
5 O	5 O
1 Mn	1 Mn
−9 charge	−9 charge

FOR PRACTICE 4.10

Balance the following redox reaction occurring in basic solution.

$$ClO^-(aq) + Cr(OH)_4^-(aq) \longrightarrow CrO_4^{2-}(aq) + Cl^-(aq)$$

Disproportionation Reactions A **disproportionation reaction** is one in which a reactant is both oxidized and reduced. For example, hydrogen peroxide (H_2O_2) decomposes to form H_2O and O_2. Some H_2O_2 is reduced, which forms H_2O, and some H_2O_2 is oxidized, which forms O_2:

$$\underset{-1}{2H_2O_2(aq)} \longrightarrow \underset{-2}{2H_2O(l)} + \underset{0}{O_2(g)}$$

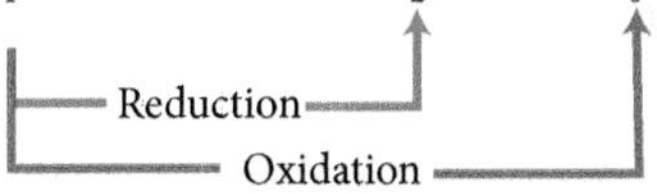

Reduction (−1 → −2)
Oxidation (−1 → 0)

To balance disproportionation reactions we follow the same method as laid out in Examples 4.9 and 4.10.

EXAMPLE 4.11 BALANCING DISPROPORTIONATION REACTIONS

Balance the disproportionation reaction of chlorine to form chloride and chlorate ions in basic solution:

$$Cl_2(aq) \longrightarrow Cl^-(aq) + ClO_3^-(aq)$$

1. Assign oxidation states to help categorize the half-reactions.	$\underset{0}{Cl_2(aq)} \longrightarrow \underset{-1}{Cl^-(aq)} + \underset{+5}{ClO_3^-(aq)}$ 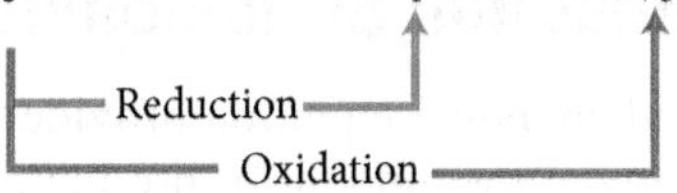 Reduction (0 → −1); Oxidation (0 → +5)
2. Separate the overall reaction into half-reactions.	**Reduction:** $Cl_2(aq) \longrightarrow Cl^-(aq)$ **Oxidation:** $Cl_2(aq) \longrightarrow ClO_3^-(aq)$
3. Balance each half-reaction with respect to mass:	
• Balance all elements other than H and O.	$Cl_2(aq) \longrightarrow 2\,Cl^-(aq)$ $Cl_2(aq) \longrightarrow 2\,ClO_3^-(aq)$
• Balance O by adding H_2O.	$Cl_2(aq) \longrightarrow 2\,Cl^-(aq)$ $Cl_2(aq) + 6\,H_2O(l) \longrightarrow 2\,ClO_3^-(aq)$
• Balance H by adding H^+.	$Cl_2(aq) \longrightarrow 2\,Cl^-(aq)$ $Cl_2(aq) + 6\,H_2O(l) \longrightarrow 2\,ClO_3^-(aq) + 12\,H^+(aq)$

(continued)

EXAMPLE 4.11 (CONTINUED)

4. Balance each half-reaction with respect to charge.	$Cl_2(aq) + 2e^- \longrightarrow 2\,Cl^-(aq)$ $Cl_2(aq) + 6\,H_2O(l) \longrightarrow 2\,ClO_3^-(aq) + 12\,H^+(aq) + 10e^-$
5. Make the number of electrons in both equations the same by multiplying each by a small whole number.	$5\,Cl_2(aq) + 10e^- \longrightarrow 10\,Cl^-(aq)$ $Cl_2(aq) + 6\,H_2O(l) \longrightarrow 2\,ClO_3^-(aq) + 12\,H^+(aq) + 10e^-$
6. Add the half-reactions together and make necessary cancellations.	$5\,Cl_2(aq) + \cancel{10e^-} \longrightarrow 10\,Cl^-(aq)$ $Cl_2(aq) + 6\,H_2O(l) \longrightarrow 2\,ClO_3^-(aq) + 12\,H^+(aq) + \cancel{10e^-}$ $6\,Cl_2(aq) + 6\,H_2O(l) \longrightarrow 2\,ClO_3^-(aq) + 10\,Cl^-(aq) + 12\,H^+(aq)$
7. Neutralize H+ by adding the same number of OH^- ions to both sides of the equation.	$6\,Cl_2(aq) + 6\,H_2O(l) + 12\,OH^-(aq) \longrightarrow 2\,ClO_3^-(aq) + 10\,Cl^-(aq) + 12\,H^+(aq) + 12\,OH^-(aq)$
The side with both H^+ and OH^- will combine to form water.	$6\,Cl_2(aq) + \cancel{6\,H_2O(l)} + 12\,OH^-(aq) \longrightarrow 2\,ClO_3^-(aq) + 10\,Cl^-(aq) + \overset{6}{\cancel{12}}\,H_2O(l)$
Then cancel as much water as possible from both sides of the equation. In this case, we can divide each stoichiometric coefficient by a factor of two.	$6\,Cl_2(aq) + 12\,OH^-(aq) \longrightarrow 2\,ClO_3^-(aq) + 10\,Cl^-(aq) + 6\,H_2O(l)$ $3\,Cl_2(aq) + 6\,OH^-(aq) \longrightarrow ClO_3^-(aq) + 5\,Cl^-(aq) + 3\,H_2O(l)$
8. Verify that the reaction is balanced with respect to mass and charge.	**Reactants** / **Products** 6 Cl / 6 Cl 6 H / 6 H 6 O / 6 O −6 charge / −6 charge

FOR PRACTICE 4.11

Balance the following disproportionation reaction of chlorine dioxide in acidic medium.

$$ClO_2 \longrightarrow ClO_2^- + ClO_3^-$$

4.7 Reaction Stoichiometry: How Much Is Produced?

A balanced chemical equation provides the exact relationship between the amount of reactant and the amount of product. For example, in a combustion reaction, the chemical equation provides a relationship between the amount of fuel burned and the amount of carbon dioxide emitted. In the following discussion, we use octane (a component of gasoline) as our fuel. The balanced equation for the combustion of octane is:

$$2\,C_8H_{18}(g) + 25\,O_2(g) \longrightarrow 16\,CO_2(g) + 18\,H_2O(l)$$

The balanced equation shows that 16 CO_2 molecules are produced for every 2 molecules of octane burned, or that 8 CO_2 molecules are produced for every mole of octane burned. It is equally correct to write a combustion reaction such as the preceding one to show only one molecule of the fuel by dividing all the coefficients by a factor of 2:

$$C_8H_{18}(g) + \tfrac{25}{2}O_2(g) \longrightarrow 8\,CO_2(g) + 9\,H_2O(l)$$

Nothing has changed; there are still 8 CO_2 molecules produced for every mole of octane burned. We can extend this numerical relationship between molecules to the amounts in moles as follows:

The coefficients in a chemical reaction specify the relative amounts in moles of each of the substances involved in the reaction.

In other words, from the equation, we know that eight *moles* of CO_2 are produced for every *mole* of octane burned. The use of the numerical relationships between chemical amounts in a balanced chemical equation are called reaction **stoichiometries**. Stoichiometry allows us to predict the amounts of products that will form in a chemical reaction based on the amounts of reactants that react. Stoichiometry also allows us to determine the amount of reactants necessary to form a given amount of product. These calculations are central to chemistry, allowing chemists to plan and carry out chemical reactions in order to obtain products in the desired quantities.

Stoichiometry is pronounced stoy-kee-om-e-tree.

Making Molecules: Mole-to-Mole Conversions

A balanced chemical equation is simply a "recipe" for how reactants combine to form products. From our balanced equation for the combustion of octane, for example, we can write the following stoichiometric ratio:

$$1\,\text{mol}\ C_8H_{18} : 8\,\text{mol}\ CO_2$$

We can use this ratio to determine how many moles of CO_2 form when a given number of moles of C_8H_{18} burns. A typical car or small truck requires 50.0 L, which is about 300 mol of octane, to fill the tank. Suppose we burn this entire tank of gas, 300 mol of C_8H_{18}; how many moles of CO_2 form? We use the ratio from the balanced chemical equation. The ratio acts as a conversion factor between the amount in moles of the reactant C_8H_{18} and the amount in moles of the product:

$$300\ \cancel{\text{mol}\ C_8H_{18}} \times \frac{8\ \text{mol}\ CO_2}{1\ \cancel{\text{mol}\ C_8H_{18}}} = 2.40 \times 10^3\ \text{mol}\ CO_2$$

The combustion of 300 mol of C_8H_{18} (1 tank of gas) adds 2400 mol of CO_2 to the atmosphere!

Making Molecules: Mass-to-Mass Conversions

Respiration is a chemical reaction where glucose reacts with oxygen to form carbon dioxide and water:

$$C_6H_{12}O_6(s) + 6\ O_2(g) \longrightarrow 6\ CO_2(g) + 6\ H_2O(l)$$

Let's estimate the mass of CO_2 that is produced by respiration of the glucose equivalent to the sugar in one chocolate bar, approximately 36.0 g. The calculation is similar to the one done in the previous section, but this time we are given the mass of fuel ($C_6H_{12}O_6$) instead of the number of moles. Consequently, we must first convert the mass (in grams) to the amount (in moles). The general conceptual plan for calculations where you are given the mass of a reactant or product in a chemical reaction and asked to find the mass of a different reactant or product takes the form:

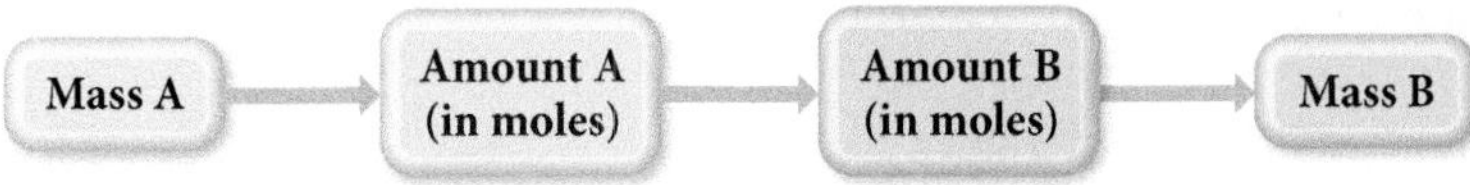

where A and B are two different substances involved in the reaction. We use the molar mass of A to convert from the mass of A to the amount of A (in moles). Then, we use the appropriate ratio from the balanced chemical equation to convert from the amount of A (in moles) to the amount of B (in moles). Finally, we use the molar mass of B to convert from the amount of B (in moles) to the mass of B. To calculate the mass of CO_2 produced from the respiration of 36.0 g of glucose, we use the following conceptual plan:

Conceptual Plan

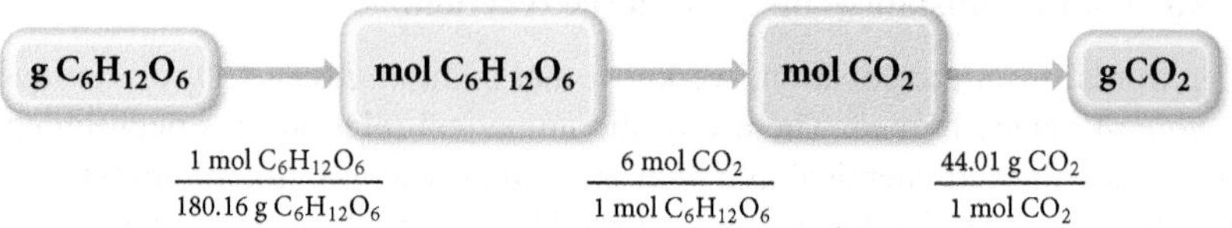

Relationships Used

1 mol $C_6H_{12}O_6$: 6 mol CO_2 (from the chemical equation)

molar mass of $C_6H_{12}O_6$ = 180.16 g mol^{-1}

molar mass of CO_2 = 44.01 g mol^{-1}

Solution

We follow the conceptual plan to solve the problem, beginning with the mass of $C_6H_{12}O_6$ and cancelling units to arrive at the mass of CO_2:

$$36.0 \text{ g } \cancel{C_6H_{12}O_6} \times \frac{1 \text{ mol } \cancel{C_6H_{12}O_6}}{180.16 \text{ g } \cancel{C_6H_{12}O_6}} \times \frac{6 \text{ mol } \cancel{CO_2}}{1 \text{ mol } \cancel{C_6H_{12}O_6}} \times \frac{44.01 \text{ g } CO_2}{1 \text{ mol } \cancel{CO_2}} = 52.8 \text{ g } CO_2$$

The following are additional examples of stoichiometric calculations.

EXAMPLE 4.12 STOICHIOMETRY

In photosynthesis, plants convert carbon dioxide and water into glucose ($C_6H_{12}O_6$) according to the following reaction:

$$6CO_2(g) + 6H_2O(l) \xrightarrow{\text{sunlight}} 6O_2(g) + C_6H_{12}O_6(aq)$$

Suppose you determine that a particular plant consumes 37.8 g of CO_2 in one week. Assuming that there is more than enough water present to react with all of the CO_2, what mass of glucose (in grams) can the plant synthesize from the CO_2?

SORT The problem gives the mass of carbon dioxide and asks you to find the mass of glucose that can be produced.

GIVEN: 37.8 g CO_2

FIND: g $C_6H_{12}O_6$

STRATEGIZE The conceptual plan follows the general pattern of mass A ⟶ amount A (in moles) ⟶ amount B (in moles) ⟶ mass B. From the chemical equation, deduce the relationship between moles of carbon dioxide and moles of glucose. Use the molar masses to convert between grams and moles.

CONCEPTUAL PLAN

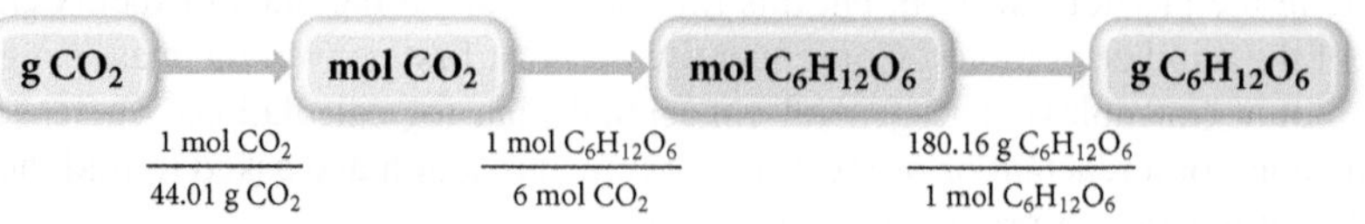

RELATIONSHIPS USED

molar mass CO_2 = 44.01 g mol^{-1}

6 mol CO_2 : 1 mol $C_6H_{12}O_6$

molar mass $C_6H_{12}O_6$ = 180.16 g mol^{-1}

SOLVE Follow the conceptual plan to solve the problem. Begin with g CO_2 and use the conversion factors to arrive at g $C_6H_{12}O_6$.

SOLUTION

$$37.8 \text{ g } \cancel{CO_2} \times \frac{1 \text{ mol } \cancel{CO_2}}{44.01 \text{ g } \cancel{CO_2}} \times \frac{1 \text{ mol } \cancel{C_6H_{12}O_6}}{6 \text{ mol } \cancel{CO_2}} \times \frac{180.16 \text{ g } C_6H_{12}O_6}{1 \text{ mol } \cancel{C_6H_{12}O_6}} = 25.8 \text{ g } C_6H_{12}O_6$$

CHECK The units of the answer are correct. The magnitude of the answer (25.8 g) is less than the initial mass of CO_2 (37.8 g). This is reasonable because each carbon in CO_2 has two oxygen atoms associated with it, while in $C_6H_{12}O_6$, each carbon has only one oxygen atom and two hydrogen atoms (which are much lighter than oxygen) associated with it. Therefore, the mass of glucose produced should be less than the mass of carbon dioxide for this reaction.

FOR PRACTICE 4.12

Magnesium hydroxide, the active ingredient in milk of magnesia, neutralizes stomach acid, primarily HCl, according to the following reaction:

$$Mg(OH)_2(aq) + 2\,HCl(aq) \longrightarrow 2\,H_2O(l) + MgCl_2(aq)$$

What mass of HCl, in grams, can be neutralized by a dose of milk of magnesia containing 3.26 g $Mg(OH)_2$?

FOR MORE PRACTICE 4.12

One component of acid rain is nitric acid, which forms when NO_2, also a pollutant, reacts with oxygen and water according to the following simplified equation:

$$4\,NO_2(g) + O_2(g) + 2\,H_2O(l) \longrightarrow 4\,HNO_3(aq)$$

The generation of the electricity used by a medium-sized home produces about 16 kg of NO_2 per year. Assuming that there is adequate O_2 and H_2O, what mass of HNO_3, in kg, can form from this amount of NO_2 pollutant?

CONCEPTUAL CONNECTION 4.3

Stoichiometry

Under certain conditions, sodium can react with oxygen to form sodium oxide according to the following reaction:

$$4\,Na(s) + O_2(g) \longrightarrow 2\,Na_2O(s)$$

A flask contains the amount of oxygen represented by the diagram on the right ▶.

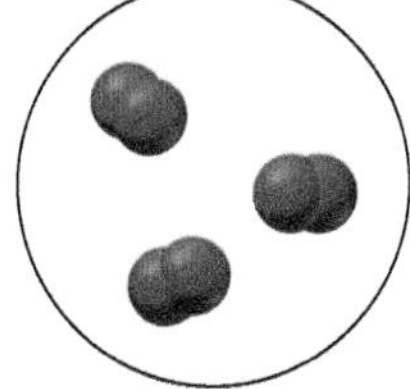

Which diagram best represents the amount of sodium required to completely react with all of the oxygen in the flask, according to the above equation?

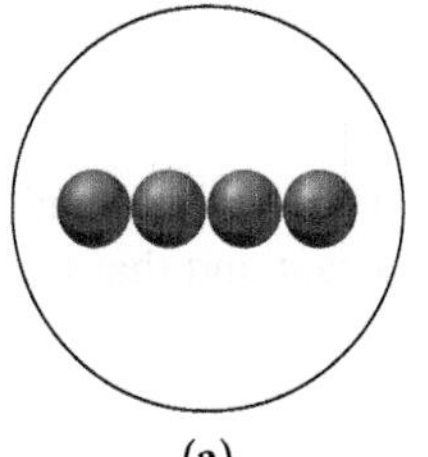

(a)

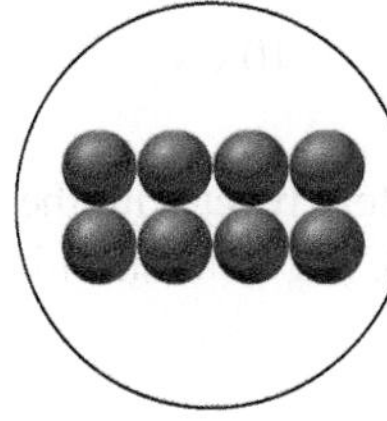

(b)

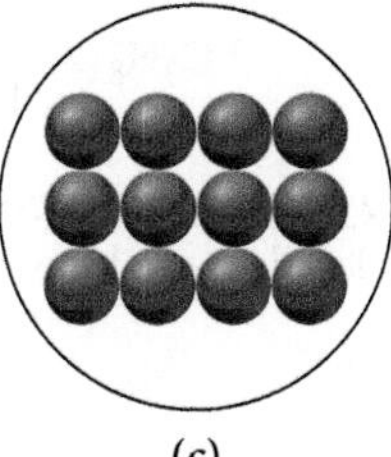

(c)

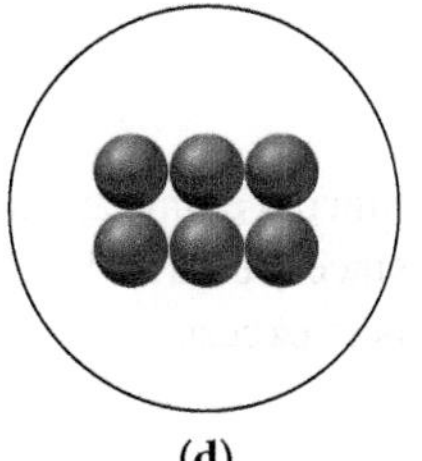

(d)

4.8 Limiting Reactant, Theoretical Yield, and Percent Yield

It is intuitive to begin with an example to understand three more important concepts in reaction stoichiometry: limiting reactant, theoretical yield, and percent yield. We will use the combustion of propane (C_3H_8), the most common barbeque fuel, as our example. The balanced equation for the combustion of propane is:

$$C_3H_8(g) + 5\,O_2(g) \longrightarrow 3\,CO_2(g) + 4\,H_2O(l)$$

   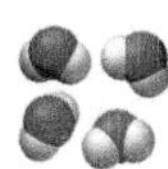

Supposing we start with 2 molecules of C_3H_8 and 15 molecules of O_2, what is the reactant that limits the amount of the products that can be formed (the **limiting reactant**)? What is the maximum amount of CO_2 that can be produced from the limiting reactant (the **theoretical yield**)? First we must calculate the number of CO_2 molecules that can be made from 2 molecules of C_3H_8:

$$2\ \cancel{C_3H_8} \times \frac{3\ CO_2}{1\ \cancel{C_3H_8}} = 6\ CO_2$$

Next, we calculate the number of CO_2 molecules that can be made from 15 O_2 molecules:

$$15\ \cancel{O_2} \times \frac{3\ CO_2}{5\ \cancel{O_2}} = 9\ CO_2$$

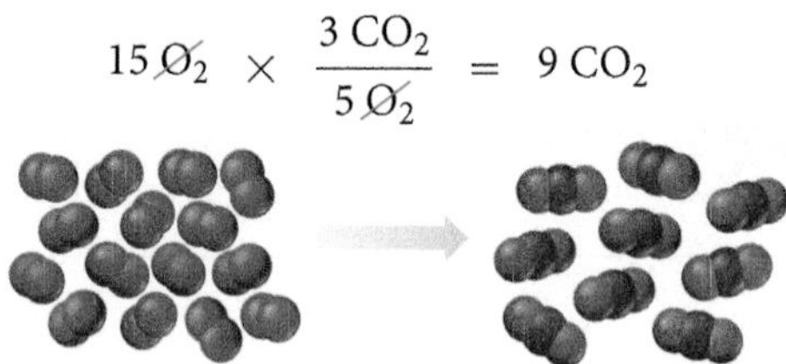

We have enough C_3H_8 to make 6 CO_2 molecules and enough O_2 to make 9 CO_2 molecules; for this reason, C_3H_8 is the *limiting reactant* and 6 molecules of CO_2 is the *theoretical yield* for our present starting mixture of 2 propane molecules and 15 O_2 molecules. O_2 is in excess.

An alternate way of calculating the limiting reactant is to pick any reactant and determine how much of the *other reactant* is necessary to completely react with it. For the reaction we just examined, we have 2 C_3H_8 molecules and 15 O_2 molecules. Let's see how much O_2 is need to completely react with the 2 molecules of C_3H_8:

$$2\ \cancel{C_3H_8} \times \frac{5\ O_2}{1\ \cancel{C_3H_8}} = 10\ O_2$$

Since we only need 10 O_2 molecules to completely react with the 2 C_3H_8 molecules and since we have 15 O_2 molecules, we know that C_3H_8 is the limiting reactant and that O_2 is in excess.

Limiting Reactant, Theoretical Yield, and Percent Yield from Initial Reactant Masses

When working in the laboratory, we normally measure the initial quantities of reactants in grams, not in number of molecules. To find the limiting reactant and theoretical yield from initial masses, we must first convert the masses to amounts in moles. Consider the following reaction:

$$2\ Mg(s) + O_2(g) \longrightarrow 2\ MgO(s)$$

A reaction mixture contains 42.5 g Mg and 33.8 g O_2; what is the limiting reactant and theoretical yield? To solve this problem, we must determine which of the given amounts of reactants makes the least amount of product.

CONCEPTUAL CONNECTION 4.4

Limiting Reactant and Theoretical Yield

Nitrogen and hydrogen gas react to form ammonia according to the following reaction:

$$N_2(g) + 3H_2(g) \longrightarrow 2\,NH_3(g)$$

If a flask contains a mixture of reactants represented by the diagram on the right ▸, which diagram best represents the mixture in the flask after the reactants have reacted as completely as possible? What is the limiting reactant? Which reactant is in excess?

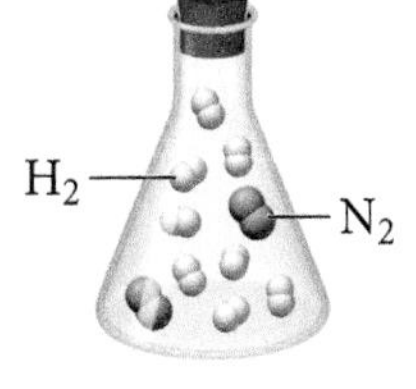

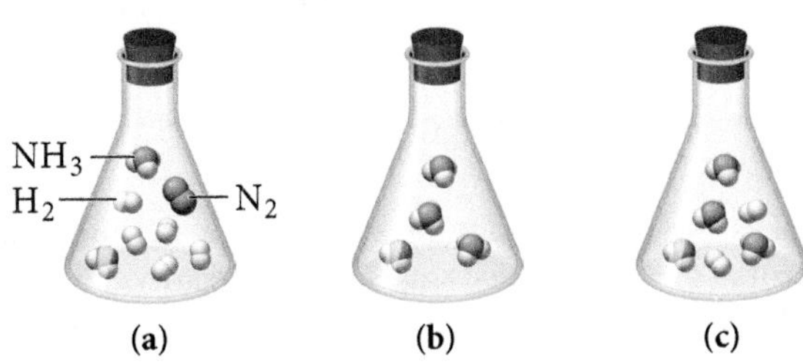

Conceptual Plan We can find the limiting reactant by calculating how much product can be made from each reactant. However, since we are given the initial quantities in grams, and stoichiometric relationships are between moles, we must first convert grams to moles. We then convert from moles of the reactant to moles of the product. The reactant that makes the *least amount of product* is the limiting reactant. The conceptual plan is as follows:

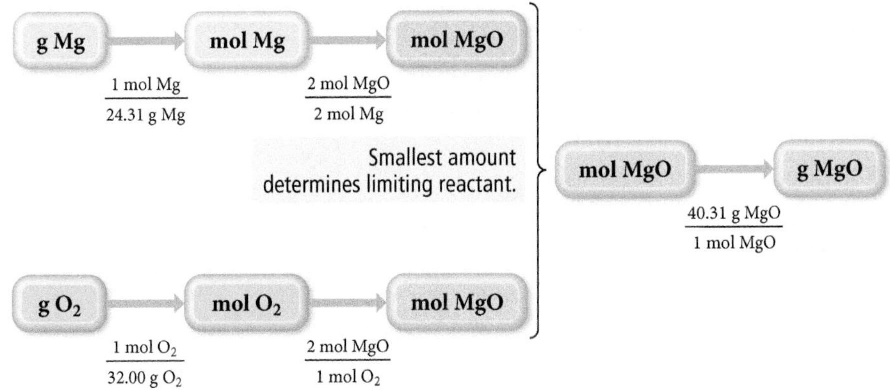

In the plan, we compare the number of moles of MgO made by each reactant and convert only the smaller amount to grams.

Relationships Used

molar mass Mg $= 24.31$ g mol^{-1}

molar mass $O_2 = 32.00$ g mol^{-1}

2 mol Mg : 2 mol MgO

1 mol O_2 : 2 mol MgO

molar mass MgO $= 40.31$ g mol^{-1}

Solution

Beginning with the masses of each reactant, we follow the conceptual plan to calculate how much product can be made from each:

$$42.5\ \text{g Mg} \times \frac{1\ \text{mol Mg}}{24.31\ \text{g Mg}} \times \frac{2\ \text{mol MgO}}{2\ \text{mol Mg}} = 1.7483\ \text{mol MgO}$$

Limiting reactant

Least amount of product

$$1.7483\ \text{mol MgO} \times \frac{40.31\ \text{g MgO}}{1\ \text{mol MgO}} = 70.5\ \text{g MgO}$$

$$33.8\ \text{g } O_2 \times \frac{1\ \text{mol } O_2}{32.00\ \text{g } O_2} \times \frac{2\ \text{mol MgO}}{1\ \text{mol } O_2} = 2.1125\ \text{mol MgO}$$

Since Mg makes the least amount of product, it is the limiting reactant, and O_2 is in excess. Notice that the limiting reactant is not necessarily the reactant with the least mass. In this case, the mass of O_2 is less than the mass of Mg, yet Mg is the limiting reactant because it makes the least amount of MgO. The theoretical yield is 70.5 g of MgO, the mass of product possible based on the moles of limiting reactant.

Suppose that after the reaction has occurred, we determine a measured yield or an **actual yield** of MgO is 55.9 g. What is the **percent yield**? We compute the percent yield as follows:

$$\%\ \text{yield} = \frac{\text{actual yield}}{\text{theoretical yield}} \times 100\% = \frac{55.9\ \text{g}}{70.5\ \text{g}} \times 100\% = 79.3\%$$

EXAMPLE 4.13 LIMITING REACTANT AND THEORETICAL YIELD

Ammonia, NH_3, can be synthesized by the following reaction:

$$2\ NO(g) + 5\ H_2(g) \longrightarrow 2\ NH_3(g) + 2\ H_2O(g)$$

Starting with 86.3 g NO and 25.6 g H_2, find the theoretical yield of ammonia in grams.

SORT You are given the mass of each reactant in grams and asked to find the theoretical yield of a product.

GIVEN: 86.3 g NO, 25.6 g H_2

FIND: theoretical yield of $NH_3(g)$

STRATEGIZE Determine which reactant makes the least amount of product by converting from grams of each reactant to moles of the reactant to moles of the product. Use molar masses to convert between grams and moles and use the stoichiometric relationships (deduced from the chemical equation) to convert between moles of reactant and moles of product. Remember that the reactant that makes *the least amount of product* is the limiting reactant. Convert the number of moles of product obtained using the limiting reactant to grams of product.

CONCEPTUAL PLAN

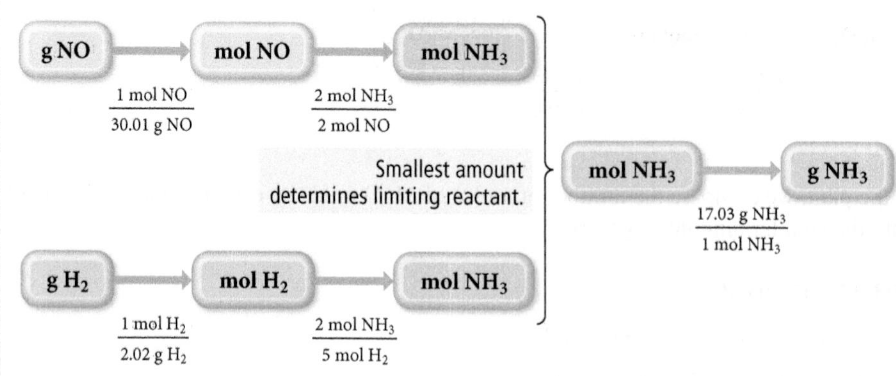

RELATIONSHIPS USED

molar mass NO $= 30.01\ \text{g mol}^{-1}$

molar mass $H_2 = 2.02\ \text{g mol}^{-1}$

2 mol NO : 2 mol NH_3 (from chemical equation)

5 mol H_2 : 2 mol NH_3 (from chemical equation)

molar mass $NH_3 = 17.03\ \text{g mol}^{-1}$

SOLVE Beginning with the given mass of each reactant, calculate the amount of product that can be made in moles. Convert the amount of product made by the limiting reactant to grams—this is the theoretical yield.

SOLUTION

$$86.3\ \text{g NO} \times \frac{1\ \text{mol NO}}{30.01\ \text{g NO}} \times \frac{2\ \text{mol NH}_3}{2\ \text{mol NO}} = 2.8757\ \text{mol NH}_3$$

Limiting reactant (86.3 g NO); Least amount of product (2.8757 mol NH_3)

$$25.6\ \text{g H}_2 \times \frac{1\ \text{mol H}_2}{2.016\ \text{g H}_2} \times \frac{2\ \text{mol NH}_3}{5\ \text{mol H}_2} = 5.0693\ \text{mol NH}_3$$

$$2.8757\ \text{mol NH}_3 \times \frac{17.03\ \text{g NH}_3}{1\ \text{mol NH}_3} = 49.0\ \text{g NH}_3$$

Since NO makes the least amount of product, it is the limiting reactant, and the theoretical yield of ammonia is 49.0 g.

CHECK The units of the answer (g NH_3) are correct. The magnitude (49.0 g) seems reasonable given that 86.3 g NO is the limiting reactant. NO contains one oxygen atom per nitrogen atom and NH_3 contains three hydrogen atoms per nitrogen atom. Since three hydrogen atoms have less mass than one oxygen atom, it is reasonable that the mass of NH_3 obtained is less than the initial mass of NO.

FOR PRACTICE 4.13

Ammonia can also be synthesized by the following reaction:

$$3\ H_2(g) + N_2(g) \longrightarrow 2\ NH_3(g)$$

What is the theoretical yield of ammonia, in kg, that we can synthesize from 5.22 kg of H_2 and 31.5 kg of N_2?

EXAMPLE 4.14 LIMITING REACTANT, THEORETICAL YIELD, AND PERCENT YIELD

Titanium metal can be obtained from its oxide according to the following balanced equation:

$$TiO_2(s) + 2\ C(s) \longrightarrow Ti(s) + 2\ CO(g)$$

When 28.6 kg of C reacts with 88.2 kg of TiO_2, 42.8 kg of Ti is produced. Find the limiting reactant, theoretical yield (in kg), and percent yield.

SORT You are given the mass of each reactant and the mass of product formed. You are asked to find the limiting reactant, theoretical yield, and percent yield.

GIVEN: 28.6 kg C, 88.2 kg TiO_2, 42.8 kg Ti produced

FIND: limiting reactant, theoretical yield, percent yield

STRATEGIZE Determine which of the reactants makes the least amount of product by converting from kilograms of each reactant to moles of product. Convert between grams and moles using molar mass. Convert between moles of reactant and moles of product using the stoichiometric relationships derived from the chemical equation. Remember that the reactant that makes the *least amount of product* is the limiting reactant.

Determine the theoretical yield (in kg) by converting the number of moles of product obtained with the limiting reactant to kilograms of product.

CONCEPTUAL PLAN

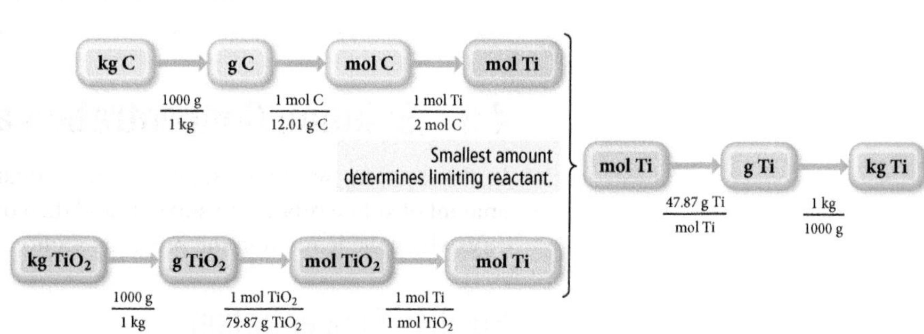

RELATIONSHIPS USED

1000 g = 1 kg

molar mass of C = 12.01 g mol^{-1}

molar mass of TiO_2 = 79.87 g mol^{-1}

1 mol TiO_2 : 1 mol Ti

2 mol C : 1 mol Ti

molar mass of Ti = 47.87 g mol^{-1}

(continued)

EXAMPLE 4.14 (CONTINUED)

SOLVE Beginning with the actual amount of each reactant, calculate the amount of product that can be made in moles. Convert the amount of product made by the limiting reactant to kilograms—this is the theoretical yield.

SOLUTION

$$28.6\ \text{kg C} \times \frac{1000\ \text{g}}{1\ \text{kg}} \times \frac{1\ \text{mol C}}{12.01\ \text{g C}} \times \frac{1\ \text{mol Ti}}{2\ \text{mol C}} = 1.1\underline{9}07 \times 10^3\ \text{mol Ti}$$

Limiting reactant — Least amount of product

$$88.2\ \text{kg TiO}_2 \times \frac{1000\ \text{g}}{1\ \text{kg}} \times \frac{1\ \text{mol TiO}_2}{79.87\ \text{g TiO}_2} \times \frac{1\ \text{mol Ti}}{1\ \text{mol TiO}_2} = 1.1\underline{0}43 \times 10^3\ \text{mol Ti}$$

$$1.1\underline{0}43 \times 10^3\ \text{mol Ti} \times \frac{47.87\ \text{g Ti}}{1\ \text{mol Ti}} \times \frac{1\ \text{kg}}{1000\ \text{g}} = 52.9\ \text{kg Ti}$$

Since TiO_2 makes the least amount of product, it is the limiting reactant, and 52.9 kg Ti is the theoretical yield.

Calculate the percent yield by dividing the actual yield (42.8 kg Ti) by the theoretical yield.

$$\%\ \text{yield} = \frac{\text{actual yield}}{\text{theoretical yield}} \times 100\% = \frac{42.8\ \text{kg}}{52.9\ \text{kg}} \times 100\% = 80.9\%$$

CHECK The theoretical yield has the correct units (kg Ti) and has a reasonable magnitude compared to the mass of TiO_2. Since Ti has a lower molar mass than TiO_2, the amount of Ti made from TiO_2 should have a lower mass. The percent yield is reasonable (under 100%, as it should be).

FOR PRACTICE 4.14

Mining companies use the following reaction to obtain iron from iron ore:

$$Fe_2O_3(s) + 3\ CO(g) \longrightarrow 2\ Fe(s) + 3\ CO_2(g)$$

The reaction of 167 g Fe_2O_3 with 85.8 g CO produces 72.3 g Fe. Find the limiting reactant, theoretical yield, and percent yield.

CONCEPTUAL CONNECTION 4.5

Reactant in Excess

Nitrogen dioxide reacts with water to form nitric acid and nitrogen monoxide according to the following equation:

$$3\ NO_2(g) + H_2O(l) \longrightarrow 2\ HNO_3(l) + NO(g)$$

Suppose that 5 mol NO_2 and 1 mol H_2O combine and react completely. How many moles of the reactant in excess are present after the reaction has completed?

4.9 Solution Concentration and Solution Stoichiometry

In this section, we first examine how to quantify the concentration of a solution (the amount of solute relative to solvent) and then turn to applying the principles of stoichiometry, which we learned in the previous section, to reactions occurring in solution.

Solution Concentration

A common way to express solution concentration is **molarity** (M, in mol L^{-1}), the amount of solute (in moles) divided by the volume of solution (in litres):

The abbreviation or symbol for molarity is M and the units of molarity are mol L^{-1}. You may see the units of molarity written as M. You may also see the concentration of a compound expressed as [X], where the square brackets denote the concentration of X in mol L^{-1}.

$$\text{molarity (in mol L}^{-1}) = \frac{\text{amount of solute (in mol)}}{\text{volume of solution (in L)}}$$

$$\text{or} \quad M = \frac{n}{V}$$

CHEMISTRY IN YOUR DAY Blended Ethanol Gasoline

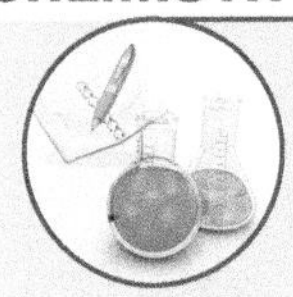

We have discussed the balanced chemical equation for the combustion of octane, a component of gasoline, as follows:

$$C_8H_{18}(g) + \frac{25}{2}O_2(g) \longrightarrow 8\,CO_2(g) + 9\,H_2O(l)$$

The equation shows that 12.5 mol of O_2 are required to completely react with a mole of C_8H_{18}. What if there is not enough O_2 in an automobile cylinder to fully react with the amount of octane that is present? For many reactions, a shortage of one reactant means that less product forms—oxygen would become the limiting reactant. However, for some reactions, a shortage of one reactant causes side reactions to occur along with the desired reaction. In the case of burning octane in an automobile, those side reactions produce pollutants such as carbon monoxide and soot or carbon. (Have you ever seen black smoke coming out of a car's tailpipe?) These side reactions are called *incomplete combustion*:

$$C_8H_{18}(g) + \frac{17}{2}O_2(g) \longrightarrow 8\,CO(g) + 9\,H_2O(l)$$

$$C_8H_{18}(g) + \frac{9}{2}O_2(g) \longrightarrow 8\,C(s) + 9\,H_2O(l)$$

Blended ethanol gasoline is a fuel where a small amount of ethanol, typically 10% by volume, is added to the gasoline. Ethanol has the molecular formula C_2H_5OH and is a partially oxidized fuel—it already contains oxygen. Blended ethanol gasoline burns cleaner—produces less emissions—as it doesn't require as much oxygen to fully oxidize to CO_2. There are other benefits of blended ethanol gasoline. Since ethanol dissolves water that might collect in the fuel tank and hoses leading to the engine, ethanol can pull it through the engine before it gums up your tank and fuel line. Ethanol is also a renewable fuel. Depending on the source of ethanol, it reduces CO_2 emissions. Ethanol from corn reduces CO_2 emissions by only about 13% but that from cellulose-based plants (sugar cane and switchgrass) can reduce CO_2 emissions by 88% compared to using fossil fuels. There are some cons associated with blended ethanol gasoline as well. Since it is partially oxidized, there is less energy content in ethanol than in a hydrocarbon such as octane. It is estimated that a 10% ethanol blend contains about 97% of the energy of gasoline, but some of the energy loss is offset by the increased combustion efficiency of the blend. In order to burn blended fuels with greater than 10% ethanol, costly modifications to the engine are required.

Finally, one of the main cons of using ethanol as fuel is that producing ethanol from corn raises the price of corn for consumption. Furthermore, if farmers decide that it is more financially beneficial to grow corn for fuel, costs of other foods will also increase. Fortunately, research into producing ethanol from cellulosic sources, such as wood and nonedible by-products from plants, is making nonfood sources of ethanol more feasible. Cellulosic ethanol was first sold to the general public in Ottawa, Ontario, from Iogen Corporation's demonstration plant on Hunt Club Road in Ottawa. The demonstration plant uses straw as the feedstock for producing ethanol. Other feedstocks for cellulosic ethanol include corn stalks and leaves (stover) left over after corn harvesting, and the fibrous material (bagasse) remaining after sugar has been extracted from sugar cane.

Plant fibre
Pretreatment
Enzymatic hydrolysis
Enzymes
Enzyme production
Separation
Power generation
Ethanol fermentation
Electricity
Distillation
Cellulosic ethanol

Notice that molarity is a ratio of the amount of solute per litre of *solution,* not per litre of solvent. To make an aqueous solution of a specified molarity, we usually put the solute into a flask and then add water to reach the desired volume of solution. For example, to make 1 L of a 1 mol L^{-1} NaCl solution, we add 1 mol of NaCl to a flask and then add enough water to make 1 L of solution (Figure 4.13 ▼). We *do not* combine 1 mol of NaCl with 1 L of water because the resulting solution would have a total volume exceeding 1 L and therefore a molarity of less than 1 mol L^{-1}. To calculate molarity, divide the amount of the solute in moles by the volume of the solution (solute *and* solvent) in litres, as shown in the following example.

▶ **FIGURE 4.13 Preparing a One-Molar NaCl Solution**

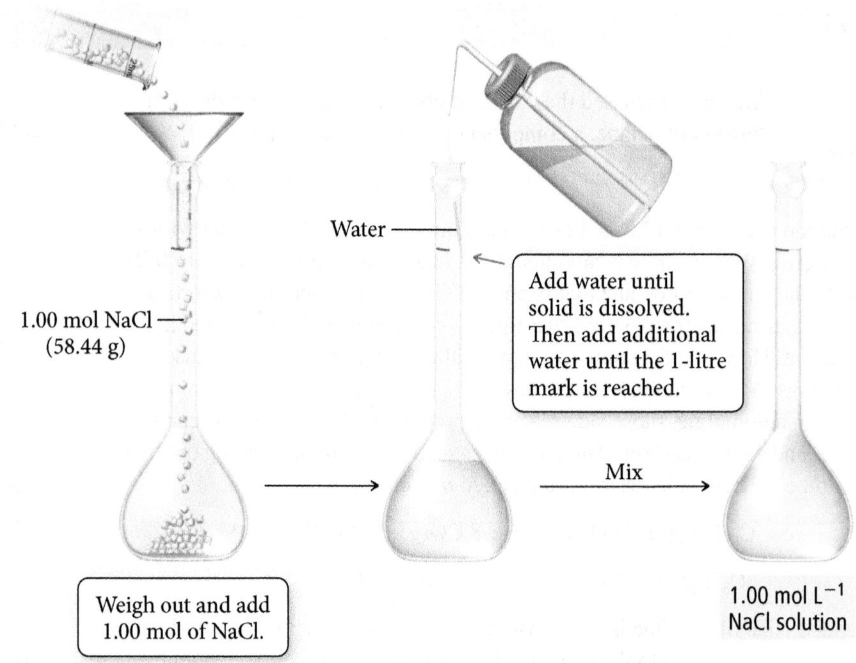
1.00 mol NaCl
(58.44 g)
Water
Add water until solid is dissolved. Then add additional water until the 1-litre mark is reached.
Mix
Weigh out and add 1.00 mol of NaCl.
1.00 mol L⁻¹ NaCl solution

EXAMPLE 4.15 CALCULATING SOLUTION CONCENTRATION

If 25.5 g KBr is dissolved in enough water to make 1.75 L of solution, what is the molarity of the solution?

SORT You are given the mass of KBr and the volume of a solution and asked to find its molarity.

GIVEN: 25.5 g KBr, 1.75 L of solution

FIND: molarity

STRATEGIZE When formulating the conceptual plan, think about the definition of molarity, the amount of solute *in moles* per litre of solution.

You are given the mass of KBr, so first use the molar mass of KBr to convert from g KBr to mol KBr.

Then use the number of moles of KBr and litres of solution to find the molarity.

CONCEPTUAL PLAN

g KBr → mol KBr

$$\frac{1\ \text{mol}}{119.00\ \text{g}}$$

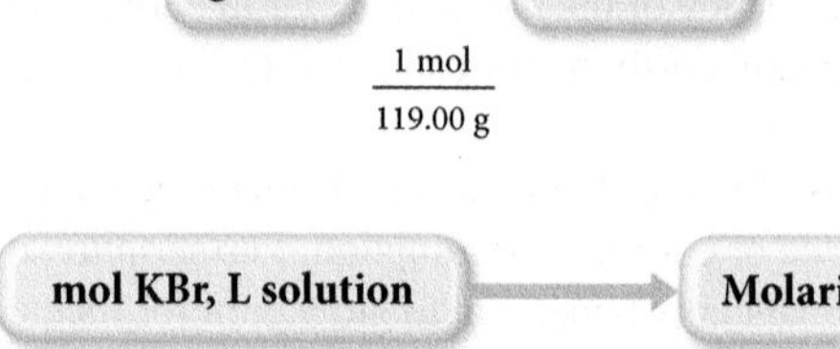
mol KBr, L solution
Molarity

$$\text{Molarity} = \frac{\text{amount of solute}}{\text{volume of solution}}$$

RELATIONSHIP USED

molar mass of KBr = $119.00\ \text{g mol}^{-1}$

SOLVE Follow the conceptual plan. Begin with g KBr and convert to mol KBr, then use mol KBr and L solution to compute molarity.

SOLUTION

$$25.5\ \text{g KBr} \times \frac{1\ \text{mol KBr}}{119.00\ \text{g KBr}} = 0.21\underline{4}29\ \text{mol KBr}$$

$$\text{molarity (M)} = \frac{\text{amount of solute (in mol)}}{\text{volume of solution (in L)}}$$

$$= \frac{0.21\underline{4}29\ \text{mol}}{1.75\ \text{L}}$$

$$= 0.122\ \text{mol L}^{-1}$$

CHECK The unit of the answer (mol L^{-1}) is correct. The magnitude is reasonable since common solutions range in concentration from 0 to about 18 mol L^{-1}. Concentrations significantly above 18 mol L^{-1} are suspect and should be double-checked.

FOR PRACTICE 4.15

Calculate the molarity of a solution made by adding 45.4 g of $NaNO_3$ to a flask and dissolving it with water to create a total volume of 2.50 L.

FOR MORE PRACTICE 4.15

What mass of KBr (in grams) do you need to make 250.0 mL of a 1.50 mol L^{-1} KBr solution?

Using Molarity in Calculations

We can use the molarity of a solution as a conversion factor between moles of the solute and litres of the solution. For example, a 0.500 mol L^{-1} NaCl solution contains 0.500 mol NaCl for every litre of solution:

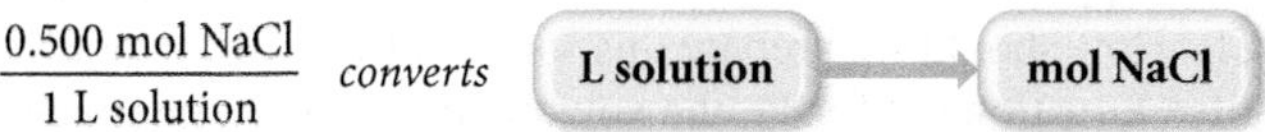

This conversion factor converts from L solution to mol NaCl. If we want to go the other way, we invert the conversion factor:

$$\frac{1 \text{ L solution}}{0.500 \text{ mol NaCl}} \quad \textit{converts} \quad \text{mol NaCl} \longrightarrow \text{L solution}$$

The following example shows how to use molarity in this way.

EXAMPLE 4.16 USING MOLARITY IN CALCULATIONS

How many litres of a 0.125 mol L^{-1} NaOH solution contains 0.255 mol of NaOH?

SORT You are given the concentration of a NaOH solution. You are asked to find the volume of the solution that contains a given amount (in moles) of NaOH.

GIVEN: 0.125 mol L^{-1} NaOH solution, 0.255 mol NaOH

FIND: volume of NaOH solution (in L)

STRATEGIZE The conceptual plan begins with mol NaOH and shows the conversion to L of solution using molarity as a conversion factor.

CONCEPTUAL PLAN

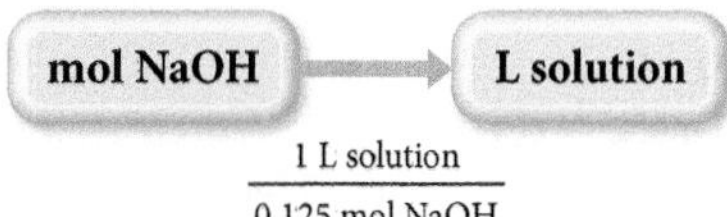

RELATIONSHIP USED

$$0.125 \text{ mol L}^{-1} \text{ NaOH} = \frac{0.125 \text{ mol NaOH}}{1 \text{ L solution}}$$

SOLVE Follow the conceptual plan. Begin with mol NaOH and convert to L solution.

SOLUTION

$$0.255 \text{ } \cancel{\text{mol NaOH}} \times \frac{1 \text{ L solution}}{0.125 \text{ } \cancel{\text{mol NaOH}}} = 2.04 \text{ L solution}$$

CHECK The units of the answer (L) are correct. The magnitude seems reasonable because the solution contains 0.125 mol per litre. Therefore, roughly 2 L contains the given amount of moles (0.255 mol).

FOR PRACTICE 4.16

How many grams of sucrose ($C_{12}H_{22}O_{11}$) are in 1.55 L of 0.758 mol L^{-1} sucrose solution?

FOR MORE PRACTICE 4.16

How many mL of a 0.155 mol L^{-1} KCl solution contains 2.55 g KCl?

CONCEPTUAL CONNECTION 4.6

Solutions

If we dissolve 25 g of salt in 251 g of water, what is the mass of the resulting solution?

(a) 251 g **(b)** 276 g **(c)** 226 g

Solution Dilution To save space while transporting and in stockrooms, it is convenient to have solutions in concentrated forms called **stock solutions**. For example, hydrochloric acid (HCl) is typically stored as a 12 mol L^{-1} stock solution. However, many lab procedures call for much less concentrated HCl solutions, so we must dilute the stock solution to the required concentration. The easiest way to solve dilution problems is to use the following dilution equation:

You may also see this equation written as $c_1V_1 = c_2V_2$; molarity (M) is just a specific case of concentration (c).

$$M_1V_1 = M_2V_2 \quad [4.2]$$

where M_1 and V_1 are the molarity and volume of the initial **concentrated solution**, and M_2 and V_2 are the molarity and volume of the final **diluted solution**. This equation works because the molarity multiplied by the volume gives the number of moles of solute, which is the same for both solutions. In other words, the number of moles of solute does not change when we dilute a solution.

For example, suppose a laboratory procedure calls for 3.00 L of a 0.500 mol L^{-1} solution of $CaCl_2$. How should we prepare this solution from a 10.0 mol L^{-1} $CaCl_2$ stock solution? We solve Equation 4.2 for V_1, the volume of the stock solution required for the dilution, and then substitute in the correct values to compute it:

$$\begin{aligned} M_1V_1 &= M_2V_2 \\ V_1 &= \frac{M_2V_2}{M_1} \\ &= \frac{0.500\ \cancel{\text{mol L}^{-1}} \times 3.00\ \text{L}}{10.0\ \cancel{\text{mol L}^{-1}}} \\ &= 0.150\ \text{L} \end{aligned}$$

We make the solution by diluting 0.150 L of the stock solution to a total volume of 3.00 L (V_2). The resulting solution will be 0.500 mol L^{-1} of $CaCl_2$ (Figure 4.14 ▼). It makes sense that we requre a small volume of the more concentrated solution to make a large volume of a more dilute solution.

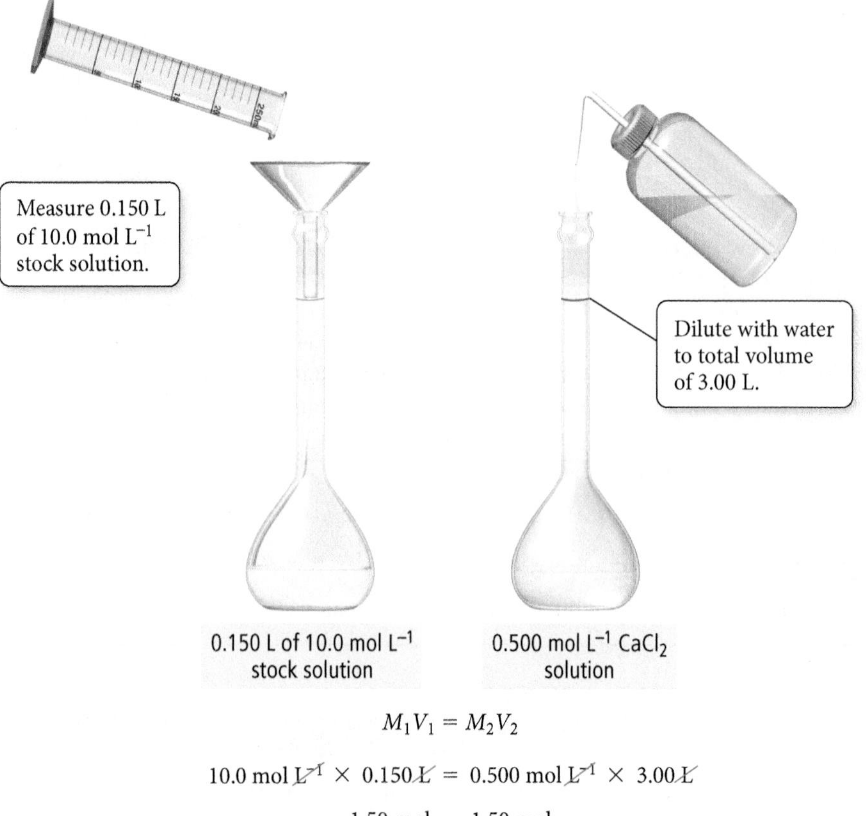

▶ **FIGURE 4.14 Preparing 3.00 L of 0.500 mol L^{-1} $CaCl_2$ from a 10.0 mol L^{-1} Stock Solution**

EXAMPLE 4.17 SOLUTION DILUTION

To what volume should you dilute 0.200 L of a 15.0 mol L^{-1} NaOH solution to obtain a 3.00 mol L^{-1} NaOH solution?

SORT You are given the initial volume, initial concentration, and final concentration of a solution, and you need to find the final volume.

GIVEN: $V_1 = 0.200$ L
$M_1 = 15.0$ mol L^{-1}
$M_2 = 3.00$ mol L^{-1}

FIND: V_2

STRATEGIZE Equation 4.2 relates the initial and final volumes and concentrations for solution dilution problems. You are asked to find V_2. The other quantities (V_1, M_1, and M_2) are all given in the problem.

CONCEPTUAL PLAN

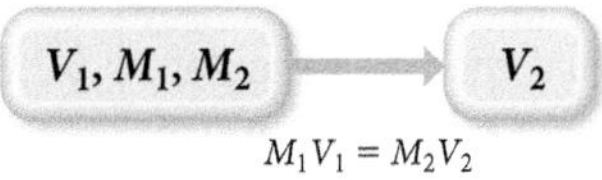

RELATIONSHIP USED
$M_1V_1 = M_2V_2$

SOLVE Begin with the solution dilution equation and solve it for V_2.

Substitute in the required quantities and compute V_2.

Make the solution by diluting 0.200 L of the stock solution to a total volume of 1.00 L (V_2). The resulting solution will have a concentration of 3.00 mol L^{-1}.

SOLUTION

$$M_1V_1 = M_2V_2$$

$$V_2 = \frac{M_1V_1}{M_2}$$

$$= \frac{15.0 \text{ mol L}^{-1} \times 0.200 \text{ L}}{3.00 \text{ mol L}^{-1}}$$

$$= 1.00 \text{ L}$$

CHECK The final unit (L) is correct. The magnitude of the answer is reasonable because the solution is diluted from 15.0 mol L^{-1} to 3.00 mol L^{-1}, a factor of five. Therefore, the volume should increase by a factor of five.

FOR PRACTICE 4.17

To what volume (in mL) should you dilute 100.0 mL of a 5.00 mol L^{-1} $CaCl_2$ solution to obtain a 0.750 mol L^{-1} $CaCl_2$ solution?

FOR MORE PRACTICE 4.17

What volume of a 6.00 mol L^{-1} $NaNO_3$ solution should you use to make 0.525 L of a 1.20 mol L^{-1} $NaNO_3$ solution?

Solution Stoichiometry

In Section 4.7, we learned how the coefficients in chemical equations are used as conversion factors between the amounts of reactants (in moles) and the amounts of products (in moles). In aqueous reactions, quantities of reactants and products are often specified in terms of volumes and concentrations. We can use the volume and concentration of a reactant or product to calculate its amount in moles. We can then use the stoichiometric coefficients in the chemical equation to convert to the amount of another reactant or product in moles. The general conceptual plan for these kinds of calculations begins with the volume of a reactant or product:

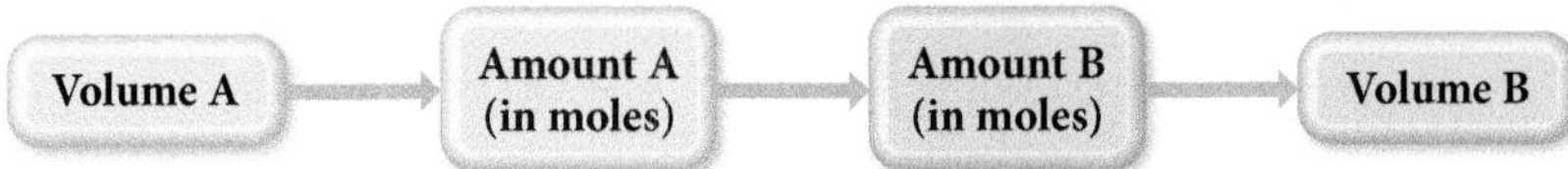

We make the conversions between solution volumes and amounts of solute in moles using the molarities of the solutions. We make the conversions between amounts in moles of A and B using the stoichiometric coefficients from the balanced chemical equation. The following example demonstrates solution stoichiometry.

EXAMPLE 4.18 SOLUTION STOICHIOMETRY

What volume of a 0.150 mol L^{-1} KCl solution will completely react with 0.150 L of a 0.175 mol L^{-1} $Pb(NO_3)_2$ solution according to the following balanced chemical equation?

$$2\ KCl(aq) + Pb(NO_3)_2(aq) \longrightarrow PbCl_2(s) + 2\ KNO_3(aq)$$

SORT You are given the volume and concentration of a $Pb(NO_3)_2$ solution. You are asked to find the volume of KCl solution (of a given concentration) required to react with it.

GIVEN: 0.150 L of $Pb(NO_3)_2$ solution, 0.175 mol L^{-1} solution, 0.150 mol L^{-1} KCl solution

FIND: volume KCl solution (in L)

STRATEGIZE The conceptual plan has the following form: volume A $\longrightarrow$ amount A (in moles) $\longrightarrow$ amount B (in moles) $\longrightarrow$ volume B. The molar concentrations of the KCl and $Pb(NO_3)_2$ solutions can be used as conversion factors between the number of moles of reactants in these solutions and their volumes. The stoichiometric coefficients from the balanced equation are used to convert between number of moles of $Pb(NO_3)_2$ and number of moles of KCl.

CONCEPTUAL PLAN

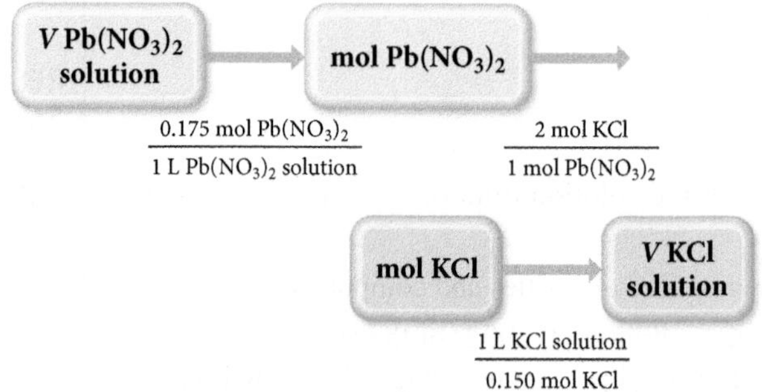

RELATIONSHIPS USED

$$[Pb(NO_3)_2] = \frac{0.175\ \text{mol}\ Pb(NO_3)_2}{1\ \text{L}\ Pb(NO_3)_2\ \text{solution}}$$

2 mol KCl : 1 mol $Pb(NO_3)_2$

$$[KCl] = \frac{0.150\ \text{mol KCl}}{1\ \text{L KCl solution}}$$

Don't forget that [X] is a shorthand way of writing the concentration of X in units of mol L^{-1}.

SOLVE Begin with L $Pb(NO_3)_2$ solution and follow the conceptual plan to arrive at the volume of KCl solution.

SOLUTION

$$0.150\ \text{L}\ \cancel{Pb(NO_3)_2\ \text{solution}} \times \frac{0.175\ \cancel{\text{mol}\ Pb(NO_3)_2}}{1\ \cancel{\text{L}\ Pb(NO_3)_2\ \text{solution}}} \times \frac{2\ \cancel{\text{mol KCl}}}{1\ \cancel{\text{mol}\ Pb(NO_3)_2}} \times \frac{1\ \text{L KCl solution}}{0.150\ \cancel{\text{mol KCl}}} = 0.350\ \text{L KCl solution}$$

CHECK The final units (L KCl solution) are correct. The magnitude (0.350 L) seems reasonable because the reaction stoichiometry requires 2 mol of KCl per mole of $Pb(NO_3)_2$. Since the concentrations of the two solutions are not very different (0.150 mol L^{-1} compared to 0.175 mol L^{-1}), the volume of KCl required should be roughly two times the 0.150 L of $Pb(NO_3)_2$ given in the problem.

FOR PRACTICE 4.18

What volume (in mL) of a 0.150 mol L^{-1} HNO_3 solution will completely react with 35.7 mL of a 0.108 mol L^{-1} Na_2CO_3 solution according to the following balanced chemical equation?

$$Na_2CO_3(aq) + 2\ HNO_3(aq) \longrightarrow 2\ NaNO_3(aq) + CO_2(g) + H_2O(l)$$

FOR MORE PRACTICE 4.18

In the reaction above, what mass (in grams) of carbon dioxide forms?

CHAPTER IN REVIEW

Key Terms

Section 4.2
chemical reaction (102)
combustion reaction (102)
chemical equation (102)
reactants (103)
products (103)
balanced chemical equation (103)

Section 4.3
solution (105)
solvent (105)
solute (105)
aqueous solution (105)
electrolyte (106)
strong electrolyte (106)
nonelectrolyte (106)
strong acid (106)
weak acid (107)
weak electrolyte (107)
soluble (107)
insoluble (107)

Section 4.4
precipitation reaction (109)
precipitate (109)
molecular equation (109)
complete ionic equation (109)
spectator ion (110)
net ionic equation (110)

Section 4.5
acid–base reaction (111)
neutralization reaction (111)
Arrhenius definitions (111)
hydronium ion (111)
polyprotic acid (112)
diprotic acid (112)
salt (112)
gas-evolution reaction (114)

Section 4.6
oxidation–reduction reaction (115)
redox reaction (115)
oxidation (116)
reduction (116)
oxidation state (117)
oxidizing agent (119)
reducing agent (119)
disproportionation reaction (123)

Section 4.7
stoichiometry (125)

Section 4.8
limiting reactant (128)
theoretical yield (128)
actual yield (130)
percent yield (130)

Section 4.9
molarity (*M*) (132)
stock solution (136)
concentrated solution (136)
diluted solution (136)

Key Concepts

Writing and Balancing Chemical Equations (4.2)

In chemistry, we represent chemical reactions with chemical equations. The substances on the left-hand side of a chemical equation are called the reactants, and the substances on the right-hand side are called the products. Chemical equations are balanced when the number of each type of atom on the left side of the equation is equal to the number on the right side.

Aqueous Solutions and Solubility (4.3)

An aqueous solution is a homogeneous mixture of water (the solvent) with another substance (the solute). Solutes that completely dissociate (or completely ionize in the case of acids) to ions in solution are strong electrolytes and are good conductors of electricity. Solutes that only partially dissociate (or partially ionize) are weak electrolytes, and solutes that do not dissociate (or ionize) at all are nonelectrolytes. A substance that dissolves in water to form a solution is soluble. The solubility rules are an empirical set of guidelines that help predict the solubilities of ionic compounds; these rules are especially useful in Section 4.4 when determining whether or not a precipitate will form.

Precipitation Reactions (4.4)

In a precipitation reaction, we mix two aqueous solutions and a solid—or precipitate—forms. Aqueous reactions, such as precipitation reactions, can be represented with a molecular equation, which shows the complete neutral formula for each compound in the reaction. Alternatively, a reaction can be represented with a complete ionic equation, which shows the dissociated nature of the aqueous ionic compounds. Finally, a third representation is the net ionic equation, in which the spectator ions—those that do not change in the course of the reaction—are left out of the equation.

Acid–Base Reactions (4.5)

An acid is a substance which produces H^+ in solution and a base is a substance which produces OH^- in solution. In an acid–base reaction, the acid and base neutralize each other, producing water (or in some cases, a weak electrolyte). In gas-evolution reactions, the acid and base combine in solution and a gas is produced.

Oxidation–Reduction Reactions (4.6)

In oxidation–reduction reactions, one substance transfers electrons to another substance. The substance that loses electrons is oxidized, and the substance that gains them is reduced. An oxidation state is a fictitious charge given to each atom in a redox reaction by assigning all shared electrons to the atom with the greater attraction for those electrons. Oxidation states are an imposed electronic bookkeeping scheme, not an actual physical state. The oxidation state of an atom increases upon oxidation and decreases upon reduction. A combustion reaction is a specific type of oxidation–reduction reaction in which a substance reacts with oxygen—emitting heat and forming one or more oxygen-containing products.

Reaction Stoichiometry (4.7)

Reaction stoichiometry refers to the numerical relationships between the reactants and products in a balanced chemical equation. Reaction stoichiometry allows us to predict, for example, the amount of product that can be formed for a given amount of reactant, or how much of one reactant is required to react with a given amount of another.

Limiting Reactant, Theoretical Yield, and Percent Yield (4.8)

When a chemical reaction actually occurs, the reactants are usually not present in the exact stoichiometric ratios specified by the balanced chemical equation. The limiting reactant is the one that is available in the smallest stoichiometric quantity—it will be completely consumed in the reaction and it limits the amount of product that can be made. Any reactant that does not limit the amount of product is said to be in excess. The amount of product that can be made from the limiting reactant is the theoretical yield. The actual yield—always equal to or less than the theoretical yield—is the amount of product that is actually made when the reaction is carried out. The percentage of the theoretical yield that is actually produced is the percent yield.

Solution Concentration and Solution Stoichiometry (4.9)

We often express the concentration of a solution in molarity, the number of moles of solute per litre of solution. We can use the molarities and volumes of reactant solutions to predict the amount of product that will form in an aqueous reaction.

Key Equations and Relationships

Mass-to-Mass Conversion: Stoichiometry (4.7)

$$\text{mass A} \longrightarrow \text{amount A (in moles)} \longrightarrow \text{amount B (in moles)} \longrightarrow \text{mass B}$$

Percent Yield (4.8)

$$\%\ \text{yield} = \frac{\text{actual yield}}{\text{theoretical yield}} \times 100\%$$

Molarity (4.9)

$$\text{molarity} = \frac{\text{amount of solute (in mol)}}{\text{volume of solution (in L)}} \quad \text{or} \quad M = \frac{n}{V}$$

Solution Dilution (4.9)

$$M_1V_1 = M_2V_2$$

Solution Stoichiometry (4.9)

$$\text{volume A} \longrightarrow \text{amount A (in moles)} \longrightarrow \text{amount B (in moles)} \longrightarrow \text{volume B}$$

Key Skills

Balancing Chemical Equations (4.2)
• Examples 4.1, 4.2 • For Practice 4.1, 4.2 • Exercises 25–34, 59, 60

Predicting Whether a Compound Is Soluble (4.3)
• Example 4.3 • For Practice 4.3 • Exercises 35–38

Writing Equations for Precipitation Reactions (4.4)
• Example 4.4 • For Practice 4.4 • For More Practice 4.4 • Exercises 39–42

Writing Equations for Acid–Base Reactions (4.5)
• Example 4.5 • For Practice 4.5 • Exercises 49–50

Writing Equations for Gas-Evolution Reactions (4.5)
• Example 4.6 • For Practice 4.6 • For More Practice 4.6 • Exercises 51–52

Assigning Oxidation States (4.6)
• Example 4.7 • For Practice 4.7 • Exercises 53–56

Identifying Redox Reactions, Oxidizing Agents, and Reducing Agents, and Using Oxidation States (4.6)
• Example 4.8 • For Practice 4.8 • Exercises 57–58

Balancing Redox Reactions in Acidic or Basic Solution; Balancing Disproportionation Reactions (4.6)
• Examples 4.9, 4.10, 4.11 • For Practice 4.9, 4.10, 4.11 • For More Practice 4.9 • Exercises 61–68

Calculations Involving the Stoichiometry of a Reaction (4.7)
• Example 4.12 • For Practice 4.12 • For More Practice 4.12 • Exercises 69–80

Determining the Limiting Reactant and Calculating Theoretical and Percent Yields (4.8)
• Examples 4.13, 4.14 • For Practice 4.13, 4.14 • Exercises 81–96

Calculating Solution Concentration and Using Molarity in Calculations (4.9)
• Examples 4.15, 4.16 • For Practice 4.15, 4.16 • For More Practice 4.15, 4.16 • Exercises 97–102

Solution Dilutions (4.9)
• Example 4.17 • For Practice 4.17 • For More Practice 4.17 • Exercises 103–106

Solution Stoichiometry (4.9)
• Example 4.18 • For Practice 4.18 • For More Practice 4.18 • Exercises 107–110

EXERCISES

Review Questions

1. What is reaction stoichiometry? What is the significance of the coefficients in a balanced chemical equation?
2. In a chemical reaction, what is the limiting reactant? The theoretical yield? The percent yield? What do we mean when we say a reactant is in excess?
3. The percent yield is normally calculated using the actual yield and theoretical yield in units of mass (g or kg). Would the percent yield be different if the actual yield and theoretical yield were in units of amount (moles)?
4. What is an aqueous solution? What is the difference between the solute and the solvent?
5. What is molarity? How is it useful?
6. Explain how a strong electrolyte, a weak electrolyte, and a nonelectrolyte differ.
7. Explain the difference between a strong acid and a weak acid.
8. What does it mean for a compound to be soluble? Insoluble?
9. What are the solubility rules? How are they useful?
10. What cations and anions have compounds that are usually soluble? What are the exceptions? What anions have compounds that are mostly insoluble? What are the exceptions?
11. What is a precipitation reaction? Give an example.
12. How can you predict whether a precipitation reaction will occur upon mixing two aqueous solutions?
13. Explain how a molecular equation, a complete ionic equation, and a net ionic equation differ.
14. What are the Arrhenius definitions of an acid and a base?
15. What is an acid–base reaction? Give an example.
16. Why can you not change the subscripts on the chemical formulas in order to balance a chemical reaction?
17. What is a gas-evolution reaction? Give an example.
18. What reactant types give rise to gas-evolution reactions?
19. What is an oxidation–reduction reaction? Give an example.
20. What are oxidation states?
21. How can oxidation states be used to identify redox reactions?
22. What happens to a substance when it becomes oxidized? Reduced?
23. In a redox reaction, which reactant is the oxidizing agent? The reducing agent?
24. What is a combustion reaction? Why are they important? Give an example.

Problems by Topic

Writing and Balancing Chemical Equations

25. Sulfuric acid is a component of acid rain formed when gaseous sulfur dioxide pollutant reacts with gaseous oxygen and liquid water to form aqueous sulfuric acid. Write a balanced chemical equation for this reaction.
26. Nitric acid is a component of acid rain that forms when gaseous nitrogen dioxide pollutant reacts with gaseous oxygen and liquid water to form aqueous nitric acid. Write a balanced chemical equation for this reaction.
27. In a popular classroom demonstration, solid sodium is added to liquid water and reacts to produce hydrogen gas and aqueous sodium hydroxide. Write a balanced chemical equation for this reaction.
28. When iron rusts, solid iron reacts with gaseous oxygen to form solid iron(III) oxide. Write a balanced chemical equation for this reaction.
29. Write a balanced chemical equation for the fermentation of sucrose ($C_{12}H_{22}O_{11}$) by yeasts in which the aqueous sugar reacts with water to form aqueous ethyl alcohol (C_2H_5OH) and carbon dioxide gas.
30. Write a balanced equation for the photosynthesis reaction in which gaseous carbon dioxide and liquid water react in the presence of chlorophyll to produce aqueous glucose ($C_6H_{12}O_6$) and oxygen gas.
31. Write a balanced chemical equation for each reaction:
    a. Solid lead(II) sulfide reacts with aqueous hydrobromic acid to form solid lead(II) bromide and dihydrogen monosulfide gas.
    b. Gaseous carbon monoxide reacts with hydrogen gas to form gaseous methane (CH_4) and liquid water.
    c. Aqueous hydrochloric acid reacts with solid manganese(IV) oxide to form aqueous manganese(II) chloride, liquid water, and chlorine gas.
    d. Liquid pentane (C_5H_{12}) reacts with gaseous oxygen to form carbon dioxide and liquid water.
32. Write a balanced chemical equation for each reaction:
    a. Solid copper reacts with solid sulfur (S_8) to form solid copper(I) sulfide.
    b. Solid iron(III) oxide reacts with hydrogen gas to form solid iron and liquid water.
    c. Sulfur dioxide gas reacts with oxygen gas to form sulfur trioxide gas.
    d. Gaseous ammonia (NH_3) reacts with gaseous oxygen to form gaseous nitrogen monoxide and gaseous water.
33. Balance each chemical equation:
    a. $CO_2(g) + CaSiO_3(s) + H_2O(l) \longrightarrow SiO_2(s) + Ca(HCO_3)_2(aq)$
    b. $Co(NO_3)_3(aq) + (NH_4)_2S(aq) \longrightarrow Co_2S_3(s) + NH_4NO_3(aq)$
    c. $Cu_2O(s) + C(s) \longrightarrow Cu(s) + CO(g)$
    d. $H_2(g) + Cl_2(g) \longrightarrow HCl(g)$
34. Balance each chemical equation:
    a. $Na_2S(aq) + Cu(NO_3)_2(aq) \longrightarrow NaNO_3(aq) + CuS(s)$
    b. $N_2H_4(l) \longrightarrow NH_3(g) + N_2(g)$
    c. $HCl(aq) + O_2(g) \longrightarrow H_2O(l) + Cl_2(g)$
    d. $FeS(s) + HCl(aq) \longrightarrow FeCl_2(aq) + H_2S(g)$

Types of Aqueous Solutions and Solubility

35. For each compound (all water soluble), would you expect the resulting aqueous solution to conduct electrical current?
a. $CsCl$ **b.** CH_3OH **c.** $Ca(NO_2)_2$ **d.** $C_6H_{12}O_6$

36. Classify each compound as a strong electrolyte or nonelectrolyte:
a. $MgBr_2$ **b.** $C_{12}H_{22}O_{11}$ **c.** Na_2CO_3 **d.** KOH

37. Determine whether each compound is soluble or insoluble. If the compound is soluble, list the ions present in solution.
a. $AgNO_3$ **b.** $Pb(C_2H_3O_2)_2$ **c.** KNO_3 **d.** $(NH_4)_2S$

38. Determine whether each compound is soluble or insoluble. For the soluble compounds, list the ions present in solution.
a. AgI **b.** $Cu_3(PO_4)_2$ **c.** $CoCO_3$ **d.** K_3PO_4

Precipitation Reactions

39. Complete and balance each equation. If no reaction occurs, write NO REACTION.
a. $LiI(aq) + BaS(aq) \longrightarrow$
b. $KCl(aq) + CaS(aq) \longrightarrow$
c. $CrBr_2(aq) + Na_2CO_3(aq) \longrightarrow$
d. $NaOH(aq) + FeCl_3(aq) \longrightarrow$

40. Complete and balance each equation. If no reaction occurs, write NO REACTION.
a. $NaNO_3(aq) + KCl(aq) \longrightarrow$
b. $NaCl(aq) + Hg_2(C_2H_3O_2)_2(aq) \longrightarrow$
c. $(NH_4)_2SO_4(aq) + SrCl_2(aq) \longrightarrow$
d. $NH_4Cl(aq) + AgNO_3(aq) \longrightarrow$

41. Write a molecular equation for the precipitation reaction that occurs (if any) when each pair of aqueous solutions is mixed. If no reaction occurs, write NO REACTION.
a. potassium carbonate and lead(II) nitrate
b. lithium sulfate and lead(II) acetate
c. copper(II) nitrate and magnesium sulfide
d. strontium nitrate and potassium iodide

42. Write a molecular equation for the precipitation reaction that occurs (if any) when each pair of aqueous solutions is mixed. If no reaction occurs, write NO REACTION.
a. sodium chloride and lead(II) acetate
b. potassium sulfate and strontium iodide
c. cesium chloride and calcium sulfide
d. chromium(III) nitrate and sodium phosphate

Ionic and Net Ionic Equations

43. Write balanced complete ionic and net ionic equations for each reaction:
a. $HCl(aq) + LiOH(aq) \longrightarrow H_2O(l) + LiCl(aq)$
b. $MgS(aq) + CuCl_2(aq) \longrightarrow CuS(s) + MgCl_2(aq)$
c. $NaOH(aq) + HNO_3(aq) \longrightarrow H_2O(l) + NaNO_3(aq)$
d. $Na_3PO_4(aq) + NiCl_2(aq) \longrightarrow Ni_3(PO_4)_2(s) + NaCl(aq)$

44. Write balanced complete ionic and net ionic equations for each reaction:
a. $K_2SO_4(aq) + CaI_2(aq) \longrightarrow CaSO_4(s) + KI(aq)$
b. $NH_4Cl(aq) + NaOH(aq) \longrightarrow H_2O(l) + NH_3(g) + NaCl(aq)$
c. $AgNO_3(aq) + NaCl(aq) \longrightarrow AgCl(s) + NaNO_3(aq)$
d. $HC_2H_3O_2(aq) + K_2CO_3(aq) \longrightarrow H_2O(l) + CO_2(g) + KC_2H_3O_2(aq)$

45. Dimercury (1+) ions (Hg_2^{2+}) can be removed from solution by precipitation with Cl^-. Suppose that a solution contains aqueous $Hg_2(NO_3)_2$. Write complete ionic and net ionic equations to show the reaction of aqueous $Hg_2(NO_3)_2$ with aqueous sodium chloride to form solid Hg_2Cl_2 and aqueous sodium nitrate.

46. Lead ions can be removed from solution by precipitation with sulfate ions. Suppose that a solution contains lead(II) nitrate. Write complete ionic and net ionic equations to show the reaction of aqueous lead(II) nitrate with aqueous potassium sulfate to form solid lead(II) sulfate and aqueous potassium nitrate.

47. Write balanced molecular and net ionic equations for the reaction between hydrobromic acid and potassium hydroxide.

48. Write balanced molecular and net ionic equations for the reaction between nitric acid and calcium hydroxide.

49. Complete and balance each acid–base equation:
a. $H_2SO_4(aq) + Ca(OH)_2(aq) \longrightarrow$
b. $HClO_4(aq) + KOH(aq) \longrightarrow$
c. $H_2SO_4(aq) + NaOH(aq) \longrightarrow$

50. Complete and balance each acid–base equation:
a. $HI(aq) + LiOH(aq) \longrightarrow$
b. $HC_2H_3O_2(aq) + Ca(OH)_2(aq) \longrightarrow$
c. $HCl(aq) + Ba(OH)_2(aq) \longrightarrow$

51. Complete and balance each gas-evolution equation:
a. $HBr(aq) + NiS(s) \longrightarrow$
b. $NH_4I(aq) + NaOH(aq) \longrightarrow$
c. $HBr(aq) + Na_2S(aq) \longrightarrow$
d. $HClO_4(aq) + Li_2CO_3(aq) \longrightarrow$

52. Complete and balance each gas-evolution equation:
a. $HNO_3(aq) + Na_2SO_3(aq) \longrightarrow$
b. $HCl(aq) + KHCO_3(aq) \longrightarrow$
c. $HC_2H_3O_2(aq) + NaHSO_3(aq) \longrightarrow$
d. $(NH_4)_2SO_4(aq) + Ca(OH)_2(aq) \longrightarrow$

Oxidation–Reduction and Combustion

53. Assign oxidation states to each atom in each element, ion, or compound:
a. Ag **b.** Ag^+ **c.** CaF_2
d. H_2S **e.** CO_3^{2-} **f.** CrO_4^{2-}

54. Assign oxidation states to each atom in each element, ion, or compound:
a. Cl_2 **b.** Fe^{3+} **c.** $CuCl_2$
d. CH_4 **e.** $Cr_2O_7^{2-}$ **f.** HSO_4^-

55. What is the oxidation state of Cr in each compound?
a. CrO **b.** CrO_3 **c.** Cr_2O_3

56. What is the oxidation state of Cl in each ion?
a. ClO^- **b.** ClO_2^- **c.** ClO_3^- **d.** ClO_4^-

57. Determine whether each reaction is a redox reaction. For each redox reaction, identify the oxidizing agent and the reducing agent.
a. $4\,Li(s) + O_2(g) \longrightarrow 2\,Li_2O(s)$
b. $Mg(s) + Fe^{2+}(aq) \longrightarrow Mg^{2+}(aq) + Fe(s)$
c. $Pb(NO_3)_2(aq) + Na_2SO_4(aq) \longrightarrow PbSO_4(s) + 2\,NaNO_3(aq)$
d. $HBr(aq) + KOH(aq) \longrightarrow H_2O(l) + KBr(aq)$

58. Determine whether each reaction is a redox reaction. For each redox reaction, identify the oxidizing agent and the reducing agent.
a. $Al(s) + 3\,Ag^+(aq) \longrightarrow Al^{3+}(aq) + 3\,Ag(s)$
b. $SO_3(g) + H_2O(l) \longrightarrow H_2SO_4(aq)$
c. $Ba(s) + Cl_2(g) \longrightarrow BaCl_2(s)$
d. $Mg(s) + Br_2(l) \longrightarrow MgBr_2(s)$

59. Complete and balance each combustion reaction equation:
   a. $S(s) + O_2(g) \longrightarrow$
   b. $C_3H_6(g) + O_2(g) \longrightarrow$
   c. $Ca(s) + O_2(g) \longrightarrow$
   d. $C_5H_{12}S(l) + O_2(g) \longrightarrow$

60. Complete and balance each combustion reaction equation:
   a. $C_4H_6(g) + O_2(g) \longrightarrow$
   b. $C(s) + O_2(g) \longrightarrow$
   c. $CS_2(s) + O_2(g) \longrightarrow$
   d. $C_3H_8O(l) + O_2(g) \longrightarrow$

Balancing Redox Reactions

61. Balance each redox reaction occurring in acidic aqueous solution.
   a. $K(s) + Cr^{3+}(aq) \longrightarrow Cr(s) + K^+(aq)$
   b. $Al(s) + Fe^{2+}(aq) \longrightarrow Al^{3+}(aq) + Fe(s)$
   c. $BrO_3^-(aq) + N_2H_4(g) \longrightarrow Br^-(aq) + N_2(g)$

62. Balance each redox reaction occurring in acidic aqueous solution.
   a. $Zn(s) + Sn^{2+}(aq) \longrightarrow Zn^{2+}(aq) + Sn(s)$
   b. $Mg(s) + Cr^{3+}(aq) \longrightarrow Mg^{2+}(aq) + Cr(s)$
   c. $MnO_4^-(aq) + Al(s) \longrightarrow Mn^{2+}(aq) + Al^{3+}(aq)$

63. Balance each redox reaction occurring in acidic aqueous solution.
   a. $PbO_2(s) + I^-(aq) \longrightarrow Pb^{2+}(aq) + I_2(s)$
   b. $SO_3^{2-}(aq) + MnO_4^-(aq) \longrightarrow SO_4^{2-}(aq) + Mn^{2+}(aq)$
   c. $S_2O_3^{2-}(aq) + Cl_2(g) \longrightarrow SO_4^{2-}(aq) + Cl^-(aq)$

64. Balance each redox reaction occurring in acidic aqueous solution.
   a. $I^-(aq) + NO_2^-(aq) \longrightarrow I_2(s) + NO(g)$
   b. $ClO_4^-(aq) + Cl^-(aq) \longrightarrow ClO_3^-(aq) + Cl_2(g)$
   c. $NO_3^-(aq) + Sn^{2+}(aq) \longrightarrow Sn^{4+}(aq) + NO(g)$

65. Balance each redox reaction occurring in basic aqueous solution.
   a. $H_2O_2(aq) + ClO_2(aq) \longrightarrow ClO_2^-(aq) + O_2(g)$
   b. $Al(s) + MnO_4^-(aq) \longrightarrow MnO_2(s) + Al(OH)_4^-(aq)$
   c. $Cl_2(g) \longrightarrow Cl^-(aq) + ClO_3^-(aq)$

66. Balance each redox reaction occurring in basic aqueous solution.
   a. $MnO_4^-(aq) + Br^-(aq) \longrightarrow MnO_2(s) + BrO_3^-(aq)$
   b. $Ag(s) + CN^-(aq) + O_2(g) \longrightarrow Ag(CN)_2^-(aq)$
   c. $NO_2^-(aq) + Al(s) \longrightarrow NH_3(g) + AlO_2^-(aq)$

67. Balance each disproportionation reaction occurring in acidic solution.
   a. $ClO^-(aq) \longrightarrow Cl^-(aq) + ClO_3^-(aq)$
   b. $Cu_2O(aq) \longrightarrow Cu(s) + Cu^{2+}(aq)$

68. Balance each disproportionation reaction occurring in acidic solution.
   a. $Sn^{2+}(aq) \longrightarrow Sn(s) + Sn^{4+}(aq)$
   b. $HNO_2(aq) \longrightarrow HNO_3(aq) + NO(g)$

Reaction Stoichiometry

69. Consider the unbalanced equation for the combustion of hexane:

$$C_6H_{14}(g) + O_2(g) \longrightarrow CO_2(g) + H_2O(g)$$

Balance the equation and determine how many moles of O_2 are required to react completely with 7.2 mol C_6H_{14}.

70. Consider the unbalanced equation for the neutralization of acetic acid:

$$CH_3COOH(aq) + Ba(OH)_2(aq) \longrightarrow H_2O(l) + (CH_3COO)_2Ba(aq)$$

Balance the equation and determine how many moles of $Ba(OH)_2$ are required to completely neutralize 0.461 mol CH_3COOH.

71. Calculate how many moles of NO_2 form when each quantity of reactant completely reacts:

$$2\ N_2O_5(g) \longrightarrow 4\ NO_2(g) + O_2(g)$$

   a. 2.5 mol N_2O_5
   b. 6.8 mol N_2O_5
   c. 15.2 g N_2O_5
   d. 2.87 kg N_2O_5

72. Calculate how many moles of NH_3 form when each quantity of reactant completely reacts:

$$3\ N_2H_4(l) \longrightarrow 4\ NH_3(g) + N_2(g)$$

   a. 2.6 mol N_2H_4
   b. 3.55 mol N_2H_4
   c. 65.3 g N_2H_4
   d. 4.88 kg N_2H_4

73. Consider the balanced equation:

$$SiO_2(s) + 3\ C(s) \longrightarrow SiC(s) + 2\ CO(g)$$

Complete the table showing the appropriate number of moles of reactants and products. If the number of moles of a *reactant* is provided, fill in the required amount of the other reactant, as well as the moles of each product formed. If the number of moles of a *product* is provided, fill in the required amount of each reactant to make that amount of product, as well as the amount of the other product that is made.

mol SiO_2	mol C	mol SiC	mol CO
3	______	______	______
______	6	______	______
______	______	______	10
2.8	______	______	______
______	1.55	______	______

74. Consider the balanced equation:

$$2\ N_2H_4(g) + N_2O_4(g) \longrightarrow 3\ N_2(g) + 4\ H_2O(g)$$

Complete the table showing the appropriate number of moles of reactants and products. If the number of moles of a *reactant* is provided, fill in the required amount of the other reactant, as well as the moles of each product formed. If the number of moles of a *product* is provided, fill in the required amount of each reactant to make that amount of product, as well as the amount of the other product that is made.

mol N_2H_4	mol N_2O_4	mol N_2	mol H_2O
2	______	______	______
______	5	______	______
______	______	______	10
2.5	______	______	______
______	4.2	______	______
______	______	11.8	______

75. Hydrobromic acid dissolves solid iron according to the reaction:

$$Fe(s) + 2\ HBr(aq) \longrightarrow FeBr_2(aq) + H_2(g)$$

What mass of HBr (in g) would you need to dissolve a 3.2 g pure iron bar on a padlock? What mass of H_2 would the complete reaction of the iron bar produce?

76. Sulfuric acid dissolves aluminum metal according to the reaction:

$$2\,Al(s) + 3\,H_2SO_4(aq) \longrightarrow Al_2(SO_4)_3(aq) + 3\,H_2(g)$$

Suppose you wanted to dissolve an aluminum block with a mass of 15.2 g. What minimum mass of H_2SO_4 (in g) would you need? What mass of H_2 gas (in g) would the complete reaction of the aluminum block produce?

77. For each of the reactions, calculate the mass (in grams) of the product formed when 3.67 g of the underlined reactant completely reacts. Assume that there is more than enough of the other reactant.

a. $\underline{Ba(s)} + Cl_2(g) \longrightarrow BaCl_2(s)$
b. $\underline{CaO(s)} + CO_2(g) \longrightarrow CaCO_3(s)$
c. $2\,\underline{Mg(s)} + O_2(g) \longrightarrow 2\,MgO(s)$
d. $4\,\underline{Al(s)} + 3\,O_2(g) \longrightarrow 2\,Al_2O_3(s)$

78. For each of the reactions, calculate the mass (in grams) of the product formed when 15.39 g of the underlined reactant completely reacts. Assume that there is more than enough of the other reactant.

a. $2\,K(s) + \underline{Cl_2(g)} \longrightarrow 2\,KCl(s)$
b. $2\,K(s) + \underline{Br_2(l)} \longrightarrow 2\,KBr(s)$
c. $4\,Cr(s) + \underline{3\,O_2(g)} \longrightarrow 2\,Cr_2O_3(s)$
d. $2\,\underline{Sr(s)} + O_2(g) \longrightarrow 2\,SrO(s)$

79. For each of the acid–base reactions, calculate the mass (in grams) of each acid necessary to completely react with and neutralize 4.85 g of the base.

a. $HCl(aq) + NaOH(aq) \longrightarrow H_2O(l) + NaCl(aq)$
b. $2\,HNO_3(aq) + Ca(OH)_2(aq) \longrightarrow 2\,H_2O(l) + Ca(NO_3)_2(aq)$
c. $H_2SO_4(aq) + 2\,KOH(aq) \longrightarrow 2\,H_2O(l) + K_2SO_4(aq)$

80. For each precipitation reaction, calculate how many grams of the first reactant are necessary to completely react with 55.8 g of the second reactant.

a. $2\,KI(aq) + Pb(NO_3)_2(aq) \longrightarrow PbI_2(s) + 2\,KNO_3(aq)$
b. $Na_2CO_3(aq) + CuCl_2(aq) \longrightarrow CuCO_3(s) + 2\,NaCl(aq)$
c. $K_2SO_4(aq) + Sr(NO_3)_2(aq) \longrightarrow SrSO_4(s) + 2\,KNO_3(aq)$

Limiting Reactant, Theoretical Yield, and Percent Yield

81. For the reaction, find the limiting reactant for each of the initial amounts of reactants.

$$2\,Na(s) + Br_2(g) \longrightarrow 2\,NaBr(s)$$

a. 2 mol Na, 2 mol Br_2
b. 1.8 mol Na, 1.4 mol Br_2
c. 2.5 mol Na, 1 mol Br_2
d. 12.6 mol Na, 6.9 mol Br_2

82. For the reaction, find the limiting reactant for each initial amount of reactants.

$$4\,Al(s) + 3\,O_2(g) \longrightarrow 2\,Al_2O_3(s)$$

a. 1 mol Al, 1 mol O_2
b. 4 mol Al, 2.6 mol O_2
c. 16 mol Al, 13 mol O_2
d. 7.4 mol Al, 6.5 mol O_2

83. Consider the reaction:

$$4\,HCl(g) + O_2(g) \longrightarrow 2\,H_2O(g) + 2\,Cl_2(g)$$

Each molecular diagram represents an initial mixture of the reactants. How many molecules of Cl_2 would be formed from the reaction mixture that produces the greatest amount of products?

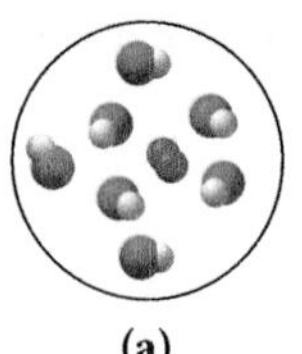
(a)

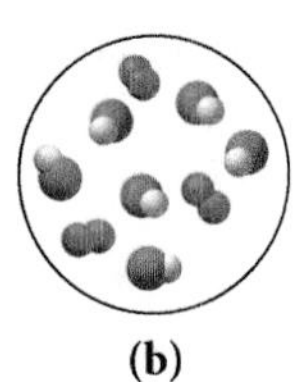
(b)

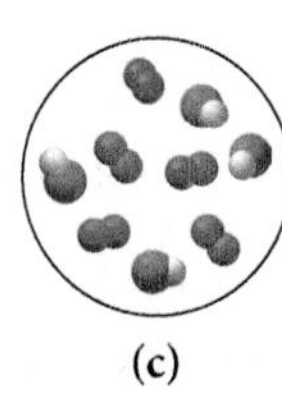
(c)

84. Consider the reaction:

$$2\,CH_3OH(g) + 3\,O_2(g) \longrightarrow 2\,CO_2(g) + 4\,H_2O(g)$$

Each of the molecular diagrams represents an initial mixture of the reactants. How many CO_2 molecules would be formed from the reaction mixture that produces the greatest amount of products?

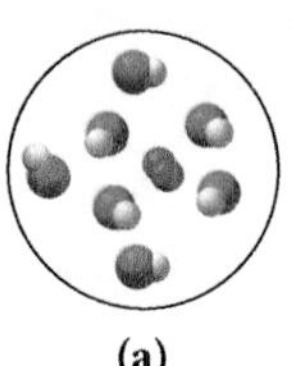
(a)

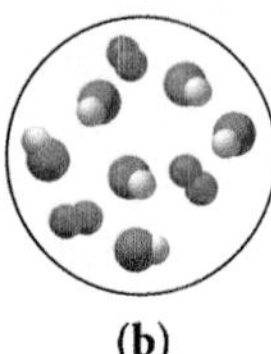
(b)

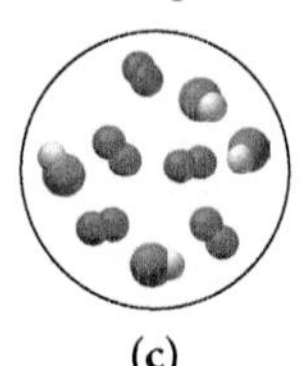
(c)

85. For the reaction, compute the theoretical yield of the product (in moles) for each initial amount of reactants.

$$Ti(s) + 2\,Cl_2(g) \longrightarrow TiCl_4(s)$$

a. 4 mol Ti, 4 mol Cl_2
b. 7 mol Ti, 17 mol Cl_2
c. 12.4 mol Ti, 18.8 mol Cl_2

86. For the reaction, compute the theoretical yield of product (in moles) for each initial amount of reactants.

$$2\,Mn(s) + 2\,O_2(g) \longrightarrow 2\,MnO_2(s)$$

a. 3 mol Mn, 3 mol O_2
b. 4 mol Mn, 7 mol O_2
c. 27.5 mol Mn, 43.8 mol O_2

87. Zinc sulfide reacts with oxygen according to the reaction:

$$2\,ZnS(s) + 3\,O_2(g) \longrightarrow 2\,ZnO(s) + 2\,SO_2(g)$$

A reaction mixture initially contains 4.2 mol ZnS and 6.8 mol O_2. Once the reaction has occurred as completely as possible, what amount (in moles) of the excess reactant is left?

88. Iron(II) sulfide reacts with hydrochloric acid according to the reaction:

$$FeS(s) + 2\,HCl(aq) \longrightarrow FeCl_2(s) + H_2S(g)$$

A reaction mixture initially contains 0.223 mol FeS and 0.652 mol HCl. Once the reaction has occurred as completely as possible, what amount (in moles) of the excess reactant is left?

89. For the reaction, compute the theoretical yield of product (in grams) for each initial amount of reactants.

$$2\,Al(s) + 3\,Cl_2(g) \longrightarrow 2\,AlCl_3(s)$$

a. 2.0 g Al, 2.0 g Cl_2
b. 7.5 g Al, 24.8 g Cl_2
c. 0.235 g Al, 1.15 g Cl_2

90. For the reaction, compute the theoretical yield of the product (in grams) for each initial amount of reactants.

$$Ti(s) + 2\,F_2(g) \longrightarrow TiF_4(s)$$

a. 5.0 g Ti, 5.0 g F_2
b. 2.4 g Ti, 1.6 g F_2
c. 0.233 g Ti, 0.288 g F_2

91. Iron(III) oxide reacts with carbon monoxide according to the equation:

$$Fe_2O_3(s) + 3\,CO(g) \longrightarrow 2\,Fe(s) + 3\,CO_2(g)$$

A reaction mixture initially contains 22.55 g Fe_2O_3 and 14.78 g CO. Once the reaction has occurred as completely as possible, what mass (in grams) of the excess reactant is left?

92. Elemental phosphorus reacts with chlorine gas according to the equation:

$$P_4(s) + 6\,Cl_2(g) \longrightarrow 4\,PCl_3(l)$$

A reaction mixture initially contains 45.69 g P_4 and 131.3 g Cl_2. Once the reaction has occurred as completely as possible, what mass (in grams) of the excess reactant is left?

93. Lead ions can be precipitated from solution with KCl according to the reaction:

$$Pb^{2+}(aq) + 2\,KCl(aq) \longrightarrow PbCl_2(s) + 2\,K^+(aq)$$

When 28.5 g KCl is added to a solution containing 25.7 g Pb^{2+}, a $PbCl_2$ precipitate forms. The precipitate is filtered and dried and found to have a mass of 29.4 g. Determine the limiting reactant, theoretical yield of $PbCl_2$, and percent yield for the reaction.

94. Magnesium oxide can be made by heating magnesium metal in the presence of oxygen. The balanced equation for the reaction is:

$$2\,Mg(s) + O_2(g) \longrightarrow 2\,MgO(s)$$

When 10.1 g Mg is allowed to react with 10.5 g O_2, 11.9 g MgO is collected. Determine the limiting reactant, theoretical yield, and percent yield for the reaction.

95. Urea (CH_4N_2O) is a common fertilizer that can be synthesized by the reaction of ammonia (NH_3) with carbon dioxide:

$$2\,NH_3(aq) + CO_2(aq) \longrightarrow CH_4N_2O(aq) + H_2O(l)$$

In an industrial synthesis of urea, a chemist combines 136.4 kg of ammonia with 211.4 kg of carbon dioxide and obtains 168.4 kg of urea. Determine the limiting reactant, theoretical yield of urea, and percent yield for the reaction.

96. Many computer chips are manufactured from silicon, which occurs in nature as SiO_2. When SiO_2 is heated to melting, it reacts with solid carbon to form liquid silicon and carbon monoxide gas. In an industrial preparation of silicon, 155.8 kg of SiO_2 reacts with 78.3 kg of carbon to produce 66.1 kg of silicon. Determine the limiting reactant, theoretical yield, and percent yield for the reaction.

Solution Concentration and Solution Stoichiometry

97. Calculate the molarity of each solution:
a. 3.25 mol LiCl in 2.78 L of solution
b. 28.33 g $C_6H_{12}O_6$ in 1.28 L of solution
c. 32.4 mg NaCl in 122.4 mL of solution

98. Calculate the molarity of each solution:
a. 0.38 mol $LiNO_3$ in 6.14 L of solution
b. 72.8 g C_2H_6O in 2.34 L of solution
c. 12.87 mg KI in 112.4 mL of solution

99. How many moles of KCl are contained in each solution?
a. 0.556 L of a 2.3 mol L^{-1} KCl solution
b. 1.8 L of a 0.85 mol L^{-1} KCl solution
c. 114 mL of a 1.85 mol L^{-1} KCl solution

100. What volume of a 0.200 mol L^{-1} ethanol solution contains each amount in moles of ethanol?
a. 0.45 mol ethanol
b. 1.22 mol ethanol
c. 1.2×10^{-2} mol ethanol

101. A laboratory procedure calls for making 400.0 mL of a 1.1 mol L^{-1} $NaNO_3$ solution. What mass of $NaNO_3$ (in grams) is needed?

102. A chemist wants to make 5.5 L of a 0.300 mol L^{-1} $CaCl_2$ solution. What mass of $CaCl_2$ (in grams) should the chemist use?

103. If 123 mL of a 1.1 mol L^{-1} glucose solution is diluted to 500.0 mL, what is the molarity of the diluted solution?

104. If 3.5 L of a 4.8 mol L^{-1} $SrCl_2$ solution is diluted to 45 L, what is the molarity of the diluted solution?

105. To what volume should you dilute 50.0 mL of a 12 mol L^{-1} stock HNO_3 solution to obtain a 0.100 mol L^{-1} HNO_3 solution?

106. To what volume should you dilute 25 mL of a 10.0 mol L^{-1} H_2SO_4 solution to obtain a 0.150 mol L^{-1} H_2SO_4 solution?

107. Consider the precipitation reaction:

$$2\,Na_3PO_4(aq) + 3\,CuCl_2(aq) \longrightarrow Cu_3(PO_4)_2(s) + 6\,NaCl(aq)$$

What volume of a 0.175 mol L^{-1} Na_3PO_4 solution is necessary to completely react with 95.4 mL of 0.102 mol L^{-1} $CuCl_2$?

108. Consider the reaction:

$$Li_2S(aq) + Co(NO_3)_2(aq) \longrightarrow 2\,LiNO_3(aq) + CoS(s)$$

What volume of a 0.150 mol L^{-1} Li_2S solution is required to completely react with 125 mL of 0.150 mol L^{-1} $Co(NO_3)_2$?

109. What is the minimum amount of 6.0 mol L^{-1} H_2SO_4 necessary to produce 25.0 g of $H_2(g)$ according to the reaction between aluminum and sulfuric acid?

$$2\,Al(s) + 3\,H_2SO_4(aq) \longrightarrow Al_2(SO_4)_3(aq) + 3H_2(g)$$

110. What is the molarity of $ZnCl_2$ that forms when 25.0 g of zinc completely reacts with $CuCl_2$ according to the following reaction? Assume a final volume of 275 mL.

$$Zn(s) + CuCl_2(aq) \longrightarrow ZnCl_2(aq) + Cu(s)$$

Cumulative Problems

111. The density of a 20.0%-by-mass ethylene glycol ($C_2H_6O_2$) solution in water is 1.03 g mL^{-1}. Find the molarity of the solution.

112. Find the percent by mass of sodium chloride in a 1.35 mol L^{-1} NaCl solution. The density of the solution is 1.05 g mL^{-1}.

113. People often use sodium bicarbonate as an antacid to neutralize excess hydrochloric acid in an upset stomach. What mass of hydrochloric acid (in grams) can 2.5 g of sodium bicarbonate neutralize? (*Hint:* Begin by writing a balanced equation for

the reaction between aqueous sodium bicarbonate and aqueous hydrochloric acid.)

114. Toilet bowl cleaners often contain hydrochloric acid, which dissolves the calcium carbonate deposits that accumulate within a toilet bowl. What mass of calcium carbonate (in grams) can 3.8 g of HCl dissolve? (*Hint:* Begin by writing a balanced equation for the reaction between hydrochloric acid and calcium carbonate.)

115. The combustion of gasoline produces carbon dioxide and water. Assume gasoline to be pure octane (C_8H_{18}) and calculate the mass (in kilograms) of carbon dioxide that is added to the atmosphere per 1.0 kg of octane burned. (*Hint:* Begin by writing a balanced equation for the combustion reaction.)

116. Many home barbeques are fuelled with propane gas (C_3H_8). What mass of carbon dioxide (in kilograms) is produced upon the complete combustion of 18.9 L of propane (approximate contents of one 5-gallon tank)? Assume that the density of the liquid propane in the tank is 0.621 g mL^{-1}. (*Hint:* Begin by writing a balanced equation for the combustion reaction.)

117. Aspirin can be made in the laboratory by reacting acetic anhydride ($C_4H_6O_3$) with salicylic acid ($C_7H_6O_3$) to form aspirin ($C_9H_8O_4$) and acetic acid ($C_2H_4O_2$). The balanced equation is:

$$C_4H_6O_3 + C_7H_6O_3 \longrightarrow C_9H_8O_4 + C_2H_4O_2$$

In a laboratory synthesis, a student begins with 3.00 mL of acetic anhydride (density = 1.08 g mL^{-1}) and 1.25 g of salicylic acid. Once the reaction is complete, the student collects 1.22 g of aspirin. Determine the limiting reactant, theoretical yield of aspirin, and percent yield for the reaction.

118. The combustion of liquid ethanol (C_2H_5OH) produces carbon dioxide and water. After 4.62 mL of ethanol (density = 0.789 g mL^{-1}) was allowed to burn in the presence of 15.55 g of oxygen gas, 3.72 mL of water (density = 1.00 g mL^{-1}) was collected. Determine the limiting reactant, theoretical yield of H_2O, and percent yield for the reaction. (*Hint:* Write a balanced equation for the combustion of ethanol.)

119. A loud classroom demonstration involves igniting a hydrogenfilled balloon. The hydrogen within the balloon reacts explosively with oxygen in the air to form water. If the balloon is filled with a mixture of hydrogen and oxygen, the explosion is even louder than if the balloon is filled only with hydrogen—the intensity of the explosion depends on the relative amounts of oxygen and hydrogen within the balloon. Look at the molecular views representing different amounts of hydrogen and oxygen in four different balloons. Based on the balanced chemical equation, which balloon will make the loudest explosion?

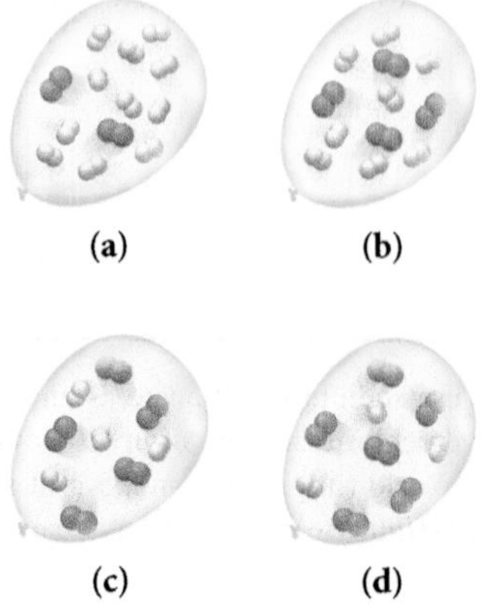

(a) (b) (c) (d)

120. A hydrochloric acid solution will neutralize a sodium hydroxide solution. Look at the molecular views showing one beaker of HCl and four beakers of NaOH. Which NaOH beaker will just neutralize the HCl beaker? Begin by writing a balanced chemical equation for the neutralization reaction.

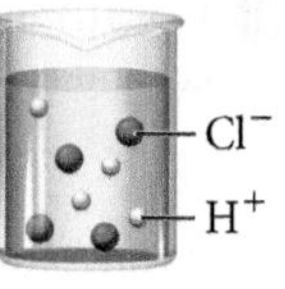

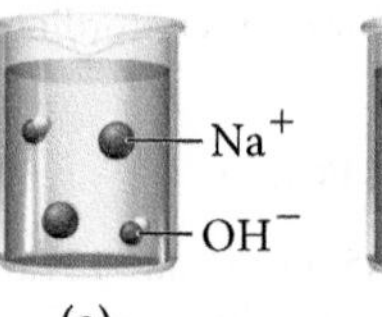

(a)

(b)

(c)

(d)

121. Predict the products and write a balanced molecular equation for each reaction. If no reaction occurs, write NO REACTION.

a. $HCl(aq) + Hg_2(NO_3)_2(aq) \longrightarrow$
b. $KHSO_3(aq) + HNO_3(aq) \longrightarrow$
c. aqueous ammonium chloride and aqueous lead(II) nitrate
d. aqueous ammonium chloride and aqueous calcium hydroxide

122. Predict the products and write a balanced molecular equation for each reaction. If no reaction occurs, write NO REACTION.

a. $H_2SO_4(aq) + HNO_3(aq) \longrightarrow$
b. $Cr(NO_3)_3(aq) + LiOH(aq) \longrightarrow$
c. liquid pentanol ($C_5H_{12}O$) and gaseous oxygen
d. aqueous strontium sulfide and aqueous copper(II) sulfate

123. Hard water often contains dissolved Ca^{2+} and Mg^{2+} ions. One way to soften water is to add phosphates. The phosphate ion forms insoluble precipitates with calcium and magnesium ions, removing them from solution. Suppose that a solution is 0.050 mol L^{-1} in calcium chloride and 0.085 mol L^{-1} in magnesium nitrate. What mass of sodium phosphate would have to be added to 1.5 L of this solution to completely eliminate the hard water ions? Assume complete reaction.

124. An acid solution is 0.100 mol L^{-1} in HCl and 0.200 mol L^{-1} in H_2SO_4. What volume of a 0.150 mol L^{-1} KOH solution would completely neutralize all the acid in 500.0 mL of this solution?

125. Find the mass of barium metal (in grams) that must react with O_2 to produce enough barium oxide to prepare 1.0 L of a 0.10 mol L^{-1} solution of OH^-.

126. A solution contains Cr^{3+} ions and Mg^{2+} ions. The addition of 1.00 L of 1.51 mol L^{-1} NaF solution is required to cause the complete precipitation of these ions as $CrF_3(s)$ and $MgF_2(s)$. The total mass of the precipitate is 49.6 g. Find the mass of Cr^{3+} in the original solution.

127. The nitrogen in sodium nitrate and in ammonium sulfate is available to plants as fertilizer. Which is the more economical source of nitrogen, a fertilizer containing 30.0% sodium nitrate by weight and costing $18 per 100 kg or one containing 20.0% ammonium sulfate by weight and costing $16.20 per 100 kg?

128. Find the volume of 0.110 mol L^{-1} of hydrochloric acid necessary to react completely with 1.52 g $Al(OH)_3$.

129. Treatment of gold metal with BrF_3 and KF produces Br_2 and $KAuF_4$, a salt of gold. Identify the oxidizing agent and the reducing agent in this reaction. Find the mass of the gold salt that forms when a 73.5 g mixture of equal masses of all three reactants is prepared.

130. We prepare a solution by mixing 0.10 L of 0.12 mol L^{-1} sodium chloride with 0.23 L of a 0.18 mol L^{-1} $MgCl_2$ solution. What volume of a 0.20 mol L^{-1} silver nitrate solution do we need to precipitate all the Cl^- ions in the solution as AgCl?

131. A solution contains one or more of the following ions: Ag^+, Ca^{2+}, and Cu^{2+}. When you add sodium chloride to the solution, no precipitate forms. When you add sodium sulfate to the solution, a white precipitate forms. You filter off the precipitate and add sodium carbonate to the remaining solution, producing another precipitate. Which ions were present in the original solution? Write net ionic equations for the formation of each of the precipitates observed.

132. A solution contains one or more of the following ions: Hg_2^{2+}, Ba^{2+}, and Fe^{2+}. When potassium chloride is added to the solution, a precipitate forms. The precipitate is filtered off, and potassium sulfate is added to the remaining solution, producing no precipitate. When potassium carbonate is added to the remaining solution, a precipitate forms. Which ions were present in the original solution? Write net ionic equations for the formation of each of the precipitates observed.

133. The reaction of NH_3 and O_2 forms NO and water. The NO can be used to convert P_4 to P_4O_6, forming N_2 in the process. The P_4O_6 can be treated with water to form H_3PO_3, which forms PH_3 and H_3PO_4 when heated. Find the mass of PH_3 that forms from the reaction of 1.00 g NH_3.

134. An important reaction that takes place in a blast furnace during the production of iron is the formation of iron metal and CO_2 from Fe_2O_3 and CO. Find the mass of Fe_2O_3 required to form 910 kg of iron. Find the amount of CO_2 that forms in this process.

135. A liquid fuel mixture contains 30.35% hexane (C_6H_{14}), 15.85% heptane (C_7H_{16}), and the rest octane (C_8H_{18}). What maximum mass of carbon dioxide is produced by the complete combustion of 10.0 kg of this fuel mixture?

136. Titanium occurs in the magnetic mineral ilmenite ($FeTiO_3$), which is often found mixed with sand. The ilmenite can be separated from the sand with magnets. The titanium can then be extracted from the ilmenite by the following set of reactions:

$$FeTiO_3(s) + 3\,Cl_2(g) + 3\,C(s) \longrightarrow 3\,CO(g) + FeCl_2(s) + TiCl_4(g)$$

$$TiCl_4(l) + 2\,Mg(s) \longrightarrow 2\,MgCl_2(l) + Ti(s)$$

Suppose that an ilmenite–sand mixture contains 22.8% ilmenite by mass and that the first reaction is carried out with a 90.8% yield. If the second reaction is carried out with an 85.9% yield, what mass of titanium can be obtained from 1.00 kg of the ilmenite–sand mixture?

Challenge Problems

137. A mixture of C_3H_8 and C_2H_2 has a mass of 2.0 g. It is burned in excess O_2 to form a mixture of water and carbon dioxide that contains 1.5 times as many moles of CO_2 as of water. Find the mass of C_2H_2 in the original mixture.

138. A mixture of 20.6 g P and 79.4 g Cl_2 reacts completely to form PCl_3 and PCl_5 as the only products. Find the mass of PCl_3 formed.

139. A solution contains Ag^+ and Hg^{2+} ions. The addition of 0.100 L of 1.22 mol L^{-1} NaI solution is just enough to precipitate all the ions as AgI and HgI_2. The total mass of the precipitate is 28.1 g. Find the mass of AgI in the precipitate.

140. Lakes that have been acidified by acid rain (HNO_3 and H_2SO_4) can be neutralized by a process called liming, in which limestone ($CaCO_3$) is added to the acidified water. What mass of limestone (in kg) would completely neutralize a 15.2 billion-litre lake that is 1.8×10^{-5} mol L^{-1} in H_2SO_4 and 8.7×10^{-6} mol L^{-1} in HNO_3?

141. We learned in Section 4.4 that sodium carbonate is often added to laundry detergents to soften hard water and make the detergent more effective. Suppose that a particular detergent mixture is designed to soften hard water that is 3.5×10^{-3} mol L^{-1} in Ca^{2+} and 1.1×10^{-3} mol L^{-1} in Mg^{2+} and that the average capacity of a washing machine is 75 L of water. If the detergent requires using 0.65 kg detergent per load of laundry, determine what percentage (by mass) of the detergent should be sodium carbonate in order to completely precipitate all of the calcium and magnesium ions in an average load of laundry water.

142. Lead poisoning is a serious condition resulting from the ingestion of lead in food, water, or other environmental sources. It affects the central nervous system, leading to a variety of symptoms such as distractibility, lethargy, and loss of motor coordination. Lead poisoning is treated with chelating agents, substances that bind to metal ions, allowing it to be eliminated in the urine. A modern chelating agent used for this purpose is succimer ($C_4H_6O_4S_2$). Suppose you are trying to determine the appropriate dose for succimer treatment of lead poisoning. What minimum mass of succimer (in milligrams) is needed to bind all of the lead in a patient's bloodstream? Assume that patient blood lead levels are 45 μg dL^{-1}, that total blood volume is 5.0 L, and that one mole of succimer binds one mole of lead.

143. A particular kind of emergency breathing apparatus—often placed in mines, caves, or other places where oxygen might become depleted or where the air might become poisoned—works via the following chemical reaction:

$$4\,KO_2(s) + 2\,CO_2(g) \longrightarrow 2\,K_2CO_3(s) + 3\,O_2(g)$$

Notice that the reaction produces O_2, which can be breathed, and absorbs CO_2, a product of respiration. Suppose you work for a company interested in producing a self-rescue breathing apparatus (based on the above reaction) that would allow the user to survive for 10 minutes in an emergency situation. What are the important chemical considerations in designing such a unit? Estimate how much KO_2 would be required for the apparatus. (Find any necessary additional information—such as human breathing rates—from appropriate sources. Assume that normal air is 20% oxygen.)

144. Metallic aluminum reacts with MnO_2 at elevated temperatures to form manganese metal and aluminum oxide. A mixture of the two reactants is 67.2% mole percent Al. Find the theoretical yield (in grams) of manganese from the reaction of 250 g of this mixture.

145. Hydrolysis of the compound B_5H_9 forms boric acid, H_3BO_3. Fusion of boric acid with sodium oxide forms a borate salt, $Na_2B_4O_7$. Without writing complete equations, find the mass (in grams) of B_5H_9 required to form 151 g of the borate salt by this reaction sequence.

146. A mixture of carbon and sulfur has a mass of 9.0 g. Complete combustion with excess O_2 gives 23.3 g of a mixture of CO_2 and SO_2. Find the mass of sulfur in the original mixture.

Conceptual Problems

 147. Consider the reaction:

$$4\,K(s) + O_2(g) \longrightarrow 2\,K_2O(s)$$

The molar mass of K is 39.10 g mol^{-1} and that of O_2 is 32.00 g mol^{-1}. Without doing any extensive calculations, pick the conditions under which potassium is the limiting reactant and explain your reasoning.

a. 170 g K, 31 g O_2
b. 16 g K, 2.5 g O_2
c. 165 kg K, 28 kg O_2
d. 1.5 g K, 0.38 g O_2

148. Consider the reaction:

$$2\,NO(g) + 5\,H_2(g) \longrightarrow 2\,NH_3(g) + 2\,H_2O(g)$$

A reaction mixture initially contains 5 moles of NO and 10 moles of H_2. Without doing any calculations, determine which set of amounts best represents the mixture after the reactants have reacted as completely as possible. Explain your reasoning.

a. 1 mol NO, 0 mol H_2, 4 mol NH_3, 4 mol H_2O
b. 0 mol NO, 1 mol H_2, 5 mol NH_3, 5 mol H_2O
c. 3 mol NO, 5 mol H_2, 2 mol NH_3, 2 mol H_2O
d. 0 mol NO, 0 mol H_2, 4 mol NH_3, 4 mol H_2O

 149. The circle below represents 1.0 L of a solution with a solute concentration of 1 mol L^{-1}:

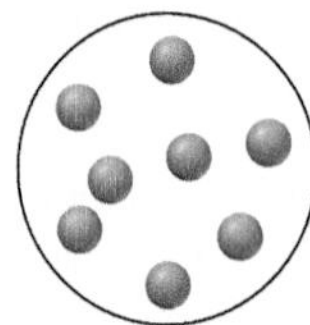

Explain what you would add (the amount of solute or volume of solvent) to the solution to obtain a solution represented by each diagram:

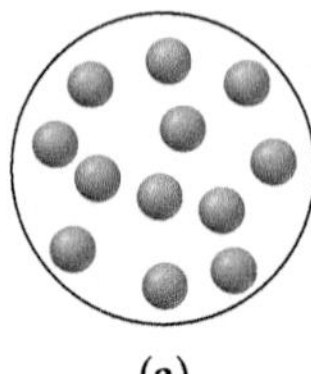

(a)

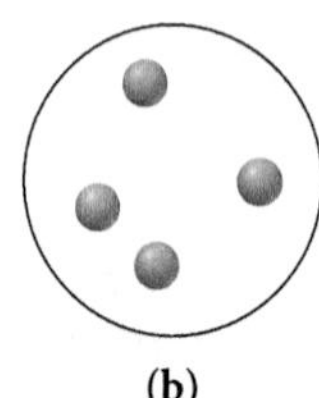

(b)

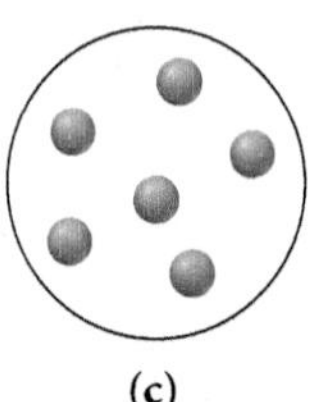

(c)

150. Consider the reaction:

$$2\,N_2H_4(g) + N_2O_4(g) \longrightarrow 3\,N_2(g) + 4\,H_2O(g)$$

Consider also this representation of an initial mixture of N_2H_4 and N_2O_4:

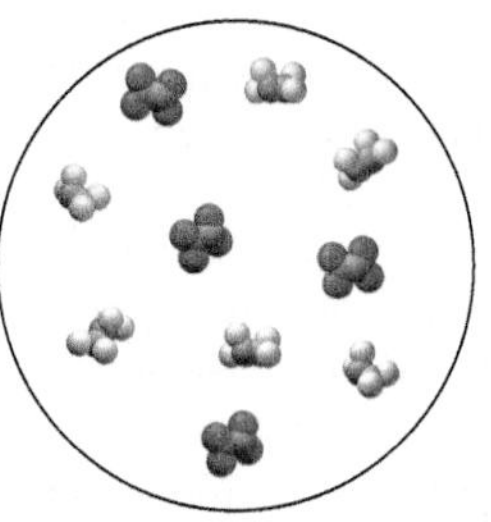

Which diagram best represents the reaction mixture after the reactants have reacted as completely as possible?

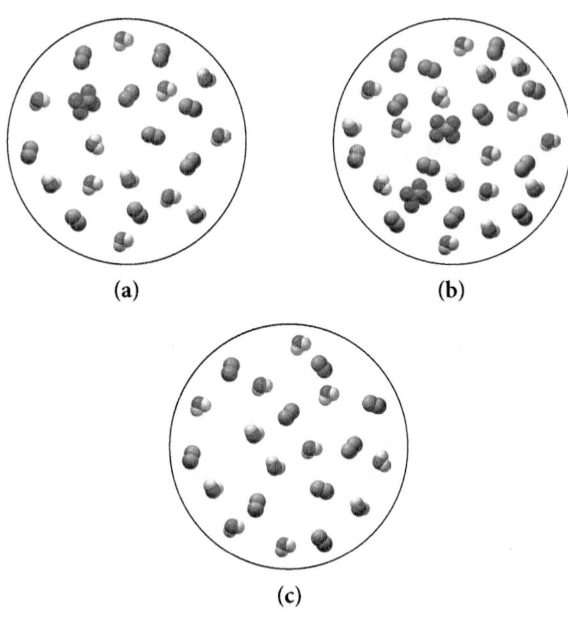

Gases

The buildup of pressure, which results from the constant collisions of gas molecules with the surfaces around them, expels the cork in a bottle of champagne.

So many of the properties of matter, especially when in the gaseous form, can be deduced from the hypothesis that their minute parts are in rapid motion, the velocity increasing with the temperature, that the precise nature of this motion becomes a subject of rational curiosity.

—James Clerk Maxwell (1831–1879)

WE CAN SURVIVE FOR WEEKS without food, days without water, but only minutes without air. Fortunately, we live at the bottom of a vast ocean of air, held to Earth by gravity. We inhale a lungful of this air every few seconds, keep some of the molecules for our own needs, add some molecules our bodies no longer have a use for, and exhale the mixture back into the surrounding air. The air around us is matter in the gaseous state. What are the fundamental properties of these gases? What laws describe their behaviour? What theory explains these properties and laws? The scientific method proceeds in this way—from observations to laws to theories—exactly the way we will proceed in this chapter. The gaseous state is the simplest and best-understood state of matter. In this chapter, we examine that state.

5.1 Breathing: Putting Pressure to Work

Every day, without even thinking about it, you move approximately 8500 litres of air into and out of your lungs. The total weight of this air is about 25 kilograms. How do you do it? The simple answer is *pressure*. You rely on your body's ability to create pressure differences to move air into and out of your lungs. **Pressure** is the force exerted per unit area by gas molecules as they strike the surfaces around them (Figure 5.1 ▼). Just as a ball exerts a force when it bounces against a wall, so

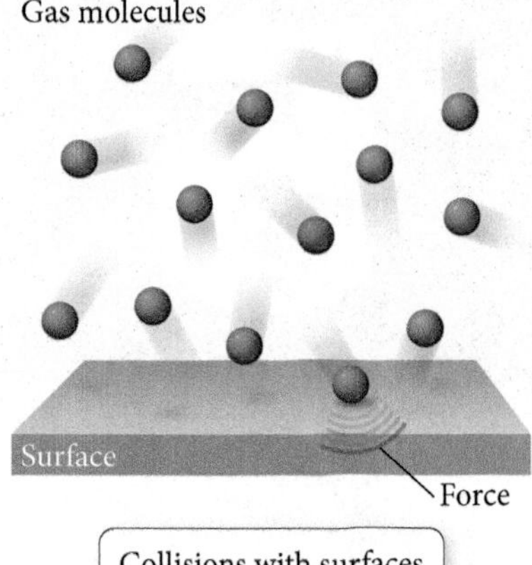

▲ **FIGURE 5.1 Gas Pressure** Pressure is the force per unit area exerted by gas molecules colliding with the surfaces around them.

a gaseous atom or molecule exerts a force when it collides with a surface. The sum of all these molecular collisions is pressure—a constant force on the surfaces exposed to any gas. The total pressure exerted by a gas depends on several factors, including the concentration of gas molecules in the sample—the higher the concentration, the greater the pressure.

When you inhale, the muscles that surround your chest cavity expand the volume of your lungs. The expanded volume results in a lower concentration of gas molecules (the number of molecules does not change, but since the volume increases, the *concentration* goes down). This in turn results in fewer molecular collisions, which results in lower pressure. The external pressure (the pressure outside of your lungs) remains relatively constant and is now higher than the pressure within your lungs. As a result, gaseous molecules flow into your lungs, from the region of higher pressure to the region of lower pressure. When you exhale, the process is reversed. The chest cavity muscles relax, which *decreases* the lung volume, increasing the pressure within the lungs and forcing air back out. In this way, within the course of a normal human lifetime, you will take about half a billion breaths, and move about 250 million litres of air through your lungs. With each breath, you create pressure differences that allow you to obtain the oxygen that you need to live.

5.2 Pressure: The Result of Molecular Collisions

Air can hold up a jumbo jet or knock down a building. How? As we just discussed, air contains gaseous atoms and molecules in constant motion. The particles collide with each other and with the surfaces around them. Each collision exerts only a small force, but when the forces of the many particles are summed, they quickly add up. The result of the constant collisions between the atoms or molecules in a gas and the surfaces around them is *pressure*. Because of pressure, we can drink from straws, inflate basketballs, and move air into and out of our lungs. Variation in pressure in Earth's atmosphere creates wind, and changes in pressure help us to predict weather. Pressure is all around us and even inside of us. The pressure that a gas sample exerts is the force per unit area that results from the collisions of gas particles with the surrounding surfaces:

$$\text{Pressure} = \frac{\text{force}}{\text{area}} = \frac{F}{A} \qquad [5.1]$$

▲ **FIGURE 5.2 Pressure and Particle Density** A low density of gas particles results in low pressure. A high density of gas particles results in high pressure.

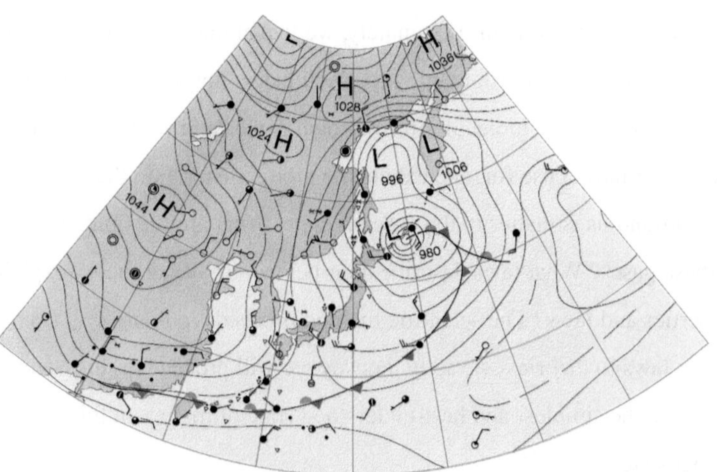

▲ Pressure variations in Earth's atmosphere create wind and weather. The H's in this map indicate regions of high pressure, usually associated with clear weather. The L's indicate regions of low pressure, usually associated with unstable weather. The map shows a typhoon off the northeast coast of Japan. The isobars, or lines of constant pressure, are labelled in hectopascals (100 Pa).

The pressure of a gas sample depends on several factors, including the number of gas particles in a given volume—the fewer the gas particles, the lower the pressure (Figure 5.2 ◀). Pressure decreases with increasing altitude because there are fewer molecules per unit

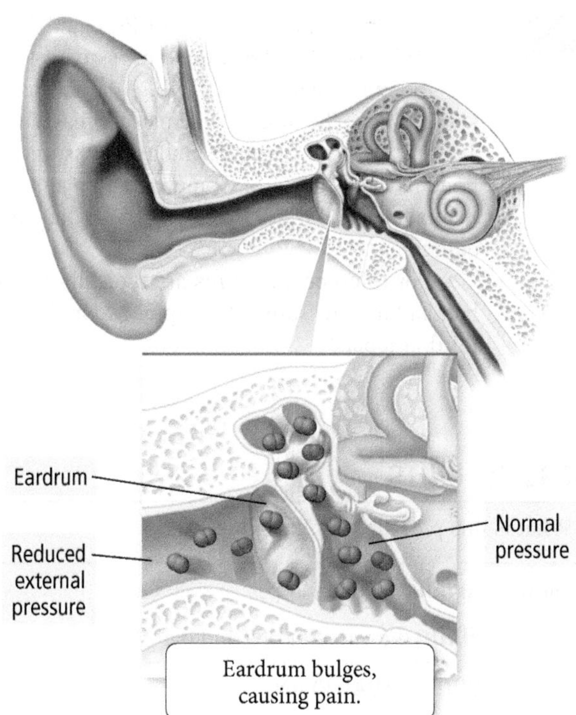

◀ **FIGURE 5.3 Pressure Imbalance** The discomfort you may feel in your ears upon ascending a mountain is caused by a pressure imbalance between the cavities in your ears and the outside air.

volume of air. Above 9100 m for example, where most commercial airplanes fly, the pressure is so low that you could pass out due to a lack of oxygen. For this reason, most airplane cabins are artificially pressurized.

You can often feel the effect of a drop in pressure as a brief pain in your ears. This pain arises within the air-containing cavities in your ear (Figure 5.3 ▲). When you ascend a mountain, the external pressure (the pressure that surrounds you) drops, while the pressure within your ear cavities (the internal pressure) remains the same. This creates an imbalance—the greater internal pressure forces your eardrum to bulge outward, causing pain. With time, and with the help of a yawn or two, the excess air within your ear's cavities escapes, equalizing the internal and external pressures and relieving the pain.

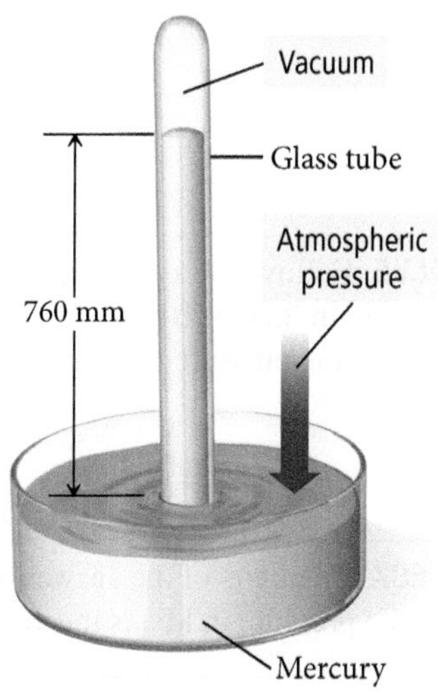

▲ **FIGURE 5.4 The Mercury Barometer** Average atmospheric pressure at sea level can support a column of mercury 760 mm in height.

Pressure Units

Pressure can be measured in several different units. A common unit of pressure, the **millimetre of mercury (mmHg)**, originates from how pressure is measured with a **barometer** (Figure 5.4 ▶). A barometer is an evacuated glass tube, the tip of which is submerged in a pool of mercury. Liquid in an evacuated tube is forced upward by atmospheric gas pressure on the liquid's surface. Because mercury is so dense (13.5 times more dense than water), atmospheric pressure can support a column of Hg that is only about 0.760 m or 760 mm tall. This makes a column of mercury a convenient way to measure pressure.

In a barometer, when the atmospheric pressure rises, the height of the mercury column rises as well. Similarly, when atmospheric pressure falls, the height of the column falls. The unit *millimetre of mercury* is often called a **torr**, after the Italian physicist Evangelista Torricelli (1608–1647) who invented the barometer.

As a convention, an SI unit that is derived from a proper name is capitalized. When the unit is spelled out in a sentence though, it begins with a lowercase letter.

$$1 \text{ mmHg} = 1 \text{ Torr}$$

The SI unit of pressure is the **pascal (Pa)**. Average sea level pressures are 101 325 Pa. This amount of pressure pushes a column of mercury to a height of 760 mmHg. The **atmosphere (atm)** is another unit of pressure that equals 760 mmHg and 101 325 Pa.

$$101\,325 \text{ Pa} = 101.325 \text{ kPa} = 760 \text{ Torr} = 1 \text{ atm}$$

TABLE 5.1 Common Units of Pressure

Pressure Measured in	Unit	Standard Pressure
bar	bar	1 bar
pascal	Pa	100 000 Pa
kilopascal	kPa	100 kPa
torr (mmHg)	Torr or mmHg	750.1 Torr
atmosphere	atm	0.98692 atm
pounds per square inch	psi	14.504 psi

The International Union of Pure and Applied Chemistry (IUPAC) has defined **standard pressure** as exactly 100 000 Pa for the purposes of specifying the properties of gaseous substances. The **bar** is a unit of pressure that is equal to 100 000 Pa, and 1 bar is standard pressure for gaseous components in a mixture. Some common units of pressure are displayed in Table 5.1, along with the standard pressure equivalent.

For reference, car tires are typically inflated to about 2.5 bar, and the pressure at the top of Mount Everest is about one-third of a bar.

EXAMPLE 5.1 CONVERTING BETWEEN PRESSURE UNITS

Aircraft tires operate at high pressures: 2.00×10^2 psi. What is this pressure in kPa and in bar?

SORT The problem gives a pressure in psi and asks you to convert the units to kPa and bar.

GIVEN: 2.00×10^2 psi

FIND: the value in kPa and bar

STRATEGIZE Table 5.1 has a direct conversion factor between bar and psi, but not for kPa and psi. However, because there is a conversion between bar and kPa, once you convert to bar, you can convert to kPa.

CONCEPTUAL PLAN

psi → bar → kPa

$\frac{1 \text{ bar}}{14.504 \text{ psi}}$ $\frac{100 \text{ kPa}}{1 \text{ bar}}$

RELATIONSHIPS USED

1 bar = 14.504 psi

100 kPa = 1 bar

SOLVE Follow the conceptual plan to solve the problem. Begin with 2.00×10^2 psi and use the conversion factors to arrive at the pressure in both bar and kPa.

SOLUTION

$$2.00 \times 10^2 \text{ psi} \times \frac{1 \text{ bar}}{14.504 \text{ psi}} = 13.8 \text{ bar}$$

$$13.8 \text{ bar} \times \frac{100 \text{ kPa}}{1 \text{ bar}} = 1.38 \times 10^3 \text{ kPa}$$

CHECK The units of the answers are correct. The magnitude of the pressure expressed in bar is smaller than the psi pressure, and the pressure in kPa is much larger, which is reasonable.

FOR PRACTICE 5.1

Barometric pressure is typically reported in hPa (h = hecto, 1 hPa = 0.1 kPa). Your local weather report says that the barometric pressure is 1005 hPa. What is the pressure in bar and in torr?

FOR MORE PRACTICE 5.1

In science labs, pressure gauges sometimes indicate pressures in vacuum chambers in **millibar (mbar)** or in Torr. A decent mechanical pump will produce a vacuum of about 1.0×10^{-2} Torr. Convert this pressure to mbar.

The Manometer: A Way to Measure Pressure in the Laboratory

We can measure the pressure of a gas sample in the laboratory with a **manometer**. A manometer is a U-shaped tube containing a dense liquid, usually mercury, as shown in Figure 5.5 ▶. In this manometer, one end of the tube is open to atmospheric pressure and the other is attached to a flask containing the gas sample. If the pressure of the gas sample is exactly equal to atmospheric pressure, then the mercury levels on both sides of the tube are the same. If the pressure of the sample is *greater than* atmospheric pressure, the mercury level on the left side of the tube is *higher than* the level on the right. If the pressure of the sample is *less than* atmospheric pressure, the mercury level on the left side will be *lower than* the level on the right. This type of manometer always measures the pressure of the gas sample relative to atmospheric pressure. The difference in height between the two levels is equal to the difference between the sample's pressure and atmospheric pressure. The manometer is a "low-tech" way to read pressure, but it can be used to measure an accurate absolute pressure. To accurately obtain the absolute pressure of a sample, you also need a barometer to measure atmospheric pressure (which varies from day to day). In chemistry labs, pressures are usually measured with a number of "higher-tech" devices that always require calibration in order to obtain absolute pressures.

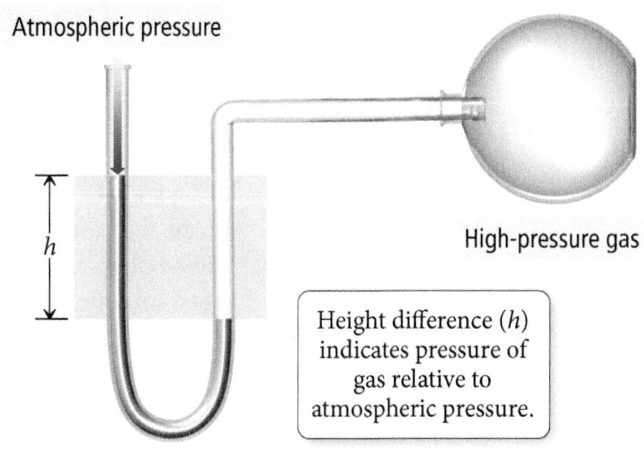
Atmospheric pressure
h
High-pressure gas
Height difference (h) indicates pressure of gas relative to atmospheric pressure.

▲ **FIGURE 5.5 The Manometer** A manometer measures the pressure exerted by a sample of gas.

CHEMISTRY AND MEDICINE Blood Pressure

Blood pressure is the force within arteries that drives the circulation of blood throughout the body. Blood pressure in the body is analogous to water pressure in a plumbing system. Just as water pressure pushes water through the pipes to faucets and fixtures throughout a house, blood pressure pushes blood to muscles and other tissues throughout the body. However, unlike the water pressure in a plumbing system—which is typically nearly constant—our blood pressure varies with each heartbeat. When the heart muscle contracts, blood pressure increases; between contractions, it decreases. Systolic blood pressure is the peak pressure during a contraction, and diastolic blood pressure is the lowest pressure between contractions. Just as excessively high water pressure in a plumbing system can damage pipes, so too can high blood pressure in a circulatory system damage the heart and arteries, resulting in increased risk of stroke and heart attack.

Medical professionals usually measure blood pressure with an instrument called a sphygmomanometer—an inflatable cuff equipped with a pressure gauge—and a stethoscope. The cuff is wrapped around the patient's arm and inflated with air. As air is pumped into the cuff, the pressure in the cuff increases. The cuff tightens around the arm and compresses the artery, momentarily stopping blood flow. The person measuring the blood pressure listens to the artery through the stethoscope while slowly releasing the pressure in the cuff. When the pressure in the cuff equals the systolic blood pressure (the peak pressure), a pulse is heard through the stethoscope. The pulse is the sound of blood getting through the compressed artery during a contraction of the heart. The pressure reading at that exact moment is the systolic blood pressure. As the pressure in the cuff continues to decrease, the blood can flow through the compressed artery even between contractions, so the pulsing sound stops. The pressure reading when the pulsing sound stops is the diastolic blood pressure (the lowest pressure).

A blood pressure measurement is usually reported as two pressures, in mmHg, separated by a slash. For example, a blood pressure measurement of 122/84 indicates that the systolic blood pressure is 122 mmHg and the diastolic blood pressure is 84 mmHg. Although the value of blood pressure can vary throughout the day, a healthy (or normal) value is usually considered to be below 120 mmHg for systolic and below 80 mmHg for diastolic (Table 5.2). High blood pressure, also called hypertension, entails the health risks mentioned previously.

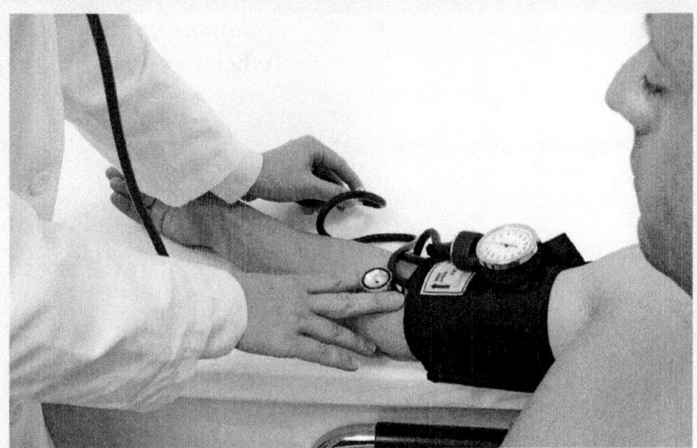

▲ A doctor or a nurse typically measures blood pressure with an inflatable cuff that compresses the main artery in the arm. A stethoscope is used to listen for blood flowing through the artery with each heartbeat.

Risk factors for hypertension include obesity, high salt (sodium) intake, high alcohol intake, lack of exercise, stress, a family history of high blood pressure, and age (blood pressure tends to increase as we get older). Mild hypertension can be managed with diet and exercise. Moderate to severe cases require doctor-prescribed medication.

TABLE 5.2 Blood Pressure Ranges

Blood Pressure	Systolic (mmHg)	Diastolic (mmHg)
Hypotension	<100	<60
Normal	100–119	60–79
Prehypertension	120–139	80–89
Hypertension Stage 1	140–159	90–99
Hypertension Stage 2	>160	>100

5.3 The Gas Laws: Boyle's Law, Charles's Law, and Avogadro's Law

We have learned about pressure and its characteristics. We now broaden our discussion to include the four basic properties of a gas sample: pressure (P), volume (V), temperature (T), and amount in moles (n). These properties are interrelated—when one changes, it affects the others. The gas laws describe the relationships between pairs of these properties. For example, how does *volume* vary with *pressure* at constant temperature and amount of gas, or with *temperature* at constant pressure and amount of gas? We can elucidate these relationships by conducting experiments in which two of the four basic properties are held constant in order to determine the relationship between the other two. We can then express the results of the experiments as laws, called the gas laws.

Boyle's Law: Volume and Pressure

In the early 1660s, the pioneering English scientist Robert Boyle (1627–1691) and his assistant Robert Hooke (1635–1703) used a J-tube (Figure 5.6 ▼) to measure the volume of a sample of gas at different pressures. They trapped a sample of air in the J-tube and added mercury to increase the pressure on the gas. Boyle and Hooke observed an *inverse relationship* between volume and pressure—an increase in one results in a decrease in the other—as shown in Figure 5.7 ▼. This relationship is now known as **Boyle's law**.

Boyle's law assumes constant temperature and constant amount of gas.

$$\text{Boyle's law:} \quad V \propto \frac{1}{P} \qquad (\text{constant } T \text{ and } n)$$

Boyle's law follows from the idea that pressure results from the collisions of the gas particles with the walls of their container. If the volume of a gas sample is decreased, the same number of gas particles is crowded into a smaller volume, resulting in more collisions with the walls and therefore an increase in the pressure (Figure 5.8 ►).

Scuba divers learn about Boyle's law during certification because it explains why they should not ascend toward the surface without continuous breathing. For every 10 m of depth that a diver descends in water, she experiences an additional 1 bar of pressure due to the weight of the water above her (Figure 5.9 ►). The pressure regulator used in scuba diving delivers air into the diver's lungs at a pressure that matches the external pressure; otherwise, the diver could not inhale the air. For example, when a diver is 20 m below

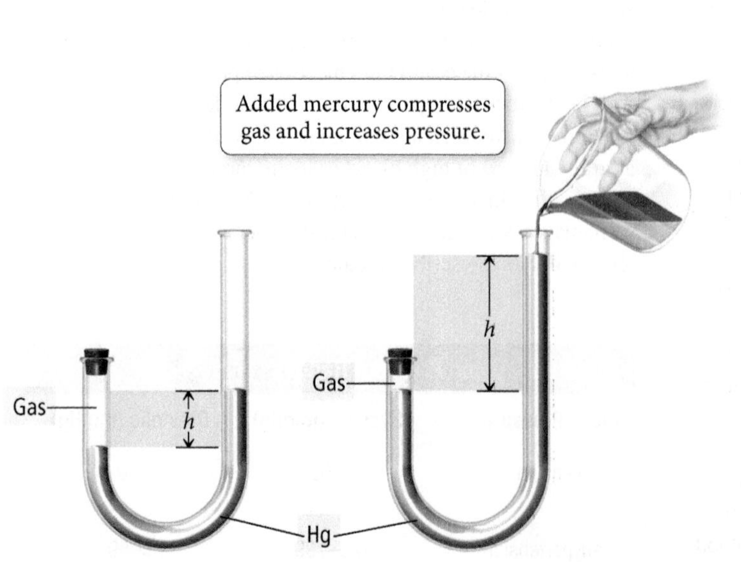

▲ **FIGURE 5.6 The J-Tube** In a J-tube, a column of mercury traps a sample of gas. The pressure on the gas can be increased by increasing the height (h) of mercury in the column.

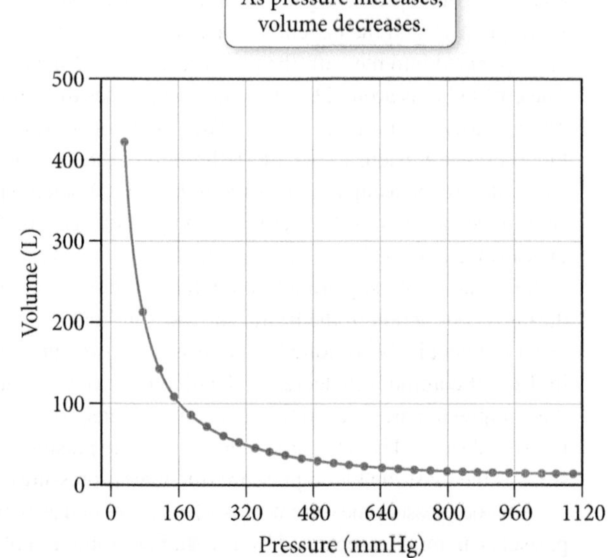

▲ **FIGURE 5.7 Volume Versus Pressure** A plot of the volume of a gas sample—as measured in a J-tube—versus pressure. The plot shows that volume and pressure are inversely related.

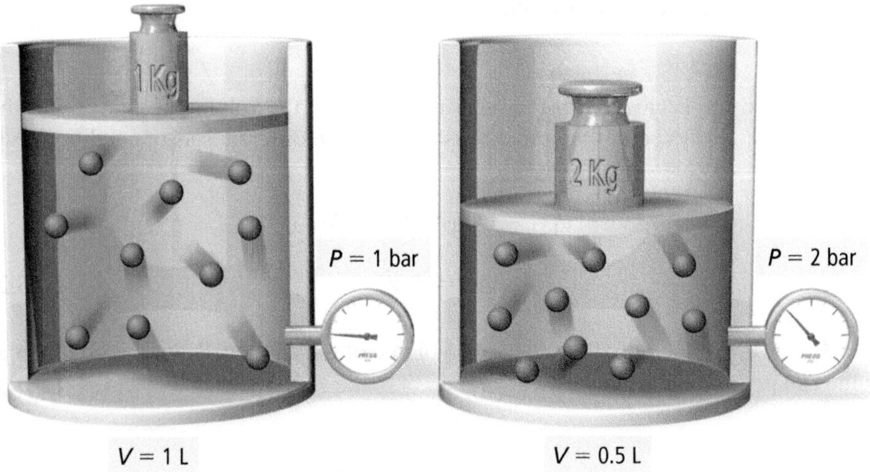

◀ **FIGURE 5.8 Molecular Interpretation of Boyle's Law** As the volume of a gas sample is decreased, gas molecules collide with surrounding surfaces more frequently, resulting in greater pressure.

the surface, the regulator delivers air at a pressure of 3 bar to match the 3 bar of pressure around the diver (1 bar due to normal atmospheric pressure and 2 additional bar due to the weight of the water at 20 m). Suppose that a diver inhaled a lungful of air at a pressure of 3 bar and swam quickly to the surface (where the pressure is 1 bar) while holding her breath. What would happen to the volume of air in her lungs? Since the pressure decreases by a factor of 3, the volume of the air in her lungs would increase by a factor of 3—a dangerous situation. Of course, the volume increase in the diver's lungs would be so great that she would not be able to hold her breath all the way to the surface—the air would force itself out of her mouth but probably not before the expanded air severely damaged her lungs, possibly killing her. Consequently, the most important rule in diving is *never hold your breath.* To avoid such catastrophic results, divers must ascend slowly and breathe continuously, allowing the regulator to bring the air pressure in their lungs back to atmospheric pressure by the time they reach the surface.

We can use Boyle's law to calculate the volume of a gas following a pressure change or the pressure of a gas following a volume change *as long as the temperature and the amount of gas remain constant.* For these types of calculations, we write Boyle's law in a slightly different way:

$$\text{Since } V \propto \frac{1}{P}, \qquad \text{then} \quad V = (\text{constant}) \times \frac{1}{P} \quad \text{or} \quad V = \frac{(\text{constant})}{P}$$

If two quantities are proportional, then one is equal to the other multiplied by a constant.

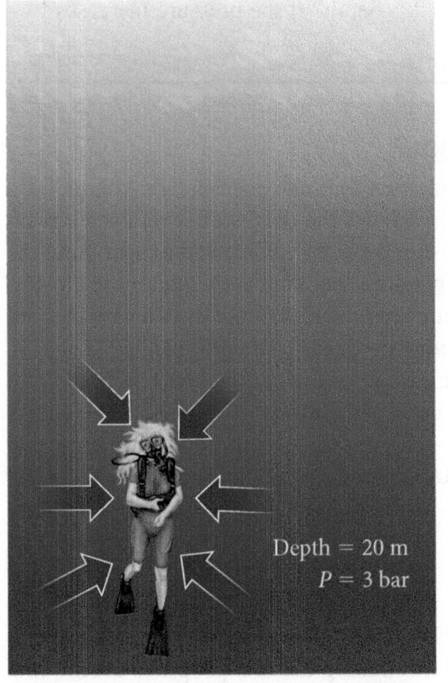

◀ **FIGURE 5.9 Increase in Pressure with Depth** For every 10 m of depth, a diver experiences approximately one additional bar of pressure due to the weight of the surrounding water. At 20 m, for example, the diver experiences approximately 3 bar of pressure (1 bar of normal atmospheric pressure plus an additional 2 bar due to the weight of the water).

If we multiply both sides by P, we get:

$$PV = \text{constant}$$

This relationship indicates that if the pressure increases, the volume decreases, but the product $P \times V$ always equals the same constant. For two different sets of conditions, we can say that:

$$P_1V_1 = \text{constant} = P_2V_2$$

or

$$P_1V_1 = P_2V_2 \qquad [5.2]$$

where P_1 and V_1 are the initial pressure and volume of the gas and P_2 and V_2 are the final volume and pressure, respectively.

EXAMPLE 5.2 BOYLE'S LAW

A cylinder equipped with a movable piston has a volume of 7.25 L under an applied pressure of 657 mbar. What is the applied pressure, in bar, required to decrease the volume of the cylinder to 2.00 L?

To solve the problem, first solve Boyle's law (Equation 5.2) for P_2 and then substitute the given quantities to calculate P_2.

SOLUTION

$$P_1V_1 = P_2V_2$$

$$P_2 = \frac{P_1V_1}{V_2}$$

$$= \frac{657\ \text{mbar} \times 7.25\ \text{L}}{2.00\ \text{L}}$$

The question also asks to provide the answer in bar, so you must convert the answer you get from Boyle's law to the units requested.

$$= 2380\ \text{mbar} \times \frac{1\ \text{bar}}{1000\ \text{mbar}}$$

$$= 2.38\ \text{bar}$$

CHECK The final volume is smaller than the initial volume by more than three times (almost four); therefore, the final pressure should be between three and four times larger, which it is.

FOR PRACTICE 5.2

A snorkeller takes a syringe filled with 16 mL of air from the surface, in which the pressure is 1.0 bar, to an unknown depth. The volume of the air in the syringe at this depth is 7.5 mL. What is the pressure at this depth? If the pressure increases by 1 bar for every 10 m of depth, how deep is the snorkeller?

Charles's Law: Volume and Temperature

Suppose we keep the pressure of a gas sample constant and measure its volume at a number of different temperatures. Figure 5.10 ▶ shows the results of several such measurements. From the plot, we can see a relationship between volume and temperature: the volume of a gas increases with increasing temperature. Looking at the plot more closely, however, reveals more—volume and temperature are *linearly related*. If two variables are linearly related, then plotting one against the other produces a straight line.

Another interesting feature emerges if we extend or *extrapolate* the line in the plot backwards from the lowest measured temperature. The dashed extrapolated line shows that the gas should occupy zero volume at –273.15 °C. Recall from Chapter 1 that –273.15 °C corresponds to 0 K (zero on the Kelvin scale), the coldest possible temperature. The extrapolated line shows that below –273.15 °C, the gas would have a negative volume, which is physically impossible. For this reason, we refer to 0 K as *absolute zero*—colder temperatures do not exist.

The first person to carefully quantify the relationship between the volume of a gas and its temperature was J. A. C. Charles (1746–1823), a French mathematician and physicist. Charles was interested in gases and was among the first people to ascend in a

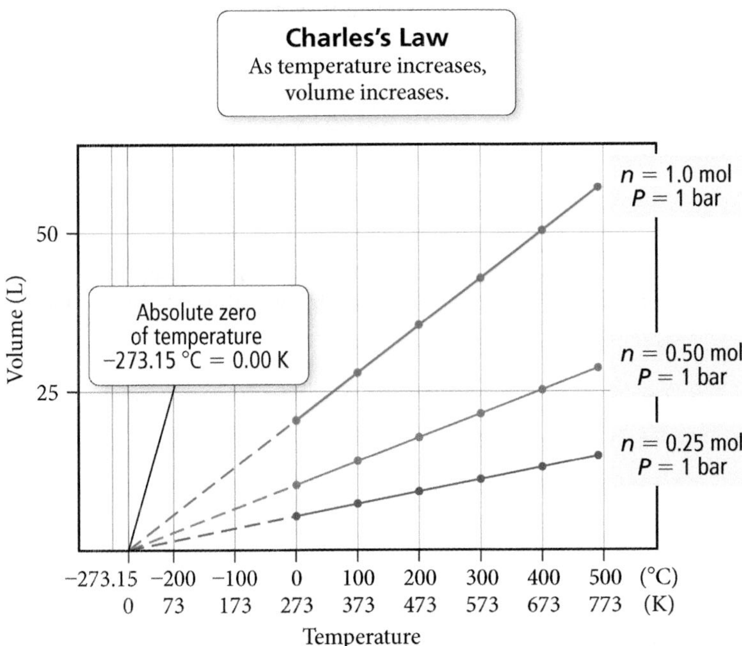

◀ **FIGURE 5.10 Volume Versus Temperature** The volume of a fixed amount of gas at a constant pressure increases linearly with increasing temperature in kelvins. (The extrapolated lines could not be measured experimentally because all gases condense into liquids before −273.15 °C is reached.)

hydrogen-filled balloon. The direct proportionality between volume and temperature is named **Charles's law** after him.

$$\text{Charles's law:} \quad V \propto T \qquad \text{(constant } P \text{ and } n\text{)}$$

Charles's law assumes constant pressure and constant amount of gas.

When the temperature of a gas sample is increased, the gas particles move faster, collisions with the walls are more frequent, and the force exerted with each collision is greater. The only way for the pressure (the force per unit area) to remain constant is for the gas to occupy a larger volume, so that collisions become less frequent and occur over a larger area (Figure 5.11 ▼).

Charles's law explains why the second floor of a house is usually warmer than the ground floor. According to Charles's law, when air is heated, its volume increases, resulting in a lower density. The warm, less dense air tends to rise in a room filled with colder, denser air. Similarly, Charles's law explains why a hot-air balloon can take flight. The gas that fills a hot-air balloon is warmed with a burner, increasing its volume and lowering its density, and causing it to float in the colder, denser surrounding air.

You can experience Charles's law directly by holding a partially inflated balloon over a warm toaster. As the air in the balloon warms, you can feel the balloon expanding. Alternatively, you can a put an inflated balloon into liquid nitrogen and see that it becomes smaller as it cools.

We can use Charles's law to calculate the volume of a gas following a temperature change or the temperature of a gas following a volume change *as long as the pressure*

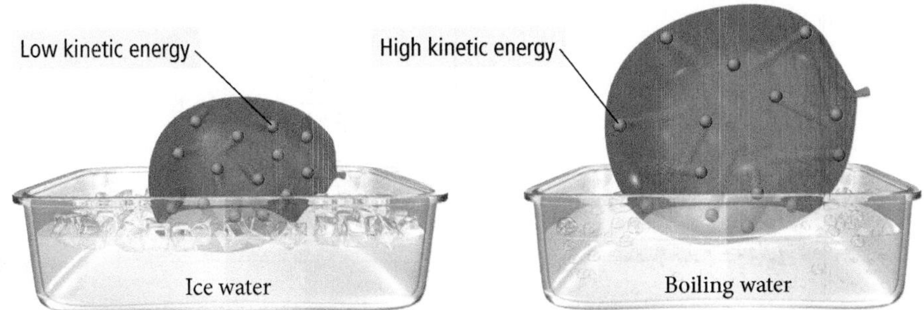

▲ **FIGURE 5.11 Molecular Interpretation of Charles's Law** If we move a balloon from an ice water bath to a boiling water bath, the temperature and therefore kinetic energy of the molecules increase, which causes the gas particles within the balloon to move faster. The end result of the temperature increase is that the volume of the gas expands.

▲ A hot-air balloon floats because the hot air is less dense than the surrounding cold air.

▲ If we place a balloon into liquid nitrogen (77 K), it shrivels up as the air within it cools and occupies less volume at the same external pressure.

and the amount of gas are constant. For these calculations, we rearrange Charles's law as follows:

$$\text{Since } V \propto T, \text{ then } V = \text{constant} \times T$$

If we divide both sides by T, we get:

$$V/T = \text{constant}$$

If the temperature increases, the volume increases in direct proportion so that the quotient, V/T, is always equal to the same constant. So, for two different measurements, we can say that:

$$V_1/T_1 = \text{constant} = V_2/T_2$$

or

$$\frac{V_1}{T_1} = \frac{V_2}{T_2} \quad [5.3]$$

where V_1 and T_1 are the initial volume and temperature of the gas and V_2 and T_2 are the final volume and temperature, respectively. *The temperatures must always be expressed in kelvins (K)*, because, as you can see in Figure 5.10, the volume of a gas is directly proportional to its absolute temperature, not its temperature in °C. For example, doubling the temperature of a gas sample from 1 °C to 2 °C does not double its volume, but doubling the temperature from 200 K to 400 K does double the volume of the gas.

Changing the temperature from 1 °C to 2 °C changes the temperature from 274 K to 275 K (an increase of 0.36%).

EXAMPLE 5.3 **CHARLES'S LAW**

A sample of gas has a volume of 2.80 L at an unknown temperature. When the sample is submerged in ice water at $T = 0.00$ °C, its volume decreases to 2.57 L. What was its initial temperature (in K and in °C)?

	SOLUTION
To solve the problem, first solve Charles's law for T_1.	$\frac{V_1}{T_1} = \frac{V_2}{T_2}$ $T_1 = \frac{V_1}{V_2} T_2$
Before you substitute the numerical values to calculate T_1, you must convert the temperature to kelvins (K). *Remember, gas law problems must always be worked with Kelvin temperatures.*	$T_2 \text{ (K)} = 0.00 + 273.15 = 273.15 \text{ K}$
Substitute T_2 and the other given quantities to calculate T_1.	$T_1 = \frac{V_1}{V_2} T_2$ $= \frac{2.80 \cancel{\text{L}}}{2.57 \cancel{\text{L}}} \cdot 273.15 \text{ K}$ $= 29\underline{7}.6 \text{ K}$
Calculate T_1 in °C by subtracting 273.15 from the value in kelvins.	$T_1 \text{ (°C)} = 29\underline{7}.6 - 273.15 = 24 \text{ °C}$

FOR PRACTICE 5.3

A gas in a cylinder with a movable piston has an initial volume of 88.2 mL. If we heat the gas from 35 °C to 155 °C, what is its final volume (in mL)?

Avogadro's Law: Volume and Amount (in Moles)

So far, we have learned the relationships between volume and pressure, and volume and temperature, but we have considered only a constant amount of a gas. What happens when the amount of gas changes? The volume of a gas sample (at constant temperature and pressure) as a function of the amount of gas (in moles) in the sample is shown in Figure 5.12 ▶. We can see that the relationship between volume and amount is linear. As we might expect, extrapolation to zero moles shows zero volume. This relationship, first stated formally by Amedeo Avogadro, is called **Avogadro's law**:

Avogadro's law: $V \propto n$ (constant T and P)

When the amount of gas in a sample increases at constant temperature and pressure, its volume increases in direct proportion because the greater number of gas particles fill more space.

You experience Avogadro's law when you inflate a balloon. With each exhaled breath, you add more gas particles to the inside of the balloon, increasing its volume. We can use Avogadro's law to calculate the volume of a gas following a change in the amount of the gas *as long as the pressure and temperature of the gas are constant.* For these types of calculations, we express Avogadro's law as:

$$\frac{V_1}{n_1} = \frac{V_2}{n_2} \quad [5.4]$$

where V_1 and n_1 are the initial volume and number of moles of the gas and V_2 and n_2 are the final volume and number of moles, respectively. In calculations, we use Avogadro's law in a manner similar to the other gas laws, as demonstrated in the following example.

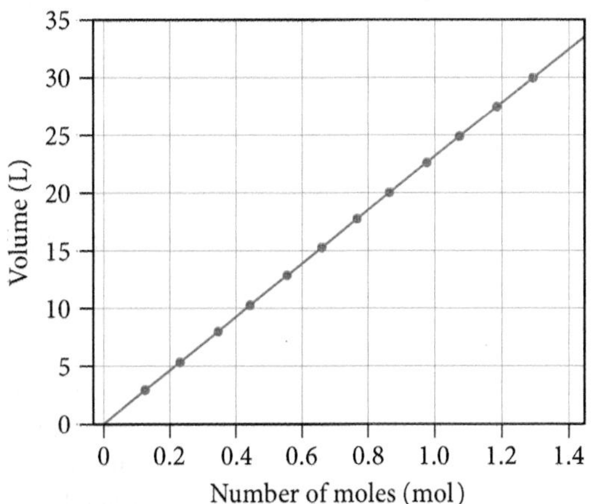

▲ **FIGURE 5.12 Volume Versus Number of Moles** The volume of a gas sample increases linearly with the number of moles of gas in the sample.

Avogadro's law assumes constant temperature and constant pressure and is independent of the identity of the gas.

EXAMPLE 5.4 AVOGADRO'S LAW

A 4.65 L sample of helium gas contains 0.225 mol of helium. How many additional moles of helium gas must we add to the sample to obtain a volume of 6.48 L? Assume constant temperature and pressure.

To solve the problem, first solve Avogadro's law for n_2. Then substitute the given quantities to calculate n_2.

SOLUTION

$$\frac{V_1}{n_1} = \frac{V_2}{n_2}$$

$$n_2 = \frac{V_2}{V_1} n_1 = \frac{6.48 \text{ L}}{4.65 \text{ L}} \cdot 0.225 \text{ mol} = 0.314 \text{ mol}$$

Since the balloon already contains 0.225 mol of gas, calculate the amount of gas to add by subtracting 0.225 mol from the value you calculated for n_2.

$$\text{moles to add} = 0.314 \text{ mol} - 0.225 \text{ mol} = 0.089 \text{ mol}$$

FOR PRACTICE 5.4

A chemical reaction occurring in a cylinder equipped with a movable piston produces 0.621 mol of a gaseous product. If the cylinder contained 0.120 mol of gas before the reaction and had an initial volume of 2.18 L, what was its volume after the reaction? (Assume constant pressure and temperature and that the initial amount of gas completely reacts.)

5.4 The Ideal Gas Law

The relationships that we have learned so far can be combined into a single law that encompasses all of them. So far, we know that:

$$V \propto \frac{1}{P} \qquad \text{(Boyle's law)}$$

$$V \propto T \qquad \text{(Charles's law)}$$

$$V \propto n \qquad \text{(Avogadro's law)}$$

Combining these three expressions, we get:

$$V \propto \frac{nT}{P}$$

The volume of a gas is directly proportional to the number of moles of gas and to the temperature of the gas, but is inversely proportional to the pressure of the gas. We can replace the proportionality sign with an equal sign by incorporating R, a proportionality constant called the *ideal gas constant*:

$$V = \frac{RnT}{P}$$

Rearranging, we get:

$$PV = nRT \qquad [5.5]$$

This equation is the **ideal gas law**, and a hypothetical gas that exactly follows this law is an **ideal gas**. The value of R, the **ideal gas constant**, is the same for all gases and has the following value:

L = litres
bar = pressure in bar
mol = moles
K = kelvins

$$R = 0.08314\frac{\text{L} \cdot \text{bar}}{\text{mol} \cdot \text{K}} = 0.08314 \text{ L bar mol}^{-1}\text{ K}^{-1}$$

The ideal gas law contains within it the three gas laws that we have learned. For example, recall that Boyle's law states that $V \propto 1/P$ when the amount of gas (n) and the temperature of the gas (T) are kept constant. We can rearrange the ideal gas law as follows:

$$PV = nRT$$

First, divide both sides by P:

$$V = \frac{nRT}{P}$$

Then put the variables that are constant, along with R, in parentheses:

$$V = (nRT)\frac{1}{P}$$

Since n and T are constant in this case, and since R is always a constant, we can write:

$$V = (\text{constant}) \times \frac{1}{P}$$

which means that $V \propto 1/P$.

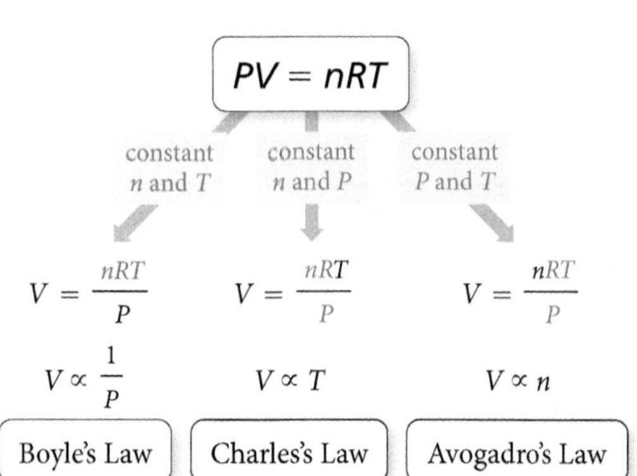

▲ The ideal gas law contains the three gas laws within it.

The ideal gas law also shows how other pairs of variables are related. For example, from Charles's law we know that $V \propto T$ at constant pressure and constant number of moles. But what if we heat a sample of gas at constant *volume* and constant number of moles? This question applies to the warning labels on aerosol cans such as hair spray or deodorants. These labels warn against excessive heating or incineration of the can, even after the contents are used up. Why? An "empty" aerosol can is not really empty but contains a fixed amount of gas trapped in a fixed volume. What would happen if you were to heat the can? Let's rearrange the ideal gas law to clearly see the relationship between pressure and temperature at constant volume and constant number of moles:

$$PV = nRT$$

Divide both sides by V.

$$P = \frac{nRT}{V} = \left(\frac{nR}{V}\right)T$$

Since n and V are constant and since R is always a constant:

$$P = (\text{constant}) \times T$$

This relationship between pressure and temperature was first shown by Guillaume Amontons in the 17th century. As the temperature of a fixed amount of gas in a fixed volume increases, the pressure increases. In an aerosol can, this pressure increase can blow the can apart, which is why aerosol cans should not be heated or incinerated. They might explode.

The ideal gas law can also be used to determine the value of any one of the four variables (P, V, n, or T) given the other three. To do so, each of the quantities in the ideal gas law *must be expressed* in the units within R:

- pressure (P) in bar
- volume (V) in L
- moles (n) in mol
- temperature (T) in K

▲ The labels on most aerosol cans warn against incineration. Since the volume of the can is constant, an increase in temperature causes an increase in pressure and possibly an explosion.

EXAMPLE 5.5 IDEAL GAS LAW I

Calculate the volume occupied by 0.845 mol of nitrogen gas at a pressure of 1.37 bar and a temperature of 315 K. Assume that nitrogen is an ideal gas under these conditions.

SORT The problem gives you the number of moles of nitrogen gas, the pressure, and the temperature. You are asked to find the volume.

GIVEN: $n = 0.845$ mol
$P = 1.37$ bar, $T = 315$ K

FIND: V

STRATEGIZE You are given three of the four variables (P, T, and n) in the ideal gas law and asked to find the fourth (V). The conceptual plan shows how the ideal gas law provides the relationship between the known quantities and the unknown quantity.

CONCEPTUAL PLAN

$n, P, T \rightarrow V$

$PV = nRT$

RELATIONSHIP USED $PV = nRT$

SOLVE To solve the problem, first solve the ideal gas law for V.

SOLUTION

$$PV = nRT$$

$$V = \frac{nRT}{P}$$

Then substitute the given quantities to calculate V.

$$V = \frac{0.845\,\cancel{\text{mol}} \times 0.08314\,\frac{\text{L}\cdot\cancel{\text{bar}}}{\cancel{\text{mol}}\cdot\cancel{\text{K}}} \times 315\,\cancel{\text{K}}}{1.37\,\cancel{\text{bar}}}$$

$$= 16.2\,\text{L}$$

CHECK The units of the answer are correct. The magnitude of the answer (16.2 L) makes sense because, as you will see in the next section, one mole of an ideal gas under standard conditions (273.15 K and 1 bar) occupies 22.7 L. Although the present conditions are not standard, they are close enough for a ballpark check of the answer. Because this gas sample contains 0.845 mol, a volume of 16.2 L is reasonable.

FOR PRACTICE 5.5

An 8.50 L tire contains 0.552 mol of gas at a temperature of 305 K. What is the pressure (in bar and in psi) of the gas in the tire?

EXAMPLE 5.6 IDEAL GAS LAW II

Calculate the number of moles of gas in a 3.24 L basketball inflated to a *total pressure* of 24.3 psi at 25 °C. (Note: the *total pressure* is not the same as the pressure read on a pressure gauge, such as the kind used for checking a car or bicycle tire. That pressure, called the *gauge pressure*, is the *difference* between the total pressure and atmospheric pressure. In this case, if atmospheric pressure is 14.7 psi, the gauge pressure would be 9.6 psi. However, for calculations involving the ideal gas law, you must use the *total pressure* of 24.3 psi.)

SORT The problem gives you the pressure, the volume, and the temperature. You are asked to find the number of moles of gas.

GIVEN: $P = 24.3\,\text{psi}, V = 3.24\,\text{L}, T = 25\,°\text{C}$

FIND: n

(continued)

EXAMPLE 5.6 (CONTINUED)

STRATEGIZE The conceptual plan shows how the ideal gas law provides the relationship between the given quantities and the quantity to be found.	**CONCEPTUAL PLAN** 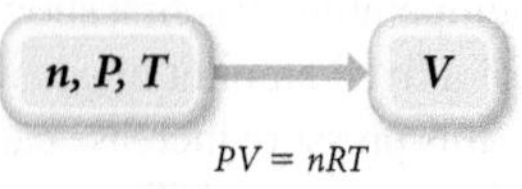 $PV = nRT$ **RELATIONSHIP USED** $PV = nRT$
SOLVE To solve the problem, first solve the ideal gas law for n.	**SOLUTION** $PV = nRT$ $n = \frac{PV}{RT}$
Before substituting into the equation, convert P and T into the correct units.	$P = 24.3\,\text{psi} \times \frac{1\,\text{bar}}{14.504\,\text{psi}} = 1.67\underline{5}4\,\text{bar}$ (Since rounding the intermediate answer would result in a slightly different final answer, we mark the least significant digit in the intermediate answer, but don't round until the end.) $T(\text{K}) = 25 + 273.15 = 298\,\text{K}$
Finally, substitute into the equation and calculate n.	$n = \frac{1.6\underline{7}54\,\text{bar} \times 3.24\,\text{L}}{0.08314\frac{\text{L}\cdot\text{bar}}{\text{mol}\cdot\text{K}} \times 298\,\text{K}} = 0.219\,\text{mol}$

CHECK The units of the answer are correct. The magnitude of the answer (0.219 mol) makes sense because, as you will see in the next section, one mole of an ideal gas under standard conditions (273.15 K and 1 bar) occupies 22.7 L. At a pressure that is 65% higher than standard conditions, the volume of 1 mol of gas would be proportionally lower. Because this gas sample occupies 3.24 L, the answer of 0.219 mol is reasonable.

FOR PRACTICE 5.6
What volume does 0.556 mol of gas occupy at a pressure of 715 Torr and a temperature of 58 °C?

FOR MORE PRACTICE 5.6
Find the pressure in mbar of a 0.133 g sample of helium gas in a 648 mL container at a temperature of 32 °C.

The molar volume of 22.7 L only applies at conditions called STP.

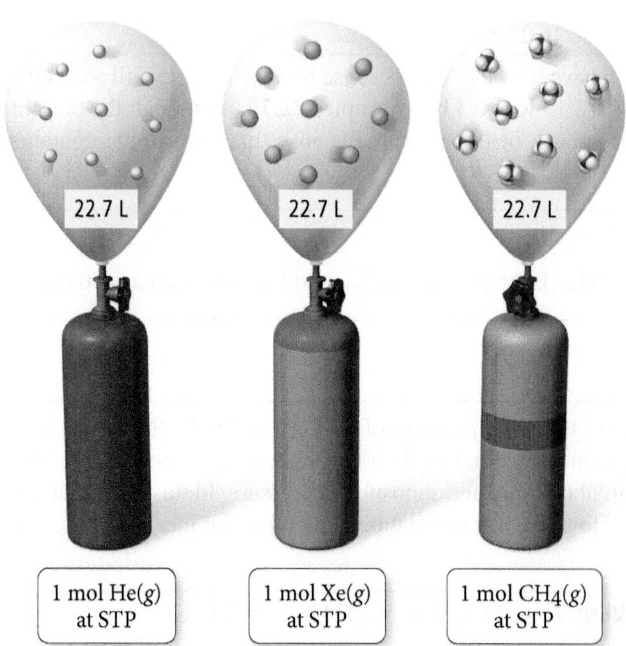

▲ One mole of any gas occupies approximately 22.7 L at standard temperature (273.15 K) and pressure (1.00 bar).

5.5 Applications of the Ideal Gas Law: Molar Volume, Density, and Molar Mass of a Gas

We just examined how we can use the ideal gas law to calculate one of the variables (P, V, T, or n) given the other three. We now turn to three other applications of the ideal gas law: molar volume, density, and molar mass.

Molar Volume at Standard Temperature and Pressure

The volume occupied by one mole of a substance is its **molar volume**. For gases, we often specify the molar volume under conditions known as **standard temperature** ($T = 0$ °C or 273.15 K) **and pressure** ($P = 1.00$ bar), abbreviated as **STP**. Using the ideal gas law, we can determine that the molar volume of ideal gas at STP is:

$$V = \frac{nRT}{P}$$

$$V = \frac{1.00\,\text{mol} \times 0.08314\frac{\text{L}\cdot\text{bar}}{\text{mol}\cdot\text{K}} \times 273.15\,\text{K}}{1.00\,\text{bar}}$$

$$= 22.7\,\text{L}$$

The molar volume of an ideal gas at STP is useful because—as we saw in the *Check* sections of Examples 5.5 and 5.6—it gives us a way to approximate the volume of an ideal gas under conditions that are close to STP.

CONCEPTUAL CONNECTION 5.1

Molar Volume

Assuming ideal behaviour, which of the following gas samples will have the greatest volume at STP?

(a) 1 g of H_2 **(b)** 1 g of O_2 **(c)** 1 g of Ar

Density of a Gas

If we know the molar volume of an ideal gas under standard conditions, we can readily calculate the density of the gas under these conditions. Since density is mass/volume, and since the mass of one mole of a gas is simply its molar mass, the *density of a gas under standard conditions* is given by the following relationship:

$$\text{density} = \frac{\text{molar mass}}{\text{molar volume}}$$

For example, we calculate the densities of helium and nitrogen gas at STP as follows:

$$d_{\text{He}} = \frac{4.003 \text{ g } \cancel{\text{mol}^{-1}}}{22.7 \text{ L } \cancel{\text{mol}^{-1}}} = 0.176 \text{ g L}^{-1} \qquad d_{N_2} = \frac{28.02 \text{ g } \cancel{\text{mol}^{-1}}}{22.7 \text{ L } \cancel{\text{mol}^{-1}}} = 1.23 \text{ g L}^{-1}$$

Notice that *the density of a gas is directly proportional to its molar mass.* The greater the molar mass of a gas, the more dense the gas. For this reason, a gas with a molar mass lower than that of air tends to rise in air. For example, both helium and hydrogen gas (molar masses of 4.003 and 2.016 g mol^{-1}, respectively) have molar masses that are lower than the average molar mass of air (approximately 28.8 g mol^{-1}). Therefore, a balloon filled with either helium or hydrogen gas floats in air.

The detailed composition of air is covered in Section 5.6. The primary components of air are nitrogen (about four-fifths) and oxygen (about one-fifth).

We can calculate the density of a gas more generally (under any conditions) by using the ideal gas law. To do so, we can arrange the ideal gas law as follows:

$$PV = nRT$$

$$\frac{n}{V} = \frac{P}{RT}$$

Since the left-hand side of this equation has units of mol L^{-1}, it represents the *molar* density. We can obtain the density in g L^{-1} from the molar density by multiplying by the molar mass (M):

$$\frac{\cancel{\text{moles}}}{\text{litre}} \times \frac{\text{grams}}{\cancel{\text{mole}}} = \frac{\text{grams}}{\text{litre}}$$

Molar density — Molar mass — Density in g L^{-1}

Therefore,

$$d = \frac{PM}{RT} \qquad [5.6]$$

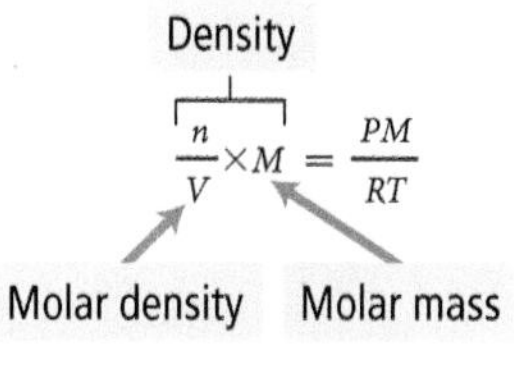

Notice that, as expected, density increases with increasing molar mass. Notice also that as we learned in Section 5.3, density decreases with increasing temperature.

EXAMPLE 5.7 DENSITY

Calculate the density of nitrogen gas at 125 °C and a pressure of 925 mbar.

SORT The problem gives you the temperature and pressure of a gas and asks you to find its density. The problem also states that the gas is nitrogen.

GIVEN: $P = 925\,\text{mbar}$, $T = 125\,°\text{C}$

FIND: d

STRATEGIZE Equation 5.6 provides the relationship between the density of a gas and its temperature, pressure, and molar mass. The temperature and pressure are given. You can calculate the molar mass from the formula of the gas, which we know is N_2.

CONCEPTUAL PLAN

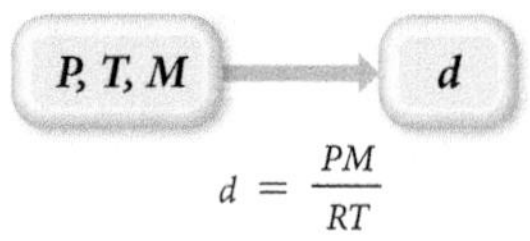

$$d = \frac{PM}{RT}$$

RELATIONSHIPS USED

$$d = \frac{PM}{RT}$$

$$M_{N_2} = 28.02\ \text{g mol}^{-1}$$

SOLVE To solve the problem, gather each of the required quantities in the correct units. Convert the temperature to kelvin and the pressure to bar.

SOLUTION

$$T(\text{K}) = 125 + 273.15 = 398\,\text{K}$$

$$P = 925\,\text{mbar} \times \frac{1\,\text{bar}}{1000\,\text{mbar}} = 0.925\,\text{bar}$$

Now substitute the quantities into the equation to calculate density.

$$d = \frac{PM}{RT}$$

$$= \frac{0.925\,\text{bar} \times 28.02\frac{\text{g}}{\text{mol}}}{0.08314\frac{\text{L}\cdot\text{bar}}{\text{mol}\cdot\text{K}} \times 398\,\text{K}}$$

$$= 0.783\,\text{g L}^{-1}$$

CHECK The units of the answer are correct. The magnitude of the answer ($0.783\ \text{g L}^{-1}$) makes sense because earlier we calculated the density of nitrogen gas at STP as $1.23\ \text{g L}^{-1}$. Because the temperature is higher than standard conditions, and the pressure is slightly lower, it follows that the density is lower.

FOR PRACTICE 5.7

Calculate the density of xenon gas at a pressure of 742 mmHg and a temperature of 45 °C.

FOR MORE PRACTICE 5.7

A gas has a density of $1.43\ \text{g L}^{-1}$ at a temperature of 23 °C and a pressure of 0.789 bar. Calculate its molar mass.

Molar Mass of a Gas

We can use the ideal gas law in combination with mass measurements to calculate the molar mass of an unknown gas. First we measure the mass and volume of an unknown gas under conditions of known pressure and temperature. Then we determine the amount of the gas in moles from the ideal gas law. Finally, we calculate the molar mass by dividing the mass (in grams) by the amount (in moles) as shown in the following example.

EXAMPLE 5.8 MOLAR MASS OF A GAS

A sample of gas has a mass of 0.311 g. Its volume is 0.225 L at a temperature of 55 °C and a pressure of 886 Torr. Find the molar mass of the gas.

SORT The problem gives you the mass of a gas sample, along with its volume, temperature, and pressure. You are asked to find the molar mass.

GIVEN: $m = 0.311\text{ g}, V = 0.225\text{ L}, T(°\text{C}) = 55\text{ °C}, P = 886\text{ Torr}$

FIND: molar mass (g mol^{-1})

STRATEGIZE The conceptual plan has two parts. In the first part, use the ideal gas law to find the number of moles of gas.

CONCEPTUAL PLAN

P, V, T → n

$PV = nRT$

In the second part, use the definition of molar mass to find the molar mass.

n, m → molar mass

$$\text{molar mass} = \frac{\text{mass }(m)}{\text{moles }(n)}$$

RELATIONSHIPS USED

$PV = nRT$

$$\text{Molar mass} = \frac{\text{mass }(m)}{\text{moles }(n)}$$

SOLVE To find the number of moles, first solve the ideal gas law for n.

SOLUTION

$$PV = nRT$$

$$n = \frac{PV}{RT}$$

Before substituting into the equation for n, convert the pressure to bar and the temperature to K.

$$P = 886\,\cancel{\text{Torr}} \times \frac{1\text{ bar}}{750.1\,\cancel{\text{Torr}}} = 1.1\underline{8}12\text{ bar}$$

$$T(\text{K}) = 55 + 273.15 = 328\text{ K}$$

Now, substitute into the equation and calculate n, the number of moles.

$$n = \frac{1.1\underline{8}12\,\cancel{\text{bar}} \times 0.225\,\cancel{\text{L}}}{0.08314\dfrac{\cancel{\text{L}}\cdot\cancel{\text{bar}}}{\text{mol}\cdot\cancel{\text{K}}} \times 328\,\cancel{\text{K}}}$$

$$= 9.7\underline{4}59 \times 10^{-3}\text{ mol}$$

Finally, use the number of moles (n) and the given mass (m) to find the molar mass.

$$M = \frac{m}{n}$$

$$= \frac{0.311\text{ g}}{9.7\underline{4}59 \times 10^{-3}\text{ mol}}$$

$$= 31.9\text{ g mol}^{-1}$$

CHECK The units of the answer are correct. The magnitude of the answer (31.9 g mol^{-1}) is a reasonable number for a molar mass. If you calculated a very small number (such as any number smaller than 1) or a very large number, you probably made some mistake. Most gases have molar masses between one and several hundred grams per mole. The gas is likely molecular oxygen.

FOR PRACTICE 5.8

A sample of gas has a mass of 827 mg. Its volume is 0.270 L at a temperature of 88 °C and a pressure of 1299 mbar. Find its molar mass.

TABLE 5.3 Composition of Dry Air

Gas	Percent by Volume (%)
Nitrogen (N_2)	78
Oxygen (O_2)	21
Argon (Ar)	0.9
Carbon dioxide (CO_2)	0.04

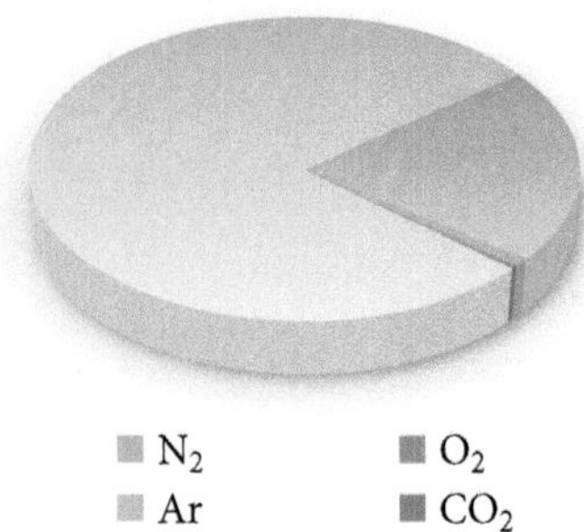

5.6 Mixtures of Gases and Partial Pressures

Many gas samples are not pure, but are mixtures of gases. Dry air, for example, is a mixture containing nitrogen, oxygen, argon, carbon dioxide, and a few other gases in trace amounts (Table 5.3).

Because the molecules in an ideal gas do not interact (as we will discuss further in Section 5.8), each of the components in an ideal gas mixture acts independently of the others. For example, the nitrogen molecules in air exert a certain pressure—78% of the total pressure—that is independent of the other gases in the mixture. Likewise, the oxygen molecules in air exert a certain pressure—21% of the total pressure—that is also independent of the other gases in the mixture. The pressure due to any individual component in a gas mixture is the **partial pressure (P_n)** of that component and can be calculated from the ideal gas law by assuming that each gas component acts independently. For a multicomponent gas mixture, we can calculate the partial pressure of each component from the ideal gas law and the number of moles of that component (n_n) as follows:

$$P_a = n_a\frac{RT}{V}; \quad P_b = n_b\frac{RT}{V}; \quad P_c = n_c\frac{RT}{V}; \quad \cdots \qquad [5.7]$$

The sum of the partial pressures of the components in a gas mixture must equal the total pressure:

$$P_{total} = P_a + P_b + P_c + \cdots \qquad [5.8]$$

where P_{total} is the total pressure and P_a, P_b, P_c, . . . are the partial pressures of the components. This relationship is known as **Dalton's law of partial pressures**.

Combining Equations 5.7 and 5.8, we get:

$$\begin{aligned} P_{total} &= P_a + P_b + P_c + \cdots \\ &= n_a\frac{RT}{V} + n_b\frac{RT}{V} + n_c\frac{RT}{V} + \cdots \\ &= (n_a + n_b + n_c + \cdots)\frac{RT}{V} \\ &= (n_{total})\frac{RT}{V} \end{aligned} \qquad [5.9]$$

The total number of moles in the mixture, when substituted into the ideal gas law, indicates the total pressure of the sample.

If we divide Equation 5.7 by Equation 5.9, we get the following result:

$$\frac{P_a}{P_{total}} = \frac{n_a\,(\cancel{RT/V})}{n_{total}\,(\cancel{RT/V})} = \frac{n_a}{n_{total}} \qquad [5.10]$$

The quantity n_a/n_{total}, the number of moles of a component in a mixture divided by the total number of moles in the mixture, is called the **mole fraction (χ_a)**:

$$\chi_a = \frac{n_a}{n_{total}} \qquad [5.11]$$

Rearranging Equation 5.10 and substituting the definition of mole fraction gives the following:

$$\frac{P_a}{P_{total}} = \frac{n_a}{n_{total}}$$

$$P_a = \frac{n_a}{n_{total}}P_{total} = \chi_a P_{total}$$

or simply

$$P_a = \chi_a P_{total} \qquad [5.12]$$

The partial pressure of a component in a gaseous mixture is its mole fraction multiplied by the total pressure. For real gases, the mole fraction of a component is equivalent to its percent by volume divided by 100%. Therefore, based on Table 5.3, we calculate the partial pressure of nitrogen (P_{N_2}) in air at 1.00 bar as follows:

$$P_{N_2} = 0.78 \times 1.00 \text{ bar}$$
$$= 0.78 \text{ bar}$$

Likewise, the partial pressure of oxygen in air at 1.00 bar is 0.21 bar and the partial pressure of Ar in air is 0.009 bar. Applying Dalton's law of partial pressures to air at 1.00 bar:

$$P_{total} = P_{N_2} + P_{O_2} + P_{Ar}$$
$$P_{total} = 0.78 \text{ bar} + 0.21 \text{ bar} + 0.009 \text{ bar}$$
$$= 1.00 \text{ bar}$$

For these purposes, we can ignore the contribution of the CO_2 and other trace gases because they are so small. However, they correspond to the 0.001 bar that is missing from the calculated sum, before rounding.

CHEMISTRY IN YOUR DAY Oxygen in Spacesuits

As is shown in Table 5.3, the air we breathe contains 78% N_2 and 21% O_2. The other 1% is a mixture of Ar, CO_2, Ne, and other trace gases. Besides oxygen, human beings can survive without any of the other gases as they fill no physiological requirements. In the low pressures of outer space, pure oxygen is exactly what astronauts breathe. For the best mobility, it is an advantage to have as low a pressure as possible in a spacesuit when astronauts go on a spacewalk. In air at a pressure of 1 bar, the partial pressure of O_2 is 207 mbar. It is not as simple as having a pressure of 207 mbar of oxygen in the spacesuit. In the alveoli of your lungs, there is a partial pressure of CO_2 (53 mbar) due to respiration and water vapour (63 mbar) from the lung tissue. This adds up to a total alveolar pressure of 116 mbar. In order to have a partial pressure of oxygen of 207 mbar, the spacesuit must be pressurized by an extra 116 mbar, to 323 mbar O_2. If the spacesuit were only pressurized to 207 mbar with pure oxygen, the partial pressure of O_2 in the lungs would be 207 – 116 = 91 mbar, about 44% of the partial pressure at sea level. This is the same as the partial pressure of oxygen at 5.5 km above sea level, which is 400 m higher than the highest permanently inhabited town in the world, Rinconada, Peru. For an astronaut, working under this low pressure of oxygen would be similar to the experience of high altitude mountain climbing.

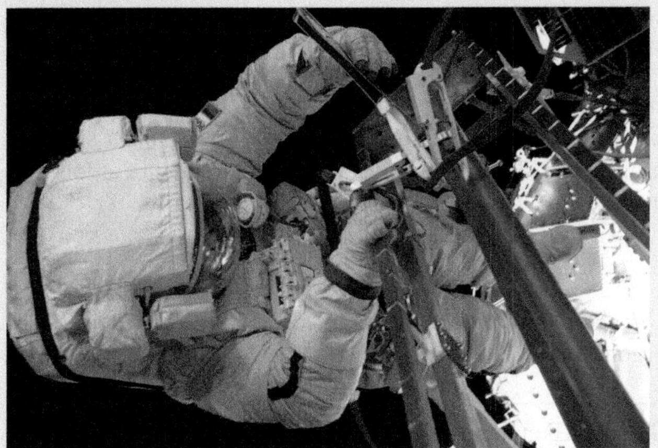

▲ Cosmonaut Sergey Volkov dons a spacesuit during a 6 hour and 23 minute spacewalk.

EXAMPLE 5.9 TOTAL PRESSURE AND PARTIAL PRESSURES

A 1.00 L mixture of helium, neon, and argon has a total pressure of 662 Torr at 298 K. If the partial pressure of helium is 341 Torr and the partial pressure of neon is 112 Torr, what mass of argon is present in the mixture?

SORT The problem gives you the partial pressures of two of the three components in a gas mixture, along with the total pressure, the volume, and the temperature, and asks you to find the mass of the third component.	**GIVEN:** $P_{He} = 341$ Torr, $P_{Ne} = 112$ Torr, $P_{total} = 662$ Torr, $V = 1.00$ L, $T = 298$ K **FIND:** m_{Ar}

(continued)

EXAMPLE 5.9 (CONTINUED)

STRATEGIZE You can find the mass of argon from the number of moles of argon, which you can calculate from the partial pressure of argon and the ideal gas law. Begin by using Dalton's law to determine the partial pressure of argon.

Then use the partial pressure of argon together with the volume of the sample and the temperature to find the number of moles of argon.

Finally, use the molar mass of argon to calculate the mass of argon from the number of moles of argon.

CONCEPTUAL PLAN

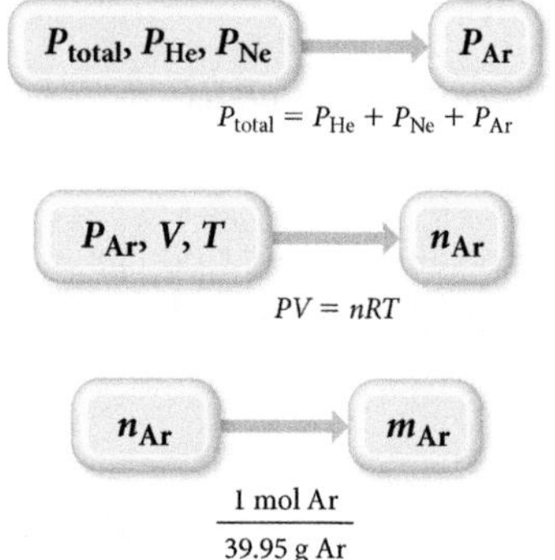

$\frac{1 \text{ mol Ar}}{39.95 \text{ g Ar}}$

RELATIONSHIPS USED

$P_{total} = P_{He} + P_{Ne} + P_{Ar}$ (Dalton's law)

$PV = nRT$ (ideal gas law)

molar mass Ar $= 39.95 \text{ g mol}^{-1}$

SOLVE Follow the conceptual plan. To find the partial pressure of argon, solve the equation for P_{Ar} and substitute the values of the other partial pressures to calculate P_{Ar}.

SOLUTION

$$P_{total} = P_{He} + P_{Ne} + P_{Ar}$$
$$P_{Ar} = P_{total} - P_{He} - P_{Ne}$$
$$= 662 \text{ Torr} - 341 \text{ Torr} - 112 \text{ Torr}$$
$$= 209 \text{ Torr}$$

Convert the partial pressure from Torr (mmHg) to bar and use it in the ideal gas law to calculate the amount of argon in moles.

$$209 \text{ Torr} \times \frac{1 \text{ bar}}{750.1 \text{ Torr}} = 0.27\underline{8}6 \text{ bar}$$

$$n = \frac{PV}{RT} = \frac{0.27\underline{8}6 \text{ bar} \times 1.00 \text{ L}}{0.08314 \frac{\text{L} \cdot \text{bar}}{\text{mol} \cdot \text{K}} \times 298 \text{ K}} = 1.1\underline{2}4 \times 10^{-2} \text{ mol}$$

Use the molar mass of argon to convert from amount of argon in moles to mass of argon.

$$m = nM = 1.1\underline{2}4 \times 10^{-2} \text{ mol} \times 39.95 \text{ g mol}^{-1} = 0.449 \text{ g}$$

CHECK The units of the answer are correct. The magnitude of the answer makes sense because the volume is 1.0 L, which at STP would contain about 1/23 mol. Since the partial pressure of argon in the mixture is about 1/3 of the total pressure, we roughly estimate about 1/69 of one molar mass of argon, which is fairly close to the answer we got.

FOR PRACTICE 5.9

A sample of hydrogen gas is mixed with water vapour. The mixture has a total pressure of 1007 mbar and the water vapour has a partial pressure of 32 mbar. What amount (in moles) of hydrogen gas is contained in 1.55 L of this mixture at 298 K?

EXAMPLE 5.10 PARTIAL PRESSURES AND MOLE FRACTIONS

A 12.5 L scuba diving tank contains a helium–oxygen (heliox) mixture made up of 24.2 g of He and 4.32 g of O_2 at 298 K. Calculate the mole fraction and partial pressure of each component in the mixture and the total pressure of the mixture.

SORT The problem gives the masses of two gases in a mixture and the volume and temperature of the mixture. You are to find the mole fraction and partial pressure of each component, as well as the total pressure.

GIVEN: $m_{He} = 24.2 \text{ g}, m_{O_2} = 4.32 \text{ g}, V = 12.5 \text{ L}, T = 298 \text{ K}$

FIND: $\chi_{He}, \chi_{O_2}, P_{He}, P_{O_2}, P_{total}$

STRATEGIZE The conceptual plan has several parts. To calculate the mole fraction of each component, you must first find the number of moles of each component. Therefore, in the first part of the conceptual plan, convert the masses to moles using the molar masses.

CONCEPTUAL PLAN

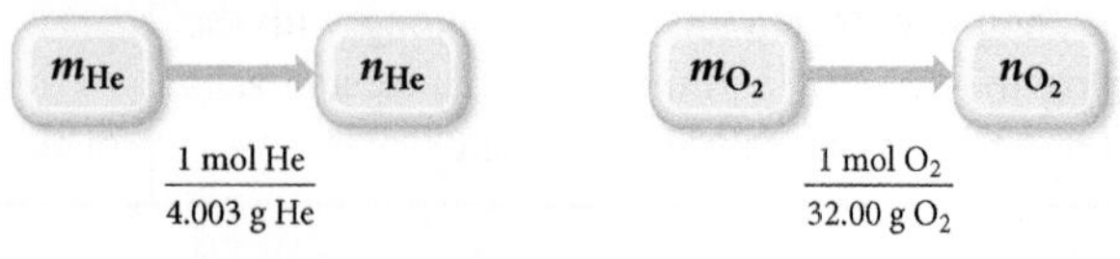

$\frac{1 \text{ mol He}}{4.003 \text{ g He}}$ $\frac{1 \text{ mol } O_2}{32.00 \text{ g } O_2}$

In the second part, calculate the mole fraction of each component using the mole fraction definition.	$\chi_{He} = \frac{n_{He}}{n_{He} + n_{O_2}}$; $\chi_{O_2} = \frac{n_{O_2}}{n_{He} + n_{O_2}}$
To calculate *partial pressures,* calculate the *total pressure* and then use the mole fractions from the previous part to calculate the partial pressures. Calculate the total pressure from the sum of the moles of both components. (Alternatively, you can calculate the partial pressures of the components individually, using the number of moles of each component. Then you can sum them to obtain the total pressure.)	$P_{total} = \frac{(n_{He} + n_{O_2})RT}{V}$ $P_{He} = \chi_{He}P_{total}$; $P_{O_2} = \chi_{O_2}P_{total}$ **RELATIONSHIPS USED** $\chi_a = n_a/n_{total}$ (mole fraction definition) $P_{total}V = n_{total}RT$ (ideal gas law) $P_a = \chi_a P_{total}$
Last, use the mole fractions of each component and the total pressure to calculate the partial pressure of each component.	
SOLVE Follow the plan to solve the problem. Begin by converting each of the masses to amounts in moles.	**SOLUTION** $24.2 \text{ g He} \times \frac{1 \text{ mol He}}{4.003 \text{ g He}} = 6.05 \text{ mol He}$ $4.32 \text{ g } O_2 \times \frac{1 \text{ mol } O_2}{32.00 \text{ g } O_2} = 0.135 \text{ mol } O_2$
Calculate each of the mole fractions.	$\chi_{He} = \frac{n_{He}}{n_{He} + n_{O_2}} = \frac{6.05}{6.05 + 0.135} = 0.978\underline{1}7$ $\chi_{O_2} = \frac{n_{O_2}}{n_{He} + n_{O_2}} = \frac{0.135}{6.05 + 0.135} = 0.021\underline{8}27$
Calculate the total pressure.	$P_{total} = \frac{(n_{He} + n_{O_2})RT}{V}$ $= \frac{(6.05 \text{ mol} + 0.135 \text{ mol})\left(0.08314 \frac{\text{L} \cdot \text{bar}}{\text{mol} \cdot \text{K}}\right)(298 \text{ K})}{12.5 \text{ L}}$ $= 12.\underline{2}59 \text{ bar}$
Finally, calculate the partial pressure of each component.	$P_{He} = \chi_{He}P_{total} = 0.97\underline{8}17 \times 12.\underline{2}59 \text{ bar} = 12.0 \text{ bar}$ $P_{O_2} = \chi_{O_2}P_{total} = 0.021\underline{8}27 \times 12.\underline{2}59 \text{ bar} = 0.268 \text{ bar}$

CHECK The units of the answers are correct and the magnitudes are reasonable.

FOR PRACTICE 5.10

A diver breathes a heliox mixture with an oxygen mole fraction of 0.050. What must the total pressure be for the partial pressure of oxygen to be 0.21 bar?

Collecting Gases over Water

When the desired product of a chemical reaction is a gas, the gas is often collected by the displacement of water. For example, suppose the following reaction is used as a source of hydrogen gas:

$$Zn(s) + 2\,HCl(aq) \longrightarrow ZnCl_2(aq) + H_2(g)$$

As the hydrogen gas forms, it bubbles through the water and gathers in the collection flask (Figure 5.13 ▼). The hydrogen gas collected in this way is not pure, however, but mixed with water vapour because some water molecules evaporate and mix with the hydrogen molecules.

We cover vapour pressure in detail in Chapter 11.

The partial pressure of water in the mixture, called its **vapour pressure**, depends on temperature (Table 5.4). Vapour pressure increases with increasing temperature because higher temperatures cause more water molecules to evaporate.

Appendix IIE contains a more complete table of the vapour pressure of water versus temperature.

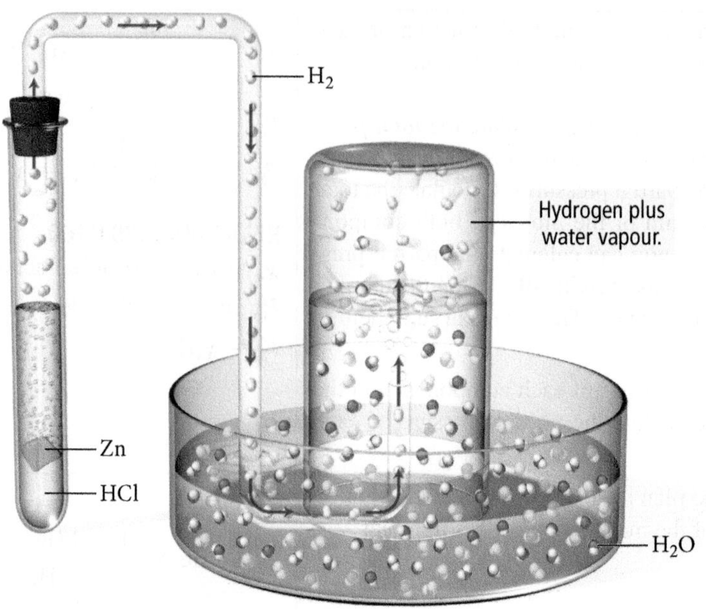

▶ **FIGURE 5.13 Collecting a Gas over Water** When the gaseous product of a chemical reaction is collected over water, the product molecules (in this case, H_2) become mixed with water molecules. The pressure of water in the final mixture is equal to the vapour pressure of water at the temperature at which the gas is collected. The partial pressure of the product is then the total pressure minus the partial pressure of water.

TABLE 5.4 Vapour Pressure of Water Versus Temperature

Temperature (°C)	Pressure (Torr)	Temperature (°C)	Pressure (Torr)
0	4.58	55	118.2
5	6.54	60	149.6
10	9.21	65	187.5
15	12.79	70	233.7
20	17.55	75	289.1
25	23.78	80	355.1
30	31.86	85	433.6
35	42.23	90	525.8
40	55.40	95	633.9
45	71.97	100	760.0
50	92.0		

Suppose we collect the hydrogen gas over water at a total pressure of 758.2 Torr and a temperature of 25 °C. What is the partial pressure of the hydrogen gas? We know that the total pressure is 758.2 Torr and we can see from Table 5.4 that the partial pressure of water is 23.78 Torr (its vapour pressure at 25 °C):

$$P_{\text{total}} = P_{H_2} + P_{H_2O}$$
$$758.2 \text{ Torr} = P_{H_2} + 23.78 \text{ Torr}$$

Therefore,

$$P_{H_2} = 758.2 \text{ Torr} - 23.78 \text{ Torr}$$
$$= 734.4 \text{ Torr}$$

The partial pressure of the hydrogen in the mixture will be 734.4 Torr.

EXAMPLE 5.11 COLLECTING GASES OVER WATER

In order to determine the rate of photosynthesis, the oxygen gas emitted by an aquatic plant was collected over water at a temperature of 293 K and a total pressure of 755.2 Torr. Over a specific time period, a total of 1.02 L of gas was collected. What mass of oxygen gas (in grams) was formed?

SORT The problem gives the volume of gas collected over water as well as the temperature and the pressure. You are to find the mass in grams of oxygen formed.	**GIVEN:** $V = 1.02 \text{ L}, P_{\text{total}} = 755.2 \text{ Torr}, T = 293 \text{ K}$ **FIND:** $\text{g } O_2$
STRATEGIZE You can determine the mass of oxygen from the amount of oxygen in moles, which you can calculate from the ideal gas law if you know the partial pressure of oxygen. Since the oxygen is mixed with water vapour, you can find the partial pressure of oxygen in the mixture by subtracting the partial pressure of water at 293 K (20 °C) from the total pressure.	**CONCEPTUAL PLAN** $P_{O_2} = P_{\text{total}} - P_{H_2O} (20 \text{ °C})$

Next, use the ideal gas law to determine the number of moles of oxygen from its partial pressure, volume, and temperature.	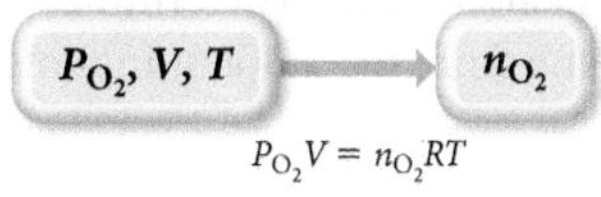 $P_{O_2}V = n_{O_2}RT$
Finally, use the molar mass of oxygen to convert the number of moles to grams.	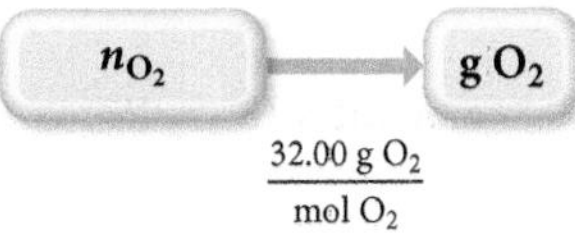 $\frac{32.00\text{ g }O_2}{\text{mol }O_2}$ **RELATIONSHIPS USED** $P_{total} = P_a + P_b + P_c + \cdots$ (Dalton's law) $PV = nRT$ (ideal gas law)
SOLVE Follow the conceptual plan to solve the problem. Begin by calculating the partial pressure of oxygen in the oxygen/water mixture. You can find the partial pressure of water at 20 °C in Table 5.4.	**SOLUTION** $P_{O_2} = P_{total} - P_{H_2O}\ (20\ °C) = 755.2\text{ Torr} - 17.55\text{ Torr} = 737.65\text{ Torr}$
Next, solve the ideal gas law for number of moles. Before substituting into the ideal gas law, you must convert the partial pressure of oxygen from torr to bar.	$n_{O_2} = \frac{P_{O_2}V}{RT}$ $P_{O_2} = 737.65\text{ Torr} \times \frac{1\text{ bar}}{750.1\text{ Torr}} = 0.98340\text{ bar}$
Next, substitute into the ideal gas law to find the number of moles of oxygen.	$n_{O_2} = \frac{(0.98340\text{ bar})(1.02\text{ L})}{\left(0.08314\frac{\text{L}\cdot\text{bar}}{\text{mol}\cdot\text{K}}\right)(293\text{ K})}$
Finally, use the molar mass of oxygen to convert to grams of oxygen.	$= 4.118 \times 10^{-2}\text{ mol}$ $m = nM = (4.118 \times 10^{-2}\text{ mol})(32.00\text{ g mol}^{-1}) = 1.32\text{ g}$

CHECK The answer is in the correct units. We can quickly check the magnitude of the answer by using molar volume. Under STP, one litre is about 1/23 of one mole. Therefore, the answer should be about 1/23 the molar mass of oxygen $(1/23 \times 32 = 1.39)$. The magnitude of our answer seems reasonable.

FOR PRACTICE 5.11

A common way to make hydrogen gas in the laboratory is to place a metal such as zinc in hydrochloric acid. The hydrochloric acid reacts with the metal to produce hydrogen gas, which is then collected over water. Suppose a student carries out this reaction and collects a total of 154.4 mL of gas at a pressure of 742 Torr and a temperature of 25 °C. What mass of hydrogen gas (in mg) did the student collect?

5.7 Gases in Chemical Reactions: Stoichiometry Revisited

In Chapter 4, we learned how we can use the coefficients in chemical equations as conversion factors between number of moles of reactants and number of moles of products in a chemical reaction. We used these conversion factors to determine, for example, the mass of product obtained in a chemical reaction based on a given mass of reactant, or the mass of one reactant needed to react completely with a given mass of another reactant. The general conceptual plan for these kinds of calculations is:

where A and B are two different substances involved in the reaction and the conversion factor between amounts (in moles) of each comes from the stoichiometric coefficients in the balanced chemical equation.

In reactions involving *gaseous* reactants or products, we often specify the quantity of a gas in terms of its volume at a given temperature and pressure. As we have seen, stoichiometric relationships always express relative amounts in moles. However, we can use

The pressures here could also be partial pressure.

the ideal gas law to determine the amount in moles from the volume, or to determine the volume from the amount in moles:

$$n = \frac{PV}{RT} \qquad V = \frac{nRT}{P}$$

The general conceptual plan for these kinds of calculations is:

The following examples demonstrate this kind of calculation.

EXAMPLE 5.12 GASES IN CHEMICAL REACTIONS

Methanol (CH_3OH) can be synthesized by the following reaction:

$$CO(g) + 2\,H_2(g) \longrightarrow CH_3OH(g)$$

What volume (in litres) of hydrogen gas, at a temperature of 355 K and a pressure of 984 mbar, is required to synthesize 35.7 g of methanol given an excess of CO gas?

SORT You are given the mass of methanol, the product of a chemical reaction. You are asked to find the required volume of one of the reactants (hydrogen gas) at a specified temperature and pressure.

GIVEN: 35.7 g CH_3OH, $T = 355$ K, $P = 984$ mbar

FIND: V_{H_2}

STRATEGIZE You can calculate the required volume of hydrogen gas from the number of moles of hydrogen gas, which you can obtain from the number of moles of methanol via the stoichiometry of the reaction.

CONCEPTUAL PLAN

First, find the number of moles of methanol from its mass by using the molar mass.

Then use the stoichiometric relationship from the balanced chemical equation to find the number of moles of hydrogen you need to form that quantity of methanol.

Finally, substitute the number of moles of hydrogen together with the pressure and temperature into the ideal gas law to find the volume of hydrogen.

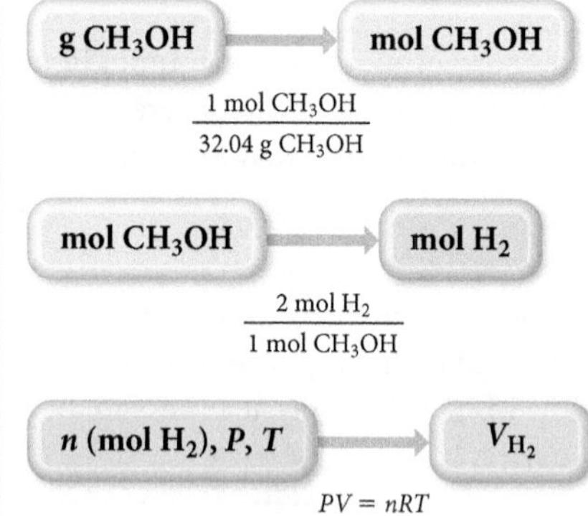

RELATIONSHIPS USED

$PV = nRT$ (ideal gas law)

2 mol H_2 : 1 mol CH_3OH (from balanced chemical equation)

molar mass CH_3OH = 32.04 g mol^{-1}

SOLVE Follow the conceptual plan to solve the problem. Begin by using the mass of methanol to determine the number of moles of methanol.

SOLUTION

$$35.7\ \text{g}\ \cancel{CH_3OH} \times \frac{1\ \text{mol}\ CH_3OH}{32.04\ \text{g}\ \cancel{CH_3OH}} = 1.1\underline{1}42\ \text{mol}\ CH_3OH$$

Next, convert the number of moles of methanol to moles of hydrogen.

$$1.1\underline{1}42\ \cancel{\text{mol}\ CH_3OH} \times \frac{2\ \text{mol}\ H_2}{1\ \cancel{\text{mol}\ CH_3OH}} = 2.2\underline{2}84\ \text{mol}\ H_2$$

Finally, use the ideal gas law to find the volume of hydrogen. Before substituting into the equation, you must convert the pressure to bar.

$$V_{H_2} = \frac{n_{H_2}RT}{P}$$

$$P = 984\ \cancel{\text{mbar}} \times \frac{1\ \text{bar}}{1000\ \cancel{\text{mbar}}} = 0.984\ \text{bar}$$

$$V_{H_2} = \frac{(2.2\underline{2}84\ \cancel{\text{mol}})\left(0.08314\ \frac{\text{L}\cdot\cancel{\text{bar}}}{\cancel{\text{mol}}\cdot\cancel{\text{K}}}\right)(355\ \cancel{\text{K}})}{(0.984\ \cancel{\text{bar}})}$$

$$= 66.8\ \text{L}$$

CHECK The units of the answer are correct. The magnitude of the answer (66.8 L) seems reasonable. You are given slightly more than one molar mass of methanol, which is therefore slightly more than one mole of methanol. From the equation, you can see that you need 2 mol hydrogen to make 1 mol methanol, so the answer must be slightly greater than 2 mol hydrogen. Under standard conditions, slightly more than 2 mol hydrogen occupies slightly more than 2 × 22.7 L = 45.4 L. At a temperature greater than standard temperature, the volume would be even greater; therefore, this answer is reasonable.

FOR PRACTICE 5.12

In the following reaction, 4.58 L of O_2 was formed at P = 745 Torr and T = 308 K. How many grams of Ag_2O must have decomposed?

$$2\,Ag_2O(s) \longrightarrow 4\,Ag(s) + O_2(g)$$

FOR MORE PRACTICE 5.12

In the above reaction, what mass of $Ag_2O(s)$ (in grams) is required to form 388 mL of oxygen gas at P = 978.7 mbar and 25.0 °C?

Molar Volume and Stoichiometry

In Section 5.5, we saw that, under standard conditions, 1 mol of an ideal gas occupies 22.7 L. Consequently, if a reaction is occurring at or near standard conditions, we can use 1 mol = 22.7 L as a conversion factor in stoichiometric calculations, as shown in the following example.

EXAMPLE 5.13 **USING MOLAR VOLUME IN GAS STOICHIOMETRIC CALCULATIONS**

How many grams of water form when 1.24 L of H_2 gas at STP completely reacts with O_2?

$$2\,H_2(g) + O_2(g) \longrightarrow 2\,H_2O(g)$$

SORT You are given the volume of hydrogen gas (a reactant) at STP and asked to determine the mass of water that forms upon complete reaction.

GIVEN: 1.24 L H_2

FIND: g H_2O

STRATEGIZE Since the reaction occurs under standard conditions, you can convert directly from the volume (in L) of hydrogen gas to the amount in moles. Then use the stoichiometric relationship from the balanced equation to find the number of moles of water formed. Finally, use the molar mass of water to obtain the mass of water formed.

CONCEPTUAL PLAN

$$\text{L H}_2 \xrightarrow{\frac{1\text{ mol H}_2}{22.7\text{ L H}_2}} \text{mol H}_2 \xrightarrow{\frac{2\text{ mol H}_2\text{O}}{2\text{ mol H}_2}} \text{mol H}_2\text{O} \xrightarrow{\frac{18.02\text{ g H}_2\text{O}}{1\text{ mol H}_2\text{O}}} \text{g H}_2\text{O}$$

RELATIONSHIPS USED

1 mol = 22.7 L (at STP)

2 mol H_2 : 2 mol H_2O (from balanced equation)

molar mass H_2O = 18.02 g mol^{-1}

SOLVE Follow the conceptual plan to solve the problem.

SOLUTION

$$1.24\text{ L H}_2 \times \frac{1\text{ mol H}_2}{22.7\text{ L H}_2} \times \frac{2\text{ mol H}_2\text{O}}{2\text{ mol H}_2} \times \frac{18.02\text{ g H}_2\text{O}}{1\text{ mol H}_2\text{O}} = 0.984\text{ g H}_2\text{O}$$

CHECK The units of the answer are correct. The magnitude of the answer (0.984 g) is about 1/18 of the molar mass of water, roughly equivalent to the approximately 1/23 of a mole of hydrogen gas given, as expected for the 1:1 stoichiometric relationship between number of moles of hydrogen and number of moles of water.

FOR PRACTICE 5.13

How many litres of oxygen (at STP) are required to form 10.5 g of H_2O?

$$2\,H_2(g) + O_2(g) \longrightarrow 2\,H_2O(g)$$

CONCEPTUAL CONNECTION 5.2

Pressure and Number of Moles

Nitrogen and hydrogen react to form ammonia according to the following equation:

$$N_2(g) + 3\,H_2(g) \longrightarrow 2\,NH_3(g)$$

Consider the following representations of the initial mixture of reactants and the resulting mixture after the reaction has been allowed to react for some time:

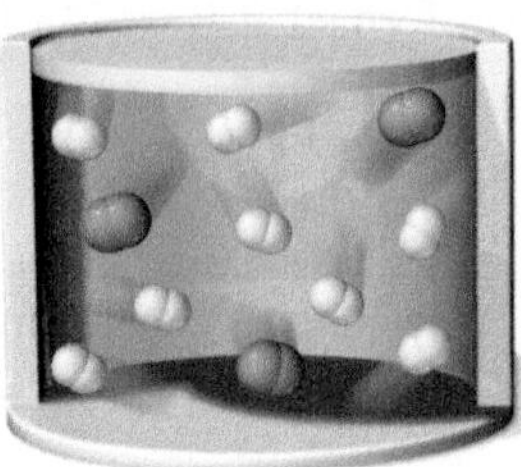

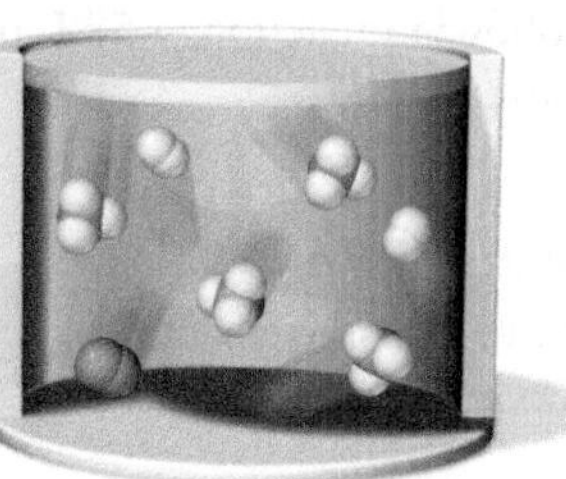

If the volume is kept constant, and nothing is added to the reaction mixture, what happens to the total pressure during the course of the reaction?

(a) the pressure increases

(b) the pressure decreases

(c) the pressure does not change

5.8 Kinetic Molecular Theory: A Model for Gases

Applying the scientific method, one proceeds from observations to laws and eventually to theories. Laws summarize behaviour—for example, Charles's law summarizes *how* the volume of a gas depends on temperature—while theories give the underlying reasons for the behaviour. A theory of gas behaviour explains, for example, *why* the volume of a gas increases with increasing temperature.

The simplest model for the behaviour of gases is the **kinetic molecular theory**. In this theory, a gas is modelled as a collection of particles (either molecules or atoms, depending on the gas) in constant motion (Figure 5.14 ◄). A single particle moves in a straight line until it collides with another particle (or with the wall of the container). The basic postulates (or assumptions) of kinetic molecular theory are as follows:

▲ **FIGURE 5.14 A Model for Gas Behaviour** In the kinetic molecular theory of gases, a gas sample is modelled as a collection of particles in constant straight-line motion. The size of the particles is negligibly small and their collisions are elastic.

1. **The size of each gas particle is negligibly small.** Kinetic molecular theory assumes that the particles themselves occupy no volume, even though they have mass. This postulate is justified because, under normal pressures, the space between atoms or molecules in a gas is very large compared to the size of an atom or molecule itself. For example, in a sample of argon gas at STP, only about 0.01% of the volume is occupied by atoms, and the average distance from one argon atom to another is 3.3 nm. In comparison, the atomic radius of argon is 97 pm. If an argon atom were the size of a golf ball, its nearest neighbour would be, on average, just over 1.3 m away at STP.
2. **The average kinetic energy of a particle is proportional to the temperature in kelvins.** The motion of atoms or molecules in a gas is due to thermal energy, which distributes itself among the particles in the gas. At any given moment, some particles are moving faster than others—there is a distribution of velocities—but the higher the temperature, the faster the overall motion, and the greater the average kinetic energy. Notice that *kinetic energy* ($\frac{1}{2}mv^2$)—not *velocity*—is proportional to temperature. The atoms in a sample of helium and a sample of argon at the same temperature have the same average *kinetic energy*, but not the same average *velocity*. Since the helium atoms are lighter, they must move faster to have the same kinetic energy as argon atoms.
3. **The collision of one particle with another (or with the walls of its container) is completely elastic.** This means that when two particles collide, they may

▲ **FIGURE 5.15 Elastic Versus Inelastic Collisions** When two billiard balls collide, the collision is elastic—the total kinetic energy of the colliding bodies is the same before and after the collision. When two lumps of clay collide, the collision is inelastic—the kinetic energy of the colliding bodies dissipates in the form of heat during the collision.

exchange energy, but there is no overall *loss of energy*. Any kinetic energy lost by one particle is completely gained by the other. In other words, the particles have no "stickiness," and they are not deformed by the collision. An encounter between two particles in kinetic molecular theory is more like the collision between two billiard balls than the collision between two lumps of clay (Figure 5.15 ▲). Between collisions, the particles do not exert any forces on one another.

If you start with the postulates of kinetic molecular theory, you can mathematically derive the ideal gas law (as we will show later). In other words, the ideal gas law follows directly from kinetic molecular theory, which gives us confidence that the assumptions of the theory are valid, at least under conditions where the ideal gas law applies. Let's see how the concept of pressure as well as each of the gas laws we have examined follow conceptually from kinetic molecular theory.

The Nature of Pressure In Section 5.2, we defined pressure as force divided by area:

$$P = \frac{F}{A}$$

According to kinetic molecular theory, a gas is a collection of particles in constant motion. The motion results in collisions between the particles and the surfaces around them. As each particle collides with a surface, it exerts a force upon that surface. The result of many particles in a gas sample exerting forces on the surfaces around them is a constant pressure.

The force (F) associated with an individual collision is given by $F = ma$, where m is the mass of the particle and a is its acceleration as it changes its direction of travel due to the collision.

Boyle's Law Boyle's law states that, for a constant number of particles at constant temperature, the volume of a gas is inversely proportional to its pressure. According to kinetic molecular theory, if you decrease the volume of a gas, you force the gas particles to occupy a smaller space. As long as the temperature remains the same, the number of collisions with the surrounding surfaces (per unit surface area) must necessarily increase, resulting in a greater pressure.

Charles's Law Charles's law states that, for a constant number of particles at constant pressure, the volume of a gas is proportional to its temperature. According to kinetic molecular theory, when you increase the temperature of a gas, the average kinetic energy—and thus the average speed—of the particles increases. Since this greater speed results in more frequent collisions and more force per collision, the pressure of the gas increases if its volume is held constant. The only way for the pressure to remain constant is for the volume to increase. The greater volume spreads the collisions out over a greater surface area, so that the pressure (defined as force per unit area) is unchanged.

Avogadro's Law Avogadro's law states that, at constant temperature and pressure, the volume of a gas is proportional to the number of particles. According to kinetic molecular theory, when you increase the number of particles in a gas sample, the number of collisions with the surrounding surfaces increases. The greater number of collisions results in a greater overall force on surrounding surfaces; the only way for the pressure to remain constant is for the volume to increase so that the number of particles per unit volume (and thus the number of collisions) remains constant.

Dalton's Law Dalton's law states that the total pressure of a gas mixture is the sum of the partial pressures of its components. In other words, according to Dalton's law, the components in a gas mixture act identically to, and independently of, one another. According to kinetic molecular theory, the particles have negligible size and they do not interact. Consequently, the only property that would distinguish one type of particle from another is its mass. However, even particles of different masses have the same average kinetic energy at a given temperature. Consequently, adding components to a gas mixture—even different *kinds* of gases—has the same effect as simply adding more particles. The partial pressures of all the components sum to the overall pressure.

Kinetic Molecular Theory and the Ideal Gas Law

We have just seen how each of the gas laws conceptually follows from kinetic molecular theory. We can also *derive* the ideal gas law from the postulates of kinetic molecular theory. In other words, the kinetic molecular theory is a quantitative model that *implies* $PV = nRT$. We now explore this derivation.

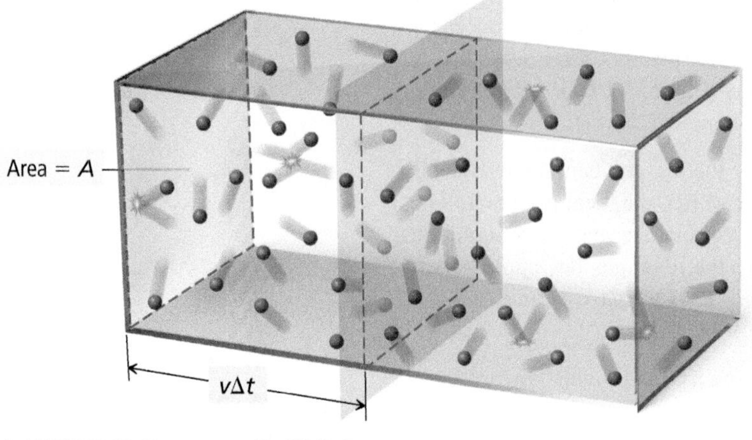

▲ **FIGURE 5.16 Pressure on the Wall of a Container** The pressure on the wall of a container can be calculated by determining the total force due to collisions of the particles with the wall.

The pressure on a wall of a container (Figure 5.16 ◄) occupied by particles in constant motion is the total force on the wall (due to the collisions) divided by the area of the wall:

$$P = \frac{F_{\text{total}}}{A} \quad [5.13]$$

From Newton's second law, the force (F) associated with an individual collision is given by $F = ma$, where m is the mass of the particle and a is its acceleration as it changes its direction of travel due to the collision. The acceleration for each collision is the change in velocity (Δv) divided by the time interval (Δt), so the force imparted for each collision is:

$$F_{\text{collision}} = m\frac{\Delta v}{\Delta t} \quad [5.14]$$

If a particle collides elastically with the wall, it bounces off the wall with no loss of energy. For a straight-line collision, the change in velocity is $2v$ (the particle's velocity was v before the collision and $-v$ after the collision; therefore, the change is $2v$). The force per collision is given by the following:

$$F_{\text{collision}} = m\frac{2v}{\Delta t} \quad [5.15]$$

The total number of collisions in the time interval Δt on a wall of surface area A is proportional to the number of particles that can reach the wall in this time interval—in other words, all particles within a distance of $v\,\Delta t$ of the wall. These particles occupy a volume given by $v\,\Delta t \times A$, and their total number is equal to this volume multiplied by the density of particles in the container (n/V):

$$\text{Number of collisions} \propto \text{number of particles within } v\,\Delta t$$

$$\propto v\,\Delta t \times A \times \frac{n}{V} \quad [5.16]$$

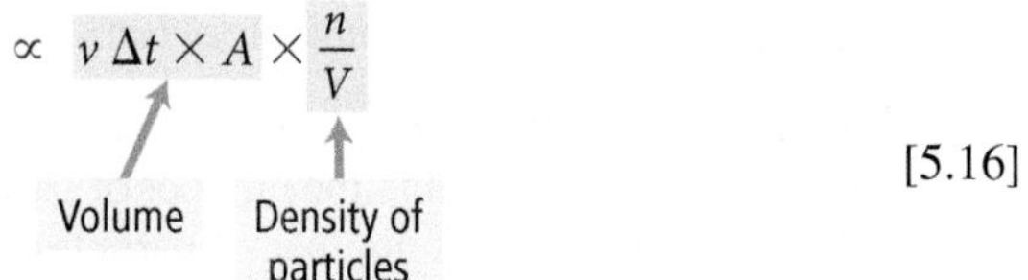

The *total force* on the wall is equal to the force per collision multiplied by the number of collisions:

$$F_{\text{total}} = F_{\text{collision}} \times \text{number of collisions}$$
$$\propto m\frac{2v}{\Delta t} \times v\,\Delta t \times A \times \frac{n}{V}$$
$$\propto mv^2 \times A \times \frac{n}{V} \qquad [5.17]$$

The pressure on the wall is equal to the total force divided by the surface area of the wall:

$$P = \frac{F_{\text{total}}}{A}$$
$$P \propto \frac{mv^2 \times A \times \frac{n}{V}}{A}$$
$$P \propto mv^2 \times \frac{n}{V} \qquad [5.18]$$

Notice that Equation 5.18 contains within it Boyle's law ($P \propto 1/V$) and Avogadro's law ($V \propto n$). We can get the complete ideal gas law from postulate 2 of the kinetic molecular theory, which states that the average kinetic energy ($\frac{1}{2}mv^2$) is proportional to the temperature in kelvins (T):

$$mv^2 \propto T \qquad [5.19]$$

By combining Equations 5.18 and 5.19, we get the following:

$$P \propto \frac{T \times n}{V}$$
$$PV \propto nT \qquad [5.20]$$

The proportionality can be replaced by an equal sign if we provide the correct constant, R:

$$PV = nRT \qquad [5.21]$$

In other words, the kinetic molecular theory (a model for how gases behave) predicts behaviour that is consistent with our observations and measurements of gases—the theory agrees with the experiment. A scientific theory is the most powerful kind of scientific knowledge. In the kinetic molecular theory, we have a model for what a gas is like. Although the model is not perfect—indeed, it breaks down under certain conditions, as we shall see later in this chapter—it predicts a great deal about the behaviour of gases. Therefore, the model is a good approximation of what a gas is actually like. A careful examination of the conditions under which the model breaks down (see Section 5.10) gives us even more insight into the behaviour of gases.

Temperature and Molecular Velocities

According to kinetic molecular theory, particles of different masses have the same average kinetic energy at a given temperature. The kinetic energy of a particle depends on its mass and velocity according to the following equation:

$$\text{KE} = \tfrac{1}{2}mv^2$$

The only way for particles of different masses to have the same kinetic energy is if they are travelling at different velocities.

In a gas at a given temperature, lighter particles travel faster (on average) than heavier ones.

In kinetic molecular theory, we define the root mean square velocity (u_{rms}) of a particle as follows:

$$u_{\text{rms}} = \sqrt{\overline{u^2}} \qquad [5.22]$$

where $\overline{u^2}$ is the average of the squares of the particle velocities. Even though the root mean square velocity of a collection of particles is not identical to the average velocity, the two are close in value and conceptually similar. Root mean square velocity is just a special *type* of average. The average kinetic energy of one mole of gas particles is then given by:

$$KE_{avg} = \tfrac{1}{2} N_A m\overline{u^2} \qquad [5.23]$$

where N_A is Avogadro's number.

Postulate 2 of the kinetic molecular theory states that the average kinetic energy is proportional to the temperature in kelvins. The constant of proportionality in this relationship is (3/2) R:

$$KE_{avg} = (3/2)\,RT \qquad [5.24]$$

where R is the gas constant, but in different units ($R = 8.314\ \text{J mol}^{-1}\ \text{K}^{-1}$) than those we use in the ideal gas law. If we combine Equations 5.23 and 5.24, and solve for $\overline{u^2}$, we get the following:

Briefly, the 3/2 R corresponds to 1/2 R for the velocity for each translational degree of freedom or dimension (i.e., x, y, z) but the derivation is beyond the scope of this text.

$$(1/2)\,N_A m\overline{u^2} = (3/2)\,RT$$

$$\overline{u^2} = \frac{(3/2)\,RT}{(1/2)\,N_A m} = \frac{3RT}{N_A m}$$

The joule (J) is a unit of energy, which we discuss in more detail in Section 6.2. $\left(1\ \text{J} = 1\ \text{kg m}^2\ \text{s}^{-2}\right)$

Taking the square root of both sides, we get:

$$\sqrt{\overline{u^2}} = u_{rms} = \sqrt{\frac{3RT}{N_A m}} \qquad [5.25]$$

In Equation 5.25, m is the mass of a particle in kg and N_A is Avogadro's number. The product $N_A m$, then, is the molar mass in kg mol^{-1}. If we call this quantity M, then the expression for the root mean square velocity as a function of temperature becomes the following important result:

$$u_{rms} = \sqrt{\frac{3RT}{M}} \qquad [5.26]$$

The root mean square velocity of a collection of gas particles is proportional to the square root of the temperature in kelvins and inversely proportional to the square root of the molar mass of the particles (because the units of M must be in kilograms per mole). The root mean square velocity of nitrogen molecules at 25 °C, for example, is 515 m s^{-1} (1854 km h^{-1}). The root mean square velocity of hydrogen molecules at room temperature is 1920 m s^{-1} (6912 km h^{-1}). Notice that the lighter molecules move much faster at a given temperature.

The root mean square velocity, as we have seen, is a kind of average velocity. Some particles are moving faster and some are moving slower than this average. The velocities of all the particles in a gas sample form distributions like those shown in Figure 5.17 ▼. We

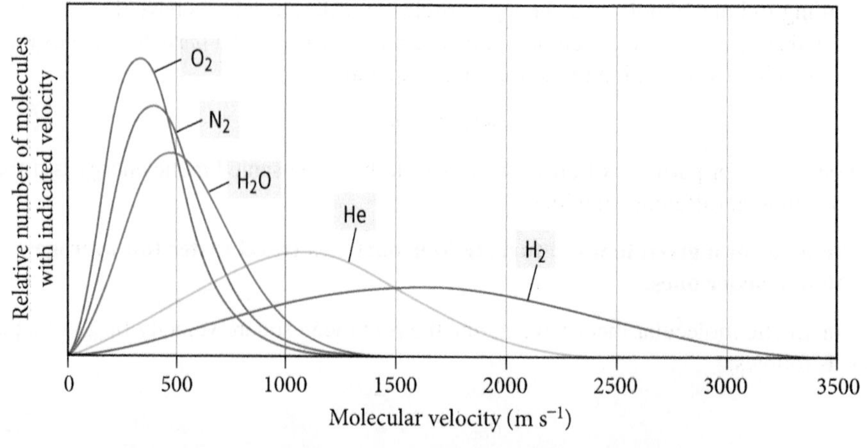

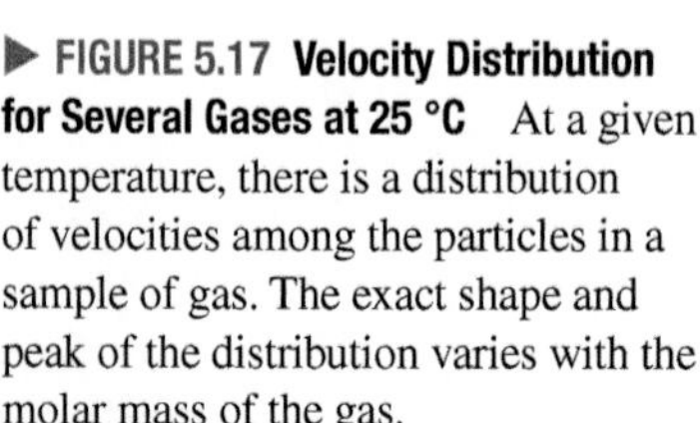

▶ **FIGURE 5.17 Velocity Distribution for Several Gases at 25 °C** At a given temperature, there is a distribution of velocities among the particles in a sample of gas. The exact shape and peak of the distribution varies with the molar mass of the gas.

can see from these distributions that some particles are indeed travelling at the root mean square velocity. However, many particles are travelling faster and many slower than the root mean square velocity. For lighter particles, such as helium and hydrogen, the velocity distribution is shifted toward higher velocities and the curve becomes broader, indicating a wider range of velocities. The velocity distribution for nitrogen at different temperatures is shown in Figure 5.18 ▶. As the temperature increases, the root mean square velocity increases and the distribution becomes broader.

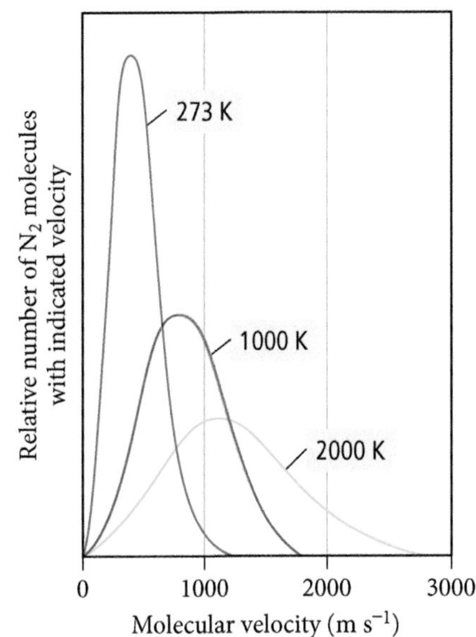

▶ **FIGURE 5.18 Velocity Distribution for Nitrogen at Several Temperatures**
As the temperature of a gas sample increases, the velocity distribution of the molecules shifts toward higher velocity and the breadth of the peak is increased.

EXAMPLE 5.14 ROOT MEAN SQUARE VELOCITY

Calculate the root mean square velocity of oxygen molecules at 25 °C.

SORT You are given the identity of the molecule and the temperature and asked to find the root mean square velocity.

GIVEN: O_2, $T = 25\ °C$

FIND: u_{rms}

STRATEGIZE The conceptual plan for this problem shows how the molar mass of oxygen and the temperature (in kelvins) can be used with the equation that defines the root mean square velocity to calculate root mean square velocity.

CONCEPTUAL PLAN

$M, T \rightarrow u_{rms}$

$$u_{rms} = \sqrt{\frac{3RT}{M}}$$

RELATIONSHIP USED

$$u_{rms} = \sqrt{\frac{3RT}{M}} \quad \text{(Equation 5.26)}$$

SOLVE First gather the required quantities in the correct units. Note that molar mass must be in kg mol^{-1}.

SOLUTION

$$T = 25 + 273.15 = 298\ K$$

$$M = \frac{32.00\ \cancel{g}\ O_2}{1\ mol\ O_2} \times \frac{1\ kg}{1000\ \cancel{g}} = \frac{32.00 \times 10^{-3}\ kg\ O_2}{1\ mol\ O_2}$$

Substitute the quantities into the equation to calculate root mean square velocity. Note that $1\ J = 1\ kg\ m^2\ s^{-2}$.

$$u_{rms} = \sqrt{\frac{3RT}{M}}$$

$$= \sqrt{\frac{3\left(8.314\ \frac{J}{\cancel{mol} \cdot \cancel{K}}\right)(298\ \cancel{K})}{\frac{32.00 \times 10^{-3}\ kg\ \cancel{O_2}}{1\ \cancel{mol}\ \cancel{O_2}}}}$$

$$= \sqrt{2.32 \times 10^5\ \frac{J}{kg}}$$

$$= \sqrt{2.32 \times 10^5\ \frac{\frac{\cancel{kg} \cdot m^2}{s^2}}{\cancel{kg}}} = 482\ m\ s^{-1}$$

CHECK The units of the answer (m s^{-1}) are correct. The magnitude of the answer seems reasonable because oxygen is slightly heavier than nitrogen and should therefore have a slightly lower root mean square velocity at the same temperature. Recall that earlier we stated that the root mean square velocity of nitrogen is 515 m s^{-1} at 25 °C.

FOR PRACTICE 5.14

Calculate the root mean square velocity of gaseous xenon atoms at 25 °C.

CONCEPTUAL CONNECTION 5.3

Kinetic Molecular Theory

Which sample of an ideal gas has the greatest pressure? Assume that the mass of each particle is proportional to its size and that all the gas samples are at the same temperature.

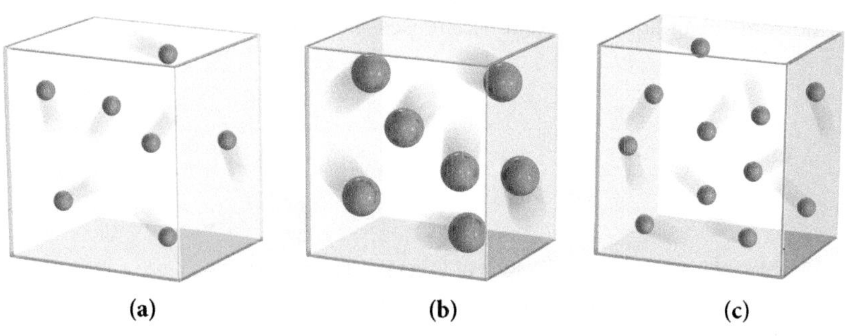

5.9 Mean Free Path, Diffusion, and Effusion of Gases

In a ventilated room, air currents also enhance the transport of gas molecules.

The average distance between collisions is the mean free path.

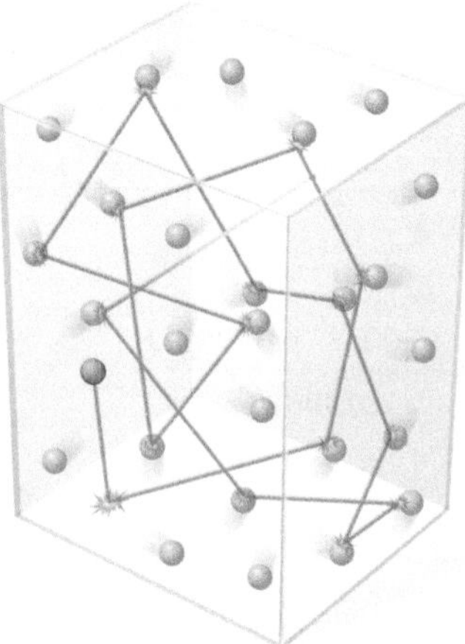

▲ **FIGURE 5.19 Mean Free Path** A molecule in a volume of gas follows a haphazard path, involving many collisions with other molecules.

We have just learned that the root mean square velocity of gas molecules at room temperature is measured in hundreds of metres per second. However, suppose that your roommate just put on too much perfume in the bathroom only 2 m away. Why does it take a minute or two before you can smell the fragrance? Although most molecules in a perfume bottle have higher molar masses than nitrogen, their velocities are still hundreds of metres per second, so why the delay? The answer is that, even though gaseous particles travel at tremendous speeds, they also travel in haphazard paths (Figure 5.19 ◀). To a perfume molecule, the path from the perfume bottle in the bathroom to your nose 2 m away is much like a bargain hunter's path through a busy shopping mall during a clearance sale. The molecule travels only a short distance before it collides with another molecule, changes direction, only to collide again, and so on. In fact, at room temperature and atmospheric pressure, a molecule in the air experiences several billion collisions per second. The average distance that a molecule travels between collisions is called its **mean free path**. At room temperature and atmospheric pressure, the mean free path of a nitrogen molecule with a molecular diameter of 300 pm (four times the covalent radius) is 93 nm, or about 310 molecular diameters. If the nitrogen molecule were the size of a golf ball, it would travel about 12 m between collisions. Mean free path increases with *decreasing* pressure. Under conditions of ultrahigh vacuum (10^{-10} Torr), the mean free path of a nitrogen molecule is hundreds of kilometres.

The process by which gas molecules spread out in response to a concentration gradient is called **diffusion**, and even though the particles undergo many collisions, the root mean square velocity still influences the rate of diffusion. Heavier molecules diffuse more slowly than lighter ones, so the first molecules you would smell from a perfume mixture (in a room with no air currents) are the lighter ones.

A process related to diffusion is **effusion**, the process by which a gas escapes from a container into a vacuum through a small hole (Figure 5.20 ▶). The rate of effusion is also related to root mean square velocity—heavier molecules effuse more slowly than lighter ones. The rate of effusion—the amount of gas that effuses in a given time—is inversely proportional to the square root of the molar mass of the gas as follows:

$$\text{rate} \propto \frac{1}{\sqrt{M}}$$

The ratio of effusion rates of two different gases is given by **Graham's law of effusion**, named after Thomas Graham (1805–1869):

$$\frac{\text{rate}_A}{\text{rate}_B} = \sqrt{\frac{M_B}{M_A}} \qquad [5.27]$$

In this expression, rate_A and rate_B are the effusion rates of gases A and B and M_A and M_B are the molar masses, respectively.

Graham's law explains, in part, why helium balloons only float for a day or so. Since helium has a such a low molar mass, it escapes from the balloon quite quickly. A balloon filled with air, by contrast, remains inflated longer.

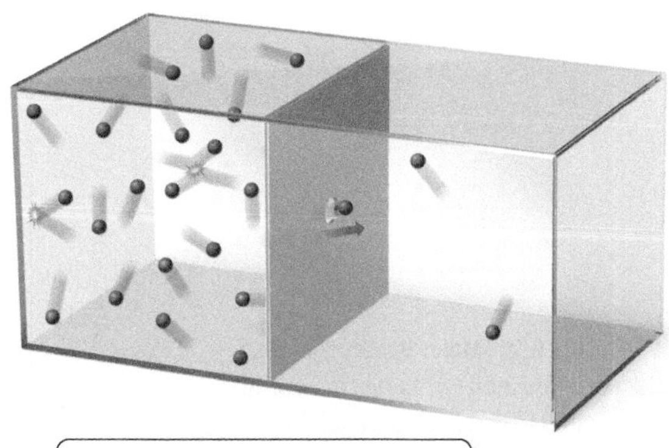

Gas escapes from a container into a vacuum through a small hole.

▲ **FIGURE 5.20 Effusion** Effusion is the escape of a gas from a container into a vacuum through a small hole.

EXAMPLE 5.15 GRAHAM'S LAW OF EFFUSION

An unknown atomic gas effuses at a rate that is 0.462 times that of nitrogen gas (at the same temperature). Calculate the molar mass of the unknown gas in g mol^{-1}.

SORT You are given the ratio of effusion rates for the unknown gas and nitrogen and asked to find the molar mass of the unknown gas.	**GIVEN:** $\frac{\text{rate}_{\text{unk}}}{\text{rate}_{N_2}} = 0.462$ **FIND:** M_{unk}
STRATEGIZE The conceptual plan uses Graham's law of effusion. You are given the ratio of rates and you know the molar mass of nitrogen. You can use Graham's law to find the molar mass of the unknown gas.	**CONCEPTUAL PLAN** $\frac{\text{rate}_{\text{unk}}}{\text{rate}_{N_2}}, M_{N_2}$ → M_{unk} $\frac{\text{rate}_{\text{unk}}}{\text{rate}_{N_2}} = \sqrt{\frac{M_{N_2}}{M_{\text{unk}}}}$ **RELATIONSHIP USED** $\frac{\text{rate}_A}{\text{rate}_B} = \sqrt{\frac{M_B}{M_A}}$ (Graham's law)
SOLVE Solve the equation for M_{unk} and substitute the correct values to calculate it.	**SOLUTION** $\frac{\text{rate}_{\text{unk}}}{\text{rate}_{N_2}} = \sqrt{\frac{M_{N_2}}{M_{\text{unk}}}}$ $M_{\text{unk}} = \frac{M_{N_2}}{\left(\frac{\text{rate}_{\text{unk}}}{\text{rate}_{N_2}}\right)^2}$ $= \frac{28.02 \text{ g mol}^{-1}}{(0.462)^2}$ $= 131 \text{ g mol}^{-1}$

CHECK The units of the answer are correct. The magnitude of the answer seems reasonable for the molar mass of a gas. In fact, from the answer, we can even conclude that the gas is probably xenon, which has a molar mass of 131.29 g mol^{-1}.

FOR PRACTICE 5.15

Find the ratio of effusion rates of hydrogen gas and krypton gas.

5.10 Real Gases: The Effects of Size and Intermolecular Forces

One mole of an ideal gas has a volume of 22.7 L at STP. Figure 5.21 ▼ shows the molar volume of several real gases at STP. As you can see, most of these gases have a volume that is very close to 22.7 L, meaning that they are acting very nearly as ideal

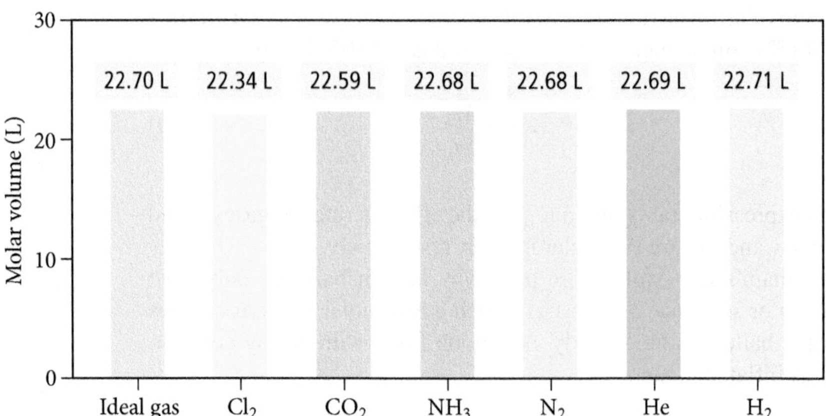

▶ **FIGURE 5.21 Molar Volumes of Real Gases** The molar volumes of several gases at STP are all close to 22.7 L, indicating that their departures from ideal behaviour are small.

gases. Gases behave ideally when both of the following are true: (a) the volume of the gas particles is small compared to the space between them, and (b) the forces between the gas particles are not significant. At STP, these assumptions are valid for most common gases. However, these assumptions break down at higher pressures or lower temperatures.

The Effect of the Finite Volume of Gas Particles

The finite volume of gas particles—that is, their actual *size*—becomes important at high pressure because the volume of the particles themselves occupies a significant portion of the total gas volume (Figure 5.22 ▼). We can see the effect of particle volume by comparing the molar volume of argon to the molar volume of an ideal gas as a function of pressure at 500 K as shown in Figure 5.23 ▼. At low pressures, the molar volume of argon is nearly identical to that of an ideal gas. But as the pressure increases, the molar volume of argon becomes *greater than* that of an ideal gas. At the higher pressures, the argon atoms themselves occupy a significant portion of the gas volume, making the actual volume greater than that predicted by the ideal gas law.

In 1873, Johannes van der Waals (1837–1923) modified the ideal gas equation to fit the behaviour of real gases. From the graph for argon in Figure 5.23, we can see that the

▲ **FIGURE 5.22 Particle Volume and Ideal Behaviour** As a gas is compressed, the gas particles themselves begin to occupy a significant portion of the total gas volume, leading to deviations from ideal behaviour.

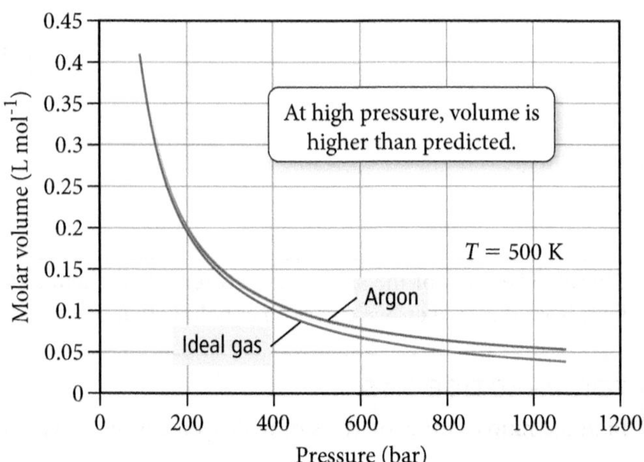

▲ **FIGURE 5.23 The Effect of Particle Volume** At high pressures, 1 mol of argon occupies a larger volume than 1 mol of an ideal gas because of the volume of the argon atoms themselves. (This example was chosen to minimize the effects of intermolecular forces, which are very small in argon at 500 K, thereby isolating the effect of particle volume.)

ideal gas law predicts a volume that is too small. Van der Waals suggested a small correction factor that accounts for the volume of the gas particles themselves:

Ideal behaviour $$V = \frac{nRT}{P}$$

Corrected for volume of gas particles $$V = \frac{nRT}{P} + nb \qquad [5.28]$$

The correction adds the quantity nb to the volume, where n is the number of moles and b is a constant that depends on the gas (see Table 5.5). We can rearrange the corrected equation as follows:

$$(V - nb) = \frac{nRT}{P} \qquad [5.29]$$

TABLE 5.5 Van der Waals Constants for Common Gases

Gas	a (L^2 bar mol^{-2})	b (L mol^{-1})
He	0.03475	0.0237
Ne	0.2135	0.0171
Ar	1.363	0.0322
Kr	2.349	0.0398
Xe	4.250	0.0511
H_2	0.2476	0.0266
N_2	1.408	0.0391
O_2	6.579	0.0562
Cl_2	6.579	0.0562
H_2O	5.536	0.0305
CH_4	2.283	0.0428
CO_2	3.640	0.0427
CCl_4	19.75	0.1383

The Effect of Intermolecular Forces

Intermolecular forces, covered in more detail in Chapter 11, are attractions between the atoms or molecules that compose any substance. These attractions are typically negligible in gases because the kinetic energy of the molecules is enough to overcome the intermolecular forces of attraction. Therefore, at high temperatures and low pressures, the weak attractions between molecules, compared with the relatively large kinetic energy between them, do not significantly affect their collisions. At lower temperatures, however, the collisions occur with less kinetic energy, and weak attractions can affect the molecular collisions and even the direction of their motion. We can understand this difference with an analogy to billiard balls. Imagine two billiard balls that are coated with a substance that makes them slightly sticky. If they collide when moving at high velocities, the stickiness will not have much of an effect—the balls bounce off one another as if the sticky substance was not even there. However, if the two billiard balls collide when moving very slowly (say, barely rolling), the sticky substance would have an effect—the billiard balls might even stick together and not bounce off one another.

The effect of these weak attractions between particles is a lower number of collisions with the surfaces of the container, thereby lowering the pressure compared to that of an ideal gas. We can see the effect of intermolecular forces by comparing the pressure of 1.0 mol of xenon gas to the pressure of 1.0 mol of an ideal gas as a function of temperature and at a fixed volume of 1.0 L, as shown in Figure 5.24 ▼. At high temperature, the pressure of the xenon gas is nearly identical to that of an ideal gas. But at lower temperatures, the pressure of xenon is *less than* that of an ideal gas. At the lower temperatures, the xenon atoms interact significantly with one another. These interactions reduce the number of collisions with the wall of the container, making the pressure less than that of an ideal gas where there are no forces of attraction between the gas molecules.

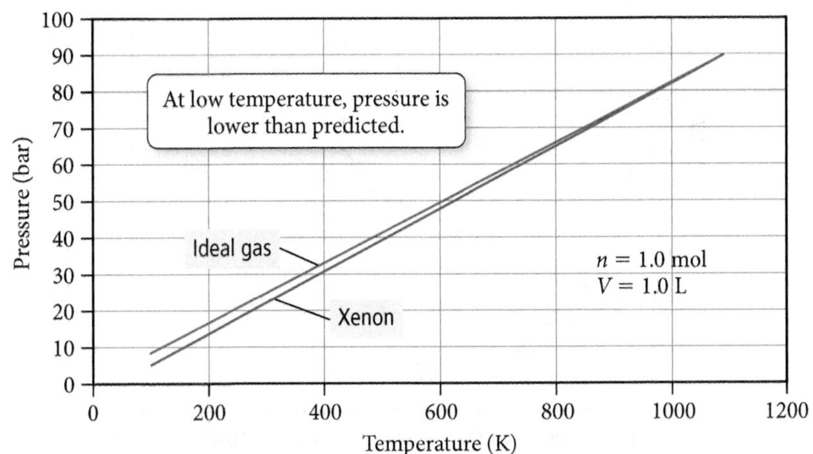

◀ **FIGURE 5.24 The Effect of Intermolecular Forces** At low temperatures, the pressure of xenon is less than an ideal gas exerts because interactions among xenon atoms reduce the number of collisions with the walls of the container.

From the graph for xenon shown in Figure 5.24, we can see that the ideal gas law predicts a pressure that is too large at low temperatures. Van der Waals suggested a small correction factor that accounts for the intermolecular forces between gas particles:

Ideal behaviour $$P = \frac{nRT}{V}$$

Corrected for intermolecular forces $$P = \frac{nRT}{V} - a\left(\frac{n}{V}\right)^2 \quad [5.30]$$

The correction subtracts the quantity $a(n/V)^2$ from the pressure, where n is the number of moles, V is the volume, and a is a constant that depends on the gas (see Table 5.5). Notice that the correction factor increases as n/V (the number of moles of particles per unit volume) increases because a greater concentration of particles makes it more likely that they will interact with one another. We can rearrange the corrected equation as follows:

$$P + a\left(\frac{n}{V}\right)^2 = \frac{nRT}{V} \quad [5.31]$$

Van der Waals Equation

We can now combine the effects of particle volume (Equation 5.29) and particle intermolecular forces (Equation 5.31) into one equation that describes nonideal gas behaviour:

$$\left[P + a\left(\frac{n}{V}\right)^2\right] \times [V - nb] = nRT \quad [5.32]$$

Correction for intermolecular forces (left term); Correction for particle volume ($[V - nb]$)

The above equation is called the **van der Waals equation** and can be used to calculate the properties of a gas under nonideal conditions. A nonideal gas—one that does not obey the assumptions that define an ideal gas—is called a **real gas**.

Real Gases

We can see the combined effects of particle volume and intermolecular forces by examining a plot of PV/RT versus P for 1 mol of a number of real gases (Figure 5.25 ▼). For an ideal gas, $PV/RT = n$, the number of moles of gas. Therefore, for 1 mol of an ideal gas, PV/RT is equal to 1, as shown in the plot. For real gases, PV/RT deviates from 1, but the deviations are not uniform. For example, carbon dioxide (CO_2) displays a large

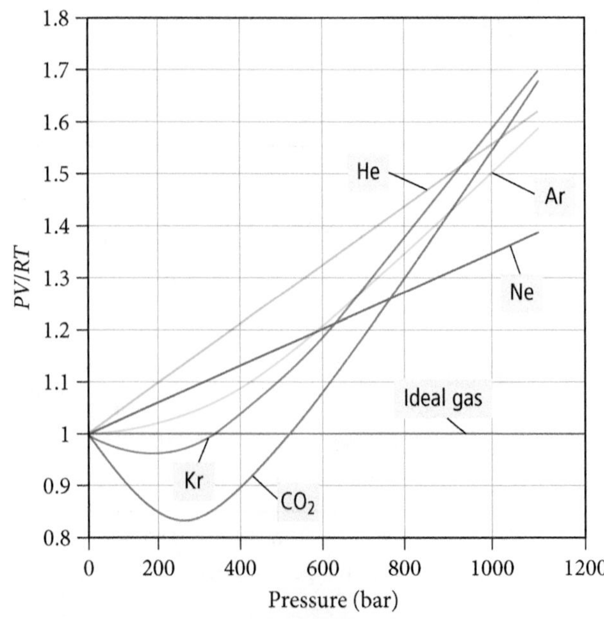

▶ **FIGURE 5.25 Real Versus Ideal Behaviour** For 1 mol of an ideal gas, PV/RT would be equal to 1. The combined effects of the volume of gas particles and the interactions among them cause each real gas to deviate from ideal behaviour in a slightly different way. These curves were calculated at a temperature of 273.15 K.

negative deviation from PV/RT because, for CO_2, the effect of intermolecular forces on lowering the pressure (relative to an ideal gas) is far greater than the effect of particle size on increasing the volume. Notice from Table 5.5 that CO_2 has a high value of a (relative to helium), the constant that corrects for intermolecular forces, but a moderate value of b, the constant that corrects for particle size. Therefore, PV/RT is lower than predicted from the ideal gas law for water.

By contrast, consider the behaviour of helium, which displays a positive deviation from the ideal behaviour. This is because helium has very weak intermolecular forces and their effect on lowering the pressure (relative to ideal gas) is small compared to the effect of particle size on increasing the volume. Therefore, PV/RT is greater than predicted from the ideal gas law for helium.

CONCEPTUAL CONNECTION 5.4

Real Gases

The graph below shows PV/RT for carbon dioxide at three different temperatures. Rank the curves in order of increasing temperature.

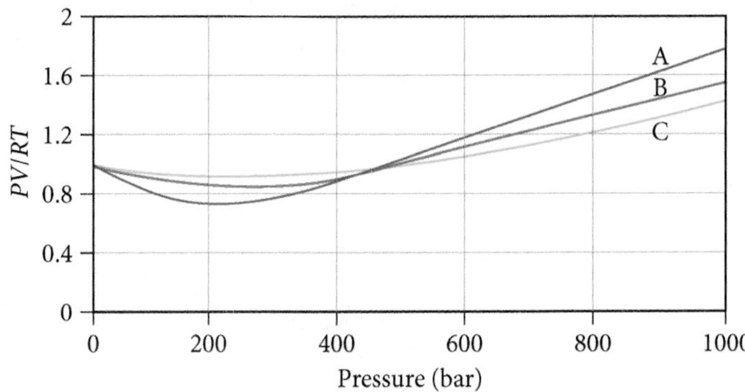

CHEMISTRY IN YOUR DAY Pressure in Outer Space

The Earth's atmospheric pressure drops from 1.01 bar at sea level to about 300 mbar at typical cruising altitudes of planes (~9 km, almost at the top of the troposphere), which is also about the altitude of the summit of Mount Everest. At high altitudes where atmospheric pressure is so low that humans cannot acclimatize to the low oxygen levels, their bodies begin to deteriorate. Most climbers must use oxygen tanks above 8 km.

At about 30 km above the Earth's surface, the middle of the stratosphere and the approximate altitude of the ozone layer (see Figure 5.26 ▼), the pressure drops to about 10 mbar. More than 99.9% of the Earth's atmosphere lies in the troposphere and stratosphere. You might wonder where the Earth's atmosphere ends and "outer space" begins. Scientists have also puzzled over this very question. In 2009, scientists at the University of Calgary designed an instrument that measures the direction and speed of ions (the Supra-Thermal Ion Imager), which allowed them to determine that space begins at 118 km above the Earth. There is a gradual transition over many tens of kilometres from the gentle winds of Earth's atmosphere to the quite violent flows of charged particles outside the atmosphere, and the midpoint of this transition is 118 km. The pressure at 118 km is about 0.001 mbar. At these small pressures, scientists usually talk about number densities rather than gas pressure. The number density is the number of molecules per unit volume—which is simply another unit of a concentration. We can solve the ideal gas law, as we did before, for concentration:

$$\frac{n}{V} = \frac{P}{RT}$$

Under standard conditions, the molar concentration (n/V) is 4.4×10^{-2} mol L^{-1}. To convert to number density, multiply by Avogadro's number to yield 2.7×10^{22} molecules L^{-1}. Scientists typically express number density in molecules cm^{-3}, so under standard conditions, the number density is 2.7×10^{19} molecules cm^{-3}; and at 118 km above sea level, where the temperature and pressure are about -10 °C and 0.001 mbar, respectively, the number density is 2.8×10^{13} molecules cm^{-3}.

In outer space, the number density can get very small. For example, there are regions of interstellar space (the space between star systems within a galaxy) with number densities as low as 1 atom dm^{-3}. Much of the matter is a plasma

(*continued*)

CHEMISTRY IN YOUR DAY (CONTINUED)

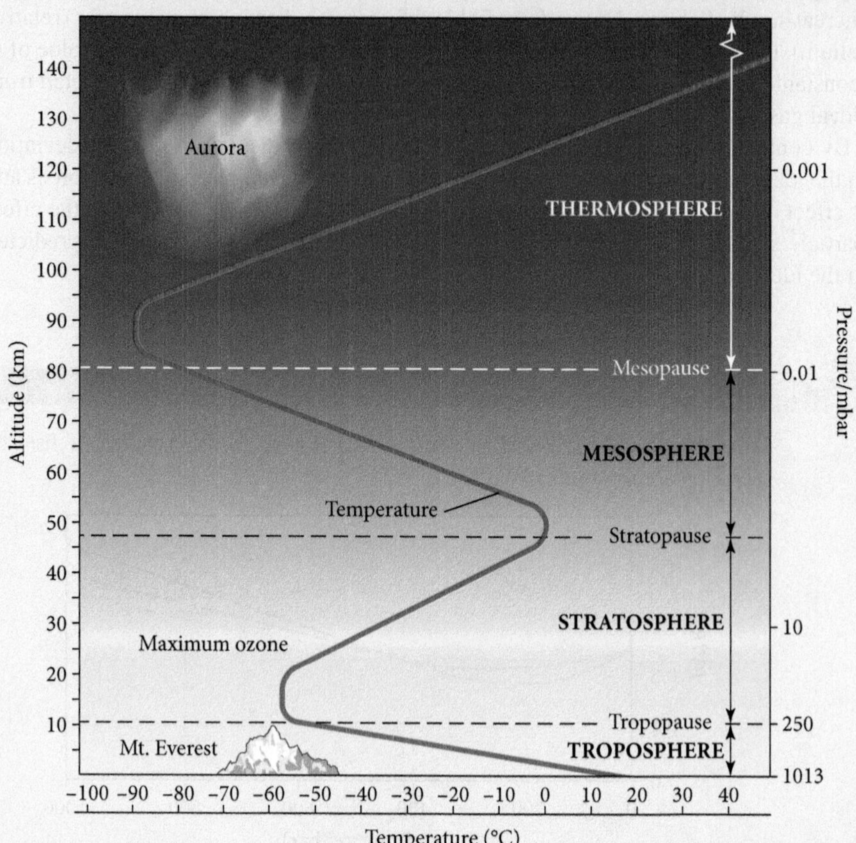

▶ **FIGURE 5.26 The Structure of the Atmosphere** Earth's atmosphere contains several different regions, including the troposphere and stratosphere.

composed of ionized hydrogen atoms. At these very low pressures, in one cubic centimetre of space, there is fewer than one collision every few hundred thousand years. In enormous molecular clouds where stars form (see Figure 5.27 ▶), the number densities are between 10^2 and 10^6 atoms and molecules cm^{-3}, and collisions occur between once every 100 years and once every hour. As chemists, we typically measure reaction rates in mol L^{-1} s^{-1}; that is, moles of product formed per litre of reaction mixture per second. At the very small molecular densities and small collision rates of interstellar space, one product molecule is formed between every hour and every 100 years for each cubic centimetre of space. That scientists have observed molecules in interstellar space is testament to both the age of our galaxy (and universe) as well as the vastness of it.

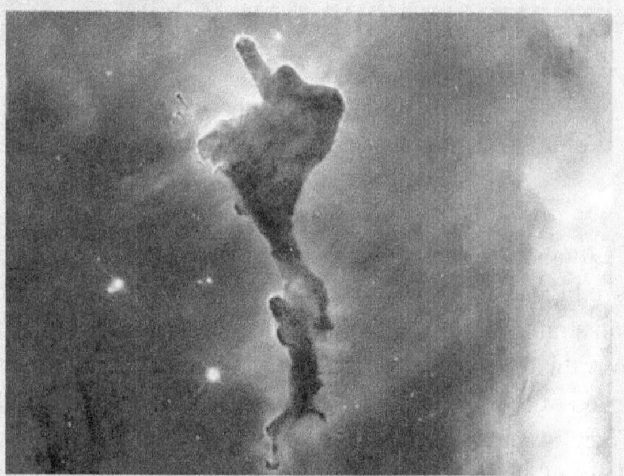

▲ **FIGURE 5.27 Molecular Cloud** This small molecular cloud, about two light years across, has broken off part of the Carina Nebula, a star-forming region about 8000 light years from Earth.

Imagine on a clear day, looking miles into the horizon and being able to see a distant mountain or hill, even though you are looking through miles of atmosphere containing more than 10^{19} molecules cm^{-3}. The small molecular cloud in Figure 5.27 has a number density of about 10^4 molecules cm^{-3}. That it is visible to telescopes at such a low number density is due to the fact that the image is about two light years across. Assuming that the composition of the cloud is molecular hydrogen, can you determine the mass that is contained in a molecular cloud that is two light years across, assuming a cubic molecular cloud? Can you determine the pressure in mbar of the molecular cloud, assuming a temperature of 30 K?

(Answer: $m = 4 \times 10^{17}$ kg, $P = 4 \times 10^{-14}$ mbar)

CHAPTER IN REVIEW

Key Terms

Section 5.1
pressure (149)

Section 5.2
millimetre of mercury (mmHg) (151)
barometer (151)
torr (151)
pascal (Pa) (151)
atmosphere (atm) (151)
standard pressure (152)
bar (152)
millibar (mbar) (152)
manometer (152)

Section 5.3
Boyle's law (154)
Charles's law (157)
Avogadro's law (159)

Section 5.4
ideal gas law (160)
ideal gas (160)
ideal gas constant (160)

Section 5.5
molar volume (162)
standard temperature and pressure (STP) (162)

Section 5.6
partial pressure (P_n) (166)
Dalton's law of partial pressures (166)
mole fraction (χ_a) (166)
vapour pressure (169)

Section 5.8
kinetic molecular theory (174)

Section 5.9
mean free path (180)
diffusion (180)
effusion (180)
Graham's law of effusion (181)

Section 5.10
van der Waals equation (184)
real gas (184)

Key Concepts

Pressure (5.1, 5.2)

Gas pressure is the force per unit area that results from gas particles colliding with the surfaces around them. Pressure is measured in a number of units, including bar, mbar, mmHg, torr, Pa, psi, and atm.

The Gas Laws (5.3)

The gas laws express relationships between pairs of variables when the other variables are held constant. Boyle's law states that the volume of a gas is inversely proportional to its pressure. Charles's law states that the volume of a gas is directly proportional to its temperature. Avogadro's law states that the volume of a gas is directly proportional to the amount (in moles).

The Ideal Gas Law and Its Applications (5.4, 5.5)

The ideal gas law, $PV = nRT$, gives the relationship among all four gas variables and contains the gas laws within it. We can use the ideal gas law to find one of the four variables given the other three. We can use it to calculate the molar volume of an ideal gas, which is 22.7 L at STP, and to calculate the density and molar mass of a gas.

Mixtures of Gases and Partial Pressures (5.6)

In a mixture of gases, each gas acts independently of the others so that any overall property of the mixture is the sum of the properties of the individual components. The pressure of any individual component is its partial pressure.

Gas Stoichiometry (5.7)

In reactions involving gaseous reactants and products, quantities are often reported in volumes at specified pressures and temperatures. We can convert these quantities to amounts (in moles) using the ideal gas law. Then we can use the stoichiometric coefficients from the balanced equation to determine the stoichiometric amounts of other reactants or products. The general form for these types of calculations is often as follows: volume A $\rightarrow$ amount A (in moles) $\rightarrow$ amount B (in moles) $\rightarrow$ quantity of B (in desired units). In cases where the reaction is carried out at STP, the molar volume at STP (22.7 L = 1 mol) can be used to convert between volume in litres and amount in moles.

Kinetic Molecular Theory and Its Applications (5.8, 5.9)

Kinetic molecular theory is a quantitative model for gases. The theory has three main assumptions: (1) the gas particles are negligibly small, (2) the average kinetic energy of a gas particle is proportional to the temperature in kelvin, and (3) the collision of one gas particle with another is completely elastic (the particles do not stick together). The gas laws all follow from the kinetic molecular theory.

We can also use the theory to derive the expression for the root mean square velocity of gas particles. This velocity is inversely proportional to the molar mass of the gas, and therefore—at a given temperature—smaller gas particles are (on average) moving more quickly than larger ones. The kinetic molecular theory also allows us to predict the mean free path of a gas particle (the distance it travels between collisions) and relative rates of diffusion or effusion.

Real Gases (5.10)

Real gases differ from ideal gases to the extent that they do not always fit the assumptions of kinetic molecular theory. These assumptions tend to break down at high pressures, where the volume is higher than predicted for an ideal gas because the particles are no longer negligibly small compared to the space between them. The assumptions also break down at low temperatures where the pressure is lower than predicted because the attraction between molecules combined with low kinetic energies causes partially inelastic collisions. The van der Waals equation predicts gas properties under nonideal conditions.

Key Equations and Relationships

Relationship Between Pressure (P), Force (F), and Area (A) (5.2)

$$P = \frac{F}{A}$$

Boyle's Law: Relationship Between Pressure (P) and Volume (V) (5.3)

$$V \propto \frac{1}{P}$$

$$P_1V_1 = P_2V_2$$

Charles's Law: Relationship Between Volume (V) and Temperature (T) (5.3)

$$V \propto T \quad (\text{in K})$$

$$\frac{V_1}{T_1} = \frac{V_2}{T_2}$$

Avogadro's Law: Relationship Between Volume (V) and Amount in Moles (n) (5.3)

$$V \propto n$$

$$\frac{V_1}{n_1} = \frac{V_2}{n_2}$$

Ideal Gas Law: Relationship Between Volume (V), Pressure (P), Temperature (T), and Amount (n) (5.4)

$$PV = nRT$$

Dalton's Law: Relationship Between Partial Pressures (P_n) in Mixture of Gases and Total Pressure (P_{total}) (5.6)

$$P_{total} = P_a + P_b + P_c + \cdots$$

$$P_a = \frac{n_aRT}{V} \qquad P_b = \frac{n_bRT}{V} \qquad P_c = \frac{n_cRT}{V}$$

Mole Fraction (χ_a) (5.6)

$$\chi_a = \frac{n_a}{n_{total}}$$

$$P_a = \chi_a P_{total}$$

Average Kinetic Energy (KE_{avg}) (5.8)

$$KE_{avg} = \frac{3}{2}RT$$

Relationship Between Root Mean Square Velocity (u_{rms}) and Temperature (T) (5.8)

$$u_{rms} = \sqrt{\frac{3RT}{M}}$$

Relationship of Effusion Rates of Two Different Gases (5.9)

$$\frac{\text{rate A}}{\text{rate B}} = \sqrt{\frac{M_B}{M_A}}$$

Van der Waals Equation: The Effects of Volume and Intermolecular Forces on Nonideal Gas Behaviour (5.10)

$$[P + a(n/V)^2] \times (V - nb) = nRT$$

Key Skills

Converting Between Pressure Units (5.2)

• Example 5.1 • For Practice 5.1 • For More Practice 5.1 • Exercises 25–30

Relating Volume and Pressure: Boyle's Law (5.3)

• Example 5.2 • For Practice 5.2 • Exercises 31, 32

Relating Volume and Temperature: Charles's Law (5.3)
• Example 5.3 • For Practice 5.3 • Exercises 33, 34

Relating Volume and Moles: Avogadro's Law (5.3)
• Example 5.4 • For Practice 5.4 • Exercises 35, 36

Determining *P*, *V*, *n*, or *T* using the Ideal Gas Law (5.4)
• Examples 5.5, 5.6 • For Practice 5.5, 5.6 • For More Practice 5.6 • Exercises 37–52

Relating the Density of a Gas to Its Molar Mass (5.5)
• Example 5.7 • For Practice 5.7 • For More Practice 5.7 • Exercises 53–56

Calculating the Molar Mass of a Gas with the Ideal Gas Law (5.5)
• Example 5.8 • For Practice 5.8 • Exercises 57–60

Calculating Total Pressure, Partial Pressures, and Mole Fractions of Gases in a Mixture (5.6)
• Examples 5.9, 5.10, 5.11 • For Practice 5.9, 5.10, 5.11 • Exercises 61–70

Relating the Amounts of Reactants and Products in Gaseous Reactions: Stoichiometry (5.7)
• Examples 5.12, 5.13 • For Practice 5.12, 5.13 • For More Practice 5.12 • Exercises 71–78

Calculating the Root Mean Square Velocity of a Gas (5.8)
• Example 5.14 • For Practice 5.14 • Exercises 81, 82

Calculating the Effusion Rate or the Ratio of Effusion Rates of Two Gases (5.9)
• Example 5.15 • For Practice 5.15 • Exercises 83–90

EXERCISES

Review Questions

1. What is pressure? What causes pressure?
2. Explain what happens when you inhale. What forces air into your lungs?
3. Explain what happens when you exhale. What forces air out of your lungs?
4. What are some common units of pressure? List these in order of smallest to largest unit.
5. What is a manometer? How does it measure the pressure of a sample of gas?
6. Summarize each of the gas laws (Boyle's law, Charles's law, and Avogadro's law). For each law, explain the relationship between the two variables and also state which variables must be kept constant.
7. Explain why scuba divers should never hold their breath as they ascend to the surface.
8. Why is it impossible to breathe air through an extra-long snorkel (greater than a couple of metres) while swimming underwater?
9. Explain why hot-air balloons float above the ground, and why the second storey of a two-storey home is often warmer than the ground storey.
10. What is the ideal gas law? Why is it useful?
11. Explain how the ideal gas law contains within it the three gas laws (show an example).
12. Define molar volume and give its value for a gas at STP.
13. How does the density of a gas depend on temperature? Pressure? How does it depend on the molar mass of the gas?
14. What is partial pressure? What is the relationship between the partial pressures of each gas in a sample and the total pressure of gas in the sample?
15. When a gas is collected over water, is the gas pure? Why or why not? How can the partial pressure of the collected gas be determined?
16. How does the vapour pressure of water change with temperature?
17. If a reaction occurs in the gas phase at STP, the mass of a product can be determined from the volumes of reactants. Explain.
18. What are the basic postulates of kinetic molecular theory? How does the concept of pressure follow from kinetic molecular theory?
19. Explain how Boyle's law, Charles's law, Avogadro's law, and Dalton's law all follow from kinetic molecular theory.
20. How is the kinetic energy of a gas related to temperature? How is the root mean square velocity of a gas related to its molar mass?
21. Describe how the molecules in a perfume bottle travel from the bottle to your nose. What is mean free path?
22. Explain the difference between diffusion and effusion. How is the effusion rate of a gas related to its molar mass?
23. Deviations from the ideal gas law are often observed at high pressure and low temperature. Explain why, in light of kinetic molecular theory.
24. If a gas were composed entirely of positive ions (this can actually be accomplished in an ion trapping mass spectrometer), and you could measure the pressure of this gas, would it be greater or less than that of an ideal gas? Explain.

Problems by Topic

Converting Between Pressure Units

25. The air pressure at Lake Louise, AB (elevation 1600 m) is about 875 mbar. Convert this pressure to:
a. atm **b.** psi **c.** Pa **d.** torr **e.** bar

26. The pressure on top of Mount Everest averages about 235 Torr. Convert this pressure to:
a. atm **b.** psi **c.** Pa **d.** mbar **e.** bar

27. The North American record for highest recorded barometric pressure is 1078 hPa set in 1989 in Northway, Alaska. Convert this pressure to:
a. atm **b.** torr **c.** kPa **d.** mbar **e.** bar

28. The world record for lowest pressure (at sea level) was 652.5 mmHg recorded inside Typhoon Tip on October 12, 1979, in the Western Pacific Ocean. Convert this pressure to:
a. torr **b.** kPa **c.** bar **d.** psi

29. Given a barometric pressure of 762.4 mmHg, calculate the pressure of each gas sample as indicated by the manometer.

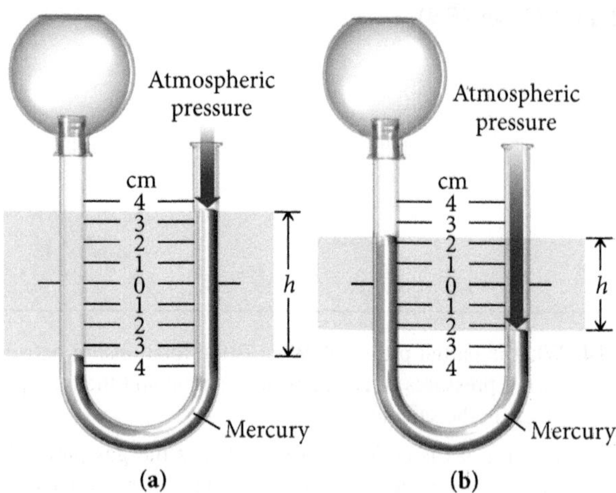

30. Given a barometric pressure of 751.5 mmHg, calculate the pressure of each gas sample as indicated by the manometer.

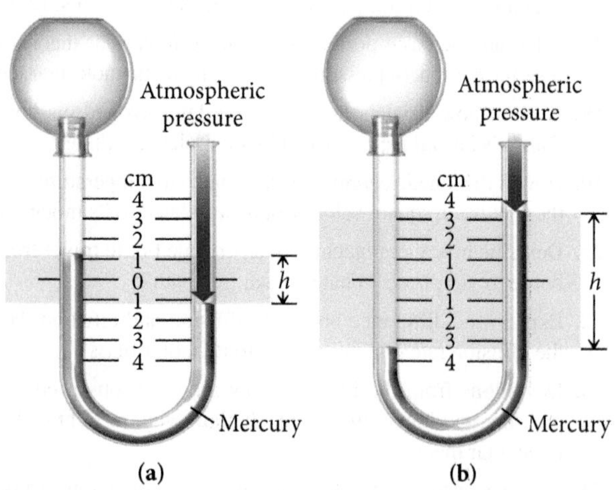

The Gas Laws

31. A sample of gas has an initial volume of 5.6 L at a pressure of 735 Torr. If the volume of the gas is increased to 9.4 L, what will the pressure be?

32. A sample of gas has an initial volume of 13.9 L at a pressure of 1.22 bar. If the sample is compressed to a volume of 10.3 L, what will its pressure be?

33. A 48.3 mL sample of gas in a cylinder is warmed from 22 °C to 87 °C. What is its volume at the final temperature?

34. A syringe containing 1.55 mL of oxygen gas is cooled from 95.3 °C to 0.0 °C. What is the final volume of oxygen gas?

35. A balloon contains 0.158 mol of gas and has a volume of 2.46 L. If an additional 0.113 mol of gas is added to the balloon (at the same temperature and pressure), what will its final volume be?

36. A cylinder with a movable piston contains 0.553 mol of gas and has a volume of 253 mL. What will its volume be if an additional 0.365 mol of gas is added to the cylinder? (Assume constant temperature and pressure.)

Ideal Gas Law

37. What is the volume occupied by 0.118 mol of helium gas at a pressure of 0.97 bar and a temperature of 305 K? Would the volume be different if the gas was argon (under the same conditions)?

38. What is the volume occupied by 12.5 g of argon gas at a pressure of 1.05 bar and a temperature of 322 K? Would the volume be different if the sample were 12.5 g of helium (under identical conditions)?

39. What is the pressure in a 10.0 L cylinder filled with 0.448 mol of nitrogen gas at a temperature of 315 K?

40. What is the pressure in a 15.0 L cylinder filled with 32.7 g of oxygen gas at a temperature of 302 K?

41. A cylinder contains 28.5 L of oxygen gas at a pressure of 1.8 bar and a temperature of 298 K. How much gas (in moles) is in the cylinder?

42. What is the temperature of 0.52 mol of gas at a pressure of 1.3 bar and a volume of 11.8 L?

43. An automobile tire has a maximum rating of 38.0 psi (gauge pressure). The tire is inflated (while cold) to a volume of 11.8 L and a gauge pressure of 36.0 psi at a temperature of 12.0 °C. Driving on a hot day, the tire warms to 65.0 °C and its volume expands to 12.2 L. Does the pressure in the tire exceed its maximum rating? (Note: the *gauge pressure* is the *difference* between the total pressure and atmospheric pressure. In this case, assume that atmospheric pressure is 14.7 psi.)

44. A weather balloon is inflated to a volume of 28.5 L at a pressure of 748 Torr and a temperature of 28.0 °C. The balloon rises in the atmosphere to an altitude of approximately 7600 m, where the pressure is 385 Torr and the temperature is –15.0 °C. Assuming the balloon can freely expand, calculate the volume of the balloon at this altitude.

45. A piece of dry ice (solid carbon dioxide) with a mass of 28.8 g sublimes (converts from solid to gas) into a large balloon. Assuming that all of the carbon dioxide ends up in the balloon, what is the volume of the balloon at a temperature of 22 °C and a pressure of 989 mbar?

46. A 1.0 L container of liquid nitrogen is kept in a closet measuring 1.0 m by 1.0 m by 2.0 m. Assuming that the container is completely full, that the temperature is 25.0 °C, and that the atmospheric pressure is 1.0 bar, calculate the percent (by volume) of air that is displaced if all of the liquid nitrogen evaporates. (Liquid nitrogen has a density of 0.807 g mL^{-1}.)

47. A wine-dispensing system uses argon canisters to pressurize and preserve wine in the bottle. An argon canister for the system has a volume of 55.0 mL and contains 26.0 g of argon. Assuming ideal gas behaviour, what is the pressure in the canister at 295 K? When the argon is released from the canister, it expands to fill the wine bottle. How many 750.0 mL wine bottles can be purged with the argon in the canister at a pressure of 1.20 bar and a temperature of 295 K?

48. Pressurized carbon dioxide inflators can be used to inflate a bicycle tire in the event of a flat. These inflators use metal cartridges that contain 16.0 g of carbon dioxide. At 298 K, to what pressure (in psi) can the carbon dioxide in the cartridge inflate a 3.45 L mountain bike tire? (Note: the *gauge pressure* is the *difference* between the total pressure and atmospheric pressure. In this case, assume that atmospheric pressure is 14.7 psi.)

49. Which gas sample representation has the greatest pressure? Explain. Assume that all the samples are at the same temperature.

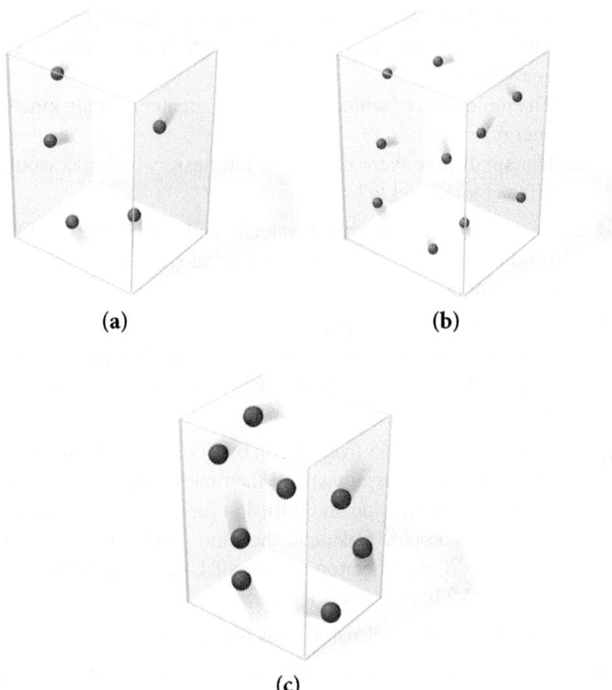

50. This picture represents a sample of gas at a pressure of 1 bar, a volume of 1 L, and a temperature of 25 °C. Draw a similar picture showing what would happen to the sample if the volume were reduced to 0.5 L and the temperature increased to 250 °C. What would happen to the pressure?

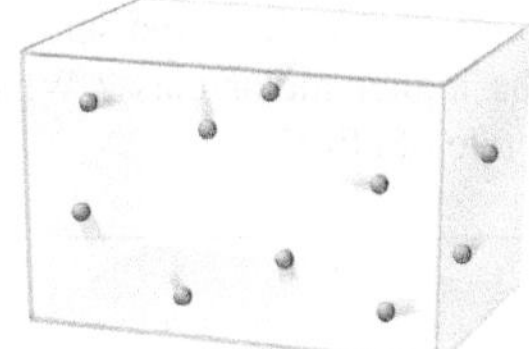

51. Aerosol cans carry clear warnings against incineration because of the high pressures that can develop upon heating. Suppose that a can contains a residual amount of gas at a pressure of 755 Torr and a temperature of 25 °C. What would the pressure be if the can were heated to 1155 °C?

52. A sample of nitrogen gas in a 1.75 L container exerts a pressure of 1.35 bar at 25 °C. What is the pressure if the volume of the container is maintained constant and the temperature is raised to 355 °C?

Molar Volume, Density, and Molar Mass of a Gas

53. Use the molar volume of a gas at STP to determine the volume (in L) occupied by 33.6 g of neon at STP.

54. Use the molar volume of a gas at STP to calculate the density (in g L^{-1}) of nitrogen gas at STP.

55. What is the density (in g L^{-1}) of hydrogen gas at 20.0 °C and a pressure of 1655 psi?

56. A sample of N_2O gas has a density of 2.85 g L^{-1} at 298 K. What is the pressure of the gas (in mbar)?

57. An experiment shows that a 248 mL gas sample has a mass of 0.433 g at a pressure of 745 Torr and a temperature of 28 °C. What is the molar mass of the gas?

58. An experiment shows that a 113 mL gas sample has a mass of 0.171 g at a pressure of 721 Torr and a temperature of 32 °C. What is the molar mass of the gas?

59. A sample of gas has a mass of 38.8 mg. Its volume is 224 mL at a temperature of 55 °C and a pressure of 1181 mbar. Find the molar mass of the gas.

60. A sample of gas has a mass of 0.555 g. Its volume is 117 mL at a temperature of 85 °C and a pressure of 753 Torr. Find the molar mass of the gas.

Partial Pressure

61. A gas mixture contains each of the following gases at the indicated partial pressures: N_2, 215 Torr; O_2, 102 Torr; and He, 117 Torr. What is the total pressure of the mixture? What mass of each gas is present in a 1.35 L sample of this mixture at 25.0 °C?

62. A gas mixture with a total pressure of 745 mbar contains each of the following gases at the indicated partial pressures: CO_2, 125 mbar; Ar, 214 mbar; and O_2, 187 mbar. The mixture also contains helium gas. What is the partial pressure of the helium gas? What mass of helium gas is present in a 12.0 L sample of this mixture at 273 K?

63. A 1.20 g sample of dry ice is added to a 755 mL flask containing nitrogen gas at a temperature of 25.0 °C and a pressure of 725 Torr. The dry ice sublimes (converts from solid to gas) and the mixture returns to 25.0 °C. What is the total pressure in the flask?

64. A 275 mL flask contains pure helium at a pressure of 752 Torr. A second flask with a volume of 475 mL contains pure argon at a pressure of 722 Torr. If the two flasks are connected through a stopcock and the stopcock is opened, what are the partial pressures of each gas and the total pressure?

65. A gas mixture contains 1.25 g N_2 and 0.85 g O_2 in a 1.55 L container at 18 °C. Calculate the mole fraction and partial pressure of each component in the gas mixture.

66. What is the mole fraction of oxygen gas in air (see Table 5.3)? What volume of air contains 10.0 g of oxygen gas at 273 K and 1.00 bar?

67. The hydrogen gas formed in a chemical reaction is collected over water at 30.0 °C at a total pressure of 732 Torr. What is the partial pressure of the hydrogen gas collected in this way? If the total volume of gas collected is 722 mL, what mass of hydrogen gas is collected?

68. The air in a bicycle tire is bubbled through water and collected at 25 °C. If the total volume of gas collected is 5.45 L at a temperature of 25 °C and a pressure of 745 Torr, how many moles of gas were in the bicycle tire?

69. The zinc within a copper-plated penny will dissolve in hydrochloric acid if the copper coating is filed down in several spots (so that the hydrochloric acid can get to the zinc). The reaction

between the acid and the zinc is $2\,H^+(aq) + Zn(s) \longrightarrow H_2(g) + Zn^{2+}(aq)$. When the zinc in a certain penny dissolves, the total volume of gas collected over water at 25 °C was 0.951 L at a total pressure of 0.990 bar. What mass of hydrogen gas was collected?

70. A heliox deep-sea diving mixture contains 2.0 g of oxygen to every 98.0 g of helium. What is the partial pressure of oxygen when this mixture is delivered at a total pressure of 8.5 bar?

Reaction Stoichiometry Involving Gases

71. Consider the chemical reaction:

$$C(s) + H_2O(g) \longrightarrow CO(g) + H_2(g)$$

How many litres of hydrogen gas are formed from the complete reaction of 15.7 g C? Assume that the hydrogen gas is collected at a pressure of 1.0 bar and a temperature of 355 K.

72. Consider the chemical reaction:

$$2\,H_2O(l) \longrightarrow 2\,H_2(g) + O_2(g)$$

What mass of H_2O is required to form 1.4 L of O_2 at a temperature of 315 K and a pressure of 0.957 bar?

73. CH_3OH can be synthesized by the reaction:

$$CO(g) + 2\,H_2(g) \longrightarrow CH_3OH(g)$$

What volume of H_2 gas (in L), at 748 Torr and 86 °C, is required to synthesize 25.8 g CH_3OH? How many litres of CO gas, measured under the same conditions, are required?

74. Oxygen gas reacts with powdered aluminum according to the reaction:

$$4\,Al(s) + 3\,O_2(g) \longrightarrow 2\,Al_2O_3(s)$$

What volume of O_2 gas (in L), measured at 782 Torr and 25 °C, completely reacts with 53.2 g Al?

75. Automobile air bags inflate following a serious impact. The impact triggers the chemical reaction:

$$2\,NaN_3(s) \longrightarrow 2\,Na(s) + 3\,N_2(g)$$

If an automobile air bag has a volume of 11.8 L, what mass of NaN_3 (in g) is required to fully inflate the air bag upon impact? Assume STP conditions.

76. Lithium reacts with nitrogen gas according to the reaction:

$$6\,Li(s) + N_2(g) \longrightarrow 2\,Li_3N(s)$$

What mass of lithium (in g) reacts completely with 58.5 mL of N_2 gas at STP?

77. Hydrogen gas (a potential future fuel) can be formed by the reaction of methane with water according to the equation:

$$CH_4(g) + H_2O(g) \longrightarrow CO(g) + 3\,H_2(g)$$

In a particular reaction, 25.5 L of methane gas (measured at a pressure of 732 Torr and a temperature of 25 °C) mixes with 22.8 L of water vapour (measured at a pressure of 702 Torr and a temperature of 125 °C). The reaction produces 26.2 L of hydrogen gas at STP. What is the percent yield of the reaction?

78. Ozone is depleted in the stratosphere by chlorine from CF_3Cl according to the set of equations:

$$CF_3Cl + \text{UV light} \longrightarrow CF_3 + Cl$$
$$Cl + O_3 \longrightarrow ClO + O_2$$
$$O_3 + \text{UV light} \longrightarrow O_2 + O$$
$$ClO + O \longrightarrow Cl + O_2$$

What total volume of ozone at a pressure of 25.0 Torr and a temperature of 225 K is destroyed when all of the chlorine from 15.0 g of CF_3Cl goes through ten cycles of the above reactions?

Kinetic Molecular Theory

79. Consider a 1.0 L sample of helium gas and a 1.0 L sample of argon gas, both at room temperature and atmospheric pressure.

a. Do the atoms in the helium sample have the same *average kinetic energy* as the atoms in the argon sample?
b. Do the atoms in the helium sample have the same *average velocity* as the atoms in the argon sample?
c. Do the argon atoms, because they are more massive, exert a greater pressure on the walls of the container? Explain.
d. Which gas sample would have the faster rate of effusion?

80. A flask at room temperature contains exactly equal amounts (in moles) of nitrogen and xenon.

a. Which of the two gases exerts the greater partial pressure?
b. The molecules or atoms of which gas have the greater average velocity?
c. The molecules of which gas have the greater average kinetic energy?
d. If a small hole were opened in the flask, which gas would effuse more quickly?

81. Calculate the root mean square velocity and kinetic energy of F_2, Cl_2, and Br_2 at 298 K. Rank these three halogens with respect to their rates of effusion.

82. Calculate the root mean square velocity and kinetic energy of CO, CO_2, and SO_3 at 298 K. Which gas has the greatest velocity? The greatest kinetic energy? The greatest effusion rate?

83. We obtain uranium-235 from U-238 by fluorinating the uranium to form UF_6 (which is a gas) and then taking advantage of the different rates of effusion and diffusion for compounds containing the two isotopes. Calculate the ratio of effusion rates for $^{238}UF_6$ and $^{235}UF_6$. The atomic mass of U-235 is 235.054 amu and that of U-238 is 238.051 amu.

84. Calculate the ratio of effusion rates for Ar and Kr.

85. A sample of neon effuses from a container in 76 seconds. The same amount of an unknown noble gas requires 155 seconds. Identify the gas.

86. A sample of N_2O effuses from a container in 42 seconds. How long would it take the same amount of gaseous I_2 to effuse from the same container under identical conditions?

87. The graph shows the distribution of molecular velocities for two different molecules (A and B) at the same temperature. Which molecule has the higher molar mass? Which molecule would have the higher rate of effusion?

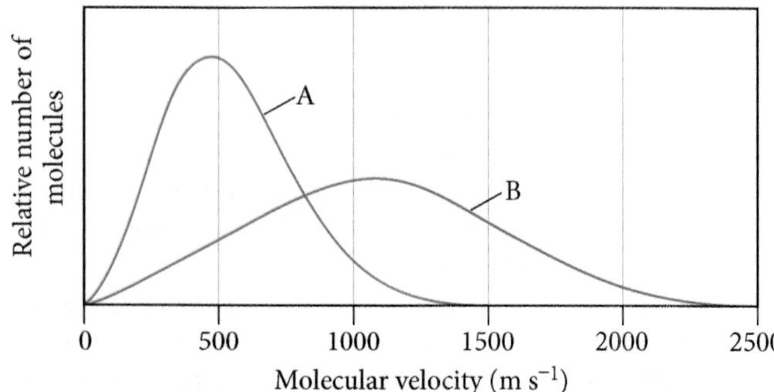

88. The graph shows the distribution of molecular velocities for the same molecule at two different temperatures (T_1 and T_2). Which temperature is greater? Explain.

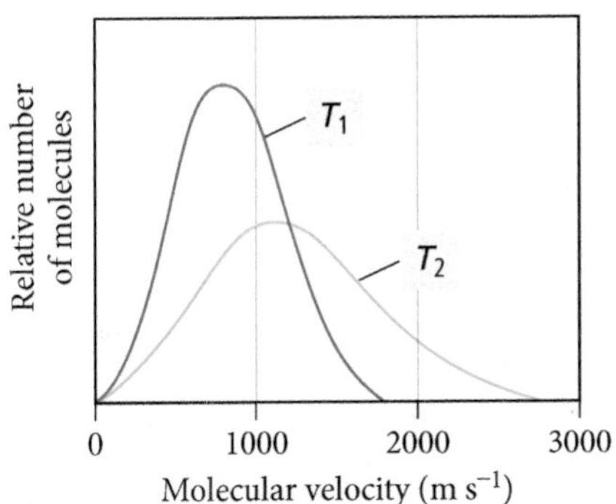

89. Oxygen (O_2) and chlorine (Cl_2) have molar masses of 32.00 and 70.90 g mol^{-1}, respectively. In one hour, 0.315 mol of chlorine effuses through a tiny hole. How much oxygen effuses through the same hole in the same amount of time?

90. The following is a plot of the distribution of molecular speeds for N_2 at 298 K. Sketch the distribution of molecular speeds for:

a. N_2 at 150 K **b.** N_2 at 500 K **c.** He at 298 K

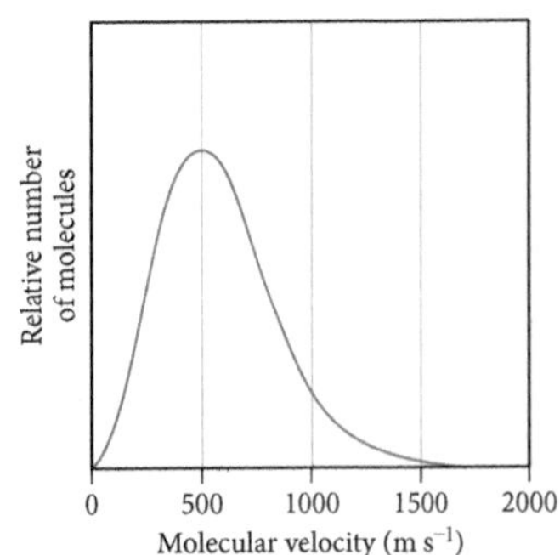

Real Gases

91. Which postulate of the kinetic molecular theory breaks down under conditions of high pressure? Explain.

92. Which postulate of the kinetic molecular theory breaks down under conditions of low temperature? Explain.

93. Use the van der Waals equation and the ideal gas equation to calculate the volume of 1.000 mol of neon at a pressure of 500.0 bar and a temperature of 355.0 K. Explain why the two values are different. (*Hint:* One way to solve the van der Waals equation for *V* is to use successive approximations. Use the ideal gas law to get a preliminary estimate for *V*.)

94. Use the van der Waals equation and the ideal gas equation to calculate the pressure exerted by 1.000 mol of Cl_2 in a volume of 5.000 L at a temperature of 273.0 K. Explain why the two values are different.

Cumulative Problems

95. Modern American pennies are composed of zinc coated with copper. A student determines the mass of a penny to be 2.482 g and then makes several scratches in the copper coating (to expose the underlying zinc). The student puts the scratched penny in hydrochloric acid, where the following reaction occurs between the zinc and the HCl (the copper remains undissolved):

$$Zn(s) + 2\,HCl(aq) \longrightarrow H_2(g) + ZnCl_2(aq)$$

The student collects the hydrogen produced over water at 25 °C. The collected gas occupies a volume of 0.899 L at a total pressure of 791 mmHg. Assuming that all the Zn in the penny dissolves, calculate the percent zinc by mass in the penny.

96. A 2.85 g sample of an unknown chlorofluorocarbon decomposes and produces 564 mL of chlorine gas at a pressure of 752 Torr and a temperature of 298 K. What is the percent chlorine (by mass) in the unknown chlorofluorocarbon?

97. The mass of an evacuated 255 mL flask is 143.187 g. The mass of the flask filled with 356 mbar of an unknown gas at 25 °C is 143.289 g. Calculate the molar mass of the unknown gas.

98. A 118 mL flask is evacuated and found to have a mass of 97.129 g. When the flask is filled with 1024 mbar of helium gas at 35 °C, it has a mass of 97.171 g. Was the helium gas pure?

99. A gaseous hydrogen and carbon–containing compound is decomposed and found to contain 82.66% carbon and 17.34% hydrogen by mass. The mass of 158 mL of the gas, measured at 556 Torr and 25 °C, was 0.275 g. What is the molecular formula of the compound?

100. A gaseous hydrogen and carbon–containing compound is decomposed and found to contain 85.63% C and 14.37% H by mass. The mass of 258 mL of the gas, measured at STP, was 0.646 g. What is the molecular formula of the compound?

101. Consider the reaction:

$$2\,NiO(s) \longrightarrow 2\,Ni(s) + O_2(g)$$

If O_2 is collected over water at 40.0 °C and a total pressure of 745 mmHg, what volume of gas will be collected for the complete reaction of 24.78 g of NiO?

102. Consider the reaction:

$$2\,Ag_2O(s) \longrightarrow 4\,Ag(s) + O_2(g)$$

If this reaction produces 15.8 g of Ag(*s*), what total volume of gas can be collected over water at a temperature of 25 °C and a total pressure of 752 Torr?

103. When hydrochloric acid is poured over potassium sulfide, 42.9 mL of hydrogen sulfide gas is produced at a pressure of 752 Torr and 25.8 °C. Write an equation for the gas-evolution reaction and determine how much potassium sulfide (in grams) reacted.

104. Consider the reaction:

$$2\,SO_2(g) + O_2(g) \longrightarrow 2\,SO_3(g)$$

a. If 285.5 mL of SO_2 reacts with 158.9 mL of O_2 (both measured at 315 K and 67 mbar), what is the limiting reactant and the theoretical yield of SO_3?

b. If 187.2 mL of SO_3 is collected (measured at 315 K and 67 mbar), what is the percent yield for the reaction?

105. Ammonium carbonate decomposes upon heating according to the balanced equation:

$$(NH_4)_2CO_3(s) \longrightarrow 2\,NH_3(g) + CO_2(g) + H_2O(g)$$

Calculate the total volume of gas produced at 22 °C and 1.02 bar by the complete decomposition of 11.83 g of ammonium carbonate.

106. Ammonium nitrate decomposes explosively upon heating according to the balanced equation:

$$2\ NH_4NO_3(s) \longrightarrow 2\ N_2(g) + O_2(g) + 4\ H_2O(g)$$

Calculate the total volume of gas (at 125 °C and 748 Torr) produced by the complete decomposition of 1.55 kg of ammonium nitrate.

107. Olympic cyclists fill their tires with helium to make them lighter. Calculate the mass of air in an air-filled tire and the mass of helium in a helium-filled tire. What is the mass difference between the two? Assume that the volume of the tire is 855 mL, that it is filled to a total pressure of 125 psi, and that the temperature is 25 °C. Also, assume an average molar mass for air of 28.8 g mol^{-1}.

108. In a common classroom demonstration, a balloon is filled with air and submerged in liquid nitrogen. The balloon contracts as the gases within the balloon cool. Suppose the balloon initially contains 2.95 L of air at a temperature of 25.0 °C and a pressure of 0.998 bar. Calculate the expected volume of the balloon upon cooling to −195.8 °C (the boiling point of liquid nitrogen). When the demonstration is carried out, the actual volume of the balloon decreases to 0.61 L. How does the observed volume of the balloon compare to your calculated value? Can you explain the difference?

109. Gaseous ammonia can be injected into the exhaust stream of a coal-burning power plant to reduce the pollutant NO to N_2 according to the reaction:

$$4\ NH_3(g) + 4\ NO(g) + O_2(g) \longrightarrow 4\ N_2(g) + 6\ H_2O(g)$$

Suppose that the exhaust stream of a power plant has a flow rate of 335 L s^{-1} at a temperature of 955 K, and that the exhaust contains a partial pressure of NO of 22.4 Torr. What should be the flow rate of ammonia delivered at 1.007 bar and 298 K into the stream to react completely with the NO if the ammonia is 65.2% pure (by volume)?

110. The emission of NO_2 by fossil fuel combustion can be prevented by injecting gaseous urea into the combustion mixture. The urea reduces NO (which oxidizes in air to form NO_2) according to the reaction:

$$2\ CO(NH_2)_2(g) + 4\ NO(g) + O_2(g) \longrightarrow 4\ N_2(g) + 2\ CO_2(g) + 4\ H_2O(g)$$

Suppose that the exhaust stream of an automobile has a flow rate of 2.55 L s^{-1} at 655 K and contains a partial pressure of NO of 16.5 mbar. What total mass of urea is necessary to react completely with the NO formed during 8.0 hours of driving?

111. An ordinary gasoline can measuring 30.0 cm by 20.0 cm by 15.0 cm is evacuated with a vacuum pump. Assuming that virtually all of the air can be removed from inside the can, and that atmospheric pressure is 1.01 bar, what is the total force (in Newtons) on the surface of the can? Do you think that the can could withstand the force?

112. Twenty-five millilitres of liquid nitrogen (density = 0.807 g mL^{-1}) is poured into a cylindrical container with a radius of 10.0 cm and a length of 20.0 cm. The container initially contains only air at a pressure of 1.01 bar and a temperature of 298 K. If the liquid nitrogen completely vaporizes, what is the total force (in N) on the interior of the container at 298 K?

113. A 160.0 L helium tank contains pure helium at a pressure of 1855 psi and a temperature of 298 K. How many 3.5 L helium balloons will the helium in the tank fill? (Assume an atmospheric pressure of 1.01 bar and a temperature of 298 K.)

114. An 11.5 mL sample of liquid butane (density = 0.573 g mL^{-1}) is evaporated in an otherwise empty container at a temperature of 28.5 °C. The pressure in the container following evaporation is 892 Torr. What is the volume of the container?

115. A scuba diver's expiration of air creates a spherical bubble with a radius of 2.5 cm at a depth of 30.0 m where the total pressure (including atmospheric pressure) is 4.00 atm. What is the radius of the bubble when it reaches the surface of the water? (Assume that the atmospheric pressure is 1.01 bar and the temperature is 298 K.)

116. A particular balloon can be stretched to a maximum surface area of 1257 cm^2. The balloon is filled with 3.0 L of helium gas at a pressure of 1.007 bar and a temperature of 298 K. The balloon is then allowed to rise in the atmosphere. If the atmospheric temperature is 273 K, at what pressure will the balloon burst? (Assume the balloon to be in the shape of a sphere.)

117. A catalytic converter in an automobile uses a palladium or platinum catalyst (a substance that increases the rate of a reaction without being consumed by the reaction) to convert carbon monoxide gas to carbon dioxide according to the reaction:

$$2\ CO(g) + O_2(g) \longrightarrow 2\ CO_2(g)$$

A chemist researching the effectiveness of a new catalyst combines a 2.0 : 1.0 mole ratio mixture of carbon monoxide and oxygen gas (respectively) over the catalyst in a 2.45 L flask at a total pressure of 993 mbar and a temperature of 552 °C. When the reaction is complete, the pressure in the flask has dropped to 552 Torr. What percentage of the carbon monoxide was converted to carbon dioxide?

118. A quantity of N_2 occupies a volume of 1.0 L at 300 K and 1.0 bar. The gas expands to a volume of 3.0 L as the result of a change in both temperature and pressure. Find the density of the gas at these new conditions.

119. A mixture of CO(*g*) and $O_2(g)$ in a 1.0 L container at 1.0×10^3 K has a total pressure of 2.2 bar. After some time, the total pressure falls to 1.9 bar as the result of the formation of CO_2. Find the mass (in grams) of CO_2 that forms.

120. The radius of a xenon atom is 1.3×10^{-8} cm. A 100 mL flask is filled with Xe at a pressure of 1.0 bar and a temperature of 273 K. Calculate the fraction of the volume that is occupied by Xe atoms. (*Hint:* The atoms are spheres.)

121. A natural gas storage tank is a cylinder with a movable top whose volume can change only as its height changes. Its radius remains fixed. The height of the cylinder is 22.6 m on a day when the temperature is 22 °C. The next day, the height of the cylinder increases to 23.8 m when the gas expands because of a heat wave. Find the temperature on the second day, assuming that the pressure and amount of gas in the storage tank have not changed.

122. A mixture of 8.0 g CH_4 and 8.0 g Xe is placed in a container and the total pressure is found to be 0.44 bar. Find the partial pressure of CH_4.

123. A steel container of volume 0.35 L can withstand pressures up to 88 bar before exploding. What mass of helium can be stored in this container at 299 K?

124. Binary compounds of alkali metals and hydrogen react with water to liberate $H_2(g)$. The H_2 from the reaction of a sample of NaH with an excess of water fills a volume of 0.490 L above the water. The temperature of the gas is 35 °C and the total pressure is 758 Torr. Determine the mass of H_2 liberated and the mass of NaH that reacted.

125. In a given diffusion apparatus, 15.0 mL of HBr gas diffused in 1.0 min. In the same apparatus and under the same conditions, 20.3 mL of an unknown gas diffused in 1.0 min. The unknown gas is a hydrocarbon. Find its molecular formula.

126. A sample of $N_2O_3(g)$ has a pressure of 0.017 bar. The temperature (in K) is then doubled and the N_2O_3 undergoes complete decomposition to $NO_2(g)$ and $NO(g)$. Find the total pressure of the mixture of gases assuming constant volume and no additional temperature change.

127. When 0.583 g of neon is added to an 800 cm^3 bulb containing a sample of argon, the total pressure of the gases is found to be 1.17 bar at a temperature of 295 K. Find the mass of the argon in the bulb.

128. A gas mixture composed of helium and argon has a density of 0.670 g L^{-1} at 1.01 bar and 298 K. What is the composition of the mixture by volume?

129. A gas mixture contains 75.2% nitrogen and 24.8% krypton by mass. What is the partial pressure of krypton in the mixture if the total pressure is 993 mbar?

130. Lightning McQueen's tires have a maximum rating of 270 kPa. When a tire is cold (12.0 °C), it is inflated to a volume of 11.8 L and a pressure of 250 kPa. While racing on a hot day, the tire warms to 65.0 °C and its volume expands slightly to 12.1 L. Does the pressure in the tire exceed the maximum rating?

131. **a.** A liquid hydrocarbon (containing only C and H) is analyzed by combustion analysis. 1.75 g of the substance was found to produce 3.17 L of CO_2 at 1.0 bar, 298 K, and 1.92 g H_2O (molar mass = 18.015 g mol^{-1}). What is the empirical formula of the compound?

b. To obtain the actual molecular formula, the liquid was analyzed by the Dumas method to determine the molar mass. The following data was obtained:

volume of flask = 247 mL temperature = 100 °C
mass of empty flask = 71.814 g pressure = 813 Torr
mass of flask and compound vapour = 72.523 g

What is the molar mass and the molecular formula of the compound?

Challenge Problems

132. A 10-litre container is filled with 0.10 mol of $H_2(g)$ and heated to 3000 K, causing some of the $H_2(g)$ to decompose into $H(g)$. The pressure is found to be 3.0 bar. Find the partial pressure of the $H(g)$ that forms from H_2 at this temperature. (Assume two significant figures for the temperature.)

133. A mixture of $NH_3(g)$ and $N_2H_4(g)$ is placed in a sealed container at 300 K. The total pressure is 0.50 bar. The container is heated to 1200 K at which time both substances decompose completely according to the equations $2\,NH_3(g) \longrightarrow N_2(g) + 3\,H_2(g)$; and $N_2H_4(g) \longrightarrow N_2(g) + 2\,H_2(g)$. After decomposition is complete, the total pressure at 1200 K is found to be 4.5 bar. Find the percent of $N_2H_4(g)$ in the original mixture. (Assume two significant figures for the temperature.)

134. A quantity of CO gas occupies a volume of 0.48 L at 1.0 atm and 275 K. The pressure of the gas is lowered and its temperature is raised until its volume is 1.3 L. Find the density of the CO under the new conditions.

135. When $CO_2(g)$ is put in a sealed container at 701 K and a pressure of 10.0 bar and is heated to 1401 K, the pressure rises to 22.5 bar. Some of the CO_2 decomposes to CO and O_2. Calculate the mole percent of CO_2 that decomposes.

136. The world burns approximately 9.0×10^{12} kg of fossil fuel per year. Use the combustion of octane as the representative reaction and determine the mass of carbon dioxide (the most significant greenhouse gas) formed per year. The current concentration of carbon dioxide in the atmosphere is approximately 387 ppm (by volume). By what percentage does the concentration increase each year due to fossil fuel combustion? Approximate the average properties of the entire atmosphere by assuming that the atmosphere extends from sea level to 15 km and that it has an average pressure of 381 Torr and average temperature of 275 K. Assume Earth is a perfect sphere with a radius of 6371 km.

137. The atmosphere slowly oxidizes hydrocarbons in a number of steps that eventually convert the hydrocarbon into carbon dioxide and water. The overall reaction of a number of such steps for methane gas is:

$$CH_4(g) + 5\,O_2(g) + 5\,NO(g) \longrightarrow CO_2(g) + H_2O(g) + 5\,NO_2(g) + 2\,OH(g)$$

Suppose that an atmospheric chemist combines 155 mL of methane at STP, 885 mL of oxygen at STP, and 55.5 mL of NO at STP in a 2.0 L flask. The flask is allowed to stand for several weeks at 275 K. If the reaction reaches 90.0% of completion (90.0% of the limiting reactant is consumed), what is the partial pressure of each of the reactants and products in the flask at 275 K? What is the total pressure in the flask?

138. Two identical balloons are filled to the same volume, one with air and one with helium. The next day, the volume of the air-filled balloon has decreased by 5.0%. By what percent has the volume of the helium-filled balloon decreased? (Assume that the air is four-fifths nitrogen and one-fifth oxygen, and that the temperature did not change.)

139. A mixture of $CH_4(g)$ and $C_2H_6(g)$ has a total pressure of 0.53 bar. Just enough $O_2(g)$ is added to the mixture to bring about its complete combustion to $CO_2(g)$ and $H_2O(g)$. The total pressure of the two product gases is found to be 2.2 bar. Assuming constant volume and temperature, find the mole fraction of CH_4 in the mixture.

140. A sample of $C_2H_2(g)$ has a pressure of 7.8 kPa. After some time, a portion of it reacts to form $C_6H_6(g)$. The total pressure of the mixture of gases is then 3.9 kPa. Assume that the volume and temperature do not change. What fraction of $C_2H_2(g)$ has undergone reaction?

Conceptual Problems

141. When the driver of an automobile applies the brakes, the passengers are pushed toward the front of the car, but a helium balloon inside the car is pushed toward the back of the car. Upon forward acceleration, the passengers are pushed toward the back of the car, but the helium balloon is pushed toward the front of the car. Why?

142. Suppose that a liquid is 10 times more dense than water. If you were to sip this liquid at sea level using a straw, what could be the maximum length of the straw?

143. This reaction occurs in a closed container:

$$A(g) + 2\,B(g) \longrightarrow 2\,C(g)$$

A reaction mixture initially contains 1.5 L of A and 2.0 L of B. Assuming that the volume and temperature of the reaction mixture remain constant, what is the percent change in pressure if the reaction goes to completion?

144. One mole of nitrogen and one mole of neon are combined in a closed container at STP. How big is the container?

145. Exactly equal amounts (in moles) of gas A and gas B are combined in a 1 L container at room temperature. Gas B has a molar mass that is twice that of gas A. Which statement is true for the mixture of gases and why?

a. The molecules of gas B have greater kinetic energy than those of gas A.
b. Gas B has a greater partial pressure than gas A.
c. The molecules of gas B have a greater average velocity than those of gas A.
d. Gas B makes a greater contribution to the average density of the mixture than gas A.

146. Which gas would you expect to deviate most from ideal behaviour under conditions of low temperature: F_2, Cl_2, or Br_2? Explain.

Thermochemistry

6

There is a fact, or if you wish, a law, governing all natural phenomena that are known to date. There is no exception to this law—it is exact as far as we know. The law is called the conservation of energy. It states that there is a certain quantity, which we call energy, that does not change in the manifold changes which nature undergoes.

—Richard P. Feynman (1918–1988)

WE HAVE SPENT THE FIRST FEW CHAPTERS of this book examining one of the two major components of our universe—matter. We now turn our attention to the other major component—energy. As far as we know, matter and energy—which can be interchanged but not destroyed—make up the physical universe. Unlike matter, energy is not something we can touch or hold in our hand, but we experience it in many ways. The warmth of sunlight, the feel of wind on our faces, and the force that presses us back when a car accelerates are all manifestations of energy and its interconversions. And, of course, energy is critical to society and to the world. The standard of living around the globe is strongly correlated with the access to and use of energy resources. Most of those resources, as we shall see, are chemical ones, and we can understand their advantages as well as their drawbacks in terms of chemistry.

6.1 Chemical Hand Warmers

Winters can be long in Canada, and many people enjoy participating in outdoor winter activities such as hockey, skating, skiing, snowboarding, ice fishing, winter hiking, and just playing in the snow. Most of us, however, don't like being cold, especially in our hands and feet. One solution is the chemical hand warmer, a small

(a)

(b)

(c)

▲ **FIGURE 6.1** **(a)** A curling stone (also known as a "rock") sliding down the ice has kinetic energy due to its motion. **(b)** When this stone collides with another, it does work and transfers energy to the second stone. **(c)** The second stone now has kinetic energy as it slides away from the collision.

pouch that comes sealed in a plastic package. The package, which is opened and placed in gloves or boots, slowly warms up and keeps your hands or feet warm all day long.

Warming your hands with chemical hand warmers involves many of the principles of **thermochemistry**, the study of the relationships between chemistry and energy. When you open the package that contains the hand warmer, the contents are exposed to air, and an *exothermic reaction* occurs. The most commonly available hand warmers use the oxidation of iron as the exothermic reaction:

$$4\,Fe(s) + 3\,O_2(g) \longrightarrow 2\,Fe_2O_3(s)$$

The most important product of this reaction is not a substance—it is *heat*. We'll define heat more carefully later, but in general, heat is what you feel when you touch something that is warmer than your hand (in this case, the hot hand warmer). Although some of the heat is lost through the minute openings in your gloves, most of it is transferred to your hands and to the pocket of air surrounding your hands, resulting in a temperature increase. The magnitude of the temperature increase depends on the size of the hand warmer and the size of your glove (as well as some other details). But in general, the size of the temperature increase is proportional to the amount of heat released by the reaction.

In this chapter, we examine the relationship between chemical reactions and energy. Specifically, we look at how chemical reactions can *exchange* energy with their surroundings and how to quantify the magnitude of those exchanges. These kinds of calculations are important, not only for chemical hand warmers, but also to many other important processes such as the heating of homes and the production of energy for our society.

6.2 The Nature of Energy: Key Definitions

Energy is the capacity to do work. In Section 1.2, we defined **work (w)** as the result of a force acting through a distance. When you push a box across the floor, you have done work. Consider another example of work: a curling stone sliding down the ice and colliding with a second stationary curling stone (Figure 6.1 ◀). The curling stone sliding down the ice has *energy* due to its motion. When it collides with another stone, it does *work* to get the second stone moving, resulting in the *transfer* of energy from one stone to the other. The second curling stone absorbs the energy and begins to move.

As we just saw with chemical hand warmers, energy can also be transferred through **heat (q)**, the flow of energy caused by a temperature difference. For example, if you hold a cup of coffee in your hand, energy is transferred in the form of heat from the hot coffee to your cooler hand. Think of *energy* as something that an object or set of objects possesses. Think of *heat* and *work* as ways that objects or sets of objects *exchange* energy.

The energy contained in the curling stone moving down the ice is an example of **kinetic energy**, the energy associated with the *motion* of an object. The energy contained in a hot cup of coffee is **thermal energy**, the energy associated with the *temperature* of an object. Thermal energy is actually a type of kinetic energy because it arises from the motions of atoms or molecules within a substance. The water at the top of a waterfall contains **potential energy**, which is the energy associated with the *position* or *composition* of an object. The potential energy of the water at the top of the waterfall is a result of its position in Earth's gravitational field, as shown in Figure 6.2 ▶. Gravity pulls the water down from the top of the falls, releasing the potential energy. The amount of potential energy is related to how high the falls are (or the object is). The greater the height, the more energy is stored as potential energy. Another example of potential energy is the energy contained in a compressed spring. When you compress a spring, you push against the forces that tend to maintain the spring's uncompressed shape, storing energy as potential energy. **Chemical energy**, the energy associated with the relative positions of electrons and nuclei in atoms and molecules, is also a form of potential energy. Some chemical compounds, such as the methane in natural gas or the iron in a chemical hand warmer, are like a compressed spring—they contain potential energy, and a chemical reaction can release that potential energy.

▲ **FIGURE 6.2 Energy Transformation: Potential and Kinetic Energy I** The water at the top of Niagara Falls has gravitational potential energy. When the water drops over the falls, the potential energy is transformed into kinetic energy—the energy of motion.

The **law of conservation of energy** states that *energy can be neither created nor destroyed.* However, energy can be transferred from one object to another, and it can assume different forms. For example, as the water from the top of the waterfall drops toward the river below, as shown in Figure 6.2, some of its potential energy is converted to kinetic energy due to its velocity. This kinetic energy can be used to turn a turbine in a power plant to transform it to electricity, another form of energy. If you release a compressed spring, the potential energy becomes kinetic energy as the spring expands outward, as shown in Figure 6.3 ▼. When iron reacts with oxygen within a chemical hand warmer, the chemical energy of the iron and oxygen becomes thermal energy that increases the temperature of your hand and glove.

A good way to understand and track energy changes is to define the **system** under investigation. For example, the system may be a beaker of chemicals in the lab, or it may be the iron reacting in a hand warmer. The system's **surroundings** are everything with which the system can exchange energy. If we define the chemicals in a beaker as the system, the surroundings may include the water that the chemicals are dissolved in (for aqueous solutions), the beaker itself, the lab bench on which the beaker sits, the air in the room, and so on. For the iron in the hand warmer, the surroundings include your hand, your glove, the air in the glove, and even the air outside of the glove.

Einstein showed that it is mass–energy that is conserved; one can be converted into the other. This equivalence becomes important in nuclear reactions, discussed in Chapter 19. In ordinary chemical reactions, however, the interconversion of mass and energy is not a significant factor, and we can regard mass and energy as independently conserved.

In an energy exchange, energy is transferred between the system and the surroundings, as shown in Figure 6.4 ▼. If the system loses energy, the surroundings gain the same exact amount of energy, and vice versa. When the iron within the chemical hand warmer reacts, the system loses energy to the surroundings, producing the desired temperature increase within your gloves.

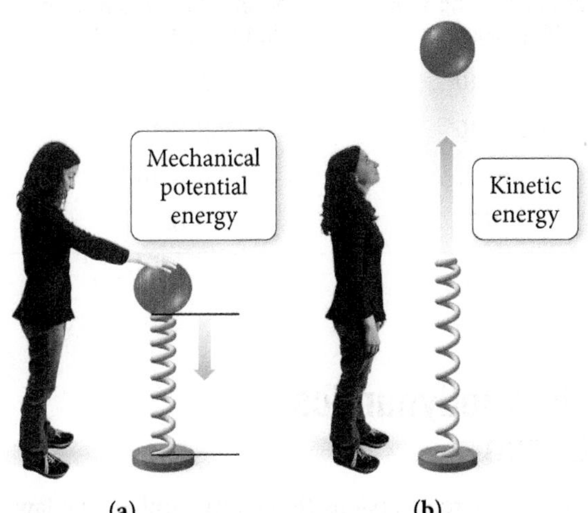

▲ **FIGURE 6.3 Energy Transformation: Potential and Kinetic Energy II** (a) A compressed spring has potential energy. (b) When the spring is released, the potential energy is transformed into kinetic energy.

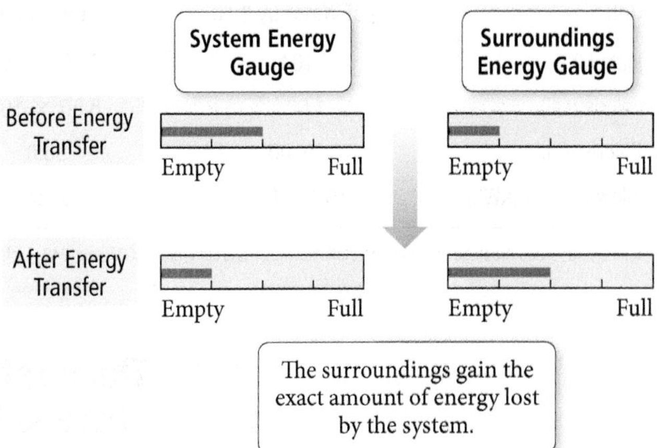

▲ **FIGURE 6.4 Energy Transfer** If a system and surroundings had energy gauges (which would measure energy content in the way a fuel gauge measures fuel content), an energy transfer in which the system transfers energy to the surroundings would result in a decrease in the energy content of the system and an increase in the energy content of the surroundings. The total amount of energy, however, must be conserved.

3.6 × 10^5 J or 0.10 kWh used in 1 hour

▲ A watt (W) is 1 J s^{-1}, so a 100W light bulb uses 100 J every second or 3.6 × 10^5 J every hour.

The "calorie" referred to on all nutritional labels (regardless of the capitalization) is always the capital *C* Calorie.

Units of Energy

We can deduce the units of energy from the definition of kinetic energy. An object of mass *m*, moving at velocity *v*, has a kinetic energy KE given by:

$$\text{KE} = \frac{1}{2}mv^2 \qquad [6.1]$$

(m: kg; v: m s^{-1})

The SI unit of mass is kg and the unit of velocity is m s^{-1}. The SI unit of energy is therefore kg m^2 s^{-2}, defined as the **joule (J)**, named after the English scientist James Joule (1818–1889).

$$1 \text{ kg m}^2 \text{s}^{-2} = 1 \text{ J}$$

One joule is a relatively small amount of energy—for example, a 100-watt light bulb uses 3.6 × 10^5 J in 1 hour. Therefore, we often use the kilojoule (kJ) in our energy discussions and calculations $(1 \text{ kJ} = 1000 \text{ J})$. A second commonly used unit of energy is the **calorie (cal)**, originally defined as the amount of energy required to raise the temperature of 1 g of water by 1 °C. The current definition is 1 cal = 4.184 J (exact); a calorie is a larger unit than a joule. A related energy unit is the nutritional, or uppercase "C" **Calorie (Cal)**, equivalent to 1000 lowercase "c" calories. The Calorie is the same as a kilocalorie (kcal): 1 Cal = 1 kcal = 1000 cal. Electricity bills typically are based on another, even larger, energy unit, the **kilowatt-hour (kWh)**: 1 kWh = 3.60 × 10^6 J. Table 6.1 shows various energy units and their conversion factors. Table 6.2 shows the amount of energy required for various processes.

TABLE 6.1 Energy Conversion Factors*

1 calorie (cal)	= 4.184 joules (J)
1 Calorie (Cal) or kilocalorie (kcal)	= 1000 cal = 4184 J
1 kilowatt-hour (kWh)	= 3.60 × 10^6 J

*All conversion factors in this table are exact.

TABLE 6.2 Energy Uses in Various Units

Unit	Amount Required to Raise Temperature of 1 g of Water by 1 °C	Amount Required to Light 100-W Bulb for 1 Hour	Amount Used by Human Body in Running 1 km (Approximate)	Average Amount of Household Electricity Used in 1 Day per Canadian
joule (J)	4.184	3.60 × 10^5	2.6 × 10^5	4.3 × 10^7
calorie (cal)	1.00	8.60 × 10^4	6.2 × 10^4	1.0 × 10^7
Calorie (Cal)	0.00100	86.0	62	1.0 × 10^4
kilowatt-hour (kWh)	1.16 × 10^{-6}	0.100	0.072	12

Source: http://oee.nrcan.gc.ca/corporate/statistics/neud/dpa/data_e/sheu07/sheu_048_1.cfm

6.3 The First Law of Thermodynamics: There Is No Free Lunch

We call the general study of energy and its interconversions **thermodynamics**. The laws of thermodynamics are among the most fundamental in all of science, governing virtually every process that involves change. The **first law of thermodynamics** is the law of energy conservation, which we can state as follows:

The total energy of the universe is constant.

In other words, since energy is neither created nor destroyed, and since the universe does not exchange energy with anything else, its energy content does not change. The first law

CHEMISTRY IN YOUR DAY Perpetual Motion Machines

In 1812, a man named Charles Redheffer appeared in Philadelphia with a machine that he claimed could run forever without any energy input—a perpetual motion machine. He set up the machine on the edge of town and charged admission to view it. He also appealed to the city for money to build a larger version of the machine. When city commissioners came out to inspect the machine, Redheffer did his best to keep them from viewing it too closely. Nonetheless, one of the commissioners noticed something suspicious: the gears that supposedly ran to an external driveshaft were cut in the wrong direction. The driveshaft that the machine was allegedly powering was instead powering the machine. Redheffer left Philadelphia exposed as a fraud.

In 2008, a man by the name of Richard Willis, from Magnacoaster Motor Company Inc. in Kitchener, Ontario, appeared on *Dragon's Den*, a popular CBC show where inventors and budding entrepreneurs pitch their ideas for a company to a panel of "dragons" (venture capitalists) in hopes that they will invest in their company. Magnacoaster claims to have invented a device in which power is injected between a set of magnets and emerges at a "higher voltage, a higher amperage, and a higher frequency of the power." In other words, it claims to have built a perpetual motion machine of the first kind that produces more energy than is put into the machine. If it works, this would provide unlimited free energy; however, the technology violates the law of conservation of energy. It is not surprising that there have been no independent verifications of the technology, and according to reports, no units have been delivered to customers as of 2015.

has many implications: the most important one being that, with energy, you do not get something for nothing. The best you can do with energy is break even—there is no free lunch. According to the first law, a device that would continually produce energy with no energy input, sometimes known as a *perpetual motion machine*, cannot exist. Occasionally, the media speculate or report on the discovery of a machine that can produce energy without the need for energy input. For example, you may have heard someone propose an electric car that recharges itself while driving, or a new motor that can create additional usable electricity as well as the electricity to power itself. Although some hybrid (electric and gasoline–powered) vehicles can capture energy from braking and use that energy to recharge their batteries, they could never run indefinitely without additional fuel. As for the motor that powers an external load as well as itself—no such thing exists. Our society has a continual need for energy, and as our current energy resources dwindle, new energy sources will be required. And those sources, whatever they may be, will follow the first law of thermodynamics—energy must be conserved.

Internal Energy

The **internal energy** (*U*) of a system is the sum of the kinetic and potential energies of all of the particles that compose the system. According to the first law of thermodynamics, the change in the internal energy of the system (ΔU) is the sum of the heat transferred (q) and the work done (w):

$$\Delta U = q + w \qquad [6.2]$$

In the above equation, and from this point forward, we follow the standard convention that ΔU (with no subscript) refers to the internal energy change of the system. As shown in Table 6.3, energy entering the system through heat or work carries a positive

TABLE 6.3 Sign Conventions for q, w, and ΔU

q (heat)	+ system *gains* thermal energy	− system *loses* thermal energy
w (work)	+ work done *on* the system	− work done *by* the system
ΔU (change in internal energy)	+ energy flows *into* the system	− energy flows *out* of the system

▶ **FIGURE 6.5 Combustion of Hydrogen** The internal energy change when burning hydrogen depends only on the states of the initial and final products, not how the hydrogen is burned. The product of the reaction, H_2O, initially is formed as a hot gas in a and b, but will eventually cool and condense to the liquid state.

sign and energy leaving the system through heat or work carries a negative sign. The system is like a chequing account—withdrawals are negative and deposits are positive. Internal energy is a **state function**, which means that its value depends only on the state of the system, not on how the system arrived at that state. The state of a chemical system is specified by parameters such as temperature, pressure, concentration, and physical state (solid, liquid, or gas).

Let's consider three different ways of reacting hydrogen and oxygen, depicted in Figure 6.5 ▲. The first way is exemplified in the historical disaster where the Hindenburg burst into flames. The H_2 from the blimp reacted with the O_2 in the atmosphere to produce water. Almost all of the internal energy for this reaction was released as heat. In engines of the space shuttle, H_2 is also reacted with O_2, but in a significantly more controlled manner than the explosion of the Hindenburg. In the space shuttle engine some of the energy is released as heat but a significant amount is used to do work, propelling the space shuttle. The third example is what happens in a fuel cell, for example, in a toy car. The H_2 and O_2 gases do not actually mix in a fuel cell. Rather electrons from H_2 in one side of the fuel cell are transferred to the O_2 side of the fuel cell where H^+, O_2, and electrons combine to form water. In the fuel cell, very little heat is produced and almost all of the energy from the H_2 and O_2 reaction is used to do work, moving the vehicle. In all three of these examples, the chemical reaction is the same:

$$H_2(g) + \frac{1}{2}O_2(g) \longrightarrow H_2O(l)$$

As long as the states (temperature and pressure) of the reactants and products are the same before and after the reaction, respectively, the change in the internal energy is the same. The change in internal energy is the difference in internal energy between the final and initial states:

$$\Delta_r U = U_{\text{products}} - U_{\text{reactants}} \qquad [6.3]$$

For the reaction of gaseous H_2 and O_2 to produce liquid water, the change in internal energy is –293 kJ mol^{-1}, no matter which path is taken. The three different paths taken can have very different amounts of heat and work associated with them, but the sum of the heat and the work $(q + w)$, the internal energy change, is the same for all three paths.

We can portray the energy changes that occur during a reaction with an energy diagram, which compares the internal energy of the reactants and products:

For a chemical reaction, the difference in internal energy is usually written as $\Delta_r U$ and has units of kJ mol^{-1}, indicating the change in internal energy per mol of reaction as written. ΔU is an internal energy change for a process in units of kJ. In this text we use $\Delta_r U$ to indicate a molar internal energy change. Note that for any process the sign of ΔU and $\Delta_r U$ will be the same.

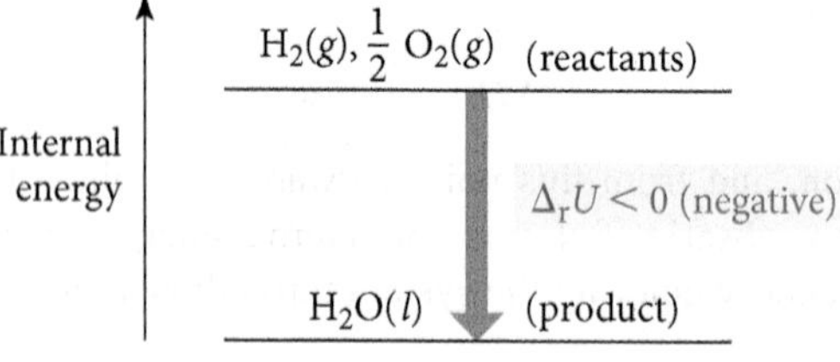

The vertical axis of the diagram is internal *energy*, which increases as you move up on the diagram. For this reaction, the reactants are *higher* on the diagram than the product because they have higher internal energy. As the reaction occurs, the reactants become products, which have lower internal energy. Therefore, energy is given off by the reaction and $\Delta_r U$ (that is, $U_{\text{products}} - U_{\text{reactants}}$) is *negative*.

Where does the energy lost by the reactants (as they transform to products) go? If we define the thermodynamic *system* as the reactants and products of the reaction, then energy flows *out of the system* and *into the surroundings*.

System → Surroundings
Energy flow
$\Delta U_{sys} < 0$ (negative) $\Delta U_{surr} > 0$ (positive)

According to the first law, energy must be conserved. Therefore, the amount of energy lost by the system must exactly equal the amount gained by the surroundings:

$$\Delta U_{sys} = -\Delta U_{surr} \qquad [6.4]$$

In the engine of the space shuttle, where H_2 and O_2 are reacted together to form water, both quantities q and w are negative as heat is released from the engine to air around the engine (part of the surroundings) and work is done on the space shuttle, moving it through the sky.

Now, suppose the reaction is reversed:

$$H_2O(l) \longrightarrow H_2(g) + \frac{1}{2}O_2(g)$$

The energy level diagram is nearly identical with one important difference: $H_2O(l)$ is now the reactant and $H_2(g)$ and $O_2(g)$ are the products. Instead of decreasing in energy as the reaction occurs, the system increases in energy.

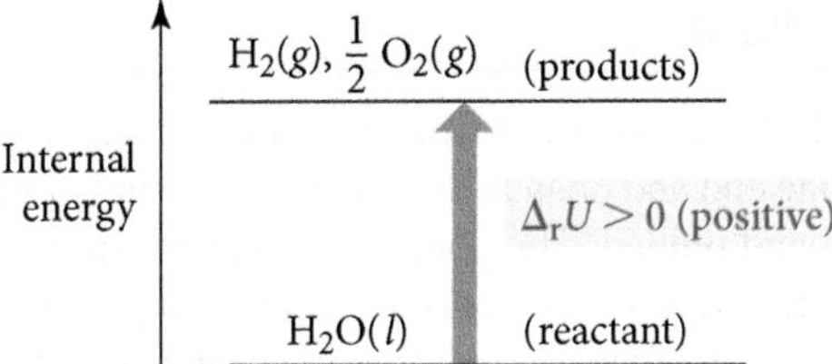

In this reversed reaction, $\Delta_r U$ is *positive* and energy flows *into the system* and *out of the surroundings*.

System ← Surroundings
Energy flow
$\Delta U_{sys} > 0$ (positive) $\Delta U_{surr} < 0$ (negative)

Summarizing Energy Flow:

- If the reactants have a higher internal energy than the products, ΔU_{sys} is negative and energy flows out of the system into the surroundings.
- If the reactants have a lower internal energy than the products, ΔU_{sys} is positive and energy flows into the system from the surroundings.

Again, recall the chequing account analogy. Energy flowing *out of* the system is like a withdrawal and therefore carries a negative sign. Energy flowing *into* the system is like a deposit and carries a positive sign.

CONCEPTUAL CONNECTION 6.1

System and Surroundings

Consider the fictitious internal energy gauges for a chemical system and its surroundings:

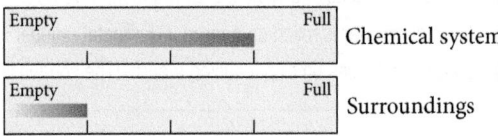

Empty Full — Chemical system

Empty Full — Surroundings

Which of the following best represents the energy gauges for the same system and surroundings following an energy exchange in which ΔU_{sys} is negative?

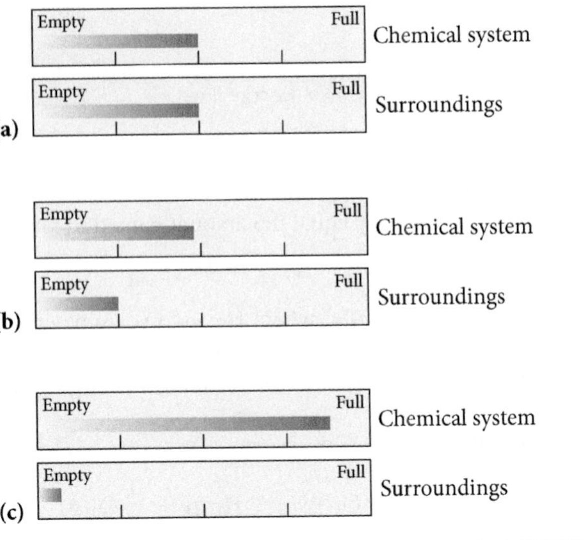

EXAMPLE 6.1 INTERNAL ENERGY, HEAT, AND WORK

The firing of a potato cannon provides a good example of the heat and work associated with a chemical reaction. In a potato cannon, a potato is stuffed into a long cylinder that is capped on one end and open at the other. Some kind of fuel is introduced under the potato at the capped end—usually through a small hole—and ignited. The potato then shoots out of the cannon, sometimes flying hundreds of metres, and the cannon emits heat to the surroundings. If the burning of the fuel performs 855 J of work on the potato and produces 1422 J of heat, what is ΔU for the burning of the fuel? (Note: A potato cannon can be dangerous and should not be constructed without proper training and experience.)

SOLUTION

To solve the problem, substitute the values of q and w into the equation for ΔU. Since work is done by the system on the surroundings, w is negative. Similarly, since heat is released by the system to the surroundings, q is also negative.	$\Delta U = q + w$ $= -1422 \text{ J} - 855 \text{ J}$ $= -2277 \text{ J}$

FOR PRACTICE 6.1

A cylinder and piston assembly (defined as the system) is warmed by an external flame. The contents of the cylinder expand, doing work on the surroundings by pushing the piston outward against the external pressure. If the system absorbs 559 J of heat and does 488 J of work during the expansion, what is the value of ΔU?

CONCEPTUAL CONNECTION 6.2
Heat and Work

Identify each of the following energy exchanges as heat or work and determine whether the sign of heat or work (relative to the system) is positive or negative.

(a) An ice cube melts and cools the surrounding beverage. (The ice cube is the system.)

(b) A metal cylinder is rolled up a ramp. (The metal cylinder is the system.)

(c) Steam condenses on skin, causing a burn. (The condensing steam is the system.)

6.4 Quantifying Heat and Work

In the previous section, we calculated ΔU based on given values of q and w. We now turn to calculating q (heat) and w (work) based on changes in temperature and volume.

Heat

As we saw in Section 6.2, *heat* is the exchange of thermal energy between a system and its surroundings caused by a temperature difference. Notice the distinction between heat and temperature. Temperature is a *measure* of the thermal energy within a sample of matter. Heat is the *transfer* of thermal energy. Thermal energy always flows from matter at higher temperatures to matter at lower temperatures. For example, a hot cup of coffee transfers thermal energy—as heat—to the lower-temperature surroundings as it cools down. Imagine a world where the cooler surroundings actually got colder as they transferred thermal energy to the hot coffee, which got hotter. Such a world exists only in our imagination (or in the minds of science fiction writers), because the spontaneous transfer of heat from a hotter object to a colder one is a fundamental principle of our universe—no exception has ever been observed. The thermal energy in the molecules that compose the hot coffee distributes itself to the molecules in the surroundings. The heat transfer from the coffee to the surroundings stops when the two reach the same temperature, a condition called **thermal equilibrium**. At thermal equilibrium, there is no additional net transfer of heat.

The reason for this one-way transfer is related to the second law of thermodynamics, which we discuss in Chapter 17.

Temperature Changes and Heat Capacity When a system absorbs heat (q), its temperature changes by ΔT:

Heat (q) → System
ΔT

Experiments show that the heat absorbed by a system and its corresponding temperature change are directly proportional: $q \propto \Delta T$. The constant of proportionality between q and ΔT is the system's *heat capacity* (C), a measure of the system's ability to absorb thermal energy without undergoing a large change in temperature:

$$q = C \times \Delta T \qquad [6.5]$$

Heat capacity

Notice that the higher the heat capacity of a system, the smaller the change in temperature for a given amount of absorbed heat. We define the **heat capacity (C)** of a system as the quantity of heat required to change its temperature by 1 °C. As we can see by solving Equation 6.5 for heat capacity, the units of heat capacity are those of heat (typically J) divided by those of temperature (typically °C):

$$C = \frac{q}{\Delta T} = \frac{\text{J}}{°\text{C}} \text{ (or J °C}^{-1}\text{)}$$

In order to understand two important concepts related to heat capacity, consider putting a steel saucepan on a kitchen flame. The saucepan's temperature rises rapidly as it absorbs heat from the flame. However, if you add some water to the saucepan, the temperature rises more slowly. Why? The first reason is that when you add the water, the same amount of heat must now warm more matter, so the temperature rises more slowly. In other words, heat capacity is an extensive property—*it depends on the amount of matter being heated* (see Section 1.3). The second (and more fundamental) reason is that *water is more resistant to temperature change than steel*—water has an intrinsically higher capacity to absorb heat without undergoing a large temperature change. The measure of the *intrinsic capacity* of a substance to absorb heat is its **specific heat capacity (C_s)**, the amount of heat required to raise the temperature of *1 gram* of the substance by 1 °C. The units of specific heat capacity (also called *specific heat*) are J g^{-1} °C^{-1}. Table 6.4 shows the values of the specific heat capacity for several substances. Heat capacity is sometimes reported as **molar heat capacity**, the amount of

TABLE 6.4 Specific Heat Capacities of Some Common Substances

Substance	Specific Heat Capacity, C_s(J g^{-1} °C^{-1})*
Elements	
Lead	0.128
Gold	0.128
Silver	0.235
Copper	0.385
Iron	0.449
Aluminum	0.903
Compounds	
Ethanol	2.440
Water	4.184
Materials	
Glass (Pyrex)	0.75
Granite	0.79
Sand	0.84

*At 298 K

▲ The high heat capacity of the water surrounding Victoria, BC, results in relatively cooler summer and warmer winter temperatures.

heat required to raise the temperature of *1 mol* of a substance by 1 °C. The units of molar heat capacity are J mol^{-1} °C^{-1}. You can see from these definitions that *specific* heat capacity and *molar* heat capacity are intensive properties—they depend on the *kind* of substance being heated, not on the amount.

Notice that water has the highest specific heat capacity of all the substances in Table 6.4—changing the temperature of water requires that a lot of heat be exchanged. If you have ever experienced the drop in temperature that occurs when travelling from an inland region to the coast during the summer, you have experienced the effects of water's high specific heat capacity.

For example, the average daily high temperature for July in Kamloops, BC, (an inland city) is 28.3 °C, whereas the average daily high temperature for July in Victoria, BC, (a coastal city) is only 21.9 °C, even though the amount of sunlight falling on these two cities is similar. In January, the average daily temperature in Kamloops is −4.2 °C and that in Victoria is 3.8 °C! In fact, the record low in Kamloops is −37.2 °C, but in Victoria the record low is −15.6 °C.

Why the large temperature difference? Victoria is at the south end of Vancouver Island, surrounded by water of the Strait of Juan de Fuca connected to the Pacific Ocean. Water, with its high heat capacity, absorbs much of the sun's heat without undergoing a large increase in temperature, which keeps Victoria cooler in the summer. Similarly, in the winter, when there is not much sunlight, the water releases heat without decreasing its temperature much and keeps Victoria warm. Kamloops is about 400 km inland. The land surrounding Kamloops, with its low heat capacity, will undergo larger fluctuations in temperature and cannot moderate the climate as the water does for Victoria. It is quite typical of coastal regions that their climates are moderate compared to inland regions.

The specific heat capacity of a substance can be used to quantify the relationship between the amount of heat added to a given amount of the substance and the corresponding temperature increase. The equation that relates these quantities is:

$$q = m \times C_s \times \Delta T \qquad [6.6]$$

Heat (J) → q; Mass (g) → m; Specific heat capacity (J g^{-1} °C^{-1}) → C_s; Temperature change (°C) → ΔT

where q is the amount of heat in J, m is the mass of the substance in g, C_s is the specific heat capacity in J g^{-1} °C^{-1}, and ΔT is the temperature change in °C. The following example demonstrates the use of this equation.

ΔT in °C is equal to ΔT in K, but not equal to ΔT in °F (Section 1.3).

EXAMPLE 6.2 **TEMPERATURE CHANGES AND HEAT CAPACITY**

Suppose you find a 2006 commemorative pure silver (99.99%) dollar in the snow. How much heat is absorbed by the silver dollar as it warms from the temperature of the snow, which is −10.0 °C, to the temperature of your body, which is 37.0 °C? The silver dollar has a mass of 25.175 g.

SORT You are given the mass of silver as well as its initial and final temperatures. You are asked to find the heat required for the given temperature change.	**GIVEN:** m = 25.175 g silver T_i = −10.0 °C T_f = 37.0 °C **FIND:** q

STRATEGIZE The equation $q = mC_s\Delta T$ gives the relationship between the amount of heat (q) and the temperature change (ΔT).	**CONCEPTUAL PLAN** $C_s, m, \Delta T \rightarrow q$ $q = m\,C_s\,\Delta T$ **RELATIONSHIPS USED** $q = mC_s\Delta T$ (Equation 6.6) $C_s = 0.235\ \text{J g}^{-1}\,°\text{C}^{-1}$ (Table 6.4)
SOLVE Gather the necessary quantities for the equation in the correct units and substitute them into the equation to compute q.	**SOLUTION** $\Delta T = T_f - T_i = 37.0°\text{C} - (-10.0\,°\text{C}) = 47.0°\text{C}$ $q = mC_s\Delta T$ $= 25.175\ \text{g} \times 0.235\ \text{J g}^{-1}\,°\text{C}^{-1} \times 47.0\ °\text{C}$ $= 278\ \text{J}$

CHECK The unit J is correct for heat. The sign of q is *positive*, as it should be since the silver dollar *absorbed* heat from the surroundings.

FOR PRACTICE 6.2

To determine whether a shiny gold-coloured rock is actually gold, a chemistry student decides to measure its heat capacity. She first weighs the rock and finds it has a mass of 4.7 g. She then finds that upon absorption of 57.2 J of heat, the temperature of the rock rises from 25 °C to 57 °C. Find the specific heat capacity of the substance composing the rock and determine whether the value is consistent with the rock being pure gold.

FOR MORE PRACTICE 6.2

A 55.0 g aluminum block initially at 27.5 °C absorbs 725 J of heat. What is the final temperature of the aluminum?

CONCEPTUAL CONNECTION 6.3

The Heat Capacity of Water

Suppose you are cold-weather camping and decide to heat some objects to bring into your sleeping bag for added warmth. You place a large water jug and a rock of equal mass near the fire. Over time, both the rock and the water jug warm to about 50 °C. If you could bring only one into your sleeping bag, which one should you choose to keep you the warmest? Why?

Thermal Energy Transfer As we noted earlier, when two substances of different temperatures are combined, thermal energy flows as heat from the hotter substance to the cooler one. If we assume that the two substances are thermally isolated from everything else, then the heat lost by one substance exactly equals the heat gained by the other (according to the law of energy conservation). If we define one substance as the system and the other as the surroundings, we can quantify the heat exchange as follows:

$$q_{sys} = -q_{surr}$$

Suppose a block of metal initially at 55 °C is submerged into water initially at 25 °C. Thermal energy transfers as heat from the metal to the water:

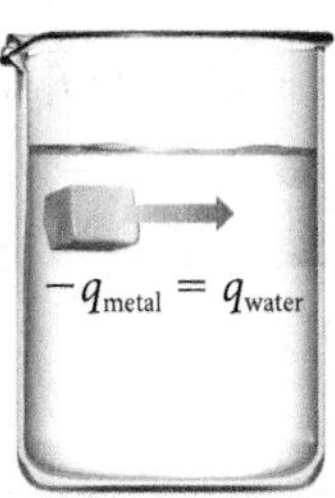

The metal will get colder and the water will get warmer until the two substances reach the same temperature (thermal equilibrium). The exact temperature change that occurs depends on the masses of the metal and the water and on their specific heat capacities. Since $q = m \times C_s \times \Delta T$, we can arrive at the following relationship:

$$-q_{\text{metal}} = q_{\text{water}}$$

$$-m_{\text{metal}} \times C_{\text{s, metal}} \times \Delta T_{\text{metal}} = m_{\text{water}} \times C_{\text{s, water}} \times \Delta T_{\text{water}}$$

The following example shows how to work with thermal energy transfer.

EXAMPLE 6.3 THERMAL ENERGY TRANSFER

A 32.5 g cube of aluminum initially at 45.8 °C is submerged into 105.3 g of water at 15.4 °C. What is the final temperature of both substances at thermal equilibrium? (Assume that the aluminum and the water are thermally isolated from everything else.)

SORT You are given the masses of aluminum and water and their initial temperatures. You are asked to find the final temperature.

GIVEN: $m_{\text{Al}} = 32.5 \text{ g}, m_{H_2O} = 105.3 \text{ g}$

$T_{\text{i, Al}} = 45.8 \text{ °C}, T_{\text{i, } H_2O} = 15.4 \text{ °C}$

FIND: T_f

STRATEGIZE The heat lost by the aluminum (q_{Al}) equals the heat gained by the water (q_{H_2O}).

CONCEPTUAL PLAN

$-q_{\text{Al}} = q_{H_2O}$

Use the relationship beween q and ΔT and the given variables to find a relationship between ΔT_{Al} and ΔT_{H_2O}.

$m_{\text{Al}}, C_{\text{s, Al}}, m_{H_2O}\ C_{\text{s, } H_2O} \rightarrow \Delta T_{\text{Al}} = \text{constant} \times \Delta T_{H_2O}$

$-m_{\text{Al}} \times C_{\text{s, Al}} \times \Delta T_{\text{Al}} = m_{H_2O} \times C_{\text{s, } H_2O} \times \Delta T_{H_2O}$

Use the relationship between ΔT_{Al} and ΔT_{H_2O} (that you just found in the previous step) along with the initial temperatures of the aluminum and the water to determine the final temperature. Note that at thermal equilibrium, the final temperature of the aluminum and the water is the same; that is, $T_{\text{f, Al}} = T_{\text{f, } H_2O} = T_f$.

$T_{\text{i, Al}}, T_{\text{i, } H_2O} \rightarrow T_f$

$\Delta T_{\text{Al}} = \text{constant} \times \Delta T_{H_2O}$

RELATIONSHIPS USED

$C_{\text{s, } H_2O} = 4.184 \text{ J g}^{-1} \text{ °C}^{-1}$, $C_{\text{s, Al}} = 0.903 \text{ J g}^{-1} \text{ °C}^{-1}$ (Table 6.4)

$q = m \times C_s \times \Delta T$ (Equation 6.6)

SOLVE Write the equation for the relationship between the heat lost by the aluminum (q_{Al}) and the heat gained by the water (q_{H_2O}) and substitute $q = m \times C_s \times \Delta T$ for each substance.

SOLUTION

$-q_{\text{Al}} = q_{H_2O}$

$-(m_{\text{Al}} \times C_{\text{s, Al}} \times \Delta T_{\text{Al}}) = m_{H_2O} \times C_{\text{s, } H_2O} \times \Delta T_{H_2O}$

Substitute the values of m (given) and C_s (from Table 6.4) for each substance and solve the equation for ΔT_{Al}. (Alternatively, you can solve the equation for ΔT_{H_2O}.)

$$-\left(32.5 \cancel{\text{g}} \times \frac{0.903 \text{ J}}{\cancel{\text{g}} \cdot \cancel{\text{°C}}} \cdot \Delta T_{\text{Al}}\right) = 105.3 \cancel{\text{g}} \times \frac{4.184 \text{ J}}{\cancel{\text{g}} \cdot \cancel{\text{°C}}} \cdot \Delta T_{H_2O}$$

$-29.3\underline{4}7 \cdot \Delta T_{\text{Al}} = 44\underline{0}.57 \cdot \Delta T_{H_2O}$

$\Delta T_{\text{Al}} = -15.\underline{0}12 \cdot \Delta T_{H_2O}$

Substitute the initial temperatures of aluminum and water into the relationship from the previous step and solve the expression for the final temperature (T_f). Remember that the final temperature for both substances will be the same.

$T_f - T_{\text{i, Al}} = -15.\underline{0}12(T_f - T_{\text{i, } H_2O})$

$T_f = -15.\underline{0}12 \cdot T_f + 15.\underline{0}12 \cdot T_{\text{i, } H_2O} + T_{\text{i, Al}}$

$16.\underline{0}12 \cdot T_f = 15.\underline{0}12 \cdot T_{\text{i, } H_2O} + T_{\text{i, Al}}$

$$T_f = \frac{15.\underline{0}12 \cdot T_{\text{i, } H_2O} + T_{\text{i, Al}}}{16.\underline{0}12} = \frac{15.\underline{0}12 \cdot 15.4 \text{ °C} + 45.8 \text{ °C}}{16.\underline{0}12}$$

$= 17.3 \text{ °C}$

CHECK The unit °C is correct. The final temperature of the mixture is closer to the initial temperature of the *water* than the *aluminum*. This makes sense for two reasons: (1) water has a higher specific heat capacity than aluminum, and (2) there is more water than aluminum. Since the aluminum loses the same amount of heat that is gained by the water, the greater mass and specific heat capacity of the water make the temperature change in the water *less than* the temperature change in the aluminum.

FOR PRACTICE 6.3

A block of copper of unknown mass has an initial temperature of 65.4 °C. The copper is immersed in a beaker containing 95.7 g of water at 22.7 °C. When the two substances reach thermal equilibrium, the final temperature is 24.2 °C. What is the mass of the copper block?

CONCEPTUAL CONNECTION 6.4

Thermal Energy Transfer

Substances A and B, initially at different temperatures, come in contact with each other and reach thermal equilibrium. The mass of substance A is twice the mass of substance B. The specific heat capacity of substance B is twice the specific heat capacity of substance A. Which statement is true about the final temperature of the two substances once thermal equilibrium is reached?

(a) The final temperature will be closer to the initial temperature of substance A than substance B.

(b) The final temperature will be closer to the initial temperature of substance B than substance A.

(c) The final temperature will be exactly midway between the initial temperatures of substances A and B.

Work: Pressure–Volume Work

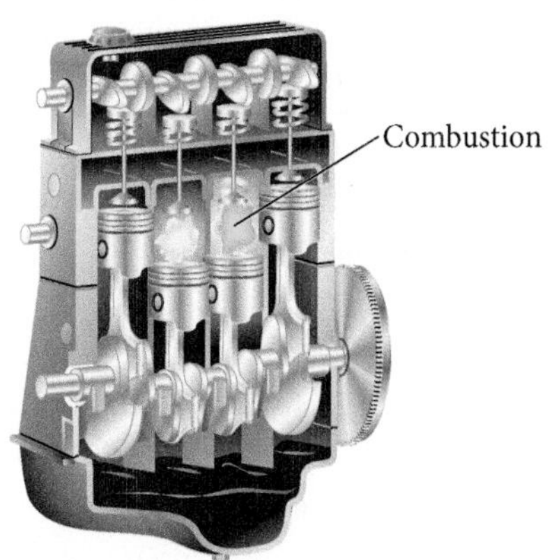

▲ The combustion of gasoline within an engine's cylinders does pressure–volume work that ultimately results in the motion of the car.

Energy transfer between a system and its surroundings can occur via heat (q) or work (w). We just saw how to calculate the *heat* associated with an observed *temperature* change. We now turn to calculating the *work* associated with an observed *volume* change. Although a chemical reaction can do several different types of work, for now we will limit our discussion to **pressure–volume work**. We have already defined work as a force acting through a distance. Pressure–volume work occurs when the force is caused by a volume change against an external pressure. For example, pressure–volume work occurs in the cylinder of an automobile engine. The combustion of gasoline causes gases within the cylinders to expand, pushing the piston outward and ultimately moving the wheels of the car.

We derive an equation for the value of the pressure–volume work from the definition of work as a force (F) acting through a distance (d):

$$w = -F \times d \qquad [6.7]$$

The force in this equation must be a constant force.

The negative sign appears because the force of the expanding gases is acting in the opposite direction of the piston's motion. When the volume of a cylinder increases (Figure 6.6 ▼), it pushes against an external force. That external force is pressure (P), which is defined as force (F) divided by area (A):

$$P = \frac{F}{A} \quad \text{or} \quad F = P \times A$$

If we substitute this expression for force into the definition of work given by Equation 6.7, we arrive at the following:

$$w = -P \times A \times d$$

The distance through which the force acts is the change in the height of the piston as it moves during the expansion (Δh). Substituting Δh for d, we get:

$$w = -P \times A \times \Delta h$$

Since the volume of a cylinder is the area of its base times its height, then $A \times \Delta h$ is actually the change in the volume (ΔV) that occurs during the expansion. Thus, the expression for work becomes:

$$w = -P\,\Delta V \qquad [6.8]$$

ΔV is the final volume minus the initial volume, $V_f - V_i$ or $V_2 - V_1$, so during an expansion ΔV is positive and the work is negative, in agreement with the convention that if the system (the expanding gases) does work on the surroundings, its sign is negative.

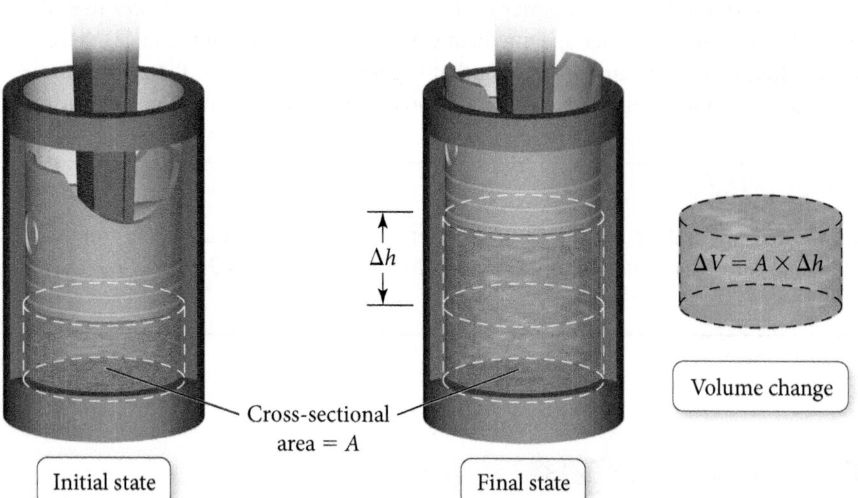

▲ **FIGURE 6.6 Piston Moving Within a Cylinder Against an External Pressure**

EXAMPLE 6.4 PRESSURE–VOLUME WORK

To inflate a balloon, you must do pressure–volume work on the surroundings. If you inflate a balloon from a volume of 0.100 L to 1.85 L against an external pressure of 1.00 bar, how much work is done (in joules)?

SORT You know the initial and final volumes of the balloon and the pressure against which it expands. The balloon and its contents are the system.

GIVEN: $V_1 = 0.100$ L, $V_2 = 1.85$ L, $P = 1.00$ bar

FIND: w

STRATEGIZE The equation $w = -P\,\Delta V$ specifies the amount of work done during a volume change against an external pressure.

CONCEPTUAL PLAN

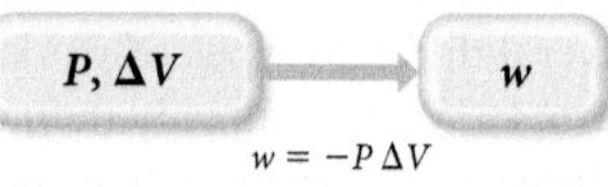

SOLVE To solve the problem, compute the value of ΔV and substitute it, together with P, into the equation.

SOLUTION

$$\begin{aligned}\Delta V &= V_2 - V_1\\ &= 1.85\text{ L} - 0.100\text{ L}\\ &= 1.75\text{ L}\end{aligned}$$

$$\begin{aligned}w &= -P\Delta V\\ &= -1.00\text{ bar} \times 1.75\text{ L}\end{aligned}$$

Convert the units of the answer (bar L) to J using 100 J = 1 bar L.

$$\begin{aligned}&= -1.75\text{ bar L} \times \frac{100\text{ J}}{1\text{ bar L}}\\ &= -175\text{ J}\end{aligned}$$

CHECK The unit J is correct for work. The sign of the work is negative, as it should be for an expansion: Work is done on the surroundings by the expanding balloon.

FOR PRACTICE 6.4

When fuel is burned in a cylinder equipped with a piston, the volume expands from 0.255 L to 1.45 L against an external pressure of 1.02 bar. In addition, 875 J is emitted as heat. What is ΔU for the burning of the fuel?

We can use Equation 6.8 to determine the work for a volume change under constant pressure. What about the work done when a chemical reaction occurs? Consider the combustion of propane at constant pressure and at 298 K:

$$C_3H_8(g) + 5\ O_2(g) \longrightarrow 3\ CO_2(g) + 4\ H_2O(l)$$

When this reaction occurs, six equivalents of gas are converted to three equivalents of gas and four equivalents of liquid water. If we assume the volume of the liquid water is negligible compared to the volume of the gases, then the system contracts by three gas equivalents (6 products – 3 reactants = contraction of 3 equivalents). If we assume that the gases behave ideally, the volume change for this chemical system is due only to the change in the amounts of gases:

$$w = -P\Delta V = -\Delta nRT$$

The work done during the chemical reaction can be computed using the equation:

$$w = -\Delta nRT \qquad [6.9]$$

Where R is the ideal gas constant (8.314 J K^{-1} mol^{-1}), T is the absolute temperature, and Δn is the difference between the stoichiometric coefficients (v, which are unitless) of gaseous products and gaseous reactants. For the combustion of propane:

$$\Delta n = v_{\text{product gases}} - v_{\text{reactant gases}} = v_{CO_2} - v_{C_3H_8} - v_{O_2} = 3-1-6=-3$$

Using Equation 6.9:

$$w = -\Delta nRT = -(-3)(8.314\ \text{J}\ \cancel{\text{K}^{-1}}\ \text{mol}^{-1})(298\ \cancel{\text{K}}) = 7.43 \times 10^3\ \text{J mol}^{-1}$$

We see that 7.43×10^3 J of work is done on the system per mol of reaction that occurs for the combustion of propane.

EXAMPLE 6.5 PRESSURE–VOLUME WORK IN A CHEMICAL REACTION

Methanoic acid (CH_2O_2) is a liquid that burns in oxygen to produce gaseous carbon dioxide and liquid water. Compute the P–V work associated with the combustion of methanoic acid at 298 K.

SORT You are given the reactants and products for a chemical reaction as well as the temperature at which you are asked to compute the P–V work associated with the chemical reaction.

GIVEN: $CH_2O_2(l)$ and $O_2(g)$ produces $CO_2(g)$, and $H_2O(l)$, $T = 298$ K

FIND: w

STRATEGIZE The equation $w = -\Delta nRT$ specifies the amount of work done during a chemical equation involving gases. To compute the change in the stoichiometric coefficient of gaseous products and reactants you also need a balanced equation.

CONCEPTUAL PLAN

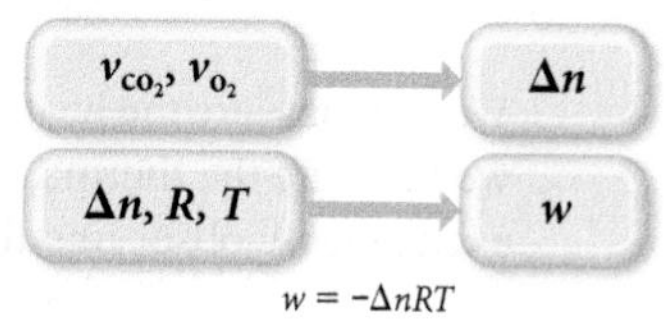

SOLVE To solve the problem, first write and balance the chemical equation.

SOLUTION

$$CH_2O_2(l) + \frac{1}{2}O_2(g) \longrightarrow CO_2(g) + H_2O(l)$$

Then determine the difference in the stoichiometric coefficients for the gaseous compounds in the chemical equation.

$$\Delta n = v_{\text{product gases}} - v_{\text{reactant gases}}$$
$$= v_{CO_2} - v_{O_2}$$
$$= 1 - \frac{1}{2} = \frac{1}{2}$$

Use the equation to calculate the work associated with the combustion of methanoic acid.

$$w = -\Delta nRT$$
$$= -\left(\frac{1}{2}\right)(8.314\ \text{J}\ \cancel{\text{K}^{-1}}\ \text{mol}^{-1})(298\ \cancel{\text{K}})$$
$$= -1.24 \times 10^3\ \text{J mol}^{-1}\ (\text{or } -1.24\ \text{kJ mol}^{-1})$$

(continued)

EXAMPLE 6.5 (CONTINUED)

CHECK The sign is negative which is correct since there is a net increase in the amount of gas for the reaction; the system expands doing work. The units J mol^{-1} of reaction are correct. Typically, energies associated with chemical reactions are reported in kJ mol^{-1}; 1.24 kJ of work being done by the system per mole of reaction is reasonable as a half a mole of gas is produced per mole of reaction.

FOR PRACTICE 6.5

The complete combustion of candle wax ($C_{31}H_{64}$) in oxygen produces CO_2 and liquid water. Calculate the work associated with this combustion reaction at 298 K in kJ mol^{-1}.

6.5 Measuring $\Delta_r U$ for Chemical Reactions: Constant-Volume Calorimetry

We now have a complete picture of how a system exchanges energy with its surroundings via heat and pressure–volume work:

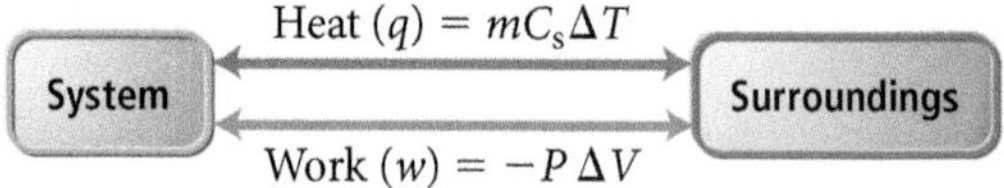

From Section 6.3, we know that the change in internal energy that occurs during a chemical reaction (ΔU) is a measure of *all of the energy* (heat and work) exchanged with the surroundings ($\Delta U = q + w$). Therefore, we can measure the changes in temperature (to calculate heat) and the changes in volume (to calculate work) that occur during a chemical reaction, and then sum them together to calculate ΔU. However, an easier way to obtain the value of ΔU for a chemical reaction is to force all of the energy change associated with a reaction to manifest itself as heat rather than work. We can then measure the temperature change caused by the heat flow.

Recall that $\Delta U = q + w$ and that $w = -P\,\Delta V$. If a reaction is carried out at constant volume, then $\Delta V = 0$ and $w = 0$. The heat evolved (or given off), called the *heat at constant volume* (q_v), is then equal to ΔU:

$$\Delta U = q_v + w \quad \text{(Equals zero at constant volume)} \qquad [6.10]$$

$$\Delta U = q_v$$

We can measure the heat evolved in a chemical reaction using *calorimetry*. In **calorimetry**, we measure the thermal energy the reaction (defined as the system) and the surroundings exchange by observing the change in temperature of the surroundings.

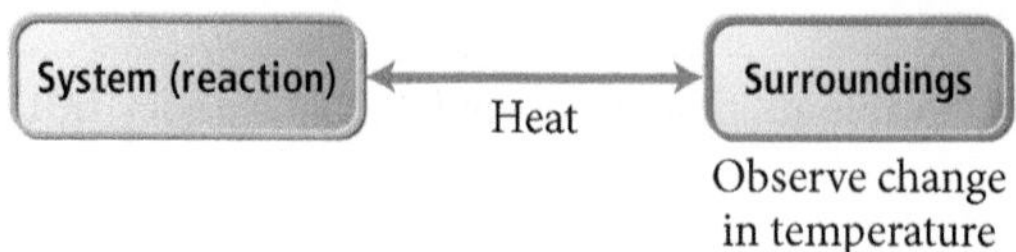

The magnitude of the temperature change in the surroundings depends on the magnitude of ΔU and on the heat capacity of the surroundings.

Figure 6.7 ▶ shows a **bomb calorimeter**, a piece of equipment designed to measure ΔU for combustion reactions. In a bomb calorimeter, the reaction occurs in a sealed container called a *bomb*, which ensures that the reaction occurs at constant volume. To use a bomb calorimeter, you put the sample to be burned (of known mass) into a cup equipped with an ignition wire. You then seal the cup into the bomb, which is filled with oxygen gas, and place the bomb in a water-filled, insulated container. The container is equipped with a stirrer and a thermometer. Finally, you ignite the sample with a wire coil, and monitor the temperature with the thermometer. The temperature change (ΔT)

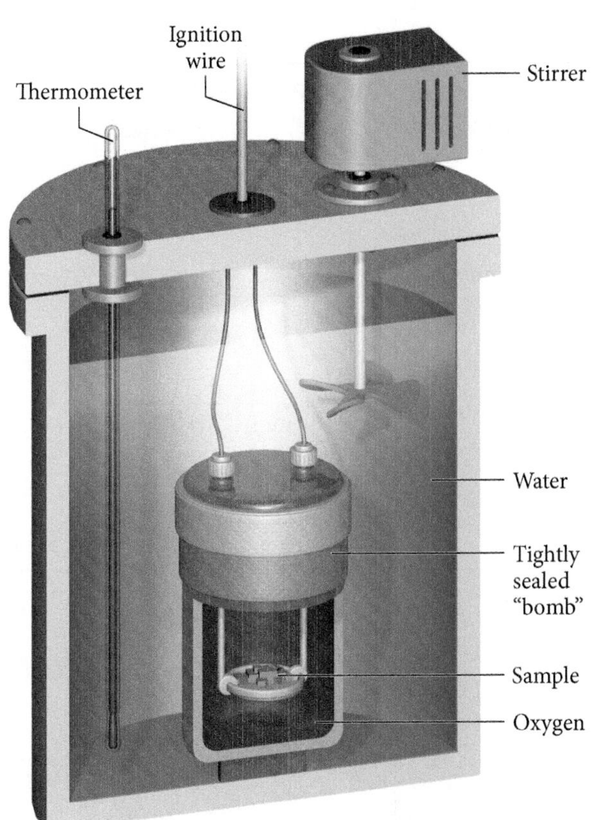

◀ **FIGURE 6.7 The Bomb Calorimeter** A bomb calorimeter measures changes in internal energy for combustion reactions.

is related to the heat absorbed by the entire calorimeter assembly (q_{cal}) by the following equation:

$$q_{cal} = C_{cal} \times \Delta T \qquad [6.11]$$

where C_{cal} is the heat capacity of the entire calorimeter assembly (which is usually determined in a separate measurement involving the burning of a substance that gives off a known amount of heat). If no heat escapes from the calorimeter, the amount of heat *gained by* the calorimeter exactly equals that *released by* the reaction (the two are equal in magnitude but opposite in sign):

$$q_{cal} = -q_r \qquad [6.12]$$

Since the reaction occurs under conditions of constant volume, $q_r = q_v = \Delta U$. This measured quantity is the change in the internal energy of the reaction for the specific amount of reactant burned. To get $\Delta_r U$ per mole of reaction—a more general quantity—you divide by the number of moles that actually reacted, as shown in the following example.

The heat capacity of the calorimeter, C_{cal}, has units of energy over temperature; its value accounts for all of the heat absorbed by all of the components within the calorimeter (including the water).

EXAMPLE 6.6 MEASURING $\Delta_r U$ IN A BOMB CALORIMETER

When 1.010 g of sucrose ($C_{12}H_{22}O_{11}$) undergoes combustion in a bomb calorimeter, the temperature rises from 24.922 °C to 28.331 °C. Find $\Delta_r U$ for the combustion of sucrose in kJ mol^{-1} sucrose. The heat capacity of the bomb calorimeter, determined in a separate experiment, is 4.901 kJ °C^{-1}. (You can ignore the heat capacity of the small sample of sucrose because it is negligible compared to the heat capacity of the calorimeter.)

SORT You are given the mass of sucrose, the heat capacity of the calorimeter, and the initial and final temperatures. You are asked to find the change in internal energy for the reaction.	**GIVEN:** 1.010 g $C_{12}H_{22}O_{11}$, $T_i = 24.922$ °C, $T_f = 28.331$ °C, $C_{cal} = 4.901$ kJ °C^{-1} **FIND:** $\Delta_r U$

(continued)

EXAMPLE 6.6 (CONTINUED)

STRATEGIZE The conceptual plan has three parts. In the first part, use the temperature change and the heat capacity of the calorimeter to find q_{cal}.

CONCEPTUAL PLAN

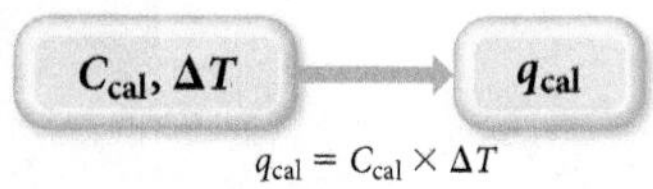

$q_{cal} = C_{cal} \times \Delta T$

In the second part, use q_{cal} to get q_r (which just involves changing the sign). Since the bomb calorimeter ensures constant volume, q_r is equivalent to ΔU for the amount of sucrose burned.

$q_{cal} \rightarrow q_r$

$q_r = -q_{cal}$

In the third part, divide q_r by the number of moles of sucrose to get $\Delta_r U$ per mole of sucrose.

$$\Delta_r U = \frac{q_r}{\text{mol } C_{12}H_{22}O_{11}}$$

RELATIONSHIPS USED

$q_{cal} = C_{cal} \times \Delta T = -q_r$

molar mass $C_{12}H_{22}O_{11}$ = 342.3 g mol^{-1}

SOLVE Gather the necessary quantities in the correct units and substitute these into the equation to calculate q_{cal}.

SOLUTION

$$\Delta T = T_f - T_i$$
$$= 28.331\ °\text{C} - 24.922\ °\text{C} = 3.409\ °\text{C}$$
$$q_{cal} = C_{cal} \times \Delta T$$
$$q_{cal} = 4.901\ \text{kJ}\ \cancel{°\text{C}^{-1}} \times 3.409\ \cancel{°\text{C}} = 16.7\underline{0}8\ \text{kJ}$$

Find q_r by taking the negative of q_{cal}.

$$q_r = -q_{cal} = -16.7\underline{0}8\ \text{kJ}$$

Find $\Delta_r U$ per mole of sucrose by dividing q_r by the number of moles of sucrose (calculated from the given mass of sucrose and its molar mass).

$$\Delta_r U = \frac{q_r}{\text{mol } C_{12}H_{22}O_{11}}$$
$$= \frac{-16.7\underline{0}8\ \text{kJ}}{1.010\ \cancel{\text{g } C_{12}H_{22}O_{11}} \times \frac{1\ \text{mol } C_{12}H_{22}O_{11}}{342.3\ \cancel{\text{g } C_{12}H_{22}O_{11}}}}$$
$$= -5663\ \text{kJ mol}^{-1}\ C_{12}H_{22}O_{11}$$

CHECK The unit of the answer (kJ mol^{-1}) is correct for a change in internal energy. The sign of $\Delta_r U$ is negative, as it should be for a combustion reaction that gives off energy.

FOR PRACTICE 6.6

When 1.550 g of liquid hexane (C_6H_{14}) undergoes combustion in a bomb calorimeter, the temperature rises from 25.87 °C to 38.13 °C. Find $\Delta_r U$ for the reaction in kJ mol^{-1} hexane. The heat capacity of the bomb calorimeter, determined in a separate experiment, is 5.73 kJ °C^{-1}.

FOR MORE PRACTICE 6.6

The combustion of toluene has a $\Delta_r U$ of -3.91×10^3 kJ mol^{-1}. When 1.55 g of toluene (C_7H_8) undergoes combustion in a bomb calorimeter, the temperature rises from 23.12 °C to 37.57 °C. Find the heat capacity of the bomb calorimeter.

6.6 Enthalpy: The Heat Evolved in a Chemical Reaction at Constant Pressure

We have just seen that when a chemical reaction occurs in a sealed container under conditions of constant volume, the energy evolves only as heat. However, when a chemical reaction occurs open to the atmosphere under conditions of constant pressure—for example, a reaction occurring in an open beaker or the burning of natural gas on a stove—the energy can evolve as both heat and work. As we have also seen, $\Delta_r U$ is a measure of the *total energy change* (both heat and work) that occurs during the reaction. However, in many cases, we are interested only in the heat exchanged, not the work done.

For example, when we burn natural gas on a stove to cook food, we do not really care how much work the combustion reaction does on the atmosphere by expanding against it—we just want to know how much heat is given off to cook the food. Under conditions of constant pressure, a thermodynamic quantity called *enthalpy* represents exactly this.

We define the **enthalpy (*H*)** of a system as the sum of its internal energy and the product of its pressure and volume:

$$H = U + PV \qquad [6.13]$$

Since internal energy, pressure, and volume are all state functions, enthalpy is also a state function. The *change in enthalpy* (ΔH) for any process occurring under constant pressure is given by the following expression:

$$\Delta H = \Delta U + P\Delta V \qquad [6.14]$$

To better understand this expression, we can interpret the two terms on the right with the help of relationships already familiar to us. We saw previously that $\Delta U = q + w$. If we represent the heat at constant pressure as q_p, then the change in internal energy at constant pressure is $\Delta U = q_p + w$. In addition, from our definition of pressure–volume work, we know that $P\Delta V = -w$. Substituting these expressions into the expression for ΔH gives us:

$$\begin{aligned} \Delta H &= \Delta U + P\Delta V \\ &= (q_p + w) + P\Delta V \\ &= q_p + w - w \\ \Delta H &= q_p \end{aligned} \qquad [6.15]$$

We can see that ΔH is equal to q_p, the heat at constant pressure.

Conceptually (and often numerically), ΔH and ΔU are similar: they both represent changes in a state function for the system. Under constant pressure conditions, ΔU is a measure of all the energy (heat and work) exchanged with the surroundings, while ΔH is a measure of only the heat exchanged. For chemical reactions that do not exchange much work with the surroundings—that is, those that do not cause a large change in reaction volume as they occur—ΔH and ΔU are nearly identical in value. For chemical reactions that produce or consume large amounts of gas, and therefore result in large volume changes, ΔH and ΔU will be slightly different in value.

As we saw earlier for ΔU and $\Delta_r U$, the difference between ΔH and $\Delta_r H$ is that the latter is a molar quantity and has units of kJ mol^{-1}, meaning an amount of energy per mol of reaction. ΔH has units of kJ.

CONCEPTUAL CONNECTION 6.5

The Difference Between $\Delta_r H$ and $\Delta_r U$

Lighters are usually fuelled by butane (C_4H_{10}). When 1 mol of butane burns at constant pressure, it produces 2658 kJ of heat and does 3 kJ of work. What are the values of $\Delta_r H$ and $\Delta_r U$ for the combustion of one mole of butane?

In the previous section, we saw how $\Delta_r U$ can be determined from bomb calorimetry experiments. For a reaction in which the number of moles of gases is different between products and reactants, we can use the relationship between $\Delta_r U$ and $\Delta_r H$ in Equation 6.14 to determine $\Delta_r H$. Again, assuming that the gases are ideal we can substitute ΔnRT for $P\Delta V$:

$$\Delta_r H = \Delta_r U + \Delta nRT \qquad [6.16]$$

EXAMPLE 6.7 DETERMINING $\Delta_r H$ FROM BOMB CALORIMETRY EXPERIMENTS

A 0.5224 g sample of liquid 2,2,4-trimethylpentane (C_8H_{18}) was combusted in a bomb calorimeter with a heat capacity of 4.901 kJ °C^{-1}. The temperature increased from 23.815 °C to 28.902 °C. Determine $\Delta_r H$ for the complete combustion of sucrose at 298 K.

SORT You are given the mass of 2,2,4-trimethylpentane, its molecular formula, the heat capacity of the calorimeter, and the initial and final temperatures. You are asked to find the change in enthalpy for the reaction, $\Delta_r H$, at 298 K.	**GIVEN:** 0.5224 g C_8H_{18} reacts with gaseous O_2 to produce gaseous CO_2 and liquid H_2O $T_f = 28.902$ °C, $T_i = 23.815$ °C, $C_{cal} = 4.901$ kJ °C^{-1}, **FIND:** $\Delta_r H$ at 298 K.

(continued)

EXAMPLE 6.7 (CONTINUED)

STRATEGIZE

Using the same strategy as in Example 6.6, we first determine $\Delta_r U$ using the calorimeter heat capacity, the temperature change of the calorimeter upon combustion, and the mass of 2,2,4-trimethylpentane.

The equation $\Delta_r H = \Delta_r U + \Delta nRT$ can then be used to determine the enthalpy of reaction. In order to use this equation, you must first write and balance the chemical equation in order to determine Δn from the stoichiometric coefficients.

CONCEPTUAL PLAN

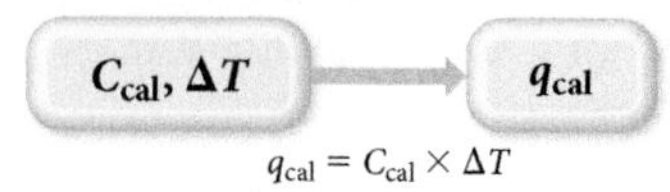

$q_{cal} = C_{cal} \times \Delta T$

$q_{cal} \rightarrow q_r$

$q_r = -q_{cal}$

$$\Delta_r U = \frac{q_r}{\text{mol } C_8H_{18}}$$

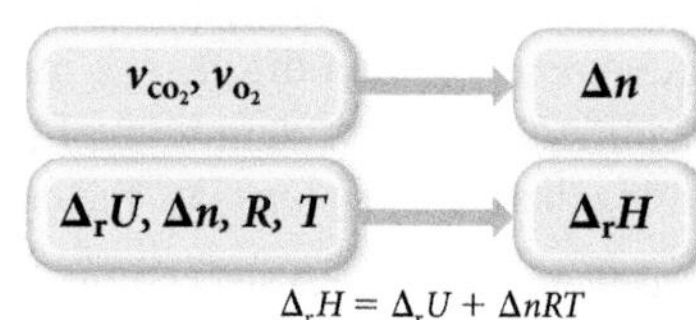

$\Delta_r H = \Delta_r U + \Delta nRT$

RELATIONSHIPS USED

$q_{cal} = C_{cal} \times \Delta T = -qr$

molar mass $C_8H_{18} = 114.231 \text{ g mol}^{-1}$

SOLVE

First determine the heat absorbed by the calorimeter.

Find q_r by taking the negative of q_{cal}.

Find $\Delta_r U$ by dividing q_r by the number of moles of 2,2,4-trimethylpentane.

Next, write and balance the chemical equation for the complete combustion of 2,2,4-trimethylpentane and determine Δn.

Finally, compute $\Delta_r H$ at 298 K by using its relationship with $\Delta_r U$ and Δn.

Don't forget to convert the ΔnRT term from J mol^{-1} to kJ mol^{-1}.

SOLUTION

$\Delta T = T_f - T_i = 28.902\ °\text{C} - 23.815\ °\text{C} = 5.087\ °\text{C}$

$$q_{cal} = C_{cal} \times \Delta T = 4.901 \text{ kJ } °\text{C}^{-1} \times 5.087\ °\text{C} = 24.93\underline{1} \text{ kJ}$$

$$q_r = -q_{cal} = -24.93\underline{1} \text{ kJ}$$

$$\Delta_r U = \frac{-24.93\underline{1} \text{ kJ}}{\left(\dfrac{0.5224 \text{ g}}{114.231 \text{ g mol}^{-1}}\right)} = -545\underline{1}.6 \text{ kJ mol}^{-1}$$

$$C_8H_{18}(l) + \frac{25}{2} O_2(g) \longrightarrow 8\ CO_2(g) + 9\ H_2O(l)$$

$$\Delta n = \nu_{\text{product gases}} - \nu_{\text{reactant gases}} = \nu_{CO_2} - \nu_{O_2} = 8 - \frac{25}{2} = -4.5$$

$$\Delta_r H = \Delta_r U + \Delta nRT$$

$$= -545\underline{1}.6 \frac{\text{kJ}}{\text{mol}} + (-4.5)\left(8.314 \frac{\text{J}}{\text{K mol}}\right)(298 \text{ K})$$

$$= -545\underline{1}.6 \frac{\text{kJ}}{\text{mol}} - 11.1 \times 10^3 \frac{\text{J}}{\text{mol}}\left(\frac{1 \text{ kJ}}{10^3 \text{ J}}\right)$$

$$= -5463 \text{ kJ mol}^{-1}$$

CHECK The units of the answer (kJ mol^{-1}) are correct and the sign of $\Delta_r H$ is correct as energy is given off during combustion. $\Delta_r H$ is more negative than $\Delta_r U$ because at constant pressure work is done on the system (positive) as it contracts because there are less moles of gas on the products side. Since $\Delta U = q + w$, the internal energy change is more positive than the enthalpy change.

FOR PRACTICE 6.7

A 1.451 g sample of solid ribose ($C_5H_{10}O_5$) was combusted in a bomb calorimeter with a heat capacity of 4.909 kJ °C^{-1}. The temperature increased from 22.107 °C to 26.730 °C. Determine $\Delta_r H$ for the complete combustion of ribose at 298 K.

The signs of ΔH and ΔU follow the same conventions as q and w. A positive ΔH indicates that heat flows into the system as the reaction occurs. A chemical reaction with a positive ΔH, called an **endothermic reaction**, absorbs heat from its surroundings. A chemical cold pack is a good example of an endothermic reaction. When a barrier separating the reactants in a chemical cold pack is broken, the substances mix, react, and absorb heat from the surroundings. The surroundings—including, say, your bruised wrist—get *colder* because they *lose* energy as the cold pack absorbs it.

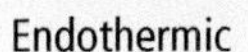

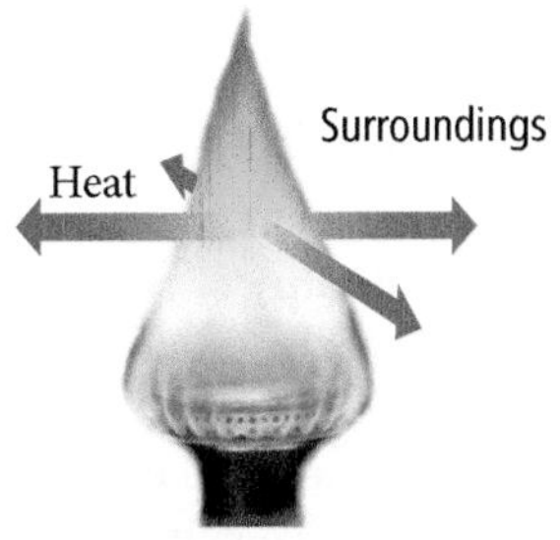

◀ The reaction that occurs in a chemical cold pack is endothermic—it absorbs energy from the surroundings. The combustion of natural gas is an exothermic reaction—it releases energy to the surroundings.

A chemical reaction with a negative $\Delta_r H$, called an **exothermic reaction**, gives off heat to its surroundings. The reaction occurring in the chemical hand warmer discussed in Section 6.1 is a good example of an exothermic reaction. As the reaction occurs, heat is given off into the surroundings (including your hand and glove), making them warmer. The burning of natural gas is another example of an exothermic reaction. As the gas burns, it gives off energy, raising the temperature of its surroundings.

Summarizing Enthalpy:

- The value of $\Delta_r H$ for a chemical reaction is the amount of heat absorbed or evolved in the reaction under conditions of constant pressure.
- An endothermic reaction has a *positive* $\Delta_r H$ and absorbs heat from the surroundings. An endothermic reaction feels cold to the touch.
- An exothermic reaction has a *negative* $\Delta_r H$ and gives off heat to the surroundings. An exothermic reaction feels warm to the touch.

Exothermic and Endothermic Processes: A Molecular View

When a chemical system undergoes a change in enthalpy, where does the energy come from or go to? For example, we just learned that an exothermic chemical reaction gives off *thermal energy*—what is the source of that energy?

First, we know that the emitted thermal energy *does not* come from the original thermal energy of the system. Recall from Section 6.2 that the thermal energy of a system is the composite kinetic energy of the atoms and molecules that compose the system. This kinetic energy *cannot* be the source of the energy given off in an exothermic reaction because, if the atoms and molecules that compose the system were to lose kinetic energy, their temperature would necessarily fall—the system would get colder. Yet, we know that in exothermic reactions, the temperature of the system and the surroundings rises. So, there must be some other source of energy.

Recall also from Section 6.2 that the internal energy of a chemical system is the sum of its kinetic energy and its *potential energy*. This potential energy is the source in an exothermic chemical reaction. Under normal circumstances, chemical potential energy (or simply chemical energy) arises primarily from the electrostatic forces between the protons and electrons that compose the atoms and molecules within the system. In an exothermic reaction, some bonds break and new ones form, and the nuclei and electrons reorganize into an arrangement with lower potential energy. As the molecules rearrange, their potential energy converts into thermal energy, the heat emitted in the reaction. In an endothermic reaction, the opposite happens: as some bonds break and others form, the nuclei and electrons reorganize into an arrangement with higher potential energy, absorbing thermal energy in the process.

CONCEPTUAL CONNECTION 6.6

Exothermic and Endothermic Reactions

If an endothermic reaction absorbs heat, then why does it feel cold to the touch?

Stoichiometry Involving $\Delta_r H$: Thermochemical Equations

The enthalpy change for a chemical reaction, abbreviated $\Delta_r H$, is also called the **enthalpy of reaction** or **heat of reaction**. We usually specify $\Delta_r H$ in combination with the balanced chemical equation for the reaction. *The magnitude of $\Delta_r H$ is for the stoichiometric amounts of reactants and products for the reaction as written.* For example, the balanced equation and $\Delta_r H$ for the combustion of propane (the main component of liquefied petroleum gas) are as follows:

$$C_3H_8(g) + 5\,O_2(g) \rightarrow 3\,CO_2(g) + 4\,H_2O(g) \qquad \Delta_r H = -2044 \text{ kJ mol}^{-1}$$

The stoichiometric coefficients are unitless, but can be thought of as 1 mol of C_3H_8 reacting with 5 mol of O_2, producing 3 mol of CO_2 and 4 mol of H_2O. The thermochemical equation means that for the reaction as written, 2044 kJ of heat is released *per mole of reaction*. In other words, when 1 mol of C_3H_8 reacts with 5 mol of O_2 to form 3 mol of CO_2 and 4 mol of H_2O, 2044 kJ of heat is emitted. We can write these relationships in the same way that we expressed stoichiometric relationships in Chapter 4: as ratios between two quantities. For example, for the reactants, we write:

$$1 \text{ mol } C_3H_8 : -2044 \text{ kJ} \qquad \text{or} \qquad 5 \text{ mol } O_2 : -2044 \text{ kJ}$$

The ratios indicate that 2044 kJ of heat evolves when 1 mol of C_3H_8 and 5 mol of O_2 completely react. We can use these ratios to construct conversion factors between amounts of reactants or products and the quantity of heat emitted (for exothermic reactions) or absorbed (for endothermic reactions). To find out how much heat is emitted upon the combustion of a certain mass in grams of C_3H_8, we would use the following conceptual plan:

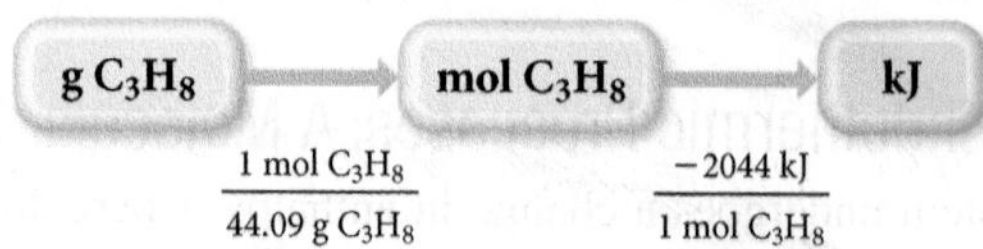

We use the molar mass to convert between grams and moles, and the stoichiometric relationship between moles of C_3H_8 and the heat of reaction to convert between moles and kilojoules, as shown in the following example.

EXAMPLE 6.8 **STOICHIOMETRY INVOLVING $\Delta_r H$**

An LP gas tank in a home barbeque contains 13.2 kg of propane, C_3H_8. Calculate the heat (in kJ) associated with the complete combustion of all of the propane in the tank.

$$C_3H_8(g) + 5\,O_2(g) \longrightarrow 3\,CO_2(g) + 4\,H_2O(g) \qquad \Delta_r H = -2044 \text{ kJ mol}^{-1}$$

SORT You are given the mass of propane and asked to find the heat evolved in its combustion.	**GIVEN:** 13.2 kg C_3H_8 **FIND:** q

STRATEGIZE Starting with kg C_3H_8, convert to g C_3H_8 and then use the molar mass of C_3H_8 to find the number of moles. Next, use the stoichiometric relationship between mol C_3H_8 and kJ to find the heat evolved.

CONCEPTUAL PLAN

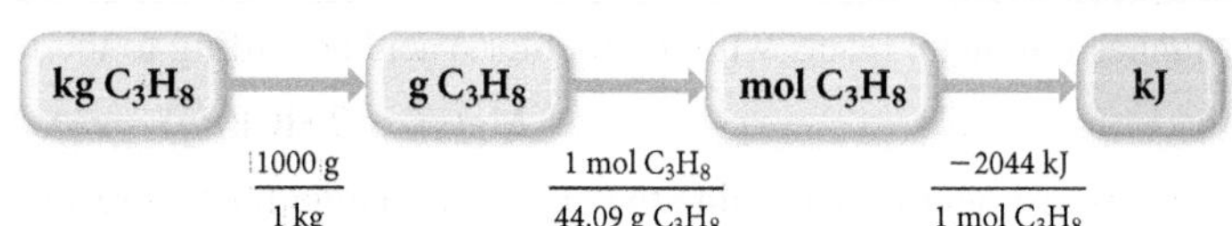

$\frac{1000\ \text{g}}{1\ \text{kg}}$ $\frac{1\ \text{mol}\ C_3H_8}{44.09\ \text{g}\ C_3H_8}$ $\frac{-2044\ \text{kJ}}{1\ \text{mol}\ C_3H_8}$

RELATIONSHIPS USED

1000 g = 1 kg
molar mass C_3H_8 = 44.09 g mol^{-1}
1 mol C_3H_8 : −2044 kJ (from balanced equation)

SOLVE Follow the conceptual plan to solve the problem. Begin with 13.2 kg C_3H_8 and multiply by the appropriate conversion factors to arrive at kJ.

SOLUTION

$$13.2\ \text{kg}\ C_3H_8 \times \frac{1000\ \text{g}}{1\ \text{kg}} \times \frac{1\ \text{mol}\ C_3H_8}{44.09\ \text{g}\ C_3H_8} \times \frac{-2044\ \text{kJ}}{1\ \text{mol}\ C_3H_8} = -6.12 \times 10^5\ \text{kJ}$$

CHECK The unit of the answer (kJ) is correct for energy. The answer is negative, as it should be for heat evolved by the reaction.

FOR PRACTICE 6.8

Ammonia reacts with oxygen according to the following equation:

$$4NH_3(g) + 5O_2(g) \longrightarrow 4NO(g) + 6H_2O(g) \qquad \Delta_r H = -906\ \text{kJ mol}^{-1}$$

Calculate the heat (in kJ) associated with the complete reaction of 155 g of NH_3.

FOR MORE PRACTICE 6.8

What mass of butane in grams is necessary to produce 1.5×10^3 kJ of heat? What mass of CO_2 is produced?

$$C_4H_{10}(g) + \tfrac{13}{2}O_2(g) \longrightarrow 4CO_2(g) + 5H_2O(g) \qquad \Delta_r H = -2658\ \text{kJ mol}^{-1}$$

6.7 Constant-Pressure Calorimetry: Measuring $\Delta_r H$

For many aqueous reactions, we can measure $\Delta_r H$ fairly simply using a **coffee-cup calorimeter** shown in Figure 6.8 ▶. The calorimeter consists of two Styrofoam coffee cups, one inserted into the other, to provide insulation from the laboratory environment. The calorimeter is equipped with a thermometer and a stirrer. The reaction occurs in a specifically measured quantity of solution within the calorimeter, so that the mass of the solution is known. During the reaction, the heat evolved (or absorbed) causes a temperature change in the solution, which the thermometer measures. If we know the specific heat capacity of the solution, normally assumed to be that of water, we can calculate q_{soln}, the heat absorbed by or lost from the solution (which is acting as the surroundings) using the following equation:

$$q_{soln} = m_{soln} \times C_{s,\,soln} \times \Delta T$$

The insulated calorimeter prevents heat from escaping, so we assume that the heat gained by the solution equals that lost by the reaction (or vice versa):

$$q_r = -q_{soln}$$

Since the reaction happens under conditions of constant pressure (open to the atmosphere), $q_r = q_p = \Delta H$. This measured quantity is the heat of reaction for the specific amount (which is measured ahead of time) of reactants that reacted. To get $\Delta_r H$ per mole of a particular reactant—a more general quantity—we divide by the number of moles that actually reacted, as shown in Example 6.9.

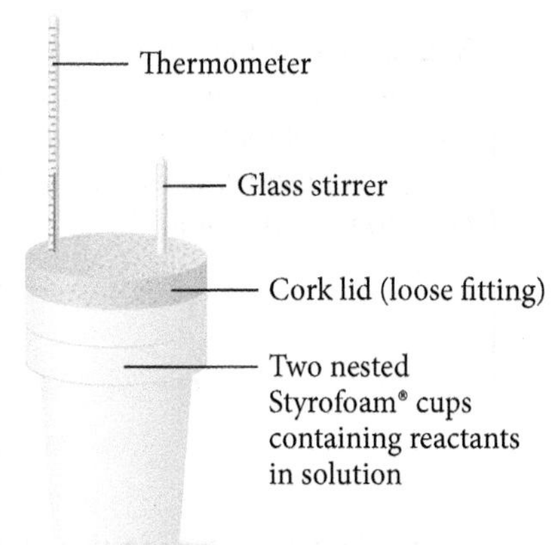

▲ **FIGURE 6.8 The Coffee-Cup Calorimeter** A coffee-cup calorimeter measures enthalpy changes for chemical reactions in solution.

This equation assumes that no heat is lost to the calorimeter itself. If heat absorbed by the calorimeter is accounted for, the equation becomes $q_r = -(q_{soln} + q_{cal})$.

Summarizing Calorimetry:

- Bomb calorimetry occurs at constant *volume* and measures $q_v = \Delta U$ for a reaction.
- Coffee-cup calorimetry occurs at constant *pressure* and measures $q_p = \Delta H$ for a reaction.

EXAMPLE 6.9 MEASURING $\Delta_r H$ IN A COFFEE-CUP CALORIMETER

Magnesium metal reacts with hydrochloric acid according to the following balanced equation:

$$Mg(s) + 2\,HCl(aq) \longrightarrow MgCl_2(aq) + H_2(g)$$

In an experiment to determine the enthalpy change for this reaction, we combine 0.158 g of Mg metal with enough HCl to make 100.0 mL of solution in a coffee-cup calorimeter. The HCl is sufficiently concentrated so that the Mg completely reacts. The temperature of the solution rises from 25.6 °C to 32.8 °C as a result of the reaction. Find $\Delta_r H$ for the reaction as written. You can assume that the aqueous solution is dilute enough that the density and heat capacity are the same as water. Use 1.00 g mL^{-1} as the density of the solution and $C_{s,\,soln} = 4.184\ J\ g^{-1}\ °C^{-1}$ as the specific heat capacity of the solution.

SORT You are given the mass of magnesium, the volume of solution, the initial and final temperatures, the density of the solution, and the heat capacity of the solution. You are asked to find the change in enthalpy for the reaction.

GIVEN: 0.158 g Mg
100.0 mL soln
$T_i = 25.6\ °C$
$T_f = 32.8\ °C$
$d = 1.00\ g\ mL^{-1}$
$C_{s,\,soln} = 4.184\ J\ g^{-1}\ °C^{-1}$

FIND: $\Delta_r H$

STRATEGIZE The conceptual plan has three parts. In the first part, use the temperature change and the other given quantities, together with the equation $q = mC_s\Delta T$, to find q_{soln}.

CONCEPTUAL PLAN

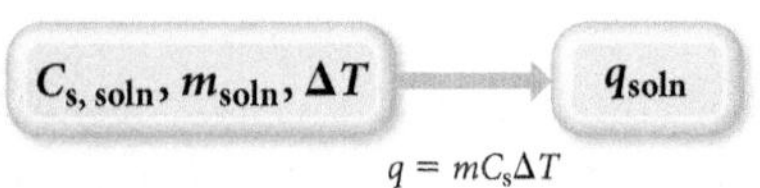

In the second part, use q_{soln} to get q_r (which simply involves changing the sign). Because the pressure is constant, q_r is equivalent to ΔH for the amount of magnesium that reacted.

q_{soln} → q_r

$q_r = -q_{soln}$

In the third part, divide q_r by the number of moles of magnesium to get $\Delta_r H$ per mole of magnesium.

$$\Delta_r H = \frac{q_r}{\text{mol Mg}}$$

RELATIONSHIPS USED $q = mC_s\Delta T$
$q_r = -q_{soln}$

SOLVE Gather the necessary quantities in the correct units for the equation $q = mC_s\Delta T$ and substitute these into the equation to compute q_{soln}. Notice that the sign of q_{soln} is *positive*, meaning that the solution *absorbed heat* from the reaction.

SOLUTION

$$C_{s,\,soln} = 4.184\ J\ g^{-1}\ °C^{-1}$$

$$m_{soln} = 100.0\ \cancel{mL\ soln} \times \frac{1.00\ g}{1\ \cancel{mL\ soln}} = 1.00 \times 10^2\ g$$

$$\Delta T = T_f - T_i$$
$$= 32.8\ °C - 25.6\ °C = 7.2\ °C$$

$$q_{soln} = m_{soln} \times C_{s,\,soln} \times \Delta T$$
$$= 1.00 \times 10^2\ \cancel{g} \times 4.184\ \frac{J}{\cancel{g} \cdot \cancel{°C}} \times 7.2\ \cancel{°C} = 3.0\underline{1} \times 10^3\ J$$

Find q_r by taking the negative of q_{soln}. Notice that q_r is negative, as expected for an *exothermic* reaction.

$$q_r = -q_{soln} = -3.0\underline{1} \times 10^3\ J$$

Finally, find $\Delta_r H$ per mole of magnesium by dividing q_r by the number of moles of magnesium that reacted. Find the number of moles of magnesium from the given mass of magnesium and its molar mass.

$$\Delta_r H = \frac{q_r}{\text{mol Mg}}$$
$$= \frac{-3.0\underline{1} \times 10^3\ J}{0.158\ \cancel{g\ Mg} \times \dfrac{1\ mol\ Mg}{24.31\ \cancel{g\ Mg}}}$$
$$= -4.6 \times 10^5\ J\ mol^{-1}\ Mg$$

Since the stoichiometric coefficient for magnesium in the balanced chemical equation is 1, the computed value represents $\Delta_r H$ for the reaction as written.

$$Mg(s) + 2\,HCl(aq) \longrightarrow MgCl_2(aq) + H_2(g)$$
$$\Delta_r H = -4.6 \times 10^5\ J\ mol^{-1}$$

CHECK The unit of the answer (J mol^{-1}) is correct for the change in enthalpy of a reaction. The sign is negative, as expected for an exothermic reaction.

FOR PRACTICE 6.9

The addition of hydrochloric acid to a silver nitrate solution precipitates silver chloride according to the following reaction:

$$AgNO_3(aq) + HCl(aq) \longrightarrow AgCl(s) + HNO_3(aq)$$

When 50.0 mL of 0.100 mol L^{-1} $AgNO_3$ is combined with 50.0 mL of 0.100 mol L^{-1} HCl in a coffee-cup calorimeter, the temperature changes from 23.40 °C to 24.21 °C. Calculate $\Delta_r H$ for the reaction as written. Use 1.00 g mL^{-1} as the density of the solution and $C = 4.184$ J g^{-1} °C^{-1} as the specific heat capacity.

CONCEPTUAL CONNECTION 6.7

Constant-Pressure Versus Constant-Volume Calorimetry

The same reaction, with exactly the same amount of reactant, is conducted in a bomb calorimeter and in a coffee-cup calorimeter. In one of the measurements, $q_r = -12.5$ kJ, and in the other, $q_r = -11.8$ kJ. Which value was obtained in the bomb calorimeter? (Assume that the reaction has a positive ΔV in the coffee-cup calorimeter.)

6.8 Relationships Involving $\Delta_r H$

The change in enthalpy for a reaction is always associated with a *particular* reaction. If we change the reaction in well-defined ways, then $\Delta_r H$ also changes in well-defined ways. We now turn our attention to three quantitative relationships between a chemical equation and $\Delta_r H$.

1. **If a chemical equation is multiplied by some factor, then $\Delta_r H$ is also multiplied by the same factor.**

We learned in Section 6.6 that $\Delta_r H$ is an extensive property; it depends on the quantity of reactants undergoing reaction. Recall also that $\Delta_r H$ is usually reported for a reaction involving stoichiometric amounts of reactants. For example, for a reaction A + 2 B $\longrightarrow$ C, $\Delta_r H$ is typically reported as the amount of heat emitted or absorbed when 1 mol A reacts with 2 mol B to form 1 mol C. Therefore, if a chemical equation is multiplied by a factor, then $\Delta_r H$ is also multiplied by the same factor. For example:

$$\begin{array}{ll} \mathrm{A} + 2\,\mathrm{B} \longrightarrow \mathrm{C} & \Delta_r H_1 \\ 2\,\mathrm{A} + 4\,\mathrm{B} \longrightarrow 2\,\mathrm{C} & \Delta_r H_2 = 2 \times \Delta_r H_1 \end{array}$$

2. **If a chemical equation is reversed, then $\Delta_r H$ changes sign.**

We learned in Section 6.6 that $\Delta_r H$ is a state function, which means that its value depends only on the initial and final states of the system.

$$\Delta_r H = H_{\text{final}} - H_{\text{initial}}$$

When a reaction is reversed, the final state becomes the initial state and vice versa. Consequently, $\Delta_r H$ changes sign, as exemplified by the following:

$$\begin{array}{ll} \mathrm{A} + 2\,\mathrm{B} \longrightarrow \mathrm{C} & \Delta_r H_1 \\ \mathrm{C} \longrightarrow \mathrm{A} + 2\,\mathrm{B} & \Delta_r H_2 = -\Delta_r H_1 \end{array}$$

3. **If a chemical equation can be expressed as the sum of a series of steps, then $\Delta_r H$ for the overall equation is the sum of the $\Delta_r H$'s for each step.**

This last relationship, known as **Hess's law**, also follows from the enthalpy of reaction being a state function. Since $\Delta_r H$ is dependent only on the initial and final states, and not on the pathway the reaction follows, then $\Delta_r H$ obtained from summing the individual steps that lead to an overall reaction must be the same as $\Delta_r H$ for that overall reaction. For example:

$$\begin{array}{ll} \mathrm{A} + 2\,\mathrm{B} \longrightarrow \cancel{\mathrm{C}} & \Delta_r H_1 \\ \cancel{\mathrm{C}} \longrightarrow 2\,\mathrm{D} & \Delta_r H_2 \\ \hline \mathrm{A} + 2\,\mathrm{B} \longrightarrow 2\,\mathrm{D} & \Delta_r H_3 = \Delta_r H_1 + \Delta_r H_2 \end{array}$$

Hess's Law
The change in enthalpy for a stepwise process is the sum of the enthalpy changes of the steps.

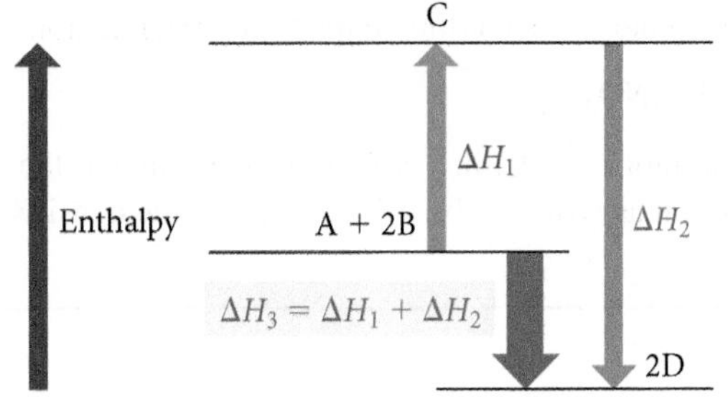

▲ **FIGURE 6.9 Hess's Law**

We illustrate Hess's law with the energy level diagram shown in Figure 6.9 ◄.

These three quantitative relationships make it possible to determine $\Delta_r H$ for a reaction without directly measuring it in the laboratory. (For some reactions, direct measurement can be difficult.) If we can find related reactions (with known $\Delta_r H$'s) that sum to the reaction of interest, we can find $\Delta_r H$ for the reaction of interest. For example, the following reaction between C(*s*) and $H_2O(g)$ is an industrially important method of generating hydrogen gas:

$$C(s) + H_2O(g) \longrightarrow CO(g) + H_2(g) \qquad \Delta_r H = ?$$

We can find $\Delta_r H$ from the following reactions with known $\Delta_r H$'s:

$$C(s) + O_2(g) \longrightarrow CO_2(g) \qquad \Delta_r H = -393.5 \text{ kJ mol}^{-1}$$
$$2\,CO(g) + O_2(g) \longrightarrow 2\,CO_2(g) \qquad \Delta_r H = -566.0 \text{ kJ mol}^{-1}$$
$$2\,H_2(g) + O_2(g) \longrightarrow 2\,H_2O(g) \qquad \Delta_r H = -483.6 \text{ kJ mol}^{-1}$$

We just have to determine how to sum these reactions to get the overall reaction of interest. We do this by manipulating the reactions with known $\Delta_r H$'s in such a way as to get the reactants of interest on the left, the products of interest on the right, and other species to cancel.

Since the first reaction has C(*s*) as a reactant, and the reaction of interest also has C(*s*) as a reactant, we write the first reaction unchanged.

$$C(s) + O_2(g) \longrightarrow CO_2(g) \qquad \Delta_r H = -393.5 \text{ kJ mol}^{-1}$$

The second reaction has 2 mol of CO(*g*) as a reactant. However, the reaction of interest has 1 mol of CO(*g*) as a product. Therefore, we reverse the second reaction, change the sign of $\Delta_r H$, and multiply the reaction and $\Delta_r H$ by ½.

$$\tfrac{1}{2} \times [2\,CO_2(g) \longrightarrow 2\,CO(g) + O_2(g)]$$
$$\Delta_r H = \tfrac{1}{2} \times (566.0 \text{ kJ mol}^{-1})$$

The third reaction has $H_2(g)$ as a reactant. In the reaction of interest, however, $H_2(g)$ is a product. Therefore, we reverse the equation and change the sign of $\Delta_r H$. In addition, to obtain coefficients that match the reaction of interest, and to cancel O_2, we must multiply the reaction and $\Delta_r H$ by ½.

$$\tfrac{1}{2} \times [2\,H_2O(g) \longrightarrow 2\,H_2(g) + O_2(g)]$$
$$\Delta_r H = \tfrac{1}{2} \times (483.6 \text{ kJ mol}^{-1})$$

Lastly, we rewrite the three reactions after multiplying through by the indicated factors and show how they sum to the reaction of interest. $\Delta_r H$ for the reaction of interest is then just the sum of the $\Delta_r H$'s for the steps.

$$C(s) + \cancel{O_2(g)} \longrightarrow \cancel{CO_2(g)} \qquad \Delta_r H = -393.5 \text{ kJ mol}^{-1}$$
$$\cancel{CO_2(g)} \longrightarrow CO(g) + \cancel{\tfrac{1}{2}O_2(g)} \qquad \Delta_r H = 283.0 \text{ kJ mol}^{-1}$$
$$H_2O(g) \longrightarrow H_2(g) + \cancel{\tfrac{1}{2}O_2(g)} \qquad \Delta_r H = 241.8 \text{ kJ mol}^{-1}$$
$$C(s) + H_2O(g) \longrightarrow CO(g) + H_2(g) \qquad \Delta_r H = 131.3 \text{ kJ mol}^{-1}$$

EXAMPLE 6.10 HESS'S LAW

Find $\Delta_r H$ for the reaction:

$$3\,C(s) + 4\,H_2(g) \longrightarrow C_3H_8(g)$$

Use these reactions with known $\Delta_r H$'s:

$$C_3H_8(g) + 5\,O_2(g) \longrightarrow 3\,CO_2(g) + 4\,H_2O(g) \qquad \Delta_r H = -2043 \text{ kJ mol}^{-1}$$
$$C(s) + O_2(g) \longrightarrow CO_2(g) \qquad \Delta_r H = -393.5 \text{ kJ mol}^{-1}$$
$$2\,H_2(g) + O_2(g) \longrightarrow 2\,H_2O(g) \qquad \Delta_r H = -483.6 \text{ kJ mol}^{-1}$$

SOLUTION

To work this and other Hess's law problems, manipulate the reactions with known $\Delta_r H$'s in such a way as to get the reactants of interest on the left, the products of interest on the right, and the other species to cancel.

The first reaction has C_3H_8 as a reactant, and the reaction of interest has C_3H_8 as a product, so you can reverse the first reaction and change the sign of $\Delta_r H$.	$3\ CO_2(g) + 4\ H_2O(g) \longrightarrow C_3H_8(g) + 5\ O_2(g) \quad \Delta_r H = 2043\ kJ\ mol^{-1}$
The second reaction has C as a reactant and CO_2 as a product, just as required in the reaction of interest. However, the coefficient for C is 1, and in the reaction of interest, the coefficient for C is 3. You need to multiply this equation and its $\Delta_r H$ by 3.	$3 \times [C(s) + O_2(g) \longrightarrow CO_2(g)] \quad \Delta_r H = 3 \times (-393.5\ kJ\ mol^{-1})$
The third reaction has $H_2(g)$ as a reactant, as required. However, the coefficient for H_2 is 2, and in the reaction of interest, the coefficient for H_2 is 4. Multiply this reaction and its $\Delta_r H$ by 2.	$2 \times [2\ H_2(g) + O_2(g) \longrightarrow 2\ H_2O(g)] \quad \Delta_r H = 2 \times (-483.6\ kJ\ mol^{-1})$
Lastly, rewrite the three reactions after multiplying through by the indicated factors and show how they sum to the reaction of interest. $\Delta_r H$ for the reaction of interest is the sum of the $\Delta_r H$'s for the steps.	$\cancel{3\ CO_2(g)} + \cancel{4\ H_2O(g)} \longrightarrow C_3H_8(g) + \cancel{5\ O_2(g)} \quad \Delta_r H = 2043\ kJ\ mol^{-1}$ $3\ C(s) + \cancel{3\ O_2(g)} \longrightarrow \cancel{3\ CO_2(g)} \quad \Delta_r H = -1181\ kJ\ mol^{-1}$ $4\ H_2(g) + \cancel{2\ O_2(g)} \longrightarrow \cancel{4\ H_2O(g)} \quad \Delta_r H = -967.2\ kJ\ mol^{-1}$ $3\ C(s) + 4\ H_2(g) \longrightarrow C_3H_8(g) \quad \Delta_r H = -105\ kJ\ mol^{-1}$

FOR PRACTICE 6.10

Find $\Delta_r H$ for the reaction:

$$N_2O(g) + NO_2(g) \longrightarrow 3\ NO(g)$$

Use these reactions with known $\Delta_r H$'s:

$$2\ NO(g) + O_2(g) \longrightarrow 2\ NO_2(g) \qquad \Delta_r H = -113.1\ kJ\ mol^{-1}$$
$$N_2(g) + O_2(g) \longrightarrow 2\ NO(g) \qquad \Delta_r H = 182.6\ kJ\ mol^{-1}$$
$$2\ N_2O(g) \longrightarrow 2\ N_2(g) + O_2(g) \qquad \Delta_r H = -163.2\ kJ\ mol^{-1}$$

FOR MORE PRACTICE 6.10

Find $\Delta_r H$ for the reaction:

$$3\ H_2(g) + O_3(g) \longrightarrow 3\ H_2O(g)$$

Use these reactions with known $\Delta_r H$'s:

$$2\ H_2(g) + O_2(g) \longrightarrow 2\ H_2O(g) \qquad \Delta_r H = -483.6\ kJ\ mol^{-1}$$
$$3\ O_2(g) \longrightarrow 2\ O_3(g) \qquad \Delta_r H = 285.4\ kJ\ mol^{-1}$$

6.9 Determining Enthalpies of Reaction from Standard Enthalpies of Formation

We have examined two ways to determine $\Delta_r H$ for a chemical reaction: experimentally through calorimetry and inferentially through Hess's law. We now turn to a third and more convenient way to determine $\Delta_r H$ for a large number of chemical reactions: from tabulated *standard enthalpies of formation*.

Standard States and Standard Enthalpy Changes

Recall that $\Delta_r H$ is the *change* in enthalpy for a chemical reaction—the difference in enthalpy between the products and the reactants. Since we are interested in changes in enthalpy (and not in absolute values of enthalpy itself), we are free to define the *zero* of enthalpy as conveniently as possible. We must define a standard for enthalpy.

The superscripted ° (pronounced "not") on $\Delta_r H°$ and $\Delta_f H°$ means "under standard conditions at the *specified temperature.*" The temperature for the value of $\Delta_f H°$ reported must always be stated.

This standard has three parts: the **standard state**, the **standard enthalpy change** (**$\Delta_r H°$**), and the **standard enthalpy of formation** (**$\Delta_f H°$**).

1. **Standard State**
   - *For a Gas:* The standard state for a gas is the pure gas at a pressure of exactly 1 bar.
   - *For a Liquid or Solid:* The standard state for a liquid or solid is the pure substance in its most stable form at a pressure of 1 bar and at the temperature of interest (often taken to be 25 °C).
   - *For a Substance in Solution:* The standard state for a substance in solution is a concentration of exactly 1 mol L^{-1}.
2. **Standard Enthalpy Change (**$\Delta_r H°$**)**
   - The change in enthalpy for a process when all reactants and products are in their standard states. The ° indicates standard states.
3. **Standard Enthalpy of Formation (**$\Delta_f H°$**)**
   - *For a Pure Compound:* The change in enthalpy when 1 mol of the compound forms from its constituent elements in their standard states.
   - *For a Pure Element in Its Standard State*: $\Delta_f H° = 0$ kJ mol^{-1}.

The standard enthalpy of formation is also called the **standard heat of formation.**

We can measure all changes in enthalpy relative to those of pure elements in their standard states. For example, consider the standard enthalpy of formation of methane gas at 25 °C:

The carbon in this equation must be graphite (the most stable form of carbon at 1 bar and 25 °C).

$$C(s, \text{graphite}) + 2\, H_2(g) \longrightarrow CH_4(g) \quad \Delta_f H° = -74.6 \text{ kJ mol}^{-1}$$

For methane, $\Delta_f H°$ is negative. The chemical equation for the enthalpy of formation of a compound is always written to form 1 mol of the compound and $\Delta_f H°$ has the units of kJ mol^{-1}. Table 6.5 shows $\Delta_f H°$ values for some selected compounds. A more complete list can be found in Appendix IIB.

TABLE 6.5 Standard Enthalpies (or Heats) of Formation ($\Delta_f H°$) at 298 K

Formula	$\Delta_f H°$ kJ mol^{-1}	Formula	$\Delta_f H°$ kJ mol^{-1}	Formula	$\Delta_f H°$ kJ mol^{-1}
Bromine		C_3H_8O(*l*, isopropanol)	−318.1	***Oxygen***	
Br(*g*)	111.9	C_6H_6(*l*)	49.1	O_2(*g*)	0
Br_2(*l*)	0	$C_6H_{12}O_6$(*s*, glucose)	−1273.3	O_3(*g*)	142.7
HBr(*g*)	−36.3	$C_{12}H_{22}O_{11}$(*s*, sucrose)	−2226.1	H_2O(*g*)	−241.8
Calcium		***Chlorine***		H_2O(*l*)	−285.8
Ca(*s*)	0	Cl(*g*)	121.3	***Silver***	
CaO(*s*)	−634.9	Cl_2(*g*)	0	Ag(*s*)	0
$CaCO_3$(*s*)	−1207.6	HCl(*g*)	−92.3	AgCl(*s*)	−127.0
Carbon		***Fluorine***		***Sodium***	
C(*s*, graphite)	0	F(*g*)	79.38	Na(*s*)	0
C(*s*, diamond)	1.88	F_2(*g*)	0	Na(*g*)	107.5
CO(*g*)	−110.5	HF(*g*)	−273.3	NaCl(*s*)	−411.2
CO_2(*g*)	−393.5	***Hydrogen***		Na_2CO_3(*s*)	−1130.7
CH_4(*g*)	−74.6	H(*g*)	218.0	$NaHCO_3$(*s*)	−950.8
CH_3OH(*l*)	−238.6	H_2(*g*)	0	***Sulfur***	
C_2H_2(*g*)	227.4	***Nitrogen***		S_8(*s*, rhombic)	0
C_2H_4(*g*)	52.4	N_2(*g*)	0	S_8(*s*, monoclinic)	0.3
C_2H_6(*g*)	−84.68	NH_3(*g*)	−45.9	SO_2(*g*)	−296.8
C_2H_5OH(*l*)	−277.6	NH_4NO_3(*s*)	−365.6	SO_3(*g*)	−395.7
C_3H_8(*g*)	−103.85	NO(*g*)	91.3	H_2SO_4(*l*)	−814.0
C_3H_6O(*l*, acetone)	−248.4	N_2O(*g*)	81.6		

EXAMPLE 6.11 **STANDARD ENTHALPIES OF FORMATION**

Write equations for the formation of **(a)** $MgCO_3(s)$ and **(b)** $C_6H_{12}O_6(s)$ from their respective elements in their standard states. Include the value of $\Delta_f H°$ for each equation.

SOLUTION

(a) $MgCO_3(s)$ Write the equation with the elements in $MgCO_3$ in their standard states as the reactants and 1 mol of $MgCO_3$ as the product.	$Mg(s) + C(s, \text{graphite}) + O_2(g) \longrightarrow MgCO_3(s)$
Balance the equation and look up $\Delta_f H°$ in Appendix IIB. (Use fractional coefficients so that the product of the reaction is 1 mol of $MgCO_3$.)	$Mg(s) + C(s, \text{graphite}) + \frac{3}{2}O_2(g) \longrightarrow MgCO_3(s)$ $\Delta_f H° = -1095.8 \text{ kJ mol}^{-1}$
(b) $C_6H_{12}O_6(s)$ Write the equation with the elements in $C_6H_{12}O_6$ in their standard states as the reactants and 1 mol of $C_6H_{12}O_6$ as the product.	$C(s, \text{graphite}) + H_2(g) + O_2(g) \longrightarrow C_6H_{12}O_6(s)$
Balance the equation and look up $\Delta_f H°$ in Appendix IIB.	$6\,C(s, \text{graphite}) + 6\,H_2(g) + 3\,O_2(g) \longrightarrow C_6H_{12}O_6(s)$ $\Delta_f H° = -1273.3 \text{ kJ mol}^{-1}$

FOR PRACTICE 6.11

Write equations for the formation of **(a)** $NaCl(s)$ and **(b)** $Pb(NO_3)_2(s)$ from their respective elements in their standard states. Include the value of $\Delta_f H°$ for each equation.

Calculating the Standard Enthalpy Change for a Reaction

We have just seen that the standard enthalpy of formation corresponds to the *formation* of a compound from its constituent elements in their standard states:

$$\text{elements} \longrightarrow \text{compound} \quad \Delta_f H°$$

Therefore, the *negative* of the standard enthalpy of formation corresponds to the *decomposition* of a compound into its constituent elements in their standard states:

$$\text{compound} \longrightarrow \text{elements} \quad -\Delta_f H°$$

We can use these two concepts—the decomposing of a compound into its elements and the forming of a compound from its elements—to calculate the enthalpy change of any reaction by mentally taking the reactants through two steps. In the first step, we *decompose the reactants* into their constituent elements in their standard states; in the second step, we *form the products* from the constituent elements in their standard states.

$$\begin{array}{lll} \text{reactants} \longrightarrow \text{elements} & \Delta_r H_1 = -\Sigma \Delta_f H°(\text{reactants}) \\ \text{elements} \longrightarrow \text{products} & \Delta_r H_2 = +\Sigma \Delta_f H°(\text{products}) \\ \hline \text{reactants} \longrightarrow \text{products} & \Delta_r H° = \Delta H_1 + \Delta H_2 \end{array}$$

In these equations, Σ means "the sum of," so that $\Delta_r H_1$ is the sum of the negatives of the heats of formation of the reactants and $\Delta_r H_2$ is the sum of the heats of formation of the products.

We can demonstrate this procedure by calculating the standard enthalpy change $\Delta_r H°$ for the combustion of methane:

$$CH_4(g) + 2\,O_2(g) \longrightarrow CO_2(g) + 2\,H_2O(g) \quad \Delta_r H° = ?$$

The energy changes associated with the decomposition of the reactants and the formation of the products are shown in Figure 6.10 ▸. Step 1 is the decomposition of 1 mol of methane into its constituent elements in their standard states. We can obtain the change

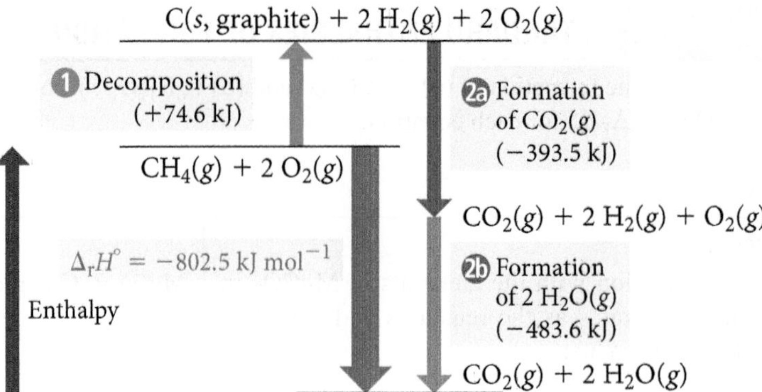

▶ **FIGURE 6.10 Calculating the Enthalpy Change for the Combustion of Methane**

in enthalpy for this step by reversing the enthalpy of formation equation for methane and changing the sign of $\Delta_f H°$:

$$\text{(1) } CH_4(g) \longrightarrow C(s, \text{graphite}) + 2\,H_2(g) \qquad -\Delta_f H° = 74.6 \text{ kJ mol}^{-1}$$

The second step, the formation of the products from their constituent elements, has two parts: (a) the formation of 1 mol CO_2, and (b) the formation of 2 mol H_2O. Since part (b) forms 2 mol H_2O, we multiply the $\Delta_f H°$ for that step by 2.

$$\text{(2a) } C(s, \text{graphite}) + O_2(g) \longrightarrow CO_2(g) \qquad \Delta_f H° = -393.5 \text{ kJ mol}^{-1}$$

$$\text{(2b) } 2 \times [H_2(g) + \tfrac{1}{2}\,O_2(g) \longrightarrow H_2O(g)] \quad 2 \times \Delta_f H° = 2 \times (-241.8 \text{ kJ mol}^{-1})$$

As we know from Hess's law, the enthalpy of reaction for the overall reaction is the sum of the enthalpies of reaction of the individual steps:

$$\begin{array}{llr} \text{(1) } CH_4(g) \longrightarrow \cancel{C(s, \text{graphite})} + \cancel{2\,H_2(g)} & -\Delta_f H° = & 74.6 \text{ kJ mol}^{-1} \\ \text{(2a) } \cancel{C(s, \text{graphite})} + O_2(g) \longrightarrow CO_2(g) & \Delta_f H° = & -393.5 \text{ kJ mol}^{-1} \\ \text{(2b) } \cancel{2\,H_2(g)} + O_2(g) \longrightarrow 2\,H_2O(g) & 2 \times \Delta_f H° = & -483.6 \text{ kJ mol}^{-1} \\ \hline CH_4(g) + 2\,O_2(g) \longrightarrow CO_2(g) + 2\,H_2O(g) & \Delta_r H° = & -802.5 \text{ kJ mol}^{-1} \end{array}$$

We can streamline and generalize this process as follows:

> **To calculate $\Delta_r H°$, subtract the enthalpies of formation of the reactants multiplied by their stoichiometric coefficients from the enthalpies of formation of the products multiplied by their stoichiometric coefficients.**

In the form of an equation, the process is:

$$\Delta_r H° = \Sigma\, \nu_p \Delta_f H°_{\text{products}} - \Sigma\, \nu_r \Delta_f H°_{\text{reactants}} \qquad [6.17]$$

In this equation, ν_p represents the stoichiometric coefficients of the products, ν_r represents the stoichiometric coefficients of the reactants, and $\Delta_f H°$ represents the standard enthalpies of formation. Keep in mind when using this equation that elements in their standard states have $\Delta_f H° = 0 \text{ kJ mol}^{-1}$. The following examples demonstrate this process.

EXAMPLE 6.12 $\Delta_r H°$ AND STANDARD ENTHALPIES OF FORMATION

Use the standard enthalpies of formation to determine $\Delta_r H°$ for the reaction:

$$4\,NH_3(g) + 5\,O_2(g) \longrightarrow 4\,NO(g) + 6\,H_2O(g)$$

SORT You are given the balanced equation and asked to find the enthalpy of reaction.	**GIVEN:** $4\,NH_3(g) + 5\,O_2(g) \longrightarrow 4\,NO(g) + 6\,H_2O(g)$ **FIND:** $\Delta_r H°$

STRATEGIZE To calculate $\Delta_r H°$ from standard enthalpies of formation, subtract the heats of formation of the reactants multiplied by their stoichiometric coefficients from the heats of formation of the products multiplied by their stoichiometric coefficients.

CONCEPTUAL PLAN

$$\Delta_r H° = \Sigma\, \nu_p \Delta_f H°_{products} - \Sigma\, \nu_r \Delta_f H°_{reactants}$$

SOLVE Begin by looking up (in Appendix IIB) the standard enthalpy of formation for each reactant and product. Remember that the standard enthalpy of formation of pure elements in their standard state is zero. Compute $\Delta_r H°$ by substituting into the equation.

SOLUTION

Reactant or Product	$\Delta_f H°$ (kJ mol^{-1}, from Appendix IIB)
$NH_3(g)$	−45.9
$O_2(g)$	0.0
$NO(g)$	91.3
$H_2O(g)$	−241.8

$$\begin{aligned}\Delta_r H° &= \Sigma\, \nu_p \Delta_f H°_{products} - \Sigma\, \nu_r \Delta_f H°_{reactants}\\ &= [4(\Delta_f H°_{NO(g)}) + 6(\Delta_f H°_{H_2O(g)})] - [4(\Delta_f H°_{NH_3(g)}) + 5(\Delta_f H°_{O_2(g)})]\\ &= [4(+91.3\text{ kJ mol}^{-1}) + 6(-241.8\text{ kJ mol}^{-1})] - [4(-45.9\text{ kJ mol}^{-1})\\ &\quad + 5(0.0\text{ kJ mol}^{-1})]\\ &= -1085.6\text{ kJ mol}^{-1} - (-183.6\text{ kJ mol}^{-1})\\ &= -902.0\text{ kJ mol}^{-1}\end{aligned}$$

CHECK The unit of the answer (kJ) is correct. The answer is negative, which means that the reaction is exothermic.

FOR PRACTICE 6.12

The thermite reaction, in which powdered aluminum reacts with iron oxide, is highly exothermic:

$$2\,Al(s) + Fe_2O_3(s) \longrightarrow Al_2O_3(s) + 2\,Fe(s)$$

Use standard enthalpies of formation to find $\Delta_r H°$ for the thermite reaction.

▶ The reaction of powdered aluminum with iron oxide, known as the thermite reaction, releases a large amount of heat.

EXAMPLE 6.13 $\Delta_r H°$ AND STANDARD ENTHALPIES OF FORMATION

A city of 100000 people uses approximately 1.0×10^{11} kJ of energy per day. Suppose all of that energy comes from the combustion of liquid octane (C_8H_{18}) to form gaseous water and gaseous carbon dioxide. Use standard enthalpies of formation to calculate $\Delta_r H°$ for the combustion of octane and then determine how many kilograms of octane would be necessary to provide this amount of energy.

SORT You are given the amount of energy used and asked to find the mass of octane required to produce the energy.

GIVEN: 1.0×10^{11} kJ

FIND: kg C_8H_{18}

(continued)

EXAMPLE 6.13 (CONTINUED)

STRATEGIZE The conceptual plan has three parts. In the first part, write a balanced equation for the combustion of octane.

In the second part, calculate $\Delta_r H°$ from the $\Delta_f H°$'s of the reactants and products.

In the third part, convert from kilojoules of energy to moles of octane using the conversion factor found in step 2, then convert from moles of octane to mass of octane using the molar mass.

CONCEPTUAL PLAN

(1) Write balanced equation.

(2)

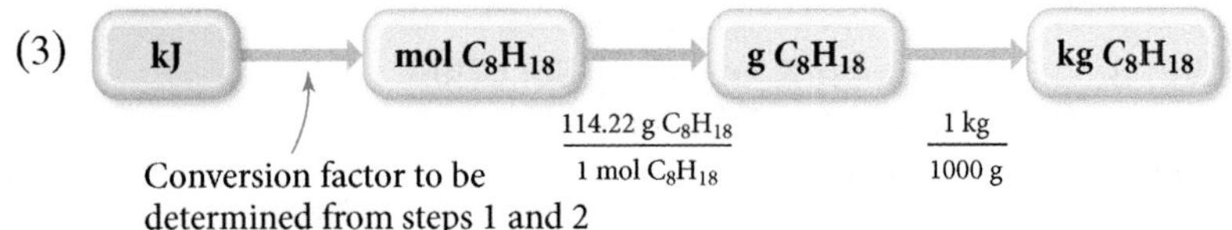

(3) kJ → mol C_8H_{18} → g C_8H_{18} → kg C_8H_{18}

Conversion factor to be determined from steps 1 and 2; $\frac{114.22 \text{ g } C_8H_{18}}{1 \text{ mol } C_8H_{18}}$; $\frac{1 \text{ kg}}{1000 \text{ g}}$

RELATIONSHIPS USED

molar mass $C_8H_{18} = 114.22 \text{ g mol}^{-1}$ $\quad$ 1 kg = 1000 g

SOLVE Begin by writing the balanced equation for the combustion of octane. For convenience, do not clear the 25/2 fraction in order to keep the coefficient on octane as 1.

SOLUTION STEP 1

$$C_8H_{18}(l) + \tfrac{25}{2} O_2(g) \longrightarrow 8\, CO_2(g) + 9\, H_2O(g)$$

Look up the standard enthalpy of formation (in Appendix IIB) for each reactant and product and then calculate $\Delta_r H°$.

SOLUTION STEP 2

Reactant or Product	$\Delta_f H°$ (kJ mol^{-1}, from Appendix IIB)
$C_8H_{18}(l)$	−250.1
$O_2(g)$	0.0
$CO_2(g)$	−393.5
$H_2O(g)$	−241.8

$$\begin{aligned}\Delta_r H° &= \Sigma\, \nu_p \Delta_f H°_{products} - \Sigma\, \nu_r \Delta_f H°_{reactants}\\ &= [8(\Delta_f H°_{CO_2(g)}) + 9(\Delta_f H°_{H_2O(g)})] - [1(\Delta_f H°_{C_8H_{18}(g)}) + \tfrac{25}{2}(\Delta_f H°_{O_2(g)})]\\ &= [8(-393.5 \text{ kJ mol}^{-1}) + 9(-241.8 \text{ kJ mol}^{-1})] - [1(-250.1 \text{ kJ mol}^{-1}) + \tfrac{25}{2}(0.0 \text{ kJ mol}^{-1})]\\ &= -5324.2 \text{ kJ mol}^{-1} - (-250.1 \text{ kJ mol}^{-1}) = -5074.1 \text{ kJ mol}^{-1}\end{aligned}$$

From steps 1 and 2, build a conversion factor between mol C_8H_{18} and kJ.

SOLUTION STEP 3

1 mol C_8H_{18} : −5074.1 kJ

Follow step 3 of the conceptual plan. Begin with -1.0×10^{11} kJ (since the city uses this much energy, the reaction must emit it, and therefore the sign is negative) and follow the steps to determine kg octane.

$$-1.0 \times 10^{11} \text{ kJ mol}^{-1} \times \frac{1 \text{ mol } C_8H_{18}}{-5074.1 \text{ kJ mol}^{-1}} \times \frac{114.22 \text{ g } C_8H_{18}}{1 \text{ mol } C_8H_{18}} \times \frac{1 \text{ kg}}{1000 \text{ g}} = 2.3 \times 10^6 \text{ kg } C_8H_{18}$$

CHECK The units of the answer (kg C_8H_{18}) are correct. The answer is positive, as it should be for mass. The magnitude is fairly large, as you would expect since this amount of octane is supposed to provide the energy for an entire city.

FOR PRACTICE 6.13

The chemical hand warmers described in Section 6.1 produce heat when they are removed from their airtight plastic wrappers. Recall that they utilize the oxidation of iron to form iron oxide according to the reaction $4\, Fe(s) + 3\, O_2(g) \longrightarrow 2\, Fe_2O_3(s)$. Calculate $\Delta_r H°$ for this reaction and compute how much heat is produced from a hand warmer containing 15.0 g of iron powder.

6.10 Energy Use and the Environment

In this chapter, we have learned about the relationship between chemical reactions and energy changes. As noted earlier, our society derives the majority of its energy from the energy changes associated with burning fossil fuels. Fossil fuels undergo combustion reactions that have large negative enthalpies of reaction (the reactions are highly exothermic). Fossil fuels have traditionally been regarded as convenient sources of energy due to their abundance, portability, and relatively low cost. In 2014, the world's primary energy consumption was equivalent to 541 exajoules (1 exajoule = 10^{18} J) or the equivalent of approximately 92 billion barrels of oil. The percentage of this consumption from oil, natural gas, and coal fossil fuels was 86.3%. The reactions for the combustion of the main or representative components of several fossil fuels, and the associated enthalpies of reaction, are as follows:

Primary Energy Sources

- Oil, 32.6%
- Gas, 23.7%
- Coal, 30.0%
- Nuclear, 4.4%
- Hydroelectric, 6.8%
- Other renewables, 2.5%

Source: *BP Statistical Review of World Energy*, June 2015.

Coal:	$C(s) + O_2(g) \longrightarrow CO_2(g)$	$\Delta_r H^\circ = -393.5\,\text{kJ mol}^{-1}$
Natural Gas:	$CH_4(g) + 2\,O_2(g) \longrightarrow CO_2(g) + 2\,H_2O\,(g)$	$\Delta_r H^\circ = -802.3\,\text{kJ mol}^{-1}$
Petroleum:	$C_8H_{18}(l) + \frac{25}{2}\,O_2(g) \longrightarrow 8\,CO_2(g) + 9\,H_2O(g)$	$\Delta_r H^\circ = -5074.1\,\text{kJ mol}^{-1}$

Implications of Dependence on Fossil Fuels

There are some serious implications to the world's current dependence on fossil fuels. One is that burning fossil fuels produces large amounts of CO_2, which has been implicated in global climate change. Whether or not CO_2 emissions are the cause of climate change, we do know that the amount of CO_2 in the atmosphere has increased from 290 to 400 ppm between 1860 and 2014. Much of this increase in CO_2 is a direct result of burning fossil fuels. At best, the effect of this increase in CO_2 in our atmosphere has an unknown effect on our global environment, which is a dangerous prospect. Another potential effect of increasing CO_2 levels in the atmosphere is increased acidity of oceans and lakes, which has an effect on marine life, especially shellfish whose shells are composed of calcium carbonate, which is more soluble in an acidic solution.

Proven Oil Reserves (billions of barrels)

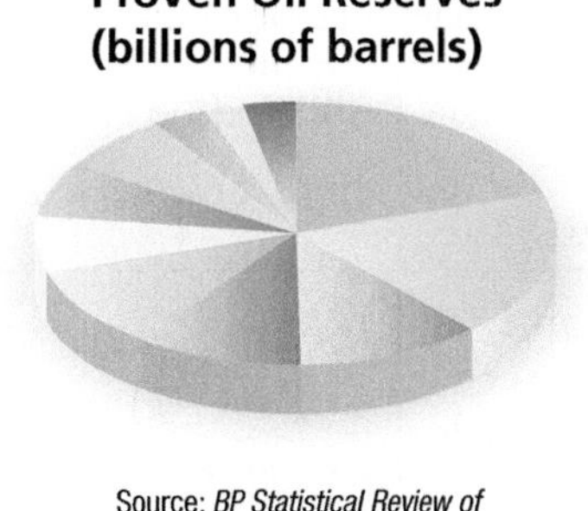

- Venezuela, 298.3
- Saudi Arabia, 267.0
- Canada, 172.9
- Iran, 157.8
- Iraq, 150.0
- Kuwait, 101.5
- United Arab Emirates, 97.8
- Russian Federation, 103.2
- Libya, 48.4
- Nigeria, 37.4
- US, 48.5

Source: *BP Statistical Review of World Energy*, June 2015.

Another major problem with our dependence on fossil fuels for energy is that they are nonrenewable. Fossil fuels originate from ancient plant and animal life and were formed over the last two billion years. Clearly, we cannot wait another two billion years to replenish the fossil fuels. At current rates of consumption, we will have depleted the proven oil reserves in about 50 years—within your lifetime! At current consumption rates and with the known reserves, natural gas will be depleted in 60–70 years, and coal will last only another 120 years. These are "world" average values and at the current usage rates. Canada, for example, has the third largest proven oil reserve when the oil sands in Alberta are included (172.9 billion barrels), and at the current rate of production of oil in Canada, we could produce oil for about 140 years. However, as the world begins to run out of oil, the price will increase and the rate of production of the oil sands will likely increase, decreasing the time to deplete our oil reserves.

We should all practice conservation, but that will only get us so far; we need energy. Indeed the world's energy demands are growing, and we are consuming ever more energy, including fossil fuels, as can be seen in Figure 6.11 ▼.

Since we cannot rely on fossil fuels in the long term, scientists and engineers are looking for solutions to the world's long-term and increasing energy demands. Over the past decades, we have been exploring and increasing the use of renewable energy sources such as wind, solar power, and biofuels such as ethanol (see Figure 6.12 ▼). As an example, every year, the sun irradiates the land with the equivalent of 139 trillion barrels of oil. If we could harvest only 0.05% of this radiation, we could do away with fossil fuels and nuclear power altogether; clearly, much research effort is required in making use of the sun's energy.

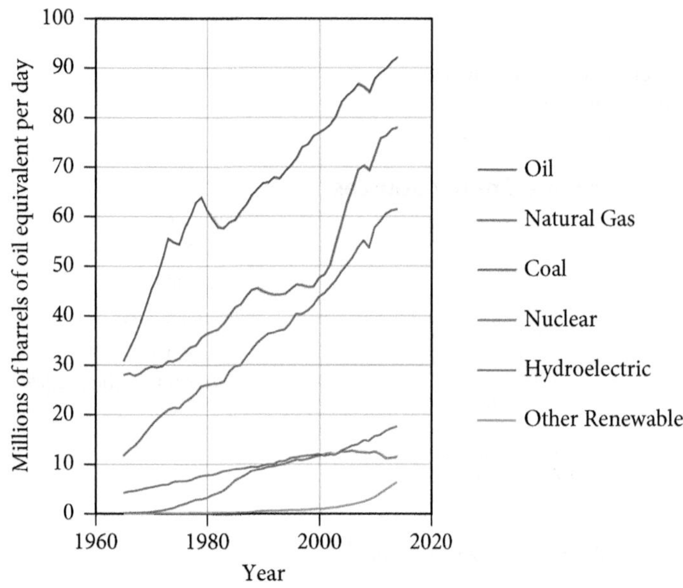

▲ **FIGURE 6.11 World Energy Consumption by Source**
Source: *BP Statistical Review of World Energy*, June 2015.

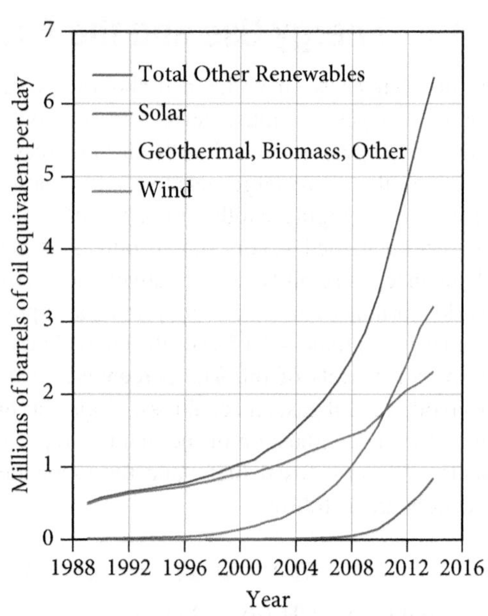

▲ **FIGURE 6.12 Consumption of Renewable Energy**
Source: *BP Statistical Review of World Energy*, June 2015.

EXAMPLE 6.14 PORTABLE ENERGY

One way to evaluate fuels is by their portability. The liquid gasoline we currently use in our vehicles is easy to transfer compared with solid fuels (such as coal) and is safer to store than gaseous fuels (such as hydrogen and natural gas, which require high pressure to store enough fuel to be useful). It is also important to have the most energy for the mass that is being carried in your vehicle. Use the combustion reactions of hydrogen, carbon, natural gas, and octane, in combination with the energy of combustion for each reaction, to determine which fuel gives the most heat per 1.00 kg of fuel.

SORT You are given 1.00 kg of each fuel and are asked to find which fuel gives the most energy per kilogram.

GIVEN: 1.00 kg of each fuel

FIND: kJ of energy provided by combustion of 1.00 kg of each fuel

STRATEGIZE You must first write the thermochemical equations for the combustion of each fuel you are asked to explore.

$$H_2(g) + \tfrac{1}{2}O_2(g) \longrightarrow H_2O(g) \qquad \Delta_r H^\circ = -241.8\ \text{kJ mol}^{-1}$$
$$C(s) + O_2(g) \longrightarrow CO_2(g) \qquad \Delta_r H^\circ = -393.5\ \text{kJ mol}^{-1}$$
$$CH_4(g) + 2\,O_2(g) \longrightarrow CO_2(g) + 2\,H_2O(g) \qquad \Delta_r H^\circ = -802.3\ \text{kJ mol}^{-1}$$
$$C_8H_{18}(l) + \tfrac{25}{2}O_2(g) \longrightarrow 8\,CO_2(g) + 9\,H_2O(g) \qquad \Delta_r H^\circ = -5074.1\ \text{kJ mol}^{-1}$$

The conceptual plan has two parts for each fuel. First, use the molar mass of the fuel to compute the number of moles of fuel.

Second, use the number of moles of fuel to compute the energy output.

CONCEPTUAL PLAN

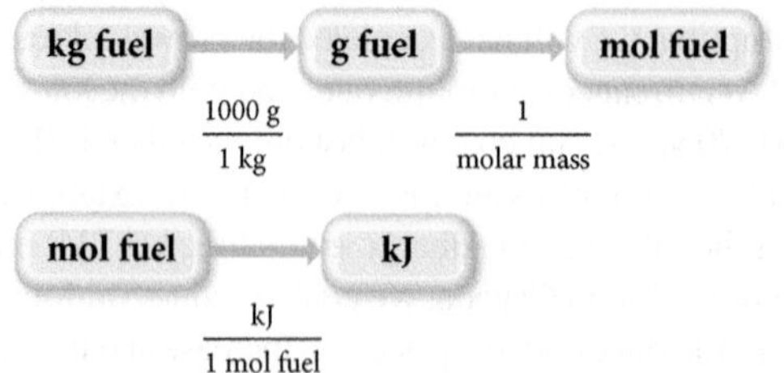

STOICHIOMETRIC RELATIONSHIPS

1 mol $H_2(g)$: -241.8 kJ 1 mol $CH_4(g)$: -802.3 kJ
1 mol $C(s)$: -393.5 kJ 1 mol $C_8H_{18}(l)$: -5074.1 kJ

OTHER RELATIONSHIPS USED

molar mass $H_2 = 2.016\ \text{g mol}^{-1}$ molar mass $CH_4 = 16.04\ \text{g mol}^{-1}$
molar mass $C = 12.01\ \text{g mol}^{-1}$ molar mass $C_8H_{18} = 114.23\ \text{g mol}^{-1}$

SOLVE Determine the number of moles contained in 1.00 kg of each fuel and then determine the heat released in the combustion of 1.00 kg of each fuel.	**SOLUTION** For H_2: $1.00\ \text{kg}\ H_2 \times \frac{1000\ \text{g}}{1\ \text{kg}} \times \frac{1\ \text{mol}\ H_2}{2.016\ \text{g}\ H_2} = 49\underline{6}.0\ \text{mol}\ H_2$ $49\underline{6}.0\ \text{mol}\ H_2 \times \frac{-241.8\ \text{kJ}}{1\ \text{mol}\ H_2} = -1.20 \times 10^5\ \text{kJ}$
Follow the same procedure for each of the other fuels. For each of the other fuels, the two steps have been simplified to one calculation.	For C: $1.00\ \text{kg}\ C \times \frac{1000\ \text{g}}{1\ \text{kg}} \times \frac{1\ \text{mol}\ C}{12.01\ \text{g}\ C} \times \frac{-393.5\ \text{kJ}}{1\ \text{mol}\ C} = -3.28 \times 10^4\ \text{kJ}$ For CH_4: $1.00\ \text{kg}\ CH_4 \times \frac{1000\ \text{g}}{1\ \text{kg}} \times \frac{1\ \text{mol}\ CH_4}{16.04\ \text{g}\ CH_4} \times \frac{-802.3\ \text{kJ}}{1\ \text{mol}\ CH_4} = -5.00 \times 10^4\ \text{kJ}$ For C_8H_{18}: $1.00\ \text{kg}\ C_8H_{18} \times \frac{1000\ \text{g}}{1\ \text{kg}} \times \frac{1\ \text{mol}\ C_8H_{18}}{114.23\ \text{g}\ C_8H_{18}} \times \frac{-5074.1\ \text{kJ}}{1\ \text{mol}\ C_8H_{18}} = -4.44 \times 10^4\ \text{kJ}$

The heat released for the combustion of 1.00 kg of H_2 produces the most heat of all the fuels, more than twice as much as the second-place CH_4. Therefore, it would be more efficient to carry around H_2 than any of the other fuels, and it would be better for the environment since it does not produce CO_2. Cost and storage issues still remain as a barrier to mass-production of automobiles that burn H_2.

CHECK Each answer is in kJ, as it should be for heat produced. Each answer is negative, as expected for exothermic reactions.

FOR PRACTICE 6.14

What mass of CO_2 (in kg) does the combustion of a 60.0 L tank of gasoline release into the atmosphere? Assume that the gasoline is pure octane (C_8H_{18}) and that it has a density of 0.70 g ml^{-1}.

CHAPTER IN REVIEW

Key Terms

Section 6.1
thermochemistry (198)

Section 6.2
energy (198)
work (w) (198)
heat (q) (198)
kinetic energy (198)
thermal energy (198)
potential energy (198)
chemical energy (199)
law of conservation of energy (199)
system (199)
surroundings (199)
joule (J) (200)
calorie (cal) (200)
Calorie (Cal) (200)
kilowatt-hour (kWh) (200)

Section 6.3
thermodynamics (200)
first law of thermodynamics (200)
internal energy (U) (201)
state function (202)

Section 6.4
thermal equilibrium (205)
heat capacity (C) (205)
specific heat capacity (C_s) (205)
molar heat capacity (205)
pressure–volume work (209)

Section 6.5
calorimetry (212)
bomb calorimeter (212)

Section 6.6
enthalpy (H) (215)
endothermic reaction (217)
exothermic reaction (217)
enthalpy (heat) of reaction ($\Delta_r H$) (218)

Section 6.7
coffee-cup calorimeter (219)

Section 6.8
Hess's law (221)

Section 6.9
standard state (224)
standard enthalpy change ($\Delta_r H°$) (224)
standard enthalpy of formation ($\Delta_f H°$) (224)
standard heat of formation ($\Delta_f H°$) (224)

Key Concepts

The Nature of Energy and Thermodynamics (6.2, 6.3)

Energy, which is measured in the SI unit of joules (J), is the capacity to do work. Work is the result of a force acting through a distance. Many different kinds of energy exist, including kinetic energy, thermal energy, potential energy, and chemical energy, a type of potential energy associated with the relative positions of electrons and nuclei in atoms and molecules. According to the first law of thermodynamics, energy can be converted from one form to another, but the total amount of energy is always conserved.

The internal energy (U) of a system is the sum of all of its kinetic and potential energy. Internal energy is a state function, which means that it depends only on the state of the system and not on the pathway by which it got to that state. A chemical system exchanges energy with its surroundings through heat (the transfer of thermal energy caused by a temperature difference) or work. The total change in internal energy is the sum of these two quantities.

Heat and Work (6.4)

Heat can be quantified using the equation $q = m \times C_s \times \Delta T$. In this expression, C_s is the specific heat capacity, the amount of heat required to change the temperature of 1 g of the substance by 1 °C. Compared to most substances, water has a very high heat capacity—it takes a lot of heat to change its temperature.

The type of work most characteristic of chemical reactions is pressure–volume work, which occurs when a gas expands against an external pressure. Pressure–volume work can be quantified with the equation $w = -P\Delta V$. For a chemical reaction involving gases we can calculate the work done using $w = -\Delta nRT$. The change in internal energy (ΔU) that occurs during a chemical reaction is the sum of the heat (q) exchanged and the work (w) done: $\Delta U = q + w$.

Enthalpy (6.6)

The heat evolved in a chemical reaction occurring at constant pressure is called the change in enthalpy (ΔH) for the reaction. Like internal energy, enthalpy is a state function. An endothermic reaction has a positive enthalpy of reaction, whereas an exothermic reaction has a negative enthalpy of reaction. The enthalpy of reaction can be used to determine stoichiometrically the heat evolved when a specific amount of reactant reacts.

Calorimetry (6.5, 6.7)

Calorimetry is a method of determining $\Delta_r U$ or $\Delta_r H$ for a reaction. In bomb calorimetry, the reaction is carried out under conditions of constant volume, so $\Delta U = q_V$. The temperature change of the calorimeter can therefore be used to calculate ΔU for the reaction. When a reaction takes place at constant pressure, energy may be released both as heat and as work. We can compute the enthalpy change for a reaction involving a change in the number of moles of gases from the internal energy change using the equation $\Delta_r H = \Delta_r U + \Delta nRT$. In coffee-cup calorimetry, a reaction is carried out under atmospheric pressure in a solution, so $q_p = \Delta H$. The temperature change of the solution is used to calculate ΔH for the reaction. Both ΔH and ΔU can be divided by the number of moles of reactant to determine $\Delta_r H$ and $\Delta_r U$ for a chemical reaction.

Calculating $\Delta_r H$ (6.8, 6.9)

The enthalpy of reaction $\Delta_r H$ can be calculated from known thermochemical data in two ways. The first method involves using the following relationships: (a) when a reaction is multiplied by a factor, $\Delta_r H$ is multiplied by the same factor; (b) when a reaction is reversed, $\Delta_r H$ changes sign; and (c) if a chemical reaction can be expressed as a sum of two or more steps, $\Delta_r H$ is the sum of the $\Delta_r H$'s for the individual steps (Hess's law). Together, these relationships can be used to determine the enthalpy change of an unknown reaction from reactions with known enthalpy changes. The second method is to calculate $\Delta_r H$ from known thermochemical data by using tabulated standard enthalpies of formation for the reactants and products of the reaction. These are usually tabulated for substances in their standard states, and the enthalpy of reaction is called the standard enthalpy of reaction ($\Delta_r H^\circ$). For any reaction, $\Delta_r H^\circ$ is obtained by subtracting the sum of the enthalpies of formation of the reactants multiplied by their stoichiometric coefficients from the sum of the enthalpies of formation of the products multiplied by their stoichiometric coefficients.

Environmental Problems Associated with Fossil Fuel Use (6.10)

Fossil fuels are nonrenewable fuels; once they are consumed, they cannot be replaced. At current rates of consumption, natural gas and petroleum reserves will be depleted in 40–120 years. In addition to their limited supply, the products of the combustion of fossil fuels—directly or indirectly formed—contribute to several environmental problems, including air pollution, acid rain, and perhaps global climate change.

Key Equations and Relationships

Kinetic Energy (6.2)

$$\text{KE} = \frac{1}{2}mv^2$$

Change in Internal Energy (ΔU) of a Chemical System (6.3)

$$\Delta_r U = U_{\text{products}} - U_{\text{reactants}}$$

Energy Flow Between System and Surroundings (6.3)

$$\Delta U_{\text{system}} = -\Delta U_{\text{surroundings}}$$

Relationship Between Internal Energy (ΔU), Heat (q), and Work (w) (6.3)

$$\Delta U = q + w$$

Relationship Between Heat (q), Temperature (T), and Heat Capacity (C) (6.4)

$$q = C \times \Delta T$$

Relationship Between Heat (q), Mass (m), Temperature (T), and Specific Heat Capacity of a Substance (C_s) (6.4)

$$q = m \times C_s \times \Delta T$$

Relationship Between Work (w), Force (F), and Distance (d) (6.4)

$$w = -F \times d$$

Relationship Between Work (w), Pressure (P), and Change in Volume (ΔV) (6.4)

$$w = -P\Delta V$$

Relationship Between Pressure–Volume Work (w) for a Reaction Involving Gases (6.4)

$$w = -\Delta nRT$$

Change in Internal Energy (ΔU) of System at Constant Volume (6.5)

$$\Delta U = q_v$$

Heat of a Bomb Calorimeter (q_{cal}) (6.5)

$$q_{cal} = C_{cal} \times \Delta T$$

Heat Exchange Between a Calorimeter and a Reaction (6.5)

$$q_{cal} = -q_r$$

Relationship Between Enthalpy (ΔH), Internal Energy (ΔU), Pressure (P), and Volume (V) (6.6)

$$\Delta H = \Delta U + P\Delta V$$
$$\Delta H = q_p$$

Relationship Between ($\Delta_r U$) and ($\Delta_r H$) for a Chemical Reaction Involving Gases (6.6)

$$\Delta_r H = \Delta_r U + \Delta nRT$$

Relationship Between Enthalpy of a Reaction ($\Delta_r H°$) and the Heats of Formation ($\Delta_f H°$) (6.9)

$$\Delta_r H° = \sum v_p \Delta_f H°_{products} - \sum v_r \Delta_f H°_{reactants}$$

Key Skills

Calculating Internal Energy from Heat and Work (6.3)
• Example 6.1 • For Practice 6.1 • Exercises 41–44, 53–54

Finding Heat from Temperature Changes (6.4)
• Example 6.2 • For Practice 6.2 • For More Practice 6.2 • Exercises 47–48

Thermal Energy Transfer (6.4)
• Example 6.3 • For Practice 6.3 • Exercises 49–50, 65–70

Finding Work from Volume Changes (6.4)
• Example 6.4 • For Practice 6.4 • Exercises 51–52

Finding Pressure–Volume Work for Chemical Reactions Involving Gases (6.4)
• Example 6.5 • For Practice 6.5 • Exercises 53–56

Using Bomb Calorimetry to Calculate $\Delta_r U$ and $\Delta_r H$ (6.5, 6.6)
• Examples 6.6, 6.7 • For Practice 6.6, 6.7 • For More Practice 6.6 • Exercises 73–74

Predicting Endothermic and Exothermic Processes (6.6)
• Example 6.6 • For Practice 6.6 • Exercises 59–60

Determining Heat from ΔH and Stoichiometry (6.6)
• Examples 6.8, 6.12 • For Practice 6.8, 6.12 • For More Practice 6.8 • Exercises 61–64

Finding $\Delta_r H$ Using Calorimetry (6.7)
• Example 6.9 • For Practice 6.9 • Exercises 75–76

Finding $\Delta_r H$ Using Hess's Law (6.8)
• Example 6.10 • For Practice 6.10 • For More Practice 6.10 • Exercises 79–82

Finding $\Delta_r H$ Using Standard Enthalpies of Formation (6.9)
• Examples 6.11, 6.12, 6.13 • For Practice 6.11, 6.12, 6.13 • Exercises 85–92

EXERCISES

Review Questions

1. What is thermochemistry? Why is it important?
2. What is energy? What is work? Give some examples of each.
3. What is kinetic energy? What is potential energy? Give some examples of each.
4. What is the law of conservation of energy? How does it relate to energy exchanges between a thermodynamic system and its surroundings?
5. What is the SI unit of energy? List some other common units of energy.
6. What is the first law of thermodynamics? What are its implications?
7. A friend claims to have constructed a machine that creates electricity, but requires no energy input. Explain why you should be suspicious of your friend's claim.
8. What is a state function? List some examples of state functions.
9. What is internal energy? Is internal energy a state function?
10. If energy flows out of a chemical system and into the surroundings, what is the sign of ΔU_{system}?
11. If the internal energy of the products of a reaction is higher than the internal energy of the reactants, what is the sign of ΔU for the reaction? In which direction does energy flow?
12. What is heat? Explain the difference between heat and temperature.
13. How is the change in internal energy of a system related to heat and work?
14. Explain how the sum of heat and work can be a state function, even though heat and work are themselves not state functions.
15. What is heat capacity? Explain the difference between heat capacity and specific heat capacity.
16. Explain how the high specific heat capacity of water can affect the weather in coastal versus inland regions.
17. If two objects, A and B, of different temperatures come into direct contact, what is the relationship between the heat lost by one object and the heat gained by the other? What is the relationship between the temperature changes of the two objects? (Assume that the two objects do not lose any heat to anything else.)
18. What is pressure–volume work? How is it calculated?
19. What is calorimetry? Explain the difference between a coffee-cup calorimeter and a bomb calorimeter. What is each designed to measure?
20. What is the change in enthalpy (ΔH) for a chemical reaction? How is ΔH different from ΔU?
21. Explain the difference between an exothermic and an endothermic reaction. Give the sign of ΔH for each type of reaction.
22. From a molecular viewpoint, where does the energy emitted in an exothermic chemical reaction come from? Why does the reaction mixture undergo an increase in temperature even though energy is emitted?
23. From a molecular viewpoint, where does the energy absorbed in an endothermic chemical reaction go? Why does the reaction mixture undergo a decrease in temperature even though energy is absorbed?
24. Is the change in enthalpy for a reaction an extensive property? Explain the relationship between ΔH for a reaction and the amounts of reactants and products that undergo reaction.
25. Explain how the value of $\Delta_r H$ for a reaction changes upon:
    a. multiplying the reaction by a factor.
    b. reversing the reaction.

    Why do these relationships hold?
26. What is Hess's law? Why is it useful?
27. What is a standard state? What is the standard enthalpy change for a reaction?
28. What is the standard enthalpy of formation for a compound? For a pure element in its standard state?
29. How can you calculate $\Delta_r H^\circ$ from tabulated standard enthalpies of formation?
30. What are the main sources of the energy consumed in the world?
31. What are the main problems associated with fossil fuel use?
32. What are renewable energy sources? State some renewable sources of energy.

Problems by Topic

Energy Units

33. Perform each conversion between energy units:
    a. 534 kWh to J
    b. 215 kJ to Cal
    c. 567 Cal to J
    d. 2.85×10^3 J to cal
34. Perform each conversion between energy units:
    a. 231 cal to kJ
    b. 132×10^4 kJ to kcal
    c. 4.99×10^3 kJ to kWh
    d. 2.88×10^4 J to Cal
35. Suppose that a person eats a diet of 2387 Calories per day. Convert this energy into each unit:
    a. J
    b. kJ
    c. kWh
36. A particular frost-free refrigerator uses about 745 kWh of electrical energy per year. Express this amount of energy in each unit:
    a. J
    b. kJ
    c. Cal

Internal Energy, Heat, and Work

37. Which statement is true of the internal energy of a system and its surroundings during an energy exchange with a negative ΔU_{sys}?
    a. The internal energy of the system increases and the internal energy of the surroundings decreases.
    b. The internal energy of both the system and the surroundings increases.

c. The internal energy of both the system and the surroundings decreases.
d. The internal energy of the system decreases and the internal energy of the surroundings increases.

38. During an energy exchange, a chemical system absorbs energy from its surroundings. What is the sign of ΔU_{sys} for this process? Explain.

39. Identify each energy exchange as primarily heat or work and determine whether the sign of ΔU is positive or negative for the system.
a. Sweat evaporates from skin, cooling the skin. (The evaporating sweat is the system.)
b. A balloon expands against an external pressure. (The contents of the balloon is the system.)
c. An aqueous chemical reaction mixture is warmed with an external flame. (The reaction mixture is the system.)

40. Identify each energy exchange as primarily heat or work and determine whether the sign of ΔU is positive or negative for the system.
a. A rolling billiard ball collides with another billiard ball. The first billiard ball (defined as the system) stops rolling after the collision.
b. A book is dropped to the floor (the book is the system).
c. A father pushes his daughter on a swing (the daughter and the swing are the system).

41. A system releases 622 kJ of heat and does 105 kJ of work on the surroundings. What is the change in internal energy of the system?

42. A system absorbs 196 kJ of heat and the surroundings do 117 kJ of work on the system. What is the change in internal energy of the system?

43. The gas in a cylinder (defined as the system) warms and absorbs 655 J of heat. The expansion performs 344 J of work on the surroundings. What is the change in internal energy for the system?

44. The air in an inflated balloon (defined as the system) warms over a toaster and absorbs 115 J of heat. As it expands, it does 77 kJ of work. What is the change in internal energy for the system?

Heat, Heat Capacity, and Work

45. We pack two identical coolers for a picnic, placing twenty-four 355 mL soft drinks and 2.5 kg of ice in each. However, the drinks that we put into cooler A were refrigerated for several hours before they were packed in the cooler, while the drinks that we put into cooler B were at room temperature. When we open the two coolers three hours later, most of the ice in cooler A is still present, while nearly all of the ice in cooler B has melted. Explain this difference.

46. A kilogram of aluminum metal and a kilogram of water are each warmed to 75 °C and placed in two identical insulated containers. One hour later, the two containers are opened and the temperature of each substance is measured. The aluminum has cooled to 35 °C, while the water has cooled to only 66 °C. Explain this difference.

47. How much heat is required to warm 1.50 L of water from 25.0 °C to 100.0 °C? (Assume a density of 1.0 g mL^{-1} for the water.)

48. How much heat is required to warm 1.50 kg of sand from 25.0 °C to 100.0 °C?

49. Suppose that 25 g of each substance is initially at 27.0 °C. What is the final temperature of each substance upon absorbing 2.35 kJ of heat?
a. gold b. silver
c. aluminum d. water

50. An unknown mass of each substance, initially at 23.0 °C, absorbs 1.95×10^3 J of heat. The final temperature is recorded as indicated. Find the mass of each substance.
a. Pyrex glass ($T_f = 55.4$ °C)
b. sand ($T_f = 62.1$ °C)
c. ethanol ($T_f = 44.2$ °C)
d. water ($T_f = 32.4$ °C)

51. How much work (in J) is required to expand the volume of a pump from 0.0 L to 2.5 L against an external pressure of 1.1 bar?

52. The average human lung expands by about 0.50 L during each breath. If this expansion occurs against an external pressure of 1.0 bar, how much work (in J) is done during the expansion?

53. The air within a piston equipped with a cylinder absorbs 565 J of heat and expands from an initial volume of 0.10 L to a final volume of 0.85 L against an external pressure of 1.0 bar. What is the change in internal energy of the air within the piston?

54. A gas is compressed from an initial volume of 5.55 L to a final volume of 1.22 L by an external pressure of 1.00 bar. During the compression, the gas releases 124 J of heat. What is the change in internal energy of the gas?

55. What is the work associated with the decomposition of liquid peroxide forming gaseous oxygen and liquid water at 298.15 K?

56. What is the work associated with decomposition of trinitrotoluene (TNT) upon detonation according to the following reaction at 298.15 K?

$$C_7H_5N_3O_6(s) \longrightarrow \frac{3}{2}N_2(g) + \frac{5}{2}H_2(g) + 6\,O_2(g) + 2\,C(s)$$

Enthalpy and Thermochemical Stoichiometry

57. When 1 mol of a fuel burns at constant pressure, it produces 3452 kJ of heat and does 11 kJ of work. What are the values of ΔU and ΔH for the combustion of the fuel?

58. The change in internal energy for the combustion of 1.0 mol of octane at a pressure of 1.0 bar is −5084.3 kJ. If the change in enthalpy is −5074.1 kJ, how much work is done during the combustion?

59. Determine whether each process is exothermic or endothermic and indicate the sign of ΔH:
a. natural gas burning on a stove
b. isopropyl alcohol evaporating from skin
c. water condensing from steam

60. Determine whether each process is exothermic or endothermic and indicate the sign of ΔH:
a. dry ice evaporating
b. a sparkler burning
c. the reaction that occurs in a chemical cold pack used to ice athletic injuries

61. Consider the thermochemical equation for the combustion of acetone (C_3H_6O), the main ingredient in nail polish remover:

$$C_3H_6O(l) + 4\,O_2(g) \longrightarrow 3\,CO_2(g) + 3\,H_2O(g) \qquad \Delta_rH^\circ = -1790 \text{ kJ mol}^{-1}$$

If a bottle of nail polish remover contains 177 mL of acetone, how much heat is released by its complete combustion? The density of acetone is 0.788 g mL^{-1}.

62. What mass of natural gas (CH_4) must burn to emit 267 kJ of heat?

$$CH_4(g) + 2\,O_2(g) \longrightarrow CO_2(g) + 2\,H_2O(g) \qquad \Delta_rH^\circ = -802.3 \text{ kJ mol}^{-1}$$

63. The propane fuel (C_3H_8) used in gas barbeques burns according to the thermochemical equation:

$$C_3H_8(g) + 5\,O_2(g) \longrightarrow 3\,CO_2(g) + 4\,H_2O(g) \quad \Delta_rH° = -2217\ \text{kJ mol}^{-1}$$

If a pork roast must absorb 1.6×10^3 kJ to fully cook, and if only 10% of the heat produced by the barbeque is actually absorbed by the roast, what mass of CO_2 is emitted into the atmosphere during the grilling of the pork roast?

64. Charcoal is primarily carbon. Determine the mass of CO_2 produced by burning enough carbon (in the form of charcoal) to produce 5.00×10^2 kJ of heat.

$$C(s) + O_2(g) \longrightarrow CO_2(g) \qquad \Delta_rH° = -393.5\ \text{kJ mol}^{-1}$$

Thermal Energy Transfer

65. A silver block, initially at 58.5 °C, is submerged into 100.0 g of water at 24.8 °C, in an insulated container. The final temperature of the mixture upon reaching thermal equilibrium is 26.2 °C. What is the mass of the silver block?

66. A 32.5 g iron rod, initially at 22.7 °C, is submerged into an unknown mass of water at 63.2 °C, in an insulated container. The final temperature of the mixture upon reaching thermal equilibrium is 59.5 °C. What is the mass of the water?

67. A 31.1 g wafer of pure gold, initially at 69.3 °C, is submerged into 64.2 g of water at 27.8 °C, in an insulated container. What is the final temperature of both substances at thermal equilibrium?

68. A 2.85 g lead weight, initially at 10.3 °C, is submerged in 7.55 g of water at 52.3 °C, in an insulated container. What is the final temperature of both substances at thermal equilibrium?

69. Two substances, A and B, initially at different temperatures, come into contact and reach thermal equilibrium. The mass of substance A is 6.15 g and its initial temperature is 20.5 °C. The mass of substance B is 25.2 g and its initial temperature is 52.7 °C. The final temperature of both substances at thermal equilibrium is 46.7 °C. If the specific heat capacity of substance B is 1.17 J g^{-1} °C^{-1}, what is the specific heat capacity of substance A?

70. A 2.74 g sample of a substance suspected of being pure gold is warmed to 72.1 °C and submerged into 15.2 g of water, initially at 24.7 °C. The final temperature of the mixture is 26.3 °C. What is the heat capacity of the unknown substance? Could the substance be pure gold?

Calorimetry

71. Exactly 1.5 g of a fuel burns under conditions of constant pressure and then again under conditions of constant volume. In measurement A, the reaction produces 25.9 kJ of heat, and in measurement B, the reaction produces 23.3 kJ of heat. Which measurement (A or B) corresponds to conditions of constant pressure? Which one corresponds to conditions of constant volume? Explain.

72. In order to obtain the largest possible amount of heat from a chemical reaction in which there is a large increase in the number of moles of gas, should you carry out the reaction under conditions of constant volume or constant pressure? Explain.

73. When 0.5141 g of biphenyl ($C_{12}H_{10}$) undergoes combustion in a bomb calorimeter, the temperature rises from 25.823 °C to 29.419 °C. Find Δ_rU and Δ_rH for the combustion of biphenyl in kJ mol^{-1} at 298 K. The heat capacity of the bomb calorimeter, determined in a separate experiment, is 5.861 kJ °C^{-1}.

74. Mothballs are composed primarily of the hydrocarbon naphthalene ($C_{10}H_8$). When 1.025 g of naphthalene burns in a bomb calorimeter, the temperature rises from 24.259 °C to 32.338 °C. Find Δ_rU and Δ_rH for the combustion of naphthalene at 298 K. The heat capacity of the calorimeter, determined in a separate experiment, is 5.112 kJ °C^{-1}.

75. Zinc metal reacts with hydrochloric acid according to the following balanced equation:

$$Zn(s) + 2\,HCl(aq) \longrightarrow ZnCl_2(aq) + H_2(g)$$

When 0.103 g of Zn(*s*) is combined with enough HCl to make 50.0 mL of solution in a coffee-cup calorimeter, all of the zinc reacts, raising the temperature of the solution from 22.5 °C to 23.7 °C. Find Δ_rH for this reaction as written. (Use 1.0 g mL^{-1} for the density of the solution and 4.184 J g^{-1} °C^{-1} as the specific heat capacity.)

76. Instant cold packs, often used to ice athletic injuries on the field, contain ammonium nitrate and water separated by a thin plastic divider. When the divider is broken, the ammonium nitrate dissolves according to the following endothermic reaction:

$$NH_4NO_3(s) \longrightarrow NH_4^+(aq) + NO_3^-(aq)$$

In order to measure the enthalpy change for this reaction, 1.25 g of NH_4NO_3 is dissolved in enough water to make 25.0 mL of solution. The initial temperature is 25.8 °C and the final temperature (after the solid dissolves) is 21.9 °C. Calculate the change in enthalpy for the reaction in kJ. (Use 1.0 g mL^{-1} as the density of the solution and 4.184 J g^{-1} °C^{-1} as the specific heat capacity.)

Quantitative Relationships Involving Δ_rH and Hess's Law

77. For each generic reaction, determine the value of Δ_rH_2 in terms of Δ_rH_1:

a. $A + B \longrightarrow 2\,C \qquad \Delta_rH_1$
$2\,C \longrightarrow A + B \qquad \Delta_rH_2 = ?$

b. $A + \frac{1}{2}B \longrightarrow C \qquad \Delta_rH_1$
$2\,A + B \longrightarrow 2\,C \qquad \Delta_rH_2 = ?$

c. $A \longrightarrow B + 2\,C \qquad \Delta_rH_1$
$\frac{1}{2}B + C \longrightarrow \frac{1}{2}A \qquad \Delta_rH_2 = ?$

78. Consider the generic reaction:

$$A + 2\,B \longrightarrow C + 3\,D \quad \Delta_rH = 155\ \text{kJ mol}^{-1}$$

Determine the value of Δ_rH for each related reaction:

a. $3\,A + 6\,B \longrightarrow 3\,C + 9\,D$

b. $C + 3\,D \longrightarrow A + 2\,B$

c. $\frac{1}{2}C + \frac{3}{2}D \longrightarrow \frac{1}{2}A + B$

79. Calculate Δ_rH for the reaction:

$$Fe_2O_3(s) + 3\,CO(g) \longrightarrow 2\,Fe(s) + 3\,CO_2(g)$$

Use the following reactions and given Δ_rH's:

$$2\,Fe(s) + \tfrac{3}{2}O_2(g) \longrightarrow Fe_2O_3(s) \quad \Delta_rH = -824.2\ \text{kJ mol}^{-1}$$
$$CO(g) + \tfrac{1}{2}O_2(g) \longrightarrow CO_2(g) \quad \Delta_rH = -282.7\ \text{kJ mol}^{-1}$$

80. Calculate Δ_rH for the reaction:

$$CaO(s) + CO_2(g) \longrightarrow CaCO_3(s)$$

Use the following reactions and given Δ_rH's:

$$Ca(s) + CO_2(g) + \tfrac{1}{2}O_2(g) \longrightarrow CaCO_3(s) \quad \Delta_rH = -812.8\ \text{kJ mol}^{-1}$$
$$2\,Ca(s) + O_2(g) \longrightarrow 2\,CaO(s) \quad \Delta_rH = -1269.8\ \text{kJ mol}^{-1}$$

81. Calculate $\Delta_r H$ for the reaction:

$$5\,C(s) + 6\,H_2(g) \longrightarrow C_5H_{12}(l)$$

Use the following reactions and given $\Delta_r H$'s:

$$C_5H_{12}(l) + 8\,O_2(g) \longrightarrow 5\,CO_2(g) + 6\,H_2O(g) \quad \Delta_r H = -3505.8\text{ kJ mol}^{-1}$$
$$C(s) + O_2(g) \longrightarrow CO_2(g) \quad \Delta_r H = -393.5\text{ kJ mol}^{-1}$$
$$2\,H_2(g) + O_2(g) \longrightarrow 2\,H_2O(g) \quad \Delta_r H = -483.5\text{ kJ mol}^{-1}$$

82. Calculate $\Delta_r H$ for the reaction:

$$CH_4(g) + 4\,Cl_2(g) \longrightarrow CCl_4(g) + 4\,HCl(g)$$

Use the following reactions and given $\Delta_r H$'s:

$$C(s) + 2\,H_2(g) \longrightarrow CH_4(g) \quad \Delta_r H = -74.6\text{ kJ mol}^{-1}$$
$$C(s) + 2\,Cl_2(g) \longrightarrow CCl_4(g) \quad \Delta_r H = -95.7\text{ kJ mol}^{-1}$$
$$H_2(g) + Cl_2(g) \longrightarrow 2\,HCl(g) \quad \Delta_r H = -92.3\text{ kJ mol}^{-1}$$

Enthalpies of Formation and $\Delta_r H$

83. Write an equation for the formation of each compound from its elements in their standard states, and find $\Delta_f H°$ for each from Appendix IIB:
   a. $NH_3(g)$ **b.** $CO_2(g)$ **c.** $Fe_2O_3(s)$ **d.** $CH_4(g)$

84. Write an equation for the formation of each compound from its elements in their standard states, and find $\Delta_f H°$ for each from Appendix IIB:
   a. $NO_2(g)$ **b.** $MgCO_3(s)$ **c.** $C_2H_4(g)$ **d.** $CH_3OH(l)$

85. Hydrazine (N_2H_4) is a fuel used by some spacecraft. It is normally oxidized by N_2O_4 according to the equation:

$$N_2H_4(l) + N_2O_4(g) \longrightarrow 2\,N_2O(g) + 2\,H_2O(g)$$

Calculate $\Delta_r H°$ for this reaction using standard enthalpies of formation.

86. Pentane (C_5H_{12}) is a component of gasoline that burns according to the following balanced equation:

$$C_5H_{12}(l) + 8\,O_2(g) \longrightarrow 5\,CO_2(g) + 6\,H_2O(g)$$

Calculate $\Delta_r H°$ for this reaction using standard enthalpies of formation. (The standard enthalpy of formation of liquid pentane is $-146.8\text{ kJ mol}^{-1}$.)

87. Use standard enthalpies of formation to calculate $\Delta_r H°$ for each reaction:
   a. $C_2H_4(g) + H_2(g) \longrightarrow C_2H_6(g)$
   b. $CO(g) + H_2O(g) \longrightarrow H_2(g) + CO_2(g)$
   c. $3\,NO_2(g) + H_2O(l) \longrightarrow 2\,HNO_3(aq) + NO(g)$
   d. $Cr_2O_3(s) + 3\,CO(g) \longrightarrow 2\,Cr(s) + 3\,CO_2(g)$

88. Use standard enthalpies of formation to calculate $\Delta_r H°$ for each reaction:
   a. $2\,H_2S(g) + 3\,O_2(g) \longrightarrow 2\,H_2O(l) + 2\,SO_2(g)$
   b. $SO_2(g) + \frac{1}{2}\,O_2(g) \longrightarrow SO_3(g)$
   c. $C(s) + H_2O(g) \longrightarrow CO(g) + H_2(g)$
   d. $N_2O_4(g) + 4\,H_2(g) \longrightarrow N_2(g) + 4\,H_2O(g)$

89. During photosynthesis, plants use energy from sunlight to form glucose ($C_6H_{12}O_6$) and oxygen from carbon dioxide and water. Write a balanced equation for photosynthesis and calculate $\Delta_r H°$.

90. Ethanol can be made from the fermentation of crops and has been used as a fuel additive to gasoline. Write a balanced equation for the combustion of ethanol and calculate $\Delta_r H°$.

91. Top fuel dragsters and funny cars burn nitromethane as fuel according to the balanced combustion equation:

$$2\,CH_3NO_2(l) + \frac{3}{2}\,O_2(g) \longrightarrow 2\,CO_2(g) + 3\,H_2O(l) + N_2(g)$$

The standard enthalpy of combustion for nitromethane is $-709.2\text{ kJ mol}^{-1}$. Calculate the standard enthalpy of formation $\Delta_f H°$ for nitromethane.

92. The explosive nitroglycerin ($C_3H_5N_3O_9$) decomposes rapidly upon ignition or sudden impact according to the balanced equation:

$$4\,C_3H_5N_3O_9(l) \longrightarrow 12\,CO_2(g) + 10\,H_2O(g) + 6\,N_2(g) + O_2(g) \quad \Delta_r H° = -5678\text{ kJ mol}^{-1}$$

Calculate the standard enthalpy of formation $\Delta_f H°$ for nitroglycerin.

Energy Use and the Environment

93. Determine the mass of CO_2 produced by burning enough of each of the following fuels to produce 1.00×10^2 kJ of heat. Which fuel contributes least to the increase in atmospheric CO_2 per kJ of heat produced?
   a. $CH_4(g) + 2\,O_2(g) \longrightarrow CO_2(g) + 2\,H_2O(g) \quad \Delta_r H° = -802.3\text{ kJ mol}^{-1}$
   b. $C_3H_8(g) + 5\,O_2(g) \longrightarrow 3\,CO_2(g) + 4\,H_2O(g) \quad \Delta_r H° = -2217\text{ kJ mol}^{-1}$
   c. $C_8H_{18}(l) + \frac{25}{2}\,O_2(g) \longrightarrow 8\,CO_2(g) + 9\,H_2O(g) \quad \Delta_r H° = -5074.1\text{ kJ mol}^{-1}$

94. Methanol (CH_3OH) has been suggested as a fuel to replace gasoline. Write a balanced equation for the combustion of methanol, find $\Delta_r H°$, and determine the mass of carbon dioxide emitted per kJ of heat produced. Use the information from the previous exercise to calculate the same quantity for octane, C_8H_{18}. How does methanol compare to octane with respect to increasing atmospheric CO_2?

95. The citizens of the world burn the fossil fuel equivalent of 7×10^{12} kg of petroleum per year. Assume that all of this petroleum is in the form of octane (C_8H_{18}) and calculate how much CO_2 (in kg) is produced by world fossil fuel combustion per year. (*Hint:* Begin by writing a balanced equation for the combustion of octane.) If the atmosphere currently contains approximately 2×10^{17} kg of CO_2, how long will it take for the world's fossil fuel combustion to double the amount of atmospheric carbon dioxide?

96. In a sunny location, sunlight has a power density of about 1 kW m^{-2}. Photovoltaic solar cells can convert this power into electricity with 15% efficiency. If a typical home uses 385 kWh of electricity per month, how many square metres of solar cells would be required to meet its energy requirements? Assume that electricity can be generated from the sunlight for eight hours per day.

▲ What area of solar cells do you need to power a home?

Cumulative Problems

97. The kinetic energy of a rolling billiard ball is given by $KE = \frac{1}{2}mv^2$. Suppose a 0.17 kg billiard ball is rolling down a pool table with an initial speed of 4.5 m s^{-1}. As it travels, it loses some of its energy as heat. The ball slows down to 3.8 m s^{-1} and then collides head-on with a second billiard ball of equal mass. The first billiard ball completely stops and the second one rolls away with a velocity of 3.8 m s^{-1}. Assume the first billiard ball is the system and calculate w, q, and ΔU for the process.

98. A 100 W light bulb is placed in a cylinder equipped with a movable piston. The light bulb is turned on for 0.015 hour, and the assembly expands from an initial volume of 0.85 L to a final volume of 5.88 L against an external pressure of 1.0 atm. Use the wattage of the light bulb and the time it is on to calculate ΔU in joules (assume that the cylinder and light bulb assembly is the system and assume two significant figures). Calculate w and q.

99. Evaporating sweat cools the body because evaporation is an endothermic process:

$$H_2O(l) \rightarrow H_2O(g)\ \Delta_r H° = 44.01 \text{ kJ mol}^{-1}$$

Estimate the mass of water that must evaporate from the skin to cool the body by 0.50 °C. Assume a body mass of 95 kg and assume that the specific heat capacity of the body is 4.0 (J g^{-1} °C^{-1}).

100. Propane gas burns according to the exothermic reaction:

$$C_3H_8(g) + 5\,O_2(g) \longrightarrow 3\,CO_2(g) + 4\,H_2O(g) \quad \Delta_r H° = -2044 \text{ kJ mol}^{-1}$$

What mass of propane gas is necessary to heat 1.5 L of water from room temperature (25.0 °C) to boiling (100.0 °C)? Assume that during heating, 15% of the heat emitted by the propane combustion reaction goes to heat the water. The rest is lost as heat to the surroundings.

101. Use standard enthalpies of formation to calculate the standard change in enthalpy for the melting of ice. (The $\Delta_f H°$ for $H_2O(s)$ is −291.8 kJ mol^{-1}.) Use this value to calculate the mass of ice required to cool 355 mL of a beverage from room temperature (25.0 °C) to 0.0 °C. Assume that the specific heat capacity and density of the beverage are the same as those of water.

102. Dry ice is solid carbon dioxide. Instead of melting, solid carbon dioxide sublimes under normal atmospheric pressure according to the equation:

$$CO_2(s) \longrightarrow CO_2(g)$$

When dry ice is added to warm water, heat from the water causes the dry ice to sublime more quickly. The evaporating carbon dioxide produces a dense fog often used to create special effects. In a simple dry ice fog machine, dry ice is added to warm water in a Styrofoam cooler. The dry ice produces fog until it evaporates away, or until the water gets too cold to sublime the dry ice quickly enough. Suppose that a small Styrofoam cooler holds 15.0 L of water heated to 85 °C. Use standard enthalpies of formation to calculate the change in enthalpy for dry ice sublimation, and calculate the mass of dry ice that should be added to the water so that the dry ice completely sublimes away when the water reaches 25 °C. Assume no heat loss to the surroundings. (The $\Delta_f H°$ for $CO_2(s)$ is −427.4 kJ mol^{-1}.)

◀ When carbon dioxide sublimes, the gaseous CO_2 is cold enough to cause water vapour in the air to condense, forming fog.

103. A 25.5 g aluminum block is warmed to 65.4 °C and plunged into an insulated beaker containing 55.2 g water initially at 22.2 °C. The aluminum and the water are allowed to come to thermal equilibrium. Assuming that no heat is lost, what is the final temperature of the water and aluminum?

104. If 50.0 mL of ethanol (density = 0.789 g mL^{-1}) initially at 7.0 °C is mixed with 50.0 mL of water (density = 1.0 g mL^{-1}) initially at 28.4 °C in an insulated beaker, and assuming that no heat is lost, what is the final temperature of the mixture?

105. Palmitic acid ($C_{16}H_{32}O_2$) is a dietary fat found in beef and butter. The caloric content of palmitic acid is typical of fats in general. Write a balanced equation for the complete combustion of palmitic acid and calculate the standard enthalpy of combustion. What is the caloric content of palmitic acid in Cal g^{-1}? Do the same calculation for table sugar (sucrose, $C_{12}H_{22}O_{11}$). Which dietary substance (sugar or fat) contains more Calories per gram? The standard enthalpy of formation of palmitic acid is −208 kJ mol^{-1} and that of sucrose is −2226.1 kJ mol^{-1}. (Use $H_2O(l)$ in the balanced chemical equations because the metabolism of these compounds produces liquid water.)

106. Hydrogen and methanol have both been proposed as alternatives to hydrocarbon fuels. Write balanced reactions for the complete combustion of hydrogen and methanol and use standard enthalpies of formation to calculate the amount of heat released per kilogram of the fuel. Which fuel contains the most energy in the least mass? How does the energy of these fuels compare to that of octane (C_8H_{18})?

107. Derive a relationship between ΔH and ΔU for a process in which the temperature of a fixed amount of an ideal gas changes.

108. Under certain nonstandard conditions, oxidation by $O_2(g)$ of 1 mol of $SO_2(g)$ to $SO_3(g)$ absorbs 89.5 kJ. The enthalpy of formation of $SO_3(g)$ is −204.2 kJ mol^{-1} under these conditions. Find the enthalpy of formation of $SO_2(g)$.

109. One tablespoon of peanut butter has a mass of 16 g. It is combusted in a calorimeter whose heat capacity is 120.0 kJ °C^{-1}. The temperature of the calorimeter rises from 22.2 °C to 25.4 °C. Find the food caloric content of peanut butter.

110. A mixture of 2.0 mol of $H_2(g)$ and 1.0 mol of $O_2(g)$ is placed in a sealed evacuated container made of a perfect insulating material at 25 °C. The mixture is ignited with a spark and it reacts to form liquid water. Find the temperature of the water.

111. A 20.0 L volume of an ideal gas in a cylinder with a piston is at a pressure of 3.0 bar. Enough weight is suddenly removed from the piston to lower the external pressure to 1.5 bar. The gas then expands at constant temperature until its pressure is 1.5 bar. Find ΔU, ΔH, q, and w for this change in state.

112. When 10.00 g of phosphorus is burned in $O_2(g)$ to form $P_4O_{10}(s)$, enough heat is generated to raise the temperature of 2950 g of water from 18.0 °C to 38.0 °C. Calculate the enthalpy of formation of $P_4O_{10}(s)$ under these conditions.

113. The $\Delta_r H$ for the oxidation of S in the gas phase to SO_3 is −204 kJ mol^{-1} and for the oxidation of SO_2 to SO_3 is 89.5 kJ mol^{-1}. Find the enthalpy of formation of SO_2 under these conditions.

114. The $\Delta_f H°$ of $TiI_3(s)$ is −328 kJ mol^{-1} and the $\Delta_r H°$ for the reaction $2\,Ti(s) + 3\,I_2(g) \longrightarrow 2\,TiI_3(s)$ is −839 kJ. Calculate the $\Delta_r H$ of sublimation of $I_2(s)$, which is a solid at 25 °C.

115. A gaseous fuel mixture contains 25.3% methane (CH_4), 38.2% ethane (C_2H_6), and the rest propane (C_3H_8) by volume. When the fuel mixture contained in a 1.55 L tank, stored at 755 Torr and 298 K, undergoes complete combustion, how much heat is emitted? (Assume that the water produced by the combustion is in the gaseous state.)

116. A gaseous fuel mixture stored at 745 Torr and 298 K contains only methane (CH_4) and propane (C_3H_8). When 11.7 L of this fuel mixture is burned, it produces 769 kJ of heat. What is the mole fraction of methane in the mixture? (Assume that the water produced by the combustion is in the gaseous state.)

117. A copper cube measuring 1.55 cm on edge and an aluminum cube measuring 1.62 cm on edge are both heated to 55.0 °C and submerged in 100.0 mL of water at 22.2 °C. What is the final temperature of the water when equilibrium is reached? (Assume a density of 0.998 g mL^{-1} for water.)

118. A pure gold ring and pure silver ring have a total mass of 14.9 g. The two rings are heated to 62.0 °C and dropped into 15.0 mL of water at 23.5 °C. When equilibrium is reached, the temperature of the water is 25.0 °C. What is the mass of each ring? (Assume a density of 0.998 g mL^{-1} for water.)

119. What volume of methane at STP would be required to convert a 2.0 kg block of ice at −15 °C to water at 15 °C, assuming that no heat is lost? The heat of fusion for ice is 6.01 kJ mol^{-1}. The heat capacity of ice is 2.108 J g^{-1} °C^{-1} and the heat of combustion for methane is 891 kJ mol^{-1}.

120. A gaseous solution of methane and propane having a mass of 4.00 g was burned in excess oxygen. Twenty-five percent of the heat produced was used to raise the temperature of 125 g of liquid water from 0.0 °C to its boiling point at 100.0 °C. What is the mass of methane and propane in the mixture?

121. Instant cold packs use ammonium nitrate as the active ingredient. When the device separating the ammonium nitrate from the water is broken, the ammonium nitrate dissolves in the water, which is an endothermic process. The enthalpy of dissolution of ammonium nitrate is 28.1 kJ mol^{-1},

$$NH_4NO_3(s) \xrightarrow{H_2O} NH_4^+(aq) + NO_3^-(aq) \quad \Delta_r H = 28.1\text{ kJ mol}^{-1}$$

Smarty Pants decides to design an instant cold pack to try to quickly cool his beer. Assume that a beer (including bottle) has a heat capacity of 1.5 kJ °C^{-1} and the cold pack contains 250 g of water (C_s = 4.184 J g^{-1} °C^{-1}), which also needs to be cooled. What mass of NH_4NO_3 is required in each cold pack to cool the beer and cold pack from 20 °C to a drinkable 9 °C? Assume also that the pack is only 35% efficient (i.e., only 35% of the "cooling power" goes into cooling the beer and cold pack).

Challenge Problems

122. A typical frostless refrigerator uses 655 kWh of energy per year in the form of electricity. Suppose that all of this electricity is generated at a power plant that burns coal containing 3.2% sulfur by mass and that all of the sulfur is emitted as SO_2 when the coal is burned. If all of the SO_2 goes on to react with rainwater to form H_2SO_4, what mass of H_2SO_4 does the annual operation of the refrigerator produce? (*Hint:* Assume that the remaining percentage of the coal is carbon, and begin by calculating $\Delta_r H°$ for the combustion of carbon.)

123. A large sport utility vehicle has a mass of 2.5×10^3 kg. Calculate the mass of CO_2 emitted into the atmosphere upon accelerating the SUV from 0.0 mph to 65.0 mph. Assume that the required energy comes from the combustion of octane with 30% efficiency. (*Hint:* Use KE = $^1/_2\,mv^2$ to calculate the kinetic energy required for the acceleration.)

124. Combustion of natural gas (primarily methane) occurs in most household heaters. The heat given off in this reaction is used to raise the temperature of the air in the house. Assuming that all the energy given off in the reaction goes to heating up only the air in the house, determine the mass of methane required to heat the air in a house by 10.0 °C. Assume the following: house dimensions are 30.0 m × 30.0 m × 3.0 m; molar heat capacity of air is 30 J K^{-1} mol^{-1}; and 1.00 mol of air occupies 22.7 L for all temperatures concerned.

125. When backpacking in the wilderness, hikers often boil water to sterilize it for drinking. Suppose that you are planning a backpacking trip and will need to boil 35 L of water for your group. What volume of fuel should you bring? Assume the following: the fuel has an average formula of C_7H_{16}; 15% of the heat generated from combustion goes to heating the water (the rest is lost to the surroundings); the density of the fuel is 0.78 g mL^{-1}; the initial temperature of the water is 25.0 °C; and the standard enthalpy of formation of C_7H_{16} is −224.4 kJ mol^{-1}.

126. An ice cube of mass 9.0 g is added to a cup of coffee. The coffee's initial temperature is 90.0 °C and the cup contains 120.0 g of liquid. Assume that the specific heat capacity of the coffee is the same as that of water. The heat of fusion of ice (the heat associated with ice melting) is 6.0 kJ mol^{-1}. Find the temperature of the coffee after the ice melts.

127. The optimum drinking temperature for a Shiraz is 15.0 °C. A certain bottle of Shiraz having a heat capacity of 3.40 kJ °C^{-1} is 23.1 °C at room temperature. The heat of fusion of ice is

6.02 kJ mol^{-1} and the heat capacity of ice is 2.108 J g^{-1} $°C^{-1}$. Assume that no heat is lost to the rest of the surroundings. What minimum mass of ice, originally at −5.0 °C, is required to bring the final temperature to 15.0 °C?

128. Find $\Delta_r H$, $\Delta_r U$, q, and w for the freezing of water at −10.0 °C. The specific heat capacity of ice is 2.04 J g^{-1} $°C^{-1}$ and its heat of fusion (the quantity of heat associated with melting) is −332 J g^{-1}.

129. Starting from the relationship between temperature and kinetic energy for an ideal gas, find the value of the molar heat capacity of an ideal gas when its temperature is changed at constant volume. Find its molar heat capacity when its temperature is changed at constant pressure.

130. An amount of an ideal gas expands from 12.0 L to 24.0 L at a constant pressure of 1.0 atm. Then the gas is cooled at a constant volume of 24.0 L back to its original temperature. Then it contracts back to its original volume. Find the total heat flow for the entire process.

131. The heat of vaporization of water at 373 K is 40.7 kJ mol^{-1}. Find q, w, ΔU, and ΔH for the evaporation of 454 g of water at this temperature.

132. Find ΔU, ΔH, q, and w for the change in state of 1.0 mol $H_2O(l)$ at 80 °C to $H_2O(g)$ at 110 °C. The molar heat capacity of $H_2O(l)$ = 75.3 J mol^{-1} K^{-1}, molar heat capacity of $H_2O(g)$ = 25.0 J mol^{-1} K^{-1}, and the heat of vaporization of H_2O is 40.7×10^3 J mol^{-1} at 100 °C.

133. The heat of combustion of liquid octane (C_8H_{18}) to carbon dioxide and liquid water at 298 K is −1303 kJ mol^{-1}. Find $\Delta_r U$ for this reaction.

134. Find $\Delta_r H$ for the combustion of ethanol (C_2H_6O) to carbon dioxide and liquid water from the following data: the heat capacity of the bomb calorimeter is 34.65 kJ K^{-1} and the combustion of 1.765 g of ethanol raises the temperature of the calorimeter from 294.33 K to 295.84 K.

Conceptual Problems

135. Which statement is true of the internal energy of the system and its surroundings following a process in which ΔU_{sys} = +65 kJ? Explain.

a. The system and the surroundings both lose 65 kJ of energy.
b. The system and the surroundings both gain 65 kJ of energy.
c. The system loses 65 kJ of energy and the surroundings gain 65 kJ of energy.
d. The system gains 65 kJ of energy and the surroundings lose 65 kJ of energy.

136. The internal energy of an ideal gas depends only on its temperature. Which statement is true of an isothermal (constant-temperature) expansion of an ideal gas against a constant external pressure? Explain.

a. ΔU is positive
b. w is positive
c. q is positive
d. ΔU is negative

137. Which expression describes the heat evolved in a chemical reaction when the reaction is carried out at constant pressure? Explain.

a. $\Delta U - w$
b. ΔU
c. $\Delta U - q$

138. Two identical refrigerators are plugged in for the first time. Refrigerator A is empty (except for air) and refrigerator B is filled with jugs of water. The compressors of both refrigerators immediately turn on and begin cooling the interiors of the refrigerators. After two hours, the compressor of refrigerator A turns off, while the compressor of refrigerator B continues to run. The next day, the compressor of refrigerator A can be heard turning on and off every few minutes, while the compressor of refrigerator B turns off and on every hour or so (and stays on longer each time). Explain these observations.

139. A 1 kg cylinder of aluminum and 1 kg jug of water, both at room temperature, are put into a refrigerator. After one hour, the temperature of each object is measured. One of the objects is much cooler than the other. Which one is cooler and why?

140. Two substances, A and B, initially at different temperatures, are thermally isolated from their surroundings and allowed to come into thermal contact. The mass of substance A is twice the mass of substance B, but the specific heat capacity of substance B is four times the specific heat capacity of substance A. Which substance will undergo a larger change in temperature?

141. When 1 mol of a gas burns at constant pressure, it produces 2418 J of heat and does 5 J of work. Identify $\Delta_r U$, $\Delta_r H$, q, and w for the process.

142. In an exothermic reaction, the reactants lose energy and the reaction feels hot to the touch. Explain why the reaction feels hot even though the reactants are losing energy. Where does the energy come from?

143. Which statement is true of a reaction in which ΔV is positive? Explain.

a. $\Delta H = \Delta U$
b. $\Delta H > \Delta U$
c. $\Delta H < \Delta U$

The Quantum-Mechanical Model of the Atom

7

Our universe contains objects that span an almost unimaginable range of sizes. This chapter is focused on the behaviour of electrons, one of the smallest particles in existence.

Anyone who is not shocked by quantum mechanics has not understood it.

—Niels Bohr (1885–1962)

THE EARLY PART OF THE TWENTIETH century brought changes that revolutionized how we think about physical reality, especially in the atomic realm. Before that time, all descriptions of the behaviour of matter had been deterministic—the present set of conditions completely determining the future. Quantum mechanics changed that. This new theory suggested that for subatomic particles—electrons, neutrons, and protons—the present does NOT completely determine the future. For example, if you shoot one electron down a path and measure where it lands, a second electron shot down the same path under the same conditions will most likely land in a different place! Quantum theory was developed by several unusually gifted scientists, including Albert Einstein, Niels Bohr, Louis de Broglie, Max Planck, Werner Heisenberg, P. A. M. Dirac, and Erwin Schrödinger. These scientists did not necessarily feel comfortable with their own theory. Bohr said, "Anyone who is not shocked by quantum mechanics has not understood it." Schrödinger wrote, "I don't like it, and I'm sorry I ever had anything to do with it." Albert Einstein disbelieved the very theory he helped create, stating, "God does not play dice with the universe." In fact, Einstein attempted to disprove quantum mechanics—without success—until he died.

But quantum mechanics was able to account for fundamental observations, including the very stability of atoms, which could not be understood within the framework of classical physics. Today, quantum mechanics forms the foundation of chemistry—explaining the periodic table and the behaviour of the elements in chemical bonding—as well as providing the practical basis for lasers, computers, and countless other applications.

7.1 Quantum Mechanics: The Theory That Explains the Behaviour of the Absolutely Small

In everyday language, small is a relative term: something is small relative to something else. A car is smaller than a house, and a person is smaller than a car. But smallness has limits. For example, a house cannot be smaller than the bricks from which it is made.

Atoms and the particles that compose them are unimaginably small. As we have learned, electrons have a mass of less than a trillionth of a trillionth of a gram, and a size so small that it is immeasurable. A single speck of dust contains more electrons than the number of people that have existed on Earth over all the centuries of time. Electrons are *small* in the absolute sense of the word—they are among the smallest particles that make up matter. And yet, an atom's electrons determine its chemical and physical properties. If we are to understand these properties, we must try to understand electrons.

The absolute smallness of electrons makes it a challenge to understand them through observation. Consider the difference between observing a baseball, for example, and observing an electron. You can measure the position of a baseball by observing the light that strikes the ball, bounces off it, and enters your eye. The baseball is large in comparison to the disturbance caused by the light, so the baseball is virtually unaffected by your observation. By contrast, imagine observing the position of an electron. If you attempt to measure its position using light, the light itself disturbs the electron. The interaction of the light with the electron actually changes its position, the very thing you are trying to measure.

The inability to observe electrons without disturbing them has significant implications. It means that when you observe an electron, it behaves differently than when you do not observe it—the act of observation changes what the electron does. It means that our knowledge of electron behaviour has limits. It means that the *absolutely small* world of the electron is different from the *large* world that we normally experience. Therefore, we need to think about subatomic particles in a different way than we think about the macroscopic world.

In this chapter, we examine the **quantum-mechanical model** of the atom, a model that explains how electrons exist in atoms and how those electrons determine the chemical and physical properties of elements. We have already learned much about those properties. We know, for example, that some elements are metals and that others are nonmetals. We know that the noble gases are chemically inert and that the alkali metals are chemically reactive. We know that sodium tends to form $1+$ ions and that fluorine tends to form $1-$ ions. But we do not know *why*. The quantum-mechanical model explains why. In doing so, it explains the modern periodic table and provides the basis for our understanding of chemical bonding.

7.2 The Nature of Light

Before we explore electrons and their behaviour within the atom, we must understand some of the properties of light. As quantum mechanics developed, light was (surprisingly) found to have many characteristics in common with electrons. Chief among these is the *wave–particle duality* of light. Certain properties of light are best described by thinking of it as a wave, while other properties are best described by thinking of it as a particle. In this section, we will first explore the wave behaviour of light, and then its particle behaviour. We will then turn to electrons to see how they also display the same wave–particle duality.

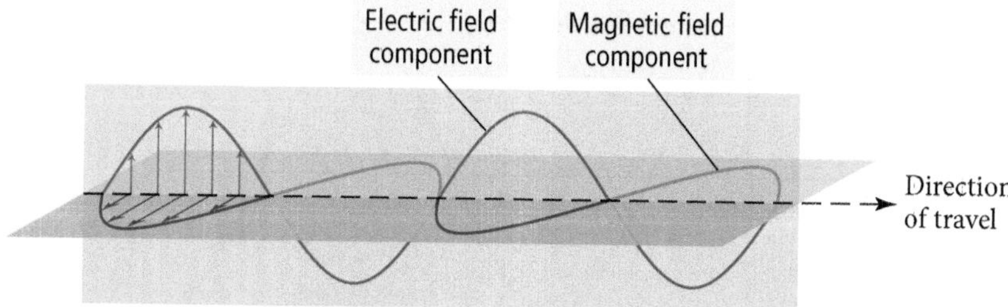

▲ **FIGURE 7.1 Electromagnetic Radiation** Electromagnetic radiation can be described as a wave composed of oscillating electric and magnetic fields. The fields oscillate in perpendicular planes.

The Wave Nature of Light

Light is **electromagnetic radiation**, a type of energy embodied in oscillating electric and magnetic fields. An *electric field* is a region of space where an electrically charged particle experiences a force. A proton, for example, has an electric field around it. If you bring another charged particle into that field, that particle will experience a force. A *magnetic field* is a region of space where a magnetic particle experiences a force. A magnet, for example, has a magnetic field around it. If you bring another magnet into that field, that magnet will experience a force.

Electromagnetic radiation can be described as a wave composed of oscillating, mutually perpendicular electric and magnetic fields propagating through space, as shown in Figure 7.1 ▲. In a vacuum, these waves move at a constant speed of 3.00×10^8 m s^{-1}—fast enough to circle the Earth in one-seventh of a second. This great speed is the reason for the delay between the moment when you see a flash of lightning and the moment you hear thunder. The light from the lightning flash reaches your eye almost instantaneously. The sound, travelling much more slowly (340 m s^{-1}), takes longer.

▲ Because light travels nearly a million times faster than sound, the flash of lightning reaches your eyes before the roll of thunder reaches your ears.

We can characterize a wave by its *amplitude* and its *wavelength*. In the graphical representation shown at the top of the next page, the **amplitude** of the wave is the vertical height of a crest (or depth of a trough). The amplitude of the electric and magnetic field waves in light determines the light's *intensity* or brightness—the greater the amplitude, the greater the intensity. The **wavelength (λ)** of the wave is the distance between adjacent crests (or any two analogous points) and is measured in units such as metres, micrometres, or nanometres.

The symbol λ is the Greek letter lambda, pronounced "lamb-duh."

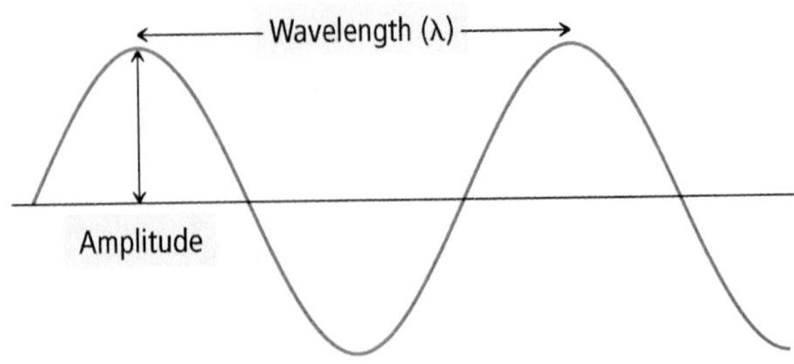

Wavelength and amplitude are both related to the quantity of energy carried by a wave. Imagine trying to swim out from a shore pounded by waves. Waves of greater amplitude (higher waves) or shorter wavelength (more closely spaced, and thus steeper, waves) will make the swim more difficult. Notice also that amplitude and wavelength can vary independently of one another, as shown in Figure 7.2 ▼. A wave can have a large amplitude or a small amplitude and a short wavelength or a long wavelength. The most energetic waves have large amplitudes and short wavelengths.

The symbol ν is the Greek letter nu, pronounced "noo."

Like all waves, light is also characterized by its **frequency (ν)**, the number of cycles (or wave crests) that pass through a stationary point in a given period of time. The units of frequency are cycles per second (cycle s^{-1}) or simply s^{-1}. An equivalent unit of frequency is the hertz (Hz), defined as 1 cycle s^{-1}. The frequency of a wave is directly proportional to the speed at which the wave is travelling—the faster the wave, the more crests will pass a fixed location per unit time. Frequency is also *inversely* proportional to the wavelength (λ)—the farther apart the crests, the fewer will pass a fixed location per unit time. For light, therefore, we can write:

$$\nu = \frac{c}{\lambda} \qquad [7.1]$$

where the speed of light, c, and the wavelength, λ, are both expressed in the same unit of distance. Therefore, wavelength and frequency represent different ways of specifying the same information—if we know one, we can readily calculate the other.

For *visible light*—light that can be seen by the human eye—wavelength (or, alternatively, frequency) determines colour. White light, produced by the sun or by a light bulb, contains a spectrum of wavelengths and therefore a spectrum of colours. We can see these colours—red, orange, yellow, green, blue, indigo, and violet—in a rainbow or

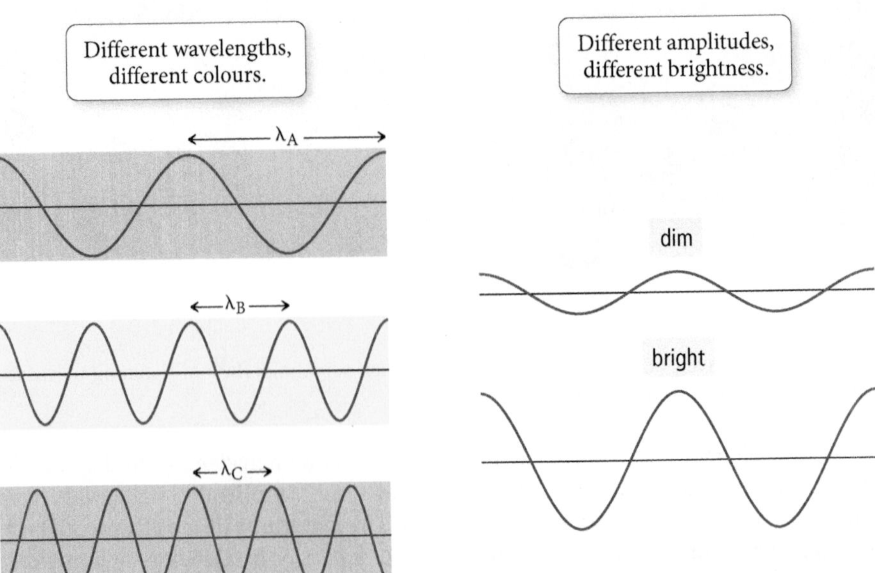

▲ **FIGURE 7.2 Wavelength and Amplitude** Wavelength and amplitude are independent properties. The wavelength of light determines its colour. The amplitude, or intensity, determines its brightness.

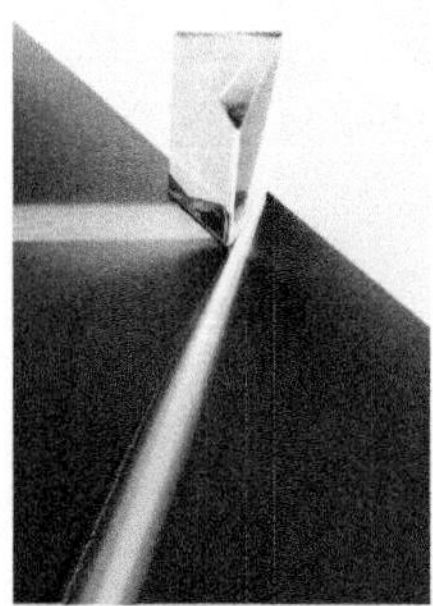

▲ **FIGURE 7.3 Components of White Light** We can pass white light through a prism and separate it into its constituent colours, each with a different wavelength. The array of colours makes up the spectrum of visible light.

▲ **FIGURE 7.4 The Colour of an Object** A red shirt is red because it reflects predominantly red light while absorbing most other colours.

when white light is passed through a prism (Figure 7.3 ▲). Red light, with a wavelength of about 750 nanometres (nm), has the longest wavelength of visible light; violet light, with a wavelength of about 400 nm, has the shortest. The presence of a variety of wavelengths in white light is responsible for the way we perceive colours in objects. When a substance absorbs some colours while reflecting others, it appears coloured. For example, a red shirt appears red because it reflects predominantly red light while absorbing most other colours (Figure 7.4 ▲). Our eyes see only the reflected light, making the shirt appear red.

nano = 10^{-9}

The Electromagnetic Spectrum

Visible light makes up only a tiny portion of the entire **electromagnetic spectrum**, which includes all wavelengths of electromagnetic radiation. Figure 7.5 ▼ shows the main regions of the electromagnetic spectrum, ranging in wavelength from 10^{-15} m (gamma rays) to 10^{5} m (radio waves). In Figure 7.5, short-wavelength, high-frequency radiation is on the right and long-wavelength, low-frequency radiation is on the left. As you can see, visible light constitutes only a small region in the middle.

As we saw previously, short-wavelength light inherently has greater energy than long-wavelength light. The most energetic forms of electromagnetic radiation have the shortest wavelengths. The form of electromagnetic radiation with the shortest wavelength is the **gamma (γ) ray**. Gamma rays are produced by the sun, other stars, and certain unstable atomic nuclei on Earth. Excessive exposure to gamma rays is dangerous to humans because the high energy of gamma rays can damage biological molecules.

Gamma rays are discussed in more detail in Chapter 19.

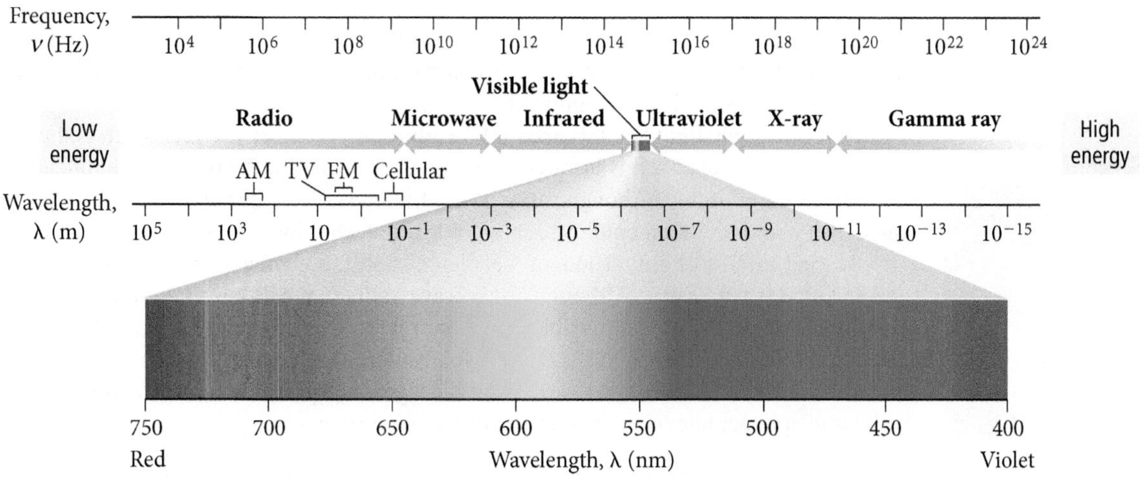

▲ **FIGURE 7.5 The Electromagnetic Spectrum** The right side of the spectrum consists of high-energy, high-frequency, short-wavelength radiation. The left side consists of low-energy, low-frequency, long-wavelength radiation. Visible light constitutes a small segment in the middle.

EXAMPLE 7.1 **WAVELENGTH AND FREQUENCY**

Calculate the wavelength (in nm) of the red light emitted by a barcode scanner that has a frequency of $4.62 \times 10^{14}\ s^{-1}$.

SOLUTION

You are given the frequency of the light and asked to find its wavelength. Use Equation 7.1, which relates frequency to wavelength. You can convert the wavelength from metres to nanometres by using the conversion factor between the two (1 nm = 10^{-9} m).

$$\nu = \frac{c}{\lambda}$$

$$\lambda = \frac{c}{\nu} = \frac{3.00 \times 10^8\ \text{m}\ \cancel{\text{s}^{-1}}}{4.62 \times 10^{14}\ \cancel{\text{s}^{-1}}}$$

$$= 6.49 \times 10^{-7}\ \text{m}$$

$$= 6.49 \times 10^{-7}\ \cancel{\text{m}} \times \frac{1\ \text{nm}}{10^{-9}\ \cancel{\text{m}}} = 649\ \text{nm}$$

FOR PRACTICE 7.1

A laser dazzles the audience in a rock concert by emitting green light with a wavelength of 515 nm. Calculate the frequency of the light.

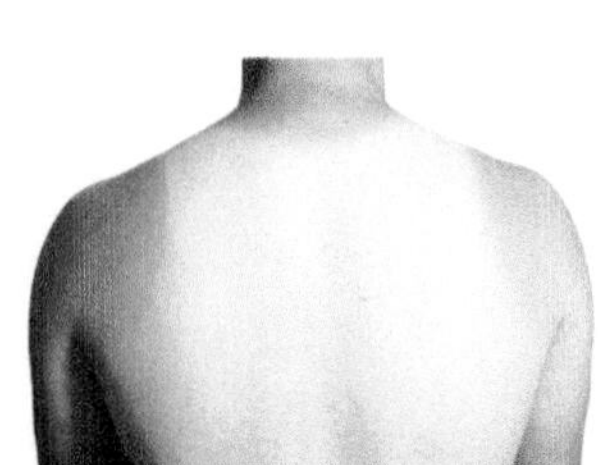

▲ Ultraviolet light from the sun produces suntans and sunburns.

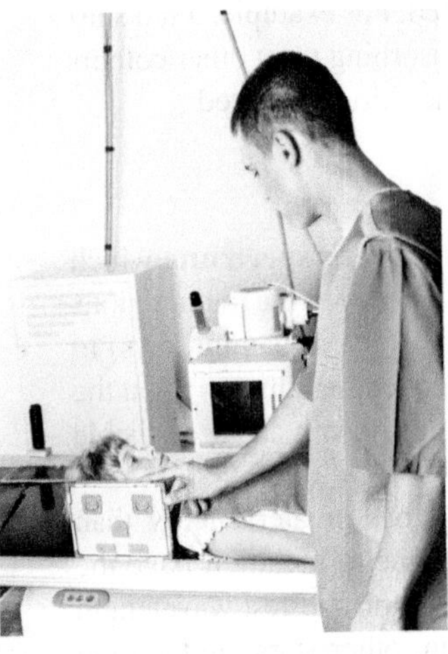

▲ To produce a medical X-ray, the patient is exposed to short-wavelength electromagnetic radiation that can pass through the skin to create an image of bones and internal organs.

Next on the electromagnetic spectrum, with longer wavelengths than gamma rays, are **X-rays**, familiar to us from their medical use. X-rays pass through many substances that block visible light and are therefore used to image bones and internal organs. Like gamma rays, X-rays are sufficiently energetic to damage biological molecules. While several yearly exposures to X-rays are relatively harmless, too much exposure to X-rays increases cancer risk.

Sandwiched between X-rays and visible light in the electromagnetic spectrum is **ultraviolet (UV) radiation**, most familiar to us as the component of sunlight that produces a sunburn or suntan. While not as energetic as gamma rays or X-rays, ultraviolet light still carries enough energy to damage biological molecules. Excessive exposure to ultraviolet light increases the risk of skin cancer and cataracts and causes premature wrinkling of the skin.

Next on the spectrum is **visible light**, ranging from violet (shorter wavelength, higher energy) to red (longer wavelength, lower energy). Visible light—at low to moderate intensity—does not carry enough energy to damage biological molecules. It does, however, cause certain molecules in our eyes to change their shape, sending a signal to our brains that results in our ability to see.

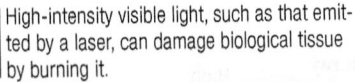

High-intensity visible light, such as that emitted by a laser, can damage biological tissue by burning it.

Beyond visible light lies **infrared (IR) radiation**. The heat you feel when you place your hand near a hot object is infrared radiation. All warm objects, including human bodies, emit infrared light. Although infrared light is invisible to our eyes, infrared sensors can detect it and are often employed in night vision technology to "see" in the dark.

Beyond infrared light, at longer wavelengths still, are **microwaves**, used for radar and in microwave ovens. Although microwave radiation has longer wavelengths and therefore lower energies than visible or infrared light, it is efficiently absorbed by water and can therefore heat substances that contain water. The longest wavelengths are those of **radio waves**, which are used to transmit the signals responsible for AM and FM radio, cellular telephone, television, and other forms of communication.

▲ Warm objects emit infrared light, which is invisible to the eye but can be captured on film or by detectors to produce an infrared photograph.

Interference and Diffraction

Waves, including electromagnetic waves, interact with each other in a characteristic way called **interference**: they can cancel each other out or build each other up, depending on

CHEMISTRY AND MEDICINE Radiation Treatment for Cancer

X-rays and gamma rays are sometimes called *ionizing radiation* because their short wavelengths correspond to high energies that can ionize atoms and molecules. When ionizing radiation interacts with biological molecules, it can permanently change or even destroy them. Consequently, we normally try to limit our exposure to ionizing radiation. However, doctors use ionizing radiation to destroy molecules within unwanted cells such as cancer cells.

In radiation therapy (or radiotherapy), doctors aim X-ray or gamma-ray beams at cancerous tumours (groups of cells that divide uncontrollably and invade surrounding healthy tissue). The ionizing radiation damages the molecules within the tumour's cells that carry genetic information—information necessary for the cell to grow and divide. Consequently, the cell dies or stops dividing. Ionizing radiation also damages molecules in healthy cells, but cancerous cells divide more quickly than normal cells, making them more susceptible to genetic damage. Nonetheless, harm to healthy tissues during treatments can result in side effects such as fatigue, skin lesions, hair loss, and organ damage. Medical workers try to reduce such effects by appropriate shielding (of healthy tissue) and by targeting the tumour from multiple directions, minimizing the exposure of healthy cells while maximizing the exposure of cancerous cells.

Another side effect of exposing healthy cells to radiation is that they too may become cancerous. If a treatment for cancer may cause cancer, why do we continue to use it? In radiation therapy, as in most other disease therapies, there is an associated risk. We take risks all the time, many of them for lesser reasons. For example, every time we fly in an airplane or drive in a car, we risk injury or even death. Why? Because we perceive the benefit—the convenience of being able to travel a significant distance in a short time—to be worth the relatively small risk. The situation is similar in cancer therapy, or any other therapy for that matter. The benefit of cancer therapy (possibly curing a cancer that might otherwise kill you) is worth the risk (a slight increase in the chance of developing a future cancer).

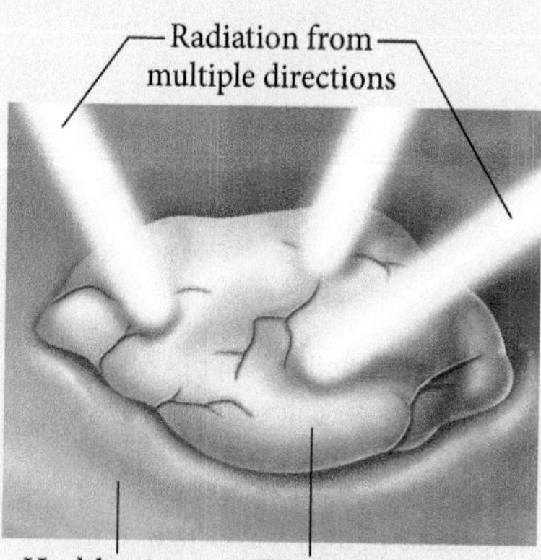

▲ During radiation therapy, a tumour is targeted from multiple directions in order to minimize the exposure of healthy cells while maximizing the exposure of cancerous cells.

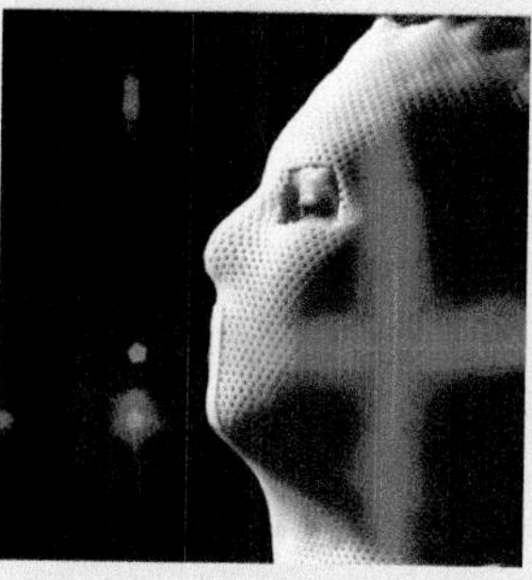
▲ In radiation therapy, highly energetic gamma rays are aimed at cancerous tumours.

Question

Why is visible light (by itself) not used to destroy cancerous tumours?

their alignment upon interaction. For example, if two waves of equal amplitude are *in phase* when they interact—that is, they align with overlapping crests—a wave with twice the amplitude results. This is called **constructive interference**.

Understanding interference in waves is critical to understanding the wave nature of the electron, as we will soon see.

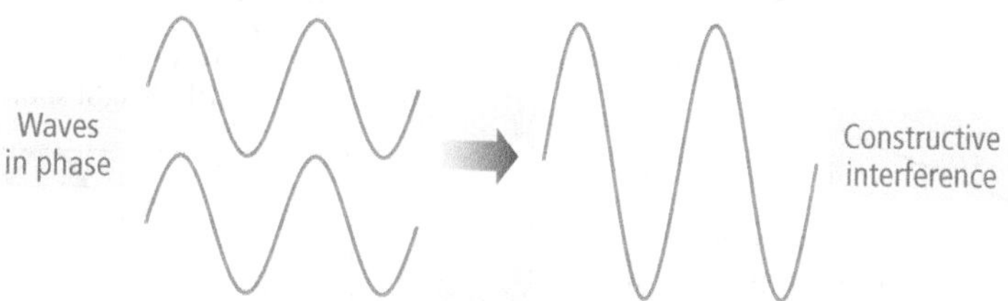

On the other hand, if two waves are completely *out of phase* when they interact—that is, they align so that the crest from one source overlaps with the trough from the other source—the waves cancel by **destructive interference**.

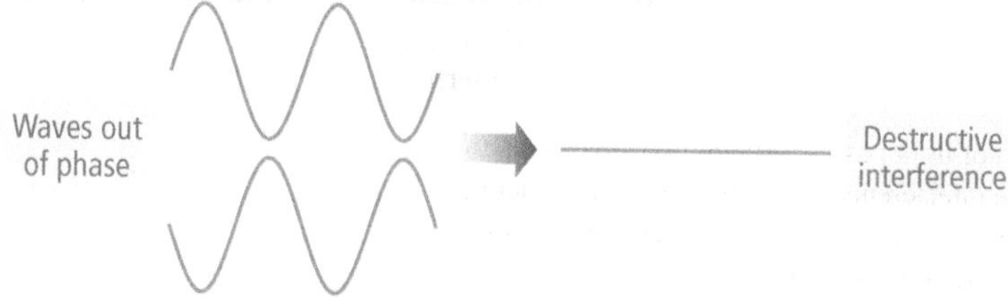

▲ When a reflected wave meets an incoming wave near the shore, the two waves interfere constructively for an instant, producing a large amplitude spike.

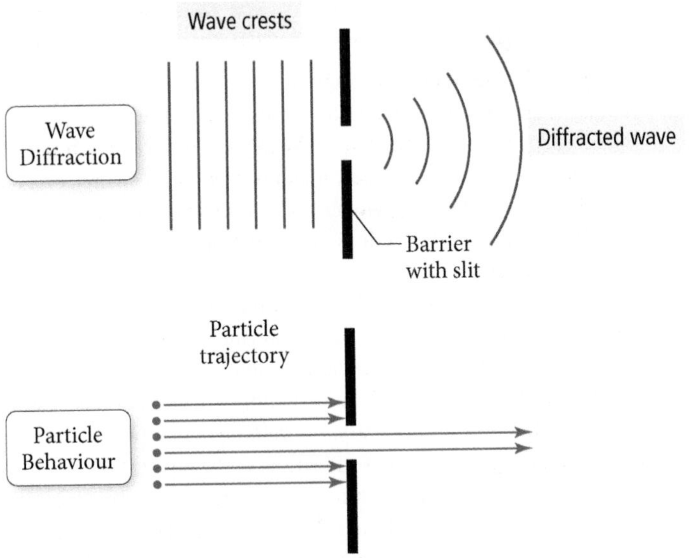

Wave crests

Wave Diffraction

Diffracted wave

Barrier with slit

Particle trajectory

Particle Behaviour

▶ **FIGURE 7.6 Diffraction** In this view from above, we can see how waves bend, or diffract, when they encounter an obstacle or slit with a size comparable to their wavelength. When a wave passes through a small opening, it spreads out. Particles, by contrast, do not diffract; they simply pass through the opening.

Waves also exhibit a characteristic behaviour called **diffraction** (Figure 7.6 ▲). When a wave encounters an obstacle or a slit that is comparable in size to its wavelength, it bends (or *diffracts*) around it. The diffraction of light through two slits separated by a distance comparable to the wavelength of the light, coupled with interference, results in an *interference pattern*, as shown in Figure 7.7 ▼. Each slit acts as a new wave source, and the two new waves interfere with each other. The resulting pattern consists of a series of bright and dark lines that can be viewed on a screen (or recorded on a film) placed at a short distance behind the slits. At the centre of the screen, the two waves travel equal distances and interfere constructively to produce a bright line. A small distance away from the centre in either direction, the two waves travel slightly different distances, so that they are out of phase. At the point where the difference in distance is one-half of one

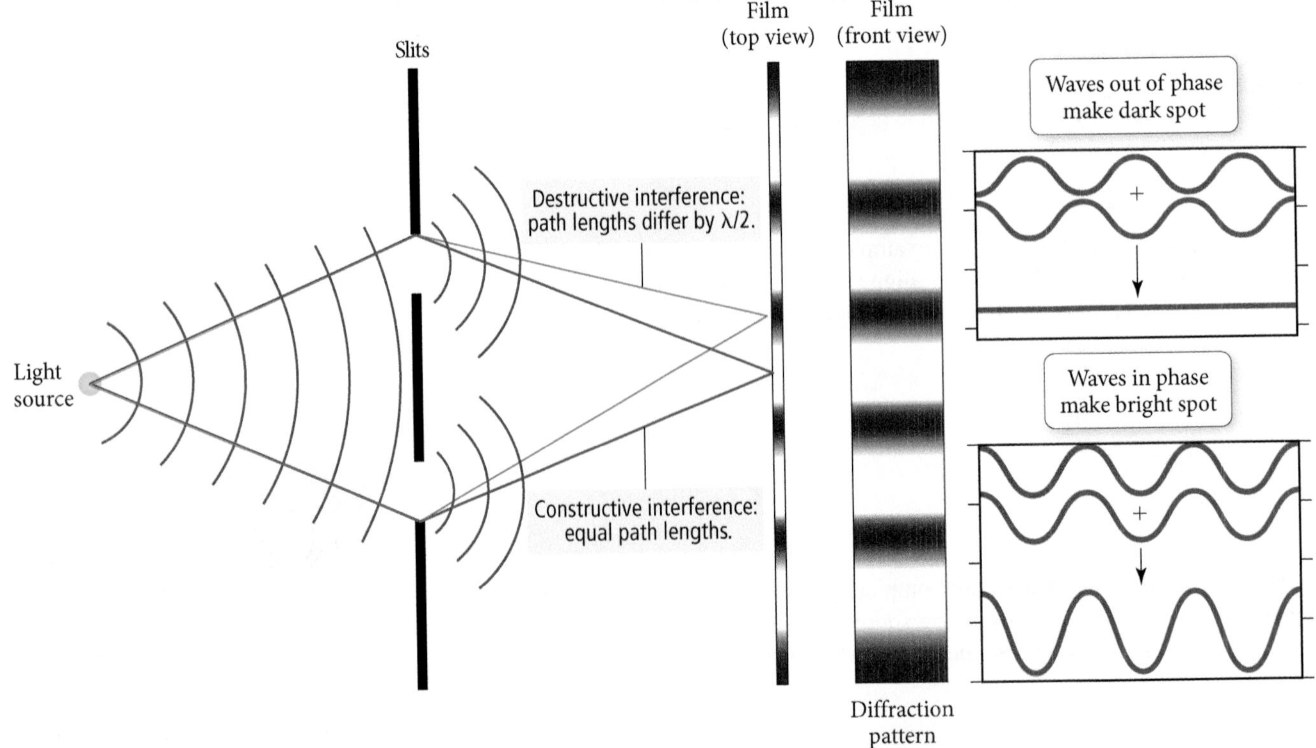

▲ **FIGURE 7.7 Interference from Two Slits** When a beam of light passes through two small slits, the two resulting waves interfere with each other. Whether the interference is constructive or destructive at any given point depends on the difference in the path lengths travelled by the waves. The resulting interference pattern appears as a series of bright and dark lines on a screen.

wavelength, the interference is destructive and a dark line appears on the screen. Moving a bit farther away from the centre produces constructive interference again because the difference between the paths is one whole wavelength. The end result is the interference pattern shown by the light and dark bars in Figure 7.7. Notice that interference is a result of the ability of a wave to diffract through two slits—this is an inherent property of waves.

The Particle Nature of Light

Prior to the early 1900s, and especially after the discovery of the diffraction of light, light was thought to be purely a wave phenomenon. Its behaviour was described adequately by classical electromagnetic theory, which treated the electric and magnetic fields that constitute light as waves propagating through space. However, a number of discoveries brought the classical view into question. Chief among these was the *photoelectric effect*.

The term *classical*, as in classical electromagnetic theory or classical mechanics, refers to descriptions of matter and energy before the advent of quantum mechanics.

The **photoelectric effect** is the observation that metals can emit electrons when light shines upon them, as shown in Figure 7.8 ▼. Classical electromagnetic theory attributed this effect to the transfer of energy from the light to an electron in the metal, which resulted in the dislodgment of the electron. If this explanation were correct, changing *either* the wavelength (colour) or the amplitude (intensity) of the light would affect the emission of electrons. In other words, according to the classical description, the rate at which electrons leave the metal due to the photoelectric effect would increase if either light of shorter wavelength or light of higher intensity (brighter light) was used. In addition, a dim light would be expected to result in a *lag time* between the initial shining of the light and the subsequent emission of an electron. The lag time would be the minimum amount of time required for the dim light to transfer sufficient energy to the electron to dislodge it.

The experimental results did not, however, follow the classical prediction. Scientists found that a high-frequency, low-intensity light produced electrons *without* the predicted lag time. Furthermore, the light used to dislodge electrons in the photoelectric effect exhibited a *threshold frequency*, below which no electrons were emitted from the metal, no matter how long the light shone on the metal. In other words, low-frequency (long-wavelength) light *would not* eject electrons from a metal regardless of its intensity or its duration. But high-frequency (short-wavelength) light *would* eject electrons, even if its intensity was low. What could explain this odd behaviour?

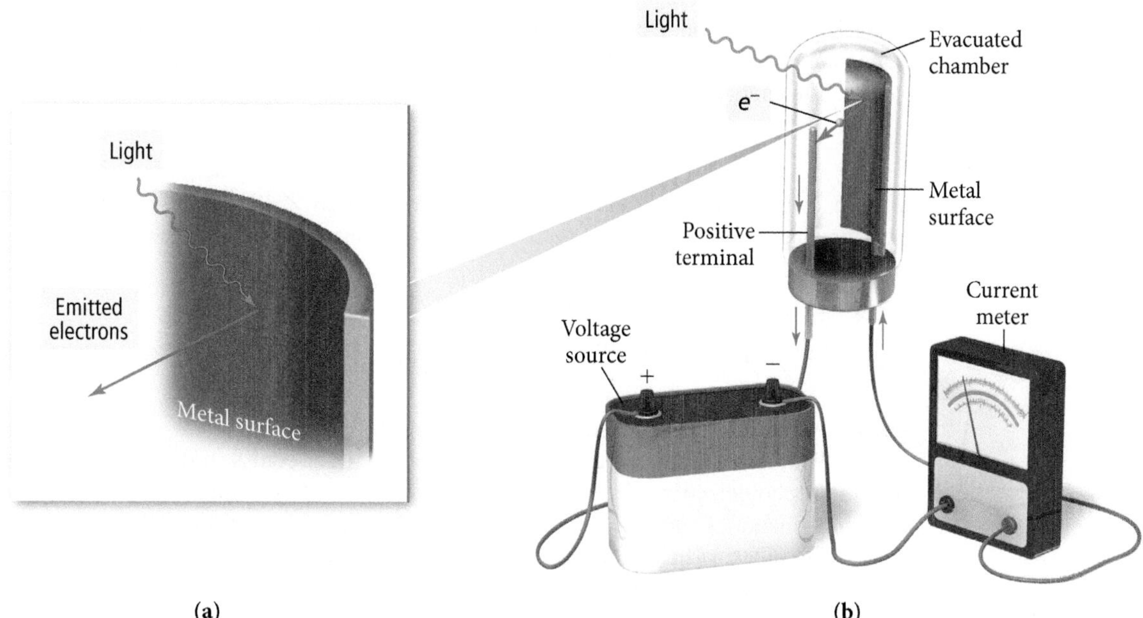

▲ **FIGURE 7.8 The Photoelectric Effect** (a) When sufficiently energetic light shines on a metal surface, the surface emits electrons. (b) The emitted electrons can be measured as an electrical current.

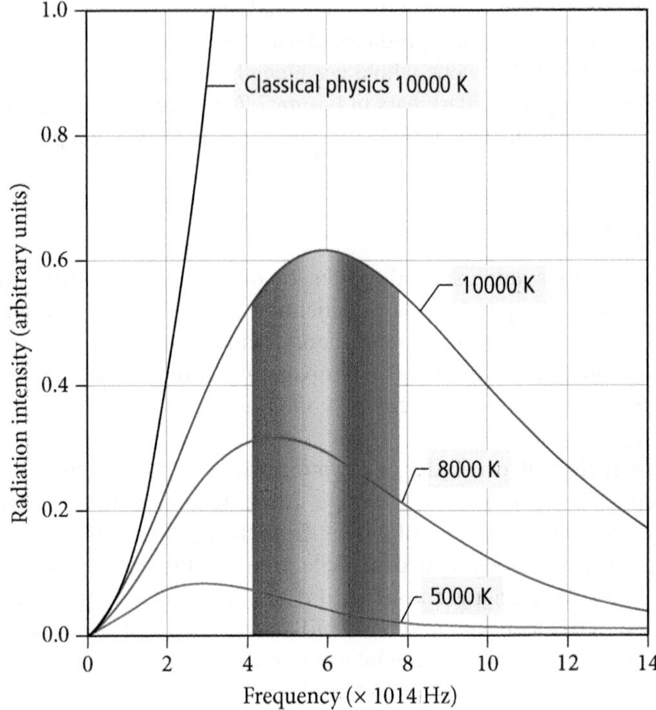

▶ **FIGURE 7.9 Blackbody Radiation Curves** Radiation density versus frequency curves for a heated body at 10000 K, 8000 K, and 5000 K. The best model for these curves according to classical physics is shown in black. Also shown is the visible range of the electromagnetic spectrum that is emitted.

Around this time, classical physics was also suffering from the inability to explain emissions—called blackbody radiation—from a heated object. All objects that are above 0 K emit radiation. An example of this is an electric stove element that emits infrared radiation as well as visible light when it is near the maximum setting. As we saw previously, your body also emits radiation, but mostly in the infrared region of the electromagnetic spectrum. The problem classical physics had was that it predicted that the density of radiation from a heated body would increase to infinity at high frequencies! In other words, your body, at 310 K, would emit an enormous amount of radiation at high frequencies such as ultraviolet light or X-rays. This is obviously not true and would make being around people very dangerous. The prediction of classical physics for an object heated to 10000 K is compared to the true blackbody radiation curve for an object at 10000 K in Figure 7.9 ▲.

This failure of classical physics was called the *Ultraviolet Catastrophe* because the theory breaks down at high frequencies. In 1900, Max Planck had developed a new theory of blackbody radiation. He could obtain agreement with the experimental blackbody radiation curve only if it was assumed that the energy was emitted in discrete packets called *quanta*. The energy of these packets was given by:

The energy of a photon is directly proportional to its frequency.

$$E = h\nu \qquad [7.2]$$

where h, called Planck's constant, has the value $h = 6.626 \times 10^{-34}\ \mathrm{J \cdot s}$. Planck obtained the following formula for the radiation density (ρ) from a heated body, which perfectly reproduced the experimental data:

$$\rho(\nu,T) = \frac{8\pi h\nu^3}{c^3}\frac{1}{e^{h\nu/kT} - 1} \qquad [7.3]$$

where k is the Boltzmann constant, $k = 1.381 \times 10^{-23}\ \mathrm{JK^{-1}}$.

In 1905, Albert Einstein used Planck's idea that light comes in discrete packets to explain the photoelectric effect. Einstein called a packet of light a **quantum** of energy (or the plural, quanta). Planck later coined the term **photon** for these discrete light packets in accord with other particles such as the electron or proton. Because $\nu = c/\lambda$, the energy of a photon can also be expressed in terms of wavelength:

The energy of a photon is inversely proportional to its wavelength.

$$E = \frac{hc}{\lambda} \qquad [7.4]$$

The idea that light occurs in discrete packets or is *quantized* was the beginning of a new era of physics. Classical physics viewed light purely as a wave whose intensity was *continuously variable*. From the new perspective, a beam of light is not a wave propagating through space, but a shower of particles, each with energy $h\nu$.

EXAMPLE 7.2 PHOTON ENERGY

A nitrogen gas laser pulse with a wavelength of 337 nm contains 3.83 mJ of energy. How many photons does it contain?

SORT You are given the wavelength and total energy of a light pulse and asked to find the number of photons it contains.

GIVEN: $E_{pulse} = 3.83$ mJ

$\lambda = 337$ nm

FIND: number of photons

STRATEGIZE In the first part of the conceptual plan, calculate the energy of an individual photon from its wavelength.

CONCEPTUAL PLAN

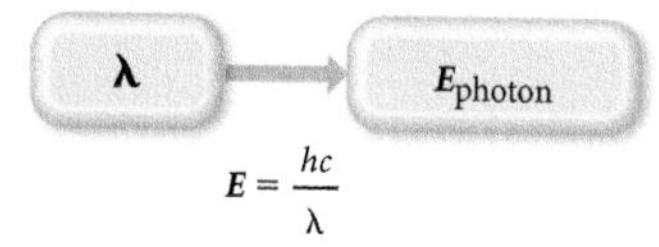

In the second part, divide the total energy of the pulse by the energy of a photon to get the number of photons in the pulse.

$$\frac{E_{pulse}}{E_{photon}} = \text{number of photons}$$

RELATIONSHIP USED $E = hc/\lambda$ (Equation 7.4)

SOLVE To execute the first part of the conceptual plan, convert the wavelength to metres and substitute it into the equation to compute the energy of a 337 nm photon.

SOLUTION

$$\lambda = 337\ \cancel{\text{nm}} \times \frac{10^{-9}\ \text{m}}{1\ \cancel{\text{nm}}} = 3.37 \times 10^{-7}\ \text{m}$$

$$E_{photon} = \frac{hc}{\lambda} = \frac{(6.626 \times 10^{-34}\ \text{J}\cdot\cancel{\text{s}})\left(3.00 \times 10^{8}\ \frac{\cancel{\text{m}}}{\cancel{\text{s}}}\right)}{3.37 \times 10^{-7}\ \cancel{\text{m}}}$$

$$= 5.89\underline{8}5 \times 10^{-19}\ \text{J}$$

To execute the second part of the conceptual plan, convert the energy of the pulse from mJ to J. Then divide the energy of the pulse by the energy of a photon to obtain the number of photons.

$$3.83\ \cancel{\text{mJ}} \times \frac{10^{-3}\ \text{J}}{1\ \cancel{\text{mJ}}} = 3.83 \times 10^{-3}\ \text{J}$$

$$\text{number of photons} = \frac{E_{pulse}}{E_{photon}} = \frac{3.83 \times 10^{-3}\ \cancel{\text{J}}}{5.89\underline{8}5 \times 10^{-19}\ \cancel{\text{J}}}$$

$$= 6.49 \times 10^{15}\ \text{photons}$$

CHECK The unit of the answer, photons, is correct. The magnitude of the answer (10^{15}) is reasonable. Photons are small and any macroscopic collection should contain a large number of them.

FOR PRACTICE 7.2

A 100 W light bulb radiates energy at a rate of 100 J s^{-1}. (The watt, W, a unit of power or energy over time, is defined as 1 J s^{-1}.) If all of the light emitted has a wavelength of 525 nm, how many photons are emitted per second? (Assume three significant figures in this calculation.)

FOR MORE PRACTICE 7.2

The energy required to dislodge electrons from sodium metal via the photoelectric effect is 275 kJ mol^{-1}. What wavelength, in nanometres of light, has sufficient energy per photon to dislodge an electron from the surface of sodium?

CONCEPTUAL CONNECTION 7.1

Arrange the three types of electromagnetic radiation—visible light, X-rays, and microwaves—in order of (i) wavelength, (ii) frequency, (iii) energy per photon.

The idea that light is quantized elegantly explains the photoelectric effect. The emission of electrons from the metal depends on whether or not a single photon has sufficient energy (as given by $h\nu$) to dislodge a single electron. For an electron bound to the metal with binding energy ϕ, the threshold frequency is reached when the energy of the photon is equal to ϕ.

The symbol ϕ is the Greek letter phi, pronounced "fi," and is also known as the work function.

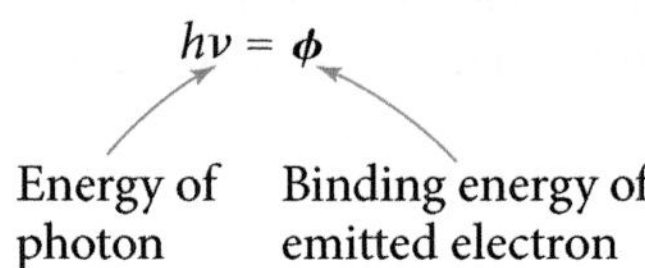

Low-frequency light does not eject electrons because no single photon has the minimum energy necessary to dislodge the electron. Increasing the *intensity* of low-frequency light simply increases the number of low-energy photons, but does not produce any single photon with sufficient energy. In contrast, increasing the *frequency* of the light, even at low intensity, increases the energy of each photon, allowing the photons to dislodge electrons with no lag time.

As the frequency of the light is increased past the threshold frequency, the excess energy of the photon (beyond what is needed to dislodge the electron) is transferred to the electron in the form of kinetic energy. The kinetic energy (KE) of the ejected electron, therefore, is the difference between the energy of the photon ($h\nu$) and the binding energy of the electron, as given by the following equation:

$$\text{KE} = h\nu - \phi \qquad [7.5]$$

Although the quantization of light explained the photoelectric effect, the wave explanation of light continued to have explanatory power as well, depending on the circumstances of the particular observation. So, the principle that slowly emerged (albeit with some measure of resistance) is what we now call the *wave–particle duality of light.* Sometimes light appears to behave like a wave—at other times, like a particle. Which behaviour you observe depends on the particular experiment.

EXAMPLE 7.3 THE PHOTOELECTRIC EFFECT

In an experiment designed to determine the work function of platinum, light with a wavelength of 30.4 nm was shone on a sample of platinum. The kinetic energy of the electrons emitted was measured to be 5.522×10^{-18} J. Determine the work function, ϕ, in kJ mol^{-1}.

SORT You are given the wavelength of the photon and the kinetic energy of the ejected electrons.	**GIVEN:** $KE = 5.522 \times 10^{-18}$ J $\lambda = 30.4\,\text{nm}$ **FIND:** the work function of platinum
STRATEGIZE In the first part of the conceptual plan, calculate the energy of the individual photon from its wavelength.	**CONCEPTUAL PLAN** $E = \dfrac{hc}{\lambda}$
Second, solve for the work function of platinum.	$\phi = h\nu - KE$
Finally, the work function will be in J, so it will be necessary to convert to kJ mol^{-1}.	$\phi(\text{J}) \times 6.022 \times 10^{23}\,\text{mol}^{-1} \times \dfrac{1\,\text{kJ}}{1000\,\text{J}} = \phi(\text{kJ mol}^{-1})$

SOLVE To execute the first part of the conceptual plan, convert the wavelength to metres and substitute it into the equation to find the energy of the 30.4 nm photon.	$\lambda = 30.4\ \cancel{\text{nm}} \times \frac{10^{-9}\ \text{m}}{\cancel{\text{nm}}} = 3.04 \times 10^{-8}\ \text{m}$ $E = \frac{hc}{\lambda} = \frac{(6.626 \times 10^{-34}\ \text{J} \cdot \cancel{\text{s}})(3.00 \times 10^{8}\ \cancel{\text{m}}\ \cancel{\text{s}^{-1}})}{(3.04 \times 10^{-8}\ \cancel{\text{m}})}$ $= 6.5\underline{3}9 \times 10^{-18}\ \text{J}$
Next, substitute the value for the kinetic energy of the ejected electron and the energy of the photon that was just calculated to obtain the work function in J.	$\phi = h\nu - KE = 6.5\underline{3}9 \times 10^{-18}\ \text{J} - 5.522 \times 10^{-18}\ \text{J}$ $= 1.0\underline{1}7 \times 10^{-18}\ \text{J}$
Finally, to execute the last step in the conceptual plan, convert the value we obtain in J, which is really the amount of energy to remove one electron from one platinum atom, to kJ mol^{-1}.	$\phi(\text{kJ mol}^{-1}) = 1.0\underline{1}7 \times 10^{-18}\ \cancel{\text{J}} \times 6.022 \times 10^{23}\ \text{mol}^{-1} \times \frac{1\ \text{kJ}}{1000\ \cancel{\text{J}}}$ $= 612\ \text{kJ mol}^{-1}$

FOR PRACTICE 7.3

The work function for calcium is 277 kJ mol^{-1}. Light from a helium discharge lamp with a wavelength of 381.96 nm was used to irradiate the calcium metal. Determine whether photoelectrons will be emitted and, if so, what the kinetic energy of these electrons would be.

CONCEPTUAL CONNECTION 7.2

The Photoelectric Effect

A metal surface was exposed, one at a time, to three different wavelengths, 325 nm, 455 nm, and 632 nm. The observations for each wavelength, labelled A, B, and C, were as follows:

Observation A: No photoelectrons were observed.

Observation B: Photoelectrons with a kinetic energy of 155 kJ mol^{-1} were observed.

Observation C: Photoelectrons with a kinetic energy of 51 kJ mol^{-1} were observed.

Which observation corresponds to which wavelength of light?

7.3 Atomic Spectroscopy and the Bohr Model

The discovery of the particle nature of light began to break down the division that existed in nineteenth-century physics between electromagnetic radiation, which was thought of as a wave phenomenon, and the small particles (protons, neutrons, and electrons) that compose atoms, which were thought to follow Newton's laws of motion. Just as the photoelectric effect suggested the particle nature of light, certain observations within atoms began to suggest a wave nature for particles. The most important of these came from *atomic spectroscopy*, the study of the electromagnetic radiation absorbed and emitted by atoms.

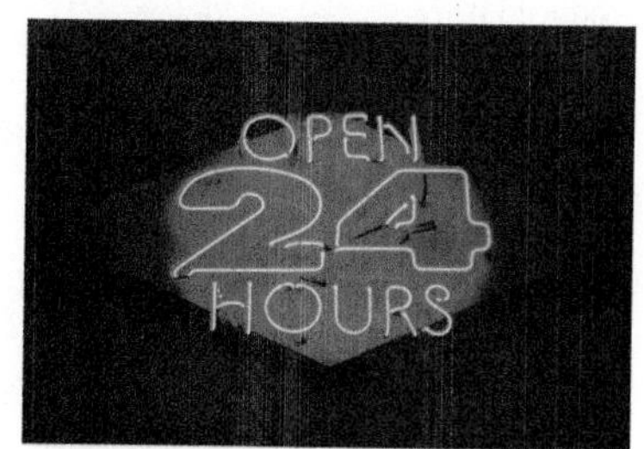

▲ The familiar red light from a neon sign is emitted by neon atoms that have absorbed electrical energy, which they re-emit as visible radiation.

When an atom absorbs energy—in the form of heat, light, or electricity—it often re-emits that energy as light. For example, a neon sign is composed of one or more glass tubes filled with neon gas. When an electric current is passed through the tube, the neon atoms absorb some of the electrical energy and re-emit it as the familiar red light of a neon sign. If the atoms in the tube are different (that is, not neon), they emit light of a different colour. In other words, atoms of each element emit light of a characteristic colour. Mercury atoms, for example, emit light that appears blue, helium atoms emit light that appears violet, and hydrogen atoms emit light that appears reddish (Figure 7.10 ▼).

Remember that the colour of visible light is determined by its wavelength.

Closer inspection of the light emitted by various atoms reveals that the light contains several distinct wavelengths. We can separate the light emitted by a single element in a glass tube into its constituent wavelengths by passing it through a prism (just

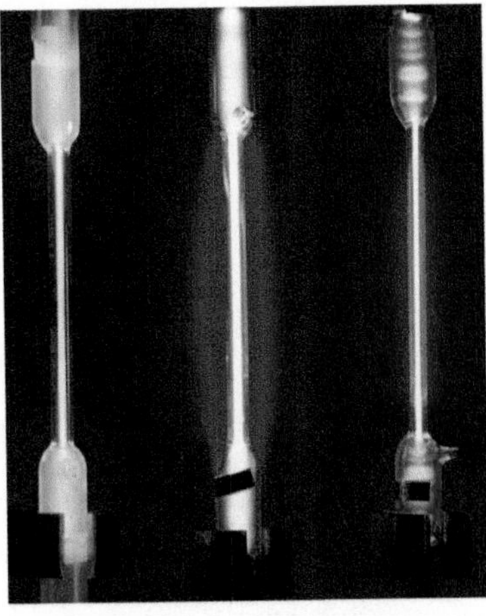

▲ **FIGURE 7.10 Mercury, Helium, and Hydrogen** Each element emits a characteristic colour.

like we separate the white light from a light bulb), as shown in Figure 7.11 ▼. The result is a series of bright lines called an **emission spectrum**. The emission spectrum of a particular element is always the same and is different from the emission spectrum of other elements. An emission spectrum can be used to identify the element. For example, light arriving from a distant star contains the emission spectra of the elements that compose the star. Analysis of the light allows us to identify the elements present in the star.

Notice the differences between a white light spectrum and the emission spectra of hydrogen, helium, and barium (as shown in Figure 7.11). The white light spectrum is *continuous*, meaning that there are no sudden interruptions in the intensity of the light as a function of wavelength—the spectrum consists of light of all wavelengths. The emission spectra of hydrogen, helium, and barium, however, are not continuous—they consist of bright lines at specific wavelengths, with complete darkness in between. That is, only certain discrete wavelengths of light are present. Classical physics could not explain why these spectra consisted of discrete lines. In fact, according to classical physics, an atom composed of an electron orbiting a nucleus should emit a continuous white light spectrum. Even more problematic, the electron should lose energy as it emits the light and spiral into the nucleus. According to classical physics, an atom should not even be stable.

Johannes Rydberg, a Swedish mathematician, analyzed many atomic spectra and developed a simple equation that predicted the wavelengths of the hydrogen emission spectrum. However, his equation (shown in the margin on the next page) gave little insight into *why* atomic spectra were discrete, *why* atoms were stable, or *why* his equation worked.

The Danish physicist Niels Bohr (1885–1962) attempted to develop a model for the atom that explained atomic spectra. In his model, electrons travel around the nucleus in circular orbits, similar to those of the planets around the sun. However, in contrast with planetary orbits—which can theoretically exist at any distance from the sun—Bohr's

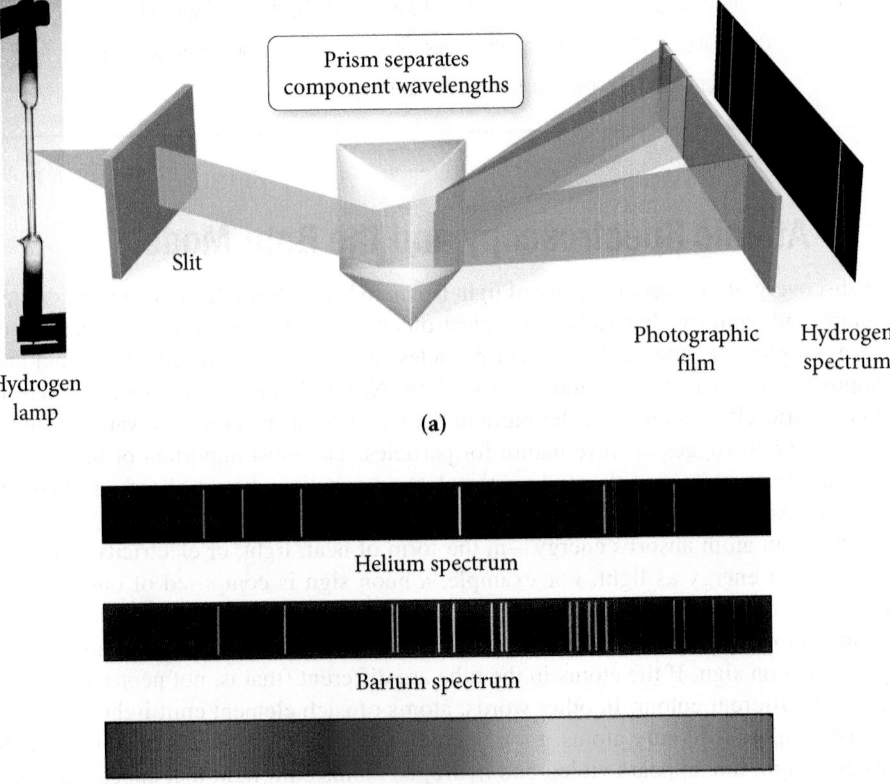

▶ **FIGURE 7.11 Emission Spectra** (**a**) The light emitted from a hydrogen, helium, or barium lamp consists of specific wavelengths, which can be separated by passing the light through a prism. (**b**) The resulting bright lines constitute an emission spectrum characteristic of the element that produced it.

orbits could exist only at specific fixed distances from the nucleus. The energy of each Bohr orbit was fixed, or *quantized*. Bohr called these orbits *stationary states* and suggested that although they obeyed the laws of classical mechanics, they also possessed "a peculiar, mechanically unexplainable, stability." We now know that the stationary states were really manifestations of the wave nature of the electron, which we will expand upon shortly. Bohr further surmised that, in contradiction to classical electromagnetic theory, no radiation was emitted by an electron orbiting the nucleus in a stationary state. It was only when an electron jumped, or made a *transition*, from one stationary state to another that radiation was emitted or absorbed (Figure 7.12 ▶). The transitions between the stationary states in a hydrogen atom are quite unlike any transition that you might imagine in the macroscopic world. The electron is never observed *between states*, only in one state or the next, and the transition between states is instantaneous.

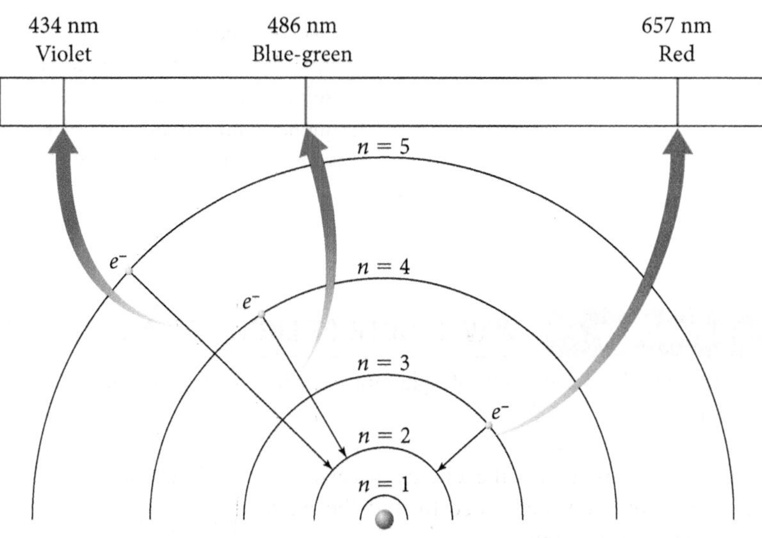

▲ **FIGURE 7.12 The Bohr Model and Emission Spectra** According to the Bohr model, each spectral line is produced when an electron falls from one stable orbit, or stationary state, to another of lower energy.

The emission spectrum of an atom consists of discrete lines because the stationary states exist only at specific, fixed energies. Each wavelength in the emission spectrum of an atom corresponds to an electron transition between two energy levels. When an atom absorbs energy, an electron in a lower energy level is excited or promoted to a higher energy level, as shown in Figure 7.13 ▼. In this new configuration, however, the atom is unstable, and the electron quickly falls back or relaxes to a lower energy level. As it does so, it releases a photon of light containing an amount of energy precisely equal to the energy difference between the two energy levels.

The Rydberg equation is $1/\lambda = R_H(1/m^2 - 1/n^2)$, where R_H is the Rydberg constant ($1.097 \times 10^7\ \text{m}^{-1}$), and m and n are integers.

The expression for the energy of an electron in any energy level in the hydrogen atom is:

$$E_n = -2.18 \times 10^{-18}\,\text{J}\left(\frac{1}{n^2}\right) \qquad [7.6]$$

where $n = 1, 2, 3, \ldots$. The difference in energy, ΔE, corresponding to a transition between two different energy levels, n_f and n_i (final and initial states), is:

$$\Delta E = -2.18 \times 10^{-18}\,\text{J}\left(\frac{1}{n_f^2}\right) - \left[-2.18 \times 10^{-18}\,\text{J}\left(\frac{1}{n_i^2}\right)\right]$$

$$\Delta E = -2.18 \times 10^{-18}\,\text{J}\left(\frac{1}{n_f^2} - \frac{1}{n_i^2}\right) \qquad [7.7]$$

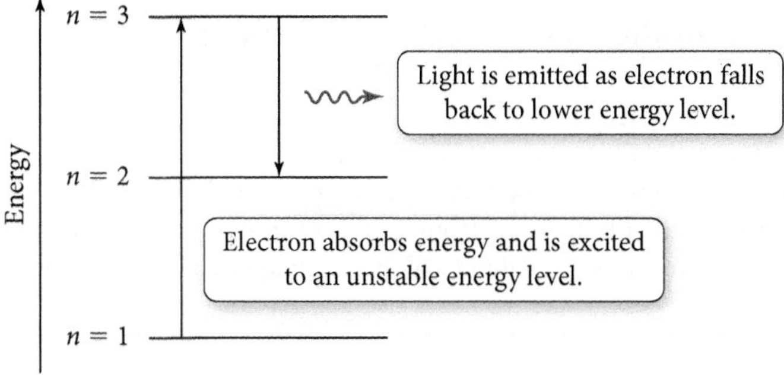

◀ **FIGURE 7.13 Excitation and Radiation** When an atom absorbs energy, an electron can be excited to a higher energy level. The electron in this excited state is unstable, however, and relaxes to a lower energy level, releasing energy in the form of electromagnetic radiation.

Notice that if $n_f < n_i$, the energy difference, ΔE, is negative because the atom emits energy as the electron relaxes from a higher energy level to a lower energy level. Conversely, if $n_f > n_i$, ΔE is positive as the atom absorbs energy. The energy determines the frequency and wavelength of the photon, and we can use Equation 7.4 to calculate the wavelength of the emitted or absorbed photon.

EXAMPLE 7.4 WAVELENGTH OF LIGHT FOR A TRANSITION IN THE HYDROGEN ATOM

Determine the wavelength of light emitted when an electron in a hydrogen atom makes a transition from an orbital in $n = 6$ to an orbital in $n = 5$.

SORT You are given the energy levels of an atomic transition and asked to find the wavelength of emitted light.

GIVEN: $n = 6 \longrightarrow n = 5$

FIND: λ

STRATEGIZE In the first part of the conceptual plan, calculate the energy of the electron in the $n = 6$ and $n = 5$ orbitals using Equation 7.7 and subtract to find ΔE_{atom}.

In the second part, find E_{photon} by taking the negative of ΔE_{atom}, and then calculate the wavelength corresponding to a photon of this energy using Equation 7.4. (The difference in sign between E_{photon} and ΔE_{atom} applies only to emission. *The energy of a photon must always be positive.*)

CONCEPTUAL PLAN

$n = 5, n = 6 \longrightarrow \Delta E_{\text{atom}}$

$\Delta E = E_5 - E_6$

$\Delta E_{\text{atom}} \longrightarrow E_{\text{photon}} \longrightarrow \lambda$

$\Delta E_{\text{atom}} = -E_{\text{photon}}$; $E = \dfrac{hc}{\lambda}$

RELATIONSHIPS USED

$E_n = -2.18 \times 10^{-18}\ \text{J}(1/n^2)$

$E = hc/\lambda$ (Equation 7.4)

SOLVE Follow the conceptual plan. Begin by computing ΔE_{atom}.

SOLUTION

$$\begin{aligned}\Delta E_{\text{atom}} &= E_5 - E_6 \\ &= -2.18 \times 10^{-18}\,\text{J}\left(\frac{1}{5^2}\right) - \left[-2.18 \times 10^{-18}\,\text{J}\left(\frac{1}{6^2}\right)\right] \\ &= -2.18 \times 10^{-18}\,\text{J}\left(\frac{1}{5^2} - \frac{1}{6^2}\right) \\ &= -2.66\underline{4}4 \times 10^{-20}\,\text{J}\end{aligned}$$

Compute E_{photon} by changing the sign of ΔE_{atom}.

$$E_{\text{photon}} = -\Delta E_{\text{atom}} = +2.66\underline{4}4 \times 10^{-20}\,\text{J}$$

Solve the equation relating the energy of a photon to its wavelength for λ. Substitute the energy of the photon and compute.

$$E = \frac{hc}{\lambda}$$

$$\begin{aligned}\lambda &= \frac{hc}{E} \\ &= \frac{(6.626 \times 10^{-34}\,\cancel{\text{J}} \cdot \cancel{\text{s}})(3.00 \times 10^8\,\text{m}\,\cancel{\text{s}^{-1}})}{2.66\underline{4}4 \times 10^{-20}\,\cancel{\text{J}}} \\ &= 7.46 \times 10^{-6}\,\text{m}\end{aligned}$$

CHECK The units of the answer (m) are correct for wavelength. The magnitude seems reasonable because 10^{-6} m is in the infrared region of the electromagnetic spectrum. We know that transitions from $n = 3$ or $n = 4$ to $n = 2$ lie in the visible region, so it makes sense that a transition between levels of higher n value (which are energetically closer to one another) would result in light of longer wavelength.

FOR PRACTICE 7.4

Determine the wavelength of the light absorbed when an electron in a hydrogen atom makes a transition from an orbital in which $n = 2$ to an orbital in which $n = 7$.

FOR MORE PRACTICE 7.4

An electron in the $n = 6$ level of the hydrogen atom relaxes to a lower energy level, emitting light of $\lambda = 93.8$ nm. Find the principal level to which the electron relaxed.

CONCEPTUAL CONNECTION 7.3

Emission Spectra

Which transition will result in emitted light with the shortest wavelength?

(a) $n = 5 \longrightarrow n = 4$

(b) $n = 4 \longrightarrow n = 3$

(c) $n = 3 \longrightarrow n = 2$

CHEMISTRY IN YOUR DAY Atomic Spectroscopy, A Bar Code for Atoms

When you check out at the grocery store, a laser scanner reads the bar code on the items that you buy. Each item has a unique code that identifies it and its price. Similarly, each element in the periodic table has a spectrum unlike that of any other element. For example, Figure 7.14 ▼ shows the emission spectra of oxygen and neon. (In Figure 7.11, we saw the emission spectra of hydrogen, helium, and barium.) Notice that each spectrum is unique and, as such, can be used to identify the substance.

The presence of intense lines in the spectra of a number of metals is the basis for *flame tests*, simple tests used to identify elements in ionic compounds even in the absence of a precise analysis of its spectrum. For example, the emission spectrum of sodium features two closely spaced, bright yellow lines. When a crystal of a sodium salt (or a drop of a solution containing a sodium salt) is put into a flame, the flame glows bright yellow (Figure 7.15 ▼). As Figure 7.15 shows, other metals exhibit similarly characteristic colours in flame tests. Each colour represents an especially bright spectral emission line (or a combination of two or more such lines). Similar emissions form the basis of the colours seen in fireworks.

▲ Fireworks typically contain the salts of such metals as sodium, calcium, strontium, barium, and copper. Emissions from these elements produce the brilliant colours of pyrotechnic displays.

Although the *emission* of light from elements is easier to detect, the *absorption* of light by elements is even more commonly used for purposes of identification. Whereas emission spectra consist of bright lines on a dark background, absorption spectra consist of dark lines on a bright background (Figure 7.16 ▼). An absorption spectrum is measured by passing white light through a sample and observing what wavelengths are *missing* due to absorption by the sample. Notice that, in the spectra shown here,

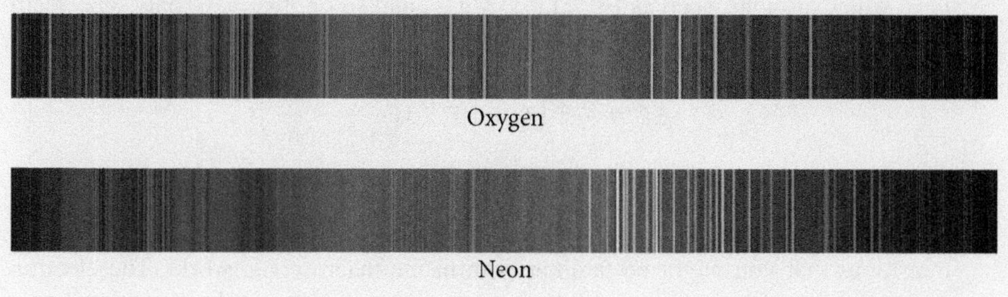

◀ **FIGURE 7.14 Emission Spectra of Oxygen and Neon** The emission spectrum of each element is unique and we can use it to identify the element.

(continued)

CHEMISTRY IN YOUR DAY (CONTINUED)

the absorption lines are at the same wavelengths as the emission lines. This is because the processes that produce them are related. In emission, an electron makes a transition from a higher energy level to a lower energy one. In absorption, the transition is between the same two energy levels, but from the lower level to the higher one.

Absorption spectrometers, found in most chemistry laboratories, typically plot the intensity of absorption as a function of wavelength. Such plots are useful both for identifying substances (qualitative analysis) and for determining the concentration of substances (quantitative analysis). Quantitative analysis is possible because the amount of light absorbed by a sample depends on the concentration of the absorbing substance within the sample. For example, the concentration of Ca^{2+} in a hard water sample can be determined by measuring the quantity of light absorbed by the calcium ion at one of its characteristic wavelengths.

▶ **FIGURE 7.15 Flame Tests for Sodium, Potassium, Lithium, and Barium** We can identify elements by the characteristic colour of the light they produce when heated. The colours derive from especially bright lines in their emission spectra.

▶ **FIGURE 7.16 Emission and Absorption Spectrum of Mercury** Elements absorb light of the same wavelengths that they radiate when heated. When these wavelengths are subtracted from a beam of white light, the result is a pattern of dark lines called an absorption spectrum.

The light emitted when an electron in a hydrogen atom makes a transition from an orbital in $n = 6$ to $n = 5$ is 7.46 μm. For an $n = 7$ to $n = 5$ transition, the wavelength of light emitted can be calculated to be 4.65 μm. The transitions between levels that are farther apart in energy produce light that is shorter in wavelength, and therefore higher in energy, than between energy levels that are closer together. Figure 7.17 ▶ shows several of the transitions in the hydrogen atom and their corresponding wavelengths.

The Bohr theory was also successful in explaining the spectra of *hydrogen-like ions*, which are ions, such as He^{+}, Li^{2+}, Mg^{3+}, and so on, that have only one electron. Equation 7.7 needs to be modified to:

$$\Delta E = -2.18 \times 10^{-18}\,\text{J}\left(\frac{Z^2}{n_f^{\,2}} - \frac{Z^2}{n_i^{\,2}}\right) \qquad [7.8]$$

where Z is the atomic number (e.g., $Z = 2$ for He^{+}, $Z = 3$ for Li^{2+}).

The transitions between stationary states in a hydrogen atom are quite unlike any transitions that you might be familiar with in the macroscopic world. The electron is *never* observed *between states*, only in one state or the next—the transition between states is instantaneous. The emission spectrum of an atom consists of discrete lines because the stationary states exist only at specific, fixed energies. The energy of the photon created when an electron makes a transition from one stationary state to another

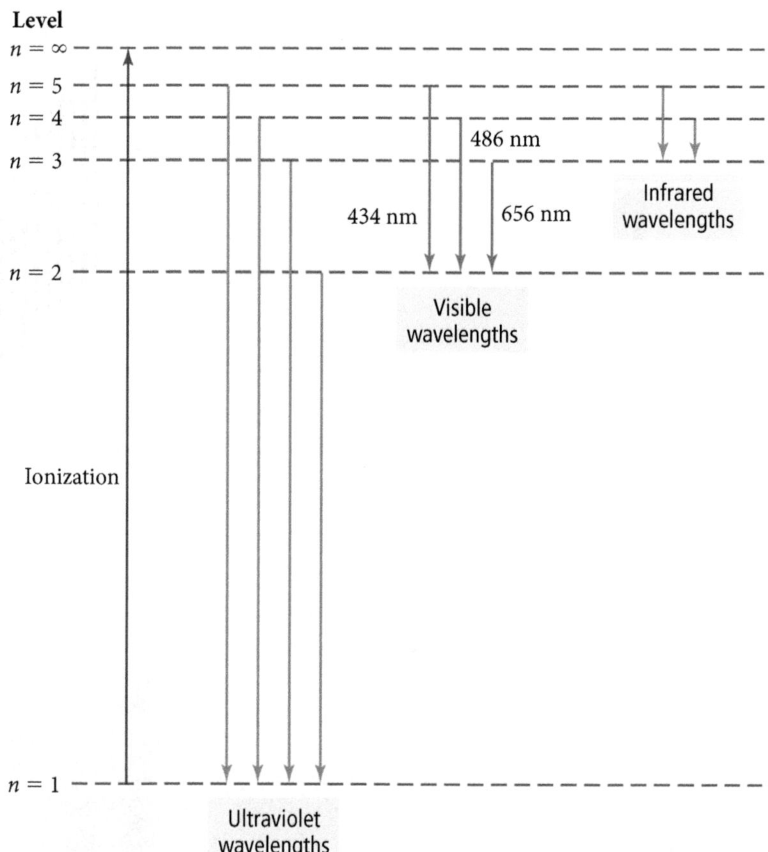

◀ **FIGURE 7.17 Hydrogen Energy Transitions and Radiation** An atomic energy level diagram for hydrogen, showing some possible electron transitions between levels and the corresponding wavelengths of emitted light.

is the energy difference between the two stationary states. Transitions between stationary states that are closer together, therefore, produce light of lower energy (longer wavelength) than transitions between stationary states that are farther apart.

In spite of its initial success in explaining the line spectrum of hydrogen, the Bohr model left many unanswered questions. It did, however, serve as an intermediate model between a classical view of the electron and a fully quantum view, and therefore has great historical and conceptual importance. Nonetheless, it was ultimately replaced by a more complete quantum theory that fully incorporated the wave nature of the electron.

7.4 The Wave Nature of Matter: The de Broglie Wavelength, the Uncertainty Principle, and Indeterminacy

The heart of the quantum theory that replaced Bohr's model is the wave nature of the electron, first proposed by Louis de Broglie (1892–1987) in 1924 and later confirmed by experiments in 1927. It seemed incredible at the time, but electrons—which were thought of as particles and known to have mass—were shown to also have a wave nature. The wave nature of the electron is seen most clearly in its diffraction. If an electron beam is aimed at two closely spaced slits, and a series (or array) of detectors is arranged to detect the electrons after they pass through the slits, an interference pattern similar to that observed for light is recorded behind the slits (Figure 7.18(a) ▼). The detectors at the centre of the array (midway between the two slits) detect a large number of electrons—exactly the opposite of what you would expect for particles (Figure 7.18(b) ▼). Moving outward from this centre spot, the detectors alternately detect small numbers of electrons and then large numbers again and so on, forming an interference pattern characteristic of waves.

The first evidence of electron wave properties was provided by the Davisson–Germer experiment of 1927, in which electrons were observed to undergo diffraction by a metal crystal.

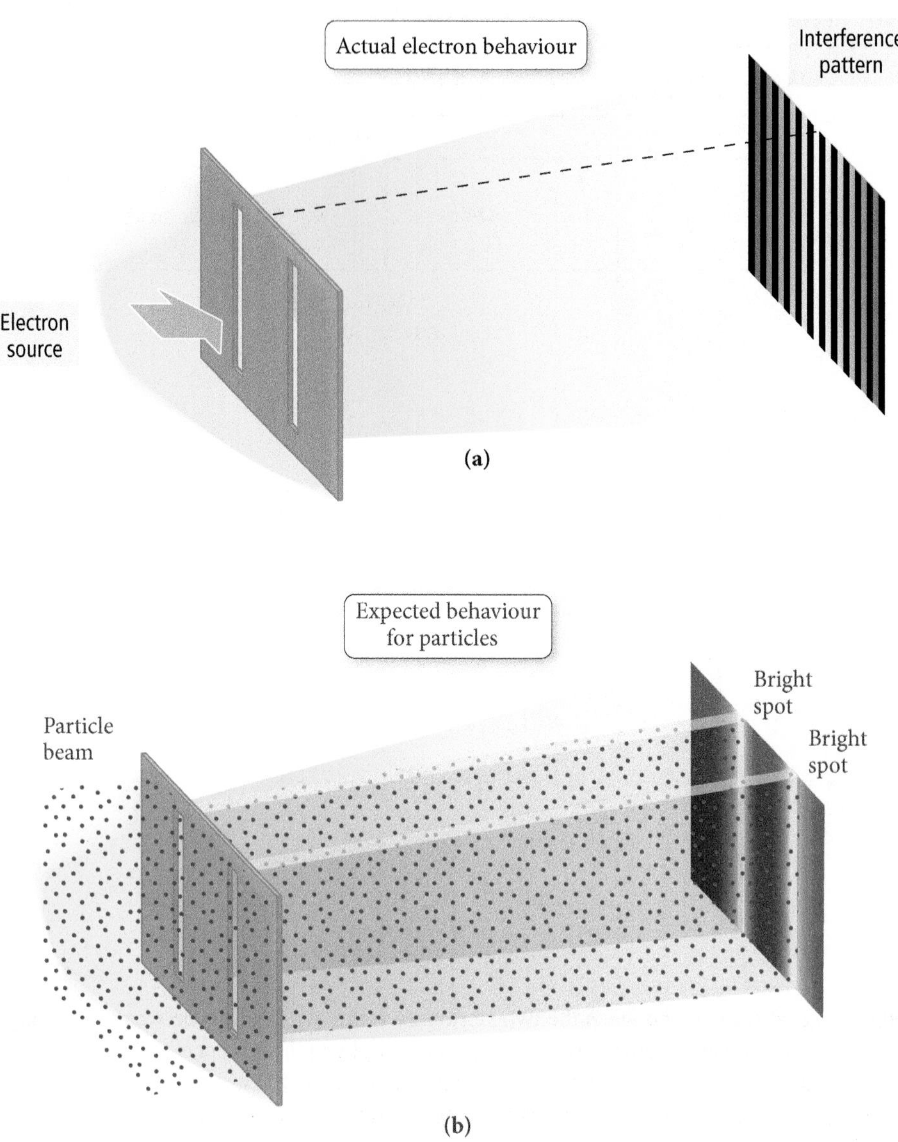

▶ **FIGURE 7.18 Electron Diffraction** When a beam of electrons goes through two closely spaced slits **(a)**, an interference pattern is created, as if the electrons were waves. By contrast, a beam of particles passing through two slits **(b)** produces two smaller beams of particles. Notice that for particle beams, there is a dark line directly behind the centre of the two slits, in contrast to wave behaviour, which produces a bright line.

Counter to what might be our initial intuition about electron interference, the interference pattern is *not caused by pairs of electrons interfering with each other, but rather by single electrons interfering with themselves*. If the electron source is turned down to a very low level so that electrons come out only one at a time, *the interference pattern remains*. In other words, we can design an experiment in which electrons come out of the source singly. We can then record where each electron strikes the detector after it has passed through the slits. If we record the positions of thousands of electrons over a long period of time, we find the same interference pattern shown in Figure 7.18(a). This leads us to an important conclusion: *the wave nature of the electron is an inherent property of individual electrons*. As it turns out, this wave nature is what explains the existence of stationary states (in the Bohr model) and prevents the electrons in an atom from crashing into the nucleus as predicted by classical physics. We now turn to three important manifestations of the electron's wave nature: the de Broglie wavelength, the uncertainty principle, and indeterminacy.

The de Broglie Wavelength

As we have seen, a single electron travelling through space has a wave nature; its wavelength is related to its kinetic energy (the energy associated with its motion). The faster the electron is moving, the higher its kinetic energy and the shorter its wavelength. The wavelength (λ) of an electron of mass m moving at velocity v is given by the **de Broglie relation**:

$$\lambda = \frac{h}{mv} \quad \text{de Broglie relation} \qquad [7.9]$$

The mass of an object (m) times its velocity (v) is its momentum. Therefore, the wavelength of an electron is inversely proportional to its momentum.

where h is Planck's constant. *Notice that the velocity of a moving electron is related to its wavelength—knowing one is equivalent to knowing the other.*

CONCEPTUAL CONNECTION 7.4
The de Broglie Wavelength of Macroscopic Objects

Since quantum theory is universal, it applies to all objects, regardless of size. Therefore, according to the de Broglie relation, a thrown baseball should also exhibit wave properties. Why do we not observe such properties at the ballpark?

The Uncertainty Principle

The wave nature of the electron is difficult to reconcile with its particle nature. How can a single entity behave as both a wave and a particle? We can begin to address this question by returning to the single-electron diffraction experiment. Specifically, we can ask the following question: How does a single electron aimed at a double slit produce an interference pattern? A possible hypothesis is that the electron splits into two, travels through both slits, and interferes with itself. This hypothesis seems testable. To do so, we would simply have to observe the single electron as it travels through the slits. If it travels through both slits simultaneously, we would know our hypothesis is correct.

The following electron diffraction experiment is designed to "watch" which slit the electron travels through by using a laser beam placed directly behind the slits.

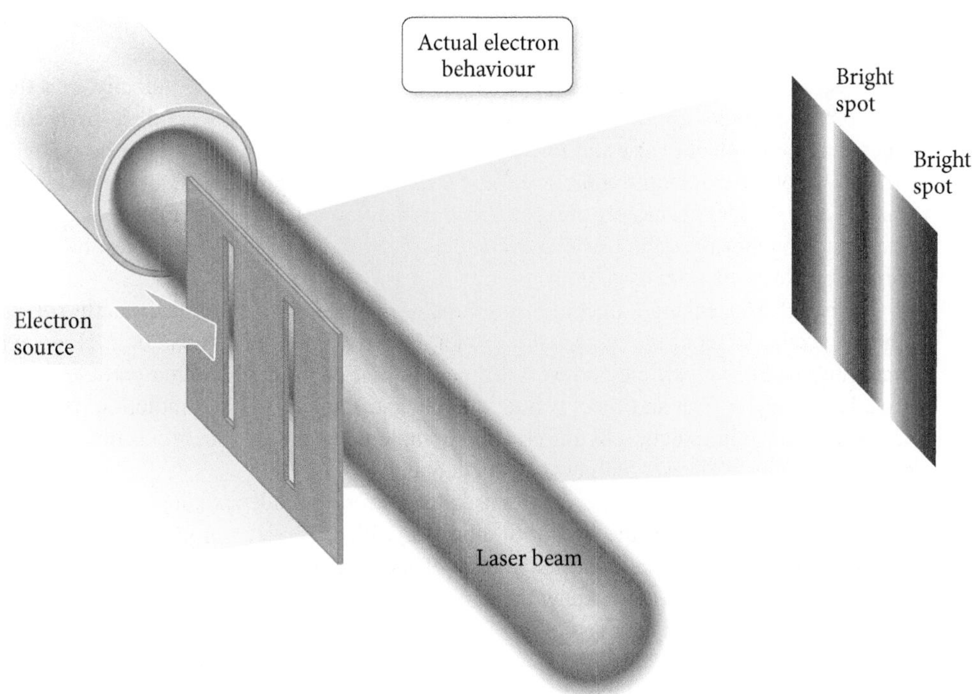

An electron that crosses the laser beam produces a tiny "flash" when a single photon is scattered at the point of crossing. If a flash shows up behind a particular slit, it indicates that an electron is passing through that slit. However, when the experiment is performed, the flash always originates either from one slit *or* the other, but *never* from both at once. Furthermore, the interference pattern, which was present without the laser, is now absent. With the laser on, the electrons hit positions directly behind each slit as if they were ordinary particles; their wave-like behaviour is no longer manifested.

Any experiment designed to observe the electron as it travels through the slits results in the detection of an electron "particle" travelling through a single slit and no interference pattern. As it turns out, no matter how hard we try, or whatever method we set up, *we can never see the interference pattern and simultaneously determine which hole the electron goes through*. It has never been done, and most scientists agree that it never will. In the words of P. A. M. Dirac,

> There is a limit to the fineness of our powers of observation and the smallness of the accompanying disturbance—a limit which is inherent in the nature of things and can never be surpassed by improved technique or increased skill on the part of the observer.

We have encountered the absolutely small and have no way of observing its behaviour without disturbing it.

The single electron diffraction experiment demonstrates that you cannot simultaneously observe both the wave nature and the particle nature of the electron. When you try to observe which hole the electron goes through (associated with the particle nature of the electron) you lose the interference pattern (associated with the wave nature of the electron). When you try to observe the interference pattern, you cannot determine which hole the electron goes through. The wave nature and particle nature of the electron are said to be **complementary properties**. Complementary properties exclude one another—the more you know about one, the less you know about the other. Which of the two complementary properties you observe depends on the experiment you perform—remember that in quantum mechanics, the observation of an event affects its outcome.

▲ Werner Heisenberg (1901–1976)

As we just saw in the de Broglie relation, the *velocity* of an electron is related to its *wave nature*. The *position* of an electron, however, is related to its *particle nature*. (Particles have well-defined position, but waves do not.) Consequently, our inability to observe the electron simultaneously as both a particle and a wave means that *we cannot simultaneously measure its position and its velocity*. Werner Heisenberg formalized this idea with the following equation:

$$\Delta x \times m\,\Delta v \geq \frac{h}{4\pi} \qquad \text{Heisenberg's uncertainty principle} \qquad [7.10]$$

where Δx is the uncertainty in the position, Δv is the uncertainty in the velocity, m is the mass of the particle, and h is Planck's constant. **Heisenberg's uncertainty principle** states that the product of Δx and $m\,\Delta v$ must be greater than or equal to a finite number ($h/4\pi$). In other words, the more accurately you know the position of an electron (the smaller Δx), the less accurately you can know its velocity (the bigger Δv) and vice versa. The complementarity of the wave nature and particle nature of the electron results in the complementarity of velocity and position.

Although Heisenberg's uncertainty principle may seem puzzling, it actually solves a great puzzle. Without the uncertainty principle, we are left with a paradox: How can something be *both* a particle and a wave? Saying that an object is both a particle and a wave is like saying that an object is both a circle and a square—a contradiction. Heisenberg solved the contradiction by introducing complementarity: an electron is observed as *either* a particle or a wave, but never both at once.

The uncertainty principle also has consequences for our understanding of the electron in an atom. Let's consider the hydrogen atom for which the electron is in its lowest energy state. We have just seen that the energy of the electron in its lowest energy state is -2.18×10^{-18} J. Suppose we know this energy to an uncertainty of 1%. Because the kinetic energy is $\frac{1}{2}mv^2$, and the mass of an electron is 9.11×10^{-31} kg, the speed of the electron is 2.19×10^6 m s^{-1}. The uncertainty in the velocity is 1.10×10^4 m s^{-1}. Using the Heisenberg uncertainty principle in Equation 7.10, the uncertainty in the position is:

$$\begin{aligned}\Delta x &= \frac{h}{4\pi} \times \frac{1}{m\Delta v} \\ &= \frac{6.626 \times 10^{-34}\,\cancel{\text{kg}}\text{ m}^2\,\cancel{\text{s}^{-1}}}{4\pi} \times \frac{1}{9.11 \times 10^{-31}\,\cancel{\text{kg}} \times 1.10 \times 10^4\,\cancel{\text{m}}\,\cancel{\text{s}^{-1}}} \\ &= 5.26 \times 10^{-9}\text{ m}\end{aligned}$$

This value is on the order of the size of an atom. What this means is that we do not, and in fact cannot, know where the electron is in the atom with any precision. One of the problems with the Bohr model of the atom was that the electrons were in precisely defined orbits with precisely defined energies that disobey the Heisenberg uncertainty principle. As we shall see shortly, we talk about the *probability* of finding an electron, not the position of the electron.

Indeterminacy and Probability Distribution Maps

According to classical physics, and Newton's laws of motion in particular, particles move in a trajectory (or path) that is determined by the particle's velocity (the speed and direction of travel), its position, and the forces acting on it. Even if you are not familiar with Newton's laws, you probably have an intuitive sense of them. For example, when a hockey player shoots the puck, a goaltender can predict where it will go by observing its path. Instantaneously, the goalie notes the initial position and velocity, and then infers its trajectory to make the save, as shown in Figure 7.19 ▼. If only the puck's velocity or position is known (imagine a still photo of the puck between the shooter and the goalie), the goalie could not make the save. In classical mechanics, both the position and velocity are required to predict a trajectory.

▲ **FIGURE 7.19 Trajectory of a Macroscopic Object** A puck follows a well-defined trajectory from the stick of the shooter to the net. The goalie is able to predict where the shot will go.

Newton's laws of motion are **deterministic**—the present determines the future. So, if two hockey pucks are shot consecutively with the same velocity from the same position under identical conditions, they will strike in exactly the same place. The same is not true of electrons. We have just seen that we cannot simultaneously know the position and velocity of an electron; therefore, we cannot know its trajectory. In quantum mechanics, trajectories are replaced with probability distribution maps, as shown in Figure 7.20 ►. A probability distribution map is a statistical map that shows where an electron is likely to be found under a given set of conditions.

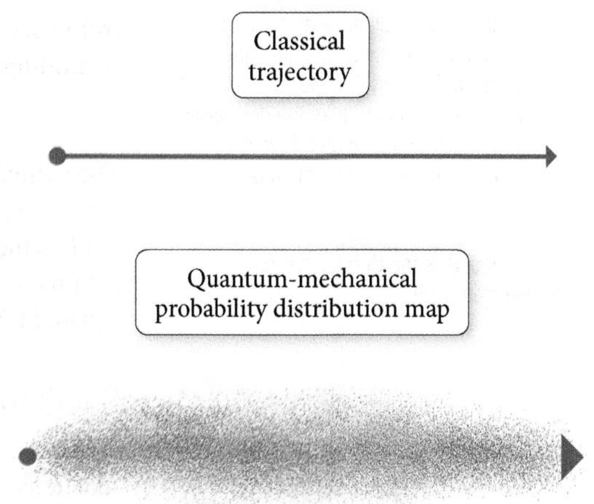

▲ **FIGURE 7.20 Trajectory Versus Probability in Quantum Mechanics** We cannot calculate deterministic trajectories. Instead, it is necessary to think in terms of probability distribution maps: statistical pictures of where a quantum particle, such as an electron, is most likely to be found. In this hypothetical map, darker shading indicates greater probability.

To understand the concept of a probability distribution, let us return to hockey. Imagine a player taking practice slapshots from the same position, trying to score on the goalie as in Figure 7.21 ▼. One of the obvious places to try to score on the goalie would be between his legs, the so-called five-hole. A good goalie can watch the puck's path, predict where it will go, and react to try to make the save. As we have seen, this would be impossible for an electron. If an electron was shot at the goalie, it would strike a different place every time, even if it was shot in exactly the same way. This behaviour is called **indeterminacy**. Unlike a puck, which has a future path that is *determined* by its position and velocity when it leaves the player's stick, the future path of an electron cannot be determined and can only be described statistically.

In the quantum world of the electron, the goalie could not know exactly where the electron will go for any given shot. However, if he kept track of hundreds of identical electron shots, the goalie could observe a reproducible, statistical pattern of where the electron will go. He could even draw a map of the five-hole region, as shown in Figure 7.21. This would be a probability distribution map. In the sections that follow, we discuss atomic orbitals which come from quantum theory, which are essentially probability distribution maps for the electrons as they exist within atoms.

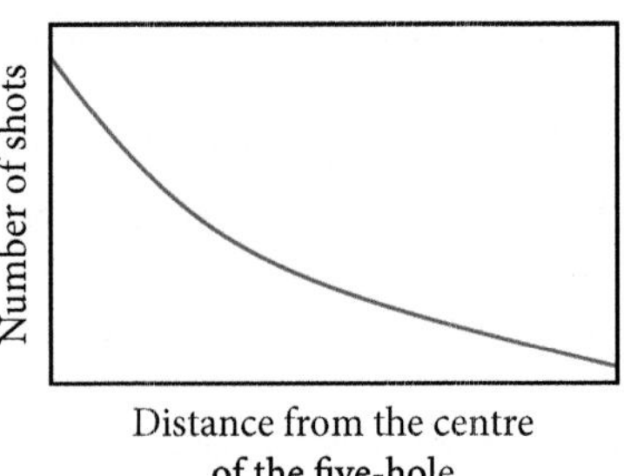

▶ **FIGURE 7.21 The Quantum-Mechanical Five-Hole** An electron does not have a well-defined trajectory. However, we can construct a probability distribution map to show the relative probability of where the electron shot will go.

7.5 Quantum Mechanics and the Atom

As we have seen, the position and velocity of the electron are complementary properties—if we know one accurately, the other becomes indeterminate. Since velocity is directly related to energy (we have seen that kinetic energy equals $\frac{1}{2}mv^2$), position and *energy* are also complementary properties—the more you know about one, the less you know about the other. Many of the properties of an element, however, depend on the energies of its electrons. For example, whether an electron is transferred from one atom to another to form an ionic bond depends in part on the relative energies of the electron in the two atoms. In the following paragraphs, we describe the probability distribution maps for electron states in which the electron has well-defined energy, but not well-defined position. In other words, for each state, we can specify the *energy* of the electron precisely, but not its location at a given instant. Instead, the electron's position is described in terms of an **orbital**, a probability distribution map showing where the electron is likely to be found. Since chemical bonding often involves the sharing of electrons between atoms to form covalent bonds, the spatial distribution of atomic electrons is important to bonding.

These states are known as energy *eigenstates*.

The mathematical derivation of energies and orbitals for electrons in atoms comes from solving the *Schrödinger* equation for the atom of interest. The general form of the Schrödinger equation is as follows:

An operator is different from a normal algebraic entity. In general, an operator transforms a mathematical function into another mathematical function. For example, d/dx is an operator that means "take the deriviative of." When d/dx operates on a function (such as x^2), it returns another function ($2x$).

$$\mathcal{H}\psi = E\psi \qquad [7.11]$$

The symbol $\mathcal{H}$ stands for the Hamiltonian operator, a set of mathematical operations that represents the total energy (kinetic and potential) of the electron within the atom. The symbol E is the actual energy of the electron. The symbol $\boldsymbol{\psi}$ is the **wave function**, a mathematical function that describes the wave-like nature of the electron. A plot of the wave function squared (ψ^2) represents an orbital, a position probability distribution map of the electron.

The symbol ψ is the Greek letter psi, pronounced "sigh."

Solutions to the Schrödinger Equation for the Hydrogen Atom

When the Schrödinger equation is solved, it yields many solutions—many possible wave functions. We will introduce graphical representations (or plots) of the orbitals that correspond to the wave functions. Each orbital is specified by three interrelated **quantum numbers**: n, the **principal quantum number**; l, the **angular momentum quantum number** (sometimes called the *azimuthal quantum number*); and m_l, the **magnetic quantum number**. These quantum numbers all have integer values, as had been hinted at by both the Rydberg equation and Bohr's model. We examine each of these quantum numbers individually.

The Principal Quantum Number (n) The principal quantum number is an integer that determines the overall size and indicates the energy level of an electron in an orbital. Its possible values are $n = 1, 2, 3$, and so on. For the hydrogen atom, the energy of an electron in an orbital with quantum number n is given by:

$$E_n = -2.18 \times 10^{-18}\ \text{J}\left(\frac{1}{n^2}\right) \qquad (n = 1, 2, 3, \ldots) \qquad [7.12]$$

The energy is negative because the electron's energy is lowered (made more negative) by its interaction with the nucleus (as described by Coulomb's law). The constant, 2.18×10^{-18} J, is known as the Rydberg constant for hydrogen (R_H). Notice that orbitals with higher values of n have greater (less negative) energies, as shown in the energy level diagram in the margin. Notice also that, as n increases, the spacing between the energy levels becomes smaller.

Energy

$n = 4$ —— $E_4 = -1.36 \times 10^{-19}$ J

$n = 3$ —— $E_3 = -2.42 \times 10^{-19}$ J

$n = 2$ —— $E_2 = -5.45 \times 10^{-19}$ J

$n = 1$ —— $E_1 = -2.18 \times 10^{-18}$ J

The Angular Momentum Quantum Number (l) The angular momentum quantum number is an integer that corresponds primarily with the shape of the orbital. We will consider these shapes in Section 7.6. The possible values of l are 0, 1, 2, . . . , $(n - 1)$. In other words, for a given value of n, l can be any integer (including 0) up to $n - 1$. For example, if $n = 1$, then the only possible value of l is 0; if $n = 2$, the possible values of l are 0 and 1. In order to avoid confusion between n and l, values of l are often assigned letters as follows:

Value of l	Letter Designation
$l = 0$	s
$l = 1$	p
$l = 2$	d
$l = 3$	f

The values of l beyond 3 are designated with letters in alphabetical order so that $l = 4$ is designated g, $l = 5$ is designated h, and so on.

The Magnetic Quantum Number (m_l) The magnetic quantum number is an integer that specifies the orientation of the orbital. We will consider these orientations in Section 7.6. The possible values of m_l are the integer values (including zero), ranging from $-l$ to $+l$. For example, if $l = 0$, then the only possible value of m_l is 0; if $l = 1$, the possible values of m_l are -1, 0, and $+1$; if $l = 2$, the possible values of m_l are -2, -1, 0, $+1$, and $+2$; and so on.

Each specific combination of n, l, and m_l specifies one atomic orbital. For example, the orbital with $n = 1$, $l = 0$, and $m_l = 0$ is known as the 1s orbital. The 1 in 1s is the value of n, and the s specifies that $l = 0$. There is only one 1s orbital in an atom, and its m_l value is zero. Orbitals with the same value of n are said to be in the same **principal level** (or **principal shell**). Orbitals with the same value of n and l are said to be in the same **sublevel** (or **subshell**). The following diagram shows all the orbitals in the first three principal levels.

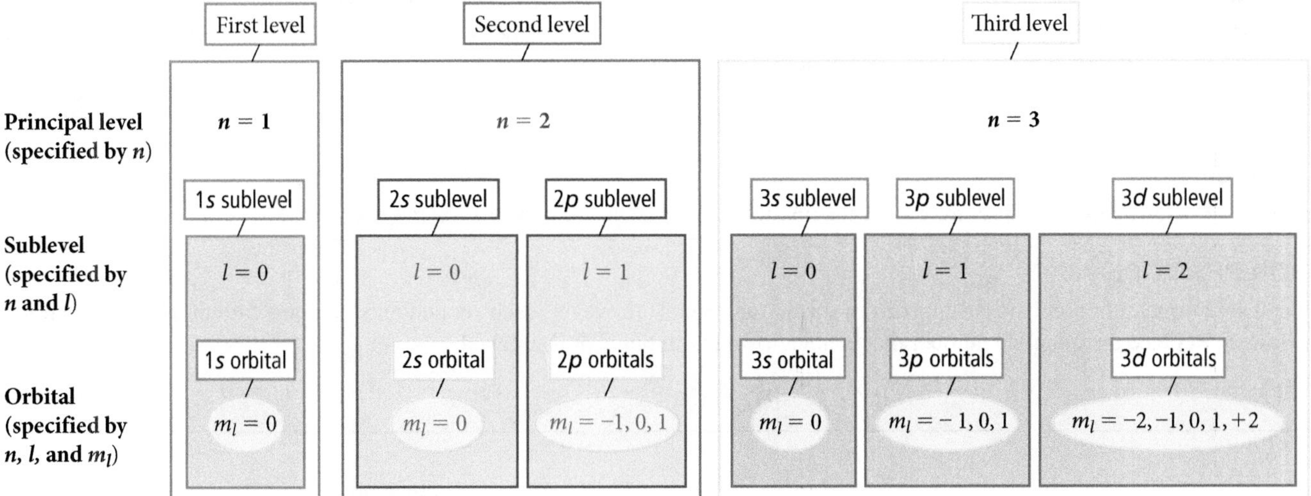

For example, the $n = 2$ level contains the $l = 0$ and $l = 1$ sublevels. Within the $n = 2$ level, the $l = 0$ sublevel—called the 2s sublevel—contains only one orbital (the 2s orbital), with $m_l = 0$. The $l = 1$ sublevel—called the 2p sublevel—contains three 2p orbitals with $m_l = -1, 0, +1$, and associated with the labels $2p_x$, $2p_y$, and $2p_z$.

In general, notice the following:

- The number of sublevels in any level is equal to n, the principal quantum number. Therefore, the $n = 1$ level has one sublevel, the $n = 2$ level has two sublevels, and so forth.

- The number of orbitals in any sublevel is equal to $2l + 1$. Therefore, the s sublevel ($l = 0$) has one orbital, the p sublevel ($l = 1$) has three orbitals, the d sublevel ($l = 2$) has five orbitals, and so forth.
- The number of orbitals in a level is equal to n^2. Therefore, the $n = 1$ level has one orbital, the $n = 2$ level has four orbitals, the $n = 3$ level has nine orbitals, and so forth.

EXAMPLE 7.5 QUANTUM NUMBERS I

What are the quantum numbers and names (for example, 2*s*, 2*p*) of the orbitals in the $n = 4$ principal level? How many $n = 4$ orbitals exist?

SOLUTION

First determine the possible values of l (from the given value of n). Then determine the possible values of m_l for each possible value of l. For a given value of n, the possible values of l are 0, 1, 2, . . . , $(n - 1)$.

$n = 4$; therefore, $l = 0$, 1, 2, and 3

For a given value of l, the possible values of m_l are the integer values (including zero), ranging from $-l$ to $+l$. The name of an orbital is its principal quantum number (n) followed by the letter corresponding to the value l. The total number of orbitals is given by n^2.

l	Possible m_l Values	Orbital Name(s)
0	0	4*s* (1 orbital)
1	−1, 0, +1	4*p* (3 orbitals)
2	−2, −1, 0, +1, +2	4*d* (5 orbitals)
3	−3, −2, −1, 0, +1, +2, +3	4*f* (7 orbitals)

Total number of orbitals $= 4^2 = 16$

FOR PRACTICE 7.5

List the quantum numbers associated with all of the 5*d* orbitals. How many 5*d* orbitals exist?

EXAMPLE 7.6 QUANTUM NUMBERS II

The sets of quantum numbers are each supposed to specify an orbital. One set, however, is erroneous. Which one and why?

(a) $n = 3; l = 0; m_l = 0$
(b) $n = 2; l = 1; m_l = -1$
(c) $n = 1; l = 0; m_l = 0$
(d) $n = 4; l = 1; m_l = -2$

SOLUTION

Choice **(d)** is erroneous because, for $l = 1$, the possible values of m_l are only -1, 0, and $+1$.

FOR PRACTICE 7.6

Each set of quantum numbers is supposed to specify an orbital. However, each set contains one quantum number that is not allowed. Replace the quantum number that is not allowed with one that is allowed.

(a) $n = 3;\ l = 3;\ m_l = +2$ **(b)** $n = 2;\ l = 1;\ m_l = -2$ **(c)** $n = 1;\ l = 1;\ m_l = 0$

7.6 The Shapes of Atomic Orbitals

As we noted previously, the shapes of atomic orbitals are important because covalent chemical bonds depend on the sharing of the electrons that occupy these orbitals. In one model of chemical bonding, for example, a bond consists of the overlap of atomic orbitals on adjacent atoms. The shapes of the overlapping orbitals determine the shape of the molecule. Although we limit ourselves to the orbitals of the hydrogen atom, we will see that the orbitals of all atoms can be approximated as being hydrogen-like and therefore have very similar shapes to those of hydrogen.

The shape of an atomic orbital is determined primarily by l, the angular momentum quantum number. As we have seen, each value of l is assigned a letter that therefore corresponds to particular orbitals. For example, the orbitals with $l = 0$ are called *s* orbitals; those with $l = 1$, *p* orbitals; those with $l = 2$, *d* orbitals; and so on. We now examine the shape of each of these orbitals.

s Orbitals ($l = 0$)

The lowest energy orbital is the spherically symmetrical 1*s* orbital shown in Figure 7.22(a) ▼. This image is actually a three-dimensional plot of the wave function squared (ψ^2), which represents **probability density**, the probability (per unit volume) of finding the electron at a point in space.

$$\psi^2 = \text{probability density} = \frac{\text{probability}}{\text{unit volume}}$$

The magnitude of ψ^2 in this plot is proportional to the density of the dots shown in the image. The high dot density near the nucleus (at the very centre of the plot) indicates a higher probability density for the electron there. As you move away from the nucleus, the probability density decreases. Figure 7.22(b) shows a plot of probability density (ψ^2) versus r, the distance from the nucleus. The plot represents a slice through the three-dimensional plot of ψ^2 and shows how the probability density decreases as r increases.

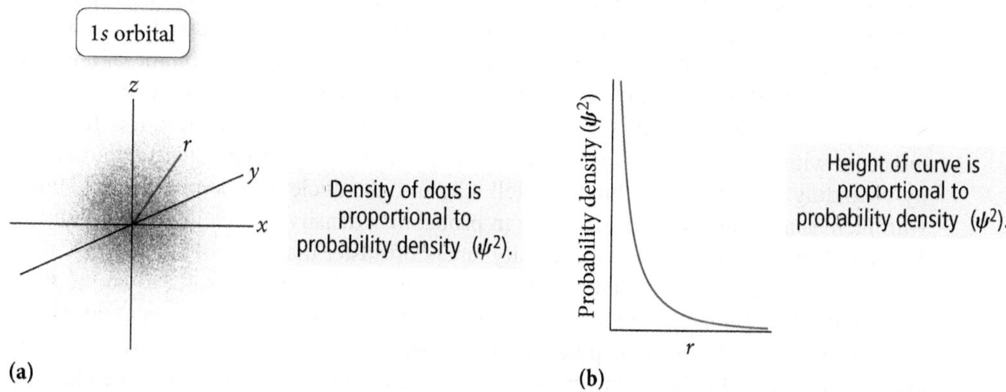

▲ **FIGURE 7.22 The 1*s* Orbital: Two Representations** In (**a**), the dot density is proportional to the electron probability density. In (**b**), the height of the curve is proportional to the electron probability density. The *x*-axis is r, the distance from the nucleus.

We can understand probability density with the help of a thought experiment. Imagine an electron in the 1*s* orbital located within the volume surrounding the nucleus. Imagine also taking a photograph of the electron every second for 10 or 15 minutes. In one photograph, the electron is very close to the nucleus; in another, it is farther away, and so on. Each photo has a dot showing the electron's position relative to the nucleus when the photo was taken. Remember that you can never predict where the electron will be for any one photo. However, if you took hundreds of photos and superimposed all of them, you would have a plot similar to Figure 7.22(a)—a statistical representation of how likely the electron is to be found at each point.

The thought experiment we just examined can result in a possible misunderstanding: that the electron is moving around (like a moth near a flame) between photographs. However, in the quantum-mechanical model, that is not the case. Between photographs, the location of the electron is uncertain—in a sense, its location is spread out over the entire volume of the orbital. Only when the photograph is taken (that is, when a measurement of its location is made) does the location of the electron become localized to one spot. Between measurements, the electron has no single location. Remember from Section 7.1, the measurement affects the outcome of any quantum system.

An atomic orbital can also be represented by a geometrical shape that encompasses the volume where the electron is likely to be found most frequently—typically 90% of the time. For example, the 1*s* orbital can be represented as the three-dimensional sphere shown in Figure 7.23 ►. If we were to superimpose the dot-density representation of the 1*s* orbital

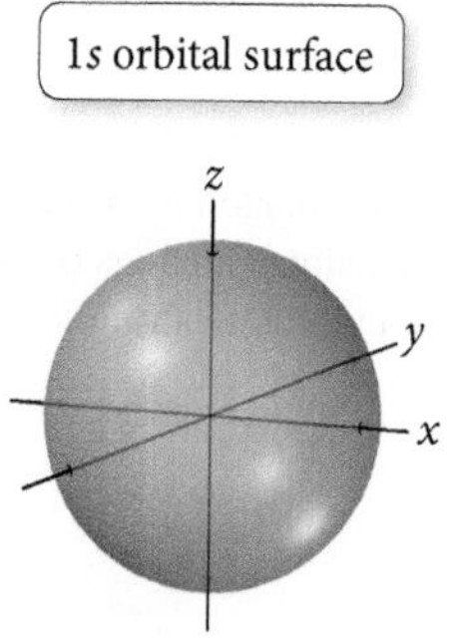

▲ **FIGURE 7.23 The 1*s* Orbital Surface** In this representation, the surface of the sphere encompasses the volume where the electron is found 90% of the time when the electron is in the 1*s* orbital.

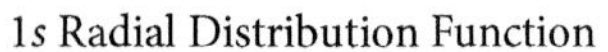

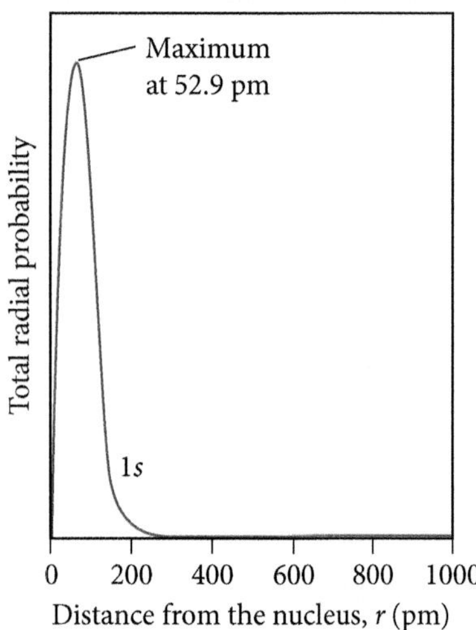

▲ **FIGURE 7.24 The Radial Distribution Function for the 1*s* Orbital** The curve shows the total probability of finding the electron within a thin shell at a distance *r* from the nucleus.

on the shape representation, 90% of the dots would be within the sphere, meaning that when the electron is in the 1*s* orbital, it has a 90% chance of being found within the sphere.

The plots we have just seen represent probability *density*. However, they are a bit misleading because they seem to imply that the electron is most likely to be found *at the nucleus*. To get a better idea of where the electron is most likely to be found, we can use a plot called the **radial distribution function**, shown in Figure 7.24 ◄ for the 1*s* orbital. The radial distribution function represents the *total probability of finding the electron within a thin spherical shell at a distance* r *from the nucleus*.

$$\text{Total radial probability (at a given } r) = \frac{\text{probability}}{\text{unit volume}} \times \text{volume of shell at } r$$

The radial distribution function represents, not probability density *at a point r*, but total probability *at a radius r*. In contrast to probability density, which has a maximum at the nucleus, the radial distribution function has a value of *zero* at the nucleus. It increases to a maximum at 52.9 pm and then decreases again with increasing *r*.

The shape of the radial distribution function is the result of multiplying together two functions with opposite trends in *r*: (1) the probability density function (ψ^2), which is the probability per unit volume and decreases with increasing *r*; and (2) the volume of the thin shell, which increases with increasing *r*. At the nucleus ($r = 0$), for example, the probability *density* is at a maximum; however, the volume of a thin spherical shell is zero, so the radial distribution function is zero. As *r* increases, the volume of the thin spherical shell increases. We can understand this by making an analogy to an onion. A spherical shell at a distance *r* from the nucleus is like a layer in an onion at a distance *r* from its centre. If the layers of the onion are all the same thickness, then the volume of any one layer—think of this as the total amount of onion in the layer—is greater as *r* increases. Similarly, the volume of any one spherical shell in the radial distribution function increases with increasing distance from the nucleus, resulting in a greater total probability of finding the electron within that shell. Close to the nucleus, this increase in volume with increasing *r* outpaces the decrease in probability density, producing a maximum at 52.9 pm. Farther out, however, the density tapers off faster than the volume increases.

The maximum in the radial distribution function, 52.9 pm, turns out to be the very same radius that Bohr had predicted for the innermost orbit of the hydrogen atom. However, there is a significant conceptual difference between the two radii. In the Bohr model, every time you probe the atom (in its lowest energy state), you would find the electron at a radius of 52.9 pm. In the quantum-mechanical model, you would generally find the electron at various radii, with 52.9 pm having the greatest probability.

1 pm = 10^{-12} m

The probability densities and radial distribution functions for the 2*s* and 3*s* orbitals are shown in Figure 7.25 ►. Like the 1*s* orbital, these orbitals are spherically symmetric. These orbitals are larger in size, however, and, unlike the 1*s* orbital, they contain radial nodes. A **node** is a point where the wave function (ψ), and therefore the probability density (ψ^2) and radial distribution function, all go through zero. A node in a wave function is much like a node in a standing wave on a vibrating string. We can see nodes in an orbital most clearly by looking at a slice through the orbital. Plots of probability density and the radial distribution function as a function of *r* both reveal the presence of nodes. The probability of finding the electron at a node is zero.

► The nodes in atomic orbitals are three-dimensional analogs of the nodes on a vibrating string.

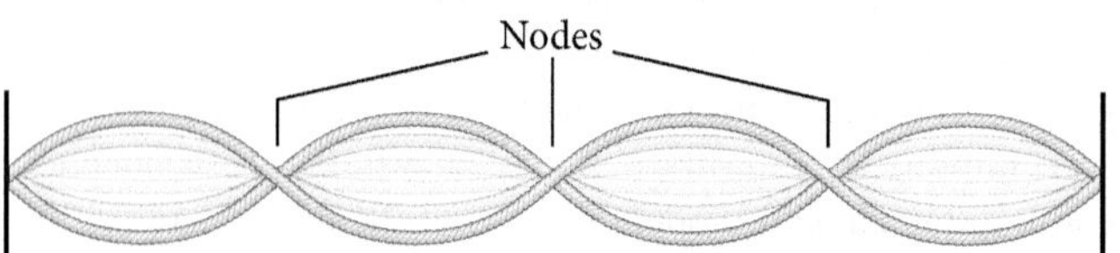

There are two types of nodes: radial and angular. For a 2*s* orbital, if you move outward from the nucleus, there will be a region in which there is zero probability of finding the electron. This is called a **radial node**, sometimes described as a **spherical node** (Figure 7.25). For a 3*s* orbital, there are two regions in which there is zero probability of finding the electron and, therefore, two radial nodes (Figure 7.25). In a probability density diagram or radial distribution function, radial nodes are the only ones that can be seen. In total, there are $n - 1$ nodes for any particular orbital and $n - l - 1$ radial nodes. For an *s*

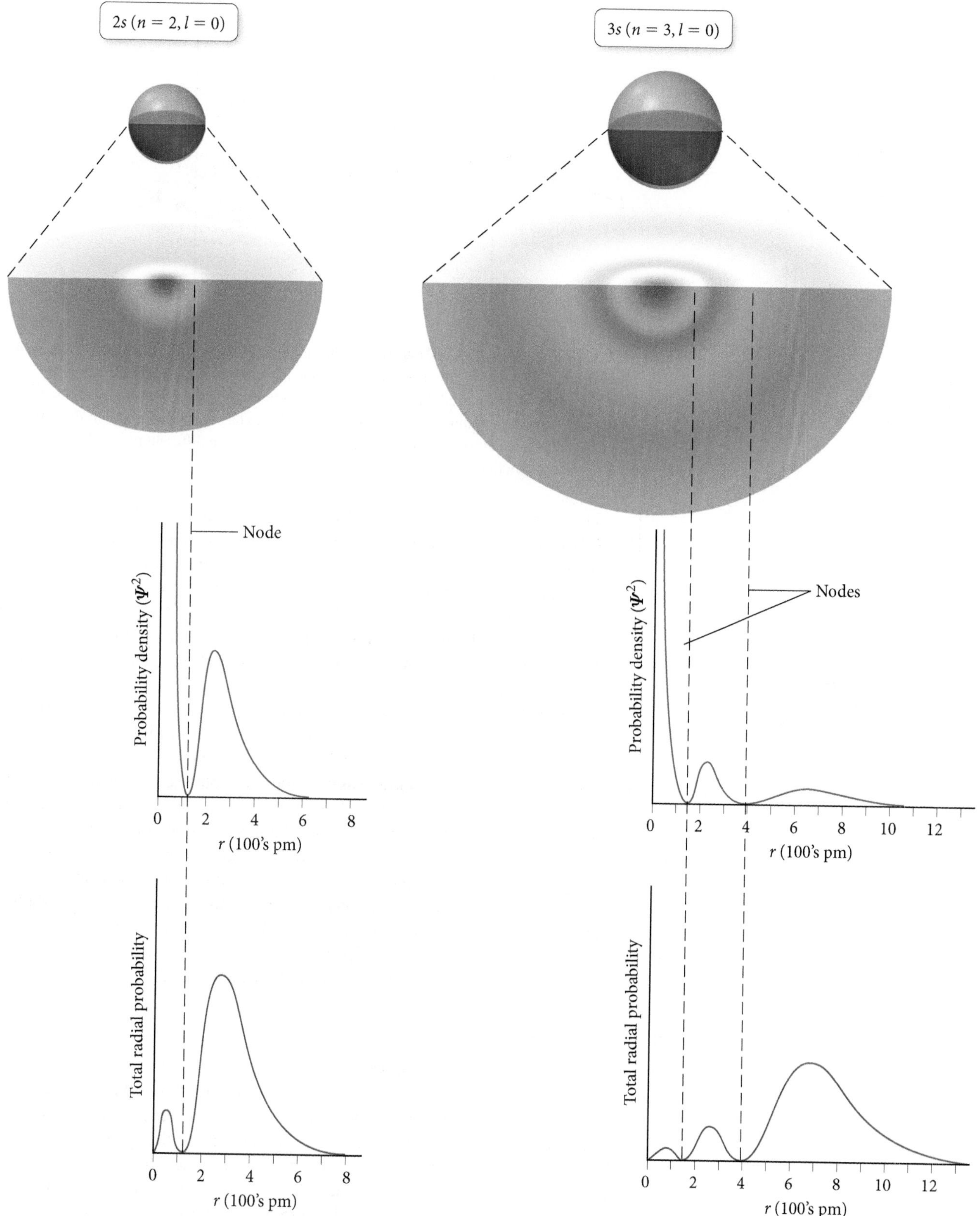

▲ **FIGURE 7.25 Probability Densities and Radial Distribution Functions for the 2*s* and 3*s* Orbitals**

orbital, there are no angular nodes; they are only encountered for $l = 1$ or higher orbitals. They will be described in the next section.

p Orbitals ($l = 1$)

Each principal level with $n = 2$ or greater contains three *p* orbitals ($m_l = -1, 0, +1$). The three 2*p* orbitals and their radial distribution functions are shown in Figure 7.26 ▼.

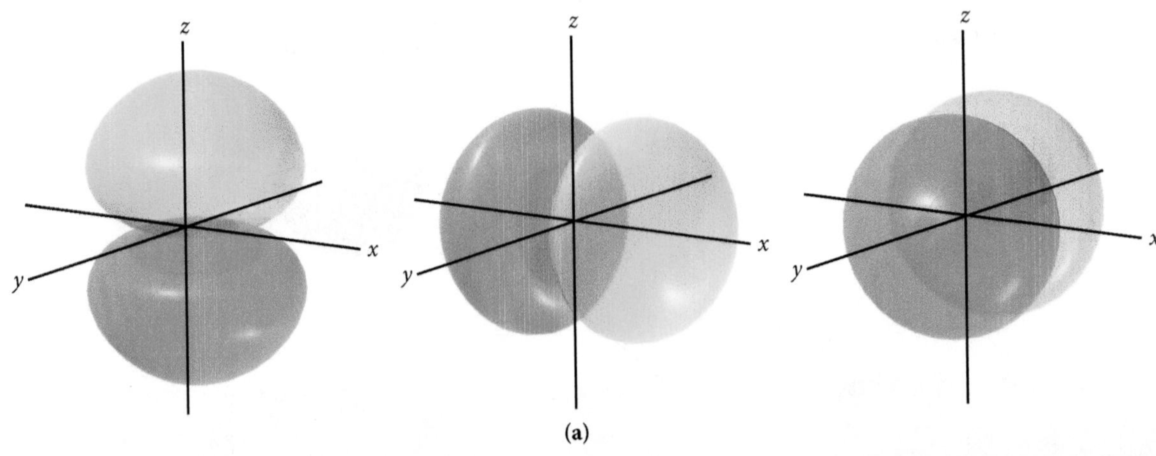

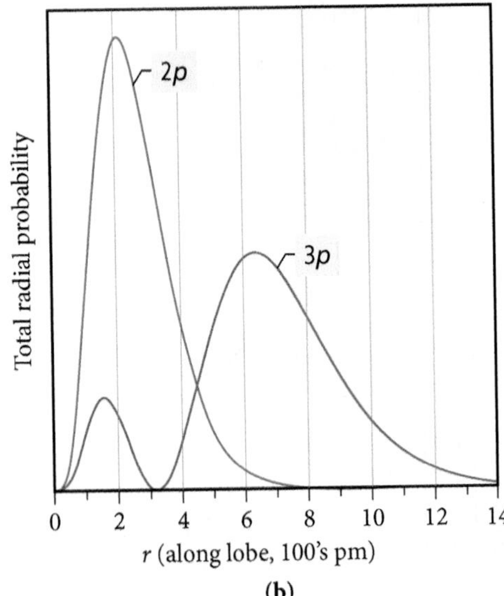

▲ **FIGURE 7.26 (a) The 2*p* Orbitals, and (b) the Radial Distribution Functions for the 2*p* and 3*p* Orbitals** The radial distribution function is the same for all 2*p* orbitals when the *r*-axis of the graph is considered the axis that contains the lobes of the orbitals. The 2*p* and 3*p* orbitals have one angular node, but the 3*p* orbital also has one radial node. In the orbital surface diagrams, the different coloured lobes represent the different phases (+/−) or signs of the wave function.

The *p* orbitals are not spherically symmetric like the *s* orbitals, but have two *lobes* of electron density on either side of the nucleus and a node located at the nucleus. The three *p* orbitals differ only in their orientation and are orthogonal (mutually perpendicular) to one another. It is convenient to define an *x*-, *y*-, and *z*-axis system and then label each *p* orbital as p_x, p_y, and p_z. The 3*p*, 4*p*, 5*p*, and higher *p* orbitals are all similar in shape to the 2*p* orbitals, but they contain additional nodes (like the higher *s* orbitals) and are progressively larger in size.

For the 2*p* orbital, there is one node ($n = 2, n - 1 = 1$ node). However, in the radial distribution function for the 2*p* orbital in Figure 7.26, there is no region of zero probability of finding the electron—no radial node. The node for the 2*p* orbital is an **angular node**. Angular nodes are planes, or surfaces where there is zero probability of finding the electron. For the $2p_x$ orbital, the plane that includes the *y*- and *z*-axes and separates the two lobes of the *p* orbital is the angular node. For any orbital, there are *l* angular nodes. For the 3*p* orbital, there is one angular node and one radial node. By comparing the radial distribution functions for the 2*p* and 3*p* orbitals, it can be seen that there is a radial node just above 300 pm on the 3*p* radial distribution function, right where the maximum occurs in the radial probability for the 2*p* orbital. Furthermore, it can be seen that the 3*p* orbital is *larger* than the 2*p* orbital; the maximum in radial probability is just below 700 pm and it extends out significantly farther from the nucleus.

d Orbitals ($l = 2$)

Each principal level with $n = 3$ or greater contains five *d* orbitals ($m_l = -2, -1, 0, +1, +2$). The five 3*d* orbitals are shown in Figure 7.27 ▶. Four of these orbitals have a cloverleaf shape, with four lobes of electron density around the nucleus and two perpendicular nodal planes. The d_{xy}, d_{xz}, and d_{yz} orbitals are oriented along the *xy*, *xz*, and *yz* planes, respectively, and their lobes are oriented *between* the corresponding axes. The four lobes of the $d_{x^2-y^2}$ orbital are oriented along the *x*- and *y*-axes. The d_{z^2} orbital is different in shape from the other four, having two lobes oriented along the *z*-axis and a doughnut-shaped ring along the *xy* plane. The 4*d*, 5*d*, 6*d* (and so on) orbitals are all similar in shape to the 3*d* orbitals, but they contain additional nodes and are progressively larger in size.

A nodal plane is a plane where the electron probability density is zero. For example, in the d_{xy} orbitals, the nodal planes lie in the *xz* and *yz* planes.

f Orbitals ($l = 3$)

Each principal level with $n = 4$ or greater contains seven *f* orbitals ($m_l = -3, -2, -1, 0, +1, +2, +3$), as shown in Figure 7.28 ▶. These *f* orbitals have more lobes and nodes than *d* orbitals.

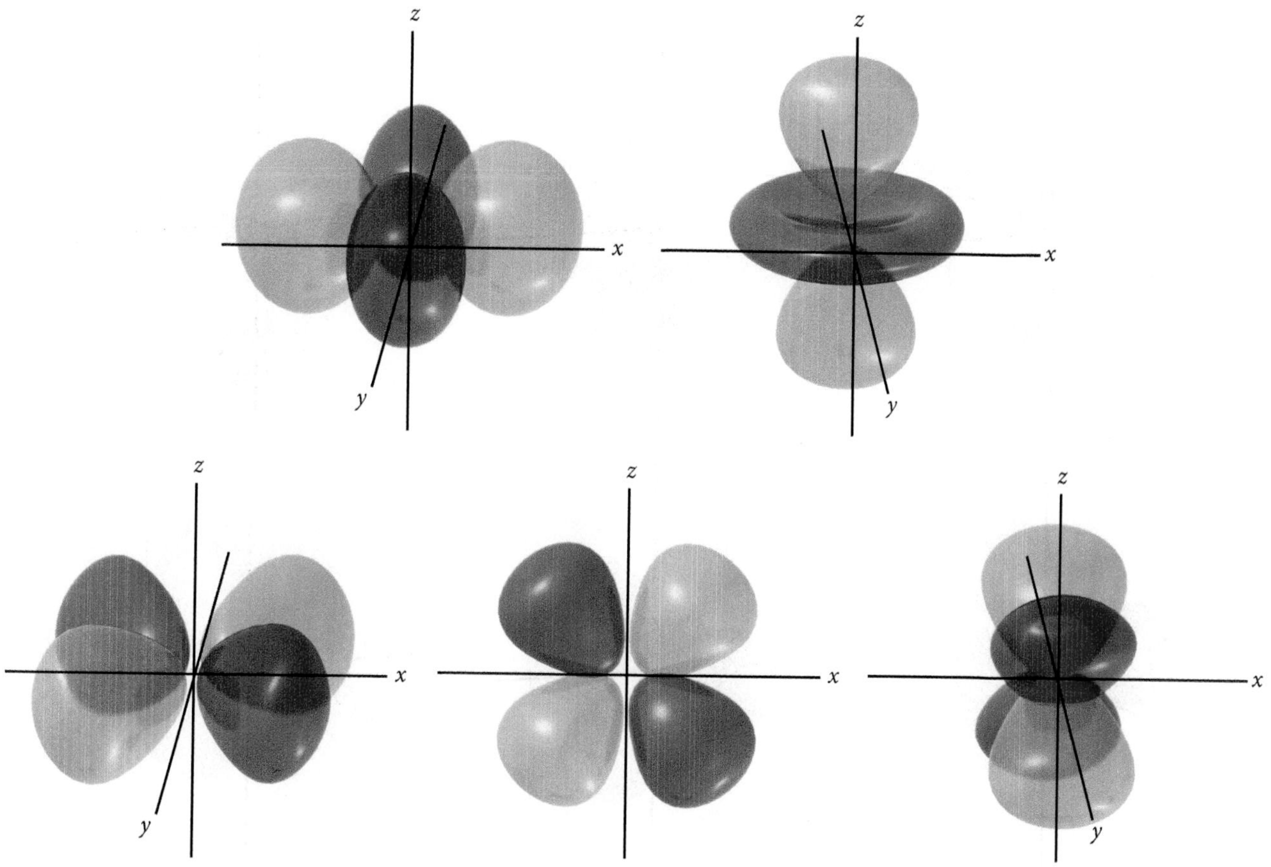

▲ **FIGURE 7.27 The 3*d* Orbitals** The different coloured lobes represent the different phases (+/−) or signs of the wave function. When these orbitals are compared for two different values of *n*, the shapes are identical; however the orbitals with the greater *n* value are larger in size.

The Phase of Orbitals

The orbitals we have just seen are three-dimensional waves. We can understand an important property of these orbitals by analogy to one-dimensional waves. Consider the following one-dimensional waves:

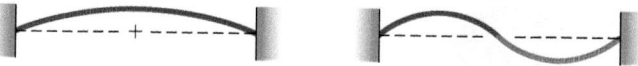

The wave on the left has a positive amplitude over its entire length, while the wave on the right has a positive amplitude over half of its length and a negative amplitude over the other half. The sign of the amplitude of a wave—positive or negative—is known as its **phase**. The phase of a wave determines how it interferes with another wave, as we saw in Section 7.2.

Just as a one-dimensional wave has components with phase, so does a three-dimensional wave. We often represent the phase of an atomic orbital with colour. For example, the phase of a 1*s* and 2*p* orbital can be represented as follows:

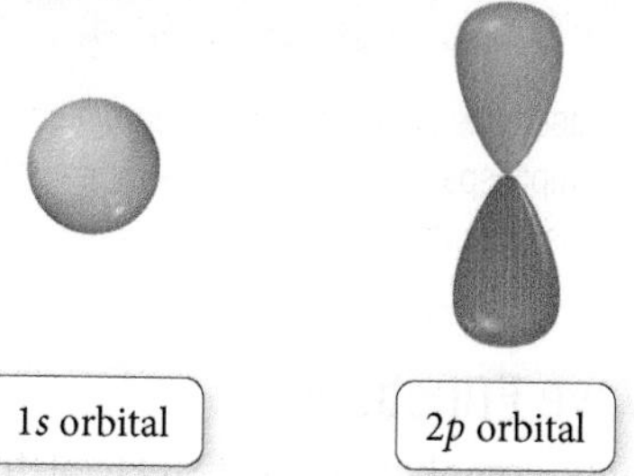

In these depictions, blue represents one phase and red represents the opposite phase. The 1*s* orbital is all one phase, while the 2*p* orbital exhibits two different phases. In Figures 7.26–7.28, the two different colours for the lobes of an orbital represent the

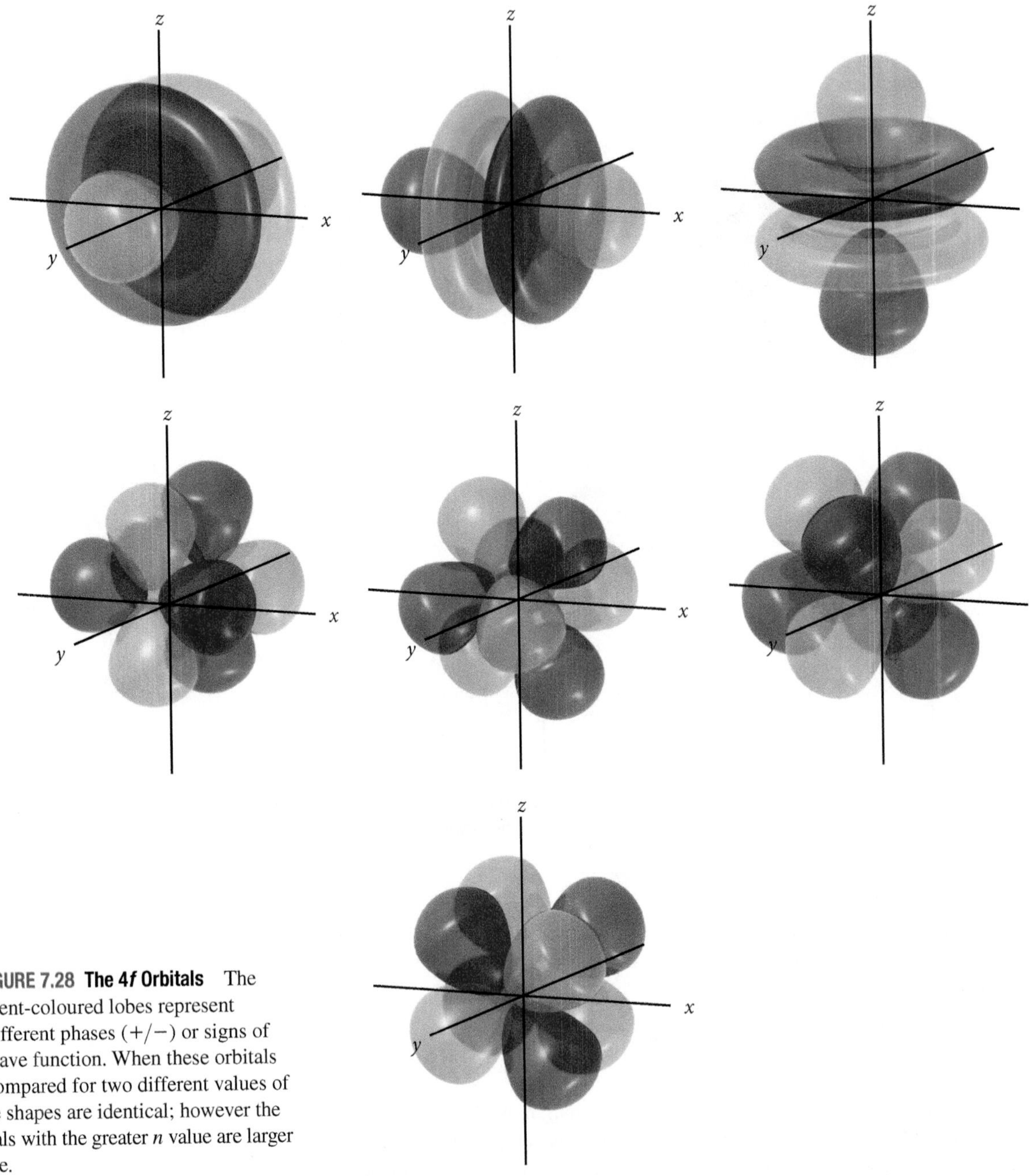

▶ **FIGURE 7.28 The 4*f* Orbitals** The different-coloured lobes represent the different phases (+/−) or signs of the wave function. When these orbitals are compared for two different values of *n*, the shapes are identical; however the orbitals with the greater *n* value are larger in size.

different phases, positive or negative. A node separates the phases of an orbital. The phase of atomic orbitals is important in bonding, as we shall see in Chapter 10.

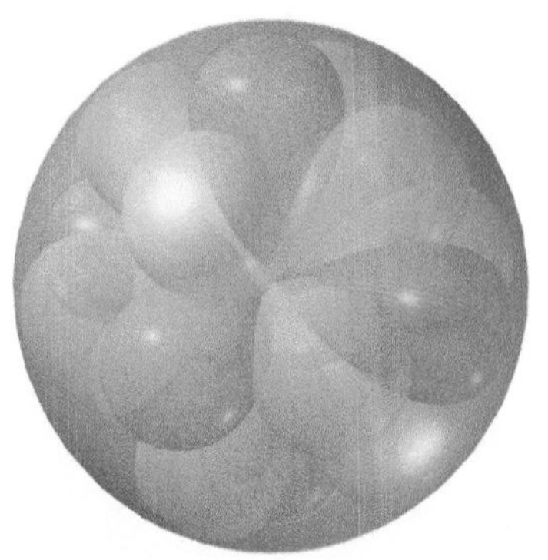

▲ **FIGURE 7.29 The Sperical Shapes of Atoms**

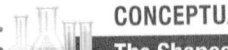

CONCEPTUAL CONNECTION 7.5

The Shapes of Atoms

If some orbitals are shaped like dumbbells and three-dimensional cloverleafs, and if most of the volume of an atom is empty space diffusely occupied by electrons in these orbitals, then why do we often depict atoms as spheres (Figure 7.29 ◀)?

The Hydrogen-Like Wave Functions

Wave functions are seemingly complicated mathematical functions, as can be seen in Table 7.1. The wave functions have been divided into two parts: the radial part (R) and the angular part (Y). The three variables r, θ, and ϕ arise from the requirement to convert Cartesian coordinates (x, y, z) to spherical polar coordinates (which we will not worry about in this text). Two issues that emerged from our discussion of the orbitals were their sizes and the presence of nodes.

TABLE 7.1 Solutions to the Schrödinger Equation (Wave Functions) for a One-Electron Atom

n	l	m_l	Orbital	Radial Part	Angular Part
1	0	0	1s	$R(1s) = 2\left(\frac{Z}{a_0}\right)^{3/2} e^{-Zr/a_0}$	$Y(s) = \frac{1}{2\sqrt{\pi}}$
2	0	0	2s	$R(2s) = \frac{1}{\sqrt{8}}\left(\frac{Z}{a_0}\right)^{3/2}\left(2 - \frac{Zr}{a_0}\right)e^{-Zr/2a_0}$	$Y(s) = \frac{1}{2\sqrt{\pi}}$
2	1	0	$2p_z$	$R(2p) = \frac{1}{\sqrt{24}}\left(\frac{Z}{a_0}\right)^{3/2}\left(\frac{Zr}{a_0}\right)e^{-Zr/2a_0}$	$Y(p_z) = \left(\frac{3}{4\pi}\right)^{1/2} \cos\theta$
2	1	1	$2p_x$		$Y(p_x) = \left(\frac{3}{4\pi}\right)^{1/2} \sin\theta \cos\phi$
2	1	−1	$2p_y$		$Y(p_y) = \left(\frac{3}{4\pi}\right)^{1/2} \sin\theta \sin\phi$
3	0	0	3s	$R(3s) = \frac{2}{81\sqrt{3}}\left(\frac{Z}{a_0}\right)^{3/2}\left(27 - 18\frac{Zr}{a_0} + 2\frac{Z^2r^2}{(a_0)^2}\right)e^{-Zr/3a_0}$	$Y(s) = \frac{1}{2\sqrt{\pi}}$
3	1	0	$3p_z$	$R(3p) = \frac{4}{81\sqrt{6}}\left(\frac{Z}{a_0}\right)^{3/2}\left(6\frac{Zr}{a_0} - \frac{Z^2r^2}{(a_0)^2}\right)e^{-Zr/3a_0}$	$Y(p_z) = \left(\frac{3}{4\pi}\right)^{1/2} \cos\theta$
3	1	1	$3p_x$		$Y(p_x) = \left(\frac{3}{4\pi}\right)^{1/2} \sin\theta \cos\phi$
3	1	−1	$3p_y$		$Y(p_y) = \left(\frac{3}{4\pi}\right)^{1/2} \sin\theta \sin\phi$
3	2	0	$3d_{z^2}$	$R(3d) = \frac{4}{81\sqrt{30}}\left(\frac{Z}{a_0}\right)^{3/2}\left(\frac{Z^2r^2}{(a_0)^2}\right)e^{-Zr/3a_0}$	$Y(d_{z^2}) = \left(\frac{5}{16\pi}\right)^{1/2}(3\cos^2\theta - 1)$

Let's consider and compare the 1*s* and 2*s* orbitals. The angular part of the 1*s* and 2*s* orbitals is the same, and is constant; there is no angular dependence, which is why the *s* orbitals are spherical in shape. The 1*s* and 2*s* orbitals both consist of a constant part and an exponential part. The radial part of the 2*s* orbital has a third term, a first-order polynomial dependent upon *r*.

$$R(1s) = \underbrace{2\left(\frac{Z}{a_0}\right)^{3/2}}_{\text{constant}} \underbrace{e^{-Zr/a_0}}_{\text{exponential}}$$

$$R(2s) = \underbrace{\frac{1}{\sqrt{8}}\left(\frac{Z}{a_0}\right)^{3/2}}_{\text{constant}} \underbrace{\left(2 - \frac{Zr}{a_0}\right)}_{\substack{\text{1st-order}\\ \text{polynomial}}} \underbrace{e^{-Zr/2a_0}}_{\text{exponential}}$$

The 1*s* orbital cannot take on the value zero. That is because the angular part as well as the exponential and constant in the radial part can never have the value zero. However, the polynomial portion of $R(2s)$ can take on the value 0. This occurs when:

$$R(2s) = 0 = \left(2 - \frac{Zr}{a_0}\right)$$

$$\text{or when } r = \frac{2a_0}{Z}$$

So, when $r = 2a_0/Z$, there is a radial node for the 2*s* orbital. The radial part of the 3*s* orbital has a portion that is a second-order polynomial and, therefore, has two values of *r* that will provide a value of zero (two roots) or two radial nodes.

For the orbitals with $n = 1$, the exponential term falls off as *r* increases. However, for the orbitals with $n = 2$, the exponential term falls off half as fast as the orbitals with $n = 1$. This

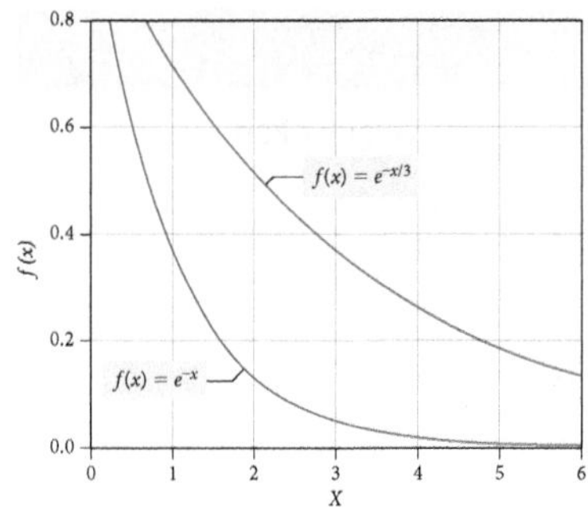

is because the exponential term is $e^{-Zr/2a_0}$ for $n = 2$ compared with e^{-Zr/a_0} when $n = 1$. The orbitals with $n = 3$ have an exponential term that falls off three times more slowly than the orbitals with $n = 1$ (for $n = 3$, $e^{-Zr/3a_0}$). Because the magnitude of the overall wave functions falls off (or decreases) more slowly due to the exponential term as n increases, the orbitals increase in size as n increases.

CONCEPTUAL CONNECTION 7.6
Radial Probabilities

Following are four radial probability diagrams for the 2*s*, 3*s*, 3*p*, and 3*d* orbitals. Assign the orbital designations to each radial probability diagram.

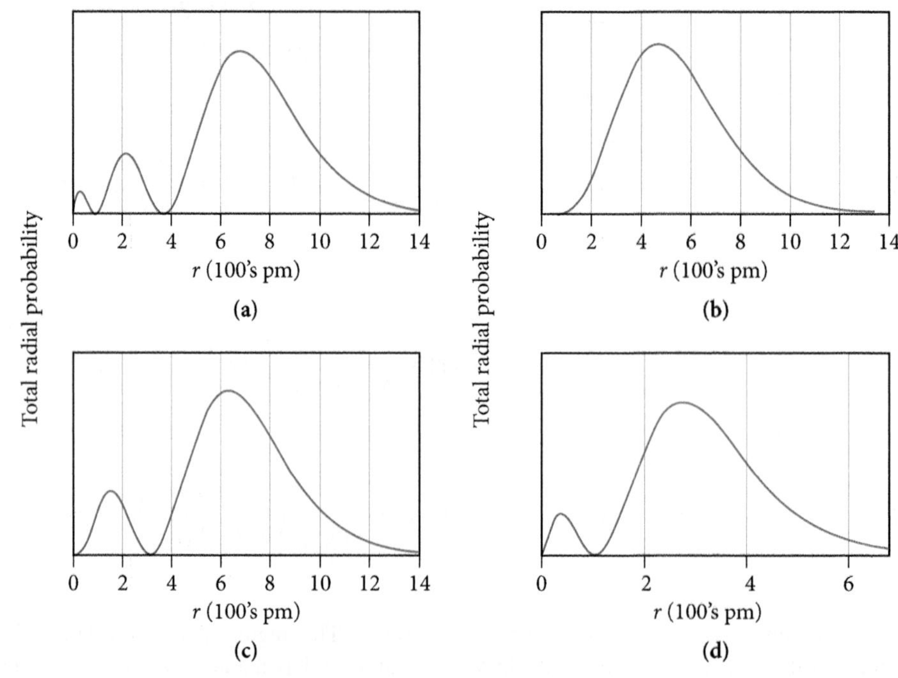

7.7 Electron Configurations: How Electrons Occupy Orbitals

Quantum theory describes the behaviour of electrons in atoms. Since chemical bonding involves the transfer or sharing of electrons, quantum theory helps us understand and describe chemical behaviour. As we have just seen, electrons exist within orbitals in atoms. An **electron configuration** for an atom shows the particular orbitals that are occupied for that atom. For example, consider the **ground state**—or lowest energy state—electron configuration for a hydrogen atom:

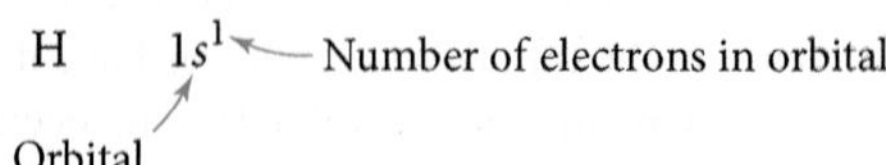

The electron configuration indicates that hydrogen's one electron is in the 1*s* orbital. Electrons generally occupy the lowest energy orbitals available. Since the 1*s* orbital is the lowest energy orbital in hydrogen (see Section 7.5), hydrogen's electron occupies that orbital. If we could write electron configurations for all the elements, we could see how the arrangements of the electrons within their atoms correlate with the element's chemical properties. However, the solutions to the Schrödinger equation (the atomic orbitals and their energies) that we just described in the previous section are for the hydrogen atom. What do the atomic orbitals of *other atoms* look like? What are their relative energies?

The Schrödinger equation for multielectron atoms is more complicated—because we must account for the interactions of the electrons with one another—and it cannot be solved exactly. However, approximate solutions indicate that the orbitals in multielectron atoms are hydrogen-like—they are similar to the *s*, *p*, *d*, and *f* orbitals. In order to see how the electrons in multielectron atoms occupy these hydrogen-like orbitals, we must examine two additional concepts: *electron spin*, a fundamental property of all electrons that affects the number of electrons allowed in one orbital; and *sublevel energy splitting*, which determines the order of orbital filling within a level.

Electron Spin and the Pauli Exclusion Principle

The electron configuration of hydrogen ($1s^1$) can be represented in a slightly different way by an **orbital diagram**, which gives similar information, but symbolizes the electron as an arrow and the orbital as a box. The orbital diagram for a hydrogen atom is:

H [↑] 1s

In orbital diagrams, the direction of the arrow (pointing up or pointing down) represents **electron spin**. Electron spin was demonstrated experimentally in 1922 by the Stern–Gerlach experiment, shown in Figure 7.30 ▼. In this experiment, a beam of silver atoms is directed through a small slit (or hole) and into a magnetic field. As the beam passes through the field, it splits into two separate beams. The splitting of the beam is caused by the spin of the electrons within the silver atoms, which creates a tiny magnetic field (on each atom) that interacts with the external magnetic field. One spin orientation causes the deflection of the beam in one direction, while the other orientation causes a deflection in the opposite direction. This experiment and others that followed it demonstrated two fundamental aspects of electron spin:

A "spinning" electron is something of a metaphor. A more accurate way to express the same idea is to say that an electron has inherent angular momentum.

1. Spin, like negative electric charge, is a basic property of all electrons. One electron does not have more or less spin than another—all electrons have the same amount of spin.
2. The orientation of the electron's spin is quantized, with only two possibilities that we can call spin up and spin down.

The spin of an electron is specified by a fourth quantum number called the **spin quantum number** (m_s). The possible values of m_s are $+\frac{1}{2}$ (spin up) and $-\frac{1}{2}$ (spin down).

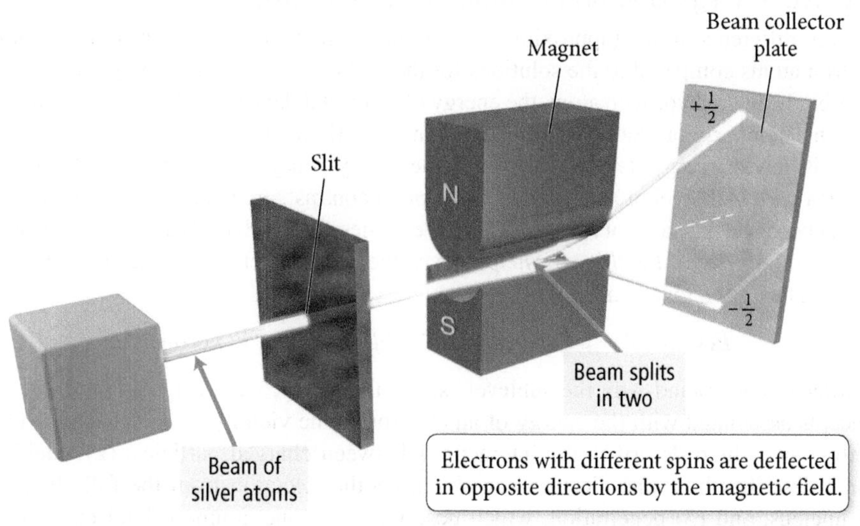

◀ **FIGURE 7.30 The Stern–Gerlach Experiment**

In an orbital diagram, $m_s = +\frac{1}{2}$ is represented with a half-arrow pointing up (↿) and $m_s = -\frac{1}{2}$ is represented with a half-arrow pointing down (⇂). In a collection of hydrogen atoms, the electrons in about half of the atoms are spin up and the electrons in the other half are spin down. Since no additional electrons are present within the hydrogen atom, we conventionally represent the hydrogen atom electron configuration with its one electron as spin up.

Helium is the first element on the periodic table that contains more than one electron. Its two electrons occupy the 1*s* orbital:

$$\text{He} \quad 1s^2$$

How do the spins of the two electrons in helium align relative to each other? The answer to this question is addressed by the **Pauli exclusion principle**, formulated by Wolfgang Pauli in 1925.

Pauli exclusion principle: No two electrons in an atom can have the same four quantum numbers.

Since two electrons occupying the same orbital have three identical quantum numbers (n, l, and m_l), they must have different spin quantum numbers. Since there are only two possible spin quantum numbers ($+\frac{1}{2}$ and $-\frac{1}{2}$), the Pauli exclusion principle implies that *each orbital can have a maximum of only two electrons, with opposing spins*. By applying the exclusion principle, we can write an electron configuration and orbital diagram for helium as follows:

Electron configuration	Orbital diagram
He $1s^2$	[↿⇂] 1*s*

The table below shows the four quantum numbers for each of the two electrons in helium.

n	l	m_l	m_s
1	0	0	$+\frac{1}{2}$
1	0	0	$-\frac{1}{2}$

The two electrons have three quantum numbers in common (because they are in the same orbital) but have different spin quantum numbers (as indicated by the opposing half-arrows in the orbital diagram).

Sublevel Energy Splitting in Multielectron Atoms

A major difference in the (approximate) solutions to the Schrödinger equation for multielectron atoms compared to the solutions for the hydrogen atom is the energy ordering of the orbitals. In the hydrogen atom, the energy of an orbital depends only on n, the principal quantum number. For example, the 3*s*, 3*p*, and 3*d* orbitals (which are empty for hydrogen in its lowest energy state) all have the same energy—they are **degenerate**. The orbitals within a principal level of a *multielectron atom*, in contrast, are not degenerate—their energy depends on the value of l. We say that the energies of the sublevels are *split*. In general, the lower the value of l *within a principal level*, the lower the energy of the corresponding orbital. Thus, for a given value of n:

$$E(s \text{ orbital}) < E(p \text{ orbital}) < E(d \text{ orbital}) < E(f \text{ orbital})$$

In order to understand why the sublevels split in this way, we must examine three key concepts associated with the energy of an electron in the vicinity of a nucleus: (1) Coulomb's law, which describes the interactions between charged particles; (2) shielding, which describes how one electron can shield another electron from the full charge of the nucleus; and (3) penetration, which describes how one atomic orbital can overlap spatially with another, thus penetrating into a region that is close to the nucleus (and therefore less shielded from nuclear charge). We will then examine how these concepts, together with the spatial distributions of electron probability for each orbital, result in the above energy ordering.

Coulomb's Law The attraction and repulsion between charged particles, first introduced in Section 2.4, are described by **Coulomb's law,** which states that the potential energy (E) of two charged particles depends on their charges (q_1 and q_2) and on their separation (r):

$$E = \frac{1}{4\pi\varepsilon_0}\frac{q_1 q_2}{r} \qquad [7.13]$$

In this equation, ε_0 is a constant ($\varepsilon_0 = 8.85 \times 10^{-12}\ C^2\ J^{-1}\ m^{-1}$). The potential energy is positive for charges of the same sign (plus $\times$ plus, or minus $\times$ minus), and negative for charges of opposite sign. The *magnitude* of the potential energy depends inversely on the separation between the charged particles. We can draw three important conclusions from Coulomb's law:

- For like charges, the potential energy (E) is positive and decreases as the particles get *farther apart* (as r increases). Since systems tend toward lower potential energy, like charges repel each other (in much the same way that like poles of two magnets repel each other).
- For opposite charges, the potential energy is negative and becomes more negative as the particles get *closer together* (as r decreases). Therefore, opposite charges (like opposite poles on a magnet) *attract each other.*
- The *magnitude* of the interaction between charged particles increases as the charges of the particles increase. Consequently, an electron with a charge of 1− is more strongly attracted to a nucleus with a charge of 2+ than it would be to a nucleus with a charge of 1+.

For example, we can compare the energy required to remove an electron (ionization energy) from H, He^+, and Li^{2+}. Each has one electron, but the charge on the nucleus is increasing. To remove the electron from H, 1312.0 $kJ\,mol^{-1}$ is required, whereas He^+ and Li^{2+} require 5250.5 and 11 815.0 $kJ\,mol^{-1}$, respectively. You will notice that the ionization energy doesn't double and triple (as you might expect from Coulomb's law) by doubling and tripling the charge on the nucleus. This is because the distance that the electron is from the nucleus is smaller in Li^{2+} than He^+, which is also smaller than in H, also contributing to the increase in ionization energy.

Shielding For multielectron atoms, any one electron experiences both the positive charge of the nucleus (attractive) and the negative charges of the other electrons (repulsive). We can think of the repulsion of one electron by other electrons as *screening* or **shielding** that electron from the full effects of the nuclear charge. For example, consider the first and second ionization energies of helium. To remove the first electron requires 2372.3 $kJ\ mol^{-1}$. This electron is partially shielded from the nucleus by the electron–electron repulsion due to the presence of a second electron in the same orbital and therefore doesn't feel the full 2+ charge from the nucleus (Figure 7.31(a) ▼). To remove the second electron (from He^+) requires 5250.5 $kJ\,mol^{-1}$, more than twice the energy required to remove the first electron. The electron in He^+ is alone and feels the entire 2+ charge from the nucleus. Electrons in an orbital closer to the nucleus shield outer electrons more efficiently than if they were in the same orbital. For example, 520.2 $kJ\,mol^{-1}$ is required to remove an electron from the lithium (Li) atom, but with the two 1s electrons removed—an excited state Li^{2+} ion—2953.8 $kJ\ mol^{-1}$ is required to remove the electron, as seen in Figure 7.31(b).

Penetration Recall from Section 7.6 that the radial distribution function for an atomic orbital shows the total probability of finding the electron within a thin spherical shell at a distance r from the nucleus. Figure 7.32 ▼ shows the radial distribution functions of the 2s and 2p orbitals superimposed on one another (that for the 1s orbital is also shown). In general, an electron in a 2p orbital has a greater probability of being found closer to

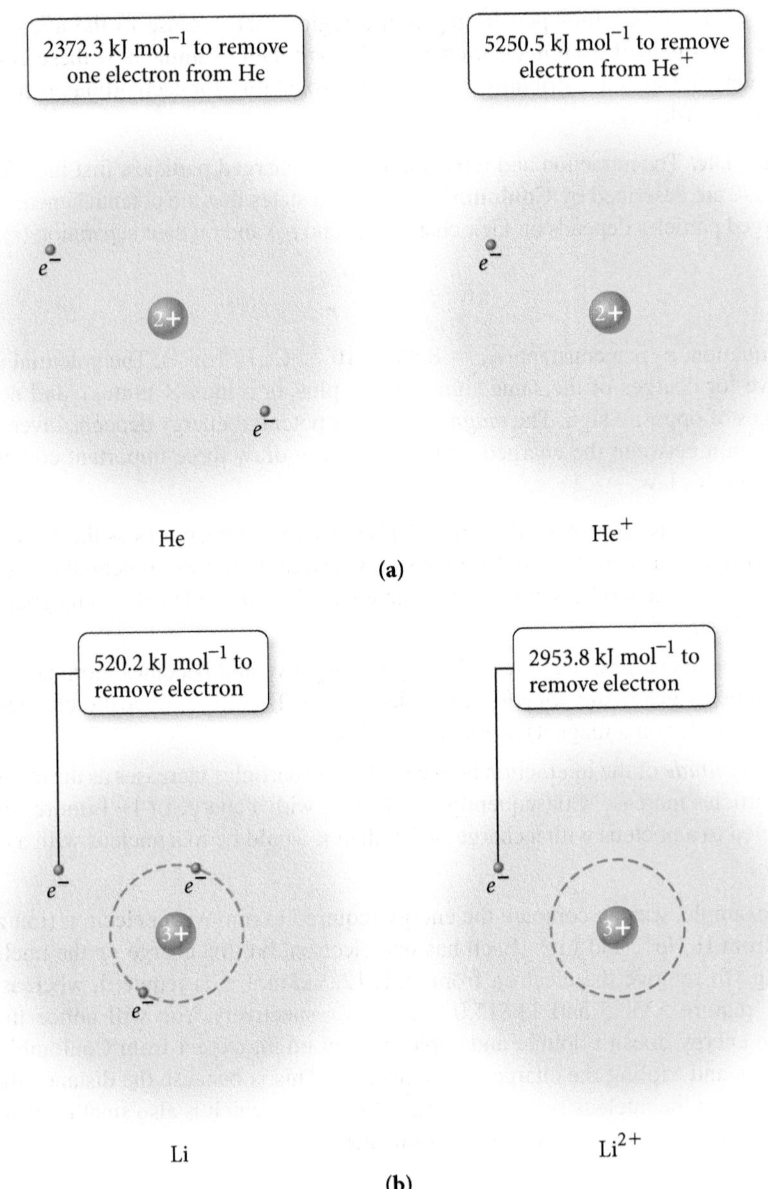

▶ **FIGURE 7.31 Shielding** (a) An electron is partially shielded by another electron in the same orbital. (b) Electrons in an inner orbital better shield electrons from the nucleus than do electrons in the same orbital.

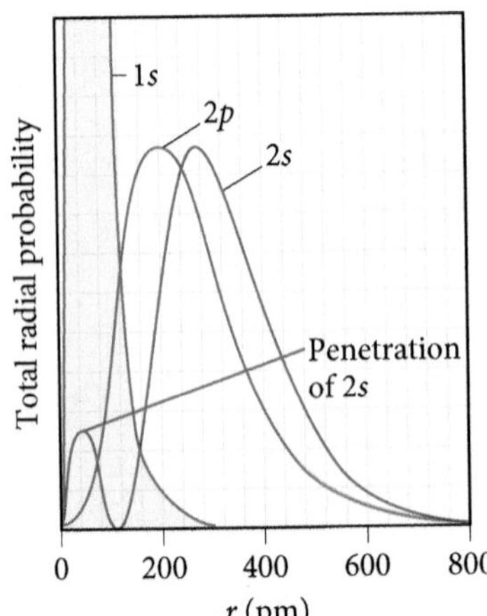

▲ **FIGURE 7.32 Radial Distribution Functions for the 1*s*, 2*s*, and 2*p* Orbitals**

the nucleus than an electron in a 2*s* orbital. However, due to the bump in the 2*s* radial distribution function near $r = 0$, which represents a significant probability of finding the 2*s* electron very close to the nucleus, we say that the electron *penetrates* the 1*s* orbital. By penetrating into the 1*s* orbital, the 2*s* orbital is not fully shielded by the 1*s* electrons. In contrast, the 2*p* orbital has most of its probability in the radial distribution function outside that for the 1*s* orbital. Electrons in the 2*s* orbital feel more of the nuclear charge than electrons in the 2*p* orbital, resulting in the 2*s* electrons being lower in energy than the 2*p* electrons. The 2*p* electrons are, therefore, easier to remove than the 2*s* electrons. As an example, we can look at the energy required to remove an electron from the 2*s* orbital in Li or from the 2*p* orbital in the first excited state of Li (Figure 7.33 ▶). As we saw previously, 520.2 kJ mol^{-1} is required to remove the outer electron from a ground-state Li atom, but in the first excited state of Li (the electron is in the 2*p* orbital), only 357.1 kJ mol^{-1} is required to remove the electron.

A similar situation arises when we compare the 3*s*, 3*p*, and 3*d* orbitals. The *s* orbitals penetrate more closely to the nucleus than the 3*p* orbitals, which in turn penetrate more fully than the 3*d* orbitals, shown in Figure 7.34 ▶.

This splitting in energy of the 2*s* and 2*p* orbitals (and 3*s*, 3*p*, and 3*d* orbitals, etc.) is a result of having more than one electron in the atom or ion. If there is only one electron in the atom or ion, the 2*s* and 2*p* orbitals would be degenerate, as we saw for hydrogen and

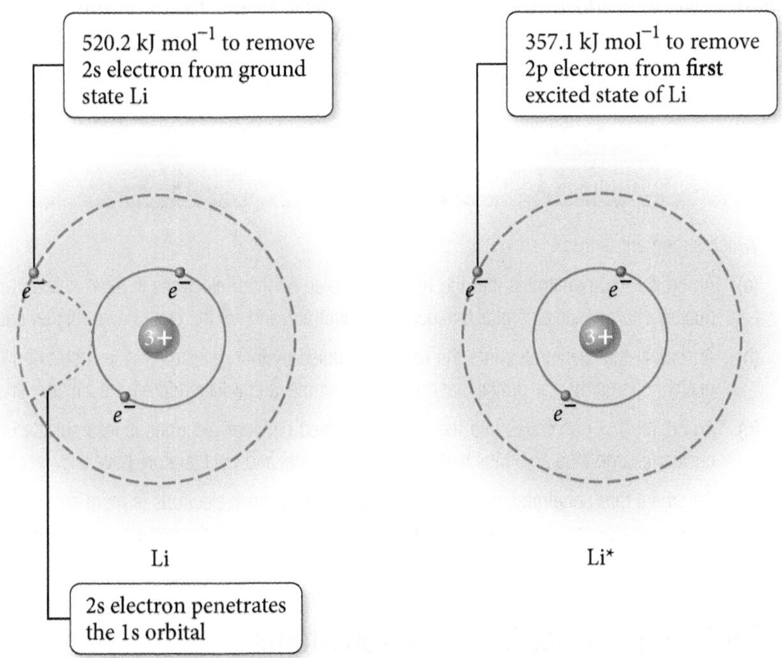

▲ **FIGURE 7.33 Penetration** The $2s$ electron penetrates close to the nucleus, lowering its energy compared with the $2p$ electron. The $2p$ electron is easier to remove compared to the $2s$ electron.

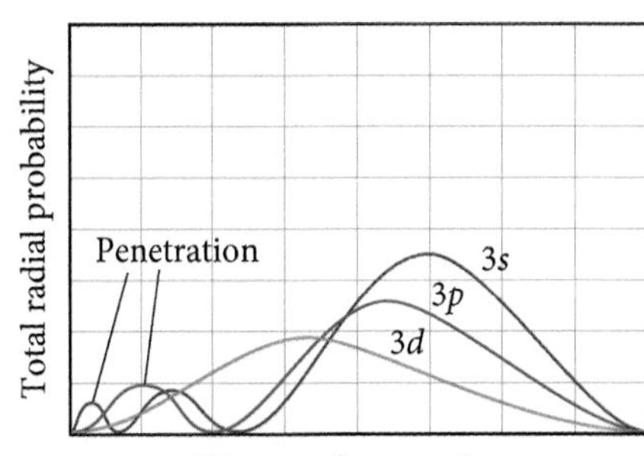

▲ **FIGURE 7.34 Radial Distribution Functions for the 3*s*, 3*p*, and 3*d* Orbitals** The $3s$ electrons penetrate most deeply into the inner orbitals, are least shielded, and experience the greatest **effective nuclear charge**. The $3d$ electrons penetrate least. This accounts for the energy ordering of the sublevels: $s < p < d$.

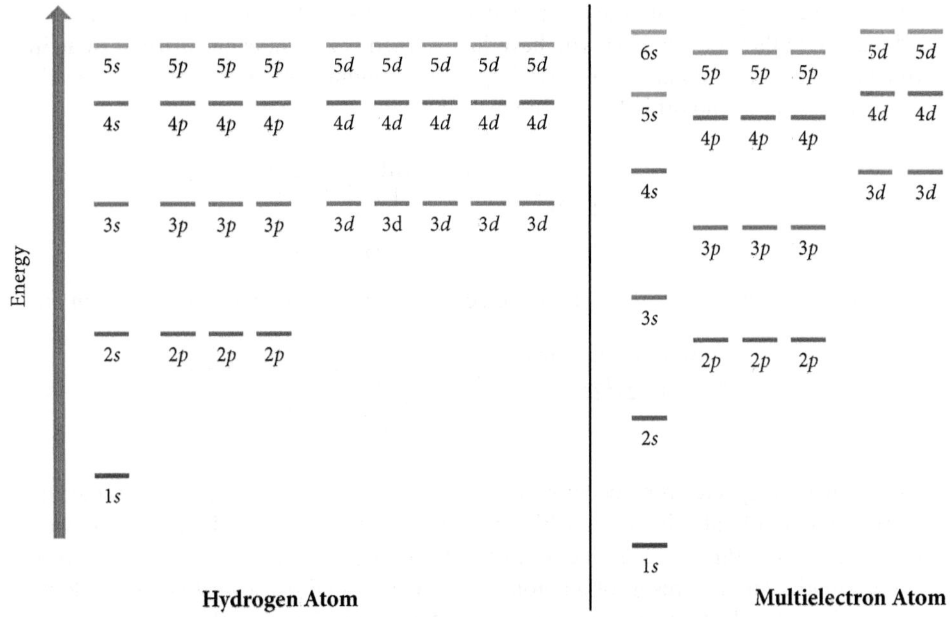

Hydrogen Atom

Multielectron Atom

▲ **FIGURE 7.35 Orbital Ordering for Hydrogen and the Multielectron Atom** Change in the energy ordering of orbitals from a one-electron atom (like hydrogen) to a multielectron atom.

hydrogen-like atoms. Figure 7.35 ▲ shows the difference between the energy ordering of a one-electron atom and a multielectron atom.

Notice these features of the diagram in Figure 7.35:

- Because of **penetration**, the sublevels of each principal level are *not* degenerate for multielectron atoms.
- In the fourth and fifth principal levels, the effects of penetration become so important that the $3d$ and $4s$ orbitals are very close in energy. The $4d$ and $5s$ orbitals are, similarly, very close in energy.

- Very shortly, we will add to the set of rules for writing electron configurations for multielectron atoms. The energy separations between one set of orbitals and the next become small for 4*s* orbitals and beyond and vary among the elements as we shall see.

CONCEPTUAL CONNECTION 7.7

Penetration and Shielding

Which statement is true?

(a) An orbital that penetrates into the region occupied by inner electrons is more shielded from nuclear charge than an orbital that does not penetrate, and will therefore have a higher energy.

(b) An orbital that penetrates into the region occupied by inner electrons is less shielded from nuclear charge than an orbital that does not penetrate, and will therefore have a higher energy.

(c) An orbital that penetrates into the region occupied by inner electrons is less shielded from nuclear charge than an orbital that does not penetrate, and will therefore have a lower energy.

(d) An orbital that penetrates into the region occupied by inner electrons is more shielded from nuclear charge than an orbital that does not penetrate, and will therefore have a lower energy.

Electron Configurations for Multielectron Atoms

Unless otherwise specified, we will use the term "electron configuration" to mean the ground-state (or lowest-energy) configuration.

Now that we know the energy ordering of orbitals in multielectron atoms, we can determine ground-state electron configurations for the rest of the elements. Since we know that electrons occupy the lowest energy orbitals available when the atom is in its ground state, and that only two electrons (with opposing spins) are allowed in each orbital, we can systematically build up the electron configurations for the elements. The pattern of orbital filling that reflects what you have just learned is known as the **aufbau principle** (the German word *aufbau* means "build up"). For lithium, with three electrons, the electron configuration and orbital diagram are:

Remember that the number of electrons in a neutral atom is equal to its atomic number.

Electron configuration		Orbital diagram	
Li	$1s^2 2s^1$	↿⇂	↿
		$1s$	$2s$

For carbon, which has six electrons, the electron configuration and orbital diagram are:

Electron configuration		Orbital diagram				
C	$1s^2 2s^2 2p^2$	↿⇂	↿⇂	↿	↿	
		$1s$	$2s$		$2p$	

Notice that the 2*p* electrons occupy the *p* orbitals (of equal energy) singly, rather than pairing in one orbital. This way of filling orbitals is in accord with **Hund's rule**, which states that *when filling degenerate orbitals, electrons fill them singly first, with parallel spins*. Hund's rule is a result of an atom's tendency to find the lowest energy state possible. When two electrons occupy separate orbitals of equal energy, the repulsive interaction between them is lower than when they occupy the same orbital because the electrons are spread out over a larger region of space.

Summarizing Orbital Filling:

- Electrons occupy orbitals so as to minimize the energy of the atom; therefore, lower energy orbitals fill before higher energy orbitals. Orbitals fill in the following order: 1*s* 2*s* 2*p* 3*s* 3*p* (4*s* or 3*d*) 4*p* (5*s* or 4*d*) 5*p* etc. (We will see shortly that orbital energy ordering and electron-electron repulsion both play important roles in whether an electron goes into the 4*s* or 3*d* orbitals.)
- Orbitals can hold no more than two electrons each. When two electrons occupy the same orbital, their spins are opposite. This is another way of expressing the Pauli exclusion principle (no two electrons in one atom can have the same four quantum numbers).

- When orbitals of identical energy are available, electrons first occupy these orbitals singly with parallel spins rather than in pairs. Once the orbitals of equal energy are half full, the electrons start to pair (Hund's rule).

Consider the electron configurations and orbital diagrams for elements after carbon, with atomic numbers 7–10.

Symbol	Number of electrons	Electron configuration	Orbital diagram
N	7	$1s^2 2s^2 2p^3$	1s: ↑↓ 2s: ↑↓ 2p: ↑ ↑ ↑
O	8	$1s^2 2s^2 2p^4$	1s: ↑↓ 2s: ↑↓ 2p: ↑↓ ↑ ↑
F	9	$1s^2 2s^2 2p^5$	1s: ↑↓ 2s: ↑↓ 2p: ↑↓ ↑↓ ↑
Ne	10	$1s^2 2s^2 2p^6$	1s: ↑↓ 2s: ↑↓ 2p: ↑↓ ↑↓ ↑↓

Notice that, as a result of Hund's rule, the p orbitals fill with single electrons before the electrons begin to pair.

The electron configuration of neon represents the complete filling of the $n = 2$ principal level. When writing electron configurations for elements beyond neon, or beyond any other noble gas, the electron configuration of the previous noble gas—sometimes called the *core electron configuration*—is often abbreviated by the symbol for the noble gas in square brackets. For example, the electron configuration of sodium is:

$$\text{Na} \quad 1s^2 2s^2 2p^6 3s^1$$

This configuration can also be written using [Ne] to represent the core electrons:

$$\text{Na} \quad [\text{Ne}]\, 3s^1$$

[Ne] represents $1s^2 2s^2 2p^6$, the electron configuration for neon. The remaining electrons, in this case the $3s$ electron, is represented. The electrons that are represented outside the core electrons are called **valence electrons**.

To write an electron configuration for an element, first find its atomic number from the periodic table—this number equals the number of electrons. Then use the order of filling to distribute the electrons in the appropriate orbitals. Remember that each orbital can hold a maximum of two electrons. Consequently,

- The s sublevel has only one orbital and can therefore hold only 2 electrons.
- The p sublevel has three orbitals and can hold 6 electrons.
- The d sublevel has five orbitals and can hold 10 electrons.
- The f sublevel has seven orbitals and can hold 14 electrons.

EXAMPLE 7.7 ELECTRON CONFIGURATIONS

Write electron configurations for each element:

(a) Mg **(b)** P **(c)** Br **(d)** Al

SOLUTION

(a) Mg Magnesium has 12 electrons. Distribute two of these into the $1s$ orbital, two into the $2s$ orbital, six into the $2p$ orbitals, and two into the $3s$ orbital. The two $3s$ electrons are valence electrons.	Mg $1s^2 2s^2 2p^6 3s^2$ or [Ne] $3s^2$

(continued)

EXAMPLE 7.7 (CONTINUED)

(b) P Phosphorus has 15 electrons. Distribute two of these into the 1*s* orbital, two into the 2*s* orbital, six into the 2*p* orbitals, two into the 3*s* orbital, and three into the 3*p* orbitals.	P $1s^2 2s^2 2p^6 3s^2 3p^3$ or [Ne] $3s^2 3p^3$
(c) Br Bromine has 35 electrons. Distribute two of these into the 1*s* orbital, two into the 2*s* orbital, six into the 2*p* orbitals, two into the 3*s* orbital, six into the 3*p* orbitals, two into the 4*s* orbital, ten into the 3*d* orbitals, and five into the 4*p* orbitals.	Br $1s^2 2s^2 2p^6 3s^2 3p^6 4s^2 3d^{10} 4p^5$ or [Ar] $4s^2 3d^{10} 4p^5$
(d) Al Aluminum has 13 electrons. Distribute two of these into the 1*s* orbital, two into the 2*s* orbital, six into the 2*p* orbitals, two into the 3*s* orbital, and one into the 3*p* orbital.	Al $1s^2 2s^2 2p^6 3s^2 3p^1$ or [Ne] $3s^2 3p^1$

FOR PRACTICE 7.7

Write electron configurations for each element:

(a) Cl **(b)** Si **(c)** Sr **(d)** O

EXAMPLE 7.8 WRITING ORBITAL DIAGRAMS

Write an orbital diagram for sulfur and determine the number of unpaired electrons.

SOLUTION

Since sulfur's atomic number is 16, it has 16 electrons and the electron configuration $1s^2 2s^2 2p^6 3s^2 3p^4$. Draw a box for each orbital, putting the lowest-energy orbital (1*s*) on the far left and proceeding to orbitals of higher energy to the right.	1*s* 2*s* 2*p* 3*s* 3*p*
Distribute the 16 electrons into the boxes representing the orbitals, allowing a maximum of two electrons per orbital and remembering Hund's rule. You can see from the diagram that sulfur has two unpaired electrons.	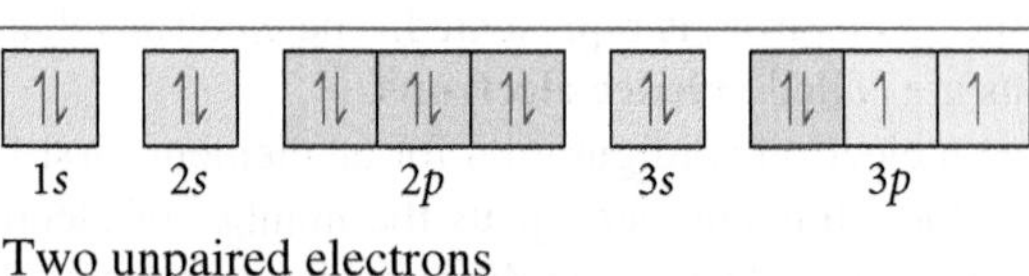 Two unpaired electrons

FOR PRACTICE 7.8

Write an orbital diagram for Ar and determine the number of unpaired electrons.

CONCEPTUAL CONNECTION 7.8

Electron Configurations and Quantum Numbers

What are the four quantum numbers for each of the two electrons in a 4*s* orbital?

Electron Configurations for Transition Metals

The next elements in the periodic table after argon (Ar) are potassium (K) and calcium (Ca). The electron configuration for Ar is $1s^2 2s^2 2p^6 3s^2 3p^6$. The $n = 3$ principal level is not yet full for Ar, so one might think the 19th electron in K might go into a 3*d* orbital. However, remember that the 4*s* and 3*d* orbitals are very close in energy. In fact, for K and Ca, the 4*s* orbitals are lower in energy than the 3*d* orbitals, so that their condensed electron configurations and orbital diagrams are:

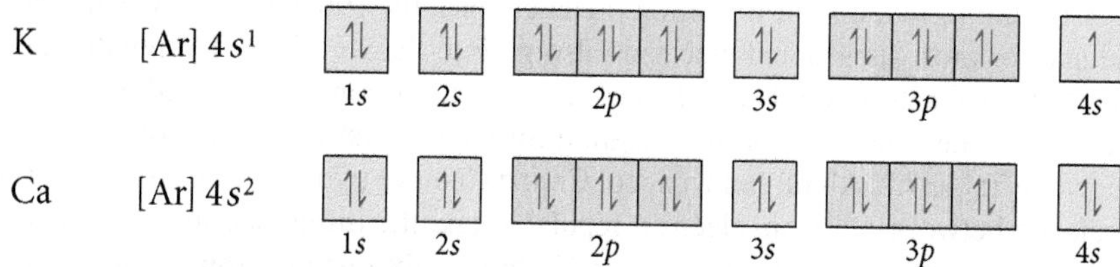

When we get to the transition metals, however, the 3*d* orbitals are lower in energy than the 4*s* orbitals. How do we know this? Let's look at the experimentally observed electron configurations of the first four transition metal cations stripped of all of their electrons down to the [Ar] core, so they all have the same electron configurations as Ar, with 18 electrons. For Sc, Ti, V, and Cr, this requires removing 3, 4, 5, and 6 electrons, respectively. When we add an electron to each of these cations, the electron occupies the lowest energy orbital, the 3*d* orbital.

18 e^-	Sc^{3+} [Ar]	Ti^{4+} [Ar]	V^{5+} [Ar]	Cr^{6+} [Ar]
19 e^-	Sc^{2+} [Ar] $3d^1$	Ti^{3+} [Ar] $3d^1$	V^{4+} [Ar] $3d^1$	Cr^{5+} [Ar] $3d^1$
20 e^-	Sc^{+} [Ar] $3d^14s^1$	Ti^{2+} [Ar] $3d^2$	V^{3+} [Ar] $3d^2$	Cr^{4+} [Ar] $3d^2$
21 e^-	Sc [Ar] $3d^14s^2$	Ti^{+} [Ar] $3d^24s^1$	V^{2+} [Ar] $3d^3$	Cr^{3+} [Ar] $3d^3$
22 e^-		Ti [Ar] $3d^24s^2$	V^{+} [Ar] $3d^4$	Cr^{2+} [Ar] $3d^4$
23 e^-			V [Ar] $3d^34s^2$	Cr^{+} [Ar] $3d^5$
24 e^-				Cr [Ar] $3d^54s^1$

As more electrons are added, an electron may go into the 3*d* or 4*s* orbital depending on the relative energies of 3*d* and 4*s* orbitals, and electron–electron repulsions. When an electron is added to Sc^{2+}, giving Sc^{+}, the electron goes into the 4*s* orbital even though the 3*d* orbitals can accommodate more electrons and are *slightly lower* in energy. Putting another electron into the smaller 3*d* orbital would introduce electron–electron repulsion, which would raise the energy of the system. The energy lost by putting the second electron in the slightly higher energy 4*s* orbital is offset by avoiding this electron–electron repulsion in the 3*d* orbital. To make neutral Sc from Sc^{+}, the third electron also goes into the 4*s* orbital. The 4*s* orbital is much larger and more diffuse than the 3*d* orbital, so there will be less electron–electron repulsion by having the two electrons in the 4*s* orbital than in the 3*d*. The resulting condensed electron configuration for neutral Sc is [Ar] $4s^23d^1$.

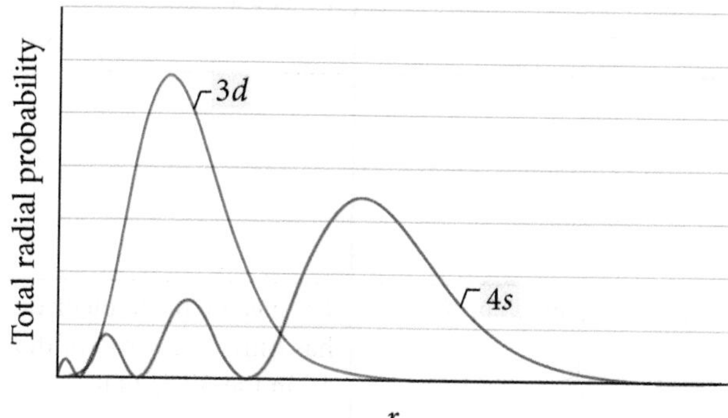

▲ The radial probability diagrams for the 3*d* orbitals and the larger, more diffuse 4*s* orbitals.

For Ti, the extra energy separation between 3*d* and 4*s* orbitals means that the 21st and 22nd electrons goes into the 4*s* orbital. For V, electrons are added to the 3*d* orbitals until the 23rd electron, at which the most stable configuration is [Ar] $3d^34s^2$. For Cr, the

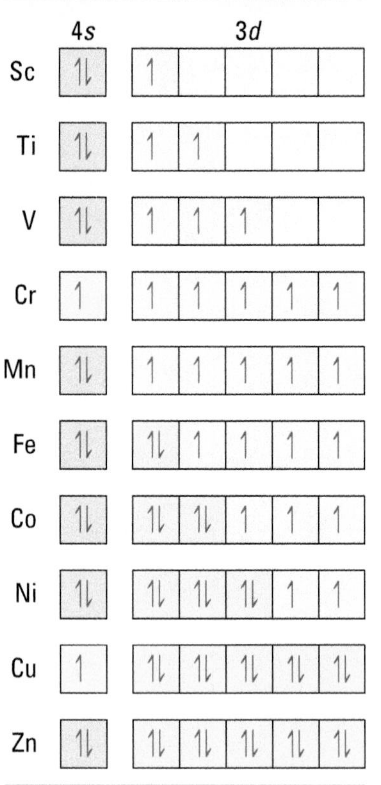

TABLE 7.2 First-Row Transition Metal Orbital Occupancy

	4s	3d				
Sc	↑↓	↑				
Ti	↑↓	↑	↑			
V	↑↓	↑	↑	↑		
Cr	↑	↑	↑	↑	↑	↑
Mn	↑↓	↑	↑	↑	↑	↑
Fe	↑↓	↑↓	↑	↑	↑	↑
Co	↑↓	↑↓	↑↓	↑	↑	↑
Ni	↑↓	↑↓	↑↓	↑↓	↑	↑
Cu	↑	↑↓	↑↓	↑↓	↑↓	↑↓
Zn	↑↓	↑↓	↑↓	↑↓	↑↓	↑↓

separation between the 3*d* and 4*s* orbitals is enough that the 3*d* orbital takes five electrons, forming Cr^+, before the sixth electron in Cr goes into the 4*s* orbital.

For the entire first row of transition metal cations, the 19th electron goes into the 3*d* orbital and for most subsequent electrons also go into the 3*d* orbital. Eventually though, due to electron–electron repulsion, the larger 4*s* orbital becomes populated before the 3*d* orbital is full. The condensed orbital diagram for the the first-row transition metal atoms are shown in Table 7.2. All of them, except Cr and Cu have two electrons in the 4*s* orbital. The balance between electron–electron repulsion and the difference in energy between the 3*d* and 4*s* orbitals is such that Cr and Cu have only one electron in the 4s orbital. For the first-row transition metals it is easy to remember that all of them have $4s^2$ in their electron configurations except for Cr and Cu which are $4s^1$ and the remaining electrons are in the 3*d* orbitals.

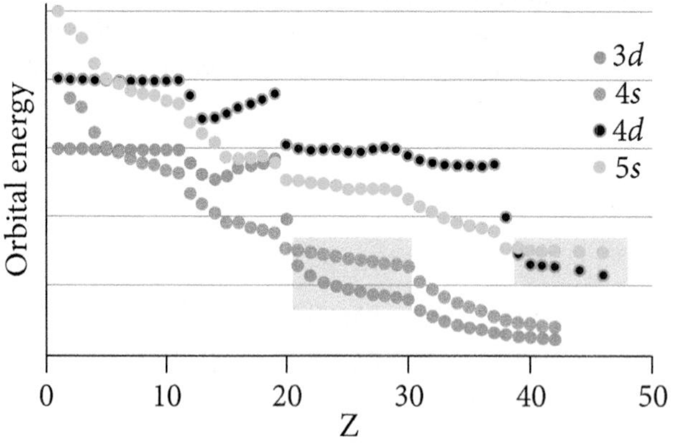

◀ The relative energies of the 3*d*, 4*s*, 4*d*, and 5*s* orbitals for the free neutral atoms with atomic numbers 1–46. The parts highlighted in grey show the first and second row transition metals. (Data from Wang, S. G.; Qiu, Y. X.; Fang, H.; Schwarz, W. H. E. *Chem. Eur. J.* 2006, 12, 4101).

For the second-row transition metals, the electron configurations are less easy to predict or remember. Only four of them have $5s^2$ in their electon configurations and five have $5s^1$ in their electron configurations. One of them, Pd, has no 5*s* electrons at all and its condensed electron configuration is [Kr] $3d^{10}$ (see Figure 8.4 in Chapter 8).

PROCEDURE FOR ... Writing Electron Configurations	**EXAMPLE 7.9 Writing Electron Configurations for Transition Metals** Write the ground-state electron configuration for Zr.	**EXAMPLE 7.10 Writing Electron Configurations for Transition Metals** Write the ground-state electron configuration for Cu.
Identify the noble gas that precedes the element and write it in square brackets.	**SOLUTION** [Kr]	**SOLUTION** [Ar]
Count down the periods to determine the outer principal quantum level—this is the quantum level for the *s* orbital.	Zr is in the fifth period, so the orbitals we use are: [Kr] 5*s*4*d*	Cu is in the fourth period, so the orbitals we use are: [Ar] 4*s*3*d*
Subtract one to obtain the quantum level for the *d* orbital. If the element is in the third or fourth transition series, include $(n - 2)f^{14}$ electrons in the configuration.		
Count across the row to see how many electrons are in the neutral atom and fill the orbitals accordingly.	Zr has four more electrons than Kr. [Kr] $5s^2 4d^2$	Cu has 11 more electrons than Ar and has only 1 electron in the 4*s* orbital and 10 in the 3*d* orbital. [Ar] $4s^1 3d^{10}$
	FOR PRACTICE 7.9 Write the ground-state electron configuration for Os.	**FOR PRACTICE 7.10** Write the ground-state electron configuration for Mo.

Electron Configurations and Magnetic Properties of Ions

Ions are simply atoms that have lost or gained electrons. We can deduce the electron configuration of a main-group monoatomic ion from the electron configuration of the neutral atom and the charge of the ion. For anions, we *add* the number of electrons indicated by the magnitude of the charge of the anion. For example, the electron configuration of fluorine (F) is $1s^2 2s^2 2p^5$ and that of the fluoride ion (F^-) is $1s^2 2s^2 2p^6$.

We determine the electron configuration of cations by *subtracting* the number of electrons indicated by the magnitude of the charge. For example, the electron configuration of lithium (Li) is $1s^2 2s^1$ and that of the lithium ion (Li^+) is $1s^2 2s^0$ (or simply $1s^2$).

When writing the electron configuration of any ion, including transition metal cations, *remove the electrons from the highest energy orbitals first—those with the highest n-value*. For example, the electron configurations of vanadium and copper are as follows:

$$\text{V} \quad [\text{Ar}]\,4s^2 3d^3 \qquad\qquad \text{Cu} \quad [\text{Ar}]\,4s^1 3d^{10}$$

Two common ions, or oxidation states, for each of these metals are V^{2+} and V^{3+} for vanadium and Cu^+ and Cu^{2+} for copper. Electrons are first removed from the higher energy 4*s* orbital and then the 3*d* orbital:

$$\text{V}^{2+} \quad [\text{Ar}]\,3d^3 \qquad\qquad \text{Cu}^{+} \quad [\text{Ar}]\,3d^{10}$$

$$\text{V}^{3+} \quad [\text{Ar}]\,3d^2 \qquad\qquad \text{Cu}^{2+} \quad [\text{Ar}]\,3d^{9}$$

The magnetic properties of transition metal ions support these assignments. Recall from Figure 7.30 that an unpaired electron generates a magnetic field due to its spin. Consequently, an atom or ion that contains unpaired electrons is attracted to an external magnetic field, and we say that the atom or ion is **paramagnetic**. For example, the magnetic properties of silver—which result in the splitting of a beam of silver atoms in the Stern–Gerlach experiment discussed earlier—is caused by silver's unpaired 5*s* electron.

Ag $[\text{Kr}]\,5s^1 4d^{10}$

5*s*	4*d*				
↑	↑↓	↑↓	↑↓	↑↓	↑↓

An atom or ion in which all electrons are paired is not attracted to an external magnetic field—it is in fact slightly repelled—and we say that the atom or ion is **diamagnetic**. The zinc atom is diamagnetic.

Zn $[\text{Ar}]\,4s^2 3d^{10}$

4*s*	3*d*				
↑↓	↑↓	↑↓	↑↓	↑↓	↑↓

The magnetic properties of the zinc ion provide confirmation that the higher energy 4*s* electrons are indeed lost before 3*d* electrons in the ionization of zinc. If zinc lost two 3*d* electrons upon ionization, then the Zn^{2+} would become paramagnetic (because the two electrons would come out of two different filled *d* orbitals, leaving each of them with one unpaired electron). But the zinc ion, like the zinc atom, is diamagnetic because the 4*s* electrons are lost instead.

Zn^{2+} $[\text{Ar}]\,3d^{10}$

4*s*	3*d*				
	↑↓	↑↓	↑↓	↑↓	↑↓

If you have the choice of removing electrons from two different orbitals with the same value of *n*, you remove the electrons from the orbital with the greatest value of *l*. The larger elements in periods 4, 5, and 6 in groups 13, 14, and 15 lose the high energy *np* electrons (where *n* is the period number and principal quantum number) followed by the *ns* electrons to form ions. This is exactly as we would expect since the *np* orbitals are higher in energy than the *ns* orbitals. For example, the electron configurations of antimony and lead are:

Sb [Kr] $5s^2 4d^{10} 5p^3$ Pb [Xe] $6s^2 4f^{14} 5d^{10} 5p^2$

Antimony commonly forms Sb^{3+} and Sb^{5+} ions and lead forms Pb^{2+} and Pb^{4+} ions. Their electron configurations are:

Sb^{3+} [Kr] $5s^2 4d^{10}$ Pb^{2+} [Xe] $6s^2 4f^{14} 5d^{10}$

Sb^{5+} [Kr] $4d^{10}$ Pb^{4+} [Xe] $4f^{14} 5d^{10}$

EXAMPLE 7.11 ELECTRON CONFIGURATIONS AND MAGNETIC PROPERTIES FOR IONS

Write the electron configuration and orbital diagram for each ion and determine whether it is diamagnetic or paramagnetic:

(a) Al^{3+} **(b)** S^{2-} **(c)** Fe^{3+} **(d)** In^{+}

SOLUTION

(a) Al^{3+} Begin by writing the electron configuration of the neutral atom. Since this ion has a 3+ charge, remove three electrons to write the electron configuration of the ion. Write the orbital diagram by drawing half-arrows to represent each electron in boxes representing the orbitals. Because there are no unpaired electrons, Al^{3+} is diamagnetic.	Al [Ne] $3s^2 3p^1$ Al^{3+} [Ne] or [He] $2s^2 2p^6$ Al^{3+} [He] ⇅ (2s) ⇅ ⇅ ⇅ (2p) Diamagnetic
(b) S^{2-} Begin by writing the electron configuration of the neutral atom. Since this ion has a 2− charge, add two electrons to write the electron configuration of the ion. Write the orbital diagram by drawing half-arrows to represent each electron in boxes representing the orbitals. Because there are no unpaired electrons, S^{2-} is diamagnetic.	S [Ne] $3s^2 3p^4$ S^{2-} [Ne] $3s^2 3p^6$ S^{2-} [Ne] ⇅ (3s) ⇅ ⇅ ⇅ (3p) Diamagnetic
(c) Fe^{3+} Begin by writing the electron configuration of the neutral atom. Since this ion has a 3+ charge, remove three electrons to write the electron configuration of the ion. As always, we remove the electrons from the highest energy orbitals first. Here, we remove the electrons from the 4*s* orbital before removing electrons from the 3*d* orbitals. Write the orbital diagram by drawing half-arrows to represent each electron in boxes representing the orbitals. Because there are unpaired electrons, Fe^{3+} is paramagnetic.	Fe [Ar] $4s^2 3d^6$ Fe^{3+} [Ar] $3d^5$ Fe^{3+} [Ar] ☐ (4s) ↿ ↿ ↿ ↿ ↿ (3d) Paramagnetic
(d) In^{+} Begin by writing the electron configuration of the neutral atom. Since this ion has a 1+ charge, remove one electron from the highest energy orbital, the 5*p* orbital. Write the orbital diagram by drawing half-arrows to represent each electron in boxes representing the orbitals. Because there are no unpaired electrons, In^{+} is diamagnetic.	In [Kr] $5s^2 4d^{10} 5p^1$ In^{+} [Kr] $5s^2 4d^{10}$ In^{+} [Kr] ⇅ (5s) ⇅ ⇅ ⇅ ⇅ ⇅ (4d) Diamagnetic

FOR PRACTICE 7.11

Write the electron configuration and orbital diagram for each ion and predict whether it will be paramagnetic or diamagnetic: **(a)** Co^{2+} **(b)** N^{3-} **(c)** Ca^{2+} **(d)** In^{3+}

CHAPTER IN REVIEW

Key Terms

Section 7.1

quantum-mechanical model (242)

Section 7.2

electromagnetic radiation (243)
amplitude (243)
wavelength (λ) (243)
frequency (ν) (244)
electromagnetic spectrum (245)
gamma (γ) rays (245)
X-rays (246)
ultraviolet (UV) radiation (246)
visible light (246)
infrared (IR) radiation (246)
microwaves (246)
radio waves (246)
interference (246)
constructive interference (247)
destructive interference (247)
diffraction (248)
photoelectric effect (249)
photon (quantum) (250)

Section 7.3

emission spectrum (254)

Section 7.4

de Broglie relation (261)
complementary properties (262)
Heisenberg's uncertainty principle (262)
deterministic (263)
indeterminacy (263)

Section 7.5

orbital (264)
wave function (ψ) (264)
quantum number (264)
principal quantum number (n) (264)
angular momentum quantum number (l) (264)
magnetic quantum number (m_l) (264)
principal level (principal shell) (265)
sublevel (subshell) (265)

Section 7.6

probability density (ψ^2) (267)
radial distribution function (268)
node (268)
radial (spherical) node (268)
angular node (270)
phase (271)

Section 7.7

electron configuration (274)
ground state (274)
orbital diagram (275)
electron spin (275)
spin quantum number (m_s) (275)
Pauli exclusion principle (276)
degenerate (276)
Coulomb's law (277)
shielding (277)
effective nuclear charge (279)
penetration (279)
aufbau principle (280)
Hund's rule (280)
paramagnetic (285)
diamagnetic (285)

Key Concepts

The Realm of Quantum Mechanics (7.1)

The theory of quantum mechanics explains the behaviour of particles, such as photons (particles of light) and electrons, in the atomic and subatomic realms. Since the electrons of an atom determine many of its chemical and physical properties, quantum mechanics is foundational to understanding chemistry.

The Nature of Light (7.2)

Light is a type of electromagnetic radiation—a form of energy embodied in oscillating electric and magnetic fields that travels though space at 3.00×10^8 m s^{-1}. Light has both a wave nature and a particle nature. The wave nature of light is characterized by its wavelength—the distance between wave crests—and its ability to experience interference (constructive or destructive) and diffraction. The particle nature of light is characterized by the specific quantity of energy carried in each photon.

The electromagnetic spectrum includes all wavelengths of electromagnetic radiation, from gamma rays (high energy per photon, short wavelength) to radio waves (low energy per photon, long wavelength). Visible light is a tiny sliver in the middle of the electromagnetic spectrum.

Atomic Spectroscopy (7.3)

Atomic spectroscopy is the study of the light absorbed and emitted by atoms when an electron makes a transition from one energy level to another. The wavelengths absorbed or emitted depend on the energy differences between the levels involved in the transition; large energy differences result in short wavelengths and small energy differences result in long wavelengths.

The Wave Nature of Matter (7.4)

Electrons have a wave nature with an associated wavelength, as quantified by the de Broglie relation. The wave nature and particle nature of matter are complementary—the more you know of one, the less you can know of the other. The wave–particle duality of electrons is quantified in Heisenberg's uncertainty principle, which states that there is a limit to how well we can know both the position of an electron (associated with the electron's particle nature) and the velocity times the mass of an electron (associated with the electron's wave nature)—the more accurately one is measured, the greater the uncertainty in measurement of the other. The inability to simultaneously know both the position and the velocity of an electron results in indeterminacy, the inability to predict a trajectory for an electron. Consequently, electron behaviour is described differently than the behaviour of everyday-sized particles. The trajectory we normally associate with macroscopic objects is replaced, for electrons, with statistical descriptions that show, not the electron's path, but the region where it is most likely to be found.

The Quantum-Mechanical Model of the Atom (7.5, 7.6)

The most common way to describe electrons in atoms according to quantum mechanics is to solve the Schrödinger equation for the energy states of the electrons within the atom. When the electron is in these states, its energy is well defined but its position is not. The position of an electron is described by a probability distribution map called an orbital.

The solutions to the Schrödinger equation (including the energies and orbitals) are characterized by three quantum numbers: n, l, and m_l. The principal quantum number (n) determines the energy of the electron and the size of the orbital, the angular momentum quantum number (l) determines the shape of the orbital, and the magnetic quantum number (m_l) determines the orientation of the orbital.

Electron Configurations (7.7)

An electron configuration for an atom simply shows which atomic orbitals are occupied by the atom's electrons. For example, the electron configuration of helium ($1s^2$) shows that helium's two electrons exist within the $1s$ orbital. The order of filling atomic orbitals in multielectron atoms is as follows: $1s$ $2s$ $2p$ $3s$ $3p$ [$4s$ $3d$] $4p$ [$5s$ $4d$] $5p$ $6s$. Beginning in period 4, the ns orbitals are lower in energy than the $(n-1)d$ orbitals, however, the $(n-1)d$ orbitals are lower in energy than the ns orbitals. However, because they are so close in energy, for most transition elements the ns orbitals are populated even though the $(n-1)d$ orbitals are not full. For example, all the first-row transition metals have $4s^2 3d^x$ except Cr and Cu which only have one $4s$ electron. The reason the higher energy $4s$ orbitals are populated in the transition elements is because, by putting one or more electrons in the ns orbitals, electron–electron repulsion is relieved in the $(n-1)d$ orbitals. According to the Pauli exclusion principle, each orbital can hold a maximum of two electrons with opposing spins. According to Hund's rule, orbitals of the same energy first fill singly with electrons with parallel spins, before pairing. The electron configuration of an ion can be determined by adding or subtracting the corresponding number of electrons to or from the electron configuration of the neutral atom. The electrons always come out of the highest energy orbitals. The highest energy orbitals are those with the highest value of n. Given the choice of electrons with the same value of n to remove, the orbital with the highest l value is depleted.

Key Equations and Relationships

Relationship Between Frequency (ν), Wavelength (λ), and the Speed of Light (c) (7.2)

$$\nu = \frac{c}{\lambda}$$

Relationship Between Energy (E), Frequency (ν), Wavelength (λ), and Planck's Constant (h) (7.2)

$$E = h\nu$$

$$E = \frac{hc}{\lambda}$$

Energy of an Electron in an Orbital with Quantum Number n in a Hydrogen Atom (7.3)

$$E_n = -2.18 \times 10^{-18}\ \text{J}\left(\frac{1}{n^2}\right) \qquad (n = 1, 2, 3, \ldots)$$

Change in Energy That Occurs for an Electron in an Atom When It Undergoes a Transition Between Levels n_{initial} and n_{final} (7.3)

$$\Delta E = -2.18 \times 10^{-18}\ \text{J}\left(\frac{1}{n_f^2} - \frac{1}{n_i^2}\right)$$

de Broglie Relation: Relationship Between Wavelength (λ), Mass (m), and Velocity (v) of a Particle (7.4)

$$\lambda = \frac{h}{mv}$$

Heisenberg's Uncertainty Principle: Relationship Between a Particle's Uncertainty in Position (Δx) and Uncertainty in Velocity (Δv) (7.4)

$$\Delta x \times m\Delta v \geq \frac{h}{4\pi}$$

Key Skills

Calculating the Wavelength and Frequency of Light (7.2)

• Example 7.1 • For Practice 7.1 • Exercises 53, 54

Calculating the Energy of a Photon (7.2)

• Example 7.2 • For Practice 7.2 • For More Practice 7.2 • Exercises 55, 56, 59, 60

Using the Photelectric Effect to Determine Work Functions (7.2)

• Example 7.3 • For Practice 7.3 • Exercises 61, 62

Relating the Wavelength of Light to Transitions in the Hydrogen Atom (7.3)
• Example 7.4 • For Practice 7.4 • For More Practice 7.4 • Exercises 65–68

Relating Quantum Numbers to One Another and to Their Corresponding Orbitals (7.5)
• Examples 7.5, 7.6 • For Practice 7.5, 7.6 • Exercises 81–84

Writing Electron Configurations (7.7)
• Example 7.7 • For Practice 7.7 • Exercises 87, 88, 91, 92

Writing Orbital Diagrams (7.7)
• Example 7.8 • For Practice 7.8 • Exercises 89, 90

Writing Electron Configurations for Transition Metals (7.7)
• Examples 7.9, 7.10 • For Practice 7.9, 7.10 • Exercises 93, 94

Electron Configurations and Magnetic Properties for Ions (7.7)
• Example 7.11 • For Practice 7.11 • Exercises 95–96

EXERCISES

Review Questions

1. What does it mean for a particle to be *absolutely* small? What particles fit this description?
2. Explain the difference between observing an object such as a baseball and observing a particle that is absolutely small.
3. Why is the quantum-mechanical model of the atom important for understanding chemistry?
4. What is light? How fast does it travel in a vacuum?
5. Define the wavelength and amplitude of a wave. How are these related to the energy of the wave?
6. Define the frequency of electromagnetic radiation. How is frequency related to wavelength?
7. What determines the colour of light? For example, describe the difference between red light and blue light.
8. What determines the colour of a coloured object? For example, explain why grass appears green.
9. Give an approximate range of wavelengths for each type of electromagnetic radiation and summarize the characteristics and/or uses of each:
   a. gamma rays
   b. X-rays
   c. ultraviolet radiation
   d. visible light
   e. infrared radiation
   f. microwave radiation
   g. radio waves
10. Explain the wave behaviour known as interference. Explain the difference between constructive and destructive interference.
11. Explain the wave behaviour known as diffraction. Draw the diffraction pattern that occurs when light travels through two slits comparable in size and separation to the light's wavelength.
12. Describe the photoelectric effect. How did experimental observations of this phenomenon differ from the predictions of classical electromagnetic theory?
13. How did the photoelectric effect lead Einstein to propose that light is quantized?
14. What is a photon? How is the energy of a photon related to its wavelength? Its frequency?
15. What is an emission spectrum? How does an emission spectrum of a gas in a discharge tube differ from a white light spectrum?
16. Describe the Bohr model for the atom. How did the Bohr model account for the emission spectra of atoms?
17. Explain electron diffraction.
18. What is the de Broglie wavelength of an electron? What determines the value of the de Broglie wavelength for an electron?
19. What are complementary properties? How does electron diffraction demonstrate the complementarity of the wave nature and particle nature of the electron?
20. Explain Heisenberg's uncertainty principle. What paradox is at least partially solved by the uncertainty principle?
21. What is a trajectory? What kind of information do you need to predict the trajectory of a particle?
22. Why does the uncertainty principle make it impossible to predict a trajectory for the electron?
23. Newton's laws of motion are *deterministic*. What does this mean?
24. An electron behaves in ways that are at least partially indeterminate. What does this mean?
25. What is a probability distribution map?
26. For each solution to the Schrödinger equation, what can be precisely specified: the electron's energy or its position? Explain.
27. What is an atomic orbital?
28. What is the Schrödinger equation? What is a wave function? How is a wave function related to an orbital?
29. What are the possible values of the principal quantum number n? What does the principal quantum number determine?
30. What are the possible values of the angular momentum quantum number l? What does the angular momentum quantum number determine?
31. What are the possible values of the magnetic quantum number m_l? What does the magnetic quantum number determine?

32. List all the orbitals in each principal level. Specify the three quantum numbers for each orbital.
a. $n = 1$ **b.** $n = 2$ **c.** $n = 3$ **d.** $n = 4$

33. Explain the difference between a plot showing the probability density for an orbital and one showing the radial distribution function.

34. Make sketches of the general shapes of the *s*, *p*, and *d* orbitals.

35. List the four different sublevels. Given that only a maximum of two electrons can occupy an orbital, determine the maximum number of electrons that can exist in each sublevel.

36. Why are atoms usually portrayed as spheres when most orbitals are not spherically shaped?

37. What is electron spin? Explain the difference between an electron with $m_s = +\frac{1}{2}$ and $m_s = -\frac{1}{2}$.

38. Describe the Stern–Gerlach experiment. How did the experiment demonstrate that the orientation of electron spin was quantized?

39. What is an electron configuration? Give an example.

40. What is Coulomb's law? Explain how the potential energy of two charged particles depends on the distance between the charged particles and on the magnitude and sign of their charges.

41. What is shielding? In an atom, which electrons tend to do the most shielding (core electrons or valence electrons)?

42. What is penetration? How does the penetration of an orbital into the region occupied by core electrons affect the energy of an electron in that orbital?

43. Why are the sublevels within a principal level split into different energies for multielectron atoms but not for the hydrogen atom?

44. What is an orbital diagram? Give an example.

45. Why is electron spin important when writing electron configurations? Explain in terms of the Pauli exclusion principle.

46. What is the difference between diamagnetism and paramagnetism?

47. Describe the similarities and differences between the radial probability diagrams for a 2*s* orbital and a 3*p* orbital.

48. Describe the similarities and differences between the radial probability diagrams for a 3*p* and a 4*p* orbital.

Problems by Topic

Electromagnetic Radiation

49. The distance from the sun to Earth is 1.496×10^8 km. How long does it take light to travel from the sun to Earth?

50. The nearest star to our sun is Proxima Centauri, at a distance of 4.3 light years from the sun. A light year is the distance that light travels in one year (365 days). How far away, in kilometres, is Proxima Centauri from the sun?

51. List these types of electromagnetic radiation in order of (i) increasing wavelength and (ii) increasing energy per photon:
a. radio waves **b.** microwaves
c. infrared radiation **d.** ultraviolet radiation

52. List these types of electromagnetic radiation in order of (i) increasing frequency and (ii) decreasing energy per photon:
a. gamma rays **b.** radio waves
c. microwaves **d.** visible light

53. Calculate the frequency of each wavelength of electromagnetic radiation:
a. 632.8 nm (wavelength of red light from helium–neon laser)
b. 503 nm (wavelength of maximum solar radiation)
c. 0.052 nm (a wavelength contained in medical X-rays)

54. Calculate the wavelength of each frequency of electromagnetic radiation:
a. 100.2 MHz (typical frequency for FM radio broadcasting)
b. 1070 kHz (typical frequency for AM radio broadcasting) (assume four significant figures)
c. 835.6 MHz (common frequency used for cell phone communication)

55. Calculate the energy of a photon of electromagnetic radiation at each of the wavelengths indicated in Problem 53.

56. Calculate the energy of a photon of electromagnetic radiation at each of the frequencies indicated in Problem 54.

57. A laser pulse with wavelength 532 of nm contains 3.85 mJ of energy. How many photons are in the laser pulse?

58. A heat lamp produces 32.8 W of power at a wavelength of 6.5 μm. How many photons are emitted per second? ($1 \text{ W} = 1 \text{ J s}^{-1}$)

59. Determine the energy of 1 mol of photons for each type of light. (assume three significant figures):
a. infrared radiation (1500 nm)
b. visible light (500 nm)
c. ultraviolet radiation (150 nm)

60. How much energy is contained in 1 mol of each?
a. X-ray photons with a wavelength of 0.135 nm
b. γ-ray photons with a wavelength of 2.15×10^{-5} nm

Photoelectric Effect

61. The work function of aluminum is 412 kJ mol^{-1}. If light corresponding to 471 kJ mol^{-1} is shone on the metal, what is the velocity of electrons that are emitted from the metal? The mass of an electron is 9.11×10^{-31} kg.

62. Sodium is a soft metal with a relatively low work function. Light corresponding to 471 kJ mol^{-1} was shone on the sodium metal, and the electrons detected had a velocity of $9.57 \times 10^5 \text{ m s}^{-1}$. What is the work function of sodium metal based on this data? The mass of an electron is 9.11×10^{-31} kg.

Atomic Spectroscopy

63. An electron in a hydrogen atom is excited with electrical energy to an excited state with $n = 2$. The atom then emits a photon. What is the value of *n* for the electron following the emission?

64. Determine whether each transition for an electron in the hydrogen atom corresponds to absorption or emission of energy:
a. $n = 3 \longrightarrow n = 1$ **b.** $n = 2 \longrightarrow n = 4$
c. $n = 4 \longrightarrow n = 3$

65. Calculate the wavelength of the light emitted when an electron in a hydrogen atom makes each transition and indicate the region of the electromagnetic spectrum (infrared, visible, ultraviolet, etc.) where the light is found:
a. $n = 2 \longrightarrow n = 1$ **b.** $n = 3 \longrightarrow n = 1$
c. $n = 4 \longrightarrow n = 2$ **d.** $n = 5 \longrightarrow n = 2$

66. Calculate the frequency of the light emitted when an electron in a hydrogen atom makes each transition:
a. $n = 4 \longrightarrow n = 3$ b. $n = 5 \longrightarrow n = 1$
c. $n = 5 \longrightarrow n = 4$ d. $n = 6 \longrightarrow n = 5$

67. An electron in the $n = 7$ level of the hydrogen atom relaxes to a lower energy level, emitting light of 397 nm. What is the value of n for the level to which the electron relaxed?

68. An electron in a hydrogen atom relaxes to the $n = 4$ level, emitting light of 114 THz. What is the value of n for the level in which the electron originated?

The Wave Nature of Matter and the Uncertainty Principle

69. Make a sketch of the interference pattern that results from the diffraction of electrons passing through two closely spaced slits.

70. What happens to the interference pattern described in Problem 61 if the rate of electrons going through the slits is decreased to one electron per hour? What happens to the pattern if we try to determine which slit the electron goes through by using a laser placed directly behind the slits?

71. The resolution limit of a microscope is roughly equal to the wavelength of light used in producing the image. Electron microscopes use an electron beam (in place of photons) to produce much higher resolution images, about 0.20 nm in modern instruments. Assuming that the resolution of an electron microscope is equal to the de Broglie wavelength of the electrons used, to what speed must the electrons be accelerated to obtain a resolution of 0.20 nm?

72. The smallest atoms can themselves exhibit quantum behaviour. Calculate the de Broglie wavelength (in pm) of a hydrogen atom travelling at 475 m s^{-1}.

73. What is the de Broglie wavelength of an electron travelling at 1.35×10^5 m s^{-1}?

74. A proton in a linear accelerator has a de Broglie wavelength of 122 pm. What is the speed of the proton?

75. Calculate the de Broglie wavelength of a 143 g baseball travelling at 42 m s^{-1}. Why is the wave nature of matter not important for a baseball? (mph = miles per hour, the conversion factor between miles and km is 1.6 km m^{-1})

76. A 0.22-calibre handgun fires a 27 g bullet at a velocity of 765 m s^{-1}. Calculate the de Broglie wavelength of the bullet. Is the wave nature of matter significant for bullets?

77. An electron has an uncertainty in its position of 552 pm. What is the uncertainty in its velocity?

78. An electron travelling at 3.7×10^5 m s^{-1} has an uncertainty in its velocity of 1.88×10^5 m s^{-1}. What is the uncertainty in its position?

Orbitals and Quantum Numbers

79. Which electron is, on average, closer to the nucleus: an electron in a 2*s* orbital or an electron in a 3*s* orbital?

80. Which electron is, on average, farther from the nucleus: an electron in a 3*p* orbital or an electron in a 4*p* orbital?

81. What are the possible values of l for each value of n?
a. 1 b. 2 c. 3 d. 4

82. What are the possible values of m_l for each value of l?
a. 0 b. 1 c. 2 d. 3

83. Which set of quantum numbers *cannot* occur together to specify an orbital?
a. $n = 2, l = 1, m_l = -1$ b. $n = 3, l = 2, m_l = 0$
c. $n = 3, l = 3, m_l = 2$ d. $n = 4, l = 3, m_l = 0$

84. Which combinations of n and l represent real orbitals and which do not exist?
a. 1*s* b. 2*p* c. 4*s* d. 2*d*

85. Make a sketch of the 1*s* and 2*p* orbitals. How would the 2*s* and 3*p* orbitals differ from the 1*s* and 2*p* orbitals?

86. Make a sketch of the 3*d* orbitals. How would the 4*d* orbitals differ from the 3*d* orbitals?

Electron Configurations of Atoms and Ions and Magnetic Properties

87. Write full electron configurations and full orbital diagrams for each element:
a. Si b. O c. K d. Ne e. F

88. Write full electron configurations and full orbital diagrams for each element:
a. C b. P c. Ar d. Na e. Ca

89. Write condensed electron configurations and orbital diagrams for each element:
a. N b. As c. As^{3+} d. Sn^{4+}

90. Write condensed electron configurations and orbital diagrams for each element:
a. S b. Se c. Te^{4+} d. Te^{2-}

91. Write electron configurations for each ion:
a. O^{2-} b. Br^- c. Sr^{2+} d. Co^{3+} e. Cu^{2+}

92. Write electron configurations for each ion:
a. Cl^- b. P^{3-} c. K^+ d. Mo^{3+} e. V^{3+}

93. Write the ground-state electron configuration for each atom or ion:
a. Ni, Ni^{2+} b. Mn, Mn^{4+} c. Y, Y^{3+} d. Ta, Ta^{5+}

94. Write the ground-state electron configuration for each atom or ion:
a. Zr, Zr^{2+} b. Co, Co^{2+} c. Mo, Mo^{2+} d. Os, Os^{4+}

95. Write orbital diagrams for each ion and determine if the ion is diamagnetic or paramagnetic.
a. V^{5+} b. Cr^{3+} c. Ni^{2+} d. Fe^{3+}

96. Write orbital diagrams for each ion and determine if the ion is diamagnetic or paramagnetic.
a. Cd^{2+} b. Au^+ c. Mo^{6+} d. Zr^{4+}

Cumulative Problems

97. Ultraviolet radiation and radiation of shorter wavelengths can damage biological molecules because they carry enough energy to break bonds within the molecules. A typical carbon–carbon bond requires 348 kJ mol^{-1} to break. What is the longest wavelength of radiation with enough energy to break carbon–carbon bonds?

98. The human eye contains a molecule called 11-*cis*-retinal that changes shape when struck with light of sufficient energy. The change in shape triggers a series of events that results in an electrical signal being sent to the brain. The minimum energy required to change the conformation of 11-*cis*-retinal within the eye is about

164 kJ mol^{-1}. Calculate the longest wavelength visible to the human eye.

99. An argon ion laser puts out 5.0 W of continuous power at a wavelength of 532 nm. The diameter of the laser beam is 5.5 mm. If the laser is pointed toward a pinhole with a diameter of 1.2 mm, how many photons will travel through the pinhole per second? Assume that the light intensity is equally distributed throughout the entire cross-sectional area of the beam. ($1\ W = 1\ J\ s^{-1}$)

100. A green leaf has a surface area of 2.50 cm^2. If solar radiation is 1000 W m^{-2}, how many photons strike the leaf every second? Assume three significant figures and an average wavelength of 504 nm for solar radiation.

101. In a technique used for surface analysis called Auger electron spectroscopy (AES), electrons are accelerated toward a metal surface. These electrons cause the emission of secondary electrons—called auger electrons—from the metal surface. The kinetic energy of the auger electrons depends on the composition of the surface. The presence of oxygen atoms on the surface results in auger electrons with a kinetic energy of approximately 506 eV. What is the de Broglie wavelength of one of these electrons?

$[KE = \frac{1}{2}mv^2;\ 1\ \text{electron volt (eV)} = 1.602 \times 10^{-19}\ J]$

102. An X-ray photon of wavelength 0.989 nm strikes a surface. The emitted electron has a kinetic energy of 969 eV. What is the binding energy of the electron in kJ mol^{-1}?

$[KE = \frac{1}{2}mv^2;\ 1\ \text{electron volt (eV)} = 1.602 \times 10^{-19}\ J]$

103. Ionization involves completely removing an electron from an atom. How much energy is required to ionize a hydrogen atom in its ground (or lowest energy) state? What wavelength of light contains enough energy in a single photon to ionize a hydrogen atom?

104. The energy required to ionize sodium is 496 kJ mol^{-1}. What minimum frequency of light is required to ionize sodium?

105. Suppose that in an alternate universe, the possible values of l were the integer values from 0 to n (instead of 0 to $n - 1$). Assuming no other differences between this imaginary universe and ours, how many orbitals would exist in each level?

a. $n = 1$ **b.** $n = 2$ **c.** $n = 3$

106. Suppose that in an alternate universe, the possible values of m_l were the integer values including 0 ranging from $-l - 1$ to $l + 1$ (instead of simply $-l$ to $+l$). How many orbitals would exist in each sublevel?

a. s sublevel **b.** p sublevel **c.** d sublevel

107. An atomic emission spectrum of hydrogen shows three wavelengths: 1875 nm, 1282 nm, and 1093 nm. Assign these wavelengths to transitions in the hydrogen atom.

108. An atomic emission spectrum of hydrogen shows three wavelengths: 121.5 nm, 102.6 nm, and 97.23 nm. Assign these wavelengths to transitions in the hydrogen atom.

109. The binding energy of electrons in a metal is 193 kJ mol^{-1}. Find the threshold frequency of the metal.

110. In order for a thermonuclear fusion reaction of two deuterons ($^2_1H^+$) to take place, the deuterons must collide with a velocity of about $1 \times 10^6\ m\ s^{-1}$ each. Find the wavelength of such a deuteron.

111. The speed of sound in air is 344 m s^{-1} at room temperature. The lowest frequency of a large organ pipe is 30 s^{-1} and the highest frequency of a piccolo is $1.5 \times 10^4\ s^{-1}$. Find the difference in wavelength between these two sounds.

112. The distance from Earth to the sun is 1.5×10^8 km. Find the number of crests in a light wave of frequency $1.0 \times 10^{14}\ s^{-1}$ travelling from the sun to the Earth.

113. The iodine molecule can be photodissociated into iodine atoms in the gas phase with light of wavelengths shorter than about 792 nm. A 100.0 mL glass tube contains 55.7 mTorr of gaseous iodine at 25.0 °C. What minimum amount of light energy must be absorbed by the iodine in the tube to dissociate 15.0% of the molecules?

114. A 5.00 mL ampule of a 0.100 M solution of naphthalene in hexane is excited with a flash of light. The naphthalene emits 15.5 J of energy at an average wavelength of 349 nm. What percentage of the naphthalene molecules emitted a photon?

115. A laser produces 20.0 mW of red light. In 1.00 h , the laser emits 2.29×10^{20} photons. What is the wavelength of the laser?

116. A particular laser consumes 150.0 W of electrical power and produces a 1.33×10^{19} per second stream of 1064 nm photons. What is the percent efficiency of the laser in converting electrical power to light?

117. Both vanadium and its 3+ ion are paramagnetic. Use electron configurations to explain why this is so.

118. Use electron configurations to explain why copper is paramagnetic while its 1+ ion is not.

119. Cr and Cu are different than the rest of the first transition metal series, having an [Ar] $4s^1 3d^x$ configuration. Write the ground-state electron configuration for the following species:

a. Cr, Cr^+, Cr^{2+}, Cr^{3+} **b.** Cu, Cu^+, Cu^{2+}

120. Of the ten second-row transition metals, five of them—Nb, Mo, Ru, Rh, and Ag—have a [Kr] $5s^1 4d^x$ configuration and Pd has a [Kr] $4d^{10}$ configuration. Write the ground-state electron configuration for each species:

a. Mo, Mo^+, Ag, Ag^+ **b.** Ru, Ru^{3+}
c. Rh, Rh^{2+} **d.** Pd, Pd^+, Pd^{2+}

Challenge Problems

121. An electron confined to a one-dimensional box has energy levels given by the equation

$$E_n = n^2h^2/8\ mL^2$$

where n is a quantum number with possible values of 1, 2, 3, . . . , m is the mass of the particle, and L is the length of the box.

a. Calculate the energies of the $n = 1$, $n = 2$, and $n = 3$ levels for an electron in a box with a length of 155 pm.

b. Calculate the wavelength of light required to make a transition from $n = 1 \longrightarrow n = 2$ and from $n = 2 \longrightarrow n = 3$. In what region of the electromagnetic spectrum do these wavelengths lie?

122. The energy of a vibrating molecule is quantized much like the energy of an electron in the hydrogen atom. The energy levels of a vibrating molecule are given by the equation

$$E_n = \left(n + \frac{1}{2}\right)h\nu$$

where n is a quantum number with possible values of 1, 2, . . . , and ν is the frequency of vibration. The vibration frequency of HCl is approximately $8.85 \times 10^{13}\ s^{-1}$. What minimum energy is required to excite a vibration in HCl? What wavelength of light is required to excite this vibration?

123. The wave functions for the 1*s* and 2*s* orbitals are as follows:

$$1s \quad \psi = (1/\pi)^{1/2}(1/a_0^{3/2})\exp(-r/a_0)$$

$$2s \quad \psi = (1/32\pi)^{1/2}(1/a_0^{3/2})(2 - r/a_0)\exp(-r/a_0)$$

where a_0 is a constant ($a_0 = 53$ pm) and r is the distance from the nucleus. Use a spreadsheet to make a plot containing both of these wave functions for values of r ranging from 0 pm to 500 pm. Describe the differences in the plots and identify the node in the 2*s* wave function.

124. Before quantum mechanics was developed, Johannes Rydberg developed an equation that predicted the wavelengths (λ) in the atomic spectrum of hydrogen:

$$1/\lambda = R_H(1/m^2 - 1/n^2)$$

In this equation, R_H is a constant and m and n are integers. Use the quantum-mechanical model for the hydrogen atom to derive the Rydberg equation.

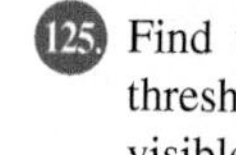
125. Find the velocity of an electron emitted by a metal whose threshold frequency is $2.25 \times 10^{14}\ s^{-1}$ when it is exposed to visible light of wavelength 5.00×10^{-7} m.

126. Water is exposed to infrared radiation of wavelength 2.8×10^{-4} cm. Assume that all the radiation is absorbed and converted to heat. How many photons will be required to raise the temperature of 2.0 g of water by 2.0 K?

127. The 2005 Nobel prize in physics was given, in part, to scientists who had made ultrashort pulses of light. These pulses are important in making measurements involving very short time periods. One challenge in making such pulses is the uncertainty principle, which can be stated with respect to energy and time as $\Delta E \cdot \Delta t \geq h/4\pi$. What is the energy uncertainty (ΔE) associated with a short pulse of laser light that lasts for only 5.0 femtoseconds (fs)? Suppose the low-energy end of the pulse had a wavelength of 722 nm. What is the wavelength of the high-energy end of the pulse that is limited only by the uncertainty principle?

128. A metal whose threshold frequency is $6.71 \times 10^{14}\ s^{-1}$ emits an electron with a velocity of $6.95 \times 10^5\ m\ s^{-1}$ when radiation of $1.01 \times 10^{15}\ s^{-1}$ strikes the metal. Use these data to calculate the mass of the electron.

129. Find the longest wavelength of a wave that can travel around in a circular orbit of radius 1.8 m.

130. The heat of fusion of ice is 6.00 kJ mol^{-1}. Find the number of photons of wavelength 6.42×10^{-6} m that must be absorbed to melt 1.00 g of ice.

131. Use Coulomb's law to calculate the ionization energy in kJ mol^{-1} of an atom composed of a proton and an electron separated by 100.00 pm. What wavelength of light would have sufficient energy to ionize the atom?

Conceptual Problems

132. Explain the difference between the Bohr model for the hydrogen atom and the quantum-mechanical model. Is the Bohr model consistent with Heisenberg's uncertainty principle?

133. Determine whether an interference pattern is observed on the other side of the slits in each experiment:

a. An electron beam is aimed at two closely spaced slits. The beam is attenuated to produce only one electron per minute.

b. An electron beam is aimed at two closely spaced slits. A light beam is placed at each slit to determine when an electron goes through the slit.

c. A high-intensity light beam is aimed at two closely spaced slits.

d. A gun is fired at a solid wall containing two closely spaced slits. (Will the bullets that pass through the slits form an interference pattern on the other side of the solid wall?)

134. The light emitted from one of the following electronic transitions ($n = 4 \longrightarrow n = 3$ or $n = 3 \longrightarrow n = 2$) in the hydrogen atom caused the photoelectric effect in a particular metal, while light from the other transition did not. Which transition caused the photoelectric effect and why?

135. According to the quantum-mechanical model for the hydrogen atom, which electron transition would produce light with the longer wavelength: $2p \longrightarrow 1s$ or $3p \longrightarrow 1s$?

8 Periodic Properties of the Elements

Beginning students of chemistry often think of the science as a mere collection of disconnected data to be memorized by brute force. Not at all! Just look at it properly and everything hangs together and makes sense.

—Isaac Asimov (1920–1992)

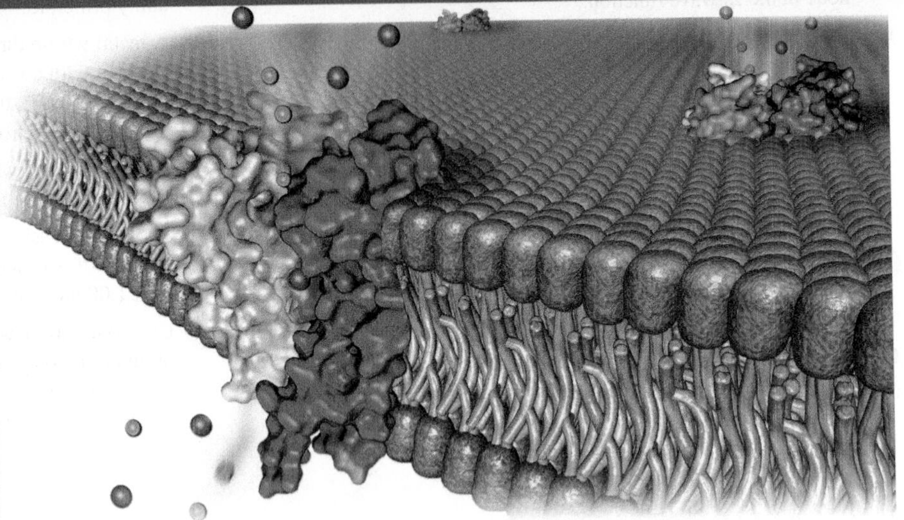

In order for a nerve cell to transmit a signal, sodium and potassium ions must flow in opposite directions through specific ion channels in the cell membrane.

GREAT ADVANCES IN SCIENCE occur not only when a scientist sees something new, but also when a scientist sees what everyone else has seen in a new way. In other words, great scientists often see patterns where others have seen only disjointed facts. Such was the case in 1869 when Dmitri Mendeleev, a Russian chemistry professor, saw a pattern in the properties of elements. Mendeleev's insight led to the periodic table, arguably the single most important tool for the chemist. Recall that scientists devise theories that explain the underlying reasons for observations. If we think of Mendeleev's periodic table as a compact way to summarize a large number of observations, then quantum mechanics (covered in Chapter 7) is the theory that explains the underlying reasons for the periodic table. The concepts of quantum mechanics explain the arrangement of elements in the periodic table by reference to the electrons within the atoms that compose the elements. In this chapter, we see a continuation of the theme we have been developing since page one of this book—the properties of macroscopic substances (in this case, the elements in the periodic table) are explained by the properties of the particles that compose them (in this case, atoms and their electrons).

8.1 Nerve Signal Transmission

As you sit reading this text, tiny pumps in the membranes of your cells are working hard to transport ions—especially sodium (Na^+) and potassium (K^+)—through those membranes. Amazingly, the ions are pumped in opposite directions. Sodium ions are pumped *out of cells*, while potassium ions are pumped *into cells*. The result is a *chemical gradient* for each ion: the concentration of sodium is higher outside the cell than within, while just the opposite is true for potassium. These ion pumps are analogous to the water pumps in a high-rise building that pump water against the force of gravity to a tank on the roof. Other structures within the membrane, called ion channels, are like the building's faucets. When these open, sodium and potassium ions flow back down their gradients—sodium flowing in and potassium flowing out. This movement of ions is the basis for the transmission of nerve signals in the brain and throughout the body. Every move you make, every thought you have, and every sensation you experience is mediated by these ion movements.

How do the pumps and channels differentiate between sodium and potassium ions to selectively move one out of the cell and the other into the cell? To answer this question, we must examine the ions more closely. Both are cations of group 1 metals. All group 1 metals tend to lose one electron to form cations with a 1+ charge, so that cannot be the decisive factor. Potassium (atomic number 19) lies directly below sodium in the periodic table (atomic number 11), indicating that it has more protons, neutrons, and electrons than sodium. How do these additional subatomic particles affect the properties of potassium? As we will see in this chapter, although a higher atomic number does not always result in a larger ion (or atom), it does in the case of potassium (relative to sodium). The potassium ion has a radius of 133 pm, while the sodium ion has a radius of 95 pm. (Recall that 1 pm $= 10^{-12}$ m.) The pumps and channels within cell membranes are so sensitive that they can distinguish between the sizes of these two ions and selectively allow only one or the other to pass.

1
3 **Li** 6.941
11 **Na** 22.99
19 **K** 39.10
37 **Rb** 85.47
55 **Cs** 132.91
87 **Fr** (223.02)

▲ The group 1 metals. Potassium is directly beneath sodium in the periodic table.

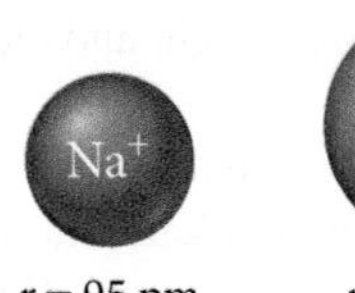

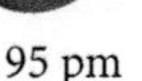

The size of sodium and potassium ions is an example of a **periodic property**: one that is predictable based on an element's position within the periodic table. In this chapter, we examine several periodic properties of elements, including atomic radius, ionization energy, and electron affinity. We will see that these properties, as well as the overall arrangement of the periodic table, are explained by quantum theory, which we examined in Chapter 7. The arrangement of elements in the periodic table—originally based on similarities in the properties of the elements—reflects how electrons fill atomic orbitals.

8.2 The Development of the Periodic Table

Prior to the 1700s, the number of known elements was relatively small, consisting mostly of the metals that had long been used for coinage, jewellery, and weapons. From the early 1700s to the mid-1800s, however, chemists discovered over 50 new elements. The first attempt to organize these elements according to similarities in their properties was made by the German chemist Johann Döbereiner (1780–1849), who grouped elements into *triads*: three elements with similar properties. For example, Döbereiner formed a triad out of barium, calcium, and strontium, three fairly reactive metals. About 50 years later, English chemist John Newlands (1837–1898) organized elements into *octaves*, in analogy to musical notes. When arranged this way, the properties of every eighth element were similar, much as every eighth note in the musical

Gallium (eka-aluminum)

	Mendeleev's predicted properties	Actual properties
Atomic mass	About 68 u	69.72 u
Melting point	Low	29.8 °C
Density	5.9 g cm^{-3}	5.90 g cm^{-3}
Formula of oxide	X_2O_3	Ga_2O_3
Formula of chloride	XCl_3	$GaCl_3$

Germanium (eka-silicon)

	Mendeleev's predicted properties	Actual properties
Atomic mass	About 72 u	72.64 u
Density	5.5 g cm^{-3}	5.35 g cm^{-3}
Formula of oxide	XO_2	GeO_2
Formula of chloride	XCl_4	$GeCl_4$

▲ **FIGURE 8.1 Eka-Aluminum and Eka-Silicon** Mendeleev's arrangement of elements in the periodic table allowed him to predict the existence of these elements, now known as gallium and germanium, and anticipate their properties.

▲ Dmitri Mendeleev is credited with the arrangement of the periodic table.

▲ Henry Moseley discovered the atomic number sequence.

scale is similar. Newlands endured some ridicule for drawing an analogy between chemistry and music, including the derisive comments of one colleague who asked Newlands if he had ever tried ordering the elements according to the first letters of their names.

The periodic table is credited primarily to the Russian chemist Dmitri Mendeleev (1834–1907), even though a similar organization had been suggested by the German chemist Julius Lothar Meyer (1830–1895). As we saw in Chapter 2, Mendeleev's table is based on the periodic law, which states that when elements are arranged in order of increasing mass, certain properties recur periodically. Mendeleev arranged the elements in a table in which mass increased from left to right and elements with similar properties fell in the same columns.

Mendeleev's arrangement was a huge success, allowing him to predict the existence and properties of yet undiscovered elements such as eka-aluminum (later discovered and named gallium) and eka-silicon (later discovered and named germanium). The properties of these elements are summarized in Figure 8.1 ▲. (As noted in Chapter 2, *eka* means "the one beyond" or "the next one" in a family of elements.) However, Mendeleev did encounter some difficulties. For example, according to accepted values of atomic masses, tellurium (with higher mass) should come *after* iodine. But based on their properties, Mendeleev placed tellurium *before* iodine and suggested that the mass of tellurium was erroneous. However, the mass was correct. Other apparent anomalies in atomic masses in the periodic table appear at argon and potassium, and cobalt and nickel. If the elements were organized by mass, these pairs of elements would be in reverse order.

The modern periodic table lists elements by atomic number, not by atomic mass. The concept of atomic number came out of experiments performed by Henry Moseley, a student of Ernest Rutherford, in 1913. Moseley was doing experiments using X-ray spectroscopy, in which a sample is bombarded with a beam of electrons from a cathode ray tube. This induces the emission of X-rays from the sample, and the frequencies of the X-rays are determined using a spectrometer. Moseley found that he could arrange the frequencies of X-rays from different elements according to a sequence of whole numbers, which he named *atomic numbers* (see Figure 8.2 ▶). Note that this was six years before the proton was discovered (1919). The atomic number sequence resolved the problems of ordering elements according to mass and happened to place elements in better correlation with elemental properties. Remarkably, Moseley could predict the existence of three undiscovered metals—rhenium, technetium, and promethium—because these atomic numbers were missing from the sequence. Technetium and promethium do not exist naturally because they are radioactive and decompose rapidly into other elements; they can only be made artificially in nuclear reactors.

Notice the scientific method in practice in the history of the periodic table. A number of related observations led to a scientific law—the periodic law. Mendeleev's table, which is really just an expression of the periodic law, had predictive power, as laws usually do. However, it did not explain *why* the properties of elements recurred, or *why* certain elements had similar properties. The theory that explains the reasons behind the periodic law is quantum theory, which we examined in Chapter 7. In this chapter, we turn to exploring the connection between the periodic table and quantum theory.

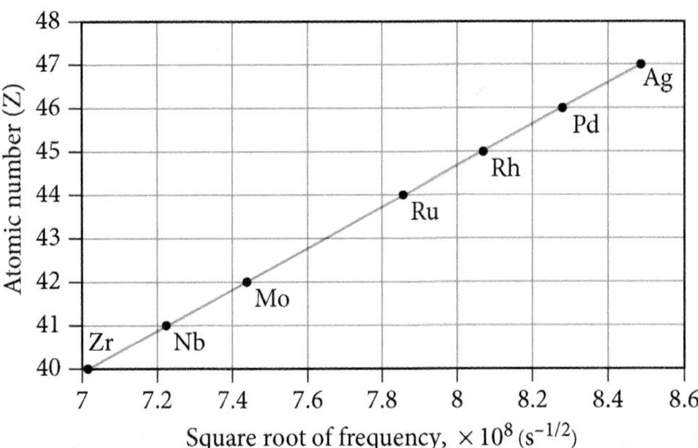

▲ **FIGURE 8.2 Graph Showing a Portion of Moseley's X-Ray Data** Integers assigned to each element are plotted against the square root of the frequency of spectral lines. Moseley obtained a perfect straight-line relationship. The integers on the y-axis are the atomic numbers of each element. The missing element at $Z = 43$, between molybdenum and ruthenium, was unknown at Moseley's time. It was later determined to be the element technetium, which does not occur naturally.

8.3 Electron Configurations, Valence Electrons, and the Periodic Table

Mendeleev arranged the periodic table so that elements with similar chemical properties lie in the same column. We can begin to make the connection between an element's properties and its electron configuration by superimposing the electron configurations of the first 18 elements onto a partial periodic table, as shown in Figure 8.3 ▼. As we move to the right across a row, the orbitals are filling in the correct order. With each subsequent row, the highest principal quantum number increases by one. Notice that as we move down a column, *the number of electrons in the outermost principal energy level (highest* n *value) remains the same.* The key connection between the macroscopic world (an element's chemical properties) and the atomic world (an atom's electronic structure) lies in these outermost electrons.

An atom's **valence electrons** are the electrons important in chemical bonding. *For main-group elements, the valence electrons are those in the outermost principal energy level.* For transition elements, we also count the outermost d electrons among the valence electrons (even though they are not in an outermost principal energy level). The chemical properties of an element depend on its valence electrons, which are instrumental in bonding because they are held most loosely (and are therefore the easiest to lose or share). We can now see *why* the elements in a column of the periodic table have similar chemical properties: *they have the same number of valence electrons.*

1							18
1 **H** $1s^1$	2	13	14	15	16	17	2 **He** $1s^2$
3 **Li** $2s^1$	4 **Be** $2s^2$	5 **B** $2s^22p^1$	6 **C** $2s^22p^2$	7 **N** $2s^22p^3$	8 **O** $2s^22p^4$	9 **F** $2s^22p^5$	10 **Ne** $2s^22p^6$
11 **Na** $3s^1$	12 **Mg** $3s^2$	13 **Al** $3s^23p^1$	14 **Si** $3s^23p^2$	15 **P** $3s^23p^3$	16 **S** $3s^23p^4$	17 **Cl** $3s^23p^5$	18 **Ar** $3s^23p^6$

▲ **FIGURE 8.3 Outer Electron Configurations of the First 18 Elements in the Periodic Table**

Valence electrons are distinguished from all the other electrons in an atom, which are called **core electrons**. The core electrons are those in *complete* principal energy levels and those in *complete d* and *f* sublevels. For example, silicon, with the electron configuration $1s^2 2s^2 2p^6 3s^2 3p^2$, has 4 valence electrons (those in the $n = 3$ principal level) and 10 core electrons.

Si $1s^2 2s^2 2p^6 3s^2 3p^2$

Core electrons — Valence electrons

EXAMPLE 8.1 VALENCE ELECTRONS AND CORE ELECTRONS

Write an electron configuration for Ge. Identify the valence electrons and core electrons.

SOLUTION

Write the electron configuration for Ge by determining the total number of electrons from germanium's atomic number (32) and then distributing them into the appropriate orbitals.	Ge $1s^2 2s^2 2p^6 3s^2 3p^6 4s^2 3d^{10} 4p^2$
Since germanium is a main-group element, its valence electrons are those in the outermost principal energy level. For germanium, the $n = 1, 2$, and 3 principal levels are complete (or full), and the $n = 4$ principal level is outermost. Consequently, the $n = 4$ electrons are valence electrons and the rest are core electrons. *Note: In this text, electron configurations are always written with the orbitals in the* order of filling. *However, writing electron configurations in* order of increasing principal quantum number *is also common. The electron configuration of germanium written in order of increasing principal quantum number is:* Ge $1s^2 2s^2 2p^6 3s^2 3p^6 3d^{10} 4s^2 4p^2$	4 valence electrons Ge $1s^2 2s^2 2p^6 3s^2 3p^6 4s^2 3d^{10} 4p^2$ 28 core electrons

FOR PRACTICE 8.1

Write an electron configuration for phosphorus. Identify the valence electrons and core electrons.

Orbital Blocks in the Periodic Table

A pattern similar to what we just saw for the first 18 elements exists for the entire periodic table, as shown in Figure 8.4 ▸. Note that, because of the filling order of orbitals, the periodic table can be divided into blocks representing the filling of particular sublevels. The first two columns on the left side of the periodic table compose the *s* block, with outer electron configurations of ns^1 (the alkali metals) and ns^2 (the alkaline earth metals). The six columns on the right side of the periodic table compose the *p* block, with outer electron configurations of $ns^2 np^1$, $ns^2 np^2$, $ns^2 np^3$ (pnictogens), $ns^2 np^4$ (chalcogens), $ns^2 np^5$ (halogens), and $ns^2 np^6$ (noble gases). The transition elements compose the *d* block, and the lanthanoids and actinoids compose the *f* block. (For compactness, the *f* block is normally printed below the *d* block instead of being imbedded within it.)

Helium is an exception. Even though it lies in the column with an outer electron configuration of $ns^2 np^6$, its electron configuration is simply $1s^2$.

You can see that *the number of columns in a block corresponds to the maximum number of electrons that can occupy the particular sublevel of that block.* The *s* block

Legend: *s*-block elements; *p*-block elements; *d*-block elements; *f*-block elements

Periods \ Groups	1	2	3	4	5	6	7	8	9	10	11	12	13	14	15	16	17	18
1	1 **H** $1s^1$																	2 **He** $1s^2$
2	3 **Li** $2s^1$	4 **Be** $2s^2$											5 **B** $2s^22p^1$	6 **C** $2s^22p^2$	7 **N** $2s^22p^3$	8 **O** $2s^22p^4$	9 **F** $2s^22p^5$	10 **Ne** $2s^22p^6$
3	11 **Na** $3s^1$	12 **Mg** $3s^2$											13 **Al** $3s^23p^1$	14 **Si** $3s^23p^2$	15 **P** $3s^23p^3$	16 **S** $3s^23p^4$	17 **Cl** $3s^23p^5$	18 **Ar** $3s^23p^6$
4	19 **K** $4s^1$	20 **Ca** $4s^2$	21 **Sc** $4s^23d^1$	22 **Ti** $4s^23d^2$	23 **V** $4s^23d^3$	24 **Cr** $4s^13d^5$	25 **Mn** $4s^23d^5$	26 **Fe** $4s^23d^6$	27 **Co** $4s^23d^7$	28 **Ni** $4s^23d^8$	29 **Cu** $4s^13d^{10}$	30 **Zn** $4s^23d^{10}$	31 **Ga** $4s^24p^1$	32 **Ge** $4s^24p^2$	33 **As** $4s^24p^3$	34 **Se** $4s^24p^4$	35 **Br** $4s^24p^5$	36 **Kr** $4s^24p^6$
5	37 **Rb** $5s^1$	38 **Sr** $5s^2$	39 **Y** $5s^24d^1$	40 **Zr** $5s^24d^2$	41 **Nb** $5s^14d^4$	42 **Mo** $5s^14d^5$	43 **Tc** $5s^24d^5$	44 **Ru** $5s^14d^7$	45 **Rh** $5s^14d^8$	46 **Pd** $4d^{10}$	47 **Ag** $5s^14d^{10}$	48 **Cd** $5s^24d^{10}$	49 **In** $5s^25p^1$	50 **Sn** $5s^25p^2$	51 **Sb** $5s^25p^3$	52 **Te** $5s^25p^4$	53 **I** $5s^25p^5$	54 **Xe** $5s^25p^6$
6	55 **Cs** $6s^1$	56 **Ba** $6s^2$		72 **Hf** $6s^25d^2$	73 **Ta** $6s^25d^3$	74 **W** $6s^25d^4$	75 **Re** $6s^25d^5$	76 **Os** $6s^25d^6$	77 **Ir** $6s^25d^7$	78 **Pt** $6s^15d^9$	79 **Au** $6s^15d^{10}$	80 **Hg** $6s^25d^{10}$	81 **Tl** $6s^26p^1$	82 **Pb** $6s^26p^2$	83 **Bi** $6s^26p^3$	84 **Po** $6s^26p^4$	85 **At** $6s^26p^5$	86 **Rn** $6s^26p^6$
7	87 **Fr** $7s^1$	88 **Ra** $7s^2$		104 **Rf** $7s^26d^2$	105 **Db** $7s^26d^3$	106 **Sg** $7s^26d^4$	107 **Bh**	108 **Hs**	109 **Mt**	110 **Ds**	111 **Rg**	112 **Cn**	113	114 **Fl**	115	116 **Lv**		

Lanthanoids	57 **La** $6s^25d^1$	58 **Ce** $6s^24f^15d^1$	59 **Pr** $6s^24f^3$	60 **Nd** $6s^24f^4$	61 **Pm** $6s^24f^5$	62 **Sm** $6s^24f^6$	63 **Eu** $6s^24f^7$	64 **Gd** $6s^24f^75d^1$	65 **Tb** $6s^24f^9$	66 **Dy** $6s^24f^{10}$	67 **Ho** $6s^24f^{11}$	68 **Er** $6s^24f^{12}$	69 **Tm** $6s^24f^{13}$	70 **Yb** $6s^24f^{14}$	71 **Lu** $6s^24f^{14}6d^1$
Actinoids	89 **Ac** $7s^26d^1$	90 **Th** $7s^26d^2$	91 **Pa** $7s^25f^26d^1$	92 **U** $7s^25f^36d^1$	93 **Np** $7s^25f^46d^1$	94 **Pu** $7s^25f^6$	95 **Am** $7s^25f^7$	96 **Cm** $7s^25f^76d^1$	97 **Bk** $7s^25f^9$	98 **Cf** $7s^25f^{10}$	99 **Es** $7s^25f^{11}$	100 **Fm** $7s^25f^{12}$	101 **Md** $7s^25f^{13}$	102 **No** $7s^25f^{14}$	103 **Lr** $7s^25f^{14}6d^1$

▲ **FIGURE 8.4 The *s*, *p*, *d*, and *f* Blocks of the Periodic Table**

has 2 columns (corresponding to one *s* orbital holding a maximum of two electrons); the *p* block has 6 columns (corresponding to three *p* orbitals with two electrons each); the *d* block has 10 columns (corresponding to five *d* orbitals with two electrons each); and the *f* block has 14 columns (corresponding to seven *f* orbitals with two electrons each).

Lastly, note that *the row number in the periodic table is equal to the number (or* n *value) of the highest principal level.* For example, because chlorine is in row 3, its highest principal level is the $n = 3$ level.

Summarizing Periodic Table Organization:

- The periodic table is divisible into four blocks corresponding to the filling of the four quantum sublevels (*s*, *p*, *d*, and *f*).
- The row number of a main-group element is equal to the highest principal quantum number of that element.

Writing an Electron Configuration for an Element from Its Position in the Periodic Table

The organization of the periodic table allows us to write the electron configuration for any element based on its position in the periodic table. For example, suppose we want to write an electron configuration for Cl. The *inner electron configuration* of Cl is that of the noble gas that precedes it in the periodic table, Ne. So, we can represent the inner electron configuration with [Ne]. The *outer electron configuration*—the configuration of the electrons beyond the previous noble gas—is obtained by tracing the elements between Ne and Cl and assigning electrons to the appropriate orbitals, as shown here. Remember that the highest n value is given by the row number (3 for chlorine).

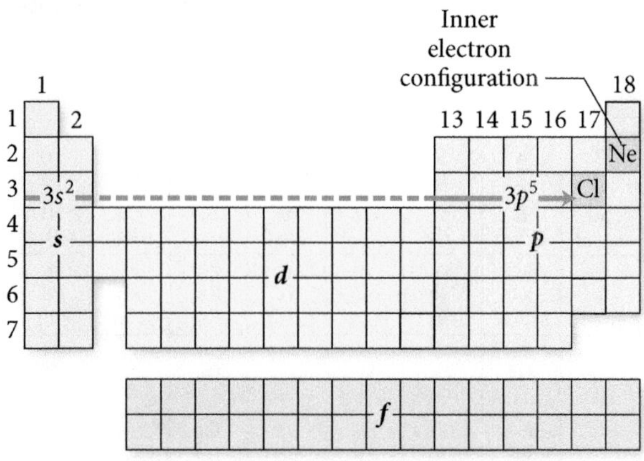

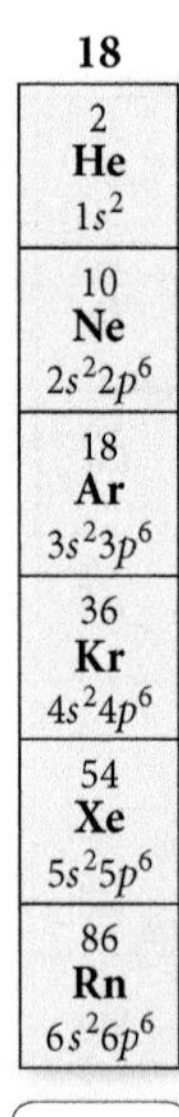

▲ The noble gases all have eight valence electrons except for helium, which has two. They have full outer energy levels and are particularly stable and unreactive.

1
3 Li $2s^1$
11 Na $3s^1$
19 K $4s^1$
37 Rb $5s^1$
55 Cs $6s^1$
87 Fr $7s^1$

Alkali metals

▲ The alkali metals all have one valence electron. Each is one electron beyond a stable electron configuration and they tend to lose that electron in their reactions.

So, we begin with [Ne], then add in the two 3*s* electrons as we trace across the *s* block, followed by five 3*p* electrons as we trace across the *p* block to Cl, which is in the fifth column of the *p* block. The electron configuration is:

$$\text{Cl} \quad [\text{Ne}]\ 3s^2 3p^5$$

Notice that Cl is in column 17 and has an outer electron configuration of ns^2np^5, and therefore has 7 valence electrons.

The *d*-Block and *f*-Block Elements

The electron configurations of the *d*-block and *f*-block elements exhibit trends that differ somewhat from those of the main-group elements. As we move to the right across a row in the *d* block, the *d* orbitals fill as shown here:

21 Sc $4s^23d^1$	22 Ti $4s^23d^2$	23 V $4s^23d^3$	24 Cr $4s^13d^5$	25 Mn $4s^23d^5$	26 Fe $4s^23d^6$	27 Co $4s^23d^7$	28 Ni $4s^23d^8$	29 Cu $4s^13d^{10}$	30 Zn $4s^23d^{10}$
39 Y $5s^24d^1$	40 Zr $5s^24d^2$	41 Nb $5s^14d^4$	42 Mo $5s^14d^5$	43 Tc $5s^24d^5$	44 Ru $5s^14d^7$	45 Rh $5s^14d^8$	46 Pd $4d^{10}$	47 Ag $5s^14d^{10}$	48 Cd $5s^24d^{10}$

Notice that *the principal quantum number of the* d *orbital being filled across each row in the transition series is equal to the row number minus one*. In the fourth row, the 3*d* orbitals fill; in the fifth row, the 4*d* orbitals fill; and so on.

Keep in mind that in the first transition series of the *d* block, the outer configuration is $4s^2 3d^x$ with two exceptions: Cr is $4s^1 3d^5$ and Cu is $4s^1 3d^{10}$. This behaviour is related to the closely spaced 3*d* and 4*s* energy levels. As shown above, it is even more difficult to predict the electron configurations of the second transition metal series, as there are $5s^1$, $5s^2$, and $5s^0$ electron configurations in no predictable order. Actual electron configurations are definitively determined experimentally (through spectroscopy) and do not always conform to simple patterns. Nonetheless, the patterns we have described allow us to accurately predict electron configurations for most of the elements in the periodic table.

As we move across the *f* block, the *f* orbitals fill. Note that, for these elements, the principal quantum number of the *f* orbital being filled across each row in the inner transition series is the row number *minus two*. (In the sixth row, the 4*f* orbitals fill, and in the seventh row, the $5f$ orbitals fill.) In addition, within the inner transition series, the close energy spacing of the $5d$ and $4f$ orbitals sometimes causes an electron to enter a $5d$ orbital instead of the expected $4f$ orbital. For example, the electron configuration of gadolinium is [Xe] $6s^2 4f^7 5d^1$, instead of the expected [Xe] $6s^2 4f^8$.

EXAMPLE 8.2 WRITING ELECTRON CONFIGURATIONS FROM THE PERIODIC TABLE

Use the periodic table to write an electron configuration for selenium (Se).

SOLUTION

The atomic number of Se is 34. The noble gas that precedes Se in the periodic table is argon, so the inner electron configuration is [Ar]. Obtain the outer electron configuration by tracing the elements between Ar and Se and assigning electrons to the appropriate orbitals. Begin with [Ar]. Because Se is in row 4, add two $4s$ electrons as you trace across the s block (n = row number). Next, add ten $3d$ electrons as you trace across the d block (n = row number − 1). Lastly, add four $4p$ electrons as you trace across the p block to Se, which is in the fourth column of the p block (n = row number).

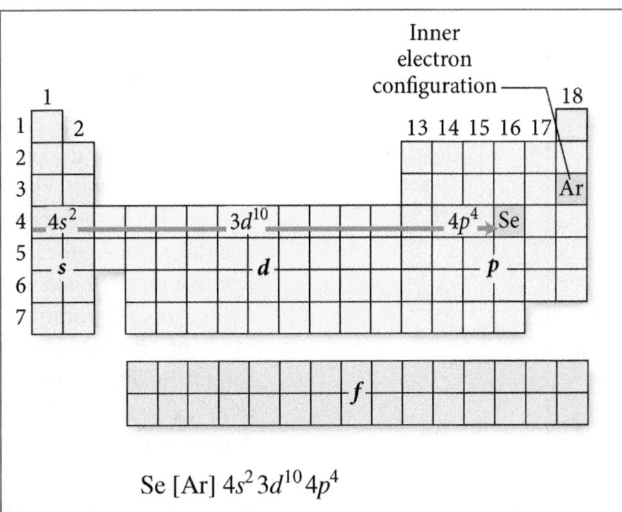

Se [Ar] $4s^2 3d^{10} 4p^4$

FOR PRACTICE 8.2

Use the periodic table to determine the electron configuration of bismuth (Bi).

FOR MORE PRACTICE 8.2

Use the periodic table to write an electron configuration for iodine (I).

8.4 The Explanatory Power of the Quantum-Mechanical Model

We can now see how the quantum-mechanical model accounts for the chemical properties of the elements, such as the inertness of helium or the reactivity of hydrogen, and (more generally) how it accounts for the periodic law. *The chemical properties of elements are largely determined by the number of valence electrons they contain.* Their properties are periodic because the number of valence electrons is periodic.

Since elements within a column in the periodic table have the same number of valence electrons, they also have similar chemical properties. The noble gases, for example, all have eight valence electrons, except for helium, which has two. Although we do not cover much of the quantitative (or numerical) aspects of the quantum-mechanical model in this text, calculations of the overall energy of atoms with eight valence electrons (or two, in the case of helium) show that they are particularly stable. In other words, when a quantum level is completely full, the overall energy of the electrons that occupy that level is particularly low. Therefore, those electrons *cannot* lower their energy by reacting with other atoms or molecules, so the corresponding atom is relatively

2
4 **Be** $2s^2$
12 **Mg** $3s^2$
20 **Ca** $4s^2$
38 **Sr** $5s^2$
56 **Ba** $6s^2$
88 **Ra** $7s^2$

Alkaline earth metals

▶ The alkaline earth metals all have two valence electrons. Each is two electrons beyond a stable electron configuration and they tend to lose those electrons in their reactions.

	1	2	3	4	5	6	7	8	9	10	11	12	13	14	15	16	17	18
1	Li^+														N^{3-}	O^{2-}	F^-	
2	Na^+	Mg^{2+}											Al^{3+}			S^{2-}	Cl^-	
3	K^+	Ca^{2+}														Se^{2-}	Br^-	
4	Rb^+	Sr^{2+}														Te^{2-}	I^-	
5	Cs^+	Ba^{2+}																

▲ **FIGURE 8.5 Elements That Form Ions with Predictable Charges** Notice that each ion has a noble gas electron configuration.

unreactive or inert. The noble gases are the most chemically stable and relatively unreactive family in the periodic table.

Elements with electron configurations *close* to those of the noble gases are the most reactive because they can attain noble gas electron configurations by losing or gaining a small number of electrons. For example, alkali metals (group 1) are among the most reactive metals because their outer electron configuration (ns^1) is one electron beyond a noble gas configuration. They readily react to lose the ns^1 electron, obtaining a noble gas configuration. This explains why—as we saw in Chapter 2—the group 1 metals tend to form 1+ cations. Similarly, alkaline earth metals, with an outer electron configuration of ns^2, also tend to be reactive metals, losing their ns^2 electrons to form 2+ cations. This does not mean that forming an ion with a noble gas configuration is in itself energetically favourable. In fact, forming cations always *requires energy*. But when the cation formed has a noble gas configuration, the energy cost of forming the cation is often less than the energy payback that occurs when that cation forms ionic bonds with anions, as we shall see in Chapter 9.

17
9 **F** $2s^22p^5$
17 **Cl** $3s^23p^5$
35 **Br** $4s^24p^5$
53 **I** $5s^25p^5$
85 **At** $6s^26p^5$

Halogens

◀ The halogens all have seven valence electrons. Each is one electron short of a stable electron configuration and they tend to gain one electron in their reactions.

On the right side of the periodic table, halogens are among the most reactive nonmetals because of their ns^2np^5 electron configurations. They are only one electron short of a noble gas configuration and tend to react to gain that one electron, forming 1− ions. Figure 8.5 ▲, first introduced in Chapter 2, shows the elements that form predictable ions. The charges of these ions reflect their electron configurations—in their reactions, these elements form ions with noble gas electron configurations.

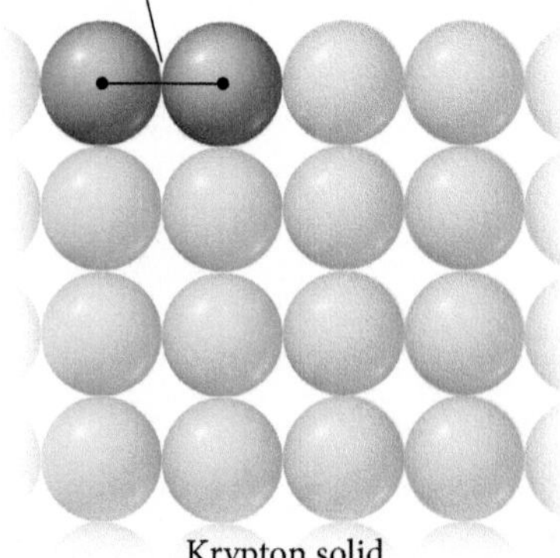

▲ The van der Waals radius of an atom is one-half the distance between adjacent nuclei in the atomic solid.

8.5 Periodic Trends in the Size of Atoms and Effective Nuclear Charge

In previous chapters, we saw that the volume of an atom is taken up primarily by its electrons (Chapter 2) occupying atomic orbitals (Chapter 7). We also saw that these orbitals do not have a definite boundary, but represent only a statistical probability distribution for where the electron is found. So, how do we define the size of an atom? One way to define atomic radii is to consider the distance between *nonbonding* atoms that are in direct contact. For example, krypton can be frozen into a solid in which the krypton atoms are touching each other but are not bonded together. The distance between the centres of adjacent krypton atoms—which can be determined from the solid's density—is then twice the radius of a krypton atom. An atomic radius determined in this way is called the **nonbonding atomic radius** or the **van der Waals radius**. The van der Waals radius represents the radius of an atom when it is not bonded to another atom.

Another way to define the size of an atom, called the **bonding atomic radius** or **covalent radius**, is defined differently for nonmetals and metals, as follows:

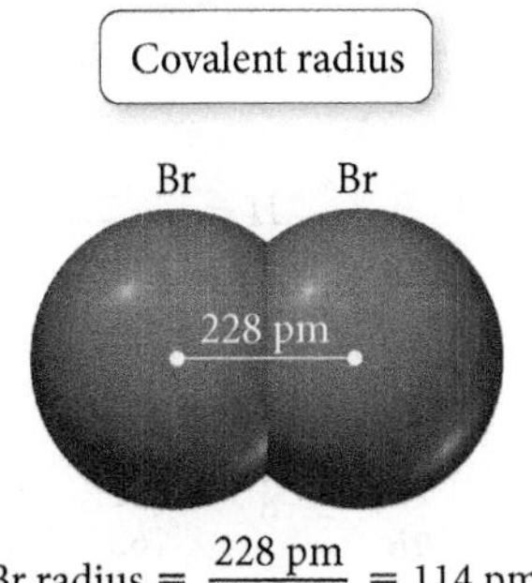

$$\text{Br radius} = \frac{228 \text{ pm}}{2} = 114 \text{ pm}$$

▲ The covalent radius of bromine is one-half the distance between two bonded bromine atoms.

Nonmetals: one-half the distance between two of the atoms bonded together

Metals: one-half the distance between two of the atoms next to each other in a crystal of the metal

For example, the distance between Br atoms in Br_2 is 228 pm; therefore, the Br covalent radius is assigned to be one-half of 228 pm or 114 pm.

Using this method, we can assign radii to all elements in the periodic table that form chemical bonds or form metallic crystals. A more general term, the **atomic radius**, refers to a set of average bonding radii determined from measurements on a large number of elements and compounds. The atomic radius represents the radius of an atom when it is bonded to another atom and is always smaller than the van der Waals radius. The approximate bond length of any two covalently bonded atoms is simply the sum of their atomic radii. For example, the approximate bond length for ICl is iodine's atomic radius (133 pm) plus chlorine's atomic radius (99 pm), for a bond length of 232 pm. (The actual experimentally measured bond length in ICl is 232.07 pm.)

Figure 8.6 ▼ shows the atomic radius plotted as a function of atomic number for the first 57 elements in the periodic table. Notice the periodic trend in the radii. Atomic radii peak with each alkali metal. Figure 8.7 ▼ is a relief map of atomic radii for most of the elements in the periodic table. The general trends in the atomic radii of main-group elements, which are the same as trends observed in van der Waals radii, are stated below.

1. As we move down a column (or family) in the periodic table, atomic radius increases.
2. As we move to the right across a period (or row) in the periodic table, atomic radius decreases.

The bonding radii of some elements, such as helium and neon, must be approximated since they do not form either chemical bonds or metallic crystals.

We can understand the observed trend in radius as we move down a column based on the trends in the sizes of atomic orbitals. The atomic radius is largely determined by the valence electrons, the electrons farthest from the nucleus. As we move down a column

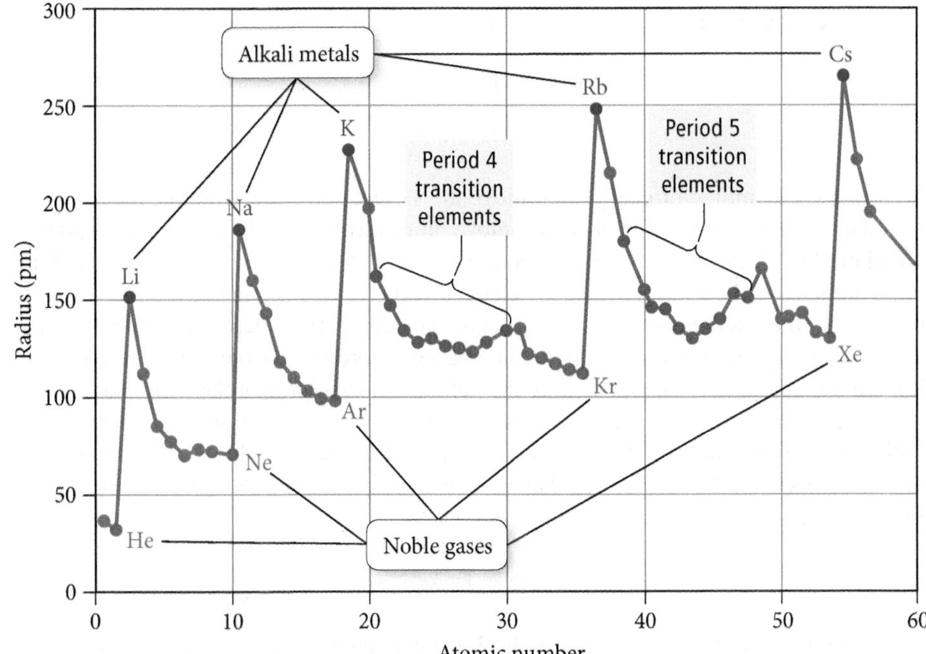

◀ **FIGURE 8.6 Atomic Radius Versus Atomic Number** Notice the periodic trend in atomic radius, starting at a peak with each alkali metal and falling to a minimum with each noble gas.

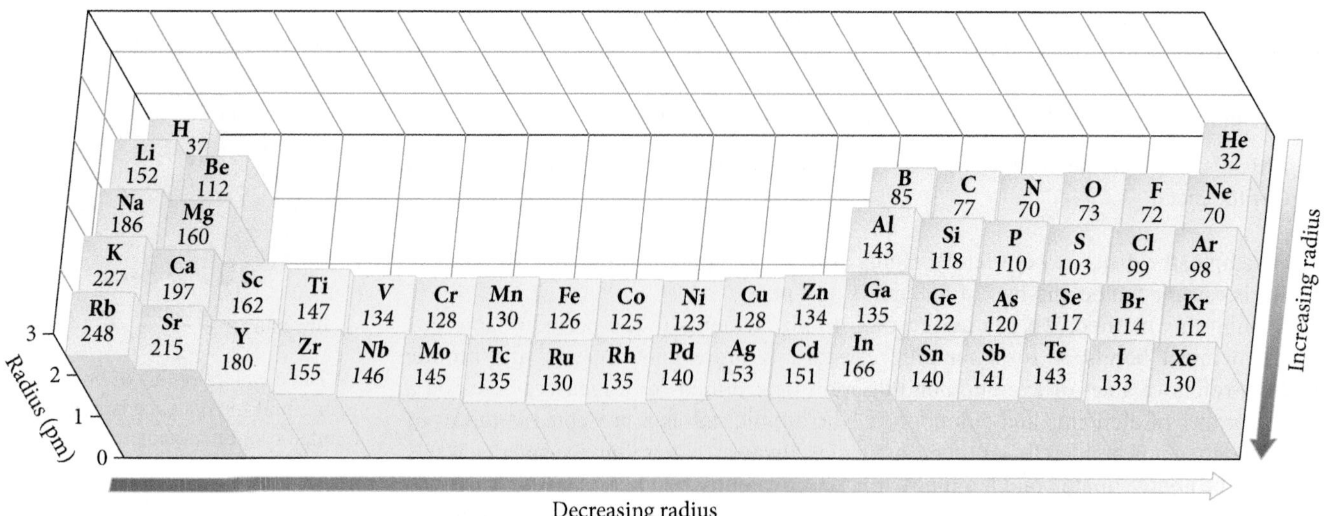

▲ **FIGURE 8.7 Trends in Atomic Radius** In general, atomic radii increase as we move down a column and decrease as we move to the right across a period in the periodic table.

in the periodic table, the highest principal quantum number (n) of the valence electrons increases. Consequently, the valence electrons occupy larger orbitals, resulting in larger atoms.

The observed trend in atomic radius as we move to the right across a row, however, is a bit more complex. To understand this trend, we revisit some concepts from Section 7.7, including effective nuclear charge and shielding.

Effective Nuclear Charge

The trend in atomic radius as we move to the right across a row in the periodic table is determined by the inward pull of the nucleus on the electrons in the outermost principal energy level (highest n value). According to Coulomb's law, the attraction between a nucleus and an electron increases with increasing magnitude of nuclear charge. For example, compare the H atom to the He^+ ion:

$$\text{H} \quad 1s^1$$

$$\text{He}^+ \quad 1s^1$$

It takes 1312 kJ mol^{-1} of energy to remove the 1s electron from 1 mol of hydrogen atoms, but 5251 kJ mol^{-1} of energy to remove an electron from the equivalent orbital in 1 mol of He^+. Why? Although each electron is in a 1s orbital, the electron in the helium ion is attracted to the nucleus with a 2+ charge, while the electron in the hydrogen atom is attracted to the nucleus by only a 1+ charge. Therefore, the electron in the helium ion is held more tightly (it has lower potential energy according to Coulomb's law), making it more difficult to remove and making the helium ion smaller than the hydrogen atom.

As we saw in Section 7.7, any one electron in a multielectron atom experiences both the positive charge of the nucleus (which is attractive) and the negative charges of the other electrons (which are repulsive). Consider again the outermost electron in the lithium atom:

$$\text{Li} \quad 1s^2 2s^1$$

As shown in Figure 8.8 ▶, even though the 2s orbital penetrates into the 1s orbital to some degree, the majority of the 2s orbital is outside of the 1s orbital. Therefore, the electron in the 2s orbital is partially *screened* or *shielded* from the 3+ charge of the nucleus by

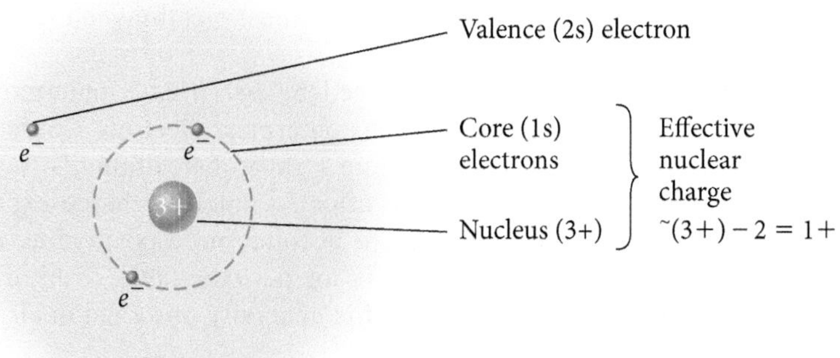

▲ **FIGURE 8.8 Screening and Effective Nuclear Charge** The valence electron in lithium experiences the 3+ charge of the nucleus through the screen of the 2− charge of the core electrons. The effective nuclear charge acting on the valence electron is approximately 1+.

the 2− charge of the 1*s* (or core) electrons, reducing the net charge experienced by the 2*s* electron.

We can define the average or net charge experienced by an electron as the *effective nuclear charge*. The effective nuclear charge experienced by a particular electron in an atom is the *actual nuclear charge* (Z) minus *the charge shielded by other electrons* (S):

$$Z_{eff} = Z - S$$

Effective nuclear charge (Z_{eff}); Actual nuclear charge (Z); Charge screened by other electrons (S)

For lithium, we estimate that the two core electrons shield the valence electron from the nuclear charge with high efficiency (*S* is nearly 2). The effective nuclear charge experienced by lithium's valence electron is therefore slightly greater than 1+.

Now consider the valence electrons in beryllium (Be), with atomic number 4. Its electron configuration is:

$$\text{Be} \quad 1s^2 2s^2$$

To estimate the effective nuclear charge experienced by the 2*s* electrons in beryllium, we must distinguish between two different types of shielding: (1) the shielding of the outermost electrons by the core electrons, and (2) the shielding of the outermost electrons by *each other*. The key to understanding the trend in atomic radius is the difference between these two types of shielding.

Core electrons efficiently shield electrons in the outermost principal energy level from nuclear charge, but outermost electrons do not efficiently shield one another from nuclear charge.

In other words, the two outermost electrons in beryllium experience the 4+ charge of the nucleus through the shield of the two 1*s* core electrons without shielding each other from that charge very much. We therefore estimate that the shielding (*S*) experienced by any one of the outermost electrons due to the core electrons is nearly 2, but that the shielding due to the other outermost electron is nearly zero. The effective nuclear charge experienced by beryllium's outermost electrons is therefore slightly greater than 2+.

The effective nuclear charge experienced by *beryllium's* outermost electrons is greater than that experienced by *lithium's* outermost electron. Consequently, beryllium's outermost electrons are held more tightly than lithium's, resulting in a smaller atomic radius for beryllium. The effective nuclear charge experienced by an atom's outermost electrons continues to become more positive as we move to the right across the rest of the second row in the periodic table, resulting in successively smaller atomic radii. The same trend is generally observed in all main-group elements.

Summarizing Atomic Radii for Main-Group Elements:

- ▶ As we move down a column in the periodic table, the principal quantum number (n) of the electrons in the outermost principal energy level increases, resulting in larger orbitals and therefore larger atomic radii.
- ▶ As we move to the right across a row in the periodic table, the effective nuclear charge (Z_{eff}) experienced by the electrons in the outermost principal energy level increases, resulting in a stronger attraction between the outermost electrons and the nucleus, and smaller atomic radii.

Slater's Rules

To this point, we have discussed shielding and effective nuclear charge in qualitative terms. To fully calculate the shielding of electrons in atoms is very complex. However, there is a simple way to estimate S, the shielding constant, in the equation $Z_{eff} = Z - S$. In 1930, the physicist John C. Slater published a set of simple rules (known as **Slater's rules**) to do just that. To calculate the shielding constant for a given electron, each other electron in the atom is assigned a shielding contribution depending on its shell and type of orbital, and these contributions are added together to give the overall shielding constant, S. The shielding contributions are shown in the following table.

	Shielding Contribution, f		
Valence Electron	Other Electrons in Valence Shell (with same n)	Core Electrons in Shell $n - 1$	Core Electrons in Shells $< n - 1$ (i.e., $n - 2$, $n - 3$ . . .)
ns or np	0.35	0.85	1.00
nd or nf	0.35	1.00	1.00

Electrons in the same shell (same n) as the valence electron have small shielding contributions because they are, on average, at similar radial distances from the nucleus as the valence electron. (Radial probability distributions were covered in Section 7.6.) The shielding contribution is the proportion of the shielding electron's charge that shields a valence electron from the nuclear charge. For example, a $2p$ electron will be shielded by 0.35 of an electron's charge by every other $2s$ and $2p$ electron. Core electrons—those in lower shells—have higher shielding contributions because they reside closer to the nucleus than valence electrons, better shielding the nuclear charge.

For ns or np valence electrons, the $n-1$ core electrons have shielding contributions of 0.85. All core electrons in shells lower than $n-1$, written as $<n-1$, have shielding contributions of 1.00.

The shielding constant is determined by taking the sum of all shielding contributions:

$$S = N_n f_n + N_{n-1} f_{n-1} + N_{<n-1} f_{<n-1}$$

where each N refers to the number of shielding electrons in given shells, and f refers to the appropriate shielding contribution for the specified type of electron as given in the previous table.

EXAMPLE 8.3 CALCULATING Z_{eff} USING SLATER'S RULES

Estimate the shielding constant, S, and the effective nuclear charge, Z_{eff}, using Slater's rules for valence electrons (i.e., those with highest n) in the following atoms:

(a) N **(b)** Co

SOLUTION

(a) N	
Begin by writing the electron configuration for N.	$1s^2 2s^2 2p^3$
The highest n electrons are $2s, 2p\ (n = 2)$. Write out the shielding amounts for the other $2s$, $2p$ electrons and the $1s$ electrons, which are in the $n-1$ shell. Notice, the electron we are considering is *not* included in the total, as an electron cannot shield itself.	$2s,\ 2p: 4 \times (0.35) = 1.40$ $1s: 2 \times (0.85) = 1.70$ $S = 1.40 + 1.70 = 3.10$
Calculate Z_{eff}, knowing that $Z = 7$.	$Z_{eff} = Z - S = 7 - 3.10 = 3.90$
(b) Co	
Begin by writing the electron configuration for Co, in order of principal quantum number, n. This makes it easier to count the number of electrons with different shielding contributions.	$1s^2 2s^2 2p^6 3s^2 3p^6 3d^7 4s^2$
The highest n electrons are $4s\ (n = 4)$. Write out the shielding amounts for the other $4s$ electron (same n) followed by all $n = 3$ electrons (i.e., $n-1$ shell) and those in lower shells ($n = 2, n = 1$).	$4s: 1 \times (0.35) = 0.35$ $3s, 3p, 3d: 15 \times (0.85) = 12.75$ $1s, 2s, 2p: 10 \times (1.00) = 10.00$ $S = 0.35 + 12.75 + 10.00 = 23.10$
Calculate Z_{eff}, knowing that $Z = 27$.	$Z_{eff} = Z - S = 27 - 23.10 = 3.90$

FOR PRACTICE 8.3

Estimate the shielding constant, S, and the effective nuclear charge, Z_{eff}, using Slater's rules for valence electrons in the following atoms:

(a) F **(b)** Ar **(c)** Rb

The estimated effective nuclear charges of atoms can be used to confirm our understanding of periodic trends in atomic radii. For example, consider the atomic radii of the third-period elements and compare them with estimated Z_{eff} from Slater's rules:

	Na	Mg	Al	Si	P	S	Cl	Ar
Z_{eff}	2.20	2.85	3.50	4.15	4.80	5.45	6.10	6.75
Radius (pm)	186	160	143	118	110	103	99	98

By examining the values in this table, there is a clear inverse relationship between Z_{eff} and atomic radius. As Z_{eff} increases, the valence electrons are pulled closer to the nucleus, reducing the size of the atom.

Atomic Radii of *d*-Block Elements

From Figure 8.7, you can see that as we go down the first two rows of a column within the transition metals, the elements follow the same general trend in atomic radii as the main-group elements (the radii get larger). However, with the exception of the first couple of elements in each transition series, the atomic radii of the transition elements *do not* follow the same trend as the main-group elements as we move to the right across a row (Figure 8.9 ▼). Instead of significantly decreasing in size, *the radii of transition elements stay roughly constant across each row*. Why? The difference is that, across a row of transition elements, the number of electrons in the outermost principal energy level (highest n value) is nearly constant (recall from Section 7.7, for example, that the $4s$ orbital fills before the $3d$). As another proton is added to the nucleus of each successive element, another electron is added as well, but the electron goes into an $n_{\text{highest}} - 1$ orbital. The number of outermost electrons stays constant and they experience a roughly constant effective nuclear charge, keeping the radius approximately constant.

Looking down a group in the *d*-block elements, we see a small but expected increase in size from the first transition metal row to the second, but the size of elements in the third row is about the same as it is for those in the second row. This pattern is also different from that of the main-group elements, especially when we consider that in any given column, the third transition row has 32 more electrons than the second row. The reason that the third row transition elements are not larger is as follows: 14 of the 32 electrons are in a large $4f$ sublevel. These electrons are not very effective at shielding the $5d$ or $6s$ electrons from the nuclear charge. Consequently, the outer electrons are held more tightly by the nucleus, offsetting the typical increase in size between the periods—an effect called the **lanthanoid contraction**.

The lanthanoid contraction is not predicted by simple Slater's rules. This is because the shielding contributions for electrons in different types of orbitals are not truly equal. For example, a $4f$ electron should have a different shielding contribution than a $4d$ electron.

CONCEPTUAL CONNECTION 8.1
Atomic Size

Which element has the larger atomic radius, Fe or W?

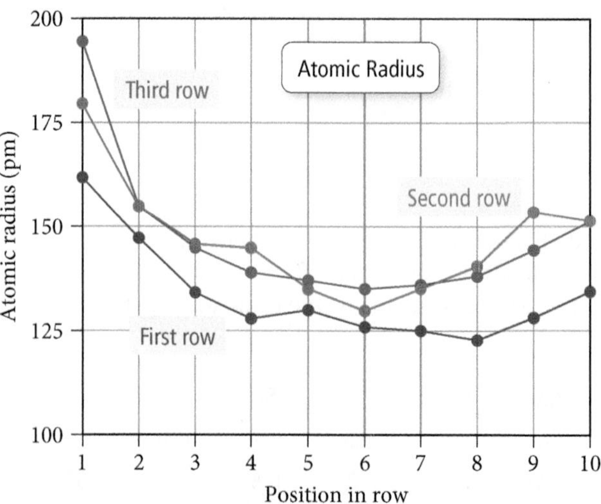

▲ **FIGURE 8.9 Trends in Atomic Radius in Transition Metals** With the exception of a decrease in radius from the first to the second element, there is only a small variation in atomic radius across a row. There is a small and expected increase in radius from the first to the second transition row, but virtually no difference in radius from the second to the third.

EXAMPLE 8.4 **ATOMIC SIZE**

On the basis of periodic trends, choose the larger atom in each pair (if possible). Explain your choices.

(a) N or F **(b)** C or Ge **(c)** N or Al **(d)** Al or Ge

SOLUTION

(a) N or F

N atoms are larger than F atoms because, as you trace the path between N and F on the periodic table, you move to the right within the same period. As you move to the right across a period, the effective nuclear charge experienced by the outermost electrons increases, resulting in a smaller radius.

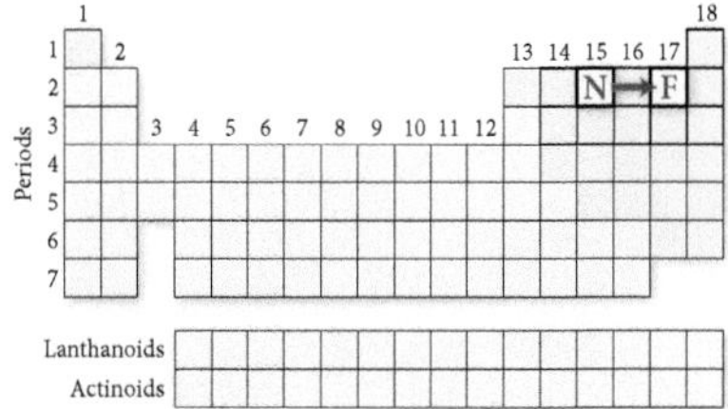

(b) C or Ge

Ge atoms are larger than C atoms because, as you trace the path between C and Ge on the periodic table, you move down a column. Atomic size increases as you move down a column because the outermost electrons occupy orbitals with a higher principal quantum number that are therefore larger, resulting in a larger atom.

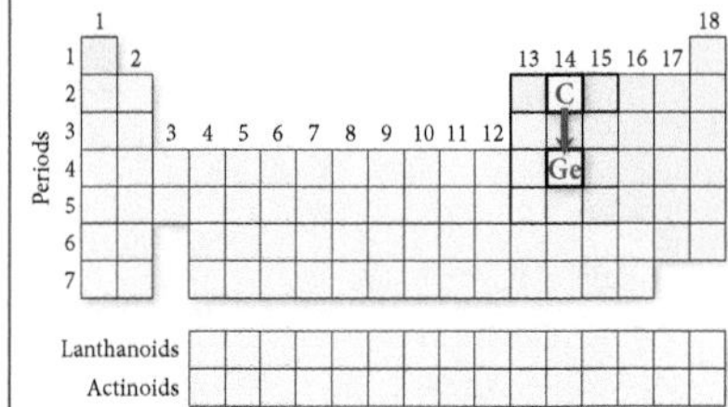

(c) N or Al

Al atoms are larger than N atoms because, as you trace the path between N and Al on the periodic table, you move down a column (atomic size increases) and then to the left across a period (atomic size increases). These effects add together for an overall increase.

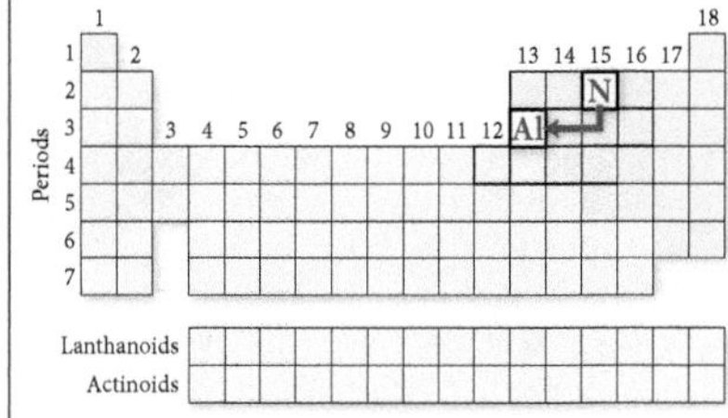

(d) Al or Ge

Based on periodic trends alone, you cannot tell which atom is larger, because as you trace the path between Al and Ge, you go to the right across a period (atomic size decreases) and then down a column (atomic size increases). These effects tend to oppose each other, and it is not easy to tell which will predominate.

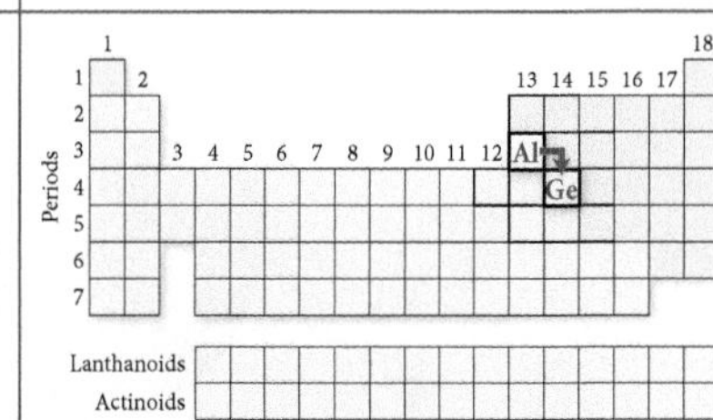

FOR PRACTICE 8.4

On the basis of periodic trends, choose the larger atom in each pair (if possible):

(a) Sn or I **(b)** Ge or Po **(c)** Cr or W **(d)** F or Se

FOR MORE PRACTICE 8.4

Arrange the elements in order of decreasing radius: S, Ca, F, Rb, Si.

8.6 Ionic Radii

What happens to the radius of an atom when it becomes a cation? An anion? Consider, for example, the difference between the Na atom and the Na^+ ion. Their electron configurations are as follows:

$$\text{Na} \quad [\text{Ne}]\,3s^1$$
$$\text{Na}^+ \quad [\text{Ne}]$$

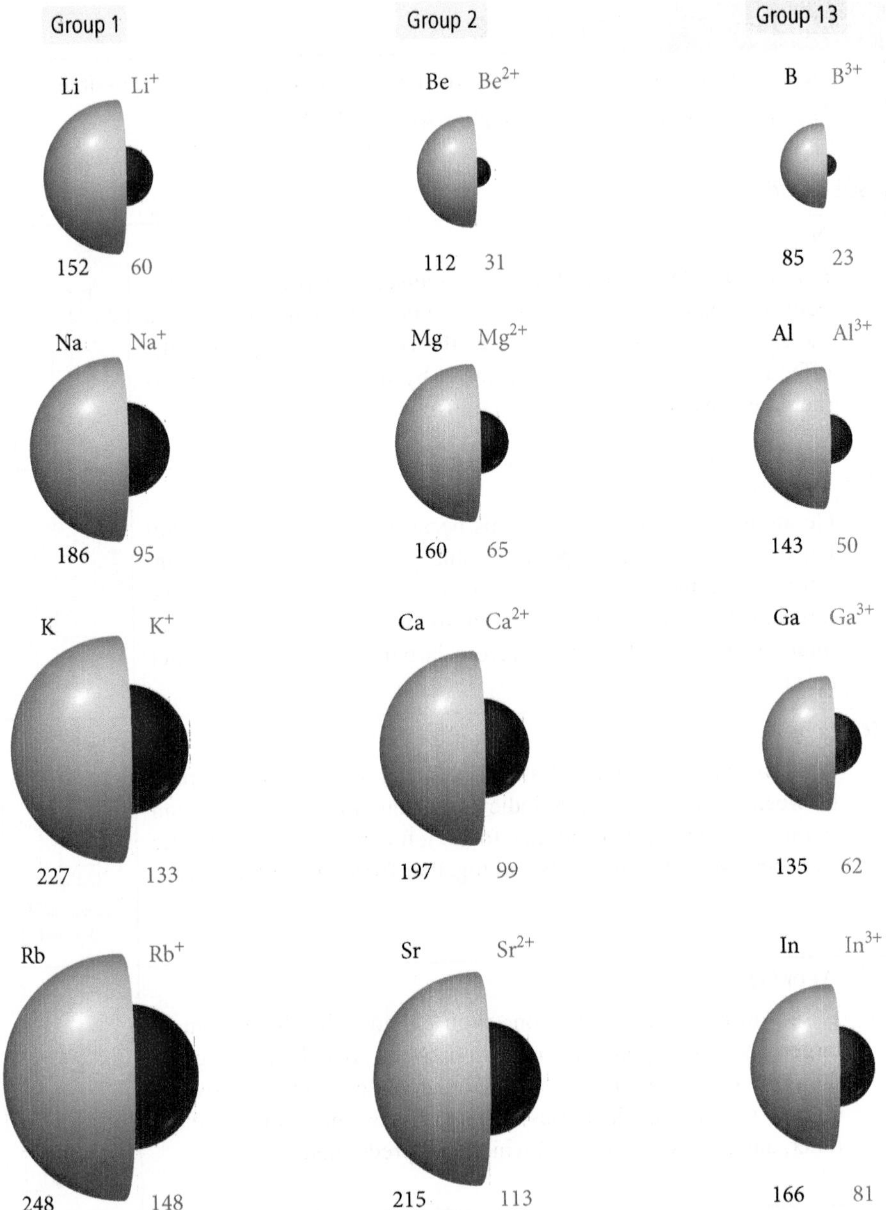

▲ **FIGURE 8.10 Sizes of Atoms and Their Cations** Atomic and ionic radii (pm) for the first three columns of main-group elements.

The sodium atom has an outer 3*s* electron and a neon core. Since the 3*s* electron is the outermost electron, and since it is shielded from the nuclear charge by the core electrons, it contributes greatly to the size of the sodium atom. The sodium cation, having lost the outermost 3*s* electron, has only the neon core and carries a charge of 1+. Without the 3*s* electron, the sodium cation (ionic radius = 95 pm) becomes much smaller than the sodium atom (covalent radius = 186 pm). The trend is the same with all cations and their atoms, as shown in Figure 8.10 ▲.

Cations are much smaller than their corresponding atoms.

What about anions? Consider, for example, the difference between Cl and Cl^-. Their electron configurations are as follows:

$$\text{Cl} \quad [\text{Ne}]\, 3s^2 3p^5$$

$$\text{Cl}^- \quad [\text{Ne}]\, 3s^2 3p^6$$

The chlorine anion has one additional outermost electron, but no additional proton to increase the nuclear charge. The extra electron increases the repulsions among the outermost electrons, resulting in a chloride anion that is larger than the chlorine atom. The trend is the same with all anions and their atoms, as shown in Figure 8.11 ▶.

Anions are much larger than their corresponding atoms.

We can observe an interesting trend in ionic size by examining the radii of an *isoelectronic* series of ions—ions with the same number of electrons. Consider the following ions and their radii:

S^{2-} (184 pm)	Cl^- (181 pm)	K^+ (133 pm)	Ca^{2+} (99 pm)
18 electrons	18 electrons	18 electrons	18 electrons
16 protons	17 protons	19 protons	20 protons

All of these ions have 18 electrons in exactly the same orbitals, but the radius of each ion gets successively smaller. Why? The reason is the progressively greater number of protons. The S^{2-} ion has 16 protons, and therefore a charge of 16+ pulling on 18 electrons. The Ca^{2+} ion, however, has 20 protons, and therefore a charge of 20+ pulling on the same 18 electrons. The result is a much smaller radius. For a given number of electrons, a greater nuclear charge results in a smaller atom or ion.

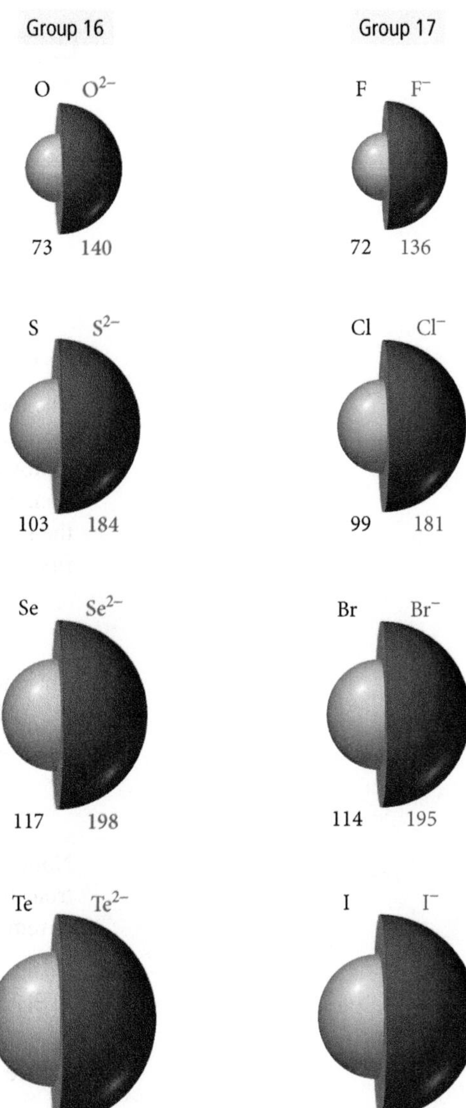

▶ **FIGURE 8.11 Sizes of Atoms and Their Anions** Atomic and ionic radii for groups 16 and 17 in the periodic table.

EXAMPLE 8.5 **ION SIZE**

Choose the larger atom or ion from each pair:

(a) S or S^{2-} **(b)** Ca or Ca^{2+} **(c)** Br^- or Kr

SOLUTION

(a) The S^{2-} ion is larger than the S atom because anions are larger than the atoms from which they are formed.

(b) The Ca atom is larger than the Ca^{2+} ion because cations are smaller than the atoms from which they are formed.

(c) The Br^- ion is larger than the Kr atom because, although they are isoelectronic, Br^- has one fewer proton than Kr, resulting in a lesser pull on the electrons and therefore a larger radius.

FOR PRACTICE 8.5

Choose the larger atom or ion from each pair:

(a) K or K^+ **(b)** F or F^- **(c)** Ca^{2+} or Cl^-

FOR MORE PRACTICE 8.5

Arrange the following in order of decreasing radius: Ca^{2+}, Ar, Cl^-.

CONCEPTUAL CONNECTION 8.2

Ions, Isotopes, and Atomic Size

In the previous sections, we have seen how the number of electrons and the number of protons affects the size of an atom or ion. However, we have not considered how the number of neutrons affects the size of an atom. Why not? Would you expect isotopes—for example, C-12 and C-13—to have different atomic radii?

8.7 Ionization Energy

The **ionization energy (IE)** of an atom or ion is the energy required to remove an electron from the atom or ion in the gaseous state. Ionization energy is always positive because removing an electron always takes energy. (The process is similar to an endothermic reaction, which absorbs heat and therefore has a positive ΔH.) The energy required to remove the first electron is called the *first ionization energy* (IE_1). For example, we represent the first ionization of sodium with the following equation:

$$Na(g) \longrightarrow Na^+(g) + 1\,e^- \qquad IE_1 = 496 \text{ kJ mol}^{-1}$$

The energy required to remove the second electron is called the *second ionization energy* (IE_2), the energy required to remove the third electron is called the *third ionization energy* (IE_3), and so on. We represent the second ionization energy of sodium as follows:

$$Na^+(g) \longrightarrow Na^{2+}(g) + 1\,e^- \qquad IE_2 = 4560 \text{ kJ mol}^{-1}$$

Notice that the second ionization energy is not the energy required to remove *two* electrons from sodium (that quantity is the sum of IE_1 and IE_2), but rather the energy required to remove one electron from Na^+. We look at trends in IE_1 and IE_2 separately.

Trends in First Ionization Energy

The first ionization energies of the elements through Xe are shown in Figure 8.12 ▼. Notice the periodic trend in ionization energy, peaking at each noble gas and bottoming

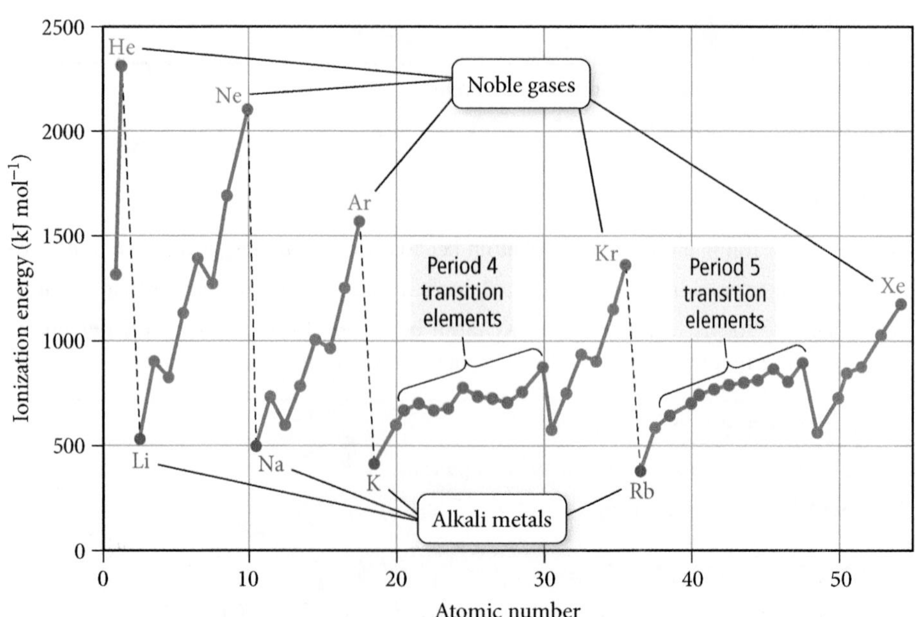

▶ **FIGURE 8.12 First Ionization Energy Versus Atomic Number for the Elements Through Xenon** Ionization energies start at a minimum with each alkali metal and rises to a peak with each noble gas.

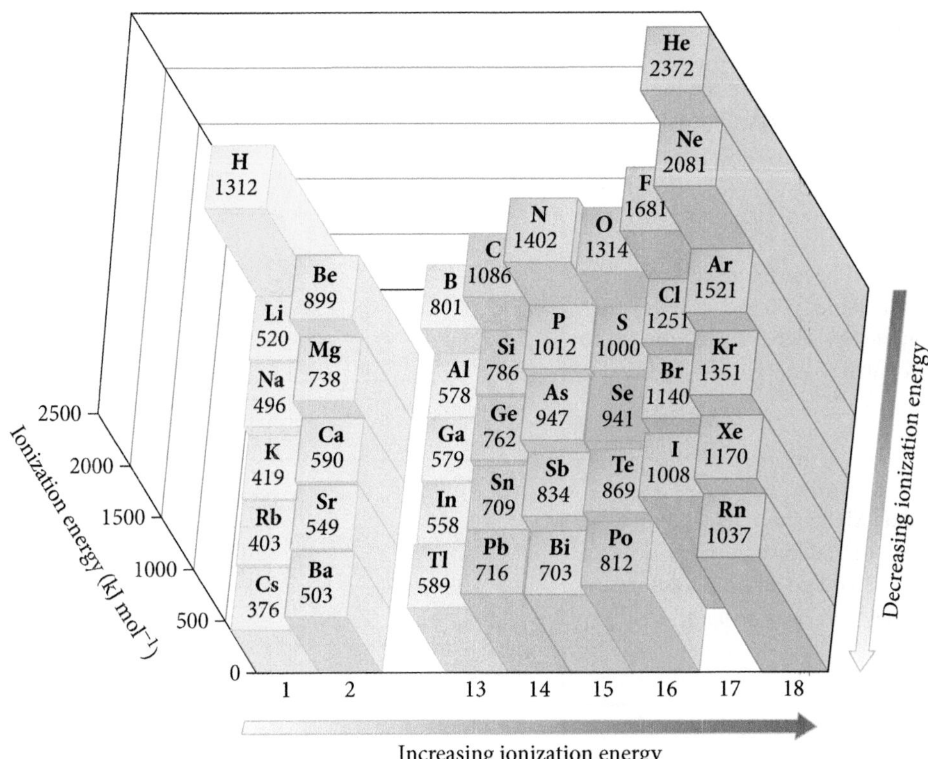

▲ **FIGURE 8.13 Trends in First Ionization Energy** Ionization energy increases as we move to the right across a period and decreases as we move down a column in the periodic table.

at each alkali metal. Based on what we have learned about electron configurations and effective nuclear charge, how can we account for the observed trend? As we have seen, the principal quantum number, n, increases as we move down a column. Within a given sublevel, orbitals with higher principal quantum numbers are larger than orbitals with smaller principal quantum numbers. Consequently, electrons in the outermost principal level are farther away from the positively charged nucleus—and are therefore held less tightly—as we move down a column. This results in a lower ionization energy as we move down a column, as shown in Figure 8.13 ▲.

What about the trend as we move to the right across a row? For example, would it take more energy to remove an electron from Na or from Cl, two elements on either end of the third row in the periodic table? We know that Na has an outer electron configuration of $3s^1$ and Cl has an outer electron configuration of $3s^2 3p^5$. As discussed previously, the outermost electrons in chlorine experience a higher effective nuclear charge than the outermost electrons in sodium (which is why chlorine has a smaller atomic radius than sodium). Consequently, we would expect chlorine to have a higher ionization energy than sodium, which is indeed the case. We can make a similar argument for the other main-group elements: ionization energy generally increases as we move to the right across a row in the periodic table, as shown in Figure 8.13.

Summarizing Ionization Energy for Main-Group Elements:

- Ionization energy generally *decreases* as we move down a column (or family) in the periodic table because electrons in the outermost principal level are increasingly farther away from the positively charged nucleus and are therefore held less tightly.
- Ionization energy generally *increases* as we move to the right across a period (or row) in the periodic table because electrons in the outermost principal energy level generally experience a greater effective nuclear charge (Z_{eff}).

EXAMPLE 8.6 IONIZATION ENERGY

On the basis of periodic trends, choose the element with the higher first ionization energy from each pair (if possible):

(a) Al or S **(b)** As or Sb **(c)** N or Si **(d)** O or Cl

SOLUTION

(a) Al or S

S has a higher ionization energy than Al because, as you trace the path between Al and S on the periodic table, you move to the right within the same period. Ionization energy increases as you go to the right due to increasing effective nuclear charge.

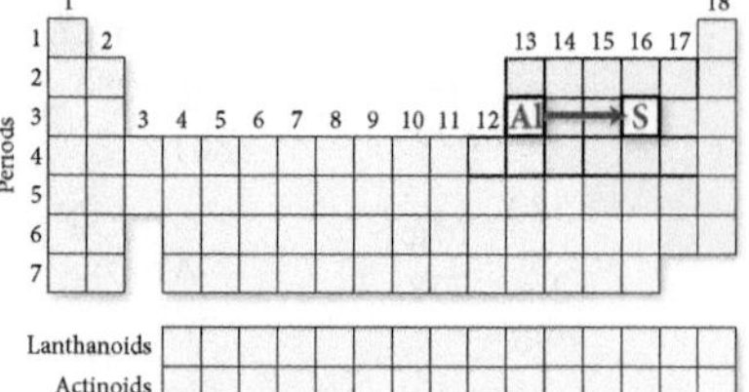

(b) As or Sb

As has a higher ionization energy than Sb because, as you trace the path between As and Sb on the periodic table, you move down a column. Ionization energy decreases as you go down a column as a result of the increasing size of orbitals with increasing *n*.

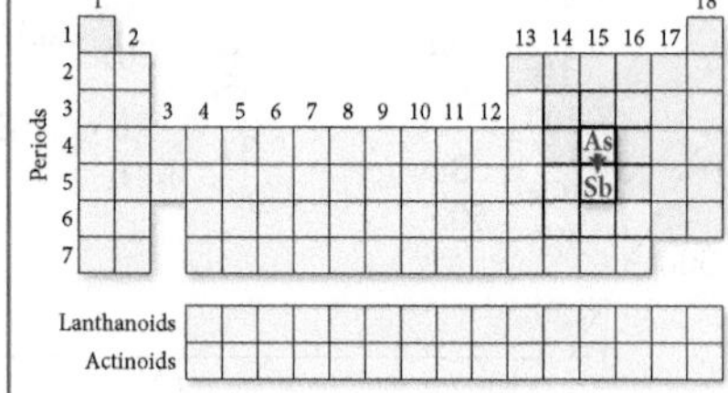

(c) N or Si

N has a higher ionization energy than Si because, as you trace the path between N and Si on the periodic table, you move down a column (ionization energy decreases) and then to the left across a period (ionization energy decreases). These effects sum together for an overall decrease.

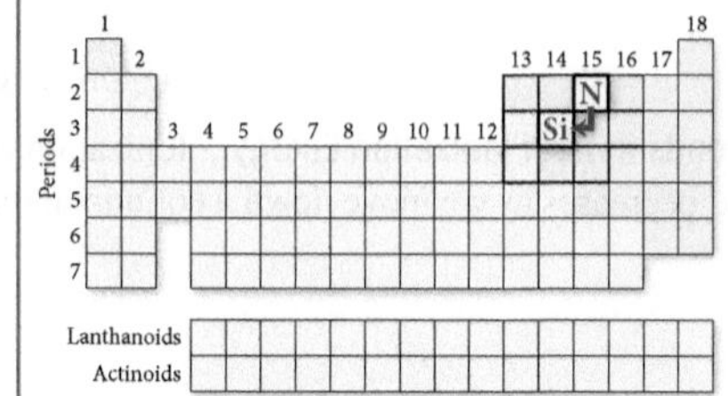

(d) O or Cl

Based on periodic trends alone, it is impossible to tell which has a higher ionization energy because, as you trace the path between O and Cl, you go to the right across a period (ionization energy increases) and then down a column (ionization energy decreases). These effects tend to oppose each other, and it is not obvious which will dominate.

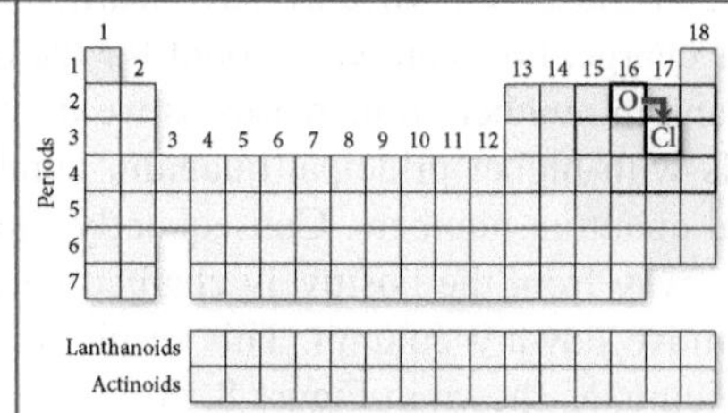

FOR PRACTICE 8.6

On the basis of periodic trends, choose the element with the higher first ionization energy from each pair (if possible):

(a) Sn or I **(b)** Ca or Sr **(c)** C or P **(d)** F or S

FOR MORE PRACTICE 8.6

Arrange the following elements in order of decreasing first ionization energy: S, Ca, F, Rb, Si.

Exceptions to Trends in First Ionization Energy

If you carefully examine Figure 8.13, you can see some exceptions to the trends in first ionization energies. For example, boron has a smaller ionization energy than beryllium, even though it lies to the right of beryllium in the same row. This exception is caused by the change in going from the *s* block to the *p* block. Recall from Section 7.7 that the 2*p* orbital penetrates into the nuclear region *less than* the 2*s* orbital. Consequently, the 1*s* electrons shield the electron in the 2*p* orbital from nuclear charge more than they shield the electrons in the 2*s* orbital. The result, as we saw in Section 7.7, is that the 2*p* orbitals are higher in energy, and therefore the electron is easier to remove (it has a lower ionization energy). Similar exceptions occur for aluminum and gallium, both directly below boron in group 13.

Another exception occurs between nitrogen and oxygen: although oxygen is to the right of nitrogen in the same row, it has a lower ionization energy. This exception is caused by the repulsion between electrons when they must occupy the same orbital. Examine the electron configurations and orbital diagrams of nitrogen and oxygen:

		1s	2s	2p		
N	$1s^2 2s^2 2p^3$	↿⇂	↿⇂	↿	↿	↿
O	$1s^2 2s^2 2p^4$	↿⇂	↿⇂	↿⇂	↿	↿

Nitrogen has three electrons in three p orbitals, while oxygen has four. In nitrogen, the $2p$ orbitals are half-filled and there are no repulsions from electrons in the same orbital. Oxygen's fourth electron must pair with another electron, making it easier to remove because of electronic repulsion. Exceptions for similar reasons occur for S and Se, directly below oxygen in group 16.

In Figure 8.12, you may also have noticed that there is always a small decrease in ionization energy on going from the d block to the p block. For example, the ionization energy of cadmium is 868 kJ mol^{-1}, and for indium it is 558 kJ mol^{-1}. This is because the $5p$ electron in indium is better shielded from the nucleus than the $5s$ electrons in cadmium.

Ionization Energies of Transition Metals

First ionization energy values of transition elements follow the expected main-group periodic trend and slowly increase across a row (Figure 8.14 ▼), but the increase is smaller than for main-group elements. As we move down a group, we see that the third transition row generally has a higher ionization energy than do the first two rows, a trend counter to that observed in the main-group elements. In the transition elements, the charge of the nucleus increases substantially from one row to the next, but there is only a small increase in atomic size between the first and second rows, and no increase in size between the second and third rows. The outer electrons are therefore held more tightly in the third transition row than in the first two rows.

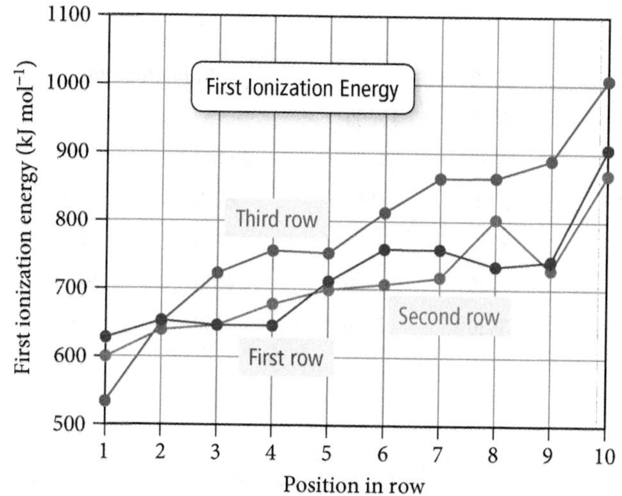

◀ **FIGURE 8.14 Trends in First Ionization Energy in Transition Metals** First ionization energy generally increases across a row, following the main-group trend. However, in contrast to the main-group trend, the third transition row has a greater ionization energy than the first and second rows.

Trends in Second and Successive Ionization Energies

Notice the trends in the first, second, and third ionization energies of sodium (group 1) and magnesium (group 2), as shown in the bar graph on the next page.

For sodium, there is a huge jump between the first and second ionization energies. For magnesium, the ionization energy roughly doubles from the first to the second, but then a huge jump occurs between the second and third ionization energies. What is the reason for these jumps?

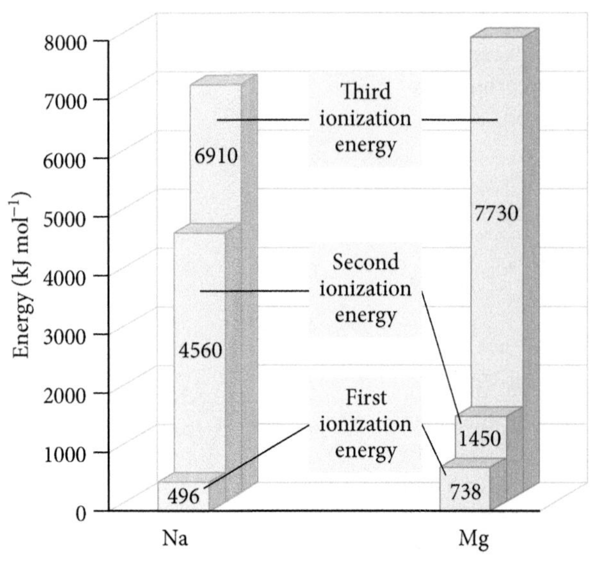

We can understand these trends by examining the electron configurations of sodium and magnesium:

Na [Ne] $3s^1$

Mg [Ne] $3s^2$

The first ionization of sodium involves removing the valence electron in the 3*s* orbital. Recall that these valence electrons are held more loosely than the core electrons, and that the resulting ion has a noble gas configuration, which is particularly stable. Consequently, the first ionization energy is fairly low. The second ionization of sodium, however, involves removing a core electron from an ion with a noble gas configuration. This requires a tremendous amount of energy, making the value of IE_2 very high.

As with sodium, the first ionization of magnesium involves removing a valence electron in the 3*s* orbital. This requires a bit more energy than the corresponding ionization of sodium because of the trends in Z_{eff} that we discussed earlier (Z_{eff} increases as we move to the right across a row). The second ionization of magnesium also involves removing an outer electron in the 3*s* orbital, but this time from an ion with a 1+ charge. This requires roughly twice the energy as is required when removing the electron from the neutral atom. The third ionization of magnesium is analogous to the second ionization of sodium—it requires removing a core electron from an ion with a noble gas configuration. This requires a tremendous amount of energy, making the value of IE_3 very high.

As shown in Table 8.1, similar trends exist for the successive ionization energies of many elements. The ionization energy increases fairly uniformly with each successive removal of an outermost electron, but then takes a large jump with the removal of the first core electron.

TABLE 8.1 Successive Values of Ionization Energies for the Elements Sodium Through Argon (kJ mol^{-1})

Element	IE_1	IE_2	IE_3	IE_4	IE_5	IE_6	IE_7
Na	496	4560					
Mg	738	1450	7730		Core electrons		
Al	578	1820	2750	11 600			
Si	786	1580	3230	4360	16 100		
P	1012	1900	2910	4960	6270	22 200	
S	1000	2250	3360	4560	7010	8500	27 100
Cl	1251	2300	3820	5160	6540	9460	11 000
Ar	1521	2670	3930	5770	7240	8780	12 000

CONCEPTUAL CONNECTION 8.3

Ionization Energies and Chemical Bonding

Based on what you just learned about ionization energies, explain why valence electrons are more important than core electrons in determining the reactivity and bonding in atoms.

8.8 Electron Affinities and Metallic Character

Two other properties that exhibit periodic trends are electron affinity and metallic character. Electron affinity is a measure of how easily an atom will accept an additional electron and is crucial to chemical bonding because bonding involves the transfer or sharing of electrons. Metallic character is important because of the high proportion of metals in the periodic table and the large role they play in our lives. Of the roughly 110 elements, 87 are metals. We examine each of these periodic properties individually.

Electron Affinity

The **electron affinity (EA)** of an atom is the energy *released* when an electron is added to the neutral atom in the gas phase. The electron affinity is usually a positive quantity because the coulombic attraction between the nucleus of an atom and the incoming electron usually results in the release of energy as the electron is gained. In some cases, the anion that forms in the gas phase is not stable, and EA is simply defined as being negative, <0. For example, we can represent the electron affinity of chlorine with the following equation:

$$Cl(g) + 1\,e^- \longrightarrow Cl^-(g)\ \ EA = 349\ kJ\ mol^{-1}$$

Figure 8.15 ▶ contains the electron affinities for a number of main-group elements. As you can see from this figure, the trends in electron affinity are not as regular as trends in other properties we have examined. For instance, we might expect electron affinities to become lower as we move down a column because the electron is entering orbitals with successively higher principal quantum numbers, and will therefore be farther from the nucleus. This trend applies to the group 1 metals but does not hold for the other columns in the periodic table.

1	2	13	14	15	16	17	18
H 73							**He** <0
Li 60	**Be** <0	**B** 27	**C** 122	**N** <0	**O** 141	**F** 328	**Ne** <0
Na 53	**Mg** <0	**Al** 43	**Si** 134	**P** 72	**S** 200	**Cl** 349	**Ar** <0
K 48	**Ca** 2	**Ga** 30	**Ge** 119	**As** 78	**Se** 195	**Br** 325	**Kr** <0
Rb 47	**Sr** 5	**In** 30	**Sn** 107	**Sb** 103	**Te** 190	**I** 295	**Xe** <0

▲ **FIGURE 8.15 Electron Affinities ($kJ\ mol^{-1}$) of Selected Main-Group Elements**

There is a more regular trend in electron affinity as we move to the right across a row, however. Based on the periodic properties we have learned so far, would you expect more energy to be released when an electron is gained by Na or Cl? We know that Na has an outer electron configuration of $3s^1$ and Cl has an outer electron configuration of $3s^2 3p^5$. Since the outermost electrons in chlorine experience a higher Z_{eff} than the outermost electrons in sodium, we would expect chlorine to have a larger electron affinity. This is, in fact, the case. For main-group elements, electron affinity generally becomes more positive as we move to the right across a row in the periodic table. The halogens (group 17) therefore have the largest electron affinities. But exceptions do occur. For example, notice that nitrogen and the other group 15 elements do not follow the general trend. These elements have $ns^2 np^3$ outer electron configurations. When an electron is added to this configuration, it must pair with another electron in an already occupied *p* orbital. The repulsion between two electrons occupying the same orbital causes the electron affinity to be smaller than for elements in the previous column.

Summarizing Electron Affinity for Main-Group Elements:

- ▶ Most groups (columns) of the periodic table do not exhibit any definite trend in electron affinity. Among the group 1 metals, however, electron affinity decreases as we move down the column.
- ▶ Electron affinity generally increases as we move to the right across a period (row) in the periodic table.

Metallic Character

As we learned in Chapter 2, metals are good conductors of heat and electricity, they can be pounded into flat sheets (malleability), they can be drawn into wires (ductility), they are often shiny, and they tend to lose electrons in chemical reactions. Nonmetals, in contrast, have more varied physical properties: some are solids at room temperature, others are gases, but in general they are typically poor conductors of heat and electricity, and they all tend to gain electrons in chemical reactions. As we move to the right across a period in the periodic table, ionization energy increases, and electron affinity becomes more positive; therefore, elements on the left side of the periodic table are more likely to lose electrons than elements on the right side of the periodic table (which are more likely

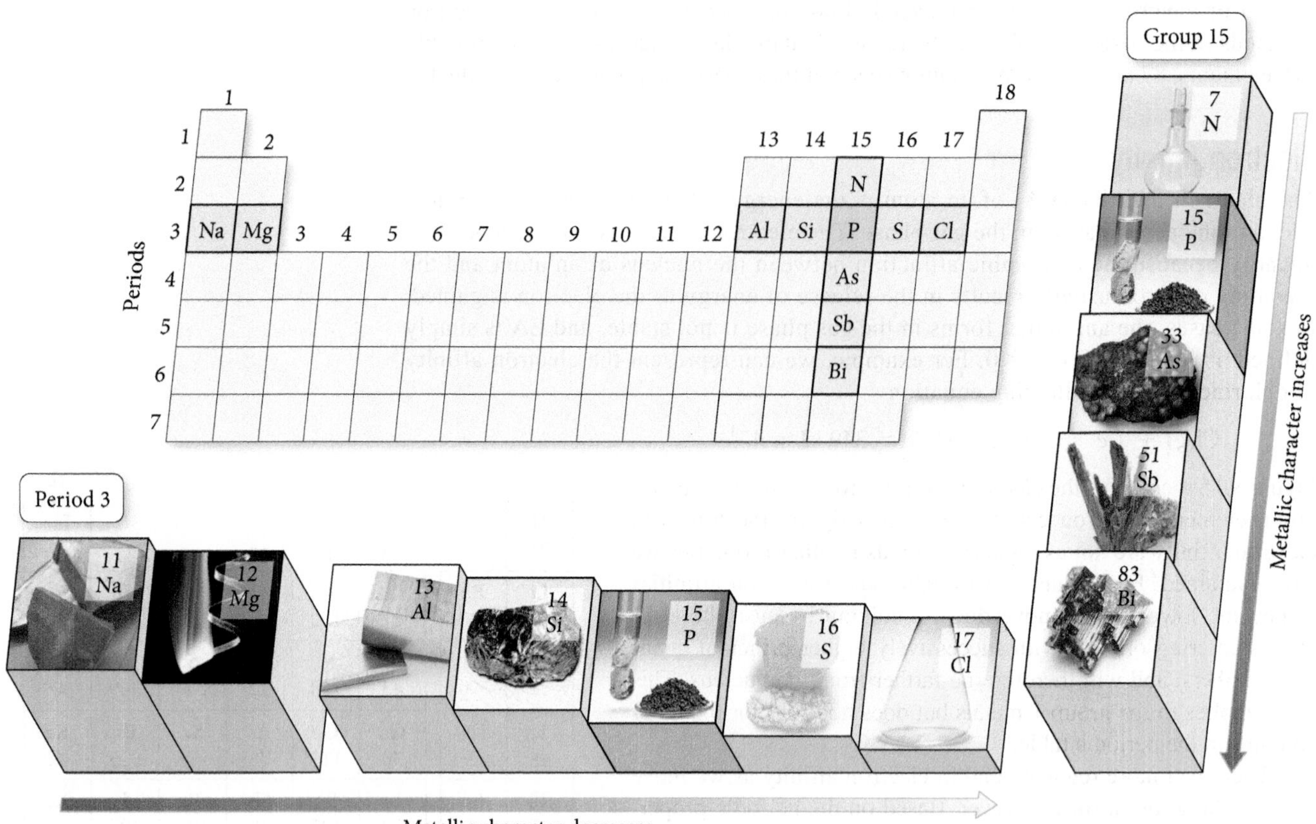

▲ **FIGURE 8.16 Trends in Metallic Character** As we move down group 15 in the periodic table, metallic character increases. As we move across period 3, metallic character decreases.

to gain them). The other properties associated with metals follow the same general trend (even though we do not quantify them here). Consequently:

> **As we move to the right across a period (or row) in the periodic table, metallic character decreases.**

As we move down a column in the periodic table, ionization energy decreases, making electrons more likely to be lost in chemical reactions. Consequently:

> **As we move down a column (or family) in the periodic table, metallic character increases.**

These trends, based on the quantum-mechanical model, explain the distribution of metals and nonmetals in the periodic table that we learned about in Chapter 2. Metals are found on the left side and toward the centre and nonmetals on the upper-right side. The change in chemical behaviour from metallic to nonmetallic can be seen most clearly as you proceed to the right across period 3, or down along group 15, as can be seen in Figure 8.16 ▲.

8.9 Some Examples of Periodic Chemical Behaviour: The Alkali Metals, Alkaline Earth Metals, Halogens, and Noble Gases

In this section, we explore some of the properties and chemical reactions of four families in the periodic table: the alkali metals, the alkaline earth metals, the halogens, and the noble gases. These families exemplify the connection between chemical behaviour and electron configuration. The alkali metals (group 1) have ns^1 outer electron configurations. The single valence electron that keeps these metals from having noble gas configurations is easily removed (the metals have low ionization energies), making these elements the most active metals in the periodic table. The alkaline earth metals (group 2) have ns^2 outer electron configurations. More energy is required to remove both valence electrons and achieve a noble gas configuration. Thus, alkaline earth metals are generally less reactive than alkali metals. The halogens (group 17) have ns^2np^5 outer electron configurations. The one electron needed to attain noble gas configurations is easily acquired (the halogens have highly positive electron affinities), making these elements among the most active nonmetals in the periodic table. The noble gases (group 18) have electron configurations with full outer principal quantum levels (ns^2np^6), and so are the most chemically inert family in the periodic table. We will examine the properties of each of these groups separately. (Even though hydrogen is often listed in group 1, it behaves like a nonmetal because of its high ionization energy: 1312 kJ mol^{-1}. We therefore do not include hydrogen in our discussion of the group 1 metals.)

The Alkali Metals (Group 1)

Table 8.2 contains some selected properties of the alkali metals. Notice that, in general, the properties of the alkali metals vary fairly regularly as we proceed down the column. As expected from periodic trends, the atomic radius increases steadily, while the first ionization energy decreases steadily.

With the exception of potassium, density increases as we move down the column. This is a general trend that occurs in other columns within the periodic table. As we move down a column, the increase in mass (due to the additional protons and neutrons) outpaces the increase in volume caused by the larger atomic radius. The result is successively greater densities. The melting points of the alkali metals as a group are anomalously low for metals, and they steadily decrease as we move down the column. (This is not a general trend for the rest of the periodic table, which shows more irregular patterns in melting points.)

Because of their generally low ionization energies, the alkali metals are excellent reducing agents—they are readily oxidized, losing electrons to other substances. Consequently, the alkali metals exist naturally in their oxidized state, either in compounds or as dissolved ions in seawater. Since ionization energy *decreases* as we go down the column, the relative reactivities of the alkali metals tend to *increase* as we move down the column. In other words, the lower the ionization energy of an alkali metal, the greater tendency it will have to lose its electron and the more reactive it will be.

The reactions of the alkali metals with nonmetals are vigorous. For example, the alkali metals (M) react with halogens (X) according to the following reaction:

$$2\,M + X_2 \longrightarrow 2\,MX$$

The reaction of sodium and chlorine to form sodium chloride is typical:

$$2\,Na(s) + Cl_2(g) \longrightarrow 2\,NaCl(s)$$

This reaction emits heat and sparks as it occurs (Figure 8.17 ▶). Each successive alkali metal reacts even more vigorously with chlorine. The alkali metals also react with water to form the dissolved alkali metal ion, the hydroxide ion, and hydrogen gas:

$$2\,M(s) + 2\,H_2O(l) \longrightarrow 2\,M^+(aq) + 2\,OH^-(aq) + H_2(g)$$

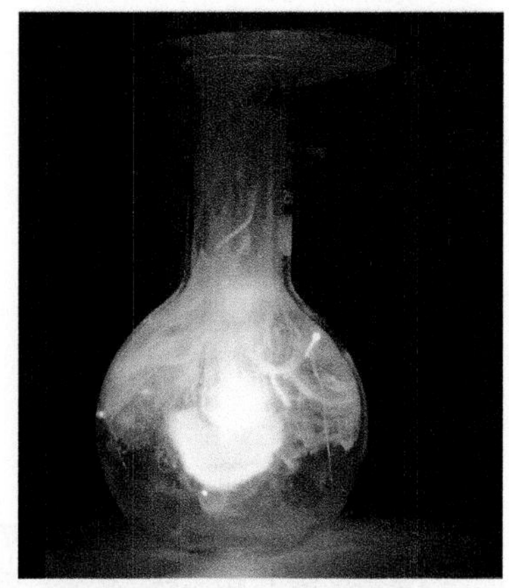

▲ **FIGURE 8.17 Reaction of Sodium and Chlorine to Form Sodium Chloride**

TABLE 8.2 Properties of the Alkali Metals*

Element	Electron Configuration	Atomic Radius (pm)	IE_1 (kJ mol^{-1})	Density at 25 °C (g cm^{-3})	Melting Point (°C)
Li	[He] $2s^1$	152	520	0.535	181
Na	[Ne] $3s^1$	186	496	0.968	102
K	[Ar] $4s^1$	227	419	0.856	98
Rb	[Kr] $5s^1$	248	403	1.532	39
Cs	[Xe] $6s^1$	265	376	1.879	29

*Francium is omitted because it has no stable isotopes.

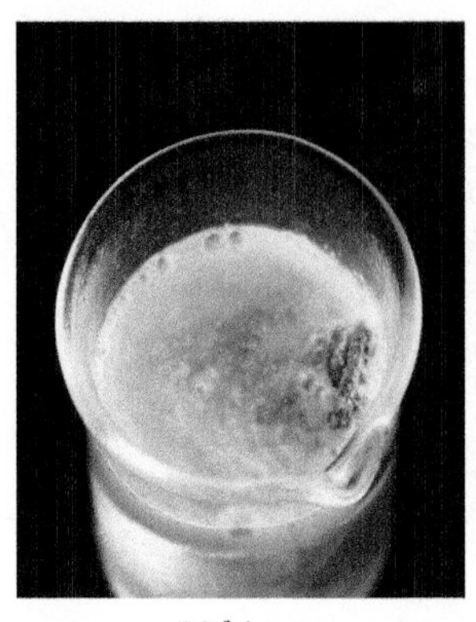

Lithium Sodium Potassium

▲ **FIGURE 8.18 Reactions of the Alkali Metals with Water**

The reaction is highly exothermic and can be explosive because the heat from the reaction can ignite the hydrogen gas (Figure 8.18 ▲).* As we see above, the alkali metal loses an electron during the course of this reaction with water. As we go down the group of alkali metals, the valence electron is less strongly held to the atom because it is in a larger *s* orbital. The easier it is to lose an electron, the more vigorous the reaction is with water, as seen in Figure 8.18.

The Alkaline Earth Metals (Group 2)

Table 8.3 lists selected physical properties of the alkaline earth metals. As with the alkali metals, atomic radius increases down the group, and ionization energy decreases down the group. Densities generally increase down the group, with anomalous densities for Mg and Ca. Melting points are much higher for the group 2 elements than corresponding group 1 elements (Table 8.2).

Alkaline earth metals exhibit similar periodic chemical behaviour to the alkali metals. For example, alkaline earth metals react with halogens:

$$Mg(s) + Cl_2(g) \longrightarrow MgCl_2(s)$$

However, group 2 elements tend to react less violently than the group 1 elements. This is because in group 2 elements, two electrons must be lost in order to obtain a noble gas electron configuration, and the energies associated with losing first and second electrons are very high compared to the loss of just one electron in group 1 elements (see Table 8.1). For example, the reactions of group 2 elements with water are much less violent than for group 1 metals. Beryllium does not react with water or steam even when it is heated until

TABLE 8.3 Properties of the Alkaline Earth Metals*

Element	Electron Configuration	Atomic Radius (pm)	IE_1 (kJ mol^{-1})	IE_2 (kJ mol^{-1})	Density at 25 °C (g cm^{-3})	Melting Point (°C)
Be	[He] $2s^2$	112	899	1755	1.85	1287
Mg	[Ne] $3s^2$	160	738	1450	1.74	650
Ca	[Ar] $4s^2$	197	590	1144	1.54	842
Sr	[Kr] $5s^2$	215	549	1063	2.64	777
Ba	[Xe] $6s^2$	222	503	964	3.62	727

*Radium is omitted because it is radioactive.

*The rate of the alkali metal reaction with water, and therefore its vigour, is enhanced by the successively lower melting points of the alkali metals as we move down the column. The low melting points of the heavier metals allow the emitted heat to actually melt the metal, increasing the reaction rate.

it is glowing red. Magnesium reacts with water only when it is hot. Calcium readily reacts with water to produce hydrogen gas:

$$Ca(s) + 2\,H_2O(l) \longrightarrow Ca^{2+}(aq) + 2\,OH^-(aq) + H_2(g)$$

However, this reaction is much less violent than the reaction of potassium with water (Figure 8.18), even though K and Ca are neighbouring elements.

The Halogens (Group 17)

Table 8.4 lists selected properties of the first four halogens. Notice that the properties of the halogens, like those of the alkali metals, vary fairly regularly as you proceed down the column. As expected from periodic trends, the atomic radius and the density increase for each successive halogen. You can see from the melting and boiling points that fluorine and chlorine are both gases at room temperature, bromine is a liquid, and iodine is a solid.

All of the halogens are powerful oxidizing agents—they are readily reduced, gaining electrons from other substances in their reactions. Fluorine is the most powerful oxidizing agent of the group—reacting with almost everything, including the heavier noble gases—and iodine is the least. The halogens all react with metals to form *metal halides* according to the following equation:

$$2\,M + n\,X_2 \longrightarrow 2\,MX_n$$

where M is the metal, X is the halogen, and MX_n is the metal halide. For example, chlorine reacts with iron according to the following equation:

$$2\,Fe(s) + 3\,Cl_2(g) \longrightarrow 2\,FeCl_3(s)$$

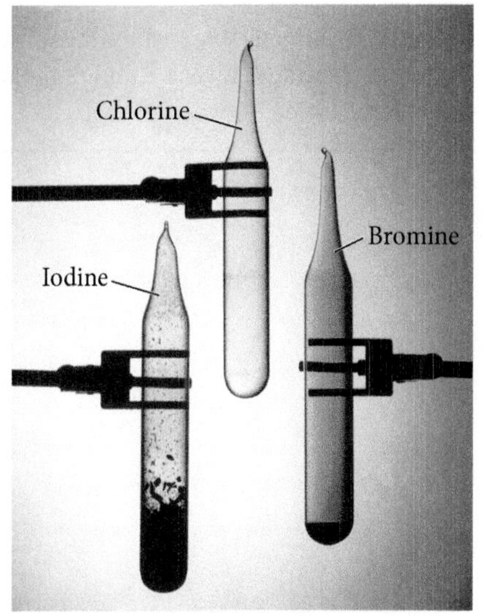

Since metals tend to lose electrons and the halogens tend to gain them, the metal halides—like all compounds that form between metals and nonmetals—contain ionic bonds.

The halogens also react with hydrogen to form *hydrogen halides* according to the following equation:

$$H_2(g) + X_2 \longrightarrow 2\,HX(g)$$

The hydrogen halides—like all compounds that form between two nonmetals—contain covalent bonds. As we saw in Chapter 3, all of the hydrogen halides form acidic solutions when combined with water.

The halogens also react with each other to form *interhalogen compounds*. For example, bromine reacts with fluorine according to the following equation:

$$Br_2(l) + F_2(g) \longrightarrow 2\,BrF(g)$$

Again, like all compounds that form between two nonmetals, the interhalogen compounds contain covalent bonds.

TABLE 8.4 Properties of the Halogens*

Element	Electron Configuration	Atomic Radius (pm)	EA (kJ mol^{-1})	Melting Point (°C)	Boiling Point (°C)	Density of Liquid (g cm^{-3})
F	[He] $2s^2 2p^5$	72	328	−219	−188	1.51
Cl	[Ne] $3s^2 3p^5$	99	349	−101	−34	2.03
Br	[Ar] $4s^2 3d^{10} 4p^5$	114	325	−7	59	3.19
I	[Kr] $5s^2 4d^{10} 5p^5$	133	295	114	184	3.96

*Astatine is omitted because it is rare and radioactive.

EXAMPLE 8.7 ALKALI METAL AND HALOGEN REACTIONS

Write a balanced chemical equation for each reaction:

(a) the reaction between potassium metal and bromine gas

(b) the reaction between rubidium metal and liquid water

(c) the reaction between gaseous chlorine and solid iodine

SOLUTION

(a) Alkali metals react with halogens to form metal halides. Write the formulas for the reactants and the metal halide product (making sure to write the correct ionic chemical formula for the metal halide, as outlined in Section 3.4), then balance the equation.	$2\ K(s) + Br_2(g) \longrightarrow 2\ KBr(s)$
(b) Alkali metals react with water to form the dissolved metal ion, the hydroxide ion, and hydrogen gas. Write the skeletal equation to include each of these, and then balance it.	$2\ Rb(s) + 2\ H_2O(l) \longrightarrow 2\ Rb^+(aq) + 2\ OH^-(aq) + H_2(g)$
(c) Halogens react with each other to form interhalogen compounds. Write the skeletal equation with each of the halogens as the reactants and the interhalogen compound as the product, and balance the equation.	$Cl_2(g) + I_2(s) \longrightarrow 2\ ICl(g)$

FOR PRACTICE 8.7

Write a balanced chemical equation for each reaction:

(a) the reaction between aluminum metal and chlorine gas

(b) the reaction between lithium metal and liquid water

(c) the reaction between gaseous hydrogen and liquid bromine

The Noble Gases (Group 18)

Table 8.5 lists selected properties of the noble gases. Notice that the properties of the noble gases, like those of the alkali metals and halogens, vary fairly regularly as we proceed down the column. As expected from periodic trends, the atomic radius and the density increase for each successive noble gas, and the ionization energy decreases. As you can see from the boiling points, all of the noble gases are gases at room temperature and must be cooled to extremely low temperatures before they liquefy. For this reason, some noble gases can be cryogenic liquids—liquids used to cool other substances to low temperatures. For example, researchers often submerse samples of interest in boiling liquid helium to cool them down to 4.2 K and study their properties at this extremely low temperature.

TABLE 8.5 Properties of the Noble Gases*

Element	Electron Configuration	Atomic Radius (pm)**	IE_1 (kJ mol^{-1})	Boiling Point (K)	Density of Gas (g L^{-1} at STP)
He	$1s^2$	32	2372	4.2	0.18
Ne	[He] $2s^2 2p^6$	70	2081	27.1	0.89
Ar	[Ne] $3s^2 3p^6$	98	1521	87.3	1.76
Kr	[Ar] $4s^2 3d^{10} 4p^6$	112	1351	119.9	3.69
Xe	[Kr] $5s^2 4d^{10} 5p^6$	130	1170	165.1	5.78

*Radon is omitted because it is radioactive.

**Since only the heavier noble gases form compounds, covalent radii for the smaller noble gases are estimated.

CHEMISTRY AND MEDICINE Potassium Iodide in Radiation Emergencies

Most governments in the world, including Canada, have plans in place for dealing with nuclear radiation emergencies. Such an emergency could occur in the very unlikely event that a nuclear reactor at a power plant was to melt down or even explode. This was the case with the well-known 1986 nuclear accident at Chernobyl, in the former Soviet Union, and the more recent meltdowns and release of radioactive materials at the Fukushima I Nuclear Power Plant, in Japan, following the Tohoku earthquake and tsunami in 2011. Nuclear emergencies could also result from accidents involving nuclear reactors powering ships, or even the re-entry of a nuclear-powered satellite into the Earth's atmosphere! There is also the risk of a terrorist strike involving a nuclear device. The health risk in these emergencies comes from exposure to radiation from the decay of radioactive isotopes that are released into the environment. This radiation can produce elevated rates of many cancers for years following exposure. The risk of developing thyroid cancer after ingesting radioactive iodine, for example, is particularly high, especially in children. The number of thyroid cancers among children and adolescents in Belarus and Ukraine (areas affected by the radioactive plume from the Chernobyl nuclear accident) is 30–100 times higher than in the normal population. The long-term effects of the Fukushima I nuclear disaster are not yet known.

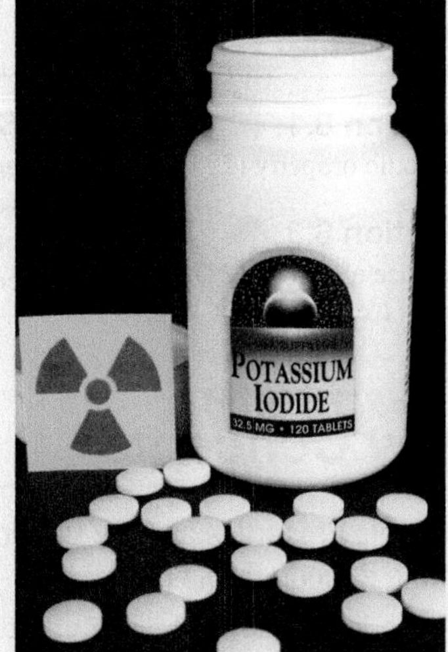

▲ Potassium iodide pills to be taken in the event of a nuclear emergency.

Depending on the severity of the nuclear radiation emergency, one emergency response is to administer potassium iodide (KI) to the population in affected areas. Although KI does not prevent exposure to radiation, it does decrease the risk of thyroid cancer that follows the intake of the radioactive isotope I-131. The chief function of the thyroid gland is to synthesize and release the hormone thyroxine, which regulates many aspects of human metabolism. In order to produce thyroxine, which contains iodine, the thyroid normally accumulates iodine in concentrations far greater than those found elsewhere in the body.

When potassium iodide is taken in the recommended doses, it floods the thyroid with nonradioactive iodine, preventing the thyroid from absorbing the cancer-causing radioactive iodine, which is then excreted in the urine.

▶ Each molecule of thyroxine, a thyroid hormone that plays a key role in metabolism, contains four iodine atoms.

The high ionization energies of the noble gases and their completely full outer quantum levels make them exceptionally unreactive. In fact, before the 1960s, no noble gas compounds were known. Since then, two of the noble gases have been shown to react with fluorine (the most reactive nonmetal on the periodic table) under fairly extreme conditions. Krypton reacts with fluorine to form KrF_2:

$$Kr + F_2 \longrightarrow KrF_2$$

Similarly, Xe reacts with fluorine to form three different xenon fluorides:

$$Xe + F_2 \longrightarrow XeF_2$$

$$Xe + 2\,F_2 \longrightarrow XeF_4$$

$$Xe + 3\,F_2 \longrightarrow XeF_6$$

▲ Liquid helium, a cryogenic liquid, cools substances to temperatures as low as 1.2 K.

Xenon can also be forced to react with oxygen to form XeO_3 and XeO_4.

The inertness of the noble gases has led to their use in situations where reactions are undesirable. For example, argon is used in light bulbs to prevent the hot tungsten filament from oxidizing, and helium is part of the mixture breathed by deep-sea divers to prevent the toxicity caused by too much oxygen and nitrogen under high pressures. (The helium replaces some of the oxygen and nitrogen in the tank, lowering the concentrations of oxygen and nitrogen in the blood.)

CHAPTER IN REVIEW

Key Terms

Section 8.1
periodic property (295)

Section 8.3
valence electrons (297)
core electrons (298)

Section 8.5
nonbonding atomic radius (302)
van der Waals radius (302)
bonding atomic radius (303)
covalent radius (303)
atomic radius (303)
Slater's rules (306)
lanthanoid contraction (308)

Section 8.7
ionization energy (IE) (312)

Section 8.8
electron affinity (EA) (317)

Key Concepts

Periodic Properties and the Development of the Periodic Table (8.1, 8.2)

The periodic table was primarily developed by Dmitri Mendeleev in the nineteenth century. Mendeleev arranged the elements in a table so that atomic mass increased from left to right in a row, and elements with similar properties fell in the same columns. Periodic properties are those that are predictable based on an element's position within the periodic table. Periodic properties include atomic radius, ionization energy, electron affinity, density, and metallic character.

Electron Configurations and the Periodic Table (8.3, 8.4)

Because atomic orbitals fill sequentially with increasing atomic number, we can infer the electron configuration of an element from its position in the periodic table. Quantum-mechanical calculations of the relative energies of electron configurations show that the most stable configurations are those with completely full principal energy levels. Therefore, the most stable and unreactive elements—those with the lowest-energy electron configurations—are the noble gases. Elements with one or two valence electrons are among the most active metals, readily losing their valence electrons to attain noble gas configurations. Elements with six or seven valence electrons are among the most active nonmetals, readily gaining enough electrons to attain a noble gas configuration.

Effective Nuclear Charge and Periodic Trends in Atomic Size (8.5)

The size of an atom is largely determined by its outermost electrons. As we move down a column in the periodic table, the principal quantum number (n) of the outermost electrons increases, resulting in successively larger orbitals and therefore larger atomic radii. As we move across a row in the periodic table, atomic radii decrease because the effective nuclear charge—the net or average charge experienced by the atom's outermost electrons—increases. The atomic radii of the transition elements stay roughly constant across each row because, as we move across a row, electrons are added to the $n_{\text{highest}} - 1$ orbitals, while the number of highest n electrons stays roughly constant.

Ion Properties (8.6, 8.7)

We can determine the electron configuration of an ion by adding or subtracting the corresponding number of electrons to the electron configuration of the neutral atom. For main-group ions, the order of removing electrons is the same as the order in which they are added in building up the electron configuration. For transition metal atoms, the *ns* electrons are removed before the $(n-1)d$ electrons. The radius of a cation is much *smaller* than that of the corresponding atom, and the radius of an anion is much *larger* than that of the corresponding atom. The ionization energy—the energy required to remove an electron from an atom in the gaseous state—generally decreases as we move down a column in the periodic table and increases when moving to the right across a row. Successive ionization energies for valence electrons increase smoothly from one to the next, but the ionization energy increases dramatically for the first core electron.

Electron Affinities and Metallic Character (8.8)

Electron affinity—the energy associated with an element in its gaseous state gaining an electron—does not show a general trend as we move down a column in the periodic table, but it generally becomes more negative (more exothermic) to the right across a row. Metallic character—the tendency to lose electrons in a chemical reaction—generally increases down a column in the periodic table and decreases to the right across a row.

The Alkali Metals, Alkaline Earth Metals, Halogens, and Noble Gases (8.9)

The most active metals are the alkali metals (group 1) and the most active nonmetals are the halogens (group 17). The alkali metals are powerful reducing agents, reacting with many nonmetals—including the halogens and water—to form ionic compounds. The halogens are powerful oxidizing agents, reacting with many metals to form ionic compounds. The halogens also react with many nonmetals to form covalent compounds. The noble gases are relatively unreactive; only krypton and xenon form compounds, typically only with fluorine, the most reactive element in the periodic table.

Key Equations and Relationships

Order of Filling Atomic Orbitals (8.3)

$$1s\ 2s\ 2p\ 3s\ 3p\ (4s \text{ or } 3d)\ 4p\ (5s \text{ or } 4d)\ 5p\ 6s$$

Shielding Constant (8.5)

$$S = N_n f_n + N_{n-1} f_{n-1} + N_{<n-1} f_{<n-1}$$

Key Skills

Valence Electrons and Core Electrons (8.3)
• Example 8.1 • For Practice 8.1 • Exercises 37, 38

Writing Electron Configurations from the Periodic Table (8.3)
• Example 8.2 • For Practice 8.2 • For More Practice 8.2 • Exercises 31, 32

Estimating Z_{eff} (8.5)
• Example 8.3 • For Practice 8.3 • Exercises 45, 46, 55–58

Using Periodic Trends to Predict Atomic Size (8.5)
• Example 8.4 • For Practice 8.4 • For More Practice 8.4 • Exercises 47–50

Using Periodic Trends to Predict Ionic Size (8.6)
• Example 8.5 • For Practice 8.5 • For More Practice 8.5 • Exercises 51–54

Using Periodic Trends to Predict Relative Ionization Energies (8.7)
• Example 8.6 • For Practice 8.6 • For More Practice 8.6 • Exercises 59–66

Writing Chemical Equations for Alkali Metal and Halogen Reactions (8.9)
• Example 8.7 • For Practice 8.7 • Exercises 73–78

EXERCISES

Review Questions

1. What are periodic properties?

2. Which periodic property is particularly important to nerve signal transmission? Why?

3. Who is first credited with arranging the periodic table? How were elements arranged in this table?

4. Explain the contributions of Meyer, Mendeleev, and Moseley to the periodic table.

5. The periodic table is a result of the periodic law. What observations led to the periodic law? What theory explains the underlying reasons for the periodic law?

6. How was the atomic number Z discovered?

7. What are valence electrons? Why are they important?

8. Copy the following blank periodic table onto a sheet of paper and label each of the blocks within the table: *s* block, *p* block, *d* block, or *f* block.

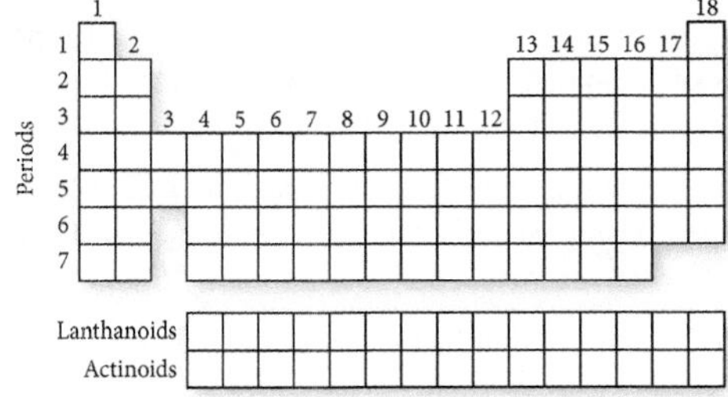

9. Explain why the *s* block in the periodic table has only two columns, while the *p* block has six.

10. Why do the rows in the periodic table get progressively longer as you move down the table? For example, the first row contains 2 elements, the second and third rows each contain 8 elements, and the fourth and fifth rows each contain 18 elements. Explain.

11. Explain the relationship between a main-group element's group number (the number of the element's column) and its valence electrons.

12. Explain the relationship between an element's row number in the periodic table and the highest principal quantum number in the element's electron configuration. How does this relationship differ for main-group elements, transition elements, and inner transition elements?

13. Explain how to write an electron configuration for an element based on its position in the periodic table.

14. Explain the relationship between the properties of an element and the number of valence electrons that it contains.

15. Give the number of valence electrons for each family in the periodic table, and explain the relationship between the number of valence electrons and the resulting chemistry of the elements in the family.
 a. alkali metals
 b. alkaline earth metals
 c. halogens
 d. oxygen family

16. Define atomic radius. For main-group elements, give the observed trends in atomic radius as you:
 a. move across a period in the periodic table.
 b. move down a column in the periodic table.

17. What is effective nuclear charge? What is shielding?

18. Use the concepts of effective nuclear charge, shielding, and *n* value of the valence orbital to explain the trend in atomic radius as you move across a period in the periodic table.

19. What are Slater's rules?

20. For transition elements, give the trends in atomic radius as you:
 a. move across a period in the periodic table.
 b. move down a column in the periodic table.

Explain the reasons for the trends in parts (a) and (b).

21. What is the lanthanoid contraction?

22. Describe the relationship between:
    a. the radius of a cation and that of the atom from which it is formed.
    b. the radius of an anion and that of the atom from which it is formed.

23. What is ionization energy? What is the difference between first ionization energy and second ionization energy?

24. What is the general trend in ionization energy as you move down a column in the periodic table? As you move across a row?

25. What are the exceptions to the periodic trends in ionization energy? Why do they occur?

26. Examination of the first few successive ionization energies for a given element usually reveals a large jump between two ionization energies. For example, the successive ionization energies of magnesium show a large jump between IE_2 and IE_3. The successive ionization energies of aluminum show a large jump between IE_3 and IE_4. Explain why these jumps occur and how you might predict them.

27. What is electron affinity? What are the observed periodic trends in electron affinity?

28. What is metallic character? What are the observed periodic trends in metallic character?

29. Write a general equation for the reaction of an alkali metal with:
    a. a halogen. b. water.

30. Write a general equation for the reaction of a halogen with:
    a. a metal. b. hydrogen.
    c. another halogen.

Problems by Topic

Electron Configurations and the Periodic Table

31. Use the periodic table to write electron configurations for each element. Represent core electrons with the symbol of the previous noble gas in brackets.
    a. P b. Ge c. Zr d. I

32. Use the periodic table to determine the element corresponding to each electron configuration:
    a. [Ar] $4s^2 3d^{10} 4p^6$ b. [Ar] $4s^2 3d^2$
    c. [Kr] $5s^2 4d^{10} 5p^2$ d. [Kr] $5s^2$

33. Use the periodic table to determine:
    a. the number of $2s$ electrons in Li.
    b. the number of $3d$ electrons in Cu.
    c. the number of $4p$ electrons in Br.
    d. the number of $4d$ electrons in Zr.

34. Use the periodic table to determine:
    a. the number of $3s$ electrons in Mg.
    b. the number of $3d$ electrons in Cr.
    c. the number of $4d$ electrons in Y.
    d. the number of $6p$ electrons in Pb.

35. Name an element in the fourth period (row) of the periodic table with:
    a. five valence electrons. b. four $4p$ electrons.
    c. three $3d$ electrons. d. a complete outer shell.

36. Name an element in the third period (row) of the periodic table with:
    a. three valence electrons.
    b. four $3p$ electrons.
    c. six $3p$ electrons.
    d. two $3s$ electrons and no $3p$ electrons.

37. Determine the number of valence electrons in each element:
    a. Ba b. Cs c. Ni d. S

38. Determine the number of valence electrons in each element. Which elements do you expect to lose electrons in their chemical reactions? Which do you expect to gain electrons?
    a. Al b. Sn c. Br d. Se

39. Which outer-electron configuration would you expect to belong to a reactive metal? To a reactive nonmetal?
    a. ns^2 b. ns^2np^6 c. ns^2np^5 d. ns^2np^2

40. Which outer-electron configurations would you expect to belong to a noble gas? To a metalloid?
    a. ns^2 b. ns^2np^6 c. ns^2np^5 d. ns^2np^2

Effective Nuclear Charge and Atomic Radius

41. Which electrons experience a greater effective nuclear charge, the valence electrons in beryllium, or the valence electrons in nitrogen? Why?

42. Arrange the atoms according to decreasing effective nuclear charge experienced by their valence electrons: S, Mg, Al, Si.

43. If core electrons completely shielded valence electrons from nuclear charge (i.e., if each core electron reduced nuclear charge by 1 unit) and if valence electrons did not shield one another from nuclear charge at all, what would be the effective nuclear charge experienced by the valence electrons of each atom?
    a. K b. Ca c. O d. C

44. In Section 8.5, we estimated the effective nuclear charge on beryllium's valence electrons to be slightly greater than 2+. What would a similar treatment predict for the effective nuclear charge on boron's valence electrons? Would you expect the effective nuclear charge to be different for boron's $2s$ electrons compared to its $2p$ electron? In what way? (*Hint:* Consider the shape of the $2p$ orbital compared to that of the $2s$ orbital.)

45. Use Slater's rules to estimate Z_{eff} for the atoms of elements in the fourth period of the periodic table, starting with potassium. Use these estimated values of Z_{eff} to explain the trend of atomic radii for this period, shown in Figure 8.7.

46. The first ionization energies for Na, S, and Cl increase across this series. Using Slater's rules, calculate Z_{eff} for these species and state whether this trend is supported by Slater's rules.

47. Choose the larger atom from each pair:
    a. Al or In b. Si or N c. P or Pb d. C or F

48. Choose the larger atom from each pair:
    a. Sn or Si b. Br or Ga c. Sn or Bi d. Se or Sn

49. Arrange these elements in order of increasing atomic radius: Ca, Rb, S, Si, Ge, F.

50. Arrange these elements in order of decreasing atomic radius: Cs, Sb, S, Pb, Se.

Ionic Radii

51. Which is the larger species in each pair?
a. Li or Li^+ b. I^- or Cs^+ c. Cr or Cr^{3+} d. O or O^{2-}

52. Which is the larger species in each pair?
a. Sr or Sr^{2+} b. N or N^{3-}
c. Ni or Ni^{2+} d. S^{2-} or Ca^{2+}

53. Arrange this isoelectronic series in order of decreasing radius: F^-, Ne, O^{2-}, Mg^{2+}, Na^+.

54. Arrange this isoelectronic series in order of increasing atomic radius: Se^{2-}, Kr, Sr^{2+}, Rb^+, Br^-.

55. The atomic radius of an oxygen atom is 73 pm, and the ionic radius of the ion O^{2-} is 140 pm. Explain the relative radii by estimating Z_{eff} for each of these species.

56. The atomic radius of a bromine atom is 114 pm, and the ionic radius of the ion Br^- is 195 pm. Explain the relative radii by estimating Z_{eff} for each of these species.

57. The atomic radius of a gallium atom is 135 pm, and the ionic radius of the ion Ga^{3+} is 62 pm. Explain the relative radii by estimating Z_{eff} for each of these species.

58. The atomic radius of a potassium atom is 227 pm, and the ionic radius of the ion K^+ is 133 pm. Explain the relative radii by estimating Z_{eff} for each of these species.

Ionization Energy

59. Choose the element with the higher first ionization energy from each pair:
a. Br or Bi b. Na or Rb c. As or At d. P or Sn

60. Choose the element with the higher first ionization energy from each pair:
a. P or I b. Si or Cl c. P or Sb d. Ga or Ge

61. Arrange these elements in order of increasing first ionization energy: Si, F, In, N.

62. Arrange these elements in order of decreasing first ionization energy: Cl, S, Sn, Pb.

63. For each element, predict where the "jump" occurs for successive ionization energies. (For example, does the jump occur between the first and second ionization energies, the second and third, or the third and fourth?)
a. Be b. N c. O d. Li

64. Consider this set of successive ionization energies:

$$IE_1 = 578 \text{ kJ mol}^{-1}$$
$$IE_2 = 1820 \text{ kJ mol}^{-1}$$
$$IE_3 = 2750 \text{ kJ mol}^{-1}$$
$$IE_4 = 11\,600 \text{ kJ mol}^{-1}$$

To which third-period element do these ionization values belong?

65. Use estimated values of Z_{eff} to explain the variation of first, second, and third ionization energies of magnesium.

66. The ions Mg^{2+} and Al^{3+} are isoelectronic. The ionization energies for these two ions are 7730 kJ mol^{-1} and 11 600 kJ mol^{-1}, respectively. Use estimated values of Z_{eff} to explain the difference.

Electron Affinities and Metallic Character

67. Choose the element with the more positive (more exothermic) electron affinity from each pair.
a. Na or Rb b. B or S c. C or N d. Li or F

68. Choose the element with the more positive (more exothermic) electron affinity from each pair.
a. Mg or S b. K or Cs c. Si or P d. Ga or Br

69. Choose the more metallic element from each pair.
a. Sr or Sb b. As or Bi c. Cl or O d. S or As

70. Choose the more metallic element from each pair.
a. Sb or Pb b. K or Ge c. Ge or Sb d. As or Sn

71. Arrange these elements in order of increasing metallic character: Fr, Sb, In, S, Ba, Se.

72. Arrange these elements in order of decreasing metallic character: Sr, N, Si, P, Ga, Al.

Periodic Chemical Behaviour

73. Write a balanced chemical equation for the reaction of solid strontium with iodine gas.

74. Based on the ionization energies of the alkali metals, which alkali metal would you expect to undergo the most exothermic reaction with chlorine gas? Write a balanced chemical equation for the reaction.

75. Write a balanced chemical equation for the reaction of solid lithium with liquid water.

76. Write a balanced chemical equation for the reaction of solid potassium with liquid water.

77. Write a balanced equation for the reaction of hydrogen gas with bromine gas.

78. Write a balanced equation for the reaction of chlorine gas with fluorine gas.

Cumulative Problems

79. Bromine is a highly reactive liquid, while krypton is an inert gas. Explain the difference based on their electron configurations.

80. Potassium is a highly reactive metal, while argon is an inert gas. Explain the difference based on their electron configurations.

81. Suppose you were trying to find a substitute for K^+ in nerve signal transmission. Where would you begin your search? What ions would be most like K^+? For each ion you propose, explain the ways in which it would be similar to K^+ and the ways it would be different. Refer to periodic trends in your discussion.

82. Suppose you were trying to find a substitute for Na^+ in nerve signal transmission. Where would you begin your search? What ions would be most like Na^+? For each ion you propose, explain the ways in which it would be similar to Na^+ and the ways it would be different. Use periodic trends in your discussion.

83. Life on Earth evolved around the element carbon. Based on periodic properties, what two or three elements would you expect to be most like carbon?

84. Which pair of elements would you expect to have the most similar atomic radii, and why?

a. Si and Ga **b.** Si and Ge

c. Si and As

85. Consider these elements: N, Mg, O, F, Al.

a. Write the ground-state electron configuration for each element.

b. Arrange the elements in order of decreasing atomic radius.

c. Arrange the elements in order of increasing ionization energy.

d. Use the electron configurations in part (a) to explain the differences between your answers to parts (b) and (c).

86. Consider these elements: P, Ca, Si, S, Ga.

a. Write the ground-state electron configuration for each element.

b. Arrange the elements in order of decreasing atomic radius.

c. Arrange the elements in order of increasing ionization energy.

d. Use the electron configurations in part (a) to explain the differences between your answers to parts (b) and (c).

87. Explain why atomic radius decreases as we move to the right across a period for main-group elements but not for transition elements.

88. Explain why vanadium (radius = 134 pm) and copper (radius = 128 pm) have nearly identical atomic radii, even though the atomic number of copper is about 25% higher than that of vanadium. What would you predict about the relative densities of these two metals? Look up the densities in a reference book, periodic table, or on the Internet. Are your predictions correct?

89. The lightest noble gases, such as helium and neon, are completely inert—they do not form any chemical compounds whatsoever. The heavier noble gases, in contrast, do form a limited number of compounds. Explain this difference in terms of trends in fundamental periodic properties.

90. The lightest halogen is also the most chemically reactive, and reactivity generally decreases as we move down the column of halogens in the periodic table. Explain this trend in terms of periodic properties.

91. Write general outer-electron configurations ($ns^x np^y$) for groups 16 and 17 in the periodic table. The electron affinity of each group 17 element is greater than that of each corresponding group 16 element. Use the electron configurations to explain why this is so.

92. The electron affinity of each group 15 element is less than that of each corresponding group 14 element. Use the outer-electron configurations for these columns to suggest a reason for this behaviour.

93. The elements with atomic numbers 35 and 53 have similar chemical properties. Based on their electronic configurations, predict the atomic number of a heavier element that also should have these chemical properties.

94. Using the appropriate electron affinities and ionization energies, estimate the enthalpy of reaction for the following reactions and state which one is most exothermic.

a. $Na(g) + O(g) \longrightarrow Na^+(g) + O^-(g)$

b. $Li(g) + Cl(g) \longrightarrow Li^+(g) + Cl^-(g)$

95. You believe you have cracked a secret code that uses elemental symbols to spell words. The code uses numbers to designate the elemental symbols. Each number is the sum of the atomic number and the highest principal quantum number of the highest occupied orbital of the element whose symbol is to be used. The message may be written forward or backward. Decode the following messages:

a. 10, 12, 58, 11, 7, 44, 63, 66

b. 9, 99, 30, 95, 19, 47, 79

96. The electron affinity of sodium is lower than that of lithium, while the electron affinity of chlorine is higher than that of fluorine. Suggest an explanation for this observation.

Challenge Problems

97. Consider the densities and atomic radii of the noble gases at 1 bar and 25 °C:

Element	Atomic Radius (pm)	Density ($g\,L^{-1}$)
He	32	0.16
Ne	70	0.81
Ar	98	—
Kr	112	3.38
Xe	130	—
Rn	—	8.96

a. Estimate the densities of argon and xenon by interpolation from the data.

b. Provide an estimate of the density of the yet undiscovered element with atomic number 118 by extrapolation from the data.

c. Use the molar mass of neon to estimate the mass of a neon atom. Then use the atomic radius of neon to calculate the average density of a neon atom. How does this density compare to the density of neon gas? What does this comparison suggest about the nature of neon gas?

d. Use the densities and molar masses of krypton and neon to calculate the number of atoms of each found in a volume of 1.0 L. Use these values to estimate the number of atoms that occur in 1.0 L of Ar. Now use the molar mass of argon to estimate the density of Ar. How does this estimate compare to that in part (a)?

98. As we have seen, the periodic table is a result of empirical observation (i.e., the periodic law), but quantum theory explains *why* the table is so arranged. Suppose that, in another universe, quantum theory was such that there were one *s* orbital but only two *p* orbitals (instead of three) and only three *d* orbitals (instead of five). Draw out the first four periods of the periodic table in this alternative universe. Which elements would be the equivalent of the noble gases? Halogens? Alkali metals?

99. Consider the metals in the first transition series. Use periodic trends to predict a trend in density as you move to the right across the series.

100. Only trace amounts of the synthetic element darmstadtium, atomic number 110, have been obtained. The element is so highly unstable that no observations of its properties have been possible. Based on its position in the periodic table, propose three different plausible valence electron configurations for this element.

101. What is the atomic number of the as yet undiscovered element in which the 8*s* and 8*p* electron energy levels fill? Predict the chemical behaviour of this element.

102. Consider the following isoelectronic series of ions and the ionic radii:

$$S^{2-}(184\,pm) \quad Cl^{-}(181\,pm) \quad K^{+}(133\,pm) \quad Ca^{2+}(99\,pm)$$

For each ion, estimate Z_{eff} using Slater's rules. Does Z_{eff} explain the variation in ionic radius? Explain why the ionic radii of the two cations are much smaller than the ionic radii of the anions.

103. Unlike the elements in groups 1 and 2, those in group 13 do not show a regular decrease in first ionization energy in going down the column. Explain the irregularities.

104. Using the data in Figures 8.12 and 8.13, calculate ΔE for the reaction:

$$Na(g) + Cl(g) \longrightarrow Na^{+}(g) + Cl^{-}(g)$$

105. Despite the fact that adding two electrons to O or S forms an ion with a noble gas electron configuration, the second electron affinity of both of these elements is negative. Explain.

106. In Section 2.7, we discussed the metalloids, which form a diagonal band separating the metals from the nonmetals. There are other instances in which elements such as lithium and magnesium that are diagonal to each other have comparable metallic character. Suggest an explanation for this observation.

107. The heaviest known alkaline earth metal is radium, atomic number 88. Find the atomic numbers of the as yet undiscovered next two members of the series.

108. Predict the electronic configurations of the first two excited states (next higher energy states above the ground state) of Pd.

109. Table 8.2 does not include francium because none of its isotopes are stable. Predict the values of the entries for Fr in Table 8.2. Predict the nature of the products of the reaction of Fr with **(a)** water, **(b)** oxygen, and **(c)** chlorine.

110. From its electronic configuration, predict which of the first 10 elements would be most similar in chemical behaviour to the as yet undiscovered element 165.

111. Using Slater's rules, estimate Z_{eff} for the group 1 metals (lithium through to rubidium). Compare these values with the atomic radii of group 1 metals shown in Figure 8.10. What consideration, besides Z_{eff}, is required to explain periodic trends down a group?

112. The trend in second ionization energy for the elements from lithium to fluorine is not a regular one. Of the elements N, O, and F, O has the highest and N the lowest second ionization energy. Explain.

Conceptual Problems

113. Imagine that in another universe, atoms and elements are identical to ours, except that atoms with six valence electrons have particular stability (in contrast to our universe, where atoms with eight valence electrons have particular stability). Give an example of an element in the alternative universe that corresponds to:

a. a noble gas.
b. a reactive nonmetal.
c. a reactive metal.

114. According to Coulomb's law, rank the interactions between the charged particles from lowest potential energy to highest potential energy:

a. A 1+ charge and a 1− charge separated by 100 pm.
b. A 2+ charge and a 1− charge separated by 100 pm.
c. A 1+ charge and a 1+ charge separated by 100 pm.
d. A 1+ charge and a 1− charge separated by 200 pm.

115. Use the trends in ionization energy and electron affinity to explain why calcium fluoride has the formula CaF_2 and not Ca_2F or CaF.

Chemical Bonding I: Lewis Theory

Theories are nets cast to catch what we call "the world": to rationalize, to explain, and to master it. We endeavour to make the mesh ever finer and finer.

—Karl Popper (1902–1994)

The AIDS drug Indinavir—shown here as the missing piece in a puzzle depicting the protein HIV-protease—was developed with the help of chemical bonding theories.

CHEMICAL BONDING IS AT THE HEART of chemistry. The bonding theories that we are about to examine are—as Karl Popper eloquently states in the above quote—nets cast to understand the world. In the next two chapters, we will examine three theories with successively finer "meshes." The first is Lewis theory, a simple model of chemical bonding, which can be carried out on the back of an envelope. With just a few dots, dashes, and chemical symbols, Lewis theory can help us to understand and predict a myriad of chemical observations. The second is valence bond theory, which treats electrons in a more quantum-mechanical manner, but stops short of viewing them as belonging to the entire molecule. The third is molecular orbital theory, essentially a full quantum-mechanical treatment of the molecule and its electrons as a whole. Molecular orbital theory has great predictive power, but at the expense of great complexity and intensive computational requirements. Which theory is "correct"? Remember that theories are models that help us understand and predict behaviour. All three of these theories are extremely useful, depending on exactly what aspect of chemical bonding we want to predict or understand.

9.1 Bonding Models and AIDS Drugs

In 1989, researchers used X-ray crystallography—a technique in which X-rays are scattered from crystals of the molecule of interest—to determine the structure of a molecule called HIV-protease. HIV-protease is a protein (a class of large biological molecules) synthesized by the human immunodeficiency virus (HIV). This particular protein is crucial to the virus's ability to multiply and cause acquired immune deficiency syndrome, or AIDS. Without HIV-protease, HIV cannot spread in the human body because the virus cannot replicate. In other words, without HIV-protease, AIDS can't develop.

X-ray crystallography is discussed in more detail in Section 11.10.

With knowledge of the HIV-protease structure, pharmaceutical companies set out to create a molecule that would disable HIV-protease by sticking to the working part of the molecule, called the active site. To design such a molecule, researchers used *bonding theories*—models that predict how atoms bond together to form molecules—to simulate the shape of potential drug molecules and how they would interact with the protease molecule. By the early 1990s, these companies had developed several drug molecules that seemed to work. Since these molecules inhibit the action of HIV-protease, they were named *protease inhibitors*. In human trials, protease inhibitors, when given in combination with other drugs, have decreased the viral count in HIV-infected individuals to undetectable levels. Although protease inhibitors do not cure AIDS, many AIDS patients are still alive today because of these drugs.

Proteins are discussed in more detail in Chapter 22.

Bonding theories are central to chemistry because they explain how atoms bond together to form molecules. They explain why some combinations of atoms are stable and others are not. For example, bonding theories explain why table salt is NaCl and not $NaCl_2$ and why water is H_2O and not H_3O. Bonding theories also predict the shapes of molecules—a topic in our next chapter—which, in turn, determine many of the physical and chemical properties of compounds. The bonding model we examine in this chapter is called **Lewis theory**, named after the American chemist G. N. Lewis (1875–1946). In Lewis theory, valence electrons are represented as dots, and we can draw **Lewis electron-dot structures** (or simply, **Lewis structures**) to depict molecules. These structures, which are fairly simple to draw, have tremendous predictive power. With minimal computation, Lewis theory can be used to predict whether a particular set of atoms will form a stable molecule and what that molecule might look like. Although we will also examine more advanced theories in the following chapter, Lewis theory remains the simplest model for making quick, everyday predictions about most molecules.

▲ G. N. Lewis

9.2 Types of Chemical Bonds

We begin our discussion of chemical bonding by asking the question, "why do bonds form in the first place?" This seemingly simple question is vitally important. Imagine our universe without chemical bonding. There would be just 91 different kinds of substances (the 91 naturally occurring elements). With such a poor diversity of substances, life would be impossible, and we would not be around to wonder why. The *answer* to this question, however, is not simple and involves not only quantum mechanics but also some thermodynamics that we do not introduce until Chapter 17. Nonetheless, we can address an important *aspect* of the answer now: *chemical bonds form because they lower the potential energy between the charged particles that compose atoms.*

As we already know, atoms are composed of particles with positive charges (the protons in the nucleus) and negative charges (the electrons). When two atoms approach each other, the electrons of one atom are attracted to the nucleus of the other according to Coulomb's law (see Section 7.7) and vice versa. However, at the same time, the electrons of each atom repel the electrons of the other, and the nucleus of each atom repels the nucleus of the other. The result is a complex set of interactions among a potentially large number of charged particles. If these interactions lead to an overall net reduction of energy between the charged particles, a chemical bond forms. Bonding theories help us to predict the circumstances under which bonds form and also the properties of the resultant molecules.

We can broadly classify chemical bonds into three types, depending on the kind of atoms involved in the bonding (Figure 9.1 ▼).

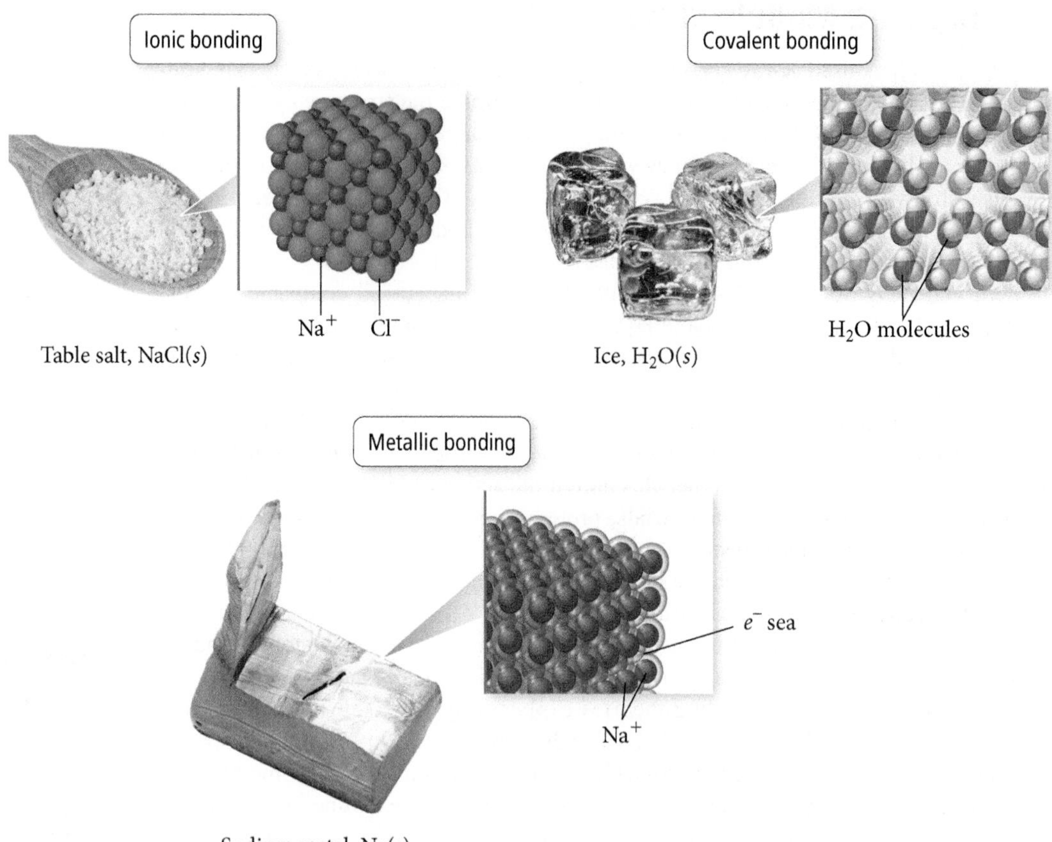

▲ **FIGURE 9.1 Ionic, Covalent, and Metallic Bonding**

Types of Atoms	Type of Bond	Characteristic of Bond
Metal and nonmetal	Ionic	Electrons transferred
Nonmetal and nonmetal	Covalent	Electrons shared
Metal and metal	Metallic	Electrons pooled

We learned in Chapter 8 that metals tend to have low ionization energies (their electrons are relatively easy to remove) and that nonmetals tend to have high electron affinities (they readily gain electrons). When a metal bonds with a nonmetal, it transfers one or more electrons to the nonmetal. The metal atom becomes a cation and the nonmetal atom an anion. These oppositely charged ions then attract one another, lowering their overall potential energy as described by Coulomb's law. The resulting bond is an **ionic bond**.

We also learned in Chapter 8 that nonmetals tend to have high ionization energies (their electrons are relatively difficult to remove). Therefore, when a nonmetal bonds with another nonmetal, neither atom transfers electrons to the other. Instead, the two atoms *share* some electrons. The shared electrons interact with the nuclei of both of the bonding atoms, lowering their potential energy in accordance with Coulomb's law. The resulting bond is a **covalent bond**.

Recall from Section 3.2 that we can understand the stability of a covalent bond by considering the most stable arrangement (the one with the lowest potential energy) of two positively charged particles separated by a small distance and a negatively charged particle. As you can see from Figure 9.2 ▸, the arrangement in which the negatively charged particle lies *between* the two positively charged ones has the lowest potential energy because, in this arrangement, the negatively charged particle interacts most strongly with *both of the positively charged ones*. In a sense, the negatively charged

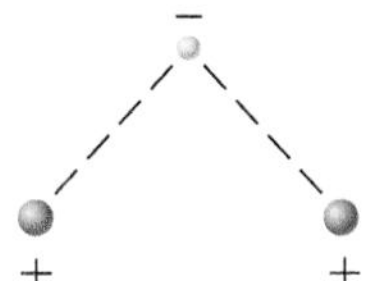

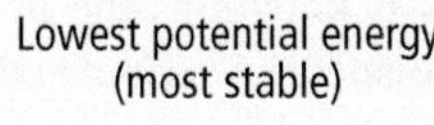

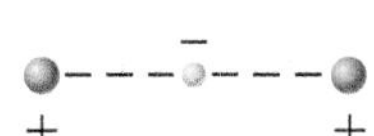

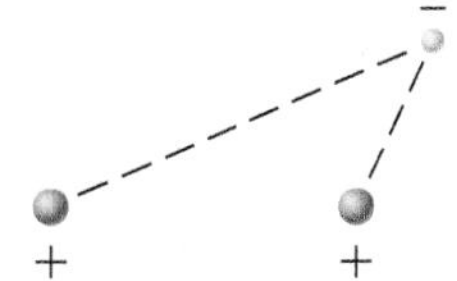

◀ **FIGURE 9.2 Possible Configurations of One Negatively Charged Particle and Two Positively Charged Ones**

particle holds the two positively charged ones together. Similarly, shared electrons in a covalent chemical bond *hold* the bonding atoms together by attracting the positive charges of their nuclei.

A third type of bonding, **metallic bonding**, occurs in metals. Since metals have low ionization energies, they tend to lose electrons easily. In the simplest model for metallic bonding—called the *electron sea* model—all of the atoms in a metal lattice pool their valence electrons. These pooled electrons are no longer localized on a single atom, but are delocalized throughout the entire metal. The positively charged metal atoms are then attracted to the sea of electrons, holding the metal together.

9.3 Representing Valence Electrons with Dots

In Chapter 8, we saw that, for main-group elements, valence electrons are those electrons in the outermost principal energy level. Since valence electrons are held most loosely, and since chemical bonding involves the transfer or sharing of electrons between two or more atoms, valence electrons are most important in bonding, so Lewis theory focuses on these. In a Lewis structure, we represent the valence electrons of main-group elements as dots surrounding the symbol for the element. For example, the electron configuration of O is:

$$1s^2 2s^2 2p^4$$

6 valence electrons

and the Lewis structure is:

$$\cdot\ddot{\underset{\cdot}{\text{O}}}:$$

6 dots representing valence electrons

Each dot represents a valence electron. The dots are placed around the element's symbol with a maximum of two dots per side. The Lewis structures for all of the period 2 elements can be drawn in a similar way:

While the exact location of dots is not critical, in this text, we will first place dots singly before pairing (except for helium, which always has two paired dots).

$$\text{Li}\cdot \quad \cdot\text{Be}\cdot \quad \cdot\dot{\text{B}}\cdot \quad \cdot\dot{\underset{\cdot}{\text{C}}}\cdot \quad \cdot\dot{\underset{\cdot}{\text{N}}}: \quad \cdot\ddot{\underset{\cdot}{\text{O}}}: \quad :\ddot{\underset{\cdot}{\text{F}}}: \quad :\ddot{\underset{\cdot\cdot}{\text{Ne}}}:$$

Lewis structures provide a simple way to visualize the number of valence electrons in a main-group atom. Notice that atoms with eight valence electrons—which are particularly stable because they have a full outer level—are easily identified because they have eight dots, an **octet**.

Helium is somewhat of an exception. Its electron configuration and Lewis structure are:

$$1s^2 \quad \text{He}:$$

The Lewis structure of helium contains only two dots. For helium, two electrons represent a stable electron configuration because the $n = 1$ quantum level fills with only two electrons.

In Lewis theory, a **chemical bond** is the sharing or transfer of electrons to attain stable electron configurations for the bonding atoms. If electrons are transferred, as occurs between a metal and a nonmetal, the bond is an *ionic bond*. If the electrons are shared, as occurs between two nonmetals, the bond is a *covalent bond*. In either case, the bonding atoms obtain stable electron configurations; since the stable configuration is usually eight electrons in the outermost shell, this is known as the **octet rule**. When applying Lewis theory, we do not try to calculate the energies associated with the attractions and repulsions between electrons and nuclei on neighbouring atoms. The energy changes that occur because of these interactions are central to chemical bonding (as we saw in Section 9.2), yet Lewis theory ignores them because calculating these energy changes is extremely complicated. Instead, Lewis theory uses the simple octet rule, a practical approach that accurately predicts what we see in nature for a large number of compounds—hence, the success and longevity of Lewis theory.

9.4 Lewis Structures: An Introduction to Ionic and Covalent Bonding

Drawing Lewis Structures for Molecular Compounds

Lewis theory provides us with a simple and useful model for covalent bonding. In this model, we represent covalent bonding by depicting neighbouring atoms as sharing some (or all) of their valence electrons in order to attain octets.

In water, these atoms share their unpaired valence electrons so that each hydrogen atom gets two electrons, and the oxygen atom gets eight electrons, or an octet:

$$\mathrm{H{:}\ddot{\underset{\cdot\cdot}{O}}{:}H}$$

The shared electrons—those that appear in the space between the two atoms—count toward the octet of oxygen or the two electrons of hydrogen. A shared pair of electrons is called a **bonding pair**, while a pair of electrons that is associated with only one atom—and therefore not involved in bonding—is called a **lone pair**. Lone-pair electrons are also called **nonbonding electrons**. It is most common to represent these shared electrons by a line between the two atoms to emphasize a chemical bond. A correct Lewis structure for water is:

$$\mathrm{H-\ddot{\underset{\cdot\cdot}{O}}-H}$$

Hydrogen doesn't obey the octet rule because to fill its valence shell requires only two electrons. Hydrogen is stable with two electrons.

In order to draw a Lewis structure for a molecule, you need to know two things: first, what atoms are bonded together in the molecule; and second, how many valence electrons need to be represented in the Lewis structure. Consider Cl_2, composed of two chlorine atoms. We know that the chlorine atoms are bonded together, so we can draw the two chlorine atoms connected by a line, or a bonding pair of electrons:

$$\mathrm{Cl-Cl}$$

Because each chlorine atom has 7 valence electrons, the Lewis structure for Cl_2 must contain a total of 14 electrons. Two have been used in the bond, leaving 12 more electrons. Because there are two chlorine atoms, it makes sense to put 6 electrons (three pairs) around each chlorine atom:

$$\mathrm{{:}\ddot{\underset{\cdot\cdot}{Cl}}-\ddot{\underset{\cdot\cdot}{Cl}}{:}}$$

Notice that each chlorine has a stable octet—each has three lone pairs, and each shares a pair of electrons. Lewis theory shows why the halogens form diatomic molecules containing single bonds—F_2, Br_2, and I_2 have similar Lewis structures to Cl_2.

In Lewis theory, two atoms can share more than one electron pair to attain an octet. As an example, let's draw a Lewis structure for O_2. Because the two oxygen atoms are bonded to one another, we draw two oxygen atoms connected by a line:

$$\mathrm{O-O}$$

Because each oxygen atom has 6 valence electrons, our Lewis structure must contain a total of 12 electrons. Two of these 12 electrons are already used in the bonding pair, so we have 10 left to incorporate into the Lewis structure. We need to divide the 10 electrons, in pairs, between the 2 oxygen atoms—three pairs on one oxygen and two on the other:

$$:\ddot{\underset{\cdot\cdot}{O}}-\ddot{O}:$$

Remember that we have to obey the octet rule if possible. In our present Lewis structure for O_2, the oxygen on the left has a complete octet, but the oxygen on the right has only six electrons. We can share a pair of electrons from the oxygen atom on the left with the electron-deficient oxygen on the right:

Keep in mind that *one* dash always stands for *two* electrons (a single bonding pair).

$$:\ddot{\underset{\cdot\cdot}{O}}-\ddot{O}: \longrightarrow :\ddot{O}=\ddot{O}:$$

Now, each oxygen atom has a full octet because the *additional bonding pair counts toward the octet of both oxygen atoms*. When two electron pairs are shared between two atoms, the resulting bond is a **double bond**. In general, a double bond is shorter and stronger than a single bond.

Atoms can also share three electron pairs. Consider the Lewis structure for N_2. Because each N has 5 valence electrons, the Lewis structure for N_2 has 10 electrons. In order to attain octets, the nitrogen atoms must share three pairs of electrons, a **triple bond**:

$$:N\equiv N:$$

Triple bonds are even shorter and stronger than double bonds. When we examine oxygen and nitrogen in nature, we find that they exist as diatomic molecules with very strong bonds, nitrogen having a significantly stronger bond than oxygen. The bond in N_2 is very difficult to break, making it relatively unreactive.

We can summarize the method for drawing Lewis structures as follows:

1. **Calculate the total number of electrons for the Lewis structure by summing the valence electrons of each atom in the molecule.** Don't worry about which electron comes from which atom—only the total number is important.
2. **Write the correct skeletal structure for the molecule drawing a bond between each set of bonding atoms.** The Lewis structure of a molecule must have the atoms in the correct positions. For example, you could try to write a Lewis structure for water if you started with the hydrogen atoms next to each other and the oxygen atom at the end (H—H—O). However, in this skeletal structure, the central H has four electrons, meaning it has two too many electrons. In nature, oxygen is the central atom, and the hydrogen atoms are *terminal* (at the ends). The correct skeletal structure for water is H—O—H. It is almost always the case with molecules containing hydrogen that hydrogen is terminal. As another guide, the central atom is usually the atom with the lower group number. In NF_3, for example, N would be central because it is in group 15, and F is in group 17. In a compound like ICl_2, with atoms in the same group, the atom that is lower in the periodic table is usually the central atom; in this case, the iodine atom would be central, and the chlorine atoms would be terminal.

Often, chemical formulas are written in a way that provides clues to how the atoms are bonded together. For example, CH_3OH indicates that three hydrogen atoms and the oxygen atom are bonded to the carbon atom, but the fourth hydrogen atom is bonded to the oxygen atom.

3. **Distribute the remaining unaccounted-for electrons, in pairs, among the atoms, giving octets (except for hydrogen) to as many atoms as possible.** Remember that each bond counts as two electrons, so you must subtract the number already accounted for in the Lewis structure as bonding pairs from the total number of electrons. Distribute the remaining electrons as lone pairs, first to terminal atoms and then to the central atom, giving octets to as many atoms as possible.
4. **If any nonhydrogen atoms lack an octet, form double or triple bonds as necessary to give them octets.** Do this by moving lone electron pairs from terminal atoms into the bonding region with the central atom.

The use of these steps to draw Lewis structures is illustrated in Examples 9.1 and 9.2.

PROCEDURE FOR ... **Drawing Lewis Structures for Covalent Compounds**	**EXAMPLE 9.1** **Drawing Lewis Structures** Draw the Lewis structure for CO_2. Carbon is the central atom.	**EXAMPLE 9.2** **Drawing Lewis Structures** Monochloroamine (NH_2Cl) is an important disinfectant and is an intermediate in the formation of rocket fuel. Draw the Lewis structure for NH_2Cl. *Hint:* The skeletal structure is similar to that of NH_3 with Cl replacing an H.
1. Calculate the total number of electrons for the Lewis structure by summing the valence electrons of each atom.	**SOLUTION** Total number of electrons for Lewis structure $= \begin{pmatrix}\text{number of}\\ \text{valence } e^-\\ \text{for C}\end{pmatrix} + 2\begin{pmatrix}\text{number of}\\ \text{valence } e^-\\ \text{for O}\end{pmatrix}$ $= 4 + 2(6) = 16$	**SOLUTION** Total number of electrons for Lewis structure $= \begin{pmatrix}\text{number of}\\ \text{valence } e^-\\ \text{for N}\end{pmatrix} + 2\begin{pmatrix}\text{number of}\\ \text{valence } e^-\\ \text{for H}\end{pmatrix} + \begin{pmatrix}\text{number of}\\ \text{valence } e^-\\ \text{for Cl}\end{pmatrix}$ $= 5 + 2(1) + 7 = 14$
2. Write the correct skeletal structure for the molecule, drawing a bond that represents a pair of electrons between each bonded atom.	Carbon is central, so we draw each of the oxygens bonded to the central carbon: O—C—O	The hint says that the structure is similar to ammonia. In ammonia, each hydrogen would be terminal, so if Cl replaces one H, the skeletal structure is: H—N—Cl (with H bonded below N)
3. Distribute the remaining electrons as pairs among the atoms, giving octets to as many atoms as possible.	With two bonds, 4 electrons are used, leaving 12 electrons to be placed in the Lewis structure. Three pairs of electrons are placed around each oxygen: :Ö—C—Ö:	A total of six electrons have been used to bond the atoms to the central atom. This leaves eight more electrons to place around the rest of the atoms in pairs. Hydrogen does not require any more electrons: H—N̈—C̈l: (with H bonded below N)
4. If any atom (except hydrogen) lacks an octet, form double or triple bonds as necessary to satisfy the octet rule.	Carbon lacks an octet. To provide an octet, C requires four more electrons. It can share one pair from each O, forming two double bonds: :Ö—C—Ö: ⟶ Ö=C=Ö	Each atom requiring an octet has one, and all 14 electrons are accounted for. No multiple bonding is required, and the Lewis structure for monochloroamine is correct as shown above.
	FOR PRACTICE 9.1 Draw the Lewis structure for CO.	**FOR PRACTICE 9.2** Draw the Lewis structure for H_2CO. Carbon is the central atom.

Lewis theory predicts the properties of molecular compounds in many ways. First, it accounts for why particular combinations of atoms form molecules and others do not. For example, why is water H_2O and not H_3O? We can write a good Lewis structure for H_2O, but not for H_3O:

H—Ö—H H—O—H (with H bonded above O)

Oxygen has nine electrons (one electron beyond an octet)

In this way, Lewis theory predicts that H_2O should be stable, while H_3O should not be, and that is in fact the case. However, if we remove an electron from H_3O, we get H_3O^+, which should be stable (according to Lewis theory) because, by removing the extra electron, oxygen has an octet:

$$\left[\begin{array}{c} \mathrm{H} \\ | \\ \mathrm{H}-\underset{\cdot\cdot}{\mathrm{O}}-\mathrm{H} \end{array}\right]^+$$

This ion, called the hydronium ion, is stable. Lewis theory predicts other possible combinations for hydrogen and oxygen as well. For example, we can write a Lewis structure for H_2O_2 as follows:

$$\mathrm{H}-\ddot{\underset{\cdot\cdot}{\mathrm{O}}}-\ddot{\underset{\cdot\cdot}{\mathrm{O}}}-\mathrm{H}$$

Indeed, H_2O_2, or hydrogen peroxide, exists and is often used as a disinfectant and a bleach.

Lewis theory also accounts for why covalent bonds are highly *directional*. The attraction between two covalently bonded atoms is due to the sharing of one or more electron pairs in the space between them. Thus, each bond links just one specific pair of atoms—*in contrast to ionic bonds, which are nondirectional and hold together an entire array of ions.* As a result, the fundamental units of covalently bonded compounds are individual molecules. These molecules can interact with one another in a number of different ways that we cover in Chapter 11. However, in covalently bonded molecular compounds, the interactions *between* molecules (intermolecular forces) are generally much weaker than the bonding interactions within a molecule (intramolecular forces), as shown in Figure 9.3 ▼. When a molecular compound melts or boils, the molecules themselves remain intact—only the relatively weak interactions between molecules must be overcome. Consequently, molecular compounds tend to have lower melting and boiling points than ionic compounds.

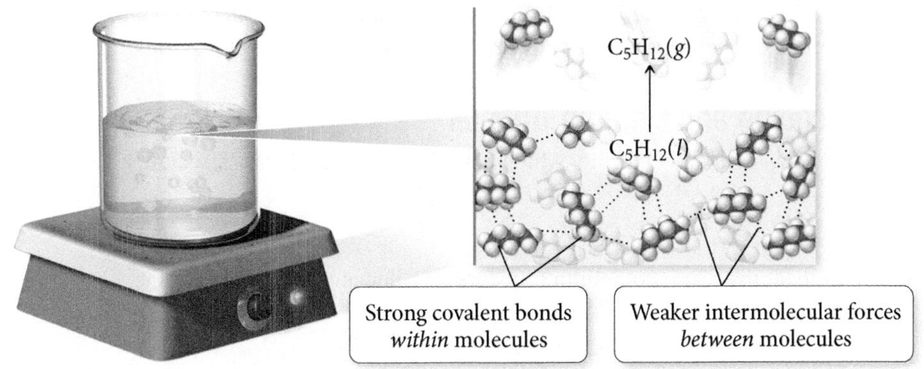

◀ **FIGURE 9.3 Intermolecular and Intramolecular Forces** The covalent bonds between atoms of a molecule are much stronger than the interactions between molecules. To boil a molecular substance, you simply have to overcome the relatively weak intermolecular forces, so molecular compounds generally have low boiling points.

CONCEPTUAL CONNECTION 9.1

Energy and the Octet Rule

What is wrong with the following statement? *Atoms form bonds in order to satisfy the octet rule.*

Writing Lewis Structures for Polyatomic Ions

We write Lewis structures for polyatomic ions by following the same procedure as the previous one, but we pay special attention to the charge of the ion when calculating the number of electrons for the Lewis structure. When counting the electrons in the first step, we add one electron for each negative charge and subtract one electron for each positive charge. The Lewis structure for a polyatomic ion is usually written within brackets with the charge of the ion in the upper-right corner, outside the bracket.

EXAMPLE 9.3 DRAWING LEWIS STRUCTURES OF POLYATOMIC IONS

Draw the Lewis Structure for the hypochlorite ion, ClO^-.

SOLUTION

Begin by counting the number of electrons to be included in the Lewis structure by summing the number of valence electrons for each atom and adding one for the negative charge.	Total number of electrons for Lewis structure $= \begin{pmatrix}\text{number of}\\ \text{valence } e^-\\ \text{for Cl}\end{pmatrix} + \begin{pmatrix}\text{number of}\\ \text{valence } e^-\\ \text{for O}\end{pmatrix} + \begin{pmatrix}1\ e^-\\ \text{to account}\\ \text{for charge}\end{pmatrix}$ $= 7 + 6 + 1 = 14$
Draw the skeletal structure, including the bond between Cl and O.	Cl—O
The bond accounts for 2 electrons, which leaves 12 more electrons to place around the atoms in pairs: 3 pairs around each of Cl and O.	:C̤̈l—Ö̤:
Because each atom has an octet, the final step is to draw the Lewis structure in brackets with the charge of the ion in the upper-right corner.	$[$:C̤̈l—Ö̤:$]^-$

FOR PRACTICE 9.3
Write a Lewis structure for the ammonium ion, NH_4^+.

Although Lewis theory's strength is in modelling covalent bonding, it can also be applied to ionic bonding. To represent ionic bonding, we move electron dots from the Lewis structure of the metal to the Lewis structure of the nonmetal and then allow the resultant ions to form a crystalline lattice composed of alternating cations and anions.

Ionic Bonding and Electron Transfer

Consider potassium and chlorine, which have the following Lewis structures:

K·   :C̤̈l:

When these atoms bond, potassium transfers its valence electron to chlorine:

K· + :C̤̈l: ⟶ K^+ $[$:C̤̈l:$]^-$

The transfer of the electron gives chlorine an octet (shown as eight dots around chlorine) and leaves potassium without any valence electrons but with an octet in the *previous* principal energy level (which is now the outermost level):

$$\text{K} \quad 1s^22s^22p^63s^23p^64s^1$$
$$\text{K}^+ \quad 1s^22s^22p^6\underbrace{3s^23p^6}_{\text{Octet in previous level}}$$

Recall that solid ionic compounds do not contain distinct molecules; they are composed of alternating positive and negative ions in a three-dimensional crystalline array.

The potassium, because it has lost an electron, becomes positively charged (a cation), while the chlorine, which has gained an electron, becomes negatively charged (an anion). The Lewis structure of an anion is usually written within brackets with the charge in the upper right-hand corner, outside the brackets. The positive and negative charges attract one another, resulting in the compound KCl.

So, we can use Lewis structures to predict the correct chemical formulas for ionic compounds. For the compound that forms between K and Cl, for example, the Lewis structures predict a ratio of one potassium cation to every one chloride anion, KCl. In nature, when we examine the compound formed between potassium and chlorine, we indeed find one potassium ion to every chloride ion. As another example, consider the ionic compound formed between sodium and sulfur. The Lewis structures for sodium and sulfur are:

$$\text{Na}\cdot \quad \cdot\ddot{\text{S}}:$$

Sodium must lose its one valence electron in order to have an octet (in the previous principal shell), while sulfur must gain two electrons to get an octet. Consequently, the compound that forms between sodium and sulfur requires a ratio of two sodium atoms to every one sulfur atom. The Lewis structure is:

$$2\text{Na}^+ \left[:\ddot{\text{S}}:\right]^{2-}$$

The two sodium atoms each lose their one valence electron, while the sulfur atom gains two electrons and gets an octet. The Lewis structures predict that the correct chemical formula is Na_2S, exactly what we see in nature.

9.5 The Ionic Bonding Model

The formation of an ionic compound from its constituent elements is usually quite exothermic. For example, when sodium chloride (table salt) forms from elemental sodium and chlorine, 411 kJ of heat is evolved in the following violent reaction:

$$\text{Na}(s) + \tfrac{1}{2}\text{Cl}_2(g) \rightarrow \text{NaCl}(s) \qquad \Delta_f H^\circ = -411 \text{ kJ mol}^{-1}$$

Where does this energy come from? We may think that it comes solely from the tendency of metals to lose electrons and nonmetals to gain electrons—but it does not. In fact, the transfer of an electron from sodium to chlorine—by itself—actually *absorbs* energy. The first ionization energy of sodium is 496 kJ mol^{-1} and the electron affinity of Cl is only 349 kJ mol^{-1}. Based only on these energies, the reaction should be *endothermic* by 147 kJ mol^{-1}. So, why is the reaction so *exothermic*?

Remember that an ionization energy of 496 kJ mol^{-1} means that 496 kJ of energy is required to remove a mole of electrons from a mole of Na atoms. An electron affinity of 349 kJ mol^{-1} means that 349 kJ of energy is released when a mole of electrons are put onto a mole of Cl atoms.

The answer lies in the **lattice energy**—the energy associated with forming a crystalline lattice of alternating cations and anions from the gaseous ions. Since the sodium ions are positively charged and the chlorine ions negatively charged, the potential energy decreases—as prescribed by Coulomb's law—when these ions come together to form a lattice. That energy is emitted as heat when the lattice forms, as shown in Figure 9.4 ▼. The exact value of the lattice energy, however, is not simple to determine because it involves a large number of interactions among many charged particles in a lattice. The easiest way to calculate lattice energy is with the *Born–Haber cycle*.

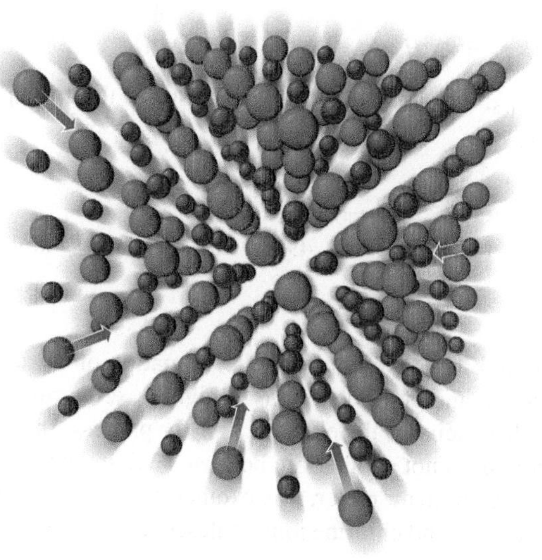

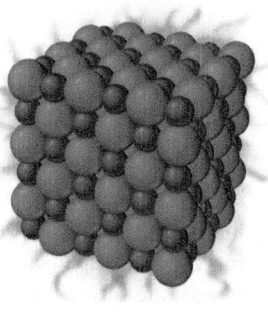

◀ **FIGURE 9.4 Lattice Energy** The lattice energy of an ionic compound is the energy associated with forming a crystalline lattice of the compound from the gaseous ions.

Recall that Hess's law states that the change in the overall enthalpy of a stepwise process is the sum of the enthalpy changes of the steps.

The Born–Haber Cycle

The **Born–Haber cycle** is a hypothetical series of steps that represents the formation of an ionic compound from its constituent elements. The steps are chosen so that the change in enthalpy of each step is known except for the last one, which is the lattice energy. The change in enthalpy for the overall process is also known. Using Hess's law (see Section 6.8), we can therefore determine the enthalpy change for the unknown last step, the lattice energy.

Consider the formation of NaCl from its constituent elements in their standard states. The enthalpy change for the overall reaction is simply the standard enthalpy of formation of NaCl(*s*):

$$\mathrm{Na}(s) + \tfrac{1}{2}\mathrm{Cl_2}(g) \longrightarrow \mathrm{NaCl}(s) \qquad \Delta_f H^\circ = -411 \text{ kJ mol}^{-1}$$

Now consider the following set of steps—the Born–Haber cycle—from which NaCl(*s*) can also be made from Na(*s*) and $Cl_2(g)$:

- The first step is the formation of gaseous sodium from solid sodium:

$$\mathrm{Na}(s) \longrightarrow \mathrm{Na}(g) \qquad \Delta_r H^\circ_{\text{step 1}} \text{ (sublimation energy of Na)} = 108 \text{ kJ mol}^{-1}$$

- The second step is the formation of a chlorine atom from a chlorine molecule:

$$\tfrac{1}{2}\mathrm{Cl_2}(g) \longrightarrow \mathrm{Cl}(g) \qquad \Delta_r H^\circ_{\text{step 2}} \text{ (bond energy of Cl}_2 \times \tfrac{1}{2}) = 122 \text{ kJ mol}^{-1}$$

- The third step is the ionization of gaseous sodium. The enthalpy change for this step is the ionization energy of sodium:

$$\mathrm{Na}(g) \longrightarrow \mathrm{Na^+}(g) + e^- \qquad \Delta_r H^\circ_{\text{step 3}} \text{ (ionization energy of Na)} = 496 \text{ kJ mol}^{-1}$$

- The fourth step is the addition of an electron to gaseous chlorine. The enthalpy change for this step is related to the electron affinity of chlorine:

$$\mathrm{Cl}(g) + e^- \longrightarrow \mathrm{Cl^-}(g) \qquad \Delta_r H^\circ_{\text{step 4}} \text{ (negative of electron affinity)} = -349 \text{ kJ mol}^{-1}$$

- The fifth and final step is the formation of the crystalline solid from the gaseous ions. The enthalpy change for this step is the lattice energy, the unknown quantity:

$$\mathrm{Na^+}(g) + \mathrm{Cl^-}(g) \longrightarrow \mathrm{NaCl}(s) \qquad \Delta_r H^\circ_{\text{step 5}} = \Delta_r H^\circ_{\text{lattice}} = ?$$

The entire Born–Haber cycle for NaCl is shown in Figure 9.5 ▶.

Since the overall reaction obtained by summing the steps in the Born–Haber cycle is equivalent to the formation of NaCl from its constituent elements, we can use Hess's law to set the overall enthalpy of formation for NaCl(*s*) equal to the sum of the steps in the Born–Haber cycle:

lattice energy ↓

$$\Delta_f H^\circ = \Delta_r H^\circ_{\text{step 1}} + \Delta_r H^\circ_{\text{step 2}} + \Delta_r H^\circ_{\text{step 3}} + \Delta_r H^\circ_{\text{step 4}} + \Delta_r H^\circ_{\text{step 5}}$$

We then solve this equation for $\Delta_r H^\circ_{\text{step 5}}$, which is $\Delta_r H^\circ_{\text{lattice}}$, and substitute the appropriate values to calculate the lattice energy:

$$\begin{aligned}\Delta_r H^\circ_{\text{lattice}} = \Delta H^\circ_{\text{step 5}} &= \Delta_f H^\circ - (\Delta_r H^\circ_{\text{step 1}} + \Delta_r H^\circ_{\text{step 2}} + \Delta_r H^\circ_{\text{step 3}} + \Delta_r H^\circ_{\text{step 4}}) \\ &= -411 \text{ kJ mol}^{-1} - (+108 \text{ kJ mol}^{-1} + 122 \text{ kJ mol}^{-1} + 496 \text{ kJ mol}^{-1} - 349 \text{ kJ mol}^{-1}) \\ &= -788 \text{ kJ mol}^{-1}\end{aligned}$$

The value of the lattice energy is a large negative number. The formation of the crystalline NaCl lattice from sodium cations and chloride anions is highly exothermic and more than compensates for the endothermicity of the electron transfer process. In other words, the formation of ionic compounds is not exothermic because sodium "wants" to lose electrons and chlorine "wants" to gain them; rather, it is exothermic because of the large amount of heat released when sodium and chlorine ions coalesce to form a crystalline lattice.

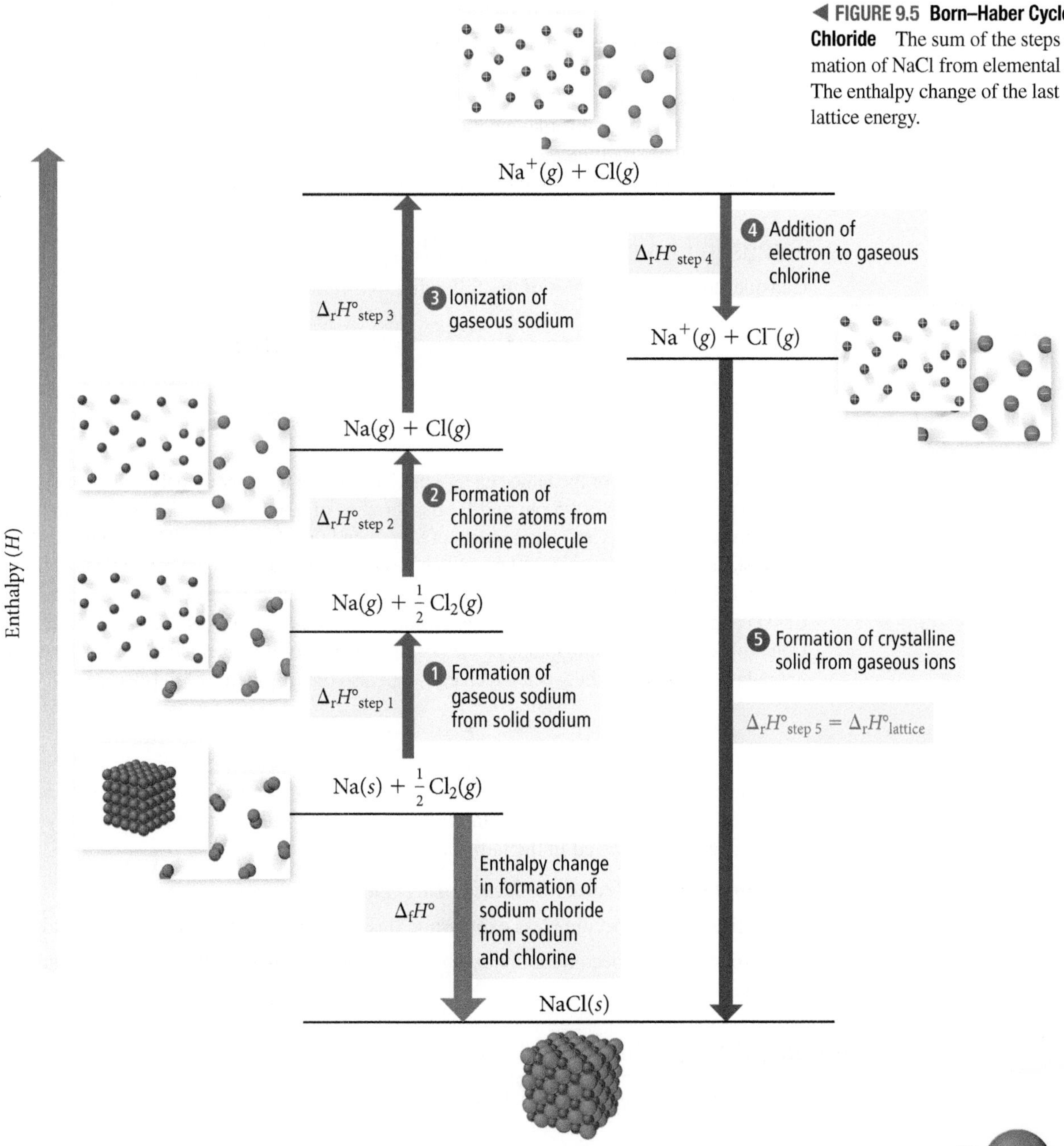

◀ **FIGURE 9.5 Born–Haber Cycle for Sodium Chloride** The sum of the steps is the formation of NaCl from elemental Na and Cl. The enthalpy change of the last step is the lattice energy.

Enthalpy (H)

$Na^+(g) + Cl(g)$

④ Addition of electron to gaseous chlorine — $\Delta_r H°_{step\ 4}$

$Na^+(g) + Cl^-(g)$

③ Ionization of gaseous sodium — $\Delta_r H°_{step\ 3}$

$Na(g) + Cl(g)$

② Formation of chlorine atoms from chlorine molecule — $\Delta_r H°_{step\ 2}$

$Na(g) + \frac{1}{2}Cl_2(g)$

① Formation of gaseous sodium from solid sodium — $\Delta_r H°_{step\ 1}$

$Na(s) + \frac{1}{2}Cl_2(g)$

⑤ Formation of crystalline solid from gaseous ions — $\Delta_r H°_{step\ 5} = \Delta_r H°_{lattice}$

Enthalpy change in formation of sodium chloride from sodium and chlorine — $\Delta_f H°$

$NaCl(s)$

Trends in Lattice Energies: Ion Size

Consider the lattice energies of the following alkali metal chlorides:

Metal Chloride	Lattice Energy (kJ mol^{-1})
LiCl	−834
NaCl	−788
KCl	−701
CsCl	−657

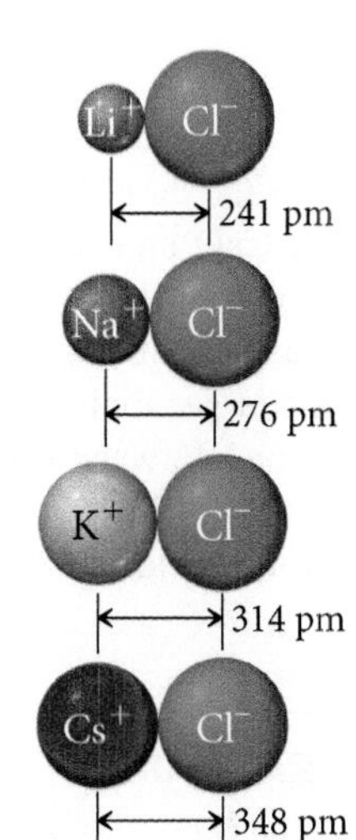

▲ Bond lengths of the group 1 metal chlorides.

Why do you suppose that the magnitude of the lattice energy decreases as we move down the column? We know from the periodic trends discussed in Chapter 8 that ionic radius increases as we move down a column in the periodic table (see Section 8.6). We also know, from our discussion of Coulomb's law in Section 7.7, that the potential energy of oppositely charged ions becomes less negative (or more positive) as the distance between the ions increases. As the size of the alkali metal ions increases down the column, so does the distance between the metal cations and the chloride anions. The magnitude of the lattice energy of the chlorides decreases accordingly, making the formation of the chlorides less exothermic. In other words, *as the ionic radii increase as we move down the column, the ions cannot get as close to each other and therefore do not release as much energy when the lattice forms.*

Trends in Lattice Energies: Ion Charge

Consider the lattice energies of the following two compounds:

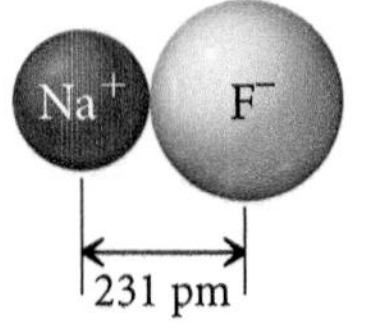

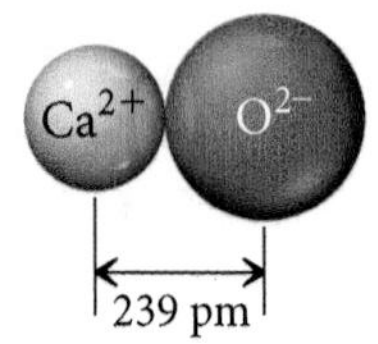

Compound	Lattice Energy (kJ mol^{-1})
NaF	−910
CaO	−3414

Why is the magnitude of the lattice energy of CaO so much greater than the lattice energy of NaF? Na^+ has a radius of 95 pm and F^- has a radius of 136 pm, resulting in a distance between ions of 231 pm. Ca^{2+} has a radius of 99 pm and O^{2-} has a radius of 140 pm, resulting in a distance between ions of 239 pm. Even though the separation between the calcium and oxygen is slightly greater (which would tend to lower the lattice energy), the lattice energy for CaO is almost four times *greater*. The explanation lies in the charges of the ions. Recall from Coulomb's law that the magnitude of the potential energy of two interacting charges depends not only on the distance between the charges, but also on the product of the charges:

$$E = \frac{1}{4\pi\varepsilon_0}\frac{q_1q_2}{r}$$

For NaF, E is proportional to $(1+)(1-) = 1-$, while for CaO, E is proportional to $(2+)(2-) = 4-$, so the relative stabilization for CaO relative to NaF is roughly four times greater, as observed in the lattice energy.

Summarizing Trends in Lattice Energies:

- Lattice energies become less exothermic (less negative) with increasing ionic radius.
- Lattice energies become more exothermic (more negative) with increasing magnitude of ionic charge.

EXAMPLE 9.4 **PREDICTING RELATIVE LATTICE ENERGIES**

Arrange these ionic compounds in order of increasing *magnitude* of lattice energy: CaO, KBr, KCl, SrO.

SOLUTION

KBr and KCl should have lattice energies of smaller magnitude than CaO and SrO because of their lower ionic charges (1+, 1− compared to 2+, 2−). When we compare KBr and KCl, we expect KBr to have a lattice energy of lower magnitude due to the larger ionic radius of the bromide ion relative to the chloride ion. Between CaO and SrO, we expect SrO to have a lattice energy of lower magnitude due to the larger ionic radius of the strontium ion relative to the calcium ion.

Order of increasing *magnitude* of lattice energy:

$$KBr < KCl < SrO < CaO$$

Actual lattice energy values:

Compound	Lattice Energy (kJ mol^{-1})
KBr	−671
KCl	−701
SrO	−3217
CaO	−3414

FOR PRACTICE 9.4

Arrange the following in order of increasing magnitude of lattice energy: LiBr, KI, and CaO.

FOR MORE PRACTICE 9.4

Which compound has a lattice energy of higher magnitude, NaCl or $MgCl_2$?

Ionic Bonding: Models and Reality

Ionic compounds do not exist as ion pairs. Rather, the model we have of an ionic solid is a lattice of alternating positive and negative ions held together by the strong coulombic forces of attraction which are equal in all directions. The value of a model is in how well it accounts for what we see in nature (through experiments). Can this model explain the properties of ionic compounds, including their high melting and boiling points, their tendency *not to conduct* electricity as solids, and their tendency *to conduct* electricity when dissolved in water or when in the molten state?

To melt the ionic solid, the coulombic forces must be overcome, which requires a significant amount of heat, as seen below. Therefore, our model accounts for the high melting points of ionic solids. In our model, electrons are transferred from the metal to the nonmetal making cations and anions, respectively. The transferred electrons remain localized on the anion. In other words, our model does not include any free electrons that might conduct electricity, and the ions themselves are fixed in place. Therefore, our model accounts for the nonconductivity of ionic solids. When we melt an ionic solid, the ions are no longer fixed in place and become mobile—they are free to move around one another. When our idealized ionic solid dissolves in water, the cations and anions dissociate from one another, forming free ions in solution. The ions in both the molten state and in solution move in response to electrical forces, creating an electrical current. Thus, our model predicts that solutions of ionic compounds and molten salts conduct electricity (which, in fact, they do).

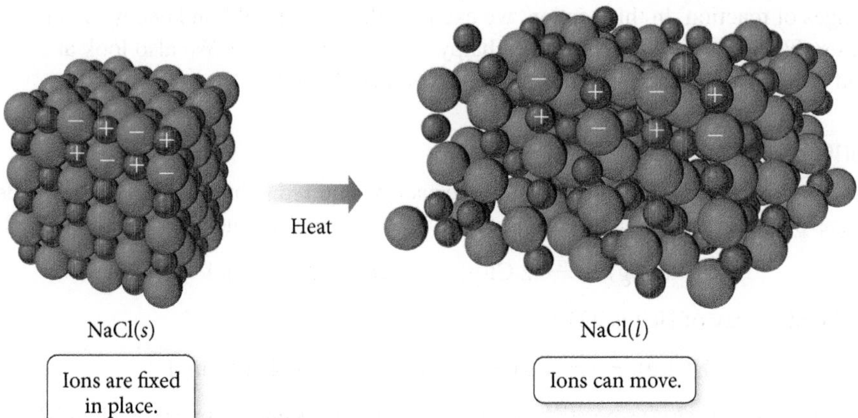

◀ The melting of solid ionic compounds such as sodium chloride requires enough heat to overcome the electrical forces holding the anions and cations together in a lattice. Thus, the melting points of ionic compounds are relatively high.

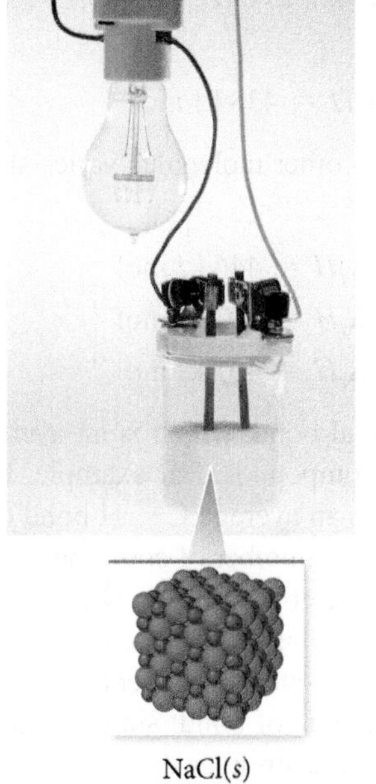

▲ Solid sodium chloride does not conduct electricity.

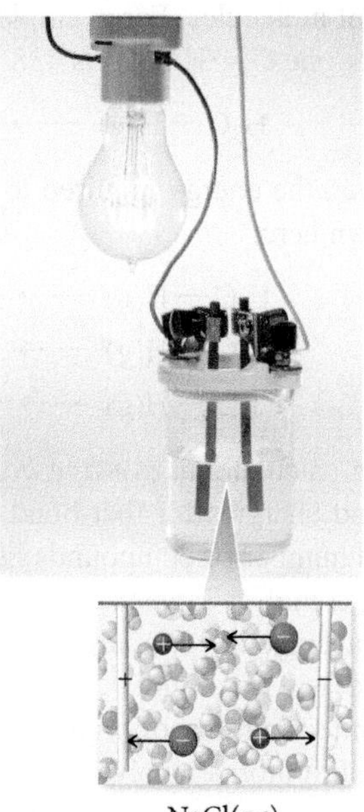

▲ When sodium chloride dissolves in water, the resulting solution contains mobile ions that can create an electric current.

CONCEPTUAL CONNECTION 9.2
Melting Points of Ionic Solids

Use the ionic bonding model to determine which has the higher melting point, NaCl or MgO. Explain the relative ordering.

9.6 Covalent Bond Energies, Lengths, and Vibrations

In Chapter 6, we learned how to calculate the standard enthalpy change for a chemical reaction ($\Delta_r H°$) from tabulated standard enthalpies of formation. However, sometimes we may not easily find standard enthalpies of formation for all of the reactants and products of a reaction. In such cases, we can use individual *bond energies* to estimate enthalpy changes of reaction. In this section, we examine the concept of bond energy and how we can use bond energies to calculate enthalpy changes of reaction. We also look at average bond lengths for a number of commonly encountered bonds.

Bond Energy

Bond energy is also called *bond enthalpy* or *bond dissociation energy.*

The **bond energy** of a chemical bond is the energy required to break 1 mol of the bonds in the gas phase. For example, the bond energy of the Cl—Cl bond in Cl_2 is 243 kJ mol^{-1}:

$$Cl_2(g) \longrightarrow 2\,Cl(g) \qquad \Delta_r H = 243 \text{ kJ mol}^{-1}$$

The bond energy of HCl is 431 kJ mol^{-1}:

$$HCl(g) \longrightarrow H(g) + Cl(g) \qquad \Delta_r H = 431 \text{ kJ mol}^{-1}$$

Bond energies are always positive because it always takes energy to break a bond. We say that the HCl bond is *stronger* than the Cl_2 bond because it requires more energy to break it. In general, compounds with stronger bonds tend to be more chemically stable, and therefore less chemically reactive, than compounds with weaker bonds. The triple bond in N_2 has a bond energy of 946 kJ mol^{-1}:

$$N_2(g) \longrightarrow N(g) + N(g) \qquad \Delta_r H = 946 \text{ kJ mol}^{-1}$$

It is a very strong and stable bond, which explains nitrogen's relative inertness.

The bond energy of a particular bond in a polyatomic molecule is a little more difficult to determine because a particular type of bond can have different bond energies in different molecules. For example, consider the C—H bond. In CH_4, the energy required to break one C—H bond is 438 kJ mol^{-1}:

$$H_3C{-}H(g) \longrightarrow H_3C(g) + H(g) \qquad \Delta_r H = 438 \text{ kJ mol}^{-1}$$

However, the energy required to break a C—H bond in other molecules varies slightly, as shown here:

$$F_3C{-}H(g) \longrightarrow F_3C(g) + H(g) \qquad \Delta_r H = 446 \text{ kJ mol}^{-1}$$
$$Br_3C{-}H(g) \longrightarrow Br_3C(g) + H(g) \qquad \Delta_r H = 402 \text{ kJ mol}^{-1}$$
$$Cl_3C{-}H(g) \longrightarrow Cl_3C(g) + H(g) \qquad \Delta_r H = 401 \text{ kJ mol}^{-1}$$

We can calculate an *average bond energy* for a chemical bond, which is an average of the bond energies for that bond in a large number of compounds. For example, for the limited number of compounds listed above, we calculate an average C—H bond energy of 422 kJ mol^{-1}. Table 9.1 lists average bond energies for a number of common chemical bonds averaged over a large number of compounds. Notice that the C—H bond energy is listed as 414 kJ mol^{-1}, which is not too different from the value we calculated from our limited number of compounds. Notice also that bond energies depend not only on the kind of atoms involved in the bond, but also on the type of bond: single, double, or triple. In general, for a given pair of atoms, triple bonds are stronger than double bonds, which are, in turn, stronger than single bonds. For example, consider the bond energies of carbon–carbon triple, double, and single bonds listed at left.

Bond	Bond Energy (kJ mol^{-1})
C≡C	837
C=C	611
C—C	347

TABLE 9.1 Average Bond Energies

Bond	Bond Energy ($kJ\ mol^{-1}$)	Bond	Bond Energy ($kJ\ mol^{-1}$)	Bond	Bond Energy ($kJ\ mol^{-1}$)
H—H	436	N—N	163	Br—F	237
H—C	414	N═N	418	Br—Cl	218
H—N	389	N≡N	946	Br—Br	193
H—O	464	N—O	222	I—Cl	208
H—S	368	N═O	590	I—Br	175
H—F	565	N—F	272	I—I	151
H—Cl	431	N—Cl	200	Si—H	323
H—Br	364	N—Br	243	Si—Si	226
H—I	297	N—I	159	Si—C	301
C—C	347	O—O	142	Si—O	450
C═C	611	O═O	498	Si—Si	226
C≡C	837	O—F	190	Si═O	523
C—N	305	O—Cl	203	Si—Cl	391
C═N	615	O—I	234	S—F	285
C≡N	891	F—F	159	S—O	265
C—O	360	Cl—F	253	S═O	515
C═O	736*	Cl—Cl	243	S—Cl	253
C≡O	1072			S—Br	218
C—Cl	339			S—S	266
				S═S	418

*799 in CO_2

Using Average Bond Energies to Estimate Enthalpy Changes for Reactions

We can use average bond energies to *estimate* the enthalpy change of a reaction. For example, consider the following reaction:

$$H_3C—H(g) + Cl—Cl(g) \longrightarrow H_3C—Cl(g) + H—Cl(g)$$

We can imagine this reaction occurring by the breaking of a C—H bond and a Cl—Cl bond and the forming of a C—Cl bond and an H—Cl bond. We know that when bonds break, the process is endothermic (positive bond energy), and when bonds form, the process is exothermic (negative bond energy). So, we can calculate the overall enthalpy change as a sum of the enthalpy changes associated with breaking the required bonds in the reactants and forming the required bonds in the products, as shown in Figure 9.6 ▼.

$$H_3C—H(g) + Cl—Cl(g) \longrightarrow H_3C—Cl(g) + H—Cl(g)$$

Bonds Broken		**Bonds Formed**	
C—H break	$+414\ kJ\ mol^{-1}$	C—Cl form	$-339\ kJ\ mol^{-1}$
Cl—Cl break	$+243\ kJ\ mol^{-1}$	H—Cl form	$-431\ kJ\ mol^{-1}$

Sum (Σ) $\Delta_r H$*'s bonds broken*: $+657\ kJ\ mol^{-1}$ *Sum* (Σ) $\Delta_r H$*'s bonds formed*: $-770\ kJ\ mol^{-1}$

$$\begin{aligned}\Delta_r H &= \Sigma(\Delta_r H\text{'s bonds broken}) + \Sigma(\Delta_r H\text{'s bonds formed})\\ &= +657\ kJ\ mol^{-1} - 770\ kJ\ mol^{-1}\\ &= -113\ kJ\ mol^{-1}\end{aligned}$$

We find that $\Delta_r H = -113\ kJ\ mol^{-1}$. Calculating $\Delta_r H^\circ$ from tabulated enthalpies of formation—as we learned in Chapter 6—gives $\Delta_r H^\circ = -101\ kJ\ mol^{-1}$—fairly close to

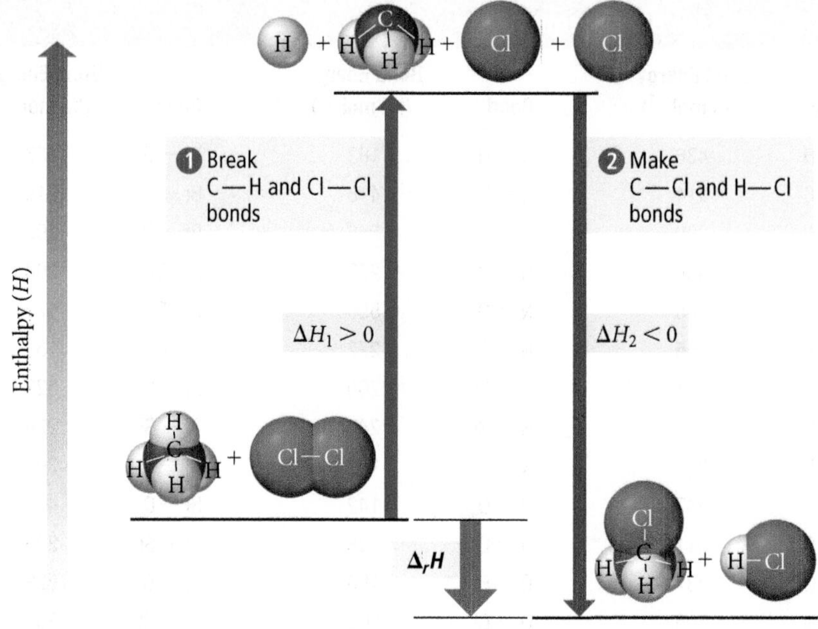

▶ **FIGURE 9.6 Estimating $\Delta_r H$ from Bond Energies** We can approximate the enthalpy change of a reaction by summing up the enthalpy changes involved in breaking old bonds and forming new ones.

the value we obtained from average bond energies. In general, you can calculate $\Delta_r H$ from average bond energies by summing the changes in enthalpy for all of the bonds that are broken and adding the sum of the enthalpy changes for all of the bonds that are formed. Remember that $\Delta_r H$ is positive for breaking bonds and negative for forming them:

$$\Delta_r H = \underbrace{\Sigma(\Delta_r H\text{'s bonds broken})}_{\text{Positive}} + \underbrace{\Sigma(\Delta_r H\text{'s bonds formed})}_{\text{Negative}}$$

As you can see from the above equation:

- A reaction is *exothermic* when weak bonds break and strong bonds form.
- A reaction is *endothermic* when strong bonds break and weak bonds form.

Scientists often say that "energy is stored in chemical bonds or in a chemical compound," which may make it sound as if breaking the bonds in the compound releases energy. For example, in biology, we often hear that energy is stored in glucose or in ATP. However, *breaking a chemical bond always requires energy.* When scientists say that energy is stored in a compound, or that a compound is energy rich, it means that the compound can undergo a reaction in which weak bonds break and strong bonds form, releasing energy. *It is always the forming of chemical bonds that releases energy.*

CONCEPTUAL CONNECTION 9.3

Bond Energies and $\Delta_r H$

The reaction between hydrogen and oxygen to form water is highly exothermic. Which of the following is true of the energies of the bonds that break and form during the reaction?

(a) The energy needed to break the required bonds is greater than the energy released when the new bonds form.

(b) The energy needed to break the required bonds is less than the energy released when the new bonds form.

(c) The energy needed to break the required bonds is about the same as the energy released when the new bonds form.

EXAMPLE 9.5 **CALCULATING $\Delta_r H$ FROM BOND ENERGIES**

Hydrogen gas, a potential fuel, can be made by the reaction of methane gas and steam:

$$CH_4(g) + 2\,H_2O(g) \longrightarrow 4\,H_2(g) + CO_2(g)$$

Use bond energies to calculate $\Delta_r H$ for this reaction.

SOLUTION

Begin by rewriting the reaction using the Lewis structures of the molecules involved.	H—C(H)(H)—H + 2 H—Ö—H ⟶ 4 H—H + Ö=C=Ö
Determine which bonds are broken in the reaction and sum the bond energies of these.	H—C(H)(H)—H + 2 H—Ö—H $\Sigma(\Delta_r H\text{'s bond broken})$ $= 4(C—H) + 4(O—H)$ $= 4(414\text{ kJ mol}^{-1}) + 4(464\text{ kJ mol}^{-1})$ $= 3512\text{ kJ mol}^{-1}$
Determine which bonds are formed in the reaction and sum the negatives of their bond energies.	4 H—H + Ö=C=Ö $\Sigma(\Delta_r H\text{'s bonds formed})$ $= -4(H—H) - 2(C=O)$ $= -4(436\text{ kJ mol}^{-1}) - 2(799\text{ kJ mol}^{-1})$ $= -3342\text{ kJ mol}^{-1}$
Find $\Delta_r H$ by summing the results of the previous two steps.	$\Delta_r H = \Sigma(\Delta_r H\text{'s bonds broken}) + \Sigma(\Delta_r H\text{'s bonds formed})$ $= 3512 - 3342$ $= 170\text{ kJ mol}^{-1}$

FOR PRACTICE 9.5

Another potential future fuel is methanol (CH_3OH). Write a balanced equation for the combustion of gaseous methanol and use bond energies to calculate the enthalpy of combustion of methanol in kJ mol^{-1}.

FOR MORE PRACTICE 9.5

Use bond energies to calculate $\Delta_r H$ for this reaction: $N_2(g) + 3\,H_2(g) \longrightarrow 2\,NH_3(g)$.

Bond Lengths

Just as we can tabulate average bond energies, which represent the average energy of a bond between two particular atoms in a large number of compounds, we can tabulate average bond lengths (Table 9.2). The average **bond length** represents the average length of a bond between two particular atoms in a large number of compounds. Like bond energies, bond lengths depend not only on the kind of atoms involved in the bond, but also on the type of bond: single, double, or triple. In general, for a particular pair of atoms, triple bonds are shorter than double bonds, which are, in turn, shorter than single bonds. For example, consider the bond lengths (along with bond strengths, repeated from earlier in this section) of carbon–carbon triple, double, and single bonds:

Bond	Bond Length (pm)	Bond Strength (kJ mol^{-1})
C≡C	120	837
C=C	134	611
C—C	154	347

TABLE 9.2 Average Bond Lengths

Bond	Bond Length (pm)	Bond	Bond Length (pm)	Bond	Bond Length (pm)
H—H	74	C—C	154	N—N	145
H—C	110	C=C	134	N=N	123
H—N	100	C≡C	120	N≡N	110
H—O	97	C—N	147	N—O	136
H—S	132	C=N	128	N=O	120
H—F	92	C≡N	116	O—O	145
H—Cl	127	C—O	143	O=O	121
H—Br	141	C=O	120	F—F	143
H—I	161	C—Cl	178	Cl—Cl	199
Br—Br	228	I—I	266		

Notice that as the bond gets longer, it also becomes weaker. This relationship between the length of a bond and the strength of a bond does not necessarily hold for all bonds. Consider the following series of nitrogen–halogen single bonds:

Bond	Bond Length (pm)	Bond Strength (kJ mol^{-1})
N—F	139	272
N—Cl	191	200
N—Br	214	243
N—I	222	159

Bond Lengths

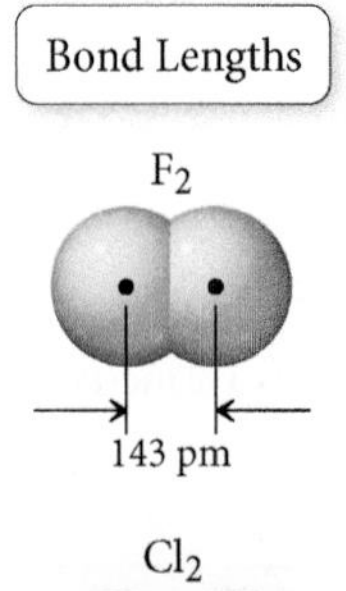

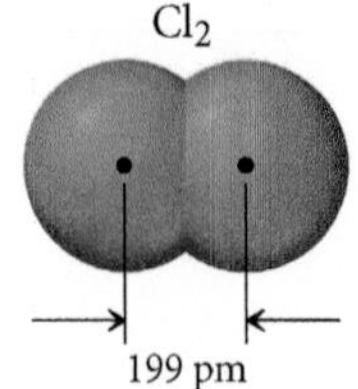

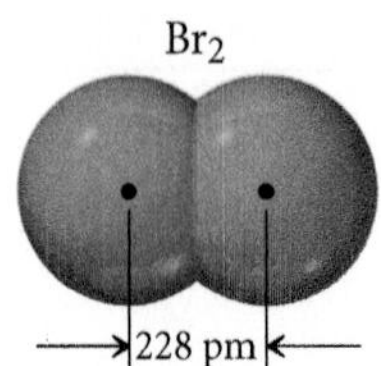

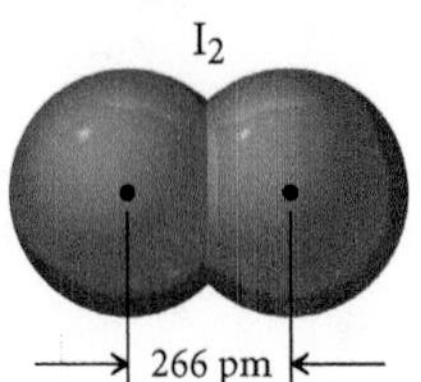

▲ Bond lengths in the diatomic halogen molecules.

Although the bonds generally get weaker as they get longer, the trend is not a smooth one.

Bond Vibrations

Bond lengths are not static. That is, when two atoms are bonded together, the distance between the atoms is not the same all the time. In fact, the two atoms move toward and away from each other continuously, like two balls attached to each other by a spring. This type of motion is called a **bond stretching vibration**, or a **stretching vibration**. Literally, the bond stretches and then contracts.

For a bond vibration to take place, energy must be supplied to the molecule. Energy can originate from molecular collisions or from the absorption of electromagnetic radiation in the infrared region because the infrared frequency range of electromagnetic radiation corresponds to the energies ($E = h\nu$) of molecular vibrations. The absorption of infrared radiation by a compound can be measured easily by irradiating the sample with an infrared source (called a glow bar) and measuring the intensity of radiation transmitted through the sample at each wavelength or frequency. This is called **infrared (IR) spectroscopy**.

In infrared absorption spectroscopy, rather than reporting the wavelength of absorptions, chemists use the reciprocal of wavelength, called the **wavenumber**, which is usually given in units of reciprocal centimetres (cm^{-1}). This unit is proportional to energy and frequency. Thus, the higher the wavenumber, the greater the energy of light that was absorbed.

In Figure 9.7 ▸, the wavenumber values of IR absorptions of HX (X=F, Cl, Br, I) molecules are plotted against the H—X bond energies. As the bond strength increases, so too does the wavenumber value of the absorption. In other words, it takes higher energy photons to excite the stretching vibration of HF, with a bond energy of 565 kJ mol^{-1}, than it does to excite the stretching vibration of HI, with a bond energy of 297 kJ mol^{-1}.

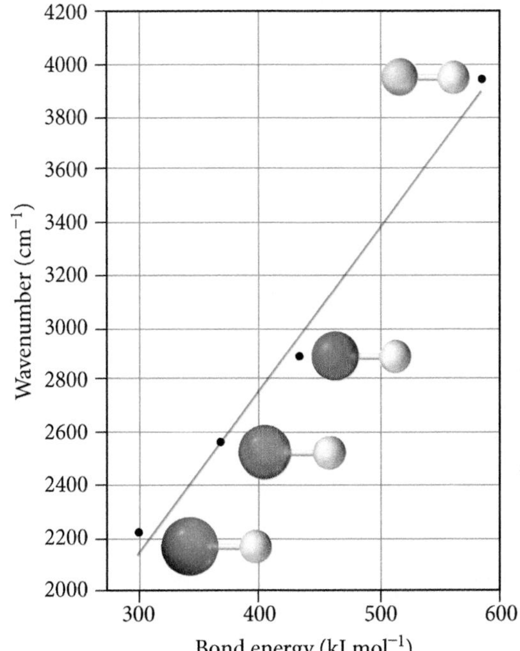

◀ **FIGURE 9.7 How Bond Strength Affects the Energy of Infrared Absorptions of H—X Stretching Vibrations** From left to right, in order of increasing bond energy, the compounds are HI, HBr, HCl, and HF.

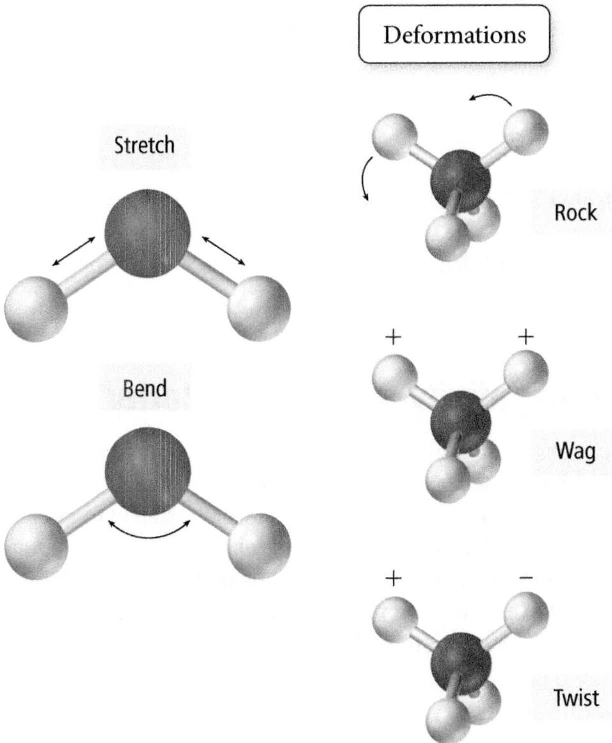

◀ **FIGURE 9.8 Some Vibrational Motions of Polyatomic Molecules** In the wag and twist deformations, the + and − signs refer to the movement of atoms in the axis perpendicular to the plane of the page.

For molecules that contain more than two atoms, other vibrational motions are possible. These include bending and deformations (Figure 9.8 ▲). Each vibrational motion requires a unique amount of energy to excite it, which means that infrared absorption spectra for different compounds are unique. Figure 9.9 ▼ shows the infrared absorption spectra for ethanol and ethanal. It is easy to tell that the two spectra are quite different, even for two similar compounds. One of these differences is that the position of the C=O stretch for ethanal is 1750 cm^{-1}, while the C—O stretch in ethanol occurs at lower energy—about 1050 cm^{-1}. The difference between the position

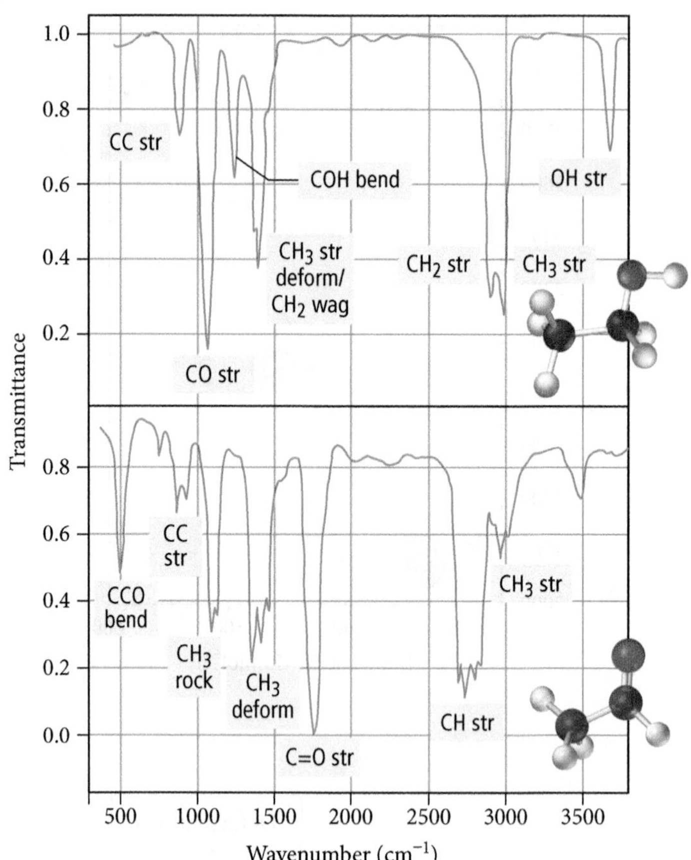

▶ **FIGURE 9.9 Infrared Absorption Spectra of Ethanol (Top Panel) and Ethanal (Lower Panel)**

of the C═O stretch and the C—O stretch is due in large part to the differences in bond energies.

In Chapter 20, we will discuss the details of how IR spectroscopy can be used to identify unknown compounds.

9.7 Electronegativity and Bond Polarity

Representing electrons with dots, as we do in Lewis theory, is a drastic oversimplification based on what we know about atomic orbitals from Chapter 7. As we have already discussed, this does not invalidate Lewis theory—which is an extremely useful theory—but we must recognize and compensate for its inherent limitations. One limitation of representing electrons as dots, and covalent bonds as lines shared between two atoms, is that the shared electrons always appear to be *equally* shared. Such is not the case. For example, consider the Lewis structure of hydrogen fluoride:

$$\mathrm{H{-}\ddot{\underset{..}{F}}\!:}$$

The two shared electron dots sitting between the H and F atoms appear to be equally shared between hydrogen and fluorine. However, based on laboratory measurements, we know they are not. When HF is put in an electric field, the molecules orient as shown in Figure 9.10 ▶. From this observation, we know that the hydrogen side of the molecule must have a slight positive charge and the fluorine side of the molecule must have a slight negative charge. We represent this partial separation of charge as follows:

$$\overset{+\!\!\longrightarrow}{\mathrm{H{-}F}} \quad or \quad \overset{\delta^+}{\mathrm{H}}{-}\overset{\delta^-}{\mathrm{F}}$$

The arrow on the left, with a positive sign on the tail, indicates that the left side of the molecule has a partial positive charge and that the right side of the molecule (the side

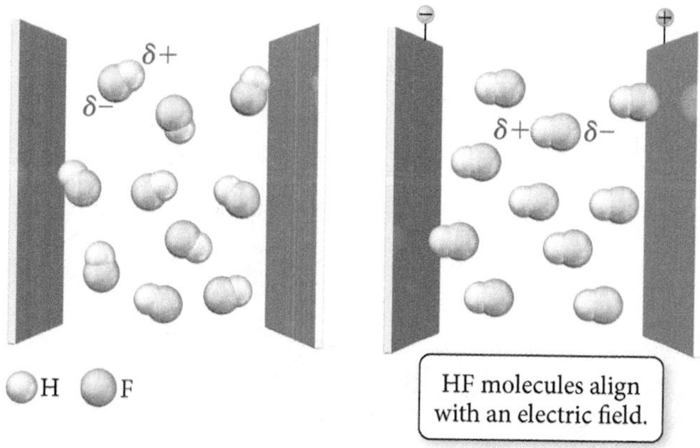

◀ **FIGURE 9.10 Orientation of Gaseous Hydrogen Fluoride in an Electric Field** Because one side of the HF molecule has a slight positive charge and the other side a slight negative charge, the molecules will align themselves with an external electric field.

the arrow is pointing *toward*) has a partial negative charge. Similarly, the δ+ (delta plus) represents a partial positive charge and the δ− (delta minus) represents a partial negative charge. Does this make the bond ionic? Not exactly. In an ionic bond, the electron is essentially *transferred* from one atom to another. In HF, the electron is *unequally shared*. In other words, even though the Lewis structure of HF portrays the bonding electrons as residing *between* the two atoms, in reality, the electron density is greater on the fluorine atom than on the hydrogen atom (Figure 9.11 ▶). The bond is said to be *polar*—having a positive pole and a negative pole. A **polar covalent bond** is intermediate in nature between a pure covalent bond and an ionic bond. In fact, the categories of pure covalent and ionic are really two extremes within a broad continuum. Most covalent bonds between dissimilar atoms are actually *polar covalent*, somewhere between the two extremes.

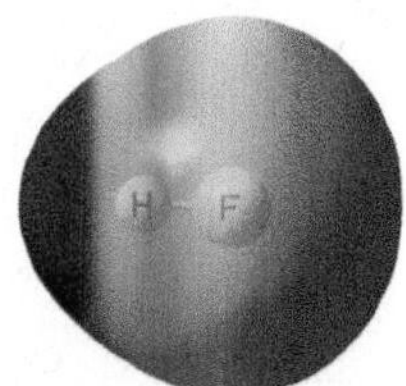

▲ **FIGURE 9.11 Electrostatic Potential Map for the HF Molecule** The F end of the molecule, with its partial negative charge, is red; the H end, with its partial positive charge, is blue.

Electronegativity

The ability of an atom to attract electrons to itself in a chemical bond (which results in polar and ionic bonds) is called **electronegativity**. We say that fluorine is more *electronegative* than hydrogen because it takes a greater share of the electron density in HF.

Electronegativity was quantified by the American chemist Linus Pauling (1901–1994) in his classic book, *The Nature of the Chemical Bond*. Pauling compared the bond energy of a heteronuclear diatomic molecule such as HF with the bond energies of its homonuclear counterparts—in this case, H_2 and F_2. The bond energies of H_2 and F_2 are 436 kJ mol^{-1} and 159 kJ mol^{-1}, respectively. Pauling reasoned that if the HF bond were purely covalent—that is, if the electrons were shared exactly equally—the bond energy of HF should simply be an average of the bond energies of H_2 and F_2, which would be 296 kJ mol^{-1}. However, the bond energy of HF is experimentally measured to be 565 kJ mol^{-1}. Pauling suggested that the additional bond energy was due to the *ionic character* of the bond. Based on many such comparisons of bond energies, and by arbitrarily assigning an electronegativity of 4.0 to fluorine (the most electronegative element on the periodic table), Pauling developed the electronegativity values shown in Figure 9.12 ▼.

▲ Electrostatic potential maps show a range of charge densities from high electron density (red) to low electron density (blue).

Pauling's "average" bond energy was actually calculated a little bit differently than the normal average shown here. He took the square root of the product of the bond energies of the homologs as the "average."

For main-group elements, notice the following periodic trends in electronegativity from Figure 9.12:

- Electronegativity generally increases across a period in the periodic table.
- Electronegativity generally decreases down a column in the periodic table.
- Fluorine is the most electronegative element.
- Francium is the least electronegative element (sometimes called the most *electropositive*).

The periodic trends in electronegativity are consistent with other periodic trends we have seen. In general, electronegativity is inversely related to atomic size—the larger the atom, the less ability it has to attract electrons to itself in a chemical bond.

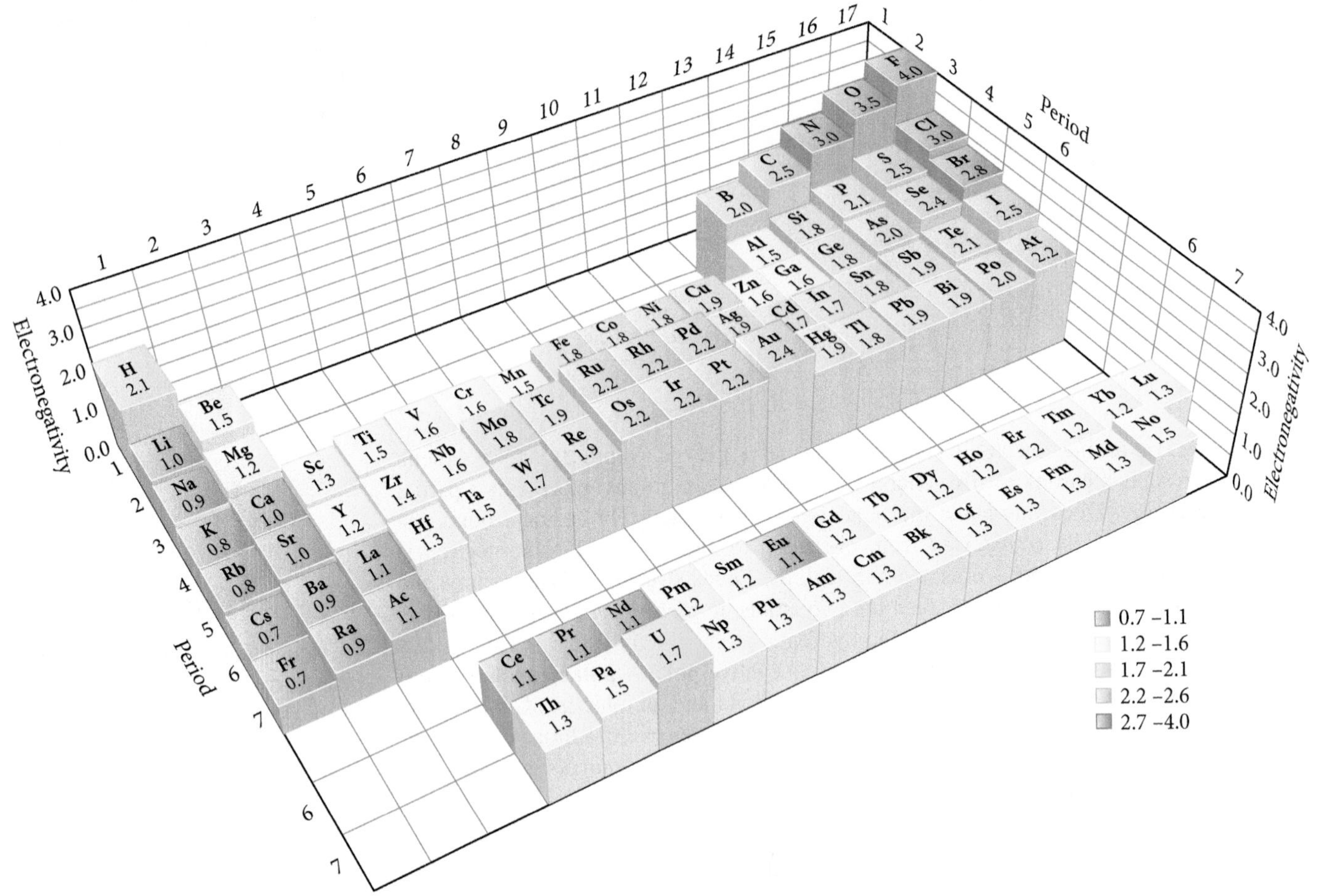

0.7 – 1.1
1.2 – 1.6
1.7 – 2.1
2.2 – 2.6
2.7 – 4.0

▲ **FIGURE 9.12 Electronegativities of the Elements** Electronegativity generally increases as we move across a row in the periodic table and decreases as we move down a column.

Bond Polarity, Dipole Moment, and Percent Ionic Character

The degree of polarity in a chemical bond depends on the electronegativity difference (sometimes abbreviated ΔEN) between the two bonding elements. The greater the electronegativity difference, the more polar the bond. If two elements with identical electronegativities form a covalent bond, they share the electrons equally, and the bond is purely covalent or *nonpolar*. For example, the chlorine molecule, composed of two chlorine atoms (which necessarily have identical electronegativities), has a covalent bond in which electrons are evenly shared:

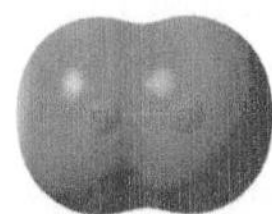

If there is a large electronegativity difference between the two elements in a bond, such as normally occurs between a metal and a nonmetal, the electron from the metal is almost completely transferred to the nonmetal, and the bond is ionic. For example, sodium and chlorine form an ionic bond:

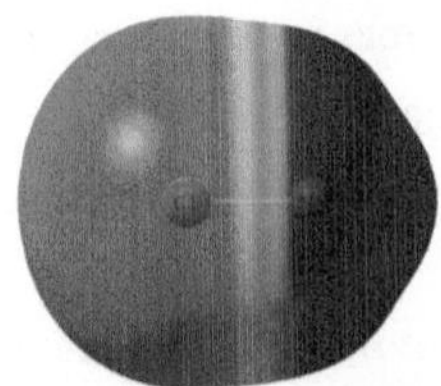

If there is an intermediate electronegativity difference between the two elements, such as between two different nonmetals, then the bond is polar covalent. For example, HCl has a polar covalent bond:

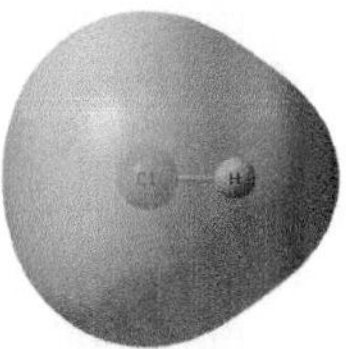

While all attempts to divide the bond polarity continuum into specific regions are necessarily arbitrary, it is helpful to classify bonds as covalent, polar covalent, and ionic based on the electronegativity difference between the bonding atoms, as shown in Table 9.3 and Figure 9.13 ▼.

TABLE 9.3 The Effect of Electronegativity Difference on Bond Type

Electronegativity Difference (ΔEN)	Bond Type	Example
Small (0–0.4)	Covalent	Cl_2
Intermediate (0.4–2.0)	Polar covalent	HCl
Large (2.0+)	Ionic	NaCl

We can quantify the polarity of a bond by the size of its dipole moment. A **dipole moment** (**μ**) occurs anytime there is a separation of positive and negative charge. The magnitude of a dipole moment created by separating two particles of equal but opposite charges of magnitude q by a distance r is given by the following equation:

$$\mu = qr \qquad [9.1]$$

We can get a sense for the dipole moment of a completely ionic bond by calculating the dipole moment that results from separating a proton and an electron ($q = 1.6 \times 10^{-19}$ C) by a distance of $r = 130$ pm (the approximate length of a short chemical bond):

$$\begin{aligned} \mu &= qr \\ &= (1.6 \times 10^{-19}\ \text{C})(130 \times 10^{-12}\ \text{m}) \\ &= 2.1 \times 10^{-29}\ \text{C} \cdot \text{m} \\ &= 6.2\ \text{D} \end{aligned}$$

The debye (D) is the unit commonly used for reporting dipole moments ($1\ \text{D} = 3.34 \times 10^{-30}\ \text{C} \cdot \text{m}$). Based on this calculation, we would expect the dipole moment of

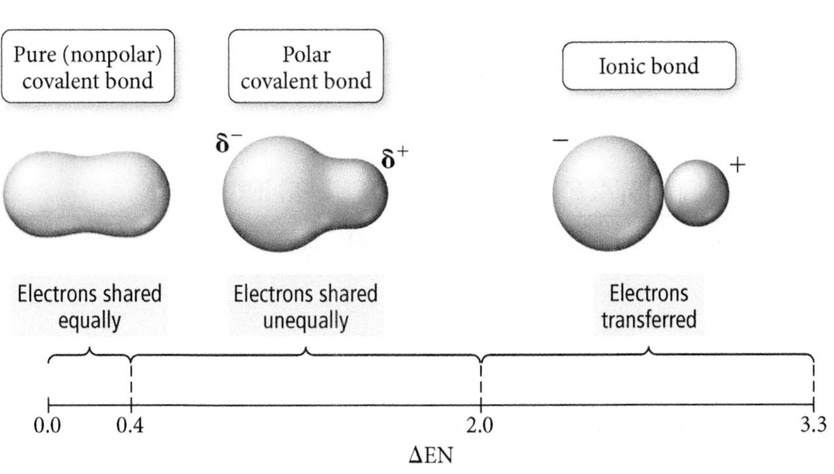

◀ **FIGURE 9.13 Electronegativity Difference (Δ EN) and Bond Type**

TABLE 9.4 Dipole Moments of Several Molecules in the Gas Phase

Molecule	ΔEN	Dipole Moment (D)
Cl_2	0	0
ClF	1.0	0.88
HF	1.9	1.82
LiF	3.0	6.33

completely ionic bonds with bond lengths close to 130 pm to be about 6 D. The smaller the magnitude of the charge separation, and the smaller the distance the charges are separated by, the smaller the dipole moment. Table 9.4 shows the dipole moments of several molecules along with the electronegativity differences of their atoms.

By comparing the *actual* dipole moment of a bond to what the dipole moment would be if the electron were completely transferred from one atom to the other, we can get a sense of the degree to which the electron is transferred (or the degree to which the bond is ionic). A quantity called the **percent ionic character** is defined as the ratio of a bond's actual dipole moment to the dipole moment it would have if the electron were completely transferred from one atom to the other, multiplied by 100%:

$$\text{Percent ionic character} = \frac{\text{measured dipole moment of bond}}{\text{dipole moment if electron were completely transferred}} \times 100\%$$

For example, suppose a diatomic molecule with a bond length of 130 pm has a dipole moment of 3.5 D. We previously calculated that separating a proton and an electron by 130 pm results in a dipole moment of 6.2 D. Therefore, the percent ionic character of the bond would be:

$$\text{Percent ionic character} = \frac{3.5\ \cancel{\text{D}}}{6.2\ \cancel{\text{D}}} \times 100\%$$

$$= 56\%$$

A bond in which an electron is completely transferred from one atom to another would have 100% ionic character (although even the most ionic bonds do not reach 100% ionic character). Figure 9.14 ▼ shows the percent ionic character of a number of diatomic gas-phase molecules plotted against the electronegativity difference between the bonding atoms. As expected, the percent ionic character generally increases as the electronegativity difference increases. However, as you can see, no bond is 100% ionic. In general, bonds with greater than 50% ionic character are referred to as ionic bonds.

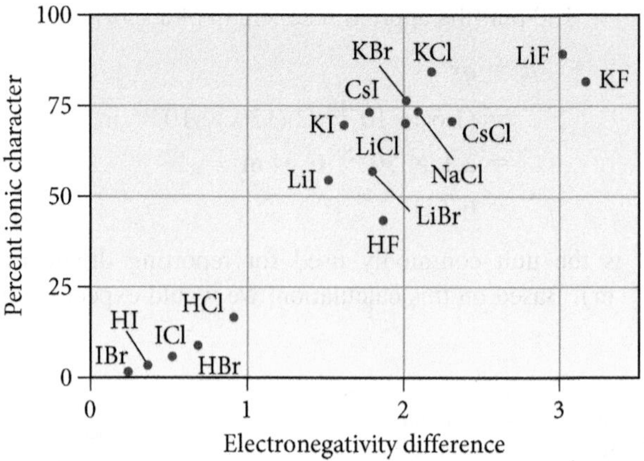

▶ **FIGURE 9.14 Percent Ionic Character Versus Electronegativity Difference for Some Compounds**

EXAMPLE 9.6 CLASSIFYING BONDS AS PURE COVALENT, POLAR COVALENT, OR IONIC

Determine whether the bond formed between each pair of atoms is pure covalent, polar covalent, or ionic:

(a) Sr and F **(b)** N and Cl **(c)** N and O

SOLUTION

(a) From Figure 9.12, we find the electronegativity of Sr (1.0) and of F (4.0). The electronegativity difference (ΔEN) is ΔEN = 4.0 − 1.0 = 3.0. Using Table 9.3, we classify this bond as ionic.

(b) From Figure 9.12, we find the electronegativity of N (3.0) and of Cl (3.0). The electronegativity difference is $\Delta EN = 3.0 - 3.0 = 0$. Using Table 9.3, we classify this bond as pure covalent.

(c) From Figure 9.12, we find the electronegativity of N (3.0) and of O (3.5). The electronegativity difference is $\Delta EN = 3.5 - 3.0 = 0.5$. Using Table 9.3, we classify this bond as polar covalent.

FOR PRACTICE 9.6

Determine whether the bond formed between each pair of atoms is pure covalent, polar covalent, or ionic:

(a) I and I **(b)** Cs and Br **(c)** P and O

CONCEPTUAL CONNECTION 9.4

Percent Ionic Character

The HCl(*g*) molecule has a bond length of 127 pm and a dipole moment of 1.08 D. Without doing detailed calculations, determine the best estimate for its percent ionic character.

(a) 5% **(b)** 15% **(c)** 50% **(d)** 80%

9.8 Resonance and Formal Charge

We need two additional concepts to help draw and interpret Lewis structures for a large number of compounds. The concepts are *resonance,* used when two or more valid Lewis structures can be drawn for the same compound, and *formal charge,* an electron bookkeeping system that allows us to discriminate between alternative Lewis structures.

Resonance

When writing Lewis structures, you may find that for some molecules, you can write more than one valid Lewis structure. For example, consider writing a Lewis structure for O_3. The following two Lewis structures, with the double bond on alternate sides, are equally correct:

$$:\ddot{O}=\ddot{O}-\ddot{\underset{\cdot\cdot}{O}}: \qquad :\ddot{\underset{\cdot\cdot}{O}}-\ddot{O}=\ddot{O}:$$

In cases such as this—where there are two or more valid Lewis structures for the same molecule—we find that in nature, the molecule exists as an *average* of the two Lewis structures. Both of the Lewis structures for O_3 predict that O_3 contains two different bonds (one double bond and one single bond). However, when we experimentally examine the structure of O_3, we find that the bonds in the O_3 molecule are equivalent and each is intermediate in strength and length between a double bond and single bond. We account for this by representing the molecule with both structures, called **resonance structures**, with a double-headed arrow between them:

$$:\ddot{O}=\ddot{O}-\ddot{\underset{\cdot\cdot}{O}}: \longleftrightarrow :\ddot{\underset{\cdot\cdot}{O}}-\ddot{O}=\ddot{O}:$$

A resonance structure is one of two or more Lewis structures that have the same skeletal formula (the atoms are in the same locations), but different electron arrangements. The actual structure of the molecule is intermediate between the two (or more) resonance structures and is called a **resonance hybrid** (Figure 9.15 ▼). The only structure that actually exists is the hybrid structure—the individual resonance structures do not exist and are merely a convenient way to describe the actual structure. Notice that the actual structure of ozone has two equivalent bonds and a bent geometry (we discuss molecular geometries in Chapter 10).

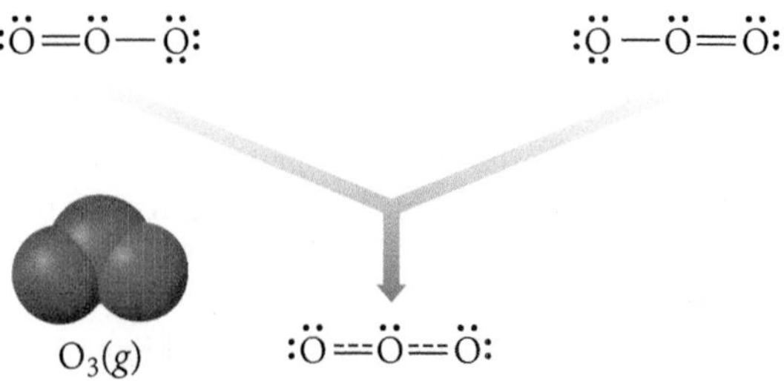

Resonance hybrid structure

▶ **FIGURE 9.15 Hybridization** The structure of a resonance hybrid is intermediate between that of the contributing resonance structures. The dashed line in the resonance hybrid structure represents a bonding electron pair.

The concept of resonance is an adaptation of Lewis theory that helps account for the complexity of actual molecules. In Lewis theory, electrons are *localized* either on one atom (lone pair) or between atoms (bonding pair). However, in nature, the electrons in molecules are often *delocalized* over several atoms or bonds. The delocalization of electrons lowers their energy; it stabilizes them (for reasons beyond the scope of this text). Resonance depicts two or more structures with the electrons in different places in an attempt to more accurately reflect the delocalization of electrons. In the real hybrid structure (an average between the resonance structures) the electrons are more spread out (or delocalized) than in any of the resonance structures. The resulting stabilization of the electrons (that is, the lowering of their potential energy due to delocalization) is sometimes called *resonance stabilization*. Resonance stabilization makes an important contribution to the stability of many molecules.

EXAMPLE 9.7 WRITING RESONANCE STRUCTURES

Write a valid Lewis structure for the NO_3^- ion. Include resonance structures.

SOLUTION

Calculate the total number of electrons for the Lewis structure by summing the number of valence electrons for each atom and adding an electron for the −1 charge.	Total number of electrons for Lewis structure $= \begin{pmatrix}\text{number of}\\ \text{valence } e^-\\ \text{for N}\end{pmatrix} + 3\begin{pmatrix}\text{number of}\\ \text{valence } e^-\\ \text{for O}\end{pmatrix} + \begin{pmatrix}1\ e^-\\ \text{to account}\\ \text{for charge}\end{pmatrix}$ $= 5 + 3(6) + 1 = 24$
Draw a skeletal structure to include the bonds between N and each of the O atoms.	O—N—O, with O bonded below N
Each bond accounts for 2 electrons, leaving 18 more electrons that need to be placed in the Lewis structure. We can place 6 electrons around each oxygen atom.	:Ö—N—Ö: with :Ö: bonded below N
All 24 electrons have been placed in the Lewis structure, but N does not have an octet. In order to provide N with an octet, share one of the lone pairs on one of the oxygens with N, forming an N=O double bond.	:Ö—N—Ö: with :Ö: bonded below N ⟶ [:O=N—Ö: with :Ö: bonded below N]$^-$

Because we can form the double bond equally well between N and any of the three O atoms, write all three possible resonance structures.	$\left[\mathrm{O{=}N(-O){-}O}\right]^- \longleftrightarrow \left[\mathrm{O{-}N(-O){=}O}\right]^- \longleftrightarrow \left[\mathrm{O{-}N({=}O){-}O}\right]^-$
Through infrared spectroscopy, it has been determined that the nitrate ion has three equivalent N—O bonds that are stronger than an N—O single bond, but not as strong as an N═O double bond.	

FOR PRACTICE 9.7

Write a valid Lewis structure for the NO_2^- ion. Include resonance structures.

In the examples of resonance hybrids that we have examined so far, the contributing structures have been equivalent (or equally valid) Lewis structures. In these cases, the true structure is an equally weighted average of the resonance structures. In some cases, however, we can write resonance structures that are not equivalent. For reasons we cover below—such as formal charge, for example—one possible resonance structure may be somewhat better than another. In such cases, the true structure is still an average of the resonance structures, but the better resonance structure contributes more to the true structure. In other words, multiple nonequivalent resonance structures may be weighted differently in their contributions to the true overall structure of a molecule (see Example 9.8).

Formal Charge

Formal charge is a fictitious charge assigned to each atom in a Lewis structure that helps us to distinguish among competing Lewis structures. The **formal charge** of an atom in a Lewis structure is *the charge it would have if all bonding electrons were shared equally between the bonded atoms*. In other words, formal charge is the calculated charge for an atom if we completely ignore the effects of electronegativity. For example, we know that because fluorine is more electronegative than hydrogen, HF has a dipole moment—the hydrogen atom has a slight positive charge and the fluorine atom has a slight negative charge. However, the *formal charges* of hydrogen and fluorine in HF (the calculated charges if we ignore their differences in electronegativity) are both zero:

H:F:

Formal charge = 0 Formal charge = 0

We can calculate the formal charge on any atom as the difference between the number of valence electrons in the atom and the number of electrons that it "owns" in a Lewis structure. An atom in a Lewis structure can be thought of as "owning" all of its nonbonding electrons and one-half of its bonding electrons:

Formal charge = number of valence electrons −
(number of nonbonding electrons + ½ number of bonding electrons)

So, we calculate the formal charge of hydrogen in HF as follows:

$$\text{Formal charge} = 1 - \left[0 + \tfrac{1}{2}(2)\right] = 0$$

Number of valence electrons for H

Number of electrons that H "owns" in the Lewis structure

Similarly, we calculate the formal charge of fluorine in HF as follows:

$$\text{Formal charge} = 7 - [6 + \tfrac{1}{2}(2)] = 0$$

Number of valence electrons for F

Number of electrons that F "owns" in the Lewis structure

When assigning formal charges, one rule must be obeyed:

The sum of the formal charges in molecules or ions must equal the overall charge of the ion or molecule.

That means that for a neutral atom, the sum of the formal charges must be zero, and for an ion, the sum of the formal charges must equal the charge of the ion.

The concept of formal charge is useful because it can help us distinguish between competing Lewis structures. To determine the best Lewis structure, the octet rule should be obeyed wherever possible. That being said, there are two guidelines to follow when drawing Lewis structures:

1. Smaller formal charges on individual atoms are better than larger ones.
2. When formal charges cannot be avoided, negative formal charges reside on the most electronegative atom.

Let's look at the Lewis structures for the cyanate ion, OCN^-, as an example. There are 16 electrons to account for in the Lewis structure. After drawing the skeletal structure, drawing bonds between the 2 pairs of atoms, there are 12 more electrons left to account for. We can put three pairs of electrons around the oxygen and the nitrogen, to complete their octets, and to leave no more electrons to account for. However, we quickly notice that the carbon atom does not have an octet. In order to complete carbon's octet, we could share one pair of electrons from each of the oxygen and nitrogen atoms, providing two double bonds and resulting in a perfectly valid Lewis structure:

$$[:\ddot{\underset{..}{O}}-C-\ddot{\underset{..}{N}}:]^- \longrightarrow [:\ddot{O}=C=\ddot{N}:]^-$$

There are two more ways that we could have completed carbon's octet. Instead of sharing one pair of electrons from each of the oxygen and nitrogen atoms, we could have shared two pairs from the oxygen atom, resulting in an O—C triple bond:

$$[:\ddot{\underset{..}{O}}-C-\ddot{\underset{..}{N}}:]^- \longrightarrow [:O\equiv C-\ddot{\underset{..}{N}}:]^-$$

or two pairs from the nitrogen atom, resulting in a C—N triple bond:

$$[:\ddot{\underset{..}{O}}-C-\ddot{\underset{..}{N}}:]^- \longrightarrow [:\ddot{\underset{..}{O}}-C\equiv N:]^-$$

Each of the three Lewis resonance structures obeys the octet rule. We can examine the formal charges in each structure to predict which structure best represents the actual bonding in the molecule. Formal charges on each atom are determined by subtracting the number of nonbonding electrons and half the number of bonding electrons from the number of valence electrons:

$$\underset{\text{A}}{[:\overset{0}{\ddot{O}}=\overset{0}{C}=\overset{-1}{\ddot{\underset{..}{N}}}:]^-} \qquad \underset{\text{B}}{[:\overset{+1}{O}\equiv\overset{0}{C}-\overset{-2}{\ddot{\underset{..}{N}}}:]^-} \qquad \underset{\text{C}}{[:\overset{-1}{\ddot{\underset{..}{O}}}-\overset{0}{C}\equiv\overset{0}{N}:]^-}$$

In structure A, the nitrogen atom has a formal charge of –1, and the carbon and oxygen atoms each have a formal charge of zero. The sum of the formal charges is equal to the overall charge of the cyanate ion, as is necessary for any resonance structure when assigning formal charges. The individual formal charges in structure A are small, which satisfies the first guideline. However, the negative charge is on nitrogen, which is not the most electronegative atom in disagreement with the second guideline. We must analyze the formal charges of the other structures as well. In structures B and C, the formal charges also add up to −1, the overall charge. In structure B, the individual formal charges are larger, and again, the nitrogen atom has a negative formal charge. In fact, carbon has a more negative formal charge than oxygen in structure B. In structure C, the formal charges are small, and oxygen, the most electronegative atom, bears the negative formal charge. We can say that structure C is the best of the three resonance structure because it fits the guidelines for preferred Lewis structures. Structure A is a less-preferred structure, and B is even less preferred. Based on this analysis, we would expect that the C—O bond is close to a single bond, but maybe a little stronger due to the influence of resonance structure A. Similarly, the C—N bond is close to a triple bond, perhaps a little weaker. These predictions agree with experimental observations. Furthermore, we would predict that the oxygen end of the molecule should be more negative than the nitrogen end.

EXAMPLE 9.8 ASSIGNING FORMAL CHARGES AND PREDICTING PREFERRED LEWIS STRUCTURES

Assign formal charges to each atom in the resonance structures for methanoic acid (or formic acid), HCOOH. Which resonance form is likely to contribute the most to the correct structure of methanoic acid?

:O: ‖ H—C—Ö—H ⟷ :Ö: | H—C=O—H

SORT You are given the resonance structures of methanoic acid. You are asked to calculate the formal charges on each atom in these structures and to determine which resonance form contributes the most to the correct structure.	**GIVEN:** Resonance structures of methanoic acid **FIND:** Formal charges Best resonance structure
STRATEGIZE Formal charges can be calculated from the number of valence electrons of the free atom and the numbers of nonbonding and bonding electrons. In the second part, to determine the best resonance form, use the following guidelines: **1.** Smaller formal charges on atoms are better. **2.** Negative formal charges should reside on electronegative atoms.	**CONCEPTUAL PLAN** Calculate formal charges in each resonance structure: → Determine the best resonance structure Relationships used: Formal charge = number of valence electrons − (number of nonbonding electrons + ½ number of bonding electrons)
SOLVE Use the numbers of valence electrons, bonding electrons, and nonbonding electrons on each atom to calculate the formal charges. The best resonance structure is the one on the left because the formal charges are small. In the other structure, there is unfavourable charge separation between the two oxygen atoms.	**SOLUTION** Left: O (top) 0; H 0; C 0; O 0; H 0 ⟷ Right: O (top) −1; H 0; C 0; O +1; H 0 preferred structure (left)

FOR PRACTICE 9.8

Assign formal charges to each atom in the resonance forms of N_2O. Which resonance form is likely to contribute most to the correct structure of N_2O?

(a) :N̈=N=Ö: (b) :N≡N—Ö: (with three lone pairs on O) (c) :N̈—N≡O: (with three lone pairs on the first N)

FOR MORE PRACTICE 9.8

Assign formal charges to each of the atoms in the nitrate ion (NO_3^-).

9.9 Exceptions to the Octet Rule: Drawing Lewis Structures for Odd-Electron Species and Incomplete Octets

When drawing Lewis structures for covalent compounds, there are a few cases in which the octet rule is not obeyed. For example, in *odd-electron species*—molecules or ions with an odd number of electrons—one atom will have an odd number of electrons, and therefore the octet rule cannot be obeyed by at least one atom. Also, compounds involving elements from groups 2 and 13 might have fewer than eight electrons around them and have *incomplete octets.*

Odd-Electron Species

Molecules and ions with an odd number of electrons in their Lewis structures are called **free radicals** (or simply, *radicals*). For example, nitrogen monoxide—a pollutant found in motor vehicle exhaust—has 11 electrons. If we try to write a Lewis structure for nitrogen monoxide, the best we can do is as follows:

The unpaired electron in nitrogen monoxide is put on the nitrogen rather than the oxygen in order to minimize formal charges.

$$:\dot{\text{N}}=\ddot{\text{O}}:$$

The nitrogen atom does not have an octet, so this Lewis structure does not satisfy the octet rule. Nitrogen monoxide does exist, especially in polluted air. In general, free radicals are quite reactive and this is mainly due to them having this unpaired electron. In fact, when the concentration of nitrogen monoxide is high enough, NO molecules will form dimers, with an N—N single bond and where the octet rule for each of the atoms is obeyed. In air, NO will react with oxygen to form NO_2, another odd-electron molecule represented by the following resonance structures with 17 electrons:

$$:\ddot{\text{O}}=\dot{\text{N}}-\underset{\cdot\cdot}{\ddot{\text{O}}}: \longleftrightarrow :\underset{\cdot\cdot}{\ddot{\text{O}}}-\dot{\text{N}}=\ddot{\text{O}}:$$

In turn, NO_2 reacts with water to form nitric acid (a component of acid rain), and also reacts with other atmospheric pollutants to form peroxyacetyl nitrate (PAN), an active component of photochemical smog.

Incomplete Octets

Beryllium compounds, such as BeH_2, also have incomplete octets.

Another significant exception to the octet rule involves those elements that tend to form *incomplete octets*. The most important of these is boron, which forms compounds with only six electrons around B, rather than eight. For example, BF_3 and BH_3 lack an octet for B:

```
     ..
    :F:                 H
     |                  |
 :F—B—F:            H—B—H
  ..    ..
```

You might be wondering why we don't just form double bonds to increase the number of electrons around B. For BH_3, of course, we can't, because there are no additional electrons to move into the bonding region. For BF_3, however, we could attempt to give B an octet by moving a lone pair from an F atom into the bonding region with B:

```
     ..
     F:
     ||
 :F—B—F:
  ..    ..
```

This Lewis structure has octets for all atoms, including boron. However, when we assign formal charges to this structure, we get the following:

```
     +1 ..
        F:
        ||
 0 :F—B—F: 0
    ..  -1  ..
```

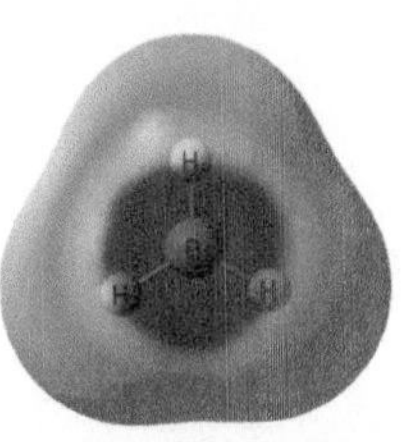

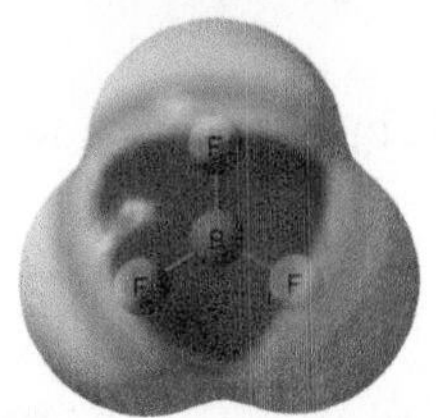

▲ Electrostatic potential plots for BH_3 and BF_3. Note the significant negative charge on the F atoms in BF_3.

CHEMISTRY IN THE ENVIRONMENT Free Radicals and the Atmospheric Vacuum Cleaner

Free radicals play a key role in much of the chemistry of the atmosphere. The free radical that is most important to atmospheric reactions is the hydroxyl radical:

$$:\dot{\underset{\cdot\cdot}{O}}\text{—H}$$

▲ $NO_2(g)$ is a pollutant found in urban air.

Many free radical structures are abbreviated by writing a single dot with the formula. Thus, the hydroxyl radical is often abbreviated as follows:

$$\cdot OH$$

In the atmosphere, the hydroxyl radical forms when excited oxygen atoms—formed from the photodecomposition of ozone—react with water vapour:

$$O_3 \xrightarrow{\text{UV light}} O_2 + O^*$$

$$O^* + H_2O \longrightarrow 2\cdot OH$$

The * next to the O above indicates that the oxygen atom has excess energy.

The resulting hydroxyl radical reacts with a wide variety of molecules from both natural sources and from air pollution that are present in the atmosphere. For example, the hydroxyl radical reacts with carbon monoxide, an atmospheric pollutant that we first encountered in Chapter 1, in the following two-step process:

$$CO + \cdot OH \longrightarrow HOCO\cdot$$

$$HOCO\cdot + O_2 \longrightarrow CO_2 + HOO\cdot$$

You can see from this reaction that the hydroxyl radical converts toxic CO into relatively nontoxic CO_2. The HOO· free radical generated by the second reaction is converted back into the hydroxyl radical when it reacts with other atmospheric substances, and the process repeats itself. Therefore, a single hydroxyl radical can convert a lot of CO into CO_2.

Do you ever wonder what happens to the hydrocarbons you accidentally spill when filling your car's gas tank, or to the natural gas that is released into the atmosphere as you light your kitchen stove? Hydrocarbons released into the atmosphere are converted to CO_2 and H_2O in a series of steps initiated by the hydroxyl free radical. Consider the following representative reaction of methane, the main hydrocarbon in natural gas:

$$CH_4 + 5\,O_2 + NO\cdot + 2\cdot OH \xrightarrow{\text{UV light}} CO_2 + H_2O + NO_2\cdot + 4\,HOO\cdot$$

Notice the similarity between this reaction and the direct combustion (or burning) of methane:

$$CH_4 + 2\,O_2 \longrightarrow CO_2 + 2\,H_2O$$

As you can see, the free radical reaction initiates a slow "burning" of CH_4 in a series of steps that produce carbon dioxide and water and some additional free radicals. The hydroxyl radical initiates similar reactions with other pollutants as well as undesirable naturally occurring atmospheric gases. Without the hydroxyl free radical—sometimes called *the atmospheric vacuum cleaner*—our atmosphere would be a much dirtier place.

▲ Hydrocarbons such as octane evaporate into the atmosphere when a motor vehicle is fuelled. What happens to them?

Question

Draw the best possible Lewis structures for the free radicals important in atmospheric chemistry: NO, NO_2, HOO, OH, CH_3.

In this Lewis structure, fluorine—the most electronegative element in the periodic table—has a positive formal charge, making this an unfavourable structure. This leaves us with the following choice: Do we complete the octet on B at the expense of giving fluorine a positive formal charge? Or do we leave B without an octet in order to avoid the positive formal charge on fluorine? The answers to these kinds of questions are not always clear because we are pushing the limits of Lewis theory. In the case of boron, we usually accept the incomplete octet as the better Lewis structure. However, doing so does not rule out the possibility that the doubly bonded Lewis structure might be a minor contributing resonance structure. The ultimate answers to these kinds of issues must be determined from experiments. Experimental measurements of the B—F bond length in BF_3 suggest that the bond may be slightly shorter than expected for a single B—F bond, indicating that it may indeed have a small amount of double-bond character.

BF_3 can complete its octet in another way: via a chemical reaction. Lewis theory predicts that BF_3 might react in ways that would complete its octet, and indeed it does. For example, BF_3 reacts with NH_3 as follows:

When nitrogen bonds to boron, the nitrogen atom provides both of the electrons. This kind of bond is called a *coordinate covalent bond*, which we discuss in Chapter 23.

$$:\ddot{F}-\underset{|}{B}(:\ddot{F}:)-\ddot{F}: + H-\ddot{N}(H)-H \longrightarrow :\ddot{F}-B(:\ddot{F}:)(:\ddot{F}:)-N(H)(H)-H$$

The product has complete octets for all atoms in the structure.

9.10 Lewis Structures for Hypercoordinate Compounds

Main-group elements in the third row of the periodic table and beyond often exhibit **hypercoordination** in which they are bonded to more than four other atoms or appear to have more than four pairs of electrons (an octet) around the central atom. The capability of these atoms to form more than four bonds is due to their larger size; elements in the second period are in general too small to bond to more than four other atoms. These hypercoordinate compounds are sometimes said to have *expanded octets* because it looks like there are more than eight electrons around the central atom in the Lewis structure. Consider the Lewis structures of arsenic pentafluoride and sulfur hexafluoride:

$$AsF_5: \; As \text{ bonded to five } :\ddot{F}: \qquad SF_6: \; S \text{ bonded to six } :\ddot{F}:$$

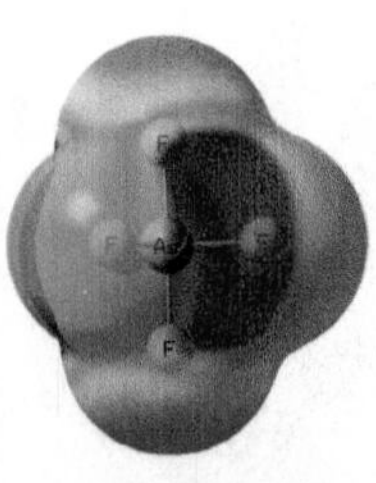

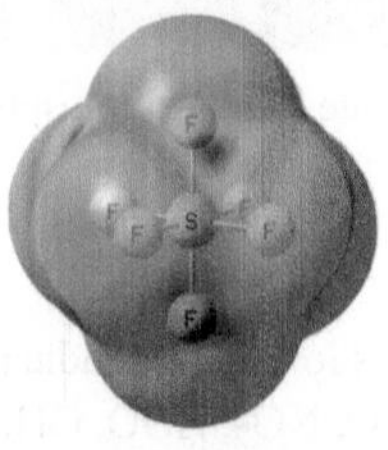

▲ Electrostatic potential maps for AsF_5 and SF_6. Both have a positive charge near the centre and a more negative charge around the outside F atoms, showing the polarity of these bonds.

In the Lewis structure of AsF_5, arsenic looks like it has an expanded octet with 10 electrons, and in SF_6, sulfur looks like it shares 12 electrons. Both of these compounds exist and are quite stable. Research has shown that when the central atom is a main-group element, it doesn't necessarily share more than eight electrons around the central atom, but by drawing a conventional Lewis structure, they look like they have an expanded octet. This is another example of extending simple Lewis theory beyond its boundaries. Remember that in Lewis theory, the electrons "belong" to a particular atom or are shared between atoms, when in reality the electrons belong to the molecule as a whole. The preceding Lewis structures are correct Lewis structures and are useful in predicting their molecular geometries, as we will see in Chapter 10.

The nature of the bonding in these species is interesting and worth discussing a little further. The Lewis structures for AsF_5 and SF_6 could be written differently:

$$As^{+1} \text{ bonded to four } :\ddot{F}:, \; :\ddot{F}:^{-1} \qquad S^{+2} \text{ bonded to four } :\ddot{F}:, \; two \; :\ddot{F}:^{-1}$$

In these **ionic resonance structures**, the octet rule is obeyed. The formal charges are shown for those atoms that do not have a formal charge of 0. In AsF_5, there are still five F atoms bonded to As, but as depicted in the previous structure, there are four covalent bonds and one ionic bond, as indicated by adjacent formal charges of +1 and −1. One could draw five equivalent Lewis structures for AsF_5, and the real structure would be considered to be a resonance hybrid of these five Lewis structures. For SF_6, the Lewis structure with a +2 formal charge on S and −1 charge on two fluorines also obeys the octet rule. Bonding could be considered to be a resonance hybrid of 15 equivalent Lewis structures, each with 4 covalent and 2 ionic bonds. So, based on these Lewis structures, the As—F and S—F bonds could be considered to be a mixture of covalent and ionic bonding. It is worth noting that the electronegativity difference between As and F is 2.0, and the difference between S and F is 1.5, so these bonds would be expected to be polar and, to some degree, ionic.

The existence of hypervalent compounds such as SF_6, AsF_5, PCl_5, and many others, while similar hydridic compounds (SH_6, AsH_5, and PH_5) do not exist can be explained using the principles of quantum theory that were developed in Chapters 7 and 8. All of the hypervalent compounds have a couple of things in common. First, the terminal atoms are smaller and very electronegative atoms, typically O, F, and Cl. Second, the central atom is large with valence electrons far from the nucleus and, relative to the terminal atoms, they are easily ionized. This combination of electronegative terminal atoms and ionizable central atoms makes the ionic resonance structures strong contributors to the overall bonding of the molecule. On the other hand, H is not very electronegative—its electronegativity is similar to many of the common central atoms in hypervalent compounds—so resonance structures for SH_6, in which H has a negative charge and S has a positive charge, are not very good. The partial ionic bonding that characterizes hypervalent compounds can not be seen in SH_6 and it does not exist.

There are many other related compounds where Lewis structures can be drawn so that there are more than four bonds to the central atom and it looks as though the central atom has more than eight electrons around it. Let's look at sulfuric acid (H_2SO_4) and the sulfate dianion (SO_4^{2-}) as examples. Lewis structures that obey the octet rule can be drawn for each of these species:

```
        :Ö:⁻¹                    ┌      :Ö:⁻¹       ┐2−
         |                       │       |          │
H—Ö⁰—S⁺²—Ö⁰—H                    │ ⁻¹:Ö—S⁺²—Ö:⁻¹    │
         |                       │       |          │
        :O:⁻¹                    └      :O:⁻¹       ┘
```

These Lewis structures are acceptable, even if there is some charge separation. The charge separation is such that the more electronegative oxygen atoms bear the formal negative charges. Let's consider the bonding in H_2SO_4. In the previous structure, there is a single covalent bond between sulfur and each of the oxygen atoms. However, there is also charge separation between sulfur (formal charge of +2) and the two oxygen atoms with formal charges of −1. These S—O bonds have significant additional ionic character and are therefore stronger than the S—OH bonds. This difference in bond strength can be observed in infrared spectroscopy experiments that show that the wavenumber positions for stretching the S—O bonds are higher than for stretching the S—OH bonds, meaning that the S—O bonds are stronger than the S—OH bonds.

For SO_4^{2-}, there appear to be single covalent bonds between sulfur and each of the oxygen atoms. Based on the formal charge separation, sulfur is also bound to each oxygen by ionic interactions. In this case, the +2 formal charge on sulfur is shared between −1 formal charges on each of the four oxygen atoms. The S—O bond strengths in the sulfate ion should be equal and intermediate in strength between the S—OH and S=O bonds in H_2SO_4. This is also observed experimentally.

The Lewis structures for H_2SO_4 and SO_4^{2-} can also be drawn with the formal charges reduced as much as possible:

```
        :Ö⁰                      ┌      :Ö⁰        ┐2−
         ||                      │       ||        │
H—Ö⁰—S⁰—Ö⁰—H                     │ ⁻¹:Ö—S⁰—Ö:⁻¹    │
         ||⁰                     │       ||⁰       │
         O:                      └       O:        ┘
```

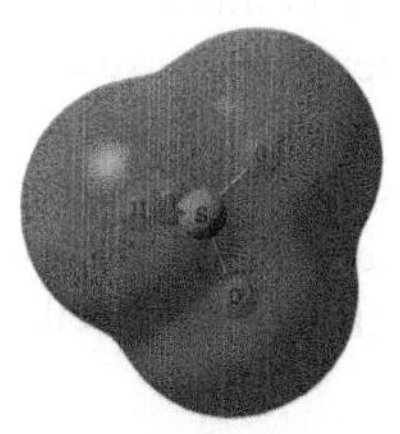

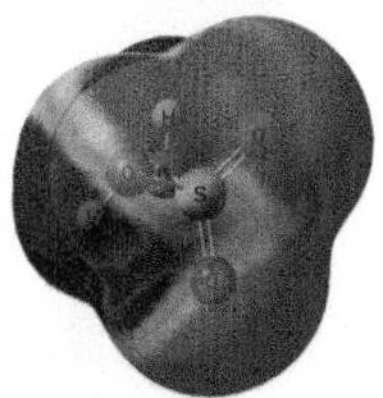

▲ Electrostatic potential maps for SO_4^{2-} and H_2SO_4.

For H_2SO_4, this Lewis structure shows that the bond order is 1 for the S—OH bond and 2 for the S=O bonds. For SO_4^{2-}, there are six equivalent resonance structures that can be drawn, and if the bond orders are averaged out, they will all be equal at 1.5. These structures, however, show that S is sharing 12 electrons, an expanded octet. Although these structures are valid, the preceding structures with formal charge separation are also valid, and it is important to realize that the bonding in these species is more complicated than can be interpreted from Lewis structures. In the next chapter, the Lewis structures we have learned to draw will be used to predict the geometries of covalent compounds, and either of the Lewis structures shown previously for H_2SO_4 and SO_4^{2-} is adequate for this purpose.

PROCEDURE FOR... Drawing Lewis Structures for Hypercoordinate Compounds	**EXAMPLE 9.9 Draw Lewis Structures for XeF_2**	**EXAMPLE 9.10 Draw Lewis Structures for $IOCl_3$**
Determine the number of valence electrons to be accounted for in the Lewis structure.	$= \begin{pmatrix}\text{number of}\\ \text{valence } e^-\\ \text{for Xe}\end{pmatrix} + 2\begin{pmatrix}\text{number of}\\ \text{valence } e^-\\ \text{for F}\end{pmatrix}$ $= 8 + 2(7) = 22$	$= \begin{pmatrix}\text{number of}\\ \text{valence } e^-\\ \text{for I}\end{pmatrix} + \begin{pmatrix}\text{number of}\\ \text{valence } e^-\\ \text{for O}\end{pmatrix} + 3\begin{pmatrix}\text{number of}\\ \text{valence } e^-\\ \text{for Cl}\end{pmatrix}$ $= 7 + 6 + 3(7) = 34$
Draw the skeletal structure, connecting the central atom to all outer atoms by a bonding pair of electrons.	F—Xe—F	O (top), Cl—I—Cl, Cl (bottom)
Distribute the remaining electrons to give octets to the outer atoms. If there are any remaining electrons, place them around the central atom.	Four electrons are accounted for by bonds, leaving 18 electrons to be placed as lone pairs. Place three pairs of electrons around each fluorine, filling their octets. The other three pairs of electrons can be placed around Xe: :F̤̈—Xë̤—F̤̈:	The skeletal structure accounts for 8 electrons, leaving 26 electrons. Fill the octets of the noncentral atoms by placing three pairs of electrons around each. This leaves two more electrons, which can be placed around the central atom as a pair: :Ö: (top), :C̤̈l—İ—C̤̈l:, :C̤l: (bottom)
The previous Lewis structures are completely valid. However, Lewis structures (ionic resonance structures) can also be drawn in which the octet rule is obeyed by the central atom as well.	If we take the bonding pair from between Xe and one F and give it to F (which is much more electronegative), all atoms have an octet: :F̤̈—Xë̤ $^{+1}$:F̤̈: $^{-1}$	There are many possible resonance structures that can be drawn. The preceding one has some formal charge distribution. We can take one of the bonding electron pairs from between I and one of the Cl atoms. Doing so will result in an octet for all atoms: :Ö: $^{-1}$ / :C̤̈l—I $^{+1}$—C̤̈l: / :C̤l: ⟷ :Ö: $^{-1}$ / :C̤̈l—I $^{+2}$:C̤̈l: $^{-1}$ / :C̤l: One can write three other resonance structures similar to the one on the right, simply by changing which Cl atom gets a formal negative charge.
	FOR PRACTICE 9.9 Draw Lewis structures for XeF_4.	**FOR PRACTICE 9.10** Draw Lewis structures for H_3PO_4. P is central, and each of the H atoms is attached to an O atom.

CHEMISTRY IN THE ENVIRONMENT The Lewis Structure of Ozone

Ozone is a form of oxygen in which three oxygen atoms bond together. Its Lewis structure consists of the following resonance structures:

$$:\ddot{O}=\ddot{O}-\ddot{\underset{..}{O}}: \longleftrightarrow :\ddot{\underset{..}{O}}-\ddot{O}=\ddot{O}:$$

Compare the Lewis structure of ozone to the Lewis structure of O_2:

$$:\ddot{O}=\ddot{O}:$$

Since double bonds are stronger and shorter than single bonds, O_2 must have a stronger bond because it is a double bond. O_3, on the other hand, has bonds that are intermediate between single and double, which are weaker bonds. The effects of this are significant. O_3 absorbs harmful ultraviolet light entering Earth's atmosphere. Ozone is ideally suited to do this because photons at wavelengths of 280–320 nm (the most harmful components of sunlight) are just strong enough to break the bonds in the O_3 molecule:

$$:\ddot{\underset{..}{O}}-\ddot{O}=\ddot{O}: + \text{UV light} \longrightarrow :\ddot{O}=\ddot{O}: + \cdot\ddot{\underset{..}{O}}:$$

In this process, the photon is absorbed. O_2 and O then recombine to re-form O_3, which can, in turn, absorb more UV light. The same wavelengths of UV light, however, do not have sufficient energy to break the stronger double bond of O_2. No other molecules in our atmosphere can do the job that ozone does. Consequently, we should continue, and even strengthen, the ban on ozone-depleting compounds.

Question

Calculate the average bond energy of one O_3 bond. What wavelength of light has just the right amount of energy to break this bond?

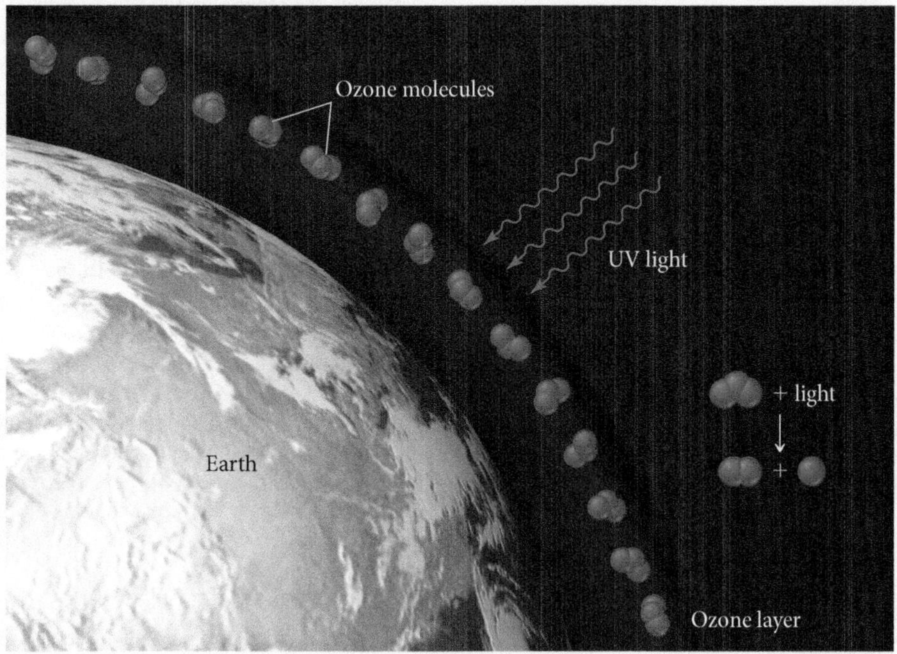

▲ Ozone protects life on Earth from harmful ultraviolet light.

CHAPTER IN REVIEW

Key Terms

Section 9.1
Lewis theory (331)
Lewis electron-dot structures (Lewis structures) (331)

Section 9.2
ionic bond (332)
covalent bond (332)
metallic bonding (333)

Section 9.3
octet (333)
chemical bond (333)
octet rule (334)

Section 9.4
bonding pair (334)
lone pair (334)
nonbonding electrons (334)
double bond (335)
triple bond (335)

Section 9.5
lattice energy (339)
Born–Haber cycle (340)

Section 9.6
bond energy (344)
bond length (347)

bond stretching vibration (stretching vibration) (348)
infrared (IR) spectroscopy (348)
wavenumber (348)

Section 9.7
polar covalent bond (351)
electronegativity (351)
dipole moment (μ) (353)
percent ionic character (354)

Section 9.8
resonance structures (355)
resonance hybrid (355)
formal charge (357)

Section 9.9
free radicals (360)

Section 9.10
hypercoordination (362)
ionic resonance structure (363)

Key Concepts

Bonding Models and AIDS Drugs (9.1)

Theories that predict how and why atoms bond together are central to chemistry because they explain compound stability and molecule shape. Bonding theories have been useful in combating HIV because they help in the design of molecules that can bind to the active site of a protein crucial for the development of AIDS.

Types of Chemical Bonds (9.2)

Chemical bonds can be divided into three general types: ionic bonds, which occur between a metal and a nonmetal; covalent bonds, which occur between two nonmetals; and metallic bonds, which occur within metals. In an ionic bond, an electron transfers from the metal to the nonmetal and the resultant ions attract each other by coulombic forces. In a covalent bond, nonmetals share electrons that interact with the nuclei of both atoms via coulombic forces, holding the atoms together. In a metallic bond, the atoms form a lattice in which each metal loses electrons to an "electron sea." The attraction of the positively charged metal ions to the electron sea holds the metal together.

Lewis Theory and Electron Dots (9.3)

In Lewis theory, chemical bonds are formed when atoms transfer (ionic bonding) or share (covalent bonding) valence electrons to attain noble gas electron configurations. Lewis theory represents valence electrons as dots surrounding the symbol for an element. When two or more elements bond together, the dots are transferred or shared so that every atom gets eight dots, an octet (or two dots—a duet—in the case of hydrogen).

Lewis Structures for Covalent Molecules and Ions (9.4)

In a covalent Lewis structure, neighbouring atoms share valence electrons to attain octets. A single shared electron pair constitutes a single bond, while two or three shared pairs constitute double or triple bonds, respectively. In an ionic Lewis structure involving main-group metals, the metal transfers its valence electrons (dots) to the nonmetal.

Ionic Bonding and Lattice Energies (9.5)

The formation of most ionic compounds is exothermic because of lattice energy, the energy released when metal cations and nonmetal anions coalesce to form the solid. The smaller the radius of the ions and the greater their charge, the more exothermic the lattice energy.

Bond Energies, Bond Lengths, and Bond Vibrations (9.6)

The bond energy of a chemical bond is the energy required to break 1 mol of the bond in the gas phase. Average bond energies for a number of different bonds are tabulated and can be used to calculate the enthalpies of reaction. Average bond lengths are also tabulated. In general, triple bonds are shorter and stronger than double bonds, which are, in turn, shorter and stronger than single bonds. Bond strengths can be compared using infrared spectroscopy. The stronger a bond between similar atoms, the higher in energy the vibration corresponding to stretching of the bond appears.

Electronegativity and Bond Polarity (9.7)

The shared electrons in a covalent bond are not always equally shared; when two dissimilar nonmetals form a covalent bond, the electron density is greater on the more electronegative element. The result is a polar bond, with one element carrying a partial positive charge and the other a partial negative charge. Electronegativity—the capability of an atom to attract electrons to itself in chemical bonding—increases as we move to the right across a period in the periodic table and decreases as we move down a group. Elements with very dissimilar electronegativities form ionic bonds; those with similar electronegativities form nonpolar covalent bonds; those with intermediate electronegativity differences form polar covalent bonds.

Resonance and Formal Charge (9.8)

Some molecules are best represented not by a single Lewis structure, but by two or more resonance structures. The actual structure of these molecules is a resonance hybrid: a combination or average of the contributing structures. The formal charge of an atom in a Lewis structure is the charge the atom would have if all bonding electrons were shared equally between bonding atoms. In general, the best Lewis structures will have the fewest atoms with formal charge and any negative formal charge will be on the most electronegative atom.

Exceptions to the Octet Rule (9.9)

Although the octet rule is normally used in drawing Lewis structures, some exceptions occur. These exceptions include odd-electron species, which necessarily have Lewis structures with only seven electrons around an atom. Such molecules, called free radicals, tend to be unstable and chemically reactive. Another exception to the octet rule include molecules with incomplete octets—usually totalling six electrons (especially important in compounds containing boron)—and molecules with expanded octets.

Lewis Structures for Hypercoordinate Compounds (9.10)

The large atoms from the third period of the periodic table and below can accommodate bonding to more than four electronegative atoms. Drawing more than four bonds to the central atom makes it look like it has more than an octet of electrons. Ionic resonance structures can be drawn with ionic bonds. The bonding in these compounds is too complicated to make sense of by using simple Lewis theory.

Key Equations and Relationships

Coulomb's Law: Potential Energy (E) of Two Charged Particles with Charges q_1 and q_2 Separated by a Distance r (9.5)

$$E = \frac{1}{4\pi\varepsilon_0}\frac{q_1 q_2}{r} \qquad \varepsilon_0 = 8.85 \times 10^{-12}\,\text{C}^2\,\text{J}^{-1}\,\text{m}^{-1}$$

Dipole Moment (μ): Separation of Two Particles of Equal but Opposite Charges of Magnitude q by a Distance r (9.6)

$$\mu = qr$$

Enthalpy Change of a Reaction ($\Delta_r H$): Relationship of Bond Energies (9.6)

$$\Delta_r H = \Sigma(\Delta_r H\text{'s bonds broken}) + \Sigma(\Delta_r H\text{'s bonds formed})$$

Percent Ionic Character (9.7)

$$\text{Percent ionic character} = \frac{\text{measured dipole moment of bond}}{\text{dipole moment if electron were completely transferred}} \times 100\%$$

Formal Charge (9.7)

$$\text{Formal charge} = \text{number of valence electrons} - (\text{number of nonbonding electrons} + \tfrac{1}{2}\,\text{number of shared electrons})$$

Key Skills

Drawing Lewis Structures for Covalent Compounds (9.4)
• Examples 9.1, 9.2 • For Practice 9.1, 9.2 • Exercises 49–52, 57

Drawing Lewis Structures for Polyatomic Ions (9.4)
• Example 9.3 • For Practice 9.3 • Exercises 58, 60

Predicting Relative Lattice Energies (9.5)
• Example 9.4 • For Practice 9.4 • For More Practice 9.4 • Exercise 44

Calculating $\Delta_r H$ from Bond Energies (9.6)
• Example 9.5 • For Practice 9.5 • For More Practice 9.5 • Exercises 75–78

Classifying Bonds: Pure Covalent, Polar Covalent, or Ionic (9.7)
• Example 9.6 • For Practice 9.6 • Exercises 53, 54

Writing Resonance Lewis Structures (9.8)
• Example 9.7 • For Practice 9.7 • Exercises 61, 62

Assigning Formal Charges to Assess Competing Resonance Structures (9.8)
• Example 9.8 • For Practice 9.8 • For More Practice 9.8 • Exercises 63, 64

Drawing Lewis Structures for Hypercoordinate Compounds (9.10)
• Examples 9.9, 9.10 • For Practice 9.9, 9.10 • Exercises 71, 72

EXERCISES

Review Questions

1. Why are bonding theories important? Give some examples of what bonding theories can predict.
2. Why do chemical bonds form? What basic forces are involved in bonding?
3. What are the two main types of chemical bonds? What happens to electrons in the bonding atoms in each case?
4. How do you determine how many dots to put around the Lewis symbol of an element?

5. Describe the octet rule in Lewis theory.
6. According to Lewis theory, what is a chemical bond?
7. How do you draw an ionic Lewis structure?
8. How can Lewis structures be used to determine the formula of ionic compounds? Give an example.
9. What is lattice energy?
10. Why is the formation of solid sodium chloride from solid sodium and gaseous chlorine exothermic, even though it takes more energy to form the Na^+ ion than the amount of energy released upon formation of Cl^-?
11. What is the Born–Haber cycle? List each of the steps in the cycle and show how the cycle is used to calculate lattice energy.
12. How does lattice energy relate to ionic radii? To ion charge?
13. How does the ionic bonding model explain the relatively high melting points of ionic compounds?
14. How does the ionic bonding model explain the nonconductivity of ionic solids and, at the same time, the conductivity of ionic solutions?
15. Within a covalent Lewis structure, what is the difference between lone-pair and bonding-pair electrons?
16. In what ways are double and triple covalent bonds different from single covalent bonds?
17. How does the Lewis model for covalent bonding account for why certain combinations of atoms are stable, while others are not?
18. How does the Lewis model for covalent bonding account for the relatively low melting and boiling points of molecular compounds (compared to ionic compounds)?
19. What is electronegativity? What are the periodic trends in electronegativity?
20. Explain the difference between a pure covalent bond, a polar covalent bond, and an ionic bond.
21. Explain what is meant by the percent ionic character of a bond. Do any bonds have 100% ionic character?
22. What is a dipole moment?
23. What is the magnitude of the dipole moment formed by separating a proton and an electron by 100 pm? 200 pm?
24. What is the basic procedure for writing a covalent Lewis structure?
25. How do you determine the number of electrons that go into the Lewis structure of a molecule? A polyatomic ion?
26. What are resonance structures? What is a resonance hybrid?
27. Do resonance structures always contribute equally to the overall structure of a molecule? Explain.
28. What is formal charge? How is formal charge calculated? How is it helpful?
29. Why does the octet rule have exceptions? Give the two major categories of exceptions and an example of each.
30. What elements can appear to have expanded octets? What elements should never have expanded octets?
31. What is bond energy? How can average bond energies be used to calculate enthalpies of reaction?
32. Explain the difference between endothermic reactions and exothermic reactions with respect to the bond energies of the bonds broken and formed.

Problems by Topic

Valence Electrons and Dot Structures

33. Write an electron configuration for N. Then write a Lewis structure for N and show which electrons from the electron configuration are included in the Lewis structure.

34. Write an electron configuration for Ne. Then write a Lewis structure for Ne and show which electrons from the electron configuration are included in the Lewis structure.

35. Write a Lewis structure for each atom or ion:
a. Al b. Na^+ c. Cl d. Cl^-

36. Write a Lewis structure for each atom or ion:
a. S^{2-} b. Mg c. Mg^{2+} d. P

Ionic Lewis Structures and Lattice Energy

37. Write a Lewis structure for each ionic compound:
a. NaF b. CaO c. $SrBr_2$ d. K_2O

38. Write a Lewis structure for each ionic compound:
a. SrO b. Li_2S c. CaI_2 d. RbF

39. Use Lewis structures to determine the formula for the compound that forms between each pair of elements:
a. Sr and Se b. Ba and Cl c. Na and S d. Al and O

40. Use Lewis structures to determine the formula for the compound that forms between each pair of elements:
a. Ca and N b. Mg and I c. Ca and S d. Cs and F

41. Explain the trend in the lattice energies of the alkaline earth metal oxides:

Metal Oxide	Lattice Energy ($kJ\ mol^{-1}$)
MgO	–3795
CaO	–3414
SrO	–3217
BaO	–3029

42. Rubidium iodide has a lattice energy of $-617\ kJ\ mol^{-1}$, while potassium bromide has a lattice energy of $-671\ kJ\ mol^{-1}$. Why is the lattice energy of potassium bromide more exothermic than the lattice energy of rubidium iodide?

43. The lattice energy of CsF is $-744\ kJ\ mol^{-1}$, whereas that of BaO is $-3029\ kJ\ mol^{-1}$. Explain this large difference in lattice energy.

44. Arrange these compounds in order of increasing magnitude of lattice energy: KCl, SrO, RbBr, CaO.

45. Use the Born–Haber cycle, data from Appendix IIB, and Chapters 8 and 9 to calculate the lattice energy of KCl. ($\Delta_{sub}H$ for potassium is $89.0\ kJ\ mol^{-1}$.)

46. Use the Born–Haber cycle, data from Appendix IIB, and Table 9.1 to calculate the lattice energy of CaO. ($\Delta_{sub}H$ for calcium is 178 kJ mol^{-1}; IE_1 and IE_2 for calcium are 590 kJ mol^{-1} and 1145 kJ mol^{-1}, respectively; EA_1 and EA_2 for O are 141 kJ mol^{-1} and −744 kJ mol^{-1}, respectively.)

Simple Covalent Lewis Structures, Electronegativity, and Bond Polarity

47. Use covalent Lewis structures to explain why each element (or family of elements) occurs as diatomic molecules:
   a. hydrogen b. the halogens
   c. oxygen d. nitrogen

48. Use covalent Lewis structures to explain why the compound that forms between nitrogen and hydrogen has the formula NH_3. Show why NH_2 and NH_4 are not stable.

49. Write a Lewis structure for each molecule:
   a. PH_3 b. SCl_2 c. HI d. CH_4

50. Write a Lewis structure for each molecule:
   a. NF_3 b. HBr c. SBr_2 d. CCl_4

51. Write a Lewis structure for each molecule:
   a. SF_2
   b. SiH_4
   c. HCOOH (both O bonded to C)
   d. CH_3SH (C and S central)

52. Write a Lewis structure for each molecule:
   a. CH_2O b. C_2Cl_4
   c. CH_3NH_2 d. $CFCl_3$ (C central)

53. Determine whether a bond between each pair of atoms would be pure covalent, polar covalent, or ionic:
   a. Br and Br b. C and Cl c. C and S d. Sr and O

54. Determine whether a bond between each pair of atoms would be pure covalent, polar covalent, or ionic.
   a. C and N b. N and S c. K and F d. N and N

55. Draw a Lewis structure for CO with an arrow representing the dipole moment. Use Figure 9.14 to estimate the percent ionic character of the CO bond.

56. Draw a Lewis structure for BrF with an arrow representing the dipole moment. Use Figure 9.14 to estimate the percent ionic character of the BrF bond.

Covalent Lewis Structures, Resonance, and Formal Charge

57. Write a Lewis structure for each molecule:
   a. CI_4 b. N_2O c. SiH_4 d. Cl_2CO

58. Write a Lewis structure for each molecule or ion:
   a. H_3COH b. OH^- c. BrO^- d. O_2^{2-}

59. Write a Lewis structure for each molecule or ion:
   a. N_2H_2 b. N_2H_4 c. C_2H_2 d. C_2H_4

60. Write a Lewis structure for each molecule or ion:
   a. H_3COCH_3 b. CN^- c. NO_2^- d. ClO^-

61. Write a Lewis structure that obeys the octet rule for each molecule or ion. Include resonance structures if necessary, and assign formal charges to each atom.
   a. SeO_2 b. CO_3^{2-} c. ClO^- d. NO_2^-

62. Write a Lewis structure that obeys the octet rule for each ion. Include resonance structures if necessary, and assign formal charges to each atom.
   a. ClO_3^- b. ClO_4^- c. NO_3^- d. NH_4^+

63. Use formal charges to determine which Lewis structure is better:

H—C(H)=S̈ H—S(H)=C̈

64. Use formal charges to determine which Lewis structure is better:

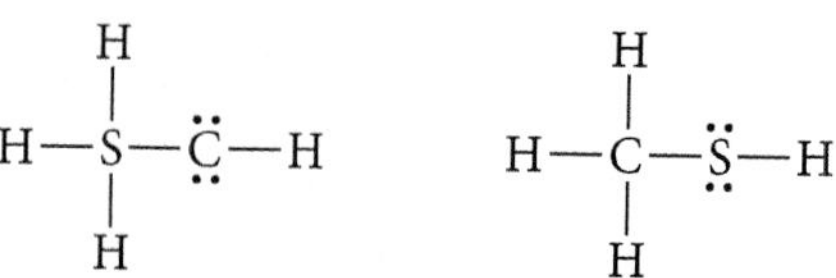

65. How important is this resonance structure to the overall structure of carbon dioxide? Explain.

:O≡C—Ö:

66. In N_2O, nitrogen is the central atom and the oxygen atom is terminal. In OF_2, however, oxygen is the central atom. Use formal charges to explain why.

Odd-Electron Species, Incomplete Octets, and Hypercoordinate Species

67. Write a Lewis structure for each molecule (octet rule not followed):
   a. BCl_3 b. NO_2 c. BH_3

68. Write a Lewis structure for each molecule (octet rule not followed):
   a. BBr_3 b. NO c. ClO_2

69. Write a Lewis structure for each ion. Include resonance structures if necessary, and assign formal charges to all atoms. If needed, expand the octet on the central atom to lower the formal charge.
   a. PO_4^{3-} b. CN^- c. SO_3^{2-} d. ClO_2^-

70. Write Lewis structures for each molecule or ion. Include resonance structures if necessary, and assign formal charges to all atoms. If needed, expand the octet on the central atom to lower formal charge.
   a. SO_4^{2-} b. HSO_4^- c. SO_3 d. BrO_2^-

71. Write Lewis structures for each molecule or ion. Use expanded octets as necessary.
   a. PF_5 b. I_3^- c. SF_4 d. GeF_4

72. Write Lewis structures for each molecule or ion. Use expanded octets as necessary.
   a. ClF_5 b. AsF_6^- c. Cl_3PO d. IF_5

Bond Energies and Bond Lengths

73. List these compounds in order of increasing carbon–carbon bond *strength* and in order of decreasing carbon–carbon bond *length*: HCCH, H_2CCH_2, H_3CCH_3.

74. Which of these compounds has the stronger nitrogen–nitrogen bond? The shorter nitrogen–nitrogen bond?

H_2NNH_2, HNNH

75. Hydrogenation reactions are used to add hydrogen across double bonds in hydrocarbons and other organic compounds. Use average bond energies to calculate Δ_rH for the hydrogenation reaction:

$$H_2C{=}CH_2(g) + H_2(g) \longrightarrow H_3C{-}CH_3(g)$$

76. Ethanol is a possible fuel. Use average bond energies to calculate $\Delta_r H$ for the combustion of ethanol:

$$CH_3CH_2OH(g) + 3\ O_2(g) \longrightarrow 2\ CO_2(g) + 3\ H_2O(g)$$

77. Hydrogen, a potential future fuel, can be produced from carbon (from coal) and steam by this reaction:

$$C(s) + 2\ H_2O(g) \longrightarrow 2\ H_2(g) + CO_2(g)$$

Use average bond energies to calculate $\Delta_r H$ for the reaction.

78. In the *Chemistry and the Environment* box on free radicals in this chapter, we discussed the importance of the hydroxyl radical in reacting with and eliminating many atmospheric pollutants. However, the hydroxyl radical does not clean up everything. For example, chlorofluorocarbons—which destroy stratospheric ozone—are not attacked by the hydroxyl radical. Consider the hypothetical reaction by which the hydroxyl radical might react with a chlorofluorocarbon:

$$OH(g) + CF_2Cl_2(g) \longrightarrow HOF(g) + CFCl_2(g)$$

Use bond energies to explain why this reaction is improbable.

79. An infrared spectrum of a mixture of methyl amine, $CH_3—NH_2$, and methylene imine, $CH_2{=}NH$, displayed absorptions at 1050 and 1640 cm^{-1}, among others. Which of these two absorptions would you expect belongs to the C—N and which to the C=N stretch? Explain your reasoning.

80. Which bond, C—Cl or C—Br, would you expect to have a stretching vibration at a higher wavenumber position? Explain your reasoning.

Cumulative Problems

81. Write an appropriate Lewis structure for each compound. Make certain to distinguish between ionic and molecular compounds.
a. BI_3 b. K_2S c. HCFO d. PBr_3

82. Write an appropriate Lewis structure for each compound. Make certain to distinguish between ionic and molecular compounds.
a. Al_2O_3 b. ClF_5 c. MgI_2 d. XeO_4

83. Each compound contains both ionic and covalent bonds. Write ionic Lewis structures for each of them, including the covalent structure for the ion in parentheses. Write resonance structures if necessary.
a. $BaCO_3$ b. $Ca(OH)_2$ c. KNO_3 d. LiIO

84. Each compound contains both ionic and covalent bonds. Write ionic Lewis structures for each of them, including the covalent structure for the ion in parentheses. Write resonance structures if necessary.
a. $RbIO_2$ b. NH_4Cl c. KOH d. $Sr(CN)_2$

85. Carbon ring structures are common in organic chemistry. Draw a Lewis structure for each carbon ring structure, including any necessary resonance structures:
a. C_4H_8 b. C_4H_4 c. C_6H_{12} d. C_6H_6

86. Amino acids are the building blocks of proteins. The simplest amino acid is glycine (H_2NCH_2COOH). Draw a Lewis structure for glycine. (*Hint:* The central atoms in the skeletal structure are nitrogen bonded to carbon, which is bonded to another carbon. The two oxygen atoms are bonded directly to the right-most carbon atom.)

87. Methanoic acid is responsible for the sting of ant bites. By mass, methanoic acid is 26.10% C, 4.38% H, and 69.52% O. The molar mass of methanoic acid is 46.02 g mol^{-1}. Find the molecular formula of methanoic acid and draw its Lewis structure.

88. Diazomethane is a highly poisonous, explosive compound because it readily evolves N_2. Diazomethane has the following composition by mass: 28.57% C, 4.80% H, and 66.64% N. The molar mass of diazomethane is 42.04 g mol^{-1}. Find the molecular formula of diazomethane, draw its Lewis structure, and assign formal charges to each atom. Why is diazomethane not very stable? Explain.

89. The reaction of $Fe_2O_3(s)$ with Al(s) to form $Al_2O_3(s)$ and Fe(s) is called the thermite reaction, and is highly exothermic. What role does lattice energy play in the exothermicity of the reaction?

90. NaCl has a lattice energy of −787 kJ mol^{-1}. Consider a hypothetical salt, XY. X^{3+} has the same radius as Na^+ and Y^{3-} has the same radius as Cl^-. Estimate the lattice energy of XY.

91. Draw a Lewis structure for nitric acid (the hydrogen atom is attached to one of the oxygen atoms). Include all three resonance structures by alternating the double bond among the three oxygen atoms. Use formal charges to determine which of the resonance structures is most important to the structure of nitric acid.

92. Phosgene (Cl_2CO) is a poisonous gas that was used as a chemical weapon during World War I. It is a potential agent for chemical terrorism today. Draw the Lewis structure of phosgene. Include all three resonance forms by alternating the double bond among the three terminal atoms. Which resonance structure is the best?

93. The cyanate ion (OCN^-) and the fulminate ion (CNO^-) share the same three atoms, but have vastly different properties. The fulminate ion forms explosive compounds. The resonance structures of the cyanate ion were explored in Section 9.8. Draw Lewis structures for the fulminate ion—including possible resonance forms.

94. The structure below is the skeletal structure for asparagine, one of the 20 common amino acids. Use this structure to draw the Lewis structure for asparagine.

```
          H  O
 H        |  |
  \N——C——C——O——H
 H/       |
      H——C——H
          |
          C——O
          |
          N
         / \
        H   H
```

95. Draw a Lewis structure for $HCSNH_2$. (The carbon and nitrogen atoms are bonded together and the sulfur atom is bonded to the carbon atom.) Label each bond in the molecule as polar or nonpolar.

96. Draw a Lewis structure for urea, H_2NCONH_2, one of the compounds in urine. (The central carbon atom is bonded to both nitrogen atoms and to the oxygen atom.) Does urea contain polar bonds? Which bond in urea is most polar?

97. Some theories of aging suggest that free radicals cause certain diseases and perhaps aging in general. As you know from Lewis theory, such molecules are not chemically stable and will quickly react with other molecules. According to certain theories, free radicals may attack molecules within the cell, such as DNA, changing them and causing cancer or other diseases. Free radicals may also attack molecules on the surfaces of cells, making them appear foreign to the body's immune system. The immune system then attacks the cells and destroys them, weakening the body. Draw Lewis structures for each free radical implicated in this theory of aging:

a. O_2^-
b. O^-
c. OH
d. CH_3OO (unpaired electron on terminal oxygen)

98. Free radicals are important in many environmentally significant reactions (see the *Chemistry in the Environment* box on free radicals in this chapter). For example, photochemical smog—smog that results from the action of sunlight on air pollutants—forms in part by these two steps:

$$NO_2 \xrightarrow{\text{UV light}} NO + O$$
$$O + O_2 \longrightarrow O_3$$

The product of this reaction, ozone, is a pollutant in the lower atmosphere. (Upper-atmospheric ozone is a natural part of the atmosphere that protects life on Earth from ultraviolet light.) Ozone is an eye and lung irritant and also accelerates the weathering of rubber products. Rewrite the above reactions using the Lewis structure of each reactant and product. Identify the free radicals.

99. If hydrogen were used as a fuel, it could be burned according to this reaction:

$$H_2(g) + {}^1\!/_2\,O_2(g) \longrightarrow H_2O(g)$$

Use average bond energies to calculate $\Delta_r H$ for this reaction and also for the combustion of methane (CH_4). Which fuel yields more energy per mole? Per gram?

100. Calculate $\Delta_r H$ for the combustion of octane (C_8H_{18}), a component of gasoline, by using average bond energies, then calculate it using enthalpies of formation from Appendix IIB. What is the percent difference between your results? Which result would you expect to be more accurate?

101. Draw Lewis structures for each compound:

a. Cl_2O_7 (no Cl—Cl bond)
b. H_3PO_3 (two OH bonds)
c. H_3AsO_4

102. The azide ion, N_3^-, is a symmetrical ion, all of whose contributing resonance structures have formal charges. Draw three important contributing structures for this ion.

103. List the following gas-phase ion pairs in order of the quantity of energy released when they form from separated gas-phase ions (start with the pair that releases the least energy): Na^+F^-, $Mg^{2+}F^-$, Na^+O^{2-}, $Mg^{2+}O^{2-}$, $Al^{3+}O^{2-}$.

104. Calculate $\Delta_r H°$ for the reaction $H_2(g) + Br_2(g) \longrightarrow 2\,HBr(g)$ using the bond energy values. The $\Delta_f H°$ of $HBr(g)$ is not equal to one-half of the value calculated. Account for the difference.

105. The heat of atomization is the heat required to convert a molecule in the gas phase into its constituent atoms in the gas phase. It is used to calculate average bond energies. Without using any tabulated bond energies, calculate the average C—Cl bond energy from the following data: the heat of atomization of CH_4 is 1660 kJ mol^{-1} and of CH_2Cl_2 is 1495 kJ mol^{-1}.

106. Calculate the heat of atomization (see previous problem) of C_2H_3Cl using the average bond energies in Table 9.1.

107. A compound composed of only carbon and hydrogen is 7.743% hydrogen by mass. Propose a Lewis structure for the compound.

108. A compound composed of only carbon and chlorine is 85.5% chlorine by mass. Propose a Lewis structure for the compound.

Challenge Problems

109. The main component of acid rain (H_2SO_4) forms from SO_2 pollutant in the atmosphere via these steps:

$$SO_2 + OH\cdot \longrightarrow HSO_3\cdot$$
$$HSO_3\cdot + O_2 \longrightarrow SO_3 + HOO\cdot$$
$$SO_3 + H_2O \longrightarrow H_2SO_4$$

Draw a Lewis structure for each of the species in these steps, and use bond energies and Hess's law to estimate $\Delta_r H$ for the overall process. (Use 265 kJ mol^{-1} for the S—O single bond energy.)

110. A 0.167 g sample of an unknown acid requires 27.8 mL of 0.100 M NaOH to titrate to the equivalence point. Elemental analysis of the acid gives the following percentages by mass: 40.00% C, 6.71% H, and 53.29% O. Determine the molecular formula, molar mass, and Lewis structure of the unknown acid.

111. Use the dipole moments of HF and HCl (given below) together with the percent ionic character of each bond (Figure 9.14) to estimate the bond length in each molecule. How well does your estimated bond length agree with the bond length given in Table 9.2?

HCl $\mu = 1.08$ D
HF $\mu = 1.82$ D

112. Use average bond energies together with the standard enthalpy of formation of C(g) (718.4 kJ mol^{-1}) to estimate the standard enthalpy of formation of gaseous benzene, $C_6H_6(g)$. (Remember that average bond energies apply to the gas phase only.) Compare the value you obtain using average bond energies to the actual standard enthalpy of formation of gaseous benzene, 82.9 kJ mol^{-1}. What does the difference between these two values tell you about the stability of benzene?

113. The standard state of phosphorus at 25 °C is P_4. This molecule has four equivalent P atoms, no double or triple bonds, and no expanded octets. Draw its Lewis structure.

114. The standard heat of formation of $CaBr_2$ is $-675\ kJ\ mol^{-1}$. The first ionization energy of Ca is 590 kJ mol^{-1} and its second ionization energy is 1145 kJ mol^{-1}. The heat of sublimation of Ca, i.e., $[Ca(s) \longrightarrow Ca(g)]$, is 178 kJ mol^{-1}. The bond energy of Br_2 is 193 kJ mol^{-1}, the heat of vaporization of $Br_2(l)$ is 31 kJ mol^{-1}, and the electron affinity of Br is +325 kJ mol^{-1}. Calculate the lattice energy of $CaBr_2$.

115. The standard heat of formation of $PI_3(s)$ is $-24.7\ kJ\ mol^{-1}$ and the PI bond energy in this molecule is 184 kJ mol^{-1}. The standard heat of formation of P(*g*) is 334 kJ mol^{-1} and that of $I_2(g)$ is 62 kJ mol^{-1}. The I_2 bond energy is 151 kJ mol^{-1}. Calculate the heat of sublimation of PI_3, i.e., $[PI_3(s) \longrightarrow PI_3(g)]$.

116. A compound has the formula C_8H_8 and does not contain any double or triple bonds. All the carbon atoms are chemically identical and all the hydrogen atoms are chemically identical. Draw a Lewis structure for this molecule.

117. Find the oxidation number of each sulfur in the molecule H_2S_4, which has a linear arrangement of its atoms.

118. Ionic solids of the O^- and O^{3-} anions do not exist, while ionic solids of the O^{2-} anion are common. Explain.

119. The standard state of sulphur is solid rhombic sulfur. Use the appropriate standard heats of formation given in Appendix II to find the average bond energy of S=O in SO_2.

Conceptual Problems

120. Which statement is true of an endothermic reaction?

a. Strong bonds break and weak bonds form.

b. Weak bonds break and strong bonds form.

c. The bonds that break and those that form are of approximately the same strength.

121. When a firecracker explodes, energy is obviously released. The compounds in the firecracker can be viewed as being "energy rich." What does this mean? Explain the source of the energy in terms of chemical bonds.

122. A fundamental difference between compounds containing ionic bonds and those containing covalent bonds is the existence of molecules. Explain why molecules exist in solid covalent compounds but do not exist in solid ionic compounds.

123. In this chapter, we looked carefully at a model for chemical bonding (Lewis theory). Why is this theory successful? What are some of the limitations of the theory?

Chemical Bonding II: Molecular Shapes, Valence Bond Theory, and Molecular Orbital Theory

10

No theory ever solves all the puzzles with which it is confronted at a given time; nor are the solutions already achieved often perfect.

—Thomas Kuhn (1922–1996)

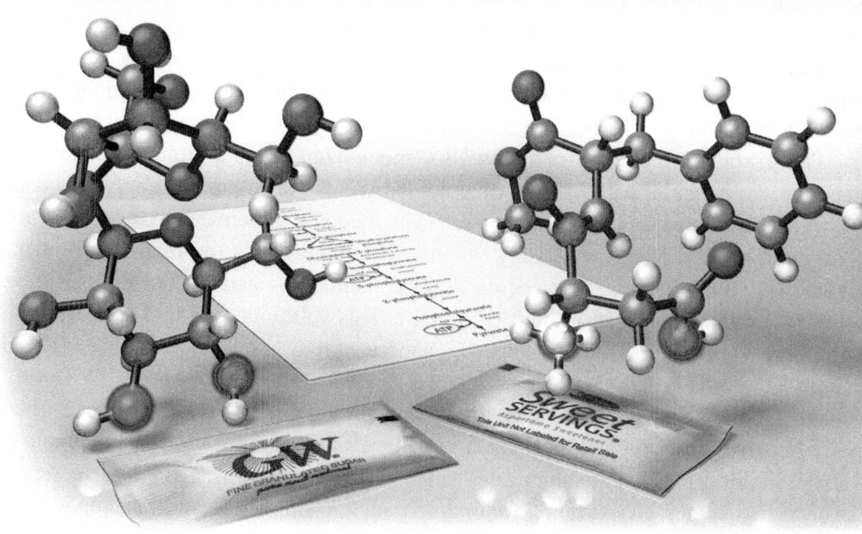

Similarities in the shapes of sugar and aspartame give both molecules the ability to stimulate a sweet taste sensation.

IN CHAPTER 9, WE EXAMINED a simple model for chemical bonding called Lewis theory. We saw how this model helps us to explain and predict the combinations of atoms that form stable molecules. When we combine Lewis theory with the idea that valence electron groups repel one another—the basis of an approach known as VSEPR theory—we can predict the general shape of a molecule from its Lewis structure. We address molecular shapes and their importance in the first part of this chapter. We then move on to explore two additional bonding theories—called valence bond theory and molecular orbital theory—that are progressively more sophisticated, but at the cost of being more complex, than Lewis theory. As you work through this chapter, our second on chemical bonding, keep in mind the importance of this topic. In our universe, elements join together to form compounds, and that makes many things possible, including our own existence.

10.1 Artificial Sweeteners: Fooled by Molecular Shape

Artificial sweeteners, such as aspartame (NutraSweet®), taste sweet but have few or no calories. Why? *Because taste and caloric value are independent properties of foods.* The caloric value of a food depends on the amount of energy released when the food is metabolized. For example, sucrose (table sugar) is metabolized by oxidation to carbon dioxide and water:

$$C_{12}H_{22}O_{11}(s) + 12\,O_2(g) \longrightarrow 12\,CO_2(g) + 11\,H_2O(l) \qquad \Delta_r H^\circ = -5644\text{ kJ mol}^{-1}$$

When your body metabolizes a mole of sucrose, it obtains 5644 kJ of energy. Some artificial sweeteners, such as saccharin, for example, are not metabolized at all—they just pass through the body unchanged—and therefore have no caloric value. Other artificial sweeteners, such as aspartame, are metabolized but have a much lower caloric content (for a given amount of sweetness) than sucrose.

The *taste* of a food, however, is independent of its metabolism. The sensation of taste originates in the tongue, where specialized cells called taste cells act as highly sensitive and specific molecular detectors. These cells can discern sugar molecules from the thousands of different types of molecules present in a mouthful of food. The main factors for this discrimination are the molecule's shape and charge distribution.

The surface of a taste cell contains specialized protein molecules called taste receptors. A particular *tastant*—a molecule that we can taste—fits snuggly into a special pocket (just as a key fits into a lock) on the taste receptor protein called the *active site.* For example, a sugar molecule precisely fits into the active site of the sugar receptor protein called T1r3. When the sugar molecule (the key) enters the active site (the lock), the different subunits of the T1r3 protein split apart. This split causes ion channels in the cell membrane to open, resulting in nerve signal transmission (see Section 8.1). The nerve signal reaches the brain and registers a sweet taste.

Artificial sweeteners taste sweet because they fit into the receptor pocket that normally binds sucrose. In fact, both aspartame and saccharin bind to the active site in the T1r3 protein more strongly than does sugar! For this reason, artificial sweeteners are "sweeter than sugar." Aspartame, for example, is 200 times sweeter than sugar, meaning that it takes 200 times as much sugar as aspartame to trigger the same amount of nerve signal transmission from taste cells.

The type of lock-and-key fit between the active site of a protein and a particular molecule is important not only to taste but to many other biological functions as well. For example, immune response, the sense of smell, and many types of drug action all depend on shape-specific interactions between molecules and proteins. In fact, the ability to determine the shapes of key biological molecules is largely responsible for the revolution in biology that has occurred over the last 50 years.

In this chapter, we look at ways to predict and account for the shapes of molecules. The molecules we examine are much smaller than the protein molecules we just discussed, but the same principles apply to both. The simple model we examine to account for molecular shape is called *valence shell electron pair repulsion* (VSEPR) theory, and we will use it in conjunction with Lewis theory. We will then proceed to explore two additional bonding theories: valence bond theory and molecular orbital theory. These bonding theories are more complex, but also more powerful, than Lewis theory. They also predict and account for molecular shape as well as other properties of molecules.

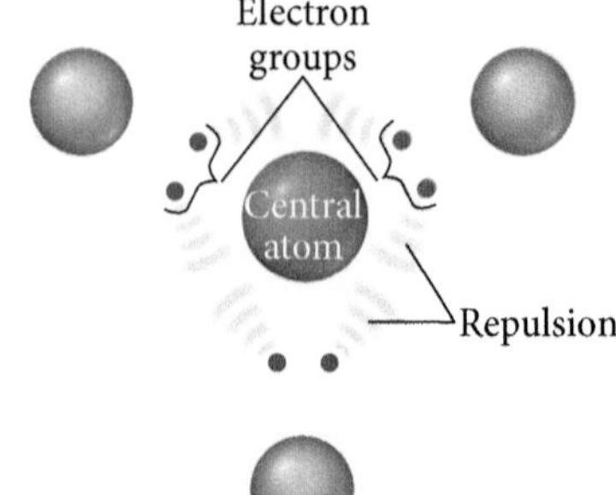

▲ **FIGURE 10.1 Repulsion Between Electron Groups** The basic idea of VSEPR theory is that repulsions between electron groups determine molecular geometry.

10.2 VSEPR Theory: The Five Basic Shapes

The first theory that we shall consider, **valence shell electron pair repulsion (VSEPR) theory**, is based on the simple idea that **electron groups**—which we define as lone pairs, single bonds, multiple bonds, and sometimes even single electrons—repel one another through coulombic forces. The electron groups, of course, are also attracted to the nucleus (otherwise, the molecule would fall apart), but VSEPR theory focuses on the repulsions. According to VSEPR theory, the repulsions between electron groups on *interior atoms* of a molecule determine the geometry of the molecule (Figure 10.1 ◄). The preferred geometry of a molecule is the one in which the electron groups have the maximum separation (and therefore, the minimum energy) possible. Consequently, for molecules having just one interior atom (the central atom), molecular geometry depends on (a) the number of electron groups around the central atom, and (b) how many of those electron groups are bonding groups and how many are lone pairs. We first look at the molecular geometries associated with two to six electron groups around the central atom when all of those groups are bonding groups (single or multiple bonds). The resulting geometries constitute the five basic shapes of molecules. We will then see how these basic shapes are modified if one or more of the electron groups are lone pairs.

Two Electron Groups: Linear Geometry

Consider the Lewis structure of $BeCl_2$, which has two electron groups (two single bonds) about the central atom:

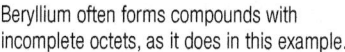

Beryllium often forms compounds with incomplete octets, as it does in this example.

:C̤̈l—Be—C̤̈l:

According to VSEPR theory, the geometry of $BeCl_2$, is determined by the repulsion between these two electron groups, which can maximize their separation by assuming a 180° bond angle or a **linear geometry**. Experimental measurements of the geometry of $BeCl_2$ indicate that the molecule is indeed linear, as predicted by the theory.

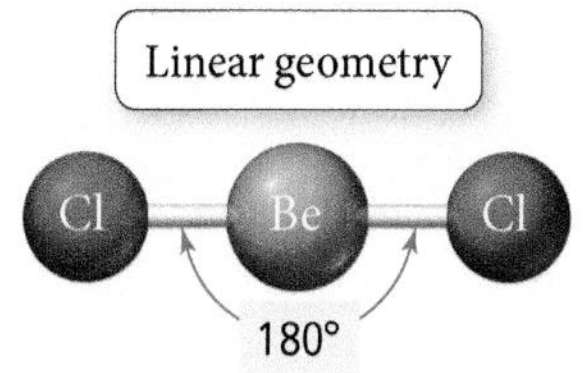

Molecules that form only two single bonds, with no lone pairs, are rare because they do not follow the octet rule. However, the same geometry is observed in all molecules that have two electron groups (and no lone pairs). For example, consider the Lewis structure of CO_2, which has two electron groups (the double bonds) around the central carbon atom:

A double bond counts as one electron group.

:Ö=C=Ö:

According to VSEPR theory, the two double bonds repel each other (just as the two single bonds in $BeCl_2$ repel each other), resulting in a linear geometry for CO_2. Experimental observations confirm that CO_2 is indeed a linear molecule.

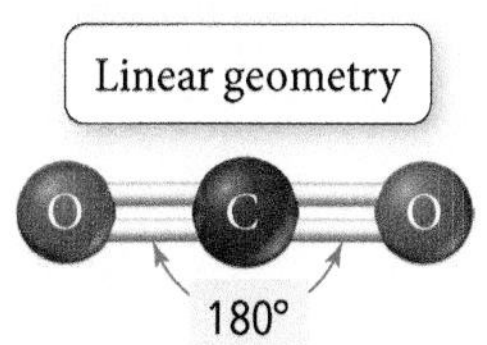

Three Electron Groups: Trigonal Planar Geometry

The Lewis structure of BF_3 (another molecule with an incomplete octet) has three electron groups around the central atom:

```
     :F̈:
      |
:F̤—B—F̤:
```

These three electron groups can maximize their separation by assuming 120° bond angles in a plane—a **trigonal planar geometry**. Experimental observations of the structure of BF_3 are again in agreement with the predictions of VSEPR theory.

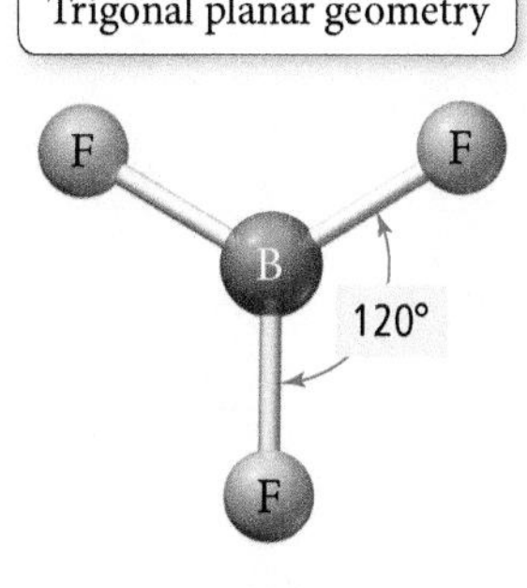

Another molecule with three electron groups, methanal (formaldehyde), has one double bond and two single bonds around the central atom:

```
   :O:
    ||
H—C—H
```

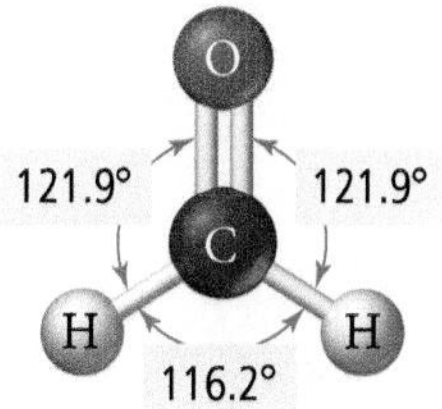

Since formaldehyde has three electron groups around the central atom, we initially predict that the bond angles should also be 120°. However, experimental observations show that the HCO bond angles are 121.9° and that the HCH bond angle is 116.2°. These bond angles are close to the idealized 120° bond angle. VSEPR theory provides a reasonable geometry for the molecule. However, it does not account for small differences from ideal bond angles. In general, we would expect bond angles for different atoms to have different values—just as single bonds connecting different atoms do not have the same length.

CONCEPTUAL CONNECTION 10.1

Electron Groups and Molecular Geometry

In determining electron geometry, why do we consider only the electron groups on the central atom? In other words, why don't we consider electron groups on terminal atoms?

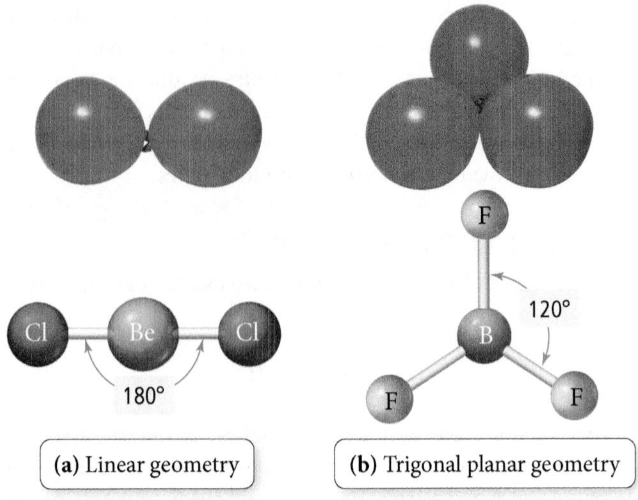

(a) Linear geometry

(b) Trigonal planar geometry

▶ **FIGURE 10.2 Representing Electron Geometry with Balloons** (**a**) The bulkiness of balloons causes them to assume a linear arrangement when two of them are tied together. Similarly, the repulsion between two electron groups produces a linear geometry. (**b**) Like three balloons tied together, three electron groups adopt a trigonal planar geometry.

Four Electron Groups: Tetrahedral Geometry

The VSEPR geometries of molecules with two or three electron groups around the central atom are two-dimensional and can therefore easily be visualized and represented on paper. For molecules with four or more electron groups around the central atom, the geometries are three-dimensional and are therefore more difficult to imagine and draw. One common way to help visualize these basic shapes is by analogy to balloons tied together. In this analogy, each electron group around a central atom is like a balloon tied to a central point. The bulkiness of the balloons causes them to spread out as much as possible, much as the repulsion between electron groups causes them to position themselves as far apart as possible. For example, if you tie two balloons together, they assume a roughly linear arrangement, as shown in Figure 10.2(a) ▲, analogous to the linear geometry of $BeCl_2$ that we just examined. Notice that the balloons do not represent atoms, but *electron groups*. Similarly, if you tie three balloons together—in analogy to three electron groups—they assume a trigonal planar geometry, as shown in Figure 10.2(b) ▲, much like our BF_3 molecule. If you tie *four* balloons together, however, they assume a three-dimensional **tetrahedral geometry** with 109.5° angles between the balloons. That is, the balloons point toward the vertices of a *tetrahedron*—a geometrical shape with four identical faces, each an equilateral triangle, as shown here:

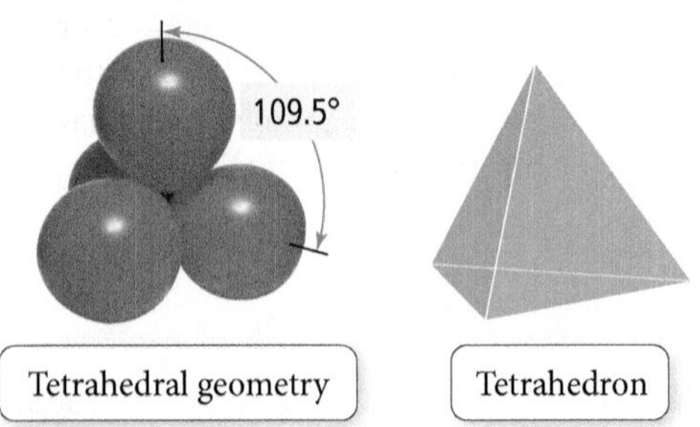

Tetrahedral geometry

Tetrahedron

Methane is an example of a molecule with four electron groups around the central atom:

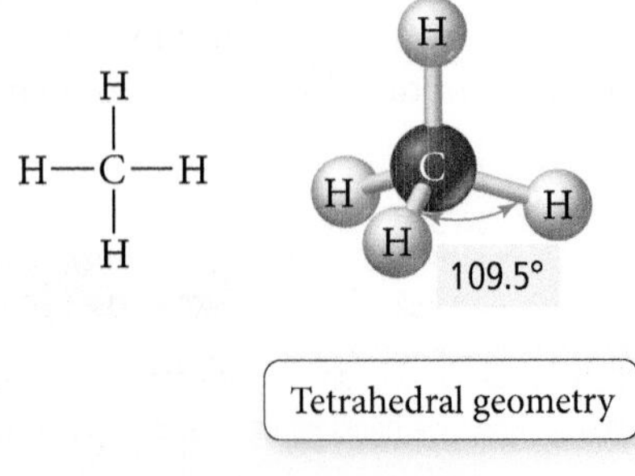

Tetrahedral geometry

For four electron groups, the tetrahedron is the three-dimensional shape that allows the maximum separation among the groups. The repulsions among the four electron groups in the C—H bonds cause the molecule to assume the tetrahedral shape. When we write the Lewis structure of CH_4 on paper, it may seem that the molecule should be square planar, with bond angles of 90°. However, in three dimensions, the electron groups can get farther away from each other by forming the tetrahedral geometry, as shown by our balloon analogy.

Five Electron Groups: Trigonal Bipyramidal Geometry

Five electron groups around a central atom assume a **trigonal bipyramidal geometry**, like that of five balloons tied together. In this structure, three of the groups lie in a single plane, as in the trigonal planar configuration, while the other two are positioned above and below this plane. The angles in the trigonal bipyramidal structure are not all the same. The angles between the *equatorial positions* (the three bonds in the trigonal plane) are 120°, while the angle between the *axial positions* (the two bonds on either side of the trigonal plane) and the trigonal plane is 90°. As an example of a molecule with five electron groups around the central atom, consider PCl_5:

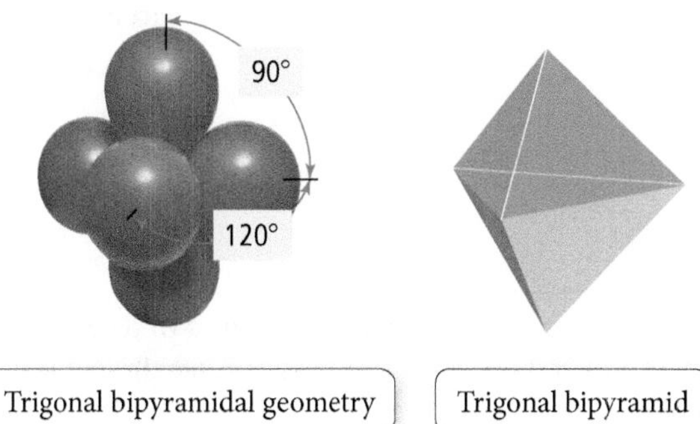

Trigonal bipyramidal geometry

Trigonal bipyramid

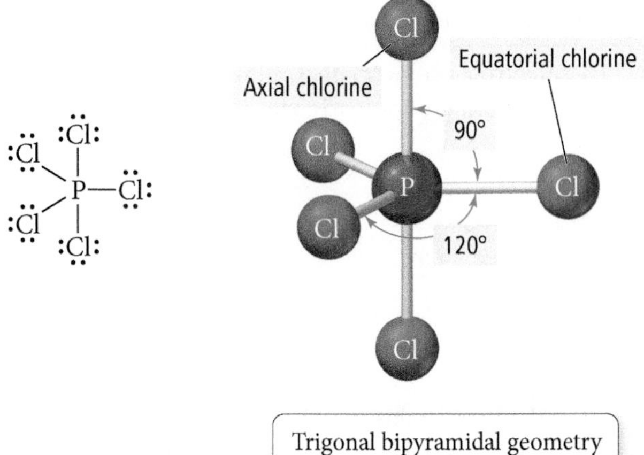

Trigonal bipyramidal geometry

The three equatorial chlorine atoms are separated by 120° bond angles and the two axial chlorine atoms are separated from the equatorial atoms by 90° bond angles.

Six Electron Groups: Octahedral Geometry

Six electron groups around a central atom assume an **octahedral geometry**, like that of six balloons tied together. In this structure—named after the eight-sided geometrical shape called the octahedron—four of the groups lie in a single plane, with a fifth group above the plane and another below it. The angles in this geometry are all 90°. As an example of a molecule with six electron groups around the central atom, consider SF_6:

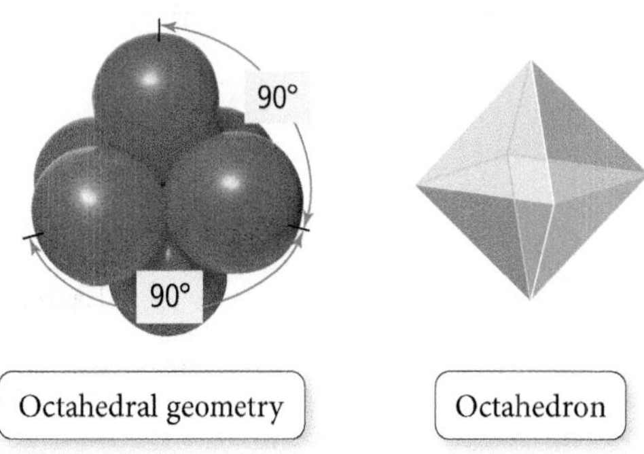

Octahedral geometry

Octahedron

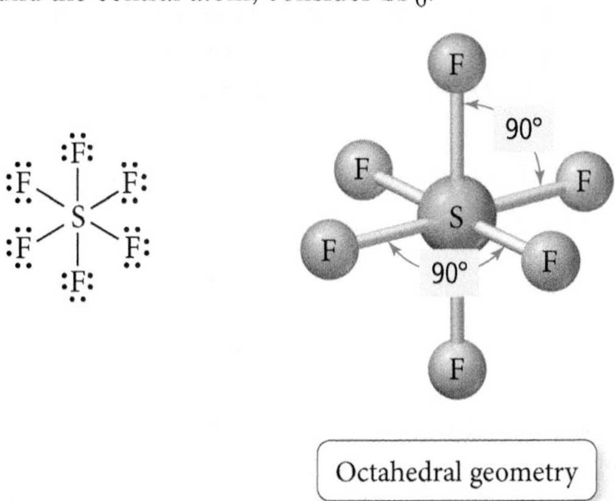

Octahedral geometry

The structure of this molecule is highly symmetrical; all six bonds are equivalent.

EXAMPLE 10.1 VSEPR THEORY AND THE BASIC SHAPES

Determine the electron geometry and molecular geometry of NO_3^-.

SOLUTION

The molecular geometry of NO_3^- is determined by the number of electron groups around the central atom (N). Begin by drawing a Lewis structure of NO_3^-.	NO_3^- has 5 + 3(6)+ 1 = 24 valence electrons. The Lewis structure is as follows: $\left[:\ddot{O}-\underset{\underset{:O:}{\Vert}}{N}-\ddot{O}:\right]^- \longleftrightarrow \left[\ddot{O}=\underset{\underset{:\ddot{O}:}{\vert}}{N}-\ddot{O}:\right]^- \longleftrightarrow \left[:\ddot{O}-\underset{\underset{:\ddot{O}:}{\vert}}{N}=\ddot{O}\right]^-$ The hybrid structure is intermediate between these three and has three equivalent bonds.
Use any one of the resonance structures to determine the number of electron groups around the central atom.	$\left[:\ddot{O}-\underset{\underset{:O:}{\Vert}}{N}-\ddot{O}:\right]^-$ The nitrogen atom has three electron groups.
Based on the number of electron groups, determine the geometry that minimizes the repulsions between the groups.	The electron geometry that minimizes the repulsions between the three electron groups is trigonal planar. 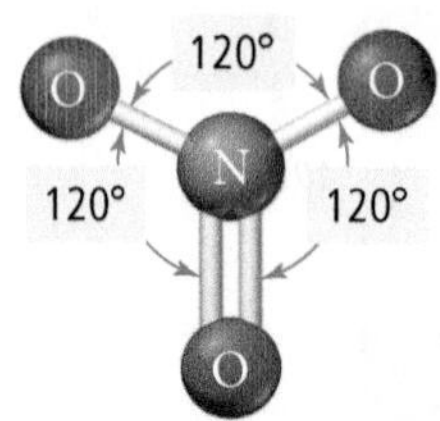 Since the three bonds are equivalent (because of the resonance structures), they each exert the same repulsion on the other two and the molecule has three equal bond angles of 120°.

FOR PRACTICE 10.1
Determine the electron geometry and molecular geometry of CCl_4.

10.3 VSEPR Theory: The Effect of Lone Pairs

Each of the examples we have just seen has only bonding electron groups around the central atom. What happens in molecules that also have lone pairs around the central atom? The lone pairs also repel other electron groups, as we see in the examples that follow.

Four Electron Groups with Lone Pairs

Consider the Lewis structure of ammonia:

$$\begin{array}{c} H \\ | \\ H-\underset{\cdot\cdot}{N}-H \end{array}$$

The central nitrogen atom has four electron groups (one lone pair and three bonding pairs) that repel one another. If we do not distinguish between bonding electron groups and lone pairs, we find that the **electron geometry**—the geometrical arrangement of the *electron groups*—is still tetrahedral, as we

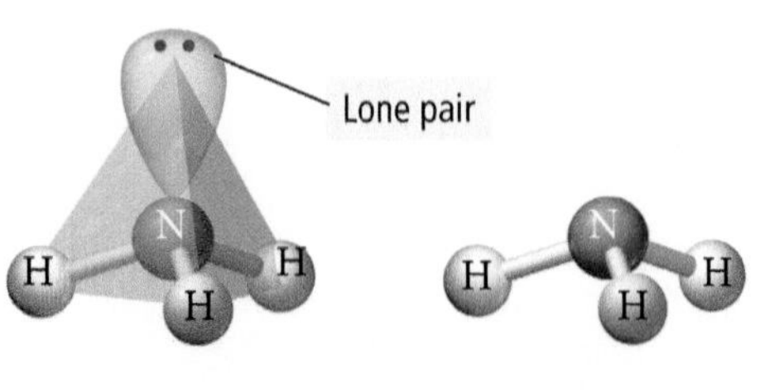

Electron geometry: tetrahedral

Molecular geometry: trigonal pyramidal

expect for four electron groups. However, the **molecular geometry**—the geometrical arrangement of the atoms—is **trigonal pyramidal**, as shown here.

Notice that although the electron geometry and the molecular geometry are different, *the electron geometry is relevant to the molecular geometry*. The lone pair exerts its influence on the bonding pairs.

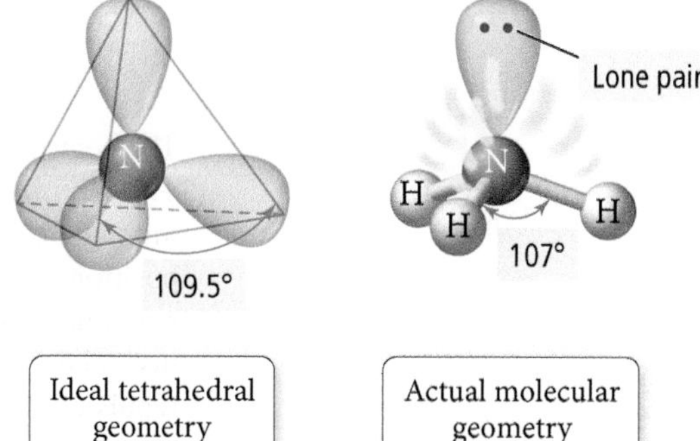

As we saw previously, different kinds of electron groups generally result in different amounts of repulsion. Lone pair electrons generally exert slightly greater repulsions than bonding electrons. If all four electron groups in NH_3 exerted equal repulsions on one another, the bond angles in the molecule would all be the ideal tetrahedral angle, 109.5°. However, the actual angle between N—H bonds in ammonia is slightly smaller: 107°. A lone electron pair is more spread out in space than a bonding electron pair because a lone pair is attracted to only one nucleus, while a bonding pair is attracted to two (Figure 10.3 ▾). The lone pair occupies more of the angular space around a nucleus, exerting a greater repulsive force on neighbouring electrons and compressing the N—H bond angles.

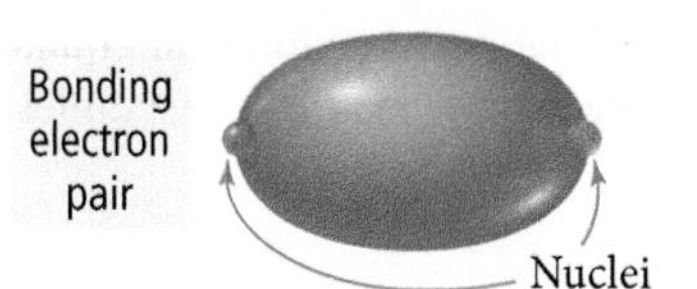

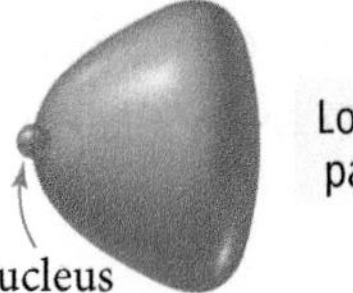

▲ **FIGURE 10.3 Nonbonding Versus Bonding Electron Pairs** A nonbonding electron pair occupies more space than a bonding pair.

A water molecule's Lewis structure is:

$$H-\ddot{\underset{\cdot\cdot}{O}}-H$$

Since it has four electron groups (two bonding pairs and two lone pairs), its *electron geometry* is also tetrahedral, but its *molecular geometry* is **bent**, as shown at right. As in NH_3, the bond angles in H_2O are smaller (104.5°) than the ideal tetrahedral bond angles because of the greater repulsion exerted by the lone-pair electrons. The bond angle in H_2O is even smaller than in NH_3 because H_2O has *two* lone pairs of electrons on the central oxygen atom. These lone pairs compress the H_2O bond angle to an even greater extent than in NH_3. In general, electron group repulsions vary as follows:

Lone pair
Lone pair
Electron geometry: tetrahedral
Molecular geometry: bent

Lone pair–lone pair > Lone pair–bonding pair > Bonding pair–bonding pair

Most repulsive — Least repulsive

We see the effects of this ordering in the progressively smaller bond angles of CH_4, NH_3, and H_2O, as shown in Figure 10.4 ▾. The relative ordering of repulsions also helps to determine the geometry of molecules with five and six electron groups when one or more of those groups are lone pairs, as we shall now see.

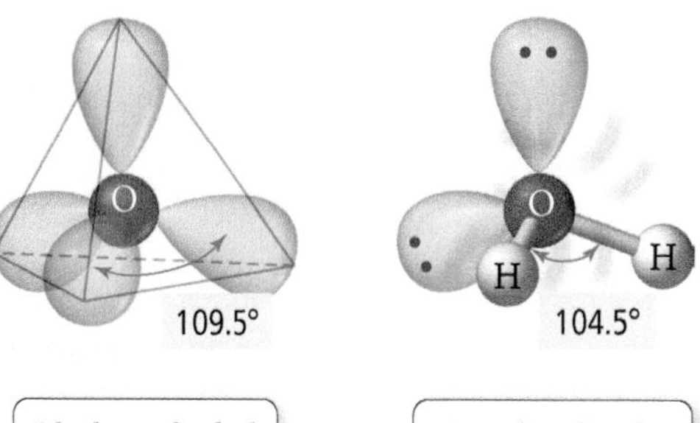

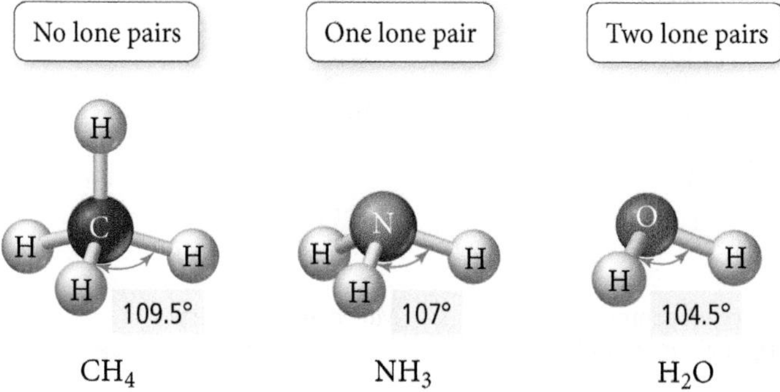

◀ **FIGURE 10.4 The Effect of Lone Pairs on Molecular Geometry** The bond angles get progressively smaller as the number of lone pairs on the central atom increases from zero in CH_4 to one in NH_3 to two in H_2O.

Five Electron Groups with Lone Pairs

Consider the Lewis structure of SF_4:

```
      :F̤:
       |
:F̤—S̤—F̤:
       |
      :F̤:
```

The central sulfur atom has five electron groups (one lone pair and four bonding pairs). The *electron geometry*, due to the five electron groups, is trigonal bipyramidal. In determining the molecular geometry, notice that the lone pair could occupy either an equatorial position or an axial position within the trigonal bipyramidal electron geometry. Which position is most favourable? To answer this question, we must consider that, as we have just seen, lone pair–bonding pair repulsions are greater than bonding pair–bonding pair repulsions. Consequently, the lone pair should occupy the position that minimizes its interaction with the bonding pairs. If the lone pair were in an axial position, it would have three 90° interactions with bonding pairs. In an equatorial position, however, it has only two 90° interactions. Consequently, the lone pair occupies an equatorial position. The resulting molecular geometry is called **seesaw**, because it resembles a seesaw (or teeter-totter):

The seesaw molecular geometry is sometimes called an *irregular tetrahedron.*

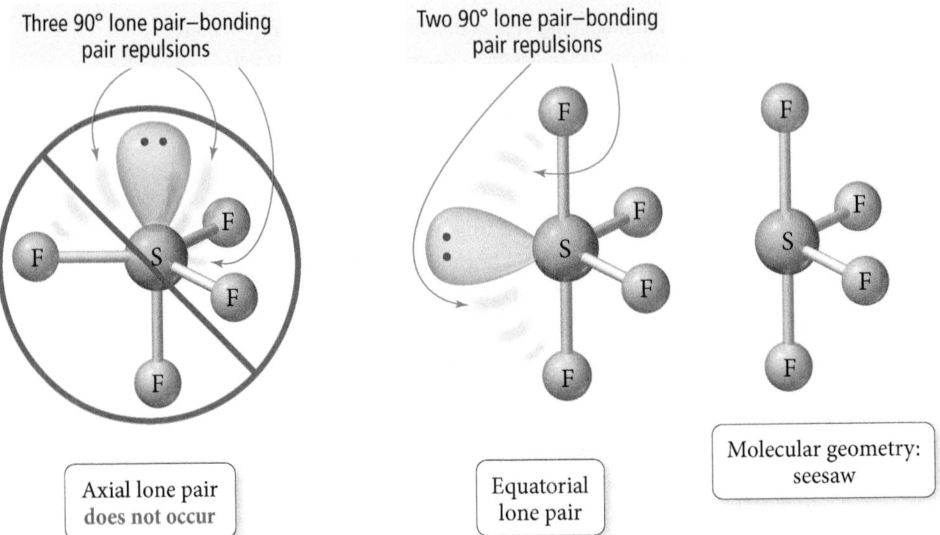

When two of the five electron groups around the central atom are lone pairs, as in BrF_3, the lone pairs occupy two of the three equatorial positions—again, minimizing 90° interactions with bonding pairs and also avoiding a lone pair–lone pair 90° repulsion. The resulting molecular geometry is **T-shaped**:

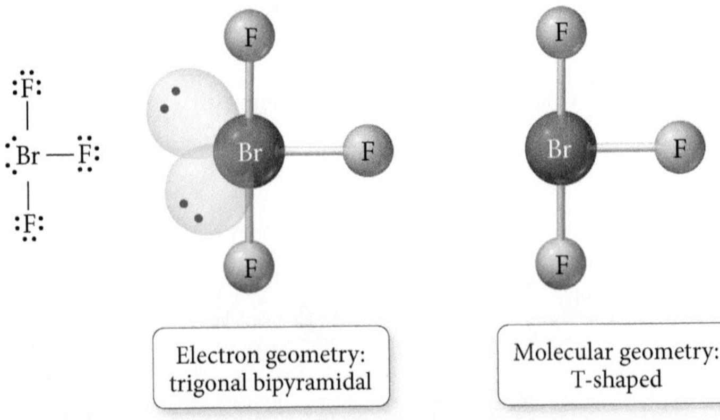

When three of the five electron groups around the central atom are lone pairs, as in XeF_2, the lone pairs occupy all three of the equatorial positions, and the resulting molecular geometry is linear:

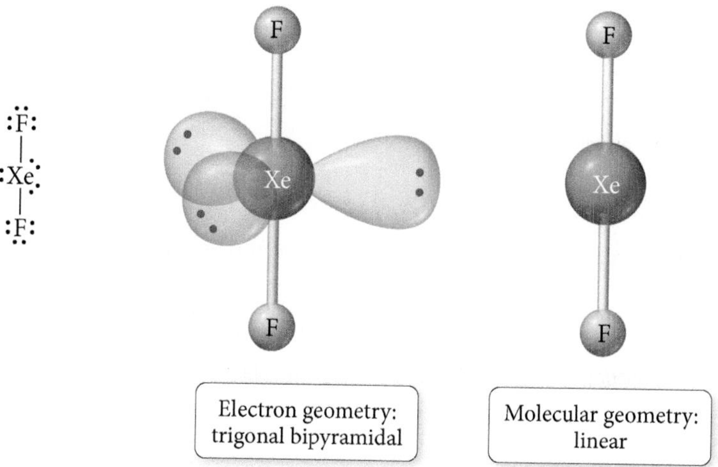

Six Electron Groups with Lone Pairs

The Lewis structure of BrF_5 is shown below. The central bromine atom has six electron groups (one lone pair and five bonding pairs). The electron geometry, due to the six electron groups, is octahedral. Since all six positions in the octahedral geometry are equivalent, the lone pair can be situated in any one of these positions. The resulting molecular geometry is **square pyramidal**:

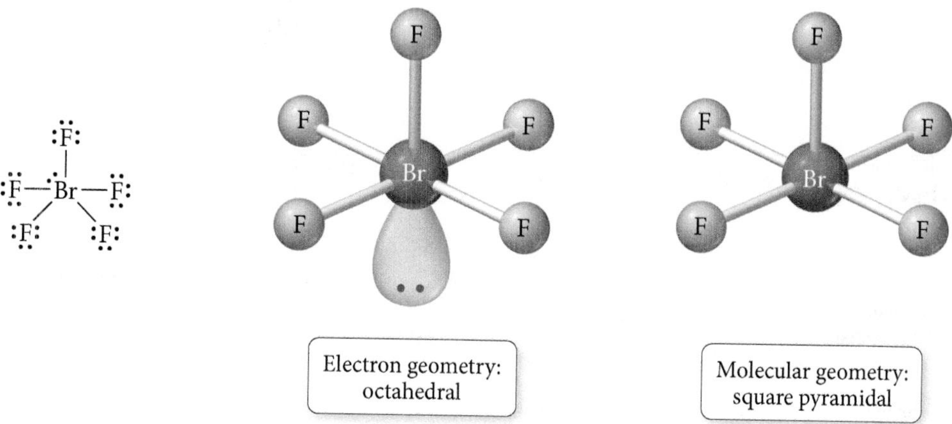

When two of the six electron groups around the central atom are lone pairs, as in XeF_4, the lone pairs occupy positions across from one another (to minimize lone pair–lone pair repulsions), and the resulting molecular geometry is **square planar**:

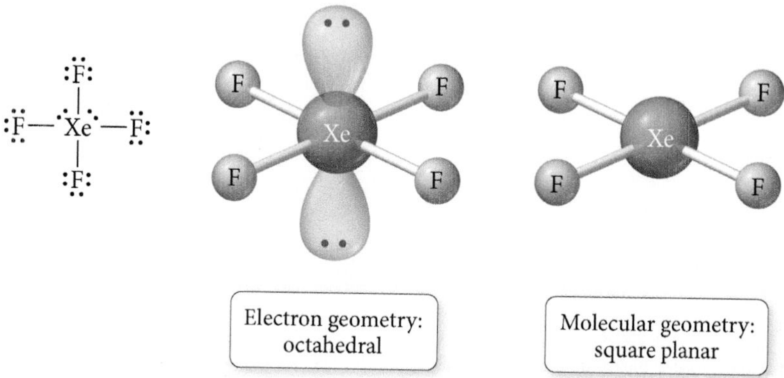

TABLE 10.1 Electron and Molecular Geometries

Electron Groups*	Bonding Groups	Lone Pairs	Electron Geometry	Molecular Geometry	Approximate Bond Angles	Example
2	2	0	Linear	Linear	180°	:Ö=C=Ö:
3	3	0	Trigonal planar	Trigonal planar	120°	:F̤—B—F̤: with :F: above B
3	2	1	Trigonal planar	Bent	<120°	:Ö=S̈—Ö:
4	4	0	Tetrahedral	Tetrahedral	109.5°	H—C—H with H above and H below C
4	3	1	Tetrahedral	Trigonal pyramidal	<109.5°	H—N̈—H with H below N
4	2	2	Tetrahedral	Bent	<109.5°	H—Ö—H
5	5	0	Trigonal bipyramidal	Trigonal bipyramidal	120° (equatorial) 90° (axial)	P with five :Cl:
5	4	1	Trigonal bipyramidal	Seesaw	<120° (equatorial) <90° (axial)	:F—S̈—F: with :F: above and :F: below S
5	3	2	Trigonal bipyramidal	T-shaped	<90°	:F—Br—F: with :F: below Br
5	2	3	Trigonal bipyramidal	Linear	180°	:F—Xe—F:
6	6	0	Octahedral	Octahedral	90°	S with six :F:
6	5	1	Octahedral	Square pyramidal	<90°	Br with five :F:
6	4	2	Octahedral	Square planar	90°	:F—Xe—F: with :F: above and :F: below Xe

*Count only the electron groups around the central atom. Each of the following is considered one electron group: a lone pair, a single bond, a double bond, a triple bond, or a single electron.

Summarizing VSEPR Theory:

- The geometry of a molecule is determined by the number of electron groups on the central atom (or on all interior atoms, if there is more than one).
- The number of electron groups can be determined from the Lewis structure of the molecule. If the Lewis structure contains resonance structures, use any one of the resonance structures to determine the number of electron groups.
- Each of the following counts as a single electron group: a lone pair, a single bond, a double bond, a triple bond, and sometimes a single electron.
- The geometry of the electron groups is determined by their repulsions, as summarized in Table 10.1. In general, electron group repulsions vary as follows:

  Lone pair–lone pair > lone pair–bonding pair > bonding pair–bonding pair

- Bond angles can vary from the idealized angles because double and triple bonds occupy more space than single bonds (they are bulkier even though they are shorter), and lone pairs occupy more space than bonding groups. The presence of lone pairs will usually make bond angles smaller than the ideal angle for the particular geometry.

CONCEPTUAL CONNECTION 10.2

Molecular Geometry and Electron Groups

Which statement is *always* true according to VSEPR theory?

(a) The shape of a molecule is determined only by repulsions among bonding electron groups.

(b) The shape of a molecule is determined only by repulsions among nonbonding electron groups.

(c) The shape of a molecule is determined by the polarity of its bonds.

(d) The shape of a molecule is determined by repulsions among all electron groups on the central atom (or interior atoms, if there is more than one).

10.4 VSEPR Theory: Predicting Molecular Geometries

To determine the geometry of a molecule, follow the procedure in the following examples. As in other examples, we provide the steps in the left column and provide two examples of applying the steps in the centre and right columns.

PROCEDURE FOR ... **Predicting Molecular Geometries**	EXAMPLE 10.2 **Predicting Molecular Geometries I** Predict the geometry and bond angles of PCl_3.	EXAMPLE 10.3 **Predicting Molecular Geometries II** Predict the geometry and bond angles of ICl_4^-.
1. Draw a Lewis structure for the molecule.	PCl_3 has 26 valence electrons. :C̈l: | :C̈l—P̤—C̈l:	ICl_4^- has 36 valence electrons. [:C̈l: | :C̈l—Ï—C̈l: | :C̤l:]$^-$
2. Determine the total number of electron groups around the central atom. Lone pairs, single bonds, double bonds, triple bonds, and single electrons each count as one group.	The central atom (P) has four electron groups.	The central atom (I) has six electron groups.

(continued)

PROCEDURE FOR... *(continued)*	**EXAMPLE 10.2** *(continued)*	**EXAMPLE 10.3** *(continued)*
3. Determine the number of bonding groups and the number of lone pairs around the central atom. These should sum to the result from step 2. Bonding groups include single bonds, double bonds, and triple bonds.	:Cl: / :Cl—P—Cl: (Lone pair) Three of the four electron groups around P are bonding groups and one is a lone pair.	Lone pairs $[$:Cl: / :Cl—I—Cl: / :Cl: $]^-$ Four of the six electron groups around I are bonding groups and two are lone pairs.
4. Use Table 10.1 to determine the electron geometry and molecular geometry. If no lone pairs are present around the central atom, the bond angles will be close to that of the ideal geometry. If lone pairs are present, the bond angles may be smaller than the ideal geometry.	The electron geometry is tetrahedral (four electron groups) and the molecular geometry—the shape of the molecule—is *trigonal pyramidal* (three bonding groups and one lone pair). Because of the presence of a lone pair, the bond angles are less than 109.5°. 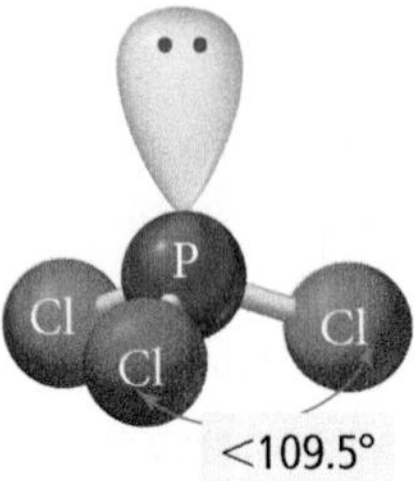 Trigonal pyramidal	The electron geometry is octahedral (six electron groups) and the molecular geometry—the shape of the molecule—is *square planar* (four bonding groups and two lone pairs). Even though lone pairs are present, the bond angles are 90° because the lone pairs are symmetrically arranged and do not compress the I—Cl bond angles. 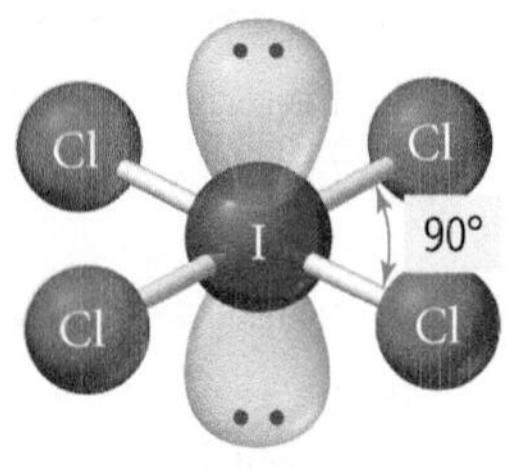 Square planar
	FOR PRACTICE 10.2 Predict the molecular geometry and bond angle of ClNO.	**FOR PRACTICE 10.3** Predict the molecular geometry and bond angle of I_3^-.

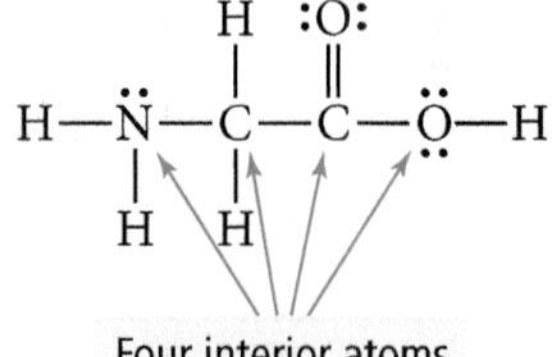

Glycine

Predicting the Shapes of Larger Molecules

Larger molecules may have two or more *interior* atoms (or what we previously called central atoms). When predicting the shapes of these molecules, the principles we just covered must be applied to each interior atom. Consider glycine, an amino acid found in many proteins (such as those involved in taste that we discussed in Section 10.1). Glycine, shown here, contains four interior atoms: one nitrogen atom, two carbon atoms, and an oxygen atom. To determine the shape of glycine, we must determine the geometry about each interior atom as follows:

Atom	Number of Electron Groups	Number of Lone Pairs	Molecular Geometry
Nitrogen	4	1	Trigonal pyramidal
Leftmost carbon	4	0	Tetrahedral
Rightmost carbon	3	0	Trigonal planar
Oxygen	4	2	Bent

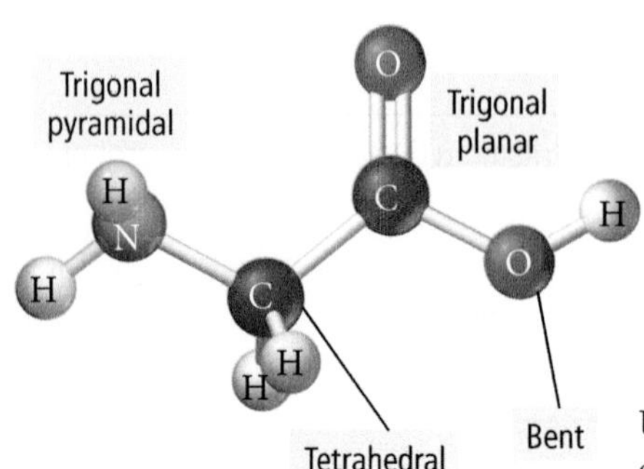

Using the geometries of each of these, we can determine the entire three-dimensional shape of the molecule as shown at left.

Since molecular geometries are three dimensional, they are often difficult to represent on two-dimensional paper. Chemists use the following notation for bonds to indicate three-dimensional structures on two-dimensional paper:

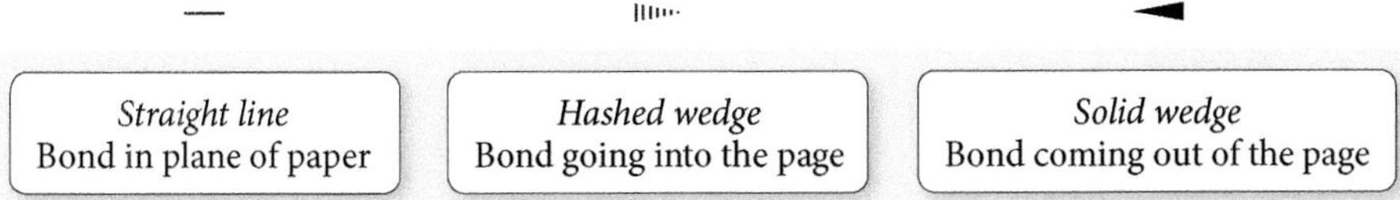

For example, a tetrahedral molecular geometry can be represented as:

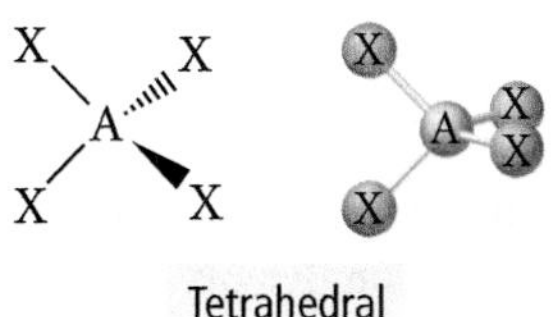

Tetrahedral

EXAMPLE 10.4 PREDICTING THE SHAPE OF LARGER MOLECULES

Predict the geometry about each interior atom in methanol (CH_3OH) and make a sketch of the molecule.

SOLUTION

Begin by drawing the Lewis structure of CH_3OH. CH_3OH contains two interior atoms: one carbon atom and one oxygen atom. To determine the shape of methanol, determine the geometry about each interior atom as follows:

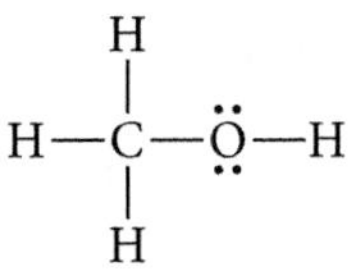

H—C(H)(H)—Ö—H

Atom	Number of Electron Groups	Number of Lone Pairs	Molecular Geometry
Carbon	4	0	Tetrahedral
Oxygen	4	2	Bent

Using the geometries of each of these, draw a three-dimensional sketch of the molecule, as shown here:

Tetrahedral — H_3C—O—H — Bent

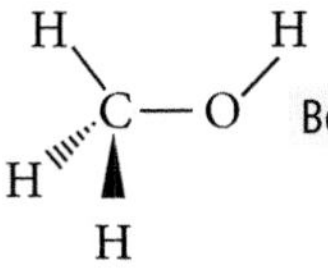

FOR PRACTICE 10.4

Predict the geometry about each interior atom in acetic acid ($H_3C—C(=O)—OH$) and make a sketch of the molecule.

10.5 Molecular Shape and Polarity

In Chapter 9, we discussed polar bonds. Entire molecules can also be polar, depending on their shape and the nature of their bonds. For example, if a diatomic molecule has a polar bond, the molecule as a whole will be polar.

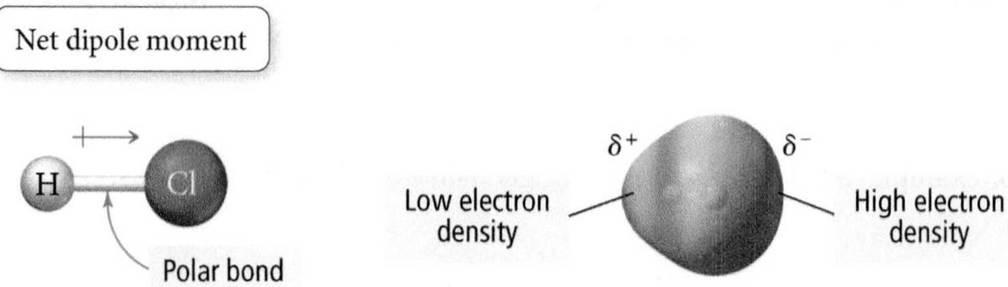

The figure above is an electrostatic potential map of HCl. Blue indicates low electron density and red indicates higher electron density. The colours between blue and red indicate intermediate electron densities. Notice that the electron density is greater around the more electronegative atom (chlorine). Thus, the molecule itself is polar. If the bond in a diatomic molecule is *nonpolar*, the molecule as a whole will be *nonpolar*.

In polyatomic molecules, the presence of polar bonds may or may not result in a polar molecule, depending on the molecular geometry. If the molecular geometry is such that the dipole moments of individual polar bonds sum together to a net dipole moment, then the molecule will be polar. But if the molecular geometry is such that the dipole moments of the individual polar bonds cancel each other (that is, sum to zero), then the molecule will be nonpolar. It all depends on the geometry of the molecule. Consider carbon dioxide:

$$:\ddot{O}=C=\ddot{O}:$$

Each C═O bond in CO_2 is polar because oxygen and carbon have significantly different electronegativities (3.5 and 2.5, respectively). However, since CO_2 is a linear molecule, the polar bonds directly oppose one another and the dipole moment of one bond exactly opposes the dipole moment of the other—the two dipole moments sum to zero and the *molecule* is nonpolar. Dipole moments can cancel each other because they are *vector quantities*: they have both a magnitude and a direction. Think of each polar bond as a vector, pointing in the direction of the more electronegative atom. The length of the vector is proportional to the electronegativity difference between the bonding atoms. In CO_2, we have two identical vectors pointing in exactly opposite directions—the vectors sum to zero, much as $+1$ and -1 sum to zero:

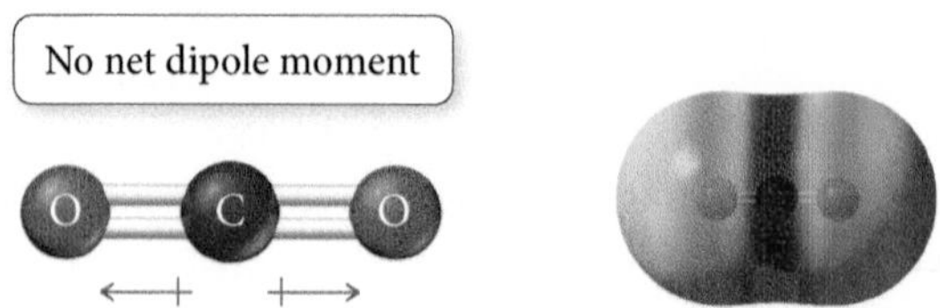

Notice that the electrostatic potential map shows regions of moderately high electron density (red and yellow) positioned symmetrically on either end of the molecule with a region of low electron density (blue) located in the middle.

In contrast, consider water:

$$H-\ddot{\underset{\cdot\cdot}{O}}-H$$

The O—H bonds in water are also polar; oxygen and hydrogen have electronegativities of 3.5 and 2.1, respectively. However, the water molecule is not linear but bent, so the two dipole moments do not sum to zero. If we imagine each bond as a vector pointing toward oxygen (the more electronegative atom), we see that because of the angle between the vectors, they do not cancel, but sum to an overall vector or a net dipole moment (shown by the dashed arrow).

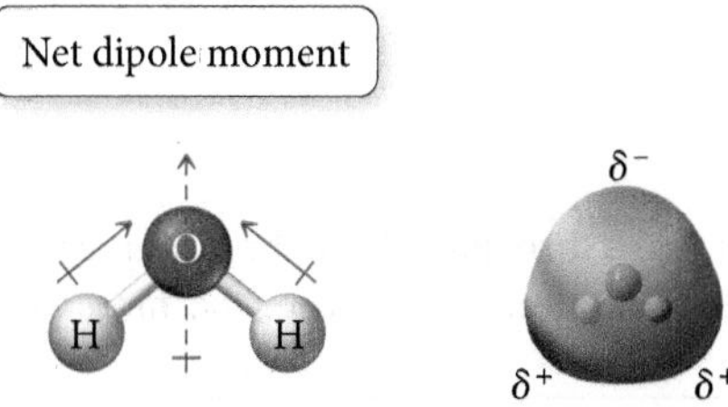

The electrostatic potential map shows a region of very high electron density at the oxygen end of the molecule. Consequently, water is a polar molecule. Table 10.2 summarizes whether or not various common geometries result in polar molecules.

TABLE 10.2 Common Cases of Adding Dipole Moments to Determine Whether a Molecule Is Polar

Linear 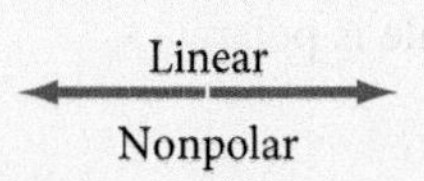 Nonpolar	Bent 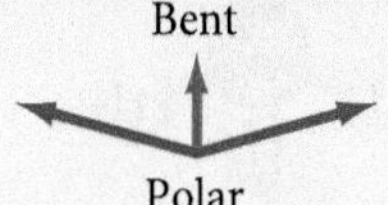 Polar	Trigonal pyramidal 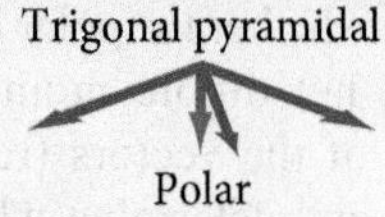 Polar
The dipole moments of two identical polar bonds pointing in opposite directions will cancel. The molecule is nonpolar. Example: CO_2.	The dipole moments of two polar bonds with an angle of less than 180° between them will not cancel. The resultant dipole moment vector is shown in red. The molecule is polar. Example: H_2O.	The dipole moments of three polar bonds in a trigonal pyramidal arrangement (109.5° from each other) will not cancel. The resultant dipole moment vector is shown in red. The molecule is polar. Example: NH_3.
Trigonal planar 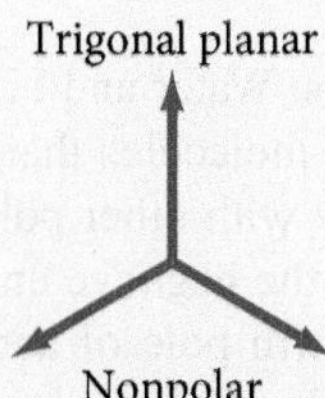 Nonpolar	Tetrahedral 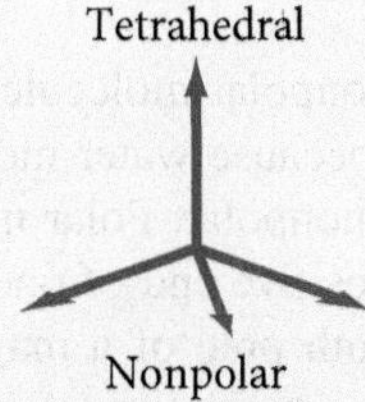 Nonpolar	
The dipole moments of three identical polar bonds at 120° from each other will cancel. The molecule is nonpolar. Example: BF_3.	The dipole moments of four identical polar bonds in a tetrahedral arrangement (109.5° from each other) will cancel. The molecule is nonpolar. Example: CH_4.	

Note: In all cases where the dipoles of two or more polar bonds cancel, the bonds are assumed to be identical. If one or more of the bonds are different from the other(s), the dipoles will not cancel and the molecule will be polar.

Summarizing Molecular Shape and Polarity:

- **Draw a Lewis structure for the molecule and determine the molecular geometry.**
- **Determine whether the molecule contains polar bonds.** A bond is polar if the two bonding atoms have sufficiently different electronegativities (see Figure 9.12 in chapter 9). If the molecule contains polar bonds, superimpose a vector, pointing toward the more electronegative atom, on each bond. Make the length of the vector proportional to the electronegativity difference between the bonding atoms.
- Determine whether the polar bonds add together to form a net dipole moment. Sum the vectors corresponding to the polar bonds together. If the vectors sum to zero, the molecule is nonpolar. If the vectors sum to a net vector, the molecule is polar.

EXAMPLE 10.5 DETERMINING WHETHER A MOLECULE IS POLAR

Determine whether NH_3 is polar.

SOLUTION

Draw a Lewis structure for the molecule and determine the molecular geometry.	H—N(H)—H with a lone pair on N The Lewis structure has three bonding groups and one lone pair about the central atom. Therefore, the molecular geometry is trigonal pyramidal.
Determine whether the molecule contains polar bonds. Sketch the molecule and superimpose a vector for each polar bond. The relative length of each vector should be proportional to the electronegativity difference between the atoms forming each bond. The vector should point in the direction of the more electronegative atom.	The electronegativities of nitrogen and hydrogen are 3.0 and 2.1, respectively. Therefore, the bonds are polar. 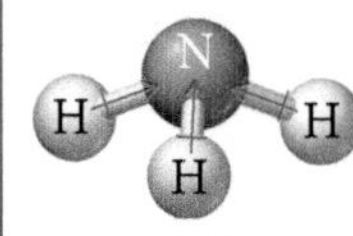
Determine whether the polar bonds add together to form a net dipole moment. Examine the symmetry of the vectors (representing dipole moments) and determine whether they cancel each other or sum to a net dipole moment.	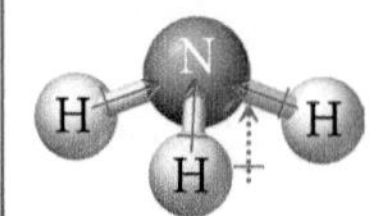 The three dipole moments sum to a net dipole moment. The molecule is polar.

FOR PRACTICE 10.5

Determine whether CF_4 is polar.

Polar and nonpolar molecules have different properties. Water and oil do not mix, for example, because water molecules are polar and the molecules that compose oil are generally nonpolar. Polar molecules interact strongly with other polar molecules because the positive end of one molecule is attracted to the negative end of another, just as the south pole of a magnet is attracted to the north pole of another magnet (Figure 10.5 ◀). A mixture of polar and nonpolar molecules is similar to a mixture of small magnetic particles and nonmagnetic ones. The magnetic particles (which are like polar molecules) clump together, excluding the nonmagnetic particles (which are like nonpolar molecules) and separate into distinct regions.

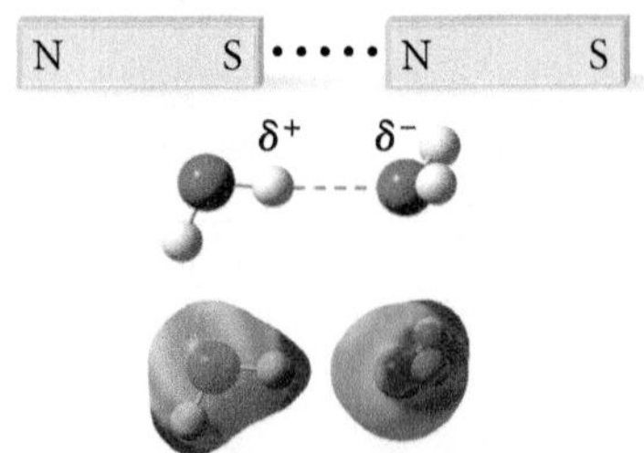

▲ **FIGURE 10.5 Interaction of Polar Molecules** The north pole of one magnet attracts the south pole of another magnet. In an analogous way, the positively charged end of one molecule attracts the negatively charged end of another (although the forces involved are different). As a result of this electrical attraction, polar molecules interact strongly with one another.

▲ A mixture of polar and nonpolar molecules is analogous to a mixture of magnetic marbles (opaque) and nonmagnetic marbles (transparent). As with the magnetic marbles, mutual attraction causes polar molecules to clump together, excluding the nonpolar molecules.

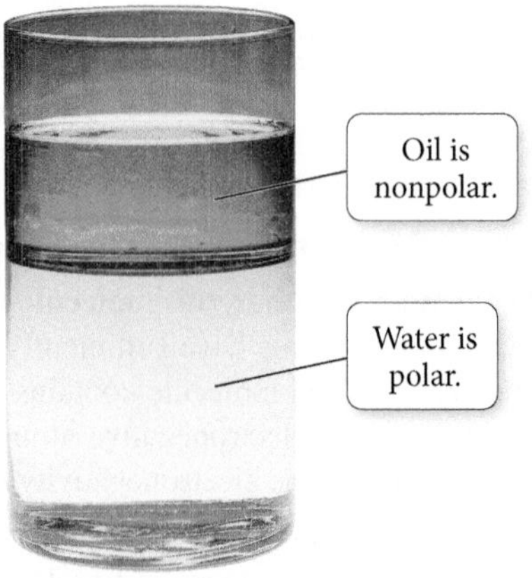

▲ Oil and water do not mix because water molecules are polar and the molecules that compose oil are nonpolar.

CHEMISTRY IN YOUR DAY How Soap Works

Imagine eating a greasy cheeseburger with both hands and without napkins. By the end of the meal, your hands are coated with grease and oil. If you try to wash them with only water, they remain greasy. However, if you add a little soap, the grease washes away. Why? As we just learned, water molecules are polar and the molecules that compose grease and oil are nonpolar. As a result, water and grease do not mix.

The molecules that compose soap, however, have a special structure that allows them to interact strongly with both water and grease. One end of a soap molecule is polar, while the other end is nonpolar.

The nonpolar end is a long hydrocarbon chain. Hydrocarbons are always nonpolar because the electronegativity difference between carbon and hydrogen is small, and because the tetrahedral arrangement about each carbon atom tends to cancel any small dipole moments of individual bonds. The polar head of a soap molecule—usually (though not always) ionic—strongly attracts water molecules, while the nonpolar tail interacts more strongly with grease and oil molecules (we examine the nature of these interactions in Chapter 11). Thus, soap acts as a sort of molecular liaison—one end interacting with water and the other end interacting with grease. Soap allows water and grease to mix, removing the grease from your hands and washing it down the drain.

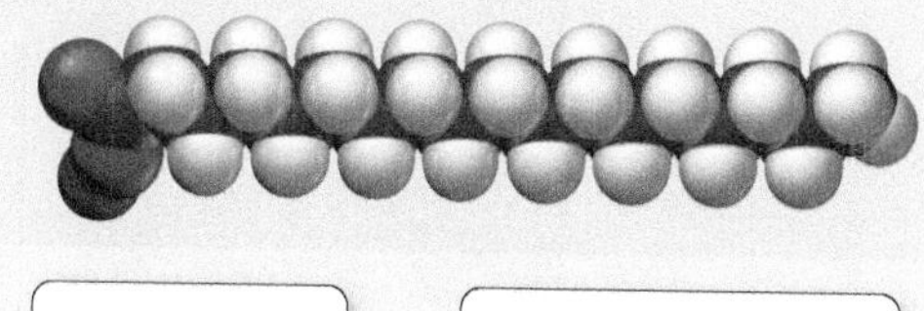

Polar head attracts water.

Nonpolar tail interacts with grease.

$CH_3(CH_2)_{11}OCH_2CH_2OH$

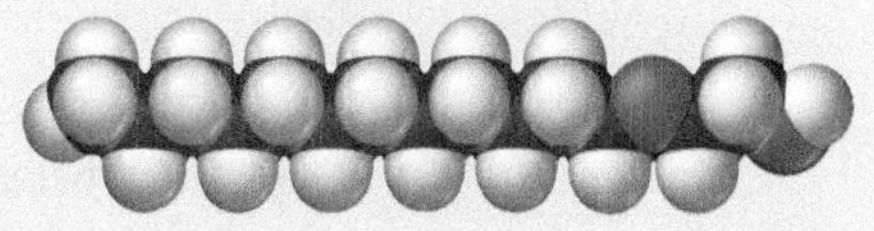

Question

Consider the detergent molecule at right. Which end do you think is polar? Which end is nonpolar?

10.6 Valence Bond Theory: Orbital Overlap as a Chemical Bond

In Lewis theory, we use "dots" to represent electrons as they are transferred or shared between bonding atoms. We know from quantum-mechanical theory, however, that such a treatment is an oversimplification. More advanced bonding theories treat electrons in a quantum-mechanical manner. In fact, these more advanced theories are actually extensions of quantum mechanics, applied to molecules. Although a detailed quantitative treatment of these theories is beyond the scope of this text, we introduce them in a *qualitative* manner in the sections that follow. Keep in mind, however, that modern *quantitative* approaches to chemical bonding using these theories can accurately predict many of the properties of molecules—such as bond lengths, bond strengths, molecular geometries, and dipole moments—that we have been discussing in this text.

The simpler of the two more advanced bonding theories is called **valence bond theory**. In valence bond theory, electrons reside in quantum-mechanical orbitals localized on individual atoms. In many cases, these orbitals are simply the standard *s*, *p*, *d*, and *f* atomic orbitals that we learned about in Chapter 7. In other cases, these orbitals are *hybridized atomic orbitals*, a kind of blend or combination of two or more standard atomic orbitals.

Valence bond theory is an application of a more general quantum-mechanical approximation method called *perturbation theory*. In perturbation theory, a system (for example, an atom) that is simpler than the actual one, is viewed as being slightly altered (or perturbed) by some additional force or interaction.

When two atoms approach each other, the electrons and nucleus of one atom interact with the electrons and nucleus of the other atom. In valence bond theory, we calculate the effect of these interactions on the energies of the electrons in the atomic orbitals. If the energy of the system is lowered because of the interactions, then a chemical bond forms. If the energy of the system is raised by the interactions, then a chemical bond does not form.

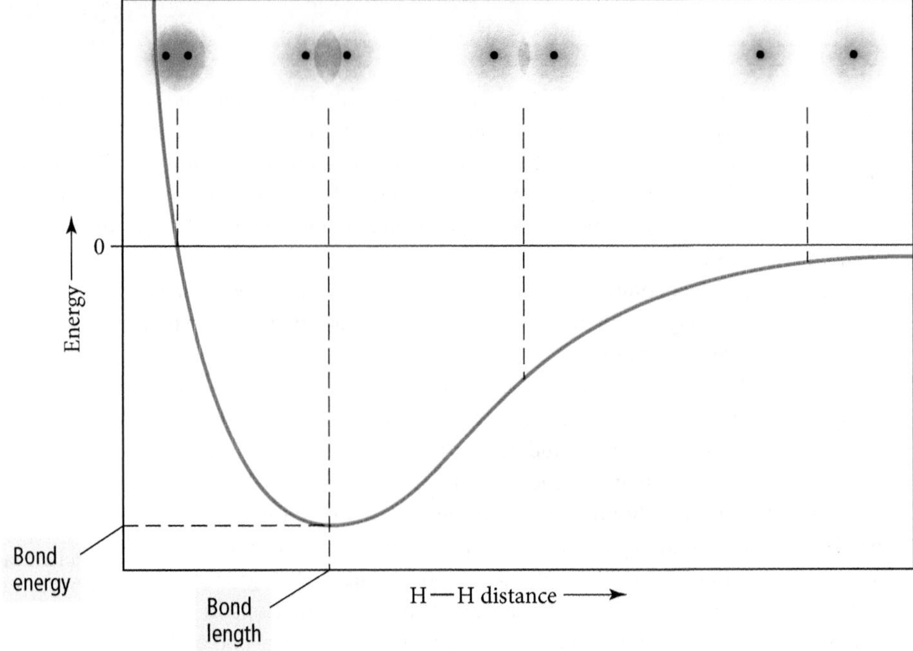

▶ **FIGURE 10.6 Energy Diagram for H_2** The potential energy of two hydrogen atoms is lowest when they are separated by a distance that allows their 1*s* orbitals a substantial degree of overlap without too much repulsion between their nuclei. This distance, at which the system is most stable, is the bond length of the H_2 molecule.

The energy of interaction is usually calculated as a function of the internuclear distance between the two bonding atoms. For example, Figure 10.6 ▲ shows the calculated energy of interaction between two hydrogen atoms as a function of the distance between them. The *y*-axis of the graph is the potential energy of the interaction between the electron and nucleus of one hydrogen atom and the electron and nucleus of the other. The *x*-axis is the separation (or internuclear distance) between the two atoms. As you can see from the graph, when the atoms are far apart (right side of the graph), the energy of interaction is nearly zero because the two atoms do not interact to any significant extent. As the atoms get closer, the overall energy becomes negative. This is a net stabilization that attracts one hydrogen atom to the other. If the atoms get too close, however, the energy begins to rise, primarily because of the mutual repulsion of the two positively charged nuclei. The most stable point on the curve occurs at the minimum in energy—this is the equilibrium bond length. At this distance, the two atomic 1*s* orbitals have a significant amount of overlap and the electrons spend time in the internuclear region where they can interact with both nuclei. The bond energy is the difference between the energy when there is no interaction and the minimum in the potential energy diagram.

When valence bond theory is applied to a number of atoms and their corresponding molecules, we can make the following general observation: *the energy of interaction is usually negative (or stabilizing) when the interacting atomic orbitals contain a total of two electrons that can spin-pair.* Most commonly, the two electrons come from two half-filled orbitals, but in some cases, the two electrons can come from one filled orbital overlapping with a completely empty orbital (this is called a coordinate covalent bond and is covered in more detail in Chapter 24). In other words, when two atoms with half-filled orbitals approach each other, the half-filled orbitals *overlap*—parts of the orbitals occupy the same space—and the electrons occupying them align with opposite spins. This results in a net energy stabilization that constitutes a covalent chemical bond. The resulting geometry of the molecule emerges from the geometry of the overlapping orbitals.

When *completely filled* orbitals overlap, the overall energy of the system increases (destabilizing interaction) and no bond forms.

Summarizing Valence Bond Theory:

- The valence electrons of the atoms in a molecule reside in quantum-mechanical atomic orbitals. The orbitals can be the standard *s*, *p*, *d*, and *f* orbitals, or they may be hybrid combinations of these.

- A chemical bond results from the overlap of two half-filled orbitals with spin-pairing of the two valence electrons (or less commonly, the overlap of a completely filled orbital with an empty orbital).
- The shape of the molecule is determined by the geometry of the overlapping orbitals.

Let's apply the general concepts of valence bond theory to explain bonding in hydrogen sulfide, H_2S. The valence electron configurations of the atoms in the molecule are as follows:

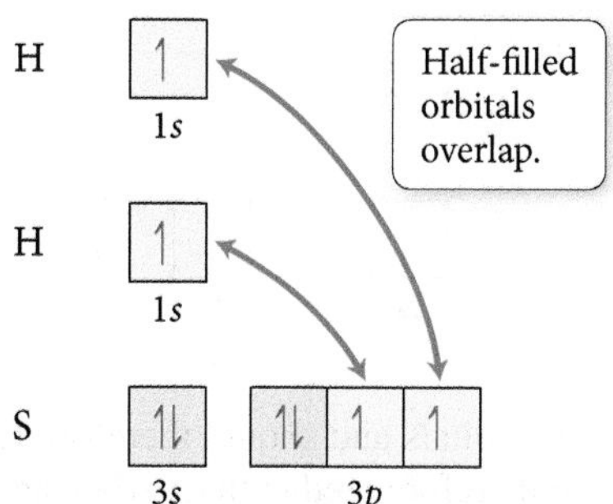

The hydrogen atoms each have one half-filled orbital, and the sulfur atom has two half-filled orbitals. The half-filled orbitals on each hydrogen atom overlap with the two half-filled orbitals on the sulfur atom, forming two chemical bonds:

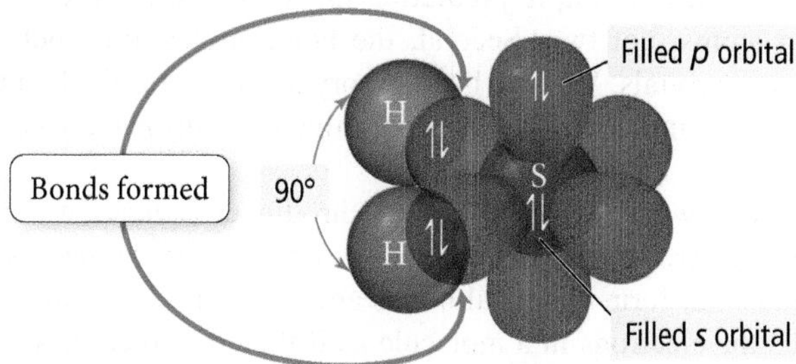

To show the spin-pairing of the electrons in the overlapping orbitals, we superimpose a half-arrow for each electron in each half-filled orbital and show that, within a bond, the electrons are spin-paired (one half-arrow pointing up and the other pointing down). We also superimpose paired half-arrows in the filled sulfur *s* and *p* orbitals to represent the lone pair electrons in those orbitals. (Since those orbitals are full, they are not involved in bonding.)

A quantitative calculation of H_2S using valence bond theory yields bond energies, bond lengths, and bond angles. In our qualitative treatment, we simply show how orbital overlap leads to bonding and make a rough sketch of the molecule based on the overlapping orbitals. Notice that, because the overlapping orbitals on the central atom (sulfur) are *p* orbitals, and because *p* orbitals are oriented at 90° to one another, the predicted bond angle is 90°. The actual bond angle in H_2S is 92°. In the case of H_2S, a simple valence bond treatment matches well with the experimentally measured bond angle (in contrast to VSEPR theory, which predicts a bond angle slightly less than 109.5°).

CONCEPTUAL CONNECTION 10.3
What Is a Chemical Bond? Part I

The answer to the question, *what is a chemical bond?* depends on the bonding model. Answer these three questions:

(a) What is a covalent chemical bond according to Lewis theory?

(b) What is a covalent chemical bond according to valence bond theory?

(c) Why are the answers different?

10.7 Valence Bond Theory: Hybridization of Atomic Orbitals

Although the overlap of half-filled *standard* atomic orbitals adequately explains the bonding in H_2S, it cannot adequately explain the bonding in many other molecules. For example, suppose we try to explain the bonding between hydrogen and carbon using the same approach. The valence electron configurations of H and C are as follows:

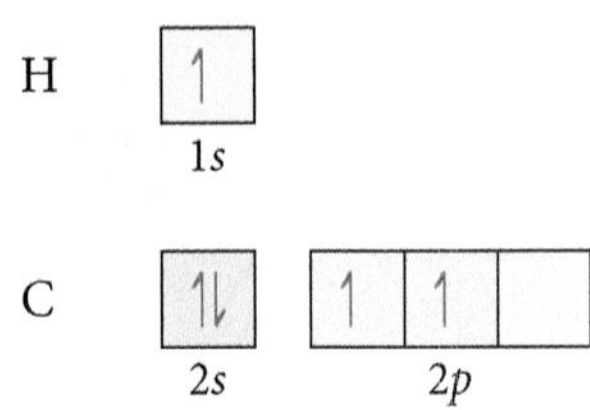

90°

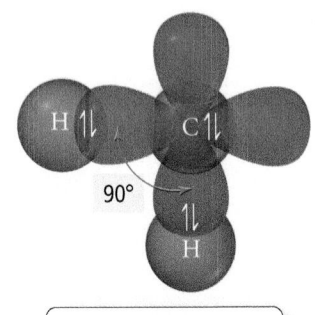

Theoretical prediction

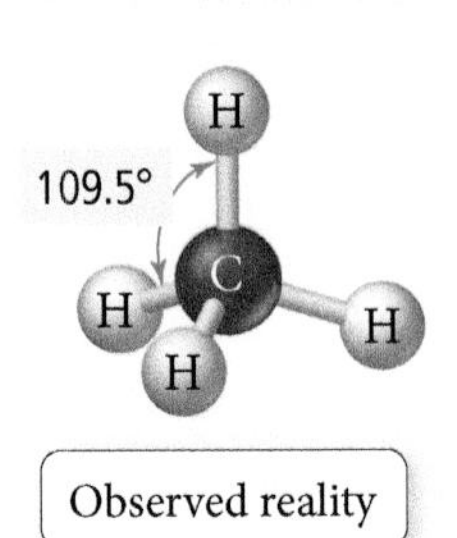

Observed reality

Carbon has only two half-filled orbitals and should therefore form only two bonds with two hydrogen atoms. We would therefore predict that carbon and hydrogen should form a molecule with the formula CH_2 and with a bond angle of 90° (corresponding to the angle between any two *p* orbitals).

However, from experiments, we know that the stable compound formed from carbon and hydrogen is CH_4 (methane), with bond angles of 109.5°. The experimental reality is different from our simple prediction in two ways. First, carbon forms bonds to four hydrogen atoms, not two. Second, the bond angles are much larger than the angle between two *p* orbitals. Valence bond theory accounts for the bonding in CH_4 and many other polyatomic molecules by incorporating an additional concept called *orbital hybridization.*

In Chapter 7, we saw that solutions to the Schrödinger equation were atomic orbitals, which we labelled $1s$, $2s$, $2p_x$, $2p_y$, $2p_z$, $3s$, and so on. So far, we have assumed that the overlapping orbitals that form chemical bonds are simply these atomic orbitals. Valence bond theory treats the electrons in a molecule as if they occupied these standard atomic orbitals, but this is a major oversimplification. The concept of hybridization in valence bond theory is essentially one step toward recognizing that the *orbitals in a molecule are not the same as the orbitals in an atom.* **Hybridization** is a procedure in which two or more of the standard atomic orbitals are mathematically mixed, forming new **hybrid atomic orbitals** or **hybrid orbitals**. These new hybrid orbitals correspond more closely to the actual distribution of electrons in chemically bonded atoms. Hybrid orbitals are still localized on individual atoms, but they have different shapes and energies from those of standard atomic orbitals.

In Section 10.8, we examine another theory called *molecular orbital theory,* which treats electrons in a molecule as occupying orbitals that belong to the molecule as a whole.

Why do we hypothesize that electrons in some molecules occupy hybrid orbitals? In valence bond theory, a chemical bond is the overlap of two orbitals that together contain two electrons. The greater the overlap, the stronger the bond and the lower the energy. In hybrid orbitals, the electron probability density is more concentrated in a single directional lobe, allowing greater overlap with the orbitals of other atoms. Hybrid orbitals *minimize* the energy of the molecule by *maximizing* the orbital overlap in a bond.

In this text, we focus on the hybridization of interior atoms—those bonded to more than one atom—in order to account for some of the geometries we encountered by applying VSEPR theory. Terminal atoms are not hybridized. Hybridization is a particularly important concept for carbon-containing compounds. We will, therefore, limit our discussion of hybridization to compounds containing carbon and other second-period atoms.

In a more detailed treatment, hybridization is not an all-or-nothing process—it can occur to varying degrees that are not always easy to predict. We saw earlier, for example, that sulfur does not hybridize very much in forming H_2S.

Although we cannot examine the procedure for obtaining hybrid orbitals in mathematical detail here, we can make the following general statements regarding hybridization:

- The *number of standard atomic orbitals* added together always equals the *number of hybrid orbitals* formed. The total number of orbitals is conserved.
- The *particular combinations* of standard atomic orbitals added together determine the *shapes and energies* of the hybrid orbitals formed.

sp^3 Hybridization

We can account for the tetrahedral geometry in CH_4 by the hybridization of the one 2*s* orbital and the three 2*p* orbitals on the carbon atom. The four new orbitals that result, called sp^3 hybrids, are shown in the following diagram:

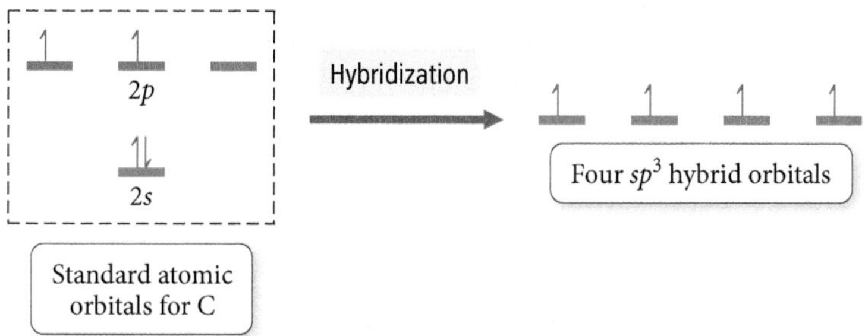

The notation "sp^3" indicates that the hybrid orbitals are mixtures of one *s* orbital and three *p* orbitals. The hybrid orbitals that are formed all have the same energy—they are degenerate. The shapes of the sp^3 hybrid orbitals are shown in Figure 10.7 ▼. The four hybrid orbitals are arranged in a tetrahedral geometry with 109.5° angles between them.

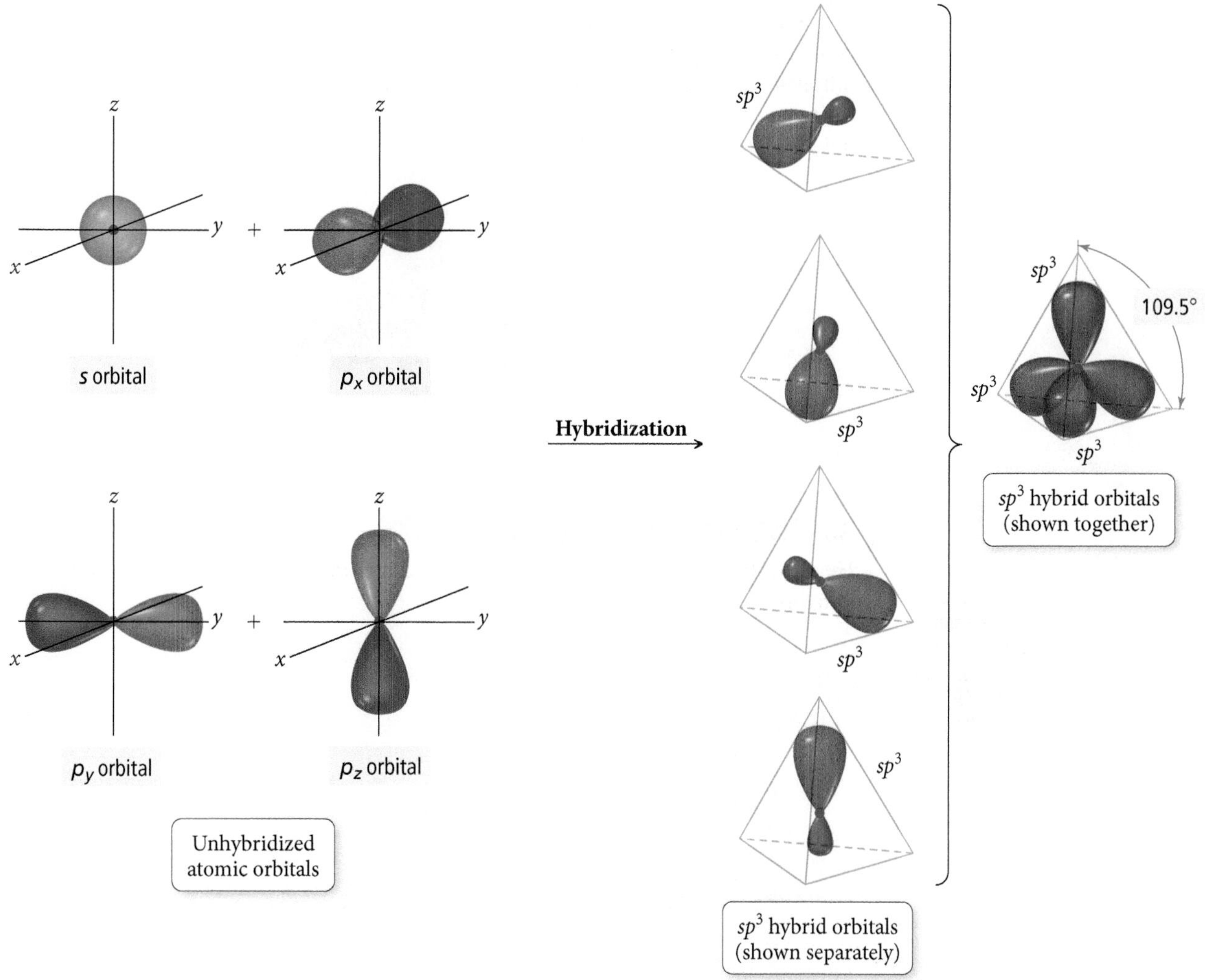

s orbital + p_x orbital

p_y orbital + p_z orbital

Unhybridized atomic orbitals

Hybridization →

sp^3 hybrid orbitals (shown separately)

sp^3 hybrid orbitals (shown together)

109.5°

▲ **FIGURE 10.7 sp^3 Hybridization** One *s* orbital and three *p* orbitals combine to form four sp^3 hybrid orbitals.

We can write an orbital diagram for carbon using these hybrid orbitals:

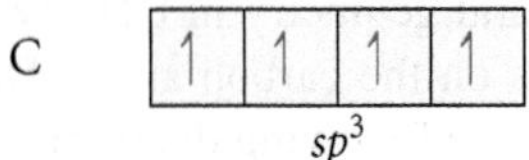

Carbon's four valence electrons occupy the orbitals singly with parallel spins as dictated by Hund's rule. With this electron configuration, carbon has four half-filled orbitals and can form four bonds with four hydrogen atoms:

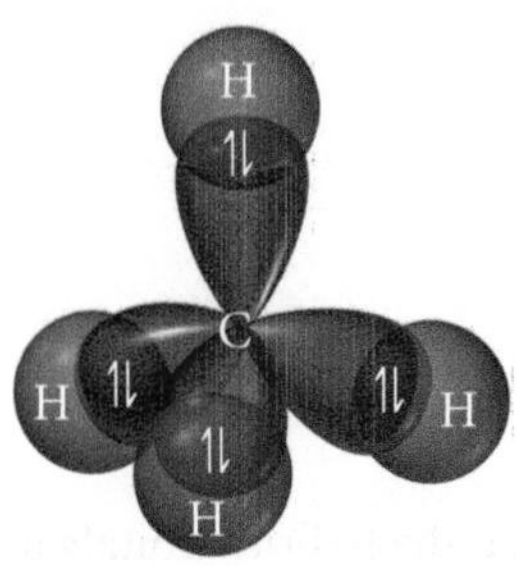

The geometry of the *overlapping orbitals* (the hybrids) is tetrahedral, with angles of 109.5° between the orbitals, so the *resulting geometry of the molecule* is tetrahedral, with 109.5° bond angles, in agreement with the experimentally measured geometry of CH_4 and with the predicted VSEPR geometry.

If the central atom of a molecule contains lone pairs, hybrid orbitals can also accommodate them. For example, the nitrogen orbitals in ammonia are sp^3 hybrids. Three of the hybrids are involved in bonding with three hydrogen atoms, but the fourth hybrid contains a lone pair. The presence of the lone pair, however, does lower the tendency of nitrogen's orbitals to hybridize. (Remember that the tendency to hybridize increases with the number of bonds formed.) Therefore, the bond angle in NH_3 is 107°, a bit closer to the unhybridized *p* orbital bond angle of 90°.

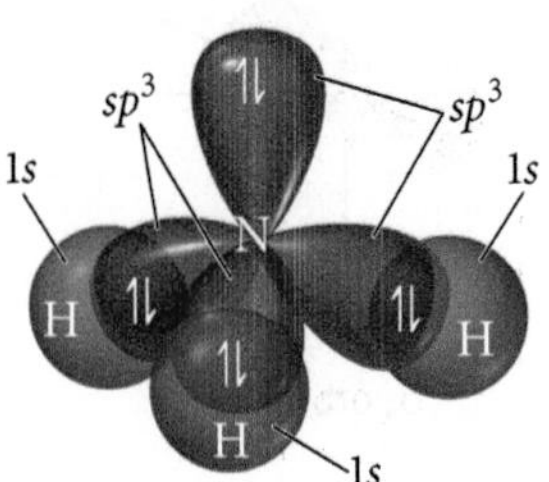

sp^2 Hybridization and Double Bonds

In valence bond theory, the particular hybridization scheme to follow (sp^2 versus sp^3, for example) for a given molecule is determined computationally, which is beyond our scope. In this text, we will determine the particular hybridization scheme from the VSEPR geometry of the molecule, as shown later in this section.

Hybridization of one *s* and two *p* orbitals results in three sp^2 hybrids and one leftover unhybridized *p* orbital:

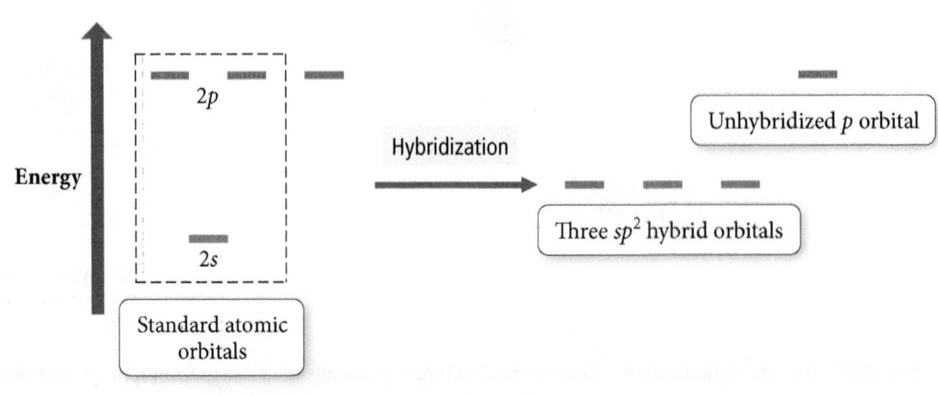

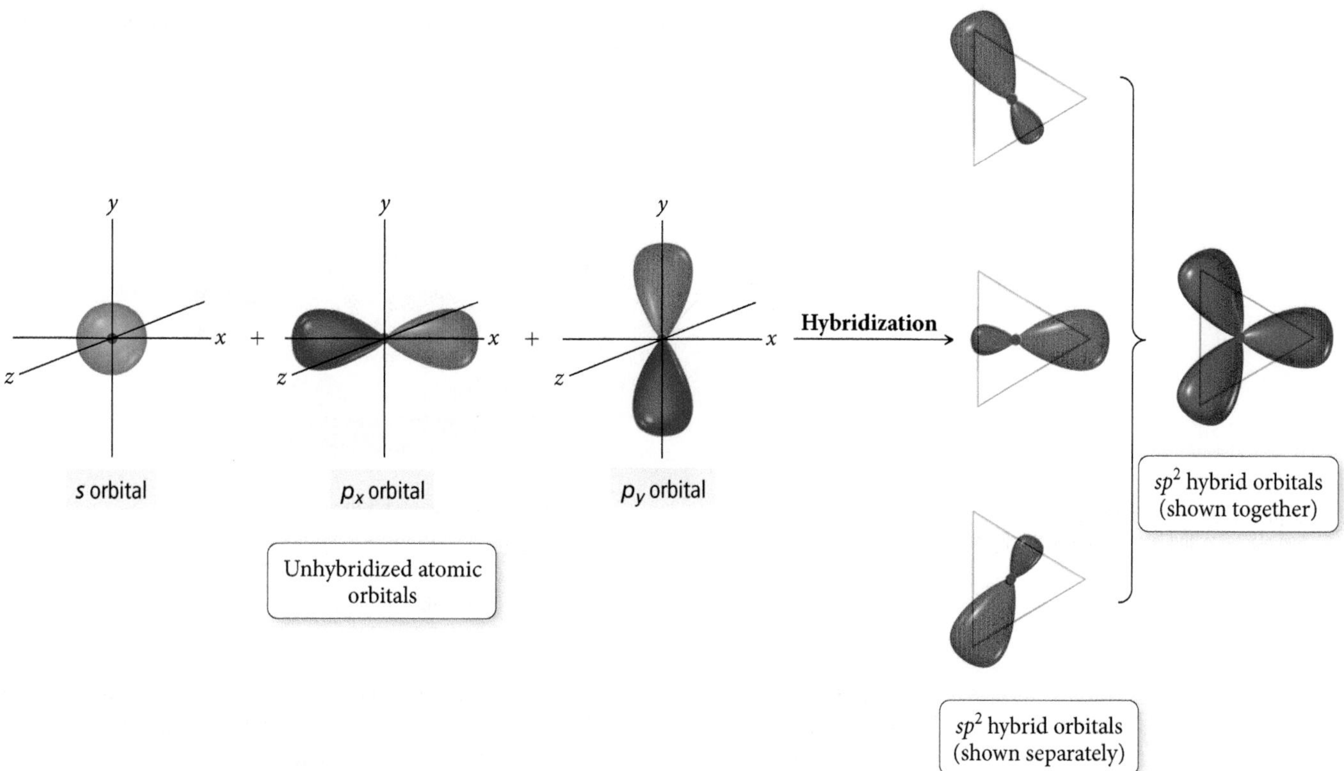

▲ **FIGURE 10.8** ***sp*² Hybridization** One *s* orbital and two *p* orbitals combine to form three sp^2 hybrid orbitals. One *p* orbital (not shown) remains unhybridized.

The notation "sp^2" indicates that the hybrids are mixtures of one *s* orbital and two *p* orbitals. The shapes of the sp^2 hybrid orbitals are shown in Figure 10.8 ▲. Notice that the three hybrid orbitals have a trigonal planar geometry with 120° angles between them. The unhybridized *p* orbital is oriented perpendicular to the three hybridized orbitals.

As an example of a molecule with sp^2 hybrid orbitals, consider H_2CO. The unhybridized valence electron configurations of each of the atoms are as follows:

H [↿] (1s)

O [⥮] (2s) [⥮][↿][↿] (2p)

C [⥮] (2s) [↿][↿][ ] (2p)

Carbon is the central atom and the hybridization of its orbitals is sp^2.

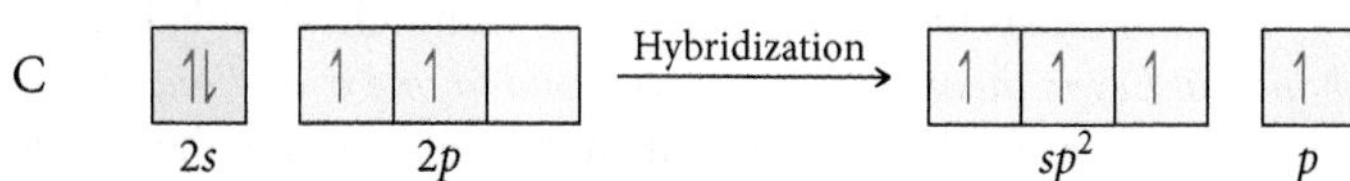

Each of the sp^2 orbitals is half-filled. The remaining electron occupies the leftover *p* orbital, even though it is slightly higher in energy. We can now see that the carbon atom has four half-filled orbitals and can therefore form four bonds: two with two hydrogen

In order to account for the trigonal planar shape of an isolated molecule such as formaldehyde, it is only necessary to hybridize central atoms. However, some chemists also hybridize the terminal atoms. For example, in some books you might see that oxygen in formaldehyde is also sp^2 hybridized. In this text, we do not hybridize terminal atoms.

atoms and two (a double bond) with the oxygen atom. We draw the molecule and the overlapping orbitals as follows:

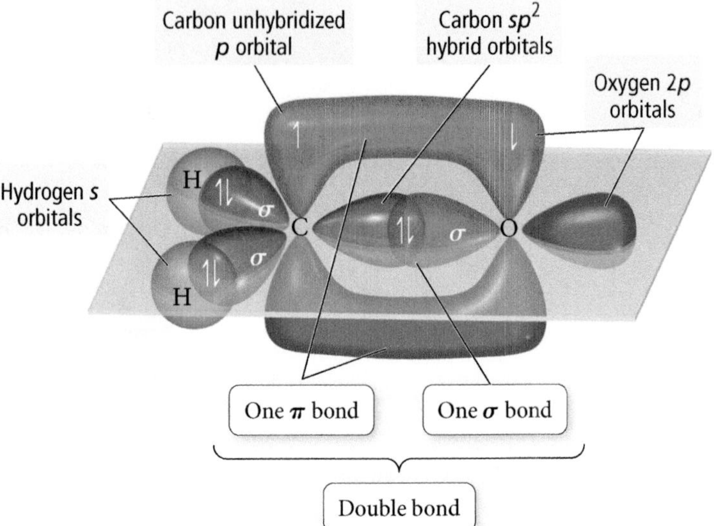

Oxygen also has a 2s orbital containing two electrons and is not shown in this figure for clarity

Notice the overlap between the half-filled *p* orbitals on the carbon and oxygen atoms. When *p* orbitals overlap this way (side by side), the resulting bond is called a **pi (π) bond**, and the electron density is above and below the internuclear axis. When orbitals overlap end to end, as in all of the rest of the bonds in the molecule, the resulting bond is called a **sigma (σ) bond** (Figure 10.9 ▸). Even though we represent the two electrons in a π bond as two half-arrows in the upper lobe, they are actually spread out over both the upper and lower lobes (this is one of the limitations we encounter when we try to represent electrons with arrows). We can now label all the bonds in the molecule using a notation that specifies the type of bond (σ or π) as well as the type of overlapping orbitals. We have included this notation, as well as the Lewis structure of H_2CO for comparison, in the bonding diagram for H_2CO:

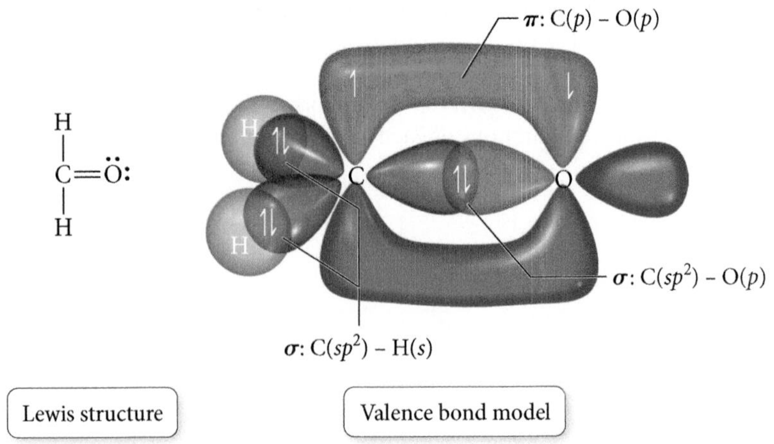

Notice the correspondence between valence bond theory and Lewis theory. In both cases, the central carbon atom is forming four bonds: two single bonds and one double bond. However, valence bond theory gives us more insight into the bonds. In the VSEPR model, the double bond between carbon and oxygen consists of two different *kinds* of bonds—one σ and one π—while in Lewis theory, the two bonds within the double bond appear identical. *Double bonds in Lewis theory always correspond to one σ and one π bond in valence bond theory*. In general, π bonds are weaker than σ bonds because the side-to-side orbital overlap tends to be less efficient than the end-to-end orbital overlap. Consequently, the π bond in a double bond is generally easier to break than the σ bond. Valence bond theory, as you can see, gives us more insight into the nature of a double bond than Lewis theory.

One—and only one—σ bond forms between any two atoms. Additional bonds must be π bonds.

Valence bond theory also gives us insight into why the rotation about a double bond is severely restricted. Because of the side-by-side overlap of the *p* orbitals, the π bond

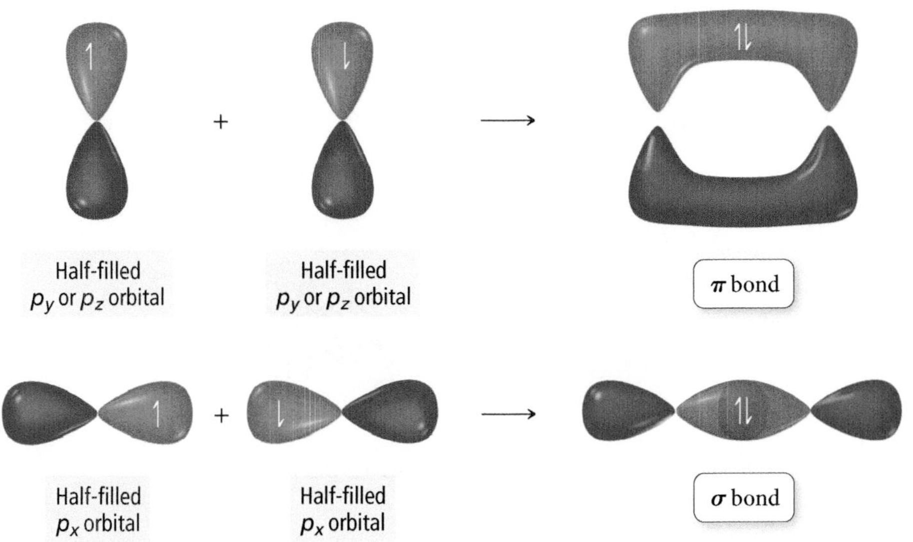

◀ **FIGURE 10.9 Sigma and Pi Bonding** When orbitals overlap side by side, the result is a pi (π) bond. When orbitals overlap end to end, they form a sigma (σ) bond. Only one σ bond can be formed between each group of two atoms. Any additional bonding between those atoms must be a π bond. A single bond is a σ bond; a double bond consists of a σ bond and a π bond; a triple bond consists of a σ bond and two π bonds.

must essentially break for rotation to occur (see *Chemistry in Your Day: The Chemistry of Vision* box on page 398). Valence bond theory shows us the types of orbitals involved in the bonding and their shapes. In H_2CO, the sp^2 hybrid orbitals on the central atom are trigonal planar with 120° angles between them, so the resulting predicted geometry of the molecule is trigonal planar with 120° bond angles. The experimentally measured bond angles in H_2CO, as discussed previously, are 121.9° for the HCO bond angle and 116.2° for the HCH bond angle, close to the predicted values.

Although rotation about a double bond is highly restricted, rotation about a single bond is relatively unrestricted. Consider, for example, the structures of two chlorinated hydrocarbons, 1,2-dichloroethane and 1,2-dichloroethene:

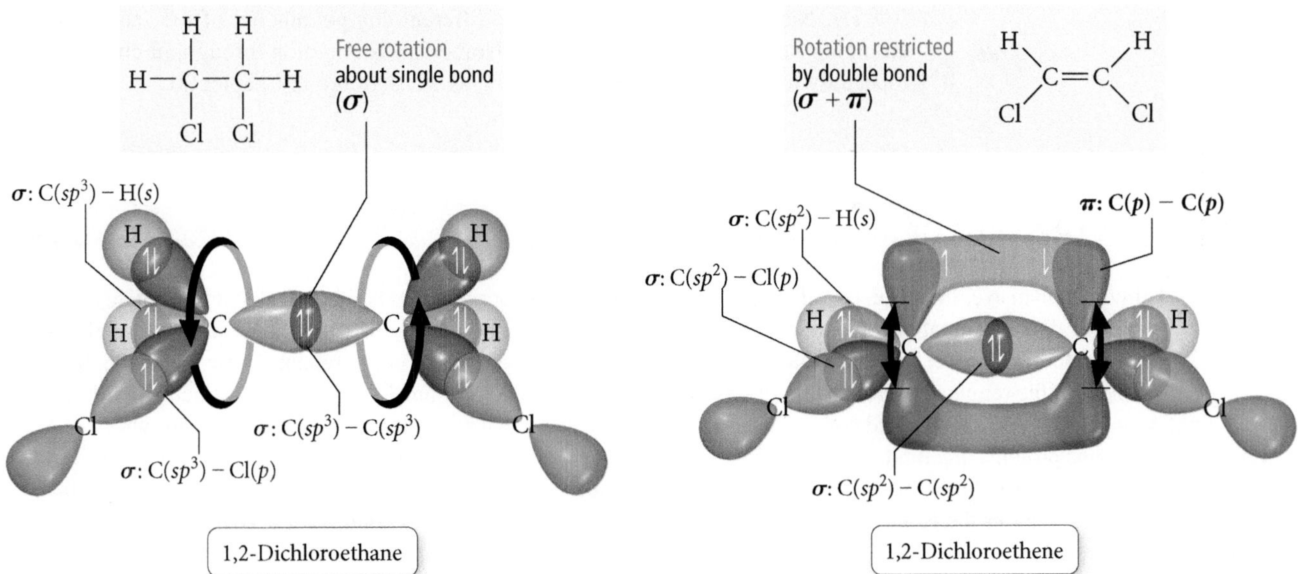

The hybridization of the carbon atoms in 1,2-dichloroethane is sp^3, resulting in relatively free rotation about the σ single bond. Consequently, there is no difference between the following two structures at room temperature because they quickly interconvert:

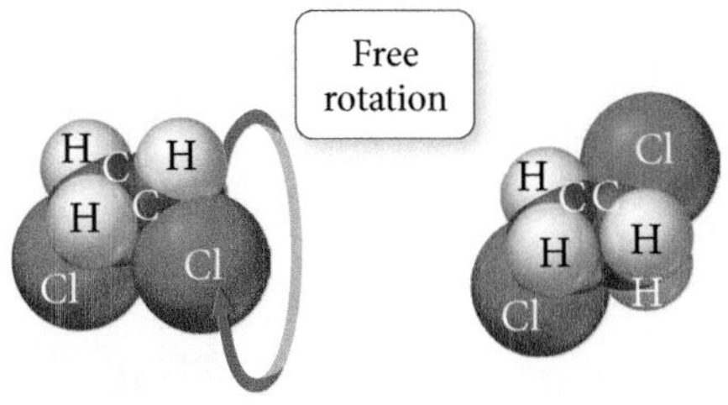

In contrast, rotation about the double bond ($\sigma + \pi$) in 1,2-dichloroethene is restricted, so that, at room temperature, 1,2-dichloroethene exists in two forms:

cis-1,2-Dichloroethene *trans*-1,2-Dichloroethene

Electrostatic potential maps of *cis*- (left) and *trans*-1,2-dichloroethene. The *cis* isomer is polar, while the *trans* isomer is nonpolar. The polarity affects their physical properties, which are discussed in Chapter 11.

IUPAC recommends using E-, and Z- labels instead of trans- and cis-, respectively and is discussed in section 20.7. The cis- and trans- labels are commonly used.

These two forms of 1,2-dichloroethene are indeed different compounds with different properties. We distinguish between them with the designations *cis* (meaning "same side") and *trans* (meaning "opposite sides"). Compounds such as these, with the same molecular formula but different structures or different spatial arrangement of atoms, are called *isomers*. Nature can—and does—make different compounds out of the same atoms by arranging the atoms in different ways. Isomerism is common throughout chemistry and especially important in organic chemistry, as we shall see in Chapter 20.

CHEMISTRY IN YOUR DAY The Chemistry of Vision

In the human eye, light is detected by a chemical switch involving the breaking and re-forming of a π bond. The back portion of the eye, the retina, is coated with millions of light-sensitive cells called rods and cones. Each of these cells contains proteins that bind a compound called 11-*cis*-retinal. When a photon of sufficient energy strikes a rod or cone, it causes the isomerization of 11-*cis*-retinal to all-*trans*-retinal:

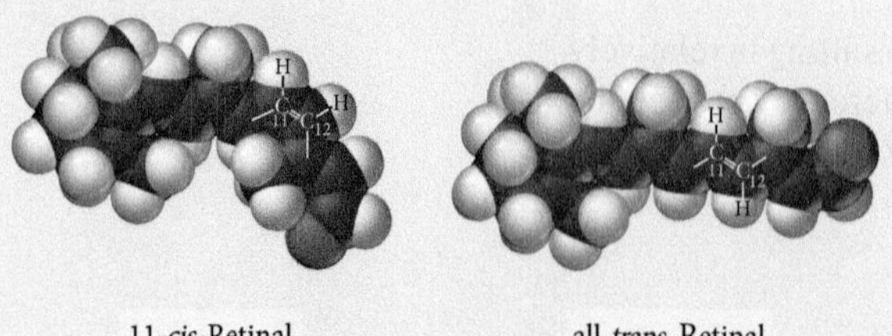

11-*cis*-Retinal all-*trans*-Retinal

The isomerization occurs because visible light contains enough energy to break the π bond between the eleventh and twelfth carbon atom in 11-*cis*-retinal. The σ bond, which is stronger, does not break, allowing the molecule to freely rotate about that bond. The π bond then re-forms with the molecule in the *trans* conformation. The different shape of the resultant all-*trans*-retinal causes conformational changes in the protein to which it is bound. These changes cause an electrical signal to be transmitted to the brain.

Question

What is the hybridization of the eleventh and twelfth carbon atoms in retinal?

CONCEPTUAL CONNECTION 10.4
Single and Double Bonds

In Section 9.6, we learned that double bonds were stronger and shorter than single bonds. For example, a C—C single bond has an average bond energy of 347 kJ mol^{-1}, while a C═C double bond has an average bond energy of 611 kJ mol^{-1}. Use valence bond theory to explain why a double bond is *not* simply twice as strong as a single bond.

sp Hybridization and Triple Bonds

Hybridization of one *s* and one *p* orbital results in two *sp* hybrid orbitals and two leftover unhybridized *p* orbitals.

The shapes of the *sp* hybrid orbitals are shown in Figure 10.10 ▼. Notice that the two *sp* hybrid orbitals are arranged in a linear geometry with a 180° angle between them. The unhybridized *p* orbitals are oriented in the plane that is perpendicular to the hybridized *sp* orbitals:

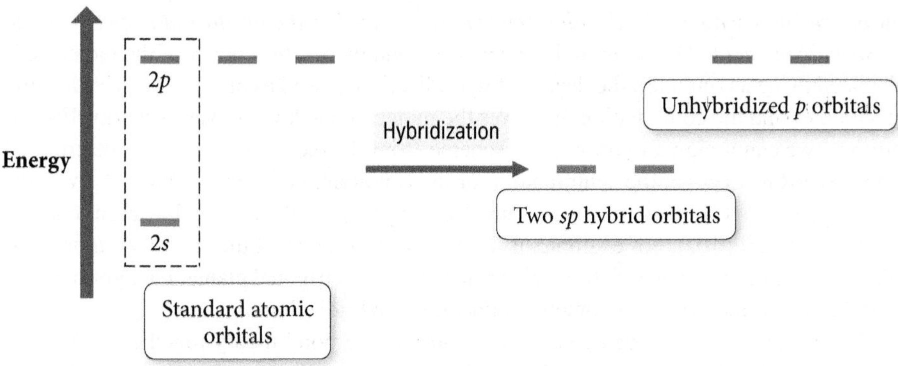

The acetylene molecule, HC≡CH, has *sp* hybrid orbitals. The four valence electrons of carbon can distribute themselves among the two *sp* hybrid orbitals and the two *p* orbitals:

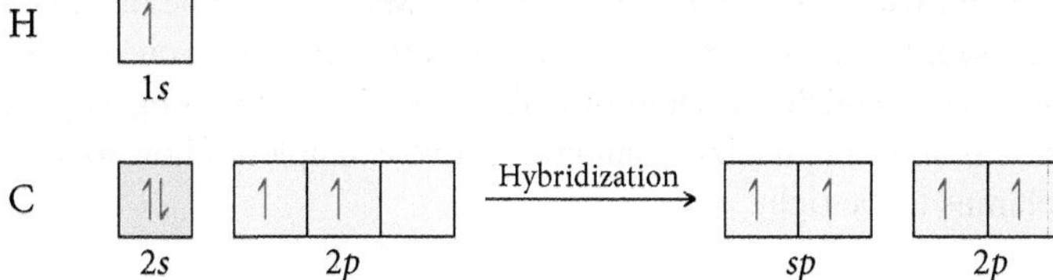

Each carbon atom then has four half-filled orbitals and can form four bonds: one with a hydrogen atom and three (a triple bond) with the other carbon atom. We draw the molecule and the overlapping orbitals as follows:

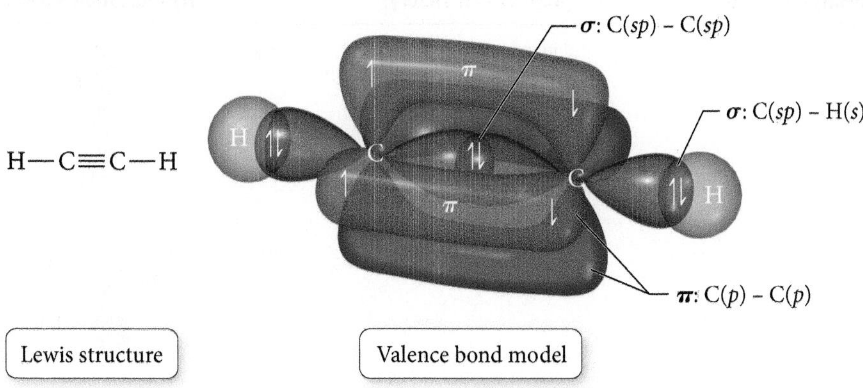

Notice that the triple bond between the two carbon atoms consists of two π bonds (overlapping *p* orbitals) and one σ bond (overlapping *sp* orbitals). The *sp* orbitals on the carbon atoms are linear with 180° between them, so the resulting geometry of the molecule is linear with 180° bond angles, in agreement with the experimentally measured geometry of HC≡CH, and also in agreement with the prediction of VSEPR theory.

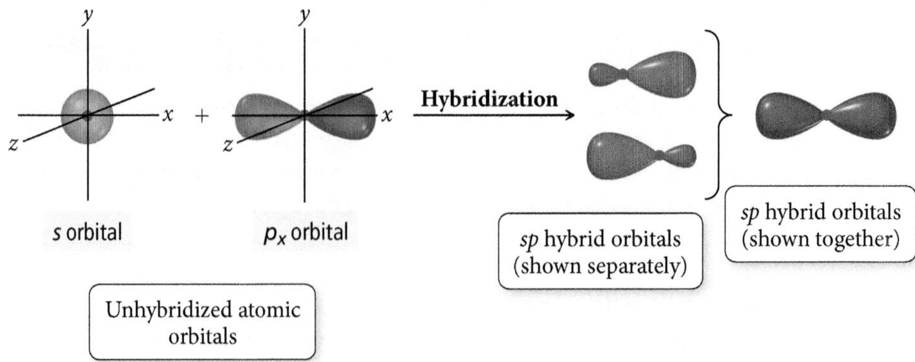

▶ **FIGURE 10.10** ***sp*** **Hybridization** One *s* orbital and one *p* orbital combine to form two *sp* hybrid orbitals. Two *p* orbitals (not shown) remain unhybridized.

Writing Hybridization and Bonding Schemes

We have now studied examples of the three main types of atomic orbital hybridization. *But how do we know which hybridization scheme best describes the orbitals of a specific atom in a specific molecule?* In computational valence bond theory, the energy of the molecule is calculated using a computer; the degree of hybridization as well as the type of hybridization are varied to find the combination that gives the molecule the lowest overall energy. For our purposes, we can assign a hybridization scheme from the electron geometry—determined using VSEPR theory—of the central atom (or interior atoms) of the molecule. The VSEPR electron geometries for two, three, and four electron groups and their hybridization schemes are shown in Table 10.3. For example, if the electron geometry of the central atom is tetrahedral, the hybridization is sp^3. If the electron geometry is trigonal planar, the hybridization is sp^2. Finally, if the electron geometry is linear, the hybridization is *sp*.

We are now ready to put Lewis theory and valence bond theory together to describe bonding in molecules. In the procedure and examples that follow, you will learn how to write a *hybridization and bonding scheme* for a molecule. This involves drawing a Lewis structure for the molecule, determining its geometry using VSEPR theory, determining the hybridization of the interior atoms, drawing the molecule with its overlapping orbitals, and labelling each bond with the σ and π notation followed by the type of overlapping orbitals. As you can see, this procedure involves virtually everything you have learned about bonding in this chapter and the previous one. The procedure for writing a hybridization and bonding scheme is shown in the left column with two examples of how to apply the procedure in the columns to the right.

TABLE 10.3 Hybridization Scheme from Electron Geometry

Number of Electron Groups	Electron Geometry (from VSEPR Theory)	Hybridization Scheme	
2	Linear	*sp*	
3	Trigonal planar	sp^2	120°
4	Tetrahedral	sp^3	109.5°

PROCEDURE FOR... **Hybridization and Bonding Scheme**	**EXAMPLE 10.6** **Hybridization and Bonding Scheme I** Write a hybridization and bonding scheme for nitrogen trifluoride, NF_3.	**EXAMPLE 10.7** **Hybridization and Bonding Scheme II** Write a hybridization and bonding scheme for ethanal: $H_3C{-}C({=}O){-}H$
1. Write a Lewis structure for the molecule.	**SOLUTION** NF_3 has 26 valence electrons and the following Lewis structure: :F̤: – N̤ – :F̤: with a third :F̤: bonded above N	**SOLUTION** Ethanal has 18 valence electrons and the following Lewis structure: H–C(H)(H)–C(=Ö:)–H
2. Use VSEPR theory to predict the electron geometry about the central atom (or interior atoms).	The nitrogen atom has four electron groups and therefore a tetrahedral electron geometry.	The leftmost carbon atom has four electron groups and a tetrahedral electron geometry. The rightmost carbon atom has three electron groups and a trigonal planar geometry.
3. Select the correct hybridization for the central atom (or interior atoms) based on the electron geometry.	A tetrahedral electron geometry corresponds to sp^3 hybridization.	The leftmost carbon atom is sp^3 hybridized, and the rightmost carbon atom is sp^2 hybridized.
4. Sketch the molecule, beginning with the central atom and its orbitals. Show overlap with the appropriate orbitals on the terminal atoms.	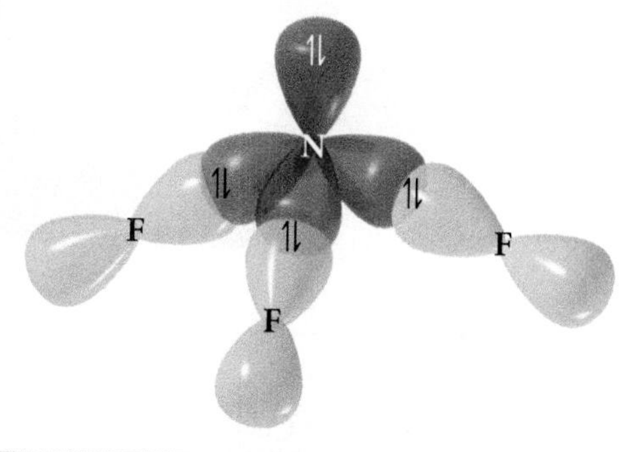	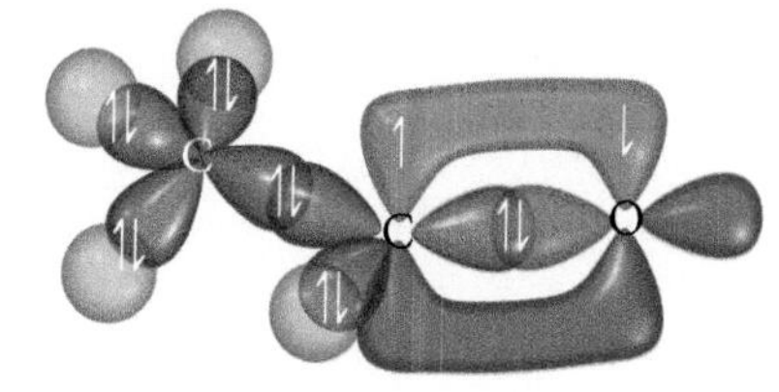
5. Label all bonds using the σ or π notation followed by the type of overlapping orbitals.	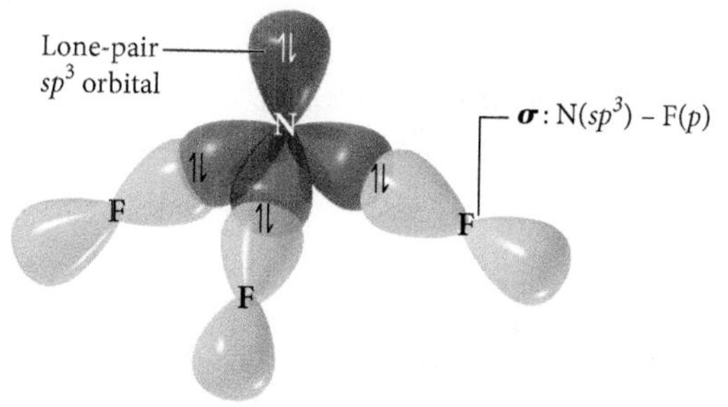	σ: C(sp^3) – H(s) π: C(p) – O(p) σ: C(sp^2) – H(s) σ: C(sp^3) – C(sp^2) σ: C(sp^2) – O(p)
	FOR PRACTICE 10.6 Write a hybridization and bonding scheme for BF_3.	**FOR PRACTICE 10.7** Write a hybridization and bonding scheme for HCN.

EXAMPLE 10.8 HYBRIDIZATION AND BONDING SCHEME III

Use valence bond theory to write a hybridization and bonding scheme for ethene, $H_2C{=}CH_2$.

SOLUTION

1. Write a Lewis structure for the molecule.	H—C(H)=C(H)—H
2. Apply VSEPR theory to predict the electron geometry about the central atom (or interior atoms).	The molecule has two interior atoms. Since each atom has three electron groups (one double bond and two single bonds), the electron geometry about each atom is trigonal planar.
3. Refer to Table 10.3 to select the correct hybridization for the central atom (or interior atoms) based on the electron geometry.	A trigonal planar geometry corresponds to sp^2 hybridization.
4. Sketch the molecule, beginning with the central atom and its orbitals. Show overlap with the appropriate orbitals on the terminal atoms.	
5. Label all bonds using the σ or π notation followed by the type of overlapping orbitals.	π: C(p) – C(p); σ: C(sp^2) – C(sp^2); σ: C(sp^2) – H(s)

FOR PRACTICE 10.8

Use valence bond theory to write a hybridization and bonding scheme for CO_2.

FOR MORE PRACTICE 10.8

What is the hybridization of the central carbon atom in acetone (CH_3COCH_3)?

10.8 Molecular Orbital Theory: Electron Delocalization

Although we have seen how valence bond theory can explain many aspects of chemical bonding—such as the rigidity of a double bond—it also has limitations. In valence bond theory, we treat electrons as if they reside in the quantum-mechanical orbitals that we calculated *for atoms*. This is a significant oversimplification that we partially compensate for by hybridization. Nevertheless, we can do better.

In Chapter 7, we learned that the mathematical derivation of energies and orbitals for electrons *in atoms* comes from solving the Schrödinger equation for the atom of interest. For a molecule, we can theoretically do the same thing. The resulting solutions to the Schrödinger equation would be the actual *molecular* orbitals of the molecule as a whole (in contrast to valence bond theory, in which the orbitals are those of individual atoms). As it turns out, however, solving the Schrödinger equation exactly for even the simplest molecules is impossible without making some approximations.

In **molecular orbital (MO) theory**, you do not actually solve the Schrödinger equation for a molecule directly. Instead, you use a trial function—an "educated guess" as to what the solution might be. In other words, rather than mathematically solving the Schrödinger equation, which would give you a mathematical function describing an orbital, you start with a trial mathematical function for the orbital. This trial function is essentially an "educated guess" that serves to approximate the true orbital. You then test the trial function to see how well it "works."

Molecular orbital theory is a specific application of a more general quantum-mechanical approximation technique called the *variational method.* In the variational method, the energy of a trial function within the Schrödinger equation is minimized.

We can understand this process by analogy to solving an algebraic equation. Suppose you want to know x in the equation $4x + 5 = 70$ without actually solving the equation. For an easy equation like this one, you might first estimate that $x = 16$. You can then determine how well your estimate works by substituting $x = 16$ into the equation. If the estimate did not work, you could try again until you found the right value of x. (In this case, you can quickly see that x must be a little more than 16.)

In molecular orbital theory, the estimating procedure is analogous. However, we need to add one more important concept to get at the heart of molecular orbital theory. In order to determine how well a trial function for an orbital "works" in molecular orbital theory, you calculate its energy. No matter how good your trial function, *you will never do better than nature at minimizing the energy of the orbital.* In other words, devise any trial function that you like for an orbital in a molecule and calculate its energy. The energy you calculate for the devised orbital will always be greater than or (at best) equal to the energy of the actual orbital.

You calculate the energy of an estimated orbital by substituting it into the Schrödinger equation and solving for the energy.

How does this help us? The best possible description of the orbital will therefore be the one with the minimum energy. In modern molecular orbital theory, computer programs are designed to try many different variations of a guessed orbital and compare the energies of each one. The variation with the lowest energy is the best approximation for the actual molecular orbital.

Linear Combination of Atomic Orbitals (LCAO)

The simplest trial functions that work reasonably well in molecular orbital theory turn out to be linear combinations of atomic orbitals, or LCAO. An LCAO molecular orbital is a *weighted linear sum—analogous to a weighted average—of the valence atomic orbitals* of the atoms in the molecule. At first glance, this concept might seem very similar to that of hybridization in valence bond theory. However, in valence bond theory, hybrid orbitals are weighted linear sums of the valence atomic orbitals of a *particular atom*, and the hybrid orbitals remain *localized* on that atom. In molecular orbital theory, the molecular orbitals are weighted linear sums of the valence atomic orbitals of *all the atoms* in a molecule, and many of the molecular orbitals are *delocalized* over the entire molecule.

When molecular orbitals are computed mathematically, it is actually the *wave functions* corresponding to the orbitals that are combined.

Consider the H_2 molecule. One of the molecular orbitals for H_2 is simply an equally weighted sum of the $1s$ orbital from one atom and the $1s$ orbital from the other. We can represent this pictorially as shown in the bottom part of Figure 10.11 ▼. The name of this

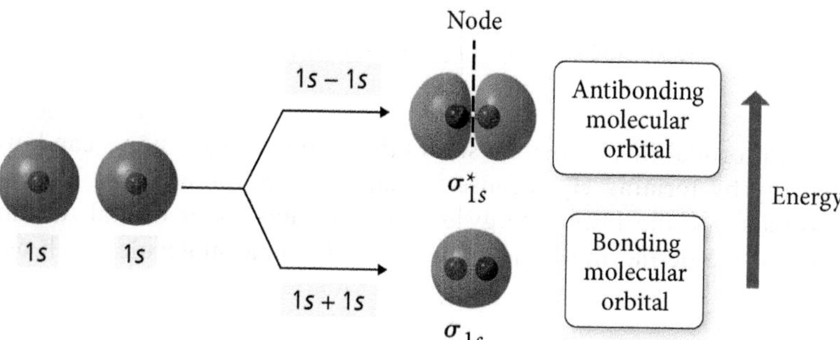

◀ **FIGURE 10.11 Formation of Bonding and Antibonding Orbitals**
Constructive interference between two atomic orbitals gives rise to a molecular orbital that is lower in energy than the atomic orbitals. This is the bonding orbital. When two atomic orbitals have opposite phases, destructive interference gives rise to a molecular orbital that is higher in energy than the atomic orbitals. This is the antibonding orbital. Red and blue signify different phases (+ and –).

molecular orbital is σ_{1s}. The σ comes from the shape of the orbital, which looks like a σ bond in valence bond theory, and the $1s$ comes from its formation by a linear sum of $1s$ orbitals. The σ_{1s} orbital is lower in energy than either of the two $1s$ atomic orbitals from which it was formed. For this reason, this orbital is called a **bonding orbital**. When electrons occupy bonding molecular orbitals, the energy of the electrons is lower than it would be if they were occupying atomic orbitals.

We can think of a molecular orbital in a molecule in much the same way that we think about an atomic orbital in an atom. Electrons will seek the lowest energy molecular orbital available, but just as an atom has more than one atomic orbital (and some may be empty), so a molecule has more than one molecular orbital (and some may be empty). The next molecular orbital of H_2 is approximated by subtracting the $1s$ orbital on one hydrogen from the $1s$ orbital on the other hydrogen atom. This is shown in the top part of Figure 10.11. The different phases of the orbitals result in *destructive* interference between them. The resulting molecular orbital therefore has a node between the two atoms. The different colours (red and blue) on either side of the node represent the different phases of the orbital (see Section 7.6). The name of this molecular orbital is σ^*_{1s}. The asterisk indicates that this orbital is an **antibonding orbital**. Electrons in antibonding orbitals have higher energies than they did in their respective atomic orbitals and therefore tend to raise the energy of the system (relative to the unbonded atoms).

In general, when two atomic orbitals are added together to form molecular orbitals, one of the resultant molecular orbitals will be lower in energy (the bonding orbital) than the atomic orbitals, and the other will be higher in energy (the antibonding orbital). Remember that electrons in orbitals behave like waves. The bonding molecular orbital arises out of constructive interference between the atomic orbitals because both orbitals have the same phase. The antibonding orbital arises out of destructive interference between the atomic orbitals because *subtracting* one from the other means the two interacting orbitals have opposite phases (Figure 10.11).

For this reason, the bonding orbital has an increased electron density in the internuclear region, while the antibonding orbital has a node in the internuclear region. Bonding orbitals have greater electron density in the internuclear region, thereby lowering their energy compared to the orbitals in nonbonded atoms. Antibonding orbitals have less electron density in the internuclear region, and their energies are generally higher than in the orbitals of nonbonded atoms.

We put all of this together in the molecular orbital energy diagram for H_2:

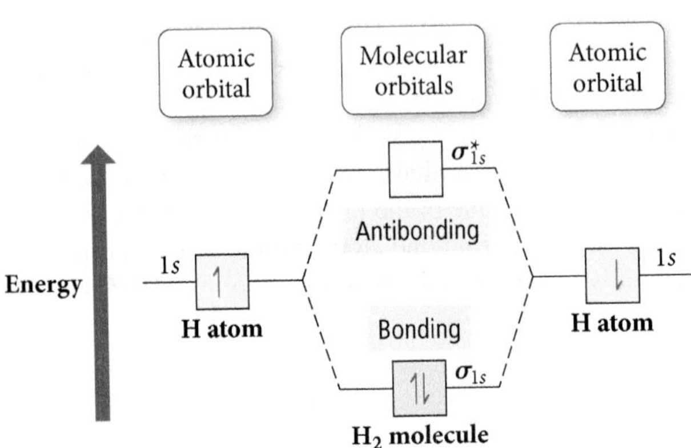

The molecular orbital (MO) diagram shows that two hydrogen atoms can lower their overall energy by forming H_2 because the electrons can move from higher-energy atomic orbitals into the lower-energy σ_{1s} bonding molecular orbital. In molecular orbital theory, we define the **bond order** of a diatomic molecule (such as H_2) as follows:

$$\text{Bond order} = \frac{(\text{number of electrons in bonding MOs}) - (\text{number of electrons in antibonding M}}{2}$$

For H_2, the bond order is:

$$H_2 \text{ bond order} = \frac{2 - 0}{2} = 1$$

A positive bond order means that there are more electrons in bonding molecular orbitals than in antibonding molecular orbitals. The electrons will therefore have lower energy than they did in the orbitals of the isolated atoms, and a chemical bond will form. In general, the higher the bond order, the stronger the bond. A negative or zero bond order indicates that a bond will *not* form between the atoms. For example, consider the MO diagram for He_2:

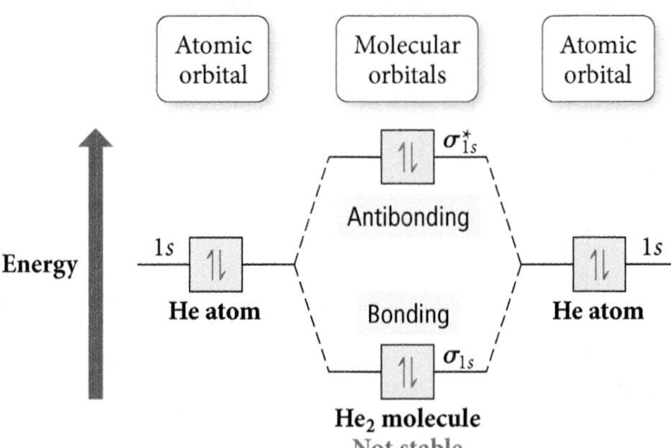

Notice that the two additional electrons must go into the higher-energy antibonding orbital. There is no net stabilization by joining two helium atoms to form a helium molecule, as indicated by the bond order:

$$He_2 \text{ bond order} = \frac{2 - 2}{2} = 0$$

So, according to MO theory, He_2 should not exist as a stable molecule, and indeed it does not. An interesting case is the helium–helium ion, He_2^+, with the following MO diagram:

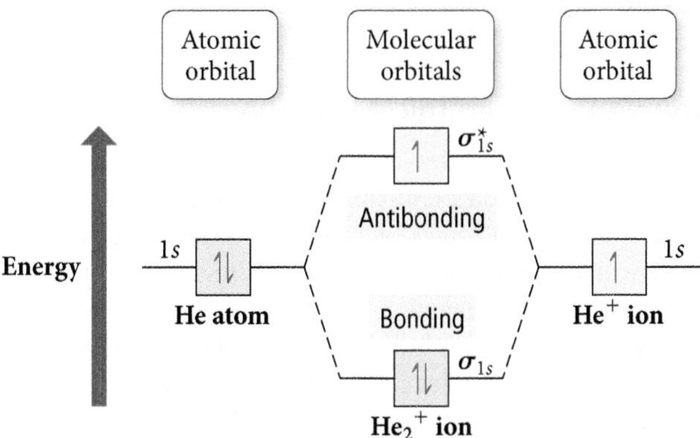

The bond order is $\frac{1}{2}$, indicating that He_2^+ should exist, and indeed it does.

Summarizing LCAO–MO Theory:

- We can approximate molecular orbitals (MOs) as a linear combination of atomic orbitals (AOs). The total number of MOs formed from a particular set of AOs will always equal the number of AOs in the set.
- When two AOs combine to form two MOs, one MO will be lower in energy (the bonding MO) and the other will be higher in energy (the antibonding MO).
- When assigning the electrons of a molecule to MOs, fill the lowest-energy MOs first with a maximum of two spin-paired electrons per orbital.
- When assigning electrons to two MOs of the same energy, follow Hund's rule—fill the orbitals singly first, with parallel spins, before pairing.
- The bond order in a diatomic molecule is the number of electrons in bonding MOs minus the number in antibonding MOs divided by two. Stable bonds require a positive bond order (more electrons in bonding MOs than in antibonding MOs).

Notice the power of the molecular orbital approach. Every electron that enters a bonding MO stabilizes the molecule or polyatomic ion, and every electron that enters an antibonding MO destabilizes it. The emphasis on electron pairs has been removed. One electron in a bonding MO stabilizes half as much as two, so a bond order of one-half is nothing mysterious.

EXAMPLE 10.9 **BOND ORDER**

Use molecular orbital theory to predict the bond order in H_2^-. Is the H_2^- bond a stronger or weaker bond than the H_2 bond?

SOLUTION

The H_2^- ion has three electrons. Assign the three electrons to the molecular orbitals, filling lower-energy orbitals first and proceeding to higher-energy orbitals.	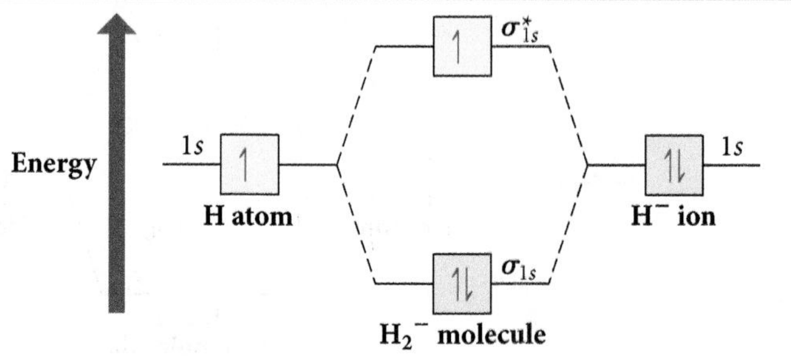
Calculate the bond order by subtracting the number of electrons in antibonding orbitals from the number in bonding orbitals and dividing the result by two.	H_2^- bond order $= \frac{2-1}{2} = +\frac{1}{2}$

Since the bond order is positive, H_2^- should be stable. However, the bond order of H_2^- is lower than the bond order of H_2 (which is 1); therefore, the bond in H_2^- is weaker than in H_2.

FOR PRACTICE 10.9

Use molecular orbital theory to predict the bond order in H_2^+. Is the H_2^+ bond a stronger or weaker bond than the H_2 bond?

Period 2 Homonuclear Diatomic Molecules

The core electrons can be ignored because, as with other models for bonding, these electrons do not contribute significantly to chemical bonding.

The homonuclear diatomic molecules (molecules made up of two atoms of the same kind) formed from second-period elements have between 2 and 16 valence electrons. To explain bonding in these molecules, we must consider the next set of higher-energy molecular orbitals, which can be approximated by linear combinations of the valence atomic orbitals of the period 2 elements.

We begin with Li_2. Even though lithium is normally a metal, we can use MO theory to predict whether or not the Li_2 molecule should exist in the gas phase. We approximate the molecular orbitals in Li_2 as linear combinations of the 2s atomic orbitals. The resulting molecular orbitals look much like those of the H_2 molecule. The MO diagram for Li_2 therefore looks a lot like the MO diagram for H_2:

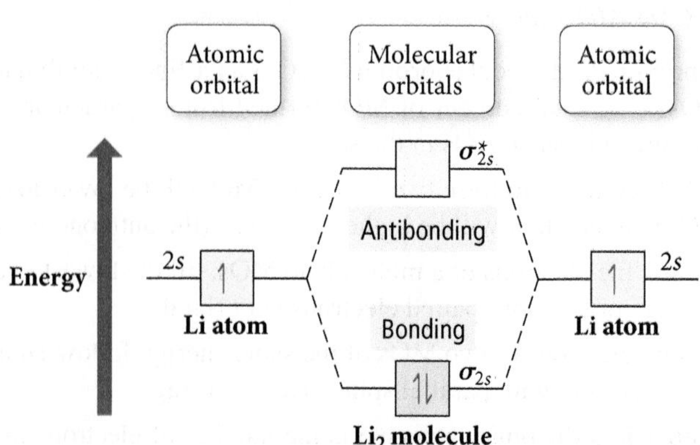

The two valence electrons of Li_2 occupy a bonding molecular orbital. We would predict that the Li_2 molecule is stable with a bond order of 1. Experiments confirm this prediction. In contrast, consider the MO diagram for Be_2:

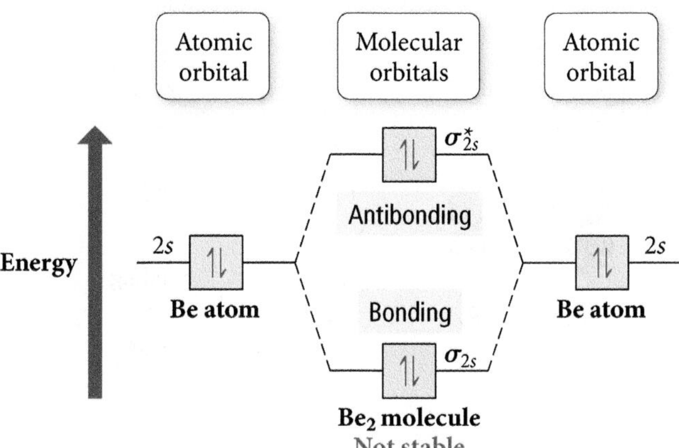

The four valence electrons of Be_2 occupy one bonding MO and one antibonding MO. The bond order is 0 and we predict that Be_2 should not be stable; again, this is consistent with experimental findings.

The next homonuclear molecule composed of second-row elements is B_2 which has six total valence electrons to accommodate. We can approximate the next higher-energy molecular orbitals for B_2 and the rest of the period 2 diatomic molecules as linear combinations of the $2p$ orbitals taken pairwise. Since the three $2p$ orbitals orient along three orthogonal axes, we must assign similar axes to the molecule. In this text, we assign the internuclear axis to be the z direction. Then the LCAO–MOs that result from combining the $2p_z$ orbitals—the ones that lie along the internuclear axis—from each atom are represented pictorially as follows:

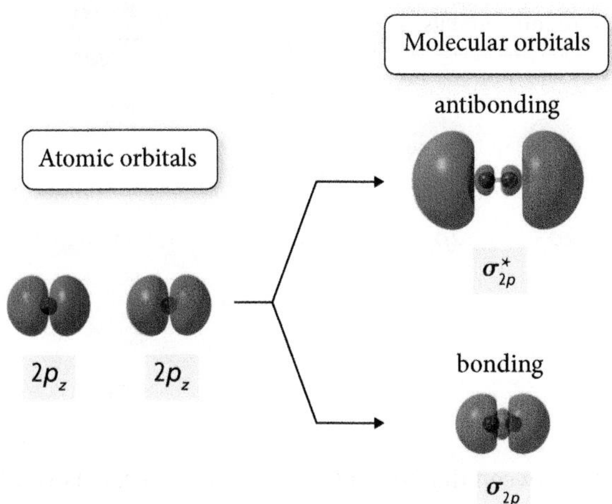

The bonding MO from this pair of atomic orbitals has increased electron density in the internuclear region due to constructive interference between the two $2p$ atomic orbitals. It has the characteristic σ shape (it is cylindrically symmetrical about the bond axis) and is therefore called the σ_{2p} bonding orbital. The antibonding orbital, called σ^*_{2p}, has a node between the two nuclei (due to destructive interference between the two $2p$ orbitals) and is higher in energy than either of the $2p_z$ orbitals.

The LCAO–MOs that result from combining the $2p_x$ orbitals from each atom are represented pictorially as follows:

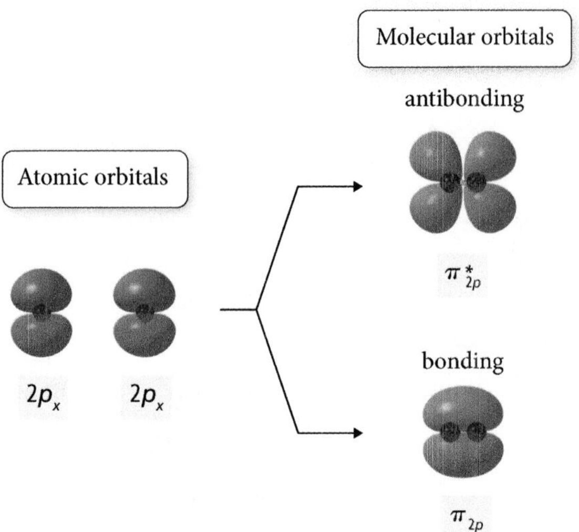

Notice that in this case, the *p* orbitals are added together in a side-by-side orientation (in contrast to the $2p_z$ orbitals, which were oriented end to end). The resultant molecular orbitals consequently have a different shape. The electron density in the bonding molecular orbital is above and below the internuclear axis with a nodal plane that includes the internuclear axis. This orbital resembles the electron density distribution of a π bond in valence bond theory. We call this orbital the π_{2p} orbital. The corresponding antibonding orbital has an additional node *between* the nuclei (perpendicular to the internuclear axis) and is called the π^*_{2p} orbital.

The LCAO–MOs that result from combining the $2p_y$ orbitals from each atom are represented pictorially as follows:

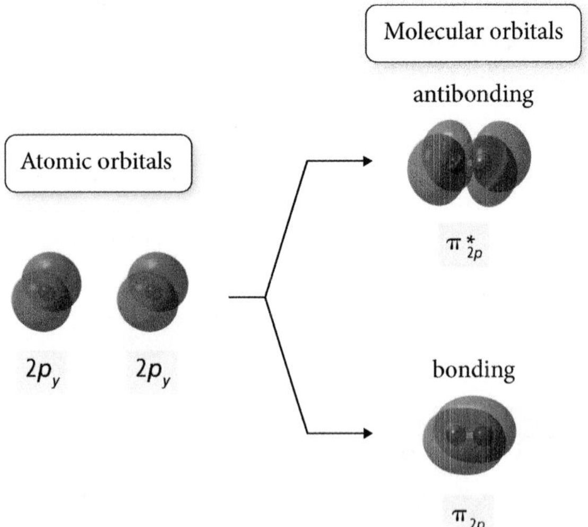

The only difference between the $2p_y$ and the $2p_x$ atomic orbitals is a 90° rotation about the internuclear axis. Consequently, the only difference between the resulting MOs is a 90° rotation about the internuclear axis. The energies and the names of the bonding and antibonding MOs obtained from the combination of the $2p_y$ AOs are identical to those obtained from the combination of the $2p_x$ AOs.

Before we can draw MO diagrams for B_2 and the other second-period diatomic molecules, we must determine the relative energy ordering of the MOs obtained from the 2*p* AO combinations. This is not a simple task. The relative ordering of MOs obtained from LCAO–MO theory is usually determined computationally. There is no single order that works for all molecules. For second-period diatomic molecules, computations reveal that the energy ordering for B_2, C_2, and N_2 is slightly different than that for O_2, F_2, and Ne_2, shown in Figure 10.12 ▶.

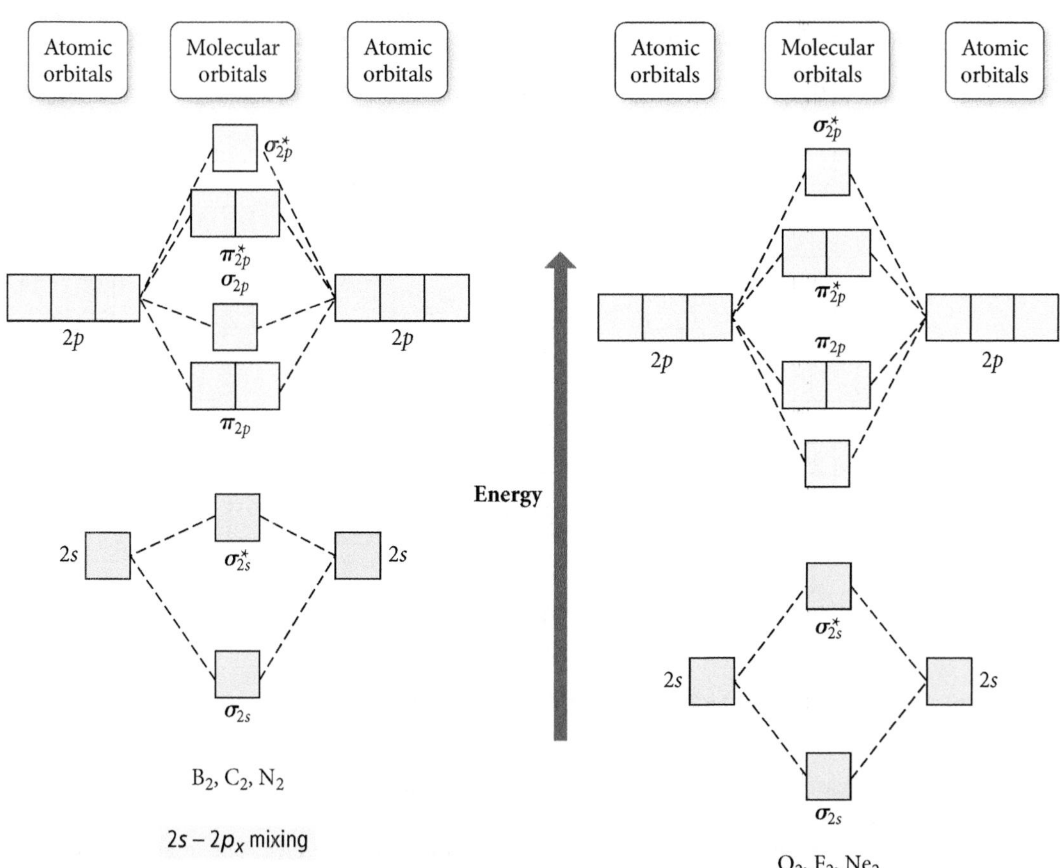

◀ **FIGURE 10.12 The Effect of 2*s*–2*p* Mixing on the Molecular Orbital Diagrams for Second-Period Diatomic Molecules** The degree of mixing between two orbitals decreases with increasing energy difference between them. Mixing of the 2*s* and $2p_z$ orbitals is therefore greater in B_2, C_2, and N_2 than in O_2, F_2, and Ne_2, because in B, C, and N, the energy levels of the atomic orbitals are more closely spaced than in O, F, and Ne. This mixing produces a change in energy ordering for the π_{2p} and σ_{2p} molecular orbitals.

The reason for the difference in energy ordering can only be explained by going back to our LCAO–MO model. In our simplified treatment, we assumed that the MOs that result from the second-period AOs could be calculated pairwise. In other words, we took the linear combination of a 2*s* from one atom with the 2*s* from another, a $2p_z$ from one atom with a $2p_z$ from the other, and so on. However, in a more detailed treatment, the MOs are formed from linear combinations that include all of the AOs that are relatively close to each other in energy and of the correct symmetry. Specifically, in a more detailed treatment, the two 2*s* orbitals and the two $2p_z$ orbitals should all be combined to form a total of four molecular orbitals. The extent to which this type of mixing affects the energy levels of the corresponding MOs depends somewhat on how close in energy the original atomic orbitals were. The energy separation of the 2*s* and 2*p* orbitals in B, C, and N are smaller than in O, F, and Ne (as seen in Figure 10.12). It is the larger nuclear charge on O, F, and Ne that causes larger energy separation of the orbitals in these atoms. The bottom line is that *s*–*p* mixing is significant in B_2, C_2, and N_2, but not in O_2, F_2, and Ne_2.

The MO energy diagrams for the rest of the second-period homonuclear diatomic molecules, as well as their bond orders, bond energies, and bond lengths, are shown in Figure 10.13 ▼. Notice that as bond order increases, the bond gets stronger (greater bond energy) and shorter (smaller bond length). For B_2, with six electrons, the bond order is 1. For C_2, the bond order is 2, and for N_2, the bond order reaches a maximum with a value of 3. Recall that the Lewis structure of N_2, has a triple bond, so both Lewis theory and MO theory predict a strong bond for N_2, which is experimentally observed.

In O_2, the two additional electrons occupy antibonding orbitals and the bond order is 2. These two electrons are unpaired—they occupy the π^*_{2p} orbitals *singly with parallel spins*, as indicated by Hund's rule. The presence of unpaired electrons in the molecular orbital diagram of oxygen is significant because oxygen is known from experiment to be *paramagnetic* (see Section 7.7)—it is attracted to a magnetic field. The paramagnetism of oxygen can be demonstrated by suspending liquid oxygen between the poles of a magnet. This magnetic property is the direct result of *unpaired electrons*, whose spin and movement around the nucleus (more accurately known as spin angular momentum and orbital angular momentum, respectively) generate tiny magnetic fields. When a paramagnetic

	Large $2s$–$2p_z$ Interaction				Small $2s$–$2p_z$ Interaction		
	B_2	C_2	N_2		O_2	F_2	Ne_2
σ^*_{2p}				σ^*_{2p}			↑↓
π^*_{2p}				π^*_{2p}	↑ ↑	↑↓ ↑↓	↑↓ ↑↓
σ_{2p}			↑↓	π_{2p}	↑↓ ↑↓	↑↓ ↑↓	↑↓ ↑↓
π_{2p}	↑ ↑	↑↓ ↑↓	↑↓ ↑↓	σ_{2p}	↑↓	↑↓	↑↓
σ^*_{2s}	↑↓	↑↓	↑↓	σ^*_{2s}	↑↓	↑↓	↑↓
σ_{2s}	↑↓	↑↓	↑↓	σ_{2s}	↑↓	↑↓	↑↓
Bond order	1	2	3		2	1	0
Bond energy (kJ mol^{-1})	290	620	946		498	159	—
Bond length (pm)	159	131	110		121	143	—

▲ **FIGURE 10.13 Molecular Orbital Energy Diagrams for Second-Row *p*-Block Homonuclear Diatomic Molecules**

substance is placed in an external magnetic field, the magnetic fields of each atom or molecule align with the external field, creating the attraction (much as two magnets attract each other when properly oriented). In contrast, when the electrons in an atom or molecule are all *paired*, the magnetic fields caused by electron spin and orbital angular momentum tend to cancel each other, resulting in diamagnetism. A *diamagnetic* substance is not attracted to a magnetic field (and is, in fact, slightly repelled).

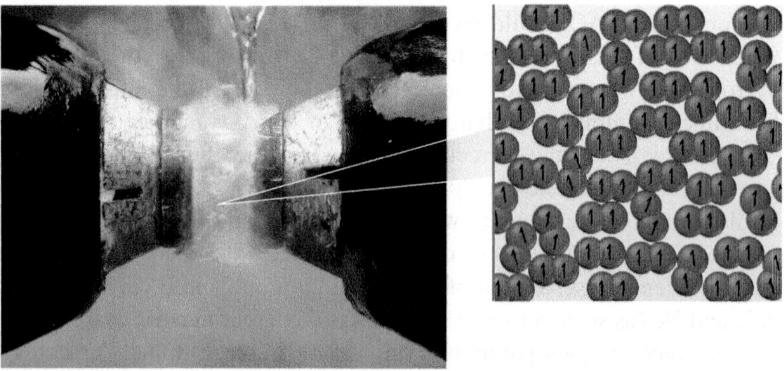

▲ Liquid oxygen can be suspended between the poles of a magnet because it is paramagnetic. It contains unpaired electrons (depicted here in the inset) that generate tiny magnetic fields, which align with and interact with the external field.

In the Lewis structure of O_2, as well as in the valence bond model of O_2, all of its electrons seem to be paired:

The *s* orbital on each O atom contains two electrons, but for clarity, neither the *s* orbitals nor the electrons that occupy them are shown.

$\ddot{\underset{\cdot\cdot}{\text{O}}}=\ddot{\underset{\cdot\cdot}{\text{O}}}$

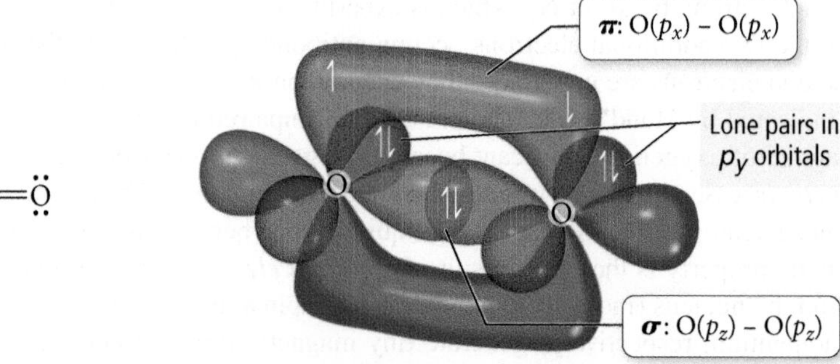

In the MO diagram for O_2, however, we can see the unpaired electrons. Molecular orbital theory is the more powerful theory in that it can account for the paramagnetism of O_2—it gives us a picture of bonding that more closely corresponds to what we see in experiment. Continuing along the second-row homonuclear diatomic molecules, we see that F_2 has a bond order of 1 and Ne_2 has a bond order of 0; again, consistent with experiment since F_2 exists and Ne_2 does not.

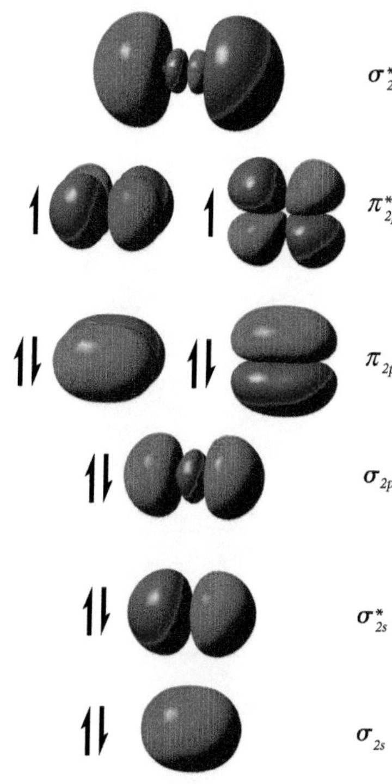

▲ Valence molecular orbitals of oxygen. The occupancies are shown to the left of each orbital.

EXAMPLE 10.10 **MOLECULAR ORBITAL THEORY**

Draw an MO energy diagram and determine the bond order for the N_2^- ion. Do you expect the bond to be stronger or weaker than in the N_2 molecule? Is N_2^- diamagnetic or paramagnetic?

SOLUTION

Write an energy level diagram for the molecular orbitals in N_2^-. Use the energy ordering for N_2.	σ^*_{2p}: [ ] π^*_{2p}: [ ][ ] σ_{2p}: [ ] π_{2p}: [ ][ ] σ^*_{2s}: [ ] σ_{2s}: [ ]
The N_2^- ion has 11 valence electrons (5 for each nitrogen atom plus 1 for the negative charge). Assign the electrons to the molecular orbitals, beginning with the lowest-energy orbitals and following Hund's rule.	σ^*_{2p}: [ ] π^*_{2p}: [↑][ ] σ_{2p}: [↑↓] π_{2p}: [↑↓][↑↓] σ^*_{2s}: [↑↓] σ_{2s}: [↑↓]
Calculate the bond order by subtracting the number of electrons in antibonding orbitals from the number in bonding orbitals and dividing the result by two.	N_2^- bond order $= \frac{8 - 3}{2} = +2.5$

The bond order is 2.5, which is a lower bond order than in the N_2 molecule (bond order = 3); therefore, the bond is weaker. The MO diagram shows that the N_2^- ion has one unpaired electron and is therefore paramagnetic.

FOR PRACTICE 10.10

Draw an MO energy diagram and determine the bond order for the N_2^+ ion. Do you expect the bond to be stronger or weaker than in the N_2 molecule? Is N_2^+ diamagnetic or paramagnetic?

FOR MORE PRACTICE 10.10

Use molecular orbital theory to determine the bond order of Ne_2.

Period 2 Heteronuclear Diatomic Molecules

Molecular orbital theory can also be applied to heteronuclear diatomic molecules (two different atoms). For example, we can draw an MO diagram for NO as follows:

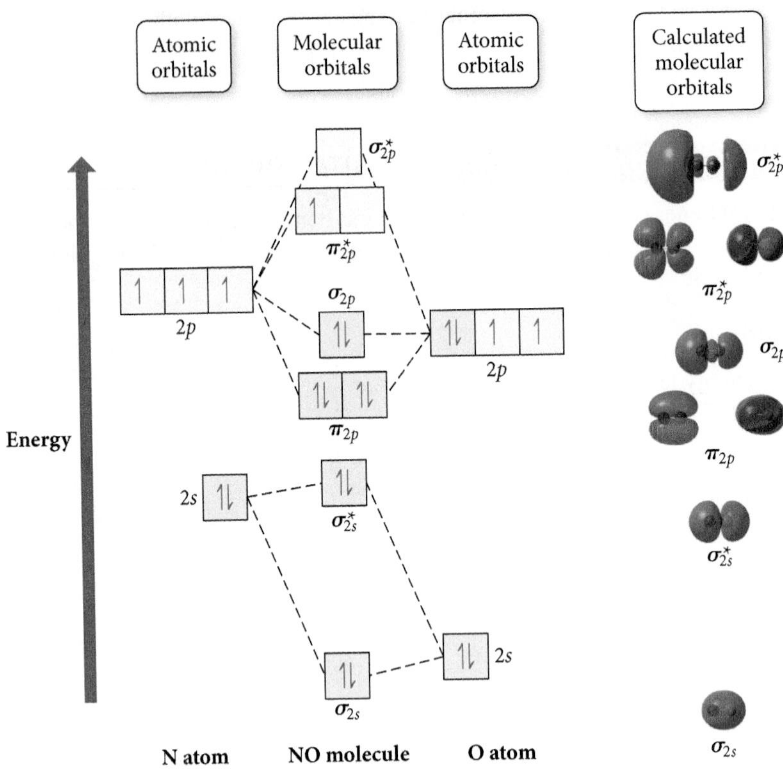

A given orbital will have lower energy in a more electronegative atom. For this reason, electronegative atoms have the ability to attract electrons to themselves.

Oxygen is more electronegative than nitrogen, so its atomic orbitals are lower in energy than nitrogen's atomic orbitals. When two atomic orbitals are identical and of equal energy, the weighting of each orbital in forming a molecular orbital is identical. However, when two atomic orbitals are different, the weighting of each orbital in forming a molecular orbital may be different. More specifically, when a molecular orbital is approximated as a linear combination of atomic orbitals of different energies, the lower-energy atomic orbital makes a greater contribution to the bonding molecular orbital, and the higher-energy atomic orbital makes a greater contribution to the antibonding molecular orbital. For example, notice that the σ_{2s} bonding orbital is closer in energy to the oxygen 2*s* orbital than to the nitrogen 2*s* orbital. We can also see this unequal weighting in the shape of the resultant molecular orbital, in which the electron density is concentrated on the oxygen atom, as shown in Figure 10.14 ◄.

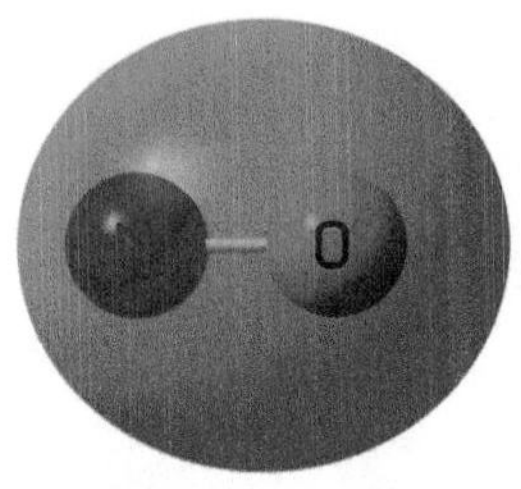

▲ **FIGURE 10.14 Shape of the σ_{2s} Bonding Orbital in NO** The molecular orbital shows more electron density at the oxygen end of the molecule because the atomic orbitals of oxygen, the more electronegative element, are lower in energy than those of nitrogen. They therefore contribute more to the bonding molecular orbital.

As another example of a heteronuclear diatomic molecule, consider the MO diagram for HF:

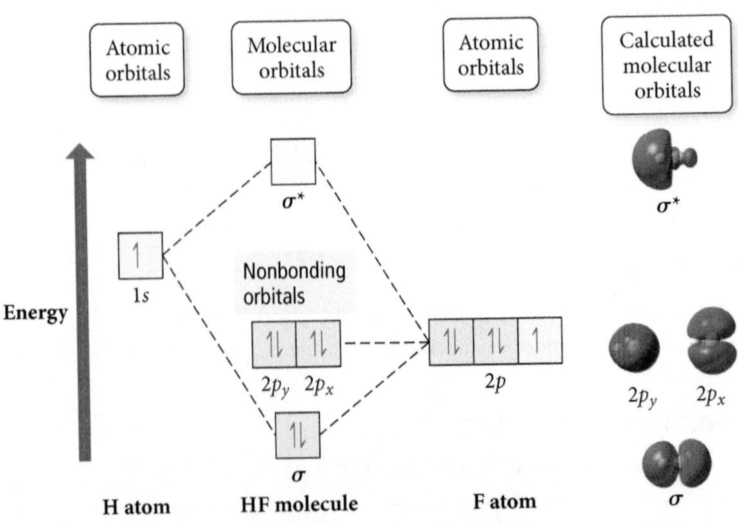

Fluorine is so electronegative that all of its atomic orbitals are lower in energy than hydrogen's atomic orbitals. In fact, fluorine's 2*s* orbital is so low in energy compared to hydrogen's 1*s* orbital that it does not contribute appreciably to the molecular orbitals. The molecular orbitals in HF are approximated by the linear combination of the fluorine $2p_z$ orbital and the hydrogen 1*s* orbital. The other 2*p* orbitals remain largely localized on the fluorine and appear in the energy diagram as **nonbonding orbitals**. The electrons in the nonbonding orbitals remain localized on the fluorine atom.

EXAMPLE 10.11 MOLECULAR ORBITAL THEORY FOR HETERONUCLEAR DIATOMIC MOLECULES AND IONS

Use molecular orbital theory to determine the bond order of the CN^- ion. Is the ion paramagnetic or diamagnetic?

SOLUTION

Determine the number of valence electrons in the molecule or ion.	Number of valence electrons = 4 (from C) + 5 (from N) + 1 (from negative charge) = 10
Write an energy level diagram, using Figure 10.13 as a guide. Fill the orbitals beginning with the lowest-energy orbital and progressing upward until all electrons have been assigned to an orbital. Remember to allow no more than two electrons (with paired spins) per orbital and to fill degenerate orbitals with single electrons (with parallel spins) before pairing.	σ^*_{2p}: [ ] π^*_{2p}: [ ][ ] σ_{2p}: [⥮] π_{2p}: [⥮][⥮] σ^*_{2s}: [⥮] σ_{2s}: [⥮]
Calculate the bond order using the appropriate formula: Bond order = $\frac{(\text{number of } e^- \text{ in bonding MOs}) - (\text{number of } e^- \text{ in antibonding MOs})}{2}$	CN^- bond order $= \frac{8-2}{2} = +3$
If the MO diagram has unpaired electrons, the molecule or ion is paramagnetic. If the electrons are all paired, the molecule or ion is diamagnetic.	Since the MO diagram has no unpaired electrons, the ion is diamagnetic.

FOR PRACTICE 10.11

Use molecular orbital theory to determine the bond order of NO^+. (Use the orbital energy ordering of N_2.) Is the molecule paramagnetic or diamagnetic?

Polyatomic Molecules

With the aid of computers, molecular orbital theory can be applied to polyatomic molecules and ions, yielding results that correlate very well with experimental measurements. (These applications are beyond the scope of this text.) However, the delocalizaton of electrons over an entire molecule is an important contribution of molecular orbital theory to our basic understanding of chemical bonding. For example, consider the Lewis structure and valence bond diagram of ozone:

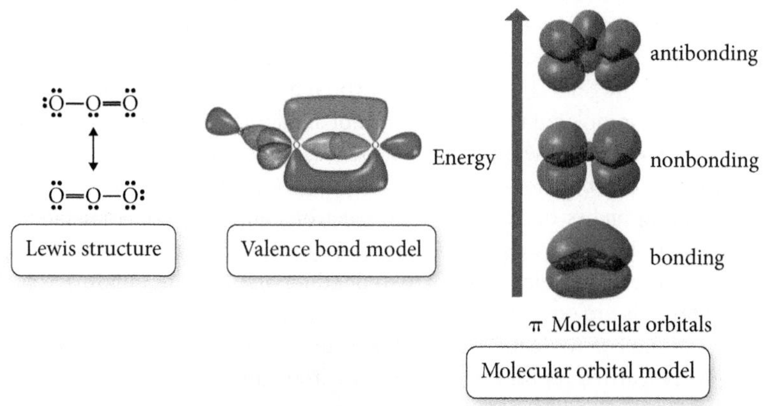

In Lewis theory, we use resonance forms to represent the two equivalent bonds; we say the real structure is a hybrid of the two resonance structures. In valence bond theory, it appears that the two oxygen–oxygen bonds are different. Both pairs of oxygen atoms have a σ bond formed by overlap of a $2p$ orbital on the terminal oxygen with an sp^2 hybrid orbital on the central oxygen. However, it appears that one pair of oxygen atoms also has a π bond by overlapping a p orbital on a terminal oxygen and a p orbital on the central oxygen. In reality though, the two oxygen–oxygen bonds are equivalent. Molecular orbital theory accounts for this. In a simplified form of MO theory, we can still think of the σ bonding framework the same way we do in the valence bond model, so there is one σ bond between each pair of oxygen atoms. However, we form π molecular orbitals using a linear combination of three $2p$ orbitals, one from each oxygen atom. From the three $2p$ orbitals, we form three molecular orbitals shown to the right of the diagram above. The bonding orbital contributes the equivalent of a single π bond between the two pairs of oxygen atoms. This accounts for the roughly one and a half bond strength we see for each oxygen–oxygen bond. In this simplified MO theory, we use valence bond theory to describe the σ-bond framework and MO theory to describe the delocalized electrons in the π molecular orbitals.

A similar situation occurs with benzene (C_6H_6). In Lewis theory, we represent the structure with two resonance forms:

```
       H       H                    H       H
        \     /                      \     /
         C—C                          C=C
        //    \\                     /     \
   H—C         C—H    <——>    H—C         C—H
        \     /                    \\     //
         C=C                          C—C
        /     \                      /     \
       H       H                    H       H
```

In the simplified MO theory, each carbon is σ-bonded to two other carbons via overlap of sp^2 hybrid orbitals and to a hydrogen atom by overlapping its third sp^2 hybrid with the hydrogen $1s$ orbital. This makes up the σ-bonding framework. The delocalized electrons in the π system are composed of six molecular orbitals formed by a linear combination of the remaining six $2p$ atomic orbitals, one from each carbon. The three lowest energy orbitals are bonding and are each occupied by two electrons. These three bonding orbitals account for about half a bond between each of the six pairs of carbon atoms. The three highest energy, antibonding orbitals are unoccupied.

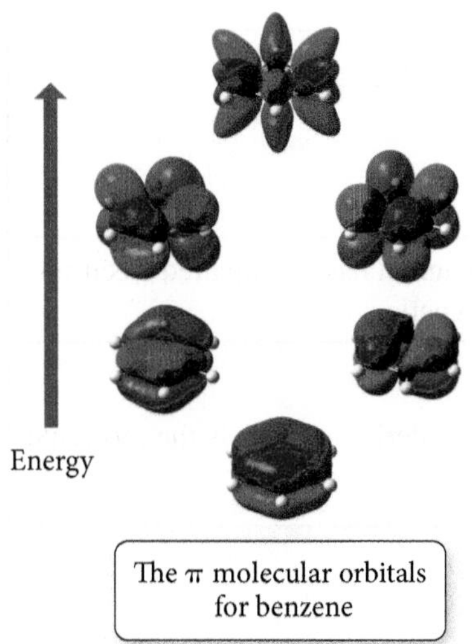

▲ The π molecular orbitals for benzene.

Larger Conjugated Pi Systems

We can extend this simplified MO theory to long chains of unsaturated hydrocarbons that Lewis theory shows as alternating double and single bonds and chemists call *conjugation*. An example is in 1,3-butadiene.

$$CH_2{=}CH_2 \qquad\qquad CH_2{=}CH{-}CH{=}CH_2$$

ethene   1,3-butadiene

However, as we shall see, the π electrons are delocalized over the entire molecule. As in benzene, each of the carbon atoms can be considered to have sp^2 hybridized orbitals which account for the σ-bonding framework. The terminal carbons are σ-bonded to another carbon and two hydrogens, whereas the internal carbons are σ-bonded to two other carbons and one hydrogen. The remaining p orbital on each of the carbon atoms combine to make up a set of π molecular orbitals. The molecular orbitals for ethene, 1,3-butadiene, and 1,3,5-hexatriene are shown in Figure 10.15 ▸. For ethene, two p atomic orbitals, one from each carbon, combine to form two π molecular orbitals. One of these π molecular orbitals is bonding and is occupied by two electrons and the other molecular orbital is an antibonding orbital and is unoccupied or empty. For 1,3-butadiene, the four p atomic orbitals form four π molecular orbitals, two bonding and two antibonding. The bonding π molecular orbitals are occupied. Finally, for 1,3,5-hexatriene, the six p atomic orbitals form three occupied π molecular orbitals and three unoccupied π molecular orbitals. This trend can be carried on for any number of carbon atoms.

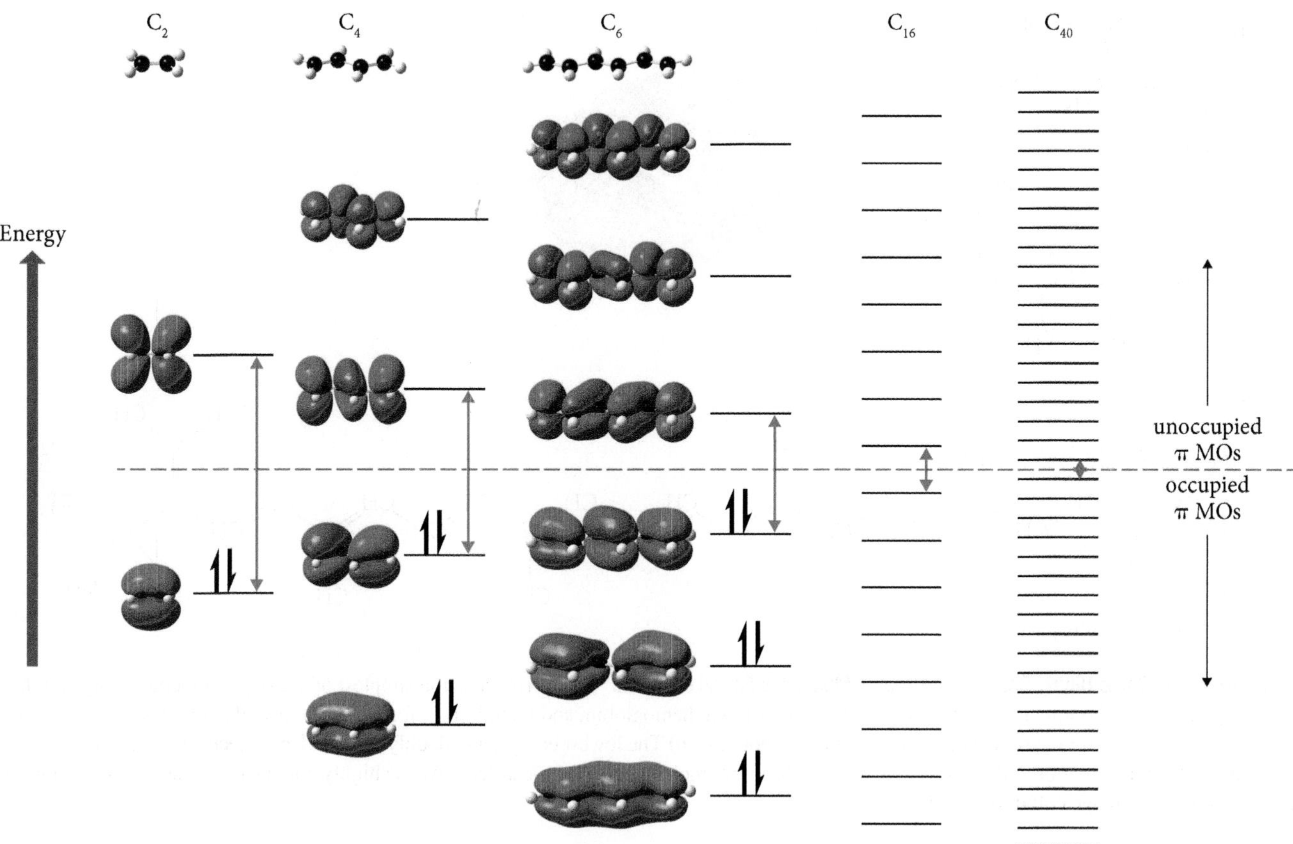

▲ **FIGURE 10.15 The π Molecular Orbitals of Ethene, 1,3-Butadiene, and 1,3,5-Hexatriene** The red double-headed arrows show the HOMO–LUMO gap for these conjugated alkenes.

The bonding π molecular orbitals are all lower in energy than the original *p* orbitals and the antibonding orbitals are all higher in energy. What we can also see from Figure 10.15 is that the difference in energy between the **highest occupied molecular orbital (HOMO)** and the **lowest unoccupied molecular orbital (LUMO)** gets smaller as the number of conjugated double bonds increases. This **HOMO–LUMO gap** can be measured by shining light on the molecule. When the right wavelength of light is shone on a sample of these molecules, an electron is promoted from the HOMO to the LUMO. The energy of light that is absorbed by these molecules to cause this promotion of an electron is a measure of this HOMO–LUMO gap. For ethene, 1,3-butadiene, and 1,3,5-hexatriene, the wavelengths of light that are absorbed to cause this electronic transition are at approximately 180 nm, 220 nm, and 260 nm, respectively—increasing in wavelength (decreasing in energy) as the number of conjugated double bonds increases in agreement with our model.

Conjugation is the word for the alternating double and single bonds in polyunsaturated hydrocarbons.

For even larger molecules with extensive unsaturation (Figure 10.16 ▼), we would expect that the wavelength of light causing the promotion of an electron from the HOMO to the LUMO gets even larger, into the visible region of the electromagnetic spectrum (approximately 400–800 nm). Because of the absorption of visible light, the molecules are coloured. Molecules such as beta-carotene, lycopene, chlorophyll, and hemoglobin all contain conjugated double bonds and are strongly coloured because they absorb light in the visible region of the electromagnetic spectrum.

An Extension of MO Theory: Band Theory of Solids

Just as the π molecular orbitals in conjugated organic molecules are delocalized, so too are the molecular orbitals in solids. If we start with a lithium atom, and build up to a macroscopic piece of metal, we can see how the electrons are delocalized in orbitals that span the entire molecule or solid. The two 2*s* orbitals in Li_2 combine to form two molecular orbitals, a σ bonding and antibonding molecular orbital. In each atom, there was one valence electron and these occupy the σ bonding molecular orbital in Li_2. Similarly, four 2*s* orbitals combine to form two bonding and two antibonding σ molecular orbitals in Li_4. The four valence electrons occupy the two lowest energy σ bonding orbitals. Continuing,

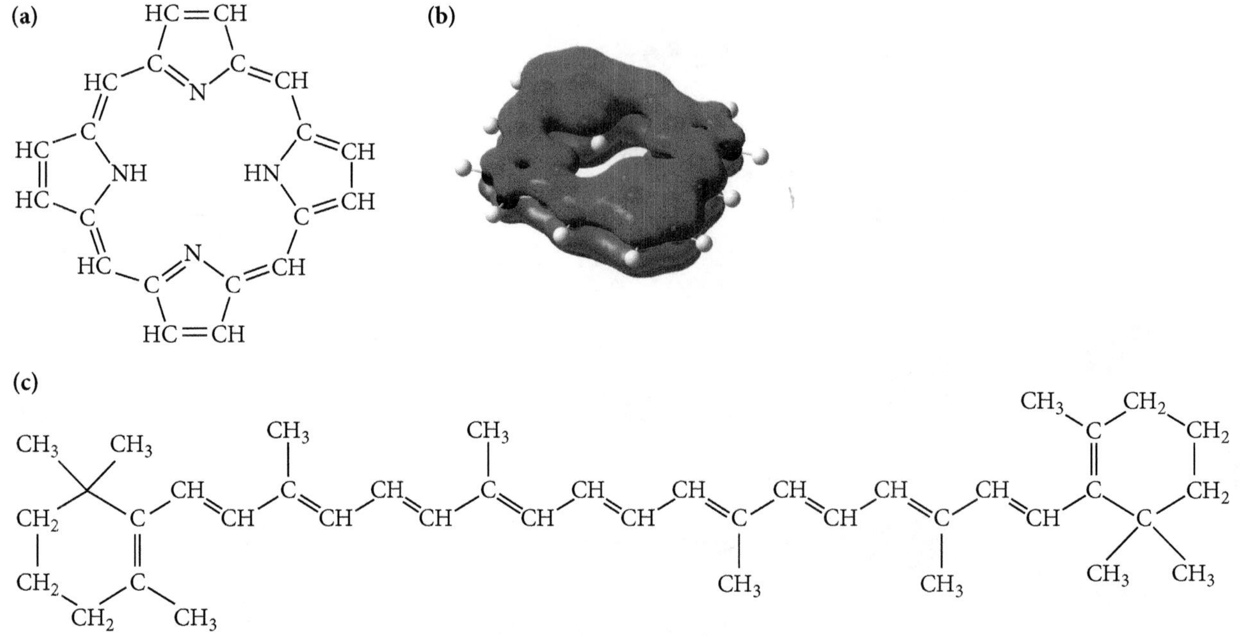

▲ **FIGURE 10.16 Some Highly Conjugated Organic Molecules Found in Nature** **(a)** Porphine is the simplest of a group of biochemically significant compounds called porphyrins. Porphyrins include chlorophyll, hemoglobin, and vitamin B_{12}, for which the heavily conjugated π molecular orbitals are responsible for the brilliant colours of these compounds. **(b)** The lowest energy, and doubly occupied π molecular orbital for porphine showing that the molecular orbitals are delocalized over the entire molecule. **(c)** Beta-carotene, whose highly conjugated π molecular orbitals are responsible for the orange colour of carrots.

there would be four occupied bonding and four unoccupied antibonding σ molecular orbitals in Li_8 as is seen in Figure 10.17 ▼. Extending this to a larger, macroscopic sample of lithium metal sees a very large number of atomic orbitals combining to give bands. The lower energy set of filled molecular orbitals is called a **valence band**, and the higher energy set of molecular orbitals, which are empty, called a **conduction band**. For a metal such as lithium, the valence and conduction bands either overlap or are very close in energy so that promotion of electrons from the valence band to the conduction band requires very little energy and the metal passes a current with little or no resistance. For some solids, the filled and empty bands are separated slightly in energy and this separation is called a **band gap**. If the band gap is small, then higher temperatures can be used to make the solid conduct electricity—these solids are called semiconductors. If the band gap is very large, then the solid is a nonconductor of electricity or an insulator.

Doping: Controlling the Conductivity of Semiconductors The conductivity of semiconductors can be increased by adding minute quantities of other substances called dopants. The addition of dopants result in additional electrons in the conduction band or electron "holes" in the valence band. For example, silicon is a group 14 semiconductor. Its valence electrons just fill

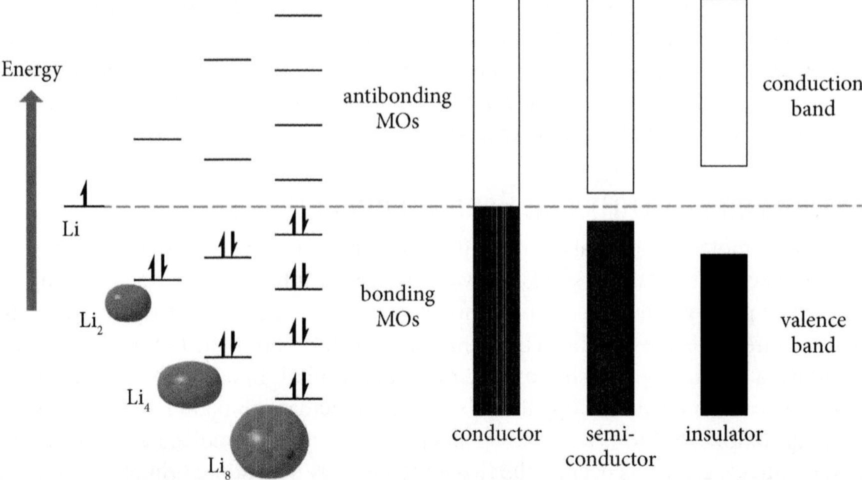

► **FIGURE 10.17 The Evolution of Atomic and Molecular Orbitals into Bands** For Li_2, Li_4, and Li_8, the lowest energy σ_{2s} molecular orbitals are shown.

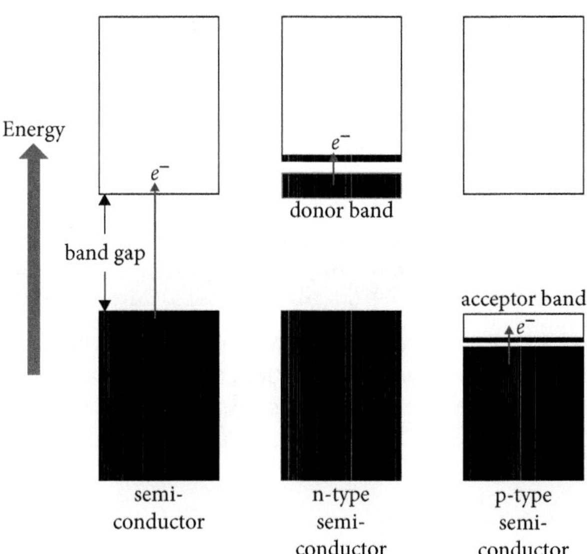

◀ **FIGURE 10.18** A semiconductor can be doped with other elements in order to promote conductivity as in an n-type or a p-type semiconductor.

its valence band. The band gap in silicon is large enough that only a few electrons are promoted into the conduction band at room temperature; therefore, silicon is a poor electrical conductor. However, silicon can be doped with phosphorus, a group 15 element with five valence electrons, to increase its conductivity. The phosphorus atoms are incorporated into the silicon crystal structure and each phosphorus atom brings with it one additional electron. Since the valence band is completely full, the additional electrons must go into the conduction band. These electrons are then somewhat mobile and can conduct electrical current (Figure 10.18 ▲). This type of semiconductor is called an **n-type semiconductor** because the charge carriers are negatively charged electrons in the conduction band.

Silicon can also be doped with a group 13 element, such as gallium, which has only three valence electrons. When gallium is incorporated into the silicon crystal structure, it results in electron "holes," or empty molecular orbitals, in the valence band. The presence of these empty molecular orbitals in the valence band also allows for the movement of electrical current because electrons in the valence band can move between holes. This type of semiconductor is called a **p-type semiconductor** because the empty molecular orbital, or hole, acts as a positive charge.

The heart of most modern electronic devices are silicon chips containing millions of **p–n junctions**, tiny spots that are p-type on one side and n-type on the other. These junctions can serve a number of functions, including acting as **diodes** (circuit elements that allow the flow of electrical current in only one direction) or amplifiers (elements that amplify a small electrical current into a larger one). One special type of diode is a light emitting diode (LED) (Figure 10.19 ▼). LEDs have been in use in home electronics, such

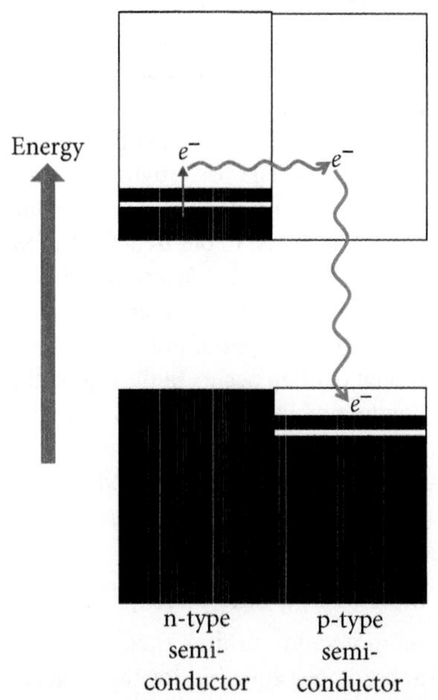

◀ **FIGURE 10.19 Molecular Orbital Diagram for a p–n Junction Light Emitting Diode** The n-type semiconductor absorbs electricity and the electron is transferred to the p-type semiconductor where the electron drops from the conduction band to the valence band, emitting a photon of light as it does.

as television convertors, for decades; the LEDs in these devices emit infrared radiation. LEDs for home lighting are becoming commonplace low energy "green" replacements for incandescent and fluorescent bulbs. LEDs consume far less energy than incandescent bulbs, which are being phased out in many countries. Unlike fluorescent and compact fluorescent (CFL) bulbs, LEDs do not use mercury and therefore do not pollute the environment when they break or come to the end of their life.

CONCEPTUAL CONNECTION 10.5
What Is a Chemical Bond? Part II

We have learned that Lewis theory portrays a chemical bond as the sharing of electrons represented as dots. Valence bond theory portrays a chemical bond as the overlap of two half-filled atomic orbitals. What is a chemical bond according to molecular orbital theory?

CHAPTER IN REVIEW

Key Terms

Section 10.2
valence shell electron pair repulsion (VSEPR) theory (374)
electron groups (374)
linear (375)
trigonal planar (375)
tetrahedral (376)
trigonal bipyramidal (377)
octahedral (377)

Section 10.3
electron geometry (378)
molecular geometry (379)
trigonal pyramidal (379)
bent (379)
seesaw (380)
T-shaped (380)
square pyramidal (381)
square planar (381)

Section 10.6
valence bond theory (389)

Section 10.7
hybridization (392)
hybrid atomic orbitals (hybrid orbitals) (392)
pi (π) bond (396)
sigma (σ) bond (396)

Section 10.8
molecular orbital (MO) theory (403)
bonding orbital (404)
antibonding orbital (404)
bond order (404)
nonbonding orbital (413)
highest occupied molecular orbital (HOMO) (415)
lowest unoccupied molecular orbital (LUMO) (415)
HOMO–LUMO gap (415)
valence band (416)
conduction band (416)
band gap (416)
n-type semiconductor (417)
p-type semiconductor (417)
p–n junctions (417)
diodes (417)

Key Concepts

Molecular Shape and VSEPR Theory (10.1–10.4)

The properties of molecules are directly related to their shapes. In VSEPR theory, molecular geometries are determined by the repulsions between electron groups on the central atom. An electron group can be a single bond, double bond, triple bond, lone pair, or even a single electron. The five basic shapes are linear (two electron groups), trigonal planar (three electron groups), tetrahedral (four electron groups), trigonal bipyramidal (five electron groups), and octahedral (six electron groups). When lone pairs are present on the central atom, the *electron* geometry is still one of the five basic shapes, but one or more positions are occupied by lone pairs. The *molecular* geometry is therefore different from the electron geometry. Lone pairs are positioned so as to minimize repulsions with other lone pairs and with bonding pairs.

Polarity (10.5)

The polarity of a polyatomic molecule containing polar bonds depends on its geometry. If the dipole moments of the polar bonds are aligned in such a way that they cancel one another, the molecule will not be polar. If they are aligned in such a way as to add together, the molecule will be polar. Highly symmetric molecules tend to be nonpolar, while asymmetric molecules containing polar bonds tend to be polar. The polarity of a molecule dramatically affects its properties.

Valence Bond Theory (10.6, 10.7)

In contrast to Lewis theory, in which a covalent chemical bond is the sharing of electrons represented by dots, in valence bond theory, a chemical bond is the overlap of half-filled atomic orbitals (or in some cases, the overlap between a completely filled orbital and an empty one). The overlapping orbitals may be the standard atomic orbitals, such as $1s$ or $2p$, or they may be hybridized atomic orbitals, which are mathematical combinations of the standard orbitals on a single atom. The basic hybridized orbitals are sp, sp^2, and sp^3. The geometry of the molecule is determined by the geometry of the overlapping orbitals. In our treatment of valence bond theory, we use the molecular geometry determined by VSEPR theory to determine the correct hybridization scheme. In valence bond theory, we distinguish between two types of bonds, σ (sigma) and π (pi). In a σ bond, the orbital overlap occurs in the region that lies directly between the two bonding atoms. In a π bond, formed from the side-by-side overlap of p orbitals, the overlap occurs above and below the region that lies directly between the two bonding atoms. Rotation about a σ bond is relatively free, while rotation about a π bond is restricted.

Molecular Orbital Theory (10.8)

In molecular orbital theory, we approximate solutions to the Schrödinger equation for the molecule *as a whole* by guessing the mathematical form of the orbitals. We differentiate between guesses by calculating the energies of guessed orbitals—the best guesses have the lowest energy. Molecular orbitals obtained in this way are properties of the molecule and are often delocalized over the entire molecule. The simplest guesses that work well are linear combinations of atomic orbitals (LCAOs), weighted averages of the atomic orbitals of the different atoms in the molecule. When two atomic orbitals are combined to form molecular orbitals, they will form one molecular orbital of lower energy (the bonding orbital) and one of higher energy (the antibonding orbital). A set of molecular orbitals are filled in much the same way as atomic orbitals. The stability of the molecule and the strength of the bond depend on the number of electrons in bonding orbitals compared to the number in antibonding orbitals.

It is useful to describe the bonding in conjugated systems (organic compounds with alternating single and double bonds) using a simplified MO theory in which the σ framework is approximated by valence bond theory (hybridization) and the π framework is composed of molecular orbitals that are delocalized over the molecule. For solids, like a metal, the molecular orbitals can be thought of as bands. The lower energy valence band is filled with electrons while the higher energy conduction band is at least partially vacant. For metallic solids, the energy difference between the valence and conduction band is very small so that electrons are easily promoted to the conduction band, therefore conducting electricity. For nonconducting solids there is a large energy difference between the valence and conduction so that electrons cannot easily be conducted.

Key Equations and Relationships

Bond Order of a Diatomic Molecule (10.8)

$$\text{Bond order} = \frac{(\text{number of electrons in bonding MOs}) - (\text{number of electrons in antibonding MOs})}{2}$$

Key Skills

Using VSEPR Theory to Predict the Basic Shapes of Molecules (10.2)
• Example 10.1 • For Practice 10.1 • Exercises 35, 36

Predicting Molecular Geometries Using VSEPR Theory and the Effects of Lone Pairs (10.4)
• Examples 10.2, 10.3 • For Practice 10.2, 10.3 • Exercises 39, 40

Predicting the Shapes of Larger Molecules (10.4)
• Example 10.4 • For Practice 10.4 • Exercises 45, 46, 49, 50

Using Molecular Shape to Determine Polarity of a Molecule (10.5)
• Example 10.5 • For Practice 10.5 • Exercises 53–56

Writing Hybridization and Bonding Schemes Using Valence Bond Theory (10.7)
• Examples 10.6, 10.7, 10.8 • For Practice 10.6, 10.7, 10.8 • For More Practice 10.8 • Exercises 65–70

Drawing Molecular Orbital Diagrams to Predict Bond Order and Magnetism of a Diatomic Molecule (10.8)
• Examples 10.9, 10.10, 10.11 • For Practice 10.9, 10.10, 10.11 • For More Practice 10.10 • Exercises 75, 76, 79–82, 85, 86

EXERCISES

Review Questions

1. Why is molecular geometry important? Give some examples.

2. According to VSEPR theory, what determines the geometry of a molecule?

3. Name and sketch the five basic electron geometries, and state the number of electron groups corresponding to each. What constitutes an *electron group*?

4. Explain the difference between electron geometry and molecular geometry. Under what circumstances are they not the same?

5. Give the correct electron and molecular geometries that correspond to each set of electron groups around the central atom of a molecule:

a. four electron groups overall; three bonding groups and one lone pair

b. four electron groups overall; two bonding groups and two lone pairs

c. five electron groups overall; four bonding groups and one lone pair

d. five electron groups overall; three bonding groups and two lone pairs

e. five electron groups overall; two bonding groups and three lone pairs

f. six electron groups overall; five bonding groups and one lone pair

g. six electron groups overall; four bonding groups and two lone pairs

6. How do you apply VSEPR theory to predict the shape of a molecule with more than one interior atom?

7. How do you determine whether a molecule is polar? Why is polarity important?

8. What is a chemical bond according to valence bond theory?

9. In valence bond theory, what determines the geometry of a molecule?

10. In valence bond theory, the interaction energy between the electrons and nucleus of one atom with the electrons and nucleus of another atom is usually negative (stabilizing) when ____________.

11. What is hybridization? Why is hybridization necessary in valence bond theory?

12. How does hybridization of the atomic orbitals in the central atom of a molecule help lower the overall energy of the molecule?

13. How is the *number* of hybrid orbitals related to the number of standard atomic orbitals that are hybridized?

14. Make sketches of each hybrid orbital:
a. sp **b.** sp^2 **c.** sp^3

15. In Lewis theory, the two bonds in a double bond look identical. However, valence bond theory shows that they are not. Describe a double bond according to valence bond theory. Explain why rotation is restricted about a double bond but not about a single bond.

16. Give the hybridization scheme that corresponds to each electron geometry:
a. linear **b.** trigonal planar **c.** tetrahedral

17. What is a chemical bond according to molecular orbital theory?

18. Explain the difference between hybrid atomic orbitals in valence bond theory and LCAO molecular orbitals in molecular orbital theory.

19. What is a bonding molecular orbital?

20. What is an antibonding molecular orbital?

21. What is the role of wave interference in determining whether a molecular orbital is bonding or antibonding?

22. In molecular orbital theory, what is bond order? Why is it important?

23. How is the number of molecular orbitals approximated by a linear combination of atomic orbitals related to the number of atomic orbitals used in the approximation?

24. Make a sketch of each molecular orbital:
a. σ_{2s} **b.** σ^*_{2s} **c.** σ_{2p}
d. σ^*_{2p} **e.** π_{2p} **f.** π^*_{2p}

25. Draw an energy diagram for the molecular orbitals of period 2 diatomic molecules. Show the difference in ordering for B_2, C_2, and N_2 compared to O_2, F_2, and Ne_2.

26. Why does the energy ordering of the molecular orbitals of the period 2 diatomic molecules change in going from N_2 to O_2?

27. Explain the difference between a paramagnetic species and a diamagnetic one.

28. When applying molecular orbital theory to heteronuclear diatomic molecules, the atomic orbitals used may be of different energies. If two atomic orbitals of different energies make two molecular orbitals, how are the energies of the molecular orbitals related to the energies of the atomic orbitals? How is the shape of the resultant molecular orbitals related to the shapes of the atomic orbitals?

29. In molecular orbital theory, what is a nonbonding orbital?

30. Write a short paragraph describing chemical bonding according to Lewis theory, valence bond theory, and molecular orbital theory. Indicate how the theories differ in their description of a chemical bond, and indicate the strengths and weaknesses of each theory. Which theory is correct?

31. In band theory of bonding for solids, what is a *band*? What is the difference between the *valence band* and the *conduction band*?

32. What is a band gap? How does the band gap differ in metals, semiconductors, and insulators?

33. Explain how doping can increase the conductivity of a semiconductor. What is the difference between an n-type semiconductor and a p-type semiconductor?

34. Explain how the number of conjugated double bonds in a molecule affects the HOMO–LUMO gap as well as the wavelength and energy of light required to cause a HOMO to LUMO electronic transition.

Problems by Topic

VSEPR Theory and Molecular Geometry

35. A molecule with the formula AB_3 has a trigonal pyramidal geometry. How many electron groups are on the central atom (A)?

36. A molecule with the formula AB_3 has a trigonal planar geometry. How many electron groups are on the central atom?

37. For each molecular geometry, give the number of total electron groups, the number of bonding groups, and the number of lone pairs on the central atom:

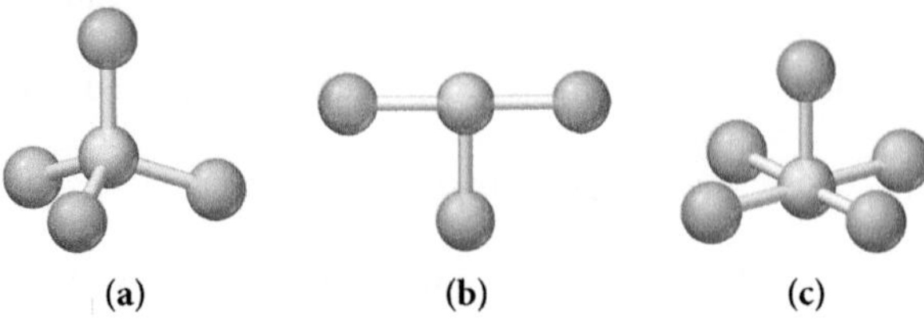

(a) (b) (c)

38. For each molecular geometry, give the number of total electron groups, the number of bonding groups, and the number of lone pairs on the central atom:

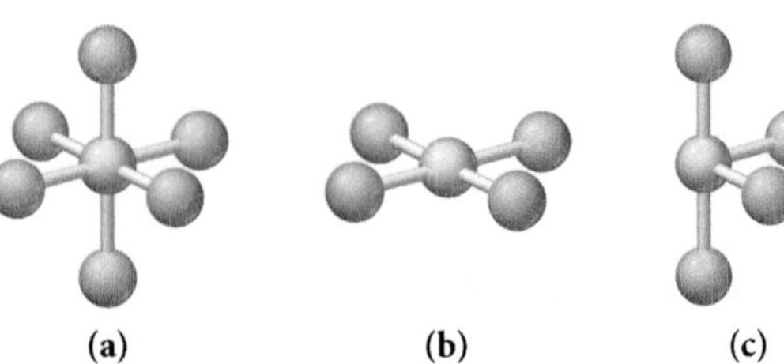

(a) (b) (c)

39. Determine the electron geometry, molecular geometry, and idealized bond angles for each molecule. In which cases do you expect deviations from the idealized bond angle?
a. PF_3 **b.** SBr_2 **c.** $CHCl_3$ **d.** CS_2

40. Determine the electron geometry, molecular geometry, and idealized bond angles for each molecule. In which cases do you expect deviations from the idealized bond angle?
a. CF_4 **b.** NF_3 **c.** OF_2 **d.** H_2S

41. Which species has the smaller bond angle, H_3O^+ or H_2O? Explain.

42. Which species has the smaller bond angle, ClO_4^- or ClO_3^-? Explain.

43. Determine the molecular geometry and make a sketch of each molecule or ion:
a. SF_4 b. ClF_3 c. IF_2^- d. IBr_4^-

44. Determine the molecular geometry and make a sketch of each molecule or ion, using the bond conventions shown on page 000:
a. BrF_5 b. SCl_6 c. PF_5 d. IF_4^+

45. Determine the molecular geometry about each interior atom and make a sketch of each molecule:
a. C_2H_2 (skeletal structure HCCH)
b. C_2H_4 (skeletal structure H_2CCH_2)
c. C_2H_6 (skeletal structure H_3CCH_3)

46. Determine the molecular geometry about each interior atom and make a sketch of each molecule:
a. N_2
b. N_2H_2 (skeletal structure HNNH)
c. N_2H_4 (skeletal structure H_2NNH_2)

47. Each ball-and-stick model shows the electron and molecular geometry of a generic molecule. Explain what is wrong with each molecular geometry and provide the correct molecular geometry, given the number of lone pairs and bonding groups on the central atom:

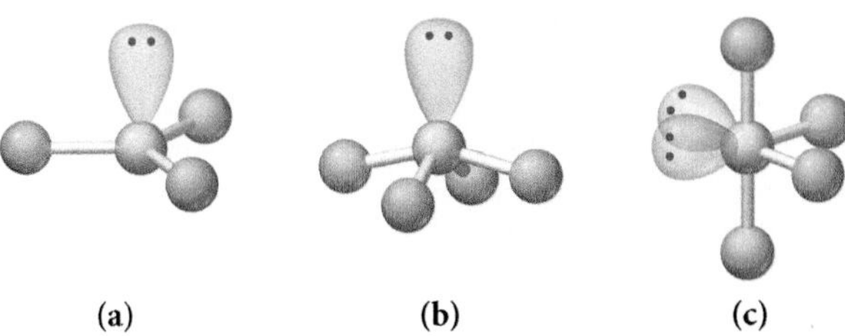

48. Each ball-and-stick model shows the electron and molecular geometry of a generic molecule. Explain what is wrong with each molecular geometry and provide the correct molecular geometry, given the number of lone pairs and bonding groups on the central atom:

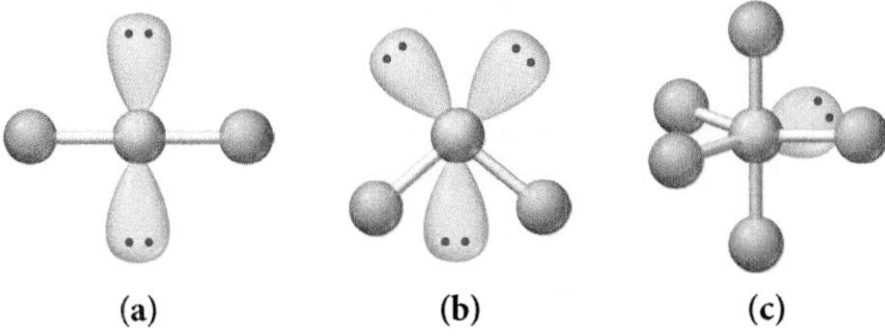

49. Determine the geometry about each interior atom in each molecule and sketch the molecule. (Skeletal structure is indicated in parentheses.)
a. CH_3OH (H_3COH) b. CH_3OCH_3 (H_3COCH_3)
c. H_2O_2 (HOOH)

50. Determine the geometry about each interior atom in each molecule and sketch the molecule. (Skeletal structure is indicated in parentheses.)
a. CH_3NH_2 (H_3CNH_2)
b. $CH_3CO_2CH_3$ ($H_3CCOOCH_3$, both O atoms attached to second C)
c. NH_2CO_2H (H_2NCOOH, both O atoms attached to C)

Molecular Shape and Polarity

51. Explain why CO_2 and CCl_4 are both nonpolar, even though they contain polar bonds.

52. CH_3F is a polar molecule, even though the tetrahedral geometry often leads to nonpolar molecules. Explain.

53. Determine whether each molecule in Exercise 39 is polar or nonpolar.

54. Determine whether each molecule in Exercise 40 is polar or nonpolar.

55. Determine whether each molecule is polar or nonpolar:
a. ClO_3^- b. SCl_2 c. SCl_4 d. $BrCl_5$

56. Determine whether each molecule is polar or nonpolar:
a. $SiCl_4$ b. CF_2Cl_2 c. SeF_6 d. IF_5

Valence Bond Theory

57. The valence electron configurations of several atoms are given. How many bonds can each atom make without hybridization?
a. Be $2s^2$ b. P $3s^23p^3$ c. F $2s^22p^5$

58. The valence electron configurations of several atoms are given. How many bonds can each atom make without hybridization?
a. B $2s^22p^1$ b. N $2s^22p^3$ c. O $2s^22p^4$

59. Write orbital diagrams (boxes with arrows in them) to represent the electron configurations—without hybridization—for all the atoms in PH_3. Circle the electrons involved in bonding. Draw a three-dimensional sketch of the molecule and show orbital overlap. What bond angle do you expect from the unhybridized orbitals? How well does valence bond theory agree with the experimentally measured bond angle of 93.3°?

60. Write orbital diagrams to represent the electron configurations—without hybridization—for all the atoms in SF_2. Circle the electrons involved in bonding. Draw a three-dimensional sketch of the molecule and show orbital overlap. What bond angle do you expect from the unhybridized orbitals? How well does valence bond theory agree with the experimentally measured bond angle of 98.2°?

61. Write orbital diagrams to represent the electron configuration of carbon before and after sp^3 hybridization.

62. Write orbital diagrams to represent the electron configurations of carbon before and after sp hybridization.

63. Which hybridization scheme allows the formation of at least one π bond?

64. Which hybridization scheme allows a boron atom to bond to three fluorine atoms?

65. Write a hybridization and bonding scheme for each molecule. Sketch the molecule, including overlapping orbitals, and label all bonds using the notation shown in Examples 10.6 and 10.7.
a. CCl_4 b. NH_3 c. OF_2 d. CO_2

66. Write a hybridization and bonding scheme for each molecule. Sketch the molecule, including overlapping orbitals, and label all bonds using the notation shown in Examples 10.6 and 10.7.
a. CH_2Br_2 b. H_2CNH c. NF_3 d. BF_3

67. Write a hybridization and bonding scheme for each molecule or ion. Sketch the structure, including overlapping orbitals, and label all bonds using the notation shown in Examples 10.6 and 10.7.
a. $COCl_2$ (carbon is the central atom) b. NH_2^-
c. CO_3^{2-}

68. Write a hybridization and bonding scheme for each molecule or ion. Sketch the structure, including overlapping orbitals, and label all bonds using the notation shown in Examples 10.6 and 10.7.
a. HCN **b.** NO_3^- **c.** CH_2CCH_2

69. Write a hybridization and bonding scheme for each molecule that contains more than one interior atom. Indicate the hybridization about each interior atom. Sketch the structure, including overlapping orbitals, and label all bonds using the notation shown in Examples 10.6 and 10.7.
a. N_2H_2 (skeletal structure HNNH)
b. N_2H_4 (skeletal structure H_2NNH_2)
c. CH_3NH_2 (skeletal structure H_3CNH_2)

70. Write a hybridization and bonding scheme for each molecule that contains more than one interior atom. Indicate the hybridization about each interior atom. Sketch the structure, including overlapping orbitals, and label all bonds using the notation shown in Examples 10.6 and 10.7.
a. C_2H_2 (skeletal structure HCCH)
b. C_2H_4 (skeletal structure H_2CCH_2)
c. C_2H_6 (skeletal structure H_3CCH_3)

71. Consider the structure of the amino acid alanine. Indicate the hybridization about each interior atom.

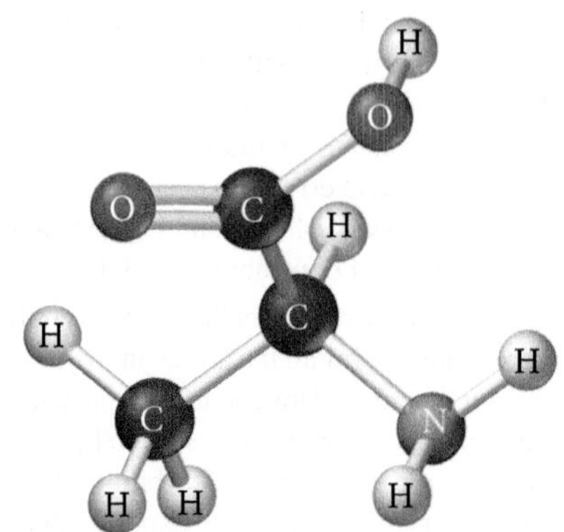

72. Consider the structure of the amino acid aspartic acid. Indicate the hybridization about each interior atom.

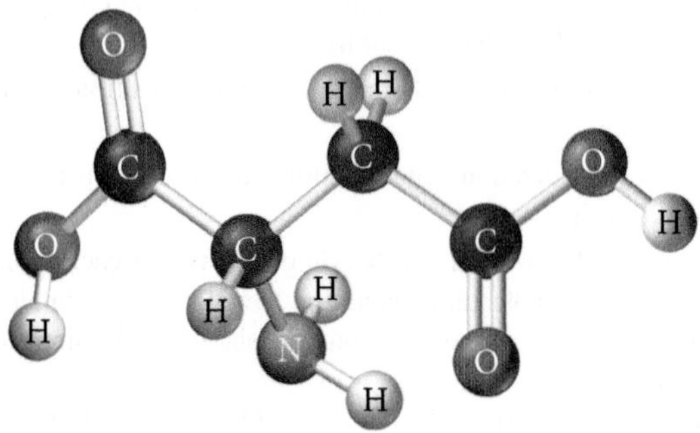

Molecular Orbital Theory

73. Sketch the bonding molecular orbital that results from the linear combination of two 1*s* orbitals. Indicate the region where interference occurs and state the kind of interference (constructive or destructive).

74. Sketch the antibonding molecular orbital that results from the linear combination of two 1*s* orbitals. Indicate the region where interference occurs and state the kind of interference (constructive or destructive).

75. Draw an MO energy diagram and predict the bond order of Be_2^+ and Be_2^-. Do you expect these molecules to exist in the gas phase?

76. Draw an MO energy diagram and predict the bond order of Li_2^+ and Li_2^-. Do you expect these molecules to exist in the gas phase?

77. Sketch the bonding and antibonding molecular orbitals that result from linear combinations of the $2p_z$ atomic orbitals in a homonuclear diatomic molecule. (The $2p_z$ orbitals are those whose lobes are oriented along the bonding axis.)

78. Sketch the bonding and antibonding molecular orbitals that result from linear combinations of the $2p_x$ atomic orbitals in a homonuclear diatomic molecule. (The $2p_x$ orbitals are those whose lobes are oriented perpendicular to the bonding axis.) How do these molecular orbitals differ from those obtained from linear combinations of the $2p_y$ atomic orbitals? (The $2p_y$ orbitals are oriented perpendicular to the bonding axis, but also perpendicular to the $2p_x$ orbitals.)

79. Using the molecular orbital energy ordering for second-row homonuclear diatomic molecules in which the π_{2p} orbitals lie at *lower* energy than the σ_{2p} orbitals, draw MO energy diagrams and predict the bond order in a molecule or ion with each number of total valence electrons. Will the molecule or ion be diamagnetic or paramagnetic?
a. 4 **b.** 6 **c.** 8 **d.** 9

80. Using the molecular orbital energy ordering for second-row homonuclear diatomic molecules in which the π_{2p} orbitals lie at *higher* energy than the σ_{2p} orbitals, draw MO energy diagrams and predict the bond order in a molecule or ion with each number of total valence electrons. Will the molecule or ion be diamagnetic or paramagnetic?
a. 10 **b.** 12 **c.** 13 **d.** 14

81. Use molecular orbital theory to predict whether or not each molecule or ion should exist in a relatively stable form:
a. H_2^{2-} **b.** Ne_2 **c.** He_2^{2+} **d.** F_2^{2-}

82. Use molecular orbital theory to predict whether or not each molecule or ion should exist in a relatively stable form:
a. C_2^{2+} **b.** Li_2 **c.** Be_2^{2+} **d.** Li_2^{2-}

83. According to MO theory, which molecule or ion has the highest bond order? Highest bond energy? Shortest bond length?

$$C_2, C_2^+, C_2^-$$

84. According to MO theory, which molecule or ion has the highest bond order? Highest bond energy? Shortest bond length?

$$O_2, O_2^-, O_2^{2-}$$

85. Draw an MO energy diagram for CO. (Use the energy ordering of N_2.) Predict the bond order and make a sketch of the lowest-energy bonding molecular orbital.

86. Draw an MO energy diagram for HCl. Predict the bond order and make a sketch of the lowest-energy bonding molecular orbital.

Band Theory

87. Which solid would you expect to have little or no band gap?
a. Zn(*s*) **b.** Si(*s*) **c.** As(*s*)

88. How many molecular orbitals are present in the valence band of a sodium crystal with a mass of 5.45 g?

89. Indicate whether each solid would form an n-type or a p-type semiconductor:
a. germanium doped with gallium
b. silicon doped with arsenic

90. Indicate whether each solid would form an n-type or a p-type semiconductor:

a. silicon doped with gallium

b. germanium doped with antimony

91. How many bonding and antibonding π molecular orbitals and how many π electrons are there in beta-carotene (see Figure 10.16)? Use Figure 10.15 to extrapolate and find the answer.

92. How many bonding and antibonding π molecular orbitals and how many π electrons are there in lycopene, the molecule responsible for the red colour of tomatoes (see below)? Use Figure 10.15 to extrapolate and find the answer.

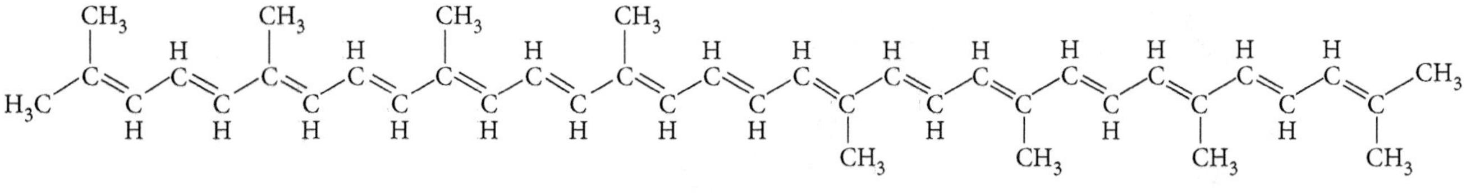

Cumulative Problems

93. For each compound, draw an appropriate Lewis structure, determine the geometry using VSEPR theory, determine whether the molecule is polar, identify the hybridization of all interior atoms, and make a sketch of the molecule according to valence bond theory, showing orbital overlap:

a. COF_2 (carbon is the central atom)

b. S_2Cl_2 (ClSSCl)

94. For each compound, draw an appropriate Lewis structure, determine the geometry using VSEPR theory, determine whether the molecule is polar, identify the hybridization of all interior atoms, and make a sketch of the molecule according to valence bond theory, showing orbital overlap:

a. CH_2CHCH_3 **b.** CH_3SH

95. Amino acids are biological compounds that link together to form proteins, the workhorse molecules in living organisms. The skeletal structures of several simple amino acids are shown here. For each skeletal structure, complete the Lewis structure, determine the geometry and hybridization about each interior atom, and make a sketch of the molecule using the bond conventions of Section 10.4.

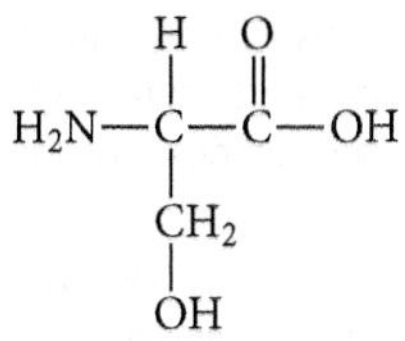

(a) serine

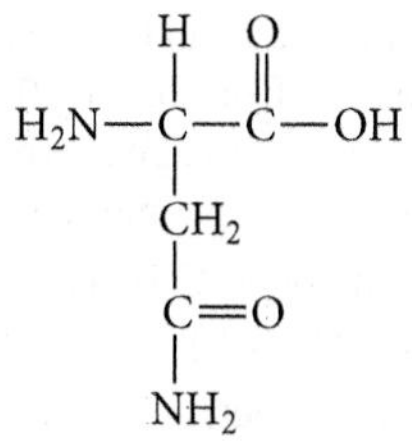

(b) asparagine

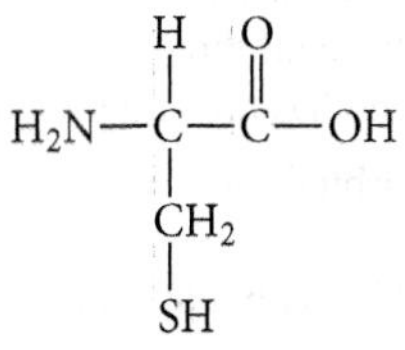

(c) cysteine

96. The genetic code is based on four different bases with the structures shown here. Assign a geometry and hybridization to each interior atom in these four bases:

a. cytosine **b.** adenine **c.** thymine **d.** guanine

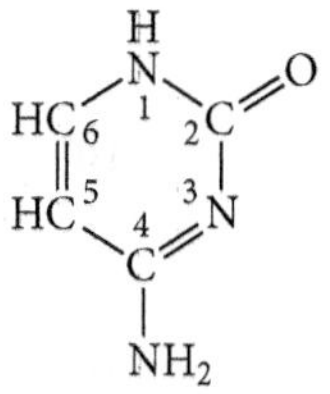

(a) 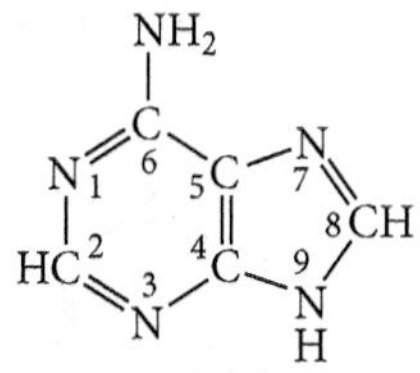 (b)

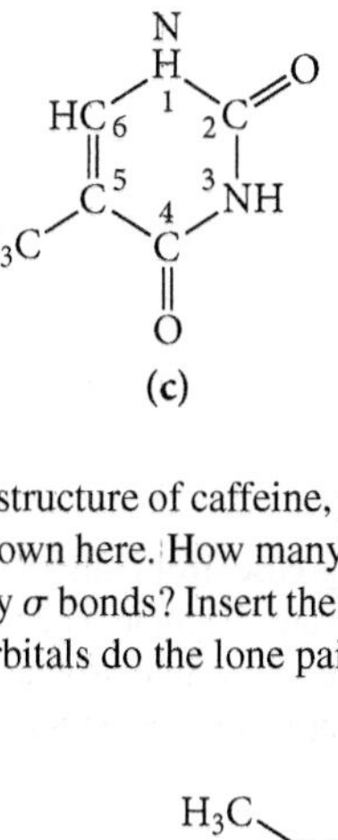

(c) 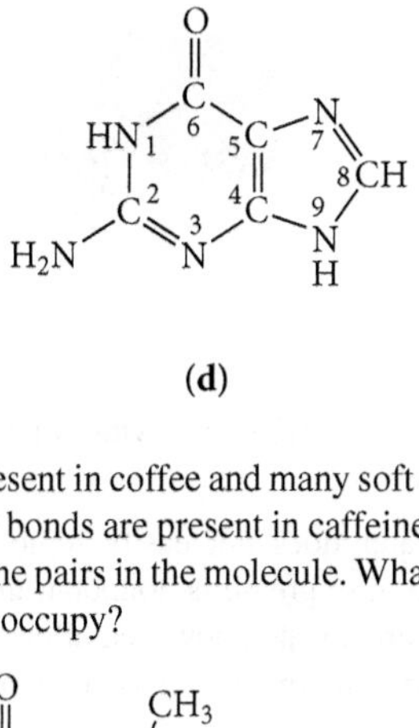 (d)

97. The structure of caffeine, present in coffee and many soft drinks, is shown here. How many π bonds are present in caffeine? How many σ bonds? Insert the lone pairs in the molecule. What kinds of orbitals do the lone pairs occupy?

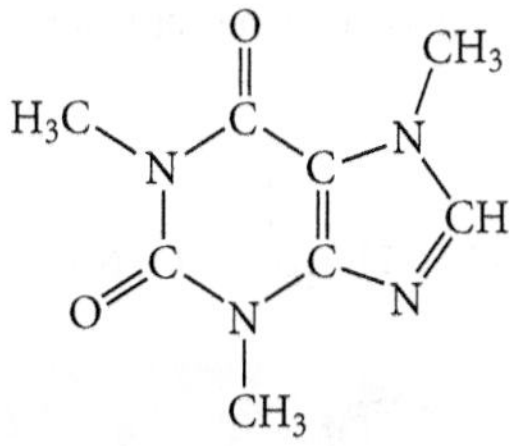

98. The structure of acetylsalicylic acid (aspirin) is shown here. How many π bonds are present in acetylsalicylic acid? How many σ bonds? What parts of the molecule are free to rotate? What parts are rigid?

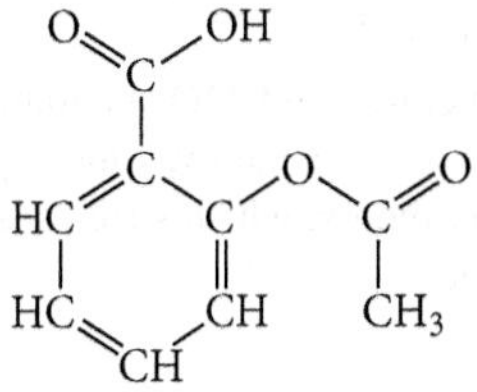

99. Most vitamins can be classified either as fat soluble, which tend to accumulate in the body (so that taking too much can be harmful), or water soluble, which tend to be quickly eliminated from the body in urine. Examine the structural formulas and space-filling models of these vitamins and determine whether they are fat soluble (mostly nonpolar) or water soluble (mostly polar).

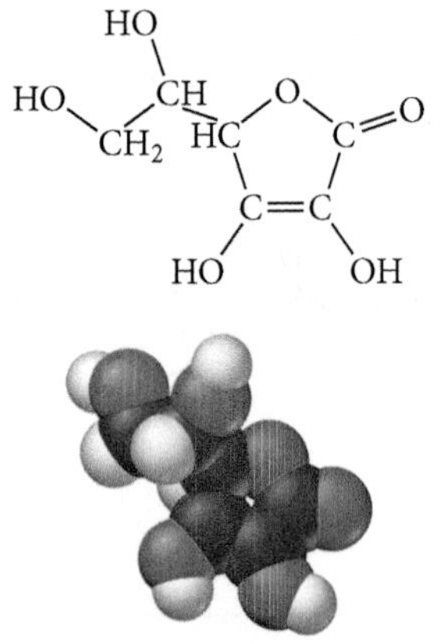

(a) vitamin C

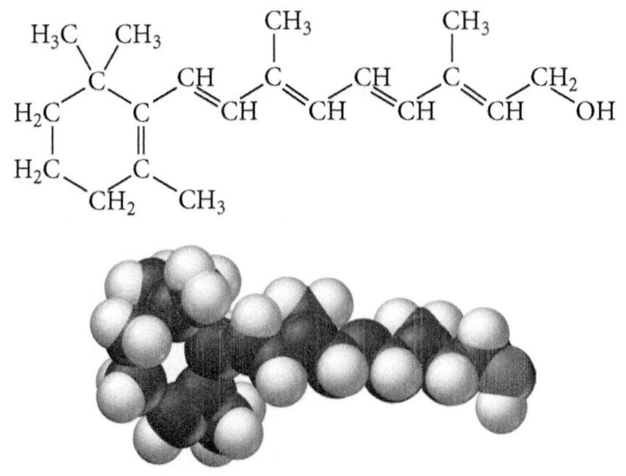

(b) vitamin A

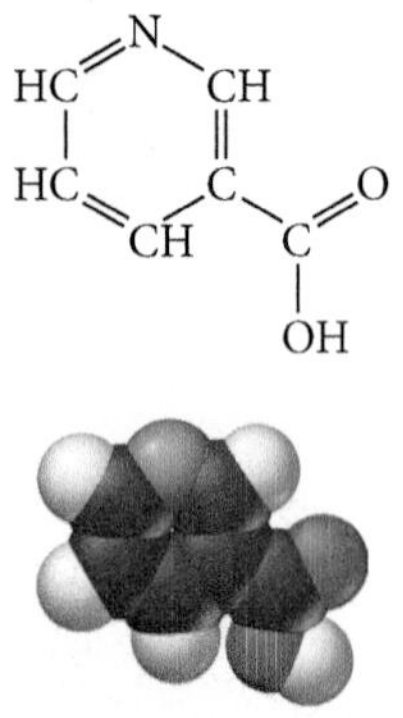

(c) niacin (vitamin B_3)

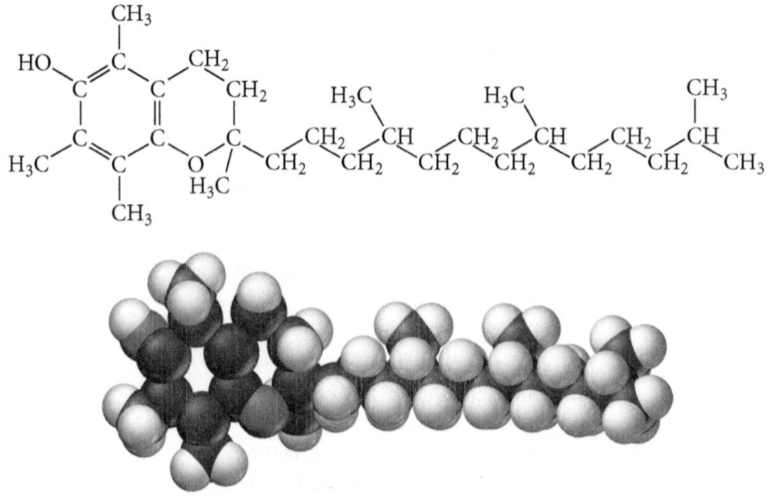

(d) vitamin E

100. Water does not easily remove grease from dishes or hands because grease is nonpolar and water is polar. The addition of soap to water, however, allows the grease to dissolve. Study the structure of sodium stearate (a soap) and suggest how it works.

$$CH_3(CH_2)_{16}\overset{O}{\overset{\|}{C}}—O^{-}Na^{+}$$

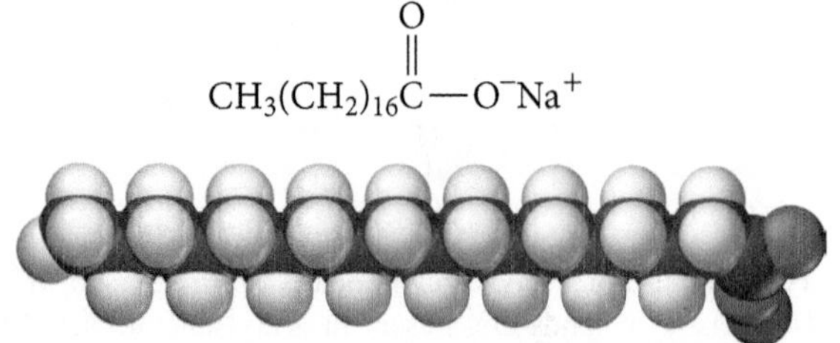

101. Draw a molecular orbital energy diagram for ClF. (Assume that the σ_p orbitals are lower in energy than the π orbitals.) What is the bond order in ClF?

102. Draw Lewis structures and MO diagrams for CN^+, CN, and CN^-. According to Lewis theory, which species is most stable? According to MO theory, which species is most stable? Do the two theories agree?

103. Bromine can form compounds or ions with any number of fluorine atoms from one to five. Write the formulas of all five of these species, assign a hybridization, and describe their electron and molecular geometries.

104. The compound C_3H_4 has two double bonds. Describe its bonding and geometry, using a valence bond approach.

105. Draw the structure of a molecule with the formula $C_4H_6Cl_2$ that has a dipole moment of 0.

106. Draw the structures of two compounds that have the composition CH_3NO_2 and have all three H atoms bonded to the C. Predict which compound has the larger ONO bond angle.

107. How many hybrid orbitals do we use to describe each molecule?
   a. N_2O_5
   b. C_2H_5NO (four C—H bonds and one O—H bond)
   c. BrCN (no formal charges)

108. Indicate which orbitals overlap to form the σ bonds in:
   a. $BeBr_2$ **b.** $HgCl_2$ **c.** ICN

Challenge Problems

109. In VSEPR theory, which uses Lewis theory to determine molecular geometry, the trend of decreasing bond angle in CH_4, NH_3, and H_2O is accounted for by the greater repulsion of lone-pair electrons compared to bonding-pair electrons. How would this trend be accounted for in valence bond theory?

110. The results of a molecular orbital calculation for H_2O are shown here. Examine each of the orbitals and classify them as bonding, antibonding, or nonbonding. Assign the correct number of electrons to the energy diagram. According to this energy diagram, is H_2O stable? Explain.

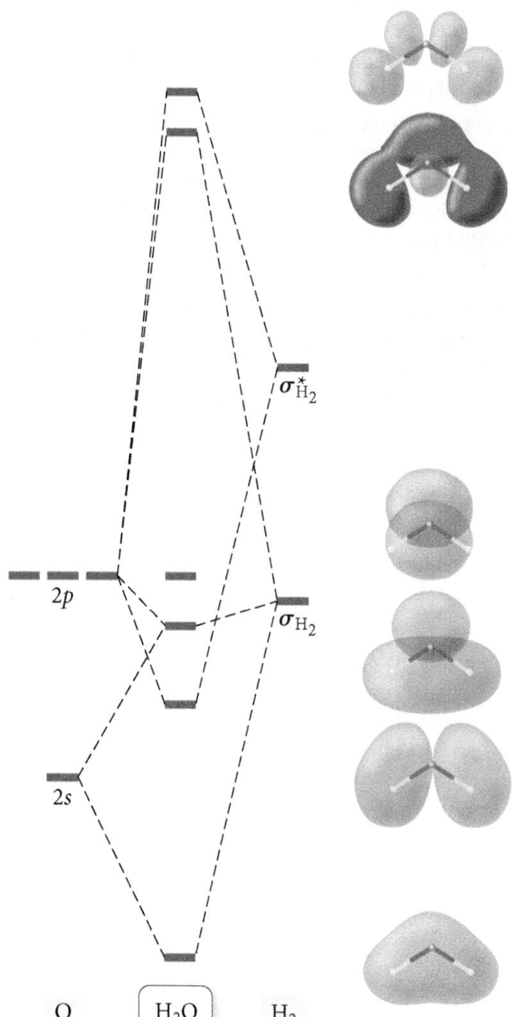

111. The results of a molecular orbital calculation for NH_3 are shown here. Examine each of the orbitals and classify them as bonding, antibonding, or nonbonding. Assign the correct number of electrons to the energy diagram. According to this energy diagram, is NH_3 stable? Explain.

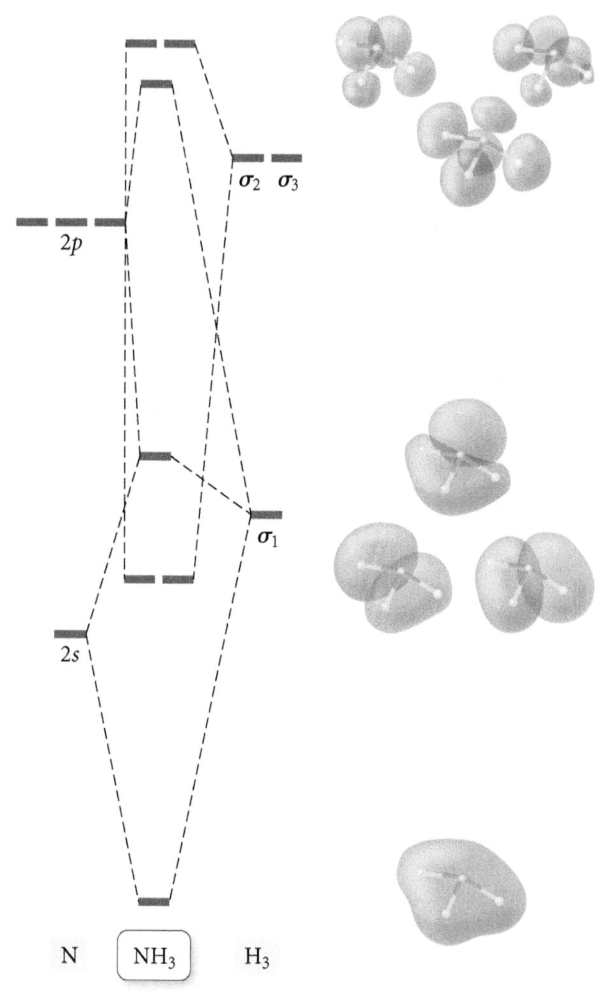

112. *cis*-2-butene isomerizes to *trans*-2-butene via the reaction:

```
H  H H  H               H  H
 \ /   \ /               \ /
H—C     C—H           H—C      H
   \   /      ⟶           \    /
    C=C                    C=C
   /   \                  /   \
  H     H                H     C—H
                              / \
                             H   H
```

a. If isomerization requires breaking the π bond, what minimum energy is required for isomerization in J mol^{-1}? In J $molecule^{-1}$?

b. If the energy for isomerization came from light, what minimum frequency of light would be required? In what portion of the electromagnetic spectrum does this frequency lie?

113. The species NO_2, NO_2^+, and NO_2^-, in which N is the central atom, have very different bond angles. Predict what these bond angles might be with respect to the ideal angles, and justify your prediction.

114. The bond angles increase steadily in the series PF_3, PCl_3, PBr_3, and PI_3. After consulting the data on atomic radii in Chapter 8, provide an explanation for this observation.

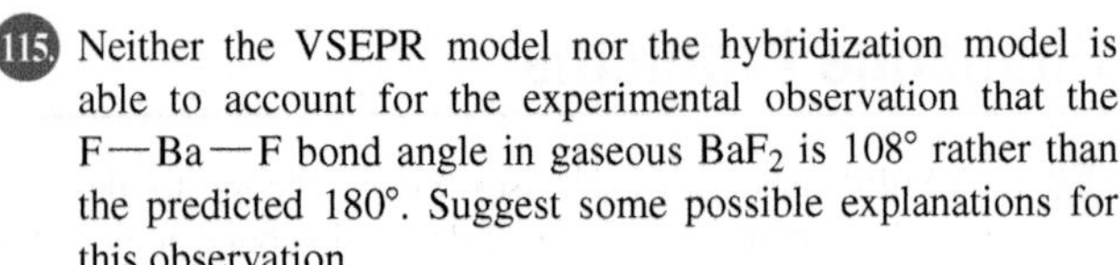

115. Neither the VSEPR model nor the hybridization model is able to account for the experimental observation that the F—Ba—F bond angle in gaseous BaF_2 is 108° rather than the predicted 180°. Suggest some possible explanations for this observation.

Conceptual Problems

116. Pick the statement that best captures the fundamental idea behind VSEPR theory. Explain what is wrong with each of the other statements.

   a. The angle between two or more bonds is determined primarily by the repulsions between the electrons within those bonds and other (lone-pair) electrons on the central atom of a molecule. Each of these electron groups (bonding electrons or lone-pair electrons) will lower its potential energy by maximizing its separation from other electron groups, thus determining the geometry of the molecule.

   b. The angle between two or more bonds is determined primarily by the repulsions between the electrons within those bonds. Each of these bonding electrons will lower its potential energy by maximizing its separation from other electron groups, thus determining the geometry of the molecule.

   c. The geometry of a molecule is determined by the shapes of the overlapping orbitals that form the chemical bonds. Therefore, to determine the geometry of a molecule, you must determine the shapes of the orbitals involved in bonding.

117. Suppose that a molecule has four bonding groups and one lone pair on the central atom. Suppose further that the molecule is confined to two dimensions (this is a purely hypothetical assumption for the sake of understanding the principles behind VSEPR theory). Make a sketch of the molecule and estimate the bond angles.

118. How does each of the three major bonding theories (Lewis theory, valence bond theory, and molecular orbital theory) define a single chemical bond? A double bond? A triple bond? How are these definitions similar? How are they different?

Liquids, Solids, and Intermolecular Forces

11

It's a wild dance floor there at the molecular level.

—Roald Hoffmann (1937–)

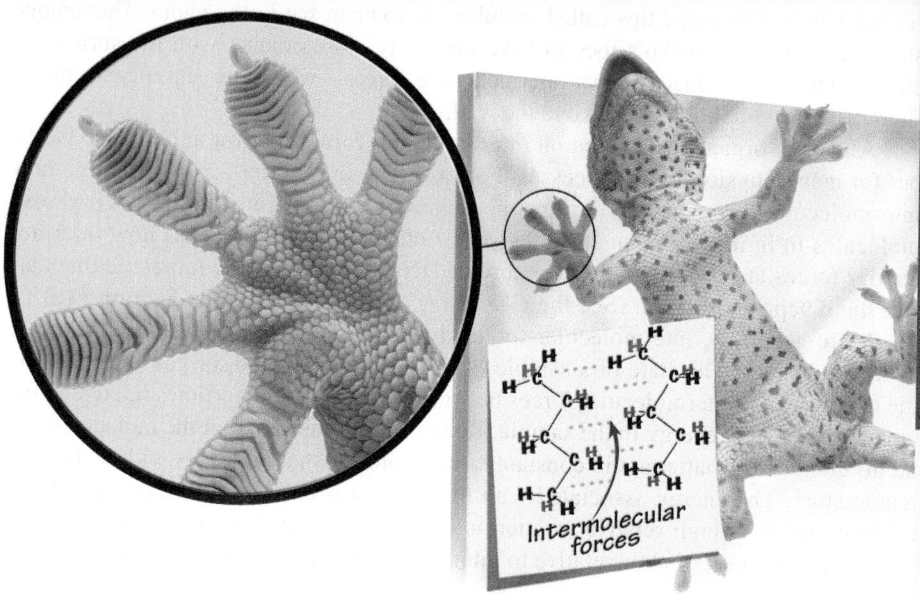

Studies suggest that the gecko's remarkable ability to climb walls and adhere to surfaces depends on intermolecular forces.

MATTER EXISTS PRIMARILY in three states (or phases): solid, liquid, and gas. In Chapter 5, we examined the gas state. In this chapter, we turn to the solid and liquid states, known collectively as the *condensed* states. The solid and liquid states are more similar to each other than they are to the gas state. In the gas state, constituent particles—atoms or molecules—are separated by large distances and therefore do not interact with each other very much. In the condensed states, constituent particles are close together and are more able to feel the moderate to strong attractive forces they have for one another. Unlike the gas state, for which we have a good, simple quantitative model (kinetic molecular theory) to describe and predict behaviour, we have no such model for the condensed states. In fact, modelling the condensed states is an active area of research. In this chapter, we focus primarily on describing the condensed states and their properties and on providing some qualitative guidelines to help us understand those properties.

11.1 Climbing Geckos and Intermolecular Forces

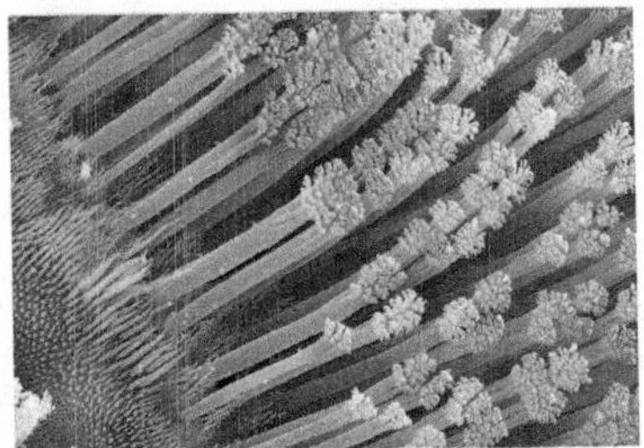

▲ Each of the millions of microhairs on a gecko's feet branches out to end in flattened tips called *spatulae*.

The gecko shown on the previous page can run up a polished glass window in seconds or even walk across a ceiling. It can support its entire weight by a single toe in contact with a surface. How? Work by several scientists points to *intermolecular forces*—attractive forces that exist *between* all molecules and atoms—as the reason that the gecko can perform its gravity-defying feats. Intermolecular forces are the forces that hold liquids and solids—such as water and ice—together.

The key to the gecko's sticky feet lies in the millions of microhairs, called setae, that line its toes. Each seta is between 30 and 130 μm long and branches out to end in several hundred flattened tips called spatulae, as you can see in the photo. This unique structure allows the gecko's toes to have unusually close contact with the surfaces it climbs. The close contact allows intermolecular forces—which are significant only at short distances—to hold the gecko to the wall.

All living organisms depend on intermolecular forces, not for adhesion to walls, but for many physiological processes. For example, in Chapter 22, we examine how intermolecular forces help determine the shapes of protein molecules (the workhorse molecules in living organisms). Later in this chapter, we will discuss how intermolecular forces are central to the structure of DNA, the inheritable molecule that carries the blueprints for life. (See the *Chemistry and Medicine* box in Section 11.3.)

More generally, intermolecular forces are responsible for the very existence of condensed states. The state of a sample of matter—solid, liquid, or gas—depends on the magnitude of intermolecular forces between the constituent particles relative to the amount of thermal energy in the sample. Recall from Chapter 6 that the molecules and atoms composing matter are in constant random motion that increases with increasing temperature. The energy associated with this motion is called *thermal energy*. When thermal energy is high relative to intermolecular forces, matter tends to be gaseous. When thermal energy is low relative to intermolecular forces, matter tends to be liquid or solid.

11.2 Solids, Liquids, and Gases: A Molecular Comparison

We are all familiar with solids and liquids. Water, gasoline, rubbing alcohol, and nail polish remover are common liquids that you have probably encountered. Ice, dry ice, and diamond are familiar solids. To begin to understand the differences between the three common states of matter, examine Table 11.1, which shows the density and molar volume of water in its three different states, along with molecular representations of each state. Notice that the densities of the solid and liquid states are much greater than the density of the gas state. Notice also that the solid and liquid states are more similar in density and molar volume to one another than they are to the gas state. The molecular representations show the reason for these differences. The molecules in liquid water and ice are in close contact with one another—essentially touching—while those in gaseous water are separated by large distances. The molecular representation of gaseous water in Table 11.1 is actually out of proportion—the water molecules in the figure should be much farther apart for their size. (Only a fraction of a molecule could be included in the figure if it were drawn to scale.) From the molar volumes, we know that 18.0 mL of liquid water (slightly more than a tablespoon) would occupy 31.0 L when converted to gas at 100 °C at standard pressure. The low density of gaseous water is a direct result of this large separation between molecules.

Notice also that, for water, the solid is slightly less dense than the liquid. This is *atypical* behaviour. Most solids are slightly denser than their corresponding liquids because the molecules move closer together upon freezing. As we will see in Section 11.9, ice is less dense than liquid water because the unique crystal structure of ice results in water molecules moving slightly further apart upon freezing.

TABLE 11.1 The Three States of Water

Phase	Temperature (°C)	Density ($g\ cm^{-3}$, at 1 bar)	Molar Volume	Molecular View
Gas (steam)	100	5.90×10^{-4}	31.0 L	
Liquid (water)	20	0.998	18.0 mL	
Solid (ice)	0	0.917	19.6 mL	

A major difference between liquids and solids is the freedom of movement of the constituent molecules or atoms. Even though the atoms or molecules in a liquid are in close contact, thermal energy partially overcomes the attractions between them, allowing them to move around one another. This is not the case in solids; the atoms or molecules in a solid are virtually locked in their positions, only vibrating back and forth about a fixed point. The properties of liquids and solids, as well as the properties of gases for comparison, are summarized in Table 11.2.

Liquids assume the shape of their containers because the atoms or molecules that compose liquids are free to flow (or move around one another). When you pour water into a beaker, the water flows and assumes the shape of the beaker (Figure 11.1 ▸). Liquids are not easily compressed because the molecules or atoms that compose them are already in close contact—they cannot be pushed much closer together. The molecules in a gas, by contrast, have a great deal of space between them and are easily forced into a smaller volume by an increase in external pressure (Figure 11.2 ▾).

Solids have a definite shape because, in contrast to liquids and gases, the molecules or atoms that compose solids are fixed in place—each molecule or atom merely vibrates about a fixed point. Like liquids, solids have a definite volume and generally cannot be compressed because the molecules or atoms composing them are already in close

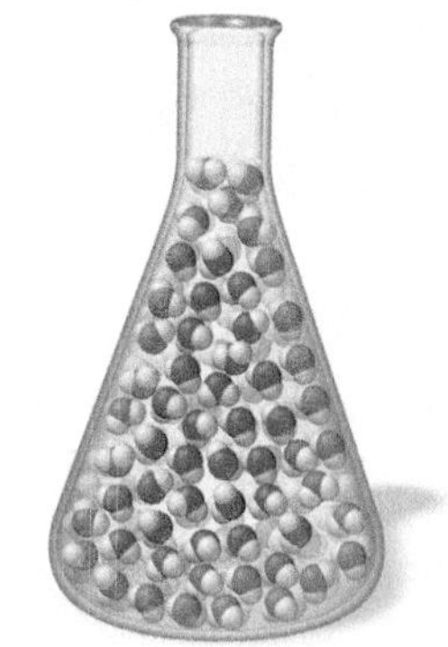

▲ **FIGURE 11.1 Liquids Assume the Shapes of Their Containers** When you pour water into a flask, it assumes the shape of the flask because water molecules are free to flow.

TABLE 11.2 Properties of the States of Matter

State	Density	Shape	Volume	Strength of Intermolecular Forces (Relative to Thermal Energy)
Gas	Low	Indefinite	Indefinite	Weak
Liquid	High	Indefinite	Definite	Moderate
Solid	High	Definite	Definite	Strong

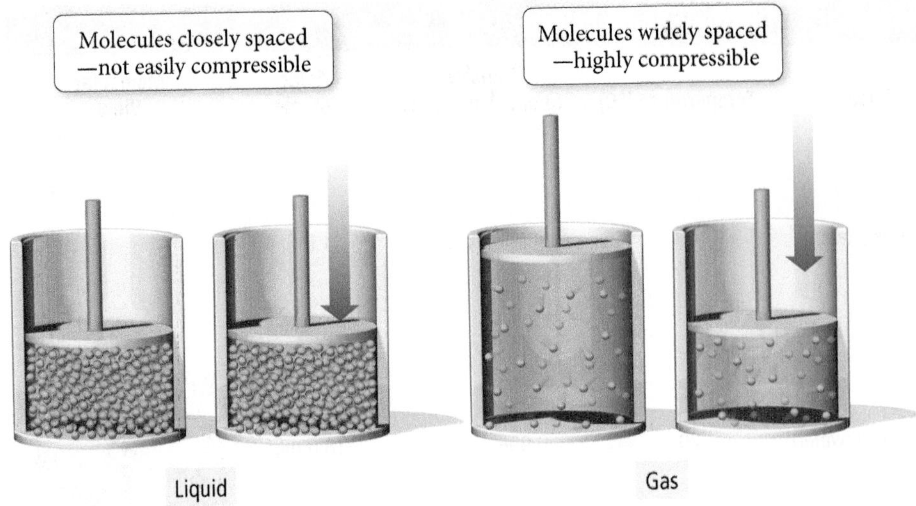

▲ **FIGURE 11.2 Gases Are Compressible** Molecules in a liquid are closely spaced and are not easily compressed. Molecules in a gas have a great deal of space between them, making gases compressible.

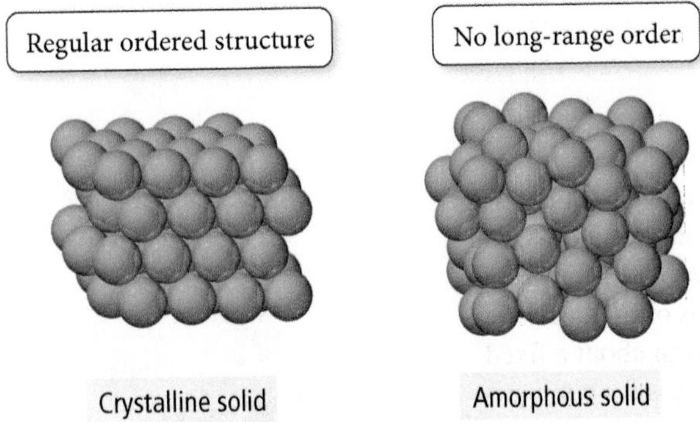

▲ **FIGURE 11.3 Crystalline and Amorphous Solids** In a crystalline solid, the arrangement of the particles displays long-range order. In an amorphous solid, the arrangement of the particles has no long-range order.

contact. Solids may be **crystalline**, in which case the atoms or molecules that compose them are arranged in a well-ordered three-dimensional array, or they may be **amorphous**, in which case the atoms or molecules that compose them have no long-range order (Figure 11.3 ◄).

Changes Between States

We can transform one state of matter to another by changing the temperature, pressure, or both. For example, we can convert solid ice to liquid water by heating, and liquid water to solid ice by cooling. The following diagram shows the three states of matter and the changes in conditions that commonly induce transitions between them:

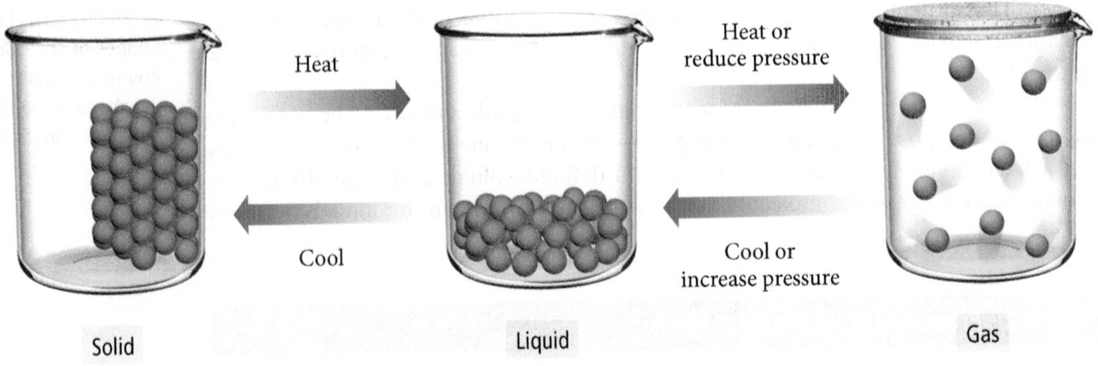

According to some definitions, an amorphous solid is considered a unique state, different from the normal solid state because it lacks any long-range order.

We can induce a transition between the liquid and gas state, not only by heating and cooling, but also through changing the pressure. In general, increases in pressure favour the denser state, so increasing the pressure of a gas sample results in a transition to the liquid state. The most familiar example of this phenomenon occurs in the LP (liquefied petroleum) gas used as a fuel for outdoor grills and lanterns. LP gas is composed primarily of propane, a gas at room temperature and atmospheric pressure. However, it liquefies at pressures exceeding about 2.7 bar. The propane you buy in a tank is under pressure and therefore in the liquid form. When you open the tank, some of the propane escapes as a gas, lowering the pressure in the tank for a brief moment. Immediately, however, some of the liquid propane evaporates, replacing the gas that escaped. Storing gases like propane as liquids is efficient because, in their liquid form, they occupy much less space.

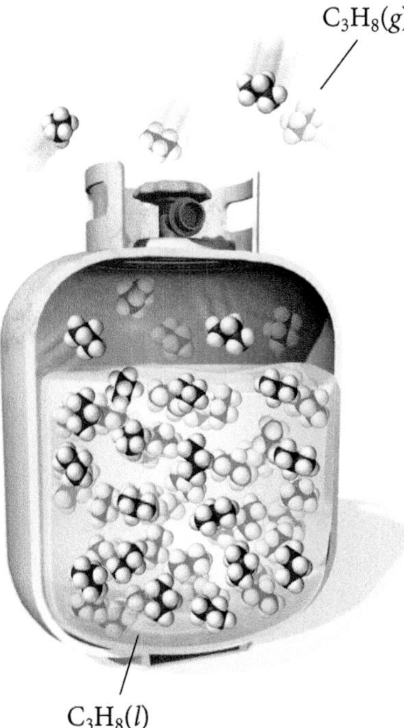

▲ The propane in an LP gas tank is in the liquid state. When you open the tank, some propane vaporizes and escapes as a gas.

CONCEPTUAL CONNECTION 11.1

State Changes

The molecular diagram below shows a sample of liquid water:

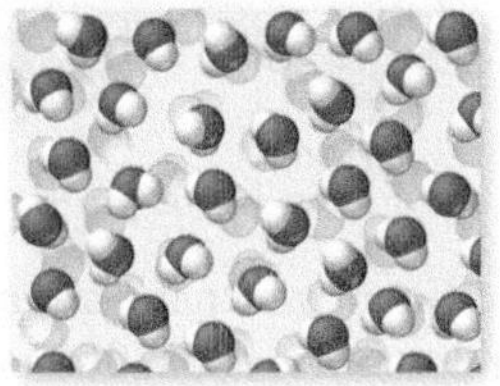

Which diagram best depicts the vapour emitted from a pot of boiling water?

(a)

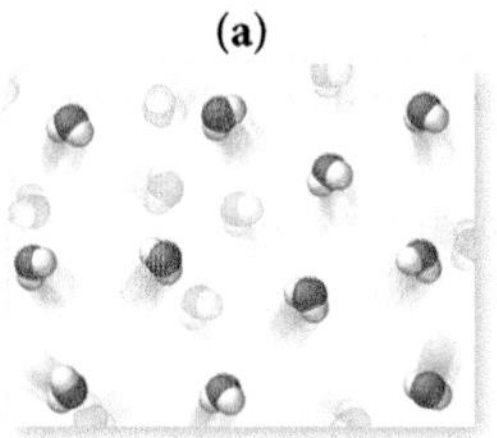

(b)

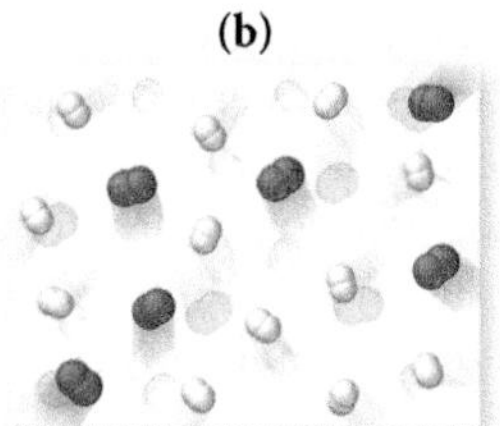

(c)

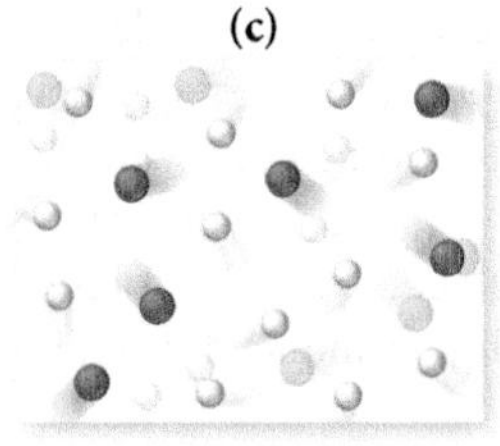

11.3 Intermolecular Forces: The Forces That Hold Condensed States Together

A candle, composed of solid paraffin wax (high-melting-point hydrocarbons), floating on liquid water, surrounded by gases such as nitrogen, oxygen, and carbon dioxide, represents three different phases of matter coexisting at the same temperature. It is the strength of the intermolecular forces between the molecules or atoms that compose a substance that determines the state—solid, liquid, or gas—at a given temperature. At room temperature, strong intermolecular forces, such as those between the wax molecules, tend to result in solids and moderate intermolecular forces, such as those between the water molecules, result in liquids. Weak intermolecular forces that exist between molecules of nitrogen, oxygen, and carbon dioxide result in gases (low melting and boiling points).

▲ Candles made of paraffin wax are solid due to strong intermolecular forces, while the water they are floating in is liquid due to moderate intermolecular forces. The surrounding air is gaseous due to weak intermolecular forces.

Intermolecular forces originate from the interactions between charges, partial charges, and temporary charges on molecules (or atoms and ions), much as bonding forces originate from interactions between charged particles in atoms. Recall from Section 7.7 that according to Coulomb's law, the potential energy (E) of two oppositely charged particles (with charges q_1 and q_2) decreases (becomes more negative) with increasing magnitude of charge and with decreasing separation (r):

$$E = \frac{1}{4\pi\varepsilon_0}\frac{q_1 q_2}{r}$$

When q_1 and q_2 are opposite in sign, E is negative and the energy of the system decreases as the two opposite charges get closer together.

Therefore, as we have seen, protons and electrons are attracted to each other because their potential energy decreases as they get closer together. Similarly, molecules with partial or temporary charges are attracted to each other because *their* potential energy decreases as they get closer together. However, intermolecular forces, even the strongest ones, are generally *much weaker* than bonding forces.

The reason for the relative weakness of intermolecular forces compared to bonding forces is also related to Coulomb's law. Bonding forces are the result of large charges (the charges on protons and electrons) interacting at very close distances. Intermolecular forces are the result of smaller charges (as we shall see in the following discussion) interacting at greater distances. For example, consider the interaction between two water molecules in liquid water:

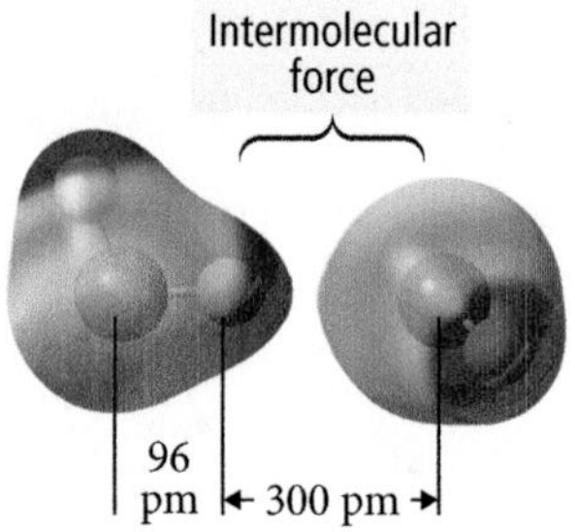

The length of an O—H bond in liquid water is 96 pm; however, the average distance between water molecules in liquid water is about 300 pm. The larger distances between molecules, as well as the smaller charges involved (partial charges on the hydrogen and oxygen atoms), result in weaker forces. To break the O—H bonds in water, you have to heat the water molecules to thousands of degrees Celsius. However, to completely overcome the intermolecular forces *between* water molecules, you have to heat water only to its boiling point, 100 °C (at sea level).

Here, we examine several different types of intermolecular forces, including ion-induced dipole forces, dispersion forces, dipole–dipole forces, hydrogen bonding, dipole-induced dipole forces, and ion–dipole forces.

Ion-Induced Dipole Force

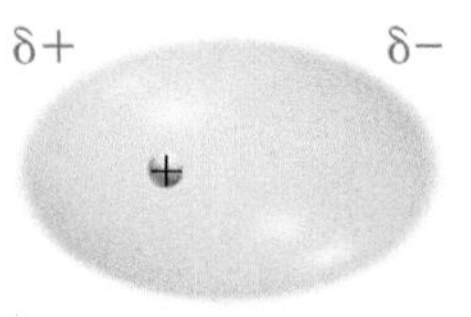

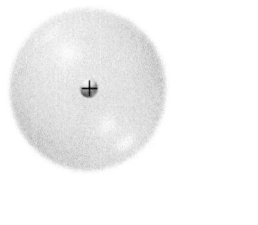

▲ **FIGURE 11.4 Ion-Induced Dipole Interactions** As an ion approaches a nonpolar atom or molecule, it distorts the electron cloud, setting up a small *induced* dipole in the atom or molecule.

When an ion approaches a nonpolar atom or molecule, it can cause a distortion of the negative electron cloud in the nonpolar atom or molecule (Figure 11.4 ◄). Since the electron cloud is distorted to one side of the atom or molecule, it has a small dipole *induced* by the presence of the ion. The magnitude of **ion-induced dipole forces** depends on the charge on the ion and how easily the electrons in the atom or molecule can move or *polarize* (a capability of electron clouds called *polarizability*) in response to the presence of the ion. The magnitude of the polarizability of an atom or molecule is in part dependent on the size (or volume) of the electron cloud. A larger electron cloud results in a greater dispersion force because the electrons are held less tightly by the nucleus and are therefore easier to polarize. We will discuss polarizability more with respect to dispersion forces in the next section. Since there is a large range of polarizabilities of atoms and molecules, the strengths of ion-induced dipole forces have a wide range of values. A typical covalent bond is approximately 400 kJ mol^{-1}, which is considerably larger than ion-induced dipole forces.

Dispersion Force

The nature of dispersion forces was first recognized by Fritz W. London (1900–1954), a German-American physicist.

The one intermolecular force present among all neutral atoms and molecules is the **dispersion force** (also called the London force). As we just saw, the electron clouds of atoms and molecules are polarizable. Dispersion forces are the result of fluctuations in the electron distribution within atoms or molecules in the *absence* of an ion. The electrons in an atom or molecule may, at any one instant, be unevenly distributed. Imagine a frame-by-frame movie of a helium atom in which each "frame" captures the position of the helium atom's two electrons:

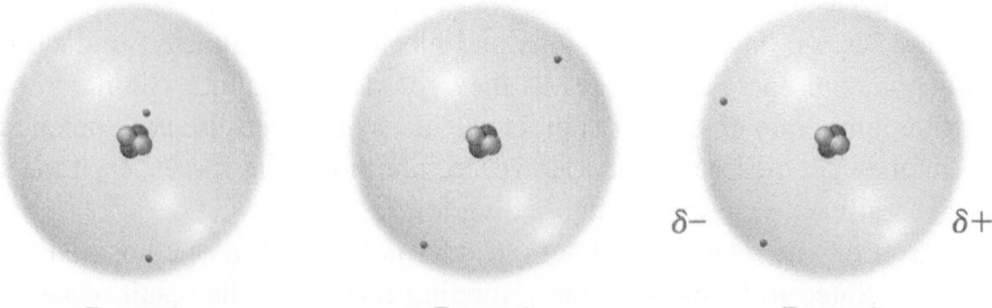

In any one frame, the electrons are not symmetrically arranged around the nucleus. In frame 3, for example, helium's two electrons are on the left side of the helium atom. At that instant, the left side will have a slightly negative charge ($\delta-$). The right side of the atom, which temporarily has no electrons, will have a slightly positive charge ($\delta+$) because of the charge of the nucleus. This fleeting charge separation is called an *instantaneous dipole* or a *temporary dipole*. As shown in Figure 11.5 ▼, an instantaneous dipole on one helium atom induces an instantaneous dipole on its neighbouring atoms because the positive end of the instantaneous dipole attracts electrons in the neighbouring atoms. The neighbouring atoms then attract one another—the positive end of one instantaneous dipole attracting the negative end of another. This attraction is the dispersion force.

An instantaneous dipole on any one helium atom induces instantaneous dipoles on neighbouring atoms, which then attract one another.

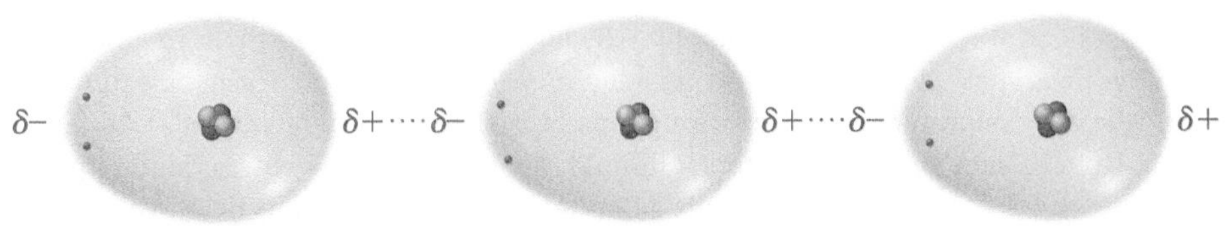

◀ **FIGURE 11.5 Dispersion Interactions** The temporary dipole in one helium atom induces a temporary dipole in its neighbour. The resulting attraction between the positive and negative charges creates the dispersion force.

To *polarize* means to form a dipole moment (see Section 9.7).

Like the ion-induced dipole force, the magnitude of the dispersion force depends on how easily the electrons in the atom or molecule can move or polarize in response to an instantaneous dipole, which partly depends on the size of the electron cloud. A larger electron cloud results in greater dispersion forces because the electrons are held less tightly by the nucleus and therefore are distorted—or polarize—more easily. If all other variables are constant, the dispersion force increases with increasing numbers of electrons, which typically increases the size of the electron cloud. For example, consider the boiling points of the noble gases displayed in Table 11.3. As the number of electrons increases, the volume of the electron cloud increases, and the greater dispersion forces result in increasing boiling points.

The number of electrons alone, however, does not determine the magnitude of the dispersion force. Compare the molar masses and boiling points of the isomeric hydrocarbons pentane and 2,2-dimethylpropane:

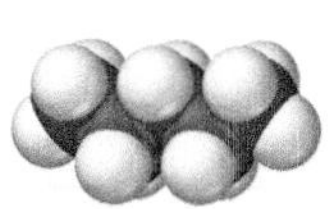

Pentane
42 electrons
boiling point = 36.1 °C

2,2-Dimethylpropane
42 electrons
boiling point = 9.5 °C

These molecules have an identical number of electrons, but pentane has a higher boiling point than 2,2-dimethylpropane. Why? Because the two molecules have different shapes. The pentane molecules are long and can interact with one another along their entire length, as shown in Figure 11.6 (a) ▼. In contrast, the bulky round shape of 2,2-dimethylpropane molecules results in a smaller area of interaction between neighbouring molecules, as shown in Figure 11.6 (b). The result is a lower boiling point for 2,2-dimethylpropane.

TABLE 11.3 Boiling Points of the Noble Gases

Noble Gas	Number of Electrons	Boiling Point (K)
He	2	4.2
Ne	10	27
Ar	18	87
Kr	36	120
Xe	54	165

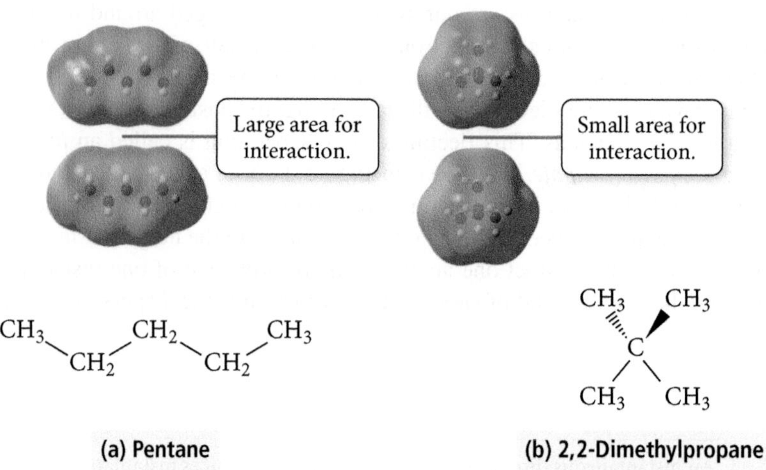

▶ **FIGURE 11.6 Dispersion Force and Molecular Shape** (a) The straight shape of pentane molecules allows them to interact with one another along the entire length of the molecules. (b) The nearly spherical shape of 2,2-dimethylpropane molecules allows for only a small area of interaction. Thus, dispersion forces are weaker in 2,2-dimethylpropane than in pentane, resulting in a lower boiling point.

Dispersion forces are the reason why we can liquefy and freeze the rare gases and small hydrocarbons, albeit at very low temperatures. Dispersion forces can be extremely weak (the dispersion forces between He atoms is 0.01 kJ mol^{-1}), but can also be fairly strong. Both helium and decane interact through dispersion forces, but the boiling point for helium is 4.2 K and that for decane is 446.9 K. Larger hydrocarbons have even higher boiling points.

Although molecular shape and other factors must always be considered in determining the magnitude of dispersion forces, the number of electrons can act as a guide when comparing dispersion forces within a family of similar elements or compounds, as shown in Figure 11.7 ▼.

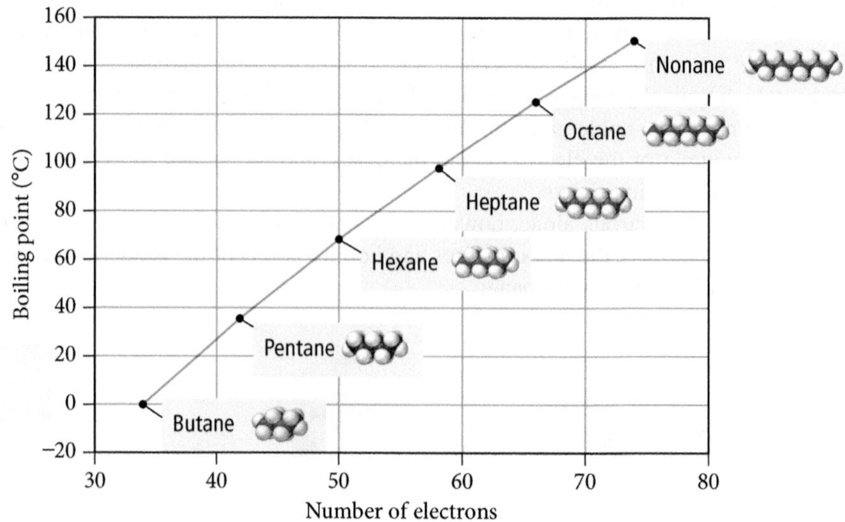

▶ **FIGURE 11.7 Boiling Points of the Alkanes** The boiling points of the alkanes rise with increasing number of electrons and the consequent stronger dispersion forces.

The positive end of a polar molecule is attracted to the negative end of its neighbour.

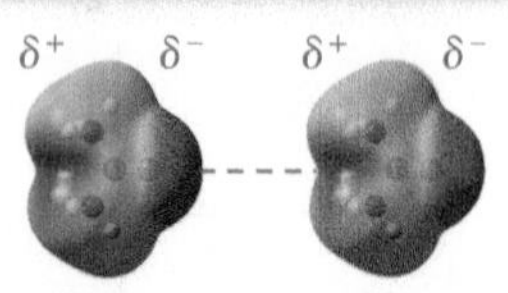

▲ **FIGURE 11.8 Dipole–Dipole Interaction** Molecules with permanent dipoles, such as propanone (acetone) are attracted to one another via dipole–dipole interactions.

Dipole–Dipole Force

Dipole–dipole forces exist in all molecules that are polar. Polar molecules have **permanent dipoles** that interact with the permanent dipoles of neighbouring molecules, as you can see in Figure 11.8 ◀. The positive end of one permanent dipole attracts the negative end of another; this attraction is the dipole–dipole force. Polar molecules, therefore, have higher melting and boiling points than nonpolar molecules with a similar number of electrons or of similar size. Remember that all molecules (including polar ones) have dispersion forces. Polar molecules have, *in addition*, dipole–dipole forces. This additional attractive force raises their melting and boiling points relative to nonpolar molecules with a similar number of electrons. For example, consider methanal and ethene:

See Section 9.6 to review how to determine whether a molecule is polar.

Name	Formula	Number of Electrons	Structure	Electrostatic Potential Map	bp (°C)	mp (°C)
Methanal (Formaldehyde)	CH_2O	16	H₂C=O		−19.3	−92
Ethene	C_2H_4	16	H₂C=CH₂		−104	−169.4

Methanal is polar, and has a higher melting point (mp) and boiling point (bp) than nonpolar ethene, even though the two compounds have the same number of electrons. Figure 11.9 ▼ shows the boiling points of a series of molecules with a similar number of electrons but progressively greater dipole moments. Notice that the boiling points increase with increasing dipole moment.

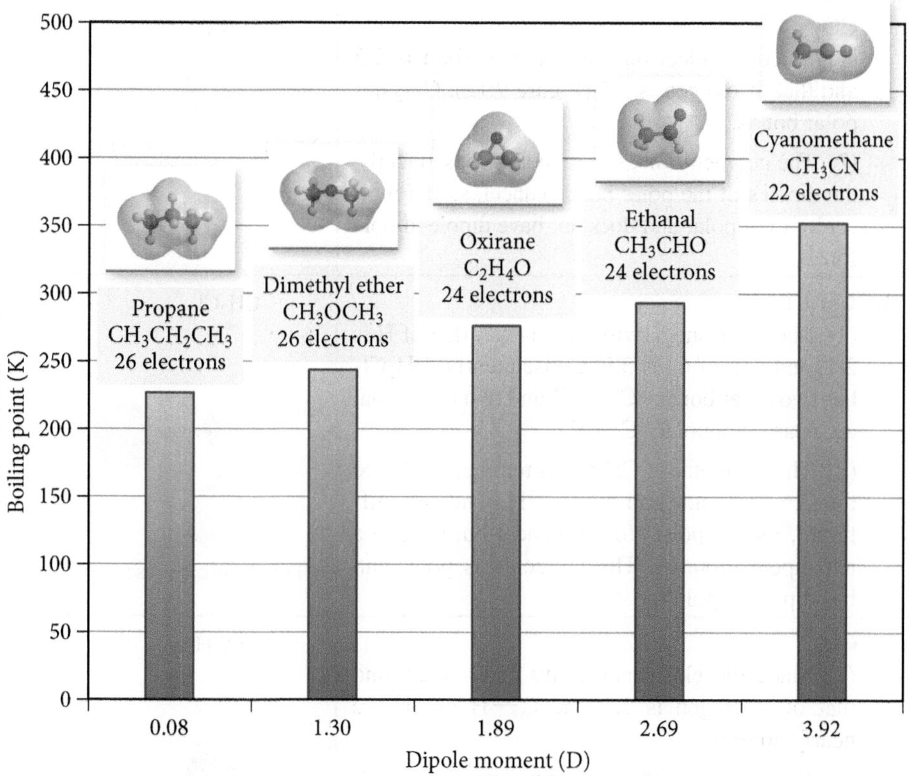

▲ **FIGURE 11.9 Dipole Moment and Boiling Point** The molecules shown here all have similar numbers of electrons but different dipole moments. The boiling points increase with increasing dipole moment.

The polarity of molecules composing liquids is also important in determining the **miscibility**—the ability to mix without separating into two states—of liquids. In general, polar liquids are miscible with other polar liquids but are not miscible with nonpolar liquids. For example, water, a polar liquid, is not miscible with pentane (C_5H_{12}) a nonpolar liquid (Figure 11.10 ▼). Similarly, water and oil (also nonpolar) do not mix. Consequently, oily hands or oily stains on clothes cannot be washed with plain water (see *Chemistry in Your Day: How Soap Works* in Section 10.5).

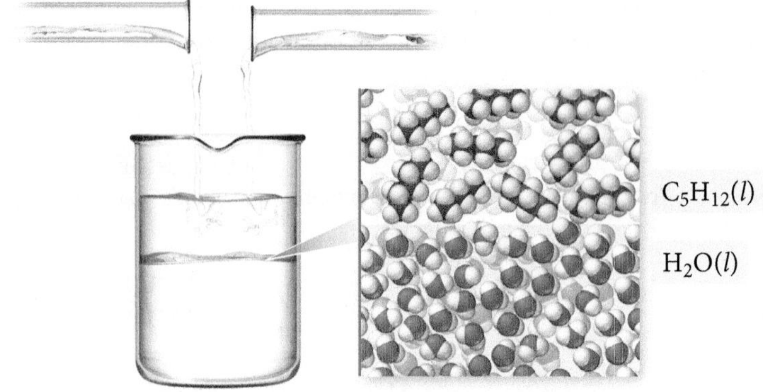

▶ **FIGURE 11.10 Polar and Nonpolar Compounds** Water and pentane do not mix because water molecules are polar and pentane molecules are nonpolar.

EXAMPLE 11.1 DIPOLE–DIPOLE FORCES

Which of these molecules have dipole–dipole forces?

(a) CO_2 **(b)** CH_2Cl_2 **(c)** CH_4

SOLUTION

A molecule has dipole–dipole forces if it is polar. To determine whether a molecule is polar, (1) *determine whether the molecule contains polar bonds*, and (2) *determine whether the polar bonds add together to form a net dipole moment* (Section 9.7).

(a) CO_2

(1) Since the electronegativity of carbon is 2.5 and that of oxygen is 3.5 (Figure 9.12), CO_2 has polar bonds.

(2) The geometry of CO_2 is linear. Consequently, the dipoles of the polar bonds cancel, so the molecule is not polar and does not have dipole–dipole forces.

O=C=O

No dipole forces present.

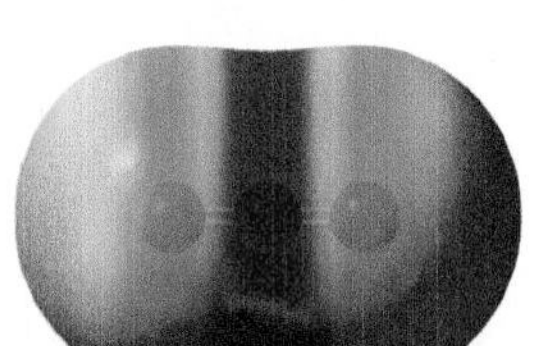

(b) CH_2Cl_2

(1) The electronegativity of C is 2.5, that of H is 2.1, and that of Cl is 3.0. Consequently, CH_2Cl_2 has two polar bonds (C—Cl) and two bonds that are nearly nonpolar (C—H).

(2) The geometry of CH_2Cl_2 is tetrahedral. Since the C—Cl bonds and the C—H bonds are different, their dipoles do not cancel but sum to a net dipole moment. The molecule is polar and has dipole–dipole forces.

CH_2Cl_2

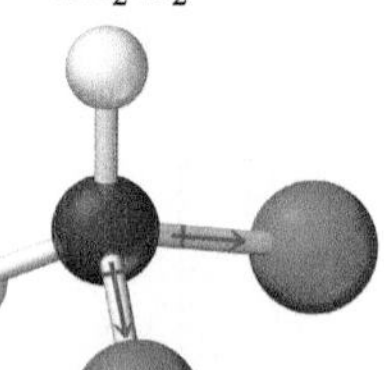

Dipole forces present.

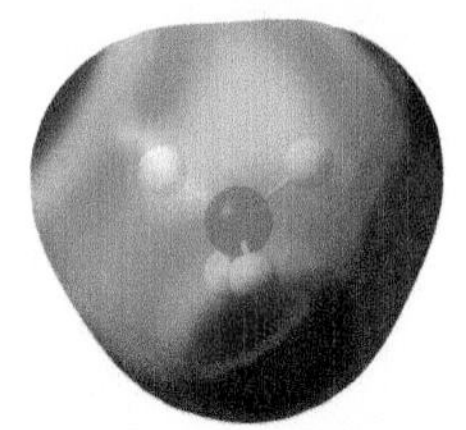

▲ Electrostatic potential maps for CO_2, dichloromethane, and methane.

(c) CH_4

(1) Since the electronegativity of C is 2.5 and that of hydrogen is 2.1, the C—H bonds are nearly nonpolar.

(2) In addition, since the geometry of the molecule is tetrahedral, any slight polarities that the bonds might have will cancel. CH_4 is therefore nonpolar and does not have dipole–dipole forces.

CH_4

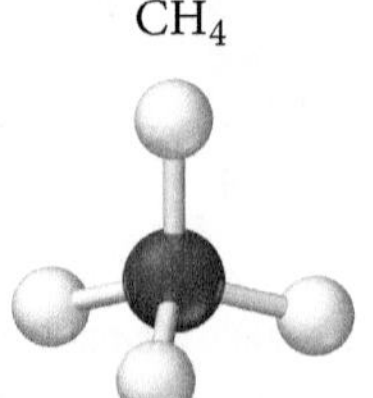

No dipole forces present.

FOR PRACTICE 11.1

Which molecules have dipole–dipole forces?

(a) CI_4 **(b)** CH_3Cl **(c)** HCl

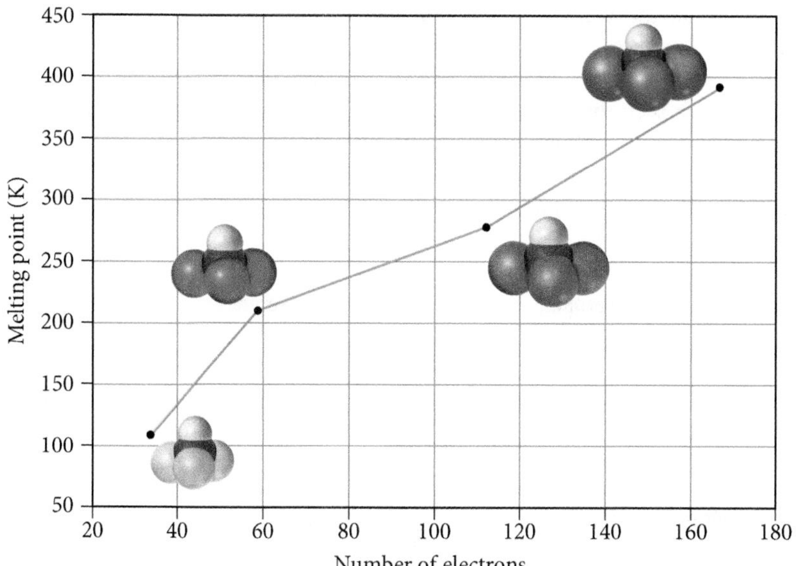

◀ **FIGURE 11.11 Dispersion Forces and Melting Points for the Polar Trihalomethanes** The increasing melting points for the larger trihalomethanes are explained by the increasing dispersion forces for the trihalomethanes with more electrons.

It is important to note that dipole–dipole interactions are not always responsible for trends in physical properties of compounds that might seem related. The dipole moments of the trihalomethanes increase in the following order:

$$CHI_3 \approx CHBr_3 < CHCl_3 < CHF_3$$

However, the melting points increase in the opposite direction: the melting points *increase* as the dipole moments *decrease*. The trend in the melting points for the trihalomethanes can be explained by their increasing dispersion forces. Remember that all atoms and molecules have dispersion forces. In Figure 11.11 ▲, the melting points of the trihalides are plotted against the number of electrons in the molecules. The electron clouds of the larger trihalomethanes are more polarizable, have greater dispersion forces, and therefore have higher melting points.

Hydrogen Bonding

Polar molecules containing hydrogen atoms bonded directly to small electronegative atoms—most importantly fluorine, oxygen, or nitrogen—exhibit an intermolecular force called **hydrogen bonding**. HF, NH_3, and H_2O, for example, all undergo hydrogen bonding. The hydrogen bond is a sort of *super* dipole–dipole force. The large electronegativity difference between hydrogen and any of these electronegative elements causes the hydrogen atom to have a fairly large partial positive charge ($\delta+$) within the bond, while the F, O, or N atom has a fairly large partial negative charge ($\delta-$). In addition, since these atoms are all quite small, the H atom on one molecule can approach the F, O, or N atom on an adjacent molecule very closely. The result is a strong attraction between the H atom on one molecule and the F, O, or N on its neighbour—an attraction called a **hydrogen bond**. For example, in HF, the hydrogen atom in one molecule is strongly attracted to the fluorine atom on a neighbouring molecule (Figure 11.12 ▶).

When H bonds directly to F, O, or N, the bonding atoms acquire relatively large partial charges, giving rise to strong dipole–dipole forces between neighbouring molecules.

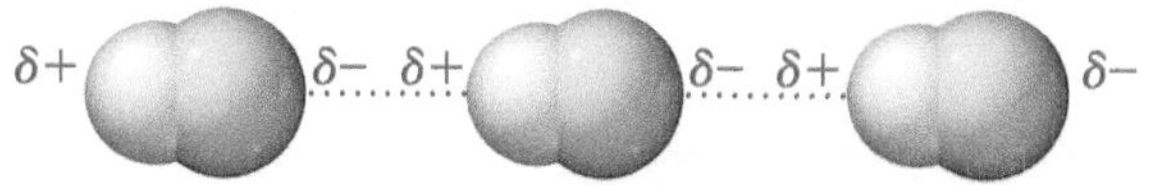

▲ **FIGURE 11.12 Hydrogen Bonding in HF** The hydrogen of one HF molecule, with its partial positive charge, is attracted to the fluorine of its neighbour with its partial negative charge. This dipole–dipole interaction is an example of a hydrogen bond.

Hydrogen bonds should not be confused with chemical bonds. Chemical bonds occur *between individual atoms within a molecule*, whereas hydrogen bonds—like dispersion forces and dipole–dipole forces—are intermolecular forces that occur *between molecules*. Typical hydrogen bonds vary in strength from about 8 to 40 kJ mol^{-1}, much weaker than a typical covalent bond. Weak hydrogen bonds are stronger than the weakest dispersion and dipole–dipole forces, but the strongest dispersion forces can be as strong as what are considered to be the strongest hydrogen bonds. Water—its dominant intermolecular forces being hydrogen bonds—boils at 100 °C, whereas we have seen that larger hydrocarbons have boiling points far in excess of this (see Figure 11.7). For small molecules with similar numbers of electrons, those that form hydrogen bonds have higher melting points. For example, consider the isomeric compounds ethanol and dimethyl ether:

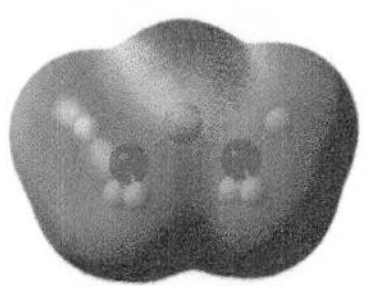

▲ Electrostatic potential maps for ethanol and dimethyl ether.

Name	Formula	Structure		bp (°C)	mp (°C)
Ethanol	C_2H_6O		CH_3CH_2OH	78.3	−114.1
Dimethyl ether	C_2H_6O		CH_3OCH_3	−22.0	−138.5

Since ethanol contains hydrogen bonded directly to oxygen, ethanol molecules form hydrogen bonds with each other, as shown in Figure 11.13 ◄. The hydrogen that is directly bonded to oxygen in an individual ethanol molecule is also strongly attracted to the oxygen on neighbouring molecules. This strong attraction makes the boiling point of ethanol 78.3 °C. Consequently, ethanol is a liquid at room temperature. In contrast, dimethyl ether is an isomer of ethanol but does not exhibit hydrogen bonding because in the dimethyl ether molecule, the oxygen atom is not bonded directly to hydrogen; this results in lower boiling and melting points and dimethyl ether is a gas at room temperature.

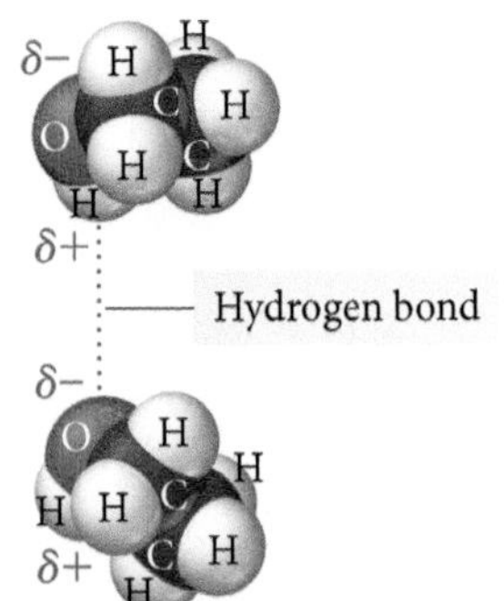

▲ **FIGURE 11.13 Hydrogen Bonding in Ethanol**

Figure 11.14(a) ▼ illustrates hydrogen bonding in water and also depicts the *directionality* of a hydrogen bond. Hydrogen bonds have an orientation to them, unlike other intermolecular interactions. The O—H bond adopts a nearly collinear geometry with the negative end of the molecule to which it is hydrogen bonded. That is, an O—H—O angle is nearly 180° for a hydrogen bond. On the other hand, if there were only dipole–dipole interactions between water molecules, the negative end of one water molecule would line up with the positive end of a neighbouring water molecule (Figure 11.14(b)). Figure 11.15 ► shows the boiling points of the simple hydrides of group 14, 15, and 16 elements, plotted against the period in which the central element occurs. For the group 14 hydrides, the boiling points increase as you go down the periodic table because of the stronger dispersion forces due to the increase in the number of electrons and, therefore, the polarizability. A similar trend holds for the group 15 and 16 elements, except for the hydrides containing nitrogen and oxygen, respectively. Because of hydrogen bonding, the boiling points of ammonia and water are much higher than expected based on their polarizability.

One might ask why water has a higher boiling point than ammonia. Water is special in that it has two lone pairs to accept hydrogen bonds and two O—H bonds to act as donors. Therefore, water can participate in four hydrogen bonds simultaneously. Since each water molecule can form four hydrogen bonds, each water molecule is effectively

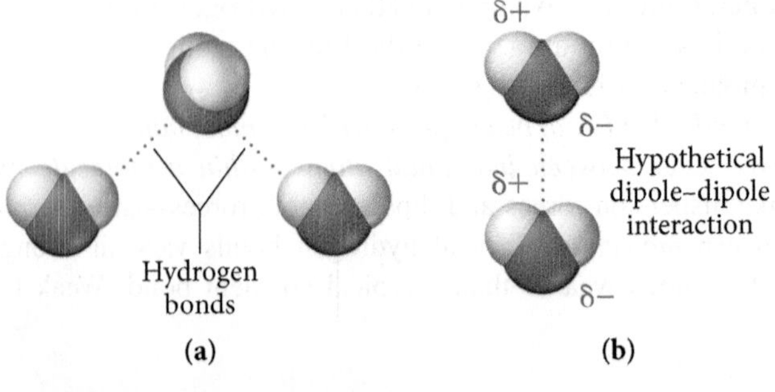

► **FIGURE 11.14 Hydrogen Bonds Versus Dipole–Dipole Interactions** Hydrogen bonds in water (**a**) are almost collinear along an O—H—O axis, whereas a dipole–dipole interaction between two water molecules (**b**), which is hypothetical, would have the positive end of one water molecule lined up with the negative end of an adjacent water molecule.

EXAMPLE 11.2 **HYDROGEN BONDING**

One of these compounds is a liquid at room temperature. Which one and why?

H—C(=O)—H Methanal

H—C(H)(H)—F Fluoromethane

H—O—O—H Hydrogen peroxide

SOLUTION

The three compounds have similar numbers of electrons:

Methanal	16 electrons
Fluoromethane	18 electrons
Hydrogen peroxide	18 electrons

So, the strengths of their dispersion forces are similar. All three compounds are also polar, so they have dipole–dipole forces. Hydrogen peroxide, however, is the only one of these compounds that also contains H bonded directly to F, O, or N. Therefore, it also has hydrogen bonding and is likely to have the highest boiling point of the three. Since the example stated that only one of the compounds was a liquid, we can safely assume that hydrogen peroxide is the liquid. Note that although fluoromethane *contains* both H and F, H is not *directly bonded* to F, so fluoromethane does not have hydrogen bonding as an intermolecular force. Similarly, methanal *contains* both H and O, but H is not *directly bonded* to O, so formaldehyde does not have hydrogen bonding, either.

FOR PRACTICE 11.2

Which has the higher boiling point: HF or HCl? Why?

hydrogen bonded to four other water molecules, which in turn are hydrogen bonded to four other water molecules. Ammonia has only one lone pair with which to accept a hydrogen bond, limiting the amount of hydrogen bonding it can participate in. Without hydrogen bonding in water, due to the high electronegativity of oxygen, and without the ability of water to participate in four hydrogen bonds (two as a donor and two as an acceptor), all the water on our planet would be gaseous.

Dipole-Induced Dipole Force

Dipole-induced dipole forces are between molecules that have a permanent dipole and an atom or molecule that is nonpolar (Figure 11.16 ▼). These intermolecular interactions occur in mixtures and are important when we discuss solutions in Chapter 12. When a nonpolar atom or molecule and a molecule with a permanent dipole approach one another, the negative or positive end of the polar molecule distorts or polarizes the electron cloud of the nonpolar atom or molecule. Since the nonpolar atom or molecule now has a small induced dipole, it can interact with the polar molecule. The magnitude of these interactions depends on the size of the dipole of the polar molecule and the polarizability of the nonpolar atom or molecule.

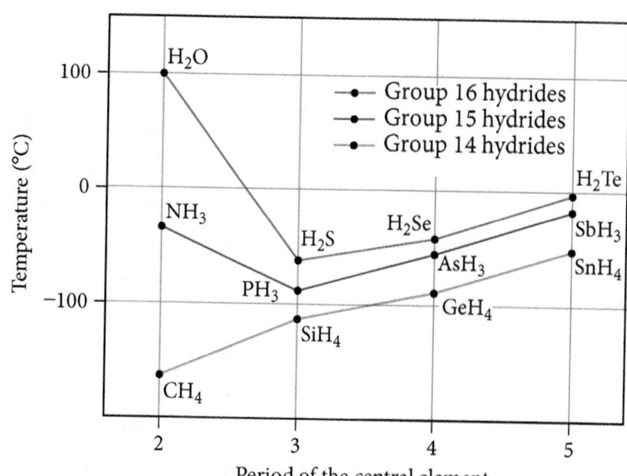

▲ **FIGURE 11.15 Boiling Points of Group 14, 15, and 16 Hydrides** Because of hydrogen bonding, the boiling points of water and ammonia are anomalous compared to the boiling points of the other hydrogen-containing compounds.

Ion–Dipole Force

The **ion–dipole force** occurs when an ionic compound is mixed with a polar compound; it is especially important in aqueous solutions of ionic compounds. For example, when sodium chloride is mixed with water, the sodium and chloride ions interact with water molecules via ion–dipole forces, as shown in Figure 11.17 ▼.

▶ **FIGURE 11.16 Dipole-Induced Dipole Forces**

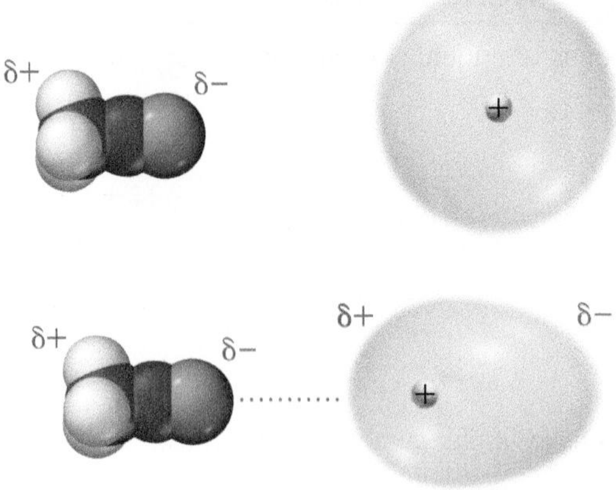

The positive sodium ions interact with the negative poles of water molecules, while the negative chloride ions interact with the positive poles. Ion–dipole forces are the strongest of the types of intermolecular forces discussed here and are responsible for the ability of ionic substances to form solutions with water. We discuss aqueous solutions more thoroughly in Chapter 12.

▶ **FIGURE 11.17 Ion–Dipole Forces** Ion–dipole forces exist between Na^+ and the negative ends of H_2O molecules and between Cl^- and the positive ends of H_2O molecules.

The positively charged end of a polar molecule such as H_2O is attracted to negative ions and the negatively charged end of the molecule is attracted to positive ions.

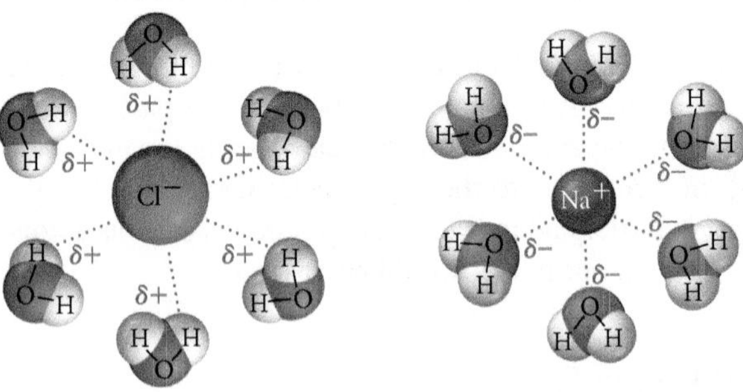

Summarizing Intermolecular Forces (as shown in Table 11.4):

- Ion-induced dipole forces occur between an ion and a nonpolar molecule, as in a dilute solution of an ionic compound in a nonpolar solvent.
- Dispersion forces are present between all molecules and atoms. These forces are weak between small atoms or molecules, but can be significant when the molecule or atom has a large number of electrons.
- Dipole–dipole forces occur between polar molecules.
- Hydrogen bonds are present in molecules containing hydrogen bonded directly to fluorine, oxygen, or nitrogen.
- Dipole-induced dipole forces occur in dilute mixtures of polar and nonpolar molecules.
- Ion–dipole forces are present in mixtures of ionic compounds and polar compounds. They can be very strong, and are especially important in aqueous solutions of ionic compounds.

TABLE 11.4 Types of Intermolecular Forces

Type	Present in	Molecular Perspective
Ion-induced dipole	Dilute mixtures of ionic compounds and nonpolar molecules	+ ···· $\delta-$ $\delta+$
Dispersion	All molecules and atoms	$\delta-$ $\delta+$ ···· $\delta-$ $\delta+$
Dipole–dipole	Polar molecules	$\delta+$ $\delta-$ ····· $\delta+$ $\delta-$
Hydrogen bonding	Molecules containing H bonded to F, O, or N	$\delta+$ $\delta+$ $\delta-$ $\delta+$ $\delta-$ $\delta-$
Dipole-induced dipole	Mixtures of polar and nonpolar molecules	$\delta+$ $\delta-$ ···· $\delta-$ $\delta+$
Ion–dipole	Mixtures of ionic compounds and polar compounds	$\delta-$ $\delta-$ $\delta-$ + $\delta-$ $\delta-$ $\delta-$

CHEMISTRY AND MEDICINE Hydrogen Bonding in DNA

DNA is a long, chain-like molecule that acts as a blueprint for each living organism. Copies of DNA are passed from parent to offspring, which is how we inherit traits from our parents. A DNA molecule is composed of thousands of repeating units called *nucleotides* (Figure 11.18 ▼). Each nucleotide contains one of four different *organic bases*: adenine, thymine, cytosine, and guanine (abbreviated A, T, C, and G). The order of these bases along the DNA encodes the information that determines the nature of the proteins that are made in the body (proteins are the molecules that do most of the work in living organisms). Our proteins, in turn, determine many of our

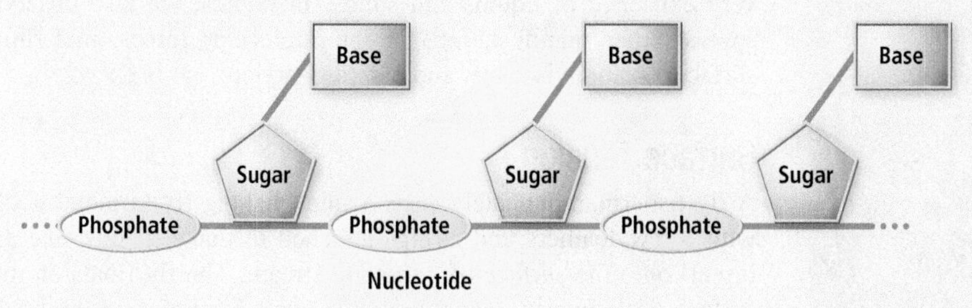

◀ **FIGURE 11.18 Nucleotides** The individual units in a DNA polymer are called nucleotides. Each nucleotide contains one of four bases: adenine, thymine, cytosine, and guanine.

(continued)

CHEMISTRY AND MEDICINE *(Continued)*

characteristics, including how we look, what diseases we are at risk of developing, and even our behaviour.

The replicating mechanism of DNA is related to its structure, which was discovered in 1953 by James Watson and Francis Crick. DNA consists of two *complementary* strands, wrapped around each other in the now famous double helix and linked by hydrogen bonds between the bases on each strand. Each base (A, T, C, and G) has a complementary partner with which it forms hydrogen bonds (Figure 11.19 ►): adenine (A) with thymine (T) and cytosine (C) with guanine (G). The hydrogen bonding is so specific that each base will pair only with its complementary partner. When a cell is going to divide, enzymes unzip the DNA molecule across the hydrogen bonds that join its two strands (Figure 11.20 ▼). Then new bases, complementary to the bases in each strand, are added along each of the original strands, forming hydrogen bonds with their complements. The result is two identical copies of the original DNA.

▲ **FIGURE 11.19 Complementary Base Pairing via Hydrogen Bonds** The individual bases in DNA interact with one another via specific hydrogen bonds that form between A and T and between C and G.

Question

Why would dispersion forces not work as a way to hold the two strands of DNA together? Why would covalent bonds not work?

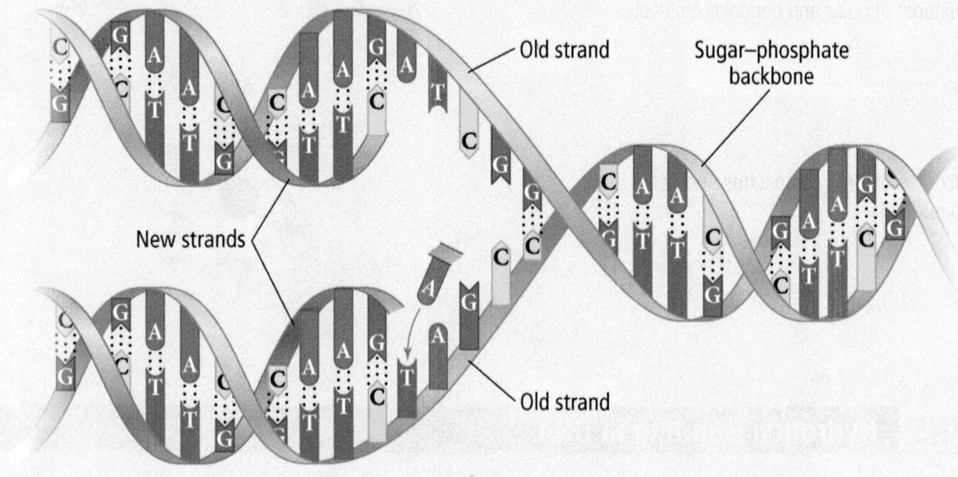

◄ **FIGURE 11.20 Copying DNA** The two strands of the DNA molecule can "unzip" by breaking the hydrogen bonds that join the base pairs. New bases complementary to the bases of each strand are assembled and joined together. The result is two molecules, each identical to the original one.

11.4 Intermolecular Forces in Action: Surface Tension, Viscosity, and Capillary Action

▲ A trout fly can float on water because of surface tension.

The most important manifestation of intermolecular forces is the very existence of liquids and solids. In liquids, we also observe several other manifestations of intermolecular forces, including surface tension, viscosity, and capillary action.

Surface Tension

A fly fisherman delicately casts a small fishing fly (a metal hook with a few feathers and strings attached to make it look like an insect) onto the surface of a moving stream. The fly floats on the surface of the water—even though the metal composing the hook is denser than water—and attracts trout. Why? The hook floats because of *surface tension*, the tendency of liquids to minimize their surface area.

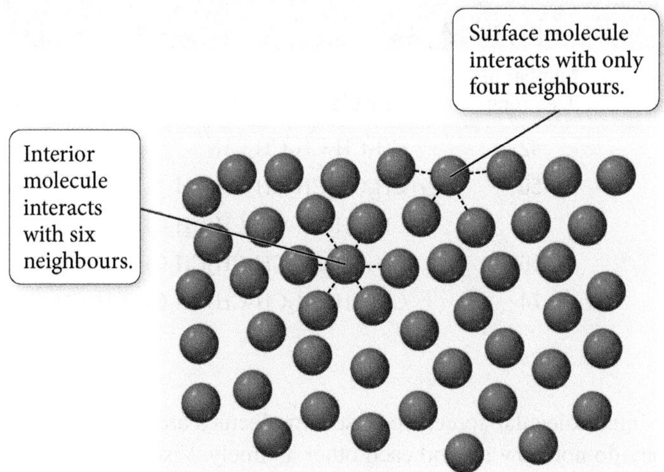
Surface molecule interacts with only four neighbours.
Interior molecule interacts with six neighbours.

◀ **FIGURE 11.21 The Origin of Surface Tension** Molecules at the liquid surface have a higher potential energy than those in the interior. As a result, liquids tend to minimize their surface area, and the surface behaves like a membrane or "skin."

We can understand surface tension by examining Figure 11.21 ▲, which depicts the intermolecular forces experienced by a molecule at the surface of the liquid compared to those experienced by a molecule in the interior. Notice that a molecule at the surface has relatively fewer neighbours with which to interact, and is therefore inherently less stable—it has higher potential energy—than those in the interior. (Remember that the attractive interactions with other molecules lower potential energy.) In order to increase the surface area of the liquid, molecules from the interior have to be moved to the surface, and, since molecules at the surface have a higher potential energy than those in the interior, this movement requires energy. Therefore, liquids tend to minimize their surface area. The **surface tension** of a liquid is the energy required to increase the surface area by a unit amount. For example, at room temperature, water has a surface tension of 72.8 mJ m^{-1}—it takes 72.8 mJ to increase the surface area of water by one square metre.

Recall from Section 11.3 that the interactions between molecules lower their potential energy in much the same way that the interaction between protons and electrons lowers their potential energy, in accordance with Coulomb's law.

Why does surface tension allow the fly fisherman's hook to float on water? The tendency for liquids to minimize their surface creates a kind of skin at the surface that resists penetration. For the fisherman's hook to sink into the water, the water's surface area must increase slightly—an increase that is resisted by the surface tension. You can observe surface tension by carefully placing a paper clip on the surface of water (Figure 11.22 ▶). The paper clip, even though it is denser than water, will float on the surface of the water. A slight tap on the clip will provide the energy necessary to overcome the surface tension and cause the clip to sink.

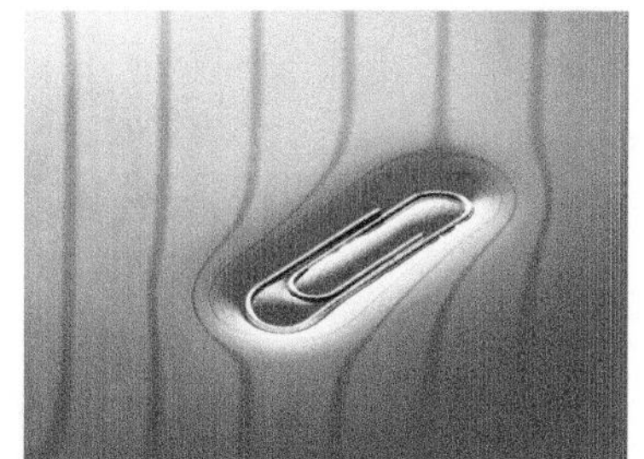

▲ **FIGURE 11.22 Surface Tension in Action** A paper clip floats on water due to surface tension.

Surface tension decreases as the strength of the intermolecular forces decrease. You can't float a paper clip on benzene, for example, because the dispersion forces among the molecules composing benzene are significantly weaker than the hydrogen bonds among water molecules. The surface tension of benzene is only 28 mJ m^{-1}—just 40% that of water.

Surface tension is also the reason that small water droplets (those not large enough to be distorted by gravity) form nearly perfect spheres. On the Space Shuttle, the complete absence of gravity allows even large samples of water to form nearly perfect spheres (Figure 11.23 ▶). Why? Just as gravity pulls the matter of a planet or star inward to form a sphere, so intermolecular forces among collections of water molecules pull the water into a sphere. A sphere is the geometrical shape with the smallest surface-area-to-volume ratio; therefore, the formation of a sphere minimizes the number of molecules at the surface, thus minimizing the potential energy of the system.

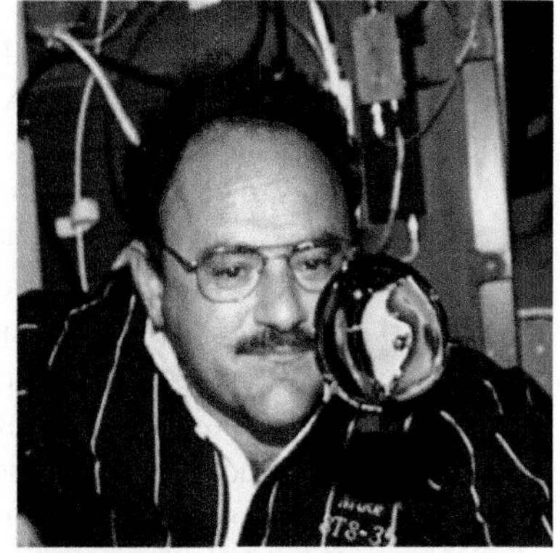

▲ **FIGURE 11.23 Spherical Water Droplets** On the Space Shuttle in orbit, under weightless conditions, water coalesces into nearly perfect spheres held together by intermolecular forces between water molecules.

Viscosity

Another manifestation of intermolecular forces is **viscosity**, the resistance of a liquid to flow. Motor oil, for example, is more viscous than gasoline, and maple syrup is more viscous than water. The SI unit of viscocity is the Pa s, but it is usually reported in a unit called the poise (P), defined as 1 g cm^{-1} s^{-1} (1 P $=$ 0.1 Pa s). The viscosity of water at room temperature is approximately one centipoise (cP). Viscosity is greater in substances

TABLE 11.5 Viscosity of Several Hydrocarbons at 20 °C

Hydrocarbon	Number of Electrons	Formula	Viscosity (cP)
Pentane	42	$CH_3CH_2CH_2CH_2CH_3$	0.240
Hexane	50	$CH_3CH_2CH_2CH_2CH_2CH_3$	0.326
Heptane	58	$CH_3CH_2CH_2CH_2CH_2CH_2CH_3$	0.409
Octane	66	$CH_3CH_2CH_2CH_2CH_2CH_2CH_2CH_3$	0.542
Nonane	74	$CH_3CH_2CH_2CH_2CH_2CH_2CH_2CH_2CH_3$	0.711

with stronger intermolecular forces because if molecules are more strongly attracted to each other, they do not flow around each other as freely. Viscosity also depends on molecular shape, increasing in longer molecules that can interact over a greater area and possibly become entangled. Table 11.5 lists the viscosity of several hydrocarbons. Notice the increase in viscosity with increasing numbers of electrons (and therefore increasing magnitude of dispersion forces) and with increasing length (and therefore increasing potential for molecular entanglement).

Viscosity also depends on temperature because thermal energy partially overcomes the intermolecular forces, allowing molecules to flow past each other more easily. Table 11.6 lists the viscosity of water as a function of temperature. Nearly all liquids become less viscous as temperature increases.

TABLE 11.6 Viscosity of Liquid Water at Several Temperatures

Temperature (°C)	Viscosity (cP)
20	1.002
40	0.653
60	0.467
80	0.355
100	0.282

Capillary Action

Medical technicians often take advantage of **capillary action**—the ability of a liquid to flow against gravity up a narrow tube—when taking a blood sample. The technician pokes the patient's finger with a pin, squeezes some blood out of the puncture, and then

CHEMISTRY IN YOUR DAY Viscosity and Motor Oil

Viscosity is an important property of the motor oil you put into your car. The oil must be thick enough to adequately coat engine surfaces to lubricate them, but also thin enough to be pumped easily into all the required engine compartments. Motor oil viscosity is usually reported on a scale called the SAE scale (named after the Society of Automotive Engineers). The higher the SAE rating, the more viscous the oil. The thinnest motor oils have SAE ratings of 5 or 10, while the thickest have SAE ratings of up to 50. Before the 1950s, most automobile owners changed the oil in their engine to accommodate seasonal changes in weather—a higher SAE rating was required in the summer months and a lower rating in the winter. Today, the advent of multigrade oils allows car owners in many climates to keep the same oil all year long. Multigrade oils, such as the 10W-40 oil shown here, contain polymers (long molecules made up of repeating structural units) that coil at low temperatures but unwind at high temperatures. At low temperatures, the coiled polymers—because of their compact shape—do not contribute very much to the oil's viscosity. As the temperature increases, however, the molecules unwind and their long shape results in intermolecular forces and molecular entanglements that prevent the viscosity from decreasing as much as it would normally. The result is an oil whose viscosity is less temperature dependent than it would be otherwise, allowing the same oil to be used over a wider range of temperatures. It is a good idea to understand what a rating such as 10W-40 means. First, *W* stands for winter grade and is a cold-temperature specification. *10W* means that it has a viscosity corresponding to a maximum of 10 on the SAE scale at low temperatures. In colder climates, it is better to use oil with a 5W rating because it is even less viscous at cold temperatures (like early in the morning when you want to start the car). The second rating, *40* for example, means that the viscosity of the oil is a maximum of 40 on the SAE scale at higher temperatures when the oil molecules are unwound.

collects the blood with a thin tube. When the tube's tip comes into contact with the blood, the blood is drawn into the tube by capillary action. The same force plays a role in the way that trees and plants draw water from the soil.

Capillary action results from a combination of two forces: the attraction between molecules in a liquid, called *cohesive forces*, and the attraction between these molecules and the surface of the tube, called *adhesive forces*. The adhesive forces cause the liquid to spread out over the surface of the tube, while the cohesive forces cause the liquid to stay together. If the adhesive forces are greater than the cohesive forces (as is the case for water in a glass tube), the attraction to the surface draws the liquid up the tube and the cohesive forces pull along those molecules not in direct contact with the tube walls (Figure 11.24 ▸). The water rises up the tube until the force of gravity balances the capillary action—the thinner the tube, the higher the rise. If the adhesive forces are smaller than the cohesive forces (as is the case for liquid mercury), the liquid does not rise up the tube at all (and, in fact, will drop to a level below the level of the surrounding liquid).

The result of the differences in the relative magnitudes of cohesive and adhesive forces can be seen by comparing the meniscus of water to the meniscus of mercury (Figure 11.25 ▸). (The meniscus is the curved shape of a liquid surface within a tube.) The meniscus of water is concave (rounded inward) because the *adhesive forces* are greater than the cohesive forces, causing the edges of the water to creep up the sides of the tube a bit, forming the familiar cupped shape. The meniscus of mercury is convex (rounded outward) because the *cohesive forces*—due to metallic bonding between the atoms—are greater than the adhesive forces. The mercury atoms crowd toward the interior of the liquid to maximize their interactions with each other, resulting in the upward bulge at the centre of the surface.

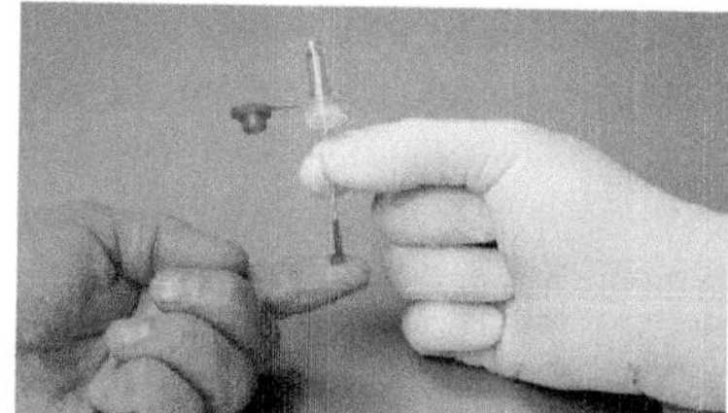

▲ Blood is drawn into a capillary tube by capillary action.

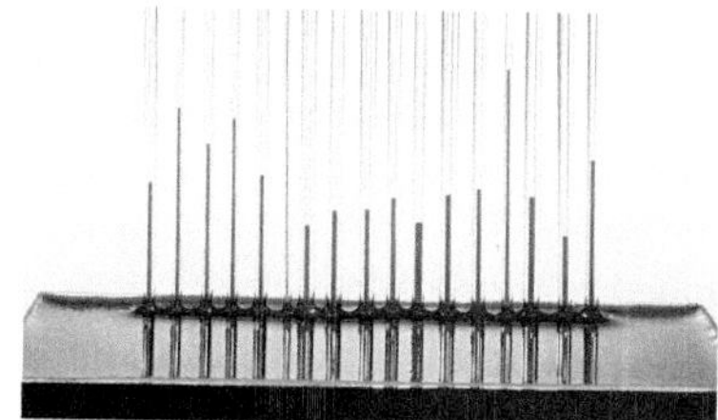

▲ **FIGURE 11.24 Capillary Action** The attraction of water molecules to the glass surface draws the liquid around the edge of the tube up the walls. The water in the rest of the column is pulled along by the attraction of water molecules to one another. As can be seen above, the narrower the tube, the higher the liquid will rise.

▲ **FIGURE 11.25 Meniscuses of Water and Mercury** The meniscus of water (dyed red for visibility at left) is concave because water molecules are more strongly attracted to the glass wall than to one another. The meniscus of mercury (right) is convex because mercury atoms are more strongly attracted to one another than to the glass walls.

11.5 Vaporization and Vapour Pressure

We now turn our attention to vaporization, the process by which thermal energy can overcome intermolecular forces and produce a state change from liquid to gas. We will first discuss the process of vaporization itself, then the energetics of vaporization, and finally the concepts of vapour pressure, dynamic equilibrium, and critical point. Vaporization is a common occurrence that we experience every day—and even depend on—to maintain proper body temperature.

The Process of Vaporization

Imagine water molecules in a beaker at room temperature and open to the atmosphere (Figure 11.26 ▾). The molecules are in constant motion due to thermal energy. If you could actually see the molecules at the surface, you would witness what Roald Hoffmann described as a "wild dance floor" (see the chapter-opening quote) because of all the vibrating, jostling, and molecular movement. *The higher the temperature, the greater the average energy of the collection of molecules.* However, at any one time, some molecules would have more thermal energy than the average and some would have less.

The distributions of thermal energies for the molecules in a sample of water at two different temperatures

◂ **FIGURE 11.26 Vaporization of Water** Some molecules in an open beaker have enough kinetic energy to vaporize from the surface of the liquid.

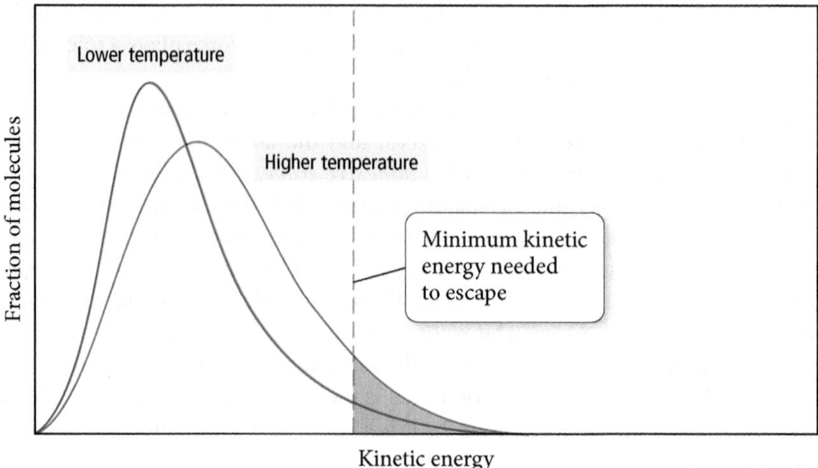

▶ **FIGURE 11.27 Distribution of Thermal Energy** The thermal energies of the molecules in a liquid are distributed over a range. The peak energy increases with increasing temperature.

are shown in Figure 11.27 ▲. The molecules at the high end of the distribution curve have enough energy to break free from the surface—where molecules are held less tightly than in the interior due to fewer neighbour–neighbour interactions—and into the gas state. This transition, from liquid to gas, is called **vaporization**. Some of the water molecules in the gas state, at the low end of the energy distribution curve for the gaseous molecules, may plunge back into the water and be captured by intermolecular forces. This transition, from gas to liquid, is the opposite of vaporization and is called **condensation**.

Although both evaporation and condensation occur in a beaker open to the atmosphere, under normal conditions, evaporation takes place at a greater rate because most of the newly evaporated molecules escape into the surrounding atmosphere and never come back. The result is a noticeable decrease in the water level within the beaker over time (usually several days).

What happens if we increase the temperature of the water within the beaker? Because of the shift in the energy distribution to higher energies (see Figure 11.27), more molecules now have enough energy to break free and evaporate, so vaporization occurs more quickly. What happens if we spill the water on the table or floor? The same amount of water is now spread over a wider area, resulting in more molecules at the surface of the liquid. Since molecules at the surface have the greatest tendency to evaporate—because they are held less tightly—vaporization also occurs more quickly in this case. You probably know from experience that water in a beaker or glass may take many days to evaporate completely, while the same amount of water spilled on a table or floor typically evaporates within a few hours (depending on the exact conditions).

See Chapter 6 to review endothermic and exothermic processes.

What happens if the liquid in the beaker is not water, but some other substance with weaker intermolecular forces, such as acetone (the main component in nail polish remover)? The weaker intermolecular forces allow more molecules to evaporate at a given temperature, again increasing the rate of vaporization. We call liquids that vaporize easily **volatile**, and those that do not vaporize easily **nonvolatile**. Acetone is more volatile than water. Motor oil is virtually nonvolatile at room temperature.

Summarizing the Process of Vaporization:

- ▶ The rate of vaporization increases with increasing temperature.
- ▶ The rate of vaporization increases with increasing surface area.
- ▶ The rate of vaporization increases with decreasing strength of intermolecular forces.

The Energetics of Vaporization

To understand the energetics of vaporization, consider again a beaker of water from the molecular point of view, except now let's imagine that the beaker is thermally insulated so that heat from the surroundings cannot enter the beaker. What happens to the temperature of the water left in the beaker as molecules evaporate? To answer this question, think about the energy distribution curve again (see Figure 11.27). The molecules that leave the beaker are the ones at the high end of the energy curve—the most energetic. If no additional heat enters the beaker, the average energy of the entire collection of molecules goes down—much as the average age on a sports team goes down if the oldest veterans retire. So, vaporization is an *endothermic* process: it takes energy to vaporize the molecules in a liquid. Another way to understand the endothermicity of vaporization is to remember that vaporization requires overcoming the intermolecular forces that hold liquids together. Since energy is needed to pull the molecules away from one another, the process is endothermic.

▲ When you sweat, water evaporates from the skin. Since evaporation is endothermic, the result is a cooling effect.

Our bodies use the endothermic nature of vaporization for cooling. When you overheat, you sweat, causing your skin to be covered with liquid water. As this water evaporates, it absorbs heat from your body, cooling your skin. A fan makes you feel cooler because it blows newly vaporized water away from your skin, allowing more sweat to vaporize and causing even more cooling. High humidity, on the other hand, slows down the net rate of evaporation, preventing cooling. When the air already contains large amounts of water vapour, the sweat evaporates more slowly, making your body's cooling system less efficient.

Condensation, the opposite of vaporization, is exothermic—heat is released when a gas condenses to a liquid. If you have ever accidentally put your hand above a steaming kettle, or opened a bag of microwaved popcorn too soon, you may have experienced a *steam burn*. As the steam condenses to a liquid on your skin, it releases a lot of heat, causing the burn. The condensation of water vapour is also the reason that winter overnight temperatures in coastal regions, which tend to have water vapour in the air, do not get as low as in deserts, which tend to have dry air. As the air temperature in a coastal area drops, water condenses out of the air, releasing heat and preventing the temperature from dropping further. In deserts, the air contains almost no moisture to condense, so the temperature drop is more extreme.

Heat of Vaporization The amount of heat required to vaporize one mole of a liquid to gas is its **heat of vaporization** ($\Delta_{vap}H^\circ$). The heat of vaporization of water at its normal boiling point of 100 °C is +40.7 kJ mol^{-1}:

The term "normal" boiling point refers to the boiling point at 1 atm or 101 325 kPa (1.01325 bar).

$$H_2O(l) \longrightarrow H_2O(g) \quad \Delta_{vap}H^\circ = 40.7 \text{ kJ mol}^{-1}$$

The heat of vaporization is always positive because the process is endothermic—energy must be absorbed to vaporize a substance. The heat of vaporization is somewhat temperature dependent. For example, at 25 °C, the heat of vaporization of water is +44.0 kJ mol^{-1}, slightly more than at 100 °C because the water contains less thermal energy at 25 °C. Table 11.7 lists the heats of vaporization of several liquids at their boiling points and at 25 °C.

The sign conventions of ΔH were introduced in Chapter 6.

When a substance condenses from a gas to a liquid, the same amount of heat is involved, but the heat is emitted rather than absorbed:

$$H_2O(g) \longrightarrow H_2O(l) \quad \Delta_r H = -\Delta_{vap}H^\circ = -40.7 \text{ kJ mol}^{-1} \text{ (at 100 °C)}$$

TABLE 11.7 Heats of Vaporization of Several Liquids at Their Boiling Points and at 25 °C

Liquid	Chemical Formula	Normal Boiling Point (°C)	$\Delta_{vap}H^\circ$ (kJ mol^{-1}) at Boiling Point	$\Delta_{vap}H^\circ$ (kJ mol^{-1}) at 25 °C
Water	H_2O	100	40.7	44.0
Rubbing alcohol (propan-2-ol)	C_3H_8O	82.3	39.9	45.4
Propanone (acetone)	C_3H_6O	56.1	29.1	31.0
Diethyl ether	$C_4H_{10}O$	34.6	26.5	27.1

When one mole of water condenses, it releases 40.7 kJ of heat. The sign of $\Delta_r H$ in this case is negative because the process is exothermic.

The heat of vaporization of a liquid can be used to calculate the amount of energy required to vaporize a given mass of the liquid (or the amount of heat given off by the condensation of a given mass of liquid), using concepts similar to those covered in Section 6.6 (stoichiometry of $\Delta_r H$). You can use the heat of vaporization as a conversion factor between number of moles of a liquid and the amount of heat required to vaporize it (or the amount of heat emitted when it condenses), as demonstrated in the following example.

EXAMPLE 11.3 USING THE HEAT OF VAPORIZATION IN CALCULATIONS

Calculate the mass of water (in grams) that can be vaporized at its boiling point with 155 kJ of heat.

SORT You are given a certain amount of heat in kilojoules and asked to find the mass of water that can be vaporized.

GIVEN: 155 kJ
FIND: g H_2O

STRATEGIZE The heat of vaporization gives the relationship between heat absorbed and moles of water vaporized. Begin with the given amount of heat (in kJ) and convert to moles of water that can be vaporized. Then use the molar mass as a conversion factor to convert from moles of water to mass of water.

CONCEPTUAL PLAN

$$\text{kJ} \xrightarrow{\frac{1 \text{ mol } H_2O}{40.7 \text{ kJ}}} \text{mol } H_2O \xrightarrow{\frac{18.02 \text{ g } H_2O}{1 \text{ mol } H_2O}} \text{g } H_2O$$

RELATIONSHIPS USED

$\Delta_{vap}H^\circ = 40.7 \text{ kJ mol}^{-1}$ (at 100 °C)
$18.02 \text{ g } H_2O = 1 \text{ mol } H_2O$

SOLVE Follow the conceptual plan to solve the problem.

SOLUTION

$$155 \text{ kJ} \times \frac{1 \text{ mol } H_2O}{40.7 \text{ kJ}} \times \frac{18.02 \text{ g } H_2O}{1 \text{ mol } H_2O} = 68.6 \text{ g } H_2O$$

FOR PRACTICE 11.3

Calculate the amount of heat (in kilojoules) required to vaporize 2.58 kg of water at its boiling point.

FOR MORE PRACTICE 11.3

Suppose that 0.48 g of water at 25 °C condenses on the surface of a 55 g block of aluminum that is initially at 25 °C. If the heat released during condensation goes only toward heating the metal, what is the final temperature (in Celsius) of the metal block? (The specific heat capacity of aluminum is 0.903 J g^{-1} °C^{-1}.)

Vapour Pressure and Dynamic Equilibrium

We have already seen that if a container of water is left uncovered at room temperature, the water slowly evaporates away. But what happens if the container is sealed? Imagine a sealed evacuated flask—one from which the air has been removed—containing liquid water, as shown in Figure 11.28 ▶. Initially, the water molecules evaporate, as they did in the open beaker. However, because of the seal, the evaporated molecules cannot escape into the atmosphere. As water molecules enter the gas state, some start condensing back into the liquid. As the concentration (or partial pressure) of gaseous water molecules increases, the rate of condensation also increases. However, as long as the water remains at a constant temperature, the rate of evaporation remains constant. Eventually, the rate of condensation and the rate of vaporization become equal—**dynamic equilibrium** has

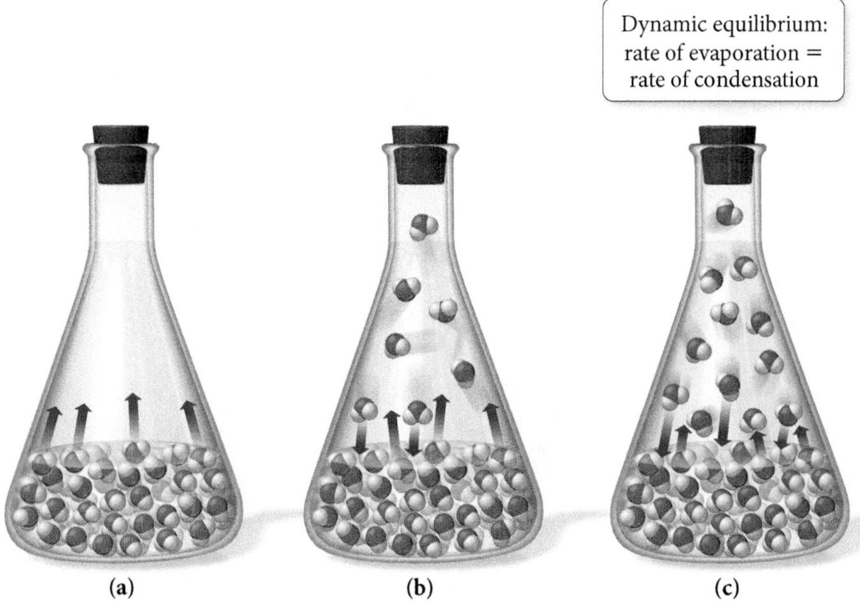

◀ **FIGURE 11.28 Vaporization in a Sealed Flask** (**a**) When water is placed into a sealed container, water molecules begin to vaporize. (**b**) As water molecules build up in the gas state, they begin to recondense into the liquid. (**c**) When the rate of evaporation equals the rate of condensation, dynamic equilibrium is reached.

been reached (Figure 11.29 ▶). Condensation and vaporization continue at equal rates and the concentration of water vapour above the liquid is constant.

The pressure of a gas in dynamic equilibrium with its liquid is called its **vapour pressure**. The vapour pressure of a particular liquid depends on the intermolecular forces present in the liquid and the temperature. Weak intermolecular forces result in volatile substances with high vapour pressures because the intermolecular forces are easily overcome by modest thermal energy. Strong intermolecular forces result in nonvolatile substances with low vapour pressures.

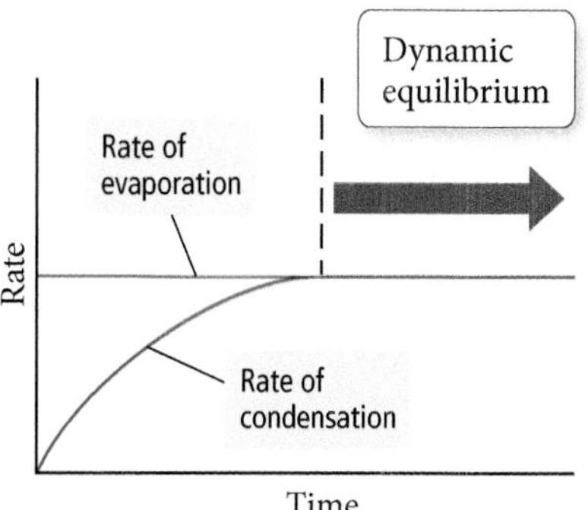

▲ **FIGURE 11.29 Dynamic Equilibrium** Dynamic equilibrium occurs when the rate of condensation is equal to the rate of evaporation.

A liquid in dynamic equilibrium with its vapour is a balanced system that tends to return to equilibrium if disturbed. For example, consider a sample of pentane (a component of gasoline) at 25 °C in a cylinder equipped with a moveable piston (Figure 11.30(a) ▼). The cylinder contains no other gases except pentane vapour in dynamic equilibrium with the liquid. Since the vapour pressure of pentane at 25 °C is 510 mmHg, the pressure in the cylinder is 510 mmHg. Now, what happens when the piston is moved upward to expand the volume within the cylinder? Initially, the pressure in the cylinder drops below 510 mmHg, in accordance with Boyle's law. Then, however, more liquid vaporizes until equilibrium is reached once again (Figure 11.30(b)). If the volume of the cylinder is expanded again, the same thing happens—the pressure initially drops and more pentane vaporizes to bring the system back into equilibrium. Further expansion will cause the same result *as long as some liquid pentane remains in the cylinder.*

| Boyle's law is discussed in Section 5.3.

Conversely, what happens if the piston is lowered, decreasing the volume in the cylinder? Initially, the pressure in the cylinder rises above 510 mmHg, but then some of the gas condenses into liquid until equilibrium is reached again (Figure 11.30(c)).

We can describe the tendency of a system in dynamic equilibrium to return to equilibrium with the following general statement:

When a system in dynamic equilibrium is disturbed, the system responds so as to minimize the disturbance and return to a state of equilibrium.

If the pressure above a liquid–vapour system in equilibrium is decreased, some of the liquid evaporates, restoring the equilibrium pressure. If the pressure is increased, some of the vapour condenses, bringing the pressure back down to the equilibrium pressure. This basic principle—Le Châtelier's principle—is applicable to any chemical system in equilibrium, as we shall see in Chapter 14.

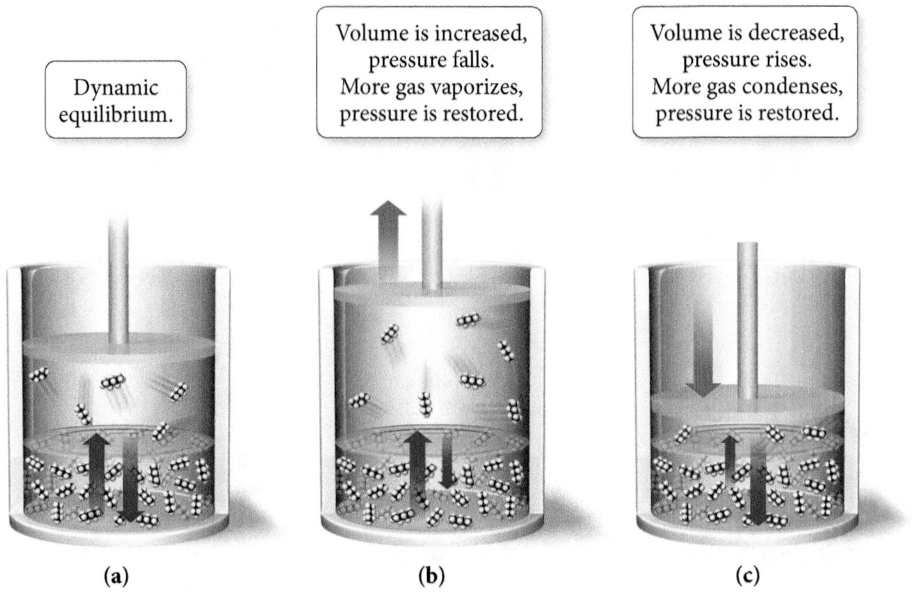

▶ **FIGURE 11.30 Dynamic Equilibrium in Pentane** (**a**) Liquid pentane is in dynamic equilibrium with its vapour. (**b**) When the volume is increased, the pressure drops and some liquid is converted to gas to bring the pressure back up. (**c**) When the volume is decreased, the pressure increases and some gas is converted to liquid to bring the pressure back down.

Dynamic equilibrium.

Volume is increased, pressure falls. More gas vaporizes, pressure is restored.

Volume is decreased, pressure rises. More gas condenses, pressure is restored.

(a) (b) (c)

CONCEPTUAL CONNECTION 11.2

Vapour Pressure

What happens to the vapour pressure of a substance when its surface area is increased at constant temperature?

(a) The vapour pressure increases.

(b) The vapour pressure remains the same.

(c) The vapour pressure decreases.

Temperature Dependence of Vapour Pressure and Boiling Point When the temperature of a liquid is increased, its vapour pressure rises because the higher thermal energy increases the number of molecules that have enough energy to vaporize (see Figure 11.27). Because of the shape of the thermal energy distribution curve, a small change in temperature makes a large difference in the number of molecules that have enough energy to vaporize, which results in a large increase in vapour pressure. For example, the vapour pressure of water at 25 °C is 23.8 Torr, while at 60 °C, the vapour pressure is 149.6 Torr. Figure 11.31 ◀ shows the vapour pressure of water and several other liquids as a function of temperature.

▼ **FIGURE 11.31 Vapour Pressure of Several Liquids at Different Temperatures** At higher temperatures, more molecules have enough thermal energy to escape into the gas state, so vapour pressure increases with increasing temperature.

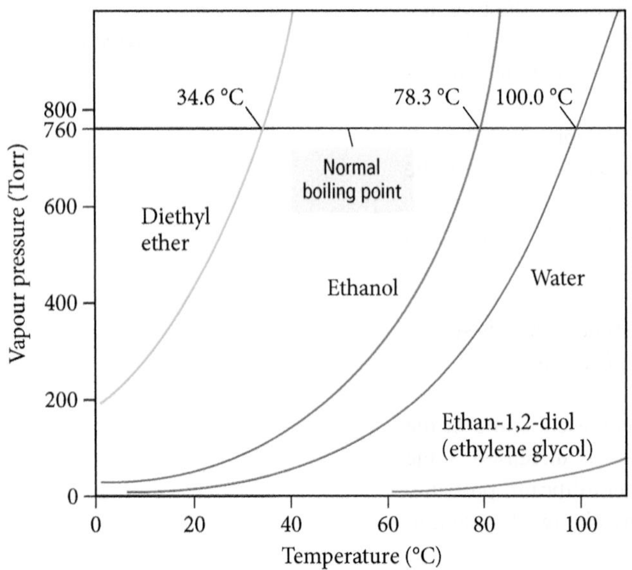

The **boiling point** of a liquid is *the temperature at which its vapour pressure equals the external pressure*. When a liquid reaches its boiling point, the thermal energy is enough for molecules in the interior of the liquid (not just those at the surface) to break free of their neighbours and enter the gas state (Figure 11.32 ▶). The bubbles in boiling water are pockets of gaseous water that have formed within the liquid water. The bubbles float to the surface and leave as gaseous water or steam.

The **normal boiling point** of a liquid is *the temperature at which its vapour pressure equals 1.01325 bar (= 1 atm = 760 Torr)*. The normal boiling point of pure water is 100 °C. However, at a lower pressure, water boils at a lower temperature. In Lake Louise, Alberta, where the altitude is about 1530 m above sea level, the average atmospheric pressure is about 83%

◀ **FIGURE 11.32 Boiling** A liquid boils when thermal energy is high enough to cause molecules in the interior of the liquid to become gaseous, forming bubbles that rise to the surface.

of what it is at sea level, and water boils at approximately 94 °C. For this reason, it takes slightly longer to cook food in boiling water in Lake Louise than in Toronto, which is at sea level. Table 11.8 shows the boiling point of water at several locations of varied altitudes.

One can also define the **standard boiling point**, which is *the temperature at which its vapour pressure equals 1 bar*. For water, the standard boiling point is 99.6 °C, slightly lower than the normal boiling point, since 1 bar is slightly lower pressure than 1 atm. Because the Celsius temperature scale is based on the melting and boiling points of water at 1 atm or 1.01325 bar (the normal melting and boiling points), standard boiling point is not nearly as common.

Sometimes you see bubbles begin to form in hot water below 100 °C. These bubbles are dissolved air—not gaseous water—leaving the liquid. Dissolved air comes out of water as you heat it because the solubility of a gas in a liquid decreases with increasing temperature (as we will see in Chapter 12).

Once the boiling point of a liquid is reached, additional heating only causes more rapid boiling; it does not raise the temperature of the liquid above its boiling point, as shown in the *heating curve* in Figure 11.33 ▶. Therefore, boiling water at 1 atm will always have a temperature of 100 °C. *As long as liquid water is present, its temperature cannot rise above its boiling point.* After all the water has been converted to steam, the temperature of the steam can continue to rise beyond 100 °C.

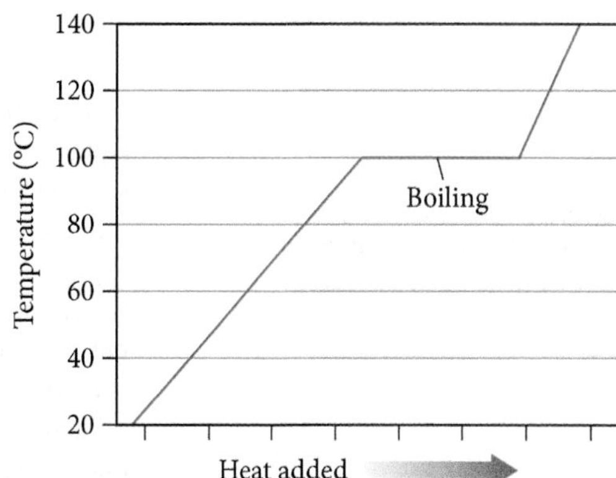

▲ **FIGURE 11.33 Temperature During Boiling** The temperature of water during boiling remains at 100 °C.

The Clausius–Clapeyron Equation Now let's return our attention to Figure 11.31. As you can see from the graph, the vapour pressure of a liquid increases with increasing temperature. However, *the relationship is not linear.* In other words, doubling the temperature results in more than a

TABLE 11.8 Boiling Points of Water at Several Locations of Varied Altitudes

Location	Elevation (m)	Approximate Pressure (atm)*	Approximate Boiling Point of Water (°C)
Mt. Everest, Tibet (highest mountain peak on Earth)	8850	0.32	71
Mt. Logan, Yukon (highest mountain peak in Canada)	5956	0.51	82
Mt. Fairweather, British Columbia (highest mountain peak on Canada's West Coast)	4671	0.60	86
Mt. Caubvick, Newfoundland and Labrador (highest mountain peak in Canada, east of Alberta)	1652	0.83	94
Toronto, Ontario (sea level)	75	1.0	100

*The atmospheric pressure in each of these locations is subject to weather conditions and can vary significantly from the values stated here.

doubling of the vapour pressure. The relationship between vapour pressure and temperature is exponential, and can be expressed as follows:

$$P_{vap} = \beta \exp\left(\frac{-\Delta_{vap}H^\circ}{RT}\right) \quad [11.1]$$

In this expression, P_{vap} is the vapour pressure, β is a constant that depends on the gas, $\Delta_{vap}H^\circ$ is the heat of vaporization, R is the gas constant (8.314 J mol^{-1} K^{-1}), and T is the temperature in kelvin. Equation 11.1 can be rearranged by taking the natural logarithm of both sides:

$$\ln(P_{vap}) = \ln\left[\beta \exp\left(\frac{-\Delta_{vap}H^\circ}{RT}\right)\right] \quad [11.2]$$

Since $\ln(AB) = \ln A + \ln B$, we can rearrange the right side of Equation 11.2:

e^x and exp(x) are equivalent ways of expressing an exponent.

$$\ln(P_{vap}) = \ln\beta + \ln\left[\exp\left(\frac{-\Delta_{vap}H^\circ}{RT}\right)\right] \quad [11.3]$$

Since $\ln e^x = x$ (see Appendix IB), we can simplify Equation 11.3:

$$\ln(P_{vap}) = \ln\beta + \left(\frac{-\Delta_{vap}H^\circ}{RT}\right) \quad [11.4]$$

A slight additional rearrangement gives us the following important result:

$$\ln(P_{vap}) = \frac{-\Delta_{vap}H^\circ}{R}\left(\frac{1}{T}\right) + \ln\beta \quad \text{Clausius–Clapeyron equation} \quad [11.5]$$

$$y = m(x) + b \quad \text{(equation for a line)}$$

Using the Clausius–Clapeyron equation in this way ignores the relatively small temperature dependence of $\Delta_{vap}H^\circ$.

Notice the parallel relationship between the **Clausius–Clapeyron equation** and the equation for a straight line. Just as a plot of y versus x for the equation of a line yields a straight line with slope m and intercept b, so a plot of $\ln P_{vap}$ (equivalent to y) versus $1/T$ (equivalent to x) gives a straight line with slope $-\Delta_{vap}H^\circ/R$ (equivalent to m) as shown in Figure 11.34 ▼. The Clausius–Clapeyron equation gives a linear relationship—not between the vapour pressure and the temperature (which have an exponential relationship)—but between the *natural log* of the vapour pressure and the *inverse* of temperature. This is a common technique in the analysis of chemical data. If two variables are not linearly related, it is often convenient to find ways to graph *functions of those variables* that are linearly related.

The Clausius–Clapeyron equation leads to a convenient way to measure the heat of vaporization in the laboratory. We just measure the vapour pressure of a liquid as a function of temperature and create a plot of the natural log of the vapour pressure versus the inverse of the temperature. We can then determine the slope of the line to find the heat of vaporization, as shown in the following example.

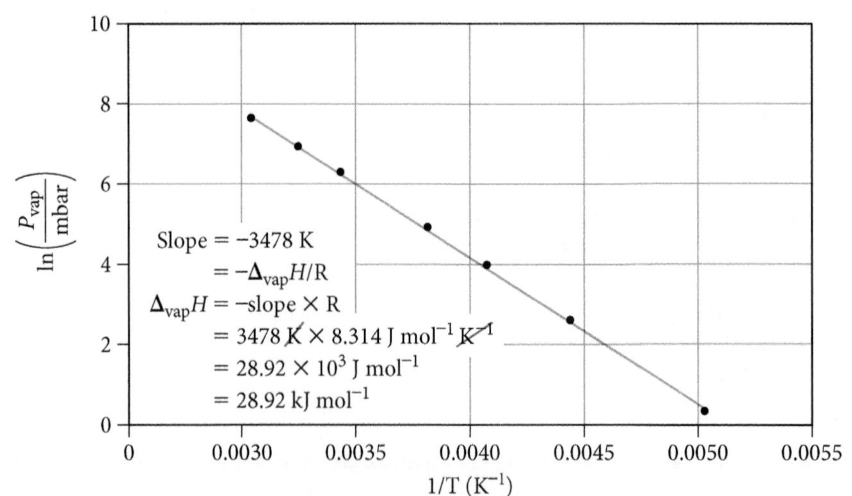

▶ **FIGURE 11.34 A Clausius–Clapeyron Plot for Diethyl Ether ($CH_3CH_2OCH_2CH_3$)** A plot of the natural logarithm of the vapour pressure versus the inverse temperature yields a straight line with a slope equal to $\Delta_{vap}H^\circ/R$.

EXAMPLE 11.4 USING THE CLAUSIUS–CLAPEYRON EQUATION TO DETERMINE HEAT OF VAPORIZATION FROM EXPERIMENTAL MEASUREMENTS OF VAPOUR PRESSURE

The vapour pressure of dichloromethane was measured as a function of temperature, and the following results were obtained:

Temperature (K)	Vapour Pressure (mbar)
200	1.1
220	6.0
240	28
260	95
280	263
300	521

Determine the heat of vaporization of dichloromethane.

SOLUTION

To find the heat of vaporization, use an Excel spreadsheet or a graphing calculator to make a plot of the natural log of vapour pressure ($\ln P_{vap}$) as a function of the inverse of the temperature in kelvin ($1/T$). Then fit the points to a line and determine the slope of the line. The slope of the best-fitting line is -3773 K. Since the slope equals $-\Delta_{vap}H^\circ/R$, we find the heat of vaporization as follows:

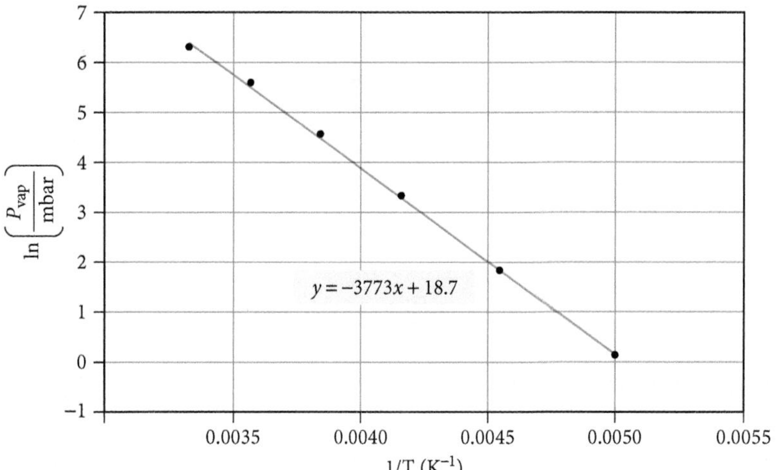

$$\begin{aligned} \text{slope} &= -\Delta_{vap}H^\circ/R \\ \Delta_{vap}H^\circ &= -\text{slope} \times R \\ &= -(-3773\ \cancel{\text{K}})(8.314\ \text{J mol}^{-1}\ \cancel{\text{K}^{-1}}) \\ &= 3.14 \times 10^4\ \text{J mol}^{-1} \\ &= 31.4\ \text{kJ mol}^{-1} \end{aligned}$$

CHECK The units of the answer are correct. The magnitude of the answer is reasonable because it is comparable to the heats of vaporization for other polar organic solvents (Table 11.7).

FOR PRACTICE 11.4

The vapour pressure of carbon tetrachloride was measured as a function of the temperature, and the following results were obtained:

Temperature (K)	Vapour Pressure (mbar)
255	15.1
265	28.0
275	49.1
285	82.0
295	132.0
300	165.1

Determine the heat of vaporization of carbon tetrachloride.

The Clausius–Clapeyron equation can also be expressed in a two-point form that we can use with just two measurements of vapour pressure and temperature to determine the heat of vaporization:

$$\ln\left(\frac{P_2}{P_1}\right) = \frac{-\Delta_{vap}H^\circ}{R}\left(\frac{1}{T_2} - \frac{1}{T_1}\right) \quad \text{Clausius–Clapeyron equation (two-point form)} \quad [11.6]$$

The two-point method is generally inferior to plotting multiple points because fewer data points results in greater possible error.

We can use this form of the equation to predict the vapour pressure of a liquid at any temperature if we know the enthalpy of vaporization and the normal boiling point (or the vapour pressure at some other temperature), as shown in the following example.

EXAMPLE 11.5 USING THE TWO-POINT FORM OF THE CLAUSIUS–CLAPEYRON EQUATION TO PREDICT THE VAPOUR PRESSURE AT A GIVEN TEMPERATURE

Methanol has a normal boiling point of 64.6 °C and a heat of vaporization ($\Delta_{vap}H°$) of 35.2 kJ mol^{-1}. What is the vapour pressure of methanol at 12.0 °C?

SORT You are given the normal boiling point of methanol, the temperature at which the vapour pressure is 1.01 bar (1 atm), and the heat of vaporization. You are asked to find the vapour pressure at a specified temperature, which is also given.

GIVEN:
$$T_1(°C) = 64.6\ °C$$
$$P_1 = 1.01\ \text{bar}$$
$$\Delta_{vap}H° = 35.2\ \text{kJ mol}^{-1}$$
$$T_2(°C) = 12.0\ °C$$

FIND: P_2

STRATEGIZE The conceptual plan is essentially the Clausius–Clapeyron equation, which relates the given and final quantities.

CONCEPTUAL PLAN

$$\ln\left(\frac{P_2}{P_1}\right) = \frac{-\Delta_{vap}H°}{R}\left(\frac{1}{T_2} - \frac{1}{T_1}\right)$$

(Clausius–Clapeyron equation, two-point form)

SOLVE First, convert T_1 and T_2 from °C to K.

SOLUTION

$$\begin{aligned} T_1(\text{K}) &= T_1(°C) + 273.15 \\ &= 64.6 + 273.15 \\ &= 337.8\ \text{K} \\ T_2(\text{K}) &= T_2(°C) + 273.15 \\ &= 12.0 + 273.15 \\ &= 285.2\ \text{K} \end{aligned}$$

Then, substitute the required values into the Clausius–Clapeyron equation and solve for P_2.

$$\ln\left(\frac{P_2}{P_1}\right) = \frac{-\Delta_{vap}H°}{R}\left(\frac{1}{T_2} - \frac{1}{T_1}\right)$$

$$\ln\left(\frac{P_2}{P_1}\right) = \frac{-35.2 \times 10^3\ \cancel{\text{J}}\ \cancel{\text{mol}^{-1}}}{8.314\ \cancel{\text{J}}\ \cancel{\text{K}^{-1}}\ \cancel{\text{mol}^{-1}}}\left(\frac{1}{285.2\ \cancel{\text{K}}} - \frac{1}{337.8\ \cancel{\text{K}}}\right) = -2.31$$

$$\left(\frac{P_2}{P_1}\right) = e^{-2.31}$$

$$\begin{aligned} P_2 &= P_1(e^{-2.31}) \\ &= 1.01\ \text{bar}\ (0.0993) \\ &= 0.100\ \text{bar (or 100 mbar)} \end{aligned}$$

CHECK The unit of the answer is correct. The magnitude of the answer makes sense because vapour pressure should be significantly lower at the lower temperature.

FOR PRACTICE 11.5

Propane has a normal boiling point of −42.0 °C and a heat of vaporization ($\Delta_{vap}H°$) of 19.04 kJ mol^{-1}. What is the vapour pressure of propane at 25.0 °C?

The Critical Point: The Transition to an Unusual State of Matter

We have considered the vaporization of a liquid in a container open to the atmosphere with and without heating, and the vaporization of a liquid in a *sealed* container without heating. We now examine the vaporization of a liquid in a *sealed* container *during heating*. Consider liquid pentane in equilibrium with its vapour in a sealed container initially at 25 °C. At this temperature, the vapour pressure of pentane is 0.68 bar. What happens if we heat the liquid? As the temperature rises, more pentane vaporizes and the pressure within the container increases. At 100 °C, the pressure is 5.6 bar, and at 190 °C the pressure is 29 bar. As the temperature and pressure increase, more and more gaseous pentane

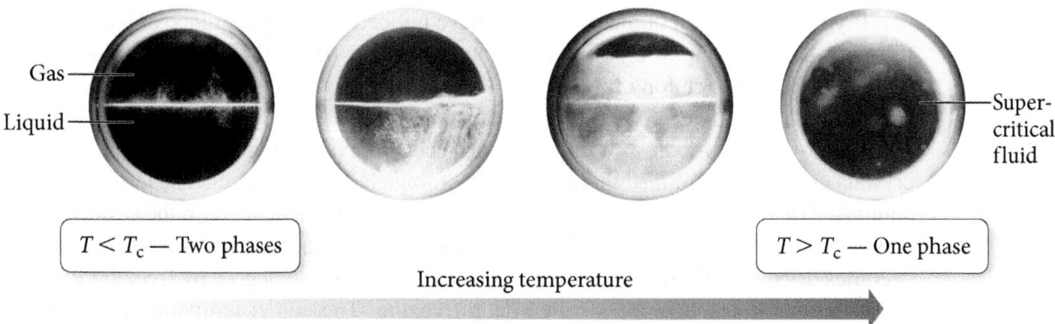

▲ **FIGURE 11.35 Critical-Point Transition** As *n*-pentane is heated in a sealed container, it undergoes a transition to a supercritical fluid. At the critical point, the meniscus separating the liquid and gas disappears, and the fluid becomes supercritical—neither a liquid nor a gas.

is forced into the same amount of space, and the density of the *gas* gets higher and higher. At the same time, the increasing temperature causes the density of the *liquid* to become lower and lower. At 197 °C, the meniscus between the liquid and gaseous *n*-pentane disappears and the gas and liquid states commingle to form a *supercritical fluid* (Figure 11.35 ▲). For any substance, the *temperature* at which this transition occurs is called the **critical temperature (T_c)**. The liquid cannot exist (regardless of pressure) above this temperature. The *pressure* at which this transition occurs is called the **critical pressure (P_c)**.

Researchers are interested in supercritical fluids because of their unique properties. A supercritical fluid has properties of both liquids and gases—it is in some sense intermediate between the two. Supercritical fluids can act as good solvents, selectively dissolving a number of compounds. For example, supercritical carbon dioxide is used as a solvent to extract caffeine from coffee beans. The caffeine dissolves in the supercritical carbon dioxide, but other substances—such as those responsible for the flavour of coffee—do not. Consequently, the caffeine can be removed without substantially altering the coffee's flavour. The supercritical carbon dioxide is easily removed from the mixture by simply lowering the pressure below the critical pressure, at which point the carbon dioxide evaporates away, leaving no residue.

11.6 Sublimation and Fusion

In Section 11.5, we examined a beaker of liquid water at room temperature from the molecular viewpoint. Now, let's examine a block of ice at −10 °C from the same molecular perspective, paying close attention to two common processes: sublimation and fusion.

Sublimation

Even though a block of ice is solid, the water molecules have thermal energy, which causes each one to vibrate about a fixed point. The motion is much less vigorous than in a liquid, but significant nonetheless. As in liquids, at any one time some molecules in the block of ice have more thermal energy than the average and some have less. The molecules with high enough thermal energy can break free from the ice surface—whereas in liquids, molecules on the surface are held less tightly than in the interior due to fewer neighbour–neighbour interactions—and go directly into the gas state (Figure 11.36 ►). This process is **sublimation**, the transition from solid to gas. Some of the water molecules in the gas state (those at the low end of the energy distribution curve for the gaseous molecules) can collide with the surface of the ice and be captured by the intermolecular forces with other molecules. This process—the opposite of sublimation—is **deposition**, the transition from gas to solid. As is the case with liquids, the pressure of a gas in dynamic equilibrium with its solid is the vapour pressure of the solid.

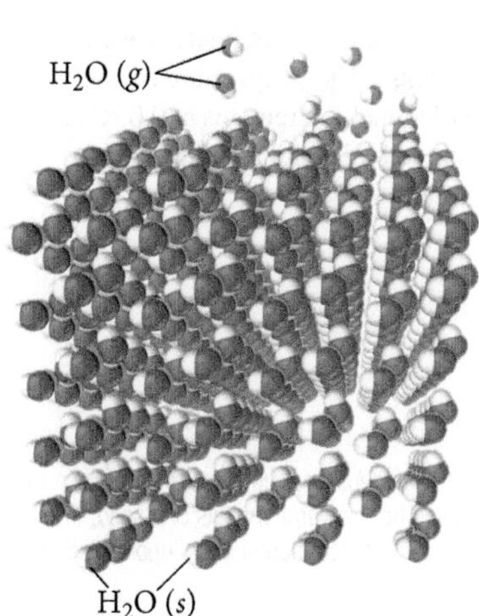

▲ **FIGURE 11.36 The Sublimation of Ice** The water molecules at the surface of an ice cube can sublime directly into the gas state.

Although both sublimation and deposition occur on the surface of an ice block open to the atmosphere at −10 °C, sublimation usually occurs at a greater rate because most of the newly sublimed molecules escape into the surrounding atmosphere and never come back. The result is a noticeable decrease in the size of the ice block over time (even though the temperature is below the melting point).

▲ The ice crystals that form on frozen food are due to sublimation of water from the food and redeposition on its surface.

If you live in a cold climate, you may have noticed the disappearance of ice and snow from the ground even though the temperature remains below 0 °C. Similarly, ice cubes left in the freezer for a long time slowly shrink, even though the freezer is always below 0 °C. In both cases, the ice is *subliming*, turning directly into water vapour. Ice also sublimes out of frozen foods. You may have noticed, for example, the gradual growth of ice crystals on the *inside* of airtight plastic food-storage bags in a freezer. The ice crystals are composed of water that has sublimed out of the food and redeposited on the surface of the bag or on the surface of the food. For this reason, food that remains frozen for too long becomes dried out. Such dehydration can be avoided to some degree by freezing foods to colder temperatures, a process called deep-freezing. The colder temperature lowers the vapour pressure of ice and preserves the food longer. Freezer burn on meats is another common manifestation of sublimation. When you improperly store meat (for example, in a container that is not airtight) sublimation continues unabated. The result is the dehydration of the surface of the meat, which becomes discoloured and loses flavour and texture.

A substance commonly associated with sublimation is solid carbon dioxide or dry ice, which does not melt under atmospheric pressure no matter what the temperature. However, at −78 °C, the CO_2 molecules have enough energy to leave the surface of the dry ice and become gaseous through sublimation.

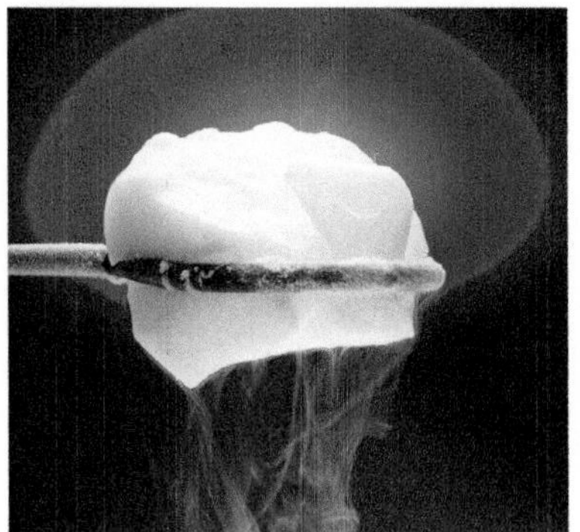

▲ Dry ice (solid CO_2) sublimes but does not melt at atmospheric pressure.

Fusion

Let's return to our ice block and examine what happens at the molecular level as we increase its temperature. The increasing thermal energy causes the water molecules to vibrate faster and faster. At the **melting point** (0 °C for water), the molecules have enough thermal energy to overcome the intermolecular forces that hold them at their stationary points, and the solid turns into a liquid. This process is **melting** or **fusion**, the transition from solid to liquid. The opposite of melting is **freezing**, the transition from liquid to solid. Once the melting point of a solid is reached, additional heating only causes more rapid melting; it does not raise the temperature of the solid above its melting point (Figure 11.37 ◄). Only after all of the ice has melted will additional heating raise the temperature of the liquid water past 0 °C. A mixture of water *and* ice will always have a temperature of 0 °C at 1.01325 bar (1 atm) pressure.

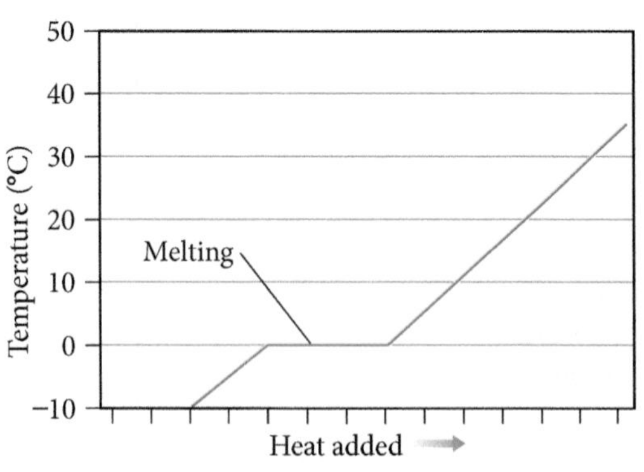

▲ **FIGURE 11.37 Temperature During Melting** The temperature of water during melting remains at 0.0 °C as long as both solid and liquid water remain.

Energetics of Melting and Freezing

The most common way to cool a beverage quickly is to drop several ice cubes into it. As the ice melts, the drink cools because melting is endothermic—the melting ice absorbs heat from the liquid. The amount of heat required to melt 1 mol of a solid is called the **heat of fusion** ($\Delta_{fus}H°$). The heat of fusion for water is 6.02 kJ mol^{-1}:

$$H_2O(s) \longrightarrow H_2O(l) \qquad \Delta_{fus}H° = 6.02 \text{ kJ mol}^{-1}$$

The heat of fusion is positive because melting is endothermic.

Freezing, the opposite of melting, is exothermic—heat is released when a liquid freezes into a solid. For example, as water in your freezer turns into ice, it releases heat, which must be removed by the refrigeration system of the freezer. If the refrigeration system did not remove the heat, the water would not completely freeze into ice. The heat released as the water began to freeze would warm the freezer, preventing further freezing. The change in enthalpy for freezing has the same magnitude as the heat of fusion but the opposite sign:

The term *fusion* is used for melting because if you heat several crystals of a solid, they *fuse* into a continuous liquid upon melting.

$$H_2O(l) \longrightarrow H_2O(s) \qquad \Delta_rH = -\Delta_{fus}H° = -6.02 \text{ kJ mol}^{-1}$$

Different substances have different heats of fusion, as shown in Table 11.9.

In general, the heat of fusion is significantly less than the heat of vaporization, as shown in Figure 11.38 ►. We have already seen that the solid and liquid states are closer to each other in many ways than they are to the gas state. It takes less energy to melt 1 mol of ice into liquid than it does to vaporize 1 mol of liquid water into gas because vaporization requires complete separation of molecules from one another, so the intermolecular forces

TABLE 11.9 Heats of Fusion of Several Substances

Liquid	Chemical Formula	Melting Point (°C)	$\Delta_{fus}H°$ (kJ mol^{-1})*
Water	H_2O	0.00	6.02
Propan-2-ol (rubbing alcohol)	C_3H_8O	−89.5	5.37
Propanone (acetone)	C_3H_6O	−94.8	5.69
Diethyl ether	$C_4H_{10}O$	−116.3	7.27

*Heats of fusion are at 1 bar and at the temperature that the phase change occurs.

must be completely overcome. Melting, however, requires that intermolecular forces be only partially overcome, allowing molecules to move around one another, while still remaining in contact.

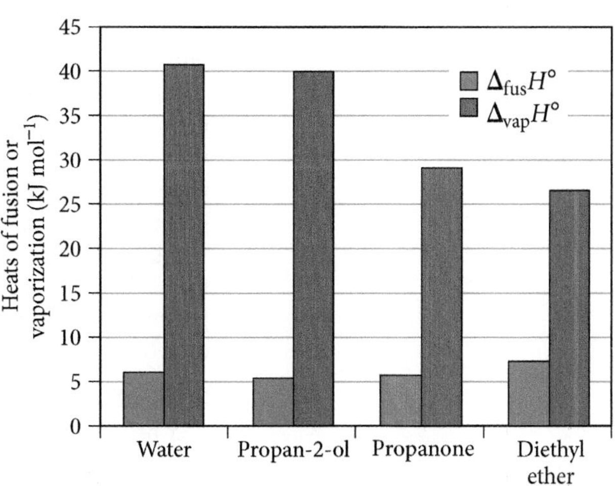

▲ **FIGURE 11.38 Heats of Fusion and Heats of Vaporization** Typical heats of fusion are significantly less than heats of vaporization.

11.7 Heating Curve for Water

We can combine and build on the concepts from the previous two sections by examining the *heating curve* for 1.00 mol of water at 1.0 atm pressure, shown in Figure 11.39 ▼. The *y*-axis of the heating curve represents the temperature of the water sample. The *x*-axis represents the amount of heat added (in kilojoules) during heating. As you can see from the diagram, the process can be divided into five segments: (1) ice warming,

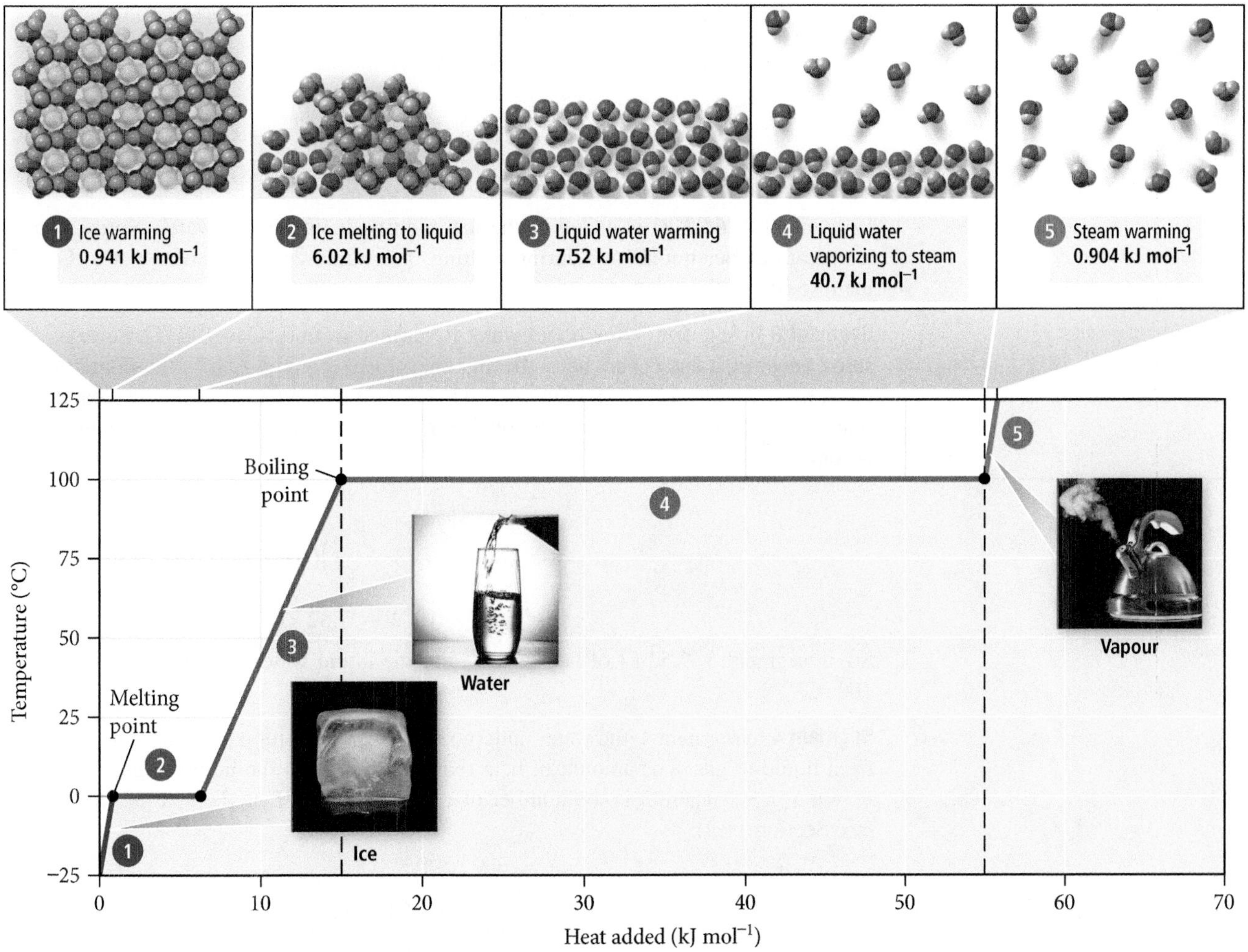

▲ **FIGURE 11.39 Heating Curve for Water**

(2) ice melting into liquid water, (3) liquid water warming, (4) liquid water vaporizing into steam, and (5) steam warming.

In two of these segments (2 and 4), the temperature is constant as heat is added because the added heat goes into producing the transition between states, not into increasing the temperature. The two states are in equilibrium during the transition and the temperature remains constant. The amount of heat required to achieve the state change is given by $q = n\,\Delta H$.

In the other three segments (1, 3, and 5), temperature increases linearly. These segments represent the heating of a single state in which the deposited heat raises the temperature in accordance with the substance's heat capacity ($q = mC_s\,\Delta T$). We examine each of these segments individually.

Segment 1 In segment 1, solid ice is warmed from −25 °C to 0 °C. Since no transition between states occurs here, the amount of heat required to heat the solid ice is given by $q = mC_s\,\Delta T$ (see Section 6.4), where C_s is the specific heat capacity of ice ($C_{s,\,ice} = 2.09\ J\ g^{-1}\ °C^{-1}$). For 1.00 mol of water (18.0 g), the amount of heat is computed as follows:

$$\begin{aligned} q &= mC_{s,\,ice}\,\Delta T \\ &= 18.0\ \cancel{g}\left(2.09\frac{J}{\cancel{g}\cdot\cancel{°C}}\right)[0.0\ \cancel{°C} - (-25.0\ \cancel{°C})] \\ &= 941\ J = 0.941\ kJ \end{aligned}$$

So, in segment 1, 0.941 kJ of heat is added to the ice, warming it from −25° C to 0 °C.

Segment 2 In segment 2, the added heat does not change the temperature of the ice and water mixture because the heat is absorbed by the transition from solid to liquid. The amount of heat required to convert the ice to liquid water is given by $q = n\,\Delta_{fus}H°$, where n is the number of moles of water and $\Delta_{fus}H°$ is the heat of fusion (see Section 11.6):

$$\begin{aligned} q &= n\,\Delta_{fus}H° \\ &= 1.00\ \cancel{mol}\left(\frac{6.02\ kJ}{\cancel{mol}}\right) \\ &= 6.02\ kJ \end{aligned}$$

In segment 2, 6.02 kJ is added to the ice, melting it into liquid water. Notice that the temperature does not change during melting. The liquid and solid coexist at 0 °C as the melting occurs.

Segment 3 In segment 3, the liquid water is warmed from 0 °C to 100 °C. Since no transition between states occurs here, the amount of heat required to heat the liquid water is given by $q = mC_s\,\Delta T$, as in segment 1. However, now we must use the heat capacity of liquid water (not ice) for the calculation. For 1.00 mol of water (18.0 g), the amount of heat is computed as follows:

$$\begin{aligned} q &= mC_{s,\,liq}\,\Delta T \\ &= 18.0\ \cancel{g}\left(4.18\frac{J}{\cancel{g}\cdot\cancel{°C}}\right)(100.0\ \cancel{°C} - 0.0\ \cancel{°C}) \\ &= 7.52 \times 10^3\ J = 7.52\ kJ \end{aligned}$$

So, in segment 3, 7.52 kJ of heat is added to the liquid water, warming it from 0 °C to 100 °C.

Segment 4 In segment 4, the water undergoes a second transition between states, this time from liquid to gas. The amount of heat required to convert the liquid to gas is given by $q = n\,\Delta_{vap}H°$, where n is the number of moles and $\Delta_{vap}H°$ is the heat of vaporization (see Section 11.5):

$$\begin{aligned} q &= n\,\Delta_{vap}H° \\ &= 1.00\ \cancel{mol}\left(\frac{40.7\ kJ}{\cancel{mol}}\right) \\ &= 40.7\ kJ \end{aligned}$$

Thus, in segment 4, 40.7 kJ is added to the water, vaporizing it into steam. Notice that the temperature does not change during boiling. The liquid and gas coexist at 100 °C as the boiling occurs.

Segment 5 In segment 5, the steam is warmed from 100 °C to 125 °C. Since no transition between states occurs here, the amount of heat required to heat the steam is given by $q = mC_s\,\Delta T$ (as in segments 1 and 3) except that we must use the heat capacity of steam ($2.01\ \text{J g}^{-1}\,°\text{C}^{-1}$):

$$
\begin{aligned}
q &= mC_{s,\,\text{steam}}\,\Delta T \\
&= 18.0\ \cancel{\text{g}}\left(2.01\frac{\text{J}}{\cancel{\text{g}}\cdot \cancel{°\text{C}}}\right)(125.0\ \cancel{°\text{C}} - 100.0\ \cancel{°\text{C}}) \\
&= 904 = 0.904\ \text{kJ}
\end{aligned}
$$

So, in segment 5, 0.904 kJ of heat is added to the steam, warming it from 100 °C to 125 °C.

CONCEPTUAL CONNECTION 11.3

Cooling of Water with Ice

We just saw that the heat capacity of ice is $C_{s,\,\text{ice}} = 2.09\ \text{J g}^{-1}\,°\text{C}^{-1}$ and that the heat of fusion of ice is $6.02\ \text{kJ mol}^{-1}$. When a small ice cube at −10 °C is put into a cup of water at room temperature, which of the following plays a larger role in cooling the liquid water: the warming of the ice from −10 °C to 0 °C, or the melting of the ice?

11.8 Phase Diagrams

Throughout most of this chapter, we have examined how the state of a substance changes with temperature and pressure. We can combine both the temperature dependence and pressure dependence of the state of a particular substance in a graph called a *phase diagram*. A **phase diagram** is a map of the state or *phase* of a substance as a function of pressure (on the *y*-axis) and temperature (on the *x*-axis). We first examine the major features of a phase diagram, then turn to navigating within a phase diagram, and finally examine and compare the phase diagrams of selected substances.

The Major Features of a Phase Diagram

We can become familiar with the major features of a phase diagram by examining the phase diagram for water as an example (Figure 11.40 ▼). The *y*-axis (or ordinate) displays

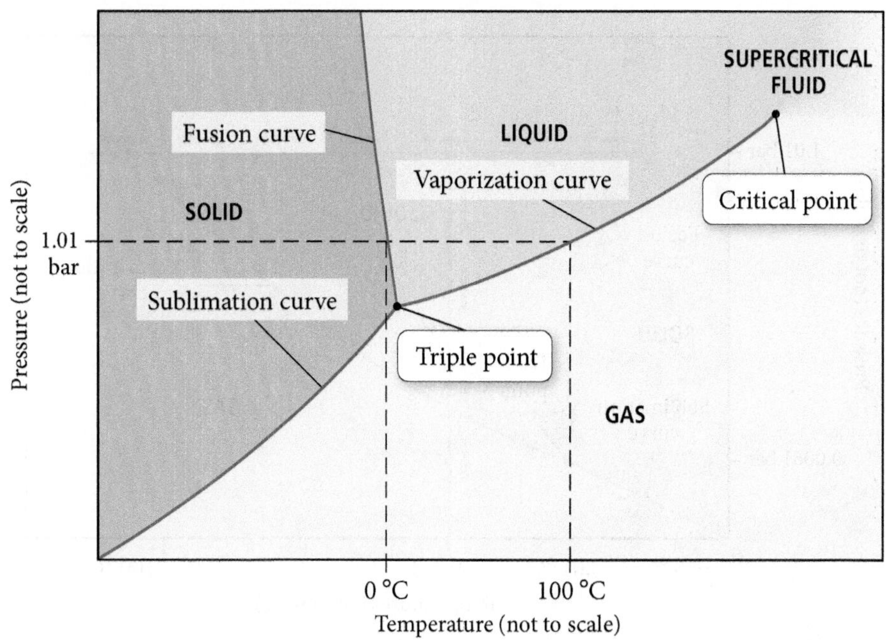

◀ **FIGURE 11.40 Phase Diagram for Water**

the pressure in bar and the x-axis (or abscissa) displays the temperature in degrees Celsius. We can categorize the main features of the phase diagram as regions, lines, and points.

Regions *Any of the three main regions—solid, liquid, and gas—in the phase diagram represents conditions where that particular state is stable.* For example, under any of the temperatures and pressures within the liquid region in the phase diagram of water, the liquid is the stable state. Notice that the point 25 °C and 1.01 bar falls within the liquid region, as we know from everyday experience. In general, low temperature and high pressure favour the solid state; high temperature and low pressure favour the gas state; and intermediate conditions favour the liquid state. A sample of matter that is not in the state indicated by its phase diagram for a given set of conditions will convert to that state when those conditions are imposed. For example, steam that is cooled to room temperature at 1.01 bar will condense to liquid.

Lines *Each of the lines (or curves) in the phase diagram represents a set of temperatures and pressures at which the substance is in equilibrium between the two states on either side of the line.* For example, in the phase diagram for water, consider the curved line beginning just beyond 0 °C separating the liquid from the gas. This line is the vaporization curve (also called the vapour pressure curve) for water that we examined in Section 11.5 (see Figure 11.31). At any of the temperatures and pressures that fall along this line, the liquid and gas states of water are equally stable and in equilibrium. For example, at 100 °C and 1.01 bar pressure, water and its vapour are in equilibrium—they are equally stable and will coexist. The other two major lines in a phase diagram are the sublimation curve (separating the solid and the gas) and the fusion curve (separating the solid and the liquid).

The triple point of a substance such as water can be reproduced anywhere to calibrate a thermometer or pressure gauge with a known temperature and pressure.

The Triple Point *The* ***triple point*** *in a phase diagram represents the unique set of conditions at which three states are equally stable and in equilibrium.* In the phase diagram for water, the triple point occurs at 0.0098 °C and 6.11×10^{-3} bar (6.11 mbar). Under these unique conditions (and only under these conditions), the solid, liquid, and gas states of water are equally stable and will coexist in equilibrium.

The Critical Point *The* ***critical point*** *in a phase diagram represents the temperature and pressure above which a supercritical fluid exists.* As we learned in Section 11.5, at the critical temperature and pressure, the liquid and gas states coalesce into a *supercritical fluid*.

Navigation Within a Phase Diagram

We can represent changes in the temperature or pressure of a sample of water as movement within the phase diagram. For example, suppose we heat a block of ice initially at 1.01 bar and −25 °C. We represent the change in temperature at constant pressure as movement along the line marked *A* in Figure 11.41 ▼. As the temperature rises, we move

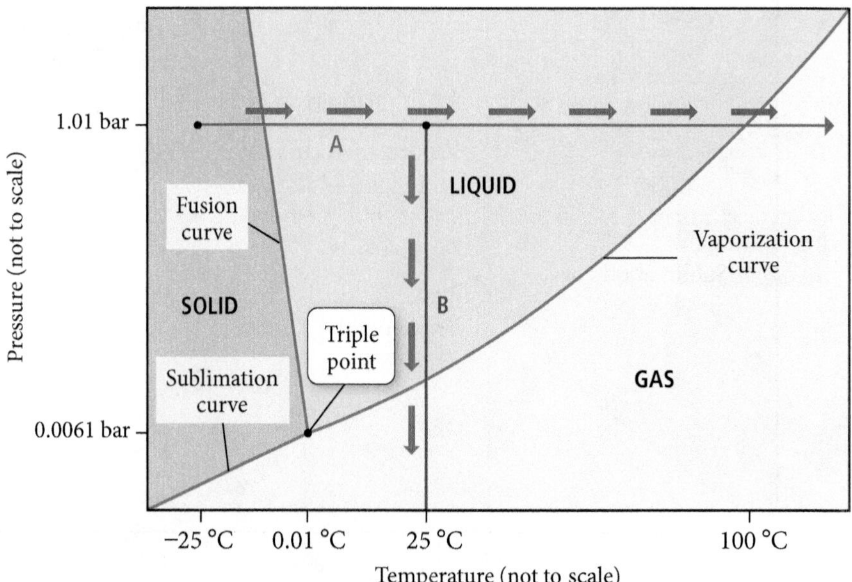

▶ **FIGURE 11.41 Navigation on the Phase Diagram for Water**

to the right along the line. At the fusion curve, the temperature stops rising and melting occurs until the solid ice is completely converted to liquid water. Crossing the fusion curve requires the complete transition from solid to liquid. Once the ice has completely melted, the temperature of the liquid water can begin to rise until the vaporization curve is reached. At this point, the temperature again stops rising and boiling occurs until all the liquid is converted to gas.

We can represent a change in pressure by a vertical line on the phase diagram. For example, suppose we lower the pressure above a sample of water initially at 1.01 bar and 25 °C. We represent the change in pressure at constant temperature as movement along the line marked *B* in Figure 11.41. As the pressure drops, we move down the line and approach the vaporization curve. At the vaporization curve, the pressure stops dropping and vaporization occurs until the liquid is completely converted to vapour. Crossing the vaporization curve requires the complete transition from liquid to gas. Only after the liquid has all vaporized can the pressure continue to drop.

The Phase Diagrams of Other Substances

Examine the phase diagrams of iodine and carbon dioxide, shown in Figure 11.42 ▼. The phase diagrams are similar to that of water in most of their general features, but some significant differences exist.

The fusion curves for both carbon dioxide and iodine have a positive slope—as the temperature increases, the pressure also increases—in contrast to the fusion curve for water, which has a negative slope. The behaviour of water is atypical. The fusion curve within the phase diagrams for most substances has a positive slope because increasing pressure favours the denser state, which for most substances is the solid state. For example, suppose the pressure on a sample of iodine is increased from 1.01 bar to 101 bar at 184 °C, as shown by line A in Figure 11.42(a). Notice that this change crosses the fusion curve, converting the liquid into a solid. In contrast, a pressure increase from 1.01 bar to 101 bar at −0.1 °C in water causes a state transition from solid to liquid. Unlike most substances, the liquid state of water is actually more dense than the solid state.

Both water and iodine have stable solid, liquid, and gaseous states at a pressure of 1.01 bar. However, notice that carbon dioxide has no stable liquid state at a pressure of 1.01 bar. If we increase the temperature of a block of solid carbon dioxide (dry ice) at 1.01 bar, as indicated by line B in Figure 11.42(b), we cross the sublimation curve at −78.5 °C. At this temperature, the solid sublimes to a gas, which is one reason that dry ice is useful (it does not melt into a liquid at atmospheric pressure). Carbon dioxide will form a liquid only above pressures of 5.2 bar.

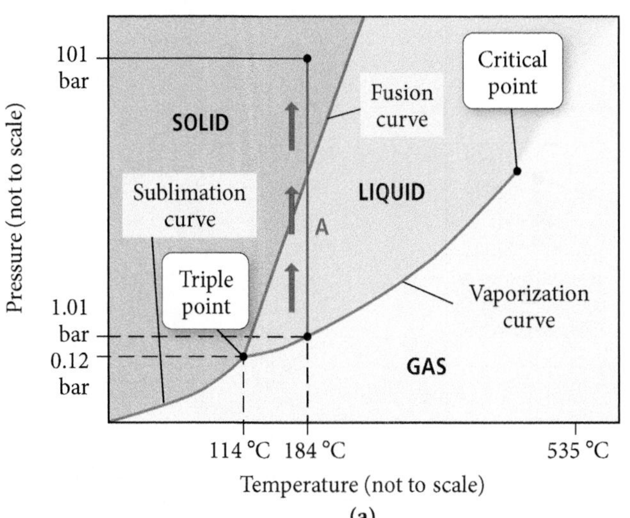

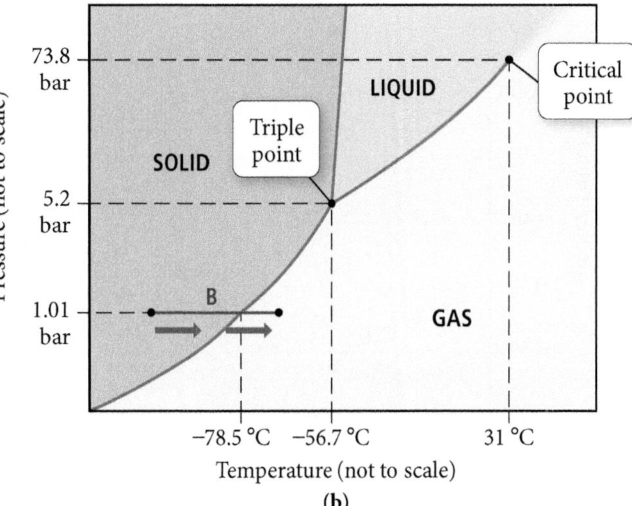

▲ **FIGURE 11.42 Phase Diagrams for Other Substances** (**a**) Iodine; (**b**) carbon dioxide.

CONCEPTUAL CONNECTION 11.4

Phase Diagrams

A substance has a triple point at −24.5 °C and 300 mbar. What is most likely to happen to a solid sample of the substance as it is warmed from −35 °C to 0 °C at a pressure of 290 mbar?

(a) The solid will melt into a liquid.

(b) The solid will sublime into a gas.

(c) Nothing (the solid will remain as a solid).

11.9 Water: An Extraordinary Substance

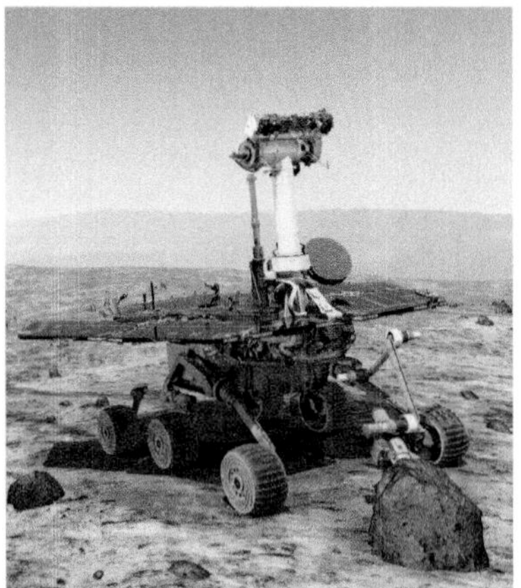

▲ A Mars Exploration Rover is looking for evidence of life in frozen water that lies below the surface of Mars's north polar region.

Water is easily the most common and important liquid on Earth. It fills our oceans, lakes, and streams. In its solid form, it caps our mountains, and in its gaseous form, it humidifies our air. We drink water, we sweat water, and we excrete bodily wastes dissolved in water. Indeed, the majority of our body mass *is* water. Life is impossible without water, and in most places on Earth where liquid water exists, life exists. Recent evidence for water on Mars in the past has fuelled hopes of finding life or evidence of past life there. And though it may not be obvious to us (because we take water for granted), this familiar substance turns out to have many remarkable properties.

Among liquids, water is unique. It has only a few electrons (10 electrons), so it is not very polarizable, yet it is a liquid at room temperature. Other main-group hydrides have many more electrons and therefore are more polarizable but have lower boiling points, as shown in Figure 11.43 ▼. No other substance of similarly low polarizability (except for HF) comes close to being a liquid at room temperature. We can understand water's high boiling point by examining its molecular structure. The bent geometry of the water molecule and the highly polar nature of the O—H bonds result in a molecule with a significant dipole moment. Water's two O—H bonds (hydrogen directly bonded to oxygen) allow a water molecule to form strong hydrogen bonds with four other water molecules (Figure 11.44 ▼), resulting in a relatively high boiling point. Water's high polarity also allows it to dissolve many other polar and ionic compounds, and even a number of nonpolar gases such as oxygen and carbon dioxide (by inducing a dipole moment in their molecules). Consequently, water is the main solvent within living organisms, transporting nutrients and other important compounds throughout the

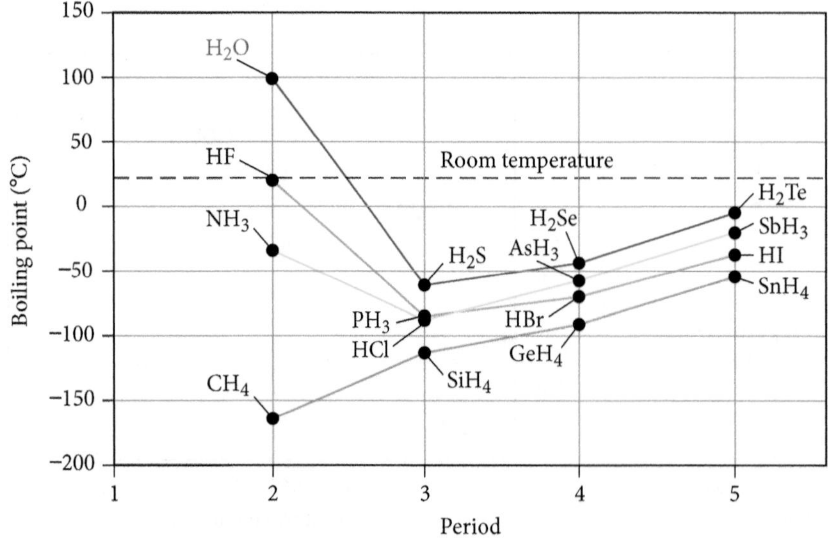

▲ **FIGURE 11.43 Boiling Points of Main-Group Hydrides** Water is the only common main-group hydride that is a liquid at room temperature.

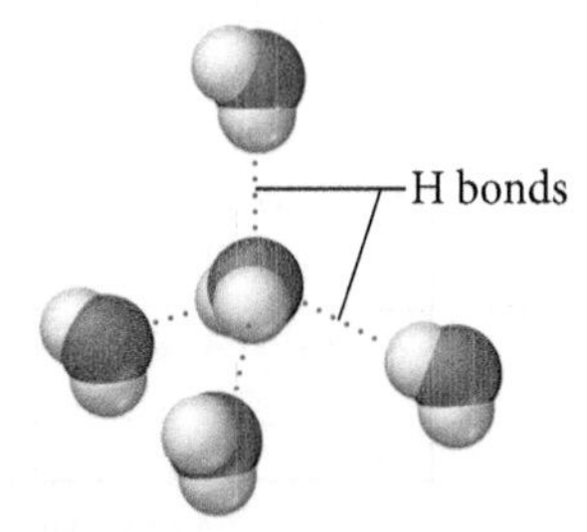

▲ **FIGURE 11.44 Hydrogen Bonding in Water** A water molecule can form four strong hydrogen bonds with four other water molecules.

body. Water is the main solvent in our environment as well, allowing aquatic animals, for example, to survive by breathing dissolved oxygen and allowing aquatic plants to survive by using dissolved carbon dioxide for photosynthesis.

We have already seen in Section 6.4 that water has an exceptionally high specific heat capacity, which has a moderating effect on the climate of coastal cities. In some cities, such as St. John's, NL, or Vancouver, BC, the daily fluctuation in temperature can be less than 10 °C. This same moderating effect occurs over the entire planet, two-thirds of which is covered by water. Without water, the daily temperature fluctuations on our planet might be more like those on Mars, where temperature fluctuations of 63 °C have been measured between early morning and midday. Imagine awakening to below freezing temperatures, only to bake at summer desert temperatures in the afternoon! The presence of water on Earth and its uniquely high specific heat capacity are largely responsible for our planet's much smaller daily fluctuations.

As we have seen, the way water freezes is also unique. Unlike other substances, which contract upon freezing, water expands upon freezing. Consequently, ice is less dense than liquid water, and it floats. This seemingly trivial property has significant consequences. The frozen layer of ice at the surface of a winter lake insulates the water in the lake from further freezing. If this ice layer sank, it would kill bottom-dwelling aquatic life and possibly allow the lake to freeze solid, eliminating virtually all life in the lake.

The expansion of water upon freezing, however, is one reason that most organisms do not survive freezing. When the water within a cell freezes, it expands and often ruptures the cell, just as water freezing within a pipe bursts the pipe. Many foods, especially those with high water content, do not survive freezing very well, either. Have you ever tried, for example, to freeze your own vegetables? If you put lettuce or spinach in the

▲ When lettuce freezes, the water within its cells expands, rupturing them.

CHEMISTRY IN THE ENVIRONMENT Water Pollution

Water quality is critical to human health. Many human diseases—especially in developing nations—are caused by poor water quality. Several kinds of pollutants, including biological and chemical contaminants, can enter water supplies.

▲ Uncontaminated, sanitary water supplies are critical to human health.

Biological contaminants are microorganisms that cause diseases such as hepatitis, cholera, dysentery, and typhoid. They get into drinking water primarily when human or animal waste is dumped into bodies of water. Drinking water in developed nations is usually chemically treated to kill microorganisms. Water containing biological contaminants poses an immediate danger to human health and should not be consumed. Most biological contaminants can be eliminated from untreated water by boiling.

Chemical contaminants enter drinking water supplies as a result of industrial dumping, pesticide and fertilizer use, and household dumping. These contaminants include organic compounds, such as carbon tetrachloride and dioxin, and inorganic elements and compounds, such as mercury, lead, and nitrates. Since many chemical contaminants are neither volatile nor alive (like biological contaminants), they are usually *not* eliminated through boiling.

The Federal-Provincial-Territorial Committee on Drinking Water has prepared guidelines for Canadian drinking water quality which is published by Health Canada (http://www.hc-sc.gc.ca/ewh-semt/pubs/water-eau/index-eng.php), most recently in October of 2014. This committee sets guidelines for biological, chemical, and radiological contaminants in water including setting maximum acceptable contamination (MAC) values for hundreds of these contaminants. They also provide guidance for issuing boil water advisories and drinking water avoidance advisories.

Question

Why does boiling not eliminate a nonvolatile contaminant such as lead?

freezer, it will be limp and damaged when you defrost it. The frozen-food industry gets around this problem by *flash freezing* vegetables and other foods. In this process, foods are frozen nearly instantaneously, which prevents water molecules from settling into their preferred crystalline structure. Consequently, the water does not expand very much and the food remains largely undamaged.

11.10 Crystalline Solids: Determining Their Structure by X-Ray Crystallography

▲ The well-defined angles and smooth faces of crystalline solids reflect the underlying order of the atoms composing them.

▲ The hexagonal shape of a snowflake derives from the hexagonal arrangement of water molecules in crystalline ice.

We have seen that crystalline solids are composed of atoms or molecules arranged in structures with long-range order (see Section 11.2). If you have ever visited the mineral section of a natural history museum and seen crystals with smooth faces and well-defined angles between them, or if you have carefully observed the hexagonal shapes of snowflakes, you have witnessed some of the effects of the underlying order in crystalline solids. The often beautiful geometric shapes that you see on the macroscopic scale are the result of specific structural patterns on the molecular and atomic scales. But how do we study these patterns? How do we look into the atomic and molecular world to determine the arrangement of the atoms and measure the distances between them? In this section, we examine **X-ray diffraction**, a powerful laboratory technique that enables us to do exactly that.

Recall from Section 7.2 that electromagnetic (or light) waves interact with each other in a characteristic way called *interference*: they can cancel each other out or reinforce each other, depending on the alignment of their crests and troughs. *Constructive interference* occurs when two waves interact with their crests and troughs in alignment. *Destructive interference* occurs when two waves interact in such a way that the crests of one align with the troughs of the other. Recall also that when light encounters two slits separated by a distance comparable to the wavelength of the light, constructive and destructive interference between the resulting beams produces a characteristic *interference pattern*, consisting of alternating bright and dark lines.

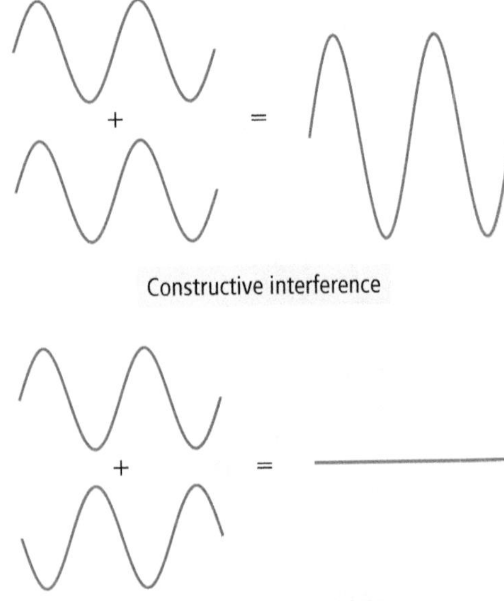

Atoms within crystal structures have spacings between them on the order of 10^2 pm, so light of similar wavelength (which happens to fall in the X-ray region of the electromagnetic spectrum) forms interference patterns or *diffraction patterns* when it interacts with those atoms. The exact pattern of diffraction reveals the spacings between planes of atoms. Consider two planes of atoms within a crystalline lattice separated by a distance d, as shown in Figure 11.45 ▶. If two rays of light with wavelength λ that are initially in phase (that is, the crests of one wave are aligned with the crests of the other)

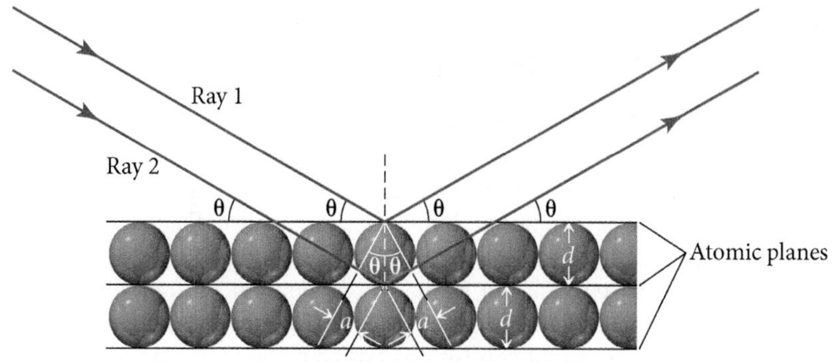

◀ **FIGURE 11.45 Diffraction from a Crystal** When X-rays strike parallel planes of atoms in a crystal, constructive interference occurs if the difference in path length between beams reflected from adjacent planes is an integral number of wavelengths.

diffract from the two planes, the diffracted rays may interfere with each other constructively or destructively, depending on the difference between the path lengths travelled by each ray. If the difference between the two path lengths ($2a$) is an integral number (n) of wavelengths, then the interference will be constructive:

$$n\lambda = 2a \quad \text{(criterion for constructive interference)} \quad [11.7]$$

Using trigonometry, we can see that the angle of reflection (θ) is related to the distance a and the separation between layers (d) by the following relation:

$$\sin\theta = \frac{a}{d} \quad [11.8]$$

Rearranging, we get:

$$a = d\sin\theta \quad [11.9]$$

By substituting Equation 11.9 into Equation 11.7, we arrive at the following important relationship:

$$n\lambda = 2d\sin\theta \qquad \text{Bragg's law}$$

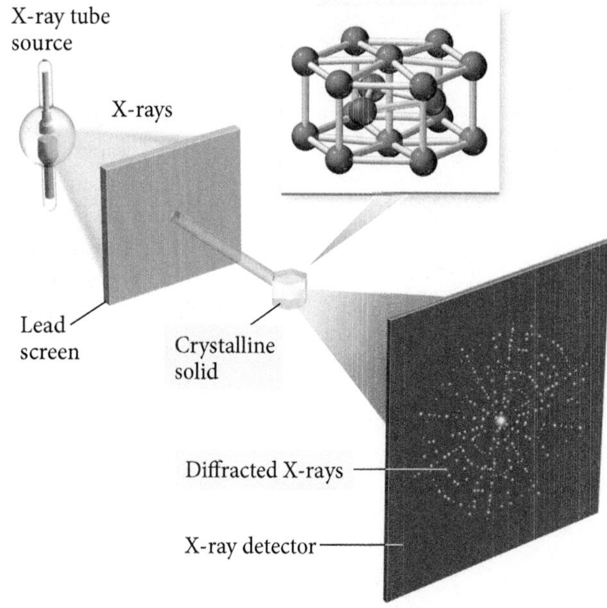

▲ **FIGURE 11.46 X-Ray Diffraction Analysis** In X-ray crystallography, an X-ray beam is passed through a sample, which is rotated to allow diffraction from different crystalline planes. The resulting patterns, representing constructive interference from various planes, are then analyzed to determine crystalline structure.

This equation is known as *Bragg's law*. For a given wavelength of light incident on atoms arranged in layers, we can measure the angle that produces constructive interference (which appears as a bright spot on the X-ray diffraction pattern) and then compute d, the distance between the atomic layers:

$$d = \frac{n\lambda}{2\sin\theta} \quad [11.10]$$

In a modern X-ray diffractometer, the diffraction pattern from a crystal (Figure 11.46 ▲) is collected and analyzed by a computer. By rotating the crystal and collecting the resulting diffraction patterns at different angles, the distances between various crystalline planes can be measured, eventually yielding the entire crystalline structure. This process is called X-ray crystallography. Researchers use X-ray crystallography to determine not only the structures of simple atomic lattices, but also the structures of proteins, DNA, and other biologically important molecules. For example, the famous X-ray diffraction photograph shown here, obtained by Rosalind Franklin and Maurice Wilkins, helped Watson and Crick determine the double-helical structure of DNA. As we learned in Section 9.1, researchers also used X-ray diffraction to determine the structure of HIV protease, a protein critical to the reproduction of HIV and the development of AIDS. That structure was then used to design drug molecules that would inhibit the action of HIV protease, thus halting the advance of the disease.

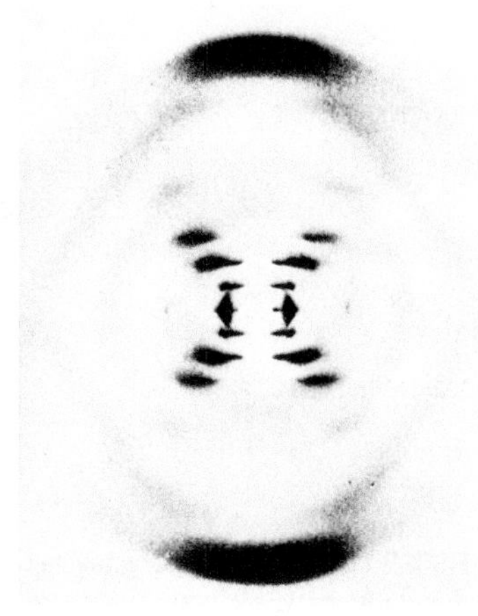

11.11 Crystalline Solids: Unit Cells and Basic Structures

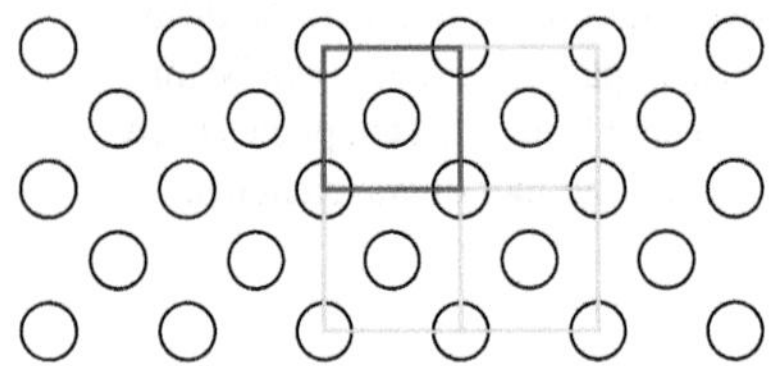

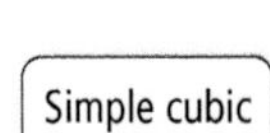

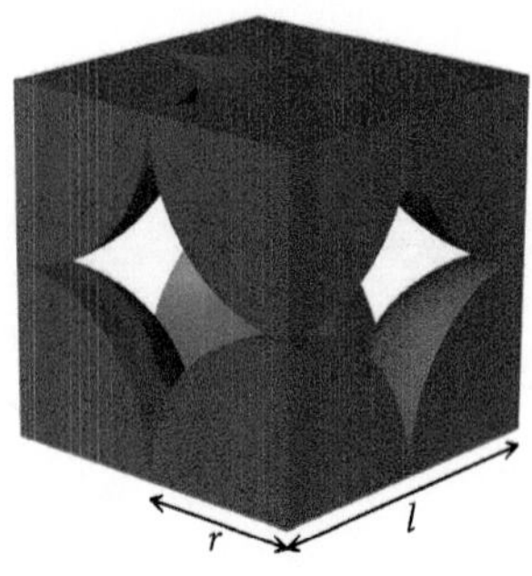

$l = 2r$

▲ In the simple cubic lattice, the atoms touch along each edge so that the edge length is $2r$.

X-ray crystallography allows us to determine the regular arrangements of atoms within a crystalline solid. This arrangement is called the **crystalline lattice**. The crystalline lattice of any solid is nature's way of aggregating the particles to minimize their energy. We can represent the crystalline lattice with a small collection of atoms, ions, or molecules called the **unit cell**. When the unit cell is repeated over and over—like the tiles of a floor or the pattern in a wallpaper design, but in three dimensions—the entire lattice can be reproduced. For example, consider the two-dimensional crystalline lattice shown at left. The unit cell for this lattice is the dark-coloured square. Each circle represents a *lattice point*, a point in space occupied by an atom, ion, or molecule. Repeating the pattern in the square throughout the two-dimensional space generates the entire lattice.

Many different unit cells exist, and we often classify unit cells by their symmetry. In this text, we focus primarily on *cubic unit cells* (although we will look at one hexagonal unit cell). Cubic unit cells are characterized by equal edge lengths and 90° angles at their corners. The three cubic unit cells—simple cubic, body-centred cubic, and face-centred cubic—along with some of their basic characteristics, are presented in Figure 11.47 ▼. We use two colours in this figure to help you visualize the different positions of the atoms; they *do not* represent different *kinds* of atoms. For these unit cells, *each atom in any one structure is identical to the other atoms in that structure.*

The **simple cubic** unit cell (Figure 11.48 ►) consists of a cube with one atom at each corner. The atoms touch along each edge of the cube, so the edge length is twice the radius of the atoms ($l = 2r$). Even though it may seem like the unit cell contains eight atoms, it actually contains only one. Each corner atom is shared by eight other unit cells. In other words, any one unit cell actually contains only one-eighth of each of the eight atoms at its corners, for a total of only one atom per unit cell.

A characteristic feature of any unit cell is the **coordination number**, the number of atoms with which each atom is in *direct contact*. The coordination number is the number of atoms with which a particular atom can strongly interact. The simple cubic unit cell has a coordination number of 6; any one atom touches only six others, as

Cubic Cell Name	Atoms per Unit Cell	Structure	Unit Cell	Coordination Number	Edge Length (in terms of r)	Packing Efficiency (fraction of volume occupied)
Simple cubic	1			6	$2r$	52%
Body-centred cubic	2			8	$\frac{4r}{\sqrt{3}}$	68%
Face-centred cubic	4			12	$(2\sqrt{2})r$	74%

▲ **FIGURE 11.47 The Cubic Crystalline Lattices** The different colours used for the atoms in this figure are for clarity only. All atoms within each structure are identical.

▲ **FIGURE 11.48 Simple Cubic Crystal Structure**

you can see in Figure 11.48. A quantity closely related to the coordination number is the **packing efficiency**, the percentage of the volume of the unit cell occupied by the spheres. The higher the coordination number, the greater the packing efficiency. The simple cubic unit cell has a packing efficiency of 52%—the simple cubic unit cell contains a lot of empty space.

The **body-centred cubic** unit cell (Figure 11.49 ▼) consists of a cube with one atom at each corner and one atom (of the same kind) in the very centre of the cube. Note that in the body-centred unit cell, the atoms *do not* touch along each edge of the cube, but instead along the diagonal line that runs from one corner, through the middle of the cube, to the opposite corner. The edge length in terms of the atomic radius is therefore $l = 4r/\sqrt{3}$, as shown in the diagram at left. The body-centred unit cell contains two atoms per unit cell

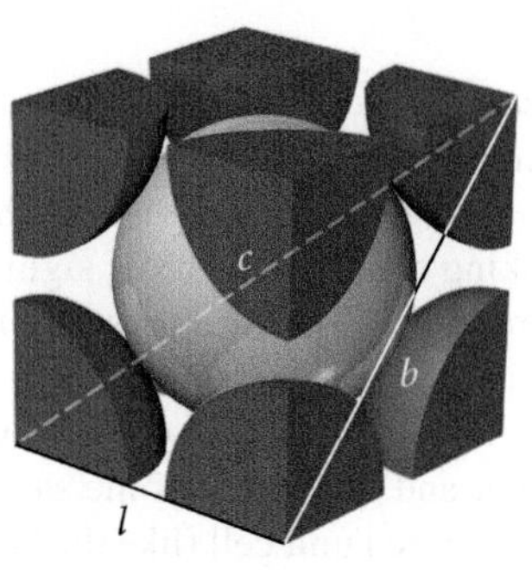

$$c^2 = b^2 + l^2 \qquad b^2 = l^2 + l^2$$
$$c = 4r \qquad b^2 = 2l^2$$
$$(4r)^2 = 2l^2 + l^2$$
$$(4r)^2 = 3l^2$$
$$l^2 = \frac{(4r)^2}{3}$$
$$l = \frac{4r}{\sqrt{3}}$$

▲ In the body-centred cubic lattice, the atoms touch only along the cube diagonal. The edge length is $4r/\sqrt{3}$.

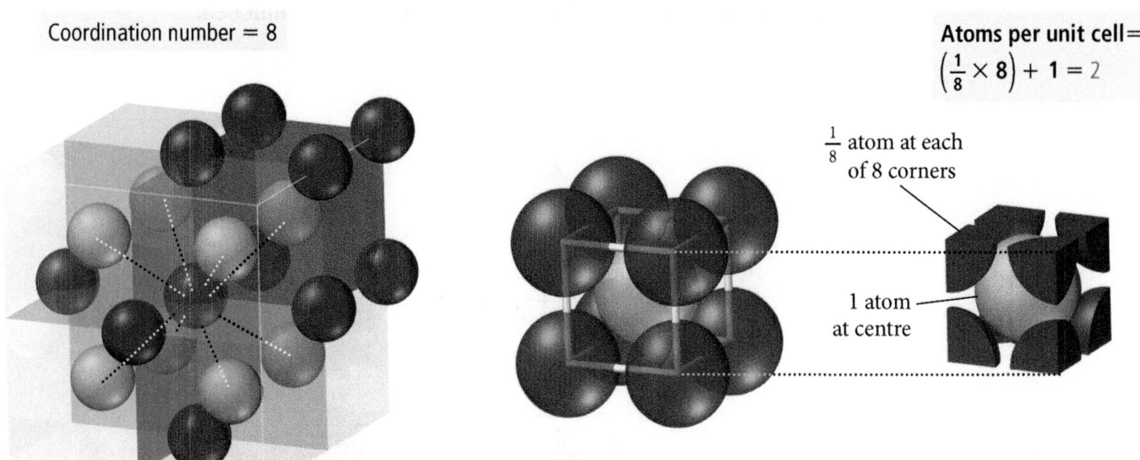

▲ **FIGURE 11.49 Body-Centred Cubic Crystal Structure** The different colours used for the atoms in this figure are for clarity only. All atoms within the structure are identical.

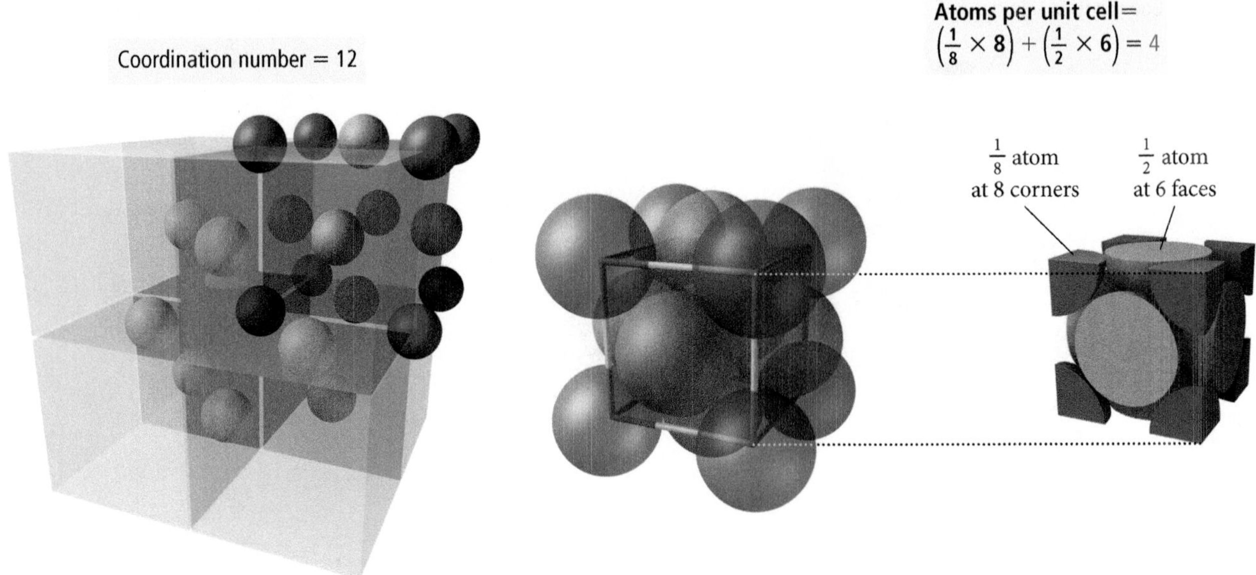

▲ **FIGURE 11.50 Face-Centred Cubic Crystal Structure** The different colours used on the atoms in this figure are for clarity only. All atoms within the structure are identical.

because the centre atom is not shared with any other neighbouring cells. The coordination number of the body-centred cubic unit cell is 8, which you can see by examining the atom in the very centre of the cube, which touches eight atoms at the corners. The packing efficiency is 68%, significantly higher than for the simple cubic unit cell. Each atom in this structure strongly interacts with more atoms than each atom in the simple cubic unit cell.

The **face-centred cubic** unit cell (Figure 11.50 ▲) is a cube with one atom at each corner and one atom (of the same kind) in the centre of each cube face. Note that in the face-centred unit cell (like the body-centred unit cell), the atoms *do not* touch along each edge of the cube. Instead, the atoms touch *along the diagonal face*. The edge length in terms of the atomic radius is therefore $l = 2\sqrt{2}r$, as shown in the figure below. The face-centred unit cell contains four atoms per unit cell because the centre atoms on each of the six faces are shared between two unit cells. There are $^1/_2 \times 6 = 3$ face-centred atoms plus $^1/_8 \times 8 = 1$ corner atoms, for a total of four atoms per unit cell. The coordination number of the face-centred cubic unit cell is 12 and its packing efficiency is 74%. In this structure, any one atom strongly interacts with more atoms than in either the simple cubic unit cell or the body-centred cubic unit cell.

Face-centred cubic

$$
\begin{aligned}
b^2 &= l^2 + l^2 = 2l^2 \\
b &= 4r \\
(4r)^2 &= 2l^2 \\
l^2 &= \frac{(4r)^2}{2} \\
l &= \frac{4r}{\sqrt{2}} \\
&= 2\sqrt{2}r
\end{aligned}
$$

b

r

l

▶ In the face-centred cubic lattice, the atoms touch along a face diagonal. The edge length is $2\sqrt{2}r$.

EXAMPLE 11.6 RELATING DENSITY TO CRYSTAL STRUCTURE

Aluminum crystallizes with a face-centred cubic unit cell. The radius of an aluminum atom is 143 pm. Calculate the density of solid crystalline aluminum in g cm^{-3}.

SORT You are given the radius of an aluminum atom and its crystal structure. You are asked to find the density of solid aluminum.

GIVEN: $r = 143$ pm, face-centred cubic

FIND: d

STRATEGIZE The conceptual plan is based on the definition of density.

Since the unit cell has the physical properties of the entire crystal, you can find the mass and volume of the unit cell and use these to calculate its density.

CONCEPTUAL PLAN

$$d = m/V$$

$$m = \text{mass of unit cell} = \text{number of atoms in unit cell} \times \text{mass of each atom}$$

$$V = \text{volume of unit cell} = (\text{edge length})^3$$

SOLVE Begin by finding the mass of the unit cell. Obtain the mass of an aluminum atom from its molar mass. Since the face-centred cubic unit cell contains four atoms per unit cell, multiply the mass of aluminum by 4 to get the mass of a unit cell.

SOLUTION

$$m(\text{Al atom}) = 26.98\frac{\text{g}}{\cancel{\text{mol}}} \times \frac{1\ \cancel{\text{mol}}}{6.022 \times 10^{23}\ \text{atoms}} = 4.480 \times 10^{-23}\ \text{g atom}^{-1}$$

$$m(\text{unit cell}) = 4\ \cancel{\text{atoms}}\ (4.480 \times 10^{-23}\ \text{g}\ \cancel{\text{atom}^{-1}}) = 1.792 \times 10^{-22}\ \text{g}$$

Next, compute the edge length (l) of the unit cell (in m) from the atomic radius of aluminum. For the face-centred cubic structure, $l = 2\sqrt{2}r$.

$$l = 2\sqrt{2}\,(143\ \text{pm}) = 2\sqrt{2}\,(143 \times 10^{-12}\ \text{m}) = 4.0\underline{4}5 \times 10^{-10}\ \text{m}$$

Compute the volume of the unit cell (in cm) by converting the edge length to cm and cubing the edge length. (We use centimetres because we want to report the density in units of g cm^{-3}.)

$$V = l^3 = \left(4.0\underline{4}5 \times 10^{-10}\ \cancel{\text{m}} \times \frac{1\ \text{cm}}{10^{-2}\ \cancel{\text{m}}}\right)^3 = 6.6\underline{1}8 \times 10^{-23}\ \text{cm}^3$$

Finally, compute the density by dividing the mass of the unit cell by the volume of the unit cell.

$$d = \frac{m}{V} = \frac{1.792 \times 10^{-22}\ \text{g}}{6.618 \times 10^{-23}\ \text{cm}^3} = 2.71\ \text{g cm}^{-3}$$

CHECK The units of the answer are correct. The magnitude of the answer is reasonable because the density is greater than 1 g cm^{-3} (as we would expect for metals), but still not too high (because aluminum is a low-density metal).

FOR PRACTICE 11.6

Chromium crystallizes with a body-centred cubic unit cell. The radius of a chromium atom is 125 pm. Calculate the density of solid crystalline chromium in g cm^{-3}.

Closest-Packed Structures

Another way to envision crystal structures, especially useful in metals where bonds are not usually directional, is to think of the atoms as stacking in layers, much as fruit is stacked at the grocery store. For example, the simple cubic structure can be envisioned as one layer of atoms arranged in a square pattern with the next layer stacking directly over the first, so that the atoms in one layer align exactly on top of the atoms in the layer beneath it, as shown here.

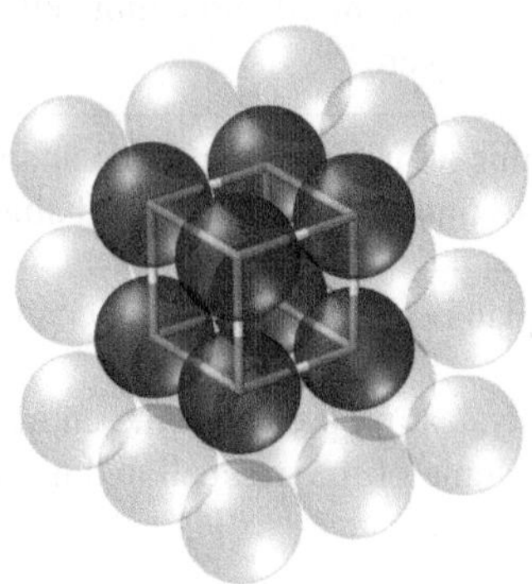

As we saw previously, this crystal structure has a great deal of empty space—only 52% of the volume is occupied by the spheres, and the coordination number is 6.

More space-efficient packing can be achieved by aligning neighbouring rows of atoms in a pattern with one row offset from the next by one-half a sphere, as shown here.

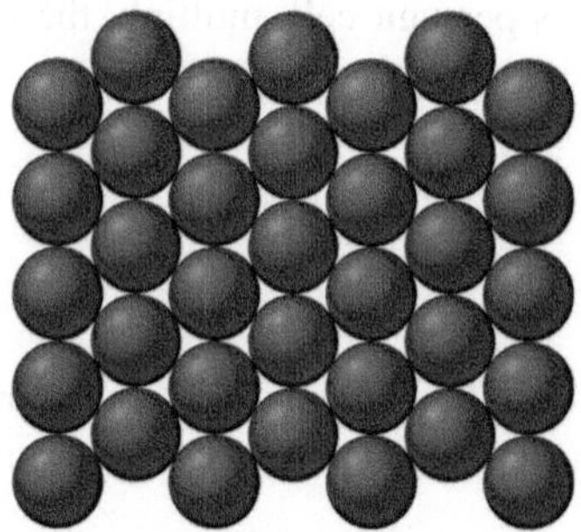

In this way, the atoms pack more closely to each other in any one layer. We can further increase the packing efficiency by placing the next layer *not directly on top of the first*, but again offset so that any one atom actually sits in the indentation formed by three atoms in the layer beneath it, as shown here:

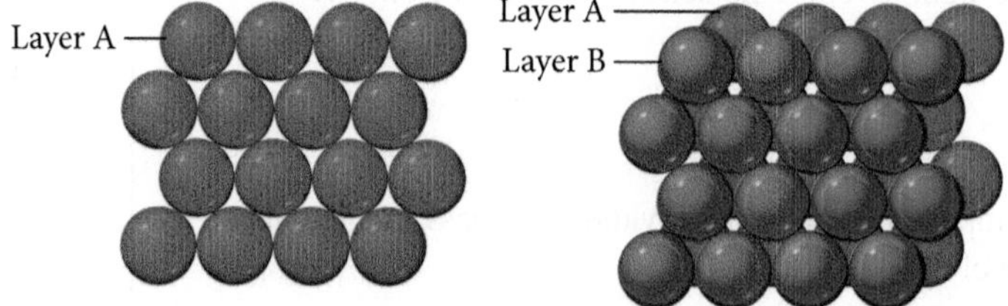

This kind of packing leads to two different crystal structures called *closest-packed structures*, both of which have a packing efficiency of 74% and a coordination number of 12. In the first of these two closest-packed structures—called **hexagonal closest packing**—the third layer of atoms aligns exactly on top of the first, as shown here.

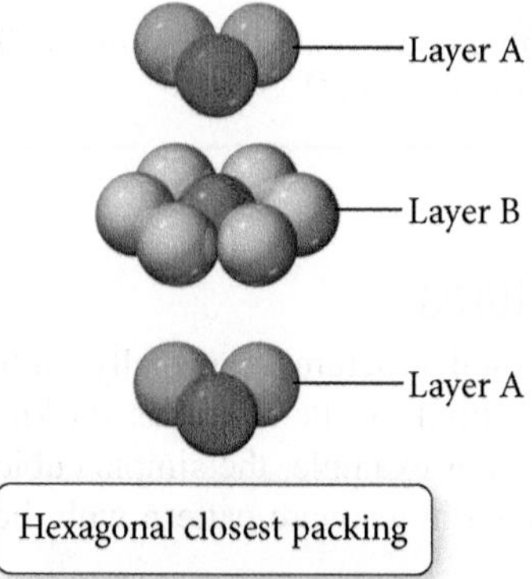

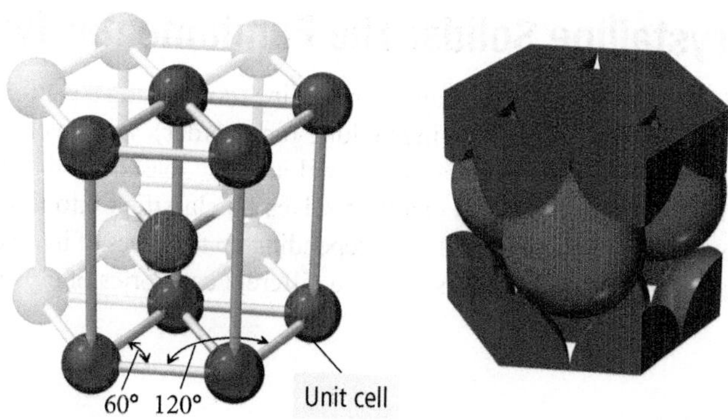

◀ **FIGURE 11.51 Hexagonal Closest-Packing Crystal Structure** The unit cell is shown in full colour in the first part of the figure.

The pattern from one layer to the next is ABAB . . . , with the third layer aligning exactly on top of the first. Notice that the central atom in layer B of this structure is touching six atoms in its own layer, three atoms in the layer above it, and three atoms in the layer below, for a coordination number of 12. The unit cell for this crystal structure is not a cubic unit cell, but a hexagonal one, as shown in Figure 11.51 ▲.

In the second of the two closest-packed structures—called **cubic closest packing**—the third layer of atoms is offset from the first, as shown here:

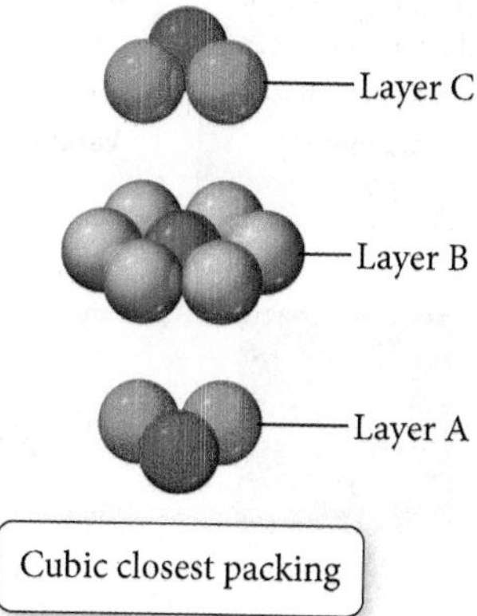

The pattern from one layer to the next is ABCABC . . . , with every fourth layer aligning with the first. Although not simple to visualize, the unit cell for cubic closest packing is the face-centred cubic unit cell, as shown in Figure 11.52 ▼. The cubic closest-packed structure is identical to the face-centred cubic unit cell structure.

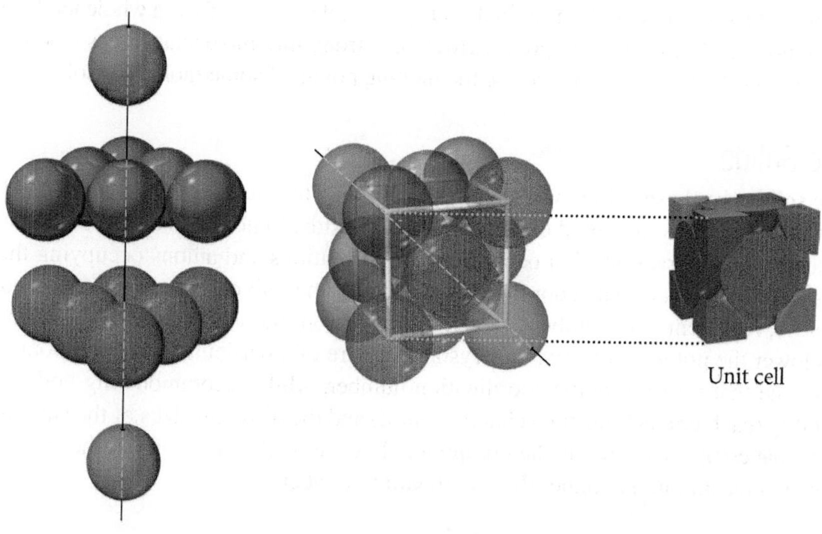

◀ **FIGURE 11.52 Cubic Closest-Packing Crystal Structure** The unit cell of the cubic closest-packed structure is face-centred cubic.

11.12 Crystalline Solids: The Fundamental Types

As we learned in Section 11.2, solids may be crystalline (comprising a well-ordered array of atoms or molecules) or amorphous (having no long-range order). We can classify crystalline solids into three categories—molecular, ionic, and atomic—based on the individual units that compose the solid. Atomic solids can themselves be classified into three categories—nonbonded, metallic, and network covalent—depending on the types of interactions between atoms within the solid. Figure 11.53 ▼ shows the different categories of crystalline solids.

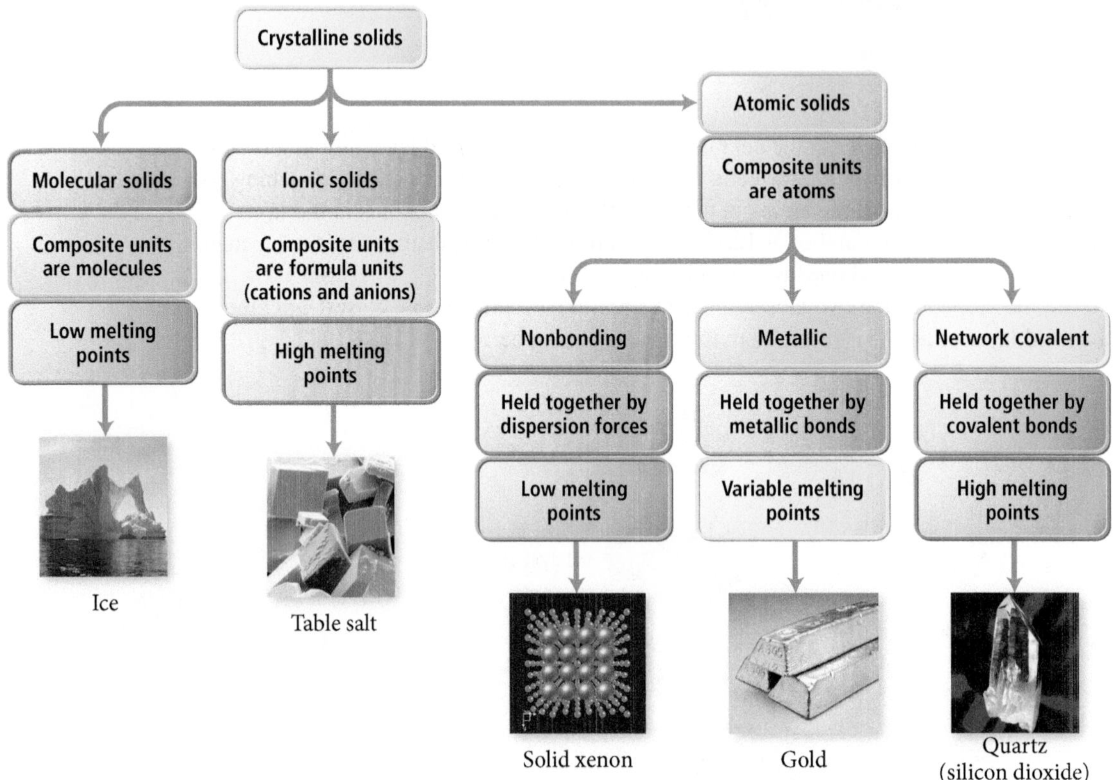

▲ **FIGURE 11.53 Types of Crystalline Solids**

Molecular Solids

Molecular solids are those solids whose composite units are *molecules*. The lattice sites in a crystalline molecular solid are therefore occupied by molecules. Ice (solid H_2O) and dry ice (solid CO_2) are examples of molecular solids. Molecular solids are held together by the kinds of intermolecular forces—dispersion forces, dipole–dipole forces, and hydrogen bonding—that we discussed earlier in this chapter. Molecular solids as a whole tend to have low to moderately low melting points. However, strong intermolecular forces (such as the hydrogen bonds in water) can increase the melting points of some molecular solids.

Ionic Solids

Ionic solids are those solids whose composite units are ions. Table salt (NaCl) and calcium fluoride (CaF_2) are good examples of ionic solids. Ionic solids are held together by the coulombic interactions that occur between the cations and anions occupying the lattice sites in the crystal. The coordination number of the unit cell for an ionic compound, therefore, represents the number of close cation–anion interactions. Since these interactions lower the potential energy, the crystal structure of a particular ionic compound will be the one that maximizes the coordination number, while accommodating both charge neutrality (each unit cell must be charge neutral) and the different sizes of the cations and anions that compose the particular compound. In general, the more similar the radii of the cation and the anion, the higher the coordination number.

Cesium chloride (CsCl) is a good example of an ionic compound with cations and anions of similar size (Cs^+ radius = 167 pm; Cl^- radius = 181 pm). In the cesium chloride structure, the chloride ions occupy the lattice sites of a simple cubic cell and one cesium ion lies in the very centre of the cell, as shown in Figure 11.54 ▸. (In this and subsequent figures of ionic crystal structures, the different-coloured spheres represent different ions.) The coordination number is 8, meaning that each cesium ion is in direct contact with eight chloride ions (and vice versa). The cesium chloride unit cell contains one chloride anion ($8 \times 1/8 = 1$) and one cesium cation, for a ratio of Cs to Cl of 1:1, as the formula for the compound indicates. (Note that complete chloride ions are shown in Figure 11.54 even though only 1/8 of each ion is in the unit cell.) Calcium sulfide (CaS) has the same structure as cesium chloride.

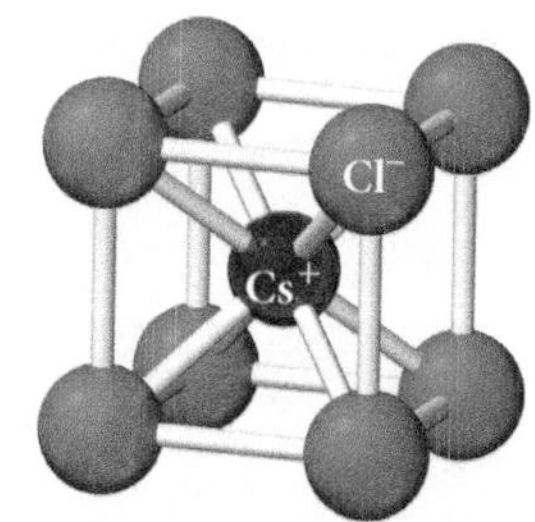

▲ **FIGURE 11.54 Cesium Chloride Unit Cell** The different-coloured spheres in this figure represent the different ions in the compound.

The crystal structure of sodium chloride must accommodate the more disproportionate sizes of Na^+ (radius = 97 pm) and Cl^- (radius = 181 pm). If ion size were the only consideration, the larger chloride anion could theoretically fit many of the smaller sodium cations around it, but charge neutrality requires that each sodium cation be surrounded by an equal number of chloride anions. Therefore, the coordination number is limited by the number of chloride anions that can fit around the relatively small sodium cation. The structure that minimizes the energy is shown in Figure 11.55 ▸ and has a coordination number of 6 (each chloride anion is surrounded by six sodium cations and vice versa). You can visualize this structure, called the *rock salt* structure, as chloride anions occupying the lattice sites of a face-centred cubic structure with the smaller sodium cations occupying the holes between the anions. (Alternatively, you can visualize this structure as the *sodium cations* occupying the lattice sites of a face-centred cubic structure with the *larger chloride anions* occupying the spaces between the cations.) Each unit cell contains four chloride anions $[(8 \times {}^1/_8) + (6 \times {}^1/_2) = 4]$ and four sodium cations $[(12 \times {}^1/_4) + 1 = 4]$, resulting in a ratio of 1:1, as the formula of the compound specifies. Other compounds exhibiting the sodium chloride structure include LiF, KCl, KBr, AgCl, MgO, and CaO.

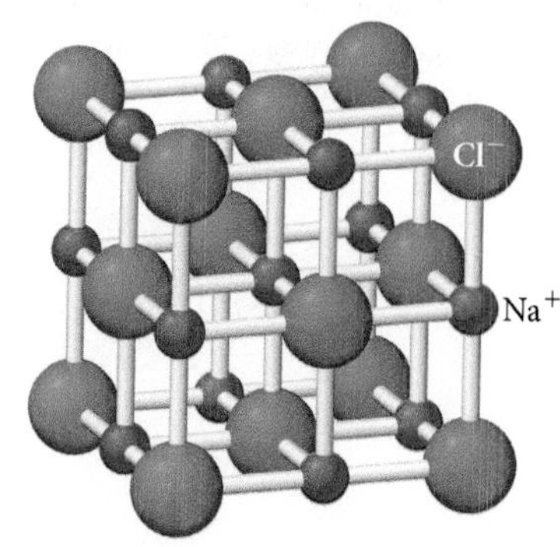

▲ **FIGURE 11.55 Sodium Chloride Unit Cell** The different-coloured spheres in this figure represent the different ions in the compound.

An even greater disproportion between the sizes of the cations and anions in a compound makes a coordination number of even 6 physically impossible. For example, in ZnS (Zn^{2+} radius = 74 pm; S^{2-} radius = 184 pm), the crystal structure, shown in Figure 11.56 ▸, has a coordination number of only 4. You can visualize this structure, called the *zinc blende* structure, as sulfide anions occupying the lattice sites of a face-centred cubic structure with the smaller zinc cations occupying four of the eight tetrahedral holes located directly beneath each corner atom. A tetrahedral hole is the empty space that lies in the centre of a tetrahedral arrangement of four atoms, as shown below. Each unit cell contains four sulfide anions $[(8 \times {}^1/_8) + (6 \times {}^1/_2 = 4)]$ and four zinc cations (each of the four zinc cations is completely contained within the unit cell), resulting in a ratio of 1:1, just as the formula of the compound indicates. Other compounds exhibiting the zinc blende structure include CuCl, AgI, and CdS.

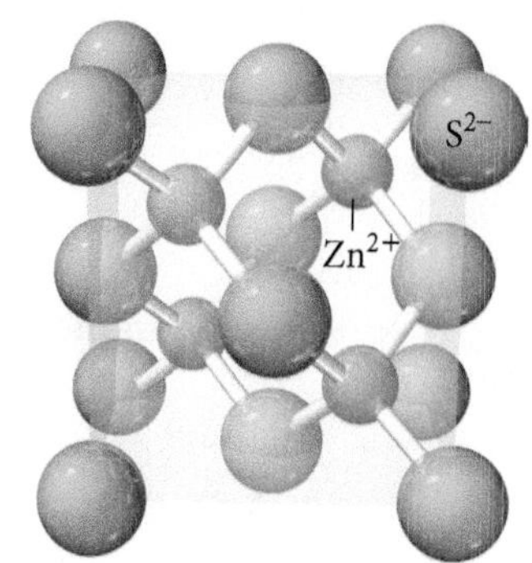

▲ **FIGURE 11.56 Zinc Sulfide (Zinc Blende) Unit Cell** The different-coloured spheres in this figure represent the different ions in the compound.

When the ratio of cations to anions is not 1:1, the crystal structure must accommodate the unequal number of cations and anions. Many compounds that contain a cation-to-anion ratio of 1:2 adopt the *fluorite* (CaF_2) *structure* shown in Figure 11.57 ▾. You can visualize this structure as calcium cations occupying the lattice sites of a face-centred cubic structure with the larger fluoride anions occupying all eight of the tetrahedral holes located directly beneath each corner atom. Each unit cell contains four calcium cations $[(8 \times {}^1/_8) + (6 \times {}^1/_2) = 4]$ and eight fluoride anions (each of the eight fluoride anions is completely contained within the unit cell), resulting in a cation-to-anion ratio of 1:2, just as in the formula of the compound. Other compounds exhibiting the fluorite structure include PbF_2, SrF_2, and $BaCl_2$. Compounds with a cation-to-anion ratio of 2:1 often exhibit the *antifluorite structure*, in which the anions occupy the lattice sites of a face-centred cubic structure and the cations occupy the tetrahedral holes beneath each corner atom.

The forces holding ionic solids together are strong coulombic forces (or ionic bonds), and since these forces are much stronger than the intermolecular forces discussed previously, ionic solids tend to have much higher melting points than molecular solids. For example, sodium chloride melts at 801 °C, while carbon disulfide (CS_2)—a molecular solid with a higher molar mass—melts at −110 °C.

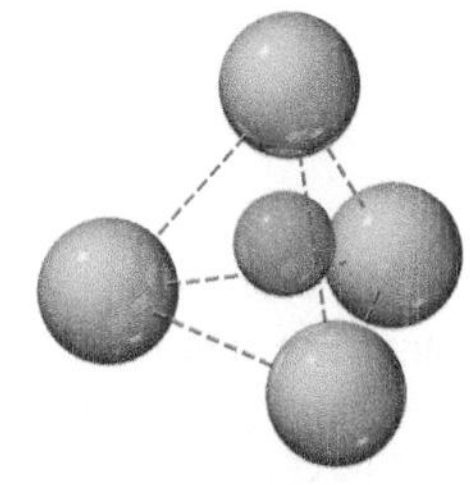
▲ A tetrahedral hole.

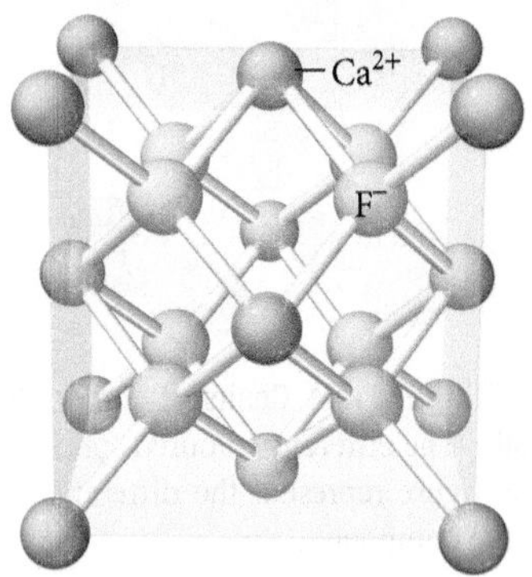

▲ **FIGURE 11.57 Calcium Fluoride Unit Cell** The different-coloured spheres in this figure represent the different ions in the compound.

Atomic Solids

Solids whose composite units are individual atoms are **atomic solids**. Solid xenon (Xe) and iron (Fe), are examples of atomic solids. Atomic solids can themselves be classified into three categories—*nonbonding atomic solids, metallic atomic solids*, and *network covalent atomic solids*—each held together by a different kind of force.

Nonbonding atomic solids are held together by relatively weak dispersion forces. In order to maximize these interactions, nonbonding atomic solids form closest-packed structures, maximizing their coordination numbers and minimizing the distance between them. Nonbonding atomic solids have very low melting points that increase uniformly with molar mass. The only nonbonding atomic solids are noble gases in their solid form. Argon, for example, has a melting point of −189 °C and xenon has a melting point of −112 °C.

Metallic atomic solids, such as iron or gold, are held together by *metallic bonds*, which in the simplest terms can be described as the metals being held together by delocalized molecular orbitals, as described in Section 10.8.

Since metallic bonds are not directional, metals also tend to form closest-packed crystal structures. For example, nickel crystallizes in the cubic closest-packed structure and zinc crystallizes in the hexagonal closest-packed structure (Figure 11.58 ▼). Metallic bonds have varying strengths. Some metals, such as mercury, have melting points below room temperature, whereas other metals, such as iron, have relatively high melting points (iron melts at 1808 K).

Network covalent solids, such as diamond, graphite, and silicon dioxide, are held together by covalent bonds. The crystal structures of these solids are more restricted by the geometrical constraints of the covalent bonds (which tend to be more directional than intermolecular forces, ionic bonds, or metallic bonds), so they *do not* tend to form closest-packed structures.

In diamond (Figure 11.59(a) ▶), each carbon atom forms four covalent bonds to four other carbon atoms in a tetrahedral geometry. This structure extends throughout the entire crystal, so a diamond crystal can be thought of as a giant molecule, held together by these covalent bonds. Since covalent bonds are very strong, covalent atomic solids have high melting points. Diamond is estimated to melt at about 3800 °C. The electrons in diamond are confined to the covalent bonds and are not free to flow. Therefore, diamond does not conduct electricity.

σ (sigma) and π (pi) bonds were discussed in Section 10.7.

In graphite (Figure 11.59(b)), carbon atoms are arranged in sheets. Within each sheet, carbon atoms are covalently bonded to each other by a network of σ and π bonds, similar to those in benzene. Just as the electrons within the π bonds in benzene are delocalized over the entire molecule, so the π bonds in graphite are delocalized over the entire sheet, making graphite a good electrical conductor along the sheets. The bond length between carbon atoms *within a sheet* is 142 pm. However, the forces *between* sheets are much

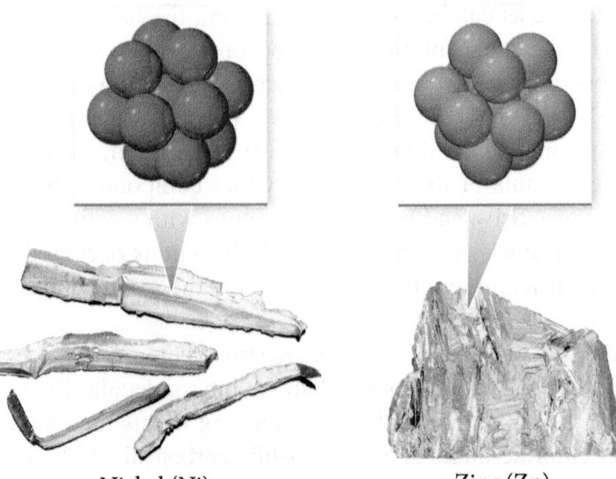

▶ **FIGURE 11.58 Closest-Packed Crystal Structures in Metals** Nickel crystallizes in the cubic closest-packed structure. Zinc crystallizes in the hexagonal closest-packed structure.

▲ **FIGURE 11.59 Network Covalent Atomic Solids** (a) In diamond, each carbon atom forms four covalent bonds to four other carbon atoms in a tetrahedral geometry. (b) In graphite, carbon atoms are arranged in sheets. Within each sheet, the atoms are covalently bonded to one another by a network of σ and π bonds. Neighbouring sheets are held together by dispersion forces.

different. The separation between sheets is 341 pm. There are no covalent bonds between sheets, only relatively weak dispersion forces. Consequently, the sheets slide past each other relatively easily, which explains the slippery feel of graphite and its extensive use as a lubricant.

The silicates (extended arrays of silicon and oxygen) are the most common network covalent solids. Geologists estimate that 90% of Earth's crust is composed of silicates; we cover these in more detail in Chapter 22. The basic silicon–oxygen compound is silica (SiO_2), which, in its most common crystalline form, is called quartz. The structure of quartz consists of an array of SiO_4 tetrahedra with shared oxygen atoms, as shown in Figure 11.60(a) ▼. The strong silicon–oxygen covalent bonds that hold quartz together result in its high melting point of about 1600 °C. Common glass is also composed of SiO_2, but in its amorphous form (Figure 11.60(b)).

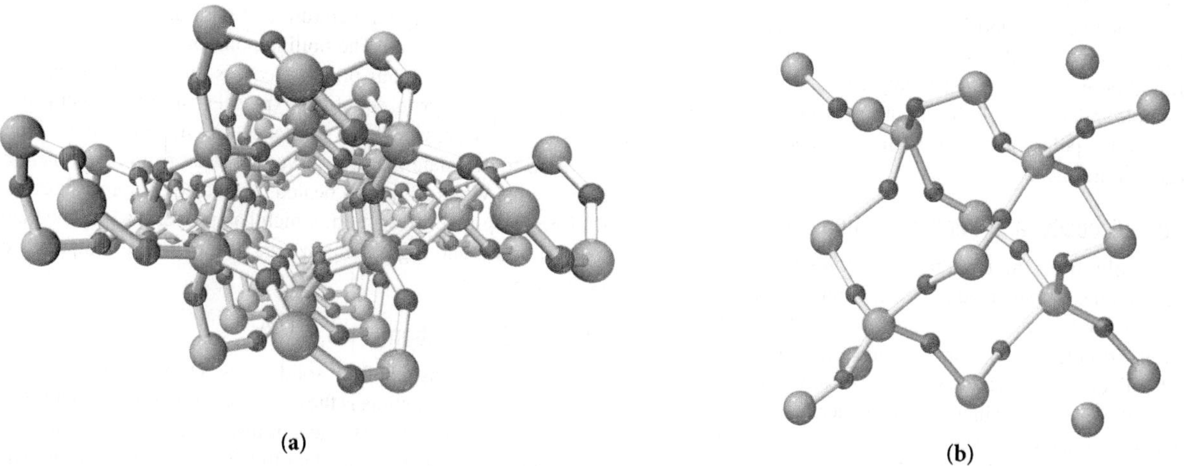

▲ **FIGURE 11.60 The Structure of Quartz** (a) Quartz consists of an array of SiO_4 tetrahedra with shared oxygen atoms. (b) Glass is amorphous SiO_2.

CHAPTER IN REVIEW

Key Terms

Section 11.2
crystalline (430)
amorphous solid (430)

Section 11.3
ion–induced dipole force (432)
dispersion force (432)
dipole–dipole force (434)
permanent dipole (434)
miscibility (435)
hydrogen bonding (437)
hydrogen bond (437)
dipole-induced dipole force (439)
ion–dipole force (439)

Section 11.4
surface tension (443)
viscosity (443)
capillary action (444)

Section 11.5
vaporization (446)
condensation (446)
volatile (446)
nonvolatile (446)
heat of vaporization ($\Delta_{\text{vap}}H°$) (447)
dynamic equilibrium (448)
vapour pressure (449)
boiling point (450)
normal boiling point (450)
standard boiling point (451)
Clausius–Clapeyron equation (452)
critical temperature (T_c) (455)
critical pressure (P_c) (455)

Section 11.6
sublimation (455)
deposition (455)
melting point (456)
melting (fusion) (456)
freezing (456)
heat of fusion ($\Delta_{\text{fus}}H°$) (456)

Section 11.8
phase diagram (459)
triple point (460)
critical point (460)

Section 11.10
X-ray diffraction (464)

Section 11.11
crystalline lattice (466)
unit cell (466)
simple cubic (466)
coordination number (466)
packing efficiency (467)
body-centred cubic (467)
face-centred cubic (468)
hexagonal closest packing (470)
cubic closest packing (471)

Section 11.12
molecular solids (472)
ionic solids (472)
atomic solids (474)
nonbonding atomic solids (474)
metallic atomic solids (474)
network covalent solids (474)

Key Concepts

Solids, Liquids, and Intermolecular Forces (11.1, 11.2, 11.3)

Intermolecular forces hold molecules or atoms together in a liquid or solid. The strength of the intermolecular forces in a substance at a fixed temperature and pressure determines its state. Dispersion forces are always present because they result from the fluctuations in electron distribution within atoms and molecules. They can be the weakest intermolecular forces, but they are significant in molecules with many electrons. Dipole–dipole forces are present in all polar molecules. Hydrogen bonding occurs in polar molecules that contain hydrogen atoms bonded directly to fluorine, oxygen, or nitrogen. In general, the weakest hydrogen bonds are stronger than the weakest dipole–dipole forces, which are stronger than the weakest dispersion forces. Ion-induced dipole and ion–dipole forces occur when ionic compounds are mixed with nonpolar and polar compounds, respectively. Ion–dipole forces are especially important in aqueous solutions. Dipole-induced dipole forces are present in mixtures containing polar and nonpolar molecules, such as aqueous solutions containing oxygen or nitrogen.

Surface Tension, Viscosity, and Capillary Action (11.4)

Surface tension results from the tendency of liquids to minimize their surface area in order to maximize the interactions between their constituent particles, thus lowering their potential energy. Surface tension causes water droplets to form spheres and allows insects and paper clips to "float" on the surface of water. Viscosity is the resistance of a liquid to flow. Viscosity increases with increasing strength of intermolecular forces and decreases with increasing temperature. Capillary action is the ability of a liquid to flow against gravity up a narrow tube. It is the result of adhesive forces, the attraction between the molecules and the surface of the tube, and cohesive forces, the attraction between the molecules in the liquid.

Vaporization and Vapour Pressure (11.5, 11.7)

Vaporization, the transition from liquid to gas, occurs when thermal energy overcomes the intermolecular forces present in a liquid. The opposite process is condensation. Vaporization is endothermic and condensation is exothermic. The rate of vaporization increases with increasing temperature, increasing surface area, and decreasing strength of intermolecular forces. The heat of vaporization ($\Delta_{\text{vap}}H°$) is the heat required to vaporize 1 mol of a liquid. In a sealed container, a solution and its vapour will come into dynamic equilibrium, at which point the rate of vaporization equals the rate of condensation. The pressure of a gas that is in dynamic equilibrium with its liquid is its vapour pressure. The vapour pressure of a substance increases with increasing temperature and with decreasing strength of its intermolecular forces. The boiling point of a liquid is the temperature at which its vapour pressure equals the external pressure. The Clausius–Clapeyron equation expresses the relationship between the vapour pressure of a substance and its temperature, and can be used to calculate the heat of vaporization from experimental measurements. When a liquid is heated in a sealed container, it eventually forms a supercritical fluid, which has properties intermediate between a liquid and a gas. This occurs at the critical temperature and critical pressure.

Fusion and Sublimation (11.6, 11.7)

Sublimation is the transition from solid to gas. The opposite process is deposition. Fusion, or melting, is the transition from solid to liquid. The opposite process is freezing. The heat of fusion ($\Delta_{\text{fus}}H°$) is the amount of heat required to melt one mole of a solid. Fusion is endothermic. The heat of fusion is generally less than the heat of vaporization because intermolecular forces do not have to be completely overcome for melting to occur.

Phase Diagrams (11.8)

A phase diagram is a map of the states of a substance as a function of its pressure (y-axis) and temperature (x-axis). The regions in a phase diagram represent conditions under which a single stable state (solid, liquid, gas) exists. The lines represent conditions under which two states are in equilibrium. The triple point represents the conditions under which all three states coexist. The critical point is the temperature and pressure above which a supercritical fluid exists.

The Uniqueness of Water (11.9)

Water is a liquid at room temperature despite having only 10 electrons and not being very polarizable. Water forms strong hydrogen bonds, resulting in its high boiling point. Its high polarity also enables it to dissolve many polar and ionic compounds, and even nonpolar gases. Water expands upon freezing, so that ice is less dense than liquid water. Water is critical both to the existence of life and to human health.

Crystalline Structures (11.10–11.12)

In X-ray crystallography, the diffraction pattern of X-rays is used to determine the crystal structure of solids. The crystal lattice is represented by a unit cell, a structure that reproduces the entire lattice when repeated in all three dimensions. Three basic cubic unit cells are the simple cubic, the body-centred cubic, and the face-centred cubic. Some crystal lattices can also be depicted as closest-packed structures, including the hexagonal closest-packing structure (not cubic) and the cubic closest-packing structure (which has a face-centred cubic unit cell). The types of crystal solids are molecular, ionic, and atomic solids. Atomic solids can be divided into three different types: nonbonded, metallic, and covalent.

Key Equations and Relationships

Clausius–Clapeyron Equation: Relationship Between Vapour Pressure (P_{vap}), Heat of Vaporization ($\Delta_{vap}H°$), and Temperature (T) (11.5)

$$\ln P_{vap} = \frac{-\Delta_{vap}H°}{RT} + \ln \beta \text{ } (\beta \text{ is a constant})$$

$$\ln\left(\frac{P_2}{P_1}\right) = \frac{-\Delta_{vap}H°}{R}\left[\frac{1}{T_2} - \frac{1}{T_1}\right]$$

Bragg's Law: Relationship Between Light Wavelength (λ), Angle of Reflection (θ), and Distance (d) Between Atomic Layers (11.10)

$$n\lambda = 2d \sin\theta \text{ } (n = \text{integer})$$

Key Skills

Determining Whether a Molecule Has Dipole–Dipole Forces (11.3)
• Example 11.1 • For Practice 11.1 • Exercises 47–58

Determining Whether a Molecule Displays Hydrogen Bonding (11.3)
• Example 11.2 • For Practice 11.2 • Exercises 47–58

Using the Heat of Vaporization in Calculations (11.5)
• Example 11.3 • For Practice 11.3 • For More Practice 11.3 • Exercises 69–72

Using the Clausius–Clapeyron Equation (11.5)
• Examples 11.4, 11.5 • For Practice 11.4, 11.5 • Exercises 73–76

Relating Density to Crystal Structure (11.11)
• Example 11.6 • For Practice 11.6 • Exercises 97–100

EXERCISES

Review Questions

1. Explain why a gecko is able to walk on a polished glass surface.
2. Why are intermolecular forces important?
3. What are the main properties of liquids (in contrast to gases and solids)?
4. What are the main properties of solids (in contrast to liquids and gases)?
5. What is the fundamental difference between an amorphous solid and a crystalline solid?
6. What factors cause changes between the solid and liquid state? The liquid and gas state?
7. Describe the relationship between the state of a substance, its temperature, and the strength of its intermolecular forces.
8. From what kinds of interactions do intermolecular forces originate?
9. Why are intermolecular forces generally much weaker than bonding forces?

10. What is the dispersion force? What does the magnitude of the dispersion force depend on? How can you predict the magnitude of the dispersion force for closely related elements or compounds?
11. What is the dipole–dipole force? How can you predict the presence of dipole–dipole forces in a compound?
12. How is the miscibility of two liquids related to their polarity?
13. What is hydrogen bonding? How can you predict the presence of hydrogen bonding in a compound?
14. What is the ion–dipole force? Why is it important?
15. What is surface tension? How does surface tension result from intermolecular forces? How is it related to the strength of intermolecular forces?
16. What is viscosity? How does viscosity depend on intermolecular forces? What other factors affect viscosity?
17. What is capillary action? How does it depend on the relative strengths of adhesive and cohesive forces?
18. Explain what happens in the processes of vaporization and condensation. Why does the rate of vaporization increase with increasing temperature and surface area?
19. Why is vaporization endothermic? Why is condensation exothermic?
20. How is the volatility of a substance related to the intermolecular forces present within the substance?
21. What is the heat of vaporization for a liquid and why is it useful?
22. Explain the process of dynamic equilibrium. How is dynamic equilibrium related to vapour pressure?
23. What happens to a system in dynamic equilibrium when it is disturbed in some way?
24. How is vapour pressure related to temperature? What happens to the vapour pressure of a substance when the temperature is increased? Decreased?
25. Define the terms *boiling point*, *normal boiling point*, and *standard boiling point*.
26. What is the Clausius–Clapeyron equation and why is it important?
27. Explain what happens to a substance when it is heated in a closed container to its critical temperature.
28. What is sublimation? Give a common example of sublimation.
29. What is fusion? Is fusion exothermic or endothermic? Why?
30. What is the heat of fusion and why is it important?
31. Examine the heating curve for water in Section 11.7 (Figure 11.39). Explain why the curve has two segments in which heat is added to the water but the temperature does not rise.
32. Examine the heating curve for water in Section 11.7 (Figure 11.39). Explain the significance of the slopes of each of the three rising segments. Why are the slopes different?
33. What is a phase diagram? Draw a generic phase diagram and label its important features.
34. What is a supercritical fluid?
35. What is the significance of crossing a line in a phase diagram?
36. How do the properties of water differ from those of most other substances?
37. Explain the basic principles involved in X-ray crystallography. Include Bragg's law in your explanation.
38. What is a crystalline lattice? How is the lattice represented with the unit cell?
39. Make a drawing of each unit cell: simple cubic, body-centred cubic, and face-centred cubic.
40. For each of the cubic cells in the previous problem, give the coordination number, edge length in terms of *r*, and number of atoms per unit cell.
41. What is the difference between hexagonal closest packing and cubic closest packing? What are the unit cells for each of these structures?
42. What are the three basic types of solids and the composite units of each? What types of forces hold each type of solid together?
43. In an ionic compound, how are the relative sizes of the cation and anion related to the coordination number of the crystal structure?
44. Show how the cesium chloride, sodium chloride, and zinc blende unit cells each contain a cation-to-anion ratio of 1:1.
45. Show how the fluorite structure accommodates a cation-to-anion ratio of 1:2.
46. What are the three basic subtypes of atomic solids? What kinds of forces hold each of these subtypes together?

Problems by Topic

Intermolecular Forces

47. Determine the kinds of intermolecular forces that are present in samples of each element or compound:
a. N_2 b. NH_3 c. CO d. CCl_4
48. Determine the kinds of intermolecular forces that are present in each element or compound:
a. Kr b. NCl_3 c. SiH_4 d. HF
49. Determine the kinds of intermolecular forces that are present in samples of each element or compound:
a. HCl b. H_2O c. Br_2 d. He
50. Determine the kinds of intermolecular forces that are present in samples of each element or compound:
a. PH_3 b. HBr c. CH_3OH d. I_2
51. Arrange these compounds in order of increasing boiling point. Explain your reasoning.
a. CH_4 b. CH_3CH_3 c. CH_3CH_2Cl d. CH_3CH_2OH
52. Arrange these compounds in order of increasing boiling point. Explain your reasoning.
a. H_2S b. H_2Se c. H_2O
53. For each pair of compounds, pick the one with the higher boiling point. Explain your reasoning.
a. CH_3OH or CH_3SH b. CH_3OCH_3 or CH_3CH_2OH
c. CH_4 or CH_3CH_3
54. For each pair of compounds, pick the one with the higher boiling point. Explain your reasoning.
a. NH_3 or CH_4 b. CS_2 or CO_2 c. CO_2 or NO_2
55. For each pair of compounds, pick the one with the higher vapour pressure at a given temperature. Explain your reasoning.
a. Br_2 or I_2 b. H_2S or H_2O c. NH_3 or PH_3
56. For each pair of compounds, pick the one with the higher vapour pressure at a given temperature. Explain your reasoning.
a. CH_4 or CH_3Cl
b. $CH_3CH_2CH_2OH$ or CH_3OH
c. CH_3OH or H_2CO

57. Which pairs of substances would you expect to form homogeneous solutions when combined? For those that form homogeneous solutions, indicate the type of forces that are involved.

a. CCl_4 and H_2O
b. KCl and H_2O
c. Br_2 and CCl_4
d. CH_3CH_2OH and H_2O

58. Which pairs of compounds would you expect to form homogeneous solutions when combined? For those that form homogeneous solutions, indicate the type of forces that are involved.

a. $CH_3CH_2CH_2CH_2CH_3$ and $CH_3CH_2CH_2CH_2CH_2CH_3$
b. CBr_4 and H_2O
c. $LiNO_3$ and H_2O
d. CH_3OH and $CH_3CH_2CH_2CH_2CH_3$

Surface Tension, Viscosity, and Capillary Action

59. Which compound would you expect to have greater surface tension: propanone $[(CH_3)_2CO]$ or water (H_2O)? Explain.

60. Water **(a)** "wets" some surfaces and beads up on others. Mercury **(b)**, in contrast, beads up on almost all surfaces. Explain this difference.

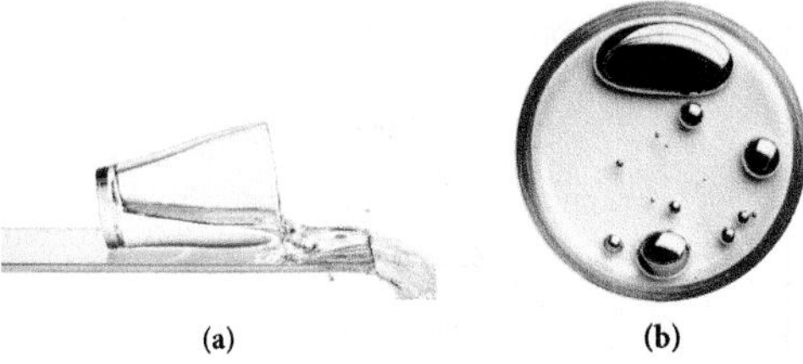

(a) (b)

61. The structures of two isomers of heptane are shown here. Which of these two compounds would you expect to have the greater viscosity?

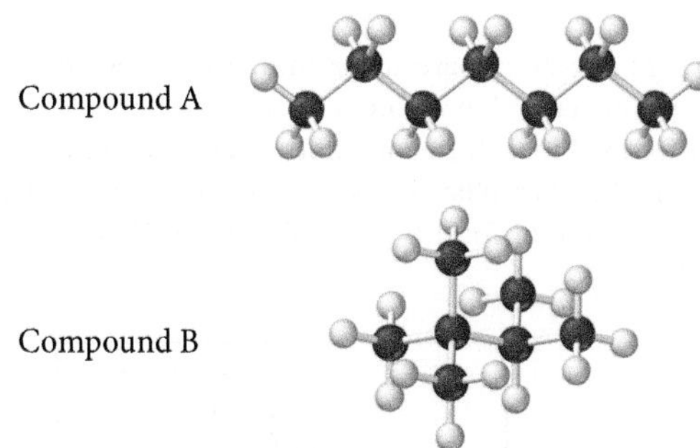

62. Explain why the viscosity of multigrade motor oils is less temperature dependent than that of single-grade motor oils.

63. Water in a glass tube that contains grease or oil residue displays a flat meniscus (left), whereas water in a clean glass tube displays a concave meniscus (right). Explain this difference.

64. When a thin glass tube is put into water, the water rises 1.4 cm. When the same tube is put into hexane, the hexane rises only 0.4 cm. Explain the difference.

Vaporization and Vapour Pressure

65. Which will evaporate more quickly: 55 mL of water in a beaker with a diameter of 4.5 cm, or 55 mL of water in a dish with a diameter of 12 cm? Will the vapour pressure of the water be different in the two containers? Explain.

66. Which will evaporate more quickly: 55 mL of water (H_2O) in a beaker or 55 mL of propanone $[(CH_3)_2CO]$ in an identical beaker under identical conditions? Is the vapour pressure of the two substances different? Explain.

67. Spilling room-temperature water over your skin on a hot day will cool you down. Spilling room-temperature vegetable oil over your skin on a hot day will not. Explain the difference.

68. Why is the heat of vaporization of water greater at room temperature than it is at its boiling point?

69. The human body obtains 915 kJ of energy from a candy bar. If this energy were used to vaporize water at 100.0 °C, how much water (in litres) could be vaporized? (Assume the density of water is 1.00 g mL^{-1}.)

70. A 100.0 mL sample of water is heated to its boiling point. How much heat (in kilojoules) is required to vaporize it? (Assume a density of 1.00 g mL^{-1}.)

71. Suppose that 0.95 g of water condenses on a 75.0 g block of iron that is initially at 22 °C. If the heat released during condensation goes only to warming the iron block, what is the final temperature (in Celsius) of the iron block? (Assume a constant enthalpy of vaporization for water of 44.0 kJ mol^{-1}.)

72. Suppose that 1.15 g of propan-2-ol (C_3H_8O) evaporates from a 65.0 g aluminum block. If the aluminum block is initially at 25 °C, what is the final temperature of the block after the evaporation of the alcohol? (Assume that the heat required for the vaporization of the alcohol comes only from the aluminum block and that the alcohol vaporizes at 25 °C.)

73. This table displays the vapour pressure of ammonia at several different temperatures. Use the data to determine the heat of vaporization and normal boiling point of ammonia.

Temperature (K)	Pressure (mbar)
200	87.1
210	179.1
220	340.9
230	608.0
235	795.9

74. This table displays the vapour pressure of nitrogen at several different temperatures. Use the data to determine the heat of vaporization and normal boiling point of nitrogen.

Temperature (K)	Pressure (mbar)
65	174.0
70	386.0
75	761.0
80	1371
85	2290

75. Ethanol has a heat of vaporization of 38.56 kJ mol^{-1} and a normal boiling point of 78.4 °C. What is the vapour pressure of ethanol at 15 °C?

76. Benzene has a heat of vaporization of 30.72 kJ mol^{-1} and a normal boiling point of 80.1 °C. At what temperature does benzene boil when the external pressure is 593 mbar?

Sublimation and Fusion

77. How much energy is released when 65.8 g of water freezes?

78. Calculate the amount of heat required to completely sublime 50.0 g of solid dry ice (CO_2) at its sublimation temperature. The heat of sublimation for carbon dioxide is 32.3 kJ mol^{-1}.

79. An 8.5 g ice cube is placed into 255 g of water. Calculate the temperature change in the water upon the complete melting of the ice. (Assume that all of the energy required to melt the ice comes from the water.)

80. How much ice (in grams) would have to melt to lower the temperature of 352 mL of water from 25 °C to 5 °C? (Assume the density of water is 1.0 g mL^{-1}.)

81. How much heat (in kilojoules) is required to warm 10.0 g of ice, initially at −10.0 °C, to steam at 110.0 °C? The heat capacity of ice is 2.09 J g^{-1} $°C^{-1}$ and that of steam is 2.01 J g^{-1} $°C^{-1}$.

82. How much heat (in kilojoules) is evolved in converting 1.00 mol of steam at 145.0 °C to ice at −50.0 °C? The heat capacity of steam is 2.01 J g^{-1} $°C^{-1}$ and of that ice is 2.09 J g^{-1} $°C^{-1}$.

Phase Diagrams

83. Consider the phase diagram shown here. Identify the states present at points *a* through *g*.

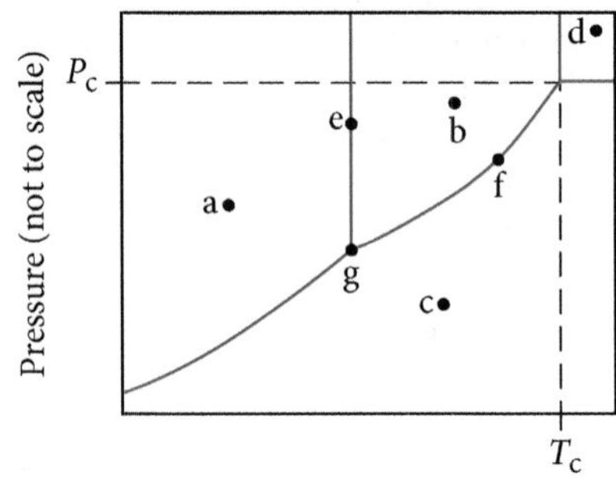

84. Consider the phase diagram for iodine shown here and answer each of the following questions:

a. What is the normal boiling point for iodine?

b. What is the melting point for iodine at 1 atm?

c. What state is present at room temperature and normal atmospheric pressure?

d. What state is present at 186 °C and 1.0 atm?

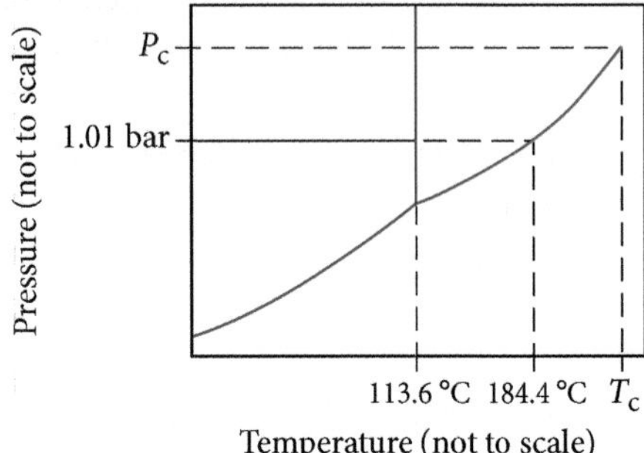

85. Nitrogen has a normal boiling point of 77.3 K and a melting point (at 1 atm) of 63.1 K. Its critical temperature is 126.2 K and critical pressure is 2.55×10^4 Torr. It has a triple point at 63.1 K and 94.0 Torr. Sketch the phase diagram for nitrogen. Does nitrogen have a stable liquid state at 1 atm?

86. Argon has a normal boiling point of 87.2 K and a melting point (at 1 atm) of 84.1 K. Its critical temperature is 150.8 K and critical pressure is 48.3 atm. It has a triple point at 83.7 K and 0.68 atm. Sketch the phase diagram for argon. Which has the greater density: solid argon or liquid argon?

87. The phase diagram for sulfur is shown below. The rhombic and monoclinic states are two solid states with different structures.

a. Below what pressure will solid sulfur sublime?

b. Which of the two solid states of sulfur is most dense?

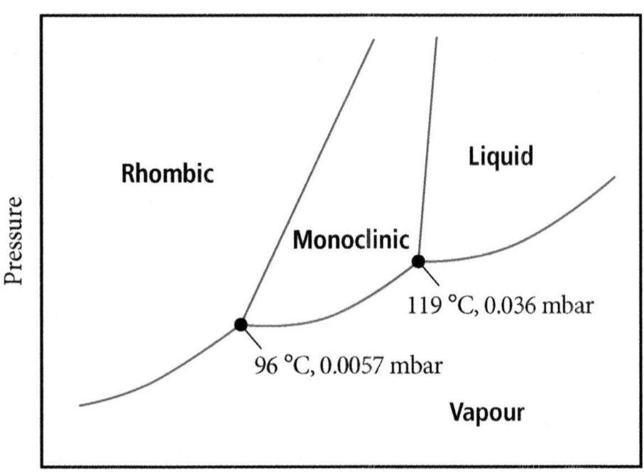

88. The high-pressure phase diagram of ice is shown here. Notice that, under high pressure, ice can exist in several different solid forms. What three forms of ice are present at the triple point marked O? What is the density of ice II compared to ice I (the familiar form of ice). Would ice III sink or float in liquid water?

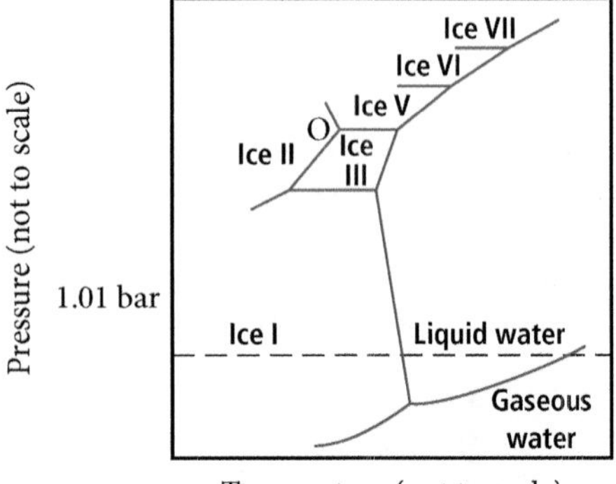

The Uniqueness of Water

89. Water has a high boiling point for its relatively low molar mass. Why?

90. Water is a good solvent for many substances. What is the molecular basis for this property and why is it significant?

91. Explain the role of water in moderating Earth's climate.

92. How is the density of solid water compared to that of liquid water atypical among substances? Why is this significant?

Types of Solids and Their Structures

93. An X-ray beam with $\lambda = 154$ pm incident on the surface of a crystal produced a maximum reflection at an angle of $\theta = 28.3°$. Assuming $n = 1$, calculate the separation between layers of atoms in the crystal.

94. An X-ray beam of unknown wavelength is diffracted from an NaCl surface. If the interplanar distance in the crystal is 286 pm, and the angle of maximum reflection is found to be 7.23°, what is the wavelength of the X-ray beam? (Assume $n = 1$.)

95. Determine the number of atoms per unit cell for each metal:

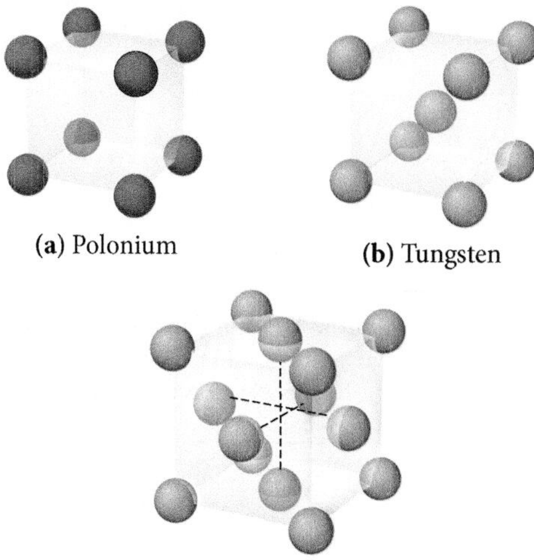

(a) Polonium (b) Tungsten (c) Nickel

96. Determine the coordination number for each structure:

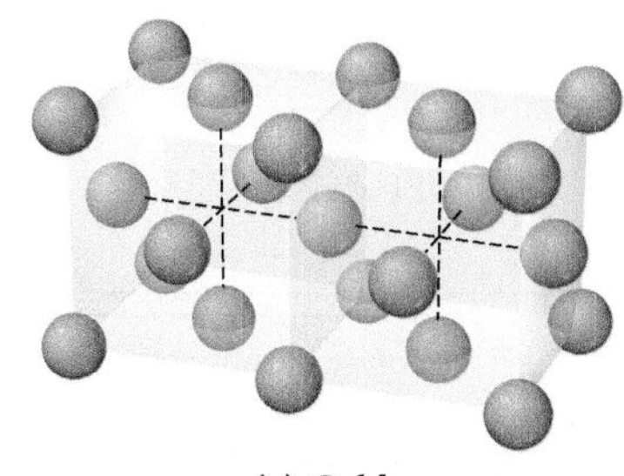

(a) Gold

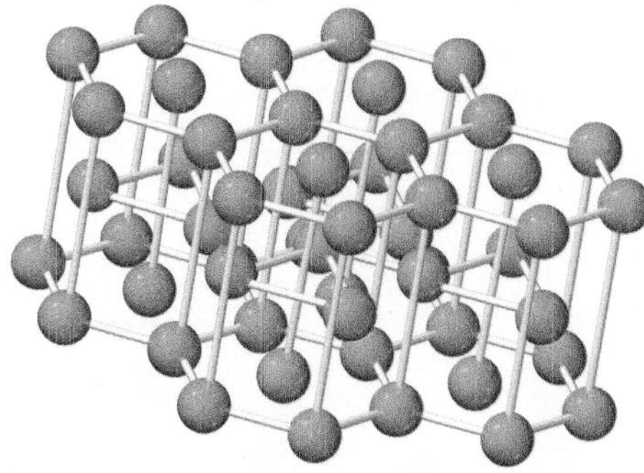

(b) Ruthenium

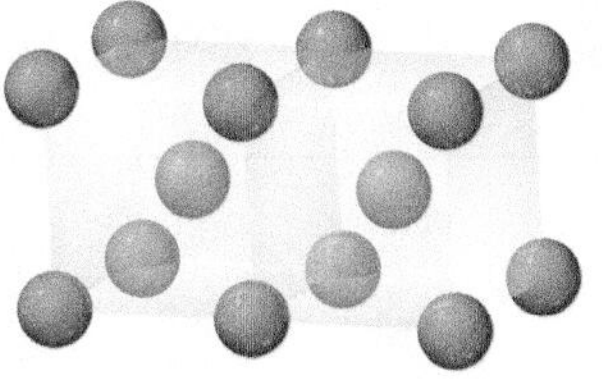

(c) Chromium

97. Platinum crystallizes with the face-centred cubic unit cell. The radius of a platinum atom is 139 pm. Calculate the edge length of the unit cell and the density of platinum in g cm^{-3}.

98. Molybdenum crystallizes with the body-centred unit cell. The radius of a molybdenum atom is 136 pm. Calculate the edge length of the unit cell and the density of molybdenum.

99. Rhodium has a density of 12.41 g cm^{-3} and crystallizes with the face-centred cubic unit cell. Calculate the radius of a rhodium atom.

100. Barium has a density of 3.59 g cm^{-3} and crystallizes with the body-centred cubic unit cell. Calculate the radius of a barium atom.

101. Polonium crystallizes with a simple cubic structure. It has a density of 9.3 g cm^{-3}, a radius of 167 pm, and a molar mass of 209 g mol^{-1}. Use this data to estimate Avogadro's number (the number of atoms in one mole).

102. Palladium crystallizes with a face-centred cubic structure. It has a density of 12.0 g cm^{-3}, a radius of 138 pm, and a molar mass of 106.42 g mol^{-1}. Use this data to estimate Avogadro's number.

103. Identify each solid as molecular, ionic, or atomic:
   a. Ar(*s*) **b.** $H_2O(s)$
   c. $K_2O(s)$ **d.** Fe(*s*)

104. Identify each solid as molecular, ionic, or atomic:
   a. $CaCl_2(s)$ **b.** $CO_2(s)$
   c. Ni(*s*) **d.** $I_2(s)$

105. Which solid has the highest melting point? Why?

   Ar(*s*), $CCl_4(s)$, LiCl(*s*), $CH_3OH(s)$

106. Which solid has the highest melting point? Why?

   C(*s*, diamond), Kr(*s*), NaCl(*s*), $H_2O(s)$

107. In each pair of solids, which one has the higher melting point and why?
   a. $CH_3OH(s)$ or HOOH(*s*) **b.** $CCl_4(s)$ or $SiCl_4(s)$
   c. Kr(*s*) or Xe(*s*) **d.** NaCl(*s*) or CaO(*s*)

108. In each pair of solids, which one has the higher melting point and why?
   a. Fe(*s*) or $CCl_4(s)$ **b.** KCl(*s*) or HCl(*s*)
   c. Ti(*s*) or Ne(*s*) **d.** $H_2O(s)$ or $H_2S(s)$

109. An oxide of titanium crystallizes with the unit cell shown here (titanium = grey; oxygen = red). What is the formula of the oxide?

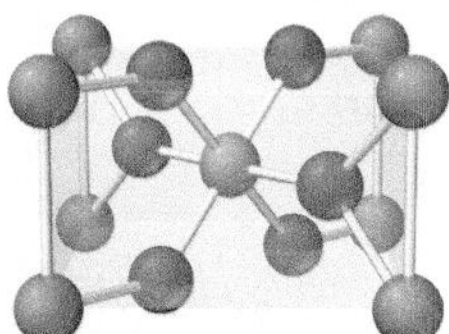

110. An oxide of rhenium crystallizes with the unit cell shown here (rhenium = grey; oxygen = red). What is the formula of the oxide?

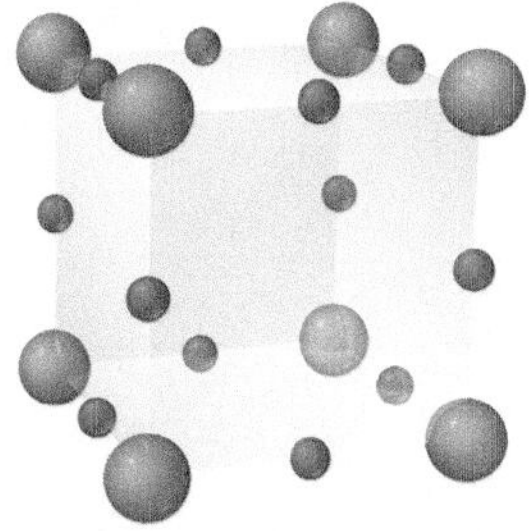

111. The unit cells for cesium chloride and barium chloride are shown below. Show that the ratio of cations to anions in each unit cell corresponds to the ratio of cations to anions in the formula of each compound.

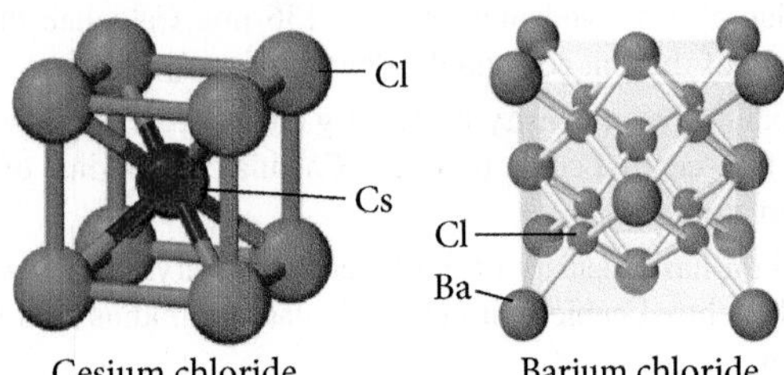

112. The unit cells for lithium oxide and silver iodide are shown here. Show that the ratio of cations to anions in each unit cell corresponds to the ratio of cations to anions in the formula of each compound.

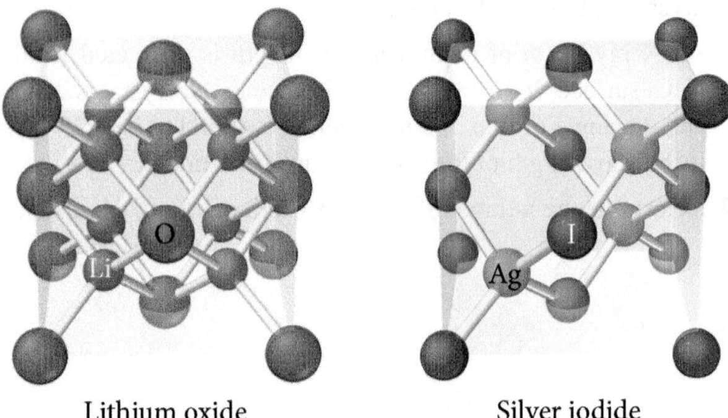

Cumulative Problems

113. Explain the observed trend in the melting points of the hydrogen halides:

HI	−50.8 °C
HBr	−88.5 °C
HCl	−114.8 °C
HF	−83.1 °C

114. Explain the observed trend in the boiling points of these compounds:

H_2Te	−2 °C
H_2Se	−41.5 °C
H_2S	−60.7 °C
H_2O	−100 °C

115. Arrange each of the following in order of *increasing* boiling points. State your reasoning.

N≡N (i) Cl—Cl (ii) O═O (iii)

a. ________ < ________ < ________

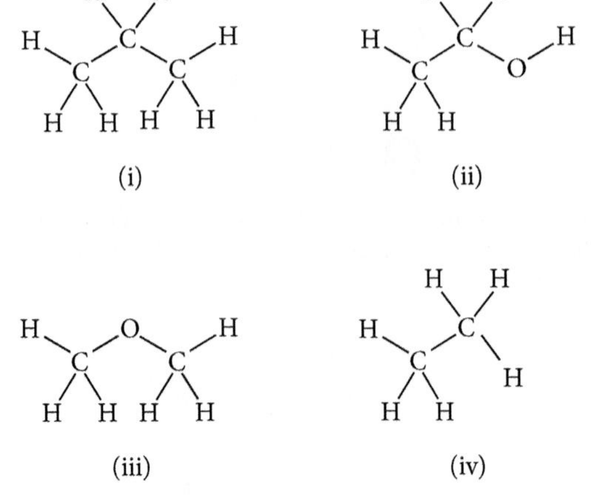

b. ______ < ______ < ______ < ______

116. The boiling points for the series of pnictogen hydrides are plotted below. The dipole moments of these five molecules decrease along the series (e.g., $NH_3 > PH_3 > AsH_3 > SbH_3 > BiH_3$).

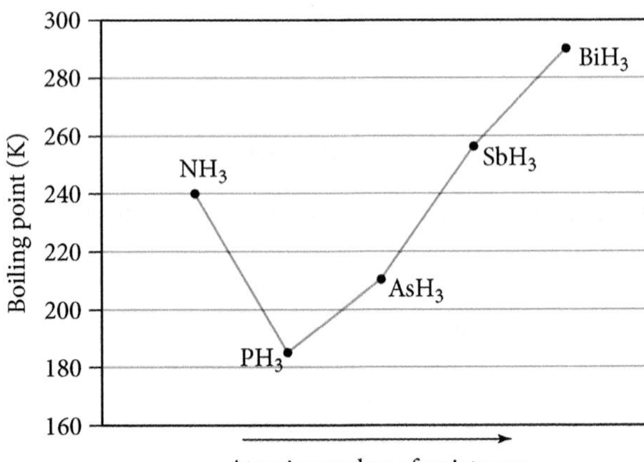

a. Why does NH_3 not follow the trend in boiling points?

b. The dipole moments decrease across the series $PH_3 > AsH_3 > SbH_3 > BiH_3$. Why do the boiling points increase?

117. The bar chart below shows the boiling points for water and four alcohols from methanol to butan-1-ol.

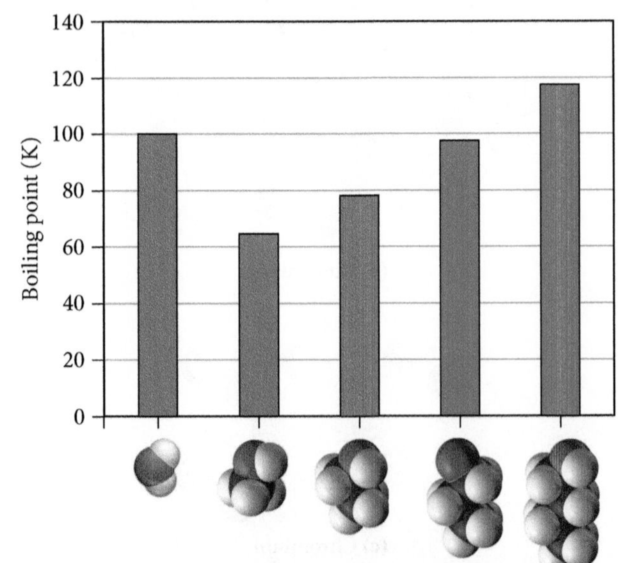

a. Explain why water seems to not follow the trend.
b. Why do the boiling points increase as the alcohol gets larger?

118. Explain the following observations.
a. CO_2 is a gas but H_2O is a liquid at room temperature.
b. H_2O is a liquid at room temperature but NH_3 and HF are gases.
c. H_2O and Br_2 are liquids at room temperature, but I_2 is a solid.
d. CH_4 is a gas at room temperature, but C_5H_{12} is a liquid.

119. The vapour pressure of water at 25 °C is 23.76 Torr. If 1.25 g of water is enclosed in a 1.5 L container, will any liquid be present? If so, what mass of liquid?

120. The vapour pressure of CCl_3F at 300 K is 856 Torr. If 11.5 g of CCl_3F is enclosed in a 1.0 L container, will any liquid be present? If so, what mass of liquid?

121. Examine the phase diagram for iodine shown in Figure 11.42(a). What state transitions occur as you uniformly increase the pressure on a gaseous sample of iodine from 0.010 bar at 185 °C to 100 bar at 185 °C? Make a graph, analogous to the heating curve for water shown in Figure 11.39 in which you plot pressure versus time during the pressure increase.

122. Carbon tetrachloride displays a triple point at 249.0 K and a melting point (at 1.01 bar) of 250.3 K. Which state of carbon tetrachloride is more dense: the solid or the liquid? Explain.

123. At 320 K and 16 atm, the molar volume of ammonia (NH_3) is approximately 10% less than that of an ideal gas. Explain this observation.

124. a. Explain the difference between the enthalpy of formation of liquid and gaseous water, −286 and −242 kJ mol^{-1}, respectively, at 298 K.
b. Explain why the enthalpy of vaporization of water at 100 °C (40.7 kJ mol^{-1}) is lower than at 25 °C (44.0 kJ mol^{-1}).

125. Four ice cubes at exactly 0 °C with a total mass of 53.5 g are combined with 115 g of water at 75 °C in an insulated container. If no heat is lost to the surroundings, what will be the final temperature of the mixture?

126. A sample of steam with a mass of 0.552 g and at a temperature of 100 °C condenses into an insulated container holding 4.25 g of water at 5.0 °C. Assuming that no heat is lost to the surroundings, what will be the final temperature of the mixture?

127. Air conditioners not only cool air, but dry it as well. Suppose that a room in a home measures 6.0 m × 10.0 m × 2.2 m. If the outdoor temperature is 30 °C and the vapour pressure of water in the air is 85% of the vapour pressure of water at this temperature, what mass of water must be removed from the air each time the volume of air in the room is cycled through the air conditioner? The vapour pressure for water at 30 °C is 31.8 Torr.

128. A sealed flask contains 0.55 g of water at 28 °C. The vapour pressure of water at this temperature is 28.36 mmHg. What is the minimum volume of the flask in order that no liquid water be present in the flask?

129. Silver iodide crystallizes in the zinc blende structure. The separation between nearest-neighbour cations and anions is approximately 325 pm and the melting point is 558 °C. Cesium chloride, by contrast, crystallizes in the cesium chloride structure shown in Figure 11.54. Even though the separation between nearest-neighbour cations and anions is greater (348 pm), the melting point is higher (645 °C). Explain.

130. Copper iodide crystallizes in the zinc blende structure. The separation between nearest-neighbour cations and anions is approximately 311 pm and the melting point is 606 °C. Potassium chloride, by contrast, crystallizes in the rock salt structure. Even though the separation between nearest-neighbour cations and anions is greater (319 pm), the melting point is higher (776 °C). Explain.

131. Consider the face-centred cubic structure shown here:

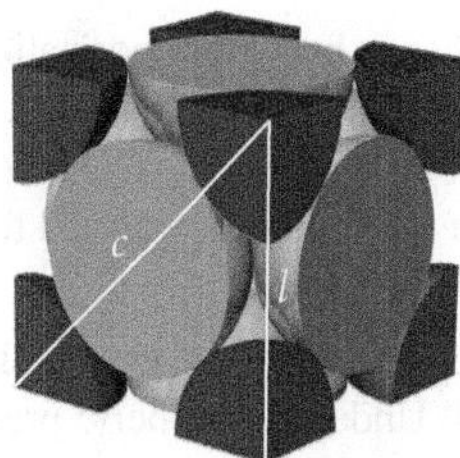

a. What is the length of the line (labelled c) that runs diagonally across one of the faces of the cube in terms of r (the atomic radius)?
b. Use the answer to part (a) and the Pythagorean theorem to derive the expression for the edge length (l) in terms of r.

132. Consider the body-centred cubic structure shown here:

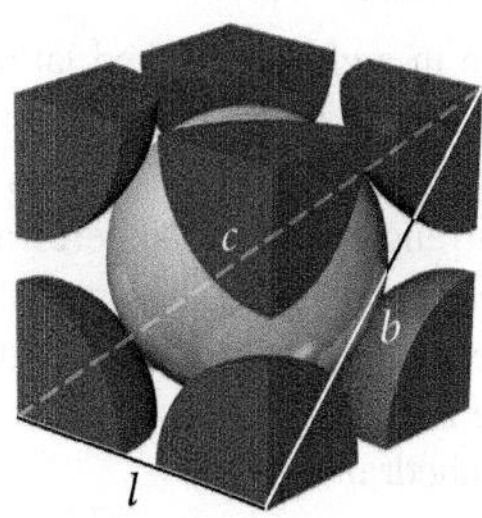

a. What is the length of the line (labelled c) that runs from one corner of the cube diagonally through the centre of the cube to the other corner in terms of r (the atomic radius)?
b. Use the Pythagorean theorem to derive an expression for the length of the line (labelled b) that runs diagonally across one of the faces of the cube in terms of the edge length (l).
c. Use the answer to parts (a) and (b) along with the Pythagorean theorem to derive the expression for the edge length (l) in terms of r.

133. The unit cell in a crystal of diamond belongs to a crystal system different from any we have discussed. The volume of a unit cell of diamond is 0.0454 nm^3 and the density of diamond is 3.52 g cm^{-3}. Find the number of carbon atoms in a unit cell of diamond.

134. The density of an unknown metal is 12.3 g cm^{-3} and its atomic radius is 0.134 nm. It has a face-centred cubic lattice. Find the atomic mass of this metal.

135. Based on the phase diagram of CO_2 shown in Figure 11.42(b), describe the state changes that occur when the temperature of CO_2 is increased from 190 K to 350 K at a constant pressure of **(a)** 1 bar, **(b)** 5.1 bar, **(c)** 10 bar, and **(d)** 100 bar.

136. Consider a planet where the pressure of the atmosphere at sea level is 2500 mmHg. Will water behave in a way that can sustain life on the planet?

137. An unknown metal is found to have a density of 7.8748 g cm^{-3} and to crystallize in a body-centred cubic lattice. The edge of the unit cell is found to be 0.28664 nm. Calculate the atomic mass of the metal.

138. When spheres of radius r are packed in a body-centred cubic arrangement, they occupy 68.0% of the available volume. Use the fraction of occupied volume to calculate the value of a, the length of the edge of the cube in terms of r.

Challenge Problems

139. Potassium chloride crystallizes in the rock salt structure. Estimate the density of potassium chloride using the ionic radii given in Chapter 8.

140. Butane (C_4H_{10}) has a heat of vaporization of 22.44 kJ mol^{-1} and a normal boiling point of −0.4 °C. A 250 mL sealed flask contains 0.55 g of butane at −22 °C. How much butane is present as a liquid? If the butane is warmed to 25 °C, how much is present as a liquid?

141. Liquid nitrogen can be used as a cryogenic substance to obtain low temperatures. Under atmospheric pressure, liquid nitrogen boils at 77 K, allowing for low temperatures to be reached. However, if the nitrogen is placed in a sealed, insulated container connected to a vacuum pump, even lower temperatures can be reached. Why? If the vacuum pump has sufficient capacity, and is left on for an extended period of time, the liquid nitrogen will start to freeze. Explain.

142. Calculate the fraction of empty space in cubic closest packing to five significant figures.

143. A tetrahedral site in a closest-packed lattice is formed by four spheres at the corners of a regular tetrahedron. This is equivalent to placing the spheres at alternate corners of a cube. In such a closest-packed arrangement, the spheres are in contact, and if the spheres have a radius r, the diagonal of the face of the cube is $2r$. The tetrahedral hole is inside the middle of the cube. Find the length of the body diagonal of this cube and then find the radius of the tetrahedral hole.

144. Given that the heat of fusion of water is −6.02 kJ mol^{-1}, that the molar heat capacity of $H_2O(l)$ is 75.2 J mol^{-1} K^{-1}, and that the molar heat capacity of $H_2O(s)$ is 37.7 J mol^{-1} K^{-1}, calculate the heat of fusion of water at −10 °C.

145. The heat of combustion of CH_4 is 890.4 kJ mol^{-1} and the molar heat capacity of H_2O is 75.2 J mol^{-1} K^{-1}. Find the volume of methane measured at 298 K and 1.00 atm required to convert 1.00 L of water at 298 K to water vapour at 373 K.

146. At a given temperature two liquids, A and B, have vapour pressures of 24 mmHg and 36 mmHg, respectively. We prepare solutions of A and B at a given temperature and measure the total pressures above the solutions. We obtain the following data:

Solution	Amt A (mol)	Amt B (mol)	*P* (mmHg)
1	1	1	30
2	2	1	28
3	1	2	32
4	1	3	33

Predict the total pressure above a solution of 5 mol A and 1 mol B.

147. Three 1.0 L flasks, maintained at 308 K, are connected to each other with stopcocks. Initially, the stopcocks are closed. One of the flasks contains 1.01 bar of N_2, the second 2.0 g of H_2O, and the third 0.50 g of ethanol, C_2H_6O. The vapour pressure of H_2O at 308 K is 42 mmHg and that of ethanol is 102 mmHg. The stopcocks are then opened and the contents mix freely. What is the pressure?

Conceptual Problems

148. One prediction of global warming is the melting of global ice, which may result in coastal flooding. A criticism of this prediction is that the melting of icebergs does not increase ocean levels any more than the melting of ice in a glass of water increases the level of liquid in the glass. Is this a valid criticism? Does the melting of an ice cube in a cup of water raise the level of the liquid in the cup? Why or why not? In response to this criticism, scientists have asserted that they are not worried about melting icebergs, but rather the melting of ice sheets that sit on the continent of Antarctica. Would the melting of this ice increase ocean levels? Why or why not?

149. The rate of vaporization depends on the surface area of the liquid. However, the vapour pressure of a liquid does not depend on the surface area. Explain.

150. Substance A has a smaller heat of vaporization than substance B. Which of the two substances will undergo a larger change in vapour pressure for a given change in temperature?

151. The density of a substance is greater in its solid state than in its liquid state. If the triple point in the phase diagram of the substance is below 1.01 bar, then which will necessarily be at a lower temperature: the triple point or the normal melting point?

152. A substance has a heat of vaporization of $\Delta_{vap}H°$ and heat of fusion of $\Delta_{fus}H°$. Express the heat of sublimation in terms of $\Delta_{vap}H°$ and $\Delta_{fus}H°$.

153. Examine the heating curve for water in Section 11.7 (Figure 11.39). If heat is added to the water at a constant rate, which of the three segments in which temperature is rising will have the least steep slope? Why?

154. A root cellar is an underground chamber used to store fruits, vegetables, and even meats. In extreme cold, farmers put large vats of water into the root cellar to prevent the fruits and vegetables from freezing. Explain why this works.

155. Suggest an explanation for the observation that the heat of fusion of a substance is always smaller than its heat of vaporization.

Solutions

Drinking seawater causes dehydration because seawater draws water out of body tissues.

One molecule of nonsaline substance (held in the solvent) dissolved in 100 molecules of any volatile liquid decreases the vapour pressure of this liquid by a nearly constant fraction, nearly 0.0105.

—François-Marie Raoult (1830–1901)

WE LEARNED IN CHAPTER 1 that most of the matter we encounter is in the form of mixtures. In this chapter, we focus on homogeneous mixtures, known as solutions. Solutions are mixtures in which atoms and molecules intermingle on the molecular and atomic scales. Some common examples of solutions include the ocean water we swim in, the gasoline we put into our cars, and the air we breathe. Why do solutions form? How are their properties different from the properties of the pure substances that compose them? As you read this chapter, keep in mind the great number of solutions that surround you at every moment, including those that exist within your own body.

12.1 Thirsty Solutions: Why You Shouldn't Drink Seawater

In a popular novel, *Life of Pi* by Yann Martel, the main character (whose name is Pi) is stranded on a lifeboat with a Bengal tiger in the middle of the Pacific Ocean for 227 days. He survives in part by rigging a solar still to distill seawater for drinking. However, in the first three days of his predicament (before he rigs the still), he becomes severely dehydrated from lack of water. He is surrounded by seawater but drinking *that* water would only have made his condition worse. Why? Seawater actually draws water *out of the body* as it passes through the stomach and intestines,

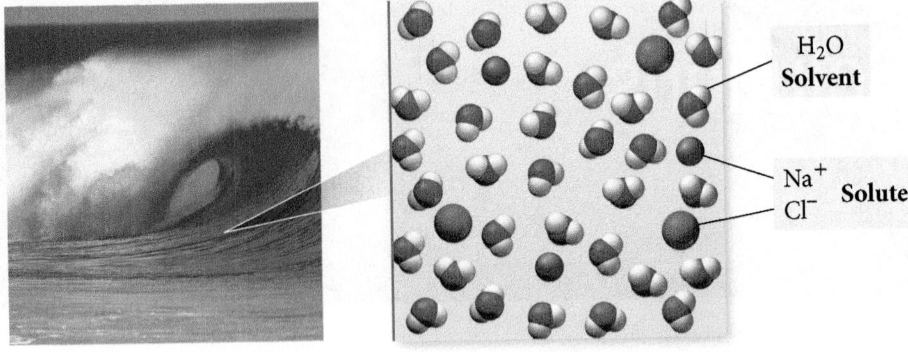

▶ **FIGURE 12.1 A Typical Solution** In seawater, sodium chloride is the primary solute. Water is the solvent.

resulting in diarrhea and further dehydration. We can think of seawater as a *thirsty solution*—one that draws more water to itself. Consequently, seawater should never be consumed as drinking water.

Seawater (Figure 12.1 ▲) is a **solution**, a homogeneous mixture of two or more substances or components. The majority component is typically called the **solvent** and the minority component is called the **solute**. In seawater, water is the solvent and sodium chloride is the main solute.

In some cases, the concepts of solute and solvent are not useful. For example, a homogeneous mixture of water and ethanol can contain equal amounts of both components, and neither component can then be identified as the solvent.

The reason that seawater draws water to itself is related to nature's tendency toward spontaneous mixing, which we discuss in more detail later in this chapter and in Chapter 17. For now, we simply observe that, unless it is highly unfavourable energetically, substances tend to combine into uniform mixtures, not separate into pure substances. For example, suppose we have pure water and a sodium chloride solution in separate compartments with a removable barrier between them, as shown in Figure 12.2(a) ▶. If we remove the barrier, the two liquids spontaneously mix together, eventually forming a more dilute sodium chloride solution of uniform concentration, as shown in Figure 12.2(b). The tendency toward mixing results in a uniform concentration of the final solution.

Seawater is a *thirsty* solution because of this tendency toward mixing. As seawater moves through the intestine, it flows past cells that line the digestive tract. These cells consist of largely fluid interiors surrounded by membranes. Cellular fluids themselves contain dissolved ions, including sodium and chloride, but the fluids are more dilute than seawater. Nature's tendency toward mixing (which tends to produce solutions of uniform concentration), together with the selective permeability of the cell membranes (which allow water to flow in and out, but restrict the flow of dissolved solids), causes a *flow of solvent out of the body's cells and into the seawater*. In this way, the two solutions become more similar in concentration (as though they had mixed)—the solution in the intestine becomes somewhat more dilute than it was and the solution in the cells becomes somewhat more concentrated. The accumulation of extra fluid in the intestines causes diarrhea, and the decreased fluid in the cells causes dehydration. If Pi had drunk the seawater instead of constructing the solar still, neither he nor his companion, the large Bengal tiger, would have survived their ordeal.

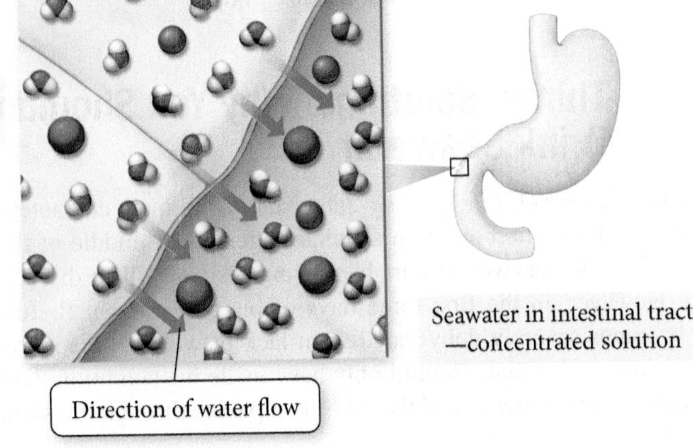

▶ Seawater is a more concentrated solution than the fluids in body cells. As a result, when seawater flows through the digestive tract, it draws water out of the surrounding tissues.

When the barrier is removed, spontaneous mixing occurs, producing a solution of uniform concentration.

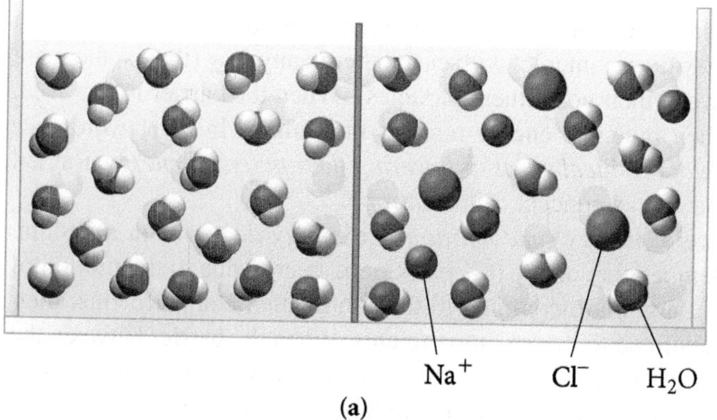

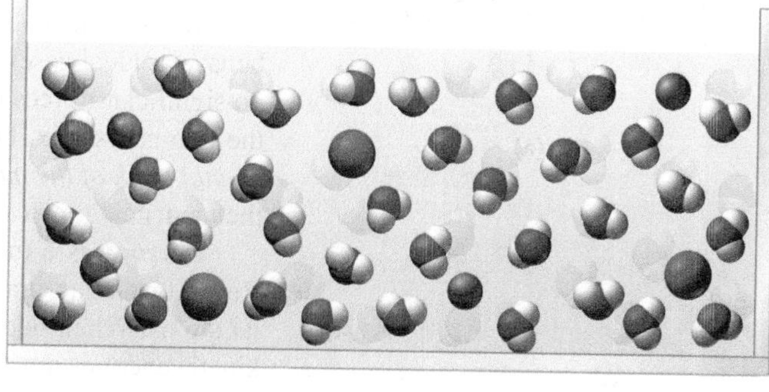

▲ **FIGURE 12.2 The Tendency to Mix** (**a**) Pure water and a sodium chloride solution are separated by a barrier. (**b**) When the barrier is removed, the two liquids spontaneously mix, producing a single solution of uniform concentration.

12.2 Types of Solutions and Solubility

A solution may be composed of a solid and a liquid (such as the salt and water that are the primary components of seawater), but may also be composed of a gas and a liquid, two different liquids, or other combinations (see Table 12.1). In **aqueous solutions**, water is the solvent, and a solid, liquid, or gas is the solute. For example, sugar water and salt water are both aqueous solutions. Similarly, ethanol—the alcohol in alcoholic beverages—readily mixes with water to form a solution, and carbon dioxide dissolves in water to form the aqueous solution that we know as club soda.

▲ Club soda is a solution of carbon dioxide and water.

You probably know from experience that a particular solvent, such as water, does not dissolve all possible solutes. For example, you cannot clean your greasy hands with just water because the water does not dissolve the grease. However, another solvent, such as paint thinner, can easily dissolve the grease. The grease is *insoluble* in water but *soluble* in the paint thinner. The **solubility** of a substance is the amount of the substance that will dissolve in a given amount of solvent. The solubility of sodium chloride in water at 25 °C is 36 g NaCl per 100 g water, while the solubility of grease in water is nearly zero. The solubility of one substance in another depends both on nature's tendency toward mixing that we discussed in Section 12.1 and on the types of intermolecular forces that we discussed in Chapter 11.

The general solubilities of a number of ionic compounds are described by the solubility rules in Section 4.3.

Nature's Tendency Toward Mixing: Entropy

So far in this text, we have seen that many physical systems tend toward lower *potential energy*. For example, two particles with opposite charges (such as a proton and an electron or a cation and an anion) move toward each other because their potential energy goes down as their separation decreases, according to Coulomb's law. The formation of a solution,

TABLE 12.1 Common Types of Solutions

Solution Phase	Solute Phase	Solvent Phase	Example
Gaseous solution	Gas	Gas	Air (mainly oxygen and nitrogen)
Liquid solution	Gas	Liquid	Club soda (CO_2 and water)
	Liquid	Liquid	Vodka (ethanol and water)
	Solid	Liquid	Seawater (salt and water)
Solid solution	Solid	Solid	Brass (copper and zinc) and other alloys

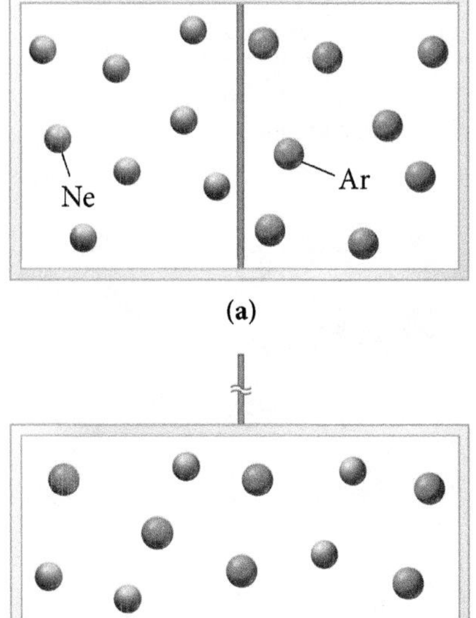

▲ **FIGURE 12.3 Spontaneous Mixing of Two Ideal Gases** (a) Neon and argon are separated by a barrier. (b) When the barrier is removed, the two gases spontaneously mix to form a uniform solution.

however, *does not necessarily* lower the potential energy of its constituent particles. The clearest example of this phenomenon is the formation of a homogeneous mixture (a *solution*) of two ideal gases. Suppose that we enclose neon and argon in a container with a removable barrier between them, as shown in Figure 12.3(a) ◄. As soon as we remove the barrier, the neon and argon mix together to form a solution, as shown in Figure 12.3(b). *Why?*

Recall that at low pressures and moderate temperatures, both neon and argon behave as ideal gases—they do not interact with each other in any way (that is, there are no significant forces between their constituent particles). When the barrier is removed, the two gases mix, but their potential energy remains unchanged. In other words, *we cannot think of the mixing of two ideal gases as lowering their potential energy*. Rather, the tendency to mix is related to a concept called *entropy*.

Entropy is a measure of *energy randomization* or *energy dispersal* in a system. Recall that a gas at any temperature above 0 K has kinetic energy due to the motion of its atoms. When neon and argon are confined to their individual compartments, their kinetic energies are also confined to those compartments. When the barrier between the compartments is removed, each gas—along with its kinetic energy—becomes *spread out* or *dispersed* over a larger volume. Thus, the mixture of the two gases has greater energy dispersal, or greater *entropy*, than the separated components.

The pervasive tendency for energy to spread out, or disperse, whenever it is not restrained from doing so is the reason that two ideal gases mix. Another common example of the tendency toward energy dispersal is the transfer of thermal energy from hot to cold. If you heat one end of an iron rod, the thermal energy deposited at the end of the rod will spontaneously spread along the entire length of the rod. In contrast to the mixing of two ideal gases—where the kinetic energy of the particles becomes dispersed over a larger volume because the particles themselves become dispersed—the thermal energy in the rod, initially concentrated in relatively fewer particles, becomes dispersed by being distributed over a larger number of particles. The tendency for energy to disperse is why thermal energy flows from the hot end of the rod to the cold one, and not the other way around. Imagine a metal rod that became spontaneously hotter on one end and ice cold on the other—this does not happen because energy does not spontaneously concentrate itself. In Chapter 17, we will see that the dispersal of energy is actually the fundamental criterion that ultimately determines the spontaneity of any process.

The Effect of Intermolecular Forces

We have just seen that, in the absence of intermolecular forces, two substances spontaneously mix to form a homogeneous solution. We know from Chapter 11, however, that solids and liquids exhibit a number of different types of intermolecular forces, including dispersion forces, dipole–dipole forces, hydrogen bonding, and ion–dipole forces (Figure 12.4 ▼). These forces may promote the formation of a solution or prevent it, depending on the nature of the forces in the particular combination of solute and solvent.

Intermolecular forces exist between: (a) the solvent and solute particles, (b) the solvent particles themselves, and (c) the solute particles themselves, as shown in Figure 12.5 ►.

▼ **FIGURE 12.4 Intermolecular Forces Involved in Solutions**

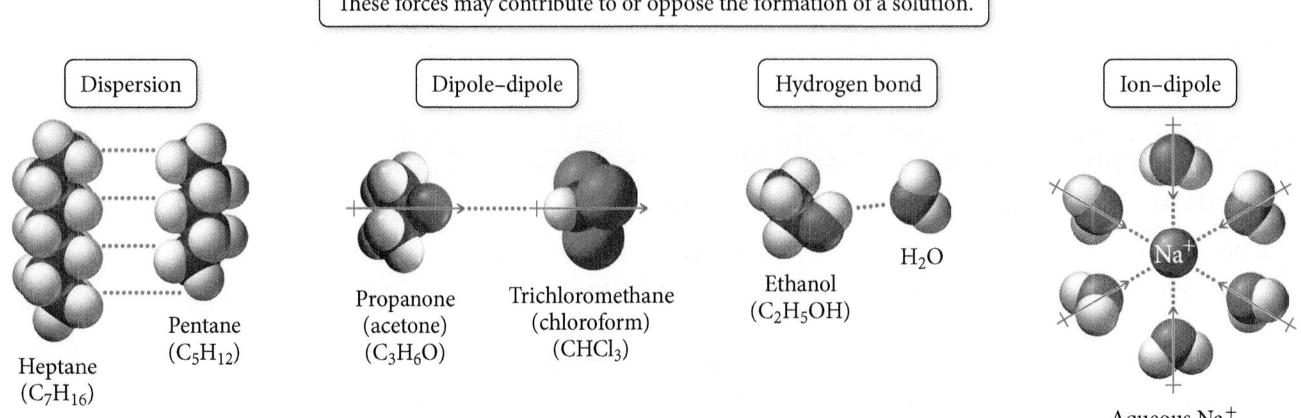

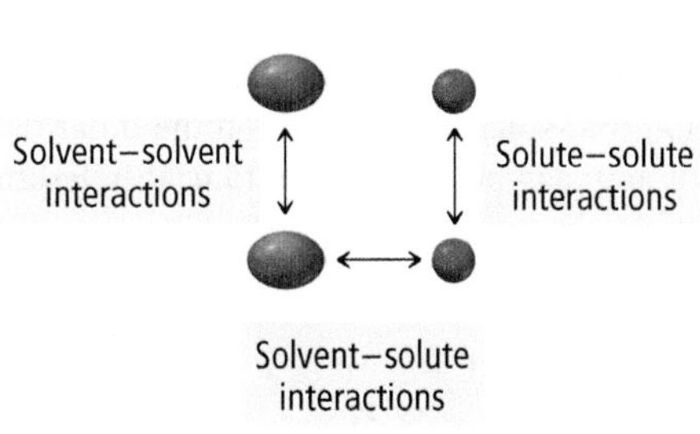

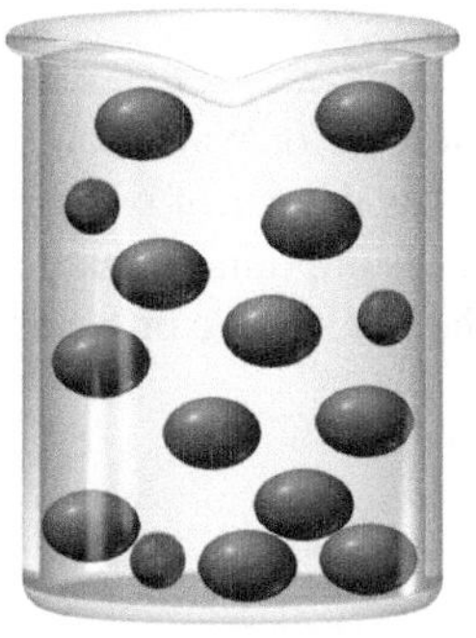

◀ **FIGURE 12.5 Forces in a Solution** The relative strengths of these three interactions determine whether a solution will form.

Solvent–solute interactions: The interactions between a solvent particle and a solute particle.

Solvent–solvent interactions: The interactions between a solvent particle and another solvent particle.

Solute–solute interactions: The interactions between a solute particle and another solute particle.

As shown in Table 12.2, a solution always forms if the solvent–solute interactions are comparable to, or stronger than, the solvent–solvent interactions and the solute–solute interactions. For example, consider mixing the hydrocarbons pentane (C_5H_{12}) and heptane (C_7H_{16}). The intermolecular forces present within both pentane and heptane are dispersion forces. Similarly, the intermolecular forces present *between* heptane and pentane are also dispersion forces. All three interactions are of similar magnitude, so the two substances are soluble in each other in all proportions—they are said to be **miscible**. The formation of the solution is driven by the tendency toward mixing, or toward greater entropy, that we just discussed.

TABLE 12.2 Relative Interactions and Solution Formation

Solvent–solute interactions	>	Solvent–solvent and solute–solute interactions	Solution forms
Solvent–solute interactions	=	Solvent–solvent and solute–solute interactions	Solution forms
Solvent–solute interactions	<	Solvent–solvent and solute–solute interactions	Solution may or may not form, depending on relative disparity

If solvent–solute interactions are weaker than solvent–solvent and solute–solute interactions—in other words, if solvent molecules and solute molecules each interact more strongly with molecules of their own kind than with molecules of the other kind—then a solution may still form, depending on the relative disparities between the interactions. If the disparity is small, the tendency to mix results in the formation of a solution, even though the process is energetically uphill. If the disparity is large, however, a solution will not form. For example, consider mixing hexane and water. The water molecules have strong hydrogen-bonding attractions to each other but cannot form hydrogen bonds with hexane. The energy required to pull water molecules away from one another is too great, and too little energy is returned when the water molecules interact with hexane molecules. As a result, a solution does not form when hexane and water are mixed. Although the tendency to mix is strong, it cannot overcome the large energy disparity between the powerful solvent–solvent interactions and the weak solvent–solute interactions.

In general, we can use the rule of thumb that *like dissolves like* when predicting the formation of solutions. Polar solvents, such as water, tend to dissolve many polar or ionic solutes, and nonpolar solvents, such as hexane, tend to dissolve many nonpolar solutes. Similar kinds of solvents dissolve similar kinds of solutes. Table 12.3 lists some common polar and nonpolar laboratory solvents.

TABLE 12.3 Common Laboratory Solvents

Common Polar Solvents	Common Nonpolar Solvents
Water (H_2O)	Hexane (C_6H_{14})
Acetone (CH_3COCH_3)	Diethyl ether ($CH_3CH_2OCH_2CH_3$)*
Methanol (CH_3OH)	Methylbenzene (toluene) (C_7H_8)
Ethanol (CH_3CH_2OH)	Carbon tetrachloride (CCl_4)

*Diethyl ether has a small dipole moment and can be considered intermediate between polar and nonpolar.

EXAMPLE 12.1 SOLUBILITY

Vitamins are often categorized as either fat soluble or water soluble. Water-soluble vitamins dissolve in body fluids and are easily eliminated in the urine, so there is little danger of overconsumption. Fat-soluble vitamins, on the other hand, can accumulate in the body's fatty deposits. Overconsumption of a fat-soluble vitamin can be detrimental to health. Examine the structure of each vitamin and classify it as either fat soluble or water soluble.

(a) Vitamin C

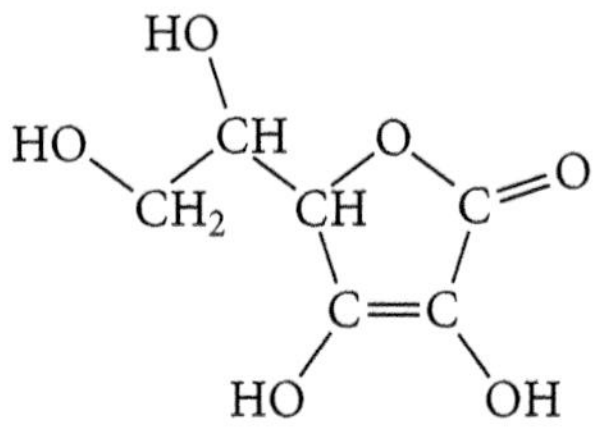

(b) Vitamin K_3

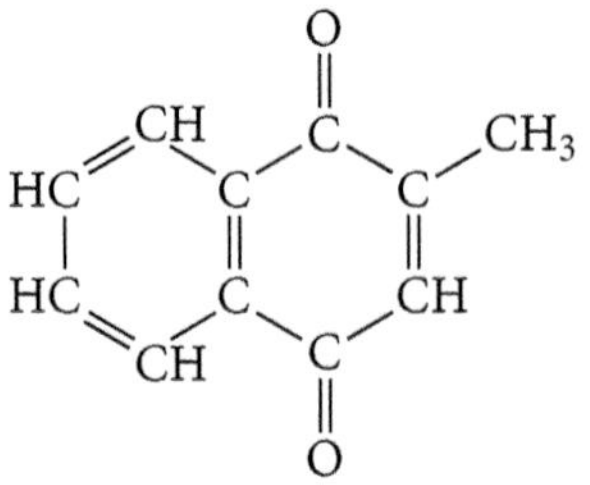

(c) Vitamin A

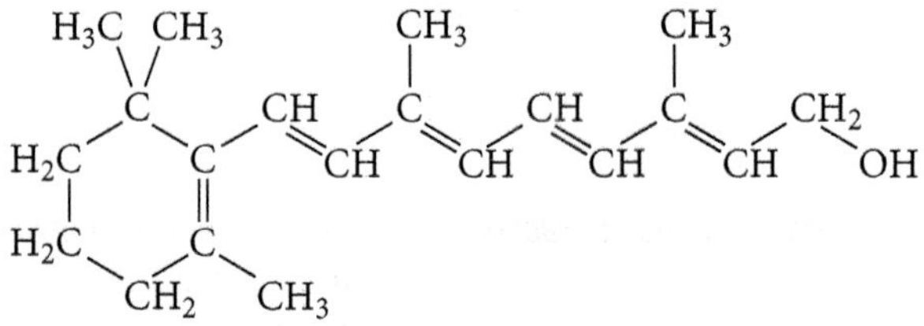

(d) Vitamin B_5

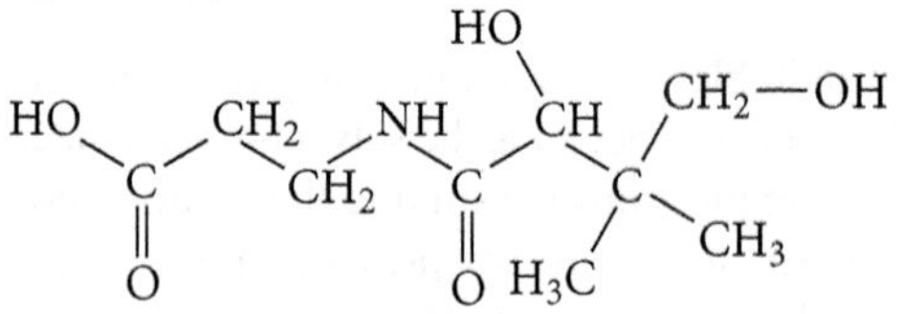

SOLUTION

(a) The four —OH bonds in vitamin C make it highly polar and allow it to hydrogen bond with water. Vitamin C is water soluble.

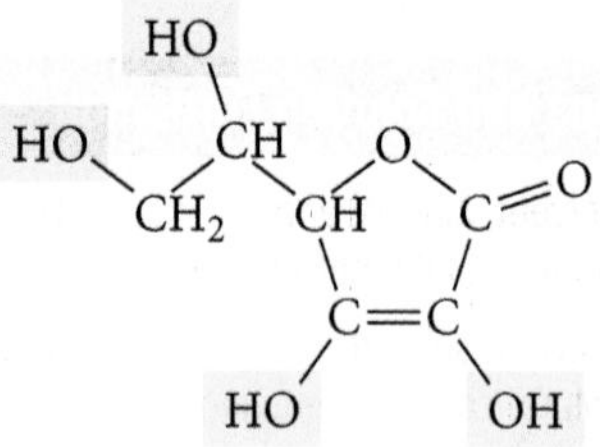

(b) The C—C bonds in vitamin K_3 are nonpolar and the C—H bonds are nearly so. The C=O bonds are polar, but the bond dipoles oppose and largely cancel each other, so the molecule is dominated by the nonpolar bonds. Vitamin K_3 is fat soluble.

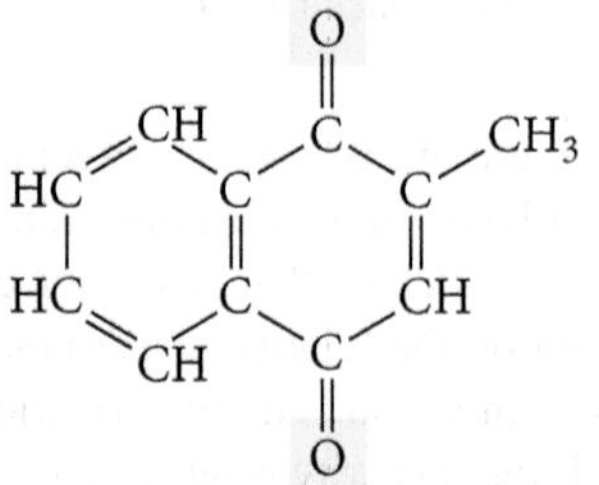

(c) The C—C bonds in vitamin A are nonpolar and the C—H bonds are nearly so. The one polar —OH bond may increase the water solubility slightly, but overall, vitamin A is nonpolar and therefore fat soluble.

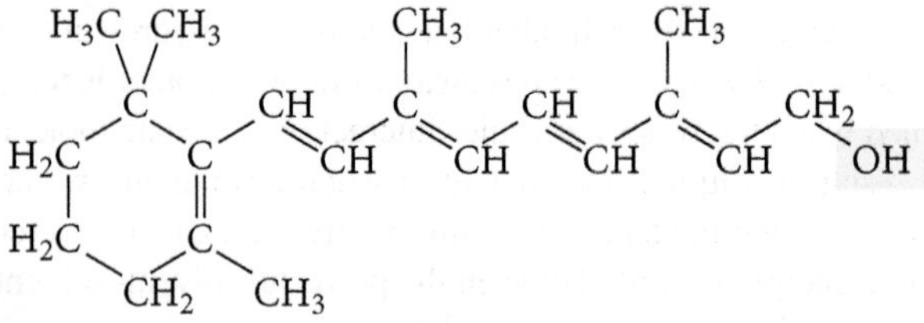

(d) The three —OH bonds and one —NH bond in vitamin B_5 make it highly polar and give it the ability to hydrogen bond with water. Vitamin B_5 is water soluble.

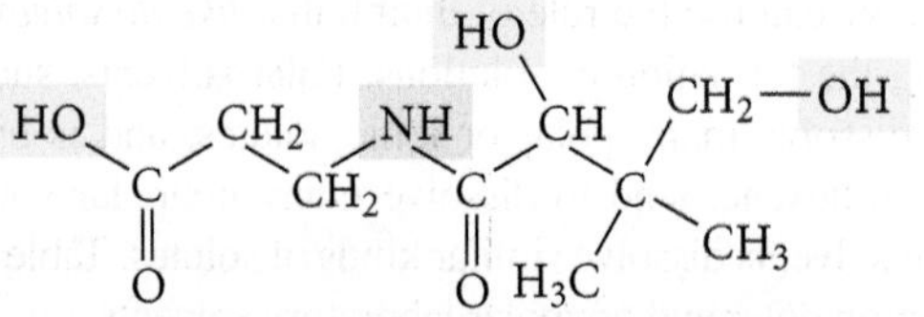

FOR PRACTICE 12.1

Determine whether each compound is soluble in hexane:

(a) water (H_2O)
(b) propane ($CH_3CH_2CH_3$)
(c) ammonia (NH_3)
(d) hydrogen chloride (HCl)

CONCEPTUAL CONNECTION 12.1
Solubility

Consider the following table showing the solubilities of several alcohols in water and in hexane. Explain the observed trend in terms of intermolecular forces.

Alcohol	Space-Filling Model	Electrostatic Potential Maps	Solubility in H_2O (mol alcohol/100 g H_2O)	Solubility in Hexane (C_6H_{14}) (mol alcohol/100 g C_6H_{14})
Methanol (CH_3OH)			Miscible	0.12
Ethanol (CH_3CH_2OH)			Miscible	Miscible
Propan-1-ol ($CH_3CH_2CH_2OH$)			Miscible	Miscible
Butan-1-ol ($CH_3CH_2CH_2CH_2OH$)			0.11	Miscible
Pentan-1-ol ($CH_3CH_2CH_2CH_2CH_2OH$)			0.030	Miscible

CHEMISTRY IN YOUR DAY Bisphenol A

Polycarbonate plastics are clear and almost shatterproof polymers that have been used to make many familiar consumer items such as baby bottles and water bottles. Polycarbonates are made with a compound called bisphenol A, which has been used in the polymer industry for more than half a century. Bisphenol A is used in many other consumer products such as dental devices and coatings on the inside of food and beverage cans. Bisphenol A is also a suspected endocrine disruptor. That means it acts like hormones in the endocrine system. It interacts with hormone receptors, interfering with processes such as reproduction and normal development of tissues and organs by changing the chemistry that occurs inside and outside the cell. In 2008, Canada became the first country to ban baby bottles made with bisphenol A, listing it as a toxic substance.

Bisphenol A
CH_3 CH_3 O n

Polycarbonate

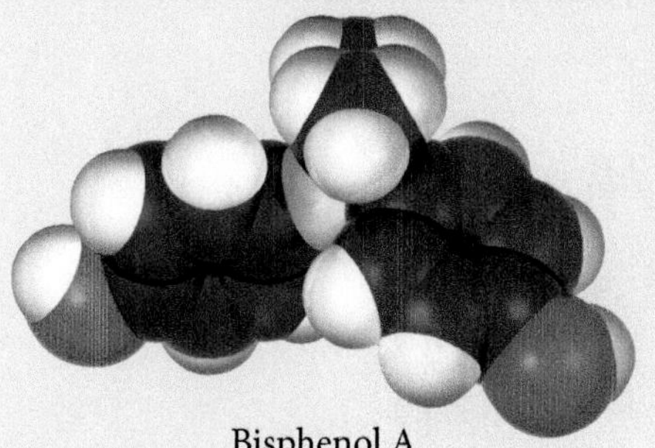

Bisphenol A

(continued)

CHEMISTRY IN YOUR DAY (continued)

By looking at the chemical structure of bisphenol A, we can conclude that it is not particularly soluble in water because it is essentially nonpolar (remember, *like dissolves like*). In fact, the water solubility is only 120–300 parts per million or 0.5–1.3 mmol L^{-1}. When we drink water that contains bisphenol A, the chemical can partition into fattier tissue. The low solubility of bisphenol A means that it is difficult to remove it from the body because the main mechanism to eliminate toxins is by urinating. Studies show that bisphenol A remains in the body for long periods of time, a phenomenon known as bioaccumulation—meaning that the concentrations inside the body can exceed the concentration found at the source of the toxin.

Studies suggest that effects of bisphenol A exposure on humans range from breast cancer to hyperactivity in children born to exposed mothers, but there is not much agreement on what exposure levels bring about adverse effects. While governments are slow to legislate a full-out ban on the chemical, it is possible to minimize exposure by using glass, stainless steel, or porcelain containers, especially for hot foods or liquids.

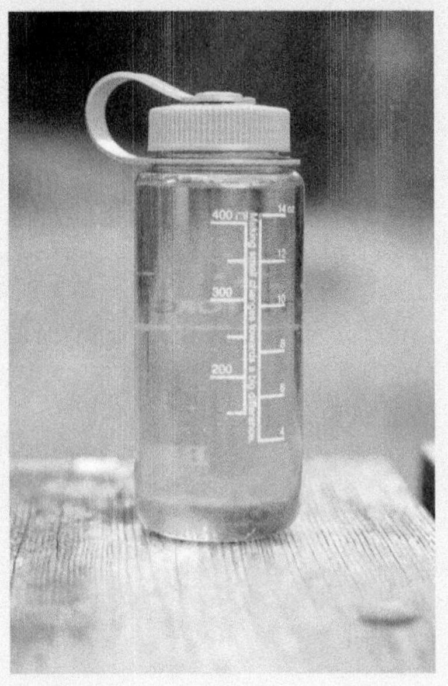

12.3 Energetics of Solution Formation

In Chapter 6, we examined the energy changes associated with chemical reactions. Similar energy changes can occur when a solution forms, depending on the magnitude of the interactions between the solute and solvent particles. For example, when we dissolve sodium hydroxide in water, heat is evolved—the solution process is *exothermic*. In contrast, when we dissolve ammonium nitrate (NH_4NO_3) in water, heat is absorbed—this solution process is *endothermic*. Other solutions, such as sodium chloride in water, barely absorb or evolve any heat upon formation. What causes these different behaviours?

We can understand the energy changes associated with solution formation by envisioning the process as occurring in the following three steps, each with an associated change in enthalpy:

1. Separating the solute into its constituent particles.

This step is always endothermic (positive ΔH) because energy is required to overcome the forces that hold the solute together.

2. Separating the solvent particles from each other to make room for the solute particles.

This step is also endothermic because energy is required to overcome the intermolecular forces among the solvent particles.

3. Mixing the solute particles with the solvent particles.

This step is exothermic, because energy is released as the solute particles interact (through intermolecular forces) with the solvent particles.

According to Hess's law, the overall enthalpy change upon solution formation, called the **enthalpy of solution ($\Delta_{soln}H$)**, is the sum of the changes in enthalpy for each step:

$$\Delta_{soln}H = \underset{\text{endothermic }(+)}{\Delta_{solute}H} + \underset{\text{endothermic }(+)}{\Delta_{solvent}H} + \underset{\text{exothermic }(-)}{\Delta_{mix}H}$$

Since the first two terms are endothermic (positive ΔH) and the third term is exothermic (negative ΔH), the overall sign of $\Delta_{soln}H$ depends on the magnitudes of the individual terms, as shown in Figure 12.6 ▼.

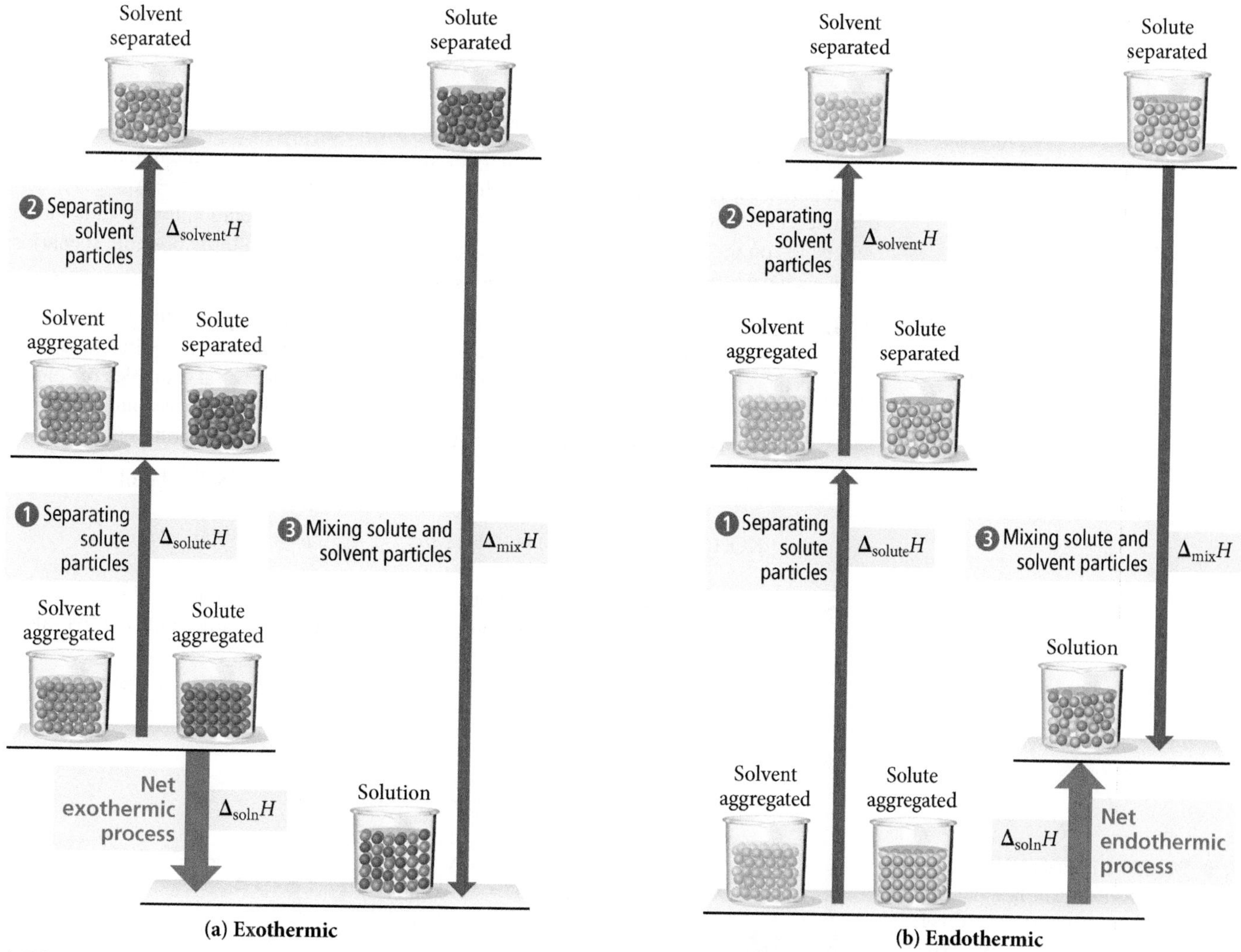

Solvent separated
Solute separated
2 Separating solvent particles $\Delta_{solvent}H$
Solvent aggregated
Solute separated
1 Separating solute particles $\Delta_{solute}H$
3 Mixing solute and solvent particles $\Delta_{mix}H$
Solvent aggregated
Solute aggregated
Net exothermic process $\Delta_{soln}H$
Solution

(a) Exothermic

Solvent separated
Solute separated
2 Separating solvent particles $\Delta_{solvent}H$
Solvent aggregated
Solute separated
1 Separating solute particles $\Delta_{solute}H$
3 Mixing solute and solvent particles $\Delta_{mix}H$
Solution
Solvent aggregated
Solute aggregated
$\Delta_{soln}H$ Net endothermic process

(b) Endothermic

▲ **FIGURE 12.6 Energetics of the Solution Process** **(a)** When $\Delta_{mix}H$ is greater in magnitude than the sum of $\Delta_{solute}H$ and $\Delta_{solvent}H$, the heat of solution is negative (exothermic). **(b)** When $\Delta_{mix}H$ is smaller in magnitude than the sum of $\Delta_{solute}H$ and $\Delta_{solvent}H$, the heat of solution is positive (endothermic).

1. *If the sum of the endothermic terms is about equal in magnitude to the exothermic term, then $\Delta_{soln}H$ is about zero.* The increasing entropy upon mixing drives the formation of a solution, while the overall energy of the system remains nearly constant.
2. *If the sum of the endothermic terms is smaller in magnitude than the exothermic term, then $\Delta_{soln}H$ is negative and the solution process is exothermic.* In this case, both the tendency toward lower energy and the tendency toward greater entropy drive the formation of a solution.
3. *If the sum of the endothermic terms is greater in magnitude than the exothermic term, then $\Delta_{soln}H$ is positive and the solution process is endothermic.* In this case, whenever $\Delta_{soln}H$ is not too large, the tendency toward greater entropy can still drive the formation of a solution. Otherwise, if $\Delta_{soln}H$ is too large, a solution will not form.

Aqueous Solutions and Heats of Hydration

Many common solutions, such as the seawater discussed in the opening section of this chapter, contain an ionic compound dissolved in water. In these aqueous solutions, $\Delta_{solvent}H$ and $\Delta_{mix}H$ can be combined into a single term called the **heat of hydration** (**$\Delta_{hyd}H$**) (Figure 12.7 ▼). The heat of hydration is the enthalpy change that occurs when 1 mol of the gaseous solute ions are dissolved in water. Because the ion–dipole interactions that occur between a dissolved ion and the surrounding water molecules (Figure 12.8 ▶) are much stronger than the hydrogen bonds in water, $\Delta_{hyd}H$ is always largely negative (exothermic) for ionic compounds. Using the heat of hydration, we can write the enthalpy of solution as a sum of just two terms, one endothermic and one exothermic:

$$\Delta_{soln}H = \Delta_{solute}H + \underbrace{\Delta_{solvent}H + \Delta_{mix}H}$$

$$\Delta_{soln}H = \underset{\substack{\text{endothermic} \\ \text{(positive)}}}{\Delta_{solute}H} + \underset{\substack{\text{exothermic} \\ \text{(negative)}}}{\Delta_{hyd}H}$$

For ionic compounds, $\Delta_{solute}H$, the energy required to separate the solute into its constituent particles, is the negative of the solute's lattice energy ($\Delta_{solute}H = -\Delta_{lattice}H$), discussed in Section 9.4. For ionic aqueous solutions, then, the overall enthalpy of solution depends on the relative magnitudes of $\Delta_{solute}H$ and $\Delta_{hyd}H$, with three possible scenarios [in each case, we refer to the *magnitude (absolute value)* of ΔH]:

1. $|\Delta_{solute}H| < |\Delta_{hyd}H|$. The amount of energy required to separate the solute into its constituent ions is less than the energy given off when the ions are hydrated. $\Delta_{soln}H$ is therefore negative and the solution process is exothermic. Good examples of solutes with negative enthalpies of solution include lithium bromide and potassium hydroxide. When these solutes dissolve in water, the resulting solutions feel warm to the touch.

$$LiBr(s) \xrightarrow[H_2O]{} Li^+(aq) + Br^-(aq) \qquad \Delta_{soln}H = -48.78 \text{ kJ mol}^{-1}$$

$$KOH(s) \xrightarrow[H_2O]{} K^+(aq) + OH^-(aq) \qquad \Delta_{soln}H = -57.56 \text{ kJ mol}^{-1}$$

2. $|\Delta_{solute}H| > |\Delta_{hyd}H|$. The amount of energy required to separate the solute into its constituent ions is greater than the energy given off when the ions are hydrated.

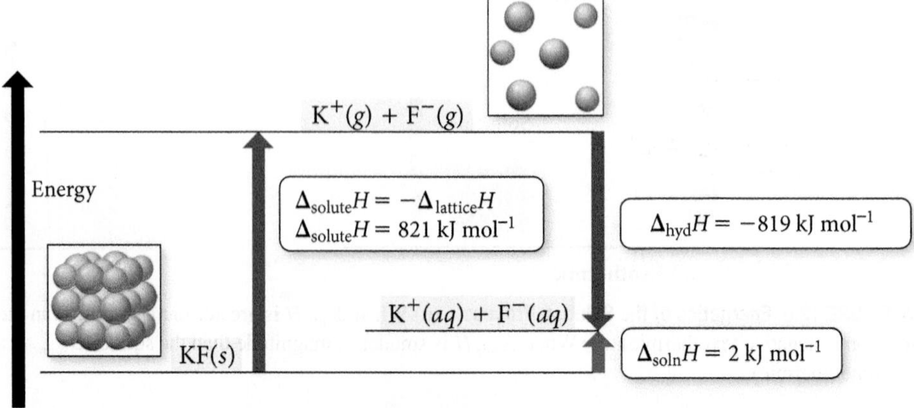

▶ **FIGURE 12.7 Heat of Hydration and Heat of Solution** The heat of hydration is the heat emitted when 1 mol of gaseous solute ions is dissolved in water. The sum of the negative of the lattice energy (which is $\Delta_{solute}H$) and the heat of hydration is the heat of solution.

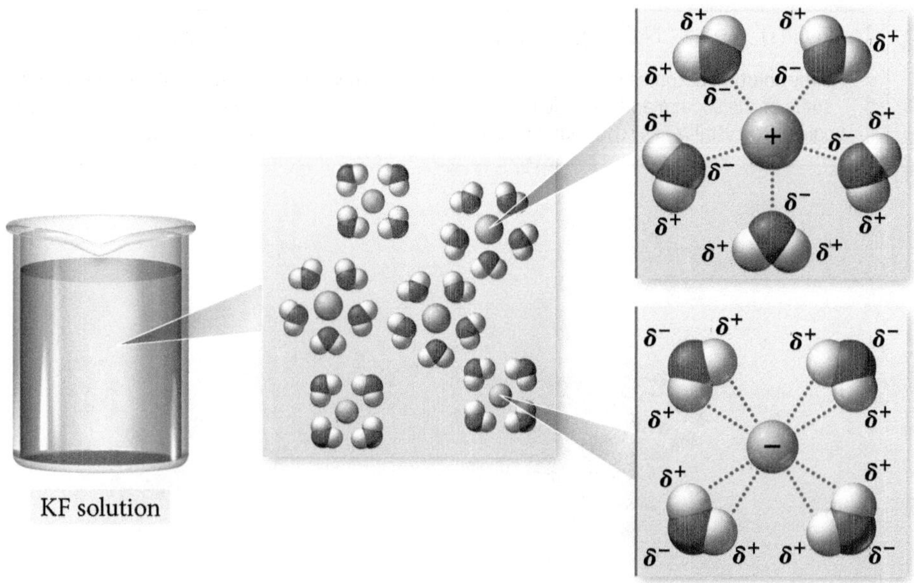

◀ **FIGURE 12.8 Ion–Dipole Interactions** Ion–dipole interactions, such as those between potassium ions, fluoride ions, and water molecules, cause the heat of hydration to be largely negative (exothermic).

$\Delta_{\text{soln}}H$ is therefore positive and the solution process is endothermic (if a solution forms at all). Good examples of solutes that form aqueous solutions with positive enthalpies of solution include ammonium nitrate and silver nitrate. When these solutes dissolve in water, the resulting solutions feel cool to the touch.

$$NH_4NO_3(s) \xrightarrow[H_2O]{} NH_4^+(aq) + NO_3^-(aq) \qquad \Delta_{\text{soln}}H = 25.67 \text{ kJ mol}^{-1}$$

$$AgNO_3(s) \xrightarrow[H_2O]{} Ag^+(aq) + NO_3^-(aq) \qquad \Delta_{\text{soln}}H = 36.91 \text{ kJ mol}^{-1}$$

3. $|\Delta_{\text{solute}}H| \approx |\Delta_{\text{hyd}}H|$. The amount of energy required to separate the solute into its constituent ions is roughly equal to the energy given off when the ions are hydrated. $\Delta_{\text{soln}}H$ is therefore approximately zero and the solution process is neither appreciably exothermic nor appreciably endothermic. Good examples of solutes with enthalpies of solution near zero include sodium chloride and sodium fluoride. When these solutes dissolve in water, the resulting solutions do not undergo a noticeable change in temperature.

$$NaCl(s) \xrightarrow{H_2O} Na^+(aq) + Cl^-(aq) \qquad \Delta_{\text{soln}}H = 3.88 \text{ kJ mol}^{-1}$$

$$NaF(s) \xrightarrow{H_2O} Na^+(aq) + F^-(aq) \qquad \Delta_{\text{soln}}H = 0.91 \text{ kJ mol}^{-1}$$

12.4 Solution Equilibrium and Factors Affecting Solubility

The dissolution of a solute in a solvent is an equilibrium process similar to the equilibrium process associated with a phase change (discussed in Chapter 11). Imagine, from a molecular viewpoint, the dissolution of a solid solute such as sodium chloride in a liquid solvent such as water (Figure 12.9 ▼). Initially, water molecules rapidly solvate sodium cations and chloride anions, resulting in a noticeable decrease in the amount of solid sodium chloride in the water. Over time, however, the concentration of dissolved sodium chloride in the solution increases. This dissolved sodium chloride can then begin to recrystallize as solid sodium chloride. Initially, the rate of dissolution far exceeds the rate of recrystallization. But as the concentration of dissolved sodium chloride increases, the rate of recrystallization also increases. Eventually, the rates of dissolution and recrystallization become equal—**dynamic equilibrium** has been reached:

$$NaCl(s) \rightleftharpoons Na^+(aq) + Cl^-(aq)$$

A solution in which the dissolved solute is in dynamic equilibrium with the solid (undissolved) solute is a **saturated solution.** *If you add additional solute to a saturated solution, it will not dissolve.* A solution containing less than the equilibrium amount of solute is an **unsaturated solution.** *If you add additional solute to an unsaturated solution, it will dissolve.*

$NaCl(s)$

When sodium chloride is first added to water, sodium and chloride ions begin to dissolve into the water.

(a) Initial

$NaCl(s) \longrightarrow Na^+(aq) + Cl^-(aq)$

As the solution becomes more concentrated, some of the sodium and chloride ions can begin to recrystallize as solid sodium chloride.

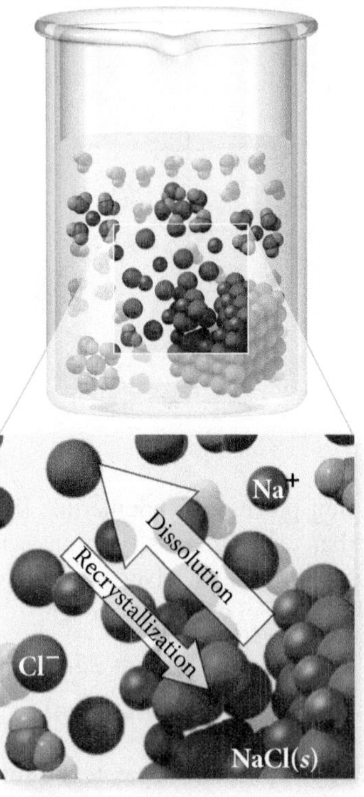

Rate of dissolution > Rate of recrystallization

(b) Dissolving

$NaCl(s) \rightleftharpoons Na^+(aq) + Cl^-(aq)$

When the rate of dissolution equals the rate of recrystallization, dynamic equilibrium has been reached.

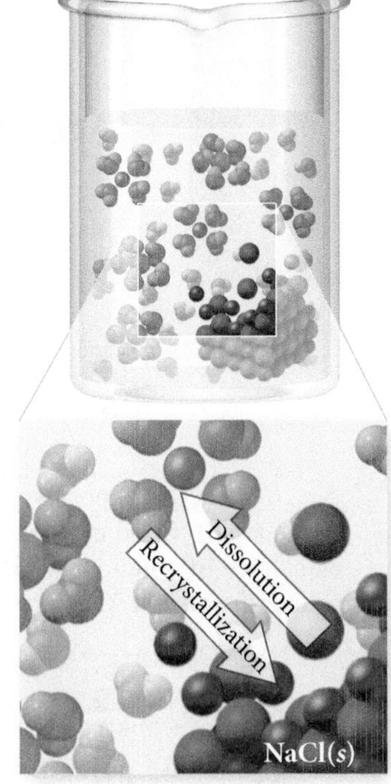

Rate of dissolution = Rate of recrystallization

(c) Dynamic equilibrium

▲ **FIGURE 12.9 Dissolution of NaCl**

Under certain circumstances, a **supersaturated solution**—one containing more than the equilibrium amount of solute—may form. Such solutions are unstable and the excess solute normally precipitates out of the solution. However, in some cases, if left undisturbed, a supersaturated solution can exist for an extended period of time. For example, in a common classroom demonstration, a tiny piece of solid sodium acetate is added to a supersaturated solution of sodium acetate. This triggers the precipitation of the solute, which crystallizes out of solution in a dramatic and often beautiful way (Figure 12.10 ▼).

The Temperature Dependence of the Solubility of Solids

The solubility of solids in water can be highly dependent on temperature. Have you ever noticed how much more sugar you can dissolve in hot tea than in cold tea? Although exceptions exist, *the solubility of most solids in water increases with increasing temperature,*

In the case of sugar dissolving in water, the higher temperature increases both *how fast* the sugar dissolves and *how much* sugar dissolves.

▶ **FIGURE 12.10 Precipitation from a Supersaturated Solution** When a small piece of solid sodium acetate is added to a supersaturated sodium acetate solution, the excess solid precipitates out of the solution.

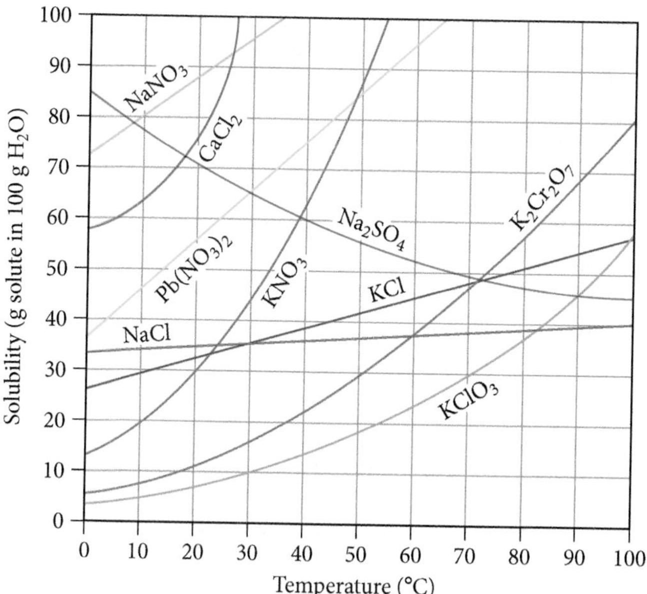

FIGURE 12.11 Solubility and Temperature The solubility of most solids increases with increasing temperature.

as shown in Figure 12.11 ▲. For example, the solubility of potassium nitrate (KNO_3) at room temperature is about 37 g KNO_3 per 100 g of water. At 50 °C, the solubility rises to 88 g KNO_3 per 100 g of water.

A common way to purify a solid is a technique called **recrystallization**. In this technique, a minimum amount of suitable recrystallization solvent at an elevated temperature is added to the solid to create a saturated solution. As the solution cools, it becomes supersaturated and the excess solid precipitates out of solution. If the solution cools slowly, the solid forms crystals as it comes out of solution. The crystalline structure tends to reject impurities, resulting in a purer solid.

You can use the temperature dependence of the solubility of solids to make rock candy. Prepare a saturated sucrose (table sugar) solution at an elevated temperature, and allow a string or stick to dangle into the solution for several days. As the solution cools and the solvent evaporates, the solution becomes supersaturated and sugar crystals grow on the string or stick. After several days, beautiful edible crystals or "rocks" of sugar cover the string.

▲ Rock candy is formed by the recrystallization of sugar.

Factors Affecting the Solubility of Gases in Water

Solutions of gases dissolved in water are common. Club soda, for example, is a solution of carbon dioxide and water, and most liquids exposed to air contain dissolved gases from air. Fish depend on the oxygen dissolved in lake or sea water for life, and our blood contains dissolved nitrogen, oxygen, and carbon dioxide. Even tap water contains dissolved gases. The solubility of a gas in a liquid is affected by both temperature and pressure.

The Effect of Temperature We can observe the effect of temperature on the solubility of a gas in water by heating ordinary tap water on a stove. Before the water reaches its boiling point, small bubbles develop in the water. These bubbles are the dissolved air (mostly nitrogen and oxygen) coming out of solution. (Once the water boils, the bubbling becomes more vigorous—these larger bubbles are composed of water vapour.) The dissolved air comes out of solution because—unlike solids, whose solubility generally increases with increasing temperature—*the solubility of gases in liquids decreases with increasing temperature.*

The inverse relationship between gas solubility and temperature is the reason that warm pop bubbles more than cold pop when you open it and warm beer goes flat faster than cold beer. More carbon dioxide comes out of solution at room temperature than at a lower temperature because the gas is less soluble at room temperature. The decreasing solubility of gases with increasing temperature is also the reason that fish don't bite much in a warm lake. The warm temperature results in a lower oxygen concentration. With lower oxygen levels, the fish become lethargic and do not strike as aggressively at the lure or bait you cast their way.

▲ Warm pop bubbles more than cold pop because carbon dioxide is less soluble in the warm solution.

CONCEPTUAL CONNECTION 12.2
Solubility and Temperature

A solution is saturated in both nitrogen gas and potassium bromide at 75 °C. When the solution is cooled to room temperature, what is most likely to happen?

(a) Some nitrogen gas bubbles out of solution.

(b) Some potassium bromide precipitates out of solution.

(c) Some nitrogen gas bubbles out of solution *and* some potassium bromide precipitates out of solution.

(d) Nothing happens.

The Effect of Pressure The solubility of gases also depends on pressure. The higher the pressure of a gas above a liquid, the more soluble the gas is in the liquid. In a sealed can of pop, for example, the carbon dioxide is maintained in solution by a high pressure of carbon dioxide within the can. When the can is opened, this pressure is released and the solubility of carbon dioxide decreases, resulting in bubbling (Figure 12.12 ▼).

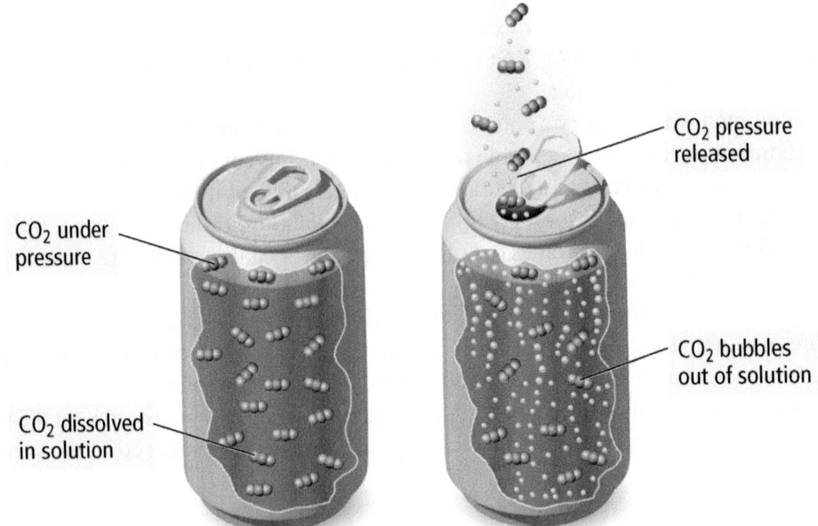

▶ **FIGURE 12.12 Pop Fizz** The bubbling that occurs when a can of pop is opened results from the reduced pressure of carbon dioxide over the liquid. At lower pressure, the carbon dioxide is less soluble and bubbles out of solution.

The increased solubility of a gas in a liquid can be understood by considering cylinders containing water and carbon dioxide gas:

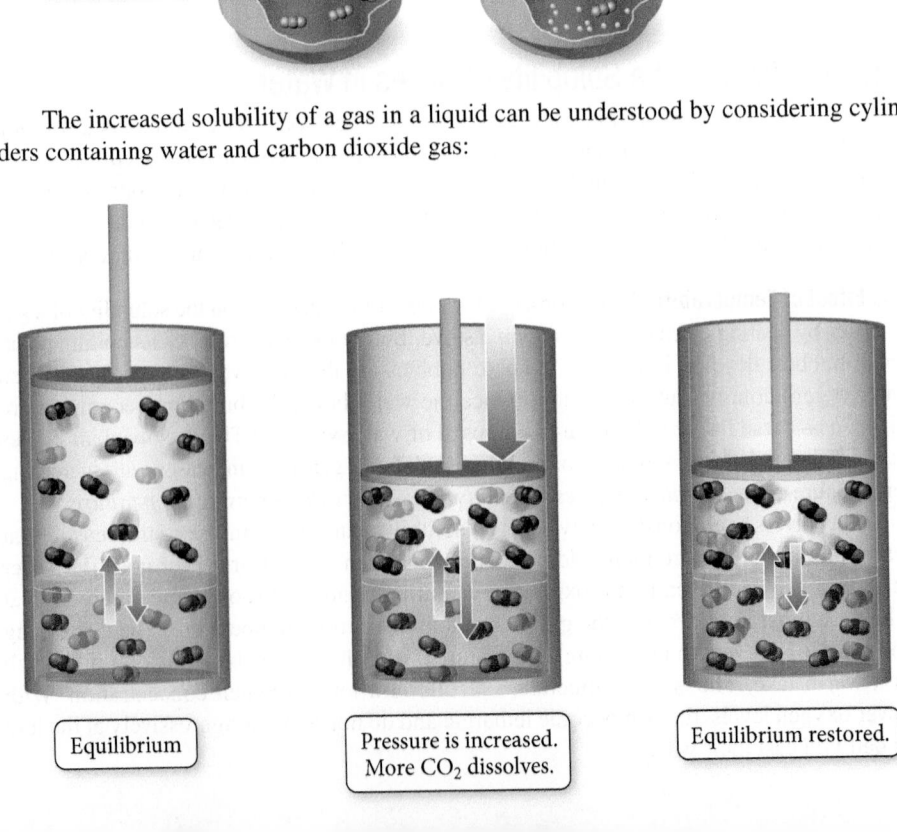

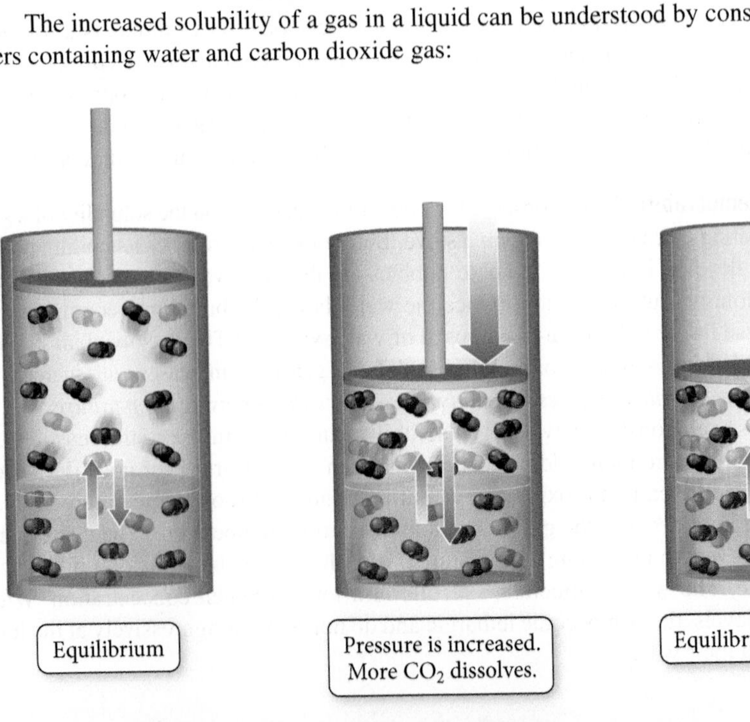

The first cylinder represents an equilibrium between gaseous and dissolved carbon dioxide—the rate of carbon dioxide molecules entering solution exactly equals the rate of molecules leaving the solution. Now imagine decreasing the volume, as shown in the second cylinder. The pressure of carbon dioxide now increases, causing the rate of molecules entering the solution to rise. The number of molecules in solution increases until equilibrium is established again, as shown in the third cylinder. However, the amount of carbon dioxide in solution is now greater.

We can quantify the solubility of gases with increasing pressure with **Henry's law**:

$$S_{gas} = k_H P_{gas}$$

where S_{gas} is the solubility of the gas (usually in mol L^{-1}), k_H is a constant of proportionality (called the *Henry's law constant*) that depends on the specific solute and solvent and also on temperature, and P_{gas} is the partial pressure of the gas. The equation shows that the solubility of a gas in a liquid is directly proportional to the pressure of the gas above the liquid. Table 12.4 lists the Henry's law constants for several common gases.

TABLE 12.4 Henry's Law Constants for Several Gases in Water at 25 °C

Gas	k_H (mol L^{-1} bar^{-1})
O_2	1.3×10^{-3}
N_2	6.1×10^{-4}
CO_2	3.4×10^{-2}
NH_3	5.8×10^{1}
He	3.7×10^{-4}

CONCEPTUAL CONNECTION 12.3

Henry's Law

Examine the Henry's law constants in Table 12.4. Why do you suppose that the constant for ammonia is higher than the others?

EXAMPLE 12.2 HENRY'S LAW

What pressure of carbon dioxide is required to keep the carbon dioxide concentration in a bottle of club soda at 0.12 mol L^{-1} at 25 °C?

SORT You are given the desired solubility of carbon dioxide and asked to find the pressure required to achieve this solubility.

GIVEN: $S_{CO_2} = 0.12 \text{ mol L}^{-1}$

FIND: P_{CO_2}

STRATEGIZE Use Henry's law to find the required pressure from the solubility. You will need the Henry's law constant for carbon dioxide.

CONCEPTUAL PLAN

$S_{CO_2} \rightarrow P_{CO_2}$

$S_{CO_2} = k_{H,CO_2} P_{CO_2}$

RELATIONSHIPS USED

$S_{gas} = k_H P_{gas}$ (Henry's law)

$k_{H, CO_2} = 3.4 \times 10^{-2} \text{ mol L}^{-1} \text{ bar}^{-1}$ (from Table 12.4)

SOLVE Solve the Henry's law equation for P_{CO_2} and substitute the other quantities to calculate it.

SOLUTION

$$S_{CO_2} = k_{H, CO_2} P_{CO_2}$$

$$P_{CO_2} = \frac{S_{CO_2}}{k_{H, CO_2}}$$

$$= \frac{0.12 \text{ mol L}^{-1}}{3.4 \times 10^{-2} \text{ mol L}^{-1} \text{ bar}^{-1}}$$

$$= 3.5 \text{ bar}$$

CHECK The answer has the correct unit and seems reasonable. A small answer (for example, less than 1 bar) would be suspect because you know that the club soda is under a pressure greater than atmospheric pressure when you open it. A very large answer (for example, over 100 bar) would be suspect because an ordinary can or bottle probably could not sustain such high pressures without bursting.

FOR PRACTICE 12.2

Determine the solubility of oxygen in water at 25 °C exposed to air at 1.0 bar. Assume a partial pressure for oxygen of 0.21 bar.

12.5 Expressing Solution Concentration

As we have seen, the amount of solute in a solution is an important property of the solution. For example, the amount of sodium chloride in a solution determines whether or not the solution will cause dehydration if consumed. A **dilute solution** is one containing small quantities of solute relative to the amount of solvent. Drinking a dilute sodium chloride solution will not cause dehydration. A **concentrated solution** is one containing large quantities of solute relative to the amount of solvent. Drinking a concentrated sodium chloride solution will cause dehydration. The common ways of reporting solution concentration include molarity, molality, parts by mass, parts by volume, mole fraction,

CHEMISTRY IN THE ENVIRONMENT Lake Nyos

Most people living near Lake Nyos in Cameroon, West Africa, began August 22, 1986, like any other day. Unfortunately, the day ended in tragedy. On that evening, a large cloud of carbon dioxide gas burped up from the depths of Lake Nyos, killing over 1700 people and about 3000 cattle. Two years before that, a similar tragedy occurred in Lake Monoun, just 96 miles away, killing 37 people. Today, scientists are taking steps to prevent these lakes, both of which are in danger of burping again, from accumulating the carbon dioxide that caused the disaster.

◀ Lake Nyos, in Cameroon, has a deceptively peaceful appearance; in the summer of 1986, more than 1700 people died around its shores.

Lake Nyos is a water-filled volcanic crater. Some 80 km beneath the surface of the lake, molten volcanic rock (magma) produces carbon dioxide gas that seeps into the lake through the volcano's plumbing system. The carbon dioxide forms a solution with the lake water. The high pressure at the bottom of the deep lake allows the solution to become highly concentrated in carbon dioxide. Over time—either because of the high concentration itself or because of some other natural trigger such as a landslide or small earthquake—some gaseous carbon dioxide escaped. The rising bubbles disrupted the stratified layers of lake water, causing water at the bottom of the lake to rise to a region of lower pressure. The drop in pressure decreased the solubility of the carbon dioxide, so more carbon dioxide bubbles formed. This, in turn, caused more churning and still more carbon dioxide release. The result was a massive cloud of carbon dioxide gas that escaped from the lake. Since carbon dioxide is heavier than air, it travelled down the sides of the volcano and into the nearby valley, displacing air and asphyxiating many of the local residents.

In an effort to keep these events from recurring, scientists have built a piping system that slowly vents carbon dioxide from the lake bottom, preventing the buildup that led to the tragedy.

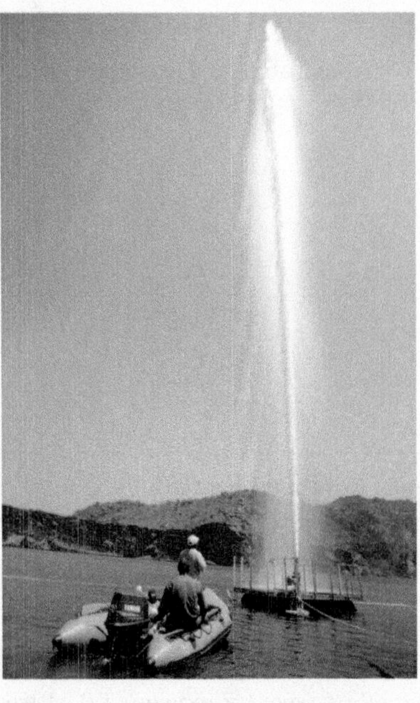

◀ In efforts to prevent another tragedy, scientists have built a plumbing system to slowly vent carbon dioxide from Lake Nyos.

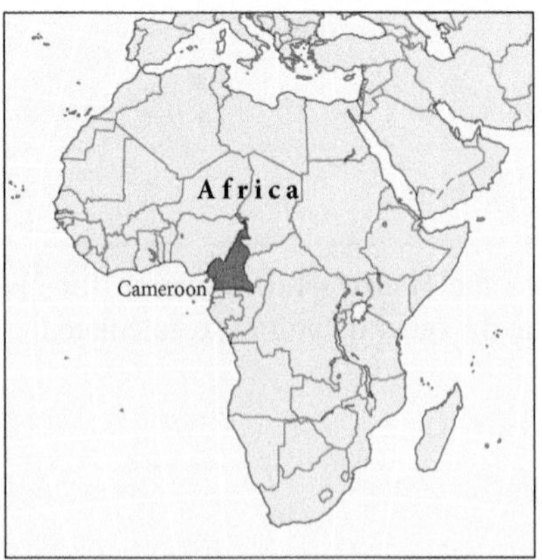

Question

Suppose that the water pressure at the bottom of Lake Nyos was 25 bar. What would the solubility of carbon dioxide be at that depth?

and mole percent, as summarized in Table 12.5. We have seen two of these units before: molarity in Section 4.9, and mole fraction in Section 5.6. In the following section, we review the terms we have already covered and introduce the new ones.

TABLE 12.5 Solution Concentration Terms

Unit Name	Definition	Units
Molarity (*M*)	$\frac{\text{Amount solute (in mol)}}{\text{Volume solution (in L)}}$	mol L^{-1}
Molality (*m*)	$\frac{\text{Amount solute (in mol)}}{\text{Mass solvent (in kg)}}$	mol kg^{-1}
Parts by mass	$\frac{\text{Mass solute}}{\text{Mass solution}} \times$ multiplication factor	
Percent by mass (%)	Multiplication factor = 100	%
Parts per million by mass (ppm)	Multiplication factor = 10^6	ppm
Parts per billion by mass (ppb)	Multiplication factor = 10^9	ppb
Parts by volume (%, ppm, ppb, ppmv, ppbv)	$\frac{\text{volume solute}}{\text{volume solution}} \times$ multiplication factor*	
Mole fraction (χ)	$\frac{\text{amount solute (in mol)}}{\text{total amount of solute and solvent (in mol)}}$	None
Mole percent (mol %)	mole fraction × 100%	%

*Multiplication factors for parts by volume are identical to those for parts by mass.

Molarity

The **molarity (*M*)** of a solution is the amount of solute (in moles) divided by the volume of solution (in litres):

$$\text{Molarity } (M) = \frac{\text{amount solute (in mol)}}{\text{volume solution (in L)}}$$

Note that molarity is moles of solute per litre of *solution*, not per litre of solvent. To make a solution of a specified molarity, we usually put the solute into a flask and then add water (or another solvent) to the desired volume of solution, as shown in Figure 12.13 ▼.

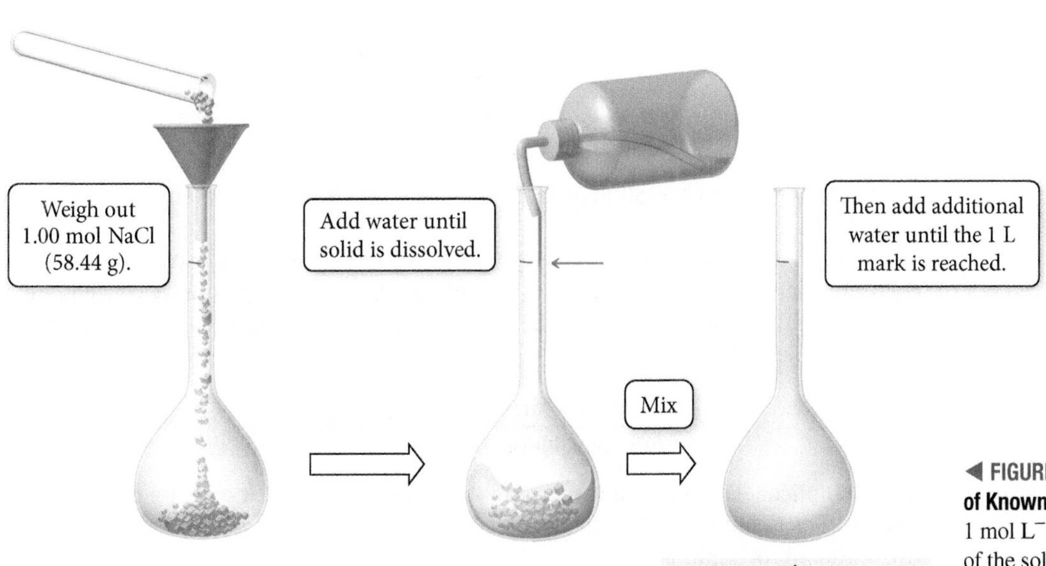
Weigh out 1.00 mol NaCl (58.44 g).
Add water until solid is dissolved.
Mix
Then add additional water until the 1 L mark is reached.
A 1.00 mol L⁻¹ NaCl solution

◀ **FIGURE 12.13 Preparing a Solution of Known Concentration** To make a 1 mol L^{-1} NaCl solution, add 1 mol of the solid to a flask and dilute with water to make 1 L of solution.

Molarity is a convenient unit to use when making, diluting, and transferring solutions because it specifies the amount of solute per unit of solution transferred.

Molality

Sometimes, M is used as a short form to represent mol L^{-1}, and m is used to represent mol kg^{-1}. For example, 12.0 M = 12.0 mol L^{-1}.

Molarity depends on volume, and since volume varies with temperature, molarity also varies with temperature. For example, a 1 mol L^{-1} aqueous solution at room temperature will be slightly less than 1 mol L^{-1} at an elevated temperature because the volume of the solution is greater at the elevated temperature. A concentration unit that is independent of temperature is **molality (*m*)**, the amount of solute (in moles) divided by the mass of solvent (in kilograms):

$$\text{Molality } (m) = \frac{\text{amount solute (in mol)}}{\text{mass solvent (in kg)}}$$

Notice that molality is defined with respect to kilograms *solvent*, not kilograms solution. Molality is particularly useful when concentrations must be compared over a range of different temperatures. For example, when the temperature of an aqueous solution is increased, its volume will increase, and therefore the concentration in molarity will decrease. However, when the temperature increases, the mass of solvent stays the same, so the concentration in molality units remains constant.

Parts by Mass and Parts by Volume

It is often convenient to report a concentration as a ratio of masses. A **parts by mass** concentration is the ratio of the mass of the solute to the mass of the solution, all multiplied by a multiplication factor:

$$\frac{\text{Mass solute}}{\text{Mass solution}} \times \text{multiplication factor}$$

The particular unit used, which determines the size of the multiplication factor, depends on the concentration of the solution. For example, the multiplication factor for **percent by mass** is 100.

$$\text{Percent by mass} = \frac{\text{mass solute}}{\text{mass solution}} \times 100\%$$

Percent means *per hundred*; a solution with a concentration of 14% by mass contains 14 g of solute per 100 g of solution.

For more dilute solutions, we can use **parts per million (ppm)**, which requires a multiplication factor of 10^6, or **parts per billion (ppb)**, which requires a multiplication factor of 10^9:

$$\text{ppm} = \frac{\text{mass solute}}{\text{mass solution}} \times 10^6$$

$$\text{ppb} = \frac{\text{mass solute}}{\text{mass solution}} \times 10^9$$

A solution with a concentration of 15 ppm by mass, for example, contains 15 g of solute per 10^6 g of solution.

Sometimes, concentrations are reported as a ratio of volumes, especially for solutions in which both the solute and solvent are liquids. A **parts by volume** concentration is usually the ratio of the volume of the solute to the volume of the solution, all multiplied by a multiplication factor:

$$\frac{\text{Volume solute}}{\text{Volume solution}} \times \text{multiplication factor}$$

The multiplication factors are identical to those just described for parts by mass concentrations. For example, a 22% ethanol solution by volume contains 22 mL of ethanol for every 100 mL of solution.

Using Parts by Mass (or Parts by Volume) in Calculations We can use the parts by mass (or parts by volume) concentration of a solution as a conversion factor between mass (or volume) of the solute and mass (or volume) of the solution. For example, for a solution containing 3.5% sodium chloride by mass, we would write the following conversion factor:

For dilute aqueous solutions near room temperature, the units of ppm are approximated as milligrams solute per litre of solution. This is because the density of a dilute aqueous solution near room temperature is very close to 1.0 g mL^{-1}, which means that 1 L has a mass of 1000 g.

$$\frac{3.5 \text{ g NaCl}}{100 \text{ g solution}}$$ converts g solution → g NaCl

This conversion factor converts from grams solution to grams NaCl. To convert the other way, we simply invert the conversion factor:

$$\frac{100 \text{ g solution}}{3.5 \text{ g NaCl}}$$ converts g NaCl → g solution

EXAMPLE 12.3 USING PARTS BY MASS IN CALCULATIONS

What volume (in mL) of a soft drink that is 10.5% sucrose ($C_{12}H_{22}O_{11}$) by mass contains 78.5 g of sucrose? (The density of the solution is 1.04 g mL^{-1}.)

SORT You are given a mass of sucrose and the concentration and density of a sucrose solution, and you are asked to find the volume of solution containing that mass.

GIVEN: 78.5 g $C_{12}H_{22}O_{11}$
10.5% $C_{12}H_{22}O_{11}$ by mass
density = 1.04 g mL^{-1}

FIND: volume in mL

STRATEGIZE Begin with the mass of sucrose in grams. Use the mass percent concentration of the solution (written as a ratio, as shown under Relationships Used) to find the number of grams of solution containing this quantity of sucrose. Then use the density of the solution to convert grams to millilitres of solution.

CONCEPTUAL PLAN

g $C_{12}H_{22}O_{11}$ → g soln → mL soln

$$\frac{100 \text{ g soln}}{10.5 \text{ g } C_{12}H_{22}O_{11}} \qquad \frac{1 \text{ mL}}{1.04 \text{ g}}$$

RELATIONSHIPS USED

$$\frac{10.5 \text{ g } C_{12}H_{22}O_{11}}{100 \text{ g soln}}$$ (percent by mass written as ratio)

$$\frac{1 \text{ mL}}{1.04 \text{ g}}$$ (given density of the solution)

SOLVE Begin with 78.5 g $C_{12}H_{22}O_{11}$ and multiply by the conversion factors to arrive at the volume of solution.

SOLUTION

$$78.5 \text{ g } C_{12}H_{22}O_{11} \times \frac{100 \text{ g soln}}{10.5 \text{ g } C_{12}H_{22}O_{11}} \times \frac{1 \text{ mL}}{1.04 \text{ g}} = 719 \text{ mL soln}$$

CHECK The unit of the answer is correct. The magnitude seems correct because the solution is approximately 10% sucrose by mass. Since the density of the solution is approximately 1 g mL^{-1}, the volume containing 78.5 g sucrose should be roughly 10 times larger, as calculated.

FOR PRACTICE 12.3

How much sucrose ($C_{12}H_{22}O_{11}$), in g, is contained in 355 mL (12 ounces) of a soft drink that is 11.5% sucrose by mass? (Assume a density of 1.04 g mL^{-1}.)

FOR MORE PRACTICE 12.3

A water sample is found to contain the pollutant chlorobenzene with a concentration of 15 ppb (by mass). What volume of this water contains 5.00×10^2 mg of chlorobenzene? (Assume a density of 1.00 g mL^{-1}.)

Mole Fraction and Mole Percent

The mole fraction can also be defined for the solvent:

$$\chi_{solvent} = \frac{n_{solvent}}{n_{solute} + n_{solvent}}$$

For some applications, especially those in which the ratio of solute to solvent can vary widely, the most useful way to express concentration is the amount of solute (in moles) divided by the total amount of solute and solvent (in moles). This ratio is called the **mole fraction (χ_{solute})**:

$$\chi_{solute} = \frac{\text{amount solute (in mol)}}{\text{total amount of solute and solvent (in mol)}} = \frac{n_{solute}}{n_{solute} + n_{solvent}}$$

Also in common use is the **mole percent (mol %)**, which is simply the mole fraction × 100 percent:

$$\text{mol } \% = \chi_{solute} \times 100\%$$

CHEMISTRY IN THE ENVIRONMENT Pharmaceuticals and Personal Care Products

Scientists around the world have been concerned about trace drugs that could affect aquatic environments and eventually make their way to tap water. According to the National Water Research Institute of Environment Canada and numerous leading scientists, pharmaceuticals and personal care products (PPCPs) is one of the leading emerging issues in environmental chemistry. At least 80 PPCPs have been identified in effluents from wastewater/sewage treatment plants (WSTPs) and surface waters worldwide. They include analgesics, antibiotics, antiepileptics, antidepressants, blood lipid regulators, and endocrine-disrupting compounds.

Many PPCPs remain unidentified, and many can be hazardous even though they are seemingly nontoxic. For example, UV filters such as 3-benzylidene camphor (3BC)—found in many PPCPs like sunscreen—protect us from exposure to UV light from the sun. These chemicals have been detected in surface water, wastewater, and fish. Short-term exposure (a month) to 3BC has been shown to affect reproduction in a dose-dependent manner in fish. Weak effects were observed on fertility at 3 μg L^{-1}, a significant decrease in fertility at 74 μg L^{-1}, and a cessation of reproduction at 285 μg L^{-1}. Furthermore, it has been shown that UV filters can bioaccumulate. This means that their concentrations build up in fish and other aquatic life to higher concentrations than in the surrounding water.

TABLE 12.6 Triclosan Concentrations from WSTP Effluent and Surface Water on the Detroit River in Windsor, Ontario

WSTP effluent (pre-UV treatment)	80 ng L^{-1}
WSTP effluent (post-UV treatment)	63 ng L^{-1}
Surface water sites downstream of WSTP	4–8 ng L^{-1}
Surface water measurements in other countries	1–140 ng L^{-1}
Toxicity level for rainbow trout and algae	1.5–350 μg L^{-1}

Source: Hua, W.; Bennett, E. R.; Letcher, R. J. *Environ. Int.* 2005, 31, 621–30.

Triclosan is another PPCP known for its antimicrobial effects and is a common component in many consumer products such as hand soaps, cleaning supplies, dish detergents, toothpaste, socks, and bedding. In fact, according to *Marketplace* on CBC.ca, Health Canada has registered 1200 cosmetics containing triclosan and has recommended avoiding antibacterial products over concerns of antibacterial resistance. These compounds eventually find their way into our wastewater, and if not completely removed, they find their way back to our water supply. Triclosan has been detected in the blood plasma of various fish species from the Detroit River and Great Lakes [M. Alaee, I. D'Sa, E. R. Bennett, and R. J. Letcher. Levels of triclosan and methyl-triclosan in fish plasma from the Detroit River, *Organohalog. Compd.* 136 (2003), pp. 136–140]. It is toxic at levels below 1.5 μg L^{-1} in rainbow trout (see Table 12.6).

Little is known about the effects of exposure or ingestion of high concentrations of PPCPs on the environment or humans. Much research is currently being conducted regarding the fate, characterization, and quantification in WSTPs, lakes, soils, and at drinking water intakes.

EXAMPLE 12.4 CALCULATING CONCENTRATIONS

A solution is prepared by dissolving 17.2 g of ethan-1,2-diol, commonly known as ethylene glycol, ($C_2H_6O_2$) in 0.500 kg of water. The final volume of the solution is 515 mL. For this solution, calculate:

(a) molarity
(b) molality
(c) percent by mass
(d) mole fraction
(e) mole percent

SOLUTION

(a) To calculate molarity, first find the amount of ethylene glycol in moles from the mass and molar mass.	$\text{mol } C_2H_6O_2 = 17.2 \text{ g } C_2H_6O_2 \times \frac{1 \text{ mol } C_2H_6O_2}{62.07 \text{ g } C_2H_6O_2} = 0.27\underline{7}1 \text{ mol } C_2H_6O_2$
Then divide the amount in moles by the volume of the solution in litres.	$\text{Molarity } (M) = \frac{\text{amount solute (in mol)}}{\text{volume solution (in L)}} = \frac{0.27\underline{7}1 \text{ mol } C_2H_6O_2}{0.515 \text{ L solution}} = 0.538 \text{ mol L}^{-1}$
(b) To calculate molality, use the amount of ethylene glycol in moles from part (a), and divide by the mass of the water in kilograms.	$\text{Molality } (m) = \frac{\text{amount solute (in mol)}}{\text{mass solvent (in kg)}} = \frac{0.27\underline{7}1 \text{ mol } C_2H_6O_2}{0.500 \text{ kg } H_2O} = 0.554 \text{ mol kg}^{-1}$
(c) To calculate percent by mass, divide the mass of the solute by the sum of the masses of the solute and solvent and multiply the ratio by 100%.	$\text{Percent by mass} = \frac{\text{mass solute}}{\text{mass solution}} \times 100\% = \frac{17.2 \text{ g}}{17.2 \text{ g} + 5.00 \times 10^2 \text{ g}} \times 100\% = 3.33\%$
(d) To calculate mole fraction, first determine the amount of water in moles from the mass of water and its molar mass.	$\text{mol } H_2O = 5.00 \times 10^2 \text{ g } H_2O \times \frac{1 \text{ mol } H_2O}{18.02 \text{ g } H_2O} = 27.\underline{7}5 \text{ mol } H_2O$
Then divide the amount of ethylene glycol in moles [from part (a)] by the total number of moles.	$\chi_{solute} = \frac{n_{solute}}{n_{solute} + n_{solvent}} = \frac{0.27\underline{7}1 \text{ mol}}{0.27\underline{7}1 \text{ mol} + 27.\underline{7}5 \text{ mol}} = 9.89 \times 10^{-3}$
(e) To calculate mole percent, simply multiply the mole fraction by 100%.	$\text{mol } \% = \chi_{solute} \times 100\% = 0.989\%$

FOR PRACTICE 12.4

A solution is prepared by dissolving 50.4 g of sucrose ($C_{12}H_{22}O_{11}$) in 0.332 kg of water. The final volume of the solution is 355 mL. Calculate the following for this solution:

(a) molarity
(b) molality
(c) percent by mass
(d) mole fraction
(e) mole percent

EXAMPLE 12.5 CONVERTING BETWEEN CONCENTRATION UNITS

What is the molarity of a 6.56%-by-mass glucose ($C_6H_{12}O_6$) solution? (The density of the solution is 1.03 g mL^{-1}.)

SORT You are given the concentration of a glucose solution in percent by mass and the density of the solution. You are asked to find the concentration of the solution in molarity.

GIVEN: 6.56% $C_6H_{12}O_6$
density = 1.03 g mL^{-1}

FIND: molarity

STRATEGIZE Begin with the mass percent concentration of the solution written as a ratio, and separate the numerator from the denominator. Convert the numerator from g $C_6H_{12}O_6$ to mol $C_6H_{12}O_6$. Convert the denominator from g soln to mL solution and then to L solution. Then divide the numerator (now in mol) by the denominator (now in L) to obtain molarity.

CONCEPTUAL PLAN

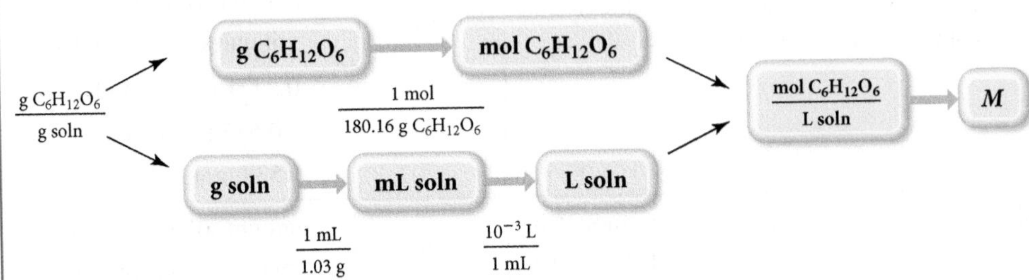

RELATIONSHIPS USED

$\frac{6.56 \text{ g } C_6H_{12}O_6}{100 \text{ g soln}}$ (percent by mass written as ratio)

$\frac{1 \text{ mol}}{180.16 \text{ g } C_6H_{12}O_6}$ (from molar mass of glucose)

$\frac{1 \text{ mL}}{1.03 \text{ g}}$ (from given density of the solution)

SOLVE Begin with the numerator (6.56 g $C_6H_{12}O_6$) and use the molar mass to convert to mol $C_6H_{12}O_6$.

SOLUTION

$$6.56 \text{ g } C_6H_{12}O_6 \times \frac{1 \text{ mol } C_6H_{12}O_6}{180.16 \text{ g } C_6H_{12}O_6} = 0.036\underline{4}12 \text{ mol } C_6H_{12}O_6$$

Then convert the denominator (100 g solution) into mL of solution (using the density) and then to L of solution.

$$100 \text{ g soln} \times \frac{1 \text{ mL}}{1.03 \text{ g}} \times \frac{10^{-3} \text{ L}}{1 \text{ mL}} = 0.0970\underline{8}7 \text{ L soln}$$

Finally, divide mol $C_6H_{12}O_6$ by L solution to arrive at molarity.

$$\frac{0.036\underline{4}12 \text{ mol } C_6H_{12}O_6}{0.0970\underline{8}7 \text{ L soln}} = 0.375 \text{ mol L}^{-1} \ C_6H_{12}O_6$$

CHECK The units of the answer are correct. The magnitude seems correct. Very high molarities (especially above 25 mol L^{-1}) should immediately appear suspect. One litre of water contains about 55 moles of water molecules, so molarities higher than 55 mol L^{-1} are physically impossible.

FOR PRACTICE 12.5
What is the molarity of a 10.5%-by-mass glucose ($C_6H_{12}O_6$) solution? (The density of the solution is 1.03 g mL^{-1}.)

FOR MORE PRACTICE 12.5
What is the molality of a 10.5%-by-mass glucose ($C_6H_{12}O_6$) solution? (The density of the solution is 1.03 g mL^{-1}.)

12.6 Colligative Properties: Vapour Pressure Lowering, Freezing Point Depression, Boiling Point Elevation, and Osmotic Pressure

▲ In winter, salt is often added to roads so that the ice will melt at lower temperatures.

Have you ever wondered why you add salt to ice in an ice-cream maker? Or why salt is scattered on icy roads in cold climates? When added to water, salt will lower the temperature at which the water freezes. The new salt water solution will have a lower freezing point than water alone, remaining liquid even below 0 °C. When salt is added to ice in the ice-cream maker, an ice/water/salt mixture (slurry) forms that can reach a temperature of about −10 °C, allowing the cream to freeze. On the winter road, the salt allows the ice to melt when the ambient temperature is below freezing.

The depression of the freezing point of ice by salt is an example of a **colligative property**, a property that depends on the number of particles dissolved in solution, not on the type of particle. In this section, we examine four colligative properties: vapour pressure lowering, freezing point depression, boiling point elevation, and osmotic pressure. Since these properties depend on the *number* of dissolved particles, nonelectrolytes must be treated slightly differently than electrolytes when determining colligative properties. When 1 mol of a nonelectrolyte dissolves in water, it forms 1 mol of dissolved particles. When 1 mol of an electrolyte dissolves in water, however, it normally forms more than 1 mol of dissolved particles (as shown in Figure 12.14 ▸). For example, when 1 mol of NaCl dissolves in water, it forms 1 mol of dissolved Na^+ ions and 1 mol of dissolved Cl^- ions. Therefore, the resulting solution will have 2 mol of dissolved particles. The colligative properties reflect this higher concentration of dissolved particles. In this section, we examine colligative properties of nonelectrolyte solutions; we then expand the concept to include electrolyte solutions in Section 12.7.

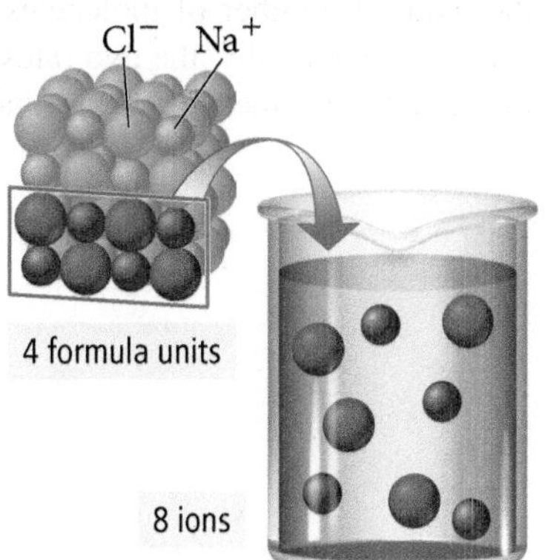

◂ **FIGURE 12.14** When sodium chloride is dissolved in water, each mole of NaCl produces 2 mol of particles: 1 mol of Na^+ and 1 mol of Cl^-.

Vapour Pressure Lowering

Recall from Section 11.5 that the vapour pressure of a liquid is the pressure of the gas above the liquid when the two are in dynamic equilibrium (that is, when the rate of vaporization equals the rate of condensation). What is the effect of a nonvolatile nonelectrolyte solute on the vapour pressure of the liquid into which it dissolves? The basic answer to this question is that *the vapour pressure of the solution will be lower than the vapour pressure of the pure solvent*. We can understand why this happens in two different ways.

The simplest explanation for why the vapour pressure of a solution is lower than that of the pure solvent is related to the concept of dynamic equilibrium itself. Consider the following representation of a liquid in dynamic equilibrium with its vapour. Here, the rate of vaporization is equal to the rate of condensation:

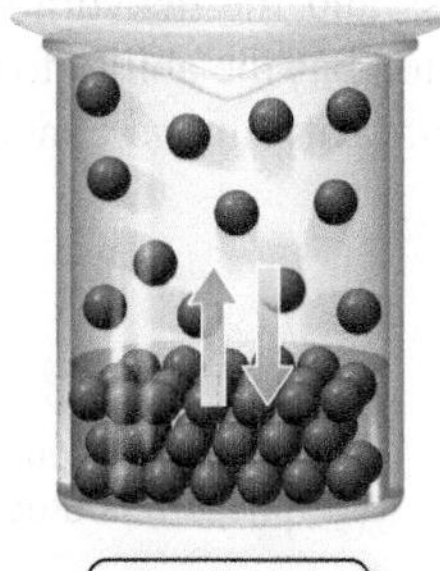

Dynamic equilibrium

When a nonvolatile solute is added, however, the solute particles (shown in red) interfere with the ability of the solvent particles (blue) to vaporize, because they occupy some of the surface area formerly occupied by the solvent. The rate of vaporization is thus diminished compared to that of the pure solvent:

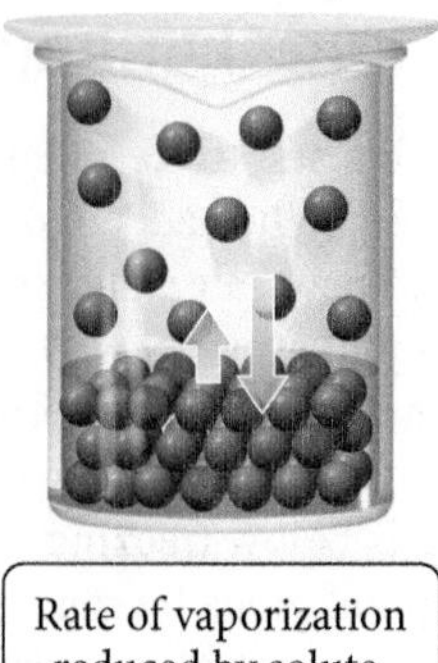
Rate of vaporization
reduced by solute.

The change in the rate of vaporization creates an imbalance in the rates: the rate of condensation is now *greater* than the rate of vaporization. The net effect is that some of the molecules that were in the gas phase condense into the liquid. As they condense, the reduced number of molecules in the gas phase causes the rate of condensation to decrease. Eventually, the two rates become equal again, but only after the concentration of solvent molecules in the gas phase has decreased:

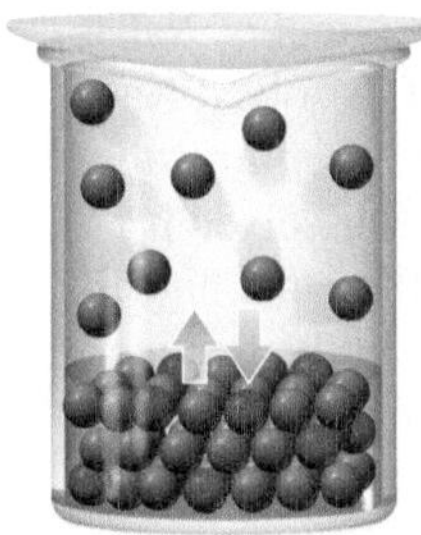
Equilibrium re-established
but with fewer molecules
in gas phase.

The result is a lower vapour pressure for the solution compared to the pure solvent.

A more fundamental explanation of why the vapour pressure of a solution is lower than that of the pure solvent is related to the tendency toward mixing (toward greater entropy) that we discussed in Sections 12.1 and 12.2. Recall from Section 12.1 that a concentrated solution is a *thirsty* solution—it has the ability to draw solvent to itself. We can observe a dramatic demonstration of this tendency by placing a concentrated solution of a nonvolatile solute and a beaker of the pure solvent in a sealed container, as shown below. Over time, the level of the pure solvent will drop and the level of the solution will rise as molecules vaporize out of the pure solvent and condense into the solution. Notice the similarity between this process and the dehydration caused by drinking seawater. In both cases, a concentrated solution has the ability to draw solvent to itself. The reason is nature's tendency to mix. If a pure solvent and concentrated solution are combined in

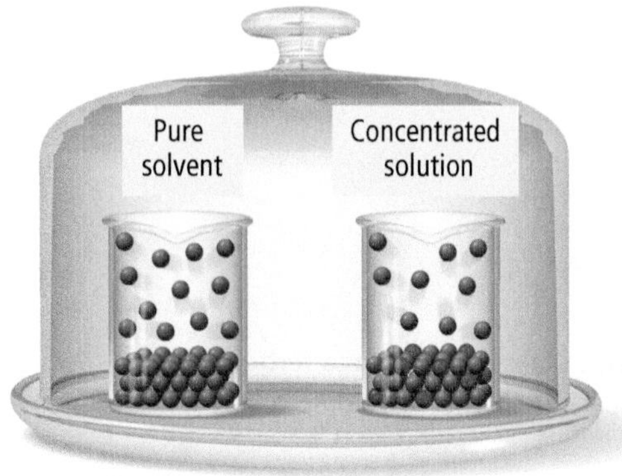
Pure
solvent
Concentrated
solution

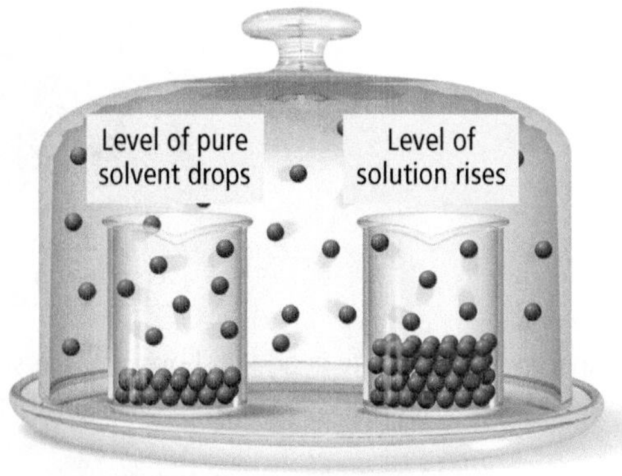
Level of pure
solvent drops
Level of
solution rises

a beaker, they naturally form a mixture in which the concentrated solution becomes less concentrated than it was initially. Similarly, if a pure solvent and concentrated solution are combined in a sealed container—even though they are in separate beakers—the two mix so that the concentrated solution becomes less concentrated.

The net transfer of solvent from the beaker containing pure solvent to the one containing the solution shows that the vapour pressure of the solution is lower than that of the pure solvent. As solvent molecules vaporize, the vapour pressure in the sealed container rises. Before dynamic equilibrium can be attained, however, the pressure exceeds the vapour pressure of the solution, causing molecules to condense into the solution (the beaker on the right). Therefore, molecules constantly vaporize from the pure solvent, but the solvent's vapour pressure is never reached because molecules are constantly leaving the beaker of pure solvent to enter the beaker of solution. The result is a continuous transfer of solvent molecules from the pure solvent to the solution.

We can quantify the vapour pressure of a solution with **Raoult's law**:

$$P_{\text{solution}} = \chi_{\text{solvent}} P^{\circ}_{\text{solvent}}$$

In this equation, P_{solution} is the vapour pressure of the solution, χ_{solvent} is the mole fraction of the solvent, and $P^{\circ}_{\text{solvent}}$ is the vapour pressure of the pure solvent at the same temperature. For example, suppose a water sample at 25 °C contains 0.90 mol of water and 0.10 mol of a nonvolatile solute such as sucrose. The pure water would have a vapour pressure of 23.8 Torr. We calculate the vapour pressure of the solution as follows:

$$\begin{aligned} P_{\text{solution}} &= \chi_{H_2O} P^{\circ}_{H_2O} \\ &= 0.90\,(23.8 \text{ Torr}) \\ &= 21.4 \text{ Torr} \end{aligned}$$

The vapour pressure of the solution is directly proportional to the amount of the solvent in the solution. Since the solvent particles compose 90% of all of the particles in the solution, the vapour pressure of the solution is 90% of the vapour pressure of the pure solvent.

To arrive at an equation that shows how much the vapour pressure is lowered by a solute, we define the **vapour pressure lowering (ΔP)** as the difference in vapour pressure between the pure solvent and the solution:

$$\Delta P = P^{\circ}_{\text{solvent}} - P_{\text{solution}}$$

Then, for a two-component solution, we can substitute $\chi_{\text{solvent}} = 1 - \chi_{\text{solute}}$ into Raoult's law as follows:

$$\begin{aligned} P_{\text{solution}} &= \chi_{\text{solvent}} P^{\circ}_{\text{solvent}} \\ P_{\text{solution}} &= (1 - \chi_{\text{solute}}) P^{\circ}_{\text{solvent}} \\ P^{\circ}_{\text{solvent}} - P_{\text{solution}} &= \chi_{\text{solute}} P^{\circ}_{\text{solvent}} \\ \Delta P &= \chi_{\text{solute}} P^{\circ}_{\text{solvent}} \end{aligned}$$

This last equation indicates that the lowering of the vapour pressure is directly proportional to the mole fraction of the solute.

EXAMPLE 12.6 CALCULATING THE VAPOUR PRESSURE OF A SOLUTION CONTAINING A NONELECTROLYTE AND NONVOLATILE SOLUTE

Calculate the vapour pressure at 25 °C of a solution containing 99.5 g sucrose ($C_{12}H_{22}O_{11}$) and 300.0 mL water. The vapour pressure of pure water at 25 °C is 23.8 Torr. Assume the density of water to be 1.00 g mL^{-1}.

SORT You are given the mass of sucrose and volume of water in a solution. You are also given the vapour pressure of pure water and asked to find the vapour pressure of the solution. The density of the pure water is also provided.	**GIVEN:** 99.5 g $C_{12}H_{22}O_{11}$ 300.0 mL H_2O $P^{\circ}_{H_2O} = 23.8$ Torr at 25 °C $d_{H_2O} = 1.00$ g mL^{-1} **FIND:** P_{solution}

(continued)

EXAMPLE 12.6 (CONTINUED)

STRATEGIZE Raoult's law relates the vapour pressure of a solution to the mole fraction of the solvent and the vapour pressure of the pure solvent. Begin by calculating the amount in moles of sucrose and water.

CONCEPTUAL PLAN

g $C_{12}H_{22}O_{11}$ → mol $C_{12}H_{22}O_{11}$

$$\frac{1 \text{ mol } C_{12}H_{22}O_{11}}{342.30 \text{ g } C_{12}H_{22}O_{11}}$$

mL H_2O → g H_2O → mol H_2O

$$\frac{1.00 \text{ g}}{1 \text{ mL}} \qquad \frac{1 \text{ mol } H_2O}{18.02 \text{ g } H_2O}$$

Calculate the mole fraction of the solvent from the calculated amounts of solute and solvent.

mol $C_{12}H_{22}O_{11}$, mol H_2O → χ_{H_2O}

$$\chi_{H_2O} = \frac{n_{H_2O}}{n_{H_2O} + n_{C_{12}H_{22}O_{11}}}$$

Then use Raoult's law to calculate the vapour pressure of the solution.

χ_{H_2O}, $P^\circ_{H_2O}$ → P_{solution}

$$P_{\text{solution}} = \chi_{H_2O} P^\circ_{H_2O}$$

SOLVE Calculate the number of moles of each solution component.

SOLUTION

$$99.5 \text{ g } C_{12}H_{22}O_{11} \times \frac{1 \text{ mol } C_{12}H_{22}O_{11}}{342.30 \text{ g } C_{12}H_{22}O_{11}} = 0.29\underline{0}7 \text{ mol } C_{12}H_{22}O_{11}$$

$$300.0 \text{ mL } H_2O \times \frac{1.00 \text{ g}}{1 \text{ mL}} \times \frac{1 \text{ mol } H_2O}{18.02 \text{ g } H_2O} = 16.\underline{6}5 \text{ mol } H_2O$$

Use the number of moles of each component to compute the mole fraction of the solvent (H_2O).

$$\chi_{H_2O} = \frac{n_{H_2O}}{n_{C_{12}H_{22}O_{11}} + n_{H_2O}}$$

$$= \frac{16.\underline{6}5 \text{ mol}}{0.29\underline{0}7 \text{ mol} + 16.\underline{6}5 \text{ mol}}$$

$$= 0.98\underline{2}8$$

Use the mole fraction of water and the vapour pressure of pure water to calculate the vapour pressure of the solution.

$$P_{\text{solution}} = \chi_{H_2O} P^\circ_{H_2O}$$

$$= 0.98\underline{2}8 \text{ (23.8 Torr)}$$

$$= 23.4 \text{ Torr}$$

CHECK The unit of the answer is correct. The magnitude of the answer seems right because the calculated vapour pressure of the solution is just below that of the pure liquid, as expected for a solution with a large mole fraction of solvent.

FOR PRACTICE 12.6

Calculate the vapour pressure at 25 °C of a solution containing 55.3 g ethylene glycol ($HOCH_2CH_2OH$) and 285.2 g water. The vapour pressure of pure water at 25 °C is 23.8 Torr.

FOR MORE PRACTICE 12.6

A solution containing ethylene glycol and water has a vapour pressure of 7.88 Torr at 10 °C. Pure water has a vapour pressure of 9.21 Torr at 10 °C. What is the mole fraction of ethylene glycol in the solution?

Vapour Pressures of Solutions Containing a Volatile (Nonelectrolyte) Solute

Over a complete range of compositions of a solution, it no longer makes sense to designate a solvent and solute, so we simply label the two components A and B.

Some solutions contain not only a volatile solvent but also a volatile *solute*. In this case, *both* the solvent and the solute contribute to the overall vapour pressure of the solution. A solution like this may be an **ideal solution** (in which case, it follows Raoult's law at all concentrations for both the solvent and the solute) or it may be nonideal (in which case, it does not follow Raoult's law). An ideal solution is similar in concept to an ideal gas. Just

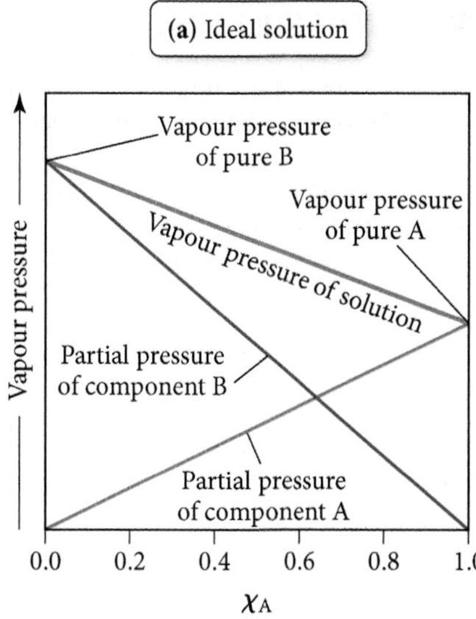

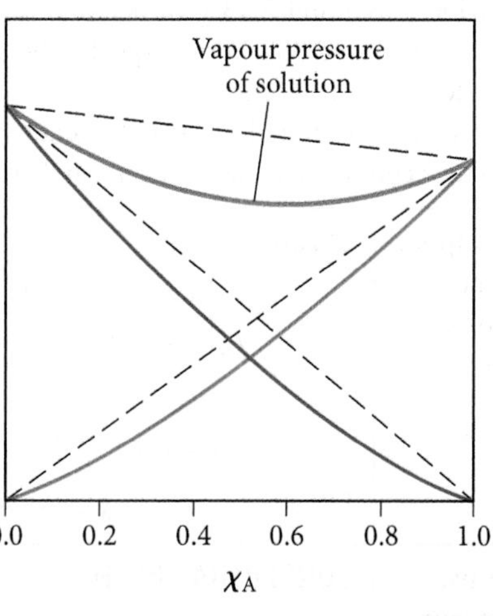

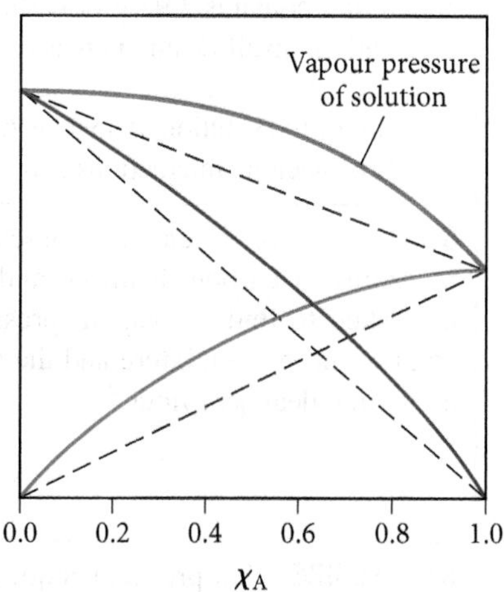

▲ **FIGURE 12.15 Behaviour of Nonideal Solutions** **(a)** An ideal solution follows Raoult's law for both components. **(b)** A solution with particularly strong solute–solvent interactions displays negative deviations from Raoult's law. **(c)** A solution with particularly weak solute–solvent interactions displays positive deviations from Raoult's law. [The dashed lines in parts (b) and (c) represent ideal behaviour.]

as an ideal gas follows the ideal gas law exactly, so an ideal solution follows Raoult's law exactly. In an ideal solution, the solute–solvent interactions are similar in magnitude to the solute–solute and solvent–solvent interactions. In this type of solution, the solute simply dilutes the solvent and ideal behaviour is observed. The vapour pressure of each of the solution components is given by Raoult's law throughout the entire composition range of the solution. For a two-component solution containing liquids A and B, we can write:

$$P_A = \chi_A P^\circ_A$$
$$P_B = \chi_B P^\circ_B$$

The total pressure above such a solution is the sum of the partial pressures of the components:

$$P_{tot} = P_A + P_B$$

Figure 12.15(a) ▲ shows a plot of vapour pressure versus solution composition for an ideal two-component solution.

In a nonideal solution, the solute–solvent interactions are either stronger or weaker than the solvent–solvent interactions. If the solute–solvent interactions are stronger, then the solute tends to prevent the solvent from vaporizing as readily as it would otherwise. If the solution is sufficiently dilute, then the effect will be small and Raoult's law works as an approximation. However, if the solution is not dilute, the effect will be significant and the vapour pressure of the solution will be *less than* that predicted by Raoult's law, as shown in Figure 12.15(b).

If, on the other hand, the solute–solvent interactions are weaker than solvent–solvent interactions, then the solute tends to allow more vaporization than would occur with just the solvent. If the solution is not dilute, the effect will be significant and the vapour pressure of the solution will be *greater than* predicted by Raoult's law, as shown in Figure 12.15(c).

CONCEPTUAL CONNECTION 12.4

Raoult's Law

A solution contains equal amounts (in moles) of liquid components A and B. The vapour pressure of pure A is 100 mmHg and that of pure B is 200 mmHg. The experimentally measured vapour pressure of the solution is 120 mmHg. What can you say about the relative strengths of the solute–solute, solute–solvent, and solvent–solvent interactions in this solution?

EXAMPLE 12.7 CALCULATING THE VAPOUR PRESSURE OF A TWO-COMPONENT SOLUTION

A solution contains 3.95 g of carbon disulfide (CS_2) and 2.43 g of acetone (CH_3COCH_3). The vapour pressures at 35 °C of pure carbon disulfide and pure acetone are 515 Torr and 332 Torr, respectively. Assuming ideal behaviour, calculate the vapour pressures of each of the components and the total vapour pressure above the solution. The experimentally measured total vapour pressure of the solution at 35 °C is 645 Torr. Is the solution ideal? If not, what can you say about the relative strengths of carbon disulfide–acetone interactions compared to the acetone–acetone and carbon disulfide–carbon disulfide interactions?

SORT You are given the masses and vapour pressures of carbon disulfide and acetone and are asked to find the vapour pressures of each component in the mixture and the total pressure, assuming ideal behaviour.

GIVEN: 3.95 g CS_2

2.43 g CH_3COCH_3

$P^{\circ}_{CS_2} = 515$ Torr (at 35 °C)

$P^{\circ}_{CH_3COCH_3} = 332$ Torr (at 35 °C)

$P_{tot}(\text{exp}) = 645$ Torr (at 35 °C)

FIND: P_{CS_2}, $P_{CH_3COCH_3}$, P_{tot} (ideal)

STRATEGIZE This problem requires the use of Raoult's law to calculate the partial pressures of each component. In order to use Raoult's law, you must first compute the mole fractions of the two components. Convert the masses of each component to moles and then use the definition of mole fraction to calculate the mole fraction of carbon disulfide. The mole fraction of acetone can easily be found because the mole fractions of the two components add up to 1.

CONCEPTUAL PLAN

3.95 g CS_2 → mol CS_2

$$\frac{1 \text{ mol } CS_2}{76.15 \text{ g } CS_2}$$

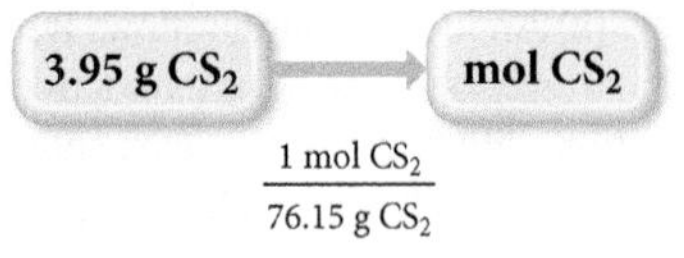

mol CS_2, mol CH_3COCH_3 → χ_{CS_2}, $\chi_{CH_3COCH_3}$

$$\chi_{CS_2} = \frac{n_{CS_2}}{n_{CS_2} + n_{CH_3COCH_3}}$$

Use the mole fraction of each component along with Raoult's law to compute the partial pressure of each component. The total pressure is the sum of the partial pressures.

$$P_{CS_2} = \chi_{CS_2} P^{\circ}_{CS_2}$$

$$P_{CH_3COCH_3} = \chi_{CH_3COCH_3} P^{\circ}_{CH_3COCH_3}$$

$$P_{tot} = P_{CS_2} + P_{CH_3COCH_3}$$

RELATIONSHIPS USED

$$\chi_A = \frac{n_A}{n_A + n_B} \text{ (mole fraction definition)}$$

$$P_A = \chi_A P^{\circ}_A \text{ (Raoult's law)}$$

SOLVE Begin by converting the masses of each component to the amounts in moles.

SOLUTION

$$3.95 \text{ g } CS_2 \times \frac{1 \text{ mol } CS_2}{76.15 \text{ g } CS_2} = 0.051\underline{8}7 \text{ mol } CS_2$$

$$2.43 \text{ g } CH_3COCH_3 \times \frac{1 \text{ mol } CH_3COCH_3}{58.08 \text{ g } CH_3COCH_3} = 0.041\underline{8}4 \text{ mol } CH_3COCH_3$$

Then calculate the mole fraction of carbon disulfide.

$$\chi_{CS_2} = \frac{n_{CS_2}}{n_{CS_2} + n_{CH_3COCH_3}}$$

$$= \frac{0.051\underline{8}7 \text{ mol}}{0.051\underline{8}7 \text{ mol} + 0.041\underline{8}4 \text{ mol}}$$

$$= 0.553\underline{5}$$

Calculate the mole fraction of acetone by subtracting the mole fraction of carbon disulfide from 1.	$\chi_{CH_3COCH_3} = 1 - 0.55\underline{3}5$ $= 0.44\underline{6}5$
Calculate the partial pressures of carbon disulfide and acetone by using Raoult's law and the given values of the vapour pressures of the pure substances.	$P_{CS_2} = \chi_{CS_2}P^{\circ}_{CS_2}$ $= 0.55\underline{3}5(515 \text{ Torr})$ $= 285 \text{ Torr}$ $P_{CH_3COCH_3} = \chi_{CH_3COCH_3}P^{\circ}_{CH_3COCH_3}$ $= 0.44\underline{6}5(332 \text{ Torr})$ $= 148 \text{ Torr}$
Calculate the total pressure by summing the partial pressures.	$P_{tot}(\text{ideal}) = 285 \text{ Torr} + 148 \text{ Torr}$ $= 433 \text{ Torr}$
Lastly, compare the calculated total pressure for the ideal case to the experimentally measured total pressure. Since the experimentally measured pressure is greater than the calculated pressure, we can conclude that the interactions between the two components must be weaker than the interactions between the components themselves.	$P_{tot}(\text{exp}) = 645 \text{ Torr}$ $P_{tot}(\text{exp}) > P_{tot}(\text{ideal})$ The solution is not ideal and shows positive deviations from Raoult's law. Therefore, carbon disulfide–acetone interactions must be weaker than acetone–acetone and carbon disulfide–carbon disulfide interactions.

CHECK The unit of the answer (Torr) is correct. The magnitude seems reasonable given the partial pressures of the pure substances.

FOR PRACTICE 12.7

A solution of benzene (C_6H_6) and toluene (C_7H_8) is 25.0% benzene by mass. The vapour pressures of pure benzene and pure toluene at 25 °C are 94.2 Torr and 28.4 Torr, respectively. Assuming ideal behaviour, calculate each of the following:

(a) The vapour pressure of each of the solution components in the mixture.
(b) The total pressure above the solution.
(c) The composition of the vapour in mass percent.

Why is the composition of the vapour different from the composition of the solution?

Freezing Point Depression and Boiling Point Elevation

Vapour pressure lowering occurs at all temperatures. We can see the effect of vapour pressure lowering over a range of temperatures by comparing the phase diagrams for a pure solvent and for a solution containing a nonvolatile solute:

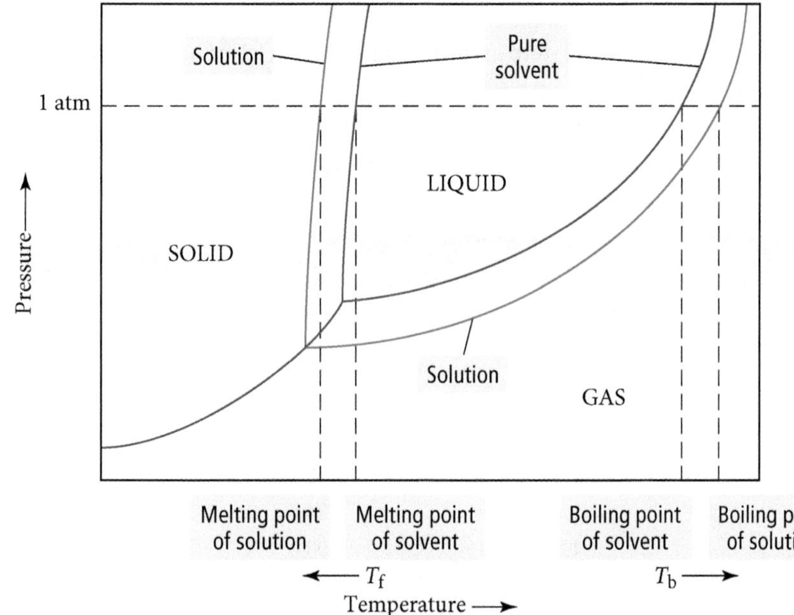

◀ A nonvolatile solute lowers the vapour pressure of a solution, resulting in a lower freezing point and an elevated boiling point.

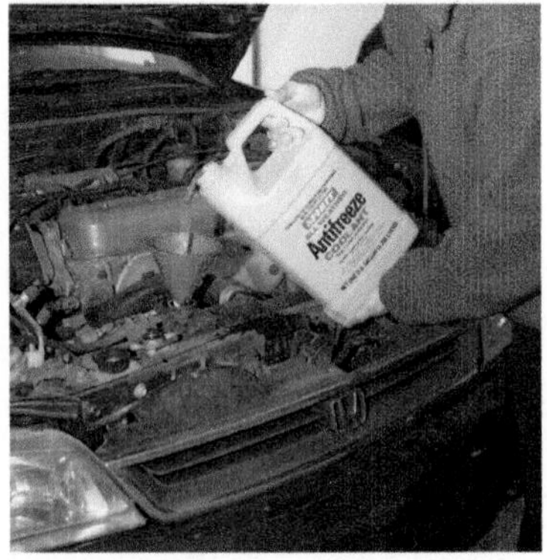

▲ Antifreeze is an aqueous solution of ethylene glycol. The solution has a lower freezing point and higher boiling point than pure water.

Notice that the vapour pressure for the solution (red curves) is shifted downward compared to that of the pure solvent. Consequently, the vapour pressure curve intersects the solid–gas curve at a lower temperature. The net effect is that the solution has a *lower melting point* and a *higher boiling point* than the pure solvent. These effects are called **freezing point depression** and **boiling point elevation**, both of which are colligative properties (like vapour pressure lowering).

The freezing point of a solution containing a nonvolatile solute is lower than the freezing point of the pure solvent. For example, antifreeze, used to prevent the freezing of engine blocks in cold climates, is an aqueous solution of ethylene glycol ($C_2H_6O_2$). The more concentrated the solution, the lower the freezing point becomes.

The amount that the freezing point is lowered is given by the equation:

$$\Delta T_f = m \times K_f \qquad [12.1]$$

where

- ▶ ΔT_f is the change in temperature of the freezing point in Celsius (relative to the freezing point of the pure solvent), usually reported as a positive number;
- ▶ m is the molality of the solution in moles of solute per kilogram solvent;
- ▶ K_f is the freezing point depression constant for the solvent.

m strictly stands for molality, but it is sometimes used to represent mol of solute per kg solvent, or just mol kg^{-1}.

For water:

$$K_f = 1.86\ °C\ m^{-1}$$

When an aqueous solution containing a dissolved solid solute freezes slowly, the ice that forms does not normally contain much of the solute. For example, when ice forms in ocean water, the ice is not salt water, but freshwater. As the ice forms, the crystal structure of the ice tends to exclude the solute particles. You can verify this yourself by partially freezing a salt water solution in the freezer. Take out the newly formed ice, rinse it several times, and taste it. Compare its taste to the taste of the original solution. The ice is much less salty.

Freezing point depression and boiling point elevation constants for several liquids are listed in Table 12.7. Calculating the freezing point of a solution involves substituting into Equation 12.1, as the following example demonstrates.

The boiling point of a solution containing a nonvolatile solute is higher than the boiling point of the pure solvent. In automobiles, antifreeze not only prevents the freezing of water within engine blocks in cold climates, it also prevents the boiling of water within engine blocks in hot climates. The amount that the boiling point rises in solutions is given by the equation:

$$\Delta T_b = m \times K_b \qquad [12.2]$$

where

- ▶ ΔT_b is the change in temperature of the boiling point in Celsius (relative to the boiling point of the pure solvent);
- ▶ m is the molality of the solution in moles of solute per kilogram solvent;
- ▶ K_b is the boiling point elevation constant for the solvent.

TABLE 12.7 Freezing Point Depression and Boiling Point Elevation Constants for Several Liquid Solvents

Solvent	Normal Freezing Point (°C)	K_f (°C m^{-1})	Normal Boiling Point (°C)	K_b (°C m^{-1})
Benzene (C_6H_6)	5.5	5.12	80.1	2.53
Carbon tetrachloride (CCl_4)	−22.9	29.9	76.7	5.03
Chloroform ($CHCl_3$)	−63.5	4.70	61.2	3.63
Ethanol (C_2H_2OH)	−114.1	1.99	78.3	1.22
Diethyl ether ($C_4H_{10}O$)	−116.3	1.79	34.6	2.02
Water (H_2O)	0.00	1.86	100.0	0.512

For water:

$$K_b = 0.512\ °\text{C}\ m^{-1}$$

The boiling point of a solution is calculated by substituting into Equation 12.2, as the following example demonstrates.

EXAMPLE 12.8 CALCULATING THE FREEZING POINT DEPRESSION

Calculate the freezing point of a 1.7 *m* aqueous ethylene glycol solution.

SORT You are given the molality of a solution and asked to find its freezing point.

GIVEN: 1.7 *m* solution

FIND: freezing point (from ΔT_f)

STRATEGIZE To solve this problem, use the freezing point depression equation.

CONCEPTUAL PLAN

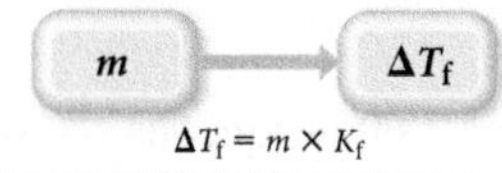

$\Delta T_f = m \times K_f$

SOLVE Substitute into the equation to calculate ΔT_f. The actual freezing point is the freezing point of pure water (0.00 °C) − ΔT_f.

SOLUTION

$$\Delta T_f = m \times K_f$$
$$= 1.7\ \cancel{m} \times 1.86\ °\text{C}\ \cancel{m^{-1}}$$
$$= 3.2\ °\text{C}$$

$$\text{Freezing point} = 0.00\ °\text{C} - 3.2\ °\text{C}$$
$$= -3.2\ °\text{C}$$

CHECK The unit of the answer is correct. The magnitude seems about right. The expected range for freezing points of an aqueous solution is anywhere from −10 °C to just below 0 °C. Any answers out of this range would be suspect.

FOR PRACTICE 12.8

Calculate the freezing point of a 2.6 *m* aqueous sucrose solution.

EXAMPLE 12.9 CALCULATING THE BOILING POINT ELEVATION

What mass of ethylene glycol ($C_2H_6O_2$), in grams, must be added to 1.0 kg of water to produce a solution that boils at 105.0 °C?

SORT You are given the desired boiling point of an ethylene glycol solution containing 1.0 kg of water and asked to find the mass of ethylene glycol required to achieve the boiling point.

GIVEN: $\Delta T_b = 5.0$ °C, 1.0 kg H_2O

FIND: g $C_2H_6O_2$

STRATEGIZE To solve this problem, use the boiling point elevation equation to calculate the desired molality of the solution from ΔT_b.

CONCEPTUAL PLAN

$\Delta T_b \rightarrow m$

$\Delta T_b = m \times K_b$

Then use the molality you just found to determine how many moles of ethylene glycol are needed per kilogram of water. Finally, calculate the molar mass of ethylene glycol and use it to convert from moles of ethylene glycol to mass of ethylene glycol.

kg H_2O → mol $C_2H_6O_2$ → g $C_2H_6O_2$

$\dfrac{\text{mol } C_2H_6O_2}{\text{kg } H_2O}$ (From first step) $\qquad \dfrac{62.07 \text{ g } C_2H_6O_2}{1 \text{ mol } C_2H_6O_2}$

RELATIONSHIPS USED

$C_2H_6O_2$ molar mass = 62.07 g mol^{-1}

$\Delta T_b = m \times K_b$ (boiling point elevation)

(continued)

EXAMPLE 12.9 (CONTINUED)

SOLVE Begin by solving the boiling point elevation equation for molality and substituting the required quantities to calculate m.

SOLUTION

$\Delta T_b = m \times K_b$

$$m = \frac{\Delta T_b}{K_b} = \frac{5.0\ \cancel{^\circ C}}{0.512\ \cancel{^\circ C}\ m^{-1}} = 9.7\underline{7}\ m$$

$$1.0\ \cancel{kg\ H_2O} \times \frac{9.7\underline{7}\ \cancel{mol\ C_2H_6O_2}}{1\ \cancel{kg\ H_2O}} \times \frac{62.07\ g\ C_2H_6O_2}{1\ \cancel{mol\ C_2H_6O_2}} = 6.1 \times 10^2\ g\ C_2H_6O_2$$

CHECK The unit of the answer is correct. The magnitude might seem a little high initially, but the boiling point elevation constant is so small that a lot of solute is required to raise the boiling point by a small amount.

FOR PRACTICE 12.9

Calculate the boiling point of a 3.60 m aqueous sucrose solution.

CHEMISTRY IN THE ENVIRONMENT Antifreeze in Frogs

Wood frogs (*Rana sylvatica)* look like most other frogs. They are a few inches long and have characteristic greenish-brown skin. However, wood frogs survive cold winters in a remarkable way—they partially freeze. In its partially frozen state, the frog has no heartbeat, no blood circulation, no breathing, and no brain activity. Within 1–2 hours of thawing, however, these vital functions return and the frog hops off to find food. How does the wood frog do this?

Most cold-blooded animals cannot survive freezing temperatures because the water within their cells freezes. As we learned in Section 11.9, when water freezes, it expands, irreversibly damaging cells. When the wood frog hibernates for the winter, however, it produces large amounts of glucose that is secreted into its bloodstream and fills the interior of its cells. When the temperature drops below freezing, extracellular body fluids, such as those in the abdominal cavity, freeze solid. Fluids within cells, however, remain liquid because the high glucose concentration lowers their freezing point. In other words, the concentrated glucose solution within the frog's cells acts as antifreeze, preventing the water within the cells from freezing and allowing the frog to survive.

▲ The wood frog survives winter by partially freezing. It protects its cells by flooding them with glucose, which acts as an antifreeze.

Question

The wood frog can survive at body temperatures as low as −8.0 °C. Calculate the molality of a glucose solution ($C_6H_{12}O_6$) required to lower the freezing point of water to −8.0 °C.

Osmotic Pressure

The process by which seawater causes dehydration (discussed in the opening section of this chapter) is called *osmosis*. **Osmosis** is the flow of solvent from a solution of lower solute concentration to one of higher solute concentration. Concentrated solutions draw solvent from more dilute solutions because of nature's tendency to mix.

Figure 12.16 ▶ shows an osmosis cell. The left side of the cell contains a concentrated salt water solution and the right side of the cell contains pure water. A **semipermeable membrane**—a membrane that selectively allows some substances to pass through but not others—separates the two halves of the cell. Water flows by osmosis from the pure-water side of the cell through the semipermeable membrane and into the salt-water side. Over

Initially

Solute particle

Water molecules

Semipermeable membrane

Water level rises

At equilibrium

Pressure of excess fluid = osmotic pressure of solution

▲ **FIGURE 12.16 An Osmosis Cell** In an osmosis cell, water flows from the pure-water side of the cell through the semipermeable membrane to the salt-water side.

time, the water level on the left side of the cell rises, while the water level on the right side of the cell falls. If external pressure is applied to the water in the left cell, this process can be opposed and even stopped. The pressure required to stop the osmotic flow, called the **osmotic pressure**, is given by the following equation:

$$\Pi = MRT$$

where M is the concentration of the solution in mol L^{-1} (molarity), T is the temperature (in kelvin), and R is the ideal gas constant 0.08314 bar L mol^{-1} K^{-1}.

EXAMPLE 12.10 DETERMINING OSMOTIC PRESSURE

The osmotic pressure of a solution containing 5.87 mg of an unknown protein per 10.0 mL of solution is 2.45 Torr at 25 °C. Find the molar mass of the unknown protein.

SORT You are given that a solution of an unknown protein contains 5.87 mg of the protein per 10.0 mL of solution. You are also given the osmotic pressure of the solution at a particular temperature and asked to find the molar mass of the unknown protein.

GIVEN: 5.87 mg protein
10.0 mL solution
$\Pi = 2.45$ Torr
$T = 25$ °C

FIND: molar mass of protein (g mol^{-1})

STRATEGIZE Step 1: Use the given osmotic pressure and temperature to find the molarity of the protein solution.

CONCEPTUAL PLAN

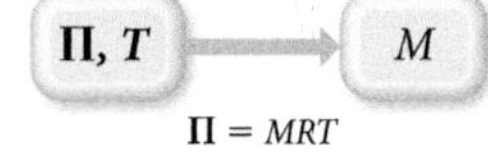

Step 2: Use the molarity calculated in step 1 to find the number of moles of protein in 10 mL of solution.

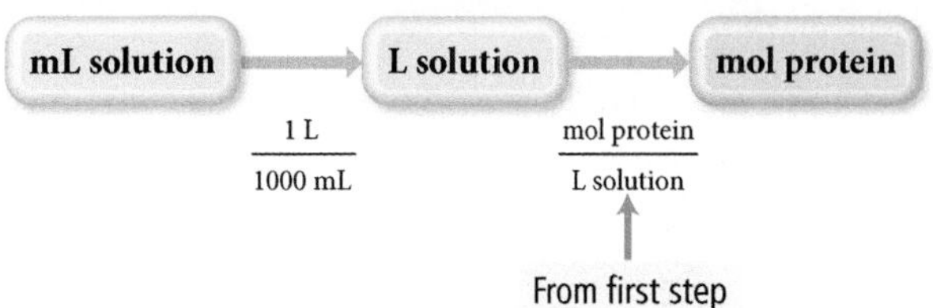

Step 3: Finally, use the number of moles of the protein calculated in step 2 and the given mass of the protein in 10.0 mL of solution to find the molar mass.

$$\text{Molar mass} = \frac{\text{mass protein}}{\text{moles protein}}$$

RELATIONSHIP USED

$\Pi = MRT$ (osmotic pressure equation)

(continued)

EXAMPLE 12.10 (CONTINUED)

SOLVE Step 1: Begin by solving the osmotic pressure equation for molarity and substituting in the required quantities in the correct units to calculate M.

SOLUTION

$$\Pi = MRT$$

$$M = \frac{\Pi}{RT} = \frac{2.45\ \text{Torr} \times \frac{1\ \text{bar}}{750\ \text{Torr}}}{0.08314\ \text{bar L mol}^{-1}\text{K}^{-1} \times 298\ \text{K}}$$

$$= 1.31\underline{8} \times 10^{-4}\ \text{mol L}^{-1}$$

Step 2: Begin with the given volume, convert to litres, then use the molarity to find the number of moles of protein.

$$n = MV$$

$$= 10.0\ \text{mL} \times \frac{1\ \text{L}}{1000\ \text{mL}} \times 1.31\underline{8} \times 10^{-4}\ \frac{\text{mol}}{\text{L}}$$

$$= 1.31\underline{8} \times 10^{-6}\ \text{mol}$$

Step 3: Use the given mass and the number of moles from step 2 to calculate the molar mass of the protein.

$$\text{Molar mass} = \frac{\text{mass protein}}{\text{moles protein}}$$

$$= \frac{5.87 \times 10^{-3}\ \text{g}}{1.31\underline{8} \times 10^{-6}\ \text{mol}} = 4.45 \times 10^{3}\ \text{g mol}^{-1}$$

CHECK The units of the answer are correct. The magnitude might seem a little high initially, but proteins are large molecules and therefore have high molar masses.

FOR PRACTICE 12.10

Calculate the osmotic pressure (in bar) of a solution containing 1.50 g ethylene glycol ($C_2H_6O_2$) in 50.0 mL of solution at 25 °C.

12.7 Colligative Properties of Strong Electrolyte Solutions

At the beginning of Section 12.6, we saw that colligative properties depend on the number of dissolved particles, and that electrolytes must therefore be treated slightly differently than nonelectrolytes when determining colligative properties. For example, the freezing point depression of a 0.10 m sucrose solution is $\Delta T_f = 0.186$ °C. However, the freezing point depression of a 0.10 m sodium chloride solution is nearly twice this large. Why? Because 1 mol of sodium chloride dissociates into nearly 2 mol of ions in solution. The ratio of moles of particles in solution to moles of formula units dissolved is called the **van't Hoff factor (i)**:

$$i = \frac{\text{moles of particles in solution}}{\text{moles of formula units dissolved}}$$

Since 1 mol of NaCl produces 2 mol of particles in solution, we expect the van't Hoff factor for NaCl to be exactly 2. In reality, this expected factor only occurs in very dilute solutions. For example, the van't Hoff factor for a 0.10 m NaCl solution is 1.87 and that for a 0.010 m NaCl solution is 1.94. The van't Hoff factor approaches the expected value at infinite dilution (as the concentration approaches zero). Table 12.8 lists the actual and expected van't Hoff factors for a number of solutes.

TABLE 12.8 Van't Hoff Factors at 0.05 m Concentration in Aqueous Solution

Solute	*i* Expected	*i* Measured
Nonelectrolyte	1	1
NaCl	2	1.9
$MgSO_4$	2	1.3
$MgCl_2$	3	2.7
K_2SO_4	3	2.6
$FeCl_3$	4	3.4

The reason that the van't Hoff factors do not exactly equal the expected values is that some ions effectively pair in solution. Ideally, we expect the dissociation of an ionic compound to be complete in solution. In reality, however, the dissociation is not complete—at any moment, some cations pair with anions (Figure 12.17 ▶), slightly reducing the number of particles in solution.

To calculate freezing point depression, boiling point elevation, and osmotic pressure of ionic solutions, use the van't Hoff factor in each equation as follows:

$$\Delta T_f = im \times K_f \text{ (freezing point depression)}$$
$$\Delta T_b = im \times K_b \text{ (boiling point elevation)}$$
$$\Pi = iMRT \text{ (osmotic pressure)}$$

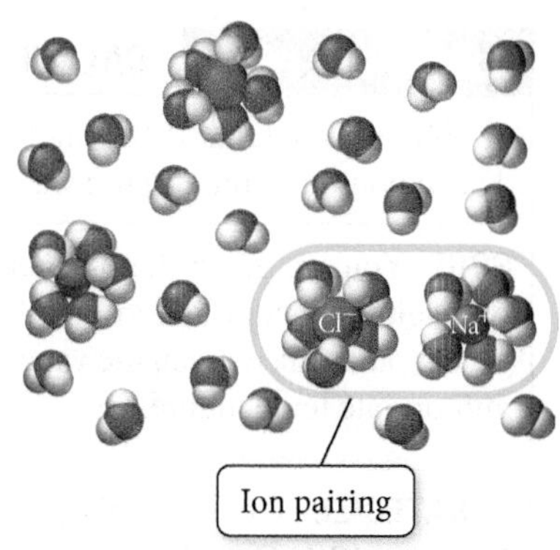

▲ **FIGURE 12.17 Ion Pairing** Hydrated anions and cations may get close enough together to effectively pair, lowering the concentration of particles below what would be expected ideally.

CONCEPTUAL CONNECTION 12.5

Colligative Properties

Which solution will have the highest boiling point?

(a) 0.50 mol L^{-1} $C_{12}H_{22}O_{11}$ **(b)** 0.50 mol L^{-1} NaCl **(c)** 0.50 mol L^{-1} $MgCl_2$

EXAMPLE 12.11 VAN'T HOFF FACTOR AND FREEZING POINT DEPRESSION

The freezing point of an aqueous 0.050 *m* $CaCl_2$ solution is −0.27 °C. What is the van't Hoff factor (i) for $CaCl_2$ at this concentration? How does it compare to the expected value of i?

SORT You are given the molality of a solution and its freezing point. You are asked to find the value of i, the van't Hoff factor, and compare it to the expected value.	**GIVEN:** 0.050 *m* $CaCl_2$ solution $\Delta T_f = 0.27$ °C **FIND:** i
STRATEGIZE To solve this problem, use the freezing point depression equation, including the van't Hoff factor.	**CONCEPTUAL PLAN** $\Delta T_f = im \times K_f$
SOLVE Solve the freezing point depression equation for i and substitute in the given quantities to calculate its value. The expected value of i for $CaCl_2$ is 3 because calcium chloride forms 3 mol of ions for each mole of calcium chloride that dissolves. The experimental value is slightly less than 3, probably because of ion pairing.	**SOLUTION** $\Delta T_f = im \times K_f$ $i = \frac{\Delta T_f}{m \times K_f}$ $= \frac{0.27\ \cancel{°C}}{0.050\ \cancel{m} \times \frac{1.86\ \cancel{°C}}{\cancel{m}}}$ $= 2.9$

CHECK The answer has no units as expected, since i is a ratio. The magnitude is about right, since it is close to the value you would expect upon complete dissociation of $CaCl_2$.

FOR PRACTICE 12.11

Calculate the freezing point of an aqueous 0.10 *m* $FeCl_3$ solution using a van't Hoff factor of 3.4.

Strong Electrolytes and Vapour Pressure

The vapour pressure of a solution containing an electrolyte solute is lowered by more than that of a solution containing the same concentration of a nonelectrolyte for the same reason that the freezing point of an electrolyte solution is depressed by a greater amount than a solution containing the same concentration of nonelectrolyte solution. The vapour pressure for a sodium chloride solution, for example, is lowered about twice as much as it is for a nonelectrolyte solution of the same concentration. To calculate the vapour pressure of a solution containing an ionic solute, we must account for the dissociation of the solute when we calculate the mole fraction of the solvent, as shown in the following example.

EXAMPLE 12.12 CALCULATING THE VAPOUR PRESSURE OF A SOLUTION CONTAINING AN IONIC SOLUTE

A solution contains 0.102 mol $Ca(NO_3)_2$ and 0.927 mol H_2O. Calculate the vapour pressure of the solution at 55 °C. The vapour pressure of pure water at 55 °C is 118.1 Torr. (Assume that the solute completely dissociates.)

SORT You are given the number of moles of each component of a solution and asked to find the vapour pressure of the solution. You are also given the vapour pressure of pure water at the appropriate temperature.

GIVEN: 0.102 mol $Ca(NO_3)_2$
0.927 mol H_2O
$P^{\circ}_{H_2O} = 118.1$ Torr (at 55 °C)

FIND: $P_{solution}$

STRATEGIZE To solve this problem, use Raoult's law as in Example 12.6. Calculate $\chi_{solvent}$ from the given amounts of solute and solvent.

CONCEPTUAL PLAN

$\chi_{H_2O}, P^{\circ}_{H_2O} \rightarrow P_{solution}$

$P_{solution} = \chi_{H_2O} P^{\circ}_{H_2O}$

SOLVE The key to this problem is to understand the dissociation of calcium nitrate. Write an equation showing the dissociation.

SOLUTION

$$Ca(NO_3)_2(s) \longrightarrow Ca^{2+}(aq) + 2\,NO_3^-(aq)$$

Since 1 mol of calcium nitrate dissociates into 3 mol of dissolved particles, the number of moles of calcium nitrate must be multiplied by 3 when computing the mole fraction.

$$\chi_{H_2O} = \frac{n_{H_2O}}{3 \times n_{Ca(NO_3)_2} + n_{H_2O}}$$
$$= \frac{0.927\ \cancel{mol}}{3(0.102)\ \cancel{mol} + 0.927\ \cancel{mol}}$$
$$= 0.75\underline{1}8$$

Use the mole fraction of water and the vapour pressure of pure water to calculate the vapour pressure of the solution.

$$P_{solution} = \chi_{H_2O} P^{\circ}_{H_2O}$$
$$= 0.75\underline{1}8(118.1\ \text{Torr})$$
$$= 88.8\ \text{Torr}$$

CHECK The unit of the answer is correct. The magnitude also seems right because the computed vapour pressure of the solution is significantly less than that of the pure solvent, as expected for a solution with a significant amount of solute.

FOR PRACTICE 12.12

A solution contains 0.115 mol H_2O and an unknown number of moles of sodium chloride. The vapour pressure of the solution at 30 °C is 25.7 Torr. The vapour pressure of pure water at 30 °C is 31.8 Torr. Calculate the number of moles of sodium chloride in the solution.

Colligative Properties and Medical Solutions

Doctors and other health-care workers often administer solutions to patients. The osmotic pressure of these solutions is controlled for the desired effect on the patient. Solutions having osmotic pressures greater than those of body fluids are called *hyperosmotic*. These solutions take water out of cells and tissues. When a human cell is placed in a hyperosmotic solution, it tends to shrivel as it loses water to the surrounding solution (Figure 12.18(b) ►). Solutions having osmotic pressures less than those of body fluids are called *hyposmotic*. These solutions pump water into cells. When a human cell is placed in a hyposmotic solution—such as pure water, for example—water enters the cell, sometimes causing it to burst (Figure 12.18(c)).

Intravenous (IV) solutions—those that are administered directly into a patient's veins—must have osmotic pressures equal to those of body fluids. These solutions are called *isosmotic* (or *isotonic*). When a patient is given an IV in a hospital, the majority of the fluid is usually an isosmotic saline solution—a solution containing 0.9 g NaCl per 100 mL of solution. In medicine and in other health-related fields, solution concentrations are often reported in units that indicate the mass of the solute per given volume

Isosmotic solution

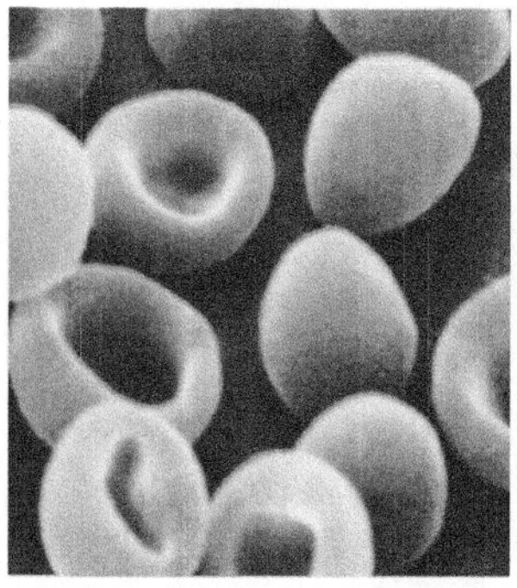

(a) Normal red blood cells

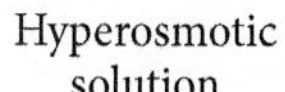

(b) Shrivelled red blood cells

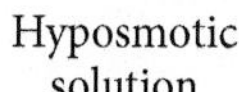

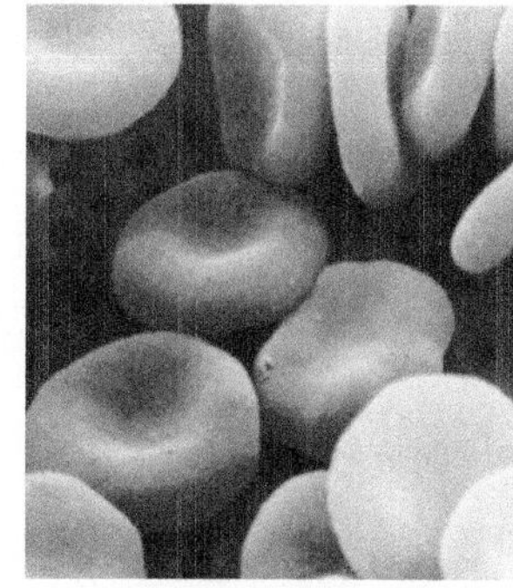

(c) Swollen red blood cells

◀ **FIGURE 12.18 Red Blood Cells and Osmosis** (**a**) In an isosmotic solution, red blood cells have the normal shape shown here. In a hyperosmotic solution (**b**), they lose water and shrivel. In a hyposmotic solution (**c**), they swell up and may burst as water flows into the cell.

of solution. Also common is *percent mass to volume*—which is simply the mass of the solute in grams divided by the volume of the solution in millilitres times 100%. In these units, the concentration of an isotonic saline solution is 0.9% mass/volume.

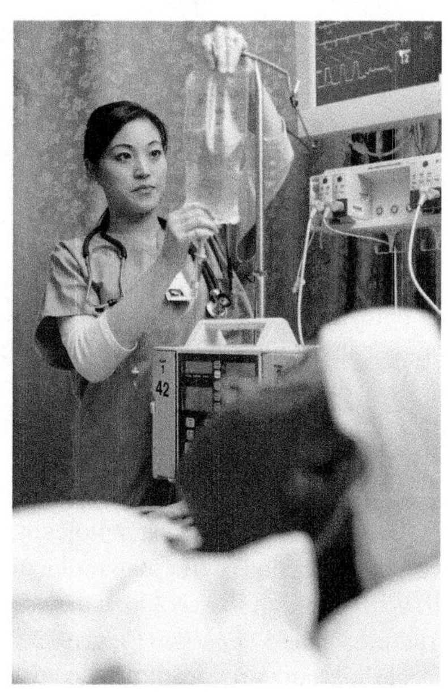

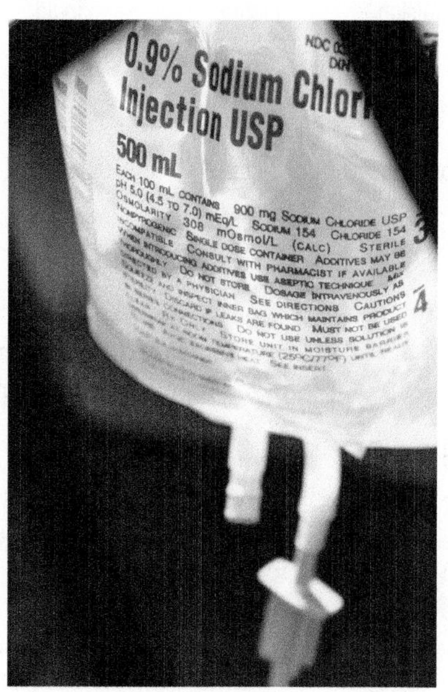

◀ Fluids used for intravenous transfusion must be isosmotic with bodily fluids—that is, they must have the same osmotic pressure.

12.8 Colloids

When you mix water and soap together, the resulting mixture has a distinctive haze (Figure 12.19 ▶). Soapy water is hazy because soap and water form a *colloidal dispersion,* rather than a true solution. A **colloidal dispersion**, or more simply a **colloid**, is a mixture in which a dispersed substance (which is solute-like) is finely divided in a dispersing medium (which is solvent-like). Examples of colloids include fog, smoke, whipped cream, and milk, as shown in Table 12.9.

Whether or not a mixture is a colloid is determined by the size of the particles it contains. If the particles are small (for example, individual small molecules), then the mixture is a solution. If the particles have a diameter greater than 1 μm (for example, grains of sand), then the mixture is a heterogeneous mixture. Sand stirred into water will slowly settle out of the water. *If the particles are between 1 nm and 1000 nm in size, the mixture is a colloid.* Colloidal particles are small enough that they stay dispersed throughout the dispersing medium by collisions with other molecules or atoms. When you view a colloidal particle dispersed in a liquid under a microscope, you can witness its jittery motion,

▲ **FIGURE 12.19 A Colloid** Soapy water is an example of a colloidal dispersion. The haze is due to the scattering of light by the colloidal particles.

TABLE 12.9 Types of Colloidal Dispersions

Classification	Dispersing Substance (solute-like)	Dispersing Medium (solvent-like)	Example
Aerosol	Liquid	Gas	Fog (water droplets in air)
Solid aerosol	Solid	Gas	Smoke (ash in air)
Foam	Gas	Liquid	Whipped cream (air bubbles in butterfat)
Emulsion	Liquid	Liquid	Milk (milk fat globules in water)
Solid emulsion	Liquid	Solid	Opal (water in silica glass)

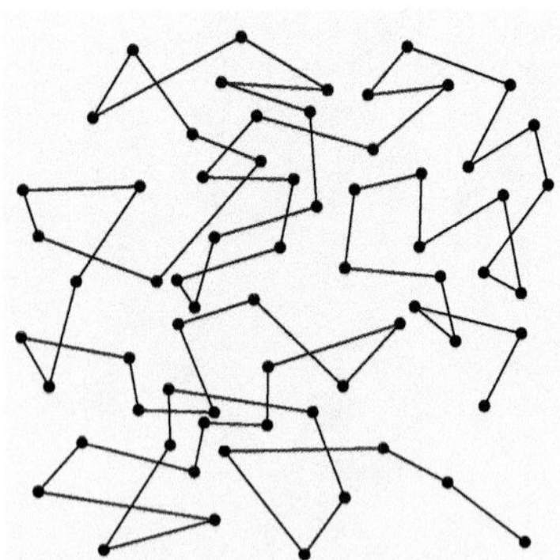

▲ **FIGURE 12.20 Brownian Motion** A colloidal particle exhibits Brownian motion, moving in a jerky, haphazard path as it undergoes collisions with other molecules.

which proceeds along a random path, as shown in Figure 12.20 ◄. This motion, called Brownian motion, is caused by collisions with molecules in the liquid. In the beginning of the twentieth century, Brownian motion was a decisive factor in confirming the molecular and atomic nature of matter.

Soap has a unique structure, shown in Figure 12.21 ▼. One end of the molecule is ionic and therefore interacts strongly with water molecules via ion–dipole interactions. However, the other end of the soap molecule is a long, nonpolar, hydrocarbon tail. When enough soap is added to water, the soap molecules aggregate in structures called *micelles* (Figure 12.22 ▼). In a micelle, the nonpolar hydrocarbon tails crowd into the centre of a sphere to maximize their interactions with one another. The ionic heads

Nonpolar tail

Ionic head

(a)

(b)

(c)

Na^+

Sodium stearate

▲ **FIGURE 12.21 Structure of Soap** A soap molecule such as sodium stearate **(a)** has an ionic head and a long nonpolar hydrocarbon tail. The electrostatic potential maps of sodium stearate show the nonpolarity of the hydrocarbon tail and the ionic nature of the –COONa group **(b)**. When dissolved in water, sodium stearate dissociates to Na^+ and the stearate anion. The electrostatic potential map of the stearate anion shows the negative $-COO^-$ and the nonpolar hydrocarbon tail **(c)**.

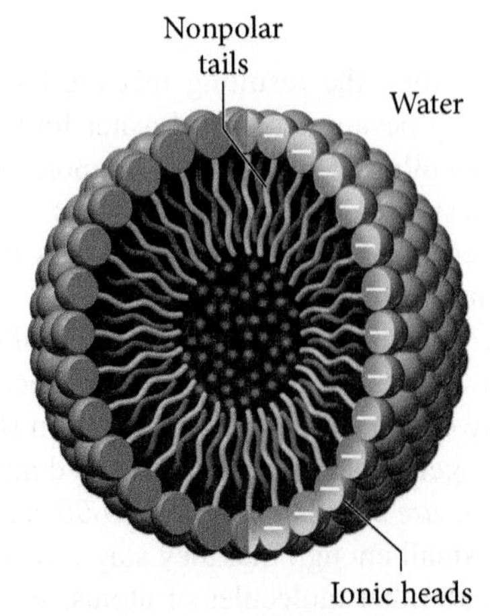

◄ **FIGURE 12.22 Micelle Structure** In a micelle, the nonpolar tails of soap molecules are oriented inward (where they can interact with one another) and the ionic heads are oriented outward (where they can interact with the polar water molecules).

▲ **FIGURE 12.23 The Tyndall Effect** When a light beam passes through a colloidal suspension (left), it is visible because the colloid particles scatter some of the light. The beam is not visible in pure water (right), nor would it be visible in a noncolloidal solution.

orient toward the surface of the sphere where they can interact with water molecules. The micelle structures are responsible for the haze seen in soapy water—they are too small to be seen by the naked eye, but they still scatter light. This scattering of light by a colloidal dispersion is known as the **Tyndall effect** (Figure 12.23 ▲). You can observe the Tyndall effect in other colloids such as fog (water droplets dispersed in air) or dusty air. In fact, you can use the Tyndall effect as a test to determine whether a mixture is a solution or a colloid, since solutions contain completely dissolved solute molecules that are too small to scatter light.

▲ Light beams are invisible when they are not scattered by colloidally dispersed particles such as dust or mist in the air.

The particles in a colloid need not be clusters of molecules. Some colloids, such as many protein solutions, contain dispersed macromolecules. For example, blood contains dispersed hemoglobin. The hemoglobin molecules are so large that they scatter light; thus, blood is considered a colloid.

Colloidal suspensions are kept stable by electrostatic repulsions that occur at their surfaces. For example, in a micelle, the ionic heads of many soap molecules compose the surface of the spherical particle (Figure 12.24 ▼). These ionic heads interact strongly with water molecules, but repel other colloid particles. Heating a colloid can destroy it because, in a heated colloid, collisions occur with enough force to overcome the electrostatic repulsions and allow the colloid particles to coalesce. Similarly, adding an electrolyte to a colloidal suspension can also disrupt the electrostatic repulsions that occur between colloid particles and thus destroy the colloid. For this reason, soap does not work well in a salt water solution.

▲ **FIGURE 12.24 Micelle Repulsions** Micelles do not coalesce because the charged surface of one micelle repels the charged surface of another.

CHAPTER IN REVIEW

Key Terms

Section 12.1
solution (486)
solvent (486)
solute (486)

Section 12.2
aqueous solution (487)
solubility (487)
entropy (488)
miscible (489)

Section 12.3
enthalpy of solution ($\Delta_{soln}H$) (493)
heat of hydration ($\Delta_{hyd}H$) (494)

Section 12.4
dynamic equilibrium (495)
saturated solution (495)
unsaturated solution (495)
supersaturated solution (496)
recrystallization (497)
Henry's law (499)

Section 12.5
dilute solution (500)
concentrated solution (500)
molarity (*M*) (501)
molality (*m*) (502)
parts by mass (502)
percent by mass (502)
parts per million (ppm) (502)
parts per billion (ppb) (502)
parts by volume (502)
mole fraction (χ_{solute}) (504)
mole percent (mol %) (504)

Section 12.6
colligative property (507)
Raoult's law (509)
vapour pressure lowering (ΔP) (509)
ideal solution (510)
freezing point depression (514)
boiling point elevation (514)
osmosis (516)
semipermeable membrane (516)
osmotic pressure (517)

Section 12.7
van't Hoff factor (*i*) (518)

Section 12.8
colloidal dispersion (colloid) (521)
Tyndall effect (523)

Key Concepts

Solutions (12.1, 12.2)

A solution is a homogeneous mixture of two or more substances. In a solution, the majority component is the solvent and the minority component is the solute. The tendency toward greater entropy (or greater energy dispersal) is the driving force for solution formation. Aqueous solutions contain water as a solvent, and a solid, liquid, or gas as the solute.

Solubility and Energetics of Solution Formation (12.2, 12.3)

The solubility of a substance is the amount of the substance that will dissolve in a given amount of solvent. The solubility of one substance in another depends on the types of intermolecular forces that exist *between* the substances as well as *within* each substance. The overall enthalpy change upon solution formation can be determined by adding the enthalpy changes for the three steps of solution formation: (1) separation of the solute particles, (2) separation of the solvent particles, and (3) mixing of the solute and solvent particles. The first two steps are both endothermic, while the last is exothermic. In aqueous solutions of an ionic compound, the change in enthalpy for steps 2 and 3 can be combined as the enthalpy of hydration which is always negative.

Solution Equilibrium (12.4)

Dynamic equilibrium in a solution occurs when the rates of dissolution and recrystallization in a solution are equal. A solution in this state is said to be saturated. Solutions containing less than or more than the equilibrium amount of solute are unsaturated or supersaturated, respectively. The solubility of most solids in water increases with increasing temperature. The solubility of gases in liquids generally decreases with increasing temperature, but increases with increasing pressure.

Concentration Units (12.5)

Common units used to express solution concentration include molarity (*M*), molality (*m*), mole fraction (χ), mole percent (mol %), percent (%) by mass or volume, parts per million (ppm) by mass or volume, and parts per billion (ppb) by mass or volume. These units are summarized in Table 12.5.

Vapour Pressure Lowering, Freezing Point Depression, Boiling Point Elevation, and Osmosis (12.6, 12.7)

The presence of a nonvolatile solute in a liquid results in a lower vapour pressure of the solution relative to the vapour pressure of the pure liquid. This lower vapour pressure is predicted by Raoult's law for an ideal solution. If the solute–solvent interactions are particularly strong, the actual vapour pressure is lower than that predicted by Raoult's law. If the solute–solvent interactions are particularly weak, the actual vapour pressure is higher than that predicted by Raoult's law. The addition of a nonvolatile solute to a liquid will result in a solution with a lower freezing point and a higher boiling point than those of the pure solvent. The flow of solvent from a solution of lower concentration to a solution of higher concentration is called osmosis. These phenomena are colligative properties and depend only on the number of solute particles added, not the type of solute particles. Electrolyte solutes have a greater effect on these properties than the corresponding amount of a nonelectrolyte solute, as specified by the van't Hoff factor.

Colloids (12.8)

A colloid is a mixture in which a substance is finely divided in a dispersing medium. Colloidal mixtures occur when the dispersed substance ranges in size from 1 nm to 1000 nm. One way to identify colloidal mixtures is by their tendency to scatter light, known as the Tyndall effect.

Key Equations and Relationships

Henry's Law: Solubility of Gases with Increasing Pressure (12.4)

$$S_{gas} = k_H P_{gas} \quad (k_H \text{ is Henry's law constant})$$

Molarity (*M*) of a Solution (12.5)

$$M = \frac{\text{amount solute (in mol)}}{\text{volume solution (in L)}}$$

Molality (*m*) of a Solution (12.5)

$$m = \frac{\text{amount solute (in mol)}}{\text{mass solvent (in kg)}}$$

Concentration of a Solution in Parts by Mass and Parts by Volume (12.5)

$$\text{Percent by mass} = \frac{\text{mass solute}}{\text{mass solution}} \times 100\%$$

$$\text{Parts per million (ppm)} = \frac{\text{mass solute}}{\text{mass solution}} \times 10^6$$

$$\text{Parts per billion (ppb)} = \frac{\text{mass solute}}{\text{mass solution}} \times 10^9$$

$$\text{Parts by volume} = \frac{\text{volume solute}}{\text{volume solution}} \times \text{multiplication factor}$$

Concentration of a Solution in Mole Fraction (χ) and Mole Percent (12.5)

$$\chi_{solute} = \frac{n_{solute}}{n_{solute} + n_{solvent}}$$

$$\text{mol \%} = \chi_{solute} \times 100\%$$

Raoult's Law: Relationship Between the Vapour Pressure of a Solution ($P_{solution}$), the Mole Fraction of the Solvent ($\chi_{solvent}$), and the Vapour Pressure of the Pure Solvent ($P^{\circ}_{solvent}$) (12.6)

$$P_{solution} = \chi_{solvent} P^{\circ}_{solvent}$$

The Vapour Pressure of a Solution Containing Two Volatile Components (12.6)

$$P_A = \chi_A P^{\circ}_A$$

$$P_B = \chi_B P^{\circ}_B$$

$$P_{tot} = P_A + P_B$$

Relationship Between Freezing Point Depression (ΔT_f), Molality (*m*), and Freezing Point Depression Constant (K_f) (12.6)

$$\Delta T_f = m \times K_f$$

Relationship Between Boiling Point Elevation (ΔT_b), Molality (*m*), and Boiling Point Elevation Constant (K_b) (12.6)

$$\Delta T_b = m \times K_b$$

Relationship Between Osmotic Pressure (Π), Molarity (*M*), the Ideal Gas Constant (R), and Temperature (T, in K) (12.6)

$$\Pi = MRT \quad (R = 0.08314 \text{ bar L mol}^{-1} \text{ K}^{-1})$$

van't Hoff Factor (*i*): Ratio of Moles of Particles in Solution to Moles of Formula Units Dissolved (12.7)

$$i = \frac{\text{moles of particles in solution}}{\text{moles of formula units dissolved}}$$

Key Skills

Determining Whether a Solute Is Soluble in a Solvent (12.2)
• Example 12.1 • For Practice 12.1 • Exercises 31–34

Using Henry's Law to Predict the Solubility of Gases with Increasing Pressure (12.4)
• Example 12.2 • For Practice 12.2 • Exercises 49, 50

Calculating Concentrations of Solutions (12.5)
• Examples 12.3, 12.4 • For Practice 12.3, 12.4 • For More Practice 12.3 • Exercises 51–56, 63, 64

Converting Between Concentration Units (12.5)
• Example 12.5 • For Practice 12.5 • For More Practice 12.5 • Exercises 65–68

Determining the Vapour Pressure of a Solution Containing a Nonelectrolyte and Nonvolatile Solute (12.6)
• Example 12.6 • For Practice 12.6 • For More Practice 12.6 • Exercises 71, 72

Determining the Vapour Pressure of a Two-Component Solution (12.6)
• Example 12.7 • For Practice 12.7 • Exercises 73–76

Calculating Freezing Point Depression (12.6)
• Example 12.8 • For Practice 12.8 • Exercises 77–80, 85, 86

Calculating Boiling Point Elevation (12.6)
• Example 12.9 • For Practice 12.9 • Exercises 77, 78, 85, 86

Determining Osmotic Pressure (12.6)
• Example 12.10 • For Practice 12.10 • Exercises 81–84

Determining and Using the van't Hoff Factor (12.7)
• Example 12.11 • For Practice 12.11 • Exercises 87–90

Calculating the Vapour Pressure of a Solution Containing an Ionic Solute (12.7)
• Example 12.12 • For Practice 12.12 • Exercises 91, 92

EXERCISES

Review Questions

1. Explain why drinking seawater results in dehydration.
2. What is a solution? What are the solute and solvent?
3. What does it mean to say that a substance is soluble in another substance? What kinds of units are used in reporting solubility?
4. Why do two ideal gases thoroughly mix when combined? What drives the mixing?
5. What is entropy? Why is entropy important in discussing the formation of solutions?
6. What kinds of intermolecular forces are involved in solution formation?
7. Explain how the relative strengths of solute–solute interactions, solvent–solvent interactions, and solvent–solute interactions affect solution formation.
8. What does the statement *like dissolves like* mean with respect to solution formation?
9. What are three steps involved in evaluating the enthalpy changes associated with solution formation?
10. What is the heat of hydration ($\Delta_{hyd}H$)? How does the enthalpy of solution depend on the relative magnitudes of $\Delta_{solute}H$ and $\Delta_{hyd}H$?
11. Explain dynamic equilibrium with respect to solution formation. What is a saturated solution? An unsaturated solution? A supersaturated solution?
12. How does the solubility of a solid in a liquid depend on temperature? How is this temperature dependence exploited to purify solids through recrystallization?
13. How does the solubility of a gas in a liquid depend on temperature? How does this temperature dependence affect the amount of oxygen available for fish and other aquatic animals?
14. How does the solubility of a gas in a liquid depend on pressure? How does this pressure dependence account for the bubbling that occurs upon opening a can of pop?
15. What is Henry's law? For what kinds of calculations is Henry's law useful?
16. What are the common units for expressing solution concentration?
17. How are parts by mass and parts by volume used in calculations?
18. What is the effect of a nonvolatile solute on the vapour pressure of a liquid? Why is the vapour pressure of a solution different from the vapour pressure of the pure liquid solvent?

19. What is Raoult's law? For what kind of calculations is Raoult's law useful?
20. Explain the difference between an ideal and a nonideal solution.
21. What is the effect on vapour pressure of a solution with particularly *strong* solute–solvent interactions? With particularly *weak* solute–solvent interactions?
22. Explain why the lower vapour pressure for a solution containing a nonvolatile solute results in a higher boiling point and lower melting point compared to the pure solvent.
23. What are colligative properties?
24. What is osmosis? What is osmotic pressure?
25. Explain the role and meaning of the van't Hoff factor in determining the colligative properties of solutions containing ionic solutes.
26. Describe a colloidal dispersion. What is the difference between a colloidal dispersion and a true solution?
27. What is the Tyndall effect and how can it be used to help identify colloidal dispersions?
28. What keeps the particles in a colloidal dispersion from coalescing?

Problems by Topic

Solubility

29. Pick an appropriate solvent from Table 12.3 to dissolve each substance. State the kind of intermolecular forces that would occur between the solute and solvent in each case:
    - **a.** motor oil (nonpolar)
    - **b.** ethanol (polar, contains an OH group)
    - **c.** lard (nonpolar)
    - **d.** potassium chloride (ionic)
30. Pick an appropriate solvent from Table 12.3 to dissolve each substance:
    - **a.** isopropyl alcohol (polar, contains an OH group)
    - **b.** sodium chloride (ionic)
    - **c.** vegetable oil (nonpolar)
    - **d.** sodium nitrate (ionic)
31. Which molecule would you expect to be more soluble in water: $CH_3CH_2CH_2OH$ or $HOCH_2CH_2CH_2OH$?
32. Which molecule would you expect to be more soluble in water: CCl_4 or CH_2Cl_2?
33. For each compound, would you expect greater solubility in water or in hexane? Indicate the kinds of intermolecular forces that occur between the solute and the solvent in which the molecule is most soluble.
    - **a.** glucose 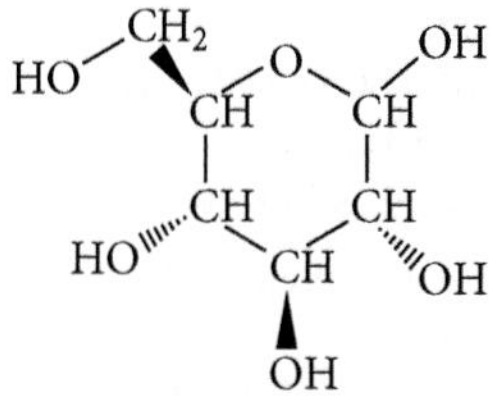
    - **b.** naphthalene 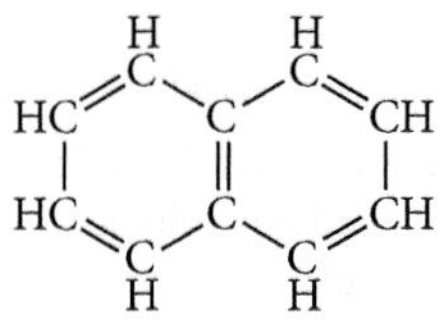
    - **c.** dimethyl ether 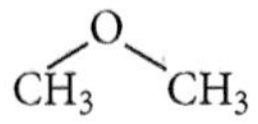
    - **d.** alanine (an amino acid) 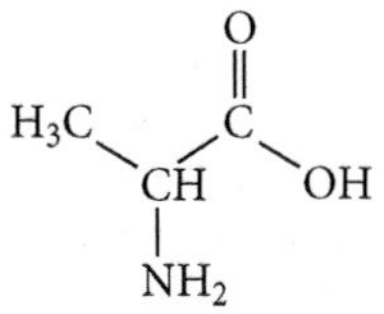
34. For each compound, would you expect greater solubility in water or in hexane? Indicate the kinds of intermolecular forces that would occur between the solute and the solvent in which the molecule is most soluble.
    - **a.** toluene 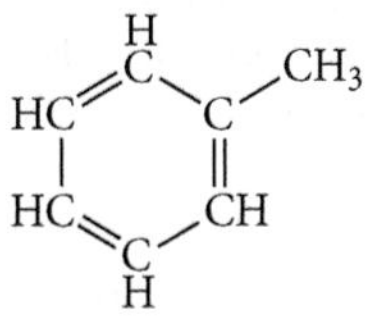
    - **b.** sucrose (table sugar) 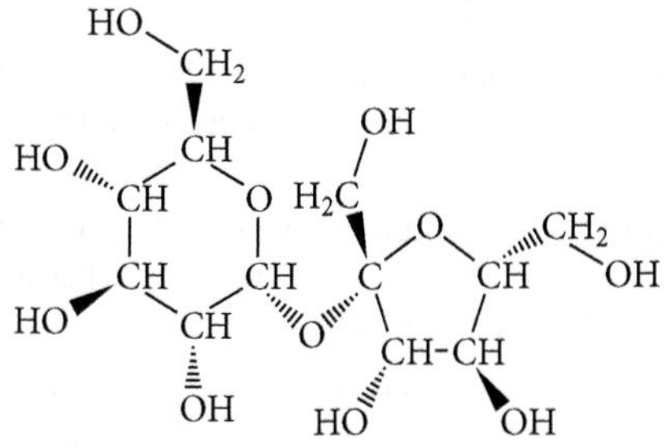
    - **c.** isobutene 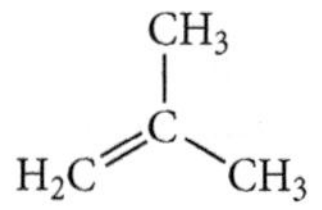
    - **d.** ethylene glycol

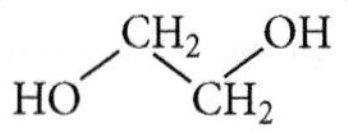

Energetics of Solution Formation

35. When ammonium chloride (NH_4Cl) is dissolved in water, the solution becomes colder.
    - **a.** Is the dissolution of ammonium chloride endothermic or exothermic?
    - **b.** What can you say about the relative magnitudes of the lattice energy of ammonium chloride and its heat of hydration?
    - **c.** Sketch a qualitative energy diagram similar to Figure 12.7 for the dissolution of NH_4Cl.
    - **d.** Why does the solution form? What drives the process?
36. When lithium iodide (LiI) is dissolved in water, the solution becomes hotter.
    - **a.** Is the dissolution of lithium iodide endothermic or exothermic?
    - **b.** What can you say about the relative magnitudes of the lattice energy of lithium iodide and its heat of hydration?
    - **c.** Sketch a qualitative energy diagram similar to Figure 12.7 for the dissolution of LiI.
    - **d.** Why does the solution form? What drives the process?

37. Silver nitrate has a lattice energy of $-820\ kJ\ mol^{-1}$ and a heat of solution of $+22.6\ kJ\ mol^{-1}$. Calculate the heat of hydration for silver nitrate.

38. Use the data to calculate the heats of hydration of lithium chloride and sodium chloride. Which of the two cations, lithium or sodium, has stronger ion–dipole interactions with water? Why?

Compound	Lattice Energy ($kJ\ mol^{-1}$)	$\Delta_{soln}H$ ($kJ\ mol^{-1}$)
LiCl	−834	−37.0
NaCl	−769	+3.88

39. Lithium iodide has a lattice energy of -7.3×10^2 ($kJ\ mol^{-1}$) and a heat of hydration of $-793\ kJ\ mol^{-1}$. Find the heat of solution for lithium iodide and determine how much heat is evolved or absorbed when 15.0 g of lithium iodide completely dissolves in water.

40. Potassium nitrate has a lattice energy of $-685.3\ kJ\ mol^{-1}$ and a heat of hydration of $-650.6\ kJ\ mol^{-1}$. How much potassium nitrate has to dissolve in water to absorb 1.00×10^2 kJ of heat?

Solution Equilibrium and Factors Affecting Solubility

41. A solution contains 25 g of NaCl per 100.0 g of water at 25 °C. Is the solution unsaturated, saturated, or supersaturated? (Use Figure 12.11.)

42. A solution contains 32 g of KNO_3 per 100.0 g of water at 25 °C. Is the solution unsaturated, saturated, or supersaturated? (Use Figure 12.11.)

43. A KNO_3 solution containing 45 g of KNO_3 per 100.0 g of water is cooled from 40 °C to 0 °C. What happens during cooling? (Use Figure 12.11.)

44. A KCl solution containing 42 g of KCl per 100.0 g of water is cooled from 60 °C to 0 °C. What happens during cooling? (Use Figure 12.11.)

45. Some laboratory procedures involving oxygen-sensitive reactants or products call for using preboiled (and then cooled) water. Explain.

46. A person preparing a fish tank uses preboiled (and then cooled) water to fill it. When the person puts the fish into the tank, it dies. Explain.

47. Scuba divers breathing air at increased pressure can suffer from nitrogen narcosis—a condition resembling drunkenness—when the partial pressure of nitrogen exceeds about 4 bar. What property of gas/water solutions causes this to happen? How could the diver reverse this effect?

48. Scuba divers breathing air at increased pressure can suffer from oxygen toxicity—too much oxygen in their bloodstream—when the partial pressure of oxygen exceeds about 1.4 bar. What happens to the amount of oxygen in a diver's bloodstream when he or she breathes oxygen at elevated pressures? How can this be reversed?

49. Calculate the mass of nitrogen dissolved at room temperature in 80.0 L the of water contained within a home aquarium. Assume a total pressure of 1.0 bar and a mole fraction for nitrogen of 0.78.

50. Use Henry's law to determine the molar solubility of helium in pure water at a pressure of 1.0 bar and temperature of 25 °C.

Concentrations of Solutions

51. An aqueous NaCl solution is made using 112 g of NaCl diluted to a total solution volume of 1.00 L. Calculate the molarity, molality, and mass percent of the solution. (Assume a density of $1.08\ g\ mL^{-1}$ for the solution.)

52. An aqueous KNO_3 solution is made using 72.5 g of KNO_3 diluted to a total solution volume of 2.00 L. Calculate the molarity, molality, and mass percent of the solution. (Assume a density of $1.05\ g\ mL^{-1}$ for the solution.)

53. To what volume should you dilute 50.0 mL of a 5.00 mol L^{-1} KI solution so that 25.0 mL of the diluted solution contains 3.05 g of KI?

54. To what volume should you dilute 125 mL of an 8.00 mol L^{-1} $CuCl_2$ solution so that 50.0 mL of the diluted solution contains 4.67 g $CuCl_2$?

55. Silver nitrate solutions are often used to plate silver onto other metals. What is the maximum amount of silver (in grams) that can be plated out of 4.8 L of an $AgNO_3$ solution containing 3.4% Ag by mass? Assume that the density of the solution is $1.01\ g\ mL^{-1}$.

56. A dioxin-contaminated water source contains 0.085% dioxin by mass. How much dioxin is present in 2.5 L of this water? Assume a density of $1.00\ g\ mL^{-1}$.

57. A hard water sample contains 0.0085% Ca by mass (in the form of Ca^{2+} ions). How much water (in grams) contains 1.2 g of Ca? (1.2 g of Ca is the recommended daily allowance of calcium for those between 19 and 24 years old.)

58. Lead is a toxic metal that affects the central nervous system. A Pb-contaminated water sample contains 0.0011% Pb by mass. How much of the water (in millilitres) contains 150 mg of Pb? (Assume a density of $1.0\ g\ mL^{-1}$.)

59. You can purchase nitric acid in a concentrated form that is 70.3% HNO_3 by mass and has a density of $1.41\ g\ mL^{-1}$. Describe exactly how you would prepare 1.15 L of 0.100 mol L^{-1} HNO_3 from the concentrated solution.

60. You can purchase hydrochloric acid in a concentrated form that is 37.0% HCl by mass and has a density of $1.20\ g\ mL^{-1}$. Describe exactly how you would prepare 2.85 L of 0.500 mol L^{-1} HCl from the concentrated solution.

61. Describe how you would prepare each solution from the dry solute and the solvent:

a. 1.00×10^2 mL of 0.500 mol L^{-1} KCl
b. 1.00×10^2 g of 0.50 *m* KCl
c. 1.00×10^2 g of 5.0% KCl solution by mass

62. Describe how you would prepare each solution from the dry solute and the solvent:

a. 125 mL of 0.100 mol L^{-1} $NaNO_3$
b. 125 g of 0.100 *m* $NaNO_3$
c. 125 g of 1.0% $NaNO_3$ solution by mass

63. A solution is prepared by dissolving 28.4 g of glucose ($C_6H_{12}O_6$) in 355 g of water. The final volume of the solution is 378 mL. For this solution, calculate the concentration in each unit:

a. molarity **b.** molality
c. percent by mass **d.** mole fraction
e. mole percent

64. A solution is prepared by dissolving 20.2 mL of methanol (CH_3OH) in 100.0 mL of water at 25 °C. The final volume of the solution is 118 mL. The densities of methanol and water at this temperature are $0.782\ g\ mL^{-1}$ and $1.00\ g\ mL^{-1}$, respectively. For this solution, calculate the concentration in each unit:

a. molarity **b.** molality
c. percent by mass **d.** mole fraction
e. mole percent

65. Household hydrogen peroxide is an aqueous solution containing 3.0% hydrogen peroxide by mass. What is the molarity of this solution? (Assume a density of $1.01\ g\ mL^{-1}$.)

66. One brand of laundry bleach is an aqueous solution containing 4.55% sodium hypochlorite (NaOCl) by mass. What is the molarity of this solution? (Assume a density of $1.02\ g\ mL^{-1}$.)

67. An aqueous solution contains 36% HCl by mass. Calculate the molality and mole fraction of the solution.

68. An aqueous solution contains 5.0% NaCl by mass. Calculate the molality and mole fraction of the solution.

Vapour Pressure of Solutions

69. A beaker contains 100.0 mL of pure water. A second beaker contains 100.0 mL of seawater. The two beakers are left side by side on a lab bench for one week. At the end of the week, the liquid level in each beaker has decreased. However, the level has decreased more in one of the beakers than in the other. Which one and why?

70. Which solution has the highest vapour pressure?
   a. 20.0 g of glucose ($C_6H_{12}O_6$) in 100.0 mL of water
   b. 20.0 g of sucrose ($C_{12}H_{22}O_{11}$) in 100.0 mL of water
   c. 10.0 g of potassium acetate ($KC_2H_3O_2$) in 100.0 mL of water

71. Calculate the vapour pressure of a solution containing 24.5 g of glycerin ($C_3H_8O_3$) in 135 mL of water at 30.0 °C. The vapour pressure of pure water at this temperature is 31.8 Torr. Assume that glycerin is not volatile and dissolves molecularly (i.e., it is not ionic) and use a density of $1.00\ g\ mL^{-1}$ for the water.

72. A solution contains naphthalene ($C_{10}H_8$) dissolved in hexane (C_6H_{14}) at a concentration of 12.35% naphthalene by mass. Calculate the vapour pressure at 25 °C of hexane above the solution. The vapour pressure of pure hexane at 25 °C is 151 Torr.

73. A solution contains 50.0 g of heptane (C_7H_{16}) and 50.0 g of octane (C_8H_{18}) at 25 °C. The vapour pressures of pure heptane and pure octane at 25 °C are 45.8 Torr and 10.9 Torr, respectively. Assuming ideal behaviour, calculate:
   a. the vapour pressure of each of the solution components in the mixture.
   b. the total pressure above the solution.
   c. the composition of the vapour in mass percent.
   d. Why is the composition of the vapour different from the composition of the solution?

74. A solution contains a mixture of pentane and hexane at room temperature. The solution has a vapour pressure of 258 Torr. Pure pentane and hexane have vapour pressures of 425 Torr and 151 Torr, respectively, at room temperature. What is the mole fraction composition of the mixture? (Assume ideal behaviour.)

75. A solution contains 4.08 g of chloroform ($CHCl_3$) and 9.29 g of acetone (CH_3COCH_3). The vapour pressures at 35 °C of pure chloroform and pure acetone are 295 Torr and 332 Torr, respectively. Assuming ideal behaviour, calculate the vapour pressures of each of the components and the total vapour pressure above the solution. The experimentally measured total vapour pressure of the solution at 35 °C was 312 Torr. Is the solution ideal? If not, what can you say about the relative strength of chloroform–acetone interactions compared to the acetone–acetone and chloroform–chloroform interactions?

76. A solution of methanol and water has a mole fraction of water of 0.312 and a total vapour pressure of 211 Torr at 39.9 °C. The vapour pressures of pure methanol and pure water at this temperature are 256 Torr and 55.3 Torr, respectively. Is the solution ideal? If not, what can you say about the relative strengths of the solute–solvent interactions compared to the solute–solute and solvent–solvent interactions?

Freezing Point Depression, Boiling Point Elevation, and Osmosis

77. A glucose solution contains 55.8 g of glucose ($C_6H_{12}O_6$) in 455 g of water. Determine the freezing point and boiling point of the solution.

78. An ethylene glycol solution contains 21.2 g of ethylene glycol ($C_2H_6O_2$) in 85.4 mL of water. Determine the freezing point and boiling point of the solution. (Assume a density of $1.00\ g\ mL^{-1}$ for water.)

79. An aqueous solution containing 17.5 g of an unknown molecular (nonelectrolyte) compound in 100.0 g of water was found to have a freezing point of −1.8 °C. Calculate the molar mass of the unknown compound.

80. An aqueous solution containing 35.9 g of an unknown molecular (nonelectrolyte) compound in 150.0 g of water was found to have a freezing point of −1.3 °C. Calculate the molar mass of the unknown compound.

81. Calculate the osmotic pressure of a solution containing 24.6 g of glycerin ($C_3H_8O_3$) in 250.0 mL of solution at 298 K.

82. What mass of sucrose ($C_{12}H_{22}O_{11}$) would you combine with 5.00×10^2 g of water to make a solution with an osmotic pressure of 8.55 bar at 298 K? (Assume a density of $1.0\ g\ mL^{-1}$ for the solution.)

83. A solution containing 27.55 mg of an unknown protein per 25.0 mL solution was found to have an osmotic pressure of 3.22 Torr at 25 °C. What is the molar mass of the protein?

84. Calculate the osmotic pressure of a solution containing 18.75 mg of hemoglobin in 15.0 mL of solution at 25 °C. The molar mass of hemoglobin is $6.5 \times 10^4\ g\ mol^{-1}$.

85. Calculate the freezing point and boiling point of each aqueous solution, assuming complete dissociation of the solute:
   a. 0.100 *m* K_2S
   b. 21.5 g of $CuCl_2$ in 4.50×10^2 g water
   c. 5.5% $NaNO_3$ by mass (in water)

86. Calculate the freezing point and boiling point in each solution, assuming complete dissociation of the solute:
   a. 10.5 g $FeCl_3$ in 1.50×10^2 g water
   b. 3.5% KCl by mass (in water)
   c. 0.150 *m* MgF_2

87. Use the van't Hoff factors in Table 12.8 to compute each colligative property:
   a. the melting point of a 0.100 *m* aqueous iron(III) chloride solution
   b. the osmotic pressure of a $0.085\ mol\ L^{-1}$ potassium sulfate solution at 298 K
   c. the boiling point of a 1.22%-by-mass magnesium chloride solution

88. Assuming the van't Hoff factors in Table 12.8, calculate the mass of solute required to make each aqueous solution:
   a. a sodium chloride solution containing 1.50×10^2 g of water that has a melting point of −1.0 °C
   b. 2.50×10^2 mL of an aqueous magnesium sulfate solution that has an osmotic pressure of 3.82 bar at 298 K
   c. an aqueous iron(III) chloride solution containing 2.50×10^2 g of water that has a boiling point of 102 °C

89. A $0.100\ mol\ L^{-1}$ ionic solution has an osmotic pressure of 8.3 bar at 25 °C. Calculate the van't Hoff factor (i) for this solution.

90. A solution contains 8.92 g of KBr in 500.0 mL of solution and has an osmotic pressure of 6.97 atm at 25 °C. Calculate the van't Hoff factor (*i*) for KBr at this concentration.

91. Calculate the vapour pressure at 25 °C of an aqueous solution that is 5.50% NaCl by mass. (Assume complete dissociation of the solute.)

92. An aqueous $CaCl_2$ solution has a vapour pressure of 81.6 mmHg at 50 °C. The vapour pressure of pure water at this temperature is 92.6 mmHg. What is the concentration of $CaCl_2$ in mass percent? (Assume complete dissociation of the solute.)

Cumulative Problems

93. The solubility of carbon tetrachloride (CCl_4) in water at 25 °C is 1.2 g L^{-1}. The solubility of chloroform ($CHCl_3$) at the same temperature is 10.1 g L^{-1}. Why is chloroform almost 10 times more soluble in water than carbon tetrachloride?

94. The solubility of phenol in water at 25 °C is 8.7 g L^{-1}. The solubility of naphthol at the same temperature is only 0.074 g L^{-1}. Examine the structures of phenol and naphthol and explain why phenol is so much more soluble than naphthol.

Phenol   Naphthol

95. Explain why methanol and water are completely miscible, while pentanol is only slightly soluble in water.

96. Using your knowledge of intermolecular forces, explain the concept of freezing point depression and boiling point elevation.

97. Potassium perchlorate ($KClO_4$) has a lattice energy of −599 kJ mol^{-1} and a heat of hydration of −548 kJ mol^{-1}. Find the heat of solution for potassium perchlorate and determine the temperature change that occurs when 10.0 g of potassium perchlorate is dissolved with enough water to make 100.0 mL of solution. (Assume a heat capacity of 4.05 J g^{-1} °C^{-1} for the solution and a density of 1.05 g mL^{-1}.)

98. Sodium hydroxide (NaOH) has a lattice energy of −887 kJ mol^{-1} and a heat of hydration of −932 kJ mol^{-1}. How much solution could be heated to boiling by the heat evolved by the dissolution of 25.0 g of NaOH? (For the solution, assume a heat capacity of 4.0 J g^{-1} °C^{-1}, an initial temperature of 25.0 °C, a boiling point of 100.0 °C, and a density of 1.05 g mL^{-1}.)

99. A saturated solution forms when 0.0537 L of argon, at a pressure of 1.0 bar and temperature of 25 °C, is dissolved in 1.0 L of water. Calculate the Henry's law constant for argon.

100. A gas has a Henry's law constant of 0.112 mol L^{-1} bar^{-1}. What total volume of solution is needed to completely dissolve 1.65 L of the gas at a pressure of 725 Torr and a temperature of 25 °C?

101. The *Safe Drinking Water Act* in Ontario sets a limit for mercury—a toxin to the central nervous system—at 0.001 ppm by mass. Water suppliers must periodically test their water to ensure that mercury levels do not exceed this limit. Suppose water becomes contaminated with mercury at four times the legal limit (0.0040 ppm). How much of this water would have to be consumed for someone to ingest 50.0 mg of mercury?

102. Water softeners often replace calcium ions in hard water with sodium ions. Since sodium compounds are soluble, the presence of sodium ions in water does not cause the white, scaly residues caused by calcium ions. However, calcium is more beneficial to human health than sodium because calcium is a necessary part of the human diet, while high levels of sodium intake are linked to increases in blood pressure. Health Canada recommends that adults ingest less than 1.5 g of sodium per day. How many litres of softened water, containing a sodium concentration of 0.050% sodium by mass, have to be consumed to exceed the Health Canada recommendation? (Assume a water density of 1.0 g mL^{-1}.)

103. An aqueous solution contains 12.5% NaCl by mass. What mass of water (in grams) is contained in 2.5 L of the vapour above this solution at 55 °C? The vapour pressure of pure water at 55 °C is 118 Torr. (Assume complete dissociation of NaCl.)

104. The vapour above an aqueous solution contains 19.5 mg water per litre at 25 °C. Assuming ideal behaviour, what is the concentration of the solute within the solution in mole percent?

105. What is the freezing point of an aqueous solution that boils at 106.5 °C?

106. What is the boiling point of an aqueous solution that has a vapour pressure of 20.5 Torr at 25 °C? (Assume a nonvolatile solute.)

107. An isotonic solution contains 0.90% NaCl mass to volume. Calculate the percent mass to volume for isotonic solutions containing each solute at 25 °C. Assume a van't Hoff factor of 1.9 for all *ionic* solutes.

a. KCl **b.** NaBr **c.** glucose ($C_6H_{12}O_6$)

108. Magnesium citrate, $Mg_3(C_6H_5O_7)_2$, belongs to a class of laxatives called *hyperosmotics*, which cause rapid emptying of the bowel. When a concentrated solution of magnesium citrate is consumed, it passes through the intestines, drawing water and promoting diarrhea, usually within six hours. Calculate the osmotic pressure of a magnesium citrate laxative solution containing 28.5 g of magnesium citrate in 235 mL of solution at 37 °C (approximate body temperature). Assume complete dissociation of the ionic compound.

109. A solution is prepared from 4.5701 g of magnesium chloride and 43.238 g of water. The vapour pressure of water above this solution is found to be 0.3672 bar at 348.0 K. The vapour pressure of pure water at this temperature is 0.3854 bar. Find the value of the van't Hoff factor (*i*) for magnesium chloride in this solution.

110. When HNO_2 is dissolved in water, it partially dissociates according to the equation $HNO_2 \rightleftharpoons H^+ + NO_2^-$. A solution is prepared that contains 7.050 g of HNO_2 in 1.000 kg of water. Its freezing point is found to be −0.2929 °C. Calculate the fraction of HNO_2 that has dissociated.

111. A solution of a nonvolatile solute in water has a boiling point of 375.3 K. Calculate the vapour pressure of water above this solution at 338 K. The vapour pressure of pure water at this temperature is 0.2467 bar.

112. The density of a 0.438 mol L^{-1} solution of potassium chromate (K_2CrO_4) at 298 K is 1.063 g mL^{-1}. Calculate the vapour pressure of water above the solution. The vapour pressure of pure water at this temperature is 0.0313 bar. Assume complete dissociation of the solute.

113. The vapour pressure of carbon tetrachloride, CCl_4, is 0.354 bar and the vapour pressure of chloroform, $CHCl_3$, is 0.526 bar at 316 K. A solution is prepared from equal masses of these two compounds at this temperature. Calculate the mole fraction of the chloroform in the vapour above the solution. If the vapour above the original solution is condensed and isolated into a separate flask, what would the vapour pressure of chloroform be above this new solution?

114. Distillation is a method of purification based on successive separations and recondensations of vapour above a solution. Use the result of the previous problem to calculate the mole fraction of chloroform in the vapour above a solution obtained by three successive separations and condensations of the vapour above the original solution of carbon tetrachloride and chloroform. Show how this result explains the use of distillation as a separation method.

115. A solution of 49.0% H_2SO_4 by mass has a density of 1.39 g cm^{-3} at 293 K. A 25.0 cm^3 sample of this solution is mixed with enough water to increase the volume of the solution to 99.8 cm^3. Find the molarity of sulfuric acid in this solution.

116. Find the mass of urea (CH_4N_2O) needed to prepare 50.0 g of a solution in water in which the mole fraction of urea is 0.0770.

117. A solution contains 10.05 g of an unknown compound dissolved in 50.0 mL of water. (Assume a density of 1.00 g mL^{-1} for water.) The freezing point of the solution is −3.16 °C. The mass percent composition of the compound is 60.97% C, 11.94% H, and the rest is O. What is the molecular formula of the compound?

118. The osmotic pressure of a solution containing 2.10 g of an unknown compound dissolved in 175.0 mL of solution at 25 °C is 1.93 bar. The combustion of 24.02 g of the unknown compound produced 28.16 g CO_2 and 8.64 g H_2O. What is the molecular formula of the compound (which contains only carbon, hydrogen, and oxygen)?

119. A 100.0 mL aqueous sodium chloride solution is 13.5% NaCl by mass and has a density of 1.12 g mL^{-1}. What would you add (solute or solvent) and what mass of it would it take to make the boiling point of the solution 104.4 °C? (Use $i = 1.8$ for NaCl.)

120. A 50.0 mL solution is initially 1.55% $MgCl_2$ by mass and has a density of 1.05 g mL^{-1}. What is the freezing point of the solution after you add an additional 1.35 g $MgCl_2$? (Use $i = 2.5$ for $MgCl_2$.)

121. Carbon disulfide has a boiling point of 46.2 °C. When 10 g of white phosphorus is dissolved in 100 mL of carbon disulfide, the boiling point increases to 47.7 °C. The density of carbon disulfide is 1.26 g cm^{-3}, and the boiling point elevation constant, K_b, is 2.37 °C kg mol^{-1}. Determine the molar mass and molecular formula of white phosphorus.

122. The freezing point of pure biphenyl, $C_{12}H_{10}$, is 69.00 °C. A solution of 100.0 g of biphenyl and 2.67 g of naphthalene, $C_{10}H_8$, has a freezing point of 68.50 °C. A solution of 100.0 g of biphenyl and 1.00 g of an unknown compound has a freezing point of 68.86 °C. What is the molar mass of the unknown compound?

Challenge Problems

123. The small bubbles that form on the bottom of a pot of water that is being heated (before boiling) are due to dissolved air coming out of solution. Use Henry's law and the solubilities given below to calculate the total volume of nitrogen and oxygen gas that should bubble out of 1.5 L of water upon warming from 25 °C to 50 °C. Assume that the water is initially saturated with nitrogen and oxygen gas at 25 °C and a total pressure of 100 kPa. Assume that the gas bubbles out at a temperature of 50 °C. The solubility of oxygen gas at 50 °C is 27.8 mg L^{-1} at an oxygen pressure of 100 kPa. The solubility of nitrogen gas at 50 °C is 14.6 mg L^{-1} at a nitrogen pressure of 100 kPa. Assume that the air above the water contains an oxygen partial pressure of 21 kPa and a nitrogen partial pressure of 78 kPa.

124. The vapour above a mixture of pentane and hexane at room temperature contains 35.5% pentane by mass. What is the mass percent composition of the solution? Pure pentane and hexane have vapour pressures of 425 Torr and 151 Torr, respectively, at room temperature.

125. A 1.10 g sample contains only glucose ($C_6H_{12}O_6$) and sucrose ($C_{12}H_{22}O_{11}$). When the sample is dissolved in water to a total solution volume of 25.0 mL, the osmotic pressure of the solution is 3.78 bar at 298 K. What is the mass percent composition of glucose and sucrose in the sample?

126. A solution is prepared by mixing 631 mL of methanol with 501 mL of water. The molarity of methanol in the resulting solution is 14.29 mol L^{-1}. The density of methanol at this temperature is 0.792 g mL^{-1}. Calculate the difference in volume between this solution and the total volume of water and methanol that were mixed to prepare the solution.

127. Two alcohols, isopropyl alcohol and propyl alcohol, have the same molecular formula, C_3H_8O. A solution of the two that is two-thirds-by-mass isopropyl alcohol has a vapour pressure of 0.110 bar at 313 K. A solution that is one-third-by-mass isopropyl alcohol has a vapour pressure of 0.089 bar at 313 K. Calculate the vapour pressure of each pure alcohol at this temperature. Explain the difference, given that the formula of propyl alcohol is $CH_3CH_2CH_2OH$ and that of isopropyl alcohol is $(CH_3)_2CHOH$.

128. A metal, M, of atomic mass 96 u, reacts with fluorine to form a salt that can be represented as MF_x. In order to determine x and therefore the formula of the salt, a boiling point elevation experiment is performed. A 9.18 g sample of the salt is dissolved in 100.0 g of water and the boiling point of the solution is found to be 374.38 K. Find the formula of the salt. Assume complete dissociation of the salt in solution.

129. Sulfuric acid in water dissociates completely into H^+ and HSO_4^- ions. The HSO_4^- ion dissociates to a limited extent into H^+ and SO_4^{2-}. The freezing point of a 0.1000 m solution of sulfuric acid in water is 272.76 K. Calculate the molality of SO_4^{2-} in the solution, assuming ideal solution behaviour.

130. A solution of 75.0 g benzene (C_6H_6) and 75.0 g toluene (C_7H_8) has a total vapour pressure of 80.9 mmHg at 303 K. Another solution of 100.0 g benzene and 50.0 g toluene has a total vapour pressure of 93.9 mmHg at this temperature. Find the vapour pressure of pure benzene and pure toluene at 303 K.

131. A solution is prepared by dissolving 11.60 g of a mixture of sodium carbonate and sodium bicarbonate in 1.00 L of water. A 300.0 cm^3 sample of the solution is then treated with excess HNO_3 and boiled to remove all the dissolved gas. A total of 0.940 L of dry CO_2 is collected at 298 K and 0.972 bar. Find the molarity of the carbonate and bicarbonate in the solution.

Conceptual Problems

132. Substance A is a nonpolar liquid and has only dispersion forces among its constituent particles. Substance B is also a nonpolar liquid and has about the same magnitude of dispersion forces among its constituent particles. When substance A and B are combined, they spontaneously mix.

a. Why do the two substances mix?

b. Predict the sign and magnitude of $\Delta_{soln}H$.

c. Give the signs and relative magnitudes of $\Delta_{solute}H$, $\Delta_{solvent}H$, and $\Delta_{mix}H$.

133. A power plant built on a river uses river water as a coolant. The water is warmed as it is used in heat exchangers within the plant. Should the warm water be immediately cycled back into the river? Why or why not?

134. The vapour pressure of a 1 mol L^{-1} ionic solution is different from the vapour pressure of a 1 mol L^{-1} nonelectrolyte solution. In both cases, the solute is nonvolatile. Which set of diagrams best represents the differences between the two solutions and their vapours?

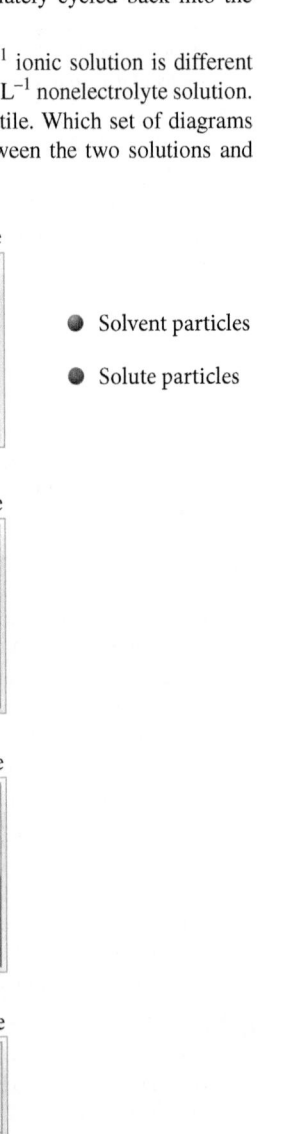

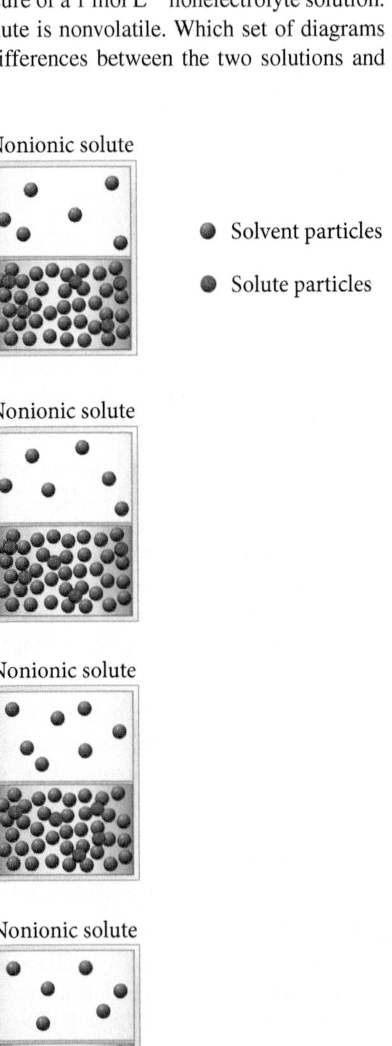

135. If each substance costs the same amount per kilogram, which would be most cost effective as a way to lower the freezing point of water? (Assume complete dissociation for all ionic compounds.) Explain.

a. $HOCH_2CH_2OH$

b. NaCl

c. KCl

d. $MgCl_2$

e. $SrCl_2$

136. A helium balloon inflated on one day will fall to the ground by the next day. The volume of the balloon decreases somewhat overnight, but not by enough to explain why it no longer floats. (If you inflate a new balloon with helium to the same size as the balloon that fell to the ground, the newly inflated balloon floats.) Explain.

137. Estimate the boiling point of 5 L of water to which a teaspoon (6 g) of salt (NaCl) has been added. Based on your result, what is the purpose of adding salt to water in which pasta or vegetables are cooked?

Chemical Kinetics

Many small animals, such as frogs, hibernate during the winter.

Nobody, I suppose, could devote many years to the study of chemical kinetics without being deeply conscious of the fascination of time and change: this is something that goes outside science into poetry. . . .

—Sir Cyril N. Hinshelwood (1897–1967)

IN THE PASSAGE QUOTED above, Oxford chemistry professor Sir Cyril Hinshelwood calls attention to an aspect of chemistry often overlooked by the casual observer—the mystery of change with time. Since the opening chapter of this text, you have learned that the goal of chemistry is to understand the macroscopic world by examining the molecular one. In this chapter, we focus on understanding how this molecular world changes with time, an area of study called chemical kinetics. The molecular world is anything but static. Thermal energy produces constant molecular motion, causing molecules to repeatedly collide with one another. In a tiny fraction of these collisions, something unique happens—the electrons on one molecule or atom are attracted to the nuclei of another. Some bonds weaken and new bonds form—a chemical reaction occurs. Chemical kinetics is the study of how these kinds of changes occur in time.

13.1 Hibernating Frogs

Hibernation is a common response of many small animals to long periods of cold weather and the lack of food. When the temperature gets too cold, amphibians like frogs enter a deep sleep. Frogs are cold-blooded, so they have no way of keeping warm during the winter. Their body temperature is almost the same as their surroundings. When they hibernate, their surroundings are typically around 0 °C and the animal's metabolism slows dramatically so that its body's energy stores are utilized only very slowly, in order to last through the winter.

Metabolism is a set of chemical reactions that occur within an organism to sustain life. So when metabolism slows down at low temperature, it is these chemical reactions that slow down. When temperatures increase in the spring, these chemical reactions speed up—metabolism speeds up—and the animal wakes from its hibernation.

The rates of chemical reactions, and the ability to control those rates, are important in hibernation and in many other phenomena and practical applications. For example, a successful rocket launch depends on the rate at which fuel burns: too quickly and the rocket can explode, too slowly and it will not leave the ground. Chemists always consider reaction rates when synthesizing new compounds. No matter how stable a compound might be, its synthesis is impossible if the rate at which it forms is too slow. As we have seen with hibernating frogs, reaction rates are important to life. In fact, the human body's ability to switch a specific reaction on or off at a specific time is achieved largely by controlling the rate of that reaction through the use of enzymes.

The first person to measure the rate of a chemical reaction carefully was Ludwig Wilhelmy. In 1850, he measured how fast sucrose, upon treatment with acid, hydrolyzed into glucose and fructose. This reaction occurred over several hours, and Wilhelmy was able to show how the rate depended on the initial amount of sugar present—the greater the initial amount, the faster the initial rate. He also examined the influence of temperature on the reaction—products were formed faster at higher temperatures. Today, we can measure the rates of reactions that occur in times as short as several femtoseconds (femto $= 10^{-15}$). The knowledge of reaction rates is not only practically important—giving us the ability to control how fast a reaction occurs—but also theoretically important. As you will see in Section 13.6, the rate of a reaction can tell us much about how the reaction occurs on the molecular scale.

13.2 The Rate of a Chemical Reaction

The rate of a chemical reaction is a measure of how fast the reaction occurs, as shown in Figure 13.1 ▶. If a chemical reaction has a slow rate, only a relatively small fraction of molecules react to form products in a given period of time. If a chemical reaction has a fast rate, a large fraction of molecules react to form products in a given period of time.

When we measure how fast something occurs, or more specifically the *rate* at which it occurs, we usually express the measurement as a change in some quantity per unit of time. For example, we measure the speed of a car—the rate at which it travels—in *kilometres per hour*, and we might measure weight loss in *kilograms per week*. We report these rates in units that represent the change in what we are measuring (distance or weight) divided by the change in time.

$$\text{Speed} = \frac{\text{change in distance}}{\text{change in time}} = \frac{\Delta x}{\Delta t} \qquad \text{Weight loss} = \frac{\text{change in weight}}{\text{change in time}} = \frac{\Delta \text{weight}}{\Delta t}$$

Similarly, the rate of a chemical reaction is measured as a change in the amounts of reactants or products (usually in concentration units) divided by the change in time. For example, consider the following gas-phase reaction between $H_2(g)$ and $I_2(g)$:

$$H_2(g) + I_2(g) \longrightarrow 2\,HI(g)$$

We can define the rate of this reaction in the time interval t_1 to t_2 as follows:

Recall that [A] means the concentration of A in mol L^{-1}.

$$\text{Rate} = -\frac{\Delta[H_2]}{\Delta t} = -\frac{[H_2]_{t_2} - [H_2]_{t_1}}{t_2 - t_1} \qquad [13.1]$$

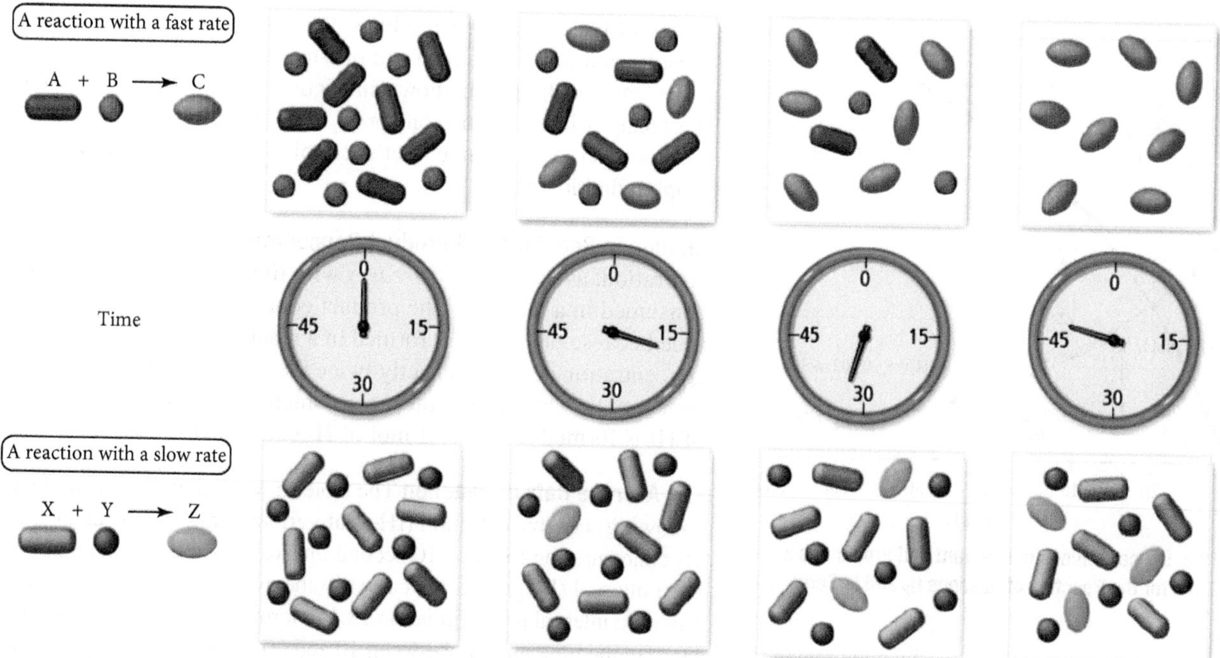

▲ **FIGURE 13.1 The Rate of a Chemical Reaction**

In this expression, $[H_2]_{t_2}$ is the hydrogen concentration at time t_2 and $[H_2]_{t_1}$ is the hydrogen concentration at time t_1. The reaction rate is defined as *the negative* of the change in concentration of a reactant divided by the change in time. The negative sign is part of the definition when the reaction rate is defined in terms of a reactant because reactant concentrations decrease as a reaction proceeds; therefore, *the change in the concentration of a reactant is negative*. The negative sign thus makes the overall *rate* positive. (By convention, reaction rates are reported as positive quantities.)

The reaction rate can also be defined with respect to the other reactant as follows:

$$\text{Rate} = -\frac{\Delta[I_2]}{\Delta t} \qquad [13.2]$$

Since 1 mol of H_2 reacts with 1 mol of I_2, the rates are defined in the same way. The rate can also be defined with respect to the *product* of the reaction as follows:

$$\text{Rate} = +\frac{1}{2}\frac{\Delta[\text{HI}]}{\Delta t} \qquad [13.3]$$

Because product concentrations *increase* as the reaction proceeds, the change in concentration of a product is positive. Therefore, when the rate is defined with respect to a product, we do not include a negative sign in the definition. The factor of $\frac{1}{2}$ in this definition is related to the stoichiometry of the reaction. In order to have a single rate for the entire reaction, the definition of the rate with respect to each reactant and product must reflect the stoichiometric coefficients of the reaction. For this particular reaction, 2 mol of HI is produced from 1 mol of H_2 and 1 mol of I_2.

The concentration of HI increases at twice the rate that the concentration of H_2 or I_2 decreases. In other words, if 1 mol of I_2 reacts per second, then 2 mol of HI are formed per second. In order for the overall rate to have the same value when defined with respect

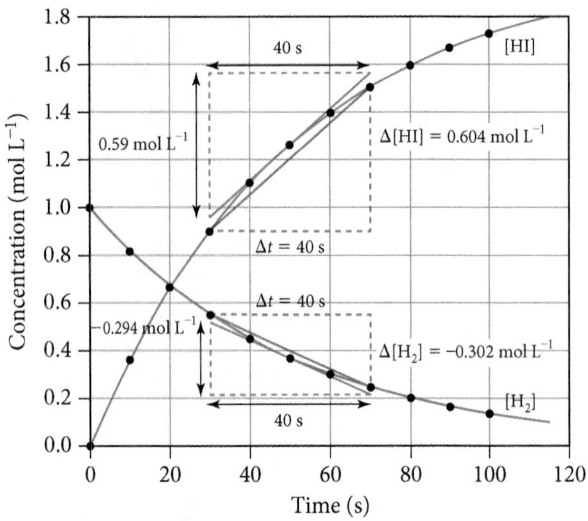

▲ **FIGURE 13.2 Concentrations of Reactant and Product as a Function of Time for the Reaction of Gaseous H_2 and I_2, Forming HI**

to any of the reactants or products, the change in HI concentration must be multiplied by a factor of one-half.

Consider the graph shown in Figure 13.2 ◄, which represents the changes in concentration for H_2 (one of the reactants) and HI (the product) versus time. Let's examine several features of this graph individually.

Change in Reactant and Product Concentrations The reactant concentration, as expected, *decreases* with time because reactants are consumed in a reaction. The product concentration *increases* with time because products are formed in a reaction. The increase in HI concentration occurs at exactly twice the rate of the decrease in H_2 concentration because of the stoichiometry of the reaction—2 mol of HI is formed for every 1 mol of H_2 consumed.

The Average Rate of Reaction The table shown below lists each of the following: H_2 concentration ($[H_2]$) at various times (t), the change in H_2 concentration for each 10-second interval, and the average rate for each interval (R_{ave}). We can calculate the average rate of reaction for any time interval using Equation 13.1 in terms of H_2. For example, the average rate of the reaction in the time interval between 10 and 20 seconds is the negative of the change in H_2 concentration divided by the change in time in that interval:

$$-\frac{\Delta[H_2]}{\Delta t} = -\frac{(-0.149 \text{ mol L}^{-1})}{10 \text{ s}} = 0.0149 \text{ mol L}^{-1}\text{ s}^{-1}$$

Similarly, the rate for the interval between 20 and 30 seconds is 0.121 mol L^{-1} s^{-1}. The average rate is not limited to 10-second intervals. The average rate between 30 and 70 seconds is 0.0076 mol L^{-1} s^{-1}. The average rate for this 40-second interval is shown graphically in Figure 13.2 (in red) for both. The change in concentration for HI is twice the change in H_2 concentration over the same time interval, but due to the factor of $\frac{1}{2}$ in Equation 13.3, the average rate calculated in terms of H_2 and HI are equal.

Notice that the average rate decreases as the reaction progresses. In other words, the reaction slows down as it proceeds. We discuss this further in the next section, where we will see that for most reactions, the rate depends on the concentrations of reactants. As the reactants transform to products their concentrations decrease, and the reaction slows down.

The Instantaneous Rate of Reaction The instantaneous rate of reaction is the rate at any one point in time, and is represented by the slope of the curve at that point. We can determine the instantaneous rate from the slope of the tangent to the curve at the time of interest.

t(s)	$[H_2]$ (mol L^{-1})	$\Delta[H_2]$ (mol L^{-1})	Δt(s)	$R_{ave} = \Delta[H_2]/\Delta t$ (mol L^{-1} s^{-1})	R_{inst} (mol L^{-1} s^{-1})
0.000	1.000				0.0200
		−0.181	10.000	0.0181	
10.000	0.819				0.0164
		−0.149	10.000	0.0149	
20.000	0.670				0.0134
		−0.121	10.000	0.0121	
30.000	0.549				0.0110
		−0.100	10.000	0.0100	
40.000	0.449				0.0090
		−0.081	10.000	0.0081	
50.000	0.368				0.0074
		−0.067	10.000	0.0067	
60.000	0.301				0.0060
		−0.054	10.000	0.0054	
70.000	0.247				0.0049
		−0.045	10.000	0.0045	
80.000	0.202				0.0040
		−0.037	10.000	0.0037	
90.000	0.165				0.0033
		−0.030	10.000	0.0030	
100.000	0.135				0.0027

In Figure 13.2, we have drawn the tangent lines for both the $[H_2]$ and [HI] curves at 50 seconds. We calculate the instantaneous rate at 50 seconds as follows:

Using $[H_2]$

$$R_{inst} = -\text{slope of the tangent to } [H_2] \text{ curve at 50 s} = \frac{-(-0.294 \text{ mol L}^{-1})}{40 \text{ s}} = 0.0074 \text{ mol L}^{-1}\text{ s}^{-1}$$

Using [HI]

$$R_{inst} = \frac{1}{2} \times \text{slope of the tangent to [HI] curve at 50 s} = \frac{1}{2}\frac{0.59 \text{ mol L}^{-1}}{40 \text{ s}} = 0.0074 \text{ mol L}^{-1}\text{ s}^{-1}$$

As we would expect, the instantaneous rate is the same whether we use one of the reactants or the product for the calculation. Notice that the instantaneous rate at 50 seconds is slightly different from the average rate for the 40 second interval calculated previously and between the average rates for the 10 second intervals just before and just after 50 seconds. This is a general observation that can be seen in the preceding table.

We can generalize our definition of reaction rates by using the following generic reaction:

$$aA + bB \longrightarrow cC + dD \qquad [13.4]$$

where A and B are reactants, C and D are products, and *a*, *b*, *c*, and *d* are the stoichiometric coefficients. We define the rate of the reaction as follows:

$$\text{Rate} = -\frac{1}{a}\frac{\Delta[A]}{\Delta t} = -\frac{1}{b}\frac{\Delta[B]}{\Delta t} = +\frac{1}{c}\frac{\Delta[C]}{\Delta t} = +\frac{1}{d}\frac{\Delta[D]}{\Delta t} \qquad [13.5]$$

From the definition, we can see that knowing the rate of change in the concentration of any one reactant or product at a point in time allows us to determine the rate of change in the concentration of any other reactant or product at that point in time (from the balanced equation). *However, predicting the rate at some future time is not possible from just the balanced equation.*

EXAMPLE 13.1 EXPRESSING REACTION RATES

Consider the following balanced chemical equation:

$$H_2O_2(aq) + 3\,I^-(aq) + 2\,H^+(aq) \longrightarrow I_3^-(aq) + 2\,H_2O(l)$$

In the first 10.0 seconds of the reaction, the concentration of I^- dropped from 1.000 mol L^{-1} to 0.868 mol L^{-1}.

(a) Calculate the average rate of this reaction in this time interval.

(b) Predict the rate of change in the concentration of H^+ (that is, $\Delta[H^+]/\Delta t$) during this time interval.

SOLUTION

(a) Use Equation 13.5 to calculate the average rate of the reaction.	$\text{Rate} = -\frac{1}{3}\frac{\Delta[I^-]}{\Delta t}$ $= -\frac{1}{3}\frac{(0.868 \text{ mol L}^{-1} - 1.000 \text{ mol L}^{-1})}{10.0 \text{ s}}$ $= 4.40 \times 10^{-3} \text{ mol L}^{-1}\text{ s}^{-1}$
(b) Use Equation 13.5 again for the relationship between the rate of the reaction and $\Delta[H^+]/\Delta t$. After solving for $\Delta[H^+]/\Delta t$, substitute the computed rate from part (a) and compute $\Delta[H^+]/\Delta t$.	$\text{Rate} = -\frac{1}{2}\frac{\Delta[H^+]}{\Delta t}$ $\frac{\Delta[H^+]}{\Delta t} = -2\text{ (Rate)}$ $= -2(4.40 \times 10^{-3} \text{ mol L}^{-1}\text{ s}^{-1})$ $= -8.80 \times 10^{-3} \text{ mol L}^{-1}\text{ s}^{-1}$

FOR PRACTICE 13.1

For the above reaction, predict the rate of change in concentration of H_2O_2 ($\Delta[H_2O_2]/\Delta t$) and I_3^- ($\Delta[I_3^-]/\Delta t$) during this time interval.

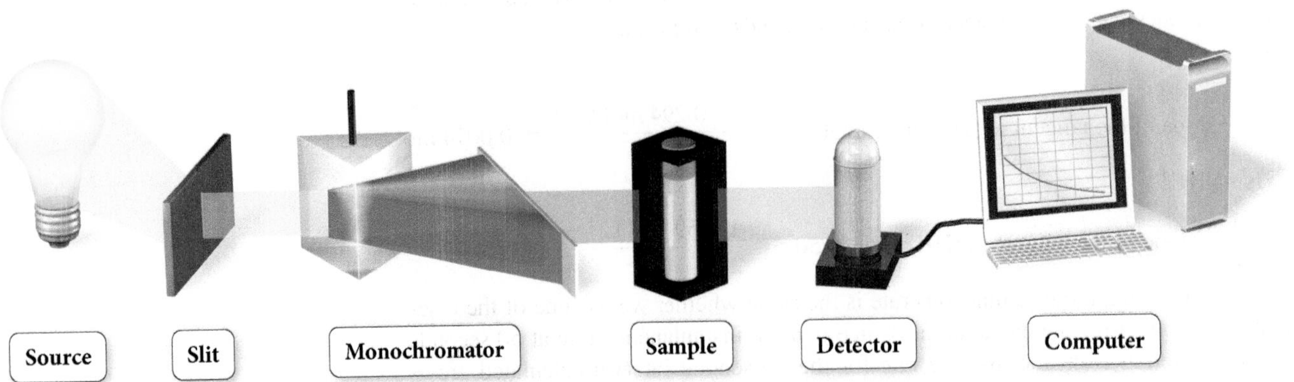

▲ **FIGURE 13.3 The Spectrometer** In a spectrometer, light of a specific wavelength is passed through the sample and the intensity of the transmitted light—which depends on how much light is absorbed by the sample—is measured and recorded.

Measuring Reaction Rates

In order to study the kinetics of a reaction, we must have an experimental way to measure the concentration of at least one of the reactants or products as a function of time. When Ludwig Wilhelmy was studying the rate of conversion of glucose to sucrose and fructose, he took advantage of the capability of sucrose to rotate polarized light. (Polarized light is light with an electric field oriented along one plane.) When a beam of polarized light is passed through a sucrose solution, the polarization of the light is rotated clockwise. In contrast, the products of the reaction rotate polarized light counterclockwise. By measuring the degree of polarization of light passing through a reacting solution—a technique known as polarimetry—Wilhelmy was able to determine the relative concentrations of the reactants and products as a function of time.

Perhaps the most common way to study the kinetics of a reaction is through spectroscopy. For example, the reaction of H_2 and I_2 to form HI can be followed spectroscopically because I_2 is violet and H_2 and HI are colourless. As I_2 reacts with H_2 to form HI, the violet colour of the reaction mixture fades. The fading colour can be monitored with a spectrometer, a device that passes light through a sample and measures how strongly the light is absorbed (Figure 13.3 ▲). If the sample contains the reacting mixture, the intensity of the light absorption will decrease as the reaction proceeds, providing a direct measure of the concentration of I_2 as a function of time. Because light travels so fast and current experimental techniques can produce very short pulses of light, spectroscopy can be used to measure reactions that happen on time scales as short as several femtoseconds.

Reactions in which the number of moles of gaseous reactants and products change as the reaction proceeds can be readily monitored by measuring changes in pressure. Consider the reaction in which dinitrogen monoxide reacts to form nitrogen and oxygen gas:

$$2\,N_2O(g) \longrightarrow 2\,N_2(g) + O_2(g)$$

For every 2 mol of N_2O that reacts, the reaction vessel will contain one additional mole of gas. As the reaction proceeds and the amount of gas increases, the pressure steadily rises. The rise in pressure can be used to determine the relative concentrations of reactants and products as a function of time.

The three techniques mentioned above—polarimetry, spectroscopy, and pressure measurement—can all be used to monitor the reaction as it occurs in the reaction vessel. Some reactions, however, occur slowly enough that samples, or *aliquots*, can be periodically withdrawn from the reaction vessel and analyzed to determine the progress of the reaction. Instrumental techniques such as gas chromatography (Figure 13.4 ▶) or mass spectrometry, as well as wet chemical techniques such as titration, can be used to measure the relative amounts of reactants or products in the aliquot. By taking aliquots at regular time intervals, the relative amounts of reactants and products can be determined as a function of time.

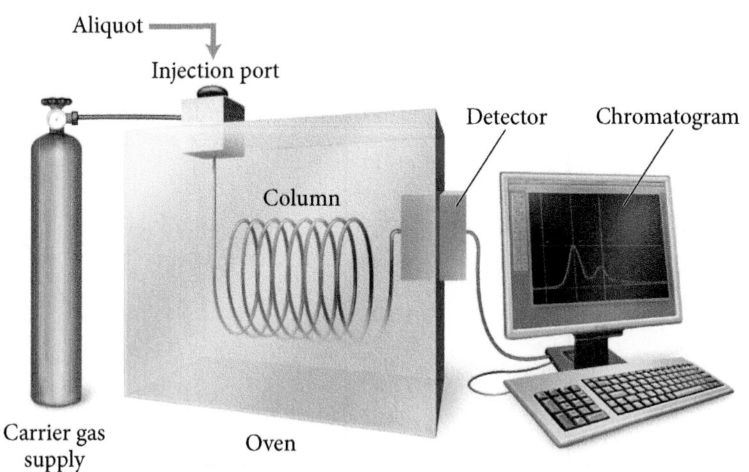

◀ **FIGURE 13.4 The Gas Chromatograph** In a gas chromatograph (GC), a sample of the reaction mixture, or aliquot, is injected into a specially constructed column. Because of their characteristic physical and chemical properties, different components of the mixture pass through the column at different rates and thus exit at different times. As each component leaves the column, it is identified electronically and a chromatogram is recorded. The area under each peak in the chromatogram is proportional to the amount of one particular component in the sample mixture.

13.3 The Rate Law: The Effect of Concentration on Reaction Rate

The rate of a reaction often depends on the concentration of one or more of the reactants. Wilhelmy noticed this effect in 1850 for the hydrolysis of sucrose. For simplicity, let's consider a reaction in which a single reactant, A, decomposes into products:

$$\text{A} \longrightarrow \text{products}$$

As long as the rate of the reverse reaction (in which the products return to reactants) is negligibly slow, we can write a relationship—called the **rate law**—between the rate of the reaction and the concentration of the reactant as follows:

$$\text{Rate} = k[\text{A}]^n \qquad [13.6]$$

where ***k*** is a constant of proportionality called the **rate constant** and ***n*** is the **reaction order**. The value of n (usually an integer) reflects how the rate depends on the concentration of the reactant.

- If the rate is independent of the concentration of A, the reaction is *zero order* and $n = 0$.
- If the rate is directly proportional to the concentration of A, the reaction is *first order* and $n = 1$.
- If the rate is proportional to the square of the concentration of A, the reaction is *second order* and $n = 2$.

By definition, $[\text{A}]^0 = 1$, so the rate is equal to k regardless of [A].

Although other orders are possible, including noninteger (or fractional) orders, these three are the most common.

In Figure 13.5 ▼ there are three plots illustrating how the *concentration of A changes with time* for the three common reaction orders with identical values for the rate constant (k). In Figure 13.6 ▼ there are three plots showing the *rate of the reaction* (the slope of the lines in Figure 13.5) *as a function of the reactant concentration* for each reaction order.

Zero-Order Reaction In a zero-order reaction, the rate of the reaction is independent of the concentration of the reactant:

$$\text{Rate} = k[\text{A}]^0 = k \qquad [13.7]$$

Consequently, for a zero-order reaction, the concentration of the reactant decreases linearly with time, as shown in Figure 13.5. The slope of the line is constant, indicating a constant rate. The rate is constant because the reaction does not slow down as the concentration of A decreases. The graph in Figure 13.6 shows that the rate of a zero-order reaction is the same at any concentration of A. Zero-order reactions occur under conditions

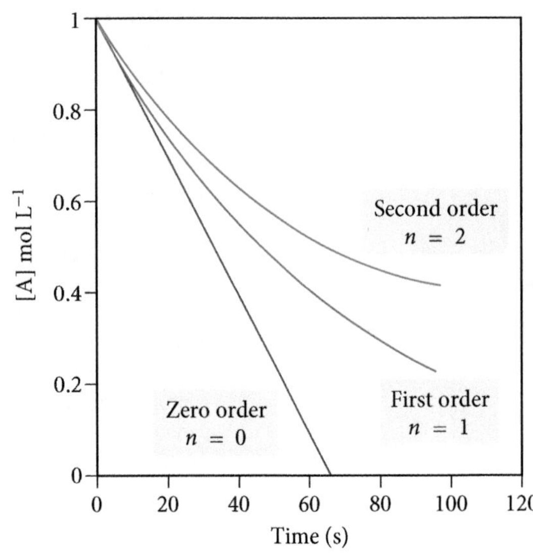

▲ **FIGURE 13.5 Reactant Concentration as a Function of Time for Different Reaction Orders**

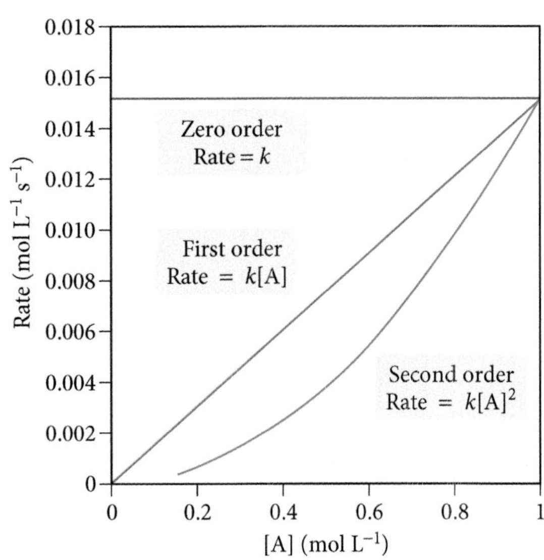

▲ **FIGURE 13.6 Reaction Rate as a Function of Reactant Concentration for Different Reaction Orders**

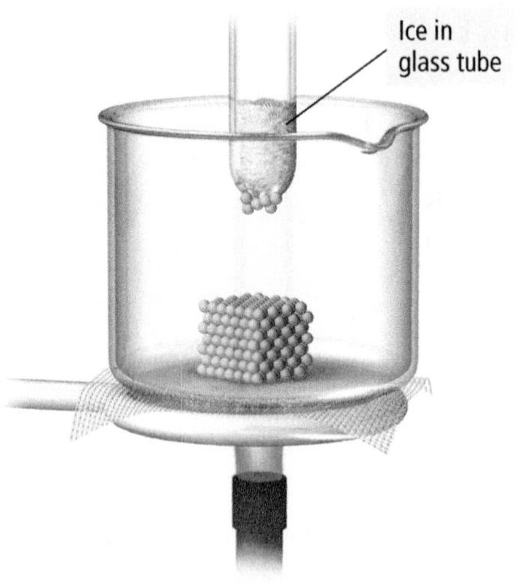

When one layer of particles sublimes, the next layer is exposed. The number of particles available to sublime remains constant.

▲ **FIGURE 13.7 Sublimation** When a layer of particles sublimes, another identical layer is just below it. Consequently, the number of particles available to sublime at any one time does not change with the total number of particles in the sample, and the process is zero order.

where the amount of reactant actually *available for reaction* is unaffected by changes in the *overall quantity of reactant*. For example, sublimation is normally zero order because only molecules at the surface can sublime, and their concentration does not change when the amount of subliming substance decreases (Figure 13.7 ◄).

First-Order Reaction In a first-order reaction, the rate of the reaction is directly proportional to the concentration of the reactant.

$$\text{Rate} = k[\text{A}]^1 = k[\text{A}] \quad [13.8]$$

For a first-order reaction the rate slows down as the reaction proceeds because the concentration of the reactant decreases. You can see this in Figure 13.5—the slope of the curve (the rate) becomes less steep (slower) with time. Figure 13.6 shows the rate as a function of the concentration of A. Notice the linear relationship—the rate is directly proportional to the concentration.

Second-Order Reaction In a second-order reaction, the rate of the reaction is proportional to the square of the concentration of the reactant.

$$\text{Rate} = k[\text{A}]^2 \quad [13.9]$$

Consequently, for a second-order reaction, the rate is even more sensitive to the reactant concentration. You can see this in Figure 13.5—the slope of the curve (the rate) flattens out more quickly than it does for a first-order reaction. Figure 13.6 shows the rate as a function of the concentration of A. Notice the quadratic relationship—the rate is proportional to the square of the concentration.

Determining the Order of a Reaction

The order of a reaction can be determined only by experiment. A common way to determine reaction order is by the *method of initial rates.* In this method, the initial rate—the rate for a short period of time at the beginning of the reaction—is measured by running the reaction several times with different initial reactant concentrations to determine the effect of the concentration on the rate. For example, let's return to our simple reaction in which a single reactant, A, decomposes into products:

$$\text{A} \longrightarrow \text{products}$$

In an experiment, the initial rate was measured at several different initial concentrations with the following results:

[A] (mol L^{-1})	Initial Rate (mol L^{-1} s^{-1})
0.10	0.015
0.20	0.030
0.40	0.060

In this data set, when the concentration of A doubles, the rate doubles—the initial rate is directly proportional to the initial concentration. The reaction is therefore first order in A and the rate law takes the first-order form:

$$\text{Rate} = k[\text{A}]$$

We can determine the value of the rate constant, k, by solving the rate law for k and substituting the concentration and the initial rate from any one of the three measurements. Using the first measurement, we get the following:

$$\text{Rate} = k[\text{A}]$$

$$k = \frac{\text{rate}}{[\text{A}]} = \frac{0.015\ \cancel{\text{mol L}^{-1}}\ \text{s}^{-1}}{0.10\ \cancel{\text{mol L}^{-1}}} = 0.15\ \text{s}^{-1}$$

The rate constant for a first-order reaction has units of s^{-1}.

The following two data sets show how measured initial rates would be different for zero-order and for second-order reactions:

Zero Order ($n = 0$)

[A] (mol L^{-1})	Initial Rate (mol L^{-1} s^{-1})
0.10	0.015
0.20	0.015
0.40	0.015

Second Order ($n = 2$)

[A] (mol L^{-1})	Initial Rate (mol L^{-1} s^{-1})
0.10	0.015
0.20	0.060
0.40	0.240

For a zero-order reaction, the initial rate is independent of the reactant concentration—the rate is the same at all measured initial concentrations. For a second-order reaction, the initial rate quadruples for a doubling of the reactant concentration—the relationship between concentration and rate is quadratic. If you are unsure about how the initial rate is changing with the initial reactant concentration, or if the numbers are not as obvious as they are in these examples, you can substitute any two initial concentrations and the corresponding initial rates into a ratio of the rate laws to determine the order (n):

$$\frac{\text{rate 2}}{\text{rate 1}} = \frac{k[\text{A}]_2^{\,n}}{k[\text{A}]_1^{\,n}}$$

For example, you can substitute the last two measurements in the above data set for the second-order reaction as follows:

$$\frac{0.240\ \cancel{\text{mol L}^{-1}\ \text{s}^{-1}}}{0.060\ \cancel{\text{mol L}^{-1}\ \text{s}^{-1}}} = \frac{k(0.40\ \cancel{\text{mol L}^{-1}})^n}{k(0.20\ \cancel{\text{mol L}^{-1}})^n}$$

$$4.0 = \left(\frac{0.40}{0.20}\right)^n = 2^n$$

$$\begin{aligned} \log(4.0) &= \log(2^n) \\ &= n \log(2) \\ n &= \frac{\log(4)}{\log(2)} \\ &= 2 \end{aligned}$$

Remember that $\log(x^n) = n \log x$.

The rate constants for zero- and second-order reactions have different units than for first-order reactions. The rate constant for a zero-order reaction has units of mol L^{-1} s^{-1} and that for a second-order reaction has units of L mol^{-1} s^{-1}.

Reaction Order for Multiple Reactants

So far, we have considered a simple reaction with only one reactant. How is the rate law defined for reactions with more than one reactant? Consider this reaction:

$$aA + bB \longrightarrow cC + dD$$

As long as the reverse reaction is negligibly slow, the rate law is proportional to the concentration of [A] raised to the *m* multiplied by the concentration of [B] raised to the *n*:

$$\text{Rate} = k[A]^m[B]^n \qquad [13.10]$$

where *m* is the reaction order with respect to A and *n* is the reaction order with respect to B. The **overall order** is the sum of the exponents $(m + n)$. For example, the reaction between hydrogen and iodine has been experimentally determined to be first order with respect to hydrogen, first order with respect to iodine, and thus second order overall.

$$H_2(g) + I_2(g) \longrightarrow 2\ HI(g) \qquad \text{Rate} = k[H_2][I_2]$$

Similarly, the reaction between hydrogen and nitrogen monoxide has been experimentally determined to be first order with respect to hydrogen, second order with respect to nitrogen monoxide, and thus third order overall.

$$2\ H_2(g) + 2\ NO(g) \longrightarrow N_2(g) + 2\ H_2O(g) \qquad \text{Rate} = k[H_2][NO]^2$$

The rate law for any reaction must always be determined by experiment, often by the method of initial rates described previously. There is no simple way merely to look at a chemical equation and determine the rate law for the reaction. When there are two or more reactants, the concentration of each reactant is usually varied independently of the others to determine the dependence of the rate on the concentration of that reactant. The following example uses the method of initial rates for determining the order of a reaction with multiple reactants.

EXAMPLE 13.2 DETERMINING THE ORDER AND RATE CONSTANT OF A REACTION

Consider the reaction between nitrogen dioxide and carbon monoxide:

$$NO_2(g) + CO(g) \longrightarrow NO(g) + CO_2(g)$$

The initial rate of the reaction was measured at several different concentrations of the reactants with the following results:

$[NO_2]$ (mol L^{-1})	[CO] (mol L^{-1})	Initial Rate (mol L^{-1} s^{-1})
0.10	0.10	0.0021
0.20	0.10	0.0083
0.30	0.20	0.0189

From the data, determine:

(a) the rate law for the reaction

(b) the rate constant (*k*) for the reaction

SOLUTION

(a) First write down the form of the rate law.

$$\text{Rate} = k[NO_2]^m[CO]^n$$

Second, examine how the rate changes for each change in concentration. Between the first two experiments, the concentration of NO_2 doubled, the concentration of CO stayed constant, and the rate quadrupled. This means that the reaction is second order in NO_2, or $m = 2$.

$[NO_2]$ (mol L^{-1})	[CO] (mol L^{-1})	Initial Rate (mol L^{-1} s^{-1})
0.10	0.10	0.0021
↓ ×2	↓ constant	↓ ×4
0.20	0.10	0.0083
↓ ×1.5	↓ ×2	↓ ×2.28
0.30	0.20	0.0189

Between the second and third experiments, the concentration of NO_2 increased by a factor of 1.5 and that of CO doubled, resulting in an increase in the initial rate by a factor of 2.28. Because both concentrations change, and the factors are not obvious, it might be best to use a ratio of the rate laws for the second and third sets of data. This analysis shows that the reaction is zero order with respect to the concentration of CO.	$\frac{\text{rate 3}}{\text{rate 2}} = \frac{k[NO_2]_3^2[CO]_3^n}{k[NO_2]_2^2[CO]_2^n}$ $\frac{0.0189 \text{ mol L}^{-1}\text{ s}^{-1}}{0.0083 \text{ mol L}^{-1}\text{ s}^{-1}} = \frac{k(0.30 \text{ mol L}^{-1})^2(0.20 \text{ mol L}^{-1})^n}{k(0.20 \text{ mol L}^{-1})^2(0.10 \text{ mol L}^{-1})^n}$ $2.28 = (1.5)^2(2.0)^n$ $1.0 = 2.0^n$ $n = 0$
Finally, write the overall rate expression.	$\text{Rate} = k[NO_2]^2[CO]^0 = k[NO_2]^2$
(b) To determine the rate constant for the reaction, solve the rate law for k and substitute the concentration and the initial rate from any one of the three measurements. In this case, we use the first measurement.	$\text{Rate} = k[NO_2]^2$ $k = \frac{\text{rate}}{[NO_2]^2} = \frac{0.0021 \text{ mol L}^{-1}\text{ s}^{-1}}{(0.10 \text{ mol L}^{-1})^2} = 0.21 \text{ L mol}^{-1}\text{ s}^{-1}$

FOR PRACTICE 13.2

Consider the reaction:

$$CHCl_3(g) + Cl_2(g) \longrightarrow CCl_4(g) + HCl(g)$$

The initial rate of the reaction was measured at several different concentrations of the reactants with the following results:

$[CHCl_3]$ (mol L^{-1})	$[Cl_2]$ (mol L^{-1})	Initial Rate (mol L^{-1} s^{-1})
0.010	0.010	0.0035
0.020	0.010	0.0069
0.030	0.030	0.0182

From the data, determine:

(a) the rate law for the reaction **(b)** the rate constant (k) for the reaction

CONCEPTUAL CONNECTION 13.1
Rate and Concentration

This reaction was experimentally determined to be first order with respect to O_2 and second order with respect to NO.

$$O_2(g) + 2\,NO(g) \longrightarrow 2\,NO_2(g)$$

These diagrams represent reaction mixtures in which the number of each type of molecule represents its relative initial concentration. Which mixture has the fastest initial rate?

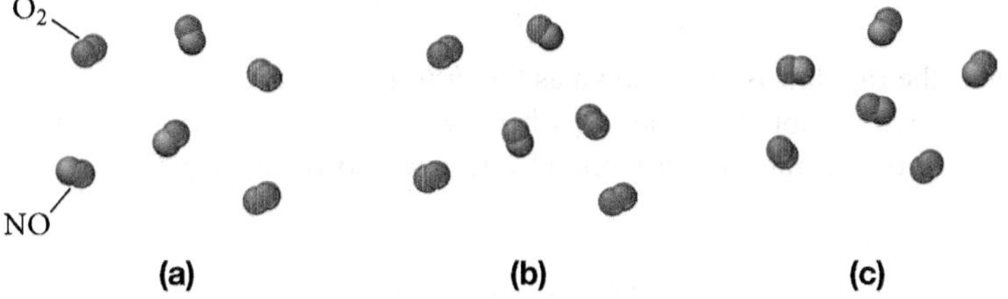

13.4 The Integrated Rate Law: The Dependence of Concentration on Time

The rate laws we have examined so far show the relationship between *the rate of a reaction and the concentration of a reactant.* But we often want to know the relationship between *the concentration of a reactant and time.* For example, the presence of

TABLE 13.1 Atmospheric Lifetimes of Several CFCs

CFC Name	Structure	Atmospheric Lifetime*
CFC-11 (CCl_3F) Trichlorofluoromethane		45 years
CFC-12 (CCl_2F_2) Dichlorodifluoromethane		100 years
CFC-113 ($C_2F_3Cl_3$) 1,1,2-Trichloro-1,2,2-trifluoroethane		85 years
CFC-114 ($C_2F_4Cl_2$) 1,2-Dichlorotetrafluoroethane		300 years
CFC-115 (C_2F_5Cl) Monochloropentafluoroethane		1700 years

*Source: EPA.

chlorofluorocarbons (CFCs) in the atmosphere threatens the ozone layer. One of the reasons that CFCs pose such a significant threat is that the reactions that consume them are so slow (see Table 13.1). Legislation has significantly reduced CFC emissions, but even if we were to completely stop adding CFCs to the atmosphere, their concentration would decrease only very slowly. Nonetheless, we would like to know how their concentration changes with time. How much will be left in 20 years? In 50 years?

The **integrated rate law** for a chemical reaction is a relationship between the concentrations of the reactants and time. For simplicity, we return to a single reactant decomposing into products:

$$\text{A} \longrightarrow \text{products}$$

The integrated rate law for this reaction depends on the order of the reaction; let's examine each of the common reaction orders individually.

First-Order Integrated Rate Law If our simple reaction is first order, the rate is directly proportional to the concentration:

$$\text{Rate} = k[\text{A}]$$

Since Rate $= -\Delta[\text{A}]/\Delta t$, we can write

$$-\frac{\Delta[\text{A}]}{\Delta t} = k[\text{A}] \qquad [13.11]$$

In this form, the rate law is also known as the *differential rate law*.

Although we do not show the steps here, we can use calculus (see End of Chapter Exercise 116) to integrate the differential rate law and obtain the first-order *integrated rate law*:

$$\ln[\text{A}]_t = -kt + \ln[\text{A}]_0 \qquad [13.12]$$

or

$$\ln\left(\frac{[\text{A}]_t}{[\text{A}]_0}\right) = -kt \qquad [13.13]$$

$$\ln[\text{A}]_t = -kt + \ln[\text{A}]_0$$
$$\ln[\text{A}]_t - \ln[\text{A}]_0 = -kt$$
$$\ln\left(\frac{[\text{A}]_t}{[\text{A}]_0}\right) = -kt$$

Remember that $\ln A - \ln B = \ln(A/B)$.

where $[\text{A}]_t$ is the concentration of A at any time t, k is the rate constant, and $[\text{A}]_0$ is the initial concentration of A. These two forms of the equation are equivalent, as shown in the margin.

Notice that the integrated rate law shown in Equation 13.12 has the form of an equation for a straight line.

$$\ln[A]_t = -kt + \ln[A]_0$$
$$y = mx + b$$

For a first-order reaction, a plot of the natural logarithm of the reactant concentration as a function of time yields a straight line with a slope of $-k$ and a y-intercept of $\ln[A]_0$, as shown in Figure 13.8 ▶. (Note that the slope is negative but that the rate constant is always positive.)

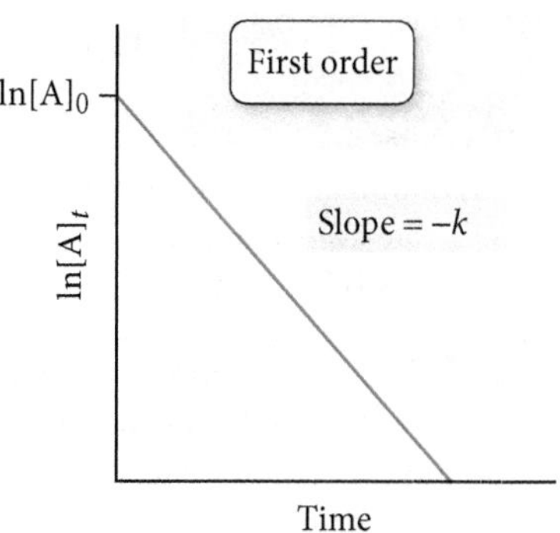

▲ **FIGURE 13.8 First-Order Integrated Rate Law** For a first-order reaction, a plot of the natural log of the reactant concentration as a function of time yields a straight line. The slope of the line is equal to $-k$ and the y-intercept is $\ln[A]_0$.

EXAMPLE 13.3 THE FIRST-ORDER INTEGRATED RATE LAW: USING GRAPHICAL ANALYSIS OF REACTION DATA

Consider the equation for the decomposition of SO_2Cl_2.

$$SO_2Cl_2(g) \longrightarrow SO_2(g) + Cl_2(g)$$

The concentration of SO_2Cl_2 was monitored at a fixed temperature as a function of time during the decomposition reaction and the following data were tabulated:

Time (s)	$[SO_2Cl_2]$ (mol L^{-1})	Time (s)	$[SO_2Cl_2]$ (mol L^{-1})
0	0.100	800	0.0793
100	0.0971	900	0.0770
200	0.0944	1000	0.0748
300	0.0917	1100	0.0727
400	0.0890	1200	0.0706
500	0.0865	1300	0.0686
600	0.0840	1400	0.0666
700	0.0816	1500	0.0647

Show that the reaction is first order and determine the rate constant for the reaction.

SOLUTION

In order to show that the reaction is first order, prepare a graph of $\ln[SO_2Cl_2]$ versus time as shown below.

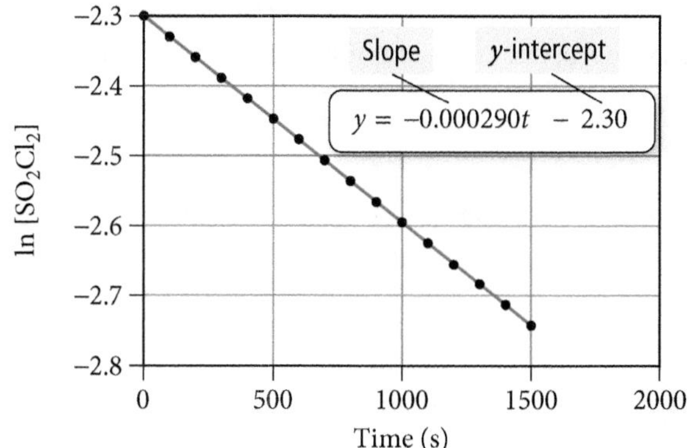

The plot is linear, confirming that the reaction is indeed first order. To obtain the rate constant, fit the data to a line. The slope of the line will be equal to $-k$. Since the slope of the best fitting line (which is most easily determined on a graphing calculator or with spreadsheet software such as Microsoft Excel) is $-2.90 \times 10^{-4}\ s^{-1}$ (notice that the slope has units!). The rate constant is therefore $2.90 \times 10^{-4}\ s^{-1}$.

FOR PRACTICE 13.3

Use the graph and the best fitting line in the previous example to predict the concentration of SO_2Cl_2 at 1900 s.

EXAMPLE 13.4 THE FIRST-ORDER INTEGRATED RATE LAW: DETERMINING THE CONCENTRATION OF A REACTANT AT A GIVEN TIME

In Example 13.3, you determined that the decomposition of SO_2Cl_2 (under the given reaction conditions) is first order and has a rate constant of $2.90 \times 10^{-4}\ s^{-1}$. If the reaction is carried out at the same temperature, and the initial concentration of SO_2Cl_2 is 0.0225 mol L^{-1}, what will the SO_2Cl_2 concentration be after 865 s?

SORT You are given the rate constant of a first-order reaction and the initial concentration of the reactant and asked to find the concentration at 865 seconds.

GIVEN: $k = 2.90 \times 10^{-4}\ s^{-1}$

$[SO_2Cl_2]_0 = 0.0225\ mol\ L^{-1}$

FIND: $[SO_2Cl_2]$ at $t = 865$ s

STRATEGIZE Refer to the first-order integrated rate law to determine the information you are asked to find from the given information.

EQUATION
$\ln[A]_t = -kt + \ln[A]_0$

SOLVE Substitute the rate constant, the initial concentration, and the time into the integrated rate law.

Solve the integrated rate law for the concentration of $[SO_2Cl_2]_t$.

SOLUTION

$$\ln[SO_2Cl_2]_t = -kt + \ln[SO_2Cl_2]_0$$

$$\ln[SO_2Cl_2]_t = -(2.90 \times 10^{-4}\ \cancel{s^{-1}})865\ \cancel{s} + \ln(0.0225)$$

$$\ln[SO_2Cl_2]_t = -0.251 - 3.79$$

$$[SO_2Cl_2]_t = e^{-4.04}$$

$$= 0.0175\ mol\ L^{-1}$$

CHECK The concentration is smaller than the original concentration as expected. If the concentration were larger than the initial concentration, this would indicate a mistake in the signs of one of the quantities on the right-hand side of the equation.

FOR PRACTICE 13.4

Cyclopropane rearranges to form propene in the gas phase.

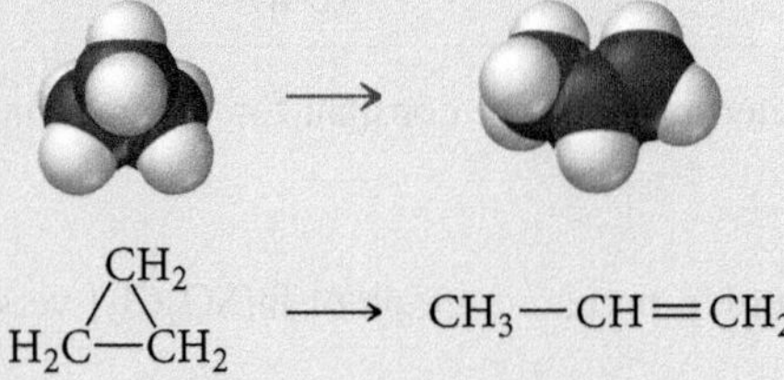

$$\underset{H_2C-CH_2}{\overset{CH_2}{/\backslash}} \longrightarrow CH_3-CH=CH_2$$

The reaction is first order in cyclopropane and has a measured rate constant of $3.36 \times 10^{-5}\ s^{-1}$ at 720 K. If the initial cyclopropane concentration is 0.0445 mol L^{-1}, what will the cyclopropane concentration be after 235.0 minutes?

Second-Order Integrated Rate Law If our simple reaction (A $\longrightarrow$ products) is second order, the rate is proportional to the square of the concentration of A:

$$\text{Rate} = k[A]^2$$

Since Rate $= -\Delta[A]/\Delta t$, we can write:

$$-\frac{\Delta[A]}{\Delta t} = k[A]^2 \qquad [13.14]$$

Again, although we do not show the steps here, this differential rate law can be integrated to obtain the *second-order integrated rate law*:

$$\frac{1}{[A]_t} = kt + \frac{1}{[A]_0} \qquad [13.15]$$

The second-order integrated rate law is also in the form of an equation for a straight line.

$$\frac{1}{[A]_t} = kt + \frac{1}{[A]_0}$$
$$y = mx + b$$

However, you must now plot the inverse of the concentration of the reactant as a function of time. The plot yields a straight line with a slope of k and an intercept of $1/[A]_0$ as shown in Figure 13.9 ▶.

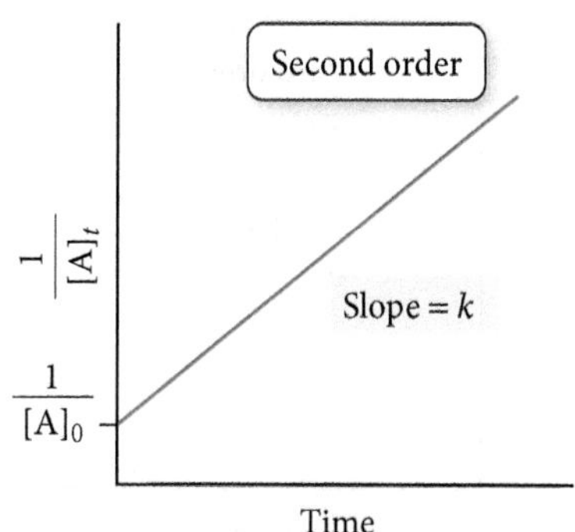

▲ **FIGURE 13.9 Second-Order Integrated Rate Law** For a second-order reaction, a plot of the inverse of the reactant concentration as a function of time yields a straight line. The slope of the line is equal to k and the y-intercept is $1/[A]_0$.

EXAMPLE 13.5 THE SECOND-ORDER INTEGRATED RATE LAW: USING GRAPHICAL ANALYSIS OF REACTION DATA

Consider the following equation for the decomposition of NO_2.

$$NO_2(g) \longrightarrow NO(g) + O(g)$$

The concentration of NO_2 was monitored at a fixed temperature as a function of time during the decomposition reaction and the data tabulated (at right). Show by graphical analysis that the reaction is not first order and that it is second order. Determine the rate constant for the reaction.

Time (s)	$[NO_2]$ (mol L^{-1})	Time (s)	$[NO_2]$ (mol L^{-1})	Time (s)	$[NO_2]$ (mol L^{-1})
0	0.01000	350	0.00528	700	0.00359
50	0.00887	400	0.00495	750	0.00343
100	0.00797	450	0.00466	800	0.00329
150	0.00723	500	0.00440	850	0.00316
200	0.00662	550	0.00416	900	0.00303
250	0.00611	600	0.00395	950	0.00292
300	0.00567	650	0.00376	1000	0.00282

SOLUTION

In order to show that the reaction is *not* first order, prepare a graph of $\ln[NO_2]$ versus time as shown in the left graph.

The plot is *not* linear (the straight line does not fit the data points), confirming that the reaction is not first order. In order to show that the reaction is second order, prepare a graph of $1/[NO_2]$ versus time as shown in the right graph.

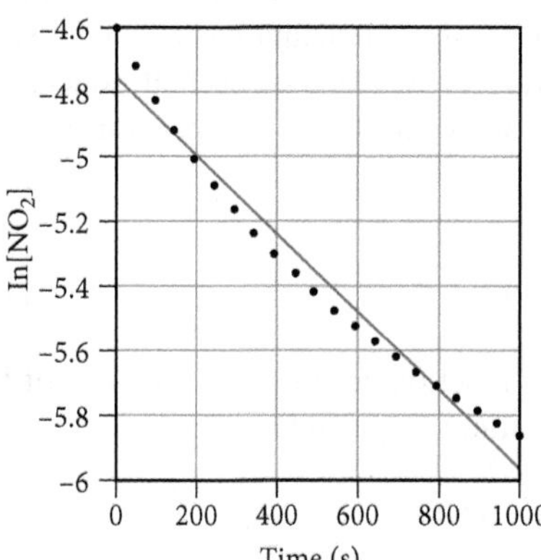

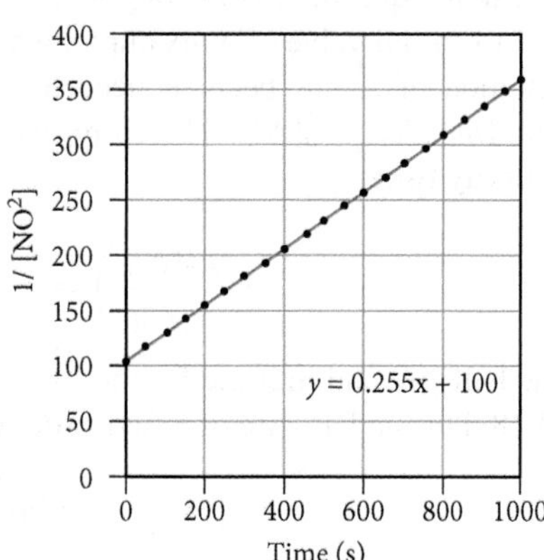

This graph is linear (the data points fit well to a straight line), confirming that the reaction is indeed second order. To obtain the rate constant, determine the slope of the best fitting line. The slope is 0.255 L mol^{-1} s^{-1}; therefore, the rate constant is 0.255 L mol^{-1} s^{-1}.

FOR PRACTICE 13.5

Use the graph and the best fitting line in Example 13.5 to predict the concentration of NO_2 at 2000 s.

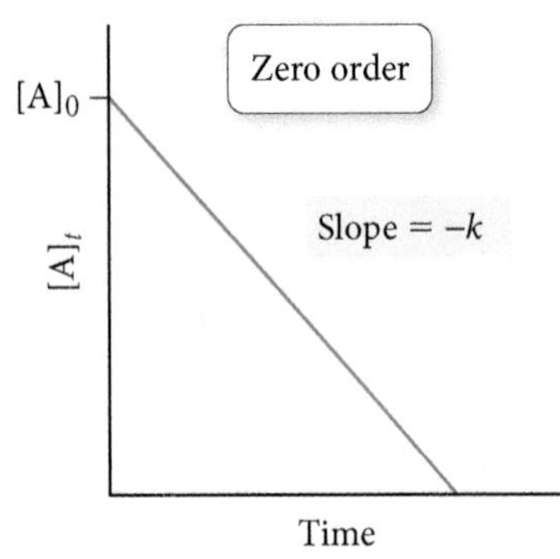

▲ **FIGURE 13.10 Zero-Order Integrated Rate Law** For a zero-order reaction, a plot of the reactant concentration as a function of time yields a straight line. The slope of the line is equal to $-k$ and the y-intercept is $[A]_0$.

Zero-Order Integrated Rate Law If our simple reaction is zero order, the rate is proportional to a constant:

$$\text{Rate} = k[A]^0 = k$$

Since Rate $= -\Delta[A]/\Delta t$, we can write:

$$-\frac{\Delta[A]}{\Delta t} = k \qquad [13.16]$$

We can integrate this differential rate law to obtain the *zero-order integrated rate law*:

$$[A]_t = -kt + [A]_0 \qquad [13.17]$$

The zero-order integrated rate law in Equation 13.17 is also in the form of an equation for a straight line. A plot of the concentration of the reactant as a function of time yields a straight line with a slope of $-k$ and an intercept of $[A]_0$, as shown in Figure 13.10 ◀.

Half-Life, Lifetime, and Decay Time

The **half-life ($t_{1/2}$)** of a reaction is the time required for the concentration of a reactant to fall to one-half of its initial value. For example, if a reaction has a half-life of 100 seconds, and if the initial concentration of the reactant is 1.0 mol L^{-1}, the concentration will fall to 0.50 mol L^{-1} in 100 s. Another common quantity is the **lifetime (τ)** of a reaction, which is the time for a reactant concentration to decrease to $1/e$ (about 1/2.7) of the starting concentration. The lifetime represents the average life expectancy of the chemical entity. The term is used in Table 13.1. Trichlorofluoromethane has a lifetime of 45 years in the atmosphere, which means that this compound is expected to exist, on average, for 45 years. The half-life and lifetime are common quantities only for first-order reactions because they are constant. As we will see, the half-life and lifetime change during the course of the reaction for reactions that are not first order.

First-Order Reactions For a first-order reaction, the integrated rate law is:

$$\ln\frac{[A]_t}{[A]_0} = -kt$$

We can ask the question: How long will it take for the concentration of reactant to drop to $1/n$ of its initial value? For example, when 90% of the reactant has reacted away, the concentration of A has been reduced to $\frac{1}{10}[A]_0$. So, when the reactant concentration drops to $1/n$, $[A]_t = \frac{1}{n}[A]_0$. Therefore, we can write the following general expression for the **decay time**:

$$\ln\left(\frac{\frac{1}{n}[A]_0}{[A]_0}\right) = -kt \quad \text{or} \quad t = \frac{\ln(n)}{k} \qquad [13.18]$$

The half-life and lifetime for the first-order reaction are just special cases of Equation 13.18. For the half-life of a first-order reaction, $t = t_{1/2}$ and $n = 2$:

$$t_{1/2} = \frac{\ln(2)}{k} = \frac{0.693}{k} \qquad [13.19a]$$

And for the lifetime of a first-order reaction $t = \tau$ and $n = e$:

$$\tau = \frac{\ln(e)}{k} = \frac{1}{k} \qquad [13.19b]$$

For a first-order reaction, these quantities are *all independent of the initial concentration*. For example, if $t_{1/2}$ is 100 s, and if the initial concentration is 1.0 mol L^{-1}, the concentration falls to 0.50 mol L^{-1} in 100 s, then to 0.25 mol L^{-1} in another 100 s, then to 0.125 mol L^{-1} in another 100 s, and so on (Figure 13.11 ▶). Constant half-lives and lifetimes are unique to first-order reactions, making this concept particularly useful for them.

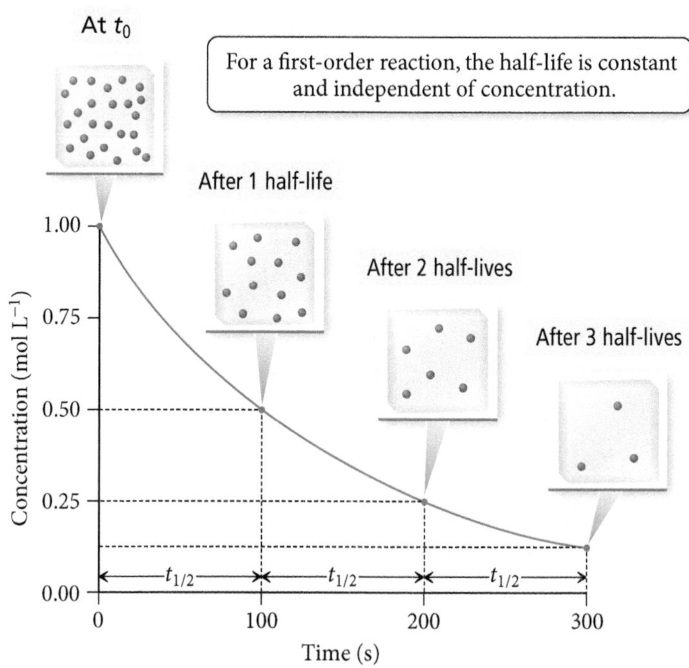

◀ **FIGURE 13.11 Half-Life: Concentration Versus Time for a First-Order Reaction** For this reaction, the concentration falls by one-half every 100 seconds ($t_{1/2} = 100$ s). The blue spheres represent reactant molecules (the products are omitted for clarity).

EXAMPLE 13.6 HALF-LIFE, LIFETIME, AND DECAY TIME

Molecular iodine dissociates at 625 K with a first-order rate constant of 0.271 s^{-1}. Calculate **(a)** the half-life, **(b)** the lifetime, and **(c)** the time for 95% of the molecular iodine to decay.

SOLUTION

(a) Because the reaction is first order, the half-life is given by Equation 13.19a. Substitute the value of k into the expression and calculate $t_{1/2}$.	$t_{1/2} = \frac{0.693}{k} = \frac{0.693}{0.271\,\text{s}^{-1}} = 2.56\,\text{s}$
(b) Substitute the value of k into the expression for τ (Equation 13.19b) to calculate the lifetime.	$\tau = \frac{1}{k} = \frac{1}{0.271\,\text{s}^{-1}} = 3.69\,\text{s}$
(c) When 95% of molecular iodine has decayed, there is 5% left. The fraction that remains is 5/100, or 1/20. Substitute k and $n = 20$ into Equation 13.18 and calculate the decay time.	$t = \frac{\ln(n)}{k} = \frac{\ln(20)}{0.271\,\text{s}^{-1}} = 11.1\,\text{s}$

CHECK The lifetime is the amount of time for molecular iodine to decay to $1/e$ or 1/2.7 of its original value. Therefore, it should be longer than the half-life, which is the amount of time to decay to 1/2 the original value—and it is. The time for molecular iodine to decay to 1/20 of its original value is even longer.

FOR PRACTICE 13.6

A first-order reaction has a half-life of 26.4 seconds. How long will it take for the concentration of the reactant in the reaction to fall to one-tenth of its initial value?

Second-Order Reactions For a second-order reaction, the integrated rate law is:

$$\frac{1}{[A]_t} = kt + \frac{1}{[A]_0}$$

At a time when the initial concentration of reactant decreases to a fraction, say $1/n$, of its initial value, ($[A]_t = \frac{1}{n}[A]_0$). We can write the following expression,

$$\frac{1}{\frac{1}{n}[A]_0} = kt + \frac{1}{[A]_0}$$

which can be solved for the decay time, t:

$$kt = \frac{1}{\frac{1}{n}[A]_0} - \frac{1}{[A]_0}$$

$$= \frac{n}{[A]_0} - \frac{1}{[A]_0}$$

$$t = \frac{n-1}{k[A]_0} \qquad [13.20]$$

A special case of the decay time is the half-life ($t_{1/2}$), when the concentration has decayed to half its original concentration, ($n = 2$):

$$t_{1/2} = \frac{1}{k[A]_0} \qquad [13.21]$$

For a second-order reaction, the decay time depends on the initial concentration. So, if the initial concentration of a reactant in a second-order reaction is 1.0 mol L^{-1}, and the half-life is 100 s, the concentration falls to 0.50 mol L^{-1} in 100 s. However, the time it takes for the concentration to fall from 0.50 mol L^{-1} to 0.25 mol L^{-1} is *twice as long*, 200 s, because the initial concentration has decreased. The half-life and decay time continue to get longer for a second-order reaction as the reaction proceeds and the concentration of reactant decreases.

Zero-Order Reactions For a zero-order reaction, the integrated rate law is:

$$[A]_t = -kt + [A]_0$$

When the concentration of reactant has decreased to $1/n$ its initial concentration:

$$\tfrac{1}{n}[A]_0 = -kt + [A]_0$$

This can then be solved for the decay time:

$$kt = [A]_0 - \tfrac{1}{n}[A]_0$$

$$t = \frac{(n-1)[A]_0}{nk} \qquad [13.22]$$

The half-life ($t_{1/2}$), when the concentration is half its original concentration ($n = 2$) is:

$$t = \frac{(n-1)[A]_0}{nk} \qquad [13.23]$$

Notice that for a zero-order reaction, the half-life depends on the initial concentration as well, but as the reaction proceeds, the half-life decreases because the concentration decreases.

Summarizing Basic Kinetic Relationships (see Table 13.2):

- The reaction order and rate law must be determined experimentally.
- The rate law relates the *rate* of the reaction to the *concentration* of the reactant(s).
- The integrated rate law (which is mathematically derived from the rate law) relates the *concentration* of the reactant(s) to *time*.
- The half-life is the time it takes for the concentration of a reactant to fall to one-half of its initial value.

- The half-life, lifetime, and decay time of a first-order reaction are independent of the initial concentration.
- The half-lives and decay times of zero-order and second-order reactions depend on the initial concentration.

CONCEPTUAL CONNECTION 13.2

Kinetics Summary

A decomposition reaction, with a rate that is observed to slow down as the reaction proceeds, is found to have a half-life that depends on the initial concentration of the reactant. Which of the following is most likely to be true of this reaction?

(a) A plot of the natural log of the concentration of the reactant as a function of time will be linear.

(b) The half-life of the reaction increases as the initial concentration increases.

(c) A doubling of the initial concentration of the reactant results in a quadrupling of the rate.

TABLE 13.2 Rate Law Summary Table

Order	Rate Law	Units of k	Integrated Rate Law	Straight-Line Plot	Half-Life Expression
0	Rate $= k[A]^0$	mol L^{-1} s^{-1}	$[A]_t = -kt + [A]_0$	Plot of $[A]_t$ vs. Time t: y-intercept $= [A]_0$; Slope $= -k$	$t_{1/2} = \frac{[A]_0}{2k}$
1	Rate $= k[A]^1$	s^{-1}	$\ln[A]_t = -kt + \ln[A]_0$ $\ln\frac{[A]_t}{[A]_0} = -kt$	Plot of $\ln[A]_t$ vs. Time t: y-intercept $= \ln[A]_0$; Slope $= -k$	$t_{1/2} = \frac{0.693}{k}$
2	Rate $= k[A]^2$	L mol^{-1} s^{-1}	$\frac{1}{[A]_t} = kt + \frac{1}{[A]_0}$	Plot of $1/[A]_t$ vs. Time t: Slope $= k$; y-intercept $= 1/[A]_0$	$t_{1/2} = \frac{1}{k[A]_0}$

13.5 The Effect of Temperature on Reaction Rate

In the opening section of this chapter, we learned that frogs and other small animals hibernate during the cold of winter. During hibernation, their body temperature drops and all the chemical reactions that occur to keep the animal alive slow down, some to within 1% of their normal rates. The rates of chemical reactions are, in general, highly sensitive to temperature. For example, at around room temperature, a 10 °C increase in temperature increases the rate of a typical reaction by two or three times. How do we explain this highly sensitive temperature dependence?

The rate law for a reaction is Rate $= k[A]^n$. *The temperature dependence of the reaction rate is contained in the rate constant,* k, which is actually a constant only when the temperature remains constant. An increase in temperature usually results in an increase in k, which results in a faster rate. In 1889, Swedish chemist Svante Arrhenius wrote a paper quantifying the temperature dependence of the rate constant. The modern form of the **Arrhenius equation** shows the relationship between the rate constant (k) and the temperature in kelvin (T):

$$k = Ae^{\frac{-E_a}{RT}} \qquad [13.24]$$

Activation energy

Frequency factor

Exponential factor

In this equation, R is the gas constant ($8.314\,\text{J mol}^{-1}\,\text{K}^{-1}$), A is a constant called the *frequency factor* (or the *pre-exponential factor*), and E_a is the *activation energy* (or *activation barrier*).

The **activation energy (E_a)** is an energy barrier that must be surmounted for the reactants to be transformed into products (Figure 13.12 ▼). We examine the frequency factor more closely in the next section; for now, we can think of the **frequency factor (A)** as the number of times that the reactants approach the activation barrier per unit time.

$$2\,H_2(g) + O_2(g) \rightleftharpoons 2\,H_2O(g)$$

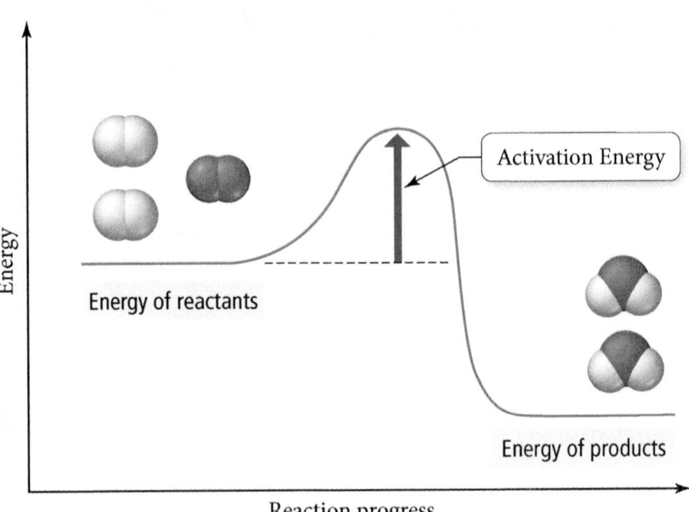

▶ **FIGURE 13.12 The Activation Energy Barrier** Even though the reaction is energetically favourable (the energy of the products is lower than that of the reactants), an input of energy is needed for the reaction to take place.

To understand each of these quantities better, consider the following simple reaction in which CH_3NC (methyl isocyanide) rearranges to form CH_3CN (methyl cyanide):

$$CH_3{-}N{\equiv}C \longrightarrow CH_3{-}C{\equiv}N$$

Let's examine the physical meaning of the activation energy, frequency factor, and exponential factor for this reaction.

The activated complex is not a chemical entity that can be isolated from the reaction mixture; it does not live long enough. It is the highest energy arrangement of the atoms along the path from reactants to products.

The Activation Energy Figure 13.13(a) ▶ shows the energy of the molecule as the reaction proceeds. The x-axis represents the progress of the reaction from left (reactant) to right (product). To get from the reactant to the product, the molecule must go through a high-energy arrangement of the atoms called the **activated complex**, or **transition state**. Even though the overall reaction is energetically downhill (exothermic), it must first go uphill to reach the activated complex because energy is required to initially weaken the $H_3C{-}N$ bond and allow the NC group to begin to rotate:

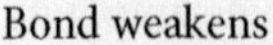

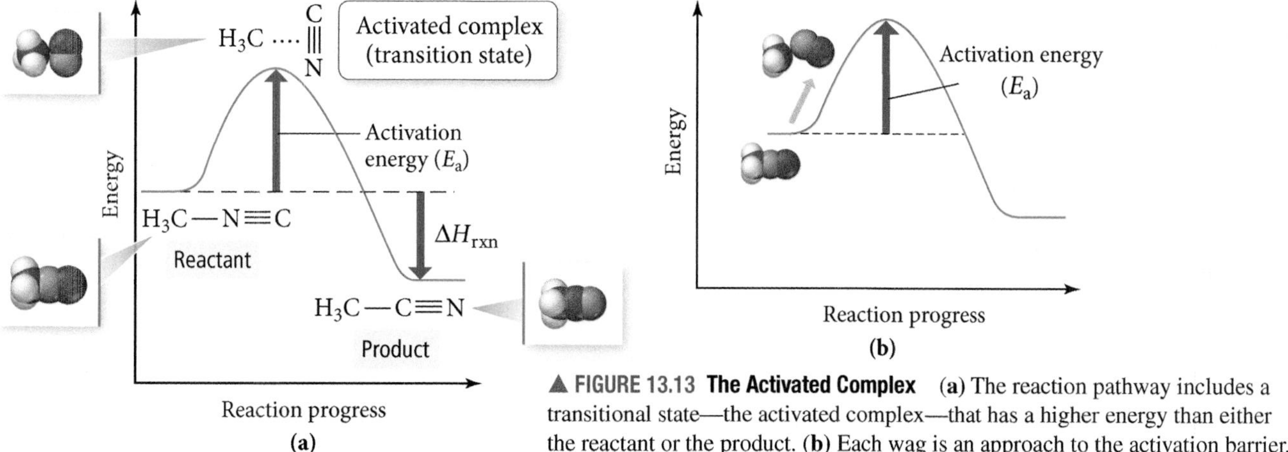

▲ **FIGURE 13.13 The Activated Complex** (**a**) The reaction pathway includes a transitional state—the activated complex—that has a higher energy than either the reactant or the product. (**b**) Each wag is an approach to the activation barrier.

The energy required to reach the activated complex is the *activation energy. The higher the activation energy, the slower the reaction rate (at a given temperature).*

The Frequency Factor We just saw that the frequency factor represents the number of approaches to the activation barrier per unit time. Any time that the NC group begins to rotate, it approaches the activation barrier. For this reaction, the frequency factor represents the rate at which the NC part of the molecule wags (vibrates side-to-side). With each wag, the reactant approaches the activation barrier (Figure 13.13(b)). However, approaching the activation barrier is not equivalent to surmounting it. Most of the approaches do not have enough total energy to make it over the activation barrier.

The Exponential Factor The **exponential factor** is a number between 0 and 1 that represents the fraction of molecules that have enough energy to make it over the activation barrier on a given approach. Another way of saying this is that the exponential factor is the fraction of approaches that are energetic enough to be successful and result in the product. For example, if the frequency factor is $10^9\ s^{-1}$ and the exponential factor is 10^{-7} at a certain temperature, then the overall rate constant at that temperature is $10^9\ s^{-1} \times 10^{-7} = 10^2\ s^{-1}$. In this case, the NC group is wagging at a rate of $10^9\ s^{-1}$. With each wag, the activation barrier is approached. However, only 1 in 10^7 molecules has sufficient energy to actually make it over the activation barrier.

The exponential factor depends on the temperature (T), which you can control, and the activation energy (E_a) of the reaction is a property of the reacting species, which you cannot control.

$$\text{Exponential factor} = e^{-E_a/RT}$$

A low activation energy and a high temperature make the negative exponent small, so that the exponential factor approaches one. For example, if the activation energy is zero, then the exponent is zero, and the exponential factor is exactly one ($e^{-0} = 1$)—every approach to the activation barrier is successful. By contrast, a large activation energy and a low temperature make the exponent a very large negative number, so that the exponential factor becomes very small. For example, as the temperature approaches 0 K, the exponent approaches an infinitely large number, and the exponential factor approaches zero ($e^{-\infty} = 0$) and the reactants can never get over the energy barrier to form products.

As the temperature increases, the number of molecules having enough thermal energy to surmount the activation barrier increases. At any given temperature, a sample of molecules will have a distribution of energies, as shown in Figure 13.14 ▼. Under common circumstances, only a small number of the molecules have enough energy to make it over the activation barrier. Because of the shape of the energy distribution curve, however, a small change in temperature results in a large difference in the number of molecules having enough energy to surmount the activation barrier. This explains the sensitivity of reaction rates to temperature.

Summarizing Temperature and Reaction Rate:

- The frequency factor is the number of times that the reactants approach the activation barrier per unit time.

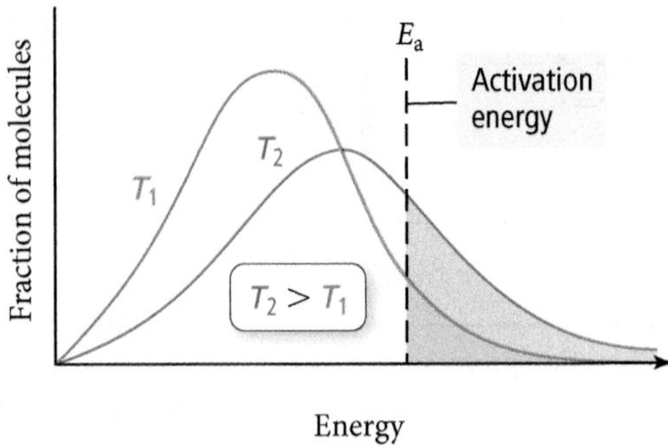
As temperature increases, the fraction of molecules with enough energy to surmount the activation energy barrier also increases.
E_a
Activation energy
T_1
T_2
$T_2 > T_1$
Fraction of molecules
Energy

▶ **FIGURE 13.14 Thermal Energy Distribution** At any given temperature, the atoms or molecules in a gas sample will have a range of energies. The higher the temperature, the wider the energy distribution and the greater the average energy. The fraction of molecules with enough energy to surmount the activation energy barrier and react increases sharply as the temperature rises.

- The exponential factor is the fraction of approaches that are successful in surmounting the activation barrier and forming products.
- The exponential factor increases with increasing temperature, but a large activation energy results in a small exponential factor.

Arrhenius Plots: Experimental Measurements of the Frequency Factor and the Activation Energy

The frequency factor and activation energy are important quantities in understanding the kinetics of any reaction. To see how we measure these factors in the laboratory, consider again Equation 13.24: $k = Ae^{-E_a/RT}$. Taking the natural logarithm of both sides of this equation, we get the following:

Remember that $\ln(A \times B) = \ln A + \ln B$.

$$\ln k = \ln(Ae^{-E_a/RT}) \qquad [13.25]$$

$$\ln k = \ln A + \ln e^{-E_a/RT}$$

Remember that $\ln e^x = x$.

$$\ln k = \ln A - \frac{E_a}{RT}$$

$$\ln k = -\frac{E_a}{R}\left(\frac{1}{T}\right) + \ln A \qquad [13.26]$$

$$y = mx + b$$

In an Arrhenius analysis, the pre-exponential factor (A) is assumed to be independent of temperature. Although the pre-exponential factor does depend on temperature to some degree, its temperature dependence is much less than that of the exponential factor and is often ignored.

Equation 13.26 is in the form of a straight line. *A plot of the natural logarithm of the rate constant (ln* k*) versus the inverse of the temperature in kelvin (1/*T*) yields a straight line with a slope of* $-E_a/R$ *and a y-intercept of ln* A. Such a plot is called an **Arrhenius plot** and is commonly used in the analysis of kinetic data, as shown in the following example.

EXAMPLE 13.7 USING AN ARRHENIUS PLOT TO DETERMINE KINETIC PARAMETERS

The decomposition of ozone shown here is important to many atmospheric reactions:

$$O_3(g) \longrightarrow O_2(g) + O(g)$$

Temperature (K)	Rate Constant (L mol^{-1} s^{-1})	Temperature (K)	Rate Constant (L mol^{-1} s^{-1})
600	3.37×10^3	1300	7.83×10^7
700	4.85×10^4	1400	1.45×10^8
800	3.58×10^5	1500	2.46×10^8
900	1.70×10^6	1600	3.93×10^8
1000	5.90×10^6	1700	5.93×10^8
1100	1.63×10^7	1800	8.55×10^8
1200	3.81×10^7	1900	1.19×10^9

A study of the kinetics of the reaction results in the data table.
Determine the value of the frequency factor and activation energy for the reaction.

SOLUTION

To find the frequency factor and activation energy, prepare a graph of the natural logarithm of the rate constant (ln k) versus the inverse of the temperature ($1/T$).

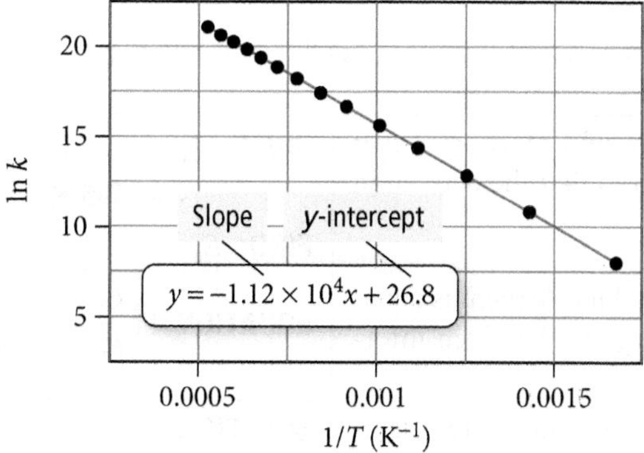

The plot is linear, as expected for Arrhenius behaviour. The line that fits best has a slope of -1.12×10^4 K and a y-intercept of 26.8. Calculate the activation energy from the slope by setting the slope equal to $-E_a/R$ and solving for E_a:

$$-1.12 \times 10^4 \text{ K} = \frac{-E_a}{R}$$

$$E_a = 1.12 \times 10^4 \text{ K}\left(8.314 \frac{\text{J}}{\text{mol} \cdot \text{K}}\right)$$

$$= 9.31 \times 10^4 \text{ J mol}^{-1}$$

$$= 93.1 \text{ kJ mol}^{-1}$$

Calculate the frequency factor (A) by setting the intercept equal to ln A.

$$26.8 = \ln A$$

$$A = e^{26.8}$$

$$= 4.36 \times 10^{11}$$

Since the rate constants were measured in units of L mol^{-1} s^{-1} the frequency factor is in the same units. Consequently, we can conclude that the reaction has an activation energy of 93.1 kJ mol^{-1} and a frequency factor of 4.36×10^{11} L mol^{-1} s^{-1}.

FOR PRACTICE 13.7

For the decomposition of ozone reaction in Example 13.7, use the results of the Arrhenius analysis to predict the rate constant at 298 K.

In some cases, when either data are limited or plotting capabilities are absent, we can calculate the activation energy if we know the rate constant at just two different temperatures. The Arrhenius expression in Equation 13.25 can be applied to the two different temperatures as follows:

$$\ln k_2 = -\frac{E_a}{R}\left(\frac{1}{T_2}\right) + \ln A \qquad \ln k_1 = -\frac{E_a}{R}\left(\frac{1}{T_1}\right) + \ln A$$

We can then subtract ln k_1 from ln k_2:

$$\ln k_2 - \ln k_1 = \left[-\frac{E_a}{R}\left(\frac{1}{T_2}\right) + \ln A\right] - \left[-\frac{E_a}{R}\left(\frac{1}{T_1}\right) + \ln A\right]$$

Rearranging, we get the two-point form of the Arrhenius equation:

$$\ln \frac{k_2}{k_1} = -\frac{E_a}{R}\left(\frac{1}{T_2} - \frac{1}{T_1}\right) \qquad [13.27]$$

The next example shows how to use this equation to calculate the activation energy from experimental measurements of the rate constant at two different temperatures.

EXAMPLE 13.8 USING THE TWO-POINT FORM OF THE ARRHENIUS EQUATION

Consider the reaction between nitrogen dioxide and carbon monoxide:

$$NO_2(g) + CO(g) \longrightarrow NO(g) + CO_2(g)$$

The rate constant at 701 K is measured as 2.57 L mol^{-1} s^{-1} and that at 895 K is measured as 567 L mol^{-1} s^{-1}. Find the activation energy for the reaction in kJ mol^{-1}.

SORT You are given the rate constant of a reaction at two different temperatures. You are asked to find the activation energy.

GIVEN: $T_1 = 701\text{ K}, k_1 = 2.57\text{ L mol}^{-1}\text{ s}^{-1}$

$T_2 = 895\text{ K}, k_2 = 567\text{ L mol}^{-1}\text{ s}^{-1}$

FIND: E_a

STRATEGIZE Use the two-point form of the Arrhenius equation, which relates the activation energy to the given information and R (a constant).

EQUATION $\ln\frac{k_2}{k_1} = -\frac{E_a}{R}\left(\frac{1}{T_2} - \frac{1}{T_1}\right)$

SOLVE Substitute the two rate constants and the two temperatures into the equation.

SOLUTION

$$\ln\frac{567\text{ L mol}^{-1}\text{ s}^{-1}}{2.57\text{ L mol}^{-1}\text{ s}^{-1}} = -\frac{E_a}{R}\left(\frac{1}{895\text{ K}} - \frac{1}{701\text{ K}}\right)$$

$$5.40 = \frac{E_a}{R}\left(\frac{3.09 \times 10^{-4}}{\text{K}}\right)$$

Solve the equation for E_a, the activation energy, and convert to kJ mol^{-1}.

$$E_a = 5.40\left(\frac{\text{K}}{3.09 \times 10^{-4}}\right)R$$

$$= 5.40\left(\frac{\text{K}}{3.09 \times 10^{-4}}\right)8.314\frac{\text{J}}{\text{mol} \cdot \text{K}}$$

$$= 1.45 \times 10^5\text{ J mol}^{-1}$$

$$= 145\text{ kJ mol}^{-1}$$

CHECK The magnitude of the answer is reasonable. Activation energies for most reactions range from tens to hundreds of kilojoules per mole.

FOR PRACTICE 13.8

Use the results from Example 13.8 and the given rate constant of the reaction at either of the two temperatures to predict the rate constant at 525 K.

The Collision Model: A Closer Look at the Frequency Factor

We suggested previously that the frequency factor in the Arrhenius equation represents the number of approaches to the activation barrier per unit time. Let's now refine that idea for a reaction involving two gas-phase reactants:

$$A(g) + B(g) \longrightarrow \text{products}$$

In the **collision model**, a chemical reaction occurs after a sufficiently energetic collision between two reactant molecules (Figure 13.15 ◀). In collision theory, therefore, each approach to the activation barrier is a collision between the reactant molecules. Consequently, the value of the frequency factor should simply be the number of collisions that occur per second. However, the frequency factors of most (though not all) gas-phase chemical reactions tend to be smaller than the number of collisions that occur per second. Why?

In the collision model, the frequency factor can be separated into two separate parts, as shown in the following equations:

$$k = Ae^{\frac{-E_a}{RT}}$$

$$= pze^{\frac{-E_a}{RT}}$$

Orientation factor (p) Collision frequency (z)

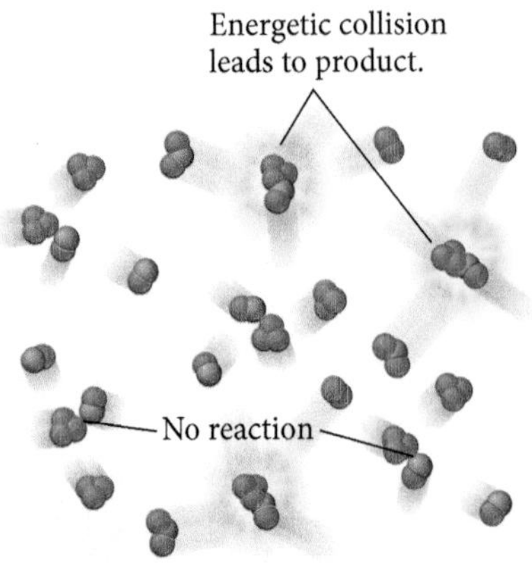

Energetic collision leads to product.

No reaction

▲ **FIGURE 13.15 The Collision Model** In the collision model, two molecules react after a sufficiently energetic collision when the correct orientation brings the reacting groups together.

where p is the **orientation factor** and z is the **collision frequency**. The collision frequency is the number of collisions that occur per unit time, which can be calculated for a gas-phase reaction from the pressure of the gases and the temperature of the reaction mixture. Under typical conditions, a single molecule undergoes on the order of 10^9 collisions every second.

We can understand the orientation factor by considering the following reaction:

$$NOCl(g) + NOCl(g) \longrightarrow 2\,NO(g) + Cl_2(g)$$

In order for the reaction to occur, two NOCl molecules must collide with sufficient energy. However, not all collisions with sufficient energy will lead to products because the reactant molecules must also be properly oriented. Consider each of the possible orientations of the reactant molecules (shown below) during a collision. The first two collisions, even if they occur with sufficient energy, will not result in a reaction because the reactant molecules are not oriented in a way that allows the chlorine atoms to bond. In other words, if two molecules are to react with each other, they must collide in such a way that allows the necessary bonds to break and form. For the reaction of NOCl(g), the orientation factor is $p = 0.16$. This means that only 16 out of 100 sufficiently energetic collisions are actually successful in forming the products.

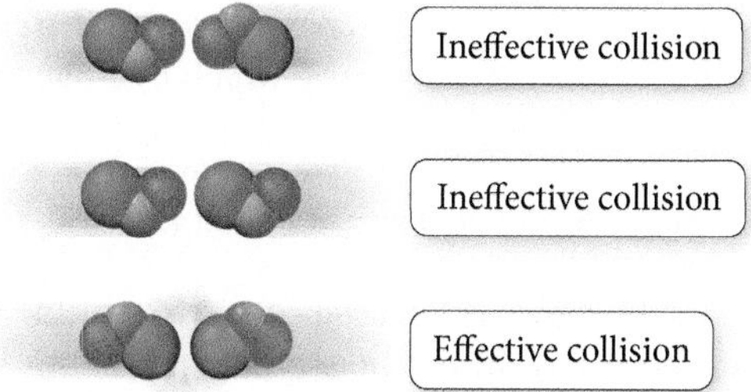

Some reactions have orientation factors that are much smaller than one. Consider the reaction between hydrogen and ethene:

$$H_2(g) + CH_2{=}CH_2(g) \longrightarrow CH_3{-}CH_3(g)$$

The orientation factor for this reaction is 1.7×10^{-6}, which means that fewer than two out of each million sufficiently energetic collisions actually form products. The small orientation factor indicates that the orientational requirements for this reaction are very stringent—the molecules must be aligned in a *very specific way* for the reaction to occur.

Reactions between *individual atoms* usually have orientation factors of approximately 1, because atoms are spherically symmetric and thus any orientation can lead to the formation of products. A few reactions have orientation factors greater than one. Consider the reaction between potassium and bromine:

$$K(g) + Br_2(g) \longrightarrow KBr(g) + Br(g)$$

This reaction has an orientation factor of $p = 4.8$. In other words, there are more reactions than collisions—the reactants do not even have to collide to react! Apparently, through a process dubbed *the harpoon mechanism,* a potassium atom can actually transfer an electron to a bromine molecule from a distance, without a collision. The resulting positive charge on the potassium and the negative charge on the bromine cause the two species to attract each other and form a bond. The potassium atom essentially *harpoons* a passing bromine molecule with an electron, and *reels it in* through the coulombic attraction between unlike charges.

We can picture a sample of reactive gases as a frenzy of collisions between the reacting atoms or molecules. At normal temperatures, the vast majority of these collisions do not have sufficient energy to overcome the activation barrier and the atoms or molecules simply bounce off one another. Of the collisions having sufficient energy to overcome the activation barrier, most do not have the proper orientation for the reaction to occur (for the majority of common reactions). When two molecules with sufficient energy *and* the correct orientation collide, something unique happens. The electrons on one of the atoms or molecules are attracted to the nuclei of the other; some bonds begin to weaken while other bonds begin to form and, if all goes well, the reactants go through the transition state and are transformed into the products. This is how a chemical reaction occurs.

CONCEPTUAL CONNECTION 13.3

Collision Theory

Which reaction would you expect to have the smallest orientation factor?

(a) $H(g) + I(g) \longrightarrow HI(g)$

(b) $H_2(g) + I_2(g) \longrightarrow 2\ HI(g)$

(c) $HCl(g) + HCl(g) \longrightarrow H_2(g) + Cl_2(g)$

13.6 Reaction Mechanisms

Most chemical reactions do not occur in a single step, but through several steps. When we write a chemical equation to represent a chemical reaction, *we usually represent the overall reaction, not the series of individual steps by which the reaction occurs.* Consider the following reaction in which hydrogen gas reacts with iodine monochloride:

$$H_2(g) + 2\ ICl(g) \longrightarrow 2\ HCl(g) + I_2(g)$$

The overall equation simply shows the substances present at the beginning of the reaction and the substances formed by the reaction. It does not show exactly how the reaction occurs—the intermediate steps that may be involved. A **reaction mechanism** is a series of individual chemical steps by which an overall chemical reaction occurs. For example, the reaction between hydrogen and iodine monochloride is proposed to occur through the following two steps:

$$\textit{Step 1}\quad H_2(g) + ICl(g) \longrightarrow HI(g) + HCl(g)$$
$$\textit{Step 2}\quad HI(g) + ICl(g) \longrightarrow HCl(g) + I_2(g)$$

An elementary step represents an actual interaction between the reactant molecules in the step. An overall reaction equation shows only the starting substances and the ending substances, not the path between them.

In the first step, an H_2 molecule collides with an ICl molecule and forms an HI molecule and an HCl molecule. In the second step, the HI molecule formed in the first step collides with a second ICl molecule to form another HCl molecule and an I_2 molecule. Each step in a reaction mechanism is an **elementary step**. Elementary steps cannot be broken down into simpler steps. Unlike the overall reaction, elementary steps occur exactly as they are written.

One of the requirements for a valid reaction mechanism is that the individual steps in the mechanism add to the overall reaction. For example, the above mechanism sums to the overall reaction as shown here:

$$\begin{array}{l} H_2(g) + ICl(g) \longrightarrow \cancel{HI(g)} + HCl(g) \\ \underline{\cancel{HI(g)} + ICl(g) \longrightarrow HCl(g) + I_2(g)} \\ H_2(g) + 2\ ICl(g) \longrightarrow 2\ HCl(g) + I_2(g) \end{array}$$

Species such as HI, formed in one step of a mechanism and consumed in a subsequent step, are called **reaction intermediates**. An intermediate is not found in the balanced equation for the overall reaction, but plays a key role in the mechanism. The mechanism specifies the individual collisions that result in the overall reaction. Knowledge of the reaction mechanism could allow chemists to make modifications to reaction conditions in order to make a reaction more efficient. As such, reaction mechanisms are highly sought-after pieces of chemical knowledge.

How do we determine reaction mechanisms? As mentioned in the opening section of this chapter, measuring rates of reactions is not only practically important (allowing us to know the rate of a particular reaction) but is also theoretically important because it can help us determine the mechanism of the reaction. Details of the reaction mechanism allow chemists to better manipulate chemical reactions. By doing experiments under different conditions, such as changing pressures or temperatures, we can propose a reaction mechanism that is consistent with the observations from these experiments.

Rate Laws for Elementary Steps

Elementary steps are characterized by their **molecularity**, the number of reactant particles involved in the step. The most common molecularities are **unimolecular** and **bimolecular**:

$$\text{A} \longrightarrow \text{products} \qquad \textbf{Unimolecular}$$

$$\text{A} + \text{A} \longrightarrow \text{products} \qquad \textbf{Bimolecular}$$

$$\text{A} + \text{B} \longrightarrow \text{products} \qquad \textbf{Bimolecular}$$

Elementary steps in which three reactant particles collide, called **termolecular** steps, are very rare because the probability of three particles simultaneously colliding is small.

Although the rate law for an overall chemical reaction cannot be deduced from the balanced chemical equation, the rate law for an elementary step can be. Since we know that an elementary step occurs through the collision of the reactant particles, the rate law is proportional to the product of the concentrations of those particles. For example, the rate for the bimolecular elementary step in which A reacts with B is as follows:

$$\text{A} + \text{B} \longrightarrow \text{products} \qquad \text{Rate} = k[\text{A}][\text{B}]$$

Similarly, the rate law for the bimolecular step in which A reacts with A is:

$$\text{A} + \text{A} \longrightarrow \text{products} \qquad \text{Rate} = k[\text{A}]^2$$

The rate laws for the common elementary steps, as well as those for the rare termolecular step, are summarized in Table 13.3.

TABLE 13.3 Rate Laws for Elementary Steps

Elementary Step	Molecularity	Rate Law
$\text{A} \longrightarrow \text{products}$	1	Rate $= k[\text{A}]$
$\text{A} + \text{A} \longrightarrow \text{products}$	2	Rate $= k[\text{A}]^2$
$\text{A} + \text{B} \longrightarrow \text{products}$	2	Rate $= k[\text{A}][\text{B}]$
$\text{A} + \text{A} + \text{A} \longrightarrow \text{products}$	3 (rare)	Rate $= k[\text{A}]^3$
$\text{A} + \text{A} + \text{B} \longrightarrow \text{products}$	3 (rare)	Rate $= k[\text{A}]^2[\text{B}]$
$\text{A} + \text{B} + \text{C} \longrightarrow \text{products}$	3 (rare)	Rate $= k[\text{A}][\text{B}][\text{C}]$

Rate-Determining Steps and Overall Reaction Rate Laws

In most chemical reactions, one of the elementary steps—called the **rate-determining step** (or **rate-limiting step**)—is much slower than the others. The rate-determining step in a chemical reaction is analogous to the narrowest section on a freeway. If a section of a freeway narrows from four lanes to two lanes, for even a short distance, the rate at which cars travel along the freeway is limited by the rate at which they can travel through the narrow section (even though the rate might be much faster along the four-lane section). Similarly, the rate-determining step in a reaction mechanism limits the overall rate of the reaction (even though the other steps occur much faster) and therefore determines *the rate law for the overall reaction.*

▶ The rate-limiting step in a reaction mechanism limits the overall rate of the reaction just as the narrowest section of a highway limits the rate at which traffic can pass.

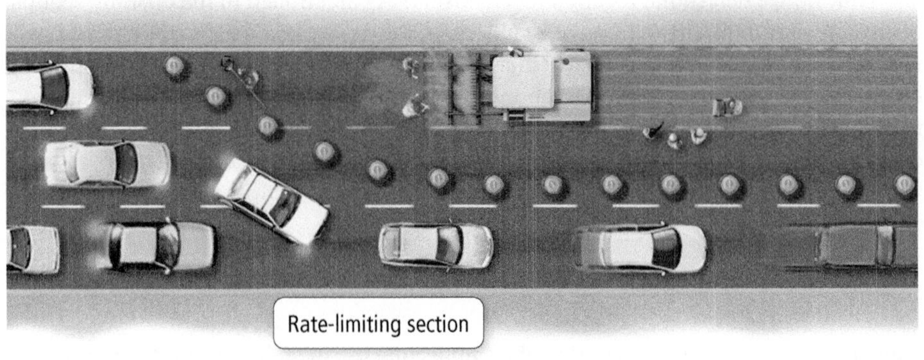

Consider the following reaction between nitrogen dioxide gas and carbon monoxide gas:

$$NO_2(g) + CO(g) \longrightarrow NO(g) + CO_2(g)$$

The experimentally determined rate law for this reaction is Rate $= k[NO_2]^2$. We can see from this rate law that the reaction must not be a single-step reaction—otherwise the rate law would be Rate $= k[NO_2][CO]$.

A mechanism proposed for this reaction is:

$$NO_2(g) + NO_2(g) \underset{k_{-1}}{\overset{k_1}{\rightleftharpoons}} NO_3(g) + NO(g)$$

$$NO_3(g) + CO(g) \xrightarrow{k_2} NO_2(g) + CO_2(g)$$

The energy diagram accompanying this mechanism is shown in Figure 13.16 ▼.

Two pieces of information can be drawn from this diagram. The preliminary step in the mechanism has a much larger activation energy barrier than the second step so that $k_1 \ll k_2$. As well, the reverse activation energy barrier for step 1 is significantly smaller than the activation energy barrier for the first step so that $k_1 \ll k_{-1}$. This means that the forward direction of step 1 is probably the rate-determining step, and the rate law is Rate $= k_1[NO_2]^2$, which is consistent with the experimentally determined rate law with $k = k_1$.

For a proposed reaction mechanism such as the previous one to be valid—mechanisms can only be validated, not proven—two conditions must be met:

1. **The elementary steps in the mechanism must sum to the overall reaction.**
2. **The rate law predicted by the mechanism must be consistent with the experimentally observed rate law.**

▶ **FIGURE 13.16 Energy Diagram for a Two-Step Mechanism**

Because E_a for Step 1 > E_a for Step 2, Step 1 has the smaller rate constant and is rate-limiting.

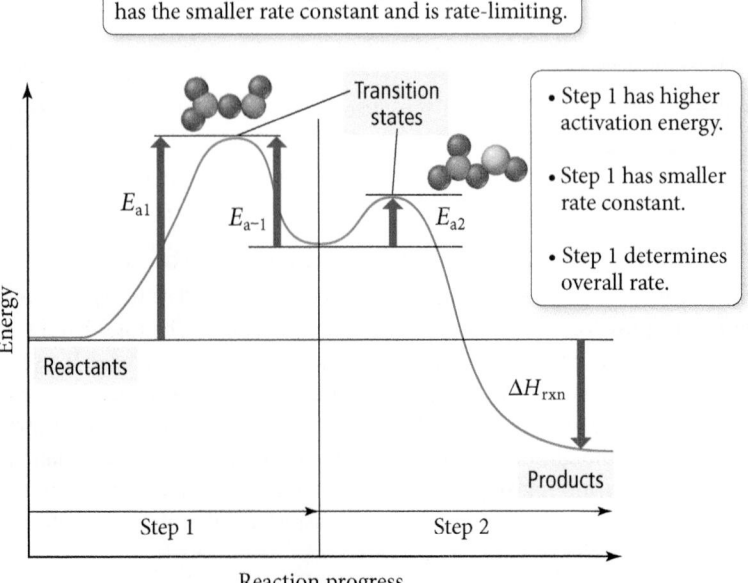

Transition states

E_{a1}

E_{a-1}

E_{a2}

• Step 1 has higher activation energy.

• Step 1 has smaller rate constant.

• Step 1 determines overall rate.

Energy

Reactants

ΔH_{rxn}

Products

Step 1

Step 2

Reaction progress

We have already seen that the rate law predicted by the preceding mechanism is consistent with the experimentally observed rate law. We can check to see whether the elementary steps sum to the overall reaction by simply adding them together:

$$\mathrm{NO_2}(g) + \cancel{\mathrm{NO_2}(g)} \underset{k_{-1}}{\overset{k_1}{\rightleftharpoons}} \cancel{\mathrm{NO_3}(g)} + \mathrm{NO}(g)$$

$$\cancel{\mathrm{NO_3}(g)} + \mathrm{CO}(g) \xrightarrow{k_2} \cancel{\mathrm{NO_2}(g)} + \mathrm{CO_2}(g)$$

$$\mathrm{NO_2}(g) + \mathrm{CO}(g) \longrightarrow \mathrm{NO}(g) + \mathrm{CO_2}(g)$$

This mechanism fulfills both requirements and is therefore valid. A valid mechanism is not a *proven* mechanism. We can only say that the given mechanism is consistent with the kinetic observations and therefore possible. Other types of data, such as experimental evidence for a proposed intermediate, like NO_3 in the previous example, can further strengthen the validity of a proposed mechanism.

The Steady-State Approximation

Most often for a proposed mechanism, the potential energy surface such as the one in Figure 13.16 is not known. It is therefore difficult to know whether the activation energy for a particular elementary step in a reaction is faster than another. Furthermore, if the concentration of CO is very small, step 1 may no longer be the rate-determining step. It is still possible, however, to obtain a rate law using a slightly different method.

We will use the same example as previously to illustrate the **steady-state approximation**. The proposed mechanism for the reaction of nitrogen dioxide and carbon monoxide to form nitrogen monoxide and carbon dioxide is:

$$\mathrm{NO_2}(g) + \mathrm{NO_2}(g) \underset{k_{-1}}{\overset{k_1}{\rightleftharpoons}} \mathrm{NO_3}(g) + \mathrm{NO}(g)$$

$$\mathrm{NO_3}(g) + \mathrm{CO}(g) \xrightarrow{k_2} \mathrm{NO_2}(g) + \mathrm{CO_2}(g)$$

The first step in determining the rate law predicted by this mechanism is to determine a preliminary expression for the rate of the reaction. Typically, but not always, the rate of reaction is defined as the rate of change in concentration of a product. For example, the rate of reaction can be defined as the rate of change in the concentration of carbon dioxide in the present example. *One could also define the rate as the rate of change in concentration of NO; the end result will be the same, but the steps to get there will be different.* Since carbon dioxide is produced in the second step, we can write a rate law for the production of CO_2:

$$\text{Rate} = \frac{\Delta[\mathrm{CO_2}]}{\Delta t} = k_2[\mathrm{NO_3}][\mathrm{CO}] \qquad [13.28]$$

The problem with this rate law is that it contains a concentration of an intermediate, NO_3. It can be difficult to know or measure the concentration of an intermediate, so we must eliminate $[NO_3]$ from the rate law. Therefore, we must obtain an expression for $[NO_3]$ in terms of other quantities and make the substitution into the preceding rate law.

Steady-state approximation:
rate of formation of intermediate = rate of consumption of intermediate

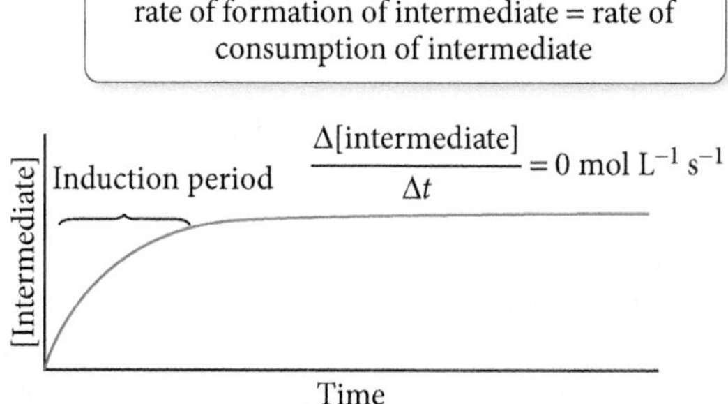

To obtain an expression for the concentration of NO_3, we assume that after a short induction period NO_3 is consumed as fast as it is produced. In other words, the concentration of NO_3 does not change with time; it has reached a *steady-state*. The steady-state approximation says that the rate of production of NO_3 is equal to the rate of consumption of NO_3. Using the elementary steps from the mechanism, we can write expressions for the rate of production and consumption of NO_3:

$$\text{rate of production of } NO_3 = k_1[NO_2]^2$$
$$\text{rate of consumption of } NO_3 = k_{-1}[NO_3][NO] + k_2[NO_3][CO]$$

Notice that there are two terms in the expression for the rate of consumption of NO_3 since it is consumed in the reverse of step 1 and in step 2. Since these two expressions are equal, we can write:

$$k_1[NO_2]^2 = k_{-1}[NO_3][NO] + k_2[NO_3][CO]$$

Factoring this expression yields:

$$k_1[NO_2]^2 = [NO_3](k_{-1}[NO] + k_2[CO])$$

This expression can be rearranged to yield the steady-state approximation expression for the concentration of NO_3:

$$[NO_3] = \frac{k_1[NO_2]^2}{k_{-1}[NO] + k_2[CO]}$$

We substitute this expression into the rate law that we determined previously (Equation 13.28):

$$\text{Rate} = \frac{k_1k_2[NO_2]^2[CO]}{k_{-1}[NO] + k_2[CO]}$$

This is the steady-state approximation rate law that, at first glance, might not look as if it is consistent with the experimental rate law, but we will now show that it is.

As we determined before, the activation energy for step 2 is smaller than the activation energy for the reverse of step 1. Therefore, $k_2 \gg k_{-1}$ and $k_2[CO] \gg k_{-1}[NO]$ so that the denominator can be simplified:

$$k_{-1}[NO] + k_2[CO] = k_2[CO]$$

The rate law then becomes:

$$\text{Rate} = \frac{k_1\cancel{k_2}[NO_2]^2\cancel{[CO]}}{\cancel{k_2}\cancel{[CO]}}$$
$$= k_1[NO_2]^2$$

This rate law, determined by using the steady-state approximation, is consistent with the experimental second-order rate law.

The steady-state approximation rate law also predicts that if the concentration of CO is very small, then:

$$k_{-1}[NO] + k_2[CO] = k_{-1}[NO]$$

and the rate law simplifies to:

$$\text{Rate} = \frac{k_1k_2[NO_2]^2[CO]}{k_{-1}[NO]}$$

Since the concentration of CO is low, the first step is no longer the rate-determining step; the second step becomes important in determining the overall rate of reaction. Since the second step is the rate-determining step, [CO] shows up in the expression for the rate law. The mechanism also predicts that as the concentration of NO increases, the rate of the reaction is predicted to slow down. This decrease in reaction rate as [NO] increases is due to the reverse of the first step becoming faster, which depletes the intermediate, NO_3, impeding the progress of the reaction.

EXAMPLE 13.9 STEADY-STATE APPROXIMATION

The reaction of gaseous NO with H_2 produces N_2O and H_2O:

$$2\,NO(g) + H_2(g) \rightarrow N_2O(g) + H_2O(g)$$

At low partial pressures of H_2, this reaction is observed to be third order and the rate law is as follows:

$$\text{Rate} = k[H_2][NO]^2$$

The following mechanism has been proposed for the reaction. Show that it is consistent with the experimentally determined rate law.

$$2\,NO(g) \underset{k_{-1}}{\overset{k_1}{\rightleftharpoons}} N_2O_2(g)$$

$$N_2O_2(g) + H_2(g) \xrightarrow{k_2} N_2O(g) + H_2O(g)$$

SOLUTION

To determine whether the mechanism is valid, you must first determine whether the steps sum to the overall reaction. Since the steps do indeed sum to the overall reaction, the first condition is met.

$$2\,NO(g) \underset{k_{-1}}{\overset{k_1}{\rightleftharpoons}} \cancel{N_2O_2}(g)$$

$$\cancel{N_2O_2}(g) + H_2(g) \xrightarrow{k_2} N_2O(g) + H_2O(g)$$

$$2\,NO(g) + H_2(g) \longrightarrow N_2O(g) + H_2O(g)$$

The second condition is that the rate law predicted by the mechanism must be consistent with the experimentally observed rate law. The rate of the reaction is equal to the rate of production of N_2O, so we can write an expression for the rate law.

$$\text{Rate} = \frac{\Delta[N_2O]}{\Delta t} = k_2[N_2O_2][H_2]$$

Since this rate law contains the concentration of an intermediate, we apply the steady-state approximation to the concentration of N_2O_2.

rate of production of N_2O_2 = rate of consumption of N_2O_2

$$k_1[NO]^2 = k_2[N_2O_2][H_2] + k_{-1}[N_2O_2]$$

$$[N_2O_2] = \frac{k_1[NO]^2}{k_2[H_2] + k_{-1}}$$

Substituting this expression for the steady-state concentration of N_2O_2 into the above rate law yields the rate law for the reaction.

$$\text{Rate} = \frac{k_1k_2[NO]^2[H_2]}{k_2[H_2] + k_{-1}}$$

If the concentration of H_2 is low, then the $k_2[H_2]$ term in the denominator will be small and can be ignored, simplifying the denominator to k_{-1}. The rate law is third order in agreement with the experiment. This is equivalent to saying that step 2 is the rate-determining step since $[H_2]$ is very low. The proposed mechanism is valid.

$$\text{Rate} = \frac{k_1k_2}{k_{-1}}[NO]^2[H_2]$$

$$\text{where}\left(k = \frac{k_1k_2}{k_{-1}}\right)$$

Furthermore, when the concentration of H_2 is very high, then step 2 is not the rate-determining step. The rate-determining step is the forward direction of step 1, the formation of N_2O_2. In this case, $k_2[H_2] + k_{-1}$; $k_2[H_2]$ so that the rate law reduces to:

$$\text{Rate} = k_1[NO]^2$$

It is second order, independent of H_2 concentration. This is equivalent to saying that the concentration of H_2 is so high that every time an N_2O_2 molecule is produced, it reacts with H_2 to form products. Under these conditions, increasing the H_2 concentration will have no more effect on the rate of reaction.

FOR PRACTICE 13.9

Predict the overall reaction and rate law that would result from the following two-step mechanism:

$$NO + Cl_2 \underset{k_{-1}}{\overset{k_1}{\rightleftharpoons}} NOCl_2$$

$$NOCl_2 + NO \xrightarrow{k_2} 2\,NOCl$$

Hint: Initially state that the rate of the reaction is:

$$\text{Rate} = \frac{1}{2}\frac{\Delta[NOCl]}{\Delta t}$$

13.7 Catalysis

Throughout this chapter, we have learned of ways to control the rates of chemical reactions. We can speed up the rate of a reaction by increasing the concentration of the reactants or by increasing the temperature. However, these approaches are not always feasible. There are limits to how concentrated we can make a reaction mixture, and increases in temperature may allow unwanted reactions—such as the decomposition of a reactant—to occur.

Alternatively, reaction rates can be increased by using a **catalyst**, a substance that increases the rate of a chemical reaction but that is not consumed by the reaction. A catalyst works by providing an alternative mechanism for the reaction—one in which the rate-determining step has a lower activation energy. For example, consider the noncatalytic destruction of ozone in the upper atmosphere, discussed in Section 5.10:

$$O_3(g) + O(g) \longrightarrow 2\,O_2(g)$$

In this reaction, an ozone molecule collides with an oxygen atom to form two oxygen molecules in a single elementary step. The reason that we have a protective ozone layer in the upper atmosphere is that the activation energy for this reaction is fairly high and the reaction, therefore, proceeds at a fairly slow rate; the ozone layer does not rapidly decompose into O_2. However, the addition of Cl atoms (which come from the photodissociation of man-made chlorofluorocarbons) to the upper atmosphere makes available another pathway by which O_3 can be destroyed. The first step in this pathway—called the catalytic destruction of ozone—is the reaction of Cl with O_3 to form ClO and O_2:

Photodissociation means *light-induced* dissociation. The energy from a photon of light can break chemical bonds and therefore dissociate, or break apart, a molecule.

$$Cl + O_3 \longrightarrow ClO + O_2$$

This is followed by a second step in which ClO reacts with O, regenerating Cl:

$$ClO + O \longrightarrow Cl + O_2$$

If we add the two reactions, the overall reaction is identical to the noncatalytic reaction:

$$\begin{array}{l} \cancel{Cl} + O_3 \longrightarrow \cancel{ClO} + O_2 \\ \underline{\cancel{ClO} + O \longrightarrow \cancel{Cl} + O_2} \\ O_3 + O \longrightarrow 2\,O_2 \end{array}$$

However, the activation energy for the rate-limiting step in this pathway is much smaller than for the first, uncatalyzed pathway (as shown in Figure 13.17 ▼), and therefore the reaction occurs much faster. Note that the Cl is not consumed in the overall reaction—this is characteristic of a catalyst.

In the case of the catalytic destruction of ozone, the catalyst speeds up a reaction that we *do not* want to happen. Most of the time, however, catalysts are used to speed up reactions that we *do* want to happen. For example, your car most likely has a catalytic converter in its exhaust system. The catalytic converter contains solid catalysts, such as

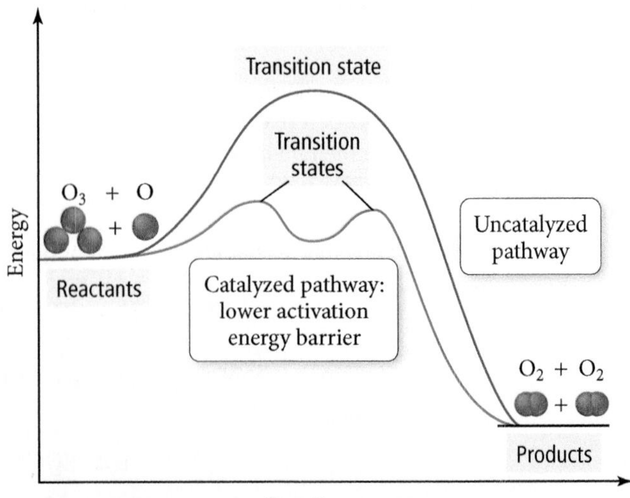

▶ **FIGURE 13.17 Catalyzed and Uncatalyzed Decomposition of Ozone** In the catalytic destruction of ozone (red), the activation barrier for the rate-limiting step is much lower than in the uncatalyzed process (blue).

platinum, rhodium, or palladium, dispersed on an underlying high-surface-area ceramic structure. These catalysts convert exhaust pollutants such as nitrogen monoxide and carbon monoxide into less harmful substances:

$$2\,NO(g) + 2\,CO(g) \xrightarrow[\text{catalyst}]{} N_2(g) + 2\,CO_2(g)$$

The catalytic converter also promotes the complete combustion of any fuel fragments present in the exhaust:

$$\underset{\text{Fuel fragment}}{CH_3CH_2CH_3(g)} + 5\,O_2(g) \xrightarrow[\text{catalyst}]{} 3\,CO_2(g) + 4\,H_2O(g)$$

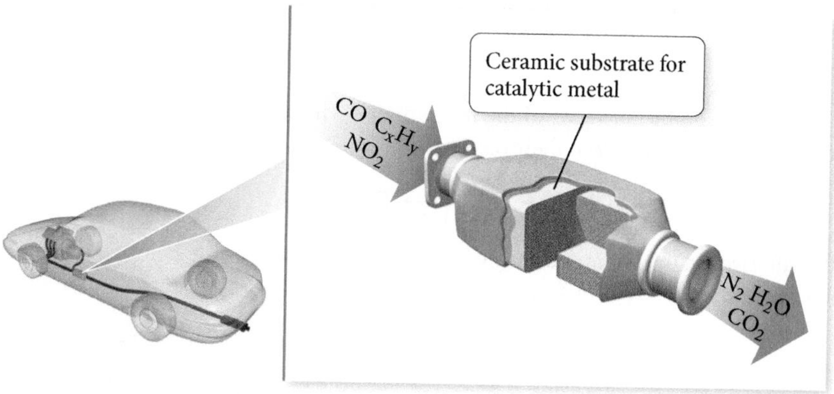

▲ The catalytic converter in the exhaust system of a car helps eliminate pollutants in the exhaust.

Fuel fragments in exhaust are harmful because they lead to the formation of ozone. We saw in Section 5.10 that although ozone is a natural part of our *upper* atmosphere that protects us from excess exposure to ultraviolet light, it is a pollutant in the *lower* atmosphere, interfering with cardiovascular function and acting as an eye and lung irritant. The use of catalytic converters in motor vehicles has resulted in lower levels of these pollutants over most Canadian cities in the last 30 years even though the number of cars on the roadways has dramatically increased (see Table 13.4).

TABLE 13.4 Change in Vehicular Emissions in Canada

Pollutant	Change 1985–2012
Sulfates	−44%
Nitrates	−38%
CO	−52%
TSP[a]	−35%

[a]Total Suspended Particulates
Source: National Pollutant Release Inventory, *Environment Canada* (http://www.ec.gc.ca/pdb/websol/emissions/ap/ap_query_e.cfm).

Homogeneous and Heterogeneous Catalysis

Catalysis can be categorized into two types: homogeneous and heterogeneous (Figure 13.18 ▼). In **homogeneous catalysis**, the catalyst exists in the same phase (or state) as the reactants. The catalytic destruction of ozone by Cl is an example of homogeneous catalysis—the chlorine atoms exist in the gas phase with the gas-phase reactants. In **heterogeneous catalysis**, the catalyst exists in a different phase than the reactants. The solid catalysts used in catalytic converters are examples of heterogeneous catalysts—they are solids while the reactants are gases. The use of solid catalysts with gas-phase or solution-phase reactants is the most common type of heterogeneous catalysis.

Studies have shown that heterogeneous catalysis is most likely responsible for the ozone hole over Antarctica. After the discovery of the Antarctic ozone hole in 1985, scientists wondered why there was such a dramatic drop in ozone over Antarctica, but not over the rest of the planet. After all, the chlorine from chlorofluorocarbons that catalyzes ozone destruction is evenly distributed throughout the entire atmosphere.

As it turns out, most of the chlorine that enters the atmosphere from chlorofluorocarbons gets bound up in chlorine reservoirs, substances such as $ClONO_2$ that hold chlorine and prevent it from catalyzing ozone destruction. The unique conditions over Antarctica—especially the cold isolated air mass that exists during the long, dark winter—result in clouds that contain solid ice particles. These unique clouds are called polar stratospheric

▲ Polar stratospheric clouds contain ice particles that catalyze reactions by which chlorine is released from its atmospheric chemical reservoirs.

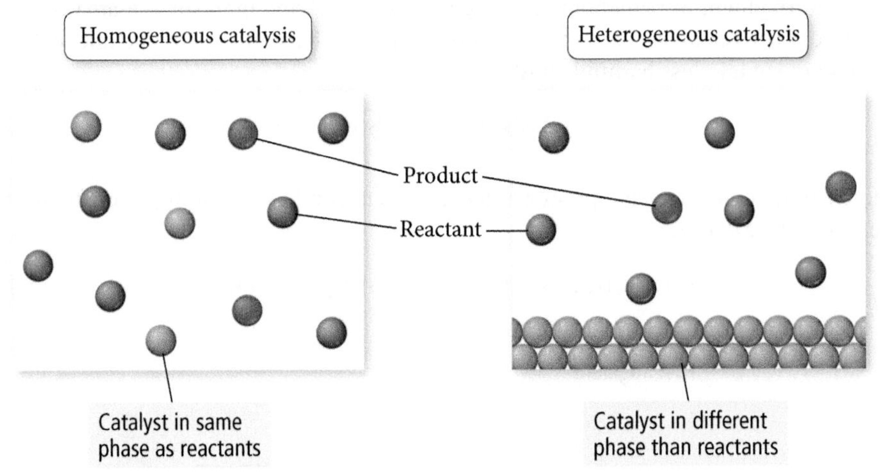

▶ **FIGURE 13.18 Homogeneous and Heterogeneous Catalysis** A homogeneous catalyst exists in the same phase as the reactants. A heterogeneous catalyst exists in a different phase than the reactants. Often a heterogeneous catalyst provides a solid surface on which the reaction can take place.

clouds (or PSCs), and the surfaces of the ice particles within these clouds appear to catalyze the release of chlorine from their reservoirs:

$$ClONO_2 + HCl \xrightarrow[\text{PSCs}]{} Cl_2 + HNO_3$$

When the sun rises in the Antarctic spring, the sunlight dissociates the chlorine molecules into chlorine atoms:

$$Cl_2 \xrightarrow[\text{light}]{} 2\ Cl$$

The chlorine atoms then catalyze the destruction of ozone by the mechanism discussed previously. This continues until the sun melts the stratospheric clouds, allowing chlorine atoms to be reincorporated into their reservoirs. The result is an ozone hole that forms every spring and lasts about 6–8 weeks (Figure 13.19 ▼).

A second example of heterogeneous catalysis involves the **hydrogenation** of double bonds within alkenes. Consider the reaction between ethene and hydrogen, which is relatively slow at normal temperatures:

$$H_2C{=}CH_2(g) + H_2(g) \longrightarrow H_3C{-}CH_3(g) \quad \text{Slow at room temperature}$$

However, in the presence of finely divided platinum, palladium, or nickel, the reaction happens rapidly. The catalysis occurs by the four-step process depicted in Figure 13.20 ▶.

1. Adsorption: the reactants are adsorbed onto the metal surface.
2. Diffusion: the reactants diffuse on the surface until they approach each other.
3. Reaction: the reactants react to form the products.
4. Desorption: the products desorb from the surface into the gas phase.

The large activation energy of the hydrogenation reaction—due primarily to the strength of the hydrogen–hydrogen bond in H_2—is greatly lowered when the reactants adsorb onto the surface.

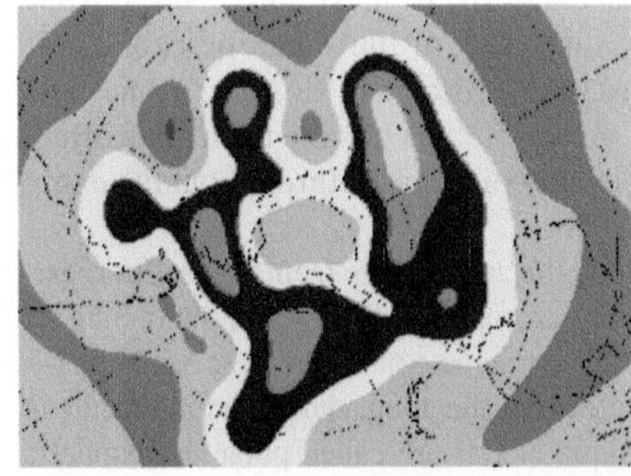

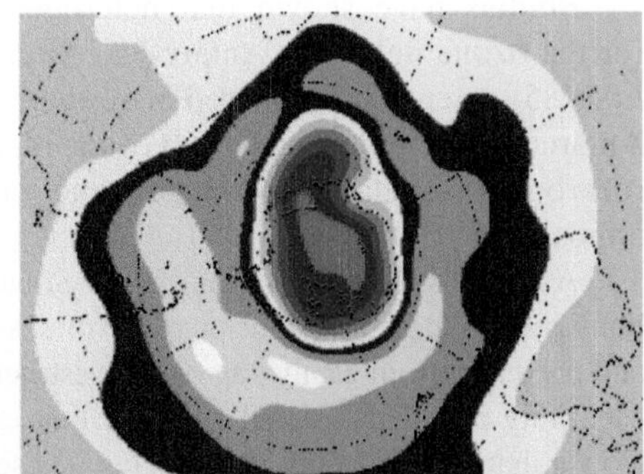

▶ **FIGURE 13.19 Ozone Depletion in the Antarctic Spring** The concentration of ozone over Antarctica drops sharply during the month of October due to the catalyzed destruction of ozone by chlorine. The image at left shows the ozone levels in May 2004 while the image at right was produced in October of the same year. (The lowest ozone levels are represented by red and deep blue.)

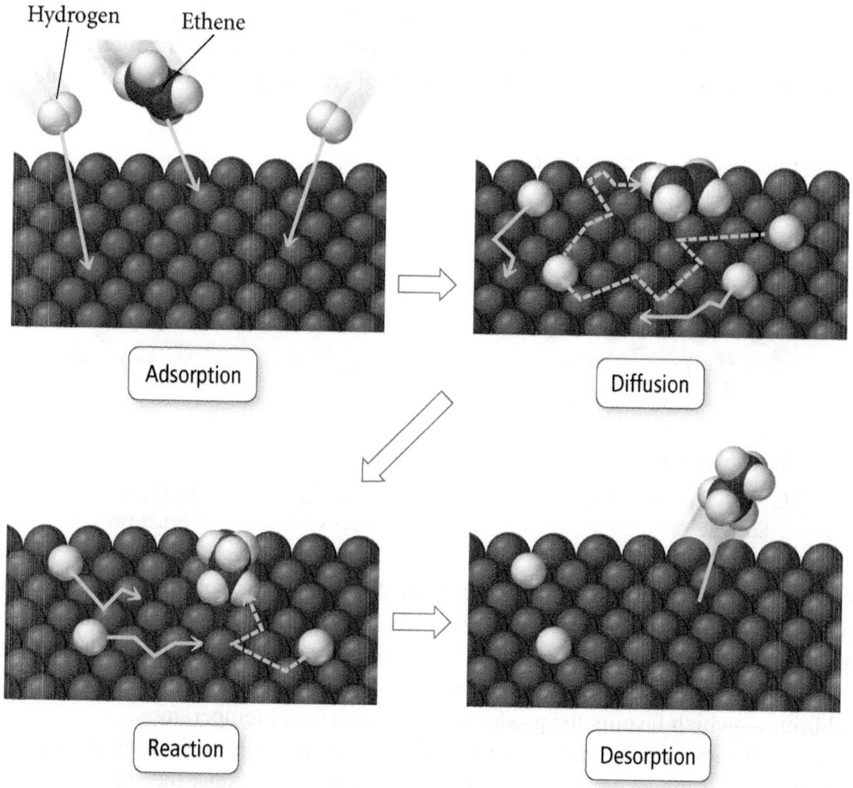

Hydrogen
Ethene

Adsorption
Diffusion
Reaction
Desorption

◀ **FIGURE 13.20 Catalytic Hydrogenation of Ethene (Ethylene)**

Enzymes: Biological Catalysts

We find perhaps the best example of chemical catalysis in living organisms. Most of the thousands of reactions that must occur for an organism to survive are too slow at normal temperatures. So living organisms rely on **enzymes**, biological catalysts that increase the rates of biochemical reactions. Enzymes are usually large protein molecules with complex three-dimensional structures. Within that structure is a specific area called the **active site**. The properties and shape of the active site are just right to bind the reactant molecule, usually called the **substrate**. When the substrate binds to the active site of the enzyme—through intermolecular forces such as hydrogen bonding and dispersion forces, or even covalent bonds—the activation energy of the reaction is greatly lowered, allowing the reaction to occur at a much faster rate (Figure 13.21 ▼). The general mechanism by which an enzyme (E) binds a substrate (S) and then reacts to form the products (P) was introduced by Michaelis and Menten in 1913:

The strategies used to speed up chemical reactions in the laboratory—high temperatures, high pressures, strongly acidic or alkaline conditions—are not available to living organisms, since they would be fatal to cells.

Maude Leonora Menten was a Canadian scientist, earning her B.A., M.B., and M.D. at the University of Toronto. She completed a Ph.D. in biochemistry in 1916 with Leonor Michaelis—part of her doctoral work resulted in the Michaelis–Menten mechanism.

$$\mathrm{E} + \mathrm{S} \underset{k_{-1}}{\overset{k_1}{\rightleftharpoons}} \mathrm{ES}$$

$$\mathrm{ES} \xrightarrow{k_2} \mathrm{P} + \mathrm{E} \qquad [13.29]$$

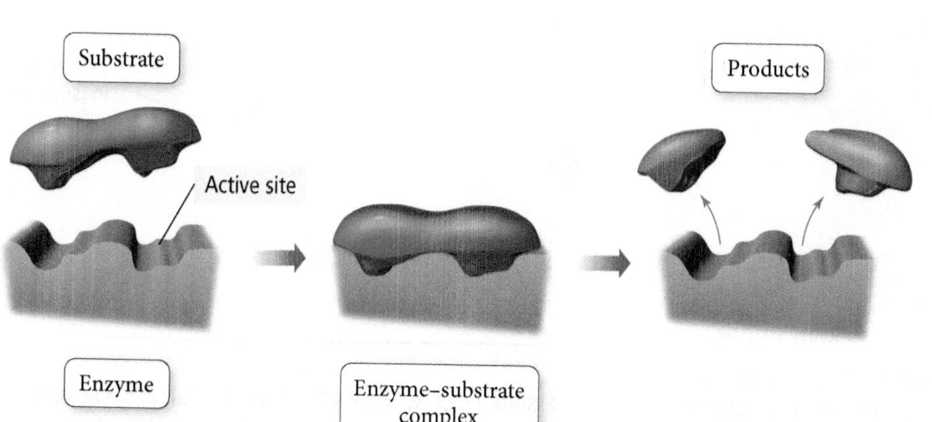

◀ **FIGURE 13.21 Enzyme–Substrate Binding** A substrate (or reactant) fits into the active site of an enzyme. It is held in place by intermolecular forces and forms an enzyme–substrate complex. (Sometimes temporary covalent bonding may also be involved.) After the reaction occurs, the products are released from the active site.

Sucrase is an enzyme that catalyzes the breaking up of sucrose (table sugar) into glucose and fructose within the body. At normal body temperature, sucrose does not break into glucose and fructose because the activation energy is high, resulting in a slow reaction rate.

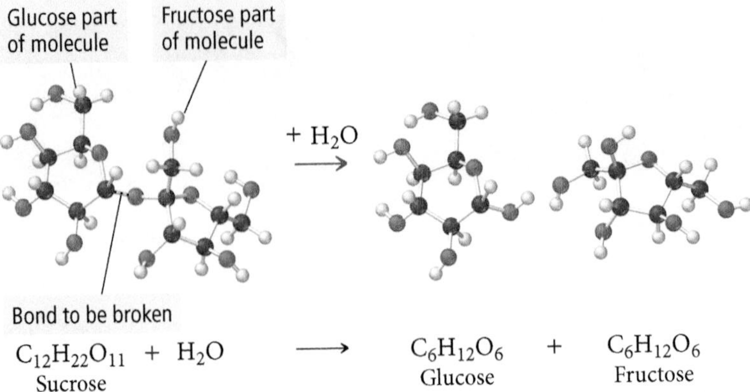

$$C_{12}H_{22}O_{11} + H_2O \longrightarrow C_6H_{12}O_6 + C_6H_{12}O_6$$
Sucrose → Glucose + Fructose

▶ Sucrose breaks up into glucose and fructose during digestion.

However, when a sucrose molecule binds to the active site within sucrase, the bond between the glucose and fructose units weakens because glucose is forced into a geometry that stresses the bond (Figure 13.22 ▼). Weakening of this bond lowers the activation energy for the reaction, increasing the reaction rate. The reaction can then proceed toward equilibrium—which favours the products—at a much lower temperature.

The behaviour of the sucrase-catalyzed reaction is depicted in Figure 13.23 ▼, in which the rate of the enzyme-catalyzed reaction is plotted against the substrate concentration for two different enzyme concentrations. Comparison of this plot with those in Figure 13.6 reveals that at low-sucrose concentrations, the reaction is first order in sucrose; but at high-sucrose concentrations, the reaction is zero order in sucrose. It also shows that the rate of reaction increases with an increase in enzyme concentration. If the mechanism in Equation 13.29 is valid, it should explain the behaviour observed in Figure 13.23. The rate of the reaction can be defined as the rate of formation of products that occurs in the second step of the mechanism:

$$\text{Rate} = k_2[\text{ES}] \quad [13.30]$$

To eliminate the concentration of the intermediate, ES, we need to apply the steady-state approximation:

$$\text{rate of production of ES} = \text{rate of consumption of ES}$$
$$k_1[\text{E}][\text{S}] = k_{-1}[\text{ES}] + k_2[\text{ES}] \quad [13.31]$$

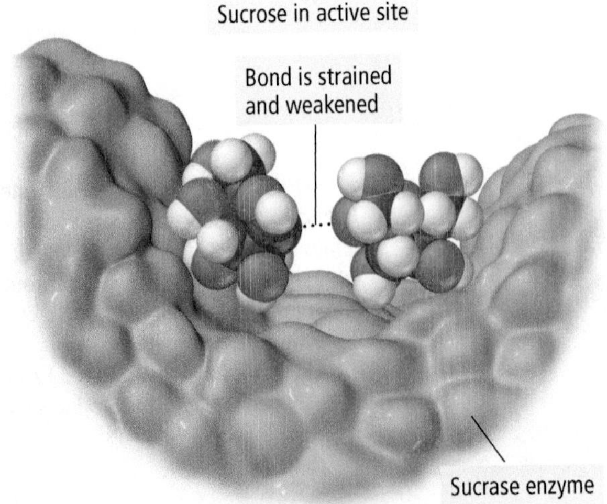

▲ **FIGURE 13.22 An Enzyme-Catalyzed Reaction** Sucrase catalyzes the conversion of sucrose into glucose and fructose by weakening the bond that joins the two rings.

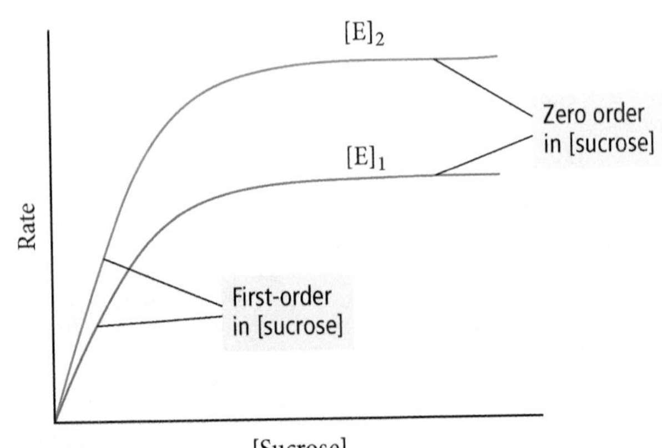

▲ **FIGURE 13.23 Michaelis–Menten Behaviour of the Sucrase-Catalyzed Conversion of Sucrose to Glucose and Fructose**

In this expression, [E] is the free enzyme in solution and [ES] is the concentration of bound enzyme–substrate complex. The sum of the concentrations of free enzyme and enzyme–substrate complex should not change during the course of the reaction and should equal the initial concentration of free enzyme, $[E]_0$:

$$[E]_0 = [ES] + [E] \quad \text{or} \quad [E] = [E]_0 - [ES]$$

Substitution of this expression for [E] into Equation 13.31 and rearranging yields:

$$[ES] = \frac{k_1[E]_0[S]}{k_1[S] + k_2 + k_{-1}} \qquad [13.32]$$

Dividing the numerator and denominator by k_1 and substituting the Michaelis constant, K_M

$$K_M = \frac{k_2 + k_{-1}}{k_1}$$

into Equation 13.32 yields:

$$[ES] = \frac{[E]_0[S]}{[S] + K_M}$$

Finally, we substitute this expression for the steady-state concentration of ES in Equation 13.30 to yield the rate law:

$$\text{Rate} = \frac{k_2[E]_0[S]}{[S] + K_M} \qquad [13.33]$$

At low concentrations of sucrose, $[S] \ll K_M$, so that $[S] + K_M ; K_M$, the rate law becomes:

$$\text{Rate} = \frac{k_2[E]_0[S]}{K_M} \qquad [13.34]$$

This explains the behaviour of the enzyme-catalyzed decomposition of sucrose at low concentrations of sucrose; it is first order in sucrose. At much higher concentrations of sucrose, $[S] \gg K_M$, so that $[S] + K_M ; [S]$, and the rate law becomes:

$$\text{Rate} = \frac{k_2[E]_0\cancel{[S]}}{\cancel{[S]}} = k_2[E]_0 \qquad [13.35]$$

which is independent of—or zero order in—sucrose concentration. The Michaelis–Menten mechanism explains the rate behaviour at low- and high-sucrose concentrations. What about observed increase in rate when enzyme concentration is increased? According to all three expressions for the rate law (Equations 13.33, 13.34, and 13.35), the rate is expected to increase with increasing enzyme concentration, as observed.

By allowing otherwise slow reactions to occur at reasonable rates, enzymes give living organisms tremendous control over which reactions occur, and when they occur. Enzymes are extremely specific (each enzyme will catalyze only one reaction or one type of reaction) and efficient, speeding up reaction rates by factors of as much as a billion. If a living organism wants to turn a particular reaction on, it produces or activates the correct enzyme to catalyze that reaction. Because organisms are so dependent on the reactions enzymes catalyze, many substances that inhibit the action of enzymes are highly toxic. Locking up a single enzyme molecule can stop the reaction of billions of substrates, much as one motorist stalled at a tollbooth can paralyze an entire highway full of cars. (For another example of enzyme action, see the *Chemistry and Medicine* box on the role of chymotrypsin in digestion.)

CHEMISTRY AND MEDICINE Enzyme Catalysis and the Role of Chymotrypsin in Digestion

When we eat foods containing proteins—such as meats, eggs, beans, and nuts—the proteins must be digested. Proteins are large biological molecules composed of individual units called amino acids. (The structure of proteins and other biologically important molecules are discussed more fully in Chapter 21.) The amino acids in proteins are linked together via peptide bonds, as shown in Figure 13.24 ▼.

$$-NH-CH_2-C(=O)-NH-CH(CH_3)-C(=O)- + H_2O \longrightarrow$$

$$-NH-CH_2-C(=O)-OH + H_2N-CH(CH_3)-C(=O)-$$

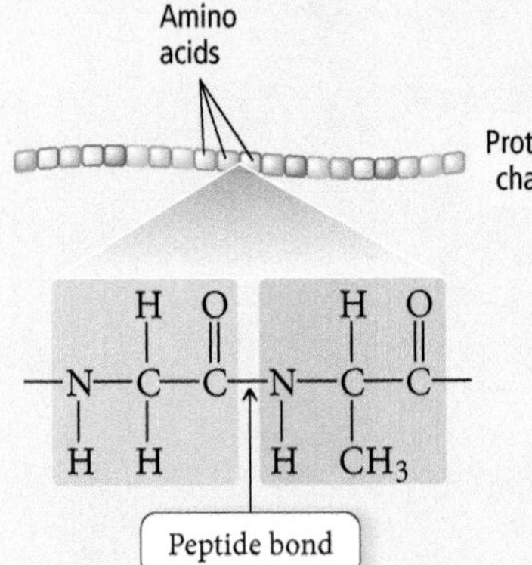
Amino acids
Protein chain
Peptide bond

◀ **FIGURE 13.24 The Structure of a Protein** Proteins are chains of amino acids linked together by peptide bonds.

During digestion, the protein must be broken up into individual amino acids (Figure 13.25 ▼), which can pass through the walls of the small intestine and into the bloodstream. However, the peptide bonds that link amino acids together are relatively stable, and under ordinary conditions the reaction is slow.

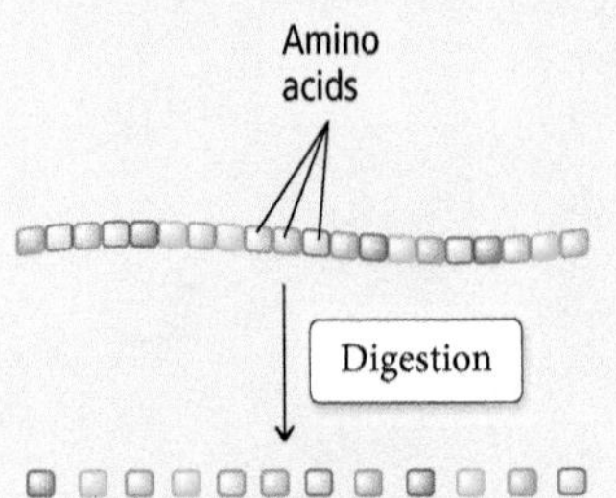
Amino acids
Digestion

◀ **FIGURE 13.25 Protein Digestion** During digestion, a protein is broken down into its component amino acids.

The pancreas secretes an enzyme called chymotrypsin (Figure 13.26 ▼) into the small intestine, where it binds protein molecules to be digested. Like many enzymes, chymotrypsin is highly selective in its action—it operates only on peptide bonds between certain kinds of amino acids. When a protein molecule containing such a pair of amino acids is attached to the active site of chymotrypsin, the peptide bond between them is weakened as the chymotrypsin forms a covalent bond with the carbon in the peptide bond. A water molecule can then come in and cleave the bond, with an —OH from the water binding to the carbon atom and the remaining —H bonding to the nitrogen (Figure 13.27 ▼).

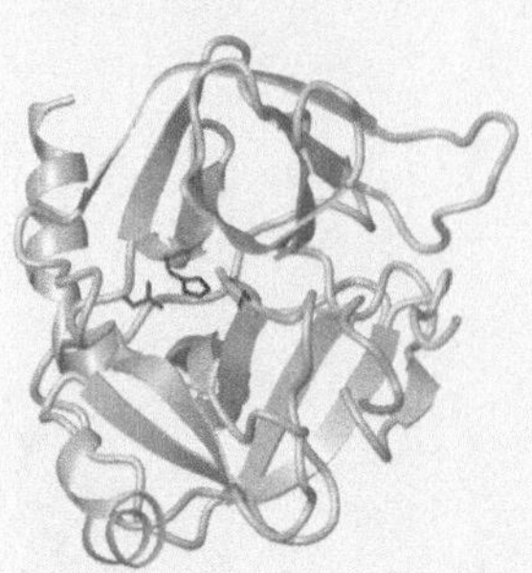

◀ **FIGURE 13.26 Chymotrypsin: A Digestive Enzyme** This model of chymotrypsin shows a section of a protein substrate in the active site.

The amino acid chain is thus clipped at the peptide bond. The products of the reaction leave the active site, another protein binds, and the process is repeated. Other digestive enzymes cleave protein chains between other pairs of amino acids. Together, these enzymes eventually reduce the entire protein to its constituent amino acids.

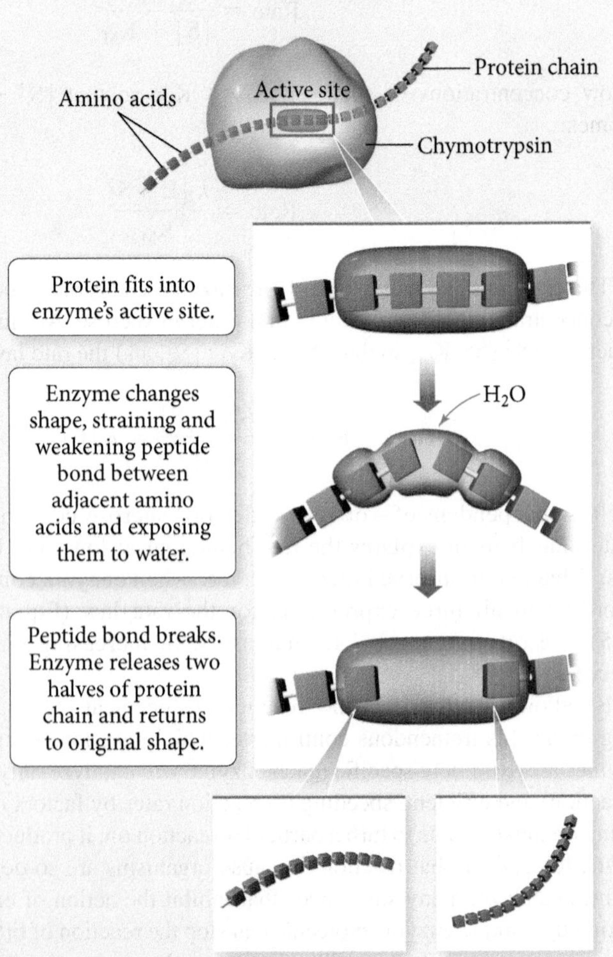
Amino acids
Active site
Protein chain
Chymotrypsin
Protein fits into enzyme's active site.
Enzyme changes shape, straining and weakening peptide bond between adjacent amino acids and exposing them to water.
H_2O
Peptide bond breaks. Enzyme releases two halves of protein chain and returns to original shape.

▲ **FIGURE 13.27 The Action of Chymotrypsin**

CHAPTER IN REVIEW

Key Terms

Section 13.3
rate law (539)
rate constant (k) (539)
reaction order (n) (539)
overall order (542)

Section 13.4
integrated rate law (544)
half-life ($t_{1/2}$) (548)
lifetime (τ) (548)
decay time (548)

Section 13.5
Arrhenius equation (552)
activation energy (E_a) (552)
frequency factor (A) (552)
activated complex (transition state) (552)
exponential factor (553)
Arrhenius plot (554)
collision model (556)
orientation factor (557)
collision frequency (557)

Section 13.6
reaction mechanism (558)
elementary step (558)
reaction intermediates (558)
molecularity (559)
unimolecular (559)
bimolecular (559)
termolecular (559)
rate-determining step (or rate-limiting step) (559)
steady-state approximation (561)

Section 13.7
catalyst (564)
homogeneous catalysis (565)
heterogeneous catalysis (565)
hydrogenation (566)
enzyme (567)
active site (567)
substrate (567)

Key Concepts

Reaction Rates, Orders, and Rate Laws (13.1–13.3)

The rate of a chemical reaction is a measure of how fast a reaction occurs. The rate reflects the change in the concentration of a reactant or product per unit time, and is usually reported in units of mol L^{-1} s^{-1}. Reaction rates generally depend on the concentration of the reactants. The rate of a first-order reaction is directly proportional to the concentration of the reactant; the rate of a second-order reaction is proportional to the square of the concentration of the reactant; and the rate of a zero-order reaction is independent of the concentration of the reactant. For a reaction with more than one reactant, the order with respect to each reactant is, in general, independent of the order with respect to other reactants. The order of a reaction with respect to a particular reactant is typically determined by measuring the rate of the reaction at several different initial concentrations of that reactant while holding the concentrations of other reactants (if there are any) constant. The rate law shows the relationship between the rate and the concentrations of each reactant.

Integrated Rate Laws (13.4)

The rate law for a reaction gives the relationship between the rate of the reaction and the concentrations of the reactants. The integrated rate law, by contrast, gives the relationship between the concentration of a reactant and time. The integrated rate law is different for each reaction order. The rate law for a zero-order reaction shows that the concentration of the reactant varies linearly with time. For a first-order reaction, the *natural log* of the concentration of the reactant varies linearly with time, and for a second-order reaction, the *inverse* of the concentration of the reactant varies linearly with time. Therefore, the order of a reaction can also be determined by plotting measurements of concentration as a function of time in these three different ways. The plot that is linear indicates the order of the reaction. The half-life, lifetime, and decay time for reactions can be derived from the integrated rate law. The half-life represents the time required for the concentration of a reactant to fall to one-half of its initial value. These quantities are independent of reactant concentration only for a first-order reaction. For reactions with other orders, such as zero or second order, the half-life and lifetime depend on the concentration and change during the course of the reaction as the concentration of reactant changes. The decay time is the time required for a specified amount of the reactant to be converted to products.

The Effect of Temperature on Reaction Rate (13.5)

The rate constant of a reaction generally depends on temperature and can be expressed by the Arrhenius equation, which consists of a frequency factor and an exponential factor. The exponential factor depends on both the temperature and the activation energy, a barrier that the reactants must overcome to become products. The frequency factor represents the number of times that the reactants approach the activation barrier per unit time. The exponential factor is the fraction of approaches that are successful in surmounting the activation barrier and forming products. The exponential factor increases with increasing temperature, but decreases with increasing activation energy. We can determine the frequency factor and activation energy for a reaction by measuring the rate constant at different temperatures and constructing an Arrhenius plot. For reactions in the gas phase, Arrhenius behaviour can be modelled with the collision model. In this model, reactions occur as a result of sufficiently energetic collisions. The colliding molecules must be oriented in such a way that the reaction can occur. The frequency factor contains two terms: p, which represents the fraction of collisions that have the proper orientation, and z, which represents the number of collisions per unit time.

Reaction Mechanisms (13.6)

Most chemical reactions occur not in a single step, but in several steps. The series of individual steps by which a reaction occurs is the reaction mechanism. In order for a mechanism to be valid, it must fulfill two conditions: (a) the steps must sum to the overall reaction; and (b) the mechanism must predict the experimentally observed rate law. For mechanisms with a slow initial step, the predicted rate law is derived from the slow step. The steady-state approximation makes no assumption of the relative rates of the elementary steps in a reaction mechanism. To eliminate the concentration of an intermediate from the rate law using the steady-state approximation, one assumes that concentration of the intermediate does not change during the course of the reaction.

Catalysis (13.7)

A catalyst is a substance that increases the rate of a chemical reaction by providing an alternative mechanism that has a lower activation energy for the rate-determining step. Catalysts can be homogeneous or heterogeneous. A homogeneous catalyst exists in the same phase as the reactants and forms a homogeneous mixture with them. A heterogeneous catalyst generally exists in a different phase than the reactants. Enzymes are biological catalysts capable of increasing the rate of specific biochemical reactions by many orders of magnitude.

Key Equations and Relationships

The Rate of Reaction (13.2)

For a reaction, $aA + bB \longrightarrow cC + dD$, the rate is defined as

$$\text{Rate} = -\frac{1}{a}\frac{\Delta[A]}{\Delta t} = -\frac{1}{b}\frac{\Delta[B]}{\Delta t} = +\frac{1}{c}\frac{\Delta[C]}{\Delta t} = +\frac{1}{d}\frac{\Delta[D]}{\Delta t}$$

The Rate Law (13.3)

$$\text{Rate} = k[A]^n \quad \text{(single reactant)}$$

$$\text{Rate} = k[A]^m[B]^n \quad \text{(multiple reactants)}$$

Integrated Rate Laws and Half-Life (13.4)

Reaction Order	Integrated Rate Law	Units of k	Half-Life Expression
0	$[A]_t = -kt + [A]_0$	$\text{mol L}^{-1}\,\text{s}^{-1}$	$t_{1/2} = \frac{[A]_0}{2k}$
1	$\ln[A]_t = -kt + \ln[A]_0$	s^{-1}	$t_{1/2} = \frac{0.693}{k}$
2	$\frac{1}{[A]_t} = kt + \frac{1}{[A]_{00}}$	$\text{L mol}^{-1}\,\text{s}^{-1}$	$t_{1/2} = \frac{1}{k[A]_0}$

Arrhenius Equation (13.5)

$$k = Ae^{-E_a/RT}$$

$$\ln k = -\frac{E_a}{R}\left(\frac{1}{T}\right) + \ln A \quad \text{(linearized form)}$$

$$\ln\frac{k_2}{k_1} = -\frac{E_a}{R}\left(\frac{1}{T_2} - \frac{1}{T_1}\right) \quad \text{(two-point form)}$$

$$k = pze^{-E_a/RT} \quad \text{(collision theory)}$$

Rate Laws for Elementary Steps (13.6)

Elementary Step	Molecularity	Rate Law
$A \longrightarrow$ products	1	$\text{Rate} = k[A]$
$A + A \longrightarrow$ products	2	$\text{Rate} = k[A]^2$
$A + B \longrightarrow$ products	2	$\text{Rate} = k[A][B]$
$A + A + A \longrightarrow$ products	3 (rare)	$\text{Rate} = k[A]^3$
$A + A + B \longrightarrow$ products	3 (rare)	$\text{Rate} = k[A]^2[B]$
$A + B + C \longrightarrow$ products	3 (rare)	$\text{Rate} = k[A][B][C]$

Key Skills

Expressing Reaction Rates (13.2)

• Example 13.1 • For Practice 13.1 • Exercises 25–34

Determining the Order, Rate Law, and Rate Constant of a Reaction (13.3)

• Example 13.2 • For Practice 13.2 • Exercises 41–44

Using Graphical Analysis of Reaction Data to Determine Reaction Order and Rate Constants (13.4)

• Examples 13.3, 13.5 • For Practice 13.3, 13.5 • Exercises 47–52

Determining the Concentration of a Reactant at a Given Time (13.4)

• Example 13.4 • For Practice 13.4 • Exercises 51–54

Working with the Half-Life of a Reaction (13.4)
• Example 13.6 • For Practice 13.6 • Exercises 53–56

Using the Arrhenius Equation to Determine Kinetic Parameters (13.5)
• Examples 13.7, 13.8 • For Practice 13.7, 13.8 • Exercises 59–70

Determining Whether a Reaction Mechanism Is Valid (13.6)
• Example 13.9 • For Practice 13.9 • Exercises 73–76

EXERCISES

Review Questions

1. How is metabolism and hibernation of some animals related to chemistry?
2. Why is knowledge of reaction rates important (both practically and theoretically)?
3. What units are typically used to express the rate of a reaction?
4. Why is the reaction rate for reactants defined as the *negative* of the change in reactant concentration with respect to time, whereas for products it is defined as the change in reactant concentration with respect to time (with a positive sign)?
5. Explain the difference between the average rate of reaction and the instantaneous rate of reaction.
6. Consider a simple reaction in which a reactant A forms products:

$$A \longrightarrow \text{products}$$

   What is the rate law if the reaction is zero order with respect to A? First order? Second order? For each case, explain how a doubling of the concentration of A would affect the rate of reaction.
7. How is the order of a reaction generally determined?
8. For a reaction with multiple reactants, how is the overall order of the reaction defined?
9. Explain the difference between the rate law for a reaction and the integrated rate law for a reaction. What relationship does each kind of rate law express?
10. Write integrated rate laws for zero-order, first-order, and second-order reactions of the form $A \longrightarrow$ products.
11. What do the terms *half-life*, *lifetime*, and *decay time* mean? Write the general expressions for the decay time and half-life for zero-, first-, and second-order reactions. Write expressions for the amount of time it takes for zero-, first-, and second-order reactions to deplete to 1/5 the original reactant concentration.
12. How do reaction rates typically depend on temperature? What part of the rate law is temperature dependent?
13. Explain the meaning of each term within the Arrhenius equation: activation energy, frequency factor, and exponential factor. Use these terms and the Arrhenius equation to explain why small changes in temperature can result in large changes in the reaction rate.
14. What is an Arrhenius plot? Explain the significance of the slope and intercept of an Arrhenius plot.
15. Explain how a chemical reaction occurs according to the collision model. Explain the meaning of the orientation factor within this model.
16. Explain the difference between a normal chemical equation for a chemical reaction and the mechanism of that reaction.
17. In a reaction mechanism, what is an elementary step? Write down the three most common elementary steps and the corresponding rate law for each one.
18. What are the two requirements for a proposed mechanism to be valid for a given reaction?
19. What is an intermediate within a reaction mechanism?
20. What is a catalyst? How does a catalyst increase the rate of a chemical reaction?
21. Explain the difference between homogeneous catalysis and heterogeneous catalysis.
22. What are the four basic steps involved in heterogeneous catalysis?
23. What are enzymes? What is the active site of an enzyme? What does the term *substrate* mean?
24. What is the general two-step mechanism by which most enzymes work?

Problems by Topic

Reaction Rates

25. Consider the reaction:

$$2\,HBr(g) \longrightarrow H_2(g) + Br_2(g)$$

   a. Express the rate of the reaction in terms of the change in concentration of each of the reactants and products.

   b. In the first 25.0 s of this reaction, the concentration of HBr dropped from 0.600 mol L^{-1} to 0.512 mol L^{-1}. Calculate the average rate of the reaction in this time interval.

   c. If the volume of the reaction vessel in part b was 1.50 L, what amount of Br_2 (in moles) was formed during the first 15.0 s of the reaction?

26. Consider the reaction:

$$2\ N_2O(g) \longrightarrow 2\ N_2(g) + O_2(g)$$

a. Express the rate of the reaction in terms of the change in concentration of each of the reactants and products.
b. In the first 15.0 s of the reaction, 0.015 mol of O_2 is produced in a reaction vessel with a volume of 0.500 L. What is the average rate of the reaction over this time interval?
c. Predict the rate of change in the concentration of N_2O over this time interval. In other words, what is $\Delta[N_2O]/\Delta t$?

27. For the reaction $2\ A(g) + B(g) \longrightarrow 3\ C(g)$,
a. Determine the expression for the rate of the reaction in terms of the change in concentration of each of the reactants and products.
b. When A is decreasing at a rate of 0.100 mol $L^{-1}\ s^{-1}$, how fast is B decreasing? How fast is C increasing?

28. For the reaction $A(g) + \frac{1}{2} B(g) \longrightarrow 2\ C(g)$,
a. Determine the expression for the rate of the reaction in terms of the change in concentration of each of the reactants and products.
b. When C is increasing at a rate of 0.025 mol $L^{-1}\ s^{-1}$, how fast is B decreasing? How fast is A decreasing?

29. Consider the reaction:

$$Cl_2(g) + 3\ F_2(g) \longrightarrow 2\ ClF_3(g)$$

Complete the table.

$\Delta[Cl_2]/\Delta t$	$\Delta[F_2]/\Delta t$	$\Delta[ClF_3]/\Delta t$	Rate
-0.012 mol $L^{-1}\ s^{-1}$			

30. Consider the reaction:

$$8\ H_2S(g) + 4\ O_2(g) \longrightarrow 8\ H_2O(g) + S_8(g)$$

Complete the table.

$\Delta[H_2S]/\Delta t$	$\Delta[O_2]/\Delta t$	$\Delta[H_2O]/\Delta t$	$\Delta[S_8]/\Delta t$	Rate
-0.080 mol $L^{-1}\ s^{-1}$				

31. Consider the reaction:

$$C_4H_8(g) \longrightarrow 2\ C_2H_4(g)$$

The following data were collected for the concentration of C_4H_8 as a function of time:

Time (s)	$[C_4H_8]$ (mol L^{-1})
0	1.000
10	0.913
20	0.835
30	0.763
40	0.697
50	0.637

a. What is the average rate of the reaction between 0 and 10 s? Between 40 and 50 s?
b. What is the rate of formation of C_2H_4 between 20 and 30 s?

32. Consider the reaction:

$$NO_2(g) \longrightarrow NO(g) + \frac{1}{2}O_2(g)$$

The tabulated data were collected for the concentration of NO_2 as a function of time:

Time (s)	$[NO_2]$ (mol L^{-1})
0	1.000
10	0.951
20	0.904
30	0.860
40	0.818
50	0.778
60	0.740
70	0.704
80	0.670
90	0.637
100	0.606

a. What is the average rate of the reaction between 10 and 20 s? Between 50 and 60 s?
b. What is the rate of formation of O_2 between 50 and 60 s?

33. Consider the reaction:

$$H_2(g) + Br_2(g) \longrightarrow 2\ HBr(g)$$

The graph below shows the concentration of Br_2 as a function of time.

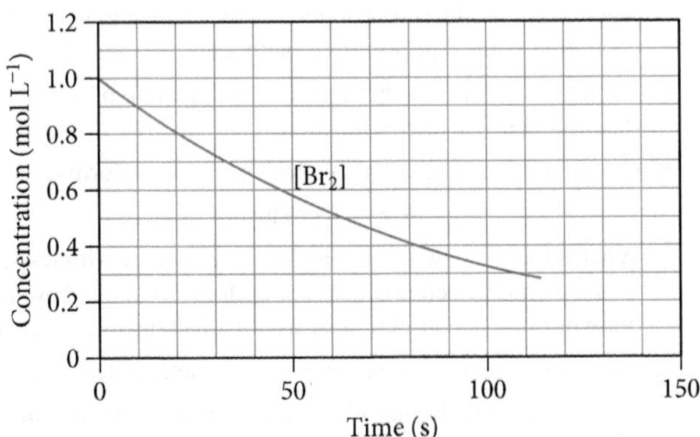

a. Use the graph to calculate each quantity:
(i) The average rate of the reaction between 0 and 25 s.
(ii) The instantaneous rate of the reaction at 25 s.
(iii) The instantaneous rate of formation of HBr at 50 s.
b. Make a rough sketch of a curve representing the concentration of HBr as a function of time. Assume that the initial concentration of HBr is zero.

34. Consider the reaction:

$$H_2O_2(aq) \longrightarrow H_2O(l) + \tfrac{1}{2}O_2(g)$$

The graph below shows the concentration of H_2O_2 as a function of time.

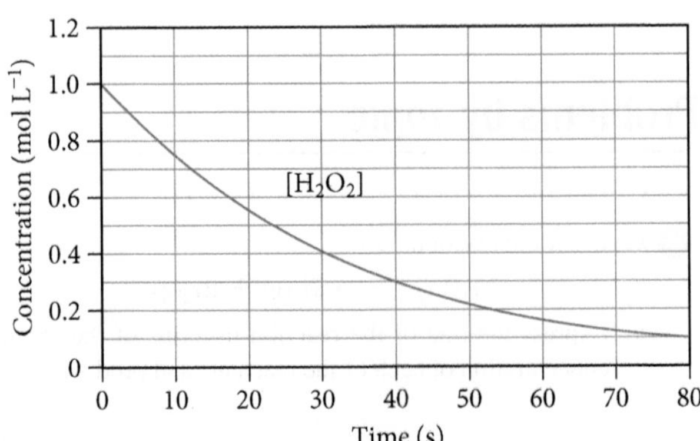

Use the graph to calculate each quantity:

a. The average rate of the reaction between 10 and 20 s.

b. The instantaneous rate of the reaction at 30 s.

c. The instantaneous rate of formation of O_2 at 50 s.

d. If the initial volume of the H_2O_2 is 1.5 L, what total amount of O_2 (in moles) is formed in the first 50 s of reaction?

The Rate Law and Reaction Orders

35. The graph below shows a plot of the rate of a reaction versus the concentration of the reactant A for the reaction A $\longrightarrow$ products.

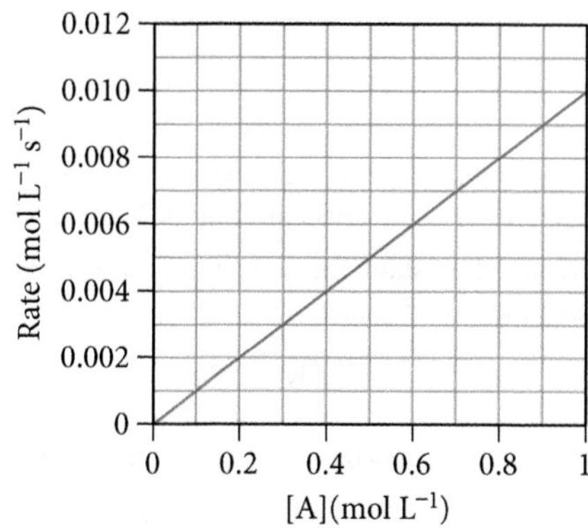

a. What is the order of the reaction with respect to A?

b. Make a rough sketch of how a plot of [A] versus *time* would appear.

c. Write a rate law for the reaction including an estimate for the value of *k*.

36. The graph below shows a plot of the rate of a reaction versus the concentration of the reactant.

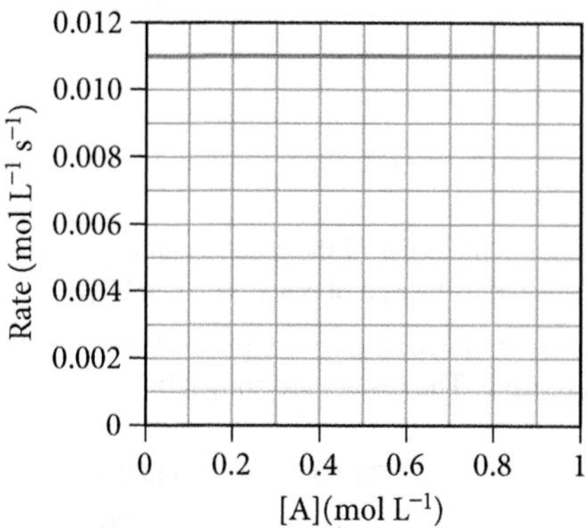

a. What is the order of the reaction with respect to A?

b. Make a rough sketch of how a plot of [A] versus *time* would appear.

c. Write a rate law for the reaction including the value of *k*.

37. What are the units of *k* for each type of reaction?

a. first-order reaction

b. second-order reaction

c. zero-order reaction

38. This reaction is first order in N_2O_5:

$$N_2O_5(g) \longrightarrow NO_3(g) + NO_2(g)$$

The rate constant for the reaction at a certain temperature is $0.053\ s^{-1}$.

a. Calculate the rate of the reaction when $[N_2O_5] = 0.055$ mol L^{-1}.

b. What would the rate of the reaction be at the same concentration as in part a if the reaction were second order? Zero order? (Assume the same *numerical* value for the rate constant with the appropriate units.)

39. A reaction in which A, B, and C react to form products is first order in A, second order in B, and zero order in C.

a. Write a rate law for the reaction.

b. What is the overall order of the reaction?

c. By what factor does the reaction rate change if [A] is doubled (and the other reactant concentrations are held constant)?

d. By what factor does the reaction rate change if [B] is doubled (and the other reactant concentrations are held constant)?

e. By what factor does the reaction rate change if [C] is doubled (and the other reactant concentrations are held constant)?

f. By what factor does the reaction rate change if the concentrations of all three reactants are doubled?

40. A reaction in which A, B, and C react to form products is zero order in A, one-half order in B, and second order in C.

a. Write a rate law for the reaction.

b. What is the overall order of the reaction?

c. By what factor does the reaction rate change if [A] is doubled (and the other reactant concentrations are held constant)?

d. By what factor does the reaction rate change if [B] is doubled (and the other reactant concentrations are held constant)?

e. By what factor does the reaction rate change if [C] is doubled (and the other reactant concentrations are held constant)?

f. By what factor does the reaction rate change if the concentrations of all three reactants are doubled?

41. Consider the data below showing the initial rate of a reaction (A $\longrightarrow$ products) at several different concentrations of A. What is the order of the reaction? Write a rate law for the reaction including the value of the rate constant, *k*.

[A] (mol L^{-1})	Initial Rate (mol L^{-1} s^{-1})
0.100	0.053
0.200	0.210
0.300	0.473

42. Consider the data below showing the initial rate of a reaction (A $\longrightarrow$ products) at several different concentrations of A. What is the order of the reaction? Write a rate law for the reaction including the value of the rate constant, *k*.

[A] (mol L^{-1})	Initial Rate (mol L^{-1} s^{-1})
0.15	0.008
0.30	0.016
0.60	0.032

43. The data below were collected for this reaction:

$$2\ NO_2(g) + F_2(g) \longrightarrow 2\ NO_2F(g)$$

$[NO_2]$ (mol L^{-1})	$[F_2]$ (mol L^{-1})	Initial Rate (mol L^{-1} s^{-1})
0.100	0.100	0.026
0.200	0.100	0.051
0.400	0.400	0.411

Write an expression for the reaction rate law and calculate the value of the rate constant, *k*. What is the overall order of the reaction?

44. The data below were collected for this reaction:

$$CH_3Cl(g) + 3\ Cl_2(g) \longrightarrow CCl_4(g) + 3\ HCl(g)$$

$[CH_3Cl]$ (mol L^{-1})	$[Cl_2]$ (mol L^{-1})	Initial Rate (mol L^{-1} s^{-1})
0.050	0.050	0.014
0.100	0.050	0.029
0.200	0.200	0.115

Write an expression for the reaction rate law and calculate the value of the rate constant, *k*. What is the overall order of the reaction?

The Integrated Rate Law and Half-Life

45. Indicate the order of reaction consistent with each observation.
a. A plot of the concentration of the reactant versus time yields a straight line.
b. The reaction has a half-life that is independent of initial concentration.
c. A plot of the inverse of the concentration versus time yields a straight line.

46. Indicate the order of reaction consistent with each observation.
a. The half-life of the reaction gets shorter as the initial concentration is increased.
b. A plot of the natural log of the concentration of the reactant versus time yields a straight line.
c. The half-life of the reaction gets longer as the initial concentration is increased.

47. The data below show the concentration of AB versus time for this reaction:

$$AB(g) \longrightarrow A(g) + B(g)$$

Time (s)	[AB] (mol L^{-1})
0	0.950
50	0.459
100	0.302
150	0.225
200	0.180
250	0.149
300	0.128
350	0.112
400	0.0994
450	0.0894
500	0.0812

Determine the order of the reaction and the value of the rate constant. Predict the concentration of AB at 25 s.

48. The data below show the concentration of N_2O_5 versus time for this reaction:

$$N_2O_5(g) \longrightarrow NO_3(g) + NO_2(g)$$

Time (s)	$[N_2O_5]$ (mol L^{-1})
0	1.000
25	0.822
50	0.677
75	0.557
100	0.458
125	0.377
150	0.310
175	0.255
200	0.210

Determine the order of the reaction and the value of the rate constant. Predict the concentration of N_2O_5 at 250 s.

49. The data below show the concentration of cyclobutane (C_4H_8) versus time for this reaction:

$$C_4H_8 \longrightarrow 2\ C_2H_4$$

Time (s)	$[C_4H_8]$ (mol L^{-1})
0	1.000
10	0.894
20	0.799
30	0.714
40	0.638
50	0.571
60	0.510
70	0.456
80	0.408
90	0.364
100	0.326

Determine the order of the reaction and the value of the rate constant. What is the rate of reaction when $[C_4H_8] = 0.25$ mol L^{-1}?

50. A reaction in which A $\longrightarrow$ products was monitored as a function of time. The results are shown below.

Time (s)	[A] (mol L^{-1})
0	1.000
25	0.914
50	0.829
75	0.744
100	0.659
125	0.573
150	0.488
175	0.403
200	0.318

Determine the order of the reaction and the value of the rate constant. What is the rate of reaction when [A] = 0.10 mol L^{-1}?

51. This reaction was monitored as a function of time:

$$A \longrightarrow B + C$$

A plot of ln[A] versus time yields a straight line with slope $-0.0045\ s^{-1}$.

a. What is the value of the rate constant (k) for this reaction at this temperature?
b. Write the rate law for the reaction.
c. What is the half-life?
d. What is the lifetime for this reaction?
e. If the initial concentration of A is 0.250 mol L^{-1}, what is the concentration after 225 s?

52. This reaction was monitored as a function of time:

$$AB \longrightarrow A + B$$

A plot of 1/[AB] versus time yields a straight line with slope 0.055 L $mol^{-1}\ s^{-1}$.

a. What is the value of the rate constant (k) for this reaction at this temperature?
b. Write the rate law for the reaction.
c. What is the half-life when the initial concentration is 0.55 mol L^{-1}?
d. How long will it take for the concentration of AB to decrease from 0.55 mol L^{-1} to 0.15 mol L^{-1}?
e. If the initial concentration of AB is 0.250 mol L^{-1}, and the reaction mixture initially contains no products, what are the concentrations of A and B after 75 s?

53. The decomposition of SO_2Cl_2 is first order in SO_2Cl_2 and has a rate constant of $1.42 \times 10^{-4}\ s^{-1}$ at a certain temperature.

a. What is the half-life for this reaction?
b. How long will it take for the concentration of SO_2Cl_2 to decrease to 30% of its initial concentration?
c. If the initial concentration of SO_2Cl_2 is 1.00 mol L^{-1}, how long will it take for the concentration to decrease to 0.78 mol L^{-1}?
d. If the initial concentration of SO_2Cl_2 is 0.150 mol L^{-1}, what is the concentration of SO_2Cl_2 after 2.00×10^2 s? After 5.00×10^2 s?

54. The decomposition of XY is second order in XY and has a rate constant of 7.02×10^{-3} L $mol^{-1}\ s^{-1}$ at a certain temperature.

a. What is the half-life for this reaction at an initial concentration of 0.100 mol L^{-1}?
b. How long will it take for the concentration of XY to decrease to 10% of its initial concentration when the initial concentration is 0.100 mol L^{-1}? When the initial concentration is 0.200 mol L^{-1}?
c. If the initial concentration of XY is 0.150 mol L^{-1}, how long will it take for the concentration to decrease to 0.062 mol L^{-1}?
d. If the initial concentration of XY is 0.050 mol L^{-1}, what is the concentration of XY after 5.0×10^1 s? After 5.50×10^2 s?

55. The half-life for the radioactive decay of U-238 is 4.5 billion years and is independent of initial concentration. How long will it take for 10% of the U-238 atoms in a sample of U-238 to decay? If a sample of U-238 initially contained 1.5×10^{18} atoms and was formed 3.8 billion years ago, how many U-238 atoms does it contain today?

56. The half-life for the radioactive decay of C-14 is 5730 years and is independent of the initial concentration. How long does it take for 25% of the C-14 atoms in a sample of C-14 to decay? If a sample of C-14 initially contains 1.5 mmol of C-14, how many millimoles are left after 2255 years?

The Effect of Temperature and the Collision Model

57. The diagram shows the energy of a reaction as the reaction progresses. Label each of the following in the diagram:

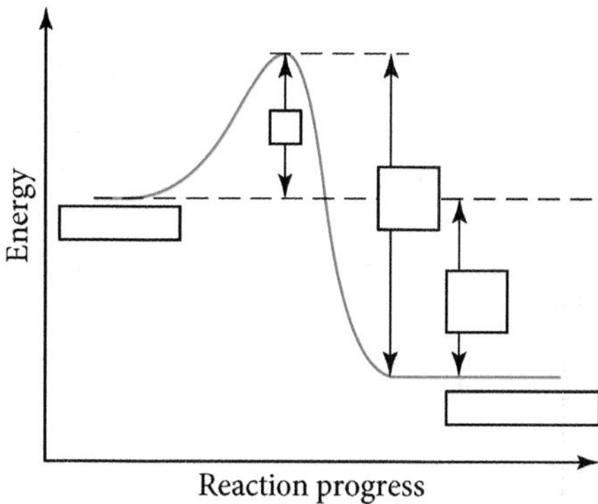

a. reactants
b. products
c. activation energy (E_a)
d. enthalpy of reaction ($\Delta_r H$)
e. reverse activation energy $E_{a,r}$

58. A chemical reaction is endothermic and has an activation energy that is twice the value of the enthalpy of the reaction. Draw a diagram depicting the energy of the reaction as it progresses. Label the position of the reactants and products and indicate the activation energy and enthalpy of reaction.

59. The activation energy of a reaction is 56.8 kJ mol^{-1} and the frequency factor is $1.5 \times 10^{11}\ s^{-1}$. Calculate the rate constant of the reaction at 25 °C.

60. The rate constant of a reaction at 32 °C is 0.055 s^{-1}. If the frequency factor is $1.2 \times 10^{13}\ s^{-1}$, what is the activation barrier?

61. The rate constant (k) for a reaction was measured as a function of temperature. A plot of ln k versus $1/T$ (in K) is linear and has a slope of -7445 K. Calculate the activation energy for the reaction.

62. The rate constant (k) for a reaction was measured as a function of temperature. A plot of ln k versus $1/T$ (in K) is linear and has a slope of -1.01×10^4 K. Calculate the activation energy for the reaction.

63. The data shown below were collected for the first-order reaction:

$$N_2O(g) \longrightarrow N_2(g) + O(g)$$

Use an Arrhenius plot to determine the activation barrier and frequency factor for the reaction.

Temperature (K)	Rate Constant (s^{-1})
800	3.24×10^{-5}
900	0.00214
1000	0.0614
1100	0.955

64. The data below show the rate constant of a reaction measured at several different temperatures. Use an Arrhenius plot to determine the activation barrier and frequency factor for the reaction.

Temperature (K)	Rate Constant (s^{-1})
300	0.0134
310	0.0407
320	0.114
330	0.303
340	0.757

65. The data shown below were collected for the second-order reaction:

$$Cl(g) + H_2(g) \longrightarrow HCl(g) + H(g)$$

Use an Arrhenius plot to determine the activation barrier and frequency factor for the reaction.

Temperature (K)	Rate Constant ($L\ mol^{-1}\ s^{-1}$)
90	0.00357
100	0.0773
110	0.956
120	7.781

66. The data below show the rate constant of a reaction measured at several different temperatures. Use an Arrhenius plot to determine the activation barrier and frequency factor for the reaction.

Temperature (K)	Rate Constant (s^{-1})
310	0.00434
320	0.0140
330	0.0421
340	0.118
350	0.316

67. A reaction has a rate constant of 0.0117 s^{-1} at 400.0 K and 0.689 s^{-1} at 450.0 K.

a. Determine the activation barrier for the reaction.

b. What is the value of the rate constant at 425 K?

68. A reaction has a rate constant of 0.000122 s^{-1} at 27 °C and 0.228 s^{-1} at 77 °C.

a. Determine the activation barrier for the reaction.

b. What is the value of the rate constant at 17 °C?

69. If a temperature increase from 10.0 °C to 20.0 °C doubles the rate constant for a reaction, what is the value of the activation barrier for the reaction?

70. If a temperature increase from 20.0 °C to 35.0 °C triples the rate constant for a reaction, what is the value of the activation barrier for the reaction?

71. Consider these two gas-phase reactions:

a. $AA(g) + BB(g) \longrightarrow 2\ AB(g)$

b. $AB(g) + CD(g) \longrightarrow AC(g) + BD(g)$

If the reactions have identical activation barriers and are carried out under the same conditions, which one would you expect to have the faster rate?

72. Which of these two reactions would you expect to have the smaller orientation factor? Explain.

a. $O(g) + N_2(g) \longrightarrow NO(g) + N(g)$

b. $NO(g) + Cl_2(g) \longrightarrow NOCl(g) + Cl(g)$

Reaction Mechanisms

73. Consider this overall reaction which is experimentally observed to be second order in AB and zero order in C:

$$AB + C \longrightarrow A + BC$$

Show that the following proposed mechanism fits the observations.

$$AB + AB \xrightarrow{k_1} AB_2 + A \quad \text{Slow}$$
$$AB_2 + C \xrightarrow{k_2} AB + BC \quad \text{Fast}$$

74. Consider this overall reaction which is experimentally observed to be second order in X and first order in Y:

$$X + Y \longrightarrow XY$$

a. Does the reaction occur in a single step in which X and Y collide?

b. Use the steady-state approximation to determine the rate law predicted by the following mechanism. Is this mechanism valid? Under what conditions?

$$2\ X \underset{k_2}{\overset{k_1}{\rightleftharpoons}} X_2$$
$$X_2 + Y \xrightarrow{k_3} XY + X$$

75. Nitrosyl chloride, NO_2Cl, is a powerful nitrating agent. It is thought to decompose via the following mechanism.

$$NO_2Cl(g) \underset{k_{-1}}{\overset{k_1}{\rightleftharpoons}} NO_2(g) + Cl(g)$$
$$NO_2Cl(g) + Cl(g) \xrightarrow{k_2} NO_2(g) + Cl_2(g)$$

a. What is the overall reaction that occurs?

b. Use the steady-state approximation to determine the rate law for this reaction.

76. Consider this two-step mechanism for a reaction:

$$NO_2(g) + Cl_2(g) \xrightarrow{k_1} ClNO_2(g) + Cl(g) \quad \text{Slow}$$
$$NO_2(g) + Cl(g) \xrightarrow{k_2} ClNO_2(g) \quad \text{Fast}$$

a. What is the overall reaction?

b. Identify the intermediates in the mechanism.

c. What is the predicted rate law?

Catalysis

77. Many heterogeneous catalysts are deposited on high surface-area supports. Why?

78. Suppose that the reaction A $\longrightarrow$ products is exothermic and has an activation barrier of 75 kJ mol^{-1}. Sketch an energy diagram showing the energy of the reaction as a function of the progress of the reaction. Draw a second energy curve showing the effect of a catalyst.

79. Suppose that a catalyst lowers the activation barrier of a reaction from 125 kJ mol^{-1} to 55 kJ mol^{-1}. By what factor would you expect the reaction rate to increase at 25 °C? (Assume that the frequency factors for the catalyzed and uncatalyzed reactions are identical.)

80. The activation barrier for the hydrolysis of sucrose into glucose and fructose is 108 kJ mol^{-1}. If an enzyme increases the rate of the hydrolysis reaction by a factor of 1 million, how much lower must the activation barrier be when sucrose is in the active site of the enzyme? (Assume that the frequency factors for the catalyzed and uncatalyzed reactions are identical and a temperature of 25 °C.)

Cumulative Problems

81. The data below were collected for this reaction at 500 °C:

$$CH_3CN(g) \longrightarrow CH_3NC(g)$$

Time (h)	$[CH_3CN]$ (mol L^{-1})
0.0	1.000
5.0	0.794
10.0	0.631
15.0	0.501
20.0	0.398
25.0	0.316

a. Determine the order of the reaction and the value of the rate constant at this temperature.
b. What is the half-life for this reaction (at the initial concentration)?
c. How long will it take for 90% of the CH_3NC to convert to CH_3CN?

82. The data below were collected for this reaction at a certain temperature:

$$X_2Y \longrightarrow 2\,X + Y$$

Time (h)	$[X_2Y]$ (mol L^{-1})
0.0	0.100
1.0	0.0856
2.0	0.0748
3.0	0.0664
4.0	0.0598
5.0	0.0543

a. Determine the order of the reaction and the value of the rate constant at this temperature.
b. What is the half-life for this reaction (at the initial concentration)?
c. What is the concentration of X after 10.0 hours?

83. Consider the reaction:

$$A + B + C \longrightarrow D$$

The rate law for this reaction is:

$$\text{Rate} = k\frac{[A][C]^2}{[B]^{1/2}}$$

Suppose the rate of the reaction at certain initial concentrations of A, B, and C is 0.0115 mol L^{-1} s^{-1}. What is the rate of the reaction if the concentrations of A and C are doubled and the concentration of B is tripled?

84. Consider the reaction:

$$2\,O_3(g) \longrightarrow 3\,O_2(g)$$

The rate law for this reaction is:

$$\text{Rate} = k\frac{[O_3]^2}{[O_2]}$$

Suppose that a 1.0 L reaction vessel initially contains 1.0 mol of O_3 and 1.0 mol of O_2. What fraction of the O_3 will have reacted when the rate falls to one-half of its initial value?

85. At 700 K acetaldehyde decomposes in the gas phase to methane and carbon monoxide. The reaction is:

$$CH_3CHO(g) \longrightarrow CH_4(g) + CO(g)$$

A sample of CH_3CHO is heated to 700 K and the pressure is measured as 220 mbar before any reaction takes place. The kinetics of the reaction are then followed by measurements of total pressure and these data are obtained:

t (s)	0	1000	3000	7000
P_{Total} (mbar)	220	240	270	310

Find the rate law, the specific rate constant, and the total pressure after 2.00×10^4 s.

86. At 400 K oxalic acid decomposes according to the reaction:

$$H_2C_2O_4(g) \longrightarrow CO_2(g) + HCOOH(g)$$

In three separate experiments, the intial pressure of oxalic acid and final total pressure after 20 000 s are measured.

Experiment	1	2	3
$P_{H_2C_2O_4}$ at $t = 0$ (kPa)	65.8	92.1	111
P_{Total} at $t = 20000$ s (kPa)	94.6	132	160

Find the rate law of the reaction and its specific rate constant.

87. Dinitrogen pentoxide decomposes in the gas phase to form nitrogen dioxide and oxygen gas. The reaction is first order in dinitrogen pentoxide and has a half-life of 2.81 h at 25 °C. If a 1.5 L reaction vessel initially contains 745 Torr of N_2O_5 at 25 °C, what partial pressure of O_2 will be present in the vessel after 215 minutes?

88. Cyclopropane (C_3H_6) reacts to form propene (C_3H_6) in the gas phase. The reaction is first order in cyclopropane and has a rate constant of 5.87×10^{-4} s^{-1} at 485 °C. If a 2.5 L reaction vessel initially contains 722 Torr of cyclopropane at 485 °C, how long will it take for the partial pressure of cyclopropane to drop to below 1.00×10^2 Torr?

89. Iodine atoms combine to form I_2 in liquid hexane solvent with a rate constant of 1.5×10^{10} L mol^{-1} s^{-1}. The reaction is second order in I. Since the reaction occurs so quickly, the only way to study the reaction is to create iodine atoms almost instantaneously, usually by photochemical decomposition of I_2. Suppose a flash of light creates an initial [I] concentration of 0.0100 mol L^{-1}. How long will it take for 95% of the newly created iodine atoms to recombine to form I_2?

90. The hydrolysis of sucrose ($C_{12}H_{22}O_{11}$) into glucose and fructose in acidic water has a rate constant of 1.8×10^{-4} s^{-1} at 25 °C. Assuming the reaction is first order in sucrose, determine the mass of sucrose that is hydrolyzed when 2.55 L of a 0.150 mol L^{-1} sucrose solution is allowed to react for 195 minutes.

91. The reaction $AB(aq) \longrightarrow A(g) + B(g)$ is second order in AB and has a rate constant of 0.0118 L mol^{-1} s^{-1} at 25.0 °C. A reaction vessel initially contains 250.0 mL of 0.100 mol L^{-1} AB which is allowed to react to form the gaseous product. The product is collected over water at 25.0 °C. How much time is required to produce 200.0 mL of the products at a barometric pressure of 755.1 mmHg? (The vapour pressure of water at this temperature is 23.8 mmHg.)

92. The reaction $2\ H_2O_2(aq) \longrightarrow 2\ H_2O(l) + O_2(g)$ is first order in H_2O_2 and under certain conditions has a rate constant of $0.00752\ s^{-1}$ at 20.0 °C. A reaction vessel initially contains 150.0 mL of 30.0% H_2O_2 by mass solution (the density of the solution is 1.11 g mL). The gaseous oxygen is collected over water at 20.0 °C as it forms. What volume of O_2 will form in 85.0 seconds at a barometric pressure of 742.5 mmHg. (The vapour pressure of water at this temperature is 17.5 mmHg.)

93. Consider this energy diagram:

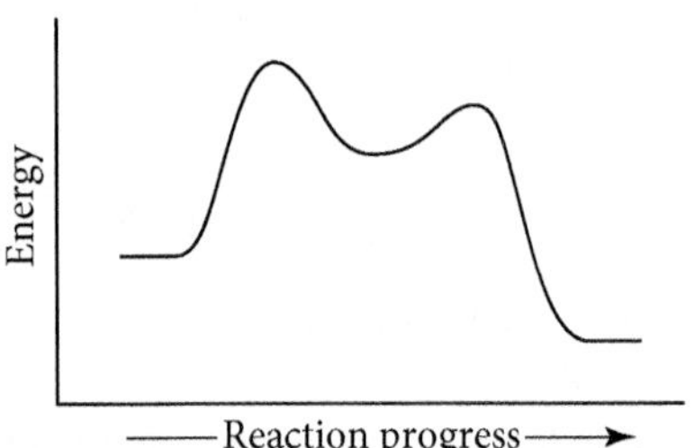

a. How many elementary steps are involved in this reaction?
b. Label the reactants, products, and intermediates.
c. Which step is rate limiting?
d. Is the overall reaction endothermic or exothermic?

94. Consider the reaction in which HCl adds across the double bond of ethene:

$$HCl + H_2C{=}CH_2 \longrightarrow H_3C{-}CH_2Cl$$

The following mechanism, with the following energy diagram, has been suggested for this reaction:

$$HCl + H_2C{=}CH_2 \underset{k_{-1}}{\overset{k_1}{\rightleftharpoons}} H_3C{-}CH_2^+ + Cl^-$$

$$H_3C{-}CH_2^+ + Cl^- \xrightarrow{k_2} H_3C{-}CH_2Cl$$

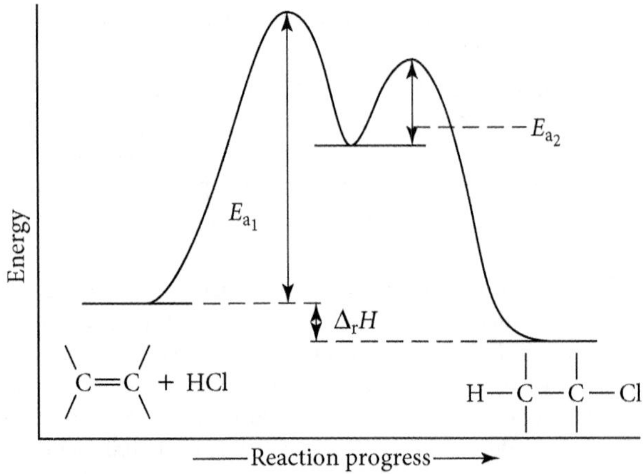

a. Based on the energy diagram, determine which step is rate limiting.
b. What is the rate law and order of the reaction based on your answer to part a?
c. Use the steady-state approximation to determine the rate law and the order of the reaction. How does it differ from the answer in part b?
d. Is the overall reaction exothermic or endothermic?

95. The desorption of a single molecular layer of butane from a single crystal of aluminum oxide was found to be first order with a rate constant of $0.128\ s^{-1}$ at 150 K.

a. What is the half-life of the desorption reaction?
b. If the surface is initially completely covered with butane at 150 K, how long will it take for 25% of the molecules to desorb? For 50% to desorb?
c. If the surface is initially completely covered, what fraction will remain covered after 10 s? After 20 s?

96. The evaporation of a 120 nm film of pentane from a single crystal of aluminum oxide is zero order with a rate constant of 1.92×10^{13} molecules $cm^{-3}\ s^{-1}$ at 120 K.

a. If the initial surface coverage is 8.9×10^{16} molecules cm^{-2}, how long will it take for one-half of the film to evaporate?
b. What fraction of the film is left after 10 s? Assume the same initial coverage as in part a.

97. The kinetics of this reaction were studied as a function of temperature. (The reaction is first order in each reactant and second order overall.)

$$C_2H_5Br(aq) + OH^-(aq) \longrightarrow C_2H_5OH(l) + Br^-(aq)$$

Temperature (°C)	k (L mol^{-1} s^{-1})
25	8.81×10^{-5}
35	0.000285
45	0.000854
55	0.00239
65	0.00633

a. Determine the activation energy and frequency factor for the reaction.
b. Determine the rate constant at 15 °C.
c. If a reaction mixture is 0.155 mol L^{-1} in C_2H_5Br, and 0.250 mol L^{-1} in OH^-, what is the initial rate of the reaction at 75 °C?

98. The reaction $2\ N_2O_5 \longrightarrow 2\ N_2O_4 + O_2$ takes place at around room temperature in solvents such as CCl_4. The rate constant at 293 K is found to be $2.35 \times 10^{-4}\ s^{-1}$ and at 303 K the rate constant is found to be $9.15 \times 10^{-4}\ s^{-1}$. Calculate the frequency factor for the reaction.

99. This reaction has an activation energy of zero in the gas phase:

$$CH_3 + CH_3 \longrightarrow C_2H_6$$

a. Would you expect the rate of this reaction to change very much with temperature?
b. Can you think of a reason for why the activation energy is zero?
c. What other types of reactions would you expect to have little or no activation energy?

100. Consider the two reactions:

$$O + N_2 \longrightarrow NO + N \qquad E_a = 315\ kJ\ mol^{-1}$$
$$Cl + H_2 \longrightarrow HCl + H \qquad E_a = 23\ kJ\ mol^{-1}$$

a. Why is the activation barrier for the first reaction so much higher than that for the second?
b. The frequency factors for these two reactions are very close to each other in value. Assuming that they are the same, compute the ratio of the reaction rate constants for these two reactions at 25 °C.

101. Anthropologists can estimate the age of a bone or other sample of organic matter by its carbon-14 content. The carbon-14 in a living organism is constant until the organism dies, after which carbon-14 decays with first-order kinetics and a half-life of 5730 years. Suppose a bone from an ancient human contains 19.5% of the C-14 found in living organisms. How old is the bone?

102. Geologists can estimate the age of rocks by their uranium-238 content. The uranium is incorporated in the rock as it hardens and then decays with first-order kinetics and a half-life of 4.5 billion years. A rock contains 83.2% of the amount of uranium-238 that it contained when it was formed. (The amount that the rock contained when it was formed can be deduced from the presence of the decay products of U-238.) How old is the rock?

103. Consider the gas-phase reaction:

$$H_2(g) + I_2(g) \longrightarrow 2\,HI(g)$$

The reaction was experimentally determined to be first order in H_2 and first order in I_2. Consider the proposed mechanisms.

Proposed mechanism I:

$$H_2(g) + I_2(g) \longrightarrow 2\,HI(g) \qquad \text{Single step}$$

Proposed mechanism II:

$$I_2(g) \underset{k_{-1}}{\overset{k_1}{\rightleftharpoons}} 2\,I(g)$$

$$H_2(g) + 2\,I(g) \xrightarrow{k_2} 2\,HI(g)$$

a. Show that proposed mechanism I is valid.
b. Use the steady-state approximation to obtain a rate predicted by proposed mechanism II. Under what conditions is this mechanism valid?
c. What order is the reaction predicted to be by proposed mechanism II at high pressures of H_2?

104. The reaction of oxygen with nitrogen dioxide

$$O_2 + NO_2 \longrightarrow O_3 + NO \quad \text{Rate} = k[NO_2]^2[O_2]$$

was found to be third order and was proposed to occur via the following mechanism:

$$NO_2 + NO_2 \underset{k_{-1}}{\overset{k_1}{\rightleftharpoons}} N_2O_4$$

$$O_2 + N_2O_4 \xrightarrow{k_2} O_3 + NO_2 + NO$$

a. Show that the mechanism predicts the overall reaction.
b. Identify the intermediate in this mechanism.
c. Use the steady-state approximation to determine the rate law predicted by this mechanism.
d. Under what conditions does the rate law predict the third-order rate law given above?
e. Under what conditions is the overall rate law second order?

105. A proposed mechanism for the reaction of NO reacting with Br_2 to give NOBr

$$2\,NO(g) + Br_2(g) \longrightarrow 2\,NOBr(g)$$

is as follows

$$NO(g) + Br_2(g) \underset{k_{-1}}{\overset{k_1}{\rightleftharpoons}} NOBr_2(g)$$

$$NO(g) + NOBr_2(g) \xrightarrow{k_2} 2\,NOBr(g)$$

a. Determine the rate law predicted by this mechanism.
b. Write the rate law at very high NO concentrations and state the order of the reaction.
c. Write the rate law at very low NO concentrations and state the order of the reaction.

106. The reaction of H_2 and NO

$$2\,H_2(g) + 2\,NO(g) \longrightarrow N_2(g) + 2\,H_2O(g)$$

is proposed to occur by the following mechanism:

$$2\,NO \underset{k_{-1}}{\overset{k_1}{\rightleftharpoons}} N_2O_2$$

$$N_2O_2 + H_2 \xrightarrow{k_2} N_2O + H_2O$$

$$N_2O + H_2 \xrightarrow{k_3} N_2 + H_2O$$

a. Identify the intermediates in this mechanism.
b. Use the steady-state approximation on the intermediate concentrations to determine the rate law for this reaction.
c. Under what conditions is the reaction (i) second order, (ii) third order?

107. A certain substance, X, decomposes. 50% of X remains after 100 minutes. How much X remains after 200 minutes if the reaction order with respect to X is **(a)** zero order, **(b)** first order, **(c)** second order?

108. The half-life for radioactive decay (a first-order process) of plutonium-239 is 24 000 years. How many years does it take for one mole of this radioactive material to decay so that just one atom remains?

109. The energy of activation for the decomposition of 2 mol of HI to H_2 and I_2 in the gas phase is 185 kJ mol^{-1}. The heat of formation of HI(g) from $H_2(g)$ and $I_2(g)$ is -5.65 kJ mol^{-1}. Find the energy of activation for the reaction of 1 mol of H_2 and 1 mol of I_2 in the gas phase.

110. Ethyl chloride vapour decomposes by the first-order reaction:

$$C_2H_5Cl \longrightarrow C_2H_4 + HCl$$

The activation energy is 249 kJ mol^{-1} and the frequency factor is 1.6×10^{14} s^{-1}. Find the value of the specific rate constant at 710 K. What fraction of the ethyl chloride decomposes in 15 minutes at this temperature? Find the temperature at which the rate of the reaction would be twice as fast.

111. Sulfuryl chloride, $SO_2Cl_2(g)$, decomposes at elevated temperatures to $SO_2(g)$ and $Cl_2(g)$. The reaction is first order in SO_2Cl_2 with a rate constant of 2.71×10^{-4} s^{-1} at 573 K.
a. A container initially contained pure sulfuryl chloride at 2.000 bar. What would be the partial pressure of sulfuryl chloride after 1.00 hour?
b. What would be the total pressure in the container after this time?

112. Consider the following reaction:

$$4\,PH_3(g) \longrightarrow P_4(g) + 6\,H_2(g)$$

In a certain experiment over a specific time period, it was determined that on average 0.0048 mol of PH_3 is consumed in a 2.0 L container per second of reaction. What is the rate of production of H_2 in mol L^{-1} s^{-1}?

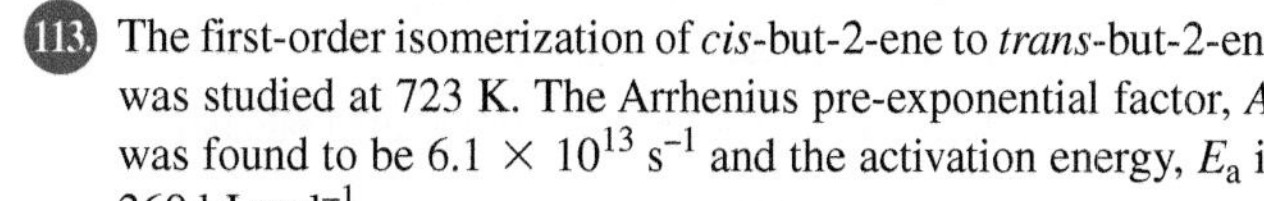

113. The first-order isomerization of *cis*-but-2-ene to *trans*-but-2-ene was studied at 723 K. The Arrhenius pre-exponential factor, A, was found to be 6.1×10^{13} s^{-1} and the activation energy, E_a is 260 kJ mol^{-1}.
a. What is the rate constant at 723 K?
b. If the temperature of a pure sample of *cis*-but-2-ene was increased to 723 K, how long would it take for 15.0% of the sample to isomerize?

114. Alcohol dehydrogenase (ADH) is a liver enzyme that catalyzes the oxidation of ethanol to acetaldehyde. The catalyzed reaction in the liver is zero order with a rate constant of 0.17 mol h^{-1}. Halogenated hydrocarbons act as a inhibitors to the ADH by binding strongly to the enzyme. The halogenated hydrocarbons can persist in the liver for days following exposure. Suppose that a worker who is exposed to halogenated hydrocarbons leaves work with 60% of their ADH inhibited. The worker decides to have a few beers which are 341 mL and 5% alcohol by volume. How many bottles of beer can the worker drink and be fully free of ethanol by the start of work the next morning, 10 hours later?

Challenge Problems

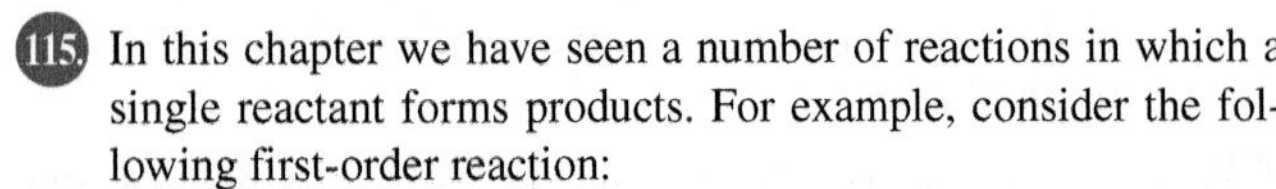

115. In this chapter we have seen a number of reactions in which a single reactant forms products. For example, consider the following first-order reaction:

$$CH_3NC(g) \longrightarrow CH_3CN(g)$$

However, we also learned that gas-phase reactions occur through collisions.

a. One possible explanation is that two molecules of CH_3NC collide with each other and form two molecules of the product in a single elementary step. If that were the case, what reaction order would you expect?

b. Another possibility is that the reaction occurs through more than one step. For example, a possible mechanism involves one step in which the two CH_3NC molecules collide, resulting in the "activation" of one of them. In a second step, the activated molecule goes on to form the product. Write down this mechanism and determine which step must be rate determining in order for the kinetics of the reaction to be first order. Show explicitly how the mechanism predicts first-order kinetics.

116. The first-order *integrated* rate law for a reaction A $\longrightarrow$ products is derived from the rate law using calculus:

$$\text{Rate} = k[\text{A}] \quad \text{(first-order rate law)}$$

$$\text{Rate} = -\frac{d[\text{A}]}{dt}$$

$$\frac{d[\text{A}]}{dt} = -k[\text{A}]$$

The above equation is a first-order, separable differential equation that can be solved by separating the variables and integrating:

$$\frac{d[\text{A}]}{[\text{A}]} = -kdt$$

$$\int_{[\text{A}]_0}^{[\text{A}]} \frac{d[\text{A}]}{[\text{A}]} = -\int_0^t kdt$$

In the above integral, $[\text{A}]_0$ is the initial concentration of A. We then evaluate the integral:

$$[\ln[\text{A}]]_{[\text{A}]_0}^{[\text{A}]} = -k[t]_0^t$$

$$\ln[\text{A}] - \ln[\text{A}]_0 = -kt$$

$$\ln[\text{A}] = -kt + \ln[\text{A}]_0 \quad \text{(integrated rate law)}$$

a. Use a procedure similar to the one above to derive an integrated rate law for a reaction A $\longrightarrow$ products which is one-half order in the concentration of A (that is, Rate $= k[\text{A}]^{1/2}$).

b. Use the result from part a to derive an expression for the half-life of a one-half-order reaction.

117. The previous exercise shows how the first-order integrated rate law is derived from the first-order differential rate law. Begin with the second-order differential rate law and derive the second-order integrated rate law.

118. The rate constant for the first-order decomposition of $N_2O_5(g)$ to $NO_2(g)$ and $O_2(g)$ is $7.48 \times 10^{-3}\ s^{-1}$ at a given temperature.

a. Find the length of time required for the total pressure in a system containing N_2O_5 at an initial pressure of 0.100 bar to rise to 0.145 bar.

b. To 0.200 bar.

c. Find the total pressure after 100 s of reaction.

119. Phosgene (Cl_2CO), a poison gas used in World War I, is formed by the reaction of Cl_2 and CO. The proposed mechanism for the reaction is:

$$Cl_2 \rightleftharpoons 2\,Cl \quad \text{(fast, equilibrium)}$$

$$Cl + CO \rightleftharpoons ClCO \quad \text{(fast, equilibrium)}$$

$$ClCO + Cl_2 \longrightarrow Cl_2CO + Cl \quad \text{(slow)}$$

What rate law is consistent with this mechanism?

120. The rate of decomposition of $N_2O_3(g)$ to $NO_2(g)$ and $NO(g)$ is followed by measuring $[NO_2]$ at different times. The following data are obtained.

$[NO_2]$ (mol L^{-1})	0	0.193	0.316	0.427	0.784
t (s)	0	884	1610	2460	50000

The reaction follows a first-order rate law. Calculate the rate constant. Assume that after 50000 s all the $N_2O_3(g)$ had decomposed.

121. At 473 K, for the elementary reaction

$$2\,NOCl(g) \underset{k_{-1}}{\overset{k_1}{\rightleftharpoons}} 2\,NO(g) + Cl_2(g)$$

$$k_1 = 7.8 \times 10^{-2}\ L\ mol^{-1}\ s^{-1} \text{ and}$$

$$k_{-1} = 4.7 \times 10^{2}\ L^2\ mol^{-2}\ s^{-1}$$

A sample of NOCl is placed in a container and heated to 473 K. When the system comes to equilibrium, [NOCl] is found to be 0.12 mol L^{-1}. Find the concentrations of NO and Cl_2.

122. Thallium(I) is oxidized by cerium(IV) in aqueous solution,

$$Tl^+ + 2\,Ce^{4+} \longrightarrow Tl^{3+} + 2\,Ce^{3+}$$

The mechanism, in the presence of manganese(II) catalyst is as follows:

$$Ce^{4+} + Mn^{2+} \xrightarrow{k_1} Ce^{3+} + Mn^{3+}$$

$$Ce^{4+} + Mn^{3+} \xrightarrow{k_2} Ce^{3+} + Mn^{4+}$$

$$Tl^{+} + Mn^{4+} \xrightarrow{k_3} Tl^{3+} + Mn^{2+}$$

Use the steady-state approximation to determine the rate law for this reaction. What is the order of the reaction?

123. We saw that the rate law predicted by the Michaelis–Menten mechanism is given by Equation 13.33 and at very high concentrations of sucrose, the rate law is reduced to Equation 13.35. Biochemists call the term $k_2[E]_0$ V_{max} since it is the maximum rate of reaction for a given enzyme concentration.

a. Using Equation 13.33, determine an expression for the Michaelis constant, K_M, when the rate of the reaction is $\frac{1}{2}V_{max}$.

b. In an experiment to determine the activity of sucrase from mouse intestine V_{max} was determined to be 1.98 mmol L^{-1} s^{-1}, and K_M was 18 mmol L^{-1}. Determine the rate of the enzyme-catalyzed reaction at 0.1 mmol L^{-1}, 1 mmol L^{-1}, 10 mmol L^{-1}, 100 mmol L^{-1}, and 1000 mmol L^{-1}. Use a spreadsheet such as Excel for these repetitive calculations.

124. In the stratosphere, atomic oxygen is formed when ultraviolet light from the sun dissociates O_2 molecules. Two free oxygen atoms can recombine to form O_2 when they collide with a third molecule, M.

$$O_2 \xrightarrow{h\nu} 2\,O \qquad k_1$$

$$2\,O + M \xrightarrow{h\nu} O_2 + M \qquad k_2$$

The ratio of atomic oxygen to molecular oxygen increases with altitude, as the atmospheric pressure decreases. Use the steady-state approximation to write an expression that shows the relationship between the concentrations of O and O_2. Use the expression to explain the observation that the relative concentration of atomic oxygen increases with altitude. (Assume that light intensity is constant at all altitudes.)

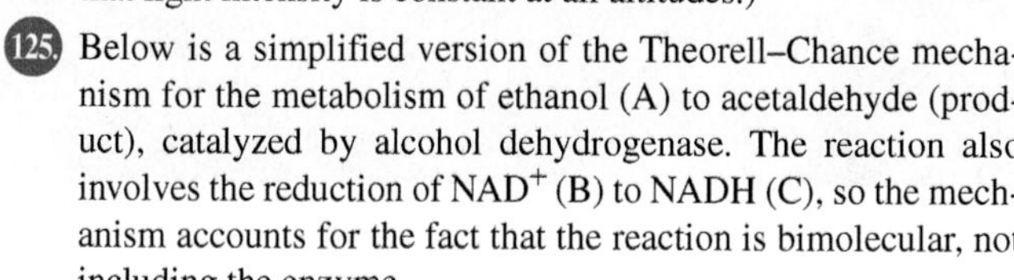

125. Below is a simplified version of the Theorell–Chance mechanism for the metabolism of ethanol (A) to acetaldehyde (product), catalyzed by alcohol dehydrogenase. The reaction also involves the reduction of NAD^+ (B) to NADH (C), so the mechanism accounts for the fact that the reaction is bimolecular, not including the enzyme.

$$E + A \underset{k_{-1}}{\overset{k_1}{\rightleftharpoons}} EA \qquad \text{(fast)}$$

$$EA + B \underset{k_{-2}}{\overset{k_2}{\rightleftharpoons}} EZ + C \qquad \text{(fast)}$$

$$EZ \xrightarrow{k_3} E + \text{Product} \qquad \text{(slow)}$$

It is known that the rate-determining step is the formation of products so that the equilibria in the first two steps are relatively fast. Assume that the rate of the forward reactions equal the rates of the reverse reactions in each of the first two steps and obtain an expression for the rate of the reaction.

Conceptual Problems

126. Consider the reaction:

$$CHCl_3(g) + Cl_2(g) \longrightarrow CCl_4(g) + HCl(g)$$

The reaction is first order in $CHCl_3$ and one-half order in Cl_2. Which reaction mixture would you expect to have the fastest initial rate?

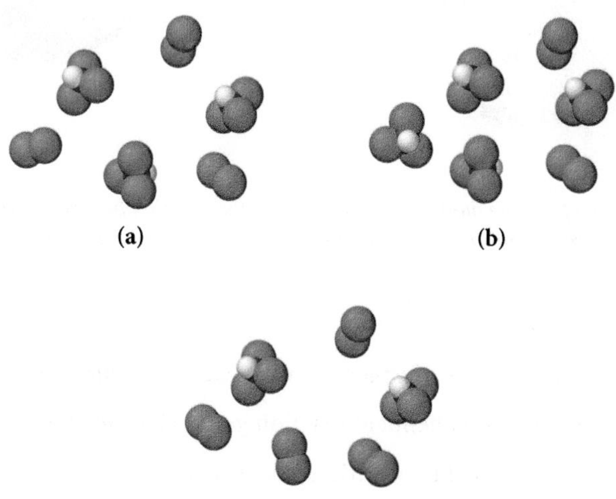

127. The graph below shows the concentration of a reactant as a function of time for two different reactions. One of the reactions is first order and the other is second order. Which of the two reactions is first order? Second order? How would you change each plot to make it linear?

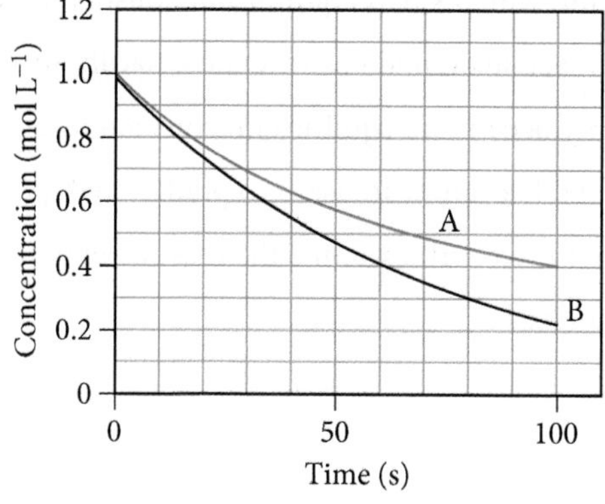

128. A particular reaction, A $\longrightarrow$ products, has a rate that slows down as the reaction proceeds. The half-life of the reaction is found to depend on the initial concentration of A. Determine whether each of the following is likely to be true or false for this reaction.

a. A doubling of the concentration of A doubles the rate of the reaction.

b. A plot of $1/[A]$ versus time is linear.

c. The half-life of the reaction gets longer as the initial concentration of A increases.

d. A plot of the concentration of A versus time has a constant slope.

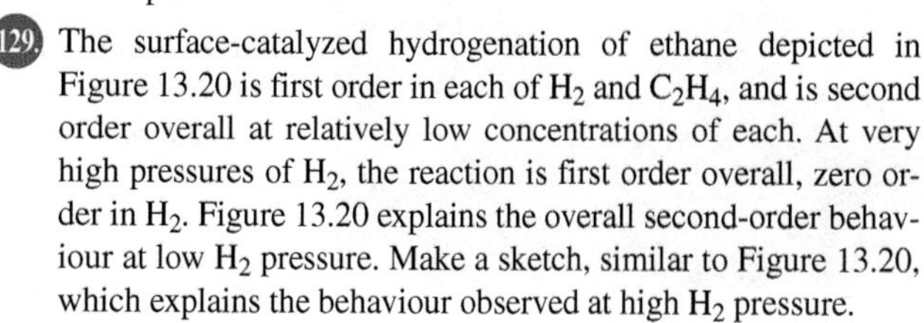

129. The surface-catalyzed hydrogenation of ethane depicted in Figure 13.20 is first order in each of H_2 and C_2H_4, and is second order overall at relatively low concentrations of each. At very high pressures of H_2, the reaction is first order overall, zero order in H_2. Figure 13.20 explains the overall second-order behaviour at low H_2 pressure. Make a sketch, similar to Figure 13.20, which explains the behaviour observed at high H_2 pressure.

14 Chemical Equilibrium

Every system in chemical equilibrium, under the influence of a change of any one of the factors of equilibrium, undergoes a transformation . . . [that produces a change] . . . in the opposite direction of the factor in question.

—Henri Le Châtelier (1850–1936)

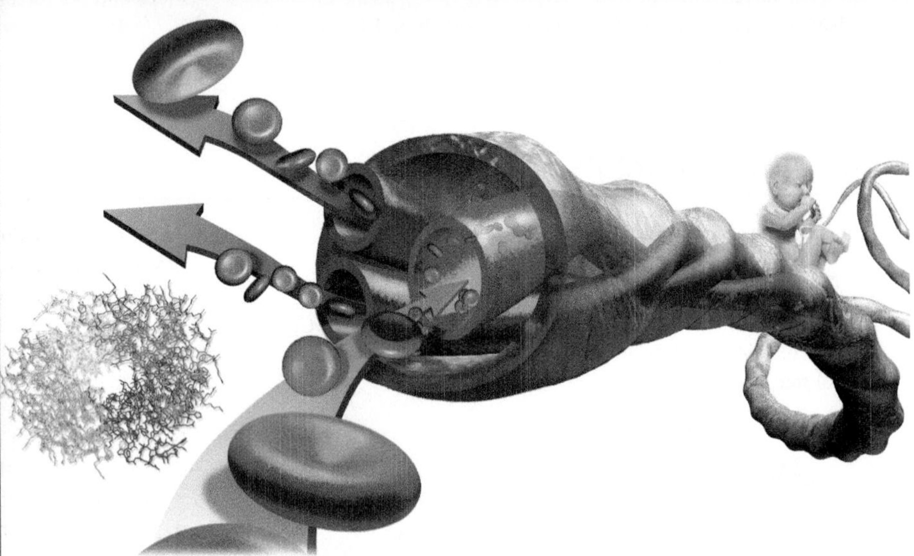

A developing fetus gets oxygen from the mother's blood because the reaction between oxygen and fetal hemoglobin has a larger equilibrium constant than the reaction between oxygen and maternal hemoglobin.

IN CHAPTER 13, we examined *how fast* a chemical reaction occurs. In this chapter, we examine *how far* a chemical reaction goes. The *speed* of a chemical reaction is determined by kinetics. The *extent* of a chemical reaction is determined by thermodynamics. In this chapter, we focus on describing and quantifying how far a chemical reaction goes based on an experimentally measurable quantity called the *equilibrium constant*. A reaction with a large equilibrium constant proceeds nearly to completion—nearly all the reactants react to form products. A reaction with a small equilibrium constant barely proceeds at all—nearly all the reactants remain as reactants, hardly forming any products. For now we simply accept the equilibrium constant as an experimentally measurable quantity and learn how to use it to predict and quantify the extent of a reaction. In Chapter 17, we will examine the reasons underlying the magnitude of equilibrium constants.

14.1 Fetal Hemoglobin and Equilibrium

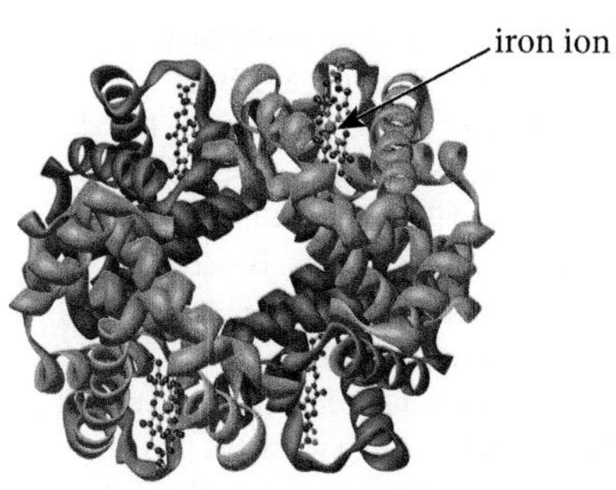

▲ Hemoglobin is the oxygen-carrying protein in red blood cells. Oxygen binds to iron ions, which are depicted here in red.

Have you ever wondered how a baby in the womb gets oxygen? A fetus does not breathe air, yet it needs oxygen. Where does that oxygen come from? After we are born, we inhale air into our lungs and that air diffuses into capillaries, where it comes into contact with the blood. Within red blood cells, a protein called hemoglobin (Hb) reacts with oxygen according to the chemical equation:

$$Hb + O_2 \rightleftharpoons HbO_2$$

The double arrows in this equation indicate that the reaction can occur in both the forward and reverse directions and can reach chemical *equilibrium.* We encountered this term in Chapters 11 and 12, and we define it more carefully in the next section. For now, understand that the concentrations of the reactants and products in a reaction at equilibrium are described by the *equilibrium constant, K*. A large value of K means that the reaction lies far to the right at equilibrium—a high concentration of products and a low concentration of reactants. A small value of K means that the reaction lies far to the left at equilibrium—a high concentration of reactants and a low concentration of products. In other words, the value of K is an indicator of how far a reaction proceeds—the larger the value of K, the more completely the reaction proceeds toward the products.

The equilibrium constant for the reaction between hemoglobin and oxygen is such that hemoglobin efficiently binds oxygen at typical lung oxygen concentrations, but can also release oxygen under the appropriate conditions. Any system at equilibrium, including the hemoglobin–oxygen system, responds to changes in ways that maintain equilibrium. If any of the concentrations of the reactants or products change, the reaction shifts to counteract that change. For the hemoglobin system, as blood flows through the lungs where oxygen concentrations are high, the equilibrium shifts to the right—hemoglobin binds oxygen:

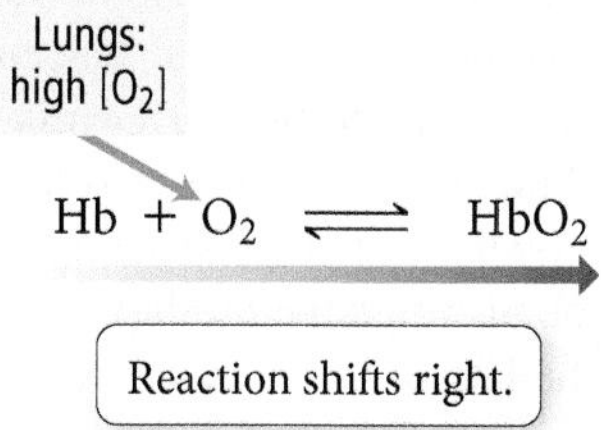

As blood flows out of the lungs and into muscles and organs where oxygen concentrations have been depleted (because muscles and organs use oxygen), the equilibrium shifts to the left—hemoglobin releases oxygen:

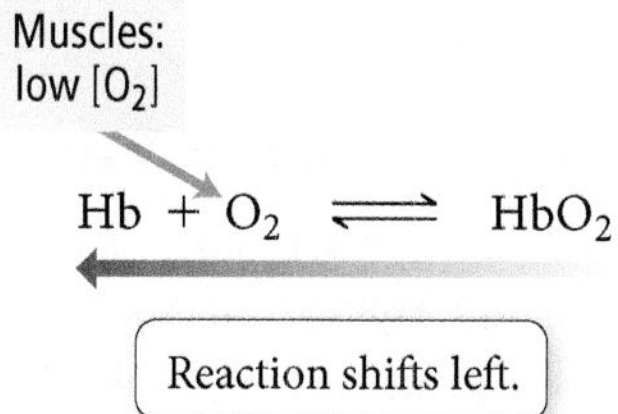

In order to maintain equilibrium, hemoglobin binds oxygen when the surrounding oxygen concentration is high, but releases oxygen when the surrounding oxygen concentration is low. In this way, hemoglobin transports oxygen from the lungs to all parts of the body that use oxygen.

A fetus has its own circulatory system. The mother's blood never flows into the fetus's body and the fetus cannot get any air in the womb. How, then, does the fetus get oxygen? The answer lies in the properties of fetal hemoglobin (HbF), which is slightly different from adult hemoglobin. Like adult hemoglobin, fetal hemoglobin is in equilibrium with oxygen:

$$HbF + O_2 \rightleftharpoons HbFO_2$$

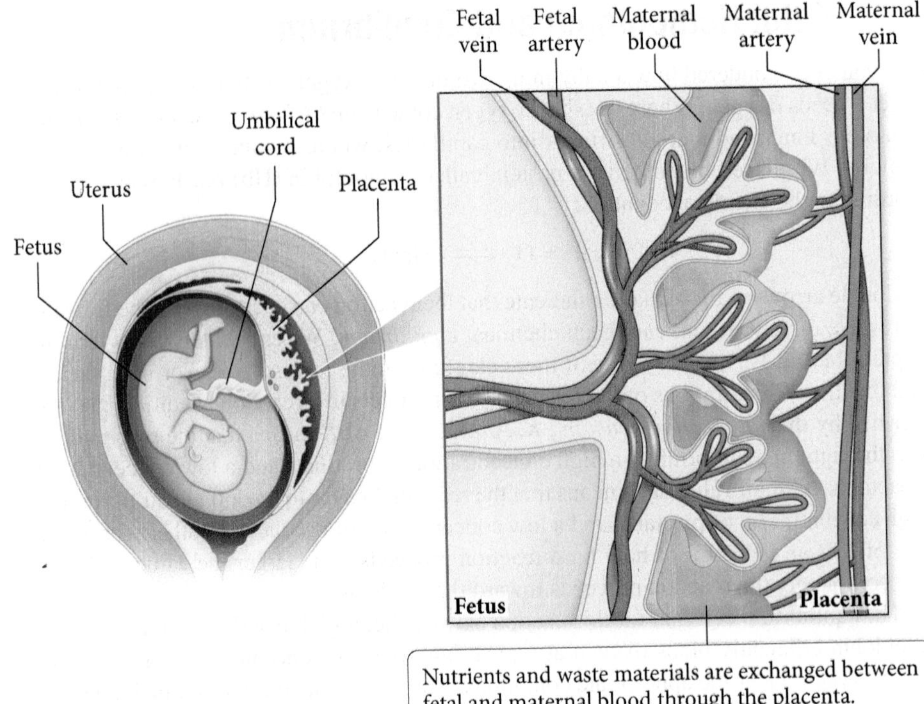

▶ **FIGURE 14.1 Oxygen Exchange Between the Maternal and Fetal Circulation** In the placenta, the blood of the fetus comes into close proximity with that of the mother although the two do not mix directly. Because the reaction of fetal hemoglobin with oxygen has a larger equilibrium constant than the reaction of maternal hemoglobin with oxygen, the fetus receives oxygen from the mother's blood.

However, the equilibrium constant for fetal hemoglobin is larger than the equilibrium constant for adult hemoglobin, meaning that the reaction tends to go farther in the direction of the product. Consequently, fetal hemoglobin loads oxygen at a lower oxygen concentration than does adult hemoglobin. In the placenta, fetal blood flows in close proximity to maternal blood. Although the two never mix, because of the different equilibrium constants, the maternal hemoglobin releases oxygen which the fetal hemoglobin then binds and carries into its own circulatory system (Figure 14.1 ▲). Nature has thus evolved a chemical system through which the mother's hemoglobin can in effect *hand off* oxygen to the hemoglobin of the fetus.

14.2 The Concept of Dynamic Equilibrium

Recall from the previous chapter that reaction rates generally increase with increasing concentration of the reactants (unless the reaction order is zero) and decrease with decreasing concentration of the reactants. With this in mind, consider the reaction between hydrogen and iodine:

$$H_2(g) + I_2(g) \rightleftharpoons 2\,HI(g)$$

Nearly all chemical reactions are at least theoretically reversible. In many cases, however, the reversibility is so small that it can be ignored.

In this reaction, H_2 and I_2 react to form 2 HI molecules, but the 2 HI molecules can also react to re-form H_2 and I_2. A reaction such as this one—that can proceed in both the forward and reverse directions—is said to be **reversible**. Suppose we begin with only H_2 and I_2 in a container (Figure 14.2 (a) ▶). What happens? Initially, H_2 and I_2 begin to react to form HI (Figure 14.2 (b)). However, as H_2 and I_2 react, their concentrations decrease, which in turn *decreases the rate of the forward reaction*. At the same time, HI begins to form. As the concentration of HI increases, the reverse reaction begins to occur at a faster and faster rate. Eventually the rate of the reverse reaction (which has been increasing) equals the rate of the forward reaction (which has been decreasing). At that point, **dynamic equilibrium** is reached (Figure 14.2 (c), (d)).

Remember from the ideal gas law that concentration and partial pressure are directly proportional:

$$c = \frac{n}{V} = \frac{P}{RT}$$

Dynamic equilibrium for a chemical reaction is the condition in which the rate of the forward reaction equals the rate of the reverse reaction.

Dynamic equilibrium is called "dynamic" because the forward and reverse reactions are still occurring; however, they are occurring at the same rate. When dynamic equilibrium

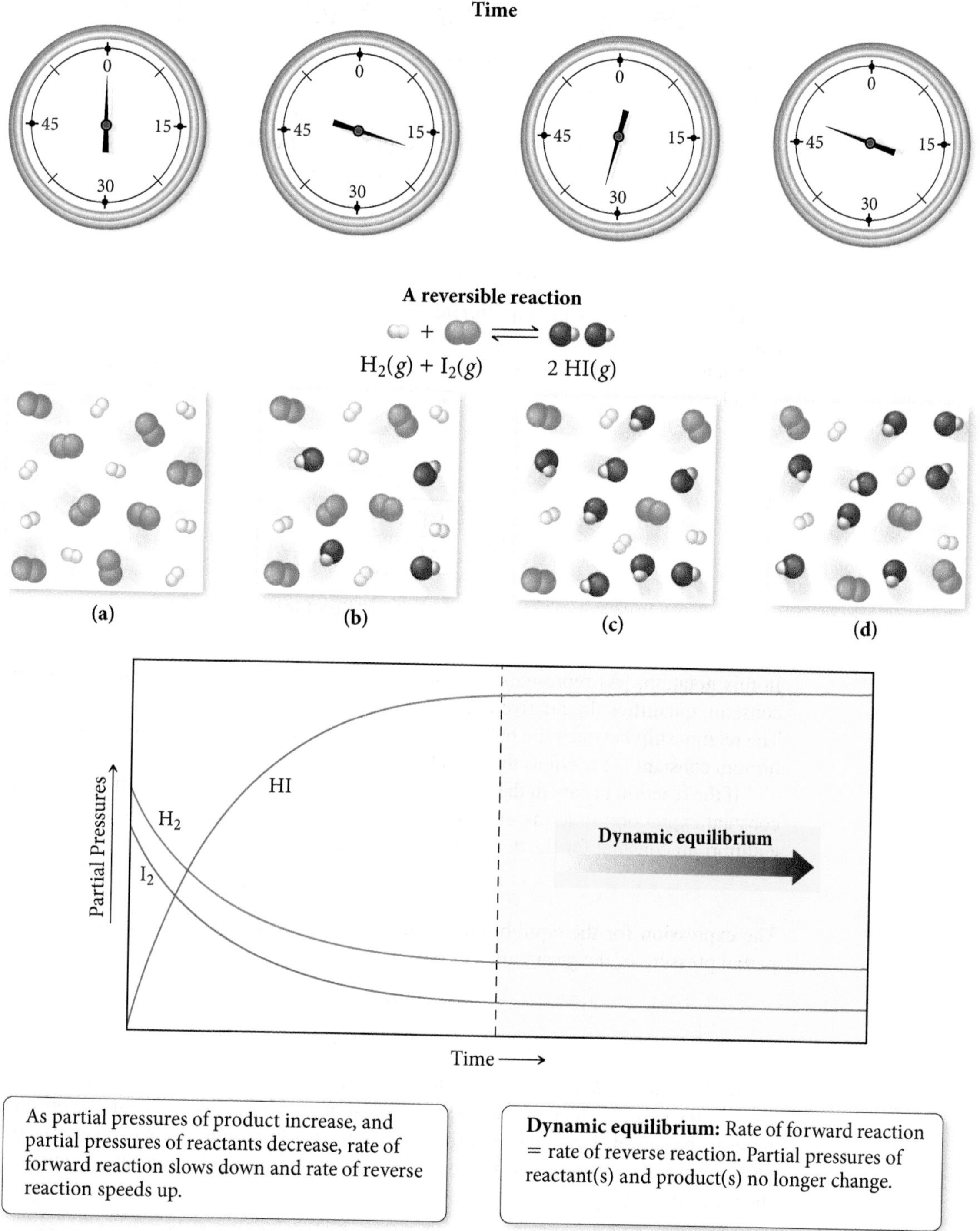

Time
0
45
15
30
A reversible reaction
$H_2(g) + I_2(g)$
$2\ HI(g)$
(a)
(b)
(c)
(d)
Partial Pressures
HI
H_2
I_2
Dynamic equilibrium
Time
As partial pressures of product increase, and partial pressures of reactants decrease, rate of forward reaction slows down and rate of reverse reaction speeds up.
Dynamic equilibrium: Rate of forward reaction = rate of reverse reaction. Partial pressures of reactant(s) and product(s) no longer change.

▲ **FIGURE 14.2 Dynamic Equilibrium** Equilibrium is reached in a chemical reaction when the partial pressures of the reactants and products no longer change. The molecular images, labelled **(a)**, **(b)**, **(c)**, and **(d)**, depict the progress of the reaction $H_2(g) + I_2(g) \rightleftharpoons 2\ HI(g)$. The graph shows the partial pressures of H_2, I_2, and HI as a function of time. When equilibrium is reached, both the forward and reverse reactions continue, but at equal rates, so the partial pressures of the reactants and products remain constant.

is reached, the concentrations of H_2, I_2, and HI no longer change. They remain the same because the reactants and products form at the same rate that they are depleted. However, just because the concentrations of reactants and products no longer change at equilibrium *does not mean that the concentrations of reactants and products are equal to one another* at equilibrium. Some reactions reach equilibrium only after most of the reactants have formed products. Others reach equilibrium when only a small fraction of the reactants have formed products.

14.3 The Expression for the Equilibrium Constant

We have just learned that the *concentrations of reactants and products* are not necessarily equal at equilibrium; instead, the rates of the *forward and reverse reactions* are equal. So what about the concentrations? The equilibrium constant is a way to quantify the relative amounts of reactants and products at equilibrium. Consider the following general chemical reaction occurring in a solution where A and B are reactants, C and D are products, and a, b, c, and d are the respective stoichiometric coefficients in the chemical equation.

$$aA(aq) + bB(aq) \rightleftharpoons cC(aq) + dD(aq)$$

The expression for the **equilibrium constant (K_c)** for a reaction is defined as the ratio of the concentrations—*at equilibrium*—of the products raised to their stoichiometric coefficients divided by the concentrations of the reactants raised to their stoichiometric coefficients:

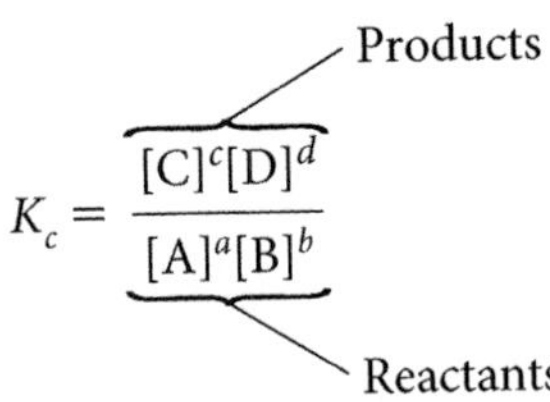

In this notation, [A] represents the concentration of A in mol L^{-1}. K_c, the equilibrium constant, quantifies the relative concentrations of reactants and products *at equilibrium*. The relationship between the balanced chemical equation and the expression of the equilibrium constant is known as the **law of mass action**.

If the reaction occurs in the gas phase, it is more convenient to write the equilibrium-constant expression in terms of pressures. For example, suppose we want to express the equilibrium constant for the decomposition of dinitrogen pentoxide:

$$2\ N_2O_5(g) \rightleftharpoons 4\ NO_2(g) + O_2(g)$$

The expression for the equilibrium constant can be written as follows, where P is the partial pressure of the gas in units of bar:

$$K_P = \frac{(P_{NO_2})^4 P_{O_2}}{(P_{N_2O_5})^2}$$

Notice that the *coefficients* in the chemical equation become the *exponents* in the expression for the equilibrium constant as was the case for K_c. The reason it is more convenient to write the equilibrium-constant expression in terms of pressures for gas-phase reactions and in terms of concentrations for solution-phase reactions will become more apparent in the following section.

Relating K_P and K_c

In the gas phase, it is possible to express the amount of gas as a pressure or as a concentration. Therefore, it is possible to express the equilibrium constant for a gas-phase reaction in terms of pressures (K_P) or concentrations (K_c) and the two equilibrium constants can be related to one another. However, because the partial pressures of the components in bar are not the same as the concentrations in mol L^{-1}, K_P and K_c are not necessarily equal to one another. As long as the gases behave ideally, we can derive a relationship between the two equilibrium constants. The concentration of an ideal gas is the number of moles of A (n_A) divided by its volume (V) in litres:

$$[A] = \frac{n_A}{V} \qquad [14.1]$$

From the ideal gas law, we can relate the quantity in Equation 14.1 to the partial pressure of A as follows:

$$P_A V = n_A RT$$

$$P_A = \frac{n_A}{V} RT \qquad [14.2]$$

Substituting Equation 14.1 into Equation 14.2, we can write:

$$P_A = [A]RT \quad \text{or} \quad [A] = \frac{P_A}{RT} \qquad [14.3]$$

Now consider the following general equilibrium:

$$aA(g) + bB(g) \rightleftharpoons cC(g) + dD(g)$$

We can write the equilibrium constant K_c as follows:

$$K_c = \frac{[C]^c[D]^d}{[A]^a[B]^b}$$

Substituting Equation 14.3 for each concentration term in K_c, we write this:

$$K_c = \frac{\left(\frac{P_C}{RT}\right)^c\left(\frac{P_D}{RT}\right)^d}{\left(\frac{P_A}{RT}\right)^a\left(\frac{P_B}{RT}\right)^b} = \frac{(P_C)^c(P_D)^d\left(\frac{1}{RT}\right)^{c+d}}{(P_A)^a(P_B)^b\left(\frac{1}{RT}\right)^{a+b}} = \frac{(P_C)^c(P_D)^d}{(P_A)^a(P_B)^b}\left(\frac{1}{RT}\right)^{(c+d)-(a+b)}$$

$$= K_P\left(\frac{1}{RT}\right)^{c+d-(a+b)}$$

Rearranging, we obtain this expression:

$$K_P = K_c(RT)^{c+d-(a+b)} \qquad [14.4]$$

Finally, the exponent on the right side of Equation 14.4 is the sum of the stoichiometric coefficients of the gaseous products minus the sum of the stoichiometric coefficients of the gaseous reactants: $\Delta n = c + d - (a + b)$. We can rewrite Equation 14.4 like this:

$$K_P = K_c(RT)^{\Delta n} \qquad [14.5]$$

Notice that if the total number of moles of gas is the same after the reaction as before, then $\Delta n = 0$ and K_P is equal to K_c.

EXAMPLE 14.1 DETERMINING K_P FROM PRESSURE MEASUREMENTS AND RELATING K_P AND K_c

Nitrogen pentoxide is of potential interest for its use in preparing explosives. It decomposes according to the following equation:

$$2\,N_2O_5(g) \rightleftharpoons 4\,NO_2(g) + O_2(g)$$

At 238 K and at equilibrium, a mixture was found to contain 3.8 bar of N_2O_5, 2.7 bar of NO_2, and 0.67 bar of O_2. Determine the equilibrium constants K_P and K_c.

SOLUTION

SORT You are given the partial pressures of the reactants and products at equilibrium and asked to find the equilibrium constants K_P and K_c.	**GIVEN:** $P_{O_2} = 0.67\,\text{bar}, P_{NO_2} = 2.7\,\text{bar}, P_{N_2O_5} = 3.8\,\text{bar}$ **FIND:** K_P and K_c
STRATEGIZE Write the equilibrium-constant expression, substitute in the partial pressures to calculate K_P, and then use Equation 14.5 to find K_c.	**EQUATION:** $K_P = K_c(RT)^{\Delta n}$

(continued)

EXAMPLE 14.1 (CONTINUED)

SOLVE	SOLUTION
First, write the expression for K_P, then substitute in the partial pressures and calculate K_P.	$K_P = \frac{(P_{NO_2})^4 P_{O_2}}{(P_{N_2O_5})^2} = \frac{(2.7\,\text{bar})^4(0.67\,\text{bar})}{(3.8\,\text{bar})^2}$ $= 2.5\,\text{bar}^3$
Second, rearrange Equation 14.5 for K_c.	$K_c = \frac{K_P}{(RT)^{\Delta n}}$
Third, calculate Δn.	$\Delta n = 5 - 2 = 3$
Substitute the required quantities to calculate K_c.	$K_c = \frac{2.5\,\text{bar}^3}{\left(0.08314\frac{\text{bar L}}{\text{mol K}} \times 248\,\text{K}\right)^3}$ $= 2.9 \times 10^{-4}\,\text{mol}^3\,\text{L}^{-3}$

CHECK The easiest way to check this answer is to substitute it back into Equation 14.5 and confirm that you get the original value for K_P.

$$K_P = 2.9 \times 10^{-4}\,\text{mol}^3\,\text{L}^{-3}\left(0.08314\frac{\text{bar L}}{\text{mol K}} \times 248\,\text{K}\right)^3$$

$$= 2.5\,\text{bar}^3$$

FOR PRACTICE 14.1

The reaction of N_2 and H_2 forms ammonia (NH_3):

$$N_2(g) + 3\,H_2(g) \rightleftharpoons 2\,NH_3(g)$$

At 600 K and at equilibrium, the concentrations of N_2, H_2, and NH_3 were found to be 0.288, 0.864, and 1.424 mol L^{-1}, respectively. Determine K_c and K_P.

The Unitless Thermodynamic Equilibrium Constant

Standard states were introduced in Section 6.9.

In Chapter 17, we will learn that we can use the equilibrium constant to determine thermochemical parameters such as the standard Gibbs energy change ($\Delta_r G^\circ$) for a chemical reaction. This requires the knowledge of the thermodynamic equilibrium constant, K, which is related to K_P and K_c, but is not exactly the same. The thermodynamic equilibrium constant is defined as the activities of the products raised to their stoichiometric coefficients divided by the activities of the reactants raised to their stoichiometric coefficients. An **activity** (a) is a measure of the deviation from the standard state. The standard states for solutes (c°) and for gases (P°) are:

- A concentration of 1 mol L^{-1} for a solute ($c^\circ = 1$ mol L^{-1})
- A pressure of 1 bar for a gas ($P^\circ = 1$ bar)

Assuming the aqueous or gaseous solutions to be ideal, the activities for a component, X, are defined as:

- $a_X = [X]/c^\circ$ for a solute
- $a_X = P_X/P^\circ$ for a gas

Ideal gases or solutes are, in simple terms, those that do not interact with one another. An activity is a measure of the "effective" partial pressure or concentration that takes into account the non-ideality of real gases or solutes.

When an ideal gas or a solute is at its standard state, the activity is 1. You will learn more about activities in higher-level chemistry courses.

Let's consider the solution-phase equilibrium between iron(III), Fe^{3+}, and the thiocyanate ion, SCN^-. A common test for Fe^{3+} is to add a source of SCN^-, which turns the solution blood red if Fe^{3+} is present. The reaction is:

$$Fe^{3+}(aq) + SCN^-(aq) \rightleftharpoons Fe(SCN)^{2+}(aq)$$

The expression for the thermodynamic equilibrium constant is written as:

$$K = \frac{a_{Fe(SCN)^{2+}}}{a_{Fe^{3+}}a_{SCN^-}} \quad [14.6]$$

Substitution of the expressions for solution activity $(a_X = [X]/c^\circ)$ into Equation 14.6 yields:

$$K = \frac{\dfrac{[Fe(SCN)^{2+}]}{c^\circ}}{\left(\dfrac{[Fe^{3+}]}{c^\circ}\right)\left(\dfrac{[SCN^-]}{c^\circ}\right)} \quad [14.7]$$

Equation 14.7 simplifies to:

$$K = \frac{[Fe(SCN)^{2+}]}{[Fe^{3+}][SCN^-]}(c^\circ) = K_c(c^\circ)$$

Assuming an ideal solution, the only difference between K and K_c for this example is that K is unitless, and K_c has units of L mol^{-1} (reciprocal concentration). In the present case, $K_c = 8.9 \times 10^2$ L mol^{-1} and $K = 8.9 \times 10^2$.

Let's consider a gas-phase reaction. The thermodynamic equilibrium constant for the decomposition of dinitrogen pentoxide

$$2\,N_2O_5(g) \rightleftharpoons 4\,NO_2(g) + O_2(g)$$

is the following:

$$K = \frac{(a_{NO_2})^4 a_{O_2}}{(a_{N_2O_5})^2} \quad [14.8]$$

Substitution of the expressions for the activity of each gas $(a_X = P_X/P^\circ)$ into Equation 14.8 yields:

$$K = \frac{\left(\dfrac{P_{NO_2}}{P^\circ}\right)^4\left(\dfrac{P_{O_2}}{P^\circ}\right)}{\left(\dfrac{P_{N_2O_5}}{P^\circ}\right)^2} \quad [14.9]$$

Equation 14.9 simplifies to:

$$K = \frac{(P_{NO_2})^2 P_{O_2}}{(P_{N_2O_5})^2}\left(\frac{1}{(P^\circ)^3}\right) = \frac{K_P}{(P^\circ)^3}$$

The only difference between K and K_P for this example is that K_P has units of bar^{-3}, and K is unitless; the magnitudes are the same. For this reaction at 298 K, $K_P = 7.7 \times 10^{-6}$ bar^{-3} and $K = 7.7 \times 10^{-6}$.

Heterogeneous Equilibria: Reactions Involving Solids and Liquids

Many chemical reactions involve pure solids or pure liquids as reactants or products. Consider, for example, this reaction, depicted in Figure 14.3 ▼:

$$2\,CO(g) \rightleftharpoons CO_2(g) + C(s)$$

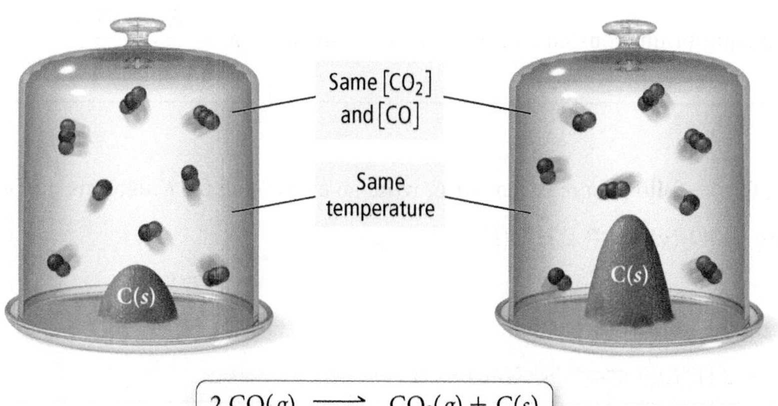

◀ **FIGURE 14.3 Heterogeneous Equilibrium** The concentration of solid carbon (the number of atoms per unit volume) is constant as long as some solid carbon is present. The same is true for pure liquids. Thus, the concentrations of solids and pure liquids are not included in equilibrium-constant expressions.

The expression for the thermodynamic equilibrium constant is:

$$K = \frac{a_{CO_2} a_c}{(a_{CO})^2} \quad [14.10]$$

In the previous section, we stated that for dilute solutions $a_X = [X]/c°$ and for gases behaving ideally $a_X = P_X/P°$, where $c°$ and $P°$ are the standard states, 1 mol L^{-1} and 1 bar, respectively. There is one more rule we must know that involves the standard states of solids and liquids (including solvents):

- For liquids and solids, the standard state is the pure liquid or solid.

The activities for a liquid or a solid are defined as:

- For a liquid, the activity is the mole fraction so for a dilute solution $a_{solvent} = 1$.
- For a solid, $a_{solid} = 1$.

In this text, we will assume the solutions are sufficiently dilute that the activity of the solvent is 1. For pure solids, the activity is also equal to 1, provided there is some solid present. Since $a_c = 1$, the equilibrium-constant expression in Equation 14.10 can be simplified to:

$$K = \frac{P_{CO_2} P°}{(P_{CO})^2} = K_P \times P° \quad \text{where} \quad K_P = \frac{P_{CO_2}}{(P_{CO})^2}$$

Since $P° = 1$ bar, K and K_P have the same value differing only by units (K_P having units of bar^{-1} for this example). It is also apparent from this example that there is no term for the solid in the equilibrium-constant expression. It is also true that for a reaction in which a liquid or solvent takes part in the reaction, we assume the liquid is pure or the solution is dilute, and we can ignore their terms in the equilibrium-constant expression. For example, the following equilibrium involving ammonia (NH_3) takes place in solution, and water takes part in the reaction:

$$NH_3(aq) + H_2O(l) \rightleftharpoons NH_4^+(aq) + OH^-(aq)$$

The equilibrium-constant expression does not include a term for liquid water:

$$K_c = \frac{[NH_4^+][OH^-]}{[NH_3]} \quad \text{and} \quad K = \frac{[NH_4^+][OH^-]}{[NH_3]c°}$$

Making the assumption that the solution is ideal, K_c and K have the same value but differ in the units.

EXAMPLE 14.2 WRITING EQUILIBRIUM EXPRESSIONS FOR REACTIONS INVOLVING A SOLID OR A LIQUID

Write an expression for the equilibrium constant K_P for the following reaction. Also, write an expression for K in terms of K_P.

$$CaCO_3(s) \rightleftharpoons CaO(s) + CO_2(g)$$

SOLUTION

Since $CaCO_3$ and CaO are both solids, they are omitted from the equilibrium-constant expressions; they are assumed to be pure and their activities are 1. K_P is in terms of pressure.	$K_P = P_{CO_2}$
K_P has units of bar. Since the thermodynamic equilibrium constant, K, is unitless, K_P must be divided by $P°$.	$K = \frac{K_P}{P°} = \frac{P_{CO_2}}{P°}$

FOR PRACTICE 14.2

Write an equilibrium-constant expression, K_P, for the following reaction. Also, write an expression for K in terms of K_P.

$$4\,HCl(g) + O_2(g) \rightleftharpoons 2\,H_2O(l) + 2\,Cl_2(g)$$

FOR MORE PRACTICE 14.2

Write an equilibrium-constant expression, K, for the following reaction:

$$Fe(s) + 2\,H^+(aq) \rightleftharpoons Fe^{2+}(aq) + H_2(g)$$

CONCEPTUAL CONNECTION 14.1

Heterogeneous Equilibria, K_P and K_c

For which reaction does $K_P = K_c$?

(a) $2\,Na_2O_2(s) + 2\,CO_2(g) \rightleftharpoons 2\,Na_2CO_3(s) + O_2(g)$

(b) $NiO(s) + CO(g) \rightleftharpoons Ni(s) + CO_2(g)$

(c) $NH_4NO_3(s) \rightleftharpoons N_2O(g) + 2\,H_2O(g)$

14.4 The Equilibrium Constant (K)

Units of Equilibrium Constants

Since there is such a close relationship between K and K_P or K_c, the question might be asked, "Why bother differentiating between the two?" The reason we use activities is that at high concentrations or high pressures the activity of the component might be very different from its concentration or partial pressure. At these higher concentrations or pressures, the intermolecular forces become important, and the molecules or ions involved in the equilibrium no longer act as "independent" particles. For our purposes, we will make the assumption that we are under conditions such that the activities are always numerically equal to the concentrations or pressures.

In the following section, we will begin to use measured values of partial pressure and concentration to calculate equilibrium constants. We will also do the reverse: use equilibrium constants to determine concentrations or partial pressures of each component at equilibrium. Formally, the values used to determine the equilibrium constants are activities. As we have seen, however, the activities can be approximated by concentrations for solutes and partial pressures for gases. *As long as the concentration units are expressed in mol L^{-1} for* K_c *and pressures are expressed in bar for* K_P, we can take a shortcut by entering the quantities directly into the equilibrium expression, dropping their corresponding units to obtain a unitless equilibrium constant that is equal to the thermodynamic equilibrium constant. Conversely, we will see that one can use unitless thermodynamic equilibrium constants (such as those tabulated in the appendices of this text) to estimate concentrations of solutes and partial pressures of gases in mol L^{-1} and bar, respectively.

The Significance of the Equilibrium Constant

We now know how to express the equilibrium constant, but what does it mean? What, for example, does a large equilibrium constant ($K \gg 1$) imply about a reaction? In general, a large equilibrium constant indicates that the numerator (which specifies the amounts of products at equilibrium) is larger than the denominator (which specifies the amounts of reactants at equilibrium). Therefore, at equilibrium the amount of products are favoured over the amount of reactants. For example, consider the reaction:

$$H_2(g) + Br_2(g) \rightleftharpoons 2\,HBr(g) \qquad K = 1.9 \times 10^{19} \text{ (at 25 °C)}$$

The equilibrium constant is large, indicating that the equilibrium point for the reaction lies far to the right—high partial pressure of products, low partial pressure of reactants (Figure 14.4 ▼). Remember that the equilibrium constant says nothing about *how fast* a reaction reaches equilibrium, only *how far* the reaction has proceeded once equilibrium is reached. A reaction with a large equilibrium constant may be kinetically very slow and take a long time to reach equilibrium.

Conversely, what does a *small* equilibrium constant ($K \ll 1$) mean? It indicates that there will be more reactants than products when equilibrium is reached. For example, consider the following reaction:

$$N_2(g) + O_2(g) \rightleftharpoons 2\,NO(g) \qquad K = 4.1 \times 10^{-31} \text{ (at 25 °C)}$$

The equilibrium constant is very small, indicating that the equilibrium point for the reaction lies far to the left—high partial pressures of reactants, low partial pressures of

▶ **FIGURE 14.4 The Meaning of a Large Equilibrium Constant** If the equilibrium constant for a reaction is large, the equilibrium point of the reaction lies far to the right—the partial pressures of the products are large and the partial pressures of the reactants are small.

$$H_2(g) + Br_2(g) \rightleftharpoons 2\,HBr(g)$$

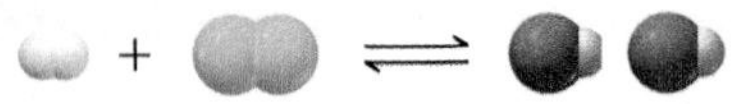

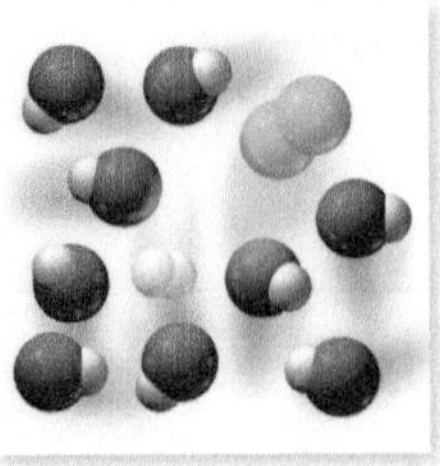

$$K = \frac{(P_{HBr})^2}{P_{H_2}P_{Br_2}} = \text{large number}$$

products (Figure 14.5 ▼). This is fortunate because N_2 and O_2 are the main components of air. If this equilibrium constant were large, much of the N_2 and O_2 in air would react to form NO, a toxic gas.

$$N_2(g) + O_2(g) \rightleftharpoons 2\,NO(g)$$

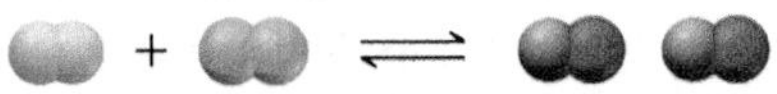

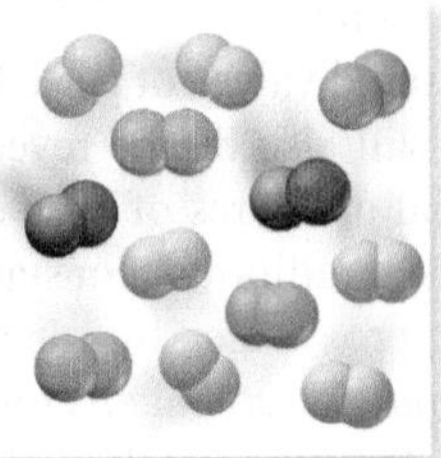

$$K = \frac{(P_{NO})^2}{P_{N_2}P_{O_2}} = \text{small number}$$

▶ **FIGURE 14.5 The Meaning of a Small Equilibrium Constant** If the equilibrium constant for a reaction is small, the equilibrium point of the reaction lies far to the left—the partial pressures of products are small and the partial pressures of reactants are large.

Summarizing the Significance of the Equilibrium Constant:

- $K \ll 1$ Reverse reaction is favoured; forward reaction does not proceed very far.
- $K \approx 1$ Neither direction is favoured; forward reaction proceeds about halfway.
- $K \gg 1$ Forward reaction is favoured; forward reaction proceeds essentially to completion.

CONCEPTUAL CONNECTION 14.2

Equilibrium Constants

The equilibrium constant for the reaction $A(g) \rightleftharpoons B(g)$ is 10. A reaction mixture initially contains 11 mol of A and 0 mol of B in a fixed volume of 1 L. When equilibrium is reached, which statement is true?

(a) The reaction mixture will contain 10 mol of A and 1 mol of B.

(b) The reaction mixture will contain 1 mol of A and 10 mol of B.

(c) The reaction mixture will contain equal amounts of A and B.

Relationships Between the Equilibrium Constant and the Chemical Equation

If a chemical equation is modified in some way, then the equilibrium constant for the equation must be changed to reflect the modification. The following modifications are common.

1. **If you reverse the equation, invert the equilibrium constant.** For example, consider this equilibrium equation:

$$A + 2\,B \rightleftharpoons 3\,C$$

CHEMISTRY AND MEDICINE Life and Equilibrium

Have you ever tried to define life? If you have, you probably know that a definition is elusive. How are living things different from nonliving things? You may try to define living things as those things that can move. But of course many living things do not move (most plants, for example), and some nonliving things, such as glaciers and Earth itself, do move. So motion is neither unique to nor definitive of life. You may try to define living things as those things that can reproduce. But again, many living things, such as mules or sterile humans, cannot reproduce; yet they are alive. In addition, some nonliving things, such as crystals, for example, reproduce (in some sense). So, what is unique about living things?

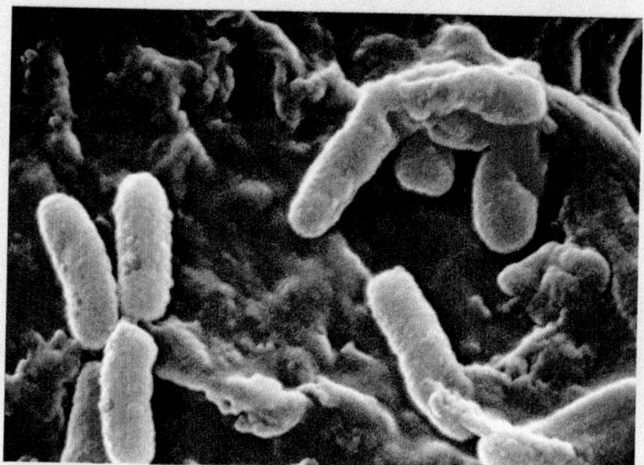

▲ What makes these cells alive?

One definition of life uses the concept of equilibrium—living things *are not* in equilibrium with their surroundings. Our body temperature, for example, is not the same as the temperature of our surroundings. If we jump into a swimming pool, the acidity of our blood does not become the same as the acidity of the surrounding water. Living things, even the simplest ones, maintain some measure of *disequilibrium* with their environment.

We must add one more concept, however, to complete our definition of life with respect to equilibrium. A cup of hot water is in disequilibrium with its environment with respect to temperature, yet it is not alive. The cup of hot water has no control over its disequilibrium, however, and will slowly come to equilibrium with its environment. In contrast, living things—as long as they are alive—maintain and *control* their disequilibrium. Your body temperature, for example, is not *only* in disequilibrium with your surroundings—it is in *controlled disequilibrium.* Your body maintains your temperature within a specific range that is not in equilibrium with the surrounding temperature.

So, one criterion for life is that living things are in *controlled disequilibrium* with their environment. Maintaining that disequilibrium is a main activity of living organisms, requiring energy obtained from their environment. Plants derive that energy from sunlight; animals eat plants (or other animals that have eaten plants), and thus they too ultimately derive their energy from the sun. A living thing comes into equilibrium with its surroundings only after it dies.

The expression for the equilibrium constant of this reaction is given by

$$K_{\text{forward}} = \frac{[\text{C}]^3}{[\text{A}][\text{B}]^2}$$

If we reverse the equation:

$$3\,\text{C} \rightleftharpoons \text{A} + 2\,\text{B}$$

then, according to the law of mass action, the expression for the equilibrium constant becomes:

$$K_{\text{reverse}} = \frac{[\text{A}][\text{B}]^2}{[\text{C}]^3} = \frac{1}{K_{\text{forward}}}$$

2. **If you multiply the coefficients in the equation by a factor, raise the equilibrium constant to the same factor.** Consider again this chemical equation and corresponding expression for the equilibrium constant:

$$\text{A} + 2\,\text{B} \rightleftharpoons 3\,\text{C} \qquad K = \frac{[\text{C}]^3}{[\text{A}][\text{B}]^2}$$

If we multiply the equation by n, we get:

$$n\,\text{A} + 2n\,\text{B} \rightleftharpoons 3n\,\text{C}$$

Applying the law of mass action, the expression for the equilibrium constant becomes:

$$K' = \frac{[\text{C}]^{3n}}{[\text{A}]^n[\text{B}]^{2n}} = \left(\frac{[\text{C}]^3}{[\text{A}][\text{B}]^2}\right)^n = K^n$$

If n is a fractional quantity, raise K to the same fractional quantity.

3. **If you add two or more individual chemical equations to obtain an overall equation, multiply the corresponding equilibrium constants by each other to obtain the overall equilibrium constant.** Consider these two chemical equations and their corresponding equilibrium constant expressions:

$$\mathrm{A} \rightleftharpoons 2\,\mathrm{B} \qquad K_1 = \frac{[\mathrm{B}]^2}{[\mathrm{A}]}$$

$$2\,\mathrm{B} \rightleftharpoons 3\,\mathrm{C} \qquad K_2 = \frac{[\mathrm{C}]^3}{[\mathrm{B}]^2}$$

The two equations sum as follows:

$$\begin{array}{r} \mathrm{A} \rightleftharpoons \cancel{2\,\mathrm{B}} \\ \cancel{2\,\mathrm{B}} \rightleftharpoons 3\,\mathrm{C} \\ \hline \mathrm{A} \rightleftharpoons 3\,\mathrm{C} \end{array}$$

According to the law of mass action, the equilibrium constant for this overall equation is then:

$$K_{\text{overall}} = \frac{[\mathrm{C}]^3}{[\mathrm{A}]}$$

Notice that K_{overall} is the product of K_1 and K_2:

$$\begin{aligned} K_{\text{overall}} &= K_1 \times K_2 \\ &= \frac{\cancel{[\mathrm{B}]^2}}{[\mathrm{A}]} \times \frac{[\mathrm{C}]^3}{\cancel{[\mathrm{B}]^2}} \\ &= \frac{[\mathrm{C}]^3}{[\mathrm{A}]} \end{aligned}$$

EXAMPLE 14.3

MANIPULATING THE EQUILIBRIUM CONSTANT TO REFLECT CHANGES IN THE CHEMICAL EQUATION

Consider the chemical equation and equilibrium constant for the synthesis of ammonia at 25 °C:

$$\mathrm{N_2}(g) + 3\,\mathrm{H_2}(g) \rightleftharpoons 2\,\mathrm{NH_3}(g) \qquad K = 3.7 \times 10^8$$

Calculate the equilibrium constant for the following reaction at 25 °C:

$$\mathrm{NH_3}(g) \rightleftharpoons \tfrac{1}{2}\mathrm{N_2}(g) + \tfrac{3}{2}\mathrm{H_2}(g) \qquad K' = ?$$

SOLUTION

You want to manipulate the given reaction and value of K to obtain the desired reaction and value of K. You can see that the given reaction is the reverse of the desired reaction, and its coefficients are twice those of the desired reaction.

Begin by reversing the given reaction and taking the inverse of the value of K.	$\mathrm{N_2}(g) + 3\,\mathrm{H_2}(g) \rightleftharpoons 2\,\mathrm{NH_3}(g) \quad K = 3.7 \times 10^8$ $2\,\mathrm{NH_3}(g) \rightleftharpoons \mathrm{N_2}(g) + 3\,\mathrm{H_2}(g) \quad K_{\text{rev}} = \dfrac{1}{3.7 \times 10^8}$
Next, multiply the reaction by $\frac{1}{2}$ and raise the equilibrium constant to the $\frac{1}{2}$ power.	$\mathrm{NH_3}(g) \rightleftharpoons \tfrac{1}{2}\mathrm{N_2}(g) + \tfrac{3}{2}\mathrm{H_2}(g)$ $K' = K_{\text{reverse}}^{1/2} = \left(\dfrac{1}{3.7 \times 10^8}\right)^{1/2}$
Calculate the value of K'.	$K' = 5.2 \times 10^{-5}$

FOR PRACTICE 14.3

Consider the following chemical equation and equilibrium constant at 25 °C:

$$2\,\mathrm{COF_2}(g) \rightleftharpoons \mathrm{CO_2}(g) + \mathrm{CF_4}(g) \qquad K = 2.2 \times 10^6$$

Compute the equilibrium constant for the following reaction at 25 °C:

$$2\,CO_2(g) + 2\,CF_4(g) \rightleftharpoons 4\,COF_2(g) \qquad K' = ?$$

FOR MORE PRACTICE 14.3

Predict the equilibrium constant for the first reaction given the equilibrium constants for the second and third reactions:

$$CO_2(g) + 3\,H_2(g) \rightleftharpoons CH_3OH(g) + H_2O(g) \qquad K_1 = ?$$
$$CO(g) + H_2O(g) \rightleftharpoons CO_2(g) + H_2(g) \qquad K_2 = 1.0 \times 10^5$$
$$CO(g) + 2\,H_2(g) \rightleftharpoons CH_3OH(g) \qquad K_3 = 1.4 \times 10^7$$

14.5 Calculating the Equilibrium Constant from Measured Quantities

The most direct way to obtain an experimental value for the equilibrium constant of a reaction is to measure the partial pressures (gases) or concentrations (solutes) of the reactants and products in a reactant mixture at equilibrium. Consider the following gaseous reaction:

$$H_2(g) + I_2(g) \rightleftharpoons 2\,HI(g)$$

Suppose a mixture of H_2 and I_2 is allowed to come to equilibrium at 640 K. The partial pressures measured at equilibrium are $P_{H_2} = 0.098\,\text{bar}$, $P_{I_2} = 0.098\,\text{bar}$, and $P_{HI} = 0.804\,\text{bar}$. What is the value of the equilibrium constant at this temperature? The expression for the equilibrium constant can be written from the balanced equation:

Since equilibrium constants depend on temperature, many equilibrium problems will state the temperature even though it has no formal part in the calculation.

$$K = \frac{(P_{HI})^2}{P_{H_2}P_{I_2}}$$

To calculate the value of K, substitute the correct equilibrium partial pressures into the expression for K:

$$K = \frac{(P_{HI})^2}{P_{H_2}P_{I_2}} = \frac{(0.804)^2}{(0.098)\,(0.098)} = 67$$

The partial pressures within K should always be written in units of bar for gas-phase reactions or mol L^{-1} for solution-phase reactions; however, as noted in Section 14.4, the units are not included when expressing the value of the thermodynamic equilibrium constant, K.

For any reaction, the partial pressures or concentrations of the reactants and products will depend on the initial values (and, in general, vary from one set of initial conditions to another). However, the equilibrium *constant* will always be the same at a given temperature regardless of the values at the beginning. For example, Table 14.1 shows several different values of the partial pressures H_2, I_2, and HI at equilibrium—each from a different set of starting values. Whether you start with only reactants or only products, the reaction components attain partial pressures in which the equilibrium constant, K, is the same.

So far, we have calculated equilibrium constants from values of the equilibrium concentrations of all the reactants and products. In most cases, however, we need only know the initial concentrations of the reactant(s) and the equilibrium concentration of any *one* reactant or product. The other equilibrium concentrations can be deduced from the stoichiometry of the reaction. For example, consider the following simple reaction:

$$A(aq) \rightleftharpoons 2\,B(aq)$$

Suppose that we have a reaction mixture in which the initial concentration of A is 1.00 mol L^{-1} and the initial concentration of B is 0.00 mol L^{-1}. When equilibrium is reached, the concentration of A is 0.75 mol L^{-1}. Since [A] has changed by -0.25 mol L^{-1}, we can deduce (based on the stoichiometry) that [B] must have changed

TABLE 14.1 Initial and Equilibrium Concentrations for the Reaction $H_2(g) + I_2(g) \rightleftharpoons 2\,HI(g)$ at 640 K

Initial Partial Pressures/Bar			Partial Pressures at Equilibrium/Bar			Equilibrium Constant
P_{H_2}	P_{I_2}	P_{HI}	P_{H_2}	P_{I_2}	P_{HI}	$K = \frac{(P_{HI})^2}{P_{H_2}P_{I_2}}$
0	0	2.000	0.196	0.196	1.608	$K = \frac{(1.608)^2}{(0.196)(0.196)} = 67$
0	0	0.500	0.049	0.049	0.402	$K = \frac{(0.402)^2}{(0.049)(0.049)} = 67$
2.000	2.000	0	0.393	0.393	3.214	$K = \frac{(3.214)^2}{(0.393)(0.393)} = 67$
1.000	0.750	0	0.331	0.081	1.338	$K = \frac{(1.338)^2}{(0.331)(0.081)} = 67$
1.000	1.000	1.000	0.295	0.295	2.410	$K = \frac{(2.41)^2}{(0.295)(0.295)} = 67$

by 2 × (+0.25 mol L^{-1}) or +0.50 mol L^{-1}. We can summarize the initial conditions, the changes, and the equilibrium conditions in the following table:

	[A]	[B]
Initial	1.00	0
Change	−0.25	+0.50
Equilibrium	0.75	0.50

This type of table is often referred to as an ICE table (I = initial, C = change, E = equilibrium). To calculate the equilibrium constant, we use the balanced equation to write an expression for the equilibrium constant and then substitute the equilibrium concentrations from the ICE table:

$$K = \frac{[B]^2}{[A]} = \frac{(0.50)^2}{(0.75)} = 0.33$$

In the examples that follow, we show the general procedure for solving these kinds of equilibrium problems in the left column and work two examples exemplifying the procedure in the centre and right columns.

PROCEDURE FOR...

Finding Equilibrium Constants from Experimental Measurements

To solve these problems, follow the procedure outlined on the next page.

EXAMPLE 14.4

Finding Equilibrium Constants from Experimental Partial Pressure Measurements

Consider the following reaction:

$$CO(g) + 2\,H_2(g) \rightleftharpoons CH_3OH(g)$$

A reaction mixture at 400 K initially contained CO and H_2 at partial pressures of 0.750 and 1.000 bar, respectively. At equilibrium, the partial pressure of CO was found to be 0.295 bar. What is the value of the equilibrium constant?

EXAMPLE 14.5

Finding Equilibrium Constants from Experimental Concentration Measurements

Consider the following reaction:

$$Ni(s) + 2\,V^{3+}(aq) \rightleftharpoons Ni^{2+}(aq) + 2\,V^{2+}(aq)$$

A chunk of solid nickel is placed into a 0.250 mol L^{-1} solution of V^{3+} at 298 K. At equilibrium the concentration of V^{3+} was found to be 0.056 mol L^{-1}. What is the value of the equilibrium constant?

1. Using the balanced equation as a guide, prepare an ICE table showing the known initial quantities of substance (partial pressures or concentrations) and the known equilibrium quantities of the reactants and products. Leave space in the middle of the table for determining the changes in partial pressure or concentration that occur during the reaction.	$CO(g) + 2\,H_2(g) \rightleftharpoons CH_3OH(g)$ P_{CO} / P_{H_2} / P_{CH_3OH} Initial: 0.750 / 1.000 / 0 Change: Equil: 0.295	$Ni(s) + 2\,V^{3+}(aq) \rightleftharpoons Ni^{2+}(aq) + 2\,V^{2+}(aq)$ $[V^{3+}]$ / $[Ni^{2+}]$ / $[V^{2+}]$ Initial: 0.250 / 0 / 0 Change: Equil: 0.056 Remember that Ni(*s*) is not in the expression for the equilibrium constant, so we do not need to account for its quantity as long as there is some solid nickel present at equilibrium.
2. For the reactant or product whose quantity is known both initially and at equilibrium, calculate the change in partial pressure or concentration that occurred.	$CO(g) + 2\,H_2(g) \rightleftharpoons CH_3OH(g)$ P_{CO} / P_{H_2} / P_{CH_3OH} Initial: 0.750 / 1.000 / 0 Change: −0.455 Equil: 0.295	$Ni(s) + 2\,V^{3+}(aq) \rightleftharpoons Ni^{2+}(aq) + 2\,V^{2+}(aq)$ $[V^{3+}]$ / $[Ni^{2+}]$ / $[V^{2+}]$ Initial: 0.250 / 0 / 0 Change: −0.194 Equil: 0.056
3. Use the change calculated in step 2 and the stoichiometric relationships from the balanced chemical equation to determine the changes in quantity of all other reactants and products. Since reactants are consumed during the reaction, the changes in their quantities are negative. Since products are formed, the changes in their quantities are positive.	$CO(g) + 2\,H_2(g) \rightleftharpoons CH_3OH(g)$ P_{CO} / P_{H_2} / P_{CH_3OH} Initial: 0.750 / 1.000 / 0 Change: −0.455 / −9.10 / +0.455 Equil: 0.295	$Ni(s) + 2\,V^{3+}(aq) \rightleftharpoons Ni^{2+}(aq) + 2\,V^{2+}(aq)$ $[V^{3+}]$ / $[Ni^{2+}]$ / $[V^{2+}]$ Initial: 0.250 / 0 / 0 Change: −0.194 / +0.097 / +0.194 Equil: 0.056
4. Sum each column for each reactant and product to determine the equilibrium quantities.	P_{CO} / P_{H_2} / P_{CH_3OH} Initial: 0.750 / 1.000 / 0 Change: −0.455 / −9.10 / +0.455 Equil: 0.295 / 0.090 / 0.455	$[V^{3+}]$ / $[Ni^{2+}]$ / $[V^{2+}]$ Initial: 0.250 / 0 / 0 Change: −0.194 / +0.097 / +0.194 Equil: 0.056 / 0.097 / 0.194
5. Use the balanced equation to write an expression for the equilibrium constant and substitute the equilibrium quantities to calculate *K*.	$K = \dfrac{P_{CH_3OH}}{P_{CO}(P_{H_2})^2} = \dfrac{0.455}{(0.295)(0.090)^2} = 190$	$K = \dfrac{[Ni^{2+}][V^{2+}]^2}{[V^{3+}]^2} = \dfrac{(0.097)(0.194)^2}{(0.056)^2} = 1.16$

FOR PRACTICE 14.4

The reaction of methane at high temperature occurs according to the following reaction:

$$2\,CH_4(g) \rightleftharpoons C_2H_2(g) + 3\,H_2(g)$$

A sample of pure methane was initially at 2.000 bar and 1277 K. When the reaction reached equilibrium, the partial pressure of methane was found to be 1.616 bar. Determine the equilibrium constant for this reaction at 1277 K.

FOR PRACTICE 14.5

Solid copper will oxidize in the presence of permanganate in aqueous solution according to the following reaction.

$$Cu(s) + MnO_4^-(aq) \rightleftharpoons Cu^+(aq) + MnO_4^{2-}(aq)$$

A sample of solid copper was placed in a 0.100 mol L^{-1} solution of permanganate. After the reaction had come to equilibrium, the copper ion concentration was found to be 0.098 mol L^{-1}. Determine the equilibrium constant.

14.6 The Reaction Quotient: Predicting the Direction of Change

When the reactants of a chemical reaction mix, they generally react to form products—we say that the reaction proceeds to the right (toward the products). The amount of products formed when equilibrium is reached depends on the magnitude of the equilibrium constant, as we have seen. However, what if a reaction mixture not at equilibrium contains both reactants *and products*? Can we predict the direction of change for such a mixture?

In order to compare the progress of a reaction to the equilibrium state of the reaction, we use a quantity called the *reaction quotient*. The definition of the reaction quotient takes the same form as the definition of the equilibrium constant, except that the reaction need not be at equilibrium. So, for the general reaction

$$aA + bB \rightleftharpoons cC + dD$$

we define the **reaction quotient (Q_c)** as the ratio—at any point in the reaction—of the concentrations of the products raised to their stoichiometric coefficients divided by the concentrations of the reactants raised to their stoichiometric coefficients. For gases, the reaction quotient is in terms of the partial pressures in place of concentrations and is called Q_P.

$$Q_c = \frac{[C]^c[D]^d}{[A]^a[B]^b} \quad Q_P = \frac{P_C{}^c P_D{}^d}{P_A{}^a P_B{}^b}$$

The difference between the reaction quotient and the equilibrium constant is that, at a given temperature, the equilibrium constant has only one value and it specifies the relative amounts of reactants and products *at equilibrium*. The reaction quotient, however, depends on the current state of the reaction and has many different values as the reaction proceeds. For example, in a reaction mixture containing only reactants, the reaction quotient is zero ($Q_c = 0$):

$$Q_c = \frac{[0]^c[0]^d}{[A]^a[B]^b} = 0$$

In a reaction mixture containing only products, the reaction quotient is infinite ($Q_c = \infty$):

$$Q_c = \frac{[C]^c[D]^d}{[0]^a[0]^b} = \infty$$

As long as reactants and products in the gas phase are expressed in bar and those in solution phase are expressed in mol L^{-1}, and we assume ideal behaviour, we can drop the subscripts, P and c, and Q is the thermodynamic reaction quotient.

The reaction quotient is useful because *the value of* Q *relative to* K *is a measure of the progress of the reaction toward equilibrium. At equilibrium, the reaction quotient is equal to the equilibrium constant.* Figure 14.6 ▸ shows a plot of Q as a function of the concentrations of A and B for the simple reaction $A(aq) \rightleftharpoons B(aq)$ which has an equilibrium constant of $K = 1.45$. The following points are representative of three possible conditions:

Q	K	Predicted Direction of Reaction
0.55	1.45	To the right (toward products)
2.55	1.45	To the left (toward reactants)
1.45	1.45	No change (at equilibrium)

For the first set of values in the table, Q is less than K and must therefore get larger as the reaction proceeds toward equilibrium. Q becomes larger as the reactant concentration decreases and the product concentration increases—the reaction proceeds to the right. For the second set of values, Q is greater than K and must therefore get smaller as the reaction

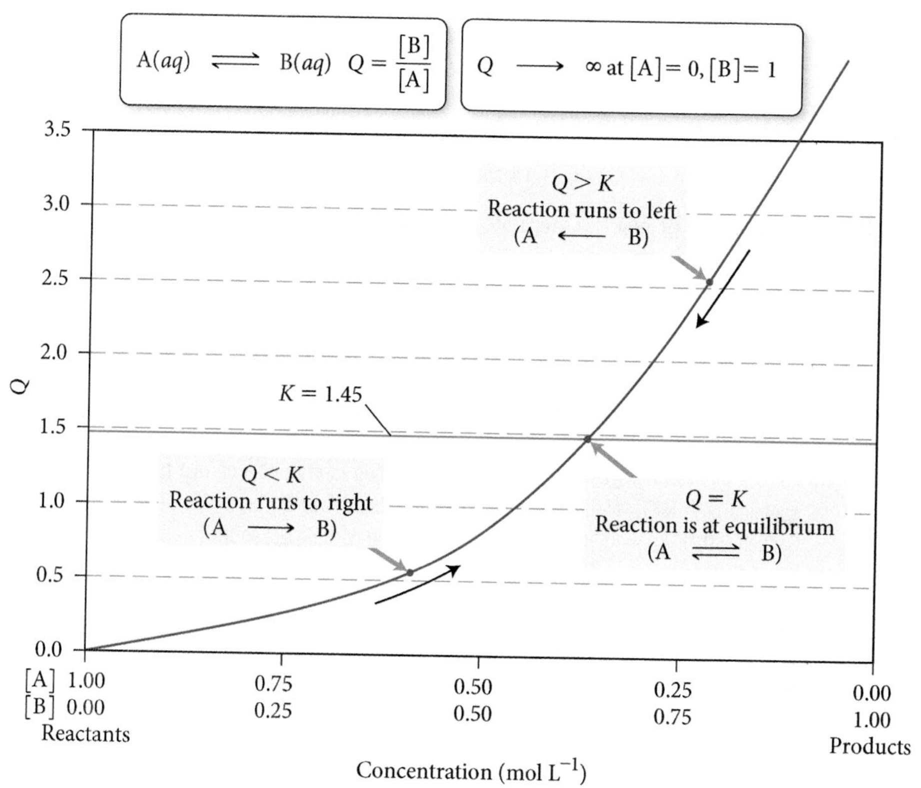

◀ **FIGURE 14.6** ***Q*, *K*, and the Direction of a Reaction** The graph shows a plot of Q as a function of the concentrations of the reactants and products in a simple reaction A $\rightleftharpoons$ B, in which $K = 1.45$ and the sum of the reactant and product concentrations is 1 mol L^{-1}. The far left of the graph represents pure reactant and the far right represents pure product. The midpoint of the graph represents an equal mixture of A and B. When Q is less than K, the reaction moves in the forward direction (A $\longrightarrow$ B). When Q is greater than K, the reaction moves in the reverse direction (A $\longleftarrow$ B). When Q is equal to K, the reaction is at equilibrium.

proceeds toward equilibrium. Q gets smaller as the reactant concentration increases and the product concentration decreases—the reaction proceeds to the left. In the third set of values, $Q = K$, implying that the reaction is at equilibrium—the reaction will not proceed in either direction.

Summarizing Direction of Change Predictions:

The reaction quotient (Q) is a measure of the progress of a reaction toward equilibrium.

- $Q < K$ Reaction goes to the right (toward products).
- $Q > K$ Reaction goes to the left (toward reactants).
- $Q = K$ Reaction is at equilibrium.

EXAMPLE 14.6 PREDICTING THE DIRECTION OF A REACTION BY COMPARING *Q* AND *K*

Consider the following reaction and its equilibrium constant:

$$I_2(g) + Cl_2(g) \rightleftharpoons 2\,ICl(g) \qquad K = 81.9$$

A reaction mixture contains $P_{I_2} = 0.114$ bar, $P_{Cl_2} = 0.102$ bar, and $P_{ICl} = 0.355$ bar. Is the reaction mixture at equilibrium? If not, in which direction will the reaction proceed?

SOLUTION

To determine the progress of the reaction relative to the equilibrium state, calculate Q.	$Q = \frac{(P_{ICl})^2}{P_{I_2}P_{Cl_2}}$ $= \frac{0.355^2}{(0.114)(0.102)}$ $= 10.8$
Compare Q to K.	$Q = 10.8; K = 81.9$ Since $Q < K$, the reaction is not at equilibrium and will proceed toward products.

(continued)

EXAMPLE 14.6 (CONTINUED)

FOR PRACTICE 14.6

Consider the following reaction and its equilibrium constant:

$$N_2O_4(g) \rightleftharpoons 2\,NO_2(g) \qquad K = 0.15 \text{ (at 298 K)}$$

A reaction mixture contains 0.631 bar of NO_2 and 0.820 bar of N_2O_4. Calculate Q and determine the direction in which the reaction will proceed.

CONCEPTUAL CONNECTION 14.3

Q* and *K

For the reaction $N_2O_4(g) \rightleftharpoons 2\,NO_2(g)$, a reaction mixture at a certain temperature initially contains both N_2O_4 and NO_2 in their standard states (see the definition of standard state in Section 6.9). If $K_P = 0.15$, which statement is true of the reaction mixture before any reaction occurs?

(a) $Q = K$; the reaction is at equilibrium.
(b) $Q < K$; the reaction will proceed to the right.
(c) $Q > K$; the reaction will proceed to the left.

14.7 Finding Equilibrium Concentrations

In Section 14.5, we learned how to calculate an equilibrium constant from the equilibrium concentrations of the reactants and products. Just as commonly, we will want to calculate equilibrium concentrations of reactants or products from the equilibrium constant. These kinds of calculations are important because they allow us to calculate the amount of a reactant or product at equilibrium. For example, in a synthesis reaction, we might want to know how much of the product forms when the reaction reaches equilibrium. Or for the hemoglobin–oxygen equilibrium discussed in Section 14.1, we might want to know the concentration of oxygenated hemoglobin present under certain oxygen concentrations within the lungs or muscles.

We can divide these types of problems into the following two categories: (1) finding equilibrium amounts when we know the equilibrium constant and all but one of the equilibrium amounts of the reactants and products; and (2) finding equilibrium amounts when we know the equilibrium constant and only initial amounts. The second category of problem is more difficult than the first. Let's examine each separately.

Finding Partial Pressures or Concentrations at Equilibrium Amounts When We Know the Equilibrium Constant and All But One of the Equilibrium Amounts of the Reactants and Products

We can use the equilibrium constant to calculate the equilibrium amounts of one of the reactants or products, given the equilibrium amounts of the others. To solve this type of problem, we can follow our general problem-solving procedure.

EXAMPLE 14.7 FINDING EQUILIBRIUM AMOUNTS WHEN YOU KNOW THE EQUILIBRIUM CONSTANT AND ALL BUT ONE OF THE EQUILIBRIUM AMOUNTS OF REACTANTS AND PRODUCTS

Consider the following reaction:

$$2\,COF_2(g) \rightleftharpoons CO_2(g) + CF_4(g) \qquad K = 0.277 \text{ at } 1750\text{ K}$$

At equilibrium, the partial pressures of COF_2 and CF_4 are 0.962 and 0.103 bar, respectively. What is the partial pressure of CO_2 at equilibrium?

SORT You are given the equilibrium constant of the reaction, together with the equilibrium partial pressures of the reactant and one product. You are asked to find the partial pressure of the other product at equilibrium.	**GIVEN:** $P_{COF_2} = 0.962$ bar $P_{CF_4} = 0.103$ bar $K = 0.277$ **FIND:** P_{CO_2}
STRATEGIZE You can calculate the partial pressure of the product using the given quantities and the expression for K.	**CONCEPTUAL PLAN** $P_{COF_2}, P_{CF_4}, K \longrightarrow P_{CO_2}$ $K = \frac{P_{CO_2}P_{CF_4}}{(P_{COF_2})^2}$
SOLVE Solve the equilibrium expression for P_{CO_2} and then substitute in the appropriate values to calculate it.	**SOLUTION** $P_{CO_2} = \frac{K \times (P_{COF_2})^2}{P_{CF_4}}$ $= \frac{(0.277) \times 0.962^2}{0.103} = 2.49$ bar

CHECK Check your answer by substituting the given quantities as well as your calculated value for P_{CO_2} back into the equilibrium expression and calculate the equilibrium constant.

$$K = \frac{P_{CO_2}P_{CF_4}}{(P_{COF_2})^2} = \frac{(2.49)(0.103)}{(0.962)^2} = 0.277$$

This procedure results in the original equilibrium constant given in the problem.

FOR PRACTICE 14.7

Diatomic iodine decomposed at high temperature to form I atoms according to the following reaction:

$$I_2(g) \rightleftharpoons 2\,I(g) \qquad K = 0.0475 \text{ at } 1173\text{ K}$$

At equilibrium, the partial pressure of I_2 is 0.125 bar. What is the partial pressure of I at equilibrium?

Finding Equilibrium Concentrations When We Know the Equilibrium Constant and Initial Concentrations or Pressures

More commonly, we know the equilibrium constant and only initial concentrations or partial pressures of reactants and need to find the *equilibrium amounts* of the reactants. These kinds of problems are generally more involved than those we just examined and require a specific procedure to solve them. The procedure has some similarities to the one used in Examples 14.4 and 14.5 in that you must set up an ICE table showing the initial conditions, the changes, and the equilibrium conditions. However, unlike Examples 14.4 and 14.5, here the changes in concentration are not known and can be represented with the variable x. For example, consider the following simple reaction:

$$A(aq) \rightleftharpoons 2B(aq)$$

Suppose that we have a reaction mixture in which the initial concentration of A is 1.0 mol L^{-1} and the initial concentration of B is 0 mol L^{-1}. We also know the equilibrium constant, $K = 0.33$, and want to find the equilibrium concentrations. Set up the ICE table with the given initial concentrations and then *represent the unknown change in [A] with the variable* x as follows:

	[A]	[B]
Initial	1.0	0
Change	$-x$	$+2x$
Equil	$1.0 - x$	$2x$

Represent changes from initial conditions with the variable x.

Notice that, due to the stoichiometry of the reaction, the change in [B] must be $+2x$. As before, each *equilibrium* concentration is the sum of the two entries above it in the ICE table. In order to find the equilibrium concentrations of A and B, we must find the value of the variable x. Since we know the value of the equilibrium constant, we can use the equilibrium expression to set up an equation in which x is the only variable:

$$K = \frac{[B]^2}{[A]} = \frac{(2x)^2}{1.0 - x} = 0.33$$

or more simply:

$$\frac{4x^2}{1.0 - x} = 0.33$$

This equation can be rearranged to:

$$4x^2 + 0.33x - 0.33 = 0$$

The above equation is a *quadratic* equation—it contains the variable x raised to the second power. In general, we can solve quadratic equations with the quadratic formula, which we introduce in Example 14.9. If the quadratic equation is a perfect square, however, it can be solved by simpler means, as shown in Example 14.8. For both of these examples, we give the general procedure in the left column and apply the procedure to the two different example problems in the centre and right columns. Later in this section, we see that quadratic equations can often be simplified by making some approximations based on our chemical knowledge.

PROCEDURE FOR...

Finding Partial Pressures at Equilibrium from Initial Pressures and the Equilibrium Constant

To solve these types of problems, follow the procedure outlined below.

EXAMPLE 14.8

Finding Partial Pressures at Equilibrium from Initial Pressures and the Equilibrium Constant

Consider the following reaction:

$$N_2(g) + O_2(g) \rightleftharpoons 2\,NO(g)$$

$$K = 0.088 \text{ (at 4000 K)}$$

A reaction mixture at 4000 K initially contains $P_{N_2} = 0.500$ bar and $P_{O_2} = 0.500$ bar. Find the partial pressures of all reactants and products at equilibrium at this temperature.

EXAMPLE 14.9

Finding Partial Pressures at Equilibrium from Initial Pressures and the Equilibrium Constant

Consider the following reaction:

$$N_2O_4(g) \rightleftharpoons 2\,NO_2(g)$$

$$K = 17 \text{ (at 373 K)}$$

A reaction mixture at 373 K initially contains $P_{NO_2} = 0.750$ bar. Find the partial pressures of NO_2 and N_2O_4 at equilibrium at this temperature.

1. **Using the balanced equation as a guide, prepare a table showing the known initial amounts of the reactants and products.** Note that the pressures in the ICE table should be in bar for gaseous reactions. Leave room in the table for the changes and for the equilibrium amounts.

Example 14.8:

$$N_2(g) + O_2(g) \rightleftharpoons 2\,NO(g)$$

	P_{N_2}	P_{O_2}	P_{NO}
Initial	0.500	0.500	0
Change			
Equil			

Example 14.9:

$$N_2O_4(g) \rightleftharpoons 2\,NO_2(g)$$

	$P_{N_2O_4}$	P_{NO_2}
Initial	0	0.750
Change		
Equil		

2. **Use the initial conditions to calculate the reaction quotient (Q). Compare Q to K to predict the direction in which the reaction will proceed.**

Example 14.8:

$$Q = \frac{(P_{NO})^2}{P_{N_2}P_{O_2}} = \frac{0^2}{(0.500)(0.500)}$$

$$= 0$$

$Q < K$, therefore the reaction will proceed to the right.

Example 14.9:

$$Q = \frac{(P_{NO_2})^2}{P_{N_2O_4}} = \frac{0.750^2}{0}$$

$$= \infty$$

$Q > K$, therefore the reaction will proceed to the left.

3. Represent the change in the amount of one of the reactants or products with the variable x. Define the changes in the amounts of the other reactants or products in terms of x.	$N_2(g) + O_2(g) \rightleftharpoons 2\,NO(g)$ | | P_{N_2} | P_{O_2} | P_{NO} | Initial | 0.500 | 0.500 | 0 Change | $-x$ | $-x$ | $+2x$ Equil | | |	$N_2O_4(g) \rightleftharpoons 2\,NO_2(g)$ | | $P_{N_2O_4}$ | P_{NO_2} | Initial | 0 | 0.750 Change | $+x$ | $-2x$ Equil | |
4. Sum each column for each reactant and product to determine the amounts at equilibrium in terms of the initial amounts and the variable x.	$N_2(g) + O_2(g) \rightleftharpoons 2\,NO(g)$ | | P_{N_2} | P_{O_2} | P_{NO} | Initial | 0.500 | 0.500 | 0 Change | $-x$ | $-x$ | $+2x$ Equil | $0.500 - x$ | $0.500 - x$ | $2x$	$N_2O_4(g) \rightleftharpoons 2\,NO_2(g)$ | | $P_{N_2O_4}$ | P_{NO_2} | Initial | 0 | 0.750 Change | $+x$ | $-2x$ Equil | x | $0.750 - 2x$
5. Substitute the expressions for the equilibrium amounts (from step 4) into the expression for the equilibrium constant and solve for the expression for the variable x. In some cases, such as Example 14.8, you can take the square root of both sides of the expression to solve for x. In other cases, such as Example 14.9, you must solve a quadratic equation to find x. Remember the quadratic formula: $ax^2 + bx + c = 0$ $x = \frac{-b \pm \sqrt{b^2 - 4ac}}{2a}$	$K = \frac{(P_{NO})^2}{P_{N_2}P_{O_2}}$ $= \frac{(2x)^2}{(0.500 - x)(0.500 - x)}$ $0.088 = \frac{(2x)^2}{(0.500 - x)^2}$ $\sqrt{0.088} = \frac{2x}{0.500 - x}$ $\sqrt{0.088}\,(0.500 - x) = 2x$ $0.148 - 0.297x = 2x$ $0.148 = 2.297x$ $x = 0.064$	$K = \frac{(P_{NO_2})^2}{P_{N_2O_4}}$ $= \frac{(0.750 - 2x)^2}{x}$ $17 = \frac{0.563 - 4x + 4x^2}{x}$ $17x = 0.563 - 4x + 4x^2$ $4x^2 - 21x + 0.563 = 0$ *(quadratic)* $x = \frac{-(-21) \pm \sqrt{(-21)^2 - 4(4)(0.563)}}{2(4)}$ $= \frac{21 \pm 20.78}{8}$ $x = 5.22$ or $x = 0.028$
6. Substitute x into the expressions for the equilibrium partial pressures of the reactants and products (from step 4) and calculate the partial pressures. In cases where you solved a quadratic and have two values for x, only one will make chemical sense; this is the one you choose (see Example 14.9).	$P_{N_2} = 0.500 - 0.064$ $= 0.436$ bar $P_{O_2} = 0.500 - 0.064$ $= 0.436$ bar $P_{NO} = 2(0.064)$ $= 0.13$ bar	We reject the root $x = 5.22$ because it gives a negative concentration for NO_2, which is not meaningful. Using $x = 0.028$, we get the following partial pressures: $P_{NO_2} = 0.750 - 2(0.028)$ $= 0.694$ bar $P_{N_2O_2} = 0.028$ bar
7. Check your answer by substituting the computed equilibrium values into the equilibrium-constant expression. The calculated value of K should match the given value of K. Note that rounding errors could cause a difference in the least significant digit when comparing values of the equilibrium constant.	$K = \frac{(P_{NO})^2}{P_{N_2}P_{O_2}}$ $= \frac{(0.13)^2}{(0.436)(0.436)} = 0.089$ Since the calculated value of K matches the given value (to within one digit in the least significant figure), the answer is valid.	$K = \frac{(P_{NO_2})^2}{P_{N_2O_4}}$ $= \frac{(0.694)^2}{(0.028)} = 16.4$ Since the calculated value of K matches the given value (to within one digit in the least significant figure), the answer is valid.

(continued)

PROCEDURE FOR... (continued) | **EXAMPLE 14.8 (continued)** | **EXAMPLE 14.9 (continued)**

FOR PRACTICE 14.8

The reaction on the previous page is carried out at 6000 K where $K = 0.51$. The reaction mixture starts with only NO at an initial pressure of 0.250 bar. Find the partial pressures of N_2, O_2, and NO at equilibrium.

FOR PRACTICE 14.9

The reaction on the previous page is carried out at 298 K where $K = 0.18$. This time the reaction mixture contains only N_2O_4 at a pressure of 0.200 bar. Find the partial pressures of NO_2 and N_2O_4 at equilibrium at this temperature.

When the reaction occurs in the solution phase instead of the gas phase, the equilibrium constant is written in terms of the concentrations rather than the partial pressures. The same procedure is used to solve for the equilibrium concentrations as previously for solving for partial pressures at equilibrium.

EXAMPLE 14.10 FINDING EQUILIBRIUM CONCENTRATIONS FROM THE EQUILIBRIUM CONSTANT AND INITIAL CONCENTRATIONS

Consider the following reaction:

$$Fe^{3+}(aq) + SCN^-(aq) \rightleftharpoons Fe(SCN)^{2+}(aq) \qquad K = 8.9 \times 10^2 \text{ (at 298 K)}$$

A reaction mixture at 298 K initially contains 0.100 mol L^{-1} Fe^{3+} and 0.150 mol L^{-1} of SCN^- and 0.100 mol L^{-1} of $Fe(SCN)^{2+}$. Find the equilibrium concentrations of each of the reactants and products.

1. Using the balanced equation as a guide, prepare a table showing the known initial concentrations of the reactants and products.

$$Fe^{3+}(aq) + SCN^-(aq) \rightleftharpoons Fe(SCN)^{2+}(aq)$$

	$[Fe^{3+}]$	$[SCN^-]$	$[Fe(SCN)^{2+}]$
Initial	0.100	0.150	0.100
Change			
Equil			

2. Use the initial concentrations to calculate the reaction quotient (Q). Compare Q to K to predict the direction in which the reaction will proceed.

$$Q = \frac{[Fe(SCN)^{2+}]}{[Fe^{3+}][SCN^-]} = \frac{0.100}{(0.100)(0.150)}$$

$$= 6.7$$

$Q < K$, therefore the reaction will proceed toward products.

3. Represent the change in the concentrations of one of the reactants or products with the variable x. Using the stoichiometry of the reaction, define the changes in the concentrations of the other reactants or products in terms of x.

$$Fe^{3+}(aq) + SCN^-(aq) \rightleftharpoons Fe(SCN)^{2+}(aq)$$

	$[Fe^{3+}]$	$[SCN^-]$	$[Fe(SCN)^{2+}]$
Initial	0.100	0.150	0.100
Change	$-x$	$-x$	$+x$
Equil			

4. Sum each column for each reactant and product to determine the equilibrium concentrations in terms of the initial concentrations and the variable x.

$$Fe^{3+}(aq) + SCN^-(aq) \rightleftharpoons Fe(SCN)^{2+}(aq)$$

	$[Fe^{3+}]$	$[SCN^-]$	$[Fe(SCN)^{2+}]$
Initial	0.100	0.150	0.100
Change	$-x$	$-x$	$+x$
Equil	$0.100 - x$	$0.150 - x$	$0.100 + x$

5. Substitute the expressions for the equilibrium concentrations (from step 4) into the expression for the equilibrium constant. Use the given value of the equilibrium constant to solve the expression for the variable x. As in this example, you may need to use the quadratic equation.	$K = \frac{[Fe(SCN)^{2+}]}{[Fe^{3+}][SCN^-]} = \frac{0.100 + x}{(0.100 - x)(0.150 - x)}$ $890 = \frac{0.100 + x}{(0.0150 - 0.25x + x^2)}$ $890(0.0150 - 0.25x + x^2) = 0.100 + x$ $890x^2 - 222.5x + 13.35 = 0.100 + x$ $890x^2 - 223.5x + 13.25 = 0$ (requiring the solution for a quadratic equation.) $x = \frac{-(-223.5) \pm \sqrt{(-223.5)^2 - 4(890)(13.25)}}{2(890)}$ $= \frac{223.5 \pm 52.75}{1780}$ $x = 0.155$ or $x = 0.096$
6. Substitute x into the expressions for the equilibrium concentrations of the reactants and products (from step 4) and calculate them.	We reject the root 0.155 because it would give negative concentrations for the reactants, which is impossible. Using $x = 0.096$, we obtain the following concentrations: $[Fe^{3+}] = 0.100 - 0.096 = 0.004 \text{ mol L}^{-1}$ $[SCN^-] = 0.150 - 0.096 = 0.054 \text{ mol L}^{-1}$ $[Fe(SCN)^{2+}] = 0.100 + 0.096 = 0.196 \text{ mol L}^{-1}$
7. Check your answer by substituting the calculated equilibrium concentrations into the equilibrium expression. The calculated value of K should match the given value.	$K = \frac{[Fe(SCN)^{2+}]}{[Fe^{3+}][SCN^-]}$ $= \frac{0.196}{(0.004)(0.054)} = 9.1 \times 10^2$

FOR PRACTICE 14.10

The reactions in Example 14.10 are carried out at the same temperature but with the following initial concentrations: $[Fe^{3+}] = 0.100 \text{ mol L}^{-1}$, $[SCN^-] = 0 \text{ mol L}^{-1}$, and $[Fe(SCN)^{2+}] = 0.575 \text{ mol L}^{-1}$. Determine the equilibrium concentrations of all three substances.

Simplifying Approximations in Working Equilibrium Problems

For some equilibrium problems of the type shown in the previous three examples, we can make an approximation that simplifies the calculations without any significant loss of accuracy. For example, if the equilibrium constant is relatively small, the reaction will not proceed very far to the right. Therefore, if the initial reactant concentration is relatively large, we can make the assumption that x is small relative to the initial concentration of reactant. To see how this approximation works, consider again the simple reaction $A \rightleftharpoons 2\,B$. Suppose that, as before, we have a reaction mixture in which the initial concentration of A is 1.0 mol L^{-1} and the initial concentration of B is 0.0 mol L^{-1}and that we want to find the equilibrium concentrations. However, suppose that in this case the equilibrium constant is much smaller, say $K = 3.3 \times 10^{-5}$. The ICE table is identical to the one we set up previously:

	[A]	[B]
Initial	1.0	0
Change	$-x$	$+2x$
Equil	$1.0 - x$	$2x$

With the exception of the value of K, we end up with the exact quadratic equation that we had before:

$$K = \frac{[B]^2}{[A]} = \frac{(2x)^2}{1.0 - x} = 3.3 \times 10^{-5}$$

or simply,

$$\frac{4x^2}{(1.0 - x)} = 3.3 \times 10^{-5}$$

We can multiply out this quadratic equation and solve it using the quadratic formula. But since K is small, the reaction will not proceed very far toward products and therefore, x will also be small. If x is much smaller than 1.0, then $(1.0 - x)$ (the quantity in the denominator) can be approximated by (1.0).

$$\frac{4x^2}{(1.0 - \cancel{x})} = 3.3 \times 10^{-5}$$

This approximation greatly simplifies the equation, which we can then solve easily for x as follows:

$$\frac{4x^2}{1.0} = 3.3 \times 10^{-5}$$

$$4x^2 = 3.3 \times 10^{-5}$$

$$x = \sqrt{\frac{3.3 \times 10^{-5}}{4}} = 0.0029$$

We can check the validity of this approximation by comparing the computed value of x to the number it was subtracted from. The ratio of x to the number it is subtracted from should be less than 0.05 (or 5%) for the approximation to be valid. In this case, x was subtracted from 1.0, and therefore the ratio of the value of x to 1.0 is calculated as follows:

$$\frac{0.0029}{1.0} \times 100\% = 0.29\%$$

The approximation is therefore valid. In the two side-by-side examples that follow, we treat two nearly identical problems—the only difference is the initial concentration of the reactant. In Example 14.11, the initial concentration of the reactant is relatively large, the equilibrium constant is small, and the *x is small* approximation works well. In Example 14.12, however, the initial concentration of the reactant is much smaller, and even though the equilibrium constant is the same, the *x is small* approximation does not work (because the initial concentration is also small). In cases such as this, we have a couple of options to solve the problem. We can either solve the equation exactly (using the quadratic formula, for example), or we can use the *method of successive approximations*, which is introduced in Example 14.12. In this method, we essentially solve for x as if it were small, and then substitute the value obtained back into the equation to solve for x again. This can be repeated until the calculated value of x stops changing with each iteration, an indication that we have arrived at an acceptable value for x.

Note that the *x is small* approximation does not imply that *x is zero*. If that were the case, the reactant and product concentrations would not change from their initial values. The *x is small* approximation just means that when x is added to or subtracted from another number, it does not change that number by very much. For example, we can calculate the value of the difference $1.0 - x$ when $x = 3.0 \times 10^{-4}$:

$$1.0 - x = 1.0 - 3.0 \times 10^{-4} = 0.9\underline{9}97 = 1.0$$

Since the value of 1.0 is known only to two significant figures, subtracting the small x does not change the value at all. This situation is similar to weighing yourself on a bathroom scale with and without a penny in your pocket. Unless your scale is unusually precise, removing the penny from your pocket will not change the reading on the scale. This does not imply that the penny is weightless, only that its weight is small when compared to your body weight. The weight of the penny can thus be neglected in reading your weight with no detectable loss in accuracy.

PROCEDURE FOR...

Finding Equilibrium Amounts in Cases with a Small Equilibrium Constant

To solve these types of problems, follow the procedure outlined below.

EXAMPLE 14.11

Finding Equilibrium Amounts in Cases with a Small Equilibrium Constant

Consider the reaction for the decomposition of hydrogen disulfide:

$$2\ H_2S(g) \rightleftharpoons 2\ H_2(g) + S_2(g) \qquad K = 5.13 \times 10^{-6}\ \text{(at 873 K)}$$

A vessel initially contains 0.250 bar of H_2S at 873 K. Find the equilibrium concentrations of H_2S, H_2, and S_2.

EXAMPLE 14.12

Finding Equilibrium Amounts in Cases with a Small Equilibrium Constant

Consider the reaction for the decomposition of hydrogen disulfide:

$$2\ H_2S(g) \rightleftharpoons 2\ H_2(g) + S_2(g) \qquad K = 5.13 \times 10^{-6}\ \text{(at 873 K)}$$

A vessel initially contains 2.50×10^{-3} bar of H_2S at 873 K. Find the equilibrium concentrations of H_2S, H_2, and S_2.

---

1. Using the balanced equation as a guide, prepare a table showing the known initial partial pressures of the reactants and products.

Example 14.11:

$2\ H_2S(g) \rightleftharpoons 2\ H_2(g) + S_2(g)$

	P_{H_2S}	P_{H_2}	P_{S_2}
Initial	0.250	0	0
Change			
Equil			

Example 14.12:

$2\ H_2S(g) \rightleftharpoons 2\ H_2(g) + S_2(g)$

	P_{H_2S}	P_{H_2}	P_{S_2}
Initial	2.50×10^{-3}	0	0
Change			
Equil			

2. Use the initial amounts to calculate the reaction quotient (Q). Compare Q to K to predict the direction in which the reaction will proceed.

Example 14.11: Since there are no products, $Q = 0$; the reaction will proceed to the right.

Example 14.12: Since there are no products, $Q = 0$; the reaction will proceed to the right.

3. Represent the change in the amount of one of the reactants or products with the variable x. Define the changes in the amounts of the other reactants or products in terms of x.

Example 14.11:

$2\ H_2S(g) \rightleftharpoons 2\ H_2(g) + S_2(g)$

	P_{H_2S}	P_{H_2}	P_{S_2}
Initial	0.250	0	0
Change	$-2x$	$+2x$	$+x$
Equil			

Example 14.12:

$2\ H_2S(g) \rightleftharpoons 2\ H_2(g) + S_2(g)$

	P_{H_2S}	P_{H_2}	P_{S_2}
Initial	2.50×10^{-3}	0	0
Change	$-2x$	$+2x$	$+x$
Equil			

4. Sum each column for each reactant and product to determine the amounts at equilibrium in terms of the initial amounts and the variable x.

Example 14.11:

$2\ H_2S(g) \rightleftharpoons 2\ H_2(g) + S_2(g)$

	P_{H_2S}	P_{H_2}	P_{S_2}
Initial	0.250	0	0
Change	$-2x$	$+2x$	$+x$
Equil	$0.250 - 2x$	$2x$	x

Example 14.12:

$2\ H_2S(g) \rightleftharpoons 2\ H_2(g) + S_2(g)$

	P_{H_2S}	P_{H_2}	P_{S_2}
Initial	2.50×10^{-3}	0	0
Change	$-2x$	$+2x$	$+x$
Equil	$2.50 \times 10^{-3} - 2x$	$2x$	x

5. Substitute the expressions for the equilibrium amounts (from step 4) into the expression for the equilibrium constant and solve for the expression for the variable x.

In this case, the resulting equation is a cubic in x. Although cubic equations can be solved, the solutions are not as

Example 14.11:

$$K = \frac{(P_{H_2})^2 P_{S_2}}{(P_{H_2S})^2} = \frac{(2x)^2 x}{(0.250 - 2x)^2}$$

Example 14.12:

$$K = \frac{(P_{H_2})^2 P_{S_2}}{(P_{H_2S})^2} = \frac{(2x)^2 x}{(2.50 \times 10^{-3} - 2x)^2}$$

(continued)

PROCEDURE FOR... (*continued*)	EXAMPLE 14.11 (*continued*)	EXAMPLE 14.12 (*continued*)
simple to obtain as for the quadratic. However, since the equilibrium constant is small, we know that the reaction does not proceed very far to the right. Therefore, x will be a small number and can be dropped from any quantities in which it is added to or subtracted from another number (as long as the number itself is not too small).	$5.13 \times 10^{-6} = \dfrac{4x^3}{(0.250 - \cancel{2x})^2}$ (*2x is small.*) $5.13 \times 10^{-6} = \dfrac{4x^3}{0.0625}$ $x = 4.31 \times 10^{-3}$	$5.13 \times 10^{-6} = \dfrac{4x^3}{(2.50 \times 10^{-3} - \cancel{2x})^2}$ (*2x is small.*) $5.13 \times 10^{-6} = \dfrac{4x^3}{6.25 \times 10^{-6}}$ $x = 2.00 \times 10^{-4}$
Check whether your approximation was valid by comparing the calculated value of $2x$ to the number it was added to or subtracted from. The ratio of the two numbers should be less than 0.05 (<5%) for the approximation to be valid. If approximation is not valid, proceed to step 5a.	Checking the $2x$ *is small* approximation: $\dfrac{8.62 \times 10^{-3}}{0.250} \times 100\% = 3.44\%$ The *x is small* approximation is valid; proceed to step 6.	Checking the $2x$ *is small* approximation: $\dfrac{4.00 \times 10^{-4}}{2.50 \times 10^{-3}} \times 100\% = 16.00\%$ The approximation does not satisfy the <5% rule; go to step 5a.
5a. If the approximation is not valid, you can solve the equation exactly by hand, by calculator, or by the method of successive approximations. In this case, we use the method of successive approximations. We can first try the solution obtained from above when we attempted to use the *x is small* approximation.		$5.13 \times 10^{-6} = \dfrac{4x^3}{(2.50 \times 10^{-3} - 2x)^2}$ try $x = 2.00 \times 10^{-4}$ $5.13 \times 10^{-6} = \dfrac{4x^3}{(2.50 \times 10^{-3} - 4.00 \times 10^{-4})^2}$ $x = 1.78 \times 10^{-4}$ Repeating this procedure with this new value for x yields $x = 1.81 \times 10^{-4}$. A third iteration yields 1.80×10^{-4}. For all subsequent iterations, the value calculated for x does not change. We have arrived at the value for x.
6. Substitute x into the expressions for the equilibrium partial pressures (from step 4) and calculate them.	$P_{H_2S} = 0.250 - 2(4.31 \times 10^{-3})$ $= 0.241$ bar $P_{H_2} = 2(4.31 \times 10^{-3})$ $= 8.62 \times 10^{-3}$ bar $P_{S_2} = 4.31 \times 10^{-3}$ bar	$P_{H_2S} = 2.50 \times 10^{-3} - 2(1.80 \times 10^{-4})$ $= 2.14 \times 10^{-3}$ bar $P_{H_2} = 2(1.80 \times 10^{-4})$ $= 3.60 \times 10^{-4}$ bar $P_{S_2} = 1.80 \times 10^{-4}$ bar
7. Check your answer by substituting the calculated equilibrium values into the equilibrium expression. The calculated value of K should match the given value of K. Note that the approximation method and rounding errors could cause a difference of up to about 10% when comparing values of the equilibrium constant.	$K = \dfrac{(8.62 \times 10^{-3})^2(4.31 \times 10^{-3})}{(0.241)^2}$ $= 5.51 \times 10^{-6}$ This calculated value of K is close enough to the given value considering the uncertainty introduced by the approximation. The answer is valid.	$K = \dfrac{(3.60 \times 10^{-4})^2(1.80 \times 10^{-4})}{(2.14 \times 10^{-3})^2}$ $= 5.09 \times 10^{-6}$ This calculated value of K is very close to the given value, only in error by less than 1%. The answer is valid.
	FOR PRACTICE 14.11 The reaction in Example 14.11 is carried out at the same temperature with the following initial partial pressures: $P_{H_2S} = 1.00$ bar, $P_{H_2} = 1.00$ bar, $P_{S_2} = 0$ bar. Find the partial pressures of each of the reactants and products at equilibrium.	**FOR PRACTICE 14.12** The reaction in Example 14.12 is carried out at the same temperature with the following initial partial pressures: $P_{H_2S} = 1.00 \times 10^{-3}$ bar, $P_{H_2} = 1.00 \times 10^{-5}$ bar, and $P_{S_2} = 0.100$ bar. Find the partial pressures of each of the reactants and products at equilibrium.

CONCEPTUAL CONNECTION 14.4

The *x is small* Approximation

For the generic reaction, $A(aq) \rightleftharpoons B(aq)$, consider each value of K and initial concentration of A. For which set will the *x is small* approximation most likely apply?

(a) $K = 1.0 \times 10^{-5}$; $[A] = 0.250 \text{ mol L}^{-1}$

(b) $K = 1.0 \times 10^{-2}$; $[A] = 0.250 \text{ mol L}^{-1}$

(c) $K = 1.0 \times 10^{-5}$; $[A] = 0.00250 \text{ mol L}^{-1}$

(d) $K = 1.0 \times 10^{-2}$; $[A] = 0.00250 \text{ mol L}^{-1}$

14.8 Le Châtelier's Principle: How a System at Equilibrium Responds to Disturbances

We have seen that a chemical system not in equilibrium tends to progress toward equilibrium and that the relative concentrations of the reactants and products at equilibrium are characterized by the equilibrium constant, K. What happens, however, when a chemical system already at equilibrium is disturbed? **Le Châtelier's principle** states that the chemical system will respond to minimize the disturbance.

Pronounced "Le-shaw-te-lyay."

Le Châtelier's principle: When a chemical system at equilibrium is disturbed, the system shifts in a direction that minimizes the disturbance.

In other words, a system at equilibrium tends to maintain that equilibrium—it bounces back when disturbed.

We can disturb a system in chemical equilibrium in several different ways, including changing the amount of a reactant or product, changing the volume or pressure, and changing the temperature. We consider each of these separately.

The Effect of Changing the Amount of Reactant or Product on Equilibrium

In this section, we will discuss what happens to the equilibrium mixture when we change the amount of a reactant or product. For these changes, we will keep the volume of the solution or the gaseous mixture constant and we will keep the temperature of the system the same. For a gas-phase reaction, increasing the amount of a reactant or product will increase its partial pressure. For a solution-phase reaction, increasing the amount of a reactant or product will increase that reactant's or product's concentration.

Consider the following reaction in chemical equilibrium:

$$N_2O_4(g) \rightleftharpoons 2\, NO_2(g)$$

Suppose we disturb the equilibrium by adding NO_2 to the equilibrium mixture (Figure 14.7 ▼). In other words, we increase the partial pressure of NO_2, the product. What happens? According to Le Châtelier's principle, the system shifts in a direction to minimize the disturbance. The reaction goes to the left (it proceeds in the reverse direction), consuming some of the added NO_2 thus bringing its partial pressure back down, as depicted graphically in Figure 14.8(a) ▼.

Add NO_2.

$$N_2O_4(g) \rightleftharpoons 2\, NO_2(g)$$

Reaction shifts left.

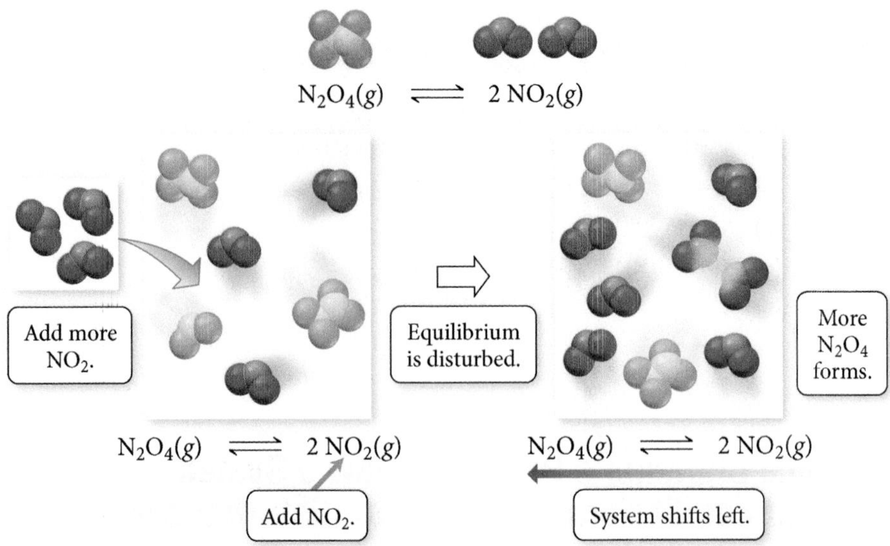

▲ **FIGURE 14.7 Le Châtelier's Principle: The Effect of Changing the Amount of Reactant or Product** Adding NO_2 causes the reaction to shift left, consuming some of the added NO_2 and forming more N_2O_4.

The reaction shifts to the left because the value of Q changes as follows:

- Before addition of NO_2: $Q = K$.
- Immediately after addition of NO_2: $Q > K$.
- Reaction shifts to left to re-establish equilibrium.

On the other hand, what happens if we add extra N_2O_4 (the reactant), increasing its partial pressure? In this case, the reaction shifts to the right, consuming some of the added N_2O_4 and bringing *its* partial pressure back down, as shown in Figure 14.8(b).

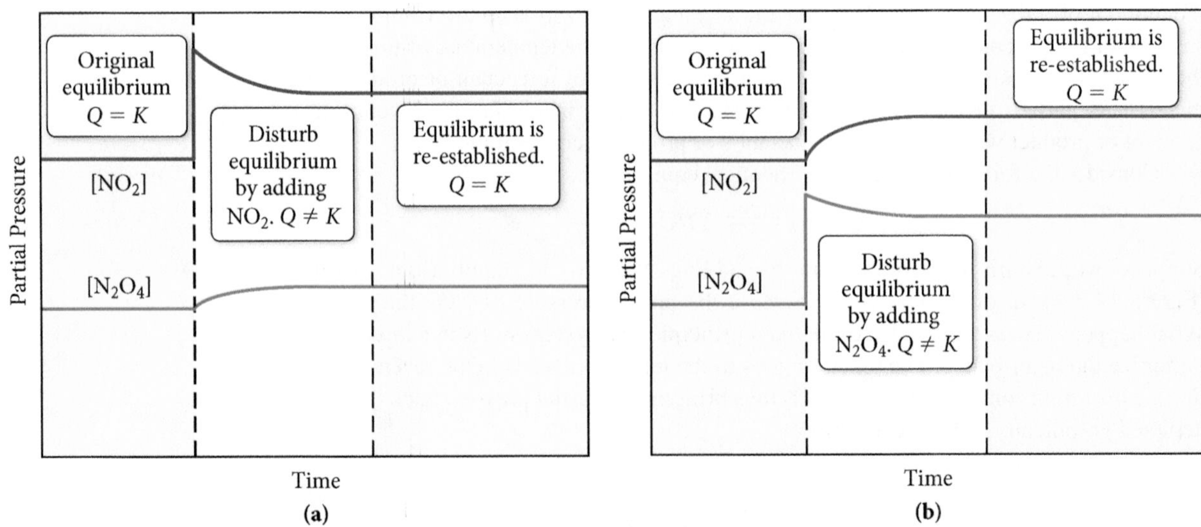

▲ **FIGURE 14.8 Le Châtelier's Principle: Changing the Amount of a Reactant or Product** The graph shows the partial pressures of NO_2 and N_2O_4 for the reaction $N_2O_4(g) \longrightarrow 2\,NO_2(g)$ in three distinct stages of the reaction: initially at equilibrium (left); upon disturbance of the equilibrium by addition of more NO_2 **(a)** or N_2O_4 **(b)** to the reaction mixture (centre); and upon re-establishment of equilibrium (right).

Add N_2O_4.

$$N_2O_4(g) \rightleftharpoons 2\,NO_2(g)$$

Reaction shifts right.

The reaction shifts to the right because the value of Q changes as follows:

- Before addition of N_2O_4: $Q = K$.
- Immediately after addition of N_2O_4: $Q < K$.
- Reaction shifts to right to re-establish equilibrium.

In both of the cases, the system shifts in a direction that minimizes the disturbance. Lowering the amount of a reactant (which makes $Q > K$) causes the system to shift in the direction of the reactants to minimize the disturbance. Lowering the concentration of a product (which makes $Q < K$) causes the system to shift in the direction of products.

Summarizing the Effect of Changing the Amount of Reactant or Product on Equilibrium:

If a chemical system is at equilibrium:

- *Increasing* the amount of one or more of the *reactants* (which makes $Q < K$) causes the reaction to *shift to the right* (in the direction of the products).
- *Increasing* the amount of one or more of the *products* (which makes $Q > K$) causes the reaction to *shift to the left* (in the direction of the reactants).
- *Decreasing* the amount of one or more of the *reactants* (which makes $Q > K$) causes the reaction to *shift to the left* (in the direction of the reactants).
- *Decreasing* the amount of one or more of the *products* (which makes $Q < K$) causes the reaction to *shift to the right* (in the direction of the products).

EXAMPLE 14.13 THE EFFECT OF CHANGING THE AMOUNT OF A REACTANT OR PRODUCT ON EQUILIBRIUM

Consider the following reaction at equilibrium.

$$CaCO_3(s) \rightleftharpoons CaO(s) + CO_2(g)$$

What is the effect of adding additional CO_2 to the reaction mixture and keeping the volume and temperature of the system the same? What is the effect of adding additional $CaCO_3$?

SOLUTION

The equilibrium-constant expression for the reaction is $K = P_{CO_2}$. Adding additional CO_2 increases the partial pressure and the reaction quotient so that $Q > K$ and the reaction can proceed to the left. Since $CaCO_3$ is a solid, and assumed to be pure, its activity will remain equal to 1. Therefore, it is not in the equilibrium-constant expression, and adding additional solid $CaCO_3$ does not affect Q and therefore does not affect the equilibrium. The reaction mixture remains at equilibrium.

FOR PRACTICE 14.13

Consider the following reaction in chemical equilibrium:

$$2\,BrNO(g) \rightleftharpoons 2\,NO(g) + Br_2(g)$$

What is the effect of adding additional Br_2 to the reaction mixture? What is the effect of adding additional BrNO?

The Effect of a Volume Change on Equilibrium

How does a system containing gaseous components in chemical equilibrium respond to a volume change? Here, we are not adding or removing any substance from the system, only changing the size of the container. Remember from Chapter 5 that changing the volume of a gas (or a gas mixture) results in a change in pressure. Remember also that pressure and volume are inversely related: a *decrease* in volume causes an *increase* in pressure, and an *increase* in volume causes a *decrease* in pressure. So, if the volume of a reaction mixture at chemical equilibrium is changed, the pressure changes and the system will shift in a direction to minimize that change. For example, consider the following reaction at equilibrium in a cylinder equipped with a moveable piston:

In considering the effect of a change in volume, we are assuming that the change in volume is carried out at constant temperature.

$$N_2(g) + 3\,H_2(g) \rightleftharpoons 2\,NH_3(g)$$

What happens if we push down on the piston, lowering the volume and raising the pressure (Figure 14.9(a) ▼)? How can the chemical system respond to bring the pressure back down? Look carefully at the reaction coefficients. If the reaction shifts to the right, 4 mol of gas particles are converted to 2 mol of gas particles. From the ideal gas law ($PV = nRT$), we know that lowering the number of moles of a gas (n) results in a lower pressure (P). Therefore, the system shifts to the right, lowering the number of gas molecules and bringing the pressure back down, minimizing the disturbance.

Consider the same reaction mixture at equilibrium again. What happens if, this time, we pull *up* on the piston, *increasing* the volume (Figure 14.9(b))? The higher volume results in a lower pressure and the system responds to bring the pressure back up. It does this by shifting to the left, converting 2 mol of gas particles into 4 mol of gas particles, increasing the pressure and minimizing the disturbance.

Summarizing the Effect of Volume Change on Equilibrium:

If a chemical system is at equilibrium:

- *Decreasing* the volume causes the reaction to shift in the direction that has *the fewer moles of gas particles.*

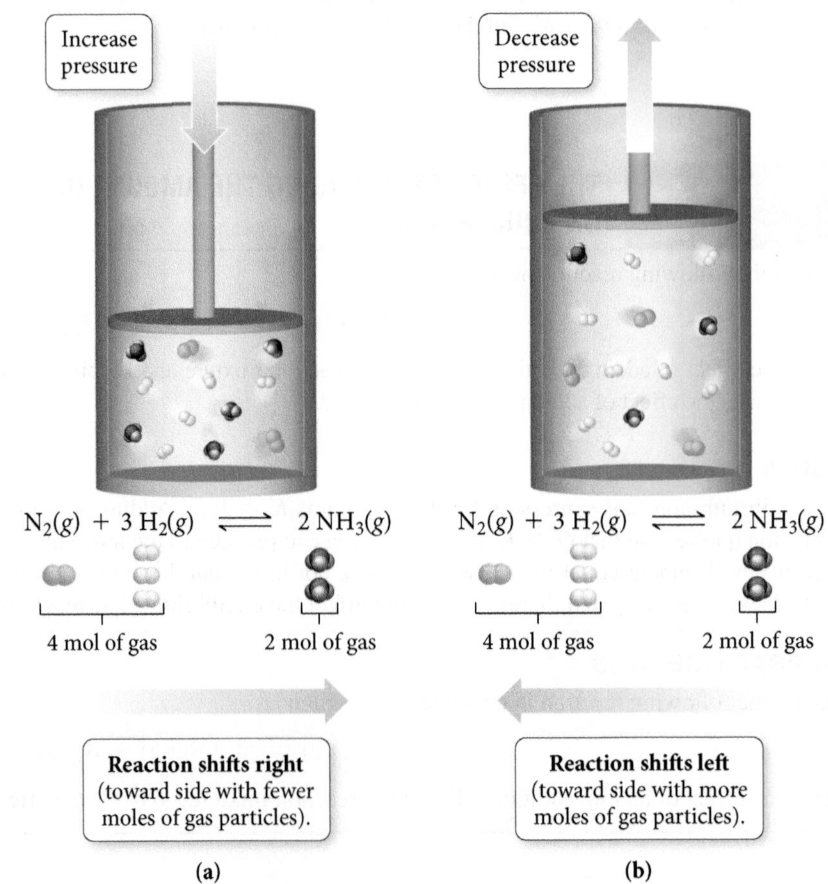

▶ **FIGURE 14.9 Le Châtelier's Principle: The Effect of a Pressure Change** (a) Decreasing the volume increases the pressure, causing the reaction to shift to the right (fewer moles of gas, lower pressure). (b) Increasing the volume reduces the pressure, causing the reaction to shift to the left (more moles of gas, higher pressure).

- *Increasing* the volume causes the reaction to shift in the direction that has *the greater number of moles of gas particles.*
- If a reaction has an equal number of moles of gas on both sides of the chemical equation, then a change in volume produces no effect on the equilibrium.

The Effect of Changing the Pressure by Adding an Inert Gas

Consider again a gaseous reaction mixture at equilibrium. What happens if this time we keep the volume the same, but increase the pressure *by adding an inert gas* to the mixture? Although the overall pressure of the mixture increases, the partial pressures of the reactants and products do not change. Since the partial pressure of the inert gas is not in the equilibrium-constant expression $Q = K$, there is no effect and the reaction does not shift in either direction.

EXAMPLE 14.14 THE EFFECT OF A VOLUME CHANGE ON EQUILIBRIUM

Consider the following reaction at chemical equilibrium:

$$2\ KClO_3(s) \rightleftharpoons 2\ KCl(s) + 3\ O_2(g)$$

What is the effect of decreasing the volume of the reaction mixture? Increasing the volume of the reaction mixture? Adding an inert gas at constant volume?

SOLUTION

The chemical equation has 3 mol of gas on the right and zero moles of gas on the left. Decreasing the volume of the reaction mixture increases the pressure and causes the reaction to shift to the left (toward the side with fewer moles of gas particles). Increasing the volume of the reaction mixture decreases the pressure and causes the reaction to shift to the right (toward the side with more moles of gas particles.) Adding an inert gas has no effect.

FOR PRACTICE 14.14

Consider the following reaction at chemical equilibrium:

$$2\ SO_2(g) + O_2(g) \rightleftharpoons 2\ SO_3(g)$$

What is the effect of decreasing the volume of the reaction mixture? Increasing the volume of the reaction mixture?

The Effect of a Temperature Change on Equilibrium

According to Le Châtelier's principle, if the temperature of a system at equilibrium is changed, the system will shift in a direction to counter that change. So, if the temperature is increased, the reaction will shift in the direction that tends to decrease the temperature and vice versa. Recall from Chapter 6 that an exothermic reaction (negative ΔH) emits heat:

In considering the effect of a change in temperature, we are assuming that the heat is added (or removed) at constant pressure.

$$\text{Exothermic reaction:}\quad A + B \rightleftharpoons C + D + \text{heat}$$

We can think of heat as a product in an exothermic reaction. In an endothermic reaction (positive ΔH), the reaction absorbs heat.

$$\text{Endothermic reaction:}\quad A + B + \text{heat} \rightleftharpoons C + D$$

We can think of heat as a reactant in an endothermic reaction.

At constant pressure, raising the temperature of an *exothermic* reaction—think of this as adding heat—is similar to adding more product, causing the reaction to shift left. For example, the reaction of nitrogen with hydrogen to form ammonia is exothermic.

Add heat

$$N_2(g) + 3\,H_2(g) \rightleftharpoons 2\,NH_3(g) + \text{heat}$$

Reaction shifts left.
Smaller K

Raising the temperature of an equilibrium mixture of these three gases causes the reaction to shift left, absorbing some of the added heat and forming less products and more reactants. Note that, unlike adding additional NH_3 to the reaction mixture (which does *not* change the value of the equilibrium constant), *changing the temperature does change the value of the equilibrium constant*. The new equilibrium mixture will have more reactants and fewer products and therefore a smaller value of K.

Conversely, lowering the temperature causes the reaction to shift right, releasing heat and producing more products because the value of K has increased.

Remove heat

$$N_2(g) + 3\,H_2(g) \rightleftharpoons 2NH_3(g) + \text{heat}$$

Reaction shifts right.
Larger K

In contrast, for an *endothermic* reaction, raising the temperature (adding heat) causes the reaction to shift right to absorb the added heat. For example, the following reaction is endothermic.

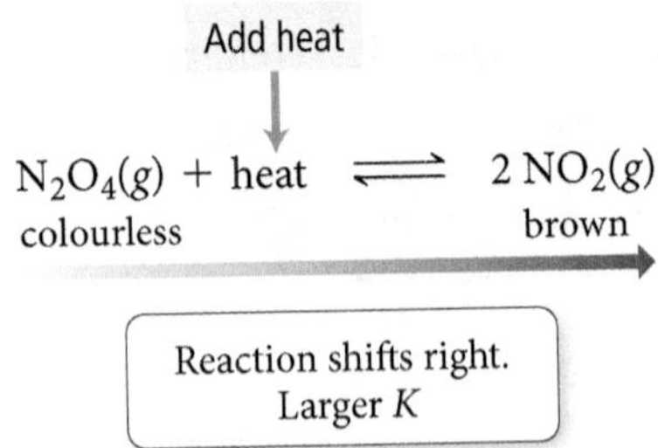

Raising the temperature of an equilibrium mixture of these two gases causes the reaction to shift right, absorbing some of the added heat and producing more products because the value of K has increased. Since N_2O_4 is colourless and NO_2 is brown, the effects of changing the temperature of this reaction are easily seen (Figure 14.10 ▶). On the other hand, lowering the temperature (removing heat) of a reaction mixture of these two gases causes the reaction to shift left, releasing heat, forming less products, and lowering the value of K.

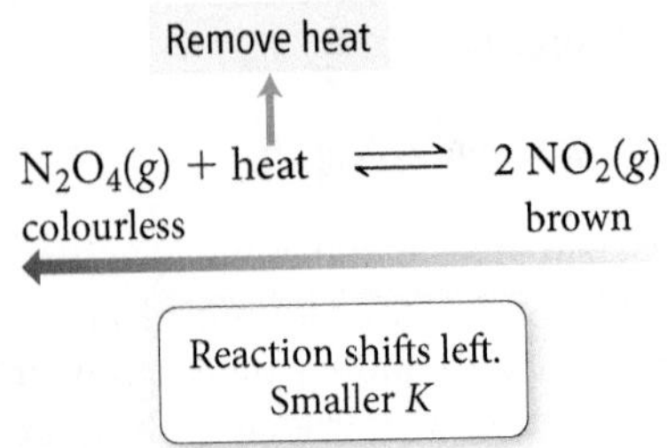

$$N_2O_4(g) + \text{heat} \rightleftharpoons 2\,NO_2(g)$$
colourless — brown

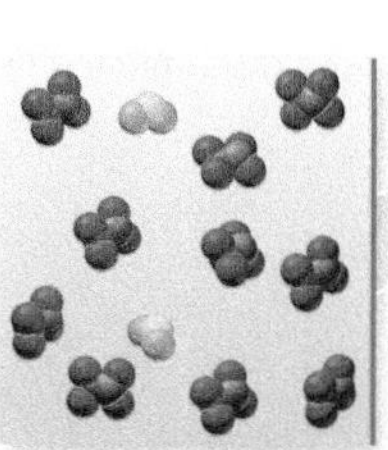
Lower temperature: N_2O_4 favoured

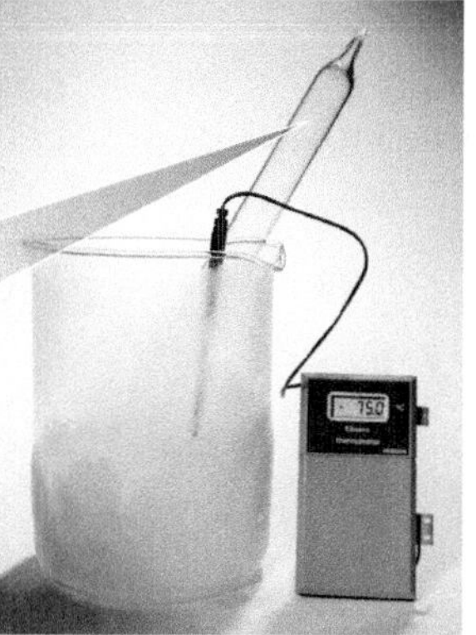

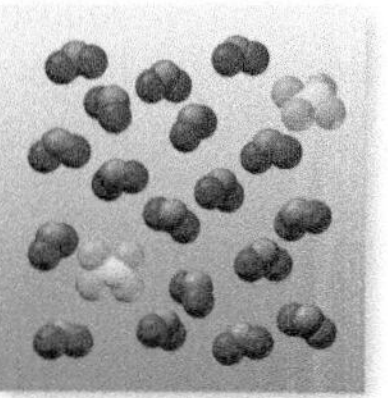
Higher temperature: NO_2 favoured

▲ **FIGURE 14.10 Le Châtelier's Principle: The Effect of a Temperature Change** Because the reaction is endothermic, raising the temperature causes a shift to the right, toward the formation of brown NO_2.

Summarizing the Effect of a Temperature Change on Equilibrium:

In an *exothermic* chemical reaction, heat is a product.

- *Increasing* the temperature causes an exothermic reaction to *shift left* (in the direction of the reactants); the value of the equilibrium constant decreases.
- *Decreasing* the temperature causes an exothermic reaction to *shift right* (in the direction of the products); the value of the equilibrium constant increases.

In an *endothermic* chemical reaction, heat is a reactant.

- *Increasing* the temperature causes an endothermic reaction to *shift right* (in the direction of the products); the equilibrium constant increases.
- *Decreasing* the temperature causes an endothermic reaction to *shift left* (in the direction of the reactants); the equilibrium constant decreases.

Adding heat favours the endothermic direction. Removing heat favours the exothermic direction.

EXAMPLE 14.15 THE EFFECT OF A TEMPERATURE CHANGE ON EQUILIBRIUM

The following reaction is endothermic:

$$CaCO_3(s) \rightleftharpoons CaO(s) + CO_2(g)$$

What is the effect of increasing the temperature of the reaction mixture? Of decreasing the temperature?

SOLUTION

Since the reaction is endothermic, we can think of heat as a reactant:

$$\text{Heat} + CaCO_3(s) \rightleftharpoons CaO(s) + CO_2(g)$$

Raising the temperature is equivalent to adding a reactant, causing the reaction to shift to the right. Lowering the temperature is equivalent to removing a reactant, causing the reaction to shift to the left.

FOR PRACTICE 14.15

The following reaction is exothermic.

$$2\,SO_2(g) + O_2(g) \rightleftharpoons 2\,SO_3(g)$$

What is the effect of increasing the temperature of the reaction mixture? Of decreasing the temperature?

CHAPTER IN REVIEW

Key Terms

Section 14.2
reversible (586)
dynamic equilibrium (586)

Section 14.3
equilibrium constant (K) (588)
law of mass action (588)
activity (590)

Section 14.6
reaction quotient (Q) (600)

Section 14.8
Le Châtelier's principle (611)

Key Concepts

The Equilibrium Constant (14.1)

The relative concentrations of the reactants and the products at equilibrium are expressed by the equilibrium constant, K. The equilibrium constant measures how far a reaction proceeds toward products: a large K (much greater than 1) indicates a high concentration of products at equilibrium and a small K (less than 1) indicates a low concentration of products at equilibrium.

Dynamic Equilibrium (14.2)

Most chemical reactions are reversible; they can proceed in either the forward or the reverse direction. When a chemical reaction is in dynamic equilibrium, the rate of the forward reaction equals the rate of the reverse reaction, so the net concentrations of reactants and products do not change. However, this does *not* imply that the concentrations of the reactants and the products are equal at equilibrium.

The Equilibrium-Constant Expression (14.3)

The equilibrium-constant expression is given by the law of mass action. For reactions in solution, the equilibrium constant, K_c, is equal to the concentrations of products, raised to their stoichiometric coefficients, divided by the concentrations of reactants, raised to their stoichiometric coefficients. For reactions in the gas phase, it is more convenient (and correct) to write the equilibrium constant, K_P, which is equal to the partial pressures of the products, raised to their stoichiometric coefficients, divided by the partial pressure of the reactants, raised to their stoichiometric coefficients. These two equilibrium constants can be related by Equation 14.5. The thermodynamic equilibrium constant, K, is written in terms of activities of the components, and for our purposes it is equal to the numerical value of K_c for solution-phase reactions or to the numerical value of K_P for gas-phase reactions. The equilibrium constant contains only partial pressures or concentrations of reactants and products that exist as gases or solutes, respectively. Pure liquids are not included in the expression for the equilibrium constant.

The Thermodynamic Equilibrium Constant (14.4)

While formally the equilibrium constants K_c and K_P have units, the thermodynamic equilibrium constant, K, written in terms of unitless activities, is unitless. As long as the equilibrium-constant expressions for K are written in terms of partial pressures in bar for gases and concentrations in mol L^{-1} for solution-phase components, we can drop the units from K_c and K_P to obtain an estimate of K from measured quantities. And from the unitless thermodynamic equilibrium constant, we can obtain quantitative values in bar for gas-phase reactions and mol L^{-1} for solution-phase reactions. When the equations for a chemical reaction are reversed, multiplied, or added to another equation, K must be modified accordingly.

Calculating *K* (14.5)

The equilibrium constant can be calculated from equilibrium concentrations or partial pressures by substituting measured values into the expression for the equilibrium constant (as obtained from the law of mass action). In most cases, the equilibrium concentrations of the reactants and products—and therefore the value of the equilibrium constant—can be calculated from the initial concentrations of the reactants and products and the equilibrium concentration of *just one* reactant or product.

The Reaction Quotient, *Q* (14.6)

The ratio of the concentrations (or partial pressures) of products raised to their stoichiometric coefficients to the concentrations of reactants raised to their stoichiometric coefficients *at any point in the reaction* is called the reaction quotient, Q. Like K, Q can be expressed in terms of concentrations (Q_c) or partial pressures (Q_P). At equilibrium, Q is equal to K; therefore, the direction in which a reaction will proceed can be determined by comparing Q to K. If $Q < K$, the reaction moves in the direction of the products; if $Q > K$, the reaction moves in the reverse direction.

Finding Equilibrium Concentrations (14.7)

There are two general types of problems in which K is given and one (or more) equilibrium amounts can be found: (1) K, initial amounts, and (at least) one equilibrium amount is given; and (2) K and *only* initial amounts is given. The first type is solved by rearranging the law of mass action and substituting given values. The second type is solved by using a variable, x, to represent the change in amounts.

Le Châtelier's Principle (14.8)

When a system at equilibrium is disturbed—by a change in the amount of a reactant or product, a change in volume, or a change in temperature—the system shifts in the direction that minimizes the disturbance.

Key Equations and Relationships

Expression for the Equilibrium Constant, K_c (14.3)

$$aA(aq) + bB(aq) \rightleftharpoons cC(aq) + dD(aq)$$

$$K_c = \frac{[C]^c[D]^d}{[A]^a[B]^b} \quad \text{(equilibrium concentrations only)}$$

Expression for the Equilibrium Constant, K_P (14.3)

$$aA(g) + bB(g) \rightleftharpoons cC(g) + dD(g)$$

$$K_P = \frac{(P_C)^c(P_D)^d}{(P_A)^a(P_B)^b} \quad \text{(equilibrium partial pressures only)}$$

Relationship Between the Equilibrium Constants, K_c and K_P (14.3)

$$K_P = K_c(RT)^{\Delta n}$$

Relationship Between the Equilibrium Constant and the Chemical Equation (14.4)

1. If you reverse the equation, invert the equilibrium constant.
2. If you multiply the coefficients in the equation by a factor, raise the equilibrium constant to the same factor.
3. If you add two or more individual chemical equations to obtain an overall equation, multiply the corresponding equilibrium constants by each other to obtain the overall equilibrium constant.

The Reaction Quotient, Q_c (14.6)

$$aA(aq) + bB(aq) \rightleftharpoons cC(aq) + dD(aq)$$

$$Q_c = \frac{[C]^c[D]^d}{[A]^a[B]^b} \quad \text{(concentrations at any point in the reaction)}$$

The Reaction Quotient, Q_p (14.6)

$$aA(g) + bB(g) \rightleftharpoons cC(g) + dD(g)$$

$$Q_P = \frac{(P_C)^c(P_D)^d}{(P_A)^a(P_B)^b} \quad \text{(partial pressures at any point in the reaction)}$$

Relationship of Q to the Direction of the Reaction (14.6)

$Q < K$ Reaction goes to the right.

$Q > K$ Reaction goes to the left.

$Q = K$ Reaction is at equilibrium.

Key Skills

Expressing Equilibrium Constants for Chemical Equations (14.3)

• Example 14.1 • For Practice 14.1 • Exercises 21, 22

Relating K_P and K_c (14.3)

• Example 14.1 • For Practice 14.1 • Exercises 31, 32

Writing Equilibrium Expressions for Reactions Involving a Solid or a Liquid (14.3)

• Example 14.2 • For Practice 14.2 • For More Practice 14.2 • Exercises 33, 34

Manipulating the Equilibrium Constant to Reflect Changes in the Chemical Equation (14.4)
• Example 14.3 • For Practice 14.3 • For More Practice 14.3 • Exercises 27–30

Finding Equilibrium Constants from Experimental Partial Pressure and Concentration Measurements (14.5)
• Examples 14.4, 14.5 • For Practice 14.4, 14.5 • Exercises 35, 36, 41, 42

Predicting the Direction of a Reaction by Comparing Q and K (14.6)
• Example 14.6 • For Practice 14.6 • Exercises 45–48

Calculating Equilibrium Concentrations from the Equilibrium Constant and One or More Equilibrium Concentrations (14.7)
• Example 14.7 • For Practice 14.7 • Exercises 37–44

Finding Equilibrium Partial Pressures from Initial Partial Pressures and the Equilibrium Constant (14.7)
• Examples 14.8, 14.9 • For Practice 14.8, 14.9 • Exercises 51, 54, 56–58

Calculating Equilibrium Concentrations from the Equilibrium Constant and Initial Concentrations (14.7)
• Example 14.10 • For Practice 14.10 • Exercise 55

Finding Equilibrium Amounts in Cases with a Small Equilibrium Constant (14.7)
• Examples 14.11, 14.12 • For Practice 14.11, 14.12 • Exercises 59, 60

Determining the Effect of Changing the Amount of a Reactant or Product on Equilibrium (14.8)
• Example 14.13 • For Practice 14.13 • Exercises 61–64

Determining the Effect of a Volume Change on Equilibrium (14.8)
• Example 14.14 • For Practice 14.14 • Exercises 65, 66

Determining the Effect of a Temperature Change on Equilibrium (14.8)
• Example 14.15 • For Practice 14.15 • Exercises 67, 68

EXERCISES

Review Questions

1. How does a developing fetus in the womb get oxygen?
2. What is dynamic equilibrium? Why is it called *dynamic*?
3. Give the general expression for the equilibrium constant for the following reactions:
   a. $aA(aq) + bB(aq) \rightleftharpoons cC(aq) + dD(aq)$
   b. $aA(g) + bB(g) \rightleftharpoons cC(g) + dD(g)$
4. What is the significance of the equilibrium constant? What does a large equilibrium constant tell us about a reaction? A small one?
5. What happens to the value of the equilibrium constant for a reaction if the reaction equation is reversed? Multiplied by a constant?
6. If two reactions sum to an overall reaction, and the equilibrium constants for the two reactions are K_1 and K_2, what is the equilibrium constant for the overall reaction?
7. Explain the difference between K, K_c, and K_P. For a given reaction, how are the two constants related?
8. What units should be used when expressing concentrations or partial pressures in the equilibrium constant? What are the units of K, K_P, and K_c? Explain.
9. Why are the concentrations of pure solids and pure liquids omitted from equilibrium constant expressions?
10. Does the value of the equilibrium constant depend on the initial amounts of the reactants and products? Do concentrations or partial pressures of the reactants and products at equilibrium depend on their initial amounts? Explain.
11. Explain how you might deduce the equilibrium constant for a reaction in which you know the initial amounts of the reactants and products and the equilibrium amount of only one reactant or product.
12. What is the definition of the reaction quotient (Q) for a reaction? What does Q measure?
13. What is the value of Q when each reactant and product is in its standard state?

14. In what direction will a reaction proceed for each condition: **(a)** $Q < K$; **(b)** $Q > K$; and **(c)** $Q = K$?

15. Many equilibrium calculations involve finding the equilibrium amounts of reactants and products given their initial concentrations or partial pressures and the equilibrium constant. Outline the general procedure used in solving these kinds of problems.

16. In equilibrium problems involving equilibrium constants that are small relative to the initial concentrations or partial pressures of reactants, we can often assume that the quantity x (which represents how far the reaction proceeds toward products) is small. When this assumption is made, the quantity x can be ignored when it is subtracted from a large number, but not when it is multiplied by a large number. In other words, $2.5 - x \approx 2.5$, but $2.5x \neq 2.5$. Explain why a small x can be ignored in the first case, but not in the second.

17. What happens to a chemical system at equilibrium when that equilibrium is disturbed?

18. What is the effect of a change in the amount of a reactant or product on a chemical reaction initially at equilibrium?

19. What is the effect of a change in volume on a chemical reaction (that includes gaseous reactants or products) initially at equilibrium?

20. What is the effect of a temperature change on a chemical reaction initially at equilibrium? How does the effect differ for an exothermic reaction compared to an endothermic one?

Problems by Topic

Equilibrium and the Equilibrium-Constant Expression

21. Find and fix each mistake in the equilibrium-constant expressions.

a. $2\,H_2S(g) \rightleftharpoons 2\,H_2(g) + S_2(g) \quad K_P = \dfrac{P_{H_2}P_{S_2}}{P_{H_2S}}$

b. $Cu(s) + 2\,Ag^+(aq) \rightleftharpoons Cu^{2+}(aq) + 2\,Ag(s)$

$$K_c = \frac{[Cu^{2+}][Ag]^2}{[Cu][Ag^+]^2}$$

c. $Li(s) + 2\,H_2O(l) \rightleftharpoons Li^+(aq) + 2\,OH^-(aq) + 2\,H_2(g)$

$$K = \frac{1}{[Li^+][OH^-]P_{H_2}}$$

22. Write an expression for the equilibrium constant of each chemical equation.

a. $CO(g) + Cl_2(g) \rightleftharpoons COCl_2(g)$

b. $SbCl_5(g) \rightleftharpoons SbCl_3(g) + Cl_2(g)$

c. $CH_4(g) + 2\,H_2S(g) \rightleftharpoons CS_2(g) + 4\,H_2(g)$

d. $HSO_4^-(aq) + H_2O(l) \rightleftharpoons SO_4^{2-}(aq) + H_3O^+(aq)$

e. $Au^{3+}(aq) + 3\,I^-(aq) \rightleftharpoons Au(s) + 3/2\,I_2(s)$

f. $2\,MnO_4^-(aq) + 6\,H^+(aq) + 5\,H_2C_2O_4(aq) \rightleftharpoons 2\,Mn^{2+}(aq) + 8\,H_2O(l) + 10\,CO_2(g)$

23. When the reaction below comes to equilibrium, will the concentrations of the reactants or products be greater? Does the answer to this question depend on the initial concentrations of the reactants and products?

$$A(aq) + B(aq) \rightleftharpoons 2\,C(aq) \quad K = 1.4 \times 10^{-5}$$

24. Ethene (C_2H_4) can be halogenated by this reaction:

$$C_2H_4(g) + X_2(g) \rightleftharpoons C_2H_4X_2(g)$$

where X_2 can be Cl_2 (green), Br_2 (brown), or I_2 (purple). Examine the three figures representing equilibrium concentrations in this reaction at the same temperature for the three different halogens. Rank the equilibrium constants for the three reactions from largest to smallest.

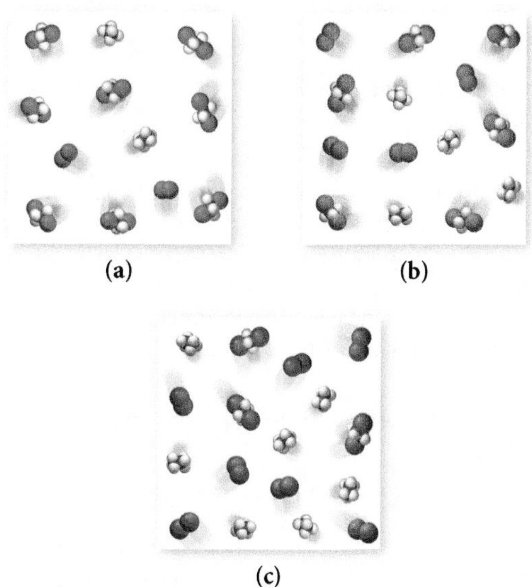

25. H_2 and I_2 are combined in a flask and allowed to react according to the reaction:

$$H_2(g) + I_2(g) \rightleftharpoons 2\,HI(g)$$

Examine the figures on the next page (sequential in time) and answer the questions:

a. Which figure represents the point at which equilibrium is reached?

b. How would the series of figures change in the presence of a catalyst?

c. Would the final figure (vi) have different amounts of reactants and products in the presence of a catalyst?

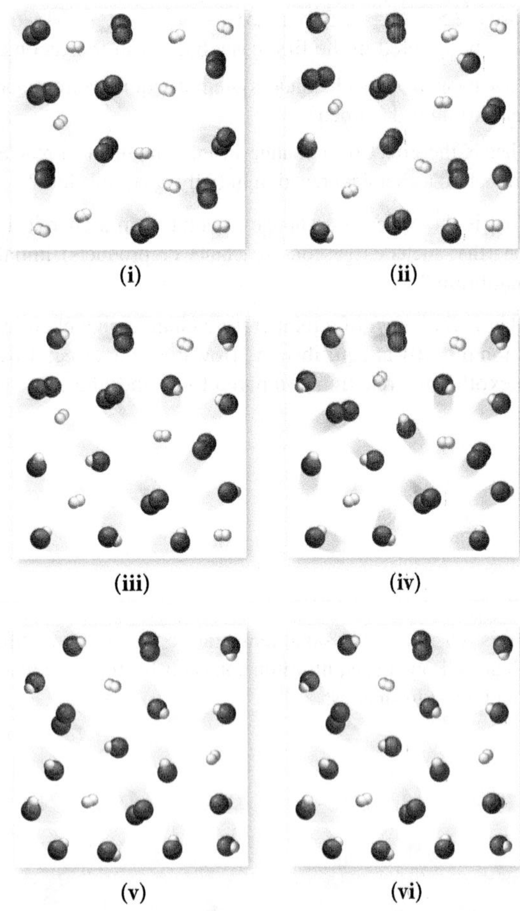

26. A chemist trying to synthesize a particular compound attempts two different synthesis reactions. The equilibrium constants for the two reactions are 23.3 and 2.2×10^4 at room temperature. However, upon carrying out both reactions for 15 minutes, the chemist finds that the reaction with the smaller equilibrium constant produces more of the desired product. Explain how this might be possible.

27. The reaction below has an equilibrium constant of $K = 9.1 \times 10^6$ at 300 K.

$$CO(g) + 2\,H_2(g) \rightleftharpoons CH_3OH(g)$$

Calculate K for each of the reactions and predict whether reactants or products will be favoured at equilibrium:

a. $CH_3OH(g) \rightleftharpoons CO(g) + 2\,H_2(g)$
b. $\frac{1}{2}CO(g) + H_2(g) \rightleftharpoons \frac{1}{2}CH_3OH(g)$
c. $2\,CH_3OH(g) \rightleftharpoons 2\,CO(g) + 4\,H_2(g)$

28. The reaction below has an equilibrium constant of $K = 2.2 \times 10^6$ at 298 K.

$$2\,COF_2(g) \rightleftharpoons CO_2(g) + CF_4(g)$$

Calculate K for each of the reactions and predict whether reactants or products will be favoured at equilibrium:

a. $COF_2(g) \rightleftharpoons \frac{1}{2}CO_2(g) + \frac{1}{2}CF_4(g)$
b. $6\,COF_2(g) \rightleftharpoons 3\,CO_2(g) + 3\,CF_4(g)$
c. $2\,CO_2(g) + 2\,CF_4(g) \rightleftharpoons 4\,COF_2(g)$

29. Consider the reactions and their respective equilibrium constants:

$NO(g) + \frac{1}{2}Br_2(g) \rightleftharpoons NOBr(g)$ $\quad K = 5.3$

$2\,NO(g) \rightleftharpoons N_2(g) + O_2(g)$ $\quad K = 2.1 \times 10^{30}$

Use these reactions and their equilibrium constants to predict the equilibrium constant for the following reaction:

$$N_2(g) + O_2(g) + Br_2(g) \rightleftharpoons 2\,NOBr(g)$$

30. Use the reactions below and their equilibrium constants to predict the equilibrium constant for the reaction, $2\,A(s) \rightleftharpoons 3\,D(g)$.

$A(s) \rightleftharpoons \frac{1}{2}B(g) + C(g)$ $\quad K_1 = 0.0334$

$3\,D(g) \rightleftharpoons B(g) + 2\,C(g)$ $\quad K_2 = 2.35$

K_P, K_C, and Heterogeneous Equilibria

31. Calculate K_c for each reaction:
a. $I_2(g) \rightleftharpoons 2\,I(g)$ $\quad K_P = 6.26 \times 10^{-22}$ (at 298 K)
b. $CH_4(g) + H_2O(g) \rightleftharpoons CO(g) + 3\,H_2(g)$ $\quad K_P = 7.7 \times 10^{24}$ (at 298 K)
c. $I_2(g) + Cl_2(g) \rightleftharpoons 2\,ICl(g)$ $\quad K_P = 81.9$ (at 298 K)

32. Calculate K_P for each reaction:
a. $N_2O_4(g) \rightleftharpoons 2\,NO_2(g)$ $\quad K_c = 5.9 \times 10^{-3}$ (at 298 K)
b. $N_2(g) + 3\,H_2(g) \rightleftharpoons 2\,NH_3(g)$ $\quad K_c = 3.7 \times 10^8$ (at 298 K)
c. $N_2(g) + O_2(g) \rightleftharpoons 2\,NO(g)$ $\quad K_c = 4.10 \times 10^{-31}$ (at 298 K)

33. Write an equilibrium-constant expression for each chemical equation involving one or more solid or liquid reactants or products.
a. $CO_3^{2-}(aq) + H_2O(l) \rightleftharpoons HCO_3^-(aq) + OH^-(aq)$
b. $2\,KClO_3(s) \rightleftharpoons 2\,KCl(s) + 3\,O_2(g)$
c. $HF(aq) + H_2O(l) \rightleftharpoons H_3O^+(aq) + F^-(aq)$
d. $NH_3(aq) + H_2O(l) \rightleftharpoons NH_4^+(aq) + OH^-(aq)$

34. Find the mistake in the equilibrium-constant expression and fix it.

$$PCl_5(g) \rightleftharpoons PCl_3(l) + Cl_2(g) \quad K = \frac{P_{PCl_3}P_{Cl_2}}{P_{PCl_5}}$$

Relating the Equilibrium Constant to Equilibrium Concentrations and Equilibrium Partial Pressures

35. Consider the reaction:

$$CO(g) + 2\,H_2(g) \rightleftharpoons CH_3OH(g)$$

An equilibrium mixture of this reaction at a certain temperature was found to have $P_{CO} = 0.105$ bar, $P_{H_2} = 0.114$ bar, and $P_{CH_3OH} = 0.185$ bar. What is the value of the equilibrium constant at this temperature?

36. Consider the reaction:

$$NH_4HS(s) \rightleftharpoons NH_3(g) + H_2S(g)$$

An equilibrium mixture of this reaction at a certain temperature was found to have $P_{NH_3} = 0.105$ bar and $P_{H_2S} = 0.114$ bar. What is the value of the equilibrium constant at this temperature?

37. Consider the reaction:

$$N_2(g) + 3\,H_2(g) \rightleftharpoons 2\,NH_3(g)$$

Complete the table. Assume that all partial pressures are equilibrium values and in bar.

T(K)	P_{N_2}	P_{H_2}	P_{NH_3}	K
350	0.121	0.105	0.565	_____
415	0.110	_____	0.128	13.2
515	0.120	0.140	_____	0.0512

38. Consider the following reaction:

$$H_2(g) + I_2(g) \rightleftharpoons 2\,HI(g)$$

Complete the table. Assume that all partial pressures are equilibrium values and in bar.

T(K)	P_{H_2}	P_{I_2}	P_{HI}	K
298	0.0302	0.0388	0.922	____
600	0.0421	____	0.387	78.2
515	0.0525	0.386	____	33.0

39. Consider the reaction:

$$2\,NO(g) + Br_2(g) \rightleftharpoons 2\,BrNO(g) \quad K = 32.9 \text{ at } 315\text{ K}$$

In a reaction mixture at equilibrium, the partial pressure of NO is 108 mbar and that of Br_2 is 126 mbar. What is the partial pressure of BrNO in the equilibrium mixture?

40. Consider the reaction:

$$SO_2Cl_2(g) \rightleftharpoons SO_2(g) + Cl_2(g) \quad K = 2.97 \times 10^3 \text{ at } 625\text{ K}$$

In a reaction mixture at equilibrium, the partial pressure of SO_2 is 137 mbar and that of Cl_2 is 285 mbar. What is the partial pressure of SO_2Cl_2?

41. Consider the reaction:

$$Fe^{3+}(aq) + SCN^-(aq) \rightleftharpoons FeSCN^{2+}(aq)$$

A solution is made containing an initial $[Fe^{3+}]$ of 2.4×10^{-4} mol L^{-1} and an initial $[SCN^-]$ of 8.0×10^{-4} mol L^{-1}. At equilibrium, $[FeSCN^{2+}] = 1.7 \times 10^{-4}$ mol L^{-1}. Calculate the value of the equilibrium constant (K_c).

42. Consider the reaction:

$$SO_2Cl_2(g) \rightleftharpoons SO_2(g) + Cl_2(g)$$

A reaction mixture is made containing an initial $P_{SO_2Cl_2} =$ 2.6 bar. At equilibrium, $P_{Cl_2} = 0.21$ bar. Calculate the value of the equilibrium constant.

43. Consider the reaction:

$$H_2(g) + I_2(g) \rightleftharpoons 2\,HI(g)$$

A reaction mixture in a 3.67 L flask at 500 K initially contains 0.371 g H_2 and 17.93 g I_2. At equilibrium, the flask contains 17.72 g HI. Calculate the equilibrium constant at this temperature.

44. Consider the reaction:

$$CO(g) + 2\,H_2(g) \rightleftharpoons CH_3OH(g)$$

A reaction mixture in a 5.19 L flask at 500 K contains 9.02 g of CO and 0.55 g of H_2. At equilibrium, the flask contains 2.31 g of CH_3OH. Calculate the equilibrium constant at this temperature.

The Reaction Quotient and Reaction Direction

45. Consider the reaction:

$$NH_4HS(s) \rightleftharpoons NH_3(g) + H_2S(g)$$

At a certain temperature, $K = 8.5 \times 10^{-3}$. A reaction mixture at this temperature containing solid NH_4HS has $P_{NH_3} = 0.266$ bar, $P_{H_2S} = 0.266$ bar. Will more of the solid form or will some of the existing solid decompose as equilibrium is reached?

46. Consider the reaction:

$$2\,H_2S(g) \rightleftharpoons 2\,H_2(g) + S_2(g)$$
$$K = 4.4 \times 10^{-4} \text{ at } 1073\text{ K}$$

A reaction mixture contains 0.112 bar of H_2, 0.055 bar of S_2, and 0.445 bar of H_2S. Is the reaction mixture at equilibrium? If not, in what direction will the reaction proceed?

47. Silver sulfate dissolves in water according to the reaction:

$$Ag_2SO_4(s) \rightleftharpoons 2\,Ag^+(aq) + SO_4^{2-}(aq)$$
$$K = 1.1 \times 10^{-5} \text{ at } 298\text{ K}$$

A 1.5 L solution contains 6.55 g of dissolved silver sulfate. If additional solid silver sulfate is added to the solution, will it dissolve?

48. Nitrogen dioxide dimerizes according to the reaction:

$$2\,NO_2(g) \rightleftharpoons N_2O_4(g) \quad K = 5.5 \text{ at } 298\text{ K}$$

A 2.25 L container contains 0.055 mol of NO_2 and 0.082 mol of N_2O_4 at 298 K. Is the reaction at equilibrium? If not, in what direction will the reaction proceed?

Finding Equilibrium Concentrations from Initial Concentrations and the Equilibrium Constant

49. Consider the reaction and associated equilibrium constant:

$$aA(aq) \rightleftharpoons bB(aq) \quad K = 4.0$$

Find the equilibrium concentrations of A and B for each value of a and b. Assume that the initial concentration of A in each case is 1.0 mol L^{-1} and that no B is present at the beginning of the reaction.

a. $a = 1$; $b = 1$
b. $a = 2$; $b = 2$
c. $a = 1$; $b = 2$

50. Consider the reaction and associated equilibrium constant:

$$aA(aq) + bB(aq) \rightleftharpoons cC(aq) \quad K = 5.0$$

Find the equilibrium concentrations of A, B, and C for each value of a, b, and c. Assume that the initial concentrations of A and B are each 1.0 mol L^{-1} and that no C is present at the beginning of the reaction.

a. $a = 1$; $b = 1$; $c = 2$
b. $a = 1$; $b = 1$; $c = 1$
c. $a = 2$; $b = 1$; $c = 1$ (set up equation for x; don't solve)

51. For the following reaction, $K = 0.538$ at 313 K.

$$N_2O_4(g) \rightleftharpoons 2\,NO_2(g)$$

If a reaction vessel initially contains an N_2O_4 concentration of 0.0500 mol L^{-1} at 313 K, what are the equilibrium concentrations of N_2O_4 and NO_2 at 313 K?

Hint: Ensure use of proper units for the equilibrium constant.

52. For the following reaction, $K = 24.6$ at 668 K.

$$CO(g) + Cl_2(g) \rightleftharpoons COCl_2(g)$$

If a reaction mixture initially contains a CO concentration of 0.1500 mol L^{-1} and a Cl_2 concentration of 0.175 mol L^{-1} at 668 K, what are the equilibrium concentrations of CO, Cl_2, and $COCl_2$ at 668 K?

Hint: Ensure use of proper units for the equilibrium constant.

53. Consider the reaction:

$$NiO(s) + CO(g) \rightleftharpoons Ni(s) + CO_2(g) \quad K = 80.3 \text{ at } 1500\text{ K}$$

If a mixture of solid nickel(II) oxide and 2.28 bar carbon monoxide is allowed to come to equilibrium at 1500 K, what will be the partial pressure of CO and CO_2 at equilibrium?

54. Consider the reaction:

$$CO(g) + H_2O(g) \rightleftharpoons CO_2(g) + H_2(g) \quad K = 130 \text{ at } 500 \text{ K}$$

If a reaction mixture initially contains 0.550 bar each of CO and H_2O, what will be the partial pressures of each of the reactants and products at equilibrium?

55. Consider the reaction:

$$CH_3COOH(aq) + H_2O(l) \rightleftharpoons H_3O^+(aq) + CH_3COO^-(aq)$$
$$K = 1.8 \times 10^{-5} \text{ at } 25\ °C$$

If a solution initially contains 0.210 mol L^{-1} CH_3COOH, what is the equilibrium concentration of H_3O^+ at 25 °C?

56. Consider the reaction:

$$SO_2(g) + Cl_2(g) \rightleftharpoons SO_2Cl_2(g) \quad K = 6.9 \times 10^{-6} \text{ at } 1000 \text{ K}$$

If a reaction mixture initially contains 0.710 bar each of SO_2 and Cl_2, what is the partial pressure of SO_2Cl_2 at equilibrium?

57. Consider the decomposition reaction of chlorine monofluoride at 1000 K:

$$2\ ClF(g) \rightleftharpoons Cl_2(g) + F_2(g) \quad K = 1.75 \times 10^{-6} \text{ at } 1000 \text{ K}$$

If a reaction mixture initially contained 0.500 bar of ClF, what are the partial pressures of all reactants and products at equilibrium?

58. Consider the reaction:

$$CO(g) + H_2O(g) \rightleftharpoons CO_2(g) + H_2(g)$$
$$K = 0.118 \text{ at } 4000 \text{ K}$$

A reaction mixture initially contains a CO partial pressure of 1344 mbar and a H_2O partial pressure of 1766 mbar at 4000 K. Calculate the equilibrium partial pressures of each of the products.

59. Consider the reaction:

$$A(aq) \rightleftharpoons B(aq) + C(aq)$$

Find the equilibrium concentrations of A, B, and C for each value of K. Assume that the initial concentration of A in each case is 1.0 mol L^{-1} and that the reaction mixture initially contains no B or C. Make any appropriate simplifying assumptions.

a. $K = 1.0$
b. $K = 0.010$
c. $K = 1.0 \times 10^{-5}$

60. Consider the reaction:

$$A(g) \rightleftharpoons 2\ B(g)$$

Find the equilibrium partial pressures of A and B for each value of K. Assume that the initial partial pressure of B in each case is 1.0 bar and that the initial partial pressure of A is 0.0 bar. Make any appropriate simplifying assumptions.

a. $K = 1.0$
b. $K = 1.0 \times 10^{-4}$
c. $K = 1.0 \times 10^{5}$

Le Châtelier's Principle

61. Consider the reaction at equilibrium:

$$CO(g) + Cl_2(g) \rightleftharpoons COCl_2(g)$$

Predict whether the reaction will shift left, shift right, or remain unchanged after each disturbance:

a. $COCl_2$ is added to the reaction mixture.
b. Cl_2 is added to the reaction mixture.
c. $COCl_2$ is removed from the reaction mixture.

62. Consider this reaction at equilibrium:

$$2\ BrNO(g) \rightleftharpoons 2\ NO(g) + Br_2(g)$$

Predict whether the reaction will shift left, shift right, or remain unchanged after each disturbance.

a. NO is added to the reaction mixture.
b. BrNO is added to the reaction mixture.
c. Br_2 is removed from the reaction mixture.

63. Consider this reaction at equilibrium:

$$2\ KClO_3(s) \rightleftharpoons 2\ KCl(s) + 3\ O_2(g)$$

Predict whether the reaction will shift left, shift right, or remain unchanged after each disturbance.

a. O_2 is removed from the reaction mixture.
b. KCl is added to the reaction mixture.
c. $KClO_3$ is added to the reaction mixture.
d. O_2 is added to the reaction mixture.

64. Consider this reaction at equilibrium:

$$C(s) + H_2O(g) \rightleftharpoons CO(g) + H_2(g)$$

Predict whether the reaction will shift left, shift right, or remain unchanged after each disturbance.

a. C is added to the reaction mixture.
b. H_2O is condensed and removed from the reaction mixture.
c. CO is added to the reaction mixture.
d. H_2 is removed from the reaction mixture.

65. Each of the following reactions is allowed to come to equilibrium and then the volume is changed as indicated. Predict the effect (shift right, shift left, or no effect) of the indicated volume change.

a. $I_2(g) \rightleftharpoons 2\ I(g)$ (volume is increased)
b. $2\ H_2S(g) \rightleftharpoons 2\ H_2(g) + S_2(g)$ (volume is decreased)
c. $I_2(g) + Cl_2(g) \rightleftharpoons 2\ ICl(g)$ (volume is decreased)

66. Each of the following reactions is allowed to come to equilibrium and then the volume is changed as indicated. Predict the effect (shift right, shift left, or no effect) of the indicated volume change.

a. $CO(g) + H_2O(g) \rightleftharpoons CO_2(g) + H_2(g)$ (volume is decreased)
b. $PCl_3(g) + Cl_2(g) \rightleftharpoons PCl_5(g)$ (volume is increased)
c. $CaCO_3(s) \rightleftharpoons CaO(s) + CO_2(g)$ (volume is increased)

67. This reaction is endothermic.

$$C(s) + CO_2(g) \rightleftharpoons 2\ CO(g)$$

Predict the effect (shift right, shift left, or no effect) of increasing and decreasing the reaction temperature. How does the value of the equilibrium constant depend on temperature?

68. This reaction is exothermic.

$$C_6H_{12}O_6(s) + 6\ O_2(g) \rightleftharpoons 6\ CO_2(g) + 6\ H_2O(g)$$

Predict the effect (shift right, shift left, or no effect) of increasing and decreasing the reaction temperature. How does the value of the equilibrium constant depend on temperature?

69. Coal, which is primarily carbon, can be converted to natural gas, primarily CH_4, by the exothermic reaction:

$$C(s) + 2\ H_2(g) \rightleftharpoons CH_4(g)$$

Which disturbance(s) will favour CH_4 at equilibrium?

a. adding more C to the reaction mixture
b. adding more H_2 to the reaction mixture
c. raising the temperature of the reaction mixture

d. lowering the volume of the reaction mixture
e. adding a catalyst to the reaction mixture
f. adding neon gas to the reaction mixture

70. Coal can be used to generate hydrogen gas (a potential fuel) by the endothermic reaction:

$$C(s) + H_2O(g) \rightleftharpoons CO(g) + H_2(g)$$

If this reaction mixture is at equilibrium, predict whether each disturbance will result in the formation of additional hydrogen gas, the formation of less hydrogen gas, or have no effect on the quantity of hydrogen gas.

a. adding more C to the reaction mixture
b. adding more H_2O to the reaction mixture
c. raising the temperature of the reaction mixture
d. increasing the volume of the reaction mixture
e. adding a catalyst to the reaction mixture
f. adding an inert gas to the reaction mixture

Cumulative Problems

71. Carbon monoxide replaces oxygen in oxygenated hemoglobin according to the reaction:

$$HbO_2(aq) + CO(aq) \rightleftharpoons HbCO(aq) + O_2(aq)$$

a. Use the reactions and associated equilibrium constants at body temperature to find the equilibrium constant for the above reaction.

$$Hb(aq) + O_2(aq) \rightleftharpoons HbO_2(aq) \quad K = 1.8$$

$$Hb(aq) + CO(aq) \rightleftharpoons HbCO(aq) \quad K = 306$$

b. Suppose that an air mixture becomes polluted with carbon monoxide at a level of 0.10%. Assuming the air contains 20.0% oxygen, and that the oxygen and carbon monoxide ratios that dissolve in the blood are identical to the ratios in the air, what would be the ratio of HbCO to HbO_2 in the bloodstream? Comment on the toxicity of carbon monoxide.

72. Nitrogen monoxide is a pollutant in the lower atmosphere that irritates the eyes and lungs and leads to the formation of acid rain. Nitrogen monoxide forms naturally in atmosphere according to the endothermic reaction:

$$N_2(g) + O_2(g) \rightleftharpoons 2\ NO(g) \quad K = 4.1 \times 10^{-31} \text{ at } 298\text{ K}.$$

Use the ideal gas law to calculate the concentrations of nitrogen and oxygen present in air at a pressure of 1.0 bar and a temperature of 298 K. Assume that nitrogen composes 78% of air by volume and that oxygen composes 21% of air. Find the "natural" equilibrium concentration of NO in air in units of molecules/cm^3. How would you expect this concentration to change in an automobile engine in which combustion is occurring?

73. The reaction $CO_2(g) + C(s) \rightleftharpoons 2\ CO(g)$ has $K = 48.3$ at 1200 K.

a. Calculate the total pressure at equilibrium when 4.45 g of CO_2 is introduced into a 10.0 L container and heated to 1200 K in the presence of 2.00 g of graphite.
b. Repeat the calculation of part (a) in the presence of 0.50 g of graphite.

74. A mixture of water and graphite is heated to 890 K in a 10.0 L container. When the system comes to equilibrium it contains 0.875 mol each of CO gas and H_2 gas and 0.289 mol of H_2O gas and some graphite. Some O_2 gas is added to the system and a spark is applied so that the H_2 reacts completely with the O_2, forming H_2O. Find the amount of CO in the flask when the system returns to equilibrium.

75. At 650 K, the reaction $MgCO_3(s) \rightleftharpoons MgO(s) + CO_2(g)$ has $K = 0.042$. A 10.0 L container at 650 K has 1.0 g of $MgO(s)$ and CO_2 at $P = 0.0260$ bar. The container is then compressed to a volume of 0.100 L. Find the mass of $MgCO_3$ that is formed.

76. A system at equilibrium contains $I_2(g)$ at a pressure of 0.21 bar and $I(g)$ at a pressure of 0.23 bar. The system is then compressed to half its volume. Find the pressure of each gas when the system returns to equilibrium.

77. Consider the exothermic reaction:

$$C_2H_4(g) + Cl_2(g) \rightleftharpoons C_2H_4Cl_2(g)$$

If you were a chemist trying to maximize the amount of $C_2H_4Cl_2$ produced, which tactic(s) might you try? Assume that the reaction mixture reaches equilibrium.

a. increasing the reaction volume
b. removing $C_2H_4Cl_2$ from the reaction mixture as it forms
c. lowering the reaction temperature
d. adding Cl_2

78. Consider the endothermic reaction:

$$C_2H_4(g) + I_2(g) \rightleftharpoons C_2H_4I_2(g)$$

If you were a chemist trying to maximize the amount of $C_2H_4I_2$ produced, which tactic(s) might you try? Assume that the reaction mixture reaches equilibrium.

a. decreasing the reaction volume
b. removing I_2 from the reaction mixture
c. raising the reaction temperature
d. adding C_2H_4 to the reaction mixture

79. Consider the reaction:

$$H_2(g) + I_2(g) \rightleftharpoons 2\ HI(g)$$

A reaction mixture at equilibrium at 600 K contains 0.170 bar H_2, 0.120 bar I_2, and 1.26 bar HI. A second reaction mixture, also at 600 K, contains 0.135 bar each of H_2 and I_2 and 1.10 bar of HI. Is the second mixture at equilibrium? If not, what will be the partial pressure of HI when the reaction reaches equilibrium at 600 K?

80. Consider the reaction:

$$2\ H_2S(g) + SO_2(g) \rightleftharpoons 3\ S(s) + 2\ H_2O(g)$$

A reaction mixture initially containing 0.600 bar each of H_2S and SO_2 was found to contain 0.0054 bar of H_2O at equilibrium at 1300 K. A second reaction mixture at the same temperature initially contains 0.500 bar of H_2S and 0.350 bar of SO_2. Calculate the equilibrium concentrations of all reactants and products at equilibrium.

81. Ammonia can be synthesized according to the reaction:

$$N_2(g) + 3\,H_2(g) \rightleftharpoons 2\,NH_3(g)$$
$$K = 5.3 \times 10^{-5} \text{ at } 725\text{ K}$$

A 200.0 L reaction container initially contains 1.27 kg of N_2 and 0.310 kg of H_2 at 725 K. Assuming ideal gas behaviour, calculate the mass of NH_3 (in g) present in the reaction mixture at equilibrium. What is the percent yield of the reaction under these conditions?

82. Hydrogen can be extracted from natural gas according to the reaction:

$$CH_4(g) + CO_2(g) \rightleftharpoons 2\,CO(g) + 2\,H_2(g)$$
$$K = 4.5 \times 10^{2} \text{ at } 1115\text{ K}$$

An 85.0 L reaction container initially contains 23.3 kg of CH_4 and 55.4 kg of CO_2 at 1115 K. Assuming ideal gas behaviour, calculate the mass of H_2 (in g) present in the reaction mixture at equilibrium. What is the percent yield of the reaction under these conditions?

83. The system described by the reaction

$$CO(g) + Cl_2(g) \rightleftharpoons COCl_2(g)$$

is at equilibrium at a given temperature when $P_{CO} = 0.30$ bar, $P_{Cl_2} = 0.10$ bar, and $P_{COCl_2} = 0.60$ bar. An additional pressure of $Cl_2(g) = 0.40$ bar is added. Find the pressure of CO when the system returns to equilibrium.

84. A reaction vessel at 1215 K contains a mixture of SO_2 ($P = 3.00$ bar) and O_2 ($P = 1.00$ bar). When a catalyst is added this reaction takes place:

$$2\,SO_2(g) + O_2(g) \rightleftharpoons 2\,SO_3(g)$$

At equilibrium the total pressure is 3.75 bar. Find the value of K.

85. At 693 K, CCl_4 decomposes to carbon and chlorine. The K for the decomposition is 0.76.

$$CCl_4(g) \rightleftharpoons C(s) + 2Cl_2(g)$$

Find the starting pressure of CCl_4 at this temperature that will produce a total pressure of 1.0 bar at equilibrium.

86. The equilibrium constant for the reaction $SO_2(g) + NO_2(g) \rightleftharpoons SO_3(g) + NO(g)$ is 15.6 at 1000 K. Find the amount of NO_2 that must be added to 2.4 mol of SO_2 in order to form 1.2 mol of SO_3 at equilibrium.

87. A sample of $CaCO_3(s)$ is introduced into a sealed container of volume 0.654 L and heated to 1000 K until equilibrium is reached. The K for the reaction

$$CaCO_3(s) \rightleftharpoons CaO(s) + CO_2(g)$$

is 3.9×10^{-2} at this temperature. Calculate the mass of CaO(s) that is present at equilibrium.

88. An equilibrium mixture contains N_2O_4 ($P = 0.28$ bar) and NO_2 ($P = 1.1$ bar) at 350 K. The volume of the container is doubled at constant temperature. Calculate the equilibrium pressures of the two gases when the system reaches a new equilibrium.

89. Carbon monoxide and chlorine gas react to form phosgene:

$$CO(g) + Cl_2(g) \rightleftharpoons COCl_2(g) \quad K = 3.10 \text{ at } 746\text{ K}$$

If a reaction mixture initially contains 215 mbar of CO and 245 mbar of Cl_2, what is the mole fraction of $COCl_2$ when equilibrium is reached?

90. Graphite can react with gaseous water to form carbon monoxide gas and hydrogen gas. The equilibrium constant for the reaction at 700.0 K is $K_P = 1.60 \times 10^{-3}$. If a 1.55 L reaction vessel initially contains 145 mbar of water at 700.0 K in contact with excess graphite, find the percent by mass of hydrogen gas of the gaseous reaction mixture at equilibrium.

Challenge Problems

91. Consider the reaction:

$$2\,NO(g) + O_2(g) \rightleftharpoons 2\,NO_2(g)$$

a. A reaction mixture at 652 K initially contains 522 mbar of NO and 421 mbar of O_2. At equilibrium, the total pressure in the reaction mixture is 748 mbar. Calculate K at this temperature.

b. A second reaction mixture at 652 K initially contains 255 mbar of NO and 185 mbar of O_2. What is the equilibrium partial pressure of NO_2 in this mixture?

92. Consider the reaction:

$$2\,SO_2(g) + O_2(g) \rightleftharpoons 2\,SO_3(g)$$
$$K = 11.4 \text{ at } 950\text{ K}$$

A 2.75 L reaction vessel at 950 K initially contains 0.100 mol of SO_2 and 0.100 mol of O_2. Calculate the total pressure in the reaction vessel when equilibrium is reached.

93. Nitric oxide reacts with chlorine gas according to the reaction:

$$2\,NO(g) + Cl_2(g) \rightleftharpoons 2\,NOCl(g)$$
$$K = 0.27 \text{ at } 700\text{ K}$$

A reaction mixture initially contains equal partial pressures of NO and Cl_2. At equilibrium, the partial pressure of NOCl was measured to be 115 mbar. What were the initial partial pressures of NO and Cl_2?

94. At a given temperature a system containing $O_2(g)$ and some oxides of nitrogen can be described by these reactions:

$$2\,NO(g) + O_2(g) \rightleftharpoons 2\,NO_2(g) \quad K = 10^4$$
$$2\,NO_2(g) \rightleftharpoons N_2O_4(g) \quad K = 0.10$$

A pressure of 1 bar of $N_2O_4(g)$ is placed in a container at this temperature. Predict which, if any, component (other than N_2O_4) will be present at a pressure greater than 0.2 bar at equilibrium.

95. A sample of pure NO_2 is heated to 337 °C at which temperature it partially dissociates according to the equation

$$2\,NO_2(g) \rightleftharpoons 2\,NO(g) + O_2(g)$$

At equilibrium, the density of the gas mixture is 0.520 g L^{-1} at 0.750 atm. Calculate K_c for the reaction.

96. When $N_2O_5(g)$ is heated, it dissociates into $N_2O_3(g)$ and $O_2(g)$ according to the reaction:

$$N_2O_5(g) \rightleftharpoons N_2O_3(g) + O_2(g) \quad K = 1.07 \times 10^{-5} \text{ at } 273\text{ K}$$

The $N_2O_3(g)$ dissociates to give $N_2O(g)$ and $O_2(g)$ according to the reaction:

$$N_2O_3(g) \rightleftharpoons N_2O(g) + O_2(g) \quad K = 1.69 \times 10^{6} \text{ at } 273\text{ K.}$$

A 1.25 L reaction vessel initially contains 0.500 mol of N_2O_5 and 273 K.

a. Determine the partial pressures of N_2O_5, N_2O, and O_2 at equilibrium.

b. Determine the partial pressure of N_2O_3 at equilibrium.

97. **a.** Silver chloride is only slightly soluble in pure water at 25 °C:

$$AgCl(s) \rightleftharpoons Ag^+(aq) + Cl^-(aq) \quad K = 1.8 \times 10^{-10}$$

Calculate the concentration of Ag^+ and Cl^- in a solution that is saturated with AgCl (i.e., the system is at equilibrium and there is still solid AgCl visible).

b. The addition of ammonia to the solution results in an increased solubility of AgCl. Ammonia complexes with Ag^+:

$$Ag^+(aq) + 2\,NH_3(aq) \rightleftharpoons Ag(NH_3)_2{}^+(aq) \quad K = 1.6 \times 10^7$$

Determine the concentration of Cl^- in a solution containing silver chloride and 0.100 mol L^{-1} NH_3 at equilibrium.

98. A sample of SO_3 is introduced into an evacuated sealed container and heated to 1233 K. The following equilibrium is established:

$$2\,SO_3(g) \rightleftharpoons 2\,SO_2(g) + O_2(g)$$

The total pressure in the system is found to be 3.0 bar and the mole fraction of O_2 is 0.12. Find K.

Conceptual Problems

99. A reaction $A(aq) \rightleftharpoons B(aq)$ has an equilibrium constant of 1.0×10^{-4}. For which of the initial reaction mixtures is the *x is small* approximation most likely to apply?

a. [A] = 0.0010 mol L^{-1}; [B] = 0 mol L^{-1}
b. [A] = 0 mol L^{-1}; [B] = 0.10 mol L^{-1}
c. [A] = 0.10 mol L^{-1}; [B] = 0.10 mol L^{-1}
d. [A] = 0.10 mol L^{-1}; [B] = 0 mol L^{-1}

100. The reaction $A(g) \rightleftharpoons 2\,B(g)$ has an equilibrium constant of $K_c = 1.0$ at a given temperature. If a reaction vessel contains equal initial amounts (in moles) of A and B, will the direction in which the reaction proceeds depend on the volume of the reaction vessel? Explain.

101. A particular reaction has an equilibrium constant of $K_P = 0.50$. A reaction mixture is prepared in which all the reactants and products are in their standard states. In which direction will the reaction proceed?

102. Consider the reaction:

$$aA(g) \rightleftharpoons bB(g)$$

Each of the entries in the table below represents equilibrium partial pressures of A and B under different initial conditions. What are the values of a and b in the reaction?

P_A (bar)	P_B (bar)
4.0	2.0
2.0	1.4
1.0	1.0
0.50	0.71
0.25	0.50

15 Acids and Bases

The differences between the various acid–base concepts are not concerned with which is right, but which is most convenient to use in a particular situation.

—James E. Huheey (1935–)

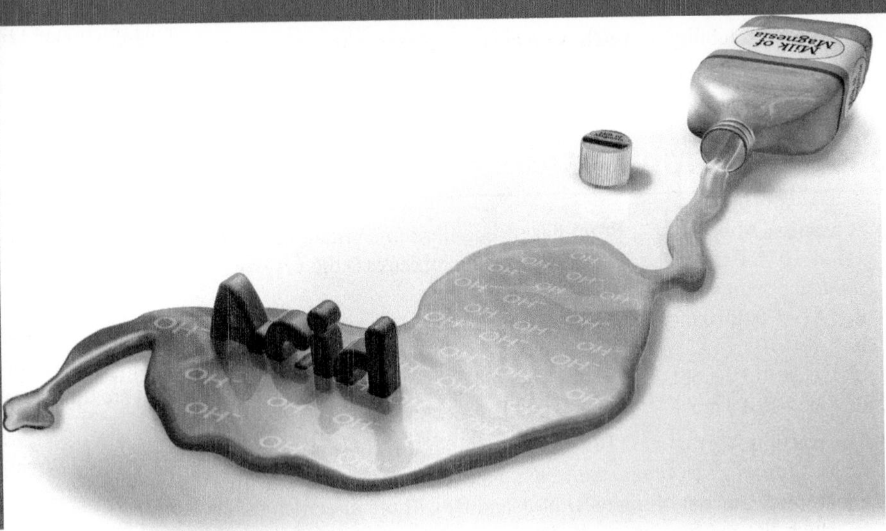

Milk of magnesia contains a base that can neutralize stomach acid and relieve heartburn.

IN THIS CHAPTER, we apply the equilibrium concepts learned in the previous chapter to acid–base phenomena. Acids are common in many foods, such as limes, lemons, and vinegar, and in a number of consumer products, such as toilet cleaners and batteries. Bases are less common in foods but are key ingredients in consumer products such as drain openers and antacids. We will examine three different models for acid–base behaviour, all of which define that behaviour differently. In spite of their differences, the three models coexist, each being useful at explaining a particular range of acid–base phenomena. We will also examine how to calculate the acidity or basicity of solutions and define a useful scale, called the pH scale, to quantify acidity and basicity. These calculations are very similar to the kind of equilibrium problems that we explored in Chapter 14.

15.1 Heartburn

Heartburn is a painful burning sensation in the esophagus (the tube that joins the throat to the stomach), just below the chest. The pain is caused by hydrochloric acid (HCl), which the stomach excretes to kill microorganisms and to activate enzymes that break down food. Hydrochloric acid sometimes backs up out of the stomach and into the esophagus, a phenomenon known as *acid reflux*. Recall from Section 4.5 that acids are substances that—by one definition that we will elaborate on shortly—produce H^+ ions in solution. When hydrochloric acid from the stomach comes in contact with the lining of the esophagus, the H^+ ions irritate the esophageal tissues, resulting in the burning sensation. Some of the acid can work its way into the lower throat and even the mouth, producing pain in the throat and a sour taste (characteristic of acids) in the mouth. Almost everyone experiences heartburn at some time, most commonly after a large meal when the stomach is full and the chances for reflux are greatest. Strenuous activity or lying in a horizontal position after a large meal increases the likelihood of stomach acid reflux and the resulting heartburn.

The simplest way to relieve mild heartburn is to swallow repeatedly. Saliva contains the bicarbonate ion (HCO_3^-), which acts as a base and, when swallowed, neutralizes some of the acid in the esophagus. Later in this chapter, we will see how bicarbonate acts as a base. You can also treat heartburn with antacids such as Tums, milk of magnesia, or Mylanta. These over-the-counter medications contain more base than our saliva does and therefore are more effective at neutralizing esophageal acid. We will look at the bases in these medicines more carefully later (see the *Chemistry and Medicine* box in Section 15.8).

Bases were first defined in Section 4.5.

For some people, heartburn becomes a chronic problem. Gastroesophageal reflux disease (GERD) is the medical condition associated with chronic heartburn. In patients with GERD, the band of muscles (called the esophageal sphincter) at the bottom of the esophagus just above the stomach does not close tightly enough, allowing the stomach contents to leak back into the esophagus on a regular basis. Medical researchers have developed a wireless sensor to help diagnose and evaluate treatment of GERD. Using a tube that goes down through the throat, a physician attaches the sensor to tissues in the patient's esophagus. The sensor reads pH—a measure of acidity that we discuss in Section 15.6—and transmits the readings to a recorder worn on the patient's body. The patient goes about his or her normal business for the next few days while the recorder monitors esophageal pH. The physician then reads the record of esophageal pH to make a diagnosis or evaluate treatment.

The concentration of stomach acid varies from about 0.01 to 0.1 mol L^{-1}.

In this chapter, we examine acid and base behaviour. Acids and bases are not only important to our health (as we have just seen), but are also found in many household products, foods, medicines, and of course in nearly every chemistry laboratory. Acid–base chemistry is central to much of biochemistry and molecular biology. The building blocks of proteins, for example, have acidic and basic properties (called amino acids) and the molecules that carry the genetic code in DNA are bases.

15.2 The Nature of Acids and Bases

Acids have the following general properties: a sour taste, the ability to dissolve many metals, the ability to turn blue litmus paper red, and the ability to neutralize bases. Some common acids are listed in Table 15.1.

Litmus paper contains certain dyes that change colour in the presence of acids and bases.

TABLE 15.1 Some Common Acids

Name	Occurrence/Uses
Hydrochloric acid (HCl)	Metal cleaning; food preparation; ore refining; primary component of stomach acid
Sulfuric acid (H_2SO_4)	Fertilizer and explosives manufacturing; dye and glue production; automobile batteries; electroplating of copper
Nitric acid (HNO_3)	Fertilizer and explosives manufacturing; dye and glue production
Ethanoic acid (acetic acid) ($HC_2H_3O_2$)	Plastic and rubber manufacturing; food preservative; active component of vinegar
Citric acid ($H_3C_6H_5O_7$)	Present in citrus fruits such as lemons and limes; used to adjust pH in foods and beverages
Carbonic acid (H_2CO_3)	Found in carbonated beverages due to the reaction of carbon dioxide with water
Hydrofluoric acid (HF)	Metal cleaning; glass frosting and etching
Phosphoric acid (H_3PO_4)	Fertilizer manufacture; biological buffering; preservative in beverages

For a review of acid naming, see Section 3.4.

The formula for acetic acid is commonly written as CH_3COOH.

You can find hydrochloric acid in most chemistry laboratories. In industry, it is used to clean metals, to prepare and process some foods, and to refine metal ores. As we have just seen, hydrochloric acid is also the main component of stomach acid.

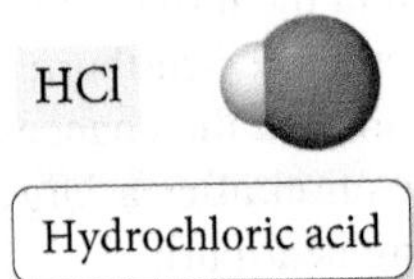

HCl

Hydrochloric acid

Sulfuric acid and nitric acid are also common in the laboratory. They play major roles in the manufacture of fertilizers, explosives, dyes, and glues. Sulfuric acid, produced in larger quantities than any other chemical, is contained in most automobile batteries.

$$\mathrm{H{-}O{-}\overset{\overset{\displaystyle O}{\|}}{\underset{\underset{\displaystyle \underset{|}{O}{-}H}{|}}{S}}{=}O}$$

H_2SO_4

Sulfuric acid

$$\mathrm{H{-}O{-}\overset{\overset{\displaystyle O}{\|}}{N}{-}O}$$

HNO_3

Nitric acid

You can probably find acetic acid in your home—it is the active component of vinegar. It is also produced in improperly stored wines. The word *vinegar* originates from the French words *vin aigre*, which means sour wine. Wine experts consider the presence of vinegar in wines a serious fault, since it makes the wine taste like salad dressing.

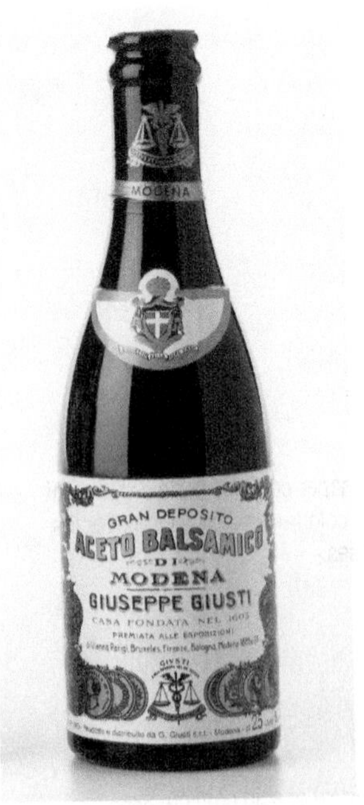

▲ Acetic acid makes vinegar taste sour.

$$\mathrm{H{-}O{-}\overset{\overset{\displaystyle O}{\|}}{C}{-}\overset{\overset{\displaystyle H}{|}}{\underset{\underset{\displaystyle H}{|}}{C}}{-}H}$$

CH_3COOH

Acetic acid

Acetic acid is a **carboxylic acid**, an acid that contains the following grouping of atoms:

$$\mathrm{H{-}O{-}\overset{\overset{\displaystyle O}{\|}}{C}{-}}$$

Carboxylic acid group

Carboxylic acids are often found in substances derived from living organisms. Other examples of carboxylic acids are citric acid, the main acid in lemons and limes, and malic acid, found in apples, grapes, and wine.

Bases have the following general properties: a bitter taste, a slippery feel, the ability to turn red litmus paper blue, and the ability to neutralize acids. Because of their bitterness, bases are less common in foods than are acids. Our aversion to the taste of bases is probably an evolutionary adaptation to warn us against **alkaloids**, organic bases found in plants that are often poisonous. (For example, the active component of hemlock—the poisonous plant that caused the death of the Greek philosopher Socrates—is the alkaloid coniine.) Nonetheless, some foods, such as coffee and chocolate (especially dark chocolate), contain small amounts of base. Many people enjoy the bitterness, but only after acquiring the taste over time.

Coffee is acidic overall, but bases present in coffee—such as caffeine—impart a bitter flavour.

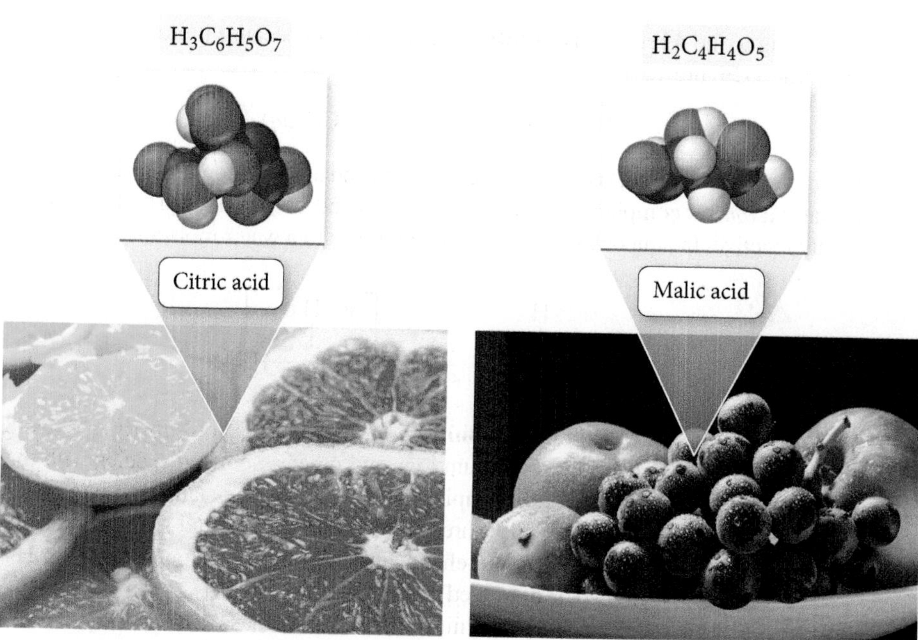

◀ Fruits contain different mixtures of organic acids. Citric acid is found in high concentrations in citrus fruits, while malic acid is one of the principal acids in grapes and apples.

Bases feel slippery because they react with oils on the skin to form soap-like substances. Some household cleaning solutions, such as ammonia, are basic and have the characteristic slippery feel of a base. Bases turn red litmus paper blue; in the laboratory, litmus paper is routinely used to test the basicity of solutions.

Some common bases are listed in Table 15.2. You can find sodium hydroxide and potassium hydroxide in most chemistry laboratories. They are used in petroleum and cotton processing, and in soap and plastic manufacturing. Sodium hydroxide is the active ingredient in products such as Drāno that unclog drains. In many homes, you can find sodium bicarbonate in the medicine cabinet (it is an active ingredient in some antacids) as well as in the kitchen (labelled as baking soda).

TABLE 15.2 Common Bases

Name	Occurrence/Uses
Sodium hydroxide (NaOH)	Petroleum processing; soap and plastic manufacturing
Potassium hydroxide (KOH)	Cotton processing; electroplating; soap production; batteries
Sodium bicarbonate ($NaHCO_3$)	Antacid; ingredient of baking soda; source of CO_2
Sodium carbonate (Na_2CO_3)	Manufacture of glass and soap; general cleanser; water softener
Ammonia (NH_3)	Detergent; fertilizer and explosives manufacturing; synthetic fibre production

▲ Many common household products and remedies contain bases.

15.3 Definitions of Acids and Bases

What are the main characteristics of the molecules and ions that exhibit acid and base behaviour? In this chapter, we examine three different definitions: the Arrhenius definition, the Brønsted–Lowry definition, and the Lewis definition. Why three definitions, and which one is correct? As Huheey noted in the quotation that opens this chapter, no single definition is "correct." Rather, each definition is useful in a given instance. We discuss the Lewis definition of acids and bases in Section 15.10; here, we discuss the other two.

The Arrhenius Definition

In the 1880s, Swedish chemist Svante Arrhenius proposed the following definitions of acids and bases:

Acid: A substance that produces H^+ ions in aqueous solution
Base: A substance that produces OH^- ions in aqueous solution

Arrhenius Acid

HCl

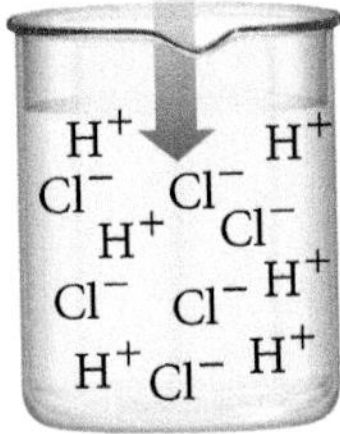

$HCl(aq) \longrightarrow H^+(aq) + Cl^-(aq)$

▲ **FIGURE 15.1 Arrhenius Acid** An Arrhenius acid produces H^+ ions in solution.

Arrhenius Base

NaOH

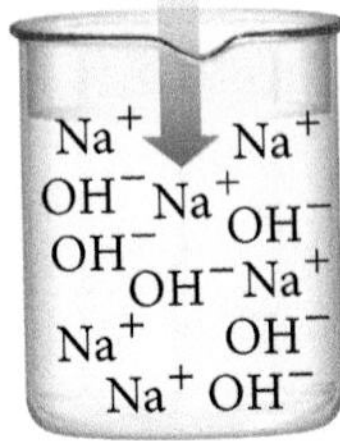

$NaOH(aq) \longrightarrow Na^+(aq) + OH^-(aq)$

▲ **FIGURE 15.2 Arrhenius Base** An Arrhenius base produces OH^- ions in solution.

According to the **Arrhenius definition**, HCl is an acid because it produces H^+ ions in solution (Figure 15.1 ◀):

$$HCl(aq) \longrightarrow H^+(aq) + Cl^-(aq)$$

Hydrogen chloride (HCl) is a covalent compound and does not contain ions. However, in water it *ionizes* completely to form $H^+(aq)$ ions and $Cl^-(aq)$ ions. The H^+ ions are highly reactive. In aqueous solution, an H^+ ion binds to a water molecule:

$$H^+ + :\ddot{O}(H)-H \longrightarrow \left[H-\ddot{O}(H)-H\right]^+$$

The H_3O^+ ion is called the **hydronium ion**. In water, H^+ ions *always* associate with H_2O molecules to form hydronium ions and other associated species with the general formula $H(H_2O)_n{}^+$. For example, an H^+ ion can associate with two water molecules to form $H(H_2O)_2{}^+$, with three to form $H(H_2O)_3{}^+$, and so on. Chemists often use $H^+(aq)$ and $H_3O^+(aq)$ interchangeably, to mean the same thing—an H^+ ion that has been solvated (or dissolved) in water.

According to the Arrhenius definition, NaOH is a base because it produces OH^- ions in solution (Figure 15.2 ◀):

$$NaOH(aq) \longrightarrow Na^+(aq) + OH^-(aq)$$

NaOH is an ionic compound and therefore contains Na^+ and OH^- ions. When NaOH is added to water, it *dissociates* or breaks apart into its component ions.

Under the Arrhenius definition, acids and bases naturally combine to form water, neutralizing each other in the process:

$$H^+(aq) + OH^-(aq) \longrightarrow H_2O(l)$$

The Brønsted–Lowry Definition

A second, more widely applicable definition of acids and bases, called the **Brønsted–Lowry definition**, was introduced in 1923. This definition focuses on the *transfer of H^+ ions* in an acid–base reaction. Since an H^+ ion is a proton—a hydrogen atom without its electron—this definition focuses on the idea of a proton donor and a proton acceptor:

Acid: proton (H^+ ion) *donor*.
Base: proton (H^+ ion) *acceptor*.

According to this definition, HCl is an acid because, in solution, it donates a proton to water:

$$HCl(aq) + H_2O(l) \longrightarrow H_3O^+(aq) + Cl^-(aq)$$

All Arrhenius acids and bases remain acids and bases under the Brønsted–Lowry definition. However, some Brønsted–Lowry acids and bases cannot be classified as Arrhenius acids and bases.

This definition clearly describes what happens to the H^+ ion from an acid—it associates with a water molecule to form H_3O^+ (a hydronium ion). The Brønsted–Lowry definition also works well with bases (such as NH_3) that do not inherently contain OH^- ions but still produce OH^- ions in solution. According to the Brønsted–Lowry definition, NH_3 is a base because it accepts a proton from water:

$$NH_3(aq) + H_2O(l) \rightleftharpoons NH_4{}^+(aq) + OH^-(aq)$$

In the Brønsted–Lowry definition, acids (proton donors) and bases (proton acceptors) always occur together. In the reaction between HCl and H_2O, HCl is the proton donor (acid) and H_2O is the proton acceptor (base):

$$\underset{\substack{\text{acid} \\ \text{(proton donor)}}}{HCl(aq)} + \underset{\substack{\text{base} \\ \text{(proton acceptor)}}}{H_2O(l)} \longrightarrow H_3O^+(aq) + Cl^-(aq)$$

In the reaction between NH_3 and H_2O, H_2O is the proton donor (acid) and NH_3 is the proton acceptor (base).

$$\underset{\substack{\text{base} \\ \text{(proton acceptor)}}}{NH_3(aq)} + \underset{\substack{\text{acid} \\ \text{(proton donor)}}}{H_2O(l)} \rightleftharpoons NH_4^+(aq) + OH^-(aq)$$

According to the Brønsted–Lowry definition, some substances—such as water in the previous two equations—can act as acids *or* bases. Substances that can act as acids or bases are **amphoteric**.

Notice what happens when we reverse an equation representing Brønsted–Lowry acid–base behaviour:

$$\underset{\substack{\text{acid} \\ \text{(proton donor)}}}{NH_4^+(aq)} + \underset{\substack{\text{base} \\ \text{(proton acceptor)}}}{OH^-(aq)} \rightleftharpoons NH_3(aq) + H_2O(l)$$

In this reaction, NH_4^+ is the proton donor (acid) and OH^- is the proton acceptor (base). The base (NH_3) in the forward reaction has become the acid (NH_4^+) in the reverse reaction and vice versa. NH_4^+ and NH_3 are often referred to as a **conjugate acid–base pair**, two substances related to each other by the transfer of a proton (Figure 15.3 ▼). A **conjugate acid** is any base to which a proton has been added, and a **conjugate base** is any acid from which a proton has been removed. Going back to the original forward reaction, we can identify the conjugate acid–base pairs:

$$\underset{\text{Base}}{NH_3(aq)} + \underset{\text{Acid}}{H_2O(l)} \rightleftharpoons \underset{\substack{\text{Conjugate} \\ \text{acid}}}{NH_4^+(aq)} + \underset{\substack{\text{Conjugate} \\ \text{base}}}{OH^-(aq)}$$

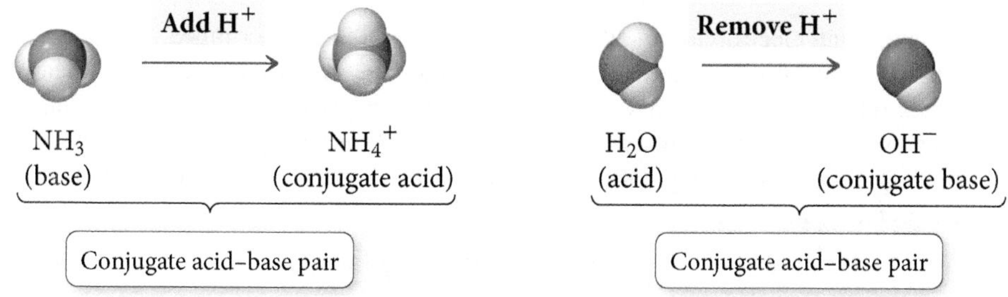

◀ **FIGURE 15.3 Conjugate Acid–Base Pairs** A conjugate acid–base pair consists of two substances related to each other by the transfer of a proton.

Summarizing the Brønsted–Lowry Definition of an Acid–Base Reaction:

- An acid donates a proton and becomes a conjugate base.
- A base accepts a proton and becomes a conjugate acid.

EXAMPLE 15.1 IDENTIFYING BRØNSTED–LOWRY ACIDS AND BASES AND THEIR CONJUGATES

In each reaction, identify the Brønsted–Lowry acid, the Brønsted–Lowry base, the conjugate acid, and the conjugate base.

(a) $H_2SO_4(aq) + H_2O(l) \longrightarrow HSO_4^-(aq) + H_3O^+(aq)$

(b) $HCO_3^-(aq) + H_2O(l) \rightleftharpoons H_2CO_3(aq) + OH^-(aq)$

SOLUTION

(a) Since H_2SO_4 donates a proton to H_2O in this reaction, it is the acid (proton donor). After H_2SO_4 donates the proton, it becomes HSO_4^-, the conjugate base. Since H_2O accepts a proton, it is the base (proton acceptor). After H_2O accepts the proton it becomes H_3O^+, the conjugate acid.

$$H_2SO_4(aq) + H_2O(l) \longrightarrow HSO_4^-(aq) + H_3O^+(aq)$$

$$\underset{\text{Acid}}{H_2SO_4(aq)} + \underset{\text{Base}}{H_2O(l)} \longrightarrow \underset{\substack{\text{Conjugate} \\ \text{base}}}{HSO_4^-(aq)} + \underset{\substack{\text{Conjugate} \\ \text{acid}}}{H_3O^+(aq)}$$

(continued)

EXAMPLE 15.1 (CONTINUED)

(b) Since H_2O donates a proton to HCO_3^- in this reaction, it is the acid (proton donor). After H_2O donates the proton, it becomes OH^-, the conjugate base. Since HCO_3^- accepts a proton, it is the base (proton acceptor). After HCO_3^- accepts the proton it becomes H_2CO_3, the conjugate acid.	$HCO_3^-(aq) + H_2O(l) \rightleftharpoons H_2CO_3(aq) + OH^-(aq)$ $HCO_3^-(aq) + H_2O(l) \rightleftharpoons H_2CO_3(aq) + OH^-(aq)$ Base, Acid, Conjugate acid, Conjugate base

FOR PRACTICE 15.1

In each reaction, identify the Brønsted–Lowry acid, the Brønsted–Lowry base, the conjugate acid, and the conjugate base.

(a) $C_5H_5N(aq) + H_2O(l) \rightleftharpoons C_5H_5NH^+(aq) + OH^-(aq)$

(b) $HNO_3(aq) + H_2O(l) \rightleftharpoons H_3O^+(aq) + NO_3^-(aq)$

CONCEPTUAL CONNECTION 15.1

Conjugate Acid–Base Pairs

Which of the following is not a conjugate acid–base pair?

(a) $(CH_3)_3N$; $(CH_3)_3NH^+$ **(b)** H_2SO_4; H_2SO_3 **(c)** HNO_2; NO_2^-

15.4 Acid Strength and the Acid Ionization Constant (K_a)

The strength of an electrolyte, first discussed in Section 4.3, is determined by the extent of its dissociation into its component ions in solution. A *strong electrolyte* completely dissociates into ions in solution whereas a *weak electrolyte* only partially dissociates. Strong and weak acids are defined accordingly. A **strong acid** completely ionizes in solution whereas a **weak acid** only partially ionizes. In other words, the strength of an acid depends on the equilibrium:

$$HA(aq) + H_2O(l) \rightleftharpoons H_3O^+(aq) + A^-(aq)$$

In this equation, HA is a generic formula for an acid. If the equilibrium lies far to the right, the acid is strong—it completely ionizes. If the equilibrium lies to the left, the acid is weak—only a small percentage of the acid molecules ionize. Of course, the range of acid strength is continuous, but for most purposes, the categories of strong and weak are useful.

When HCl dissolves in water, it ionizes completely.

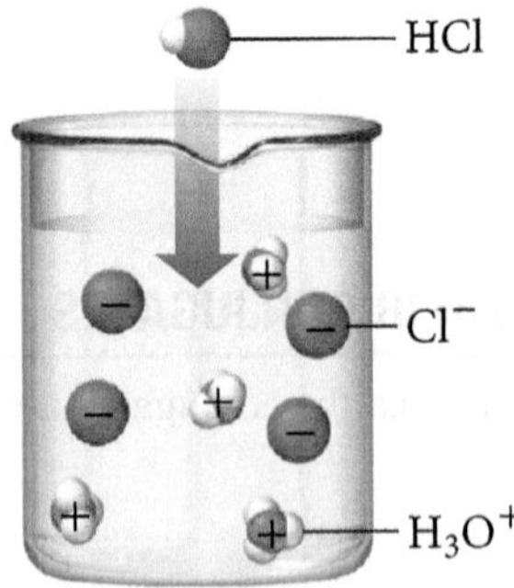

▲ **FIGURE 15.4 Ionization of a Strong Acid** When HCl dissolves in water, it completely ionizes to form H_3O^+ and Cl^-. The solution contains virtually no intact HCl.

Strong Acids

Hydrochloric acid (HCl) is an example of a strong acid.

Single arrow indicates complete ionization.

$$HCl(aq) + H_2O(l) \longrightarrow H_3O^+(aq) + Cl^-(aq)$$

An HCl solution contains virtually no intact HCl; the HCl has essentially all ionized to form $H_3O^+(aq)$ and $Cl^-(aq)$ (Figure 15.4 ◀). A 1.0 mol L^{-1} HCl solution will have an H_3O^+ concentration of 1.0 mol L^{-1}. Abbreviating the concentration of H_3O^+ as $[H_3O^+]$, we say that a 1.0 mol L^{-1} HCl solution has $[H_3O^+] = 1.0$ mol L^{-1}.

Table 15.3 lists the six important strong acids. The first five acids in the table are **monoprotic acids**, acids containing only one ionizable proton. Sulfuric acid is an example of a **diprotic acid**, an acid containing two ionizable protons. We will see shortly that the reaction involving the second proton in H_2SO_4 actually occurs to a far lesser extent than the reaction involving the first proton.

An ionizable proton is one that ionizes in solution. We discuss polyprotic acids in more detail in Section 15.9.

TABLE 15.3 Strong Acids

Hydrochloric acid (HCl)	Nitric acid (HNO_3)
Hydrobromic acid (HBr)	Perchloric acid ($HClO_4$)
Hydriodic acid (HI)	Sulfuric acid (H_2SO_4) (*diprotic*)

Weak Acids

In contrast to HCl, HF is a weak acid, one that will only partially ionize in solution.

Equilibrium arrow indicates partial ionization.

$$HF(aq) + H_2O(l) \rightleftharpoons H_3O^+(aq) + F^-(aq)$$

The terms *strong* and *weak* acids are often confused with the terms *concentrated* and *dilute* acids. Can you articulate the difference between these terms?

An HF solution contains a large number of intact (or un-ionized) HF molecules; it also contains some $H_3O^+(aq)$ and $F^-(aq)$ (Figure 15.5 ▼). In other words, a 1.0 mol L^{-1} HF solution has $[H_3O^+]$ that is much less than 1.0 mol L^{-1} because only some of the HF molecules ionize to form H_3O^+.

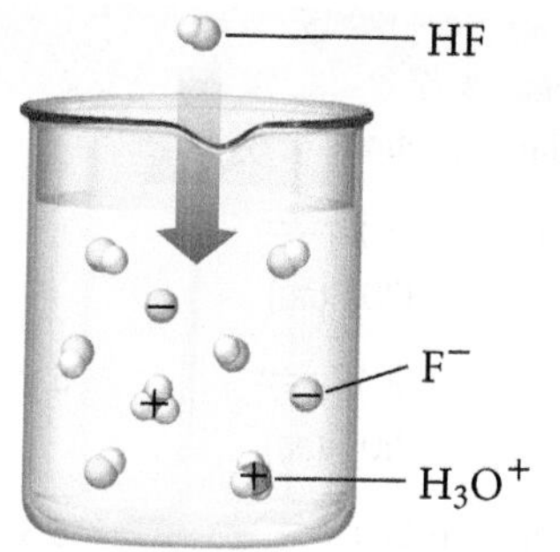
When HF dissolves in water, only a fraction of the molecules ionize.
HF
F$^-$
H$_3$O$^+$

◀ **FIGURE 15.5 Ionization of a Weak Acid** When HF dissolves in water, only a fraction of the dissolved molecules ionize to form H_3O^+ and F^-. The solution contains many intact HF molecules.

The degree to which an acid is strong or weak depends on the attraction between the anion of the acid (the conjugate base) and the hydrogen ion, relative to the attractions of these ions to water. Recall that HA is a generic formula for an acid. Then, the degree to which the following reaction proceeds in the forward direction depends on the strength of the attraction between H^+ and A^-.

$$\underset{\text{acid}}{HA(aq)} + H_2O(l) \rightleftharpoons H_3O^+(aq) + \underset{\text{conjugate base}}{A^-(aq)}$$

If the attraction between H^+ and A^- is *weak*, then the reaction favours the forward direction and the acid is *strong*. If the attraction between H^+ and A^- is *strong*, then the reaction favours the reverse direction and the acid is *weak*, as shown in Figure 15.6 ▶.

For example, in HCl, the conjugate base (Cl^-) has a relatively weak attraction to H^+—the reverse reaction does not occur to any significant extent. In HF, on the other hand, the conjugate base (F^-) has a greater attraction to H^+—the reverse reaction occurs to a significant degree. *In general, the stronger the acid, the weaker the conjugate base and vice versa.* If the forward reaction (that of the acid) has a high tendency to occur, then the reverse reaction (that of the conjugate base) has a low tendency to occur. Table 15.4 lists some common weak acids.

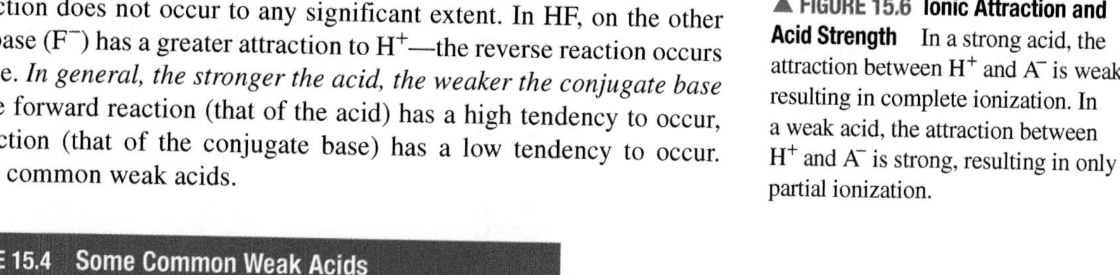

Strong acid: H$^+$ — A$^-$ — Weak attraction, **Complete ionization**

Weak acid: H$^+$ — A$^-$ — Strong attraction, **Partial ionization**

▲ **FIGURE 15.6 Ionic Attraction and Acid Strength** In a strong acid, the attraction between H^+ and A^- is weak, resulting in complete ionization. In a weak acid, the attraction between H^+ and A^- is strong, resulting in only partial ionization.

TABLE 15.4 Some Common Weak Acids

Hydrofluoric acid (HF)	Sulfurous acid (H_2SO_3) (*diprotic*)
Acetic acid (CH_3COOH)	Carbonic acid (H_2CO_3) (*diprotic*)
Methanoic acid (HCOOH)	Phosphoric acid (H_3PO_4) (*triprotic*)

Notice that two of the weak acids in Table 15.4 are diprotic, meaning that they have two ionizable protons, and one is **triprotic** (three ionizable protons). We discuss polyprotic acids in more detail in Section 15.9.

The Acid Ionization Constant (K_a)

Sometimes K_a is also referred to as the acid dissociation constant.

We can quantify the relative strengths of weak acids with the **acid ionization constant** **(K_a)**, which is the equilibrium constant for the ionization reaction of a weak acid. As we saw in Section 14.3, for the following reaction:

$$HA(aq) + H_2O(l) \rightleftharpoons H_3O^+(aq) + A^-(aq)$$

the equilibrium constant is

Recall from Chapter 14 that the concentrations of pure solids or pure liquids are not included in the expression for K_c; therefore, $H_2O(l)$ is not included in the expression for K_a.

$$K_a = \frac{[H_3O^+][A^-]}{[HA]}$$

Although the ionization constants for all weak acids are relatively small (otherwise the acid would not be a weak acid), they do vary in magnitude. The smaller the constant, the less the acid ionizes, and the weaker the acid. Table 15.5 lists the acid ionization constants for a number of common weak acids in order of decreasing acid strength.

TABLE 15.5 Acid Ionization Constants (K_a) for Some Monoprotic Weak Acids at 25 °C

Acid	Formula	Structural Formula	Ionization Reaction	K_a
Chlorous acid	$HClO_2$	H—O—Cl=O	$HClO_2(aq) + H_2O(l) \rightleftharpoons H_3O^+(aq) + ClO_2^-(aq)$	1.1×10^{-2}
Nitrous acid	HNO_2	H—O—N=O	$HNO_2(aq) + H_2O(l) \rightleftharpoons H_3O^+(aq) + NO_2^-(aq)$	5.6×10^{-4}
Hydrofluoric acid	HF	H—F	$HF(aq) + H_2O(l) \rightleftharpoons H_3O^+(aq) + F^-(aq)$	6.3×10^{-4}
Methanoic acid	HCOOH	H—O—C(=O)—H	$HCOOH(aq) + H_2O(l) \rightleftharpoons H_3O^+(aq) + HCOO^-(aq)$	1.8×10^{-4}
Benzoic acid	C_6H_5COOH	H—O—C(=O)—C ring (C=C, CH, C—C with H atoms)	$C_6H_5COOH(aq) + H_2O(l) \rightleftharpoons H_3O^+(aq) + C_6H_5COO^-(aq)$	6.3×10^{-5}
Acetic acid	CH_3COOH	H—O—C(=O)—CH_3	$CH_3COOH(aq) + H_2O(l) \rightleftharpoons H_3O^+(aq) + CH_3COO^-(aq)$	1.8×10^{-5}
Hypochlorous acid	HClO	H—O—Cl	$HClO(aq) + H_2O(l) \rightleftharpoons H_3O^+(aq) + ClO^-(aq)$	4.0×10^{-8}
Hydrocyanic acid	HCN	H—C≡N	$HCN(aq) + H_2O(l) \rightleftharpoons H_3O^+(aq) + CN^-(aq)$	6.2×10^{-10}
Phenol	C_6H_5OH	HO—C ring (C=C, CH, C—C with H atoms)	$C_6H_5OH(aq) + H_2O(l) \rightleftharpoons H_3O^+(aq) + C_6H_5O^-(aq)$	1.3×10^{-10}

CONCEPTUAL CONNECTION 15.2

Conjugate Bases

Consider the following two acids and their K_a values:

HF	$K_a = 6.3 \times 10^{-4}$
HClO	$K_a = 4.0 \times 10^{-8}$

Which conjugate base, F^- or ClO^-, is stronger?

15.5 Base Solutions

Strong Bases

Just as we define a strong acid as one that completely ionizes in solution, analogously we define a **strong base** as a base that completely dissociates in solution. NaOH, for example, is a strong base:

$$NaOH(aq) \longrightarrow Na^+(aq) + OH^-(aq)$$

An NaOH solution contains virtually no intact NaOH—it has all dissociated to form $Na^+(aq)$ and $OH^-(aq)$ (Figure 15.7 ▸). In other words, a 1.0 mol L^{-1} NaOH solution has $[OH^-] = 1.0$ mol L^{-1} and $[Na^+] = 1.0$ mol L^{-1}. The common strong bases are listed in Table 15.6.

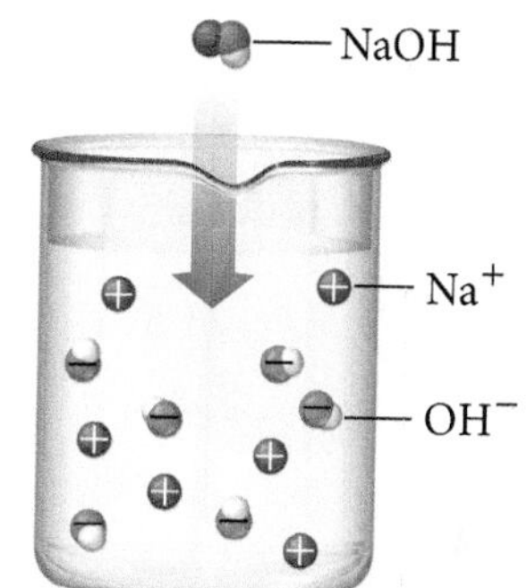

▲ **FIGURE 15.7 Ionization of a Strong Base** When NaOH dissolves in water, it dissociates almost completely into Na^+ and OH^-. The solution contains virtually no intact NaOH.

TABLE 15.6 Common Strong Bases

Lithium hydroxide (LiOH)	Strontium hydroxide [$Sr(OH)_2$]
Sodium hydroxide (NaOH)	Calcium hydroxide [$Ca(OH)_2$]
Potassium hydroxide (KOH)	Barium hydroxide [$Ba(OH)_2$]

As you can see, most strong bases are group 1 or group 2 metal hydroxides. The group 1 metal hydroxides are highly soluble in water and can form concentrated base solutions. The group 2 metal hydroxides, however, are only slightly soluble, a useful property for some applications (see the *Chemistry and Medicine* box in Section 15.8). Notice that the general formula for the group 2 metal hydroxides is $M(OH)_2$. When they dissolve in water, they produce 2 mol of OH^- per mole of the base. For example, $Sr(OH)_2$ dissociates as follows:

$$Sr(OH)_2(aq) \longrightarrow Sr^{2+}(aq) + 2\,OH^-(aq)$$

Unlike diprotic acids, which ionize in two steps, bases containing two OH^- ions dissociate in one step.

Weak Bases

A **weak base** is analogous to a weak acid. Unlike strong bases that contain OH^- and *dissociate* in water, the most common weak bases produce OH^- by accepting a proton from water, ionizing water to form OH^- according to the general equation:

$$B(aq) + H_2O(l) \rightleftharpoons BH^+(aq) + OH^-(aq)$$

In this equation, B is a generic symbol for a weak base. Ammonia, for example, ionizes water as follows:

$$NH_3(aq) + H_2O(l) \rightleftharpoons NH_4^+(aq) + OH^-(aq)$$

The double arrow indicates that the ionization is not complete. An NH_3 solution contains mostly NH_3 with only some NH_4^+ and OH^- (Figure 15.8 ▸). A 1.0 mol L^{-1} NH_3 solution will have $[OH^-] < 1.0$ mol L^{-1}.

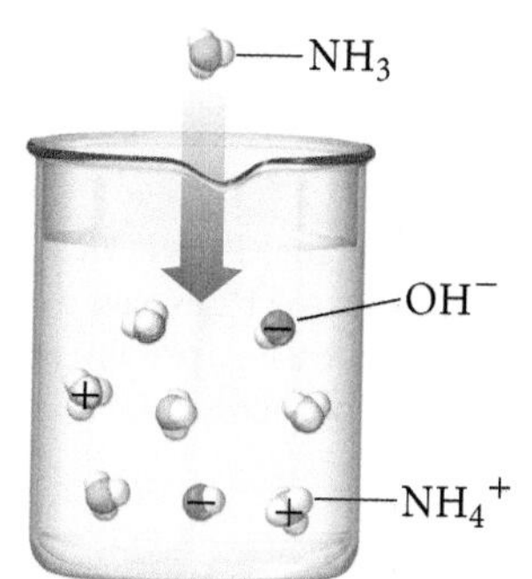

▲ **FIGURE 15.8 Ionization of a Weak Base** When NH_3 dissolves in water, it partially ionizes water to form NH_4^+ and OH^-. Most of the NH_3 molecules in solution remain as NH_3.

TABLE 15.7 Some Common Weak Bases

Weak Base	Ionization Reaction	K_b
Carbonate ion (CO_3^{2-})*	$CO_3^{2-}(aq) + H_2O(l) \rightleftharpoons HCO_3^-(aq) + OH^-(aq)$	1.8×10^{-4}
Methylamine (CH_3NH_2)	$CH_3NH_2(aq) + H_2O(l) \rightleftharpoons CH_3NH_3^+(aq) + OH^-(aq)$	4.4×10^{-4}
Ethylamine ($C_2H_5NH_2$)	$C_2H_5NH_2(aq) + H_2O(l) \rightleftharpoons C_2H_5NH_3^+(aq) + OH^-(aq)$	4.5×10^{-4}
Ammonia (NH_3)	$NH_3(aq) + H_2O(l) \rightleftharpoons NH_4^+(aq) + OH^-(aq)$	1.76×10^{-5}
Bicarbonate ion (HCO_3^-) (or hydrogen carbonate)*	$HCO_3^-(aq) + H_2O(l) \rightleftharpoons H_2CO_3(aq) + OH^-(aq)$	2.3×10^{-8}
Pyridine (C_5H_5N)	$C_5H_5N(aq) + H_2O(l) \rightleftharpoons C_5H_5NH^+(aq) + OH^-(aq)$	1.7×10^{-9}
Aniline ($C_6H_5NH_2$)	$C_6H_5NH_2(aq) + H_2O(l) \rightleftharpoons C_6H_5NH_3^+(aq) + OH^-(aq)$	7.5×10^{-10}

*The carbonate and bicarbonate ions must occur with a positively charged ion such as Na^+ that serves to balance the charge but does not have any part in the ionization reaction. For example, it is the bicarbonate ion that makes sodium bicarbonate ($NaHCO_3$) basic. We look more closely at ionic bases in Section 15.8.

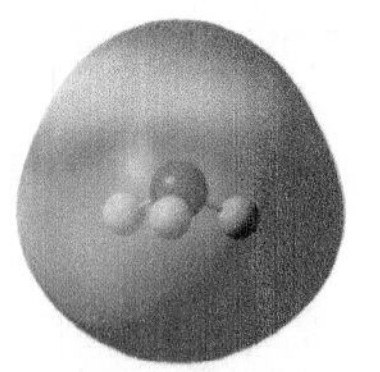

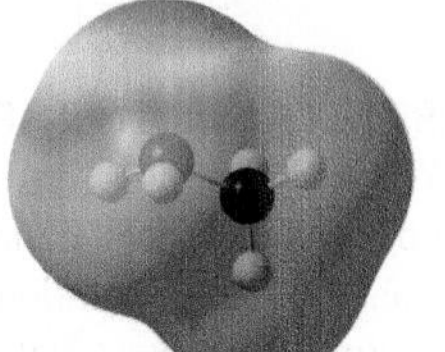

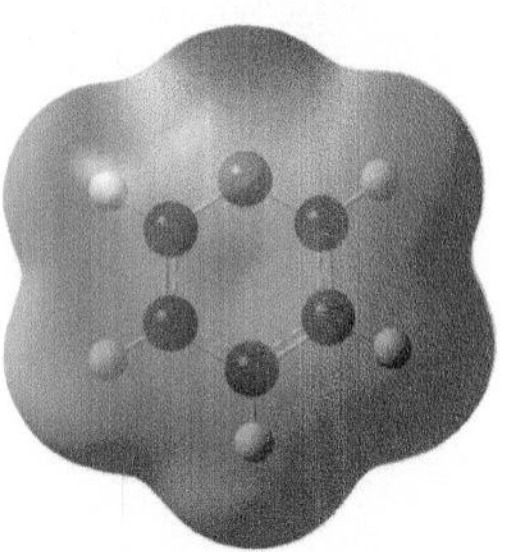

▲ Electrostatic potential maps of ammonia methylamine and pyridine. Common among bases is a region of high negative electrostatic potential (shown by the red regions).

The extent of ionization of a weak base is quantified with the **base ionization constant (K_b)**. For the general reaction in which a weak base ionizes water, we define K_b as follows:

$$B(aq) + H_2O(l) \rightleftharpoons BH^+(aq) + OH^-(aq) \qquad K_b = \frac{[BH^+][OH^-]}{[B]}$$

By analogy with K_a, the smaller the value of K_b, the weaker the base. Table 15.7 lists some common weak bases, their ionization reactions, and values for K_b.

All but two of the weak bases listed in Table 15.7 are either ammonia or *amines*, which we can think of as ammonia with one or more hydrocarbon groups substituted for one or more hydrogen atoms. All of these bases have a nitrogen atom with a lone pair (Figure 15.9 ▼). This lone pair acts as the proton acceptor that makes the substance a base, as shown in the reactions for ammonia and methylamine:

$$H{-}\ddot{N}H{-}H\,(aq) + H{-}\ddot{O}{-}H\,(l) \rightleftharpoons H{-}NH_2^{+}{-}H\,(aq) + {}^{-}{:}\ddot{O}{-}H\,(aq)$$

$$H_3C{-}\ddot{N}H{-}H\,(aq) + H{-}\ddot{O}{-}H\,(l) \rightleftharpoons H_3C{-}NH_2^{+}{-}H\,(aq) + {}^{-}{:}\ddot{O}{-}H\,(aq)$$

▶ **FIGURE 15.9 Lone Pairs in Weak Bases** Many weak bases have a nitrogen atom with a lone pair that acts as the proton acceptor.

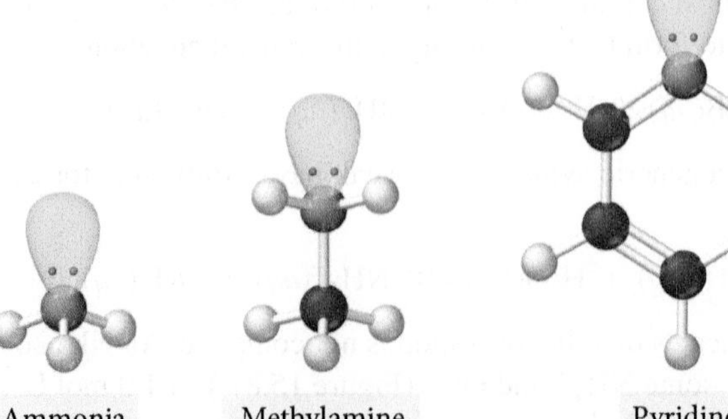

15.6 Autoionization of Water and pH

We saw earlier that water acts as a base when it reacts with HCl and as an acid when it reacts with NH_3:

Water acting as a base

$$HCl(aq) + H_2O(l) \longrightarrow H_3O^+(aq) + Cl^-(aq)$$

Acid (proton donor) **Base** (proton acceptor)

Water acting as an acid

$$NH_3(aq) + H_2O(l) \rightleftharpoons NH_4^+(aq) + OH^-(aq)$$

Base (proton acceptor) **Acid** (proton donor)

Water is *amphoteric*; it can act as either an acid or a base. Even when pure, water acts as an acid and a base with itself, a process called **autoionization**:

Water acting as both an acid and a base

$$H_2O(l) + H_2O(l) \rightleftharpoons H_3O^+(aq) + OH^-(aq)$$

Acid (proton donor) **Base** (proton acceptor)

The autoionization reaction is sometimes written as:

$$H_2O(l) \rightleftharpoons H^+(aq) + OH^-(aq)$$

We can quantify the autoionization of water with the equilibrium constant for the autoionization reaction.

$$K_w = [H_3O^+][OH^-] = [H^+][OH^-]$$

This equilibrium constant is the **ion product constant for water (K_w)** (sometimes called the *dissociation constant for water*). At 25 °C, $K_w = 1.0 \times 10^{-14}$. In pure water, since H_2O is the only source of these ions, the concentrations of H_3O^+ and OH^- are equal. Such a solution is said to be **neutral**. Since the concentrations are equal, they can be easily calculated from K_w.

$$[H_3O^+] = [OH^-] = \sqrt{K_w} = 1.0 \times 10^{-7}\ \text{mol L}^{-1} \qquad \text{(in pure water at 25 °C)}$$

As you can see, in pure water, the concentrations of H_3O^+ and OH^- are *very small* (1.0×10^{-7} mol L^{-1}) at room temperature.

An **acidic solution** contains an acid that creates additional H_3O^+ ions, causing $[H_3O^+]$ to increase. However, the *ion product constant still applies*:

$$[H_3O^+][OH^-] = K_w = 1.0 \times 10^{-14}$$

The concentration of H_3O^+ times the concentration of OH^- will always be 1.0×10^{-14} at 25 °C. If $[H_3O^+]$ increases, then $[OH^-]$ must decrease for the ion product constant to remain 1.0×10^{-14}. For example, if $[H_3O^+] = 1.0 \times 10^{-3}$ mol L^{-1} by adding some acid to water, then $[OH^-]$ can be found by solving the ion product constant expression for $[OH^-]$:

$$(1.0 \times 10^{-3})\,[OH^-] = 1.0 \times 10^{-14}$$

$$[OH^-] = \frac{1.0 \times 10^{-14}}{1.0 \times 10^{-3}} = 1.0 \times 10^{-11}\ \text{mol L}^{-1}$$

In an acidic solution $[H_3O^+] > [OH^-]$.

A **basic solution** contains a base that creates additional OH^- ions, causing $[OH^-]$ to increase and $[H_3O^+]$ to decrease, but again the *ion product constant still applies.* Suppose $[OH^-] = 1.0 \times 10^{-2}\ \text{mol L}^{-1}$; then $[H_3O^+]$ can be found by solving the ion product constant expression for $[H_3O^+]$:

$$[H_3O^+](1.0 \times 10^{-2}) = 1.0 \times 10^{-14}$$

$$[H_3O^+] = \frac{1.0 \times 10^{-14}}{1.0 \times 10^{-2}} = 1.0 \times 10^{-12}\ \text{mol L}^{-1}$$

In a basic solution $[OH^-] > [H_3O^+]$.

Notice that changing $[H_3O^+]$ in an aqueous solution produces an inverse change in $[OH^-]$ and vice versa.

Summarizing K_w:

- A *neutral solution* contains $[H_3O^+] = [OH^-] = 1.0 \times 10^{-7}\ \text{mol L}^{-1}$ (at 25 °C).
- An *acidic solution* contains $[H_3O^+] > [OH^-]$.
- A *basic solution* contains $[OH^-] > [H_3O^+]$.
- In *all aqueous solutions* both H_3O^+ and OH^- are present, with $[H_3O^+][OH^-] = K_w = 1.0 \times 10^{-14}$ (at 25 °C).

EXAMPLE 15.2 USING K_W IN CALCULATIONS

Calculate $[OH^-]$ at 25 °C for each solution and determine whether it is acidic, basic, or neutral.

(a) $[H_3O^+] = 7.5 \times 10^{-5}\ \text{mol L}^{-1}$
(b) $[H_3O^+] = 1.5 \times 10^{-9}\ \text{mol L}^{-1}$
(c) $[H_3O^+] = 1.0 \times 10^{-7}\ \text{mol L}^{-1}$

SOLUTION

(a) To find $[OH^-]$, use the ion product constant. Substitute the given value for $[H_3O^+]$ and solve the equation for $[OH^-]$. Since $[H_3O^+] > [OH^-]$, the solution is acidic.	$[H_3O^+][OH^-] = K_w = 1.0 \times 10^{-14}$ $(7.5 \times 10^{-5})[OH^-] = 1.0 \times 10^{-14}$ $[OH^-] = \frac{1.0 \times 10^{-14}}{7.5 \times 10^{-5}} = 1.3 \times 10^{-10}\ \text{mol L}^{-1}$ Acidic solution
(b) Substitute the given value for $[H_3O^+]$ and solve the acid ionization equation for $[OH^-]$. Since $[H_3O^+] < [OH^-]$, the solution is basic.	$(1.5 \times 10^{-9})[OH^-] = 1.0 \times 10^{-14}$ $[OH^-] = \frac{1.0 \times 10^{-14}}{1.5 \times 10^{-9}} = 6.7 \times 10^{-6}\ \text{mol L}^{-1}$ Basic solution
(c) Substitute the given value for $[H_3O^+]$ and solve the acid ionization equation for $[OH^-]$. Since $[H_3O^+] = 1.0 \times 10^{-7}$ and $[OH^-] = 1.0 \times 10^{-7}$, the solution is neutral.	$(1.0 \times 10^{-7})[OH^-] = 1.0 \times 10^{-14}$ $[OH^-] = \frac{1.0 \times 10^{-14}}{1.0 \times 10^{-7}} = 1.0 \times 10^{-7}\ \text{mol L}^{-1}$ Neutral solution

FOR PRACTICE 15.2

Calculate $[H_3O^+]$ at 25 °C for each solution and determine whether it is acidic, basic, or neutral.

(a) $[OH^-] = 1.5 \times 10^{-2}\ \text{mol L}^{-1}$
(b) $[OH^-] = 1.0 \times 10^{-7}\ \text{mol L}^{-1}$
(c) $[OH^-] = 8.2 \times 10^{-10}\ \text{mol L}^{-1}$

The pH Scale: A Way to Quantify Acidity and Basicity

The pH scale is a compact way to specify the acidity of a solution. We define **pH** as follows:

$$pH = -\log[H_3O^+]$$

A solution with $[H_3O^+] = 1.0 \times 10^{-3}$ mol L^{-1} (acidic) has a pH of:

$$\begin{aligned} pH &= -\log[H_3O^+] \\ &= -\log(1.0 \times 10^{-3}) \\ &= -(-3.00) \\ &= 3.00 \end{aligned}$$

The log of a number is the exponent to which 10 must be raised to obtain that number. Thus, $\log 10^1 = 1$; $\log 10^2 = 2$; $\log 10^{-1} = -1$; $\log 10^{-2} = -2$, etc. (see Appendix 1B).

Notice that the pH is reported to two *decimal places* here. This is because only the numbers to the right of the decimal point are significant in a logarithm. Since our original value for the concentration had two significant figures, the log of that number has two decimal places.

When you take the log of a quantity, the result should have the same number of decimal places as the number of significant figures in the original quantity (see Section 1.4).

2 significant digits → 2 decimal places

$$\log 1.0 \times 10^{-3} = 3.00$$

If the original number had three significant digits, the log would be reported to three decimal places:

3 significant digits → 3 decimal places

$$\log 1.00 \times 10^{-3} = 3.000$$

A solution with $[H_3O^+] = 1.0 \times 10^{-7}$ mol L^{-1} (neutral) has a pH of

$$\begin{aligned} pH &= -\log[H_3O^+] \\ &= -\log(1.0 \times 10^{-7}) \\ &= -(-7.00) \\ &= 7.00 \end{aligned}$$

In general, at 25 °C:

- $pH < 7$ The solution is *acidic.*
- $pH > 7$ The solution is *basic.*
- $pH = 7$ The solution is *neutral.*

Table 15.8 lists the pH of some common substances. As we discussed in Section 15.2, many foods, especially fruits, are acidic and have low pH values. Relatively few foods are basic. The foods with the lowest pH values are limes and lemons, and they are among the sourest. Since the pH scale is a *logarithmic scale*, a change of 1 pH unit corresponds to a 10-fold change in H_3O^+ concentration (Figure 15.10 ▼). For example, a lime with a pH of 2.0 is 10 times more acidic than a plum with a pH of 3.0 and 100 times more acidic than a cherry with a pH of 4.0.

TABLE 15.8 The pH of Some Common Substances

Substance	pH
Gastric juice (human stomach)	1.0–3.0
Limes	1.8–2.0
Lemons	2.2–2.4
Soft drinks	2.0–4.0
Plums	2.8–3.0
Wines	2.8–3.8
Apples	2.9–3.3
Peaches	3.4–3.6
Cherries	3.2–4.0
Beers	4.0–5.0
Rainwater (unpolluted)	5.6
Human blood	7.3–7.4
Egg whites	7.6–8.0
Milk of magnesia	10.5
Household ammonia	10.5–11.5
4% NaOH solution	14

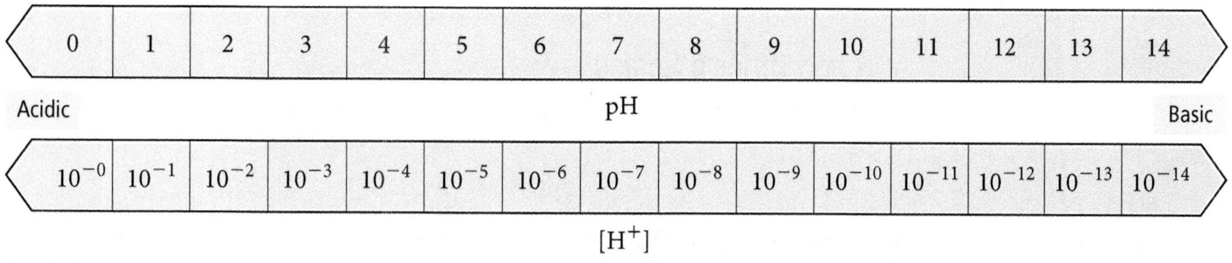

0	1	2	3	4	5	6	7	8	9	10	11	12	13	14

Acidic pH Basic

10^{-0}	10^{-1}	10^{-2}	10^{-3}	10^{-4}	10^{-5}	10^{-6}	10^{-7}	10^{-8}	10^{-9}	10^{-10}	10^{-11}	10^{-12}	10^{-13}	10^{-14}

$[H^+]$

▲ **FIGURE 15.10 The pH Scale** An increase of 1 on the pH scale corresponds to a decrease in $[H^+]$ by a factor of 10.

EXAMPLE 15.3 **CALCULATING pH FROM $[H^+]$ OR $[OH^-]$**

Calculate the pH of each solution at 25 °C and indicate whether it is acidic or basic.

(a) $[H_3O^+] = 1.8 \times 10^{-4}$ mol L^{-1} **(b)** $[OH^-] = 1.3 \times 10^{-2}$ mol L^{-1}

SOLUTION

(a) To calculate pH, substitute the given $[H_3O^+]$ into the pH equation. Since pH < 7, this solution is acidic.	$\text{pH} = -\log[H_3O^+]$ $= -\log(1.8 \times 10^{-4})$ $= -(-3.74)$ $= 3.74$ (acidic)
(b) First use K_w to find $[H_3O^+]$ from $[OH^-]$.	$[H_3O^+][OH^-] = K_w = 1.0 \times 10^{-14}$ $[H_3O^+](1.3 \times 10^{-2}) = 1.0 \times 10^{-14}$ $[H_3O^+] = \dfrac{1.0 \times 10^{-14}}{1.3 \times 10^{-2}} = 7.7 \times 10^{-13}$ mol L^{-1}
Then substitute $[H_3O^+]$ into the pH equation to find pH. Since pH > 7, this solution is basic.	$\text{pH} = -\log[H_3O^+]$ $= -\log(7.7 \times 10^{-13})$ $= -(-12.11)$ $= 12.11$ (basic)

FOR PRACTICE 15.3

Calculate the pH of each solution and indicate whether it is acidic or basic.

(a) $[H_3O^+] = 9.5 \times 10^{-9}$ mol L^{-1} **(b)** $[OH^-] = 7.1 \times 10^{-3}$ mol L^{-1}

EXAMPLE 15.4 **CALCULATING $[H_3O^+]$ FROM pH**

Calculate the H_3O^+ concentration for a solution with a pH of 4.80.

SOLUTION

To find the $[H_3O^+]$ from pH, start with the equation that defines pH. Substitute the given value of pH and then solve for $[H_3O^+]$. Since the given pH value was reported to two decimal places, the $[H_3O^+]$ is written to two significant figures. (Remember that $10^{\log x} = x$ (see Appendix 1B). Some calculators use an inv log key to represent this function.)	$\text{pH} = -\log[H_3O^+]$ $4.80 = -\log[H_3O^+]$ $-4.80 = \log[H_3O^+]$ $10^{-4.80} = 10^{\log[H_3O^+]}$ $10^{-4.80} = [H_3O^+]$ $[H_3O^+] = 1.6 \times 10^{-5}$ mol L^{-1}

FOR PRACTICE 15.4

Calculate the H_3O^+ concentration for a solution with a pH of 8.37.

pOH and Other p Scales

The pOH scale is analogous to the pH scale but is defined with respect to $[OH^-]$ instead of $[H_3O^+]$.

$$\text{pOH} = -\log[OH^-]$$

Notice that p is the mathematical operator $-\log$; thus, $\text{p}X = -\log X$.

A solution having an $[OH^-]$ of 1.0×10^{-3} mol L^{-1} (basic) has a pOH of 3.00. On the pOH scale, a pOH less than 7 is basic and a pOH greater than 7 is acidic. A pOH of 7 is

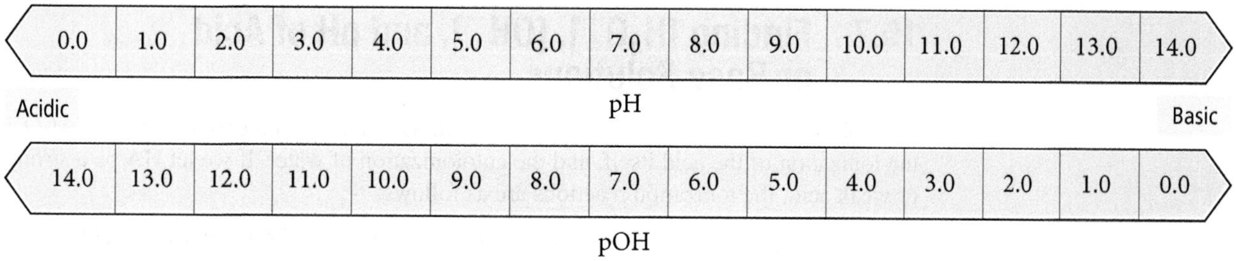

0.0	1.0	2.0	3.0	4.0	5.0	6.0	7.0	8.0	9.0	10.0	11.0	12.0	13.0	14.0

Acidic pH Basic

14.0	13.0	12.0	11.0	10.0	9.0	8.0	7.0	6.0	5.0	4.0	3.0	2.0	1.0	0.0

pOH

▲ **FIGURE 15.11 pH and pOH**

neutral (Figure 15.11 ▲). We can derive a relationship between pH and pOH at 25 °C from the expression for K_w:

$$[H_3O^+][OH^-] = 1.0 \times 10^{-14}$$

Taking the log of both sides, we get

$$\begin{aligned} \log([H_3O^+][OH^-]) &= \log(1.0 \times 10^{-14}) \\ \log[H_3O^+] + \log[OH^-] &= -14.00 \\ -\log[H_3O^+] - \log[OH^-] &= 14.00 \\ \text{pH} + \text{pOH} &= 14.00 \end{aligned}$$

The sum of pH and pOH is always equal to 14.00 at 25 °C. Therefore, a solution with a pH of 3 has a pOH of 11.

Another common p scale is the pK_a scale defined as follows:

$$pK_a = -\log K_a$$

The pK_a of a weak acid is another way to quantify its strength. The smaller the pK_a, the stronger the acid. For example, chlorous acid, with a K_a of 1.1×10^{-2}, has a pK_a of 1.96 and methanoic acid, with a K_a of 1.8×10^{-4}, has a pK_a of 3.74. This tells us that chlorous acid is stronger than methanoic acid.

CHEMISTRY AND MEDICINE Ulcers

An ulcer is a lesion on the wall of the stomach or small intestine. Under normal circumstances, a thick layer of mucous lines the stomach wall and protects it from the hydrochloric acid and other gastric juices in the stomach. If that mucous layer is damaged, however, stomach juices come in direct contact with the stomach wall and begin to digest it, resulting in an ulcer. The main symptom of an ulcer is a burning or gnawing pain in the stomach.

Acidic drugs, such as aspirin, and acidic foods, such as citrus fruits and pickling fluids, irritate ulcers. When consumed, these substances increase the acidity of the stomach juices, exacerbating the irritation to the stomach wall. On the other hand, antacids—which contain bases—relieve ulcers. Common antacids include Tums (active ingredient: calcium carbonate) and milk of magnesia (active ingredient: magnesium hydroxide).

The causes of ulcers are manifold. For many years, a stressful lifestyle and a rich diet were blamed. More recent research, however, has shown that a bacterial infection of the stomach lining is responsible for many ulcers. (The 2005 Nobel Prize in Physiology or Medicine was awarded to Australians Barry J. Marshall and J. Robin Warren, for their discovery of the bacterial cause of ulcers.) Long-term use of some over-the-counter pain relievers, such as aspirin, is also believed to produce ulcers.

Question

Which dessert would be less likely to irritate an ulcer, key lime pie or meringue (made of egg whites)?

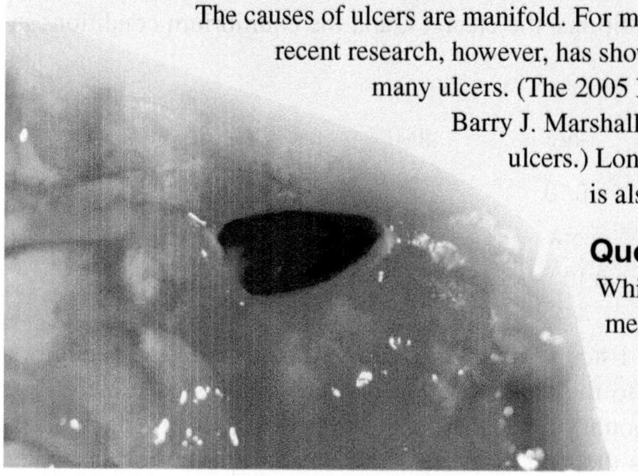

◀ An ulcer is a lesion in the stomach wall.

15.7 Finding $[H_3O^+]$, $[OH^-]$, and pH of Acid or Base Solutions

In a solution containing a strong or weak acid, there are two potential sources of H_3O^+: the ionization of the acid itself, and the autoionization of water. If we let HA be a strong or weak acid, the ionization reactions are as follows:

$$HA(aq) + H_2O(l) \rightleftharpoons H_3O^+(aq) + A^-(aq) \qquad \text{Strong or Weak Acid}$$
$$H_2O(l) + H_2O(l) \rightleftharpoons H_3O^+(aq) + OH^-(aq) \qquad K_w = 1.0 \times 10^{-14}$$

Except in extremely dilute acid solutions, the autoionization of water contributes a negligibly small amount of H_3O^+ compared to the ionization of the strong or weak acid. Recall from the previous section that autoionization in pure water produces an H_3O^+ concentration of 1.0×10^{-7} mol L^{-1}. In a strong or weak acid solution, the additional H_3O^+ from the acid causes the autoionization of water equilibrium to shift left (as described by Le Châtelier's principle). Consequently, in most strong or weak acid solutions, the autoionization of water produces even less H_3O^+ than in pure water and can be ignored. Therefore, we can focus exclusively on the amount of H_3O^+ produced by the acid.

The autoionization of water is only important in extremely dilute ($<10^{-5}$ mol L^{-1}) strong acid solutions.

Strong Acids

Because strong acids, by definition, completely ionize in solution, and because we can (in nearly all cases) ignore the contribution of the autoionization of water, *the concentration of H_3O^+ in a strong acid solution is simply equal to the concentration of the strong acid.* For example, a 0.10 mol L^{-1} HCl solution has an H_3O^+ concentration of 0.10 mol L^{-1} and a pH of 1.00.

$$0.10 \text{ mol L}^{-1} \text{ HCl} \Rightarrow [H_3O^+] = 0.10 \text{ mol L}^{-1} \Rightarrow \text{pH} = -\log(0.10) = 1.00$$

Weak Acids

Finding the pH of a weak acid solution is more complicated because the concentration of H_3O^+ is *not equal* to the concentration of the weak acid. For example, if we make solutions of 0.10 mol L^{-1} HCl (a strong acid) and 0.10 mol L^{-1} acetic acid (a weak acid) in the laboratory and measure the pH of each, we get the following results:

$$0.10 \text{ mol L}^{-1} \text{ HCl} \qquad \text{pH} = 1.00$$
$$0.10 \text{ mol L}^{-1} \text{ CH}_3\text{COOH} \qquad \text{pH} = 2.87$$

The pH of the acetic acid solution is higher (it is less acidic) because acetic acid only partially ionizes. Calculating the $[H_3O^+]$ formed by the ionization of a weak acid requires solving an equilibrium problem similar to those introduced in Chapter 14. Consider, for example, a 0.10 mol L^{-1} solution of the generic weak acid HA with an acid ionization constant K_a. Since we can ignore the contribution of the autoionization of water, we only have to determine the concentration of H_3O^+ formed by the following equilibrium:

$$HA(aq) + H_2O(l) \rightleftharpoons H_3O^+(aq) + A^-(aq) \qquad K_a$$

ICE tables were first introduced in Section 14.5.

We can summarize the initial conditions, the changes, and the equilibrium conditions in the following ICE table:

	[HA]	$[H_3O^+]$	$[A^-]$
Initial	0.10	≈ 0	0
Change	$-x$	$+x$	$+x$
Equilibrium	$0.10 - x$	x	x

The initial H_3O^+ concentration is listed as *approximately* zero because of the negligibly small contribution of H_3O^+ due to the autoionization of water (discussed previously). The variable x represents the amount of HA that ionizes. As discussed in Chapter 14, each *equilibrium* concentration is the sum of the two entries above it in the ICE table. In order to find the equilibrium concentration of H_3O^+, we must find the value of the variable x. We can use the equilibrium expression to set up an equation in which x is the only variable:

$$K_a = \frac{[H_3O^+][A^-]}{[HA]} = \frac{x^2}{0.10 - x}$$

As is often the case with equilibrium problems, we arrive at a quadratic equation in x, which we can solve using the quadratic formula. However, in many cases we can apply the *x is small* approximation (discussed in Section 14.7). Next, we examine the general procedure for weak acid equilibrium problems in the left column and two examples of applying the procedure in the centre and right columns. For both of these examples, the *x is small* approximation works well. In Example 15.7, we solve a problem in which the *x is small* approximation does not work. In such cases, we can solve the quadratic equation explicitly, or apply the method of successive approximations, also discussed in Section 14.7. Finally, in Example 15.8, we work a problem in which we must find the equilibrium constant of a weak acid from its pH.

PROCEDURE FOR...

Finding the pH (or $[H_3O^+]$) of a Weak Acid Solution

To solve these types of problems, follow the procedure outlined below.

EXAMPLE 15.5

Finding the $[H_3O^+]$ of a Weak Acid Solution

Find the $[H_3O^+]$ of a 0.100 mol L^{-1} HCN solution.

EXAMPLE 15.6

Finding the pH of a Weak Acid Solution

Find the pH of a 0.500 mol L^{-1} HNO_2 solution.

Write the balanced equation for the ionization of the acid and use it as a guide to prepare an ICE table showing the given concentration of the weak acid as its initial concentration. Leave room in the table for the changes in concentrations and for the equilibrium concentrations.

(Note that the $[H_3O^+]$ concentration is listed as approximately zero because the autoionization of water produces a negligibly small amount of H_3O^+.)

Example 15.5:

$$HCN(aq) + H_2O(l) \rightleftharpoons H_3O^+(aq) + CN^-(aq)$$

	[HCN]	$[H_3O^+]$	$[CN^-]$
Initial	0.100	≈0	0
Change			
Equil			

Example 15.6:

$$HNO_2(aq) + H_2O(l) \rightleftharpoons H_3O^+(aq) + NO_2^-(aq)$$

	$[HNO_2]$	$[H_3O^+]$	$[NO_2^-]$
Initial	0.500	≈0	0
Change			
Equil			

Represent the change in the concentration of H_3O^+ with the variable x. Define the changes in the concentrations of the other reactants and products in terms of x. Always keep in mind the stoichiometry of the reaction.

Example 15.5:

$$HCN(aq) + H_2O(l) \rightleftharpoons H_3O^+(aq) + CN^-(aq)$$

	[HCN]	$[H_3O^+]$	$[CN^-]$
Initial	0.100	≈0	0
Change	$-x$	$+x$	$+x$
Equil			

Example 15.6:

$$HNO_2(aq) + H_2O(l) \rightleftharpoons H_3O^+(aq) + NO_2^-(aq)$$

	$[HNO_2]$	$[H_3O^+]$	$[NO_2^-]$
Initial	0.500	≈0	0
Change	$-x$	$+x$	$+x$
Equil			

Sum each column to determine the equilibrium concentrations in terms of the initial concentrations and the variable x.

Example 15.5:

$$HCN(aq) + H_2O(l) \rightleftharpoons H_3O^+(aq) + CN^-(aq)$$

	[HCN]	$[H_3O^+]$	$[CN^-]$
Initial	0.100	≈0	0
Change	$-x$	$+x$	$+x$
Equil	$0.100 - x$	x	x

Example 15.6:

$$HNO_2(aq) + H_2O(l) \rightleftharpoons H_3O^+(aq) + NO_2^-(aq)$$

	$[HNO_2]$	$[H_3O^+]$	$[NO_2^-]$
Initial	0.200	≈0	0
Change	$-x$	$+x$	$+x$
Equil	$0.500 - x$	x	x

(continued)

PROCEDURE FOR... (continued)	EXAMPLE 15.5 (continued)	EXAMPLE 15.6 (continued)
Substitute the expressions for the equilibrium concentrations (from step 3) into the expression for the acid ionization constant (K_a). In many cases, you can make the approximation that *x is small* (as discussed in Section 14.7). **Substitute the value of the acid ionization constant (from Table 15.5) into the K_a expression and solve for *x*.** Confirm that the *x is small* approximation is valid by computing the ratio of *x* to the number it was subtracted from in the approximation. The ratio should be less than 0.05 (or 5%).	$K_a = \frac{[H_3O^+][CN^-]}{[HCN]}$ $= \frac{x^2}{0.100 - x}$ (*x is small*) $6.2 \times 10^{-10} = \frac{x^2}{0.100}$ $\sqrt{6.2 \times 10^{-10}} = \sqrt{\frac{x^2}{0.100}}$ $x = \sqrt{(0.100)(6.2 \times 10^{-10})}$ $= 7.9 \times 10^{-6}$ $\frac{7.9 \times 10^{-6}}{0.100} \times 100\% = 7.9 \times 10^{-3}\%$ Therefore the approximation is valid.	$K_a = \frac{[H_3O^+][NO_2^-]}{[HNO_2]}$ $= \frac{x^2}{0.500 - x}$ (*x is small*) $5.6 \times 10^{-4} = \frac{x^2}{0.500}$ $\sqrt{5.6 \times 10^{-4}} = \sqrt{\frac{x^2}{0.500}}$ $x = \sqrt{(0.500)(5.6 \times 10^{-4})}$ $= 1.7 \times 10^{-2}$ $\frac{1.7 \times 10^{-2}}{0.200} \times 100\% = 3.3\%$ Therefore the approximation is valid.
Determine the $[H_3O^+]$ concentration from the computed value of *x* and compute the pH if necessary.	$[H_3O^+] = 7.9 \times 10^{-6}$ mol L^{-1} (pH was not asked for in this problem.)	$[H_3O^+] = 1.7 \times 10^{-2}$ mol L^{-1} pH $= -\log[H_3O^+]$ $= -\log(1.7 \times 10^{-2})$ $= 1.77$
Check your answer by substituting the computed equilibrium values into the acid ionization expression. The computed value of K_a should match the given value of K_a. Note that rounding errors and the *x is small* approximation could result in a difference in the least significant digit when comparing values of K_a.	$K_a = \frac{[H_3O^+][CN^-]}{[HCN]} = \frac{(7.9 \times 10^{-6})^2}{0.100}$ $= 6.2 \times 10^{-10}$ Since the computed value of K_a matches the given value, the answer is valid.	$K_a = \frac{[H_3O^+][NO_2^-]}{[HNO_2]} = \frac{(1.7 \times 10^{-2})^2}{0.500}$ $= 5.8 \times 10^{-4}$ Since the computed value of K_a is very close to the given value, the answer is valid. The difference in values is due to rounding.
	FOR PRACTICE 15.5 Find the H_3O^+ concentration of a 0.500 mol L^{-1} hydrofluoric acid solution.	**FOR PRACTICE 15.6** Find the pH of a 0.0150 mol L^{-1} acetic acid solution.

EXAMPLE 15.7 FINDING THE pH OF A WEAK ACID SOLUTION IN CASES WHERE THE *x* IS SMALL APPROXIMATION DOES NOT WORK

Find the pH of a 0.100 mol L^{-1} $HClO_2$ solution.

SOLUTION

Write the balanced equation for the ionization of the acid and use it as a guide to prepare an ICE table showing the given concentration of the weak acid as its initial concentration.

(Note that the H_3O^+ concentration is listed as approximately zero. Although a little H_3O^+ is present from the autoionization of water, this amount is negligibly small compared to the amount of H_3O^+.)

$$HClO_2(aq) + H_2O(l) \rightleftharpoons H_3O^+(aq) + ClO_2^-(aq)$$

	$[HClO_2]$	$[H_3O^+]$	$[ClO_2^-]$
Initial	0.100	≈0	0
Change			
Equil			

Represent the change in $[H_3O^+]$ with the variable x. Define the changes in the concentrations of the other reactants and products in terms of x.	$HClO_2(aq) + H_2O(l) \rightleftharpoons H_3O^+(aq) + ClO_2^-(aq)$ | | $[HClO_2]$ | $[H_3O^+]$ | $[ClO_2^-]$ | Initial 0.100 ≈0 0 Change $-x$ $+x$ $+x$ Equil
Sum each column to determine the equilibrium concentrations in terms of the initial concentrations and the variable x.	$HClO_2(aq) + H_2O(l) \rightleftharpoons H_3O^+(aq) + ClO_2^-(aq)$ | | $[HClO_2]$ | $[H_3O^+]$ | $[ClO_2^-]$ | Initial 0.100 ≈0 0 Change $-x$ $+x$ $+x$ Equil $0.100 - x$ x x
Substitute the expressions for the equilibrium concentrations (from step 3) into the expression for the acid ionization constant (K_a). Make the *x is small* approximation and substitute the value of the acid ionization constant (from Table 15.5) into the K_a expression. Solve for x.	$K_a = \frac{[H_3O^+][ClO_2^-]}{[HNO_2]}$ $= \frac{x^2}{0.100 - \cancel{x}}$ (*x is small*) $0.011 = \frac{x^2}{0.100}$ $\sqrt{0.011} = \sqrt{\frac{x^2}{0.100}}$ $x = \sqrt{(0.100)(0.011)}$ $= 0.033$
Check to see if the *x is small* approximation is valid by computing the ratio of x to the number it was subtracted from in the approximation. The ratio should be less than 0.05 (or 5%).	$\frac{0.033}{0.100} \times 100\% = 33\%$ Therefore, the *x is small* approximation is *not valid.*
If the *x is small* approximation is not valid, solve the quadratic equation explicitly or use the method of successive approximations to find x. In this case, we solve the quadratic equation.	$0.011 = \frac{x^2}{0.100 - x}$ $0.011(0.100 - x) = x^2$ $0.0011 - 0.011x = x^2$ $x^2 + 0.011x - 0.0011 = 0$ $x = \frac{-b \pm \sqrt{b^2 - 4ac}}{2a}$ $= \frac{-(0.011) \pm \sqrt{(0.011)^2 - 4(1)(-0.0011)}}{2(1)}$ $= \frac{-0.011 \pm 0.06\underline{7}2}{2}$ $x = -0.039$ or $x = 0.028$ Since x represents the concentration of H_3O^+, and since concentrations cannot be negative, we reject the negative root. $x = 0.028$
Determine the H_3O^+ concentration from the calculated value of x and calculate the pH (if necessary).	$[H_3O^+] = 0.028 \text{ mol L}^{-1}$ $pH = -\log[H_3O^+]$ $= -\log 0.028$ $= 1.55$

(continued)

EXAMPLE 15.7 (CONTINUED)

Check your answer by substituting the calculated equilibrium values into the acid ionization expression. The calculated value of K_a should match the given value of K_a. Note that rounding errors could result in a difference in the least significant digit when comparing values of K_a.	$K_a = \frac{[H_3O^+][ClO_2^-]}{[HClO_2]} = \frac{0.028^2}{0.100 - 0.028}$ $= 0.011$ Since the calculated value of K_a matches the given value, the answer is valid.

FOR PRACTICE 15.7

Find the pH of a 0.0101 mol L^{-1} HNO_2 solution.

EXAMPLE 15.8 FINDING THE EQUILIBRIUM CONSTANT FROM pH

A 0.100 mol L^{-1} weak acid (HA) solution has a pH of 4.25. Find K_a for the acid.

SOLUTION

Use the given pH to find the equilibrium concentration of $[H_3O^+]$. Then write the balanced equation for the ionization of the acid and use it as a guide to prepare an ICE table showing all known concentrations.

$pH = -\log[H_3O^+]$

$4.25 = -\log[H_3O^+]$

$[H_3O^+] = 5.6 \times 10^{-5}\ mol\ L^{-1}$

$HA(aq) + H_2O(l) \rightleftharpoons H_3O^+(aq) + A^-(aq)$

	[HA]	$[H_3O^+]$	$[A^-]$
Initial	0.100	≈0	0
Change			
Equil		5.6×10^{-5}	

Use the equilibrium concentration of H_3O^+ and the stoichiometry of the reaction to predict the changes and equilibrium concentration for all species. For most weak acids, the initial and equilibrium concentrations of the weak acid (HA) are equal because the amount that ionizes is usually very small compared to the initial concentration.

$HA(aq) + H_2O(l) \rightleftharpoons H_3O^+(aq) + A^-(aq)$

	[HA]	$[H_3O^+]$	$[A^-]$
Initial	0.100	≈0	0
Change	-5.6×10^{-5}	$+5.6 \times 10^{-5}$	$+5.6 \times 10^{-5}$
Equil	$(0.100 - 5.6 \times 10^{-5})$ ≈0.100	5.6×10^{-5}	5.6×10^{-5}

Substitute the equilibrium concentrations into the expression for K_a and calculate its value.

$$K_a = \frac{[H_3O^+][A^-]}{[HA]}$$

$$= \frac{(5.6 \times 10^{-5})(5.6 \times 10^{-5})}{0.100}$$

$$= 3.1 \times 10^{-8}$$

FOR PRACTICE 15.8

A 0.175 mol L^{-1} weak acid solution has a pH of 3.25. Find K_a for the acid.

CONCEPTUAL CONNECTION 15.3

The *x is small* Approximation

The initial concentration and K_a's of several weak acid (HA) solutions are listed below. For which of these is the *x is small* approximation *least* likely to work in finding the pH of the solution?

(a) initial [HA] = 0.100 mol L^{-1}; $K_a = 1.0 \times 10^{-5}$

(b) initial [HA] = 1.00 mol L^{-1}; $K_a = 1.0 \times 10^{-6}$

(c) initial [HA] = 0.0100 mol L^{-1}; $K_a = 1.0 \times 10^{-3}$

(d) initial [HA] = 1.0 mol L^{-1}; $K_a = 1.5 \times 10^{-3}$

Percent Ionization of a Weak Acid

We can quantify the ionization of a weak acid according to the percentage of acid molecules that actually ionize. For instance, in Example 15.6, we found that a 0.500 mol L^{-1} HNO_2 solution contains 1.7×10^{-2} mol L^{-1} H_3O^+. We define the **percent ionization** of a weak acid as the ratio of the ionized acid concentration to the initial acid concentration, multiplied by 100%:

$$\text{Percent ionization} = \frac{\text{concentration of ionized acid}}{\text{initial concentration of acid}} \times 100\% = \frac{[H_3O^+]_{equil}}{[HA]_{init}} \times 100\%$$

Since the concentration of ionized acid is equal to the H_3O^+ concentration at equilibrium (for a monoprotic acid), we can use $[H_3O^+]_{equil}$ and $[HA]_{init}$ in the formula to calculate the percent ionization. The 0.500 mol L^{-1} HNO_2 solution therefore has the following percent ionization:

$$\begin{aligned}\%\ \text{ionization} &= \frac{[H_3O^+]_{equil}}{[HA]_{init}} \times 100\% \\ &= \frac{1.7 \times 10^{-2}\ \cancel{\text{mol L}^{-1}}}{0.500\ \cancel{\text{mol L}^{-1}}} \times 100\% \\ &= 3.3\%\end{aligned}$$

As you can see, the percent ionization is relatively small. In this case, even though HNO_2 has the second largest K_a in Table 15.5, less than four molecules out of one hundred ionize. For most other weak acids (with smaller K_a values) the percent ionization is even less.

In the example that follows, we calculate the percent ionization of a more concentrated HNO_2 solution. As you read through the example, notice that the calculated H_3O^+ concentration is much greater (as we would expect for a more concentrated solution), but the *percent ionization* is actually smaller.

EXAMPLE 15.9 FINDING THE PERCENT IONIZATION OF A WEAK ACID

Find the percent ionization of a 2.5 mol L^{-1} HNO_2 solution.

SOLUTION

To find the percent ionization, you must find the equilibrium concentration of H_3O^+. Follow the procedure in Example 15.5, shown in condensed form here.

$$HNO_2(aq) + H_2O(l) \rightleftharpoons H_3O^+(aq) + NO_2^-(aq)$$

	$[HNO_2]$	$[H_3O^+]$	$[NO_2^-]$
Initial	2.5	≈ 0	0
Change	$-x$	$+x$	$+x$
Equil	$2.5 - x$	x	x

$$K_a = \frac{[H_3O^+][NO_2^-]}{[HNO_2]} = \frac{x^2}{2.5 - \cancel{x}} \quad (x \text{ is small})$$

$$5.6 \times 10^{-4} = \frac{x^2}{2.5}$$

$$x = 0.037$$

Therefore, $[H_3O^+] = 0.037$ mol L^{-1}.

Use the definition of percent ionization to calculate it. (Since the percent ionization is less than 5%, the *x is small* approximation is valid.)

$$\begin{aligned}\%\ \text{ionization} &= \frac{[H_3O^+]_{equil}}{[HA]_{init}} \times 100\% \\ &= \frac{0.037\ \cancel{\text{mol L}^{-1}}}{2.5\ \cancel{\text{mol L}^{-1}}} \times 100\% \\ &= 1.5\%\end{aligned}$$

FOR PRACTICE 15.9

Find the percent ionization of a 0.250 mol L^{-1} CH_3COOH solution.

Let us now summarize the results of Examples 15.6 and 15.9:

$[HNO_2]$	$[H_3O^+]$	Percent Dissociation
0.500	0.017	3.3%
2.5	0.037	1.7%

The trend you can see in the above table applies to all weak acids:

- **The *equilibrium H_3O^+ concentration* of a weak acid *increases* with increasing initial concentration of the acid.**
- **The *percent ionization* of a weak acid *decreases* with increasing concentration of the acid.**

In other words, as the concentration of a weak acid solution increases, the concentration of the hydronium ion also increases, but the increase is not linear. The H_3O^+ concentration increases more slowly than the concentration of the acid because as the acid concentration increases, a smaller fraction of weak acid molecules ionize.

We can understand this behaviour by analogy with Le Châtelier's principle. Consider the following weak acid ionization equilibrium:

$$\underset{\text{1 mol dissolved particles}}{HA(aq)} \rightleftharpoons \underset{\text{2 mol dissolved particles}}{H^+(aq) + A^-(aq)}$$

If we dilute a weak acid solution initially at equilibrium, the system (according to Le Châtelier's principle) responds to minimize the disturbance. Thus, the equilibrium shifts to the right because the right side of the equation contains more particles in solution (2 mol versus 1 mol) than the left side. If the system shifts to the right, the percent ionization is greater in the more dilute solution, which is what we observe.

CONCEPTUAL CONNECTION 15.4

Percent Ionization

Which acetic acid solution has the greatest percent ionization? Which solution has the lowest (most acidic) pH?

(a) 0.100 mol L^{-1} CH_3COOH **(b)** 0.500 mol L^{-1} CH_3COOH **(c)** 0.0100 mol L^{-1} CH_3COOH

Mixtures of Acids

Finding the pH of a mixture of acids may seem difficult when first considered. However, in many cases, the relative strengths of the acids in the mixture allow us to neglect the weaker acid and focus only on the stronger one. Here, we consider two possible acid mixtures: a strong acid with a weak acid, and a weak acid with another weak acid.

A Strong Acid and a Weak Acid Consider a mixture that is 0.10 mol L^{-1} in HCl (*aq*) and 0.10 mol L^{-1} in HCOOH (*aq*). We now have three sources of H_3O^+ ions: the strong acid (HCl), the weak acid (HCOOH), and the autoionization of water.

$$HCl(aq) + H_2O(l) \longrightarrow H_3O^+(aq) + Cl^-(aq) \qquad \text{Strong}$$
$$HCOOH(aq) + H_2O(l) \rightleftharpoons H_3O^+(aq) + HCOO^-(aq) \qquad K_a = 1.8 \times 10^{-4}$$
$$H_2O(l) + H_2O(l) \rightleftharpoons H_3O^+(aq) + OH^-(aq) \qquad K_w = 1.0 \times 10^{-14}$$

Since HCl is strong, we know that it completely ionizes to produce a significant concentration of H_3O^+ (0.10 mol L^{-1}). The H_3O^+ formed by HCl then *suppresses* the formation of additional H_3O^+ formed by the ionization of HCOOH or the autoionization of water. In other words, according to Le Châtelier's principle, the formation of H_3O^+ by the strong acid causes the weak acid to ionize even less than it would in the absence of the strong acid. To see this clearly, let us calculate $[H_3O^+]$ and $[HCOO^-]$ in this solution.

In an initial estimate of $[H_3O^+]$, we can neglect the contribution of HCOOH and H_2O. The concentration of H_3O^+ is then equal to the initial concentration of HCl.

$$[H_3O^+] = [HCl] = 0.10 \text{ mol L}^{-1}$$

To find $[HCOO^-]$ we must solve an equilibrium problem. However, the initial concentration of H_3O^+ in this case is not negligible (as it has been in all the other weak acid equilibrium problems that we have worked so far) because HCl has formed a significant amount of H_3O^+. The concentration of H_3O^+ formed by HCl becomes the *initial* concentration of H_3O^+ in the ICE table for HCOOH, as shown here:

$$HCOOH(aq) + H_2O(l) \rightleftharpoons H_3O^+(aq) + HCOO^-(aq)$$

	HCOOH	$[H_3O^+]$	$[HCOO^-]$
Initial	0.10	0.10	0.00
Change	$-x$	$+x$	$+x$
Equil	$0.10 - x$	$0.10 + x$	x

We then use the equilibrium expression to set up an equation in which x is the only variable.

$$K_a = \frac{[H_3O^+][HCOO^-]}{[HCOOH]} = \frac{(0.10 + x)x}{0.10 - x}$$

Since the equilibrium constant is small relative to the initial concentration of the acid, we can make the *x is small* approximation.

$$K_a = \frac{(0.10 + \cancel{x})x}{0.10 - \cancel{x}}$$

$$1.8 \times 10^{-4} = \frac{(0.10)x}{0.10}$$

$$x = 1.8 \times 10^{-4}$$

Checking the *x is small* approximation,

$$\frac{1.8 \times 10^{-4}}{0.10} \times 100\% = 0.18\%$$

We find that the approximation is valid. Therefore, $[HCOO^-] = 1.8 \times 10^{-4}\,\text{mol L}^{-1}$. We can now see that we can completely ignore the ionization of the weak acid (HCOOH) in calculating $[H_3O^+]$ for the mixture. The contribution to the concentration of H_3O^+ by the weak acid must necessarily be equal to the concentration of $HCOO^-$ that we just calculated (because of the stoichiometry of the ionization reaction). Therefore, we have the following contributions to $[H_3O^+]$:

HCl contributes $0.10\,\text{mol L}^{-1}$

HCOOH contributes $1.8 \times 10^{-4}\,\text{mol L}^{-1}$ or $0.00018\,\text{mol L}^{-1}$

Total $[H_3O^+] = 0.10\,\text{mol L}^{-1} + 0.00018\,\text{mol L}^{-1} = 0.10\,\text{mol L}^{-1}$

As you can see, since the significant figure rules for addition limit the answer to two decimal places, the amount of H_3O^+ contributed by HCOOH is completely negligible. The amount of H_3O^+ contributed by the autoionization of water is even smaller and therefore similarly negligible.

A Mixture of Two Weak Acids When two weak acids are mixed, we again have three potential sources of H_3O^+ to consider: each of the two weak acids and the autoionization of water. However, if the K_a's of the two weak acids are sufficiently different in magnitude (if they differ by more than a factor of several hundred), then as long as the concentrations of the two acids are similar in magnitude (or the concentration of the stronger one is greater than that of the weaker), we can assume that the weaker acid will not make a significant contribution to the concentration of H_3O^+. We make this assumption for the same reason that we made a similar assumption for a mixture of a strong acid and a weak one: the stronger acid suppresses the ionization of the weaker one, in accordance with Le Châtelier's principle. Example 15.10 shows how to calculate the concentration of H_3O^+ in a mixture of two weak acids.

EXAMPLE 15.10 **MIXTURES OF WEAK ACIDS**

Find the pH of a mixture that is 0.350 mol L^{-1} in HF and 0.100 mol L^{-1} in HClO.

SOLUTION

The three possible sources of H_3O^+ ions are HF, HClO, and H_2O. Write the ionization equations for the three sources and their corresponding equilibrium constants. Since the equilibrium constant for the ionization of HF is about 16 000 times larger than that for the ionization of HClO, the contribution of HF to $[H_3O^+]$ is by far the greatest. We can therefore simply calculate the $[H_3O^+]$ formed by HF and neglect the other two potential sources of H_3O^+.	$HF(aq) + H_2O(l) \rightleftharpoons H_3O^+(aq) + F^-(aq)$ $K_a = 6.3 \times 10^{-4}$ $HClO(aq) + H_2O(l) \rightleftharpoons H_3O^+(aq) + ClO^-(aq)$ $K_a = 4.0 \times 10^{-8}$ $H_2O(l) + H_2O(l) \rightleftharpoons H_3O^+(aq) + OH^-(aq)$ $K_w = 1.0 \times 10^{-14}$
Write the balanced equation for the ionization of HF and use it as a guide to prepare an ICE table.	$HF(aq) + H_2O(l) \rightleftharpoons H_3O^+(aq) + F^-(aq)$ (ICE table below)
Substitute the expressions for the equilibrium concentrations into the expression for the acid ionization constant (K_a). Since the equilibrium constant is small relative to the initial concentration of HF, you can make the *x is small* approximation. Substitute the value of the acid ionization constant (from Table 15.5) into the K_a expression and solve for *x*.	$K_a = \frac{[H_3O^+][F^-]}{[HF]} = \frac{x^2}{0.350 - \cancel{x}}$ (*x is small*) $6.3 \times 10^{-4} = \frac{x^2}{0.350}$ $\sqrt{(0.350)(6.3 \times 10^{-4})} = \sqrt{x^2}$
Confirm that the *x is small* approximation is valid by calculating the ratio of *x* to the number it was subtracted from in the approximation. The ratio should be less than 0.05 (or 5%).	$x = 1.5 \times 10^{-2}$ $\frac{1.5 \times 10^{-2}}{0.350} \times 100\% = 4.3\%$ Therefore the approximation is valid.
Determine the H_3O^+ concentration from the calculated value of *x* and find the pH.	$[H_3O^+] = 1.5 \times 10^{-2}$ mol L^{-1} $pH = -\log(1.5 \times 10^{-2}) = 1.82$

ICE table:

	[HF]	$[H_3O^+]$	$[F^-]$
Initial	0.350	≈ 0	0
Change	$-x$	$+x$	$+x$
Equil	$0.350 - x$	x	x

FOR PRACTICE 15.10

Find the ClO^- concentration of the above mixture of HF and HClO.

CONCEPTUAL CONNECTION 15.5

Strong and Weak Acids

Which solution is most acidic (that is, has the lowest pH)?

(a) 1.0 mol L^{-1} HCl

(b) 2.0 mol L^{-1} HF

(c) A solution that is 1.0 mol L^{-1} in HF and 1.0 mol L^{-1} in HClO

Finding the $[OH^-]$ and pH of Basic Solutions

Finding the $[OH^-]$ and pH of a strong base solution is relatively straightforward, as shown in the following example. As in calculating the $[H_3O^+]$ in strong acid solutions, we can neglect the contribution of the autoionization of water to the $[OH^-]$ and focus solely on the strong base itself.

EXAMPLE 15.11 FINDING THE $[OH^-]$ AND pH OF A STRONG BASE SOLUTION

What is the OH^- concentration and pH in each solution?

(a) 0.225 mol L^{-1} KOH **(b)** 0.0015 mol L^{-1} $Sr(OH)_2$

SOLUTION

(a) Since KOH is a strong base, it completely dissociates into K^+ and OH^- in solution. The concentration of OH^- will therefore be the same as the given concentration of KOH.	$KOH(aq) \longrightarrow K^+(aq) + OH^-(aq)$ $[OH^-] = 0.225$ mol L^{-1}
Use this concentration and K_w to find $[H_3O^+]$.	$[H_3O^+][OH^-] = K_w = 1.00 \times 10^{-14}$ $[H_3O^+](0.225) = 1.00 \times 10^{-14}$ $[H_3O^+] = 4.44 \times 10^{-14}$ mol L^{-1}
Then substitute $[H_3O^+]$ into the pH expression to find the pH.	$pH = -\log[H_3O^+]$ $= -\log(4.44 \times 10^{-14})$ $= 13.352$
(b) Since $Sr(OH)_2$ is a strong base, the $Sr(OH)_2$ that dissolves in water will dissociate completely. For every Sr^{2+} in solution, there are two OH^-. The concentration of OH^- will therefore be twice the given concentration of $Sr(OH)_2$.	$Sr(OH)_2(aq) \longrightarrow Sr^{2+}(aq) + 2\ OH^-(aq)$ $[OH^-] = 2(0.0015)$ mol L^{-1} $= 0.0030$ mol L^{-1}
Use this concentration and K_w to find $[H_3O^+]$.	$[H_3O^+][OH^-] = K_w = 1.0 \times 10^{-14}$ $[H_3O^+](0.0030) = 1.0 \times 10^{-14}$ $[H_3O^+] = 3.3 \times 10^{-12}$ mol L^{-1}
Substitute $[H_3O^+]$ into the pH expression to find the pH.	$pH = -\log[H_3O^+]$ $= -\log(3.3 \times 10^{-12})$ $= 11.48$

FOR PRACTICE 15.11

Find the $[OH^-]$ and pH of a 0.010 mol L^{-1} $Ba(OH)_2$ solution.

Finding the $[OH^-]$ and pH of a *weak base* solution is analogous to finding the $[H_3O^+]$ and pH of a weak acid. Similarly, we can neglect the contribution of the autoionization of water to the $[OH^-]$ and focus solely on the weak base itself. We find the contribution of the weak base by preparing an ICE table showing the relevant concentrations of all species and then use the base ionization constant expression to find the $[OH^-]$. The following example shows how to find the $[OH^-]$ and pH of a weak base solution.

EXAMPLE 15.12 FINDING THE $[OH^-]$ AND pH OF A WEAK BASE SOLUTION

Find the $[OH^-]$ and pH of a 0.100 mol L^{-1} NH_3 solution.

SOLUTION

Write the balanced equation for the ionization of water by the base and use it as a guide to prepare an ICE table showing the given concentration of the weak base as its initial concentration. Leave room in the table for the changes in concentrations and for the equilibrium concentrations. (Note that we list the OH^- concentration as approximately zero. Although a little OH^- is present from the autoionization of water, this amount is negligibly small compared to the amount of OH^- formed by the base.)

$$NH_3(aq) + H_2O(l) \rightleftharpoons NH_4^+(aq) + OH^-(aq)$$

	$[NH_3]$	$[NH_4^+]$	$[OH^-]$
Initial	0.100	0	≈0
Change			
Equil			

(continued)

EXAMPLE 15.12 (CONTINUED)

Represent the change in the concentration of OH^- with the variable x. Define the changes in the concentrations of the other reactants and products in terms of x.	$NH_3(aq) + H_2O(l) \rightleftharpoons NH_4^+(aq) + OH^-(aq)$ | | $[NH_3]$ | $[NH_4^+]$ | $[OH^-]$ | Initial: 0.100, 0, ≈0 Change: $-x$, $+x$, $+x$ Equil
Sum each column to determine the equilibrium concentrations in terms of the initial concentrations and the variable x.	$NH_3(aq) + H_2O(l) \rightleftharpoons NH_4^+(aq) + OH^-(aq)$ | | $[NH_3]$ | $[NH_4^+]$ | $[OH^-]$ | Initial: 0.100, 0, ≈0 Change: $-x$, $+x$, $+x$ Equil: $0.100 - x$, x, x
Substitute the expressions for the equilibrium concentrations (from step 3) into the expression for the base ionization constant. In many cases, you can make the approximation that *x is small* (as discussed in Chapter 14). Substitute the value of the base ionization constant (from Table 15.7) into the K_b expression and solve for x.	$K_b = \frac{[NH_4^+][OH^-]}{[NH_3]}$ $= \frac{x^2}{0.100 - \cancel{x}}$ (*x is small*) $1.76 \times 10^{-5} = \frac{x^2}{0.100}$ $\sqrt{1.76 \times 10^{-5}} = \sqrt{\frac{x^2}{0.100}}$ $x = \sqrt{(0.100)(1.76 \times 10^{-5})}$ $= 1.33 \times 10^{-3}$
Confirm that the *x is small* approximation is valid by calculating the ratio of x to the number it was subtracted from in the approximation. The ratio should be less than 0.05 (or 5%).	$\frac{1.33 \times 10^{-3}}{0.100} \times 100\% = 1.33\%$ Therefore the approximation is valid.
Determine the OH^- concentration from the calculated value of x. Use the expression for K_w to find $[H_3O^+]$. Substitute $[H_3O^+]$ into the pH equation to find pH.	$[OH^-] = 1.33 \times 10^{-3}$ mol L^{-1} $[H_3O^+][OH^-] = K_w = 1.00 \times 10^{-14}$ $[H_3O^+](1.33 \times 10^{-3}) = 1.00 \times 10^{-14}$ $[H_3O^+] = 7.52 \times 10^{-12}$ mol L^{-1} $pH = -\log[H_3O^+]$ $= -\log(7.52 \times 10^{-12})$ $= 11.124$

FOR PRACTICE 15.12

Find the $[OH^-]$ and pH of a 0.33 mol L^{-1} methylamine solution.

15.8 The Acid–Base Properties of Ions and Salts

We have already seen that some ions act as bases. For example, the bicarbonate ion acts as a base according to the following equation:

$$HCO_3^-(aq) + H_2O(l) \rightleftharpoons H_2CO_3(aq) + OH^-(aq)$$

The bicarbonate ion, like any ion, does not exist by itself—in order to be charge neutral, it must pair with a counter ion (in this case a cation) to form an ionic compound, called a *salt*. For example, the sodium salt of bicarbonate is sodium bicarbonate. Like all sodium salts, sodium bicarbonate completely dissociates in solution to form a sodium cation and bicarbonate anion:

$$NaHCO_3(s) \rightleftharpoons Na^+(aq) + HCO_3^-(aq)$$

The sodium ion has neither acidic nor basic properties (it does not ionize water), as we will see shortly. The bicarbonate ion, by contrast, acts as a weak base, ionizing water as just shown to form a basic solution. Consequently, the pH of a sodium bicarbonate solution is above 7 (the solution is basic). In this section, we consider some of the acid–base properties of salts and the ions they contain. Some salts are pH-neutral when put into water, others are acidic, and still others are basic, depending on their constituent anions and cations. In general, anions tend to form either *basic* or neutral solutions, while cations tend to form either *acidic* or neutral solutions.

Anions as Weak Bases

We can think of any anion as the conjugate base of an acid. For example, consider the following anions and their corresponding acids:

This anion	is the conjugate base of	this acid
Cl^-		HCl
F^-		HF
NO_3^-		HNO_3
CH_3COO^-		CH_3COOH

CHEMISTRY AND MEDICINE What's in My Antacid?

In the opening section of this chapter, we discussed heartburn and its treatment with antacids. Some common antacids and their active ingredients include the following:

Amphogel	$Al(OH)_3$
Milk of magnesia	$Mg(OH)_2$
Maalox	$Mg(OH)_2$ and $Al(OH)_3$
Mylanta	$Mg(OH)_2$ and $Al(OH)_3$
Tums	$CaCO_3$

We categorize antacids into three main groups: calcium-based, magnesium-based, and aluminum-based. Calcium-based antacids may cause acid rebound—which means that, although they initially relieve heartburn, they can also cause the stomach to produce more acid, resulting in a quick return of the symptoms. Aluminum- and magnesium-based antacids do not cause acid rebound, but have downsides of their own. Aluminum-based antacids tend to cause constipation and magnesium-based ones tend to cause diarrhea. (In fact, milk of magnesia is sometimes used as a laxative.) A person who takes repeated doses of these antacids should alternate between the two or choose a product that contains both.

Notice the absence of group 1 metal hydroxides, such as KOH or NaOH, from the list of antacids. Why are those substances—which are completely soluble and act as strong bases—not used in antacids? Because a solution containing sufficient KOH or NaOH to neutralize stomach acid would also burn the mouth and throat. In contrast, $Mg(OH)_2$ and $Al(OH)_3$ are only slightly soluble. Therefore, liquid antacids containing these are actually *suspensions* of $Mg(OH)_2$ and $Al(OH)_3$—they are heterogeneous mixtures in which the solid is finely divided into the liquid. As a result, the concentration of OH^- in these suspensions is relatively small compared to what it would be with a group 1 metal hydroxide.

▶ Antacids contain a variety of bases that effectively neutralize excess stomach acid.

Initially, it might seem as though the relatively lower OH^- concentration would make the antacid much less effective. However, the solid $Mg(OH)_2$ or $Al(OH)_3$ continues to dissolve as the OH^- neutralizes stomach acid. For example, a suspension of magnesium hydroxide contains solid $Mg(OH)_2$ in equilibrium with dissolved Mg^{2+} and OH^- ions:

$$Mg(OH)_2(s) \rightleftharpoons Mg^{2+}(aq) + 2\,OH^-(aq)$$

As stomach acid is neutralized, OH^- is used up, and the equilibrium shifts to the right providing additional OH^- ions. In this way, a suspension of $Mg(OH)_2$ provides a steady concentration of dissolved OH^- ions to neutralize stomach acid.

Question

Write chemical equations showing the reactions of each of the bases in the antacids discussed here with stomach acid (HCl).

In general, the anion A^- is the conjugate base of the acid HA. Since every anion can be envisioned as the conjugate base of an acid, every anion itself can potentially act as a base. However, *not every anion does act as a base*—it depends on the strength of the corresponding acid. In general:

- An anion that is the conjugate base of a *weak acid* is itself a *weak base.*
- An anion that is the conjugate base of a *strong acid* is pH-*neutral* (forms solutions that are neither acidic nor basic).

For example, the Cl^- anion is the conjugate base of HCl, a strong acid. Therefore the Cl^- anion is pH-neutral (neither acidic nor basic). The F^- anion, however, is the conjugate base of HF, a weak acid. Therefore the F^- ion is itself a weak base and ionizes water according to the reaction:

$$F^-(aq) + H_2O(l) \rightleftharpoons OH^-(aq) + HF(aq)$$

We can understand why the conjugate base of a weak acid is basic by asking ourselves why an acid is weak to begin with. Hydrofluoric acid is a weak acid because the following equilibrium lies to the left:

$$HF(aq) + H_2O(l) \rightleftharpoons H_3O^+(aq) + F^-(aq)$$

The equilibrium lies to the left because the F^- ion has a significant affinity for H^+ ions. Consequently, when F^- is put into water, its affinity for H^+ ions allows it to remove H^+ ions from water molecules, thus acting as a weak base. In general, as shown in Figure 15.12 ▼, the weaker the acid, the stronger the conjugate base (as we saw in Section 15.4). In contrast, the conjugate base of a strong acid, such as Cl^-, does not act as a base because the following reaction lies far to the right:

$$HCl(aq) + H_2O(l) \longrightarrow H_3O^+(aq) + Cl^-(aq)$$

The reaction lies far to the right because the Cl^- ion has a low affinity for H^+ ions. Consequently, when Cl^- is put into water, it does not remove H^+ ions from water molecules.

▶ FIGURE 15.12 Strength of Conjugate Acid–Base Pairs The stronger an acid, the weaker is its conjugate base, and vice versa.

Acid Strength	Acid	Base	Base Strength
Strong	HCl	Cl^-	Neutral
Strong	H_2SO_4	HSO_4^-	Neutral
Strong	HNO_3	NO_3^-	Neutral
Strong	H_3O^+	H_2O	Neutral
Weak	HSO_4^-	SO_4^{2-}	Weak
Weak	H_2SO_3	HSO_3^-	Weak
Weak	H_3PO_4	$H_2PO_4^-$	Weak
Weak	HF	F^-	Weak
Weak	CH_3COOH	CH_3COO^-	Weak
Weak	H_2CO_3	HCO_3^-	Weak
Weak	H_2S	HS^-	Weak
Weak	HSO_3^-	SO_3^{2-}	Weak
Weak	$H_2PO_4^-$	HPO_4^{2-}	Weak
Weak	HCN	CN^-	Weak
Weak	NH_4^+	NH_3	Weak
Weak	HCO_3^-	CO_3^{2-}	Weak
Weak	HPO_4^{2-}	PO_4^{3-}	Weak
Weak	H_2O	OH^-	Weak
Negligible	HS^-	S^{2-}	Strong
Negligible	OH^-	O^{2-}	Strong

EXAMPLE 15.13 **DETERMINING WHETHER AN ANION IS BASIC OR pH-NEUTRAL**

Classify each anion as a weak base or pH-neutral:

(a) NO_3^- **(b)** NO_2^- **(c)** CH_3COO^-

SOLUTION

(a) From Table 15.3, we can see that NO_3^- is the conjugate base of a strong acid (HNO_3) and and is therefore pH-neutral.

(b) From Table 15.5 (or from its absence in Table 15.3), we know that NO_2^- is the conjugate base of a weak acid (HNO_2) and is therefore a weak base.

(c) From Table 15.5 (or from its absence in Table 15.3), we know that CH_3COO^- is the conjugate base of a weak acid (CH_3COOH) and and is therefore a weak base.

FOR PRACTICE 15.13

Classify each anion as a weak base or pH-neutral:

(a) $HCOO^-$ **(b)** ClO_4^-

We can determine the pH of a solution containing an anion that acts as a weak base in a manner similar to how we determine the pH of any weak base solution. However, we need to know K_b for the anion acting as a base, which we can readily determine from K_a of the corresponding acid. Recall from Section 15.4 the expression for K_a for a generic acid HA:

$$HA(aq) + H_2O(l) \rightleftharpoons H_3O^+(aq) + A^-(aq)$$

$$K_a = \frac{[H_3O^+][A^-]}{[HA]}$$

Similarly, the expression for K_b for the conjugate base (A^-) is:

$$A^-(aq) + H_2O(l) \rightleftharpoons OH^-(aq) + HA(aq)$$

$$K_b = \frac{[OH^-][HA]}{[A^-]}$$

If we multiply the expressions for K_a and K_b we get K_w:

$$K_a \times K_b = \frac{[H_3O^+]\cancel{[A^-]}}{\cancel{[HA]}}\frac{[OH^-]\cancel{[HA]}}{\cancel{[A^-]}} = [H_3O^+][OH^-] = K_w$$

Or simply,

$$K_a \times K_b = K_w$$

The product of K_a for an acid and K_b for its conjugate base is K_w (1.0×10^{-14} at 25 °C). Consequently, we can find K_b for an anion acting as a base from the value of K_a for the corresponding acid. For example, for acetic acid (CH_3COOH), $K_a = 1.8 \times 10^{-5}$. We can calculate K_b for the conjugate base (CH_3COO^-) by substituting into the equation:

$$K_a \times K_b = K_w$$

$$K_b = \frac{K_w}{K_a} = \frac{1.0 \times 10^{-14}}{1.8 \times 10^{-5}} = 5.6 \times 10^{-10}$$

Knowing K_b, we can find the pH of a solution containing an anion acting as a base, as demonstrated in Example 15.14.

EXAMPLE 15.14 DETERMINING THE pH OF A SOLUTION CONTAINING AN ANION ACTING AS A BASE

Find the pH of a 0.100 mol L^{-1} HCOONa solution. The salt completely dissociates into $Na^+(aq)$ and $HCOO^-(aq)$ and the Na^+ ion has no acid or base properties.

SOLUTION

Since the Na^+ ion does not have any acidic or basic properties, you can ignore it. Write the balanced equation for the ionization of water by the basic anion and use it as a guide to prepare an ICE table showing the given concentration of the weak base as its initial concentration.

$$HCOO^-(aq) + H_2O(l) \rightleftharpoons HCOOH(aq) + OH^-(aq)$$

	[HCOO⁻]	[HCOOH]	[OH⁻]
Initial	0.100	0	≈0
Change			
Equil			

Represent the change in the concentration of OH^- with the variable x. Define the changes in the concentrations of the other reactants and products in terms of x.

$$HCOO^-(aq) + H_2O(l) \rightleftharpoons HCOOH(aq) + OH^-(aq)$$

	[HCOO⁻]	[HCOOH]	[OH⁻]
Initial	0.100	0	≈0
Change	$-x$	$+x$	$+x$
Equil			

Sum each column to determine the equilibrium concentrations in terms of the initial concentrations and the variable x.

$$HCOO^-(aq) + H_2O(l) \rightleftharpoons HCOOH(aq) + OH^-(aq)$$

	[HCOO⁻]	[HCOOH]	[OH⁻]
Initial	0.100	0	≈0
Change	$-x$	$+x$	$+x$
Equil	$0.100 - x$	x	x

Find K_b from K_a (for the conjugate acid).

$$K_a \times K_b = K_w$$

$$K_b = \frac{K_w}{K_a} = \frac{1.0 \times 10^{-14}}{1.8 \times 10^{-4}} = 5.6 \times 10^{-11}$$

Substitute the expressions for the equilibrium concentrations (from step 3) into the expression for K_b. In many cases, you can make the approximation that x *is small* (as discussed in Chapter 14).

$$K_b = \frac{[HCOOH][OH^-]}{[HCOO^-]} = \frac{x^2}{0.100 - \cancel{x}}$$

Substitute the value of K_b into the K_b expression and solve for x.

$$5.6 \times 10^{-11} = \frac{x^2}{0.100}$$

$$x = 2.4 \times 10^{-6}$$

Confirm that the x *is small* approximation is valid by calculating the ratio of x to the number it was subtracted from in the approximation. The ratio should be less than 0.05 (or 5%).

$$\frac{2.4 \times 10^{-6}}{0.100} \times 100\% = 0.0024\%$$

Therefore the approximation is valid.

Determine the OH^- concentration from the calculated value of x.

$$[OH^-] = 2.4 \times 10^{-6} \text{ mol L}^{-1}$$

Use the expression for K_w to find $[H_3O^+]$.

$$[H_3O^+][OH^-] = K_w = 1.0 \times 10^{-14}$$

$$[H_3O^+](2.4 \times 10^{-6}) = 1.0 \times 10^{-14}$$

$$[H_3O^+] = 4.2 \times 10^{-9} \text{ mol L}^{-1}$$

Substitute $[H_3O^+]$ into the pH equation to find pH.

$$pH = -\log[H_3O^+] = -\log(4.2 \times 10^{-9}) = 8.38$$

FOR PRACTICE 15.14

Find the pH of a 0.250 mol L^{-1} CH_3COONa solution.

Cations as Weak Acids

In contrast to anions, which in some cases act as weak bases, cations can in some cases act as *weak acids*. We can generally divide cations into three categories: cations that are the counterions of strong bases; cations that are the conjugate acids of *weak* bases; and cations that are small, highly charged metals. We examine each individually.

Cations That Are the Counterions of Strong Bases Strong bases such as NaOH or KOH generally contain hydroxide ions and a counterion. In solution, a strong base completely dissociates to form $OH^-(aq)$ and the solvated (in solution) counterion. Although these counterions interact with water molecules via ion–dipole forces, they do not ionize water and they do not contribute to the acidity or basicity of the solution. In general, *cations that are the counterions of strong bases are themselves pH-neutral* (they form solutions that are neither acidic nor basic). For example, Na^+ and K^+ are the counterions of the strong bases NaOH and KOH, respectively, and are therefore themselves pH-neutral.

Cations That Are the Conjugate Acids of Weak Bases A cation can be formed from any non-ionic weak base by adding a proton (H^+) to its formula. The cation will be the conjugate acid of the base. Consider the following cations and their corresponding weak bases.

This cation	is the conjugate acid of	this weak base
NH_4^+		NH_3
$C_2H_5NH_3^+$		$C_2H_5NH_2$
$CH_3NH_3^+$		CH_3NH_2

Any of these cations, with the general formula BH^+, will act as a weak acid according to the equation:

$$BH^+(aq) + H_2O(aq) \rightleftharpoons H_3O^+(aq) + B(aq)$$

In general, *a cation that is the conjugate acid of a weak base is a weak acid.*

The pH of a solution containing the conjugate acid of a weak base can be calculated just like that of any other weakly acidic solution. However, the value of K_a for the acid must be derived from K_b using the previously derived relationship: $K_a \times K_b = K_w$.

Cations That Are Small, Highly Charged Metals *Small, highly charged metal cations such as Al^{3+} and Fe^{3+} form weakly acidic solutions.* For example, when Al^{3+} is dissolved in water, it becomes hydrated according to the equation:

$$Al^{3+}(aq) + 6\,H_2O(l) \longrightarrow Al(H_2O)_6{}^{3+}(aq)$$

The hydrated form of the ion then acts as a Brønsted–Lowry acid:

$$Al(H_2O)_6{}^{3+}(aq) + H_2O(aq) \rightleftharpoons Al(H_2O)_5(OH)^{2+}(aq) + H_3O^+(aq)$$

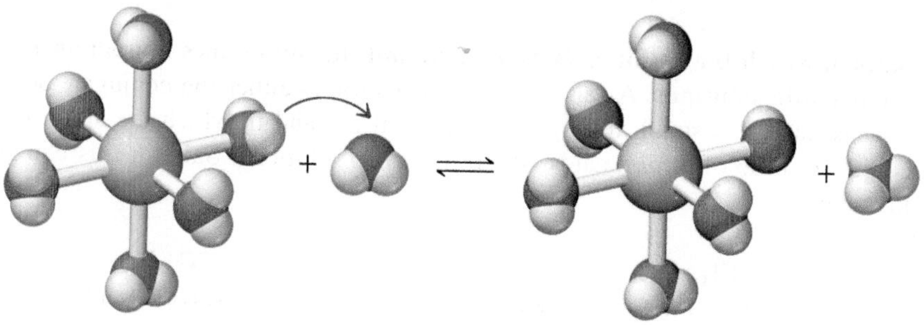

Neither the alkali metal cations nor the alkaline earth metal cations ionize water in this way, but the cations of many other metals do. The smaller and more highly charged the cation, the more acidic its behaviour.

EXAMPLE 15.15 DETERMINING WHETHER A CATION IS ACIDIC OR pH-NEUTRAL

Classify each cation as a weak acid or pH-neutral:

(a) $C_5H_5NH^+$ **(b)** Cs^+ **(c)** Cr^{3+}

SOLUTION

(a) The $C_5H_5NH^+$ cation is the conjugate acid of a weak base and is therefore a weak acid.

(b) Since all alkali metal ions are completely soluble, Cs^+ does not react with water and is therefore pH-neutral (neither acidic nor basic).

(c) The Cr^{3+} cation is a small, highly charged metal cation and is therefore a weak acid.

FOR PRACTICE 15.15

Classify each cation as a weak acid or pH-neutral:

(a) Li^+ **(b)** $CH_3NH_3^+$ **(c)** Fe^{3+}

Classifying Salt Solutions as Acidic, Basic, or Neutral

Since salts contain both a cation and an anion, they can form acidic, basic, or neutral solutions when dissolved in water. The pH of the solution depends on the specific cation and anion involved. We examine the four possibilities individually.

1. **Salts in which neither the cation nor the anion acts as an acid or a base form pH-neutral solutions.** A salt in which the cation is the counterion of a strong base and in which the anion is the conjugate base of strong acid will form *neutral* solutions. Some salts in this category include:

NaCl	$Ca(NO_3)_2$	KBr
sodium chloride	calcium nitrate	potassium bromide

Cations are pH-neutral. Anions are conjugate bases of strong acids.

2. **Salts in which the cation does not act as an acid and the anion acts as a base form basic solutions.** A salt in which the cation is an alkali metal and in which the anion is the conjugate base of *weak* acid will form *basic* solutions. Salts in this category include:

NaF	$KOOCCH_3$	KNO_2
sodium fluoride	potassium acetate	potassium nitrate

Cations are pH-neutral. Anions are conjugate bases of weak acids.

3. **Salts in which the cation acts as an acid and the anion does not act as a base form acidic solutions.** A salt in which the cation is either the conjugate acid of a weak base or a small, highly charged metal ion and in which the anion is the conjugate base of *strong* acid will form *acidic* solutions. Salts in this category include:

$FeCl_3$	$Al(NO_3)_3$	NH_4Br
iron(III) chloride	aluminum nitrate	ammonium bromide

Cations are conjugate acids of *weak* bases or small, highly charged metal ions. Anions are conjugate bases of strong acids.

4. Salts in which the cation acts as an acid and the anion acts as a base form solutions in which the pH depends on the relative strengths of the acid and the base. A salt in which the cation is either the conjugate acid of a weak base or a small, highly charged metal ion and in which the anion is the conjugate base of a *weak* acid will form a solution in which the pH depends on the relative strengths of the acid and base. Salts in this category include:

FeF_3	$Al(CH_3COO)_3$	NH_4NO_2
iron(III) fluoride	aluminum acetate	ammonium nitrate

Cations are conjugate acids of *weak* bases or small, highly charged metal ions.

Anions are conjugate bases of *weak* acids.

We can determine the overall pH of a solution containing one of these salts by comparing the K_a of the acid to the K_b of the base—the ion with the higher value of K dominates and determines whether the solution will be acidic or basic, as shown in part (e) of Example 15.16. All these possibilities are summarized in Table 15.9.

TABLE 15.9 pH of Salt Solutions

		ANION	
		Conjugate base of strong acid	**Conjugate base of weak acid**
CATION	**Conjugate acid of weak base**	*Acidic*	*Depends on relative strengths*
	Small, highly charged metal ion	*Acidic*	*Depends on relative strengths*
	Counterion of strong base	*Neutral*	*Basic*

EXAMPLE 15.16 DETERMINING THE OVERALL ACIDITY OR BASICITY OF SALT SOLUTIONS

Determine whether the solution formed by each salt is acidic, basic, or neutral:

(a) KCl **(c)** $CH_3NH_3NO_3$ **(e)** NH_4F

(b) $AlBr_3$ **(d)** $NaHCOO$ (or $HCOONa$)

SOLUTION

(a) The K^+ cation does not react with water and therefore is pH-neutral. The Cl^- anion is the conjugate base of a strong acid (HCl) and is pH-neutral as well. The KCl solution will therefore be pH-neutral (neither acidic nor basic).

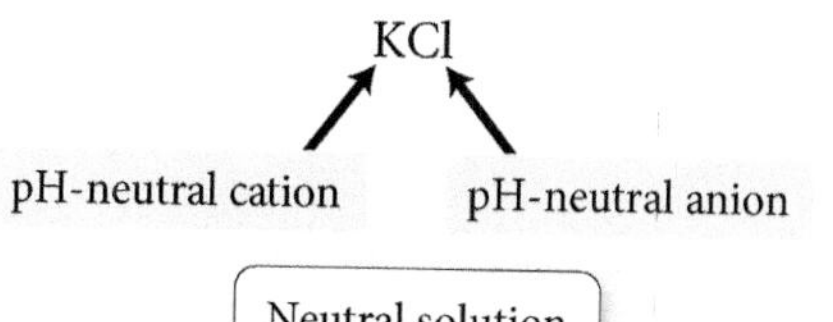

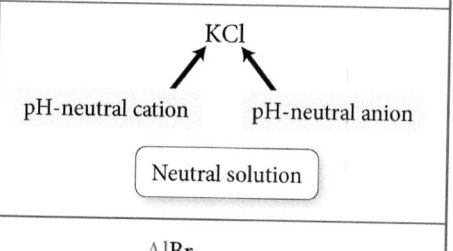

(b) The Al^{3+} cation is a small, highly charged metal ion (that is not an alkali metal or an alkaline earth metal) and is a weak acid. The Br^- anion is the conjugate base of a strong acid (HBr) and is pH-neutral. The $AlBr_3$ solution will therefore be acidic.

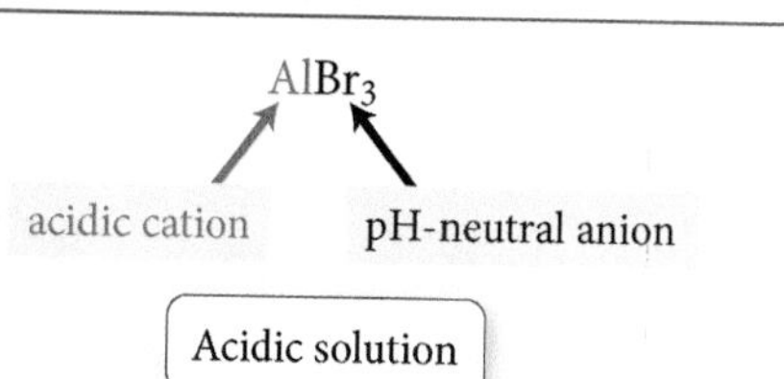

(continued)

EXAMPLE 15.16 (CONTINUED)

(c) The $CH_3NH_3^+$ ion is the conjugate acid of a weak base (CH_3NH_2) and is acidic. The NO_3^- anion is the conjugate base of a strong acid (HNO_3) and is pH-neutral. The $CH_3NH_3NO_3$ solution will therefore be acidic.	$CH_3NH_3NO_3$ acidic cation — pH-neutral anion Acidic solution
(d) The Na^+ cation does not react with water and is pH-neutral. The $HCOO^-$ anion is the conjugate base of a weak acid and is basic. The NaHCOO solution will therefore be basic.	NaHCOO pH-neutral cation — basic anion Basic solution
(e) The NH_4^+ ion is the conjugate acid of a weak base (NH_3) and is acidic. The F^- ion is the conjugate base of a weak acid and is basic. To determine the overall acidity or basicity of the solution, compare the values of K_a for the acidic cation and K_b for the basic anion. Obtain each value of K from the conjugate by using $K_a \times K_b = K_w$.	NH_4F acidic cation — basic anion $K_a(NH_4^+) = \dfrac{K_w}{K_b(NH_3)} = \dfrac{1.0 \times 10^{-14}}{1.76 \times 10^{-5}} = 5.68 \times 10^{-10}$ $K_b(F^-) = \dfrac{K_w}{K_a(HF)} = \dfrac{1.0 \times 10^{-14}}{6.3 \times 10^{-4}} = 1.6 \times 10^{-11}$
Since K_a is greater than K_b, the solution is acidic.	$K_a > K_b$ Acidic solution

FOR PRACTICE 15.16

Determine whether the solutions formed by each salt will be acidic, basic, or neutral:

(a) $NaHCO_3$ **(b)** $CH_3CH_2NH_3Cl$ **(c)** KNO_3 **(d)** $Fe(NO_3)_3$

15.9 Polyprotic Acids

In Section 15.4, we learned that some acids, called polyprotic acids, contain two or more ionizable protons. Recall that sulfurous acid (H_2SO_3) is a diprotic acid containing two ionizable protons and phosphoric acid (H_3PO_4) is a triprotic acid containing three ionizable protons. Typically, a **polyprotic acid** ionizes in successive steps, each with its own K_a. For example, sulfurous acid ionizes in two steps:

$$H_2SO_3(aq) \rightleftharpoons H^+(aq) + HSO_3^-(aq) \qquad K_{a_1} = 1.6 \times 10^{-2}$$

$$HSO_3^-(aq) \rightleftharpoons H^+(aq) + SO_3^{2-}(aq) \qquad K_{a_2} = 6.4 \times 10^{-8}$$

where K_{a_1} is the acid ionization constant for the first step and K_{a_2} is the acid ionization constant for the second step. Notice that K_{a_2} is smaller than K_{a_1}. This is true for all polyprotic acids and makes physical sense because the first proton separates from a neutral molecule while the second must separate from an anion. The negatively charged anion holds the positively charged proton more tightly, making the proton more difficult to remove and resulting in a smaller value of K_a. Table 15.10 lists some common polyprotic acids and their acid ionization constants. Notice that in all cases, the values of K_a for each step become successively smaller. The value of K_{a_1} for sulfuric acid is listed as strong because sulfuric acid is strong in the first step and weak in the second.

TABLE 15.10 Common Polyprotic Acids and Ionization Constants

Name (Formula)	Structure	Space-Filling Model	K_{a_1}	K_{a_2}	K_{a_3}
Sulfuric Acid (H_2SO_4)	O=S(=O)(—OH)—OH		Strong	1.2×10^{-2}	
Oxalic Acid ($H_2C_2O_4$)	HO—C(=O)—C(=O)—OH		6.0×10^{-2}	6.1×10^{-5}	
Sulfurous Acid (H_2SO_3)	HO—S(=O)—OH		1.6×10^{-2}	6.4×10^{-8}	
Phosphoric Acid (H_3PO_4)	HO—P(=O)(—OH)—OH		7.5×10^{-3}	6.2×10^{-8}	4.2×10^{-13}
Citric Acid ($H_3C_6H_5O_7$)	HO—C(=O)—CH$_2$—C(OH)(C(=O)OH)—CH$_2$—C(=O)—OH		7.4×10^{-4}	1.7×10^{-5}	4.0×10^{-7}
Ascorbic Acid ($H_2C_6H_6O_6$)	HO—CH$_2$—CH(OH)—HC (ring: HC—O—C(=O)—C(OH)=C(OH)—)		8.0×10^{-5}	1.6×10^{-12}	
Carbonic Acid (H_2CO_3)	HO—C(=O)—OH		4.3×10^{-7}	5.6×10^{-11}	

Finding the pH of Polyprotic Acid Solutions

Finding the pH of a polyprotic acid solution is less difficult than we might first imagine because, for most polyprotic acids, K_{a_1} is much larger than K_{a_2} (or K_{a_3} for triprotic acids). Therefore, the amount of H_3O^+ formed by the first ionization step is much larger than that formed by the second or third ionization step. In addition, the formation of H_3O^+ by the first step inhibits the formation of additional H_3O^+ by the second step (because of Le Châtelier's principle). Consequently, we treat most polyprotic acid solutions as if the first step were the only one that contributes to the H_3O^+ concentration, as shown in Example 15.17. A major exception is a dilute solution of sulfuric acid, which we examine in Example 15.18.

EXAMPLE 15.17 FINDING THE pH OF A POLYPROTIC ACID SOLUTION

Find the pH of a 0.100 mol L^{-1} ascorbic acid ($H_2C_6H_6O_6$) solution.

SOLUTION

To find the pH, you must find the equilibrium concentration of H_3O^+. Treat the problem as a weak acid pH problem with a single ionizable proton. The second proton contributes a negligible amount to the concentration of H_3O^+ and can be ignored. Follow the procedure in Example 15.6, shown in condensed form here. Use K_{a_1} for ascorbic acid from Table 15.10.

$$H_2C_6H_6O_6(aq) + H_2O(l) \rightleftharpoons H_3O^+(aq) + HC_6H_6O_6^-(aq)$$

	$[H_2C_6H_6O_6]$	$[H_3O^+]$	$[HC_6H_6O_6^-]$
Initial	0.100	≈0	0
Change	$-x$	$+x$	$+x$
Equil	$0.100 - x$	x	x

$$K_{a_1} = \frac{[H_3O^+][HC_6H_6O_6^-]}{[H_2C_6H_6O_6]}$$

$$= \frac{x^2}{0.100 - \cancel{x}} \quad (x \text{ is small})$$

$$8.0 \times 10^{-5} = \frac{x^2}{0.100}$$

$$x = 2.8 \times 10^{-3}$$

Confirm that the *x is small* approximation is valid by calculating the ratio of x to the number it was subtracted from in the approximation. The ratio should be less than 0.05 (or 5%).

$$\frac{2.8 \times 10^{-3}}{0.100} \times 100\% = 2.8\%$$

The approximation is valid. Therefore,

Calculate the pH from H_3O^+ concentration.

$$[H_3O^+] = 2.8 \times 10^{-3} \text{ mol L}^{-1}.$$

$$pH = -\log(2.8 \times 10^{-3}) = 2.55$$

FOR PRACTICE 15.17

Find the pH of a 0.050 mol L^{-1} H_2CO_3 solution.

EXAMPLE 15.18 DILUTE H_2SO_4 SOLUTIONS

Find the pH of a 0.0100 mol L^{-1} sulfuric acid (H_2SO_4) solution.

SOLUTION

Sulfuric acid is strong in its first ionization step and weak in its second. Begin by writing the equations for the two steps. As the concentration of an H_2SO_4 solution becomes smaller, the second ionization step becomes more significant because the percent ionization increases (as discussed in Section 15.6). Therefore, for a concentration of 0.0100 mol L^{-1}, you can't neglect the H_3O^+ contribution from the second step, as you can for other polyprotic acids. You must calculate the H_3O^+ contributions from both steps.

$$H_2SO_4(aq) + H_2O(l) \longrightarrow H_3O^+(aq) + HSO_4^-(aq) \quad \text{Strong}$$

$$HSO_4^-(aq) + H_2O(l) \rightleftharpoons H_3O^+(aq) + SO_4^{2-}(aq) \quad K_{a_2} = 0.012$$

The $[H_3O^+]$ that results from the first ionization step is 0.0100 mol L^{-1} (because the first step is strong). To determine the $[H_3O^+]$ formed by the second step, prepare an ICE table for the second step in which the initial concentration of H_3O^+ is 0.0100 mol L^{-1}. The initial concentration of HSO_4^- must also be 0.0100 mol L^{-1} (due to the stoichiometry of the ionization reaction).	<table><tr><th></th><th>[HSO₄⁻]</th><th>[H₃O⁺]</th><th>[SO₄²⁻]</th></tr><tr><td>Initial</td><td>0.0100</td><td>≈0.0100</td><td>0</td></tr><tr><td>Change</td><td>−x</td><td>+x</td><td>+x</td></tr><tr><td>Equil</td><td>0.0100 − x</td><td>0.0100 + x</td><td>x</td></tr></table>
Substitute the expressions for the equilibrium concentrations (from the table above) into the expression for K_{a_2}. In this case, you cannot make the *x is small* approximation because the equilibrium constant (0.012) *is not small* relative to the initial concentration (0.0100).	$K_{a_2} = \frac{[H_3O^+][SO_4^{2-}]}{[HSO_4^-]} = \frac{(0.0100 + x)x}{0.0100 - x}$
Substitute the value of K_{a_2} and multiply out the expression to arrive at the standard quadratic form.	$0.012 = \frac{0.0100x + x^2}{0.0100 - x}$ $0.012(0.0100 - x) = 0.0100x + x^2$ $0.00012 - 0.012x = 0.0100x + x^2$ $x^2 + 0.022x - 0.00012 = 0$
Solve the quadratic equation using the quadratic formula.	$x = \frac{-b \pm \sqrt{b^2 - 4ac}}{2a} = \frac{-(0.022) \pm \sqrt{(0.022)^2 - 4(1)(-0.00012)}}{2(1)} = \frac{-0.022 \pm 0.031}{2}$ $x = -0.027$ or $x = 0.0045$ Since x represents a concentration, and since concentrations cannot be negative, we reject the negative root. $x = 0.00\underline{4}5$
Determine the H_3O^+ concentration from the calculated value of x and calculate the pH. Notice that the second step produces almost half as much H_3O^+ as the first step—an amount that must not be neglected. This will always be the case with dilute H_2SO_4 solutions.	$[H_3O^+] = 0.0100 + x = 0.0100 + 0.0045 = 0.01\underline{4}5$ mol L^{-1} $pH = -\log[H_3O^+] = -\log(0.01\underline{4}5) = 1.84$

FOR PRACTICE 15.18

Find the pH and $[SO_4^{2-}]$ of a 0.0075 mol L^{-1} sulfuric acid solution.

Finding the Concentration of the Anions for a Weak Diprotic Acid Solution

In some cases, we may want to know the concentrations of the anions formed by a polyprotic acid. Consider the following generic polyprotic acid H_2X and its ionization steps:

$$H_2X(aq) + H_2O(l) \rightleftharpoons H_3O^+(aq) + HX^-(aq) \qquad K_{a_1}$$

$$HX^-(aq) + H_2O(l) \rightleftharpoons H_3O^+(aq) + X^{2-}(aq) \qquad K_{a_2}$$

In Examples 15.17 and 15.18, we discovered how to find the concentration of H_3O^+ for such a solution, which is equal to the concentration of HX^-. What if instead we needed to find the concentration of X^{2-}? To find the concentration of X^{2-}, we use the concentration of HX^- and H_3O^+ (from the first ionization step) as the initial concentrations for the second ionization step. We then solve a second equilibrium problem using the second ionization equation and K_{a_2}, as shown in Example 15.19.

EXAMPLE 15.19 **FINDING THE CONCENTRATION OF THE ANIONS FOR A WEAK DIPROTIC ACID SOLUTION**

Find the $[C_6H_6O_6^{2-}]$ of the 0.100 mol L^{-1} ascorbic acid ($H_2C_6H_6O_6$) solution in Example 15.17.

SOLUTION

To find the $[C_6H_6O_6^{2-}]$, use the concentrations of $[HC_6H_6O_6^-]$ and H_3O^+ produced by the first ionization step (as calculated in Example 15.17) as the initial concentrations for the second step. Because of the 1:1 stoichiometry, $[HC_6H_6O_6^-] = [H_3O^+]$. Then solve an equilibrium problem for the second step similar to that of Example 15.6, shown in condensed form here. Use K_{a_2} for ascorbic acid from Table 15.10.

$$HC_6H_6O_6^-(aq) + H_2O(l) \rightleftharpoons H_3O^+(aq) + C_6H_6O_6^{2-}(aq)$$

	$[HC_6H_6O_6^-]$	$[H_3O^+]$	$[C_6H_6O_6^{2-}]$
Initial	2.8×10^{-3}	2.8×10^{-3}	0
Change	$-x$	$+x$	$+x$
Equil	$2.8 \times 10^{-3} - x$	$2.8 \times 10^{-3} + x$	x

$$K_{a_2} = \frac{[H_3O^+][C_6H_6O_6^{2-}]}{[HC_6H_6O_6^-]}$$

$$= \frac{(2.8 \times 10^{-3} + \cancel{x})x}{2.8 \times 10^{-3} - \cancel{x}} \quad (x \text{ is small})$$

$$= \frac{(\cancel{2.8 \times 10^{-3}})x}{\cancel{2.8 \times 10^{-3}}}$$

$$x = K_{a_2} = 1.6 \times 10^{-12}$$

Since x is much smaller than 2.8×10^{-3}, the *x is small* approximation is valid. Therefore,

$$[C_6H_6O_6^{2-}] = 1.6 \times 10^{-12} \text{ mol L}^{-1}.$$

FOR PRACTICE 15.19

Find the $[CO_3^{2-}]$ of the 0.050 mol L^{-1} carbonic acid (H_2CO_3) solution in For Practice 15.17.

Notice from the results of Example 15.19 that the concentration of X^{2-} for a weak diprotic acid H_2X is equal to K_{a_2}. This general result applies to all diprotic acids in which the *x is small* approximation is valid. Notice also that the concentration of H_3O^+ produced by the second ionization step of a diprotic acid is very small compared to the concentration produced by the first step, as shown in Figure 15.13 ▼.

$$H_2C_6H_6O_6(aq) + H_2O(l) \rightleftharpoons H_3O^+(aq) + HC_6H_6O_6^-(aq)$$

$$[H_3O^+] = 2.8 \times 10^{-3} \text{ mol L}^{-1}$$

$$HC_6H_6O_6^-(aq) + H_2O(l) \rightleftharpoons H_3O^+(aq) + C_6H_6O_6^{2-}(aq)$$

$$[H_3O^+] = 1.6 \times 10^{-12} \text{ mol L}^{-1}$$

$$\text{Total } [H_3O^+] = 2.8 \times 10^{-3} \text{ mol L}^{-1} + 1.6 \times 10^{-12} \text{ mol L}^{-1}$$

$$= 2.8 \times 10^{-3} \text{ mol L}^{-1}$$

0.100 mol L^{-1} $H_2C_6H_6O_6$

▲ **FIGURE 15.13 Dissociation of a Polyprotic Acid** A 0.100 mol L^{-1} $H_2C_6H_6O_6$ solution contains an H_3O^+ concentration of 2.8×10^{-3} mol L^{-1} from the first step. The amount of H_3O^+ contributed by the second step is only 1.6×10^{-12} mol L^{-1}, which is insignificant compared to the amount produced by the first step.

15.10 Lewis Acids and Bases

We began our definitions of acids and bases with the Arrhenius model. We then saw how the Brønsted–Lowry model, by introducing the concept of a proton donor and proton acceptor, expanded the range of substances that we consider acids and bases. We now introduce a third model which further broadens the range of substances that we can consider acids. This third model is called the *Lewis model*, after G. N. Lewis, the American chemist who devised the electron-dot representation of chemical bonding (see Section 9.1). While the Brønsted–Lowry model focuses on the transfer of a proton, the Lewis model focuses on the transfer of an electron pair. Consider the simple acid–base reaction between the H^+ ion and NH_3, shown here with Lewis structures:

$$H^+ + :NH_3 \longrightarrow [H:NH_3]^+$$

Brønsted–Lowry model focuses on the proton

Lewis model focuses on the electron pair

According to the Brønsted–Lowry model, the ammonia accepts a proton, thus acting as a base. According to the Lewis model, the ammonia acts as a base by *donating an electron pair*. The general definitions of acids and bases according to the Lewis model focus on the electron pair:

Lewis acid: electron pair acceptor

Lewis base: electron pair donor

Under the Lewis definition, H^+ in the above reaction is acting as an acid because it is accepting an electron pair from NH_3. NH_3 is acting as a Lewis base because it is donating an electron pair to H^+.

Although the Lewis model does not significantly expand what can be considered a base—because all proton acceptors must have an electron pair to bind the proton—it does significantly expand what can be considered an acid. Under the Lewis model, a substance need not even contain hydrogen to be an acid. For example, consider the following gas-phase reaction between boron trifluoride and ammonia:

$$\underset{\text{Lewis acid}}{BF_3} + \underset{\text{Lewis base}}{:NH_3} \longrightarrow \underset{\text{adduct}}{F_3B:NH_3}$$

Boron trifluoride has an empty orbital that can accept the electron pair from ammonia and form the product (the product of a Lewis acid–base reaction is sometimes called an *adduct*). The above reaction demonstrates an important property of Lewis acids:

A Lewis acid has an empty orbital (or can rearrange electrons to create an empty orbital) that can accept an electron pair.

Consequently, the Lewis definition subsumes a whole new class of acids. Next we examine a few examples.

Molecules That Act as Lewis Acids

Since molecules with incomplete octets have empty orbitals, they can serve as Lewis acids. For example, both $AlCl_3$ and BCl_3 have incomplete octets:

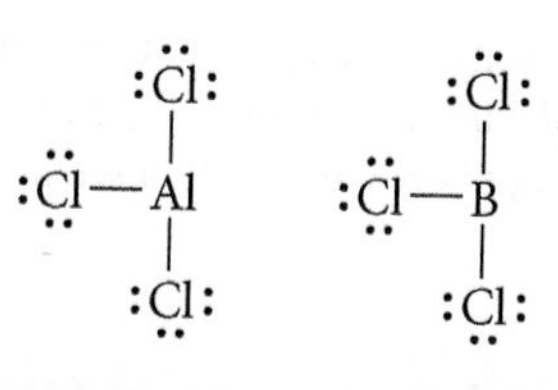

:C̈l:
:C̈l—Al
:C̈l:

:C̈l:
:C̈l—B
:C̈l:

These both act as Lewis acids, as shown in the following reactions:

$$AlCl_3 + :NH_3 \longrightarrow Cl_3Al:NH_3$$

$$BCl_3 + H_3C\text{–}CH_2\text{–}\ddot{O}\text{–}CH_2\text{–}CH_3 \longrightarrow H_3C\text{–}CH_2\text{–}O(BCl_3)\text{–}CH_2\text{–}CH_3$$

Some molecules that may not initially contain empty orbitals can rearrange their electrons to act as Lewis acids. Consider the reaction between carbon dioxide and water:

The curly arrows represent the movement of an electron pair.

$$H_2\ddot{O} + O{=}C{=}O \longrightarrow H\text{–}\overset{+}{O}(H)\text{–}C(O^-){=}O \longrightarrow H\text{–}O\text{–}C(OH){=}O$$

Water — Lewis base; Carbon dioxide — Lewis acid; Carbonic acid

The electrons in the double bond on carbon move to the terminal oxygen atom, allowing carbon dioxide to act as a Lewis acid by accepting an electron pair from water. The molecule then undergoes a rearrangement in which the hydrogen atom shown in red bonds with the terminal oxygen atom instead of the internal one.

Cations That Act as Lewis Acids

Some cations, since they are positively charged and have lost some electrons, have empty orbitals that allow them to also act as Lewis acids. Consider the hydration process of the Al^{3+} ion discussed in Section 15.8.

$$Al^{3+}(aq) + 6\,[H\text{–}\ddot{O}\text{–}H](l) \longrightarrow Al[H\text{–}\ddot{O}\text{–}H]_6^{\;3+}(aq)$$

Lewis acid; Lewis base

The aluminum ion acts as a Lewis acid, accepting lone pairs from six water molecules to form the hydrated ion. Many other small, highly charged metal ions also act as Lewis acids in this fashion.

15.11 Strengths of Acids and Bases and Molecular Structure

We have not yet explored why some hydrogen-containing molecules act as acids while others do not, or why some acids and bases are strong and others are weak. For example, why is H_2S acidic while CH_4 is not? Or why is HF a weak acid while HCl is a strong acid, and why is methylamine a stronger base than ammonia? We will divide our discussion about acid strengths into two categories: binary acids (those containing hydrogen and only one other element) and oxyacids (those containing hydrogen bonded to an oxygen atom that is bonded to another element). We will also discuss molecular factors that make one base stronger than another.

Binary Acids

A binary acid is a compound consisting of hydrogen and some other generic element (which we will call Y). Binary acids include diatomic molecules such as HF, and polyatomic molecules such as H_2O. The acid dissociation reaction of HY is:

$$H{-}Y \rightleftharpoons H^+ + Y^-$$

The factors affecting the acidity of HY include the electron affinity of Y and the strength of the H—Y bond.

Electron Affinity of Y When H—Y dissociates to give H^+, the electrons in the H—Y bond remain with the Y atom. This leaves Y with a negative charge. The stability of Y^-, the conjugate base, is related to the electron affinity of Y. We can explain some of the acid–base behaviour of binary acids on the basis of electron affinities.

For example, when going across the second period from carbon to fluorine, binary acid strength increases. The electron affinities of CH_3, NH_2, OH, and F also increase in that order (the same trend that is observed for C, N, O, and F). The higher the electron affinity, the more stable the conjugate base. This gives a stronger acid.

Increasing electron affinity of Y →

$$H{-}CH_3 < H{-}NH_2 < H{-}OH < H{-}F$$

Increasing acidity →

We can also explain why metal hydrides are not Brønsted–Lowry acids. For example, lithium hydride, LiH, does not dissociate to give H^+ and Li^-. Rather, it dissociates to give H^- and Li^+. The electron affinity of hydrogen is 73 kJ mol^{-1}, whereas the electron affinity of lithium is 60 kJ mol^{-1} (see Figure 8.15 in Chapter 8). It is energetically more favourable for the electron pair to remain with hydrogen than with lithium. In fact, the electron affinities of metals are all less than that of hydrogen.

Bond Strength The strength of the H—Y bond also affects the strength of the corresponding acid. As you might expect, the stronger the bond, the weaker the acid because the more tightly the hydrogen atom is held, the less likely it is to come off. We can see the effect of bond strength by comparing the bond strengths and acidities of the hydrogen halides.

Acid	Bond Energy (kJ mol^{-1})	Type of Acid
H—F	570	weak
H—Cl	432	strong
H—Br	366	strong
H—I	298	strong

HCl, HBr, and HI with their weaker bonds are strong acids, while H—F, with its stronger bond, is a weak acid. This is the case despite the higher electron affinity of F.

The Combined Effect of Electron Affinity and Bond Strength We can see the combined effect of electron affinity and bond strength by examining the trends in acidity of the binary

Acidity of binary acid increases because electron affinity of Y increases →

H—Y	H—CH_3	H—NH_2	H—OH	H—F
Bond Energy (kJ mol^{-1})	438	450	498	570
EA(Y) (kJ mol^{-1})	9	71	178	328
K_a	1×10^{-49}	1×10^{-34}	1.8×10^{-16}	6.3×10^{-4}
		H—PH_2	H—SH	H—Cl
		351	381	432
		112	222	349
		1×10^{-27}	8.9×10^{-9}	1×10^{7}
			H—SeH	H—Br
			335	366
			213	325
			1.3×10^{-4}	1×10^{9}
			H—TeH	H—I
			277	298
			204	295
			2.3×10^{-3}	1×10^{10}

↓ Acidity of binary acid increases because H—Y bond energy decreases

▶ **FIGURE 15.14 Acidity Trends in the Periodic Table** From left to right, the binary acids become more acidic. From top to bottom, the binary acids also become more acidic as can be seen by the K_a values. The electron affinities in the figure are for the Y group, not the central atom.

acids (Figure 15.14 ▲). The binary acids become more acidic going from left to right on the periodic table because the electron affinity of Y increases—and the bond energy remains roughly constant. The binary acids also become more acidic going from the top of the periodic table to the bottom because the H—Y bond gets significantly weaker, while the electron affinities of Y remain relatively constant.

Oxyacids

Oxyacids are sometimes called oxoacids.

Oxyacids contain a hydrogen atom bonded to an oxygen atom. The oxygen atom is in turn bonded to another atom (which we will call Y):

$$\text{H—O—Y} \lessgtr$$

Y may or may not be bonded to yet other atoms. The factors affecting the ease with which the hydrogen in an oxyacid will be donated (and therefore be acidic) are the *electronegativity of the element Y* and the *number of oxygen atoms attached to the element Y.*

The Electronegativity of Y The more electronegative the element Y, the more it weakens and polarizes the H—O bond and the more acidic the oxyacid is. We can see this effect by comparing the electronegativity of Y and the acid ionization constants of the following oxyacids:

Acid	Electronegativity of Y	K_a
H—O—I	2.5	2.3×10^{-11}
H—O—Br	2.8	2.0×10^{-9}
H—O—Cl	3.0	4.0×10^{-8}

Chlorine is the most electronegative of the three elements and the corresponding acid has the greatest K_a.

The Number of Oxygen Atoms Bonded to Y Oxyacids may contain additional oxygen atoms bonded to the element Y. Since these additional oxygen atoms are electronegative, they draw electron density away from Y, which in turn draws electron density away from the H—O bond, further weakening and polarizing it, and leading to increasing acidity. We can see this effect by comparing the following series of acid ionization constants:

Acid	Structure	K_a
$HClO_4$	O ‖ H—O—Cl=O ‖ O	Strong
$HClO_3$	O ‖ H—O—Cl=O	1
$HClO_2$	H—O—Cl=O	1.1×10^{-2}
$HClO$	H—O—Cl	4.0×10^{-8}

The greater the number of oxygen atoms bonded to Y, the stronger the acid. On this basis we would predict that H_2SO_4 is a stronger acid than H_2SO_3 and that HNO_3 is stronger than HNO_2. As we have seen in this chapter, both H_2SO_4 and HNO_3 are strong acids, while H_2SO_3 and HNO_2 are weak acids, as predicted.

Organic acids such as methanoic acid and acetic acid are also oxyacids. Methanoic acid is more acidic than acetic acid. Chloroacetic acid is also more acidic than acetic acid. Can we justify the acidic properties of these acids based on their molecular structures?

```
      O               H   O                H   O
      ‖               |   ‖                |   ‖
  H—C—O—H         H—C—C—O—H          Cl—C—C—O—H
                      |                    |
                      H                    H
```

Methanoic acid, $K_a = 1.8 \times 10^{-4}$

Acetic acid, $K_a = 1.8 \times 10^{-5}$

Chloroacetic acid, $K_a = 1.4 \times 10^{-3}$

Electronegative elements such as the halogens are what we call *electron withdrawing*. They pull electron density from the rest of the molecule and ultimately weaken the O—H, making the acid stronger. Chloroacetic acid is a stronger acid than acetic acid due to the electronegative chlorine atom. Atoms that are not electronegative are what we call *electron donating*. They have the opposite effect than electronegative atoms; they donate electrons to the rest of the molecule and actually strengthen the O—H bond, weakening the acid. Because it has more electrons, CH_3 is more electron donating than H. Therefore, acetic acid is a weaker acid than methanoic acid. The effect of a larger alkyl group is negligible. For example, propanoic acid has a K_a of 1.6×10^{-5}, similar to that of acetic acid.

CONCEPTUAL CONNECTION 15.6
Acid Strength and Molecular Structure

Which of the protons shown in red is more acidic?

```
      O               H
      ‖               |
  H—C—O—H         H—C—O—H
                      |
                      H
    (a)              (b)
```

Amine Bases

To explain why some bases are stronger than others, it is convenient to use the Lewis definition of a base: a base is an electron pair donor. Factors that will make a base a better electron donor will put more electron density onto the basic centre, ultimately making a stronger bond between the base and the proton. Electron-donating groups will make the base more effective at donating an electron pair, resulting in a stronger base. On the other hand, electronegative elements are electron-withdrawing groups and make the base less effective in donating electrons, weakening the base.

H—N—H with H	H—N—H with CH_3	H—N—H with OH
Ammonia	Methylamine	Hydroxylamine
$K_b = 1.8 \times 10^{-5}$	$K_b = 4.2 \times 10^{-4}$	$K_b = 1.1 \times 10^{-8}$

Since a methyl group is less electronegative than N, it donates electron density to N, making methylamine a stronger base than ammonia. The effect of substituting a methyl group for H on ammonia is opposite to that of substituting a methyl group for H on methanoic acid, which makes a weaker acid. Substituting an electronegative element such as oxygen has the effect of withdrawing electron density from N, making hydroxylamine a weaker base than ammonia.

CONCEPTUAL CONNECTION 15.7

Amine Base Strength and Molecular Structure

Rank the four nitrogens (a, b, c, and d) in order of expected strength as bases.

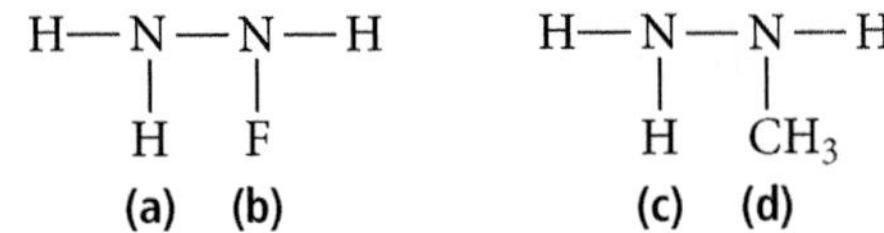

15.12 Ocean Acidification

Since the start of the Industrial Revolution, when humans began combusting large quantities of fossil fuels for energy, the atmospheric concentration of carbon dioxide has been steadily increasing. We know this from direct measurements taken at places such as the Mauna Loa Observatory in Hawaii (Figure 15.15 ▶), for which data is available since 1958. To measure the atmospheric CO_2 from preindustrial times, scientists use other sampling techniques such as obtaining small bubbles of air that were trapped in ice from long ago. From ice core samples, scientists can extract small amounts of air trapped from hundreds or even thousands of years ago, and measure the concentrations of different gases. We know that prior to the Industrial Revolution, atmospheric CO_2 never exceeded about 280 ppm. The current CO_2 concentration is around 400 ppm. Based on projections of continuing future use of carbon-based fuels, atmospheric CO_2 is expected to increase to over 500 ppm.

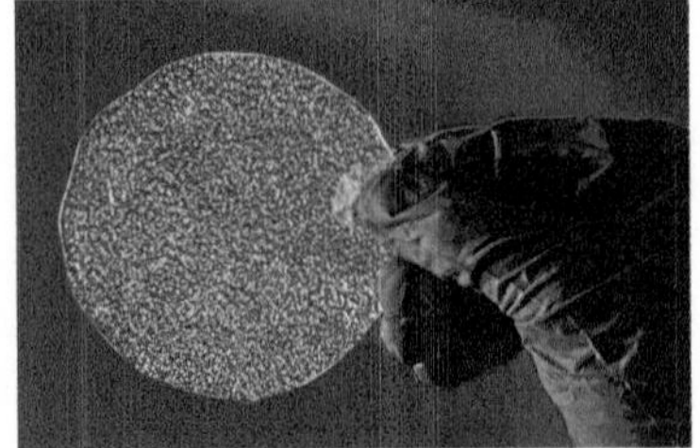

▲ Ancient air bubbles in an ice core sample.

CO_2 is a greenhouse gas, and the increasing levels of atmospheric CO_2 have resulted in climate changes and overall global warming. Another consequence of increasing atmospheric CO_2 is ocean acidification. This phenomenon is caused by shifts in chemical equilibria that are the result of CO_2 dissolving in the oceans.

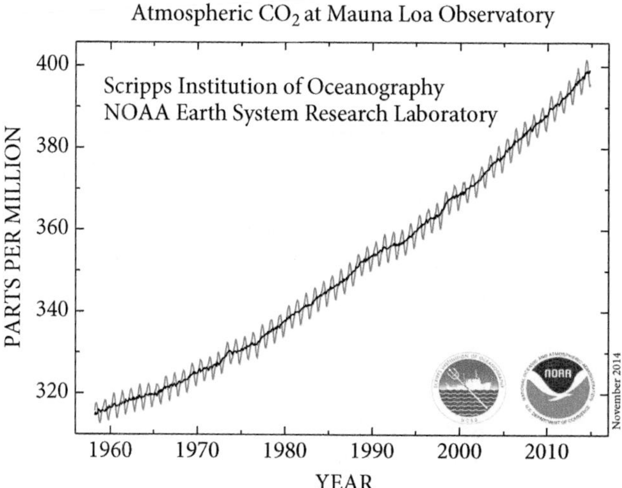

◀ **FIGURE 15.15 Increase in Atmospheric CO_2 since 1958.** Source: National Oceanic and Amospheric Administration.

In Section 12.4, we discussed the solubility of gases in water and showed that Henry's law allows us to quantify the aqueous solubility of gases with increasing pressure:

$$S_{gas} = k_H P_{gas}$$

There is a direct relationship with increasing partial pressure of a gas and its solubility in water. Since the partial pressure of CO_2 has increased, we know that the solubility of CO_2 in the oceans has also increased. It has been estimated that approximately half of the CO_2 generated by human activity has been dissolved in the oceans.

When CO_2 is dissolved in water, it forms H_3O^+ by the following reaction:

$$CO_2(aq) + 2\,H_2O(l) \rightarrow H_3O^+(aq) + HCO_3^-(aq)$$

The concentration of H_3O^+ in oceans has been increasing, which means that the pH is decreasing. The change in pH has been small. The preindustrial ocean pH is estimated to have been around 8.2. This value comes partly from our knowledge of atmospheric CO_2 concentrations from ice core samples and Henry's law. Currently, the pH of the ocean is around 8.1, and it is decreasing. 0.1 on the pH scale may not look like much of a decrease, but we need to remember that pH is the negative logarithm of $[H_3O^+]$. A small decrease in pH corresponds to a much larger relative change in $[H_3O^+]$. In this case, the change of 0.1 units of pH corresponds to a 26% increase in $[H_3O^+]$.

The increase in $[H_3O^+]$ formed from the reaction of dissolved CO_2 with water reduces the relative concentration of $CO_3^{2-}(aq)$:

$$CO_3^-(aq) + H_3O^+(aq) \rightleftarrows H_2O(l) + HCO_3^-(aq)$$

This shift in equilibrium is significant for marine calcifiers—organisms that produce calcium carbonate structures such as shells. Biocalcification depends on the presence of dissolved Ca^{2+} and CO_3^{2-}. At lower concentrations of CO_3^{2-}, calcifying organisms must expend more energy to produce calcium carbonate structures. And, at lower pH values, $CaCO_3$ is more likely to dissolve away, which affects the strength and integrity of shells and coral reefs. Scientists are actively studying how continued ocean acidification will affect many types of marine organisms. As atmospheric CO_2 continues to increase to over 500 ppm in coming decades, ocean pH is expected to fall below 8.0.

▲ Clam and coral are two types of calcifying organisms that are affected by ocean acidification.

CHAPTER IN REVIEW

Key Terms

Section 15.2
carboxylic acid (630)
alkaloid (630)

Section 15.3
Arrhenius definitions (of acids and bases) (632)
hydronium ion (632)
Brønsted–Lowry definitions (of acids and bases) (632)
amphoteric (633)
conjugate acid–base pair (633)
conjugate acid (633)
conjugate base (633)

Section 15.4
strong acid (634)
weak acid (634)
monoprotic acid (634)
diprotic acid (634)
triprotic (636)
acid ionization constant (K_a) (636)

Section 15.5
strong base (637)
weak base (637)
base ionization constant (K_b) (638)

Section 15.6
autoionization (639)
ion product constant for water (K_w) (639)
neutral (639)
acidic solution (639)
basic solution (640)
pH (641)

Section 15.7
percent ionization (649)

Section 15.9
polyprotic acid (662)

Section 15.10
Lewis acid (667)
Lewis base (667)

Key Concepts

Heartburn (15.1)
Hydrochloric acid from the stomach sometimes contacts the esophageal lining, resulting in irritation called heartburn. Heartburn is treated with antacids, bases that neutralize stomach acid.

The Nature of Acids and Bases (15.2)
Acids generally taste sour, dissolve metals, turn blue litmus paper red, and neutralize bases. Common acids are hydrochloric, sulfuric, nitric, and carboxylic acids. Bases generally taste bitter, feel slippery, turn red litmus paper blue, and neutralize acids. Common bases are sodium hydroxide, sodium bicarbonate, and potassium hydroxide.

Definitions of Acids and Bases (15.3)
The Arrhenius definition of acids and bases states that in an aqueous solution, an acid produces hydrogen ions and a base produces hydroxide ions. According to the Brønsted–Lowry definition, an acid is a proton (hydrogen ion) donor and a base is a proton acceptor. In the Brønsted–Lowry definition two substances related by the transfer of a proton are a conjugate acid–base pair.

Acid Strength and the Acid Ionization Constant, K_a (15.4)
In a solution, a strong acid completely ionizes but a weak acid only partially ionizes. Generally, the stronger the acid, the weaker the conjugate base, and vice versa. The extent of dissociation of a weak acid is quantified by the acid ionization constant, K_a, which is the equilibrium constant for the ionization of the weak acid.

Base Solutions (15.5)
A strong base dissociates completely; a weak base does not. The base ionization constant, K_b, describes the extent of ionization. Most weak bases produce hydroxide ions through the ionization of water.

Autoionization of Water and pH (15.6)
In an acidic solution, the concentration of hydrogen ions will always be greater than the concentration of hydroxide ions. $[H_3O^+]$ multiplied by $[OH^-]$ is always constant at a constant temperature. There are two types of logarithmic acid–base scales: pH and pOH. At 25 °C, the sum of the pH and pOH is always 14.

Finding the $[H_3O^+]$, $[OH^-]$, and pH of Acid or Base Solutions (15.7)
In a strong acid solution, the hydrogen ion concentration equals the initial concentration of the acid. In a weak acid solution, the hydrogen ion concentration—which can be determined by solving an equilibrium problem—is lower than the initial acid concentration. The percent ionization of weak acids decreases as the acid (and hydrogen ion) concentration increases. In mixtures of two acids with large K_a differences, the concentration of hydrogen ions can usually be determined by considering only the stronger of the two acids.

The Acid–Base Properties of Ions and Salts (15.8)
A cation will be a weak acid if it is the conjugate acid of a weak base; it will be neutral if it is the conjugate acid of a strong base. Conversely, an anion will be a weak base if it is the conjugate base of a weak acid; it will be neutral if it is the conjugate base of a strong acid. To calculate the pH of a basic anion, we find K_b from K_w and K_a ($K_a \times K_b = K_w$).

Polyprotic Acids (15.9)
Polyprotic acids contain two or more ionizable protons. Generally, polyprotic acids ionize in successive steps, with the values of K_a becoming smaller for each step. In many cases, we can determine the $[H_3O^+]$ of a polyprotic acid solution by considering only the first ionization step. In those cases, the concentration of the acid anion formed in the second ionization step is equivalent to the value of K_{a_2}.

Lewis Acids and Bases (15.10)
The third model of acids and bases, the Lewis model, defines a base as an electron pair donor and an acid as an electron pair acceptor; therefore, an acid does not have to contain hydrogen. According to this definition an acid can be a compound with an empty orbital—or one that will rearrange to make an empty orbital—or a cation.

Strengths of Acids and Bases and Molecular Structure (15.11)

For binary acids, acid strength decreases with increasing bond energy, and increases with increasing electron affinity. Oxyacid strength increases with the electronegativity of the atoms bonded to the oxygen atom and also increases with the number of oxygen atoms in the molecule.

Carboxylic acid strengths increase with the addition of electronegative groups (Cl) and decrease with the addition of electron-donating groups such as a methyl group. Amine base strength, on the contrary, decreases by substitution with electronegative groups but increases with the addition of an alkyl group.

Ocean Acidification (15.12)

The combustion of fossil fuels has increased the atmospheric concentration of CO_2, which has led to an increase in dissolved CO_2 in the oceans. The resulting carbonic acid has decreased ocean pH. At lower pH values, the concentration of carbonate is lower, and marine calcifying organisms, such as mollusks and corals, need to consume more energy to make calcium carbonate structures. This is a direct consequence of increased atmospheric CO_2 from human activity.

Key Equations and Relationships

Note: in all of these equations $[H^+]$ is interchangeable with $[H_3O^+]$.

Expression for the Acid Ionization Constant, K_a (15.4)

$$K_a = \frac{[H_3O^+][A^-]}{[HA]}$$

The Ion Product Constant for Water, K_w (15.6)

$$K_w = [H_3O^+][OH^-] = 1.0 \times 10^{-14} \text{ (at 25 °C)}$$

Expression for the pH Scale (15.6)

$$pH = -\log[H_3O^+]$$

Expression for the pOH Scale (15.6)

$$pOH = -\log[OH^-]$$

Relationship Between pH and pOH (15.6)

$$pH + pOH = 14.00$$

Expression for the pK_a Scale (15.6)

$$pK_a = -\log K_a$$

Expression for Percent Ionization (15.7)

$$\text{Percent ionization} = \frac{\text{concentration of ionized acid}}{\text{initial concentration of acid}} \times 100\% = \frac{[H_3O^+]_{equil}}{[HA]_{init}} \times 100\%$$

Relationship Between K_a, K_b, and K_w (15.8)

$$K_a \times K_b = K_w$$

Key Skills

Identifying Brønsted–Lowry Acids and Bases and Their Conjugates (15.3)
- Example 15.1 • For Practice 15.1 • Exercises 33–36

Using K_w in Calculations (15.6)
- Example 15.2 • For Practice 15.2 • Exercises 47–54

Calculating pH from $[H_3O^+]$ or $[OH^-]$ (15.6)
- Examples 15.3, 15.4 • For Practice 15.3, 15.4 • Exercises 55–58

Finding the pH of a Weak Acid Solution (15.7)
- Examples 15.5, 15.6, 15.7 • For Practice 15.5, 15.6, 15.7 • Exercises 59–64

Finding the Acid Ionization Constant from pH (15.7)
• Example 15.8 • For Practice 15.8 • Exercises 67, 68

Finding the Percent Ionization of a Weak Acid (15.7)
• Example 15.9 • For Practice 15.9 • Exercises 69–72

Mixtures of Weak Acids (15.7)
• Example 15.10 • For Practice 15.10 • Exercises 77, 78

Finding the $[OH^-]$ and pH of a Strong Base Solution (15.7)
• Example 15.11 • For Practice 15.11 • Exercises 79, 80

Finding the $[OH^-]$ and pH of a Weak Base Solution (15.7)
• Example 15.12 • For Practice 15.12 • Exercises 87–90

Determining Whether an Anion Is Basic or Neutral (15.8)
• Example 15.13 • For Practice 15.13 • Exercises 93, 94

Determining the pH of a Solution Containing an Anion Acting as a Base (15.8)
• Example 15.14 • For Practice 15.14 • Exercises 95, 96

Determining Whether a Cation Is Acidic or Neutral (15.8)
• Example 15.15 • For Practice 15.15 • Exercises 97, 98

Determining the Overall Acidity or Basicity of Salt Solutions (15.8)
• Example 15.16 • For Practice 15.16 • Exercises 99, 100

Finding the pH of a Polyprotic Acid Solution (15.9)
• Example 15.17 • For Practice 15.17 • Exercises 109, 110

Finding the $[H_3O^+]$ in Dilute H_2SO_4 Solutions (15.9)
• Example 15.18 • For Practice 15.18 • Exercise 113

Finding the Concentration of the Anions for a Weak Diprotic Acid Solution (15.9)
• Example 15.19 • For Practice 15.19 • Exercises 111, 112

EXERCISES

Review Questions

1. What causes heartburn? What are some possible ways to alleviate heartburn?
2. What are the general physical and chemical properties of acids? Of bases?
3. What is a carboxylic acid? Give an example.
4. What is the Arrhenius definition of an acid? Of a base?
5. What is a hydronium ion? Does H^+ exist in solution by itself?
6. What is the Brønsted–Lowry definition of an acid? Of a base?
7. Why is there more than one definition of acid–base behaviour? Which definition is the right one?
8. Describe amphoteric behaviour and give an example.
9. What is a conjugate acid–base pair? Give an example.
10. Explain the difference between a strong acid and a weak acid and list one example of each.
11. What are diprotic and triprotic acids? List an example of each.
12. Define the acid ionization constant and explain its significance.
13. Write an equation for the autoionization of water and an expression for the ion product constant for water (K_w). What is the value of K_w at 25 °C?
14. What happens to the $[OH^-]$ of a solution when the $[H_3O^+]$ is increased? Decreased?
15. Define pH. What pH range is considered acidic? Basic? Neutral?
16. Define pOH. What pOH range is considered acidic? Basic? Neutral?
17. In most solutions containing a strong or weak acid, the autoionization of water can be neglected when calculating $[H_3O^+]$. Explain why this is so.
18. When calculating $[H_3O^+]$ for weak acid solutions, we can often use the *x is small* approximation. Explain the nature of this approximation and why it is valid.
19. What is the percent ionization of an acid? Explain what happens to the percent ionization of a weak acid as a function of the concentration of the weak acid solution.
20. In calculating $[H_3O^+]$ for a mixture of a strong acid and weak acid, the weak acid can often be neglected. Explain why this is so.
21. Write a generic equation showing how a weak base ionizes water.
22. How can you determine whether an anion will act as a weak base? Write a generic equation showing the reaction by which an anion, A^-, acts as a weak base.

23. What is the relationship between the acid ionization constant for a weak acid (K_a) and the base ionization constant for its conjugate base (K_b)?

24. What kinds of cations act as weak acids? List some examples.

25. When calculating the $[H_3O^+]$ for a polyprotic acid, the second ionization step can often be neglected. Explain why this is so.

26. For a weak diprotic acid H_2X, what is the relationship between $[X^{2-}]$ and K_{a_2}? Under what conditions does this relationship exist?

27. For a binary acid, H—Y, what factors affect the relative ease with which the acid ionizes?

28. What factors affect the relative acidity of an oxyacid?

29. What is the Lewis definition of an acid? Of a base?

30. What is a general characteristic of a Lewis acid? Of a Lewis base?

31. How do increases in atmospheric CO_2 result in acidification of oceans?

32. What are the main detrimental effects of ocean acidification?

Problems by Topic

The Nature and Definitions of Acids and Bases

33. Identify each substance as an acid or a base and write a chemical equation showing how it is an acid or a base according to the Arrhenius definition.
a. $HNO_3(aq)$ **b.** $NH_4^+(aq)$ **c.** $KOH(aq)$ **d.** $HC_2H_3O_2(aq)$

34. Identify each substance as an acid or a base and write a chemical equation showing how it is an acid or a base according to the Arrhenius definition.
a. $NaOH(aq)$ **b.** $H_2SO_4(aq)$ **c.** $HBr(aq)$ **d.** $Sr(OH)_2(aq)$

35. For each reaction, identify the Brønsted–Lowry acid, the Brønsted–Lowry base, the conjugate acid, and the conjugate base.
a. $H_2CO_3(aq) + H_2O(l) \rightleftharpoons H_3O^+(aq) + HCO_3^-(aq)$
b. $NH_3(aq) + H_2O(l) \rightleftharpoons NH_4^+(aq) + OH^-(aq)$
c. $HNO_3(aq) + H_2O(l) \longrightarrow H_3O^+(aq) + NO_3^-(aq)$
d. $C_5H_5N(aq) + H_2O(l) \rightleftharpoons C_5H_5NH^+(aq) + OH^-(aq)$

36. For each reaction, identify the Brønsted–Lowry acid, the Brønsted–Lowry base, the conjugate acid, and the conjugate base.
a. $HI(aq) + H_2O(l) \longrightarrow H_3O^+(aq) + I^-(aq)$
b. $CH_3NH_2(aq) + H_2O(l) \rightleftharpoons CH_3NH_3^+(aq) + OH^-(aq)$
c. $CO_3^{2-}(aq) + H_2O(l) \rightleftharpoons HCO_3^-(aq) + OH^-(aq)$
d. $HBr(aq) + H_2O(l) \longrightarrow H_3O^+(aq) + Br^-(aq)$

37. Write the formula for the conjugate base of each acid.
a. HCl **b.** H_2SO_3 **c.** $HCHO_2$ **d.** HF

38. Write the formula for the conjugate acid of each base.
a. NH_3 **b.** ClO_4^- **c.** HSO_4^- **d.** CO_3^{2-}

39. Both H_2O and $H_2PO_4^-$ are amphoteric. Write an equation to show how each substance can act as an acid, and another equation to show how it can act as a base.

40. Both HCO_3^- and HS^- are amphoteric. Write an equation to show how each substance can act as an acid, and another equation to show how it can act as a base.

Acid Strength and K_a

41. Classify each acid as strong or weak. If the acid is weak, write an expression for the acid ionization constant (K_a).
a. HNO_3 **b.** HCl **c.** HBr **d.** H_2SO_3

42. Classify each acid as strong or weak. If the acid is weak, write an expression for the acid ionization constant (K_a).
a. HF **b.** $HCOOH$ **c.** H_2SO_4 **d.** H_2CO_3

43. The three diagrams represent three different solutions of the binary acid HA. Water molecules have been omitted for clarity and hydronium ions (H_3O^+) are represented by hydrogen ions (H^+). Rank the acids in order of decreasing acid strength.

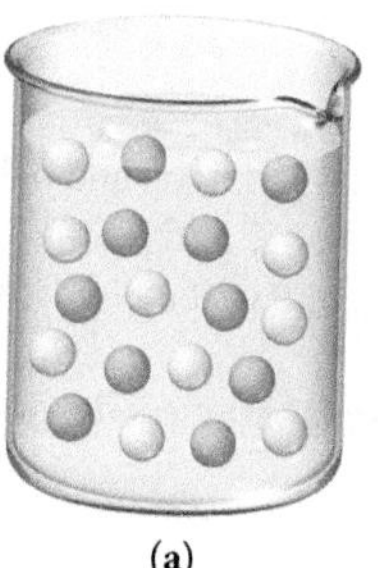
(a)

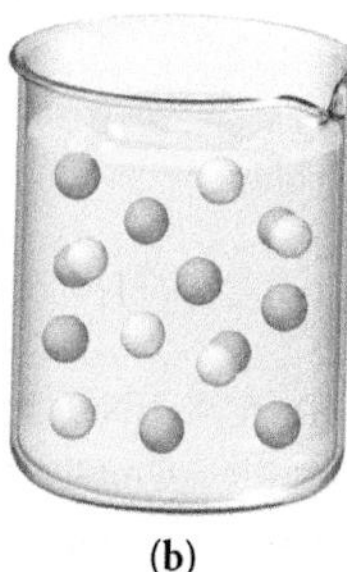
(b)

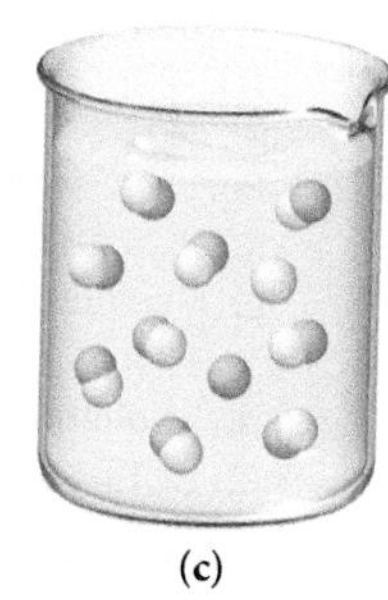
(c)

44. Rank the solutions in order of decreasing $[H_3O^+]$: 0.10 mol L^{-1} HCl; 0.10 mol L^{-1} HF; 0.10 mol L^{-1} HClO; 0.10 mol L^{-1} C_6H_5OH.

45. Pick the stronger base from each pair:
a. F^- or Cl^- **b.** NO_2^- or NO_3^- **c.** F^- or ClO^-

46. Pick the stronger base from each pair:
a. ClO_4^- or ClO_2^- **b.** Cl^- or H_2O **c.** CN^- or ClO^-

Autoionization of Water and pH

47. Calculate $[OH^-]$ in each aqueous solution at 25 °C, and classify the solution as acidic or basic.
a. $[H_3O^+] = 1.2 \times 10^{-8}$ mol L^{-1}
b. $[H_3O^+] = 8.5 \times 10^{-5}$ mol L^{-1}
c. $[H_3O^+] = 3.5 \times 10^{-2}$ mol L^{-1}

48. Calculate $[H_3O^+]$ in each aqueous solution at 25 °C, and classify each solution as acidic or basic.
a. $[OH^-] = 1.1 \times 10^{-9}$ mol L^{-1}
b. $[OH^-] = 2.9 \times 10^{-2}$ mol L^{-1}
c. $[OH^-] = 6.9 \times 10^{-12}$ mol L^{-1}

49. Calculate the pH and pOH of each solution.
a. $[H_3O^+] = 1.7 \times 10^{-8}$ mol L^{-1}
b. $[H_3O^+] = 1.0 \times 10^{-7}$ mol L^{-1}
c. $[H_3O^+] = 2.2 \times 10^{-6}$ mol L^{-1}

50. Calculate $[H_3O^+]$ and $[OH^-]$ for each solution.
a. pH = 8.55 **b.** pH = 11.23 **c.** pH = 2.87

51. Complete the table. (All solutions are at 25 °C.)

$[H_3O^+]$	$[OH^-]$	pH	Acidic or Basic
____	____	3.15	____
3.7×10^{-9}	____	____	____
____	____	11.1	____
____	1.6×10^{-11}	____	____

52. Complete the table. (All solutions are at 25 °C.)

$[H_3O^+]$	$[OH^-]$	pH	Acidic or Basic
3.5×10^{-3}	______	______	______
______	3.8×10^{-7}	______	______
1.8×10^{-9}	______	______	______
______	______	7.15	______

53. Like all equilibrium constants, the value of K_w depends on temperature. At body temperature (37 °C), $K_w = 2.4 \times 10^{-14}$. What is the $[H_3O^+]$ and pH of pure water at body temperature?

54. The value of K_w increases with increasing temperature. Is the autoionization of water endothermic or exothermic?

Acid Solutions

55. For each strong acid solution, determine $[H_3O^+]$, $[OH^-]$, and pH.
   a. 0.25 mol L^{-1} HCl **b.** 0.015 mol L^{-1} HNO_3
   c. a solution that is 0.052 mol L^{-1} in HBr and 0.020 mol L^{-1} in HNO_3
   d. a solution that is 0.655% HNO_3 by mass. (Assume a density of 1.01 g mL^{-1} for the solution.)

56. Determine the pH of each solution.
   a. 0.048 mol L^{-1} HI
   b. 0.0895 mol L^{-1} $HClO_4$
   c. a solution that is 0.045 mol L^{-1} in $HClO_4$ and 0.048 mol L^{-1} in HCl
   d. a solution that is 1.09% HCl by mass. (Assume a density of 1.01 g mL^{-1} for the solution.)

57. What mass of HI should be present in 0.250 L of solution to obtain a solution with each pH value?
   a. pH = 1.25 **b.** pH = 1.75 **c.** pH = 2.85

58. What mass of $HClO_4$ should be present in 0.500 L of solution to obtain a solution with each pH value?
   a. pH = 2.50 **b.** pH = 1.50 **c.** pH = 0.50

59. What is the pH of a solution in which 224 mL of HCl(*g*), measured at 27.2 °C and 1.02 atm, is dissolved in 1.5 L of aqueous solution?

60. What volume of a concentrated HCl solution, which is 36.0% HCl by mass and has a density of 1.179 g mL^{-1}, should be used to make 5.00 L of an HCl solution with a pH of 1.8?

61. Determine the $[H_3O^+]$ and pH of a 0.100 mol L^{-1} solution of benzoic acid.

62. Determine the $[H_3O^+]$ and pH of a 0.200 mol L^{-1} solution of formic acid.

63. Determine the pH of an HNO_2 solution of each concentration. In which cases can you *not* make the simplifying assumption that *x is small*?
   a. 0.500 mol L^{-1} **b.** 0.100 mol L^{-1} **c.** 0.0100 mol L^{-1}

64. Determine the pH of an HF solution of each concentration. In which cases can you *not* make the simplifying assumption that *x is small*?
   a. 0.250 mol L^{-1} **b.** 0.0500 mol L^{-1} **c.** 0.0250 mol L^{-1}

65. If 15.0 mL of glacial acetic acid (pure $HC_2H_3O_2$) is diluted to 1.50 L with water, what is the pH of the resulting solution? The density of glacial acetic acid is 1.05 g mL^{-1}.

66. Calculate the pH of a formic acid solution that contains 1.35% formic acid by mass. (Assume a density of 1.01 g mL^{-1} for the solution.)

67. A 0.185 mol L^{-1} solution of a weak acid (HA) has a pH of 2.95. Calculate the acid ionization constant (K_a) for the acid.

68. A 0.115 mol L^{-1} solution of a weak acid (HA) has a pH of 3.29. Calculate the acid ionization constant (K_a) for the acid.

69. Determine the percent ionization of a 0.125 mol L^{-1} HCN solution.

70. Determine the percent ionization of a 0.225 mol L^{-1} solution of benzoic acid.

71. Calculate the percent ionization of an acetic acid solution having the given concentration.
   a. 1.00 mol L^{-1} **c.** 0.100 mol L^{-1}
   b. 0.500 mol L^{-1} **d.** 0.0500 mol L^{-1}

72. Calculate the percent ionization of a formic acid solution having the given concentration.
   a. 1.00 mol L^{-1} **c.** 0.100 mol L^{-1}
   b. 0.500 mol L^{-1} **d.** 0.0500 mol L^{-1}

73. A 0.148 mol L^{-1} solution of a monoprotic acid has a percent ionization of 1.55%. Determine the acid ionization constant (K_a) for the acid.

74. A 0.085 mol L^{-1} solution of a monoprotic acid has a percent ionization of 0.59%. Determine the acid ionization constant (K_a) for the acid.

75. Find the pH and percent ionization of each HF solution:
   a. 0.250 mol L^{-1} HF **c.** 0.050 mol L^{-1} HF
   b. 0.100 mol L^{-1} HF

76. Find the pH and percent ionization of a 0.100 mol L^{-1} solution of a weak monoprotic acid having the given K_a values.
   a. $K_a = 1.0 \times 10^{-5}$ **c.** $K_a = 1.0 \times 10^{-1}$
   b. $K_a = 1.0 \times 10^{-3}$

77. Find the pH of each mixture of acids.
   a. 0.115 mol L^{-1} in HBr and 0.125 mol L^{-1} in CH_3COO^-
   b. 0.150 mol L^{-1} in HNO_2 and 0.085 mol L^{-1} in HNO_3
   c. 0.185 mol L^{-1} in $HCHO_2$ and 0.225 mol L^{-1} in CH_3COOH
   d. 0.050 mol L^{-1} in acetic acid and 0.050 mol L^{-1} in hydrocyanic acid

78. Find the pH of each mixture of acids.
   a. 0.075 mol L^{-1} in HNO_3 and 0.175 mol L^{-1} in $HC_7H_5O_2$
   b. 0.020 mol L^{-1} in HBr and 0.015 mol L^{-1} in $HClO_4$
   c. 0.095 mol L^{-1} in HF and 0.225 mol L^{-1} in C_6H_5OH
   d. 0.100 mol L^{-1} in formic acid and 0.050 mol L^{-1} in hypochlorous acid

Base Solutions

79. For each strong base solution, determine $[OH^-]$, $[H_3O^+]$, pH, and pOH.
   a. 0.15 mol L^{-1} NaOH
   b. 1.5×10^{-3} mol L^{-1} $Ca(OH)_2$
   c. 4.8×10^{-4} mol L^{-1} $Sr(OH)_2$
   d. 8.7×10^{-5} mol L^{-1} KOH

80. For each strong base solution, determine $[OH^-]$, $[H_3O^+]$, pH, and pOH.
   a. 8.77×10^{-3} mol L^{-1} LiOH
   b. 0.0112 mol L^{-1} $Ba(OH)_2$
   c. 1.9×10^{-4} mol L^{-1} KOH
   d. 5.0×10^{-4} mol L^{-1} $Ca(OH)_2$

81. Determine the pH of a solution that is 3.85% KOH by mass. Assume that the solution has density of 1.01 g mL^{-1}.

82. Determine the pH of a solution that is 1.55% NaOH by mass. Assume that the solution has density of 1.01 g mL^{-1}.

83. What volume of 0.855 mol L^{-1} KOH solution is required to make 3.55 L of a solution with pH of 12.4?

84. What volume of a 15.0% by mass NaOH solution, which has a density of 1.116 g mL^{-1}, should be used to make 5.00 L of an NaOH solution with a pH of 10.8?

85. Write equations showing how each weak base ionizes water to form OH^-. Also write the corresponding expression for K_b.
a. NH_3 b. HCO_3^- c. CH_3NH_2

86. Write equations showing how each weak base ionizes water to form OH^-. Also write the corresponding expression for K_b.
a. CO_3^{2-} b. $C_6H_5NH_2$ c. $C_2H_5NH_2$

87. Determine the $[OH^-]$, pH, and pOH of a 0.15 mol L^{-1} ammonia solution.

88. Determine the $[OH^-]$, pH, and pOH of a solution that is 0.125 mol L^{-1} in CO_3^{2-}.

89. Caffeine ($C_8H_{10}N_4O_2$) is a weak base with a pK_b of 10.4. Calculate the pH of a solution containing a caffeine concentration of 455 mg L^{-1}.

90. Amphetamine ($C_9H_{13}N$) is a weak base with a pK_b of 4.2. Calculate the pH of a solution containing an amphetamine concentration of 225 mg L^{-1}.

91. Morphine is a weak base. A 0.150 mol L^{-1} solution of morphine has a pH of 10.5. What is K_b for morphine?

92. A 0.135 mol L^{-1} solution of a weak base has a pH of 11.23. Determine K_b for the base.

Acid–Base Properties of Ions and Salts

93. Determine whether each anion acts as a weak base in solution. For those anions that are basic, write an equation that shows how the anion acts as a base.
a. Br^- b. ClO^- c. CN^- d. Cl^-

94. Determine whether each anion is basic or neutral. For those anions that are basic, write an equation that shows how the anion acts as a base.
a. $C_7H_5O_2^-$ b. I^- c. NO_3^- d. F^-

95. Determine the $[OH^-]$ and pH of a solution that is 0.140 mol L^{-1} in F^-.

96. Determine the $[OH^-]$ and pH of a solution that is 0.250 mol L^{-1} in HCO_3^-.

97. Determine whether each cation is acidic or pH-neutral. For those cations that are acidic, write an equation that shows how the cation acts as an acid.
a. NH_4^+ b. Na^+ c. Co^{3+} d. $CH_2NH_3^+$

98. Determine whether each cation is acidic or pH-neutral. For those cations that are acidic, write an equation that shows how the cation acts as an acid.
a. Cs^+ b. Mn^{3+} c. $C_5H_5NH^+$ d. Li^+

99. Determine whether each salt will form a solution that is acidic, basic, or pH-neutral.
a. $FeCl_3$ b. NaF c. NH_4Br d. $C_6H_5NH_3NO_2$

100. Determine whether each salt will form a solution that is acidic, basic, or pH-neutral.
a. $Al(NO_3)_3$
b. $C_2H_5NH_3NO_3$
c. K_2CO_3
d. RbI
e. NH_4ClO

101. Arrange the solutions in order of increasing acidity:
NaCl, NH_4Cl, $NaHCO_3$, NH_4ClO_2, NaOH

102. Arrange the solutions in order of increasing basicity:
CH_3NH_3Br, KOH, KBr, KCN, $C_5H_5NHNO_2$

103. Determine the pH of each solution:
a. 0.10 mol L^{-1} NH_4Cl
b. 0.10 mol L^{-1} CH_3COONa
c. 0.10 NaCl

104. Determine the pH of each solution:
a. 0.20 mol L^{-1} $KCHO_2$
b. 0.20 mol L^{-1} CH_3NH_3I
c. 0.20 mol L^{-1} KI

105. Calculate the concentration of all species in a 0.15 mol L^{-1} KF solution.

106. Calculate the concentration of all species in a 0.225 mol L^{-1} $C_6H_5NH_3Cl$ solution.

Polyprotic Acids

107. Write chemical equations and corresponding equilibrium expressions for each of the three ionization steps of phosphoric acid.

108. Write chemical equations and corresponding equilibrium expressions for each of the two ionization steps of carbonic acid.

109. Calculate the $[H_3O^+]$ and pH of each polyprotic acid solution:
a. 0.350 mol L^{-1} H_3PO_4 b. 0.350 mol L^{-1} $H_2C_2O_4$

110. Calculate the $[H_3O^+]$ and pH of each polyprotic acid solution:
a. 0.125 mol L^{-1} H_2CO_3 b. 0.125 mol L^{-1} $H_3C_6H_5O_7$

111. Calculate the concentration of all species in a 0.500 mol L^{-1} solution of H_2SO_3.

112. Calculate the concentration of all species in a 0.155 mol L^{-1} solution of H_2CO_3.

113. Calculate the $[H_3O^+]$ and pH of each H_2SO_4 solution. At approximately what concentration does the *x is small* approximation break down?
a. 0.50 mol L^{-1} b. 0.10 mol L^{-1} c. 0.050 mol L^{-1}

114. Consider a 0.10 *M* solution of a weak polyprotic acid (H_2A) with the possible values of K_{a_1} and K_{a_2} given below.
a. $K_{a_1} = 1.0 \times 10^{-4}$; $K_{a_2} = 5.0 \times 10^{-5}$
b. $K_{a_1} = 1.0 \times 10^{-4}$; $K_{a_2} = 1.0 \times 10^{-5}$
c. $K_{a_1} = 1.0 \times 10^{-4}$; $K_{a_2} = 1.0 \times 10^{-6}$

Calculate the contributions to $[H_3O^+]$ from each ionization step. At what point can the contribution of the second step be neglected?

Molecular Structure and Acid Strength

115. Based on their molecular structure, pick the stronger acid from each pair of binary acids. Explain your reasoning.
a. HF and HCl b. H_2O or HF c. H_2Se or H_2S

116. Based on molecular structure, arrange the binary compounds in order of increasing acid strength. Explain your reasoning.
H_2Te, HI, H_2S, NaH

117. Based on their molecular structure, pick the stronger acid from each pair of oxyacids. Explain your reasoning.
a. H_2SO_4 or H_2SO_3
b. $HClO_2$ or HClO
c. HClO or HBrO
d. CCl_3COOH or CH_3COOH

118. Based on molecular structure, arrange the oxyacids in order of increasing acid strength. Explain your reasoning.
$HClO_3$, HIO_3, $HBrO_3$

119. Which is a stronger base, S^{2-} or Se^{2-}? Explain.

120. Which is a stronger base, PO_4^{3-} or AsO_4^{3-}? Explain.

121. Which of the sites on 4-methylpyrimidine (i or ii) do you think will be most basic? Explain.

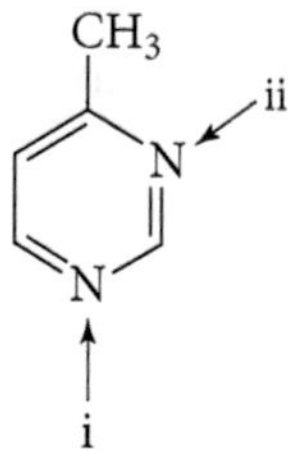

122. Which of the following do you expect to be a stronger acid? Explain.

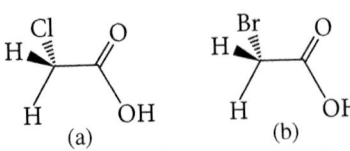

(a) (b)

Lewis Acids and Bases

123. Classify each species as either a Lewis acid or a Lewis base.
 a. Fe^{3+} b. BH_3 c. NH_3 d. F^-

124. Classify each species as either a Lewis acid or a Lewis base.
 a. $BeCl_2$ b. OH^- c. $B(OH)_3$ d. CN^-

125. Identify the Lewis acid and Lewis base from among the reactants in each equation:
 a. $Fe^{3+}(aq) + 6\,H_2O(l) \rightleftharpoons Fe(H_2O)_6{}^{3+}(aq)$
 b. $Zn^{2+}(aq) + 4\,NH_3(aq) \rightleftharpoons Zn(NH_3)_4{}^{2+}(aq)$
 c. $(CH_3)_3N(g) + BF_3(g) \rightleftharpoons (CH_3)_3NBF_3(s)$

126. Identify the Lewis acid and Lewis base from among the reactants in each equation:
 a. $Ag^+(aq) + 2\,NH_3(aq) \rightleftharpoons Ag(NH_3)_2{}^+(aq)$
 b. $AlBr_3 + NH_3 \rightleftharpoons H_3NAlBr_3$
 c. $F^-(aq) + BF_3(aq) \rightleftharpoons BF_4{}^-(aq)$

Cumulative Problems

127. Based on these molecular views, determine whether the acid is weak or strong.

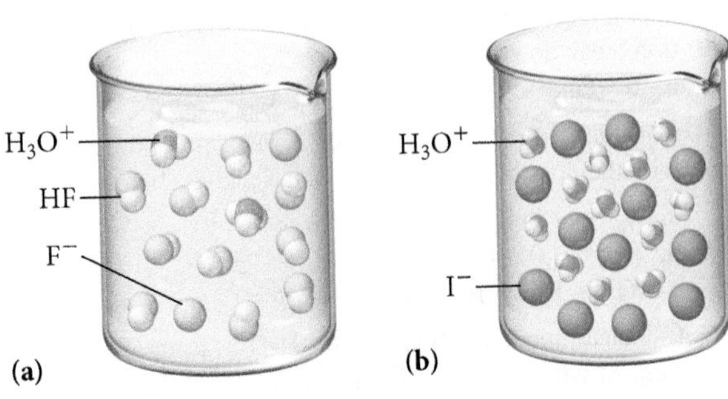

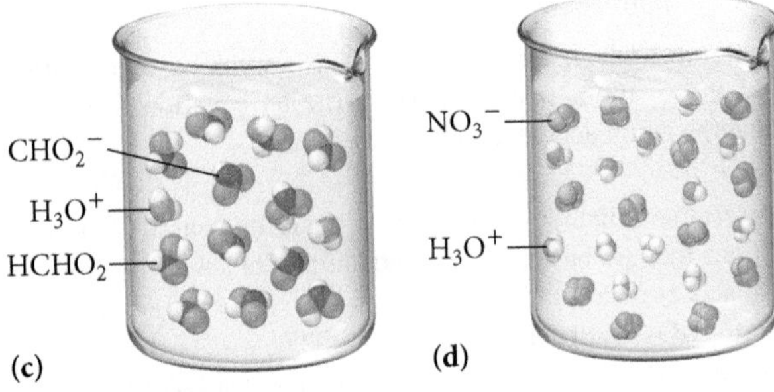

128. Based on these molecular views, determine whether the base is weak or strong.

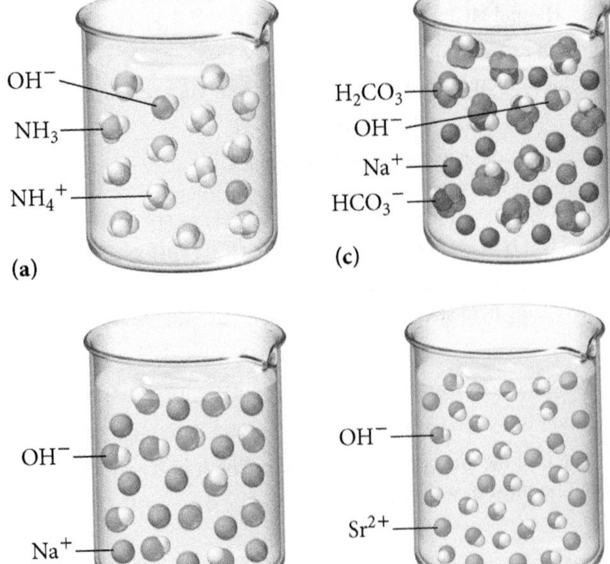

129. The binding of oxygen by hemoglobin in the blood involves the equilibrium reaction:

$$HbH^+(aq) + O_2(aq) \rightleftharpoons HbO_2(aq) + H^+(aq)$$

In this equation, Hb is hemoglobin. The pH of normal human blood is highly controlled within a range of 7.35 to 7.45. Given the above equilibrium, why is this important? What would happen to the oxygen-carrying capacity of hemoglobin if blood became too acidic (a dangerous condition known as acidosis)?

130. Carbon dioxide levels in the atmosphere have increased dramatically over the last century, resulting in ocean acidification. The preindustrial ocean pH has been estimated to have been 8.2. If the ocean pH drops to 7.9 by the end of this century, what would be the percentage increase in $[H_3O^+]$ compared to preindustrial times?

131. Milk of magnesia is often taken to reduce the discomfort associated with acid stomach or heartburn. The recommended dose is 1 teaspoon, which contains 4.00×10^2 mg of $Mg(OH)_2$. What volume of an HCl solution with a pH of 1.300 can be neutralized by one dose of milk of magnesia? If the stomach contains 2.00×10^2 mL of pH 1.300 solution, will all the acid be neutralized? If not, what fraction is neutralized?

132. Lakes that have been acidified by acid rain can be neutralized by liming, the addition of limestone ($CaCO_3$). How much limestone (in kg) is required to completely neutralize a 4.3 billion litre lake with a pH of 5.5?

▲ Liming a lake.

133. Acid rain over the Great Lakes has a pH of about 4.5. Calculate the $[H_3O^+]$ of this rain and compare that value to the $[H_3O^+]$ of rain over the West Coast that has a pH of 5.4. How many times more concentrated is the acid in rain over the Great Lakes?

134. White wines tend to be more acidic than red wines. Find the $[H_3O^+]$ in a Sauvignon Blanc with a pH of 3.23 and a Cabernet Sauvignon with a pH of 3.64. How many times more acidic is the Sauvignon Blanc?

135. Common aspirin is acetylsalicylic acid, which has the structure shown below and a pK_a of 3.5.

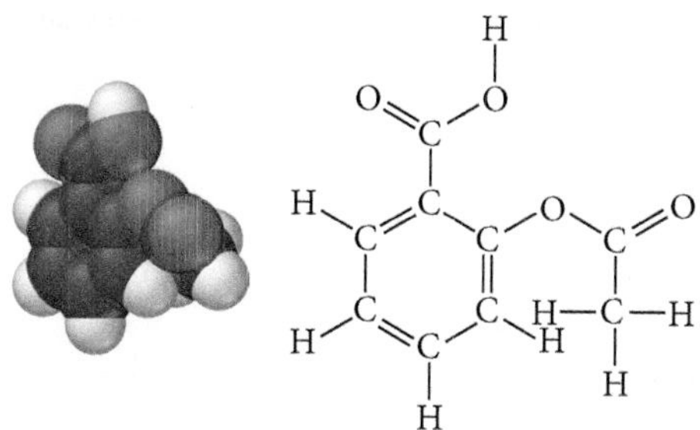

Calculate the pH of a solution in which one normal adult dose of aspirin (6.5×10^2 mg) is dissolved in 0.24 L of water.

136. The AIDS drug stavudine (also known as d4T) is a weak base with the structure shown below and a pK_b of 9.8.

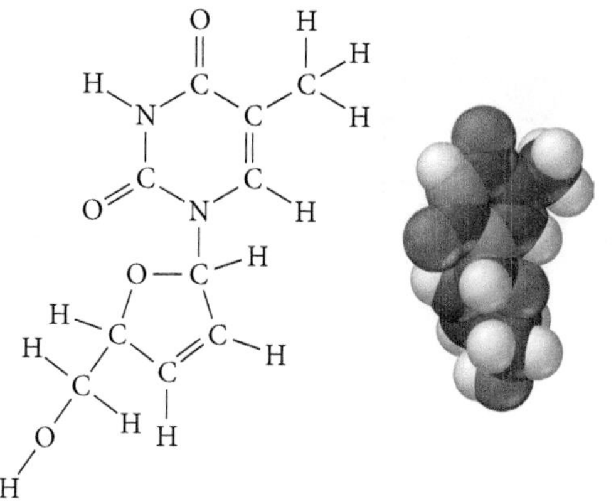

What percentage of the base is protonated in an aqueous zalcitabine solution containing 565 mg L^{-1}?

137. Determine the pH of each solution:

a. 0.0100 mol L^{-1} $HClO_4$
b. 0.115 mol L^{-1} $HClO_2$
c. 0.045 mol L^{-1} $Sr(OH)_2$
d. 0.0852 mol L^{-1} KCN
e. 0.155 mol L^{-1} NH_4Cl

138. Determine the pH of each solution:

a. 0.0650 mol L^{-1} HNO_3
b. 0.150 mol L^{-1} HNO_2
c. 0.0195 mol L^{-1} KOH
d. 0.245 mol L^{-1} CH_3NH_3I
e. 0.318 mol L^{-1} KC_6H_5O

139. Determine the pH of each two-component solution.

a. 0.0550 mol L^{-1} in HI and 0.00850 mol L^{-1} in HF
b. 0.112 mol L^{-1} in NaCl and 0.0953 mol L^{-1} in KF
c. 0.132 mol L^{-1} in NH_4Cl and 0.150 mol L^{-1} HNO_3
d. 0.0887 mol L^{-1} in sodium benzoate and 0.225 mol L^{-1} in potassium bromide
e. 0.0450 mol L^{-1} in HCl and 0.0225 mol L^{-1} in HNO_3

140. Determine the pH of each two-component solution.

a. 0.050 mol L^{-1} KOH and 0.015 mol L^{-1} $Ba(OH)_2$
b. 0.265 mol L^{-1} NH_4NO_3 and 0.102 mol L^{-1} HCN
c. 0.075 mol L^{-1} RbOH and 0.100 mol L^{-1} $NaHCO_3$
d. 0.088 mol L^{-1} $HClO_4$ and 0.022 mol L^{-1} KOH
e. 0.115 mol L^{-1} NaClO and 0.0500 mol L^{-1} KI

141. Write net ionic equations for the reactions that take place when aqueous solutions of the following substances are mixed:

a. sodium cyanide and nitric acid
b. ammonium chloride and sodium hydroxide
c. sodium cyanide and ammonium bromide
d. potassium hydrogen sulfate and lithium acetate
e. sodium hypochlorite and ammonia

142. Morphine has the formula $C_{17}H_{19}NO_3$. It is a base and accepts one proton per molecule. It is isolated from opium. A 0.682 g sample of opium is found to require 8.92 mL of a 0.0116 mol L^{-1} solution of sulfuric acid for neutralization. Assuming that morphine is the only acid or base present in opium, calculate the percentage of morphine in the sample of opium.

143. The pH of a 1.00 mol L^{-1} solution of urea, a weak organic base, is 7.050. Calculate the K_a of protonated urea.

144. A solution is prepared by dissolving 0.10 mol of acetic acid and 0.10 mol of ammonium chloride in enough water to make 1.0 L of solution. Find the concentration of ammonia in the solution.

145. Lactic acid is a weak acid found in milk. Its calcium salt is a source of calcium for growing animals. A saturated solution of this salt, which we can represent as $Ca(Lact)_2$, has a $[Ca^{2+}] = 0.26$ mol L^{-1} and a pH $= 8.40$. Assuming the salt is completely dissociated, calculate the K_a of lactic acid.

146. A solution of 0.23 mol of the chloride salt of protonated quinine (QH^+), a weak organic base, in 1.0 L of solution has pH $= 4.58$. Find the K_b of quinine (Q).

147. 2,4-Dichlorophenoxyacetic acid ("2,4-D") is a widely used herbicide with the molecular formula $C_8H_6Cl_2O_3$. The pK_a of 2,4-D is 2.73. A certain water-based herbicide product contains 190 g L^{-1} of 2,4-D. What is the pH of the 2,4-D solution?

148. Ascorbic acid (or vitamin C), $H_2C_6H_6O_6$, is a diprotic acid. It is an antioxidant, which means that it scavenges free-radicals produced by oxidation reactions, thereby inhibiting further oxidation reactions that can damage cells. Under physiological conditions, vitamin C loses only one proton to a significant extent according to the following reaction:

$$H_2C_6H_6O_6(aq) + H_2O(l) \rightleftharpoons HC_6H_6O_6^-(aq) + H_3O^+(aq)$$

a. Write the equilibrium-constant expression for the ionization of ascorbic acid.
b. The acid ionization constant for this reaction is 8.0×10^{-5}. Calculate the concentration of ascorbic acid, ascorbate ion, and hydronium ion at equilibrium following the dissolution of a 1000 mg tablet of ascorbic acid to make 100.0 mL of solution. Also, calculate the pH of the solution.
c. The second acid ionization constant for ascorbic acid is 2.5×10^{-12}. Write the reaction corresponding to the second acid ionization constant and determine whether a solution of sodium ascorbate will be acidic or basic. What is the pH of a 0.100 mol L^{-1} solution of sodium ascorbate?
d. The dissociation of ascorbic acid in water is endothermic by 22.8 kJ mol^{-1}. Using the value for the first acid ionization constant from part (b), a 298 K value, determine the first acid ionization constant at physiological temperature, 335 K. Also determine the pH of a solution such as the one in part (b) but at 335 K.

Challenge Problems

149. A student mistakenly calculates the pH of a 1.0×10^{-7} mol L^{-1} HI solution to be 7.0. Explain why this calculation is incorrect and calculate the correct pH.

150. When 2.55 g of an unknown weak acid (HA) with a molar mass of 85.0 g mol^{-1} is dissolved in 250.0 g of water, the freezing point of the resulting solution is −0.257 °C. Calculate K_a for the unknown weak acid.

151. Calculate the pH of a solution that is 0.00115 mol L^{-1} in HCl and 0.0100 mol L^{-1} in $HClO_2$.

152. To what volume should 1 L of a solution of a weak acid HA be diluted to reduce the $[H^+]$ to one-half of that in the original solution?

153. HA, a weak acid, with $K_a = 1.0 \times 10^{-8}$, also forms the ion HA_2^-. The reaction is $HA(aq) + A^-(aq) \rightleftharpoons HA_2^-(aq)$ and its $K = 4.0$. Calculate the $[H^+]$, $[A^-]$, and $[HA_2^-]$ in a 1.0 mol L^{-1} solution of HA.

154. Basicity in the gas phase can be defined as the proton affinity of the base, for example, $CH_3NH_2(g) + H^+(g) \rightleftharpoons CH_3NH_3^+(g)$. In the gas phase, $(CH_3)_3N$ is more basic than CH_3NH_2, while in solution the reverse is true. Account for this observation.

155. Calculate the pH of a solution prepared from 0.200 mol of NH_4CN and enough water to make 1.00 L of solution.

156. To 1.0 L of a 0.30 mol L^{-1} solution of $HClO_2$ is added 0.20 mol of NaF. Calculate the $[HClO_2]$ at equilibrium.

157. A mixture of Na_2CO_3 and $NaHCO_3$ has a mass of 82.2 g. It is dissolved in 1.00 L of water and the pH is found to be 9.95. Find the mass of $NaHCO_3$ in the mixture.

158. A mixture of NaCN and $NaHSO_4$ consists of a total of 0.60 mol. When the mixture is dissolved in 1.0 L of water and comes to equilibrium the pH is found to be 9.9. Find the amount of NaCN in the mixture.

Conceptual Problems

159. Without doing any calculations, determine which solution would be most acidic.
a. 0.0100 mol L^{-1} in HCl and 0.0100 mol L^{-1} in KOH
b. 0.0100 mol L^{-1} in HF and 0.0100 mol L^{-1} in KBr
c. 0.0100 mol L^{-1} in NH_4Cl and 0.0100 mol L^{-1} in CH_3NH_3Br
d. 0.100 mol L^{-1} in NaCN and 0.100 mol L^{-1} in $CaCl_2$

160. Without doing any calculations, determine which solution would be most basic.
a. 0.100 mol L^{-1} in NaClO and 0.100 mol L^{-1} in NaF
b. 0.0100 mol L^{-1} in KCl and 0.0100 mol L^{-1} in $KClO_2$
c. 0.0100 mol L^{-1} in HNO_3 and 0.0100 mol L^{-1} in NaOH
d. 0.0100 mol L^{-1} in NH_4Cl and 0.0100 mol L^{-1} in HCN

161. Rank the acids in order of increasing acid strength.

CH_3COOH $CH_2ClCOOH$ $CHCl_2COOH$ CCl_3COOH

162. Rank the oxygen atoms on uracil (left) and thymine (right) from the most basic to the least basic. Explain.

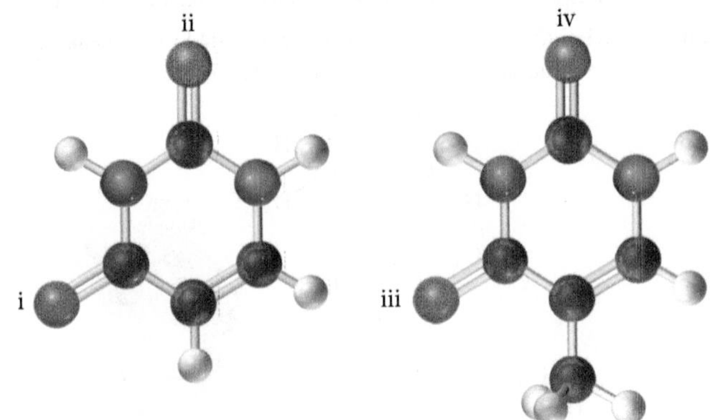

Aqueous Ionic Equilibrium

16

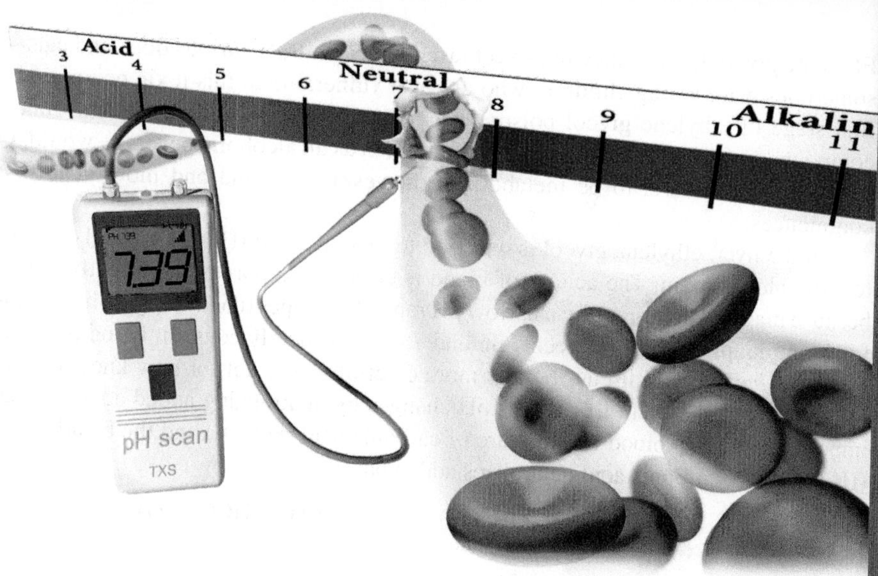

Human blood is held at nearly constant pH by the action of buffers, a main topic of this chapter.

In the strictly scientific sense of the word, insolubility does not exist, and even those substances characterized by the most obstinate resistance to the solvent action of water may properly be designated as extraordinarily difficult of solution, not as insoluble.

—Otto N. Witt (1853–1915)

WE HAVE ALREADY seen the importance of aqueous solutions, first in Chapters 4, 12, and 14, and most recently in Chapter 15 on acids and bases. We now turn our attention to two additional topics involving aqueous solutions: buffers (solutions that resist pH change) and solubility equilibria (the extent to which slightly soluble ionic compounds dissolve in water). Buffers are tremendously important in biology because nearly all physiological processes must occur within a narrow pH range. Solubility equilibria are related to the solubility rules that we learned in Chapter 4. In this chapter, we will find a more complicated picture: solids that we considered insoluble under the simple "solubility rules" are actually better described as being only very slightly soluble, as the chapter-opening quotation suggests. Solubility equilibria are important in predicting not only solubility, but also precipitation reactions that might occur when aqueous solutions are mixed.

16.1 The Danger of Antifreeze

Every year, thousands of dogs and cats die from consuming a common household product: antifreeze that was improperly stored or that leaked out of a car radiator. Most types of antifreeze used in cars are aqueous solutions of ethylene glycol (ethan-1,2-diol):

$HOCH_2CH_2OH$

Ethylene glycol has a somewhat sweet taste that can attract curious dogs and cats—and sometimes even young children, who are also vulnerable to this toxic compound. The first stage of ethylene glycol poisoning is a state resembling drunkenness. Since the compound is an alcohol, it affects the brain much as an alcoholic beverage would. Once ethylene glycol starts to be metabolized, however, a second and more deadly stage commences.

In the liver, ethylene glycol is oxidized to glycolic acid ($HOCH_2COOH$), which enters the bloodstream. The acidity of blood is critically important, and tightly regulated, because many proteins require a narrow pH range for proper functioning. In human blood, for example, pH is held between 7.36 and 7.42. This nearly constant blood pH is maintained by *buffers*. We discuss buffers more carefully later, but for now know that a buffer is a chemical system that resists pH changes by neutralizing added acid or base. An important buffer in blood is a mixture of carbonic acid (H_2CO_3) and the bicarbonate ion (HCO_3^-). The carbonic acid neutralizes added base:

$$H_2CO_3(aq) + \underset{\text{added base}}{OH^-(aq)} \longrightarrow H_2O(l) + HCO_3^-(aq)$$

The bicarbonate ion neutralizes added acid:

$$HCO_3^-(aq) + \underset{\text{added acid}}{H^+(aq)} \longrightarrow H_2CO_3(aq)$$

In this way, the carbonic acid and bicarbonate ion buffering system keeps blood pH constant.

When the glycolic acid generated by antifreeze consumption first enters the bloodstream, the acid's tendency to lower blood pH is countered by the buffering action of the bicarbonate ion. However, if the quantities of consumed antifreeze are large enough, the glycolic acid overwhelms the capacity of the buffer (discussed in Section 16.3), causing blood pH to drop to dangerously low levels.

Low blood pH results in a condition called *acidosis*; the acid affects the equilibrium between hemoglobin (Hb) and oxygen:

$$HbH^+(aq) + O_2(g) \rightleftharpoons HbO_2(aq) + \overset{\text{Excess } H^+ \downarrow}{H^+(aq)}$$

Shift left (←)

The excess acid causes the equilibrium to shift to the left, reducing the blood's ability to carry oxygen. At this point, the cat or dog may begin hyperventilating in an effort to overcome the acidic blood's lowered oxygen-carrying capacity. If no treatment is administered, the animal will eventually go into a coma and die.

One treatment for ethylene glycol poisoning is the administration of ethanol (the alcohol found in alcoholic beverages). The two molecules are similar enough that the liver enzyme that catalyzes the metabolism of ethylene glycol also acts on ethanol, but the enzyme has a higher affinity for ethanol than for ethylene glycol. Consequently, the enzyme preferentially metabolizes ethanol, allowing the unmetabolized ethylene glycol to escape through the urine. If administered early, this treatment can save the life of a dog or cat that has consumed ethylene glycol.

16.2 Buffers: Solutions That Resist pH Change

Most solutions change pH rapidly upon the addition of an acid or base. As we have just learned, however, a **buffer** resists pH change by neutralizing added acid or added base. A buffer contains significant amounts of both *a weak acid and its conjugate base* (or a weak base and its conjugate acid). For example, we saw that the buffer in blood was composed of carbonic acid (H_2CO_3) and its conjugate base, the bicarbonate ion (HCO_3^-). When additional base is added to a buffer, the weak acid reacts with the base, neutralizing it. When additional acid is added to a buffer, the conjugate base reacts with the acid, neutralizing it. In this way, a buffer can maintain a nearly constant pH.

A weak acid by itself, even though it partially ionizes to form some of its conjugate base, does not contain sufficient base to be a buffer. Similarly, a weak base by itself, even though it partially ionizes water to form some of its conjugate acid, does not contain sufficient acid to be a buffer. *A buffer must contain significant amounts of both a weak acid and its conjugate base.* Consider the simple buffer made by dissolving acetic acid (CH_3COOH) and sodium acetate (CH_3COONa) in water (Figure 16.1 ▼).

Suppose that we add a strong base, such as NaOH, to this solution. The acetic acid reacts with the OH^- from NaOH, neutralizing the base according to the following net ionic equation:

$$OH^-(aq) + CH_3COOH(aq) \longrightarrow H_2O(l) + CH_3COO^-(aq)$$

CH_3COO^- (acetate ion) is the conjugate base of CH_3COOH. It can be added to a solution in the form of the sodium salt, CH_3COONa (sodium acetate), which completely dissociates in solution.

As long as the amount of added NaOH is less than the amount of CH_3COOH in solution, the buffer neutralizes the added NaOH and the resulting pH change is small. Suppose, on the other hand, that we add a strong acid, such as HCl, to the solution. In this case, the HCl completely reacts with water to yield hydronium ion, H_3O^+, which is neutralized by the conjugate base, CH_3COO^-, according to the following net ionic equation:

$$H_3O^+(aq) + CH_3COO^-(aq) \longrightarrow H_2O(l) + CH_3COOH(aq)$$

As long as the amount of added HCl is less than the amount of CH_3COONa in solution, the buffer neutralizes the added HCl and the resulting pH change is small.

Summarizing Buffer Characteristics:

- Buffers resist pH change.
- A buffer contains significant amounts of both a weak acid and its conjugate base.

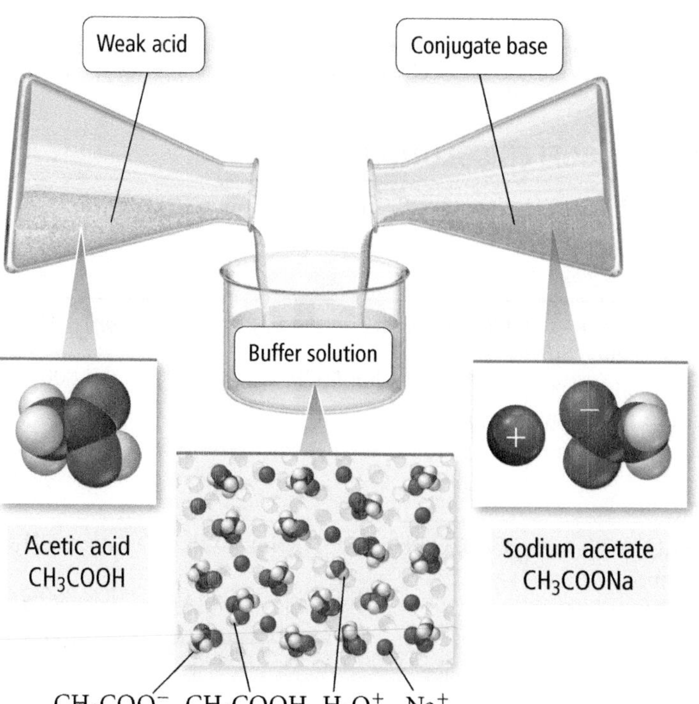

◀ **FIGURE 16.1 A Buffer Solution** A buffer typically consists of a weak acid (which can neutralize added base) and its conjugate base (which can neutralize added acid).

The molecular formula for sodium acetate is commonly written as CH_3COONa to emphasize that the sodium ion has replaced a proton in acetic acid, CH_3COOH.

- The weak acid neutralizes added base.
- The conjugate base neutralizes added acid.

Calculating the pH of a Buffer Solution

In Chapter 15, we learned how to calculate the pH of a solution containing either a weak acid or its conjugate base, but not both. How do we calculate the pH of a buffer—a solution containing both? Consider a solution that initially contains CH_3COOH and CH_3COONa, each at a concentration of 0.100 mol L^{-1}. The acetic acid ionizes according to the reaction:

$$CH_3COOH(aq) + H_2O(l) \rightleftharpoons H_3O^+(aq) + CH_3COO^-(aq)$$

Initial concentration: 0.100 mol L^{-1} 0.100 mol L^{-1}

Le Châtelier's principle is discussed in Section 14.8.

However, the ionization of CH_3COOH in the solution is suppressed compared to its ionization in a solution that does not initially contain any CH_3COO^- because the presence of CH_3COO^- *shifts the equilibrium to the left* (as we would expect from Le Châtelier's principle). In other words, the presence of the $CH_3COO^-(aq)$ ion causes the acid to ionize even less than it normally would (Figure 16.2 ▼), resulting in a less acidic solution (higher pH). This effect is known as the **common ion effect**, so named because the solution contains two substances (CH_3COOH and CH_3COONa) that share a common ion (CH_3COO^-). To find the pH of a buffer solution containing common ions, we work an equilibrium problem in which the initial concentrations include both the acid and its conjugate base, as shown in Example 16.1.

pH = 2.9

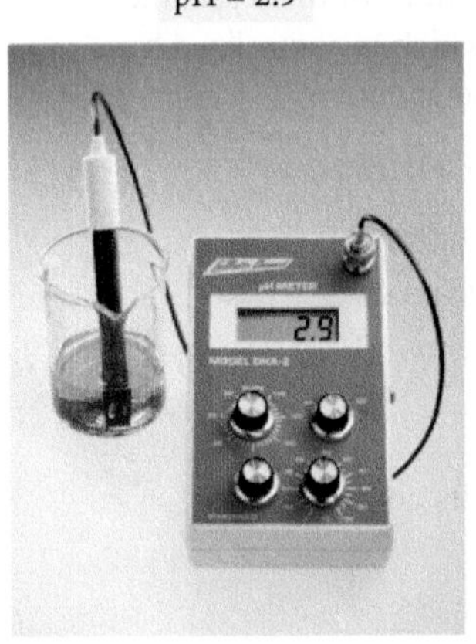

0.100 mol L^{-1} CH_3COOH

pH = 8.9

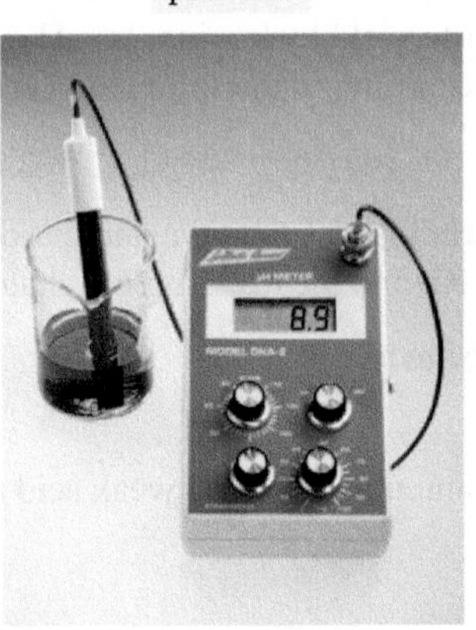

0.100 mol L^{-1} CH_3COONa

pH = 4.7

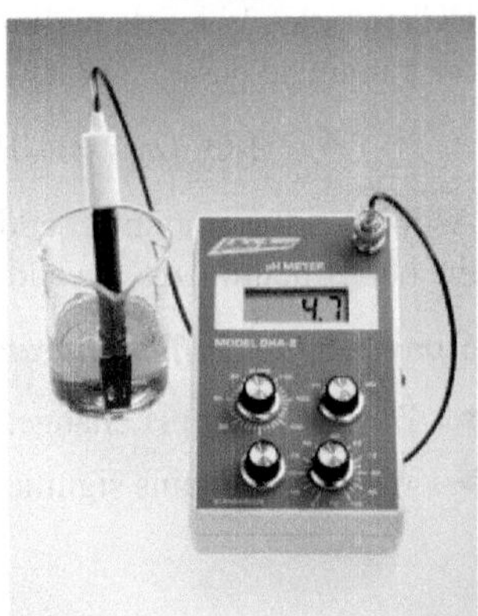

0.100 mol L^{-1} CH_3COOH
0.100 mol L^{-1} CH_3COONa

▶ **FIGURE 16.2 The Common Ion Effect** The pH of a 0.100 mol L^{-1} acetic acid solution is 2.9. The pH of a 0.100 mol L^{-1} sodium acetate solution is 8.9. The pH of a solution that is 0.100 mol L^{-1} in acetic acid and 0.100 mol L^{-1} in sodium acetate is 4.7.

EXAMPLE 16.1 CALCULATING THE pH OF A BUFFER SOLUTION

Calculate the pH of a buffer solution that is 0.100 mol L^{-1} in CH_3COOH and 0.100 mol L^{-1} in CH_3COONa.

SOLUTION

1. Write the balanced equation for the ionization of the acid and use it as a guide to prepare an ICE table showing the given concentrations of the acid and its conjugate base as the initial concentrations. Leave room in the table for the changes in concentrations and for the equilibrium concentrations.

$$CH_3COOH(aq) + H_2O(l) \rightleftharpoons H_3O^+(aq) + CH_3COO^-(aq)$$

	$[CH_3COOH]$	$[H_3O^+]$	$[CH_3COO^-]$
Initial	0.100	≈0	0.100
Change			
Equil			

2. Represent the change in the concentration of H_3O^+ with the variable x. Express the changes in the concentrations of the other reactants and products in terms of x.

$$CH_3COOH(aq) + H_2O(l) \rightleftharpoons H_3O^+(aq) + CH_3COO^-(aq)$$

	$[CH_3COOH]$	$[H_3O^+]$	$[CH_3COO^-]$
Initial	0.100	≈0	0.100
Change	$-x$	$+x$	$+x$
Equil			

3. Sum each column to determine the equilibrium concentrations in terms of the initial concentrations and the variable x.	$CH_3COOH(aq) + H_2O(l) \rightleftharpoons H_3O^+(aq) + CH_3COO^-(aq)$ | | $[CH_3COOH]$ | $[H_3O^+]$ | $[CH_3COO^-]$ | Initial | 0.100 | ≈0 | 0.100 Change | $-x$ | $+x$ | $+x$ Equil | $0.100 - x$ | x | $0.100 + x$
4. Substitute the expressions for the equilibrium concentrations (from step 3) into the expression for the acid ionization constant. In most cases, you can make the approximation that *x is small.* Substitute the value of the acid ionization constant (from Table 15.5) into the K_a expression and solve for x. Confirm that *x is small* by calculating the ratio of x and the number it was subtracted from in the approximation. The ratio should be less than 0.05 (or 5%). (See Sections 14.7 and 15.7 to review the *x is small* approximation.)	$K_a = \frac{[H_3O^+][CH_3COO^-]}{[CH_3COOH]}$ $= \frac{x(0.100 + \cancel{x})}{0.100 - \cancel{x}}$ (*x is small*) $1.8 \times 10^{-5} = \frac{x(\cancel{0.100})}{\cancel{0.100}}$ $x = 1.8 \times 10^{-5}$ $\frac{1.8 \times 10^{-5}}{0.100} \times 100\% = 0.018\%$ Therefore the approximation is valid.
5. Determine the H_3O^+ concentration from the computed value of x and substitute into the pH equation to find pH.	$[H_3O^+] = x = 1.8 \times 10^{-5}$ mol L^{-1} $pH = -\log[H_3O^+]$ $= -\log(1.8 \times 10^{-5})$ $= 4.74$

FOR PRACTICE 16.1

Calculate the pH of a buffer solution that is 0.200 mol L^{-1} in CH_3COOH and 0.100 mol L^{-1} in CH_3COONa.

FOR MORE PRACTICE 16.1

Calculate the pH of the buffer that results from mixing 60.0 mL of 0.250 mol L^{-1} formic acid (HCOOH) and 15.0 mL of 0.500 mol L^{-1} sodium formate (NaHCOO).

The Henderson–Hasselbalch Equation

Finding the pH of a buffer solution can be simplified by deriving an equation that relates the pH of the solution to the initial concentrations of the buffer components. Consider a buffer containing the weak acid HA and its conjugate base A^-. The acid ionizes as follows:

$$HA(aq) + H_2O(l) \rightleftharpoons H_3O^+(aq) + A^-(aq)$$

We can derive an expression for the concentration of H_3O^+ from the acid ionization equilibrium expression by solving the expression for $[H_3O^+]$.

$$K_a = \frac{[H_3O^+][A^-]}{[HA]}$$

$$[H_3O^+] = K_a \frac{[HA]}{[A^-]} \qquad [16.1]$$

If we make the same *x is small* approximation that we make for weak acid or weak base equilibrium problems, *we can consider the equilibrium concentrations of HA and A^- to be essentially identical to the initial concentrations of HA and A^-* (see fourth step of Example 16.1). Therefore, to determine $[H_3O^+]$ for any buffer solution, we multiply K_a by the ratio of the concentrations of the acid and the conjugate base. To find the $[H_3O^+]$ of the buffer in Example 16.1 (a solution that is 0.100 mol L^{-1} in CH_3COOH

Recall that the variable x in a weak acid equilibrium problem represents the change in the initial acid concentration. The *x is small* approximation is valid because so little of the weak acid ionizes compared to its initial concentration.

and 0.100 mol L^{-1} in CH_3COONa), we substitute the concentrations of CH_3COOH and CH_3COO^- into Equation 16.1:

$$[H_3O^+] = K_a \frac{[CH_3COOH]}{[CH_3COO^-]} = K_a \frac{0.100}{0.100} = K_a$$

In this buffer solution, as in any in which the acid and conjugate base concentrations are equal, $[H_3O^+]$ is equal to K_a.

We can derive an equation for the pH of a buffer by taking the logarithm of both sides of Equation 16.1:

$$[H_3O^+] = K_a \frac{[HA]}{[A^-]}$$

$$\log[H_3O^+] = \log\left(K_a \frac{[HA]}{[A^-]}\right)$$

$$\log[H_3O^+] = \log K_a + \log \frac{[HA]}{[A^-]} \qquad [16.2]$$

Multiplying both sides of Equation 16.2 by −1 and rearranging, we get:

$$-\log[H_3O^+] = -\log K_a - \log \frac{[HA]}{[A^-]}$$

$$-\log[H_3O^+] = -\log K_a + \log \frac{[A^-]}{[HA]}$$

Since $pH = -\log[H_3O^+]$ and since $pK_a = -\log K_a$, we obtain the result:

$$pH = pK_a + \log \frac{[A^-]}{[HA]}$$

Since A^- is a weak base and HA is a weak acid, we can generalize the equation:

Note that, as expected, the pH of a buffer increases with an increase in the amount of base relative to the amount of acid.

$$pH = pK_a + \log \frac{[base]}{[acid]} \qquad [16.3]$$

where the base is the conjugate base of the acid or the acid is the conjugate acid of the base. This equation, known as the **Henderson–Hasselbalch equation**, allows us to quickly calculate the pH of a buffer solution from the initial concentrations of the buffer components *as long as the x is small approximation is valid*. In the following example, we show how to find the pH of a buffer in two ways: in the left column we solve a common ion effect equilibrium problem using a method similar to the one we used to solve Example 16.1; in the right column, we use the Henderson–Hasselbalch equation.

EXAMPLE 16.2 CALCULATING THE pH OF A BUFFER SOLUTION AS AN EQUILIBRIUM PROBLEM AND WITH THE HENDERSON–HASSELBALCH EQUATION

Calculate the pH of a buffer solution that is 0.050 mol L^{-1} in benzoic acid (C_6H_5COOH) and 0.150 mol L^{-1} in sodium benzoate (C_6H_5COONa). For benzoic acid, $K_a = 6.3 \times 10^{-5}$.

SOLUTION

Equilibrium Approach	Henderson–Hasselbalch Approach
Write the balanced equation for the ionization of the acid and use it as a guide to prepare an ICE table.	To find the pH of this solution, determine which component is the acid and which is the base and substitute their concentrations into the Henderson–Hasselbalch equation to calculate pH.

$C_6H_5COOH(aq) + H_2O(l) \rightleftharpoons H_3O^+(aq) + C_6H_5COO^-(aq)$

	$[C_6H_5COOH]$	$[H_3O^+]$	$[C_6H_5COO^-]$
Initial	0.050	≈ 0	0.150
Change	$-x$	$+x$	$+x$
Equil	$0.050 - x$	x	$0.150 + x$

Substitute the expressions for the equilibrium concentrations into the expression for the acid ionization constant. Make the *x is small* approximation and solve for *x*.

$$K_a = \frac{[H_3O^+][C_6H_5COO^-]}{[C_6H_5COOH]}$$

$$= \frac{x(0.150 + \cancel{x})}{0.050 - \cancel{x}} \quad (x \text{ is small})$$

$$6.3 \times 10^{-5} = \frac{x(0.150)}{0.050}$$

$$x = 2.1 \times 10^{-5}$$

Since $[H_3O^+] = x$, we calculate pH as follows:

$$pH = -\log[H_3O^+]$$

$$= -\log(2.1 \times 10^{-5})$$

$$= 4.68$$

C_6H_5COOH is the acid and C_6H_5COONa is the base. Therefore, we calculate the pH as follows:

$$pH = pK_a + \log\frac{[\text{base}]}{[\text{acid}]}$$

$$= -\log(6.3 \times 10^{-5}) + \log\frac{0.150}{0.050}$$

$$= 4.2\underline{0}1 + 0.4\underline{7}7$$

$$= 4.68$$

Confirm that the *x is small* approximation is valid by calculating the ratio of *x* to the number it was subtracted from in the approximation. The ratio should be less than 0.05 (or 5%). (See Sections 14.7 and 15.7 to review the *x is small* approximation.)

$$\frac{2.1 \times 10^{-5}}{0.050} \times 100\% = 0.042\%$$

The approximation is valid.

Confirm that the *x is small* approximation is valid by calculating the $[H_3O^+]$ from the pH. Since $[H_3O^+]$ is formed by ionization of the acid, the calculated $[H_3O^+]$ has to be less than 0.05 (or 5%) of the initial concentration of the acid in order for the *x is small* approximation to be valid.

$$pH = 4.68 = -\log[H_3O^+]$$

$$[H_3O^+] = 10^{-4.68} = 2.1 \times 10^{-5}\ \text{mol L}^{-1}$$

$$\frac{2.1 \times 10^{-5}}{0.050} \times 100\% = 0.042\%$$

The approximation is valid.

FOR PRACTICE 16.2

Calculate the pH of a buffer solution that is 0.250 mol L^{-1} in HCN and 0.170 mol L^{-1} in KCN. For HCN, $K_a = 6.2 \times 10^{-10}$ ($pK_a = 9.31$). Use both the equilibrium approach and the Henderson–Hasselbalch approach.

When Can You Use the Henderson–Hasselbalch Equation? The Henderson–Hasselbalch equation can only be used when the *x is small* approximation is valid. However, as you can see from Example 16.2, checking the *x is small* approximation is not as convenient as it is with the equilibrium approach. A general rule of thumb is that the *x is small* approximation is valid when the concentrations of *each* weak acid–base conjugate pair are 100 times greater than the equilibrium constant:

$$K_a < 100 \times [HA] \text{ and } K_a < 100 \times [A^-]$$

For many practical buffer solutions, K_a values are 10^{-4} or smaller, and buffer concentrations are 10^{-2} mol L^{-1} or higher, and the Henderson–Hasselbalch equation can be used.

CONCEPTUAL CONNECTION 16.1

pH of Buffer Solutions

A buffer contains the weak acid HA and its conjugate base A^-. The weak acid has a pK_a of 4.82 and the buffer has a pH of 4.25. Which statement is true of the relative concentrations of the weak acid and conjugate base in the buffer?

(a) $[HA] > [A^-]$ **(b)** $[HA] < [A^-]$ **(c)** $[HA] = [A^-]$

Which buffer component would you add to change the pH of the buffer to 4.72?

Calculating pH Changes in a Buffer Solution

When an acid or a base is added to a buffer, the buffer resists a pH change. Nonetheless, the pH does change by a small amount. Calculating the pH change requires breaking up the problem into two parts: (1) a stoichiometry calculation (in which we calculate how the addition changes the relative amounts of acid and conjugate base); and (2) an equilibrium calculation (in which we calculate the pH based on the new amounts of acid and conjugate base). We demonstrate this calculation with a 1.0 L buffer solution that is 0.100 mol L^{-1} in the generic acid HA and 0.100 mol L^{-1} in its conjugate base A^-. Since the concentrations of the weak acid and the conjugate base are equal, the pH of the buffer is equal to p*K*a. Let's calculate the pH of the solution after we add 0.025 mol of strong acid (H^+) (assuming that the change in volume from adding the acid is negligible).

The Stoichiometry Calculation As the added acid is neutralized, it converts a stoichiometric amount of the base into its conjugate acid through the neutralization reaction (Figure 16.3(a) ▼):

$$\underset{\text{added acid}}{H_3O^+(aq)} + \underset{\text{weak base in buffer}}{A^-(aq)} \longrightarrow H_2O(l) + HA(aq)$$

Neutralizing 0.025 mol of the strong acid (H_3O^+) requires 0.025 mol of the weak base (A^-). Consequently, the amount of A^- *decreases* by 0.025 mol and the amount of HA *increases* by 0.025 mol (because of the 1:1:1 stoichiometry of the neutralization reaction). We can track these changes in tabular form as follows:

It is best to work with amounts in moles instead of concentrations when tracking these changes, as explained below.

	$H_3O^+(aq)$	+	$A^-(aq)$	$\longrightarrow$	$HA(aq)$
Before addition	0 mol		0.100 mol		0.100 mol
Addition	+0.025 mol		—		—
After addition	0 mol		0.075 mol		0.125 mol

Notice that this table *is not an ICE table.* This table simply tracks the stoichiometric changes that occur during the neutralization of the added acid.

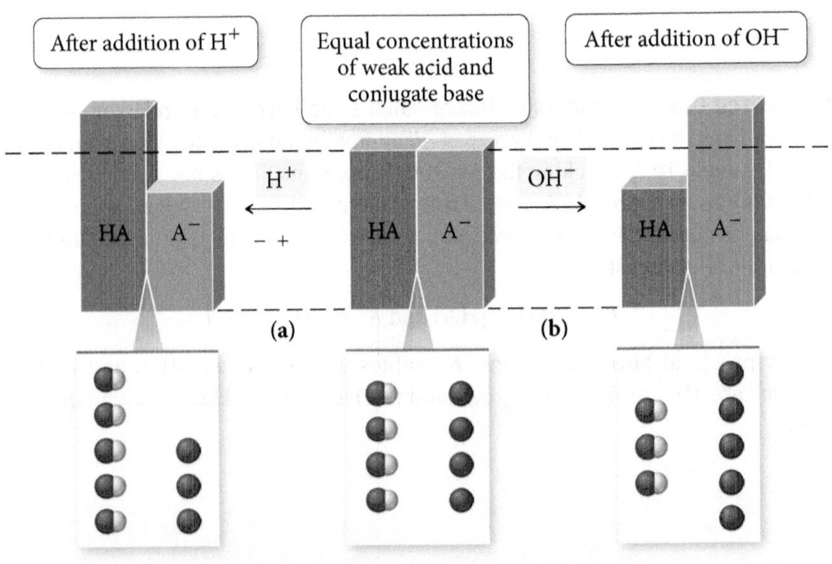

▶ **FIGURE 16.3 Buffering Action** (a) When an acid is added to a buffer, a stoichiometric amount of the weak base is converted to the conjugate acid. (b) When a base is added to a buffer, a stoichiometric amount of the weak acid is converted to the conjugate base.

The Equilibrium Calculation We have just seen that adding a small amount of acid to a buffer is equivalent to changing the initial concentrations of the acid and conjugate base present in the buffer (in this case, since the volume is 1.0 L, [HA] increased from 0.100 mol L^{-1} to 0.125 mol L^{-1}, and [A^-] decreased from 0.100 mol L^{-1} to 0.075 mol L^{-1}). Knowing these new initial concentrations, we can calculate the new pH in the same way that we calculate the pH of any buffer: either by working a full equilibrium problem or by using the Henderson–Hasselbalch equation (see Examples 16.1 and 16.2). In this case, we work the full equilibrium problem. We begin by writing the balanced equation for the ionization of the acid and using it as a guide to prepare an ICE table. The initial concentrations for the ICE table are those that we calculated in the stoichiometry part of the calculation.

$$HA(aq) + H_2O(l) \rightleftharpoons H_3O^+(aq) + A^-(aq)$$

	[HA]	[H_3O^+]	[A^-]
Initial	0.125	≈0	0.075
Change	$-x$	$+x$	$+x$
Equil	$0.125 - x$	x	$0.075 + x$

From stoichiometry calculation

We then substitute the expressions for the equilibrium concentrations into the expression for the acid ionization constant. As long as K_a is sufficiently small relative to the initial concentrations, we can make the *x is small* approximation and solve for x, which is equal to [H_3O^+].

$$K_a = \frac{[H_3O^+][A^-]}{[HA]}$$

$$= \frac{x(0.075 + \cancel{x})}{0.125 - \cancel{x}} \quad (x \text{ is small})$$

$$K_a = \frac{x(0.075)}{0.125}$$

$$x = [H_3O^+] = K_a \frac{0.125}{0.075}$$

Once we calculate [H_3O^+], we can calculate the pH with the equation pH $= -\log[H_3O^+]$.

Notice that, since the above expression for x contains a *ratio* of concentrations [HA]/[A^-], the *amounts of acid and base in moles* may be substituted in place of concentration because, in a single buffer solution, the volume is the same for both the acid and the base. Therefore the volumes cancel:

$$[HA]/[A^-] = \frac{\frac{n_{HA}}{\cancel{V}}}{\frac{n_{A^-}}{\cancel{V}}} = n_{HA}/n_{A^-}$$

The effect of adding a small amount of strong base to the buffer is exactly the opposite of adding acid. The added base converts a stoichiometric amount of the acid into its conjugate base through the neutralization reaction (Figure 16.3(b) ◂):

$$\underset{\text{added base}}{OH^-(aq)} + \underset{\text{weak acid in buffer}}{HA(aq)} \longrightarrow H_2O(l) + A^-(aq)$$

If we add 0.025 mol of OH^-, then the amount of A^- goes *up* by 0.025 mol and the amount of HA goes *down* by 0.025 mol, as shown in the following table:

	$OH^-(aq)$	+	$HA(aq)$	⟶	$H_2O(l)$	+	$A^-(aq)$
Before addition	0 mol		0.100 mol				0.100 mol
Addition	+0.025 mol		—				—
After addition	0 mol		0.075 mol				0.125 mol

When you calculate the pH of a buffer after adding small amounts of acid or base, remember:

The easiest way to remember these changes is relatively simple: adding acid creates more acid; adding base creates more base.

- Adding a small amount of strong acid to a buffer converts a stoichiometric amount of the base to the conjugate acid.
- Adding a small amount of strong base to a buffer converts a stoichiometric amount of the acid to the conjugate base.

The net effect of small additions of acid or base to the buffer solution is a change in concentration of HA and A^-, which uses up the added H_3O^+ or OH^-. This **buffering action** maintains a fairly constant pH.

The following example and For Practice problems involve calculating pH changes in a buffer solution after small amounts of strong acid or strong base are added. As we have seen, these problems generally have two parts.

- Part I. Stoichiometry—use the stoichiometry of the neutralization equation to calculate the changes in the amounts (in moles) of the buffer components upon addition of the acid or base.
- Part II. Equilibrium—use the new amounts of buffer components to work an equilibrium problem to find pH. (For most buffers, this can also be done with the Henderson–Hasselbalch equation.)

EXAMPLE 16.3 CALCULATING THE pH CHANGE IN A BUFFER SOLUTION AFTER THE ADDITION OF A SMALL AMOUNT OF STRONG ACID OR BASE

A 1.0 L buffer solution contains 0.100 mol CH_3COOH and 0.100 mol CH_3COONa. The value of K_a for CH_3COOH is 1.8×10^{-5}. Since the initial amounts of acid and conjugate base are equal, the pH of the buffer is equal to $pK_a = -\log(1.8 \times 10^{-5}) = 4.74$. Calculate the new pH after adding 0.010 mol of solid NaOH to the buffer. For comparison, calculate the pH after adding 0.010 mol of solid NaOH to 1.0 L of pure water. (Ignore any small changes in volume that might occur upon addition of the base.)

SOLUTION

Part I: Stoichiometry. The addition of the base converts a stoichiometric amount of acid to the conjugate base (adding base creates more base). Write an equation showing the neutralization reaction and then set up a table to track the changes.

$$OH^-(aq) + CH_3COOH(aq) \longrightarrow H_2O(l) + CH_3COO^-(aq)$$

	$OH^-(aq)$	$CH_3COOH(aq)$	$CH_3COO^-(aq)$
Before addition	0 mol	0.100 mol	0.100 mol
Addition	0.010 mol	—	—
After addition	0 mol	0.090 mol	0.110 mol

Part II: Equilibrium. Write the balanced equation for the ionization of the acid and use it as a guide to prepare an ICE table. Use the amounts of acid and conjugate base from part I as the initial amounts of acid and conjugate base in the ICE table.

$$CH_3COOH(aq) + H_2O(l) \rightleftharpoons H_3O^+(aq) + CH_3COO^-(aq)$$

	$[CH_3COOH]$	$[H_3O^+]$	$[CH_3COO^-]$
Initial	0.090	0	0.110
Change	$-x$	$+x$	$+x$
Equil	$0.090 - x$	x	$0.110 + x$

Substitute the expressions for the equilibrium concentrations of acid and conjugate base into the expression for the acid ionization constant. Make the *x is small* approximation and solve for x. Calculate the pH from the value of x, which is equal to $[H_3O^+]$.

$$K_a = \frac{[H_3O^+][CH_3COO^-]}{[CH_3COOH]}$$

$$= \frac{x(0.110 + \cancel{x})}{0.090 - \cancel{x}} \quad (x \text{ is small})$$

$$1.8 \times 10^{-5} = \frac{x(0.110)}{0.090}$$

$$x = [H_3O^+] = 1.4\underline{7} \times 10^{-5}\ \text{mol L}^{-1}$$

$$\text{pH} = -\log[H_3O^+]$$

$$= -\log(1.4\underline{7} \times 10^{-5})$$

$$= 4.83$$

Confirm that the *x is small* approximation is valid by calculating the ratio of x to the smallest number it was subtracted from in the approximation. The ratio should be less than 0.05 (or 5%).

$$\frac{1.4\underline{7} \times 10^{-5}}{0.090} \times 100\% = 0.016\%$$

The approximation is valid.

Part II: Equilibrium Alternative (using the Henderson–Hasselbalch equation). As long as the *x is small* approximation is valid, you can substitute the quantities of acid and conjugate base after the addition (from part I) into the Henderson–Hasselbalch equation and calculate the new pH.	$\text{pH} = \text{p}K_a + \log\frac{[\text{base}]}{[\text{acid}]}$ $= -\log(1.8 \times 10^{-5}) + \log\frac{0.110}{0.090}$ $= 4.74 + 0.087$ $= 4.83$
The pH of 1.0 L of water after adding 0.010 mol of NaOH is calculated from the $[OH^-]$. For a strong base, $[OH^-]$ is simply the number of moles of OH^- divided by the number of litres of solution.	$[\text{OH}^-] = \frac{0.010\text{ mol}}{1.0\text{ L}} = 0.010\text{ mol L}^{-1}$ $\text{pOH} = -\log[\text{OH}^-] = -\log(0.010)$ $= 2.00$ $\text{pOH} + \text{pH} = 14.00$ $\text{pH} = 14.00 - \text{pOH}$ $= 14.00 - 2.00$ $= 12.00$

CHECK Notice that the buffer solution changed from pH = 4.74 to pH = 4.83 upon addition of the base (a small fraction of a single pH unit). In contrast, the pure water changed from pH = 7.00 to pH = 12.00, five whole pH units (a factor of 10^5). Notice also that even the buffer solution got slightly more basic upon addition of a base, as we would expect. To check your answer, always make sure the pH goes in the direction you expect: adding base should make the solution more basic (higher pH); adding acid should make the solution more acidic (lower pH).

FOR PRACTICE 16.3

Calculate the pH of the original buffer solution in Example 16.3 upon addition of 0.015 mol of NaOH to the original buffer.

FOR MORE PRACTICE 16.3

Calculate the pH in the solution upon addition of 10.0 mL of 1.00 mol L^{-1} HCl to the original buffer in Example 16.3.

CONCEPTUAL CONNECTION 16.2

Adding Acid or Base to a Buffer

A buffer contains equal amounts of a weak acid and its conjugate base and has a pH of 5.25. Which would be a reasonable value of buffer pH after the addition of a small amount of acid?

(a) 4.15 **(b)** 5.15 **(c)** 5.35 **(d)** 6.35

Buffers Containing a Base and Its Conjugate Acid

So far, we have seen examples of buffers composed of an acid and its conjugate base (where the conjugate base is an ion). A buffer can also be composed of a base and its conjugate acid (where the conjugate acid is an ion). For example, a solution containing both NH_3 and NH_4Cl will act as a buffer (Figure 16.4 ▼). The NH_3 is a weak base that neutralizes small amounts of added acid and the NH_4^+ ion is the conjugate acid that neutralizes small amounts of added base. We can calculate the pH of a solution like this in the same way we did for a buffer containing a weak acid and its conjugate base. When using the Henderson–Hasselbalch equation, however, we must first calculate $\text{p}K_a$ for the conjugate acid of the weak base. Recall from Section 15.8 that for a conjugate acid–base pair, $K_a \times K_b = K_w$. Taking the negative logarithm of both sides of this equation, we get:

$$-\log(K_a \times K_b) = -\log K_w$$
$$-\log K_a - \log K_b = -\log K_w$$

Since $-\log K_a = \text{p}K_a$ and $-\log K_b = \text{p}K_b$, and substituting 10^{-14} for K_w, we arrive at the following result (valid at 25 °C):

$$\text{p}K_a + \text{p}K_b = -\log 10^{-14}$$
$$\text{p}K_a + \text{p}K_b = 14 \qquad [16.4]$$

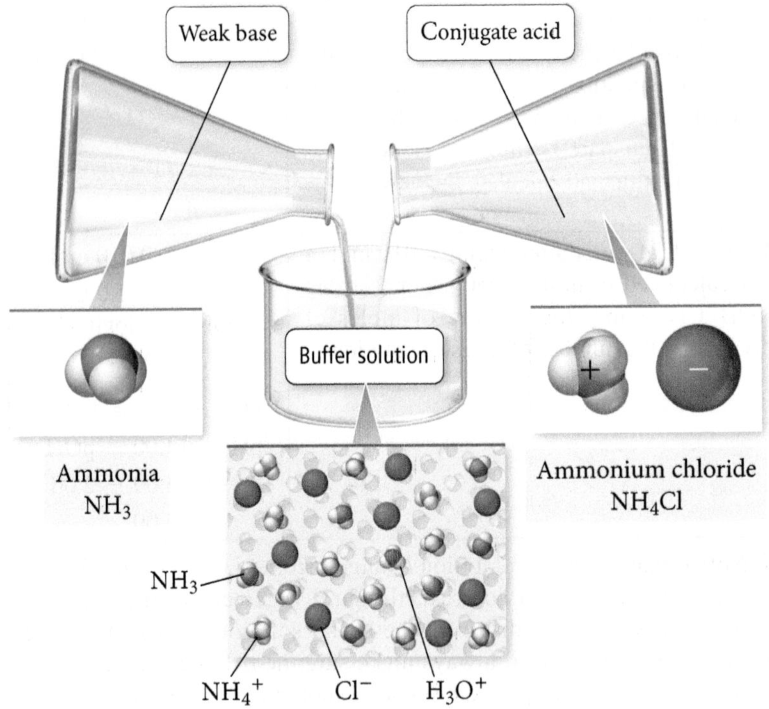

▶ **FIGURE 16.4 Buffer Containing a Base** A buffer can also consist of a weak base and its conjugate acid.

We can then find pK_a of the conjugate acid by subtracting pK_b of the weak base from 14. The following example illustrates the procedure for calculating the pH of a buffer composed of a weak base and its conjugate acid.

EXAMPLE 16.4 USING THE HENDERSON–HASSELBALCH EQUATION TO CALCULATE THE pH OF A BUFFER SOLUTION COMPOSED OF A WEAK BASE AND ITS CONJUGATE ACID

Use the Henderson–Hasselbalch equation to calculate the pH of a buffer solution that is 0.50 mol L^{-1} in NH_3 and 0.20 mol L^{-1} in NH_4Cl. For ammonia, $pK_b = 4.75$.

SOLUTION

Since K_b for NH_3 (1.8×10^{-5}) is much smaller than the initial concentrations in this problem, you can use the Henderson–Hasselbalch equation to calculate the pH of the buffer. First calculate pK_a from pK_b by using Equation 16.4.

$$pK_a + pK_b = 14$$

$$\begin{aligned} pK_a &= 14 - pK_b \\ &= 14 - 4.75 \\ &= 9.25 \end{aligned}$$

Then substitute the given quantities into the Henderson–Hasselbalch equation and calculate pH.

$$\begin{aligned} pH &= pK_a + \log \frac{[\text{base}]}{[\text{acid}]} \\ &= 9.25 + \log \frac{0.50}{0.20} \\ &= 9.25 + 0.40 \\ &= 9.65 \end{aligned}$$

FOR PRACTICE 16.4

Calculate the pH of 1.0 L of the buffer in Example 16.4 upon addition of 0.010 mol of solid NaOH.

FOR MORE PRACTICE 16.4

Calculate the pH of 1.0 L of the buffer in Example 16.4 upon addition of 30.0 mL of 1.0 mol L^{-1} HCl.

16.3 Buffer Effectiveness: Buffer Range and Buffer Capacity

An effective buffer neutralizes small to moderate amounts of added acid or base. As we saw in the opening section of this chapter, however, a buffer can be destroyed by the addition of too much acid or too much base. What factors influence the effectiveness of a buffer? In this section, we look at two such factors: *the relative amounts of the acid and conjugate base* and *the absolute concentrations of the acid and conjugate base*. We then define the *range of a buffer* (the pH range over which a particular acid and its conjugate base can be effective) and the *capacity of a buffer* (how much added acid or base it can effectively neutralize).

Relative Amounts of Acid and Base

A buffer is most effective (most resistant to pH changes) when the concentrations of acid and conjugate base are equal. Let's explore this idea by considering the behaviour of a generic buffer composed of HA and A^- for which $pK_a = 5.00$ and calculating the percent change in pH upon addition of 0.010 mol of NaOH for two different 1.0 litre solutions of this buffer system. Both solutions have 0.20 mol of *total* acid and conjugate base. However, solution I has equal amounts of acid and conjugate base (0.10 mol of each), while solution II has much more acid than conjugate base (0.18 mol HA and 0.020 mol A^-). We can calculate the initial pH values of each solution using the Henderson–Hasselbalch equation. Solution I has an initial pH of 5.00 and solution II has an initial pH of 4.05.

Solution I: 0.10 mol HA and 0.10 mol A^-; initial pH = 5.00

	$OH^-(aq)$ +	$HA(aq)$ ⟶	$H_2O(l)$ +	$A^-(aq)$
Before addition	0 mol	0.100 mol		0.100 mol
Addition	0.010 mol	—		—
After addition	0 mol	0.090 mol		0.110 mol

$$\begin{aligned} pH &= pK_a + \log\frac{[\text{base}]}{[\text{acid}]} \\ &= 5.00 + \log\frac{0.110}{0.090} \\ &= 5.09 \end{aligned}$$

$$\begin{aligned} \%\ \text{change} &= \frac{5.09 - 5.00}{5.00} \times 100\% \\ &= 1.8\% \end{aligned}$$

Solution II: 0.18 mol HA and 0.020 mol A^-; initial pH = 4.05

	$OH^-(aq)$ +	$HA(aq)$ ⟶	$H_2O(l)$ +	$A^-(aq)$
Before addition	0 mol	0.18 mol		0.020 mol
Addition	0.010 mol	—		—
After addition	0 mol	0.17 mol		0.030 mol

$$\begin{aligned} pH &= pK_a + \log\frac{[\text{base}]}{[\text{acid}]} \\ &= 5.00 + \log\frac{0.030}{0.17} \\ &= 4.25 \end{aligned}$$

$$\begin{aligned} \%\ \text{change} &= \frac{4.25 - 4.05}{4.05} \times 100\% \\ &= 5.0\% \end{aligned}$$

As you can see, the buffer with equal amounts of acid and conjugate base is more resistant to pH change and is therefore the more effective buffer. A buffer becomes less effective as the difference in the relative amounts of acid and conjugate base increases. As a guideline, we can say that an effective buffer must have a [base]/[acid] ratio in the range of 0.10 to 10. *In order for a buffer to be reasonably effective, the relative concentrations of acid and conjugate base should not differ by more than a factor of 10.*

Absolute Concentrations of the Acid and Conjugate Base

A buffer is most effective (most resistant to pH changes) when the concentrations of acid and conjugate base are high. Let's explore this idea by again considering a generic buffer composed of HA and A^- and a pK_a of 5.00 and calculating the percent change in pH upon addition of 0.010 mol of NaOH for two 1.0 L solutions of this buffer system. In this case, both the acid and the base in solution I are 10 times more concentrated than the acid and base in solution II. Both solutions have equal relative amounts of acid and conjugate base and therefore have the same initial pH of 5.00.

Solution I: 0.50 mol HA and 0.50 mol A^-; initial pH = 5.00

	$OH^-(aq)$ +	$HA(aq)$ ⟶	$H_2O(l)$ +	$A^-(aq)$
Before addition	0 mol	0.50 mol		0.50 mol
Addition	0.010 mol	—		—
After addition	0 mol	0.49 mol		0.51 mol

$$\begin{aligned} pH &= pK_a + \log \frac{[\text{base}]}{[\text{acid}]} \\ &= 5.00 + \log \frac{0.51}{0.49} \\ &= 5.02 \end{aligned}$$

$$\begin{aligned} \%\ \text{change} &= \frac{5.02 - 5.00}{5.00} \times 100\% \\ &= 0.4\% \end{aligned}$$

Solution II: 0.050 mol HA and 0.050 mol A^-; initial pH = 5.00

	$OH^-(aq)$ +	$HA(aq)$ ⟶	$H_2O(l)$ +	$A^-(aq)$
Before addition	0 mol	0.050 mol		0.050 mol
Addition	0.010 mol	—		—
After addition	0 mol	0.040 mol		0.060 mol

$$\begin{aligned} pH &= pK_a + \log \frac{[\text{base}]}{[\text{acid}]} \\ &= 5.00 + \log \frac{0.060}{0.040} \\ &= 5.18 \end{aligned}$$

$$\begin{aligned} \%\ \text{change} &= \frac{5.18 - 5.00}{5.00} \times 100\% \\ &= 3.6\% \end{aligned}$$

As you can see, the buffer with greater amounts of acid and conjugate base is more resistant to pH changes and therefore the more effective buffer. The more dilute the buffer components, the less effective the buffer.

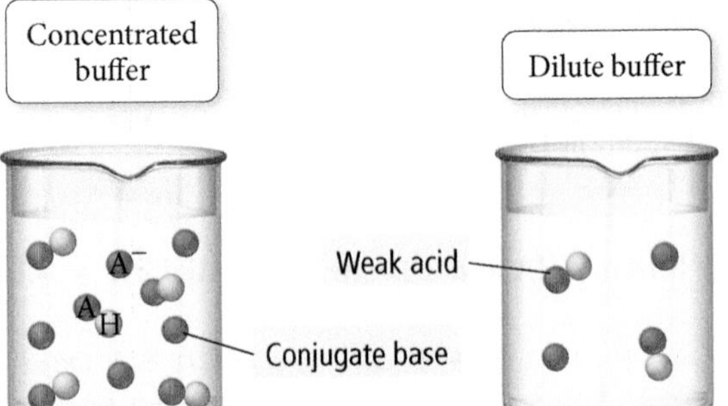

▲ A concentrated buffer contains more of the weak acid and its conjugate base than a weak buffer does. It can therefore neutralize more added acid or added base.

Buffer Range

Referring to our guideline which states that the relative concentrations of acid and conjugate base should not differ by more than a factor of 10 in order for a buffer to be reasonably effective, we can calculate the pH range over which a particular acid and its conjugate base can be used to make an effective buffer. Since the pH of a buffer is given by the Henderson–Hasselbalch equation, we can calculate the outermost points of the effective range as follows:

Lowest pH for effective buffer occurs when the base is one-tenth as concentrated as the acid.

$$\begin{aligned} pH &= pK_a + \log \frac{[\text{base}]}{[\text{acid}]} \\ &= pK_a + \log 0.10 \\ &= pK_a - 1 \end{aligned}$$

Highest pH for effective buffer occurs when the base is 10 times as concentrated as the acid.

$$\begin{aligned} pH &= pK_a + \log \frac{[\text{base}]}{[\text{acid}]} \\ &= pK_a + \log 10 \\ &= pK_a + 1 \end{aligned}$$

The effective range for a buffering system is one pH unit on either side of pK_a. For example, a buffering system with a weak acid pK_a of 5.0 can be used to prepare a buffer in the range of 4.0–6.0. We can adjust the relative amounts of acid and conjugate base to achieve any pH within this range. As we noted earlier, however, the buffer would be most effective at pH 5.0, because the buffer components would be exactly equal at that pH. The next example demonstrates how to pick an acid/conjugate base system for a buffer, and how to calculate the relative amounts of acid and conjugate base required for a desired pH.

EXAMPLE 16.5 PREPARING A BUFFER

Which acid would you choose to combine with its sodium salt to make a solution buffered at pH 4.25? For the best choice, calculate the ratio of the conjugate base to the acid required to attain the desired pH.

chlorous acid ($HClO_2$)	$pK_a = 1.95$	methanoic acid (HCOOH)	$pK_a = 3.74$
nitrous acid (HNO_2)	$pK_a = 3.34$	hypochlorous acid (HClO)	$pK_a = 7.54$

SOLUTION

The best choice would be methanoic acid because its pK_a lies closest to the desired pH. The ratio of conjugate base ($HCOO^-$) to acid (HCOOH) required can be calculated from the Henderson–Hasselbalch equation as follows:

$$pH = pK_a + \log\frac{[\text{base}]}{[\text{acid}]}$$

$$4.25 = 3.74 + \log\frac{[\text{base}]}{[\text{acid}]}$$

$$\log\frac{[\text{base}]}{[\text{acid}]} = 4.25 - 3.74$$

$$= 0.51$$

$$\frac{[\text{base}]}{[\text{acid}]} = 10^{0.51}$$

$$= 3.24$$

FOR PRACTICE 16.5

Which acid in Example 16.5 would you choose to create a buffer with pH = 7.35? If you had 500.0 mL of a 0.10 mol L^{-1} solution of the acid, what mass of the corresponding sodium salt of the conjugate base would you need to make the buffer?

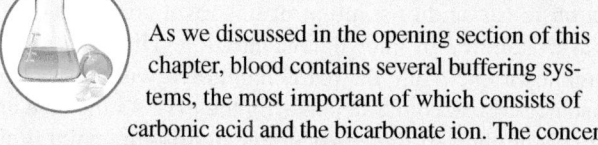

CHEMISTRY AND MEDICINE Buffer Effectiveness in Human Blood

As we discussed in the opening section of this chapter, blood contains several buffering systems, the most important of which consists of carbonic acid and the bicarbonate ion. The concentrations of these buffer components in normal blood plasma are $[HCO_3^-] = 0.024$ mol L^{-1} and $[H_2CO_3] = 0.0012$ mol L^{-1}. The pK_a for carbonic acid at body temperature is 6.1. If we substitute these quantities into the Henderson–Hasselbalch equation, we can calculate the normal pH of blood:

$$pH = pK_a + \log\frac{[\text{base}]}{[\text{acid}]}$$

$$= 6.1 = \log\frac{[HCO_3^-]}{[H_2CO_3]}$$

$$= 6.1 + \log\frac{0.024 \text{ mol L}^{-1}}{0.0012 \text{ mol L}^{-1}}$$

$$= 7.4$$

Normal blood has a pH of 7.4. Notice that the concentration of the bicarbonate ion is 20 times higher than the concentration of carbonic acid and the pH of the buffer is more than one pH unit away from pK_a. Why?

The higher bicarbonate ion concentration in blood makes the buffer capacity of blood greater for acid than for base, which is necessary because the products of metabolism that enter blood are mostly acidic. For example, when we exercise, our bodies produce lactic acid ($HC_3H_5O_3$). The lactic acid enters the bloodstream and must be neutralized. The bicarbonate ion neutralizes the lactic acid according to the equation:

$$HCO_3^-(aq) + HC_3H_5O_3(aq) \longrightarrow H_2CO_3(aq) + C_3H_5O_3^-(aq)$$

An enzyme called carbonic anhydrase then catalyzes the conversion of carbonic acid into carbon dioxide and water:

$$H_2CO_3(aq) \rightleftharpoons CO_2(g) + H_2O(l)$$

We eliminate the carbon dioxide from our blood when we breathe. When large amounts of lactic acid are produced, we must breathe faster to keep up with the need to eliminate carbon dioxide.

Question

A 70 kg person has a total blood volume of about 5.0 L. Given the carbonic acid and bicarbonate concentrations stated above, what volume (in mL) of 6.0 mol L^{-1} HCl can be neutralized by blood without the blood pH dropping below 7.0 (which would result in death)?

▶ Normal blood has a pH of 7.4.

Buffer Capacity

Buffer capacity is the amount of acid or base that you can add to a buffer without causing a large change in pH. Given what we just learned about the absolute concentrations of acid and conjugate base in an effective buffer, we can conclude that the *buffer capacity increases with increasing absolute concentrations of the buffer components*. The more concentrated the weak acid and conjugate base that compose the buffer, the higher the buffer capacity. In addition, *overall buffer capacity increases as the relative concentrations of the buffer components become more similar to each other.* As the ratio of the buffer components gets closer to 1, the *overall* capacity of the buffer (the ability to neutralize added acid *and* added base) becomes greater. In some cases, however, a buffer that must neutralize primarily added acid (or primarily added base) may be overweighted in one of the buffer components, as shown in the *Chemistry and Medicine* box in this section.

CONCEPTUAL CONNECTION 16.3

Buffer Capacity

A 1.0 L buffer solution is 0.10 mol L^{-1} in HF and 0.050 mol L^{-1} in NaF. Which action will destroy the buffer?

(a) adding 0.050 mol of HCl **(b)** adding 0.050 mol of NaOH

(c) adding 0.050 mol of NaF **(d)** None of the above

16.4 Titrations and pH Curves

In an **acid–base titration**, a basic (or acidic) solution of unknown concentration is reacted with an acidic (or basic) solution of known concentration. The known solution is slowly added to the unknown one while the pH is monitored with either a pH meter or an **indicator** (a substance whose colour depends on the pH). As the acid and base combine, they neutralize each other. At the **equivalence point**—the point in the titration when the number of moles of base is stoichiometrically equal to the number of moles of acid—the titration is complete. When the equivalence point is reached, neither reactant is in excess and the number of moles of the reactants are related by the reaction stoichiometry (Figure 16.5 ▶).

In this section, we examine acid–base titrations more closely, concentrating on the pH changes that occur during the titration. A plot of the pH of the solution during a titration is known as a *titration curve* or *pH curve.* Figure 16.6 ▶ shows a pH curve for the titration of HCl with NaOH. Before any base is added to the solution, the pH is low (as expected for a solution of HCl). As the NaOH is added, the solution becomes less acidic because the NaOH begins to neutralize the HCl. The point of inflection in the middle of the curve is the equivalence point. Notice that the pH changes very quickly near the equivalence point (small amounts of added base cause large changes in pH). Beyond the equivalence point, the solution is basic because the HCl has been completely neutralized and excess base is being added to the solution. The exact shape of the pH curve depends on several factors, including the strength of the acid or base being titrated. Let's consider several combinations individually.

The Titration of a Strong Acid with a Strong Base

Consider the titration of 25.0 mL of 0.100 mol L^{-1} HCl with 0.100 mol L^{-1} NaOH. We begin by calculating the volume of base required to reach the equivalence point, and then the pH at several points during the titration.

Volume of NaOH Required to Reach the Equivalence Point During the titration, the added sodium hydroxide neutralizes the hydrochloric acid:

$$HCl(aq) + NaOH(aq) \longrightarrow H_2O(l) + NaCl(aq)$$

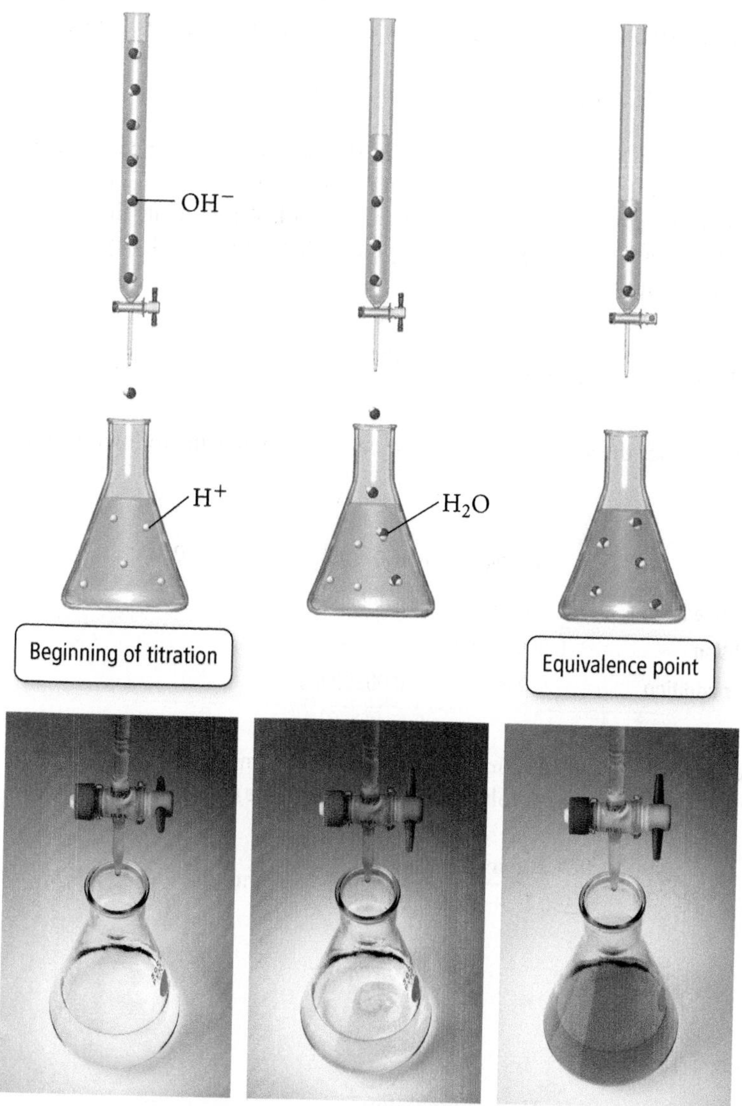

▲ **FIGURE 16.5 Acid–Base Titration** As OH^- is added in a titration, it neutralizes the H^+, forming water. At the equivalence point, the titration is complete.

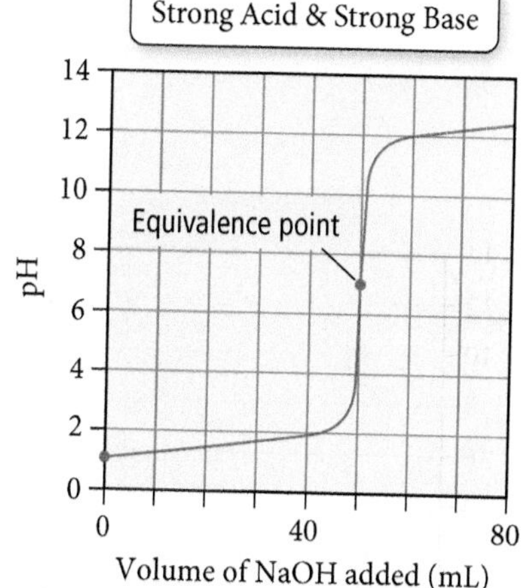

▲ **FIGURE 16.6 Titration Curve: Strong Acid + Strong Base** This curve represents the titration of 50.0 mL of 0.100 mol L^{-1} HCl with 0.100 mol L^{-1} NaOH.

The equivalence point is reached when the number of moles of base added equals the number of moles of acid initially in solution. We calculate the amount of acid initially in solution from its volume and its concentration:

$$\text{Initial mol HCl} = 0.0250\ \cancel{\text{L}} \times \frac{0.100\ \text{mol}}{1\ \cancel{\text{L}}} = 0.00250\ \text{mol HCl}$$

The amount of NaOH that must be added is 0.00250 mol NaOH. We calculate the volume of NaOH required from its concentration:

$$\text{Volume NaOH solution} = 0.00250\ \cancel{\text{mol}} \times \frac{1\ \text{L}}{0.100\ \cancel{\text{mol}}} = 0.0250\ \text{L}$$

The equivalence point is reached when 25.0 mL of NaOH has been added. In this case, the concentrations of both solutions are identical, so the volume of NaOH solution required to reach the equivalence point is equal to the volume of the HCl solution that is being titrated.

Initial pH (Before Adding Any Base) The initial pH of the solution is simply the pH of a 0.100 mol L^{-1} HCl solution. Since HCl is a strong acid, the concentration of H_3O^+ is also 0.100 mol L^{-1} and the pH is 1.00.

$$\begin{aligned} \text{pH} &= -\log[H_3O^+] \\ &= -\log(0.100) \\ &= 1.00 \end{aligned}$$

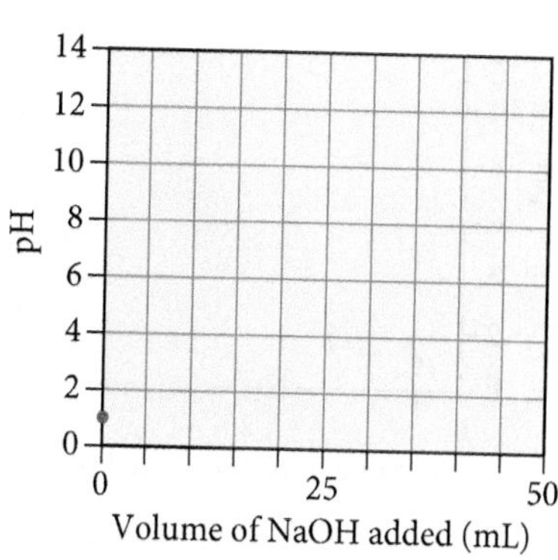

pH After Adding 5.00 mL NaOH As NaOH is added to the solution, it neutralizes H_3O^+:

$$OH^-(aq) + H_3O^+(aq) \longrightarrow 2\,H_2O(l)$$

We calculate the amount of H_3O^+ at any given point (before the equivalence point) by using the reaction stoichiometry—1 mol of NaOH neutralizes 1 mol of H_3O^+. The initial number of moles of H_3O^+ (as calculated above) is 0.00250 mol. We calculate the number of moles of NaOH added at 5.00 mL by multiplying the added volume (in L) by the concentration of the NaOH solution:

In titration calculations, some chemists prefer to use concentration units of mmol L^{-1} (i.e., 10^{-3} mol L^{-1}) and mL for volume instead of L. This is because titration volumes are usually measured in mL, and titrant concentrations are frequently in the range 10^{-2}–10^{-4} mol L^{-1}. Since concentration and volume are each converted by the same factor of 10^3, any mole calculation gives the same answer as when the units mol L^{-1} and L are used.

$$\text{mol NaOH added} = 0.00500\,\cancel{L} \times \frac{0.100\text{ mol}}{1\,\cancel{L}} = 0.000500\text{ mol NaOH}$$

The addition of OH^- causes the amount of H^+ to decrease as shown in the following table:

	$OH^-(aq)$	$+\ H_3O^+(aq)$	$\longrightarrow 2\,H_2O(l)$
Before addition	≈0 mol	0.00250 mol	
Addition	0.000500 mol	—	
After addition	≈0 mol	0.00200 mol	

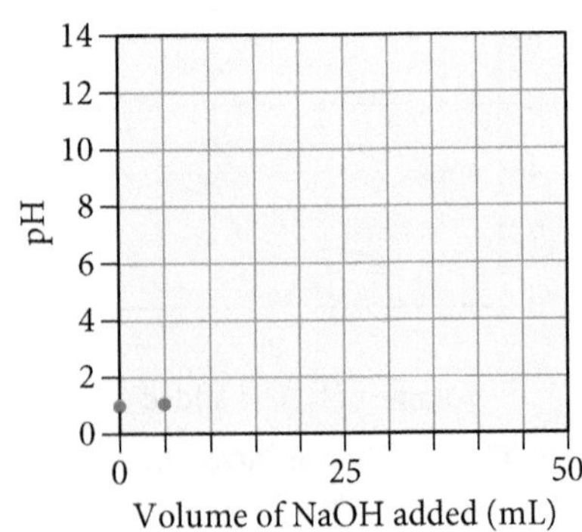

We can calculate the H_3O^+ concentration by dividing the number of moles of H_3O^+ remaining by the *total volume* (initial volume plus added volume).

$$[H_3O^+] = \frac{0.00200\text{ mol }H_3O^+}{0.0250\text{ L} + 0.00500\text{ L}} = 0.0667\text{ mol L}^{-1}$$

Initial volume   Added volume

The pH is therefore 1.18:

$$\begin{aligned} pH &= -\log 0.0667 \\ &= 1.18 \end{aligned}$$

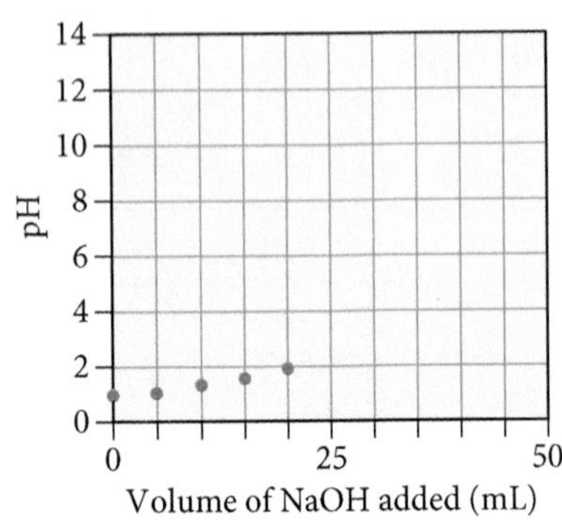

pH's After Adding 10.0, 15.0, and 20.0 mL NaOH As more NaOH is added, it further neutralizes the H_3O^+ in the solution. We calculate the pH at each of these points in the same way that we calculated the pH at the 5.00 mL point. Keep in mind that the volume changes as more base is added and this must be accounted for in the calculation. The results are tabulated as follows:

Added Volume (mL)	pH
10.0	1.37
15.0	1.60
20.0	1.95

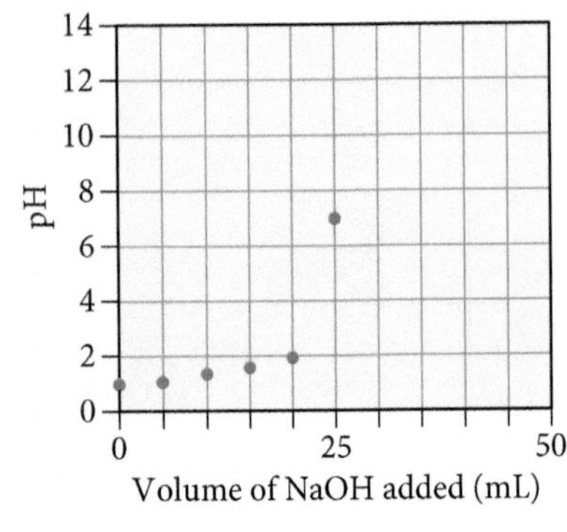

pH After Adding 25.0 mL NaOH (Equivalence Point) The pH at the equivalence point of a strong acid–strong base titration will always be 7.00 (at 25 °C). At the equivalence point, the strong base has completely neutralized the strong acid. The only source of hydronium ions then is the ionization of water. The $[H_3O^+]$ at 25 °C from the ionization of water is 1.00×10^{-7} mol L^{-1} and the pH is 7.00.

pH After Adding 30.00 mL NaOH As NaOH is added beyond the equivalence point, it becomes the excess reagent. We calculate the amount of OH^- at any given point (past the equivalence point) by subtracting the initial amount of H_3O^+ from the amount of OH^- added. The number of moles of OH^- added at 30.00 mL is

$$\text{mol OH}^- \text{ added} = 0.0300\,\cancel{\text{L}} \times \frac{0.100 \text{ mol}}{1\,\cancel{\text{L}}} = 0.00300 \text{ mol OH}^-$$

The number of moles of OH^- remaining after neutralization is shown in the following table:

	$OH^-(aq)$	+ $H_3O^+(aq)$	$\longrightarrow$ 2 $H_2O(l)$
Before addition	≈0 mol	0.00250 mol	
Addition	0.00300 mol	—	
After addition	0.00050 mol	≈0 mol	

We calculate the OH^- concentration by dividing the number of moles of OH^- remaining by the *total volume* (initial volume plus added volume):

$$[OH^-] = \frac{0.000500 \text{ mol OH}^-}{0.0250 \text{ L} + 0.0300 \text{ L}} = 0.00909 \text{ mol L}^{-1}$$

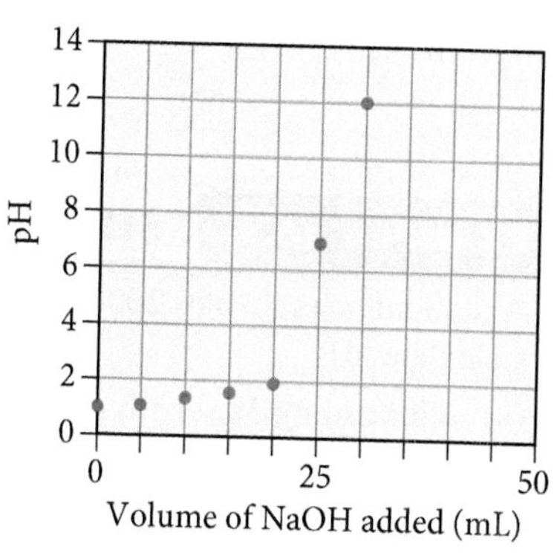

We can then calculate the $[H_3O^+]$ and pH:

$$[H_3O^+][OH^-] = 10^{-14}$$

$$[H_3O^+] = \frac{10^{-14}}{[OH^-]} = \frac{10^{-14}}{0.00909}$$

$$= 1.10 \times 10^{-12} \text{ mol L}^{-1}$$

$$\text{pH} = -\log(1.10 \times 10^{-12})$$

$$= 11.96$$

pH's After Adding 35.0, 40.0, and 50.0 mL NaOH As more NaOH is added, it further increases the basicity of the solution. We calculate the pH at each of these points in the same way that we calculated the pH at the 30.00 mL point. The results are tabulated as follows:

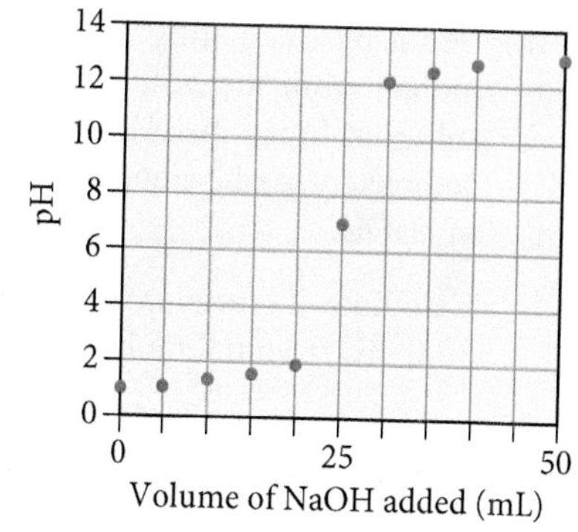

Added Volume (mL)	pH
35.0	12.22
40.0	12.36
50.0	12.52

The Overall pH Curve The overall pH curve for the titration of a strong acid with a strong base has the characteristic *S*-shape we just plotted. The overall curve is as follows:

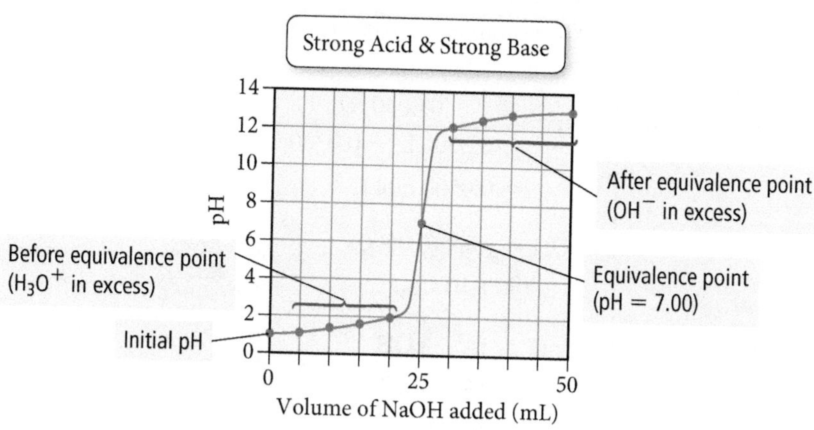

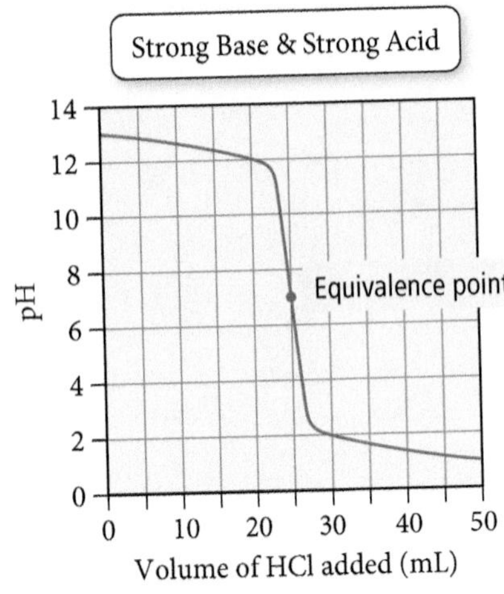

▲ **FIGURE 16.7 Titration Curve: Strong Base + Strong Acid** This curve represents the titration of 25.0 mL of 0.100 mol L^{-1} NaOH with 0.100 mol L^{-1} HCl.

Summarizing the Titration of a Strong Acid with a Strong Base:

- The initial pH is simply the pH of the strong acid solution to be titrated.
- Before the equivalence point, H_3O^+ is in excess. Calculate the $[H_3O^+]$ by subtracting the number of moles of added OH^- from the initial number of moles of H_3O^+ and dividing by the *total* volume.
- At the equivalence point, neither reactant is in excess and the pH = 7.00.
- Beyond the equivalence point, OH^- is in excess. Calculate the $[OH^-]$ by subtracting the initial number of moles of H_3O^+ from the number of moles of added OH^- and dividing by the *total* volume.

The pH curve for the titration of a strong base with a strong acid is shown in Figure 16.7 ◄. Calculating the points along this curve is very similar to calculating the points along the pH curve for the titration of a strong acid with a strong base. The main difference is that the curve starts basic and then becomes acidic after the equivalence point (instead of vice versa).

EXAMPLE 16.6 **STRONG ACID–STRONG BASE TITRATION pH CURVE**

A 50.0 mL sample of 0.200 mol L^{-1} sodium hydroxide is titrated with 0.200 mol L^{-1} nitric acid. Calculate pH:

(a) after adding 30.00 mL of HNO_3 **(b)** at the equivalence point

SOLUTION

(a) Begin by calculating the initial amount of NaOH (in moles) from the volume and molarity of the NaOH solution. Since NaOH is a strong base, it dissociates completely, so the amount of OH^- is equal to the amount of NaOH.

$$\text{moles NaOH} = 0.0500\ \cancel{L} \times \frac{0.200\ \text{mol}}{1\ \cancel{L}} = 0.0100\ \text{mol}$$

$$\text{moles OH}^- = 0.0100\ \text{mol}$$

Calculate the amount of HNO_3 (in moles) added at 30.0 mL from the molarity of the HNO_3 solution.

$$\text{mol HNO}_3\ \text{added} = 0.0300\ \cancel{L} \times \frac{0.200\ \text{mol}}{1\ \cancel{L}} = 0.00600\ \text{mol HNO}_3$$

As HNO_3 is added to the solution, it neutralizes some of the OH^-. Calculate the number of moles of OH^- remaining by setting up a table based on the neutralization reaction that shows the amount of OH^- before the addition, the amount of H_3O^+ added, and the amounts left after the addition.

	$OH^-(aq)$ +	$H_3O^+(aq)$	$\longrightarrow 2\,H_2O(l)$
Before addition	0.0100 mol	0 mol	
Addition	—	0.00600 mol	
After addition	0.0040 mol	0 mol	

Calculate the OH^- concentration by dividing the amount of OH^- remaining by the *total volume* (initial volume plus added volume).

$$[OH^-] = \frac{0.0040\ \text{mol}}{0.0500\ \text{L} + 0.0300\ \text{L}} = 0.0500\ \text{mol L}^{-1}$$

Calculate the pOH from $[OH^-]$.

$$\text{pOH} = -\log(0.0500) = 1.30$$

Calculate the pH from the pOH using the equation pH + pOH = 14.

$$\text{pH} = 14 - \text{pOH} = 14 - 1.30 = 12.70$$

(b) At the equivalence point, the strong base has completely neutralized the strong acid. The $[H_3O^+]$ at 25 °C from the ionization of water is 1.00×10^{-7} mol L^{-1} and the pH is therefore 7.00.	pH = 7.00

FOR PRACTICE 16.6

Calculate the pH in the titration in Example 16.6 after the addition of 60.0 mL of 0.200 mol L^{-1} HNO_3.

The Titration of a Weak Acid with a Strong Base

Consider the titration of 25.0 mL of 0.100 mol L^{-1} HCOOH with 0.100 mol L^{-1} NaOH. In a solution of NaOH, it is hydroxide ion, OH^-, that reacts with the weak acid. The net ionic equation is:

$$OH^-(aq) + HCOOH(aq) \longrightarrow H_2O(l) + HCOO^-(aq)$$

The concentrations and the volumes here are identical to those in our previous titration, in which we calculated the pH curve for the titration of a *strong* acid with a strong base. The only difference is that HCOOH is a *weak* acid rather than a strong one. We begin our calculation by determining the volume required to reach the equivalence point of the titration.

Volume of NaOH Required to Reach the Equivalence Point From the stoichiometry of the equation, we can see that the equivalence point occurs when the amount (in moles) of added base equals the amount (in moles) of acid initially in solution.

$$\text{Initial mol HCOOH} = 0.0250\,\cancel{L} \times \frac{0.100\text{ mol}}{1\,\cancel{L}} = 0.00250\text{ mol HCOOH}$$

The amount of NaOH that must be added is 0.00250 mol NaOH. The volume of NaOH required is therefore:

$$\text{Volume NaOH solution} = 0.00250\,\cancel{\text{mol}} \times \frac{1\text{ L}}{0.100\,\cancel{\text{mol}}} = 0.0250\text{ L NaOH solution}$$

The equivalence point occurs when 25.0 mL of base has been added. Notice that the volume of NaOH required to reach the equivalence point is identical to that required for a strong acid. *The volume at the equivalence point in an acid–base titration does not depend on whether the acid being titrated is a strong acid or a weak acid; it depends only on the amount (in moles) of acid present in solution before the titration begins and on the concentration of the added base.*

Initial pH (Before Adding Any Base) The initial pH of the solution is the pH of a 0.100 mol L^{-1} HCOOH solution. Since HCOOH is a weak acid, we calculate the concentration of H_3O^+ and the pH by doing an equilibrium problem for the ionization of HCOOH. The procedure for solving weak acid ionization problems is given in Examples 15.5 and 15.6. We show a highly condensed calculation below (K_a for HCOOH is 1.8×10^{-4}).

$$HCOOH(aq) + H_2O(l) \rightleftharpoons H_3O^+(aq) + HCOO^-(aq)$$

	[HCOOH]	$[H_3O^+]$	$[HCOO^-]$
Initial	0.100	≈0	0
Change	$-x$	$+x$	$+x$
Equil	$0.100 - x$	x	x

$$K_a = \frac{[H_3O^+][HCOO^-]}{[HCOOH]}$$

$$= \frac{x^2}{0.100 - \cancel{x}} \quad (x \text{ is small})$$

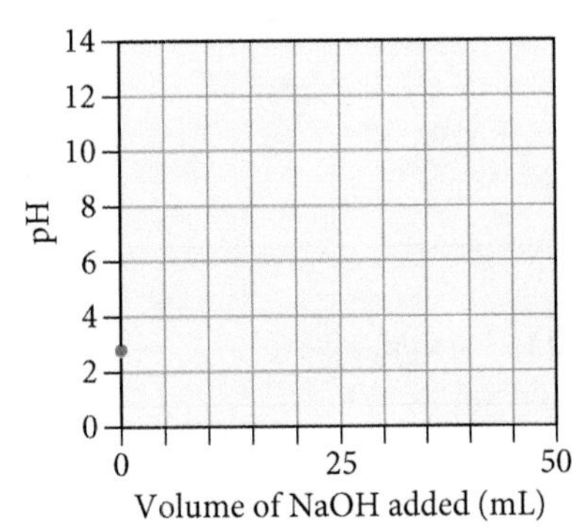

$$1.8 \times 10^{-4} = \frac{x^2}{0.100}$$

$$x = 4.24 \times 10^{-3}$$

Therefore, $[H_3O^+] = 4.24 \times 10^{-3}$ mol L^{-1}.

$$\text{pH} = -\log(4.24 \times 10^{-3})$$
$$= 2.37$$

Notice that the pH is initially at a higher value (less acidic) than it is for a strong acid of the same concentration, as we would expect because the acid is weak.

pH After Adding 5.00 mL NaOH When titrating a *weak acid* with a strong base, the added NaOH *converts a stoichiometric amount of the acid into its conjugate base.* As we calculated previously, 5.00 mL of the 0.100 mol L^{-1} NaOH solution contains 0.000500 mol OH^-. When the 0.000500 mol OH^- is added to the weak acid solution, the OH^- reacts stoichiometrically with HCOOH causing the amount of HCOOH to *decrease* by 0.000500 mol and the amount of $HCOO^-$ to *increase* by 0.000500 mol. This is very similar to what happens when you add strong base to a buffer, and is summarized in the following table:

	$OH^-(aq)$	+	$HCOOH(aq)$	$\longrightarrow$ $H_2O(l)$	+ $HCOO^-(aq)$
Before addition	0 mol		0.00250 mol	—	0 mol
Addition	0.000500 mol		—	—	—
After addition	0 mol		0.00200 mol	—	0.000500 mol

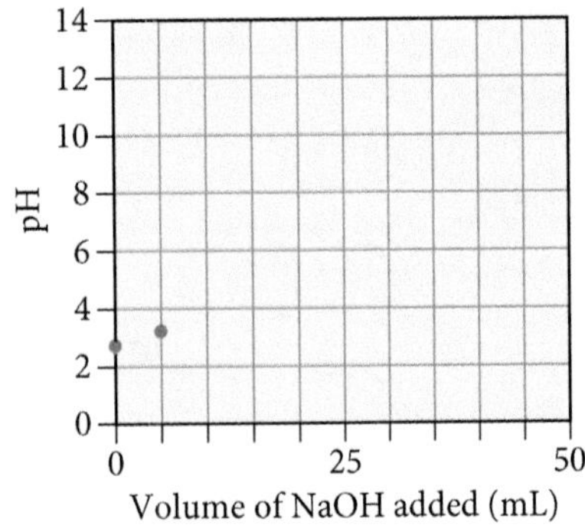

Notice that, after the addition, the solution contains significant amounts of both an acid (HCOOH) and its conjugate base ($HCOO^-$)—*the solution is now a buffer*. To calculate the pH of a buffer (when the *x is small* approximation applies, as it does here), we can use the Henderson–Hasselbalch equation and pK_a for HCOOH (which is 3.74).

$$\text{pH} = pK_a + \log\frac{[\text{base}]}{[\text{acid}]}$$
$$= 3.74 + \log\frac{0.000500}{0.00200}$$
$$= 3.74 - 0.60$$
$$= 3.14$$

Half-equivalence point (pH = pK_a)

pH's After Adding 10.0, 12.5, 15.0, and 20.0 mL NaOH As more NaOH is added, it converts more HCOOH into $HCOO^-$. We calculate the relative amounts of HCOOH and $HCOO^-$ at each of these volumes using the reaction stoichiometry, and then calculate the pH of the resulting buffer using the Henderson–Hasselbalch equation (as we did for the pH at 5.00 mL). The amounts of HCOOH and $HCOO^-$ (after addition of the OH^-) at each volume and the corresponding pH's are tabulated as follows:

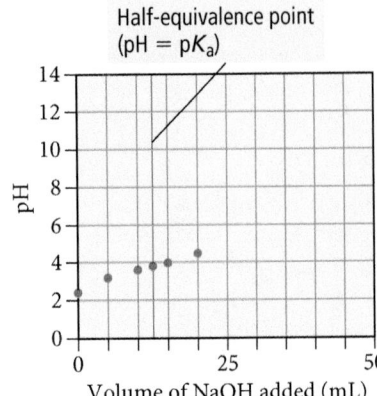

Added Volume (mL)	mol HCOOH	mol $HCOO^-$	pH
10.0	0.00150	0.00100	3.56
12.5	0.00125	0.00125	3.74
15.0	0.00100	0.00150	3.92
20.0	0.00050	0.00200	4.34

As the titration proceeds, more of the HCOOH is converted to the conjugate base ($HCOO^-$). Notice that an added NaOH volume of 12.5 mL corresponds to one-half of the equivalence point. At this volume, one-half of the initial amount of HCOOH has been converted to $HCOO^-$ resulting in *equal amounts of weak acid and conjugate base.*

For any buffer in which the amounts of weak acid and conjugate base are equal, the $pH = pK_a$:

$$pH = pK_a + \log \frac{[\text{base}]}{[\text{acid}]}$$

If [base] = [acid], then [base]/[acid] = 1.

$$\begin{aligned} pH &= pK_a + \log 1 \\ &= pK_a + 0 \\ &= pK_a \end{aligned}$$

Since $pH = pK_a$ halfway to the equivalence point, titrations can be used to measure the pK_a of an acid.

pH After Adding 25.0 mL NaOH (Equivalence Point) At the equivalence point, 0.000250 mol of OH^- have been added and therefore all of the HCOOH has been converted into its conjugate base ($HCOO^-$) as tabulated below:

	$OH^-(aq)$ +	$HCOOH(aq)$ ⟶	$H_2O(l)$ +	$HCOO^-(aq)$
Before addition	0 mol	0.00250 mol	—	0 mol
Addition	0.00250 mol	—	—	—
After addition	0 mol	0 mol	—	0.00250 mol

The solution is no longer a buffer (it no longer contains significant amounts of both a weak acid and its conjugate base). Instead, the solution contains an ion ($HCOO^-$) acting as a weak base. We learned how to calculate the pH of solutions such as this in Section 15.8 (see Example 15.14) by solving an equilibrium problem involving the ionization of water by the weak base ($HCOO^-$):

$$HCOO^-(aq) + H_2O(l) \rightleftharpoons HCOOH(aq) + OH^-(aq)$$

We calculate the initial concentration of $HCOO^-$ for the equilibrium problem by dividing the number of moles of $HCOO^-$ (0.00250 mol) by the *total* volume at the equivalence point (initial volume plus added volume).

Moles $HCOO^-$ at equivalence point

$$HCOO^- = \frac{0.00250\text{ mol}}{0.0250\text{ L} + 0.0250\text{ L}} = 0.0500\text{ mol L}^{-1}$$

Initial volume (0.0250 L); Added volume at equivalence point (0.0250 L)

We then proceed to solve the equilibrium problem as shown in condensed form as follows:

$$HCOO^-(aq) + H_2O(l) \rightleftharpoons HCOOH(aq) + OH^-(aq)$$

	$HCOO^-$	HCOOH	$[OH^-]$
Initial	0.0500	0.00	≈0
Change	$-x$	$+x$	$+x$
Equil	$0.0500 - x$	x	x

Before substituting into the expression for K_b, we find the value of K_b from K_a for methanoic acid ($K_a = 1.8 \times 10^{-4}$) and K_w:

$$K_a \times K_b = K_w$$

$$K_b = \frac{K_w}{K_a} = \frac{1.0 \times 10^{-14}}{1.8 \times 10^{-4}} = 5.6 \times 10^{-11}$$

Then we can substitute the equilibrium concentrations from the table on the previous page into the expression for K_b:

$$K_b = \frac{[HCOOH][OH^-]}{[HCOO^-]}$$

$$= \frac{x^2}{0.0500 - \not{x}} \quad (x \text{ is small})$$

$$5.6 \times 10^{-11} = \frac{x^2}{0.0500}$$

$$x = 1.7 \times 10^{-6}$$

Remember that x represents the concentration of the hydroxide ion. We calculate $[H_3O^+]$ and pH:

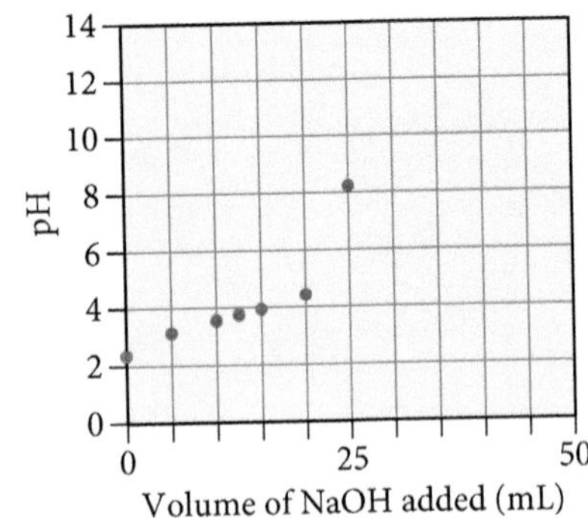

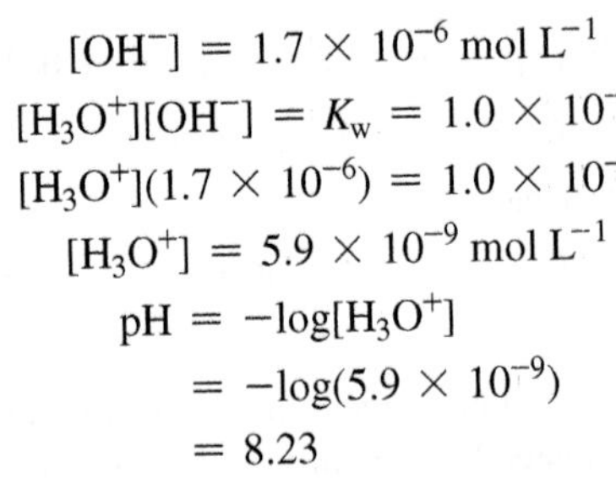

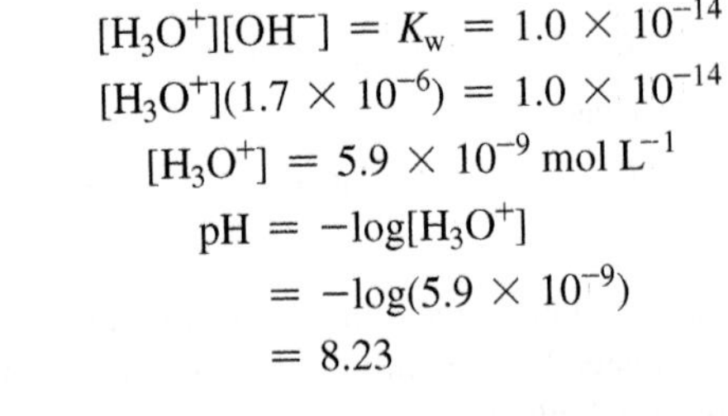

$$[OH^-] = 1.7 \times 10^{-6} \text{ mol L}^{-1}$$

$$[H_3O^+][OH^-] = K_w = 1.0 \times 10^{-14}$$

$$[H_3O^+](1.7 \times 10^{-6}) = 1.0 \times 10^{-14}$$

$$[H_3O^+] = 5.9 \times 10^{-9} \text{ mol L}^{-1}$$

$$pH = -\log[H_3O^+]$$

$$= -\log(5.9 \times 10^{-9})$$

$$= 8.23$$

Notice that the pH at the equivalence point is *not* neutral but basic. *The titration of a weak acid by a strong base will always have a basic equivalence point* because, at the equivalence point, all of the acid has been converted into its conjugate base, resulting in a weakly basic solution.

pH After Adding 30.00 mL NaOH At this point in the titration, 0.00300 mol of OH^- have been added. NaOH has thus become the excess reagent as shown in the following table:

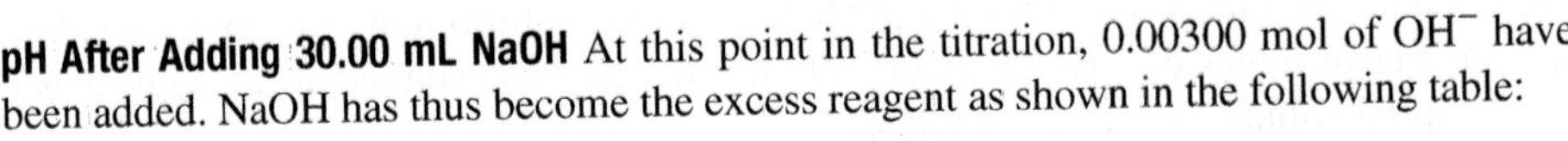

	$OH^-(aq)$	+ $HCOOH(aq)$ ⟶	$H_2O(l)$ +	$HCOO^-(aq)$
Before addition	0 mol	0.00250 mol	—	0 mol
Addition	0.00300 mol	—	—	—
After addition	0.00050 mol	0 mol	—	0.00250 mol

The solution is now a mixture of a strong base (NaOH) and a weak base ($HCOO^-$). The strong base completely overwhelms the weak base and we can calculate the pH by considering the strong base alone (as we did for the titration of a strong acid and a strong base). We calculate the OH^- concentration by dividing the amount of OH^- remaining by the *total volume* (initial volume plus added volume):

$$[OH^-] = \frac{0.00050 \text{ mol } OH^-}{0.0250 \text{ L} + 0.0300 \text{ L}} = 0.0091 \text{ mol L}^{-1}$$

We can then calculate the $[H_3O^+]$ and pH:

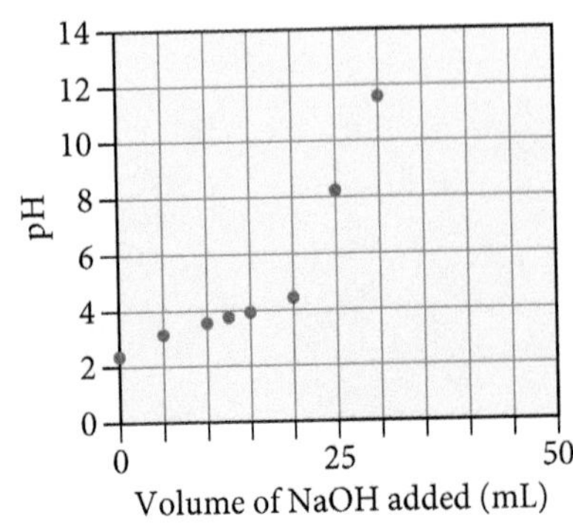

$$[H_3O^+][OH^-] = 10^{-14}$$

$$[H_3O^+] = \frac{10^{-14}}{[OH^-]} = \frac{10^{-14}}{0.0091} = 1.10 \times 10^{-12} \text{ mol L}^{-1}$$

$$pH = -\log(1.10 \times 10^{-12})$$

$$= 11.96$$

pH's After Adding 35.0, 40.0, and 50.0 mL NaOH As more NaOH is added, the basicity of the solution increases further. We calculate the pH at each of these volumes in the same way we calculated the pH at 30.00 mL of added NaOH. The results are tabulated as follows:

Added Volume (mL)	pH
35.0	12.22
40.0	12.36
50.0	12.52

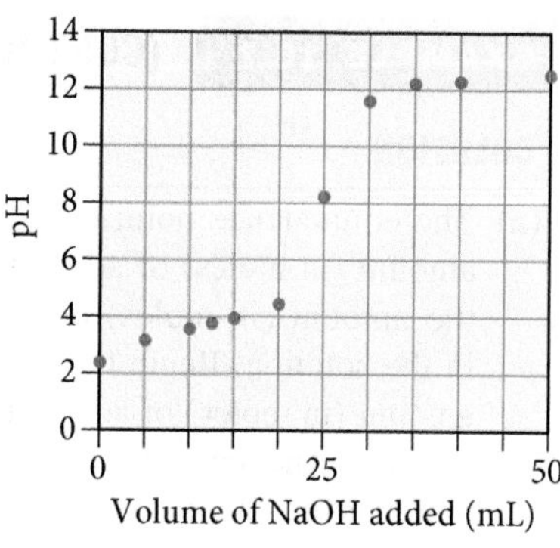

The Overall pH Curve The overall pH curve for the titration of a weak acid with a strong base has a characteristic *S*-shape similar to that for the titration of a strong acid with a strong base. The main difference is that the equivalence point pH is basic (not neutral). Notice that calculating the pH in different regions throughout the titration involves working different kinds of acid–base problems, all of which we have encountered before.

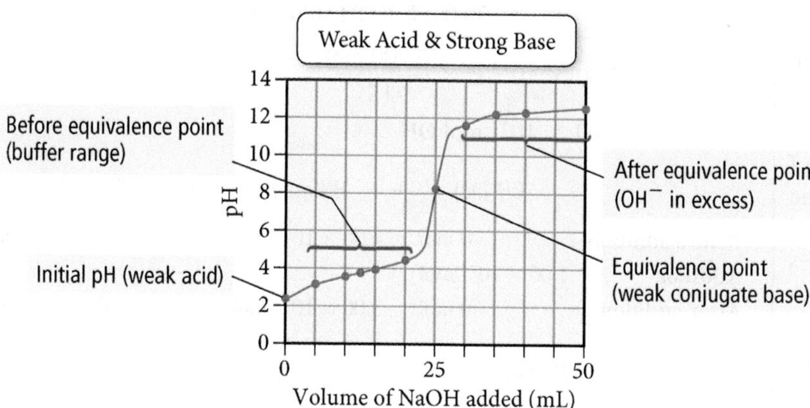

Summarizing Titration of a Weak Acid with a Strong Base:

- The initial pH is that of the weak acid solution to be titrated. Calculate the pH by working an equilibrium problem (similar to Examples 15.5 and 15.6) using the concentration of the weak acid as the initial concentration.
- Between the initial pH and the equivalence point, the solution becomes a buffer. Use the reaction stoichiometry to calculate the amounts of each buffer component and then use the Henderson–Hasselbalch equation to calculate the pH (as in Example 16.3).
- Halfway to the equivalence point, the molar quantities of the buffer components are exactly equal and pH $= pK_a$.
- At the equivalence point, the acid has all been converted into its conjugate base. Calculate the pH by working an equilibrium problem for the ionization of water by the ion acting as a weak base (similar to Example 15.14). (Calculate the concentration of the ion acting as a weak base by dividing the number of moles of the ion by the total volume at the equivalence point.)
- Beyond the equivalence point, OH^- is in excess. Ignore the weak base and calculate the $[OH^-]$ by subtracting the initial number of moles of H_3O^+ from the number of moles of added OH^- and dividing by the *total* volume.

EXAMPLE 16.7 WEAK ACID–STRONG BASE TITRATION pH CURVE

A 40.0 mL sample of 0.100 mol L^{-1} HNO_2 is titrated with 0.200 mol L^{-1} KOH. Calculate:

(a) the volume required to reach the equivalence point

(b) the pH after adding 5.00 mL of KOH

(c) the pH at one-half the equivalence point

(continued)

EXAMPLE 16.7 (CONTINUED)

SOLUTION

(a) The equivalence point occurs when the amount (in moles) of added base equals the amount (in moles) of acid initially in the solution. Begin by calculating the amount (in moles) of acid initially in the solution. The amount (in moles) of KOH that must be added is equal to the amount of the weak acid.

$$\text{mol } HNO_2 = 0.0400\ \cancel{\text{L}} \times \frac{0.100\ \text{mol}}{\cancel{\text{L}}} = 4.00 \times 10^{-3}\ \text{mol}$$

$$\text{mol KOH required} = 4.00 \times 10^{-3}\ \text{mol}$$

Calculate the volume of KOH required from the number of moles of KOH and the molarity.

$$\text{volume KOH solution} = 4.00 \times 10^{-3}\ \cancel{\text{mol}} \times \frac{1\ \text{L}}{0.200\ \cancel{\text{mol}}} = 0.0200\ \text{L KOH solution} = 20.0\ \text{mL KOH solution}$$

(b) Use the concentration of the KOH solution to calculate the amount (in moles) of OH^- in 5.00 mL of the solution.

$$\text{mol } OH^- = 5.00 \times 10^{-3}\ \cancel{\text{L}} \times \frac{0.200\ \text{mol}}{1\ \cancel{\text{L}}} = 1.00 \times 10^{-3}\ \text{mol } OH^-$$

Prepare a table showing the amounts of HNO_2 and NO_2^- before and after the addition of 5.00 mL KOH. The addition of the KOH stoichiometrically reduces the concentration of HNO_2 and increases the concentration of NO_2^-.

	$OH^-(aq)$	+ $HNO_2(aq)$	$\longrightarrow H_2O(l)$	+ $NO_2^-(aq)$
Before addition	0 mol	4.00×10^{-3} mol	—	0 mol
Addition	1.00×10^{-3} mol	—	—	—
After addition	0 mol	3.00×10^{-3} mol	—	1.00×10^{-3} mol

Since the solution now contains significant amounts of a weak acid and its conjugate base, use the Henderson–Hasselbalch equation and pK_a for HNO_2 (which is 3.25) to calculate the pH of the solution.

$$\text{pH} = pK_a + \log \frac{[\text{base}]}{[\text{acid}]} = 3.25 + \log \frac{1.00 \times 10^{-3}}{3.00 \times 10^{-3}} = 3.25 - 0.48 = 2.77$$

(c) At one-half the equivalence point, the amount of added base is exactly one-half the initial amount of acid. The base converts exactly half of the HNO_2 into NO_2^-, resulting in equal amounts of the weak acid and its conjugate base. The pH is therefore equal to pK_a.

	$OH^-(aq)$	+ $HNO_2(aq)$	$\longrightarrow H_2O(l)$	+ $NO_2^-(aq)$
Before addition	0 mol	4.00×10^{-3} mol	—	0 mol
Addition	2.00×10^{-3} mol	—	—	—
After addition	0 mol	2.00×10^{-3} mol	—	2.00×10^{-3} mol

$$\text{pH} = pK_a + \log \frac{[\text{base}]}{[\text{acid}]} = 3.25 + \log \frac{2.00 \times 10^{-3}}{2.00 \times 10^{-3}} = 3.25 + 0 = 3.25$$

FOR PRACTICE 16.7

Determine the pH at the equivalence point for the titration of HNO_2 and KOH in Example 16.7.

The Titration of a Weak Base with a Strong Acid

The pH curve for the titration of a weak base with a strong acid is shown in Figure 16.8 ▶. Calculating the points along this curve is very similar to calculating the points along the pH curve for the titration of a weak acid with a strong base (which we just did). The main differences are that the curve starts basic and has an acidic equivalence point.

The Titration of a Polyprotic Acid

When a diprotic acid is titrated with a strong base, and if K_{a_1} and K_{a_2} are sufficiently different, the pH curve will have two equivalence points. For example, Figure 16.9 ▶ shows

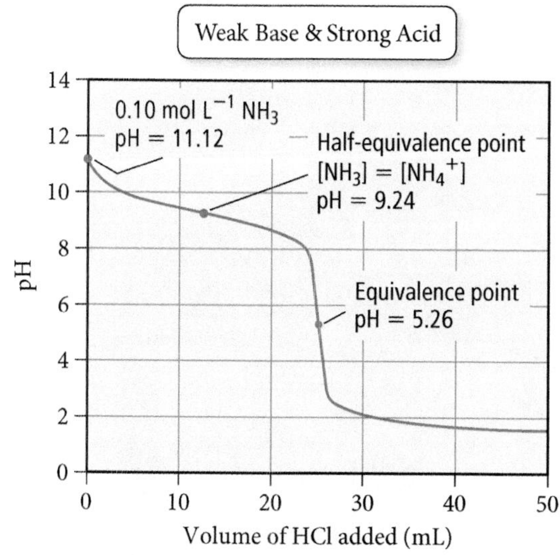

▲ **FIGURE 16.8 Titration Curve: Weak Base with Strong Acid** This curve represents the titration of 0.100 mol L^{-1} NH_3 with 0.100 mol L^{-1} HCl.

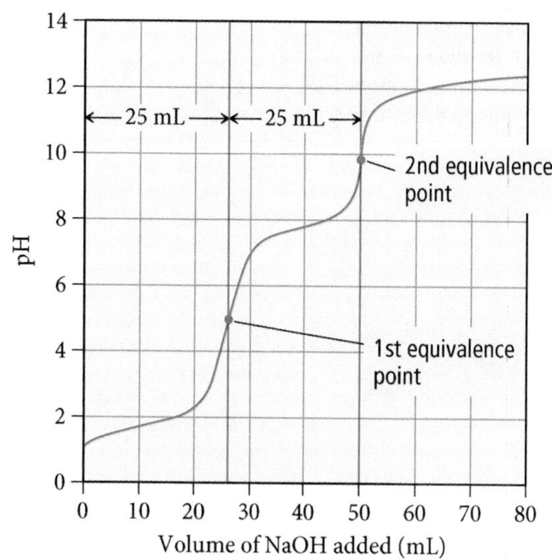

▲ **FIGURE 16.9 Titration Curve: Diprotic Acid with Strong Base** This curve represents the titration of 25.0 mL of 0.100 mol L^{-1} H_2SO_3 with 0.100 mol L^{-1} NaOH.

the pH curve for the titration of sulfurous acid (H_2SO_3) with sodium hydroxide. Recall from Section 15.9 that sulfurous acid ionizes in two steps as follows:

$$H_2SO_3(aq) \rightleftharpoons H^+(aq) + HSO_3^-(aq) \qquad K_{a_1} = 1.6 \times 10^{-2}$$

$$HSO_3^-(aq) \rightleftharpoons H^+(aq) + SO_3^{2-}(aq) \qquad K_{a_2} = 6.4 \times 10^{-8}$$

The first equivalence point in the titration curve represents the titration of the first proton while the second equivalence point represents the titration of the second proton. Notice that the volume required to reach the first equivalence point is identical to the volume required to the reach the second one because the number of moles of H_2SO_3 in the first step determines the number of moles of HSO_3^- in the second step.

CONCEPTUAL CONNECTION 16.4

Acid–Base Titrations

Consider these three titrations:

(i) the titration of 25.0 mL of a 0.100 mol L^{-1} monoprotic weak acid with 0.100 mol L^{-1} NaOH

(ii) the titration of 25.0 mL of a 0.100 mol L^{-1} diprotic weak acid with 0.100 mol L^{-1} NaOH

(iii) the titration of 25.0 mL of a 0.100 mol L^{-1} strong acid with 0.100 mol L^{-1} NaOH

Which statement is most likely to be true?

(a) All three titrations have the same initial pH.

(b) All three titrations have the same pH at their first equivalence point.

(c) All three titrations require the same volume of NaOH to reach their first equivalence point.

Indicators: pH-Dependent Colours

The pH of a titration can be monitored with either a pH meter or an indicator. The direct monitoring of pH with a meter yields data like the pH curves we have examined previously, allowing determination of the equivalence point from the pH curve itself, as shown in Figure 16.10 ▼. With an indicator, we rely on the point where the indicator changes colour—called the **endpoint**—to determine the equivalence point, as shown in

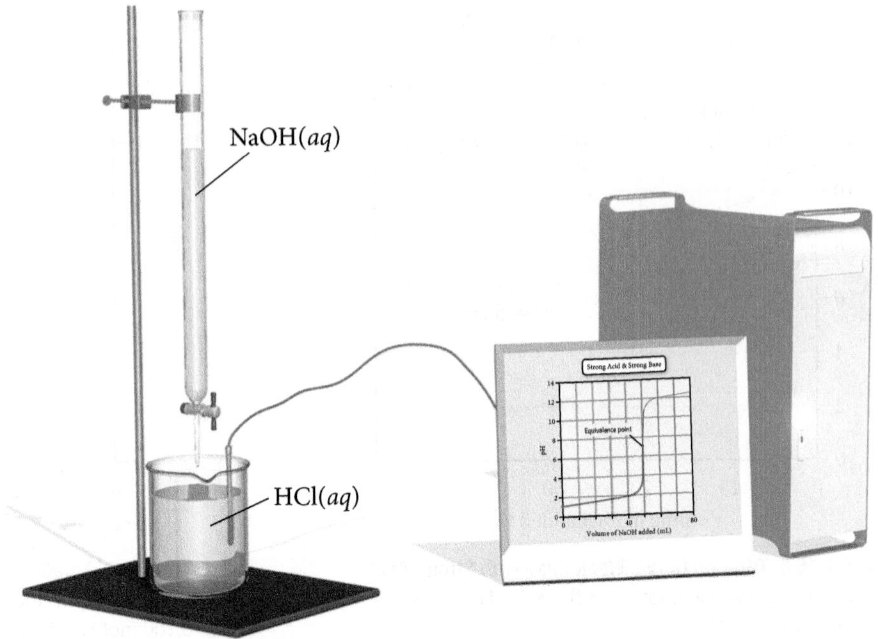

▶ **FIGURE 16.10 Monitoring the pH During a Titration** A pH meter monitors pH during titration. The inflection point in the resulting pH curve signifies the equivalence point.

Figure 16.11 ▼. With the correct indicator, the endpoint of the titration (indicated by the colour change) occurs near the equivalence point (when the amount of acid equals the amount of base).

An indicator is a weak organic acid that has a different colour in solution than its conjugate base. For example, phenolphthalein (whose structure is shown in Figure 16.12 ▶) is a common indicator whose acid form is colourless and conjugate base form is pink. If we let HIn represent the acid form of a generic indicator and In^- the conjugate base form, we have the following equilibrium:

$$\underset{\text{colour 1}}{HIn(aq)} + H_2O(l) \rightleftharpoons H_3O^+(aq) + \underset{\text{colour 2}}{In^-(aq)}$$

Because its colour is intense, only a small amount of indicator is required—an amount that will not affect the pH of the solution or the equivalence point of the neutralization reaction. When the $[H_3O^+]$ changes during the titration, the equilibrium shifts in response. At low pH, the $[H_3O^+]$ is high and the equilibrium lies far to the left, resulting in a solution of colour 1. As the titration proceeds, the $[H_3O^+]$ decreases, shifting the equilibrium

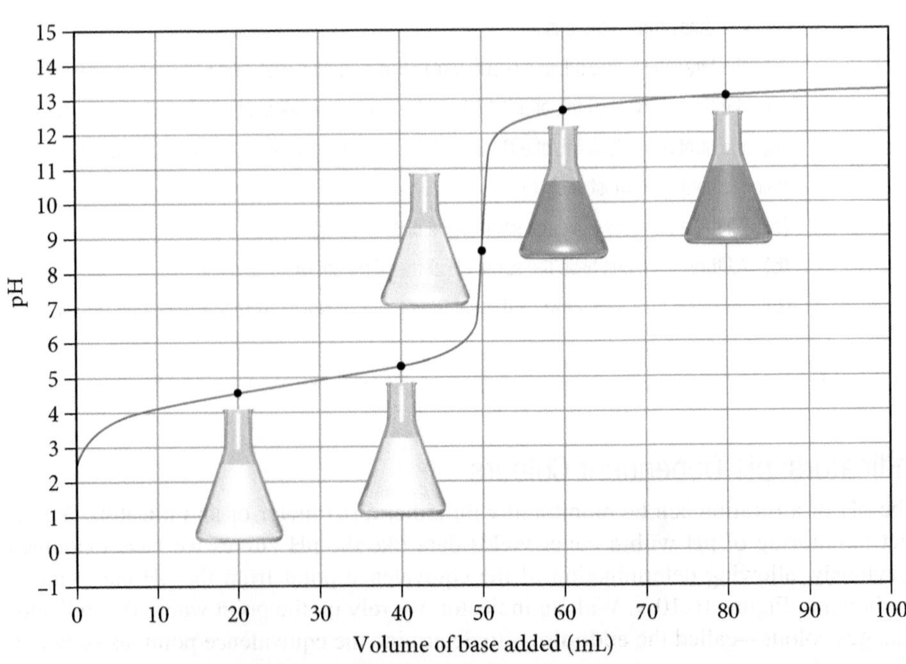

▶ **FIGURE 16.11 Monitoring the Colour Change During a Titration** Titration of 0.100 mol L^{-1} CH_3COOH with 0.100 mol L^{-1} NaOH. The endpoint of a titration is signalled by a colour change in an appropriate indicator (in this case, phenolphthalein).

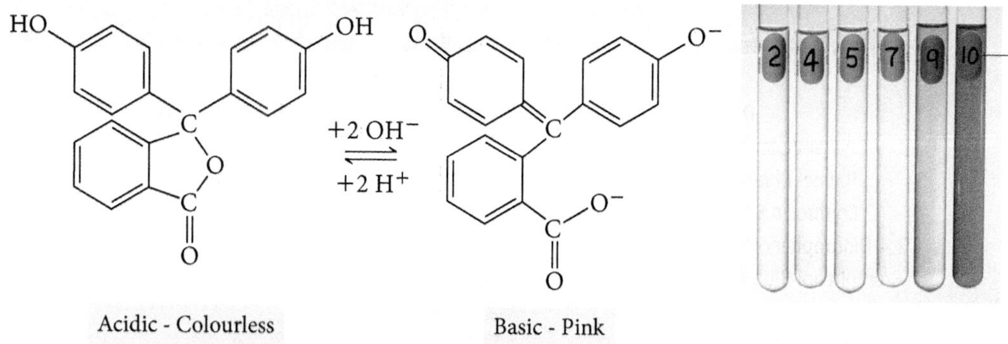

Acidic - Colourless

$\xrightleftharpoons[+2\,H^+]{+2\,OH^-}$

Basic - Pink

pH

▲ **FIGURE 16.12 Phenolphthalein** Phenolphthalein, a weakly acidic compound, is colourless. Its conjugate base is pink.

to the right. Since the pH change is large near the equivalence point of the titration, there is a large change in $[H_3O^+]$ near the equivalence point. Provided that the correct indicator is chosen, there will also be a correspondingly significant change in colour. For the titration of a strong acid with a strong base, one drop of the base near the endpoint is usually enough to change the indicator from colour 1 to colour 2.

The colour of a solution containing an indicator depends on the relative concentrations of HIn and In^-. As a useful guideline, we can assume the following:

If $\dfrac{[In^-]}{[HIn]} = 1$, the indicator solution will be intermediate in colour.

If $\dfrac{[In^-]}{[HIn]} > 10$, the indicator solution will be the colour of In^-.

If $\dfrac{[In^-]}{[HIn]} < 0.1$, the indicator solution will be the colour of HIn.

From the Henderson–Hasselbalch equation, we can derive an expression for the ratio of $[In^-]/[HIn]$:

$$\begin{aligned} pH &= pK_a + \log\frac{[base]}{[acid]} \\ &= pK_a + \log\frac{[In^-]}{[HIn]} \end{aligned}$$

$$\log\frac{[In^-]}{[HIn]} = pH - pK_a$$

$$\frac{[In^-]}{[HIn]} = 10^{(pH - pK_a)}$$

Consider the following three pH values relative to pK_a and the corresponding colours of the indicator solution:

pH (relative to p*Ka*)	$[In^-]/[HIn]$	Colour of Indicator Solution
$pH = pK_a$	$\dfrac{[In^-]}{[HIn]} = 10^0 = 1$	Intermediate colour
$pH = pK_a + 1$	$\dfrac{[In^-]}{[HIn]} = 10^1 = 10$	Colour of In^-
$pH = pK_a - 1$	$\dfrac{[In^-]}{[HIn]} = 10^{-1} = 0.10$	Colour of HIn

When the pH of the solution equals the pK_a of the indicator, the solution will have an intermediate colour. When the pH is 1 unit (or more) above pK_a, the indicator will be the colour of In^-, and when the pH is 1 unit (or more) below pK_a, the indicator will be the colour of HIn. As you can see, the indicator changes colour within a range of two pH units centred at pK_a (Figure 16.13 ▶). Table 16.1 shows various indicators and their colours as a function of pH.

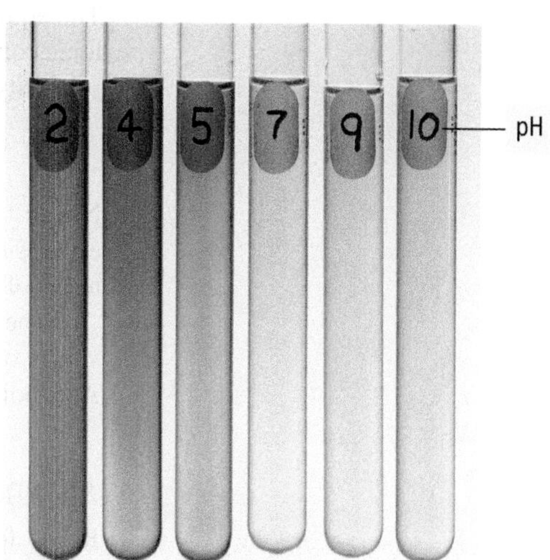

▲ **FIGURE 16.13 Indicator Colour Change** An indicator (in this case, methyl red) generally changes colour within a range of two pH units. (The pH for each solution is marked on its test tube.)

TABLE 16.1 Ranges of Colour Changes for Several Acid–Base Indicators

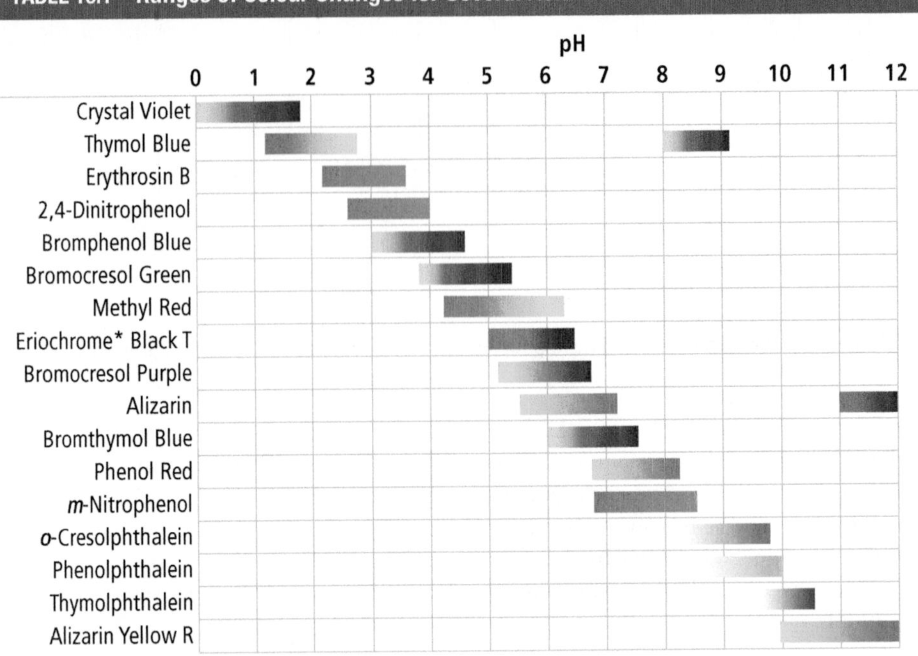

*Trademark of CIBA GEIGY CORP.

16.5 Solubility Equilibria and the Solubility Product Constant

Recall from Chapter 4 that a compound is considered *soluble* if it dissolves in water and *insoluble* if it does not. Recall also that, through the *solubility rules* (see Table 4.2), we classified ionic compounds simply as soluble or insoluble. Now we have the tools to examine *degrees* of solubility.

We can better understand the solubility of an ionic compound by applying the concept of equilibrium to the process of dissolution. For example, we can represent the dissolution of calcium fluoride in water as an equilibrium:

$$CaF_2(s) \rightleftharpoons Ca^{2+}(aq) + 2\,F^-(aq)$$

The equilibrium expression for a chemical equation representing the dissolution of an ionic compound is the **solubility product constant (K_{sp})**. For CaF_2, the expression of the solubility product constant is:

$$K_{sp} = [Ca^{2+}][F^-]^2$$

Notice that, as we discussed in Section 14.4, solids are omitted from the equilibrium expression. (Remember that the true thermodynamic equilibrium constant is written in terms of activities, and by definition, the activity of a solid is equal to one.)

The value of K_{sp} is a measure of the solubility of a compound. Table 16.2 lists the values of K_{sp} for a number of ionic compounds. A more complete list can be found in Appendix IIC.

K_{sp} and Molar Solubility

Recall from Section 12.2 that the *solubility* of a compound is the quantity of the compound that dissolves in a certain amount of liquid. The **molar solubility** is the solubility in units of moles per litre (mol L^{-1}). We can calculate the molar solubility of a compound directly from K_{sp}. Consider silver chloride:

$$AgCl(s) \rightleftharpoons Ag^+(aq) + Cl^-(aq) \qquad K_{sp} = 1.77 \times 10^{-10}$$

TABLE 16.2 Selected Solubility Product Constants (K_{sp})

Compound	Formula	K_{sp}	Compound	Formula	K_{sp}
Barium fluoride	BaF_2	2.45×10^{-5}	Lead(II) chloride	$PbCl_2$	1.17×10^{-5}
Barium sulfate	$BaSO_4$	1.07×10^{-10}	Lead(II) bromide	$PbBr_2$	4.67×10^{-6}
Calcium carbonate	$CaCO_3$	4.96×10^{-9}	Lead(II) sulfate	$PbSO_4$	1.82×10^{-8}
Calcium fluoride	CaF_2	1.46×10^{-10}	Lead(II) sulfide	PbS	9.04×10^{-29}
Calcium hydroxide	$Ca(OH)_2$	4.68×10^{-6}	Magnesium carbonate	$MgCO_3$	6.82×10^{-6}
Calcium sulfate	$CaSO_4$	7.10×10^{-5}	Magnesium hydroxide	$Mg(OH)_2$	2.06×10^{-13}
Copper(II) sulfide	CuS	1.27×10^{-36}	Silver chloride	$AgCl$	1.77×10^{-10}
Iron(II) carbonate	$FeCO_3$	3.07×10^{-11}	Silver chromate	Ag_2CrO_4	1.12×10^{-12}
Iron(II) hydroxide	$Fe(OH)_2$	4.87×10^{-17}	Silver bromide	$AgBr$	5.35×10^{-13}
Iron(II) sulfide	FeS	3.72×10^{-19}	Silver iodide	AgI	8.51×10^{-17}

Notice that K_{sp} is *not* the molar solubility, but the solubility product constant. The solubility product constant has only one value at a given temperature. The solubility, however, can have different values in different kinds of solutions. For example, due to the common ion effect, the solubility of AgCl in pure water is different from its solubility in an NaCl solution, even though the solubility product constant is the same for both solutions. Notice also that the solubility of AgCl is directly related (by the reaction stoichiometry) to the amount of Ag^+ or Cl^- present in solution when equilibrium is reached. Consequently, finding molar solubility from K_{sp} involves solving an equilibrium problem. For AgCl, we set up an ICE table for the dissolution of AgCl into its ions in pure water:

$$AgCl(s) \rightleftharpoons Ag^+(aq) + Cl^-(aq)$$

	$[Ag^+]$	$[Cl^-]$
Initial	0	0
Change	$+S$	$+S$
Equil	S	S

We let S represent the concentration of AgCl that dissolves (which is the molar solubility), and then represent the concentrations of the ions formed in terms of S. In this case, for every 1 mol of AgCl that dissolves, 1 mol of Ag^+ and 1 mol of Cl^- are produced. Therefore, the concentrations of Ag^+ or Cl^- present in solution are equal to S. Substituting the equilibrium concentrations of Ag^+ and Cl^- into the expression for the solubility product constant, we get

Alternatively, the variable x can be used in place of S, as it was for other equilibrium calculations.

$$\begin{aligned} K_{sp} &= [Ag^+][Cl^-] \\ &= S \times S \\ &= S^2 \end{aligned}$$

Therefore,

$$\begin{aligned} S &= \sqrt{K_{sp}} \\ &= \sqrt{1.77 \times 10^{-10}} \\ &= 1.33 \times 10^{-5}\ \text{mol L}^{-1} \end{aligned}$$

The molar solubility of AgCl is 1.33×10^{-5} moles per litre.

EXAMPLE 16.8 CALCULATING MOLAR SOLUBILITY FROM K_{sp}

Calculate the molar solubility of $PbCl_2$ in pure water.

SOLUTION

Begin by writing the reaction by which solid $PbCl_2$ dissolves into its constituent aqueous ions and write the corresponding expression for K_{sp}.	$PbCl_2(s) \rightleftharpoons Pb^{2+}(aq) + 2\,Cl^-(aq)$ $K_{sp} = [Pb^{2+}][Cl^-]^2$
Refer to the stoichiometry of the reaction and prepare an ICE table, showing the equilibrium concentrations of Pb^{2+} and Cl^- relative to S, the amount of $PbCl_2$ that dissolves.	$PbCl_2(s) \rightleftharpoons Pb^{2+}(aq) + 2\,Cl^-(aq)$ [ICE table below]
Substitute the equilibrium expressions for $[Pb^{2+}]$ and $[Cl^-]$ from the previous step into the expression for K_{sp}.	$K_{sp} = [Pb^{2+}][Cl^-]^2$ $= S(2S)^2 = 4S^3$
Solve for S and substitute the numerical value of K_{sp} (from Table 16.2) to calculate S.	$S = \sqrt[3]{\frac{K_{sp}}{4}}$ $S = \sqrt[3]{\frac{1.17 \times 10^{-5}}{4}} = 1.43 \times 10^{-2}\ \text{mol L}^{-1}$

	$[Pb^{2+}]$	$[Cl^-]$
Initial	0	0
Change	$+S$	$+2S$
Equil	S	$2S$

FOR PRACTICE 16.8
Calculate the molar solubility of $Fe(OH)_2$ in pure water.

CHEMISTRY IN YOUR DAY Hard Water

In many parts of the world, the water supply contains significant concentrations of $CaCO_3$ and $MgCO_3$ that dissolve into rainwater runoff as it flows through soils rich in these compounds. Water containing dissolved calcium and magnesium ions is known as hard water. Hard water is not a health hazard because both calcium and magnesium are part of a healthy diet. However, their presence in water can be a nuisance. Because of their relatively low solubility, the water becomes saturated with $CaCO_3$ and $MgCO_3$ as it evaporates. If evaporation continues, some dissolved ions precipitate out as salts. These precipitates show up as scaly deposits on faucets, sinks, or cookware. Washing cars or dishes with hard water leaves spots of $CaCO_3$ and $MgCO_3$.

Water can be softened with water softeners. These devices replace the Ca^{2+} and Mg^{2+} ions present in hard water with soluble ions, most commonly Na^+, which do not form scaly deposits the way that Ca^{2+} and Mg^{2+} do. The sodium content of softened water is considered to be low; however, people who are concerned with their sodium intake can use resins that exchange the Ca^{2+} and Mg^{2+} with K^+. Using potassium ions is safer for people with high blood pressure, but is more expensive.

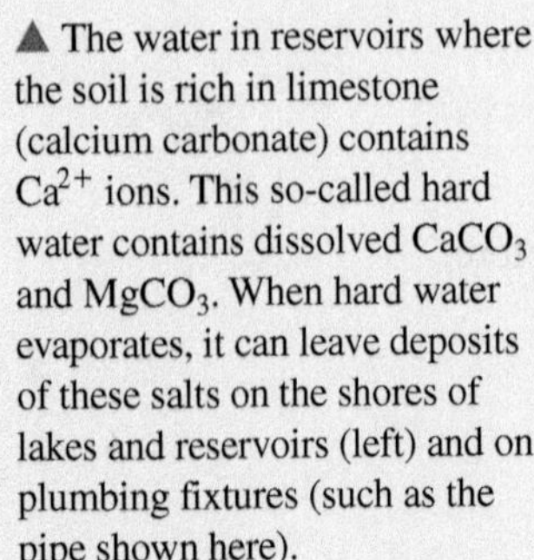

▲ The water in reservoirs where the soil is rich in limestone (calcium carbonate) contains Ca^{2+} ions. This so-called hard water contains dissolved $CaCO_3$ and $MgCO_3$. When hard water evaporates, it can leave deposits of these salts on the shores of lakes and reservoirs (left) and on plumbing fixtures (such as the pipe shown here).

Question

Use the K_{sp} values from Table 16.2 to calculate the molar solubility of $CaCO_3$ and $MgCO_3$. What mass of $CaCO_3$ (in grams) is in 5 L of water that is saturated with $CaCO_3$?

EXAMPLE 16.9 CALCULATING K_{sp} FROM MOLAR SOLUBILITY

The molar solubility of Ag_2SO_4 in pure water is 1.2×10^{-5} mol L^{-1}. Calculate K_{sp}.

SOLUTION

Begin by writing the reaction by which solid Ag_2SO_4 dissolves into its constituent aqueous ions and write the corresponding expression for K_{sp}.

$$Ag_2SO_4(s) \rightleftharpoons 2\,Ag^+(aq) + SO_4^{2-}(aq)$$
$$K_{sp} = [Ag^+]^2[SO_4^{2-}]$$

Use an ICE table to define $[Ag^+]$ and $[SO_4^{2-}]$ in terms of S, the amount of Ag_2SO_4 that dissolves.

$$Ag_2SO_4(s) \rightleftharpoons 2\,Ag^+(aq) + SO_4^{2-}(aq)$$

	$[Ag^+]$	$[SO_4^{2-}]$
Initial	0	0
Change	$+2S$	$+S$
Equil	$2S$	S

Substitute the expressions for $[Ag^+]$ and $[SO_4^{2-}]$ from the previous step into the expression for K_{sp}. Substitute the given value of the molar solubility for S and calculate K_{sp}.

$$\begin{aligned} K_{sp} &= [Ag^+]^2[SO_4^{2-}] \\ &= (2S)^2S \\ &= 4S^3 \\ &= 4(1.2 \times 10^{-5})^3 \\ &= 6.9 \times 10^{-15} \end{aligned}$$

FOR PRACTICE 16.9

The molar solubility of AgBr in pure water is 7.3×10^{-7} mol L^{-1}. Calculate K_{sp}.

K_{sp} and Relative Solubility

As we have just seen, molar solubility and K_{sp} are related, and each can be calculated from the other; however, you cannot generally use the K_{sp} values of two different compounds to directly compare their relative solubilities. For example, consider the following compounds, their K_{sp} values, and their molar solubilities:

Compound	K_{sp}	Solubility
$Mg(OH)_2$	2.06×10^{-13}	3.72×10^{-5} mol L^{-1}
$FeCO_3$	3.07×10^{-11}	5.54×10^{-6} mol L^{-1}

Magnesium hydroxide has a smaller K_{sp} than iron(II) carbonate, but a higher molar solubility. Why? The relationship between K_{sp} and molar solubility depends on the stoichiometry of the dissociation reaction. Consequently, any direct comparison of K_{sp} values for different compounds can only be made if the compounds have the same dissociation stoichiometry. Consider the following compounds with the same dissociation stoichiometry, their K_{sp} values, and their molar solubilities:

Compound	K_{sp}	Solubility
$Mg(OH)_2$	2.06×10^{-13}	3.72×10^{-5} mol L^{-1}
CaF_2	1.46×10^{-10}	3.32×10^{-4} mol L^{-1}

In this case, magnesium hydroxide and calcium fluoride have the same dissociation stoichiometry (1 mol of each compound produces 3 mol of dissolved ions); therefore, the K_{sp} values can be directly compared as a measure of relative solubility.

The Effect of a Common Ion on Solubility

How is the solubility of an ionic compound affected when the compound is dissolved in a solution that already contains one of its ions? For example, what is the solubility of CaF_2 in a solution that is 0.100 mol L^{-1} in NaF? We can determine the change in solubility by considering the common ion effect, which we first encountered in Section 16.2. We can represent the dissociation of CaF_2 in a 0.100 mol L^{-1} NaF solution as follows:

Common ion
0.100 mol L^{-1} $F^-(aq)$

$$CaF_2(s) \rightleftharpoons Ca^{2+}(aq) + 2\,F^-(aq)$$

Equilibrium shifts left.

In accordance with Le Châtelier's principle, the presence of the F^- ion in solution causes the equilibrium to shift to the left (compared to its position in pure water), which means that less CaF_2 dissolves—that is, its solubility is decreased.

In general, the solubility of an ionic compound is lower in a solution containing a common ion than in pure water.

We can calculate the exact value of the solubility by working an equilibrium problem in which the concentration of the common ion is accounted for in the initial conditions, as shown in the following example.

EXAMPLE 16.10 CALCULATING MOLAR SOLUBILITY IN THE PRESENCE OF A COMMON ION

What is the molar solubility of CaF_2 in a solution containing 0.100 mol L^{-1} NaF?

SOLUTION

Begin by writing the reaction by which solid CaF_2 dissolves into its constituent aqueous ions. Write the corresponding expression for K_{sp}.

$$CaF_2(s) \rightleftharpoons Ca^{2+}(aq) + 2\,F^-(aq)$$
$$K_{sp} = [Ca^{2+}][F^-]^2$$

Use the stoichiometry of the reaction to prepare an ICE table showing the initial concentration of the common ion. Fill in the equilibrium concentrations of Ca^{2+} and F^- relative to S, the amount of CaF_2 that dissolves.

$$CaF_2(s) \rightleftharpoons Ca^{2+}(aq) + 2\,F^-(aq)$$

	$[Ca^{2+}]$	$[F^-]$
Initial	0	0.100
Change	$+S$	$+2S$
Equil	S	$0.100 + 2S$

Substitute the equilibrium expressions for $[Ca^{2+}]$ and $[F^-]$ from the previous step into the expression for K_{sp}. Since K_{sp} is small, we can make the approximation that $2S$ is much less than 0.100 and will therefore be insignificant when added to 0.100 (this is similar to the *x is small* approximation that we make for many equilibrium problems).

$$K_{sp} = [Ca^{2+}][F^-]^2$$
$$= S(0.100 + 2S)^2 \quad (S \text{ is small})$$
$$= S(0.100)^2$$

Solve for S and substitute the numerical value of K_{sp} (from Table 16.2) to calculate S.

Note that the calculated value of S is indeed small compared to 0.100; our approximation is valid.

$$K_{sp} = S(0.100)^2$$
$$S = \frac{K_{sp}}{0.0100} = \frac{1.46 \times 10^{-10}}{0.0100} = 1.46 \times 10^{-8} \text{ mol L}^{-1}$$

For comparison, the molar solubility of CaF_2 in pure water is 3.32×10^{-4} mol L^{-1}, which means CaF_2 is over 20000 times more soluble in water than in the NaF solution. (Confirm this for yourself by calculating its solubility in pure water from the value of K_{sp}.)

FOR PRACTICE 16.10
Calculate the molar solubility of CaF_2 in a solution containing 0.250 mol L^{-1} $Ca(NO_3)_2$.

The Effect of an Uncommon Ion on Solubility (Salt Effect)

Consider a saturated solution of Ag_2SO_4.

$$Ag_2SO_4(s) \rightleftharpoons 2Ag^+(aq) + SO_4^{2-}(aq)$$

From the previous section, we know that the addition of $AgNO_3$ or K_2SO_4—which produce Ag^+ and SO_4^{2-}, respectively—to this solution results in precipitation of some Ag_2SO_4 due to the common ion effect. What effect would the addition of $NaNO_3$ have on the solubility of Ag_2SO_4? $NaNO_3$ dissolves completely to give Na^+ and NO_3^-, which do not appear in the Ag_2SO_4 solubility equilibrium and are therefore called *uncommon ions*. At relatively low concentrations of the uncommon ions, there is no effect on the solubility equilibrium. At higher concentrations, the solvent can no longer keep the ions separate and ion pairs form. For example, Na^+ is known to associate with SO_4^{2-} to form an ion pair in aqueous solution:

$$Na^+(aq) + SO_4^{2-}(aq) \rightleftharpoons Na^+/SO_4^{2-}(aq)$$

Since SO_4^{2-} is no longer free but is paired with Na^+, more Ag_2SO_4 will dissolve. The effect of adding high concentrations of uncommon ions is to slightly *increase* the solubility of an insoluble salt and is called the *uncommon ion effect* or *salt effect*.

The Effect of pH on Solubility

The pH of a solution can affect the solubility of a compound in that solution. For example, consider the dissociation of $Mg(OH)_2$, the active ingredient in milk of magnesia:

$$Mg(OH)_2(s) \rightleftharpoons Mg^{2+}(aq) + 2\,OH^-(aq)$$

The solubility of this compound is highly dependent on the pH of the solution into which it dissolves. If the pH is high, then the concentration of OH^- in the solution is high. In accordance with the common ion effect, this shifts the equilibrium to the left, lowering the solubility.

High $[OH^-]$

$$Mg(OH)_2(s) \rightleftharpoons Mg^{2+}(aq) + 2\,OH^-(aq)$$

Equilibrium shifts left.

If the pH is low, then the concentration of $H_3O^+(aq)$ in the solution is high. As the $Mg(OH)_2$ dissolves, these H_3O^+ ions neutralize the newly dissolved OH^- ions, driving the reaction to the right.

H_3O^+ reacts with OH^-

$$Mg(OH)_2(s) \rightleftharpoons Mg^{2+}(aq) + 2\,OH^-(aq)$$

Equilibrium shifts right.

Consequently, the solubility of $Mg(OH)_2$ in an acidic solution is higher than in a pH-neutral or basic solution.

In general, the solubility of an ionic compound with a strongly basic or weakly basic anion increases with increasing acidity (decreasing pH).

Common basic anions include OH^-, S^{2-}, and CO_3^{2-}. Therefore, hydroxides, sulfides, and carbonates are more soluble in acidic water than in pure water. Since rainwater is naturally acidic due to dissolved carbon dioxide, it can dissolve rocks high in limestone ($CaCO_3$) as it flows through the ground, sometimes resulting in large underground caverns and

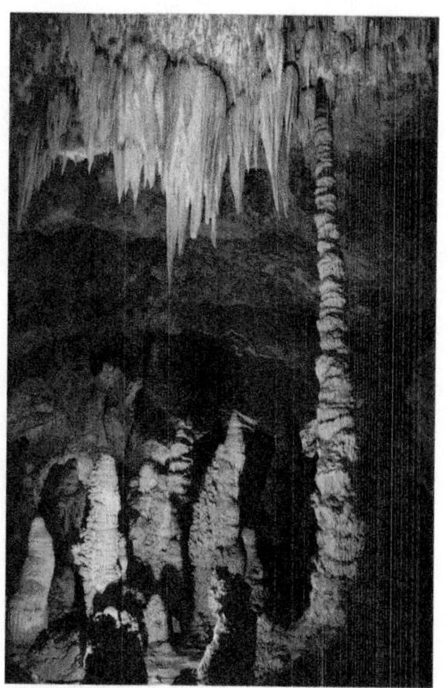

▲ Stalactites (which hang from the ceiling) and stalagmites (which grow up from the ground) form as calcium carbonate precipitates out of the water evaporating in underground caves.

tunnels called *solution caves*. Solution caves can be found across Canada, for example, in the Rocky Mountains of British Columbia and Alberta, in Saint John, New Brunswick, as well as in Eganville (Bonnechere Caves) and Peterborough (Warsaw Caves) in Ontario. Dripping water saturated in $CaCO_3$ within the cave creates the dramatic mineral formations known as stalagmites and stalactites.

EXAMPLE 16.11 THE EFFECT OF pH ON SOLUBILITY

Determine whether each compound is more soluble in an acidic solution than in a neutral solution.

(a) BaF_2 **(b)** AgI **(c)** $Ca(OH)_2$

SOLUTION

(a) The solubility of BaF_2 will be greater in acidic solution because the F^- ion is a weak base. (F^- is the conjugate base of the weak acid HF, and is therefore a weak base.)

(b) The solubility of AgI will not be greater in acidic solution because the I^- is *not* a base. (I^- is the conjugate base of the *strong* acid HI, and is therefore pH-neutral.)

(c) The solubility of $Ca(OH)_2$ will be greater in acidic solution because the OH^- ion is a strong base.

FOR PRACTICE 16.11

Which compound, $FeCO_3$ or $PbBr_2$, is more soluble in acid than in base? Why?

16.6 Precipitation

In Chapter 4, we learned that a precipitation reaction can occur upon the mixing of two solutions containing ionic compounds when one of the possible cross products—the combination of a cation from one solution and the anion from the other—is insoluble. As we have seen, however, the terms *soluble* and *insoluble* are extremes in a continuous range of solubility—many compounds are slightly soluble and even those that we categorized as insoluble in Chapter 4 actually have some limited degree of solubility (they have very small solubility product constants).

We can better understand precipitation reactions by revisiting a concept from Chapter 14—the reaction quotient (Q). The reaction quotient for the reaction by which an ionic compound dissolves is the product of the concentrations of the ionic components raised to their stoichiometric coefficients. For example, consider the reaction by which CaF_2 dissolves:

$$CaF_2(s) \rightleftharpoons Ca^{2+}(aq) + 2\,F^-(aq)$$

The reaction quotient for this reaction is

$$Q = [Ca^{2+}][F^-]^2$$

The difference between Q and K_{sp} is that K_{sp} is the value of this product *at equilibrium only*, whereas Q is the value of the product under any conditions. We can therefore use the value of Q to compare a solution containing any concentrations of the component ions to a solution that is at equilibrium.

For example, consider a solution of calcium fluoride in which Q is less than K_{sp}. Recall from Chapter 14 that if Q is less than K_{sp}, the reaction will proceed to the right (toward products). Consequently, if the solution contains any solid CaF_2, the CaF_2 will continue to dissolve. If all of the solid has already dissolved, the solution will simply remain as it is, containing less than the equilibrium amount of the dissolved ions. Such a solution is called an *unsaturated solution*. If more solid is added to an unsaturated solution, the solid will dissolve, as long as Q remains less than K_{sp}.

Now consider a solution in which Q is exactly equal to K_{sp}. In this case, the reaction is at equilibrium and will not make progress in either direction. Such a solution most likely contains at least a small amount of the solid in equilibrium with its component ions. However, the amount of solid may be too small to be visible. Such a solution is called a *saturated solution.*

Finally, consider a solution in which Q is greater than K_{sp}. In this case, the reaction will proceed to the left (toward the reactants) and solid calcium fluoride will form from the dissolved calcium and fluoride ions. In other words, the solid normally precipitates out of a solution in which Q is greater than K_{sp}. Under certain circumstances, however, Q can remain greater than K_{sp} for an unlimited period of time. Such a solution, called a *supersaturated solution,* is unstable and will form a precipitate when sufficiently disturbed. Figure 16.14 ▶ shows a supersaturated solution of sodium acetate. When a small seed crystal of solid sodium acetate is dropped into the solution, it triggers the precipitation reaction.

▲ **FIGURE 16.14 Precipitation from a Supersaturated Solution** The excess solute in a supersaturated solution of sodium acetate precipitates out if a small sodium acetate crystal is added.

Summarizing the Relationship of Q and K_{sp} in Solutions Containing an Ionic Compound:

- If $Q < K_{sp}$, the solution is unsaturated and more of the solid ionic compound can dissolve in the solution.
- If $Q = K_{sp}$, the solution is saturated. The solution is holding the equilibrium amount of the dissolved ions and additional solid will not dissolve in the solution.
- If $Q > K_{sp}$, the solution is supersaturated. Under most circumstances, the excess solid will precipitate out of a supersaturated solution.

We can use Q to predict whether a precipitation reaction will occur upon the mixing of two solutions containing dissolved ionic compounds. For example, consider mixing a silver nitrate solution with a potassium iodide solution to form a mixture that is 0.010 mol L^{-1} in $AgNO_3$ and 0.015 mol L^{-1} in KI. Will a precipitate form in the newly mixed solution? From Chapter 4 we know that one of the cross products, KNO_3, is soluble and will therefore not precipitate. The other cross product, AgI, *may* precipitate if the concentrations of Ag^+ and I^- are high enough in the newly mixed solution; we can compare Q to K_{sp} to determine if a precipitate will form. For AgI, $K_{sp} = 8.51 \times 10^{-17}$. For the newly mixed solution, $[Ag^+] = 0.010 \text{ mol L}^{-1}$ and $[I^-] = 0.015 \text{ mol L}^{-1}$. We calculate Q as follows:

$$Q = [Ag^+][I^-] = (0.010)(0.015) = 1.5 \times 10^{-4}$$

The value of Q is much greater than K_{sp}; therefore, AgI should precipitate out of the newly mixed solution.

EXAMPLE 16.12 PREDICTING PRECIPITATION REACTIONS BY COMPARING Q AND K_{sp}

A solution containing lead(II) nitrate is mixed with one containing sodium bromide to form a solution that is 0.0150 mol L^{-1} in $Pb(NO_3)_2$ and 0.00350 mol L^{-1} in NaBr. Will a precipitate form in the newly mixed solution?

SOLUTION

First, determine the possible cross products and their K_{sp} values (Table 16.2). Any cross products that are soluble will *not* precipitate (see Table 4.2).	Possible cross products: $NaNO_3$ soluble $PbBr_2$ $K_{sp} = 4.67 \times 10^{-6}$

(continued)

EXAMPLE 16.12 (CONTINUED)

Calculate Q and compare it to K_{sp}. A precipitate will only form if $Q > K_{sp}$.	$Q = [Pb^{2+}][Br^-]^2$ $= (0.0150)(0.00350)^2$ $= 1.84 \times 10^{-7}$ $Q < K_{sp}$; therefore, no precipitate forms.

FOR PRACTICE 16.12

If the original solutions in Example 16.12 are concentrated through evaporation and mixed again to form a solution that is 0.0600 mol L^{-1} in $Pb(NO_3)_2$ and 0.0158 mol L^{-1} in NaBr, will a precipitate form in this newly mixed solution?

Selective Precipitation

A solution may contain several different dissolved metal cations which can often be separated by **selective precipitation**, a process involving the addition of a reagent that forms a precipitate with one of the dissolved cations but not the others. For example, seawater contains dissolved magnesium and calcium cations with the concentrations $[Mg^{2+}] = 0.059$ mol L^{-1} and $[Ca^{2+}] = 0.011$ mol L^{-1}. We could separate these ions by adding a reagent that will precipitate one of the ions but not the other. From Table 16.2, we find that $Mg(OH)_2$ has a K_{sp} of 2.06×10^{-13} and that $Ca(OH)_2$ has a K_{sp} of 4.68×10^{-6}, indicating that the hydroxide ion forms a precipitate with magnesium at a much lower concentration than it does with calcium. Consequently, a soluble hydroxide—such as KOH or NaOH—is a good choice for the precipitating reagent. When we add an appropriate amount of KOH or NaOH to seawater, the hydroxide ion causes the precipitation of $Mg(OH)_2$ (the compound with the lowest K_{sp}) but not $Ca(OH)_2$. Calculations for this selective precipitation are shown in the following examples. In these calculations, you compare Q to K_{sp} to determine the concentration that triggers precipitation.

The difference in K_{sp} values required for selective precipitation is a factor of at least 10^3.

EXAMPLE 16.13 FINDING THE MINIMUM REQUIRED REAGENT CONCENTRATION FOR SELECTIVE PRECIPITATION

The magnesium and calcium ions present in seawater ($[Mg^{2+}] = 0.059$ mol L^{-1} and $[Ca^{2+}] = 0.011$ mol L^{-1}) can be separated by selective precipitation with KOH. What minimum $[OH^-]$ triggers the precipitation of the Mg^{2+} ion?

SOLUTION

The precipitation will commence when the value of Q for the precipitating compound just equals the value of K_{sp}. Set the expression for Q for magnesium hydroxide equal to the value of K_{sp}, and solve for $[OH^-]$. This will be the concentration above which $Mg(OH)_2$ precipitates.	$Q = [Mg^{2+}][OH^-]^2$ $= (0.059)[OH^-]^2$ When $Q = K_{sp}$, $(0.059)[OH^-]^2 = K_{sp} = 2.06 \times 10^{-13}$. $[OH^-]^2 = \frac{2.06 \times 10^{-13}}{0.059}$ $[OH^-] = 1.9 \times 10^{-6}$ mol L^{-1}

FOR PRACTICE 16.13

If the concentration of Mg^{2+} in the above solution was 0.025 mol L^{-1}, what minimum $[OH^-]$ triggers precipitation of the Mg^{2+} ion?

EXAMPLE 16.14 **FINDING THE CONCENTRATIONS OF IONS LEFT IN SOLUTION AFTER SELECTIVE PRECIPITATION**

You add potassium hydroxide to the solution in Example 16.13. When the $[OH^-]$ reaches 1.9×10^{-6} mol L^{-1} (as you just calculated), magnesium hydroxide begins to precipitate out of solution. As you continue to add KOH, the magnesium hydroxide continues to precipitate. However, at some point, the $[OH^-]$ becomes high enough to begin to precipitate the calcium ions as well. What is the concentration of Mg^{2+} when Ca^{2+} begins to precipitate?

SOLUTION

First, find the OH^- concentration at which Ca^{2+} begins to precipitate by writing the expression for Q for calcium hydroxide and substituting the concentration of Ca^{2+} from Example 16.13.	$Q = [Ca^{2+}][OH^-]^2$ $= (0.011)[OH^-]^2$
Set the expression for Q equal to the value of K_{sp} for calcium hydroxide and solve for $[OH^-]$. This will be the concentration above which $Ca(OH)_2$ precipitates.	When $Q = K_{sp}$, $(0.011)[OH^-]^2 = K_{sp} = 4.68 \times 10^{-6}$. $[OH^-]^2 = \dfrac{4.68 \times 10^{-6}}{0.011}$ $[OH^-] = 2.0\underline{6} \times 10^{-2}$ mol L^{-1}
Find the concentration of Mg^{2+} when OH^- reaches the concentration you just calculated by writing the expression for Q *for magnesium hydroxide* and substituting the concentration of OH^- that you just calculated. Then set the expression for Q equal to the value of K_{sp} for magnesium hydroxide and solve for $[Mg^{2+}]$. This will be the concentration of Mg^{2+} that remains when $Ca(OH)_2$ begins to precipitate.	$Q = [Mg^{2+}][OH^-]^2$ $= [Mg^{2+}](2.0\underline{6} \times 10^{-2})^2$ When $Q = K_{sp}$, $[Mg^{2+}](2.0\underline{6} \times 10^{-2})^2 = K_{sp} = 2.06 \times 10^{-13}$. $[Mg^{2+}] = \dfrac{2.06 \times 10^{-13}}{(2.0\underline{6} \times 10^{-2})^2}$ $[Mg^{2+}] = 4.9 \times 10^{-10}$ mol L^{-1}

As you can see from the results, the selective precipitation worked very well. The concentration of Mg^{2+} dropped from 0.059 mol L^{-1} to 4.9×10^{-10} mol L^{-1} before any calcium began to precipitate, which means that we separated 99.99% of the magnesium out of the solution.

FOR PRACTICE 16.14

A solution is 0.085 mol L^{-1} in Pb^{2+} and 0.025 mol L^{-1} in Ag^+. **(a)** If selective precipitation is to be achieved using NaCl, what minimum concentration of NaCl do you need to begin to precipitate the ion that precipitates first? **(b)** What is the concentration of each ion left in solution at the point where the second ion begins to precipitate?

16.7 Qualitative Chemical Analysis

Selective precipitation, as discussed in Section 16.6, can be used in a systematic way to determine which metal ions are present in an unknown solution. Such an analysis is known as **qualitative analysis**. The word *qualitative* means *involving quality or kind.* Qualitative analysis involves finding the *kind* of ions present in the solution. This stands in contrast to **quantitative analysis**, which is concerned with quantity, or the amounts of substances in a solution or mixture.

In the past, qualitative analysis by selective precipitation was used extensively to determine the metals present in a sample. This method of analysis—dubbed *wet chemistry* because it involves the mixing of many aqueous solutions in the lab—has been replaced by more precise and less time-intensive instrumental techniques. Nonetheless, both for the sake of history and also because of the principles involved, we now examine a traditional qualitative analysis scheme. You may use such a scheme in your general chemistry laboratory as an exercise in qualitative analysis.

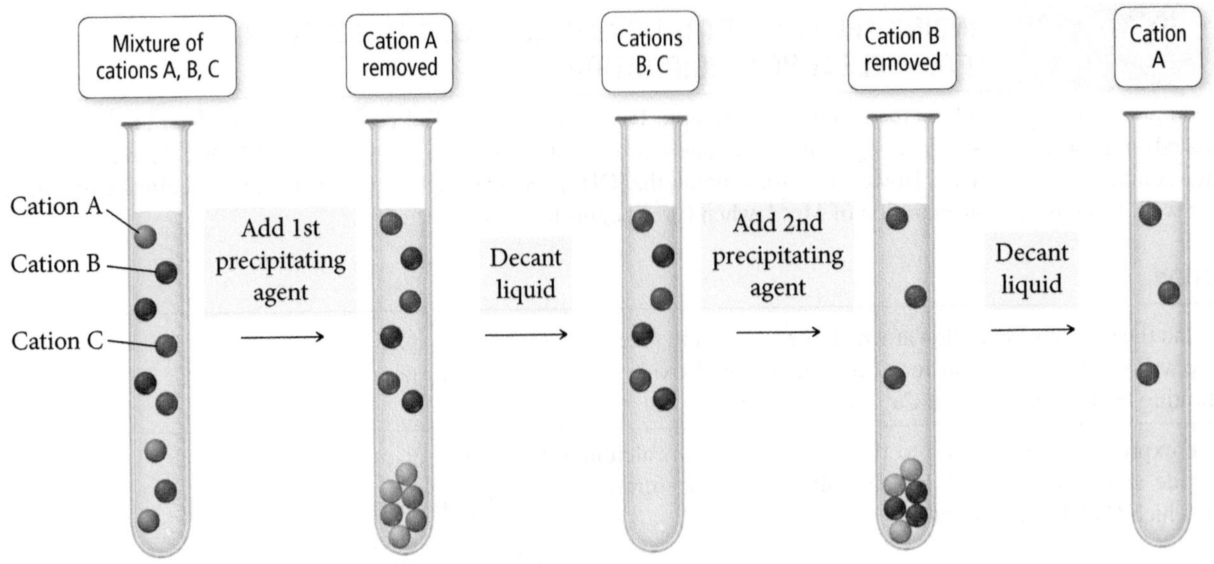

▲ **FIGURE 16.15 Qualitative Analysis** In qualitative analysis, specific ions are precipitated successively by the addition of appropriate reagents.

The basic idea behind qualitative analysis is straightforward. A sample containing a mixture of metal cations is subjected to the addition of several precipitating agents. At each step, some of the metal cations—those that form sparingly soluble compounds with the precipitating agent—precipitate from the mixture and are separated out as solids. The remaining aqueous mixture is then subjected to the next precipitating agent, and so on (Figure 16.15 ▲).

A general qualitative analysis scheme is diagrammed in Figure 16.16 ▼. The scheme involves separating a mixture of the common ions into five groups by sequentially adding

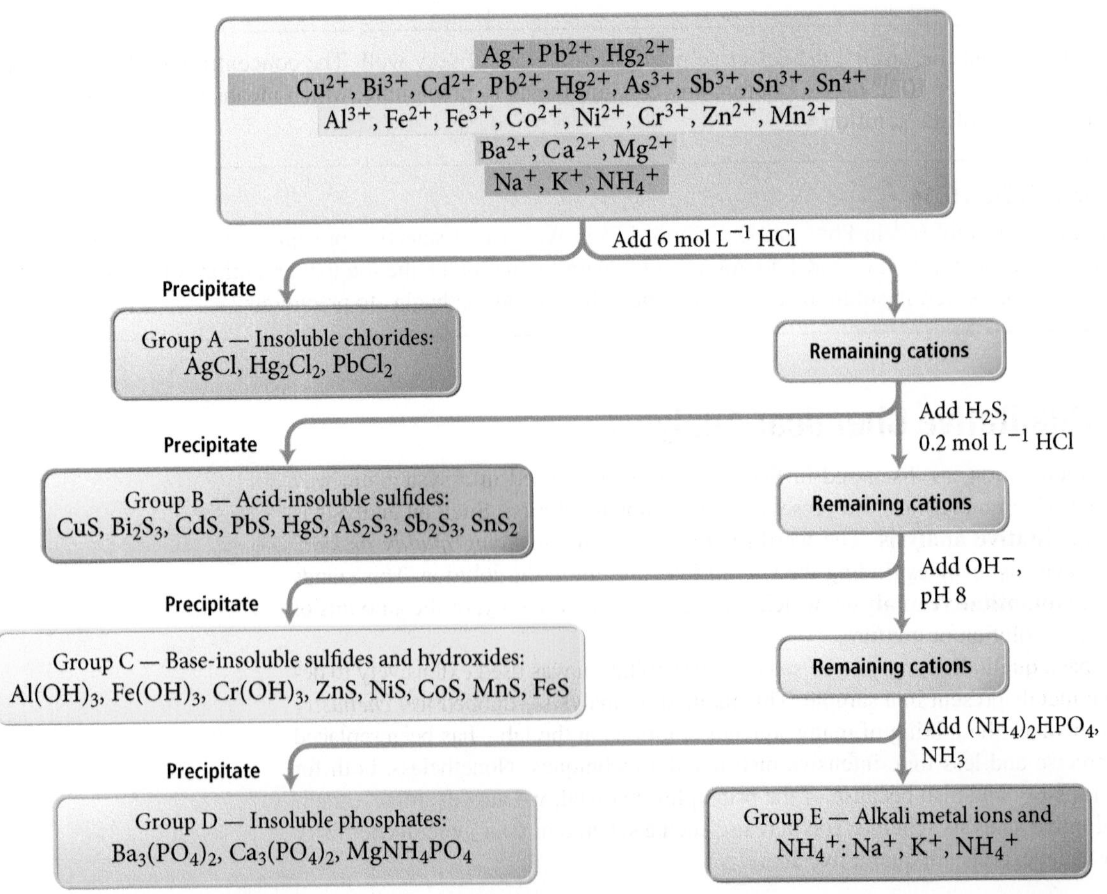

▲ **FIGURE 16.16 A General Qualitative Analysis Scheme**

five different precipitating agents. After each precipitating agent is added, the mixture is put into a centrifuge to separate the solid from the liquid. The liquid is decanted for the next step, and the solid is set aside for subsequent analysis. We examine each group separately.

Group A: Insoluble Chlorides

In the first step, the aqueous mixture containing the metal cations is treated with 6 mol L^{-1} HCl. Since most chlorides are soluble, the chloride ions *do not form* a precipitate with the majority of the cations in mixture. However, Ag^+, Pb^{2+}, and Hg_2^{2+} *do form* sparingly soluble chlorides. So, if any of those metal cations are present, they precipitate out. The absence of a precipitate constitutes a negative test for Ag^+, Pb^{2+}, and Hg_2^{2+}. If a precipitate forms, one or more of these ions is present. After the solid is separated from the liquid, the solution is ready for the next step.

Group B: Acid-Insoluble Sulfides

In the second step, the acidic aqueous mixture containing the remaining metal cations is treated with H_2S, a weak diprotic acid that dissociates in two steps:

$$H_2S \rightleftharpoons H^+ + HS^-$$
$$HS^- \rightleftharpoons H^+ + S^{2-}$$

The concentration of S^{2-} ions in an H_2S solution is pH-dependent. At low pH (high H^+ concentration) the equilibria shift left, minimizing the amount of available S^{2-}. At high pH (low H^+ concentration) the equilbria shift right, maximizing the amount of available S^{2-}. At this stage, the solution is acidic (from the addition of HCl in the previous step), and the concentration of S^{2-} in solution is relatively low. Only the most sparingly soluble metal sulfides (those with the smallest K_{sp} values) precipitate under these conditions. These include Hg^{2+}, Cd^{2+}, Bi^{3+}, Cu^{2+}, Sn^{4+}, As^{3+}, Pb^{2+}, and Sb^{3+}. If any of these metal cations are present, they precipitate out as sulfides. After the solid is separated from the liquid, the solution is ready for the next step.

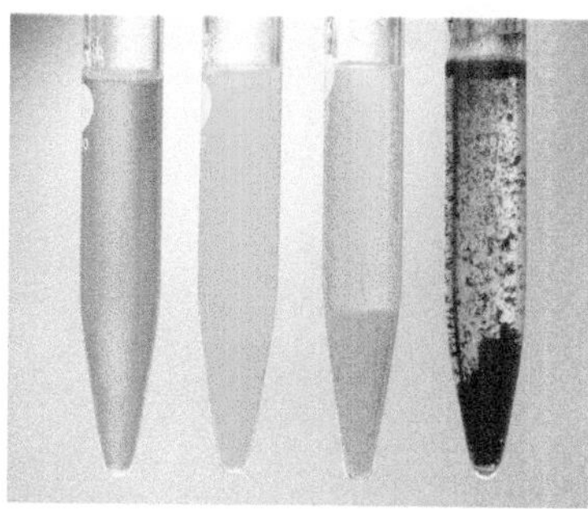

$(NH_4)_2S$ CdS Sb_2S_3 PbS

Group C: Base-Insoluble Sulfides and Hydroxides

In the third step, additional base and H_2S are added to the acidic aqueous mixture containing the remaining metal cations. The added base reacts with acid, shifting the H_2S ionization equilibria to the right and creating a higher S^{2-} concentration. This causes the precipitation of those sulfides that were too soluble to precipitate out in the previous step but not soluble enough to prevent precipitation with the higher sulfide ion concentration. The ions that precipitate as sulfides at this point (if they are present) are Fe^{2+}, Co^{2+}, Zn^{2+}, Mn^{2+}, and Ni^{2+}. In addition, the additional base causes Cr^{3+}, Fe^{3+}, and Al^{3+} to precipitate as hydroxides. After the solid is separated from the liquid, the solution is ready for the next step.

Group D: Insoluble Phosphates

At this stage, all of the cations have precipitated except those belonging to the alkali metal family (group 1 in the periodic table) and the alkaline earth metal family (group 2 in the periodic table). The alkaline earth metal cations can be precipitated by adding $(NH_4)_2HPO_4$ to the solution, causing Mg^{2+}, Ca^{2+}, and Ba^{2+} to precipitate as metal phosphates, which are separated from the liquid.

Group E: Alkali Metals and NH_4^+

The only dissolved ions that the liquid decanted from the previous step can now contain are Na^+, K^+, and NH_4^+. These cations do not form sparingly soluble compounds with any anions and cannot be precipitated from the solution. Their presence can be determined, however, by other means. Sodium and potassium ions, for example, are usually identified through flame tests. The sodium ion produces a yellow-orange flame and the potassium ion produces a violet flame, as shown in Figure 16.17 ▼.

Sodium

Potassium

▲ **FIGURE 16.17 Flame Tests** The sodium ion produces a yellow-orange flame. The potassium ion produces a violet flame.

By applying the procedure on the previous page, nearly two dozen metal cations can be separated from a solution initially containing all of them. Each of the groups can be further analyzed to determine which specific ions are present. The specific procedures for these steps are found in many general chemistry laboratory manuals.

16.8 Complex–Ion Equilibria

We have discussed several different types of equilibria so far, including acid–base equilibria and solubility equilibria. We now turn to equilibria of another type, which primarily involve transition metal ions in solution. Transition metal ions tend to be good electron acceptors (good Lewis acids). In aqueous solutions, water molecules can act as electron donors (Lewis bases) to hydrate transition metal ions. For example, silver ions are hydrated by water in solution to form $Ag(H_2O)_2^+(aq)$. Chemists often write $Ag^+(aq)$ as a shorthand notation for the hydrated silver ion, but the bare ion does not really exist by itself in solution.

Species such as $Ag(H_2O)_2^{2+}$ are known as *complex ions*. A **complex ion** contains a central metal ion bound to one or more *ligands*. A **ligand** is a neutral molecule or ion that acts as a Lewis base with the central metal ion. In $Ag(H_2O)_2^+$, water is the ligand. If a stronger Lewis base is put into a solution containing $Ag(H_2O)_2^+$, the stronger Lewis base displaces the water in the complex ion. For example, ammonia reacts with $Ag(H_2O)_2^+$ according to the following reaction:

We cover complex ions in more detail in Chapter 24. Here, we focus on the equilibria associated with their formation.

$$Ag(H_2O)_2^+(aq) + 2\,NH_3(aq) \rightleftharpoons Ag(NH_3)_2^+(aq) + 2\,H_2O(l)$$

For simplicity, water is often left out and the reaction is written as follows:

$$Ag^+(aq) + 2\,NH_3(aq) \rightleftharpoons Ag(NH_3)_2^+(aq) \quad K_f = 1.7 \times 10^7$$

The equilibrium constant associated with the reaction for the formation of a complex ion, such as the one shown above, is called the **formation constant (K_f)**. The expression for K_f is determined by the law of mass action, like any equilibrium constant. For $Ag(NH_3)_2^+$, the expression for K_f is:

$$K_f = \frac{[Ag(NH_3)_2^+]}{[Ag^+][NH_3]^2}$$

Notice that the value of K_f for $Ag(NH_3)_2^+$ is large, indicating that the formation of the complex ion is highly favoured. Table 16.3 lists the formation constants for a number of complex ions. You can see that, in general, values of K_f are very large, indicating that the formation of complex ions is highly favoured in each case. The following example shows how to use K_f in calculations.

TABLE 16.3 Formation Constants of Selected Complex Ions in Water at 25 °C

Complex Ion	K_f	Complex Ion	K_f
$Ag(CN)_2^-$	1×10^{21}	$Cu(NH_3)_4^{2+}$	1.7×10^{13}
$Ag(NH_3)_2^+$	1.7×10^7	$Fe(CN)_6^{4-}$	1.5×10^{35}
$Ag(S_2O_3)_2^{3-}$	2.8×10^{13}	$Fe(CN)_6^{3-}$	2×10^{43}
AlF_6^{3-}	7×10^{19}	$Hg(CN)_4^{2-}$	1.8×10^{41}
$Al(OH)_4^-$	3×10^{33}	$HgCl_4^{2-}$	1.1×10^{16}
$CdBr_4^{2-}$	5.5×10^3	HgI_4^{2-}	2×10^{30}
CdI_4^{2-}	2×10^6	$Ni(NH_3)_6^{2+}$	2.0×10^8
$Cd(CN)_4^{2-}$	3×10^{18}	$Pb(OH)_3^-$	8×10^{13}
$Co(NH_3)_6^{3+}$	2.3×10^{33}	$Sn(OH)_3^-$	3×10^{25}
$Co(OH)_4^{2-}$	5×10^9	$Zn(CN)_4^{2-}$	2.1×10^{19}
$Co(SCN)_4^{2-}$	1×10^3	$Zn(NH_3)_4^{2+}$	2.8×10^9
$Cr(OH)_4^-$	8.0×10^{29}	$Zn(OH)_4^{2-}$	2×10^{15}
$Cu(CN)_4^{2-}$	1.0×10^{25}		

EXAMPLE 16.15 COMPLEX–ION EQUILIBRIA

A 200.0 mL sample of a solution that is 1.5×10^{-3} mol L^{-1} in $Cu(NO_3)_2$ is mixed with a 250.0 mL sample of a solution that is 0.20 mol L^{-1} in NH_3. After the solution reaches equilibrium, what concentration of $Cu^{2+}(aq)$ remains?

SOLUTION

Write the balanced equation for the complex ion equilibrium that occurs and look up the value of K_f in Table 16.3. Since this is an equilibrium problem, you have to create an ICE table, which requires the initial concentrations of Cu^{2+} and NH_3. Calculate those concentrations from the given values.

$$Cu^{2+}(aq) + 4\,NH_3(aq) \rightleftharpoons Cu(NH_3)_4^{2+}(aq)$$

$$K_f = 1.7 \times 10^{13}$$

$$[Cu^{2+}]_{initial} = \frac{0.200\,\cancel{L} \times \dfrac{1.5 \times 10^{-3}\,\text{mol}}{\cancel{L}}}{0.200\,L + 0.250\,L} = 6.7 \times 10^{-4}\,\text{mol L}^{-1}$$

$$[NH_3]_{initial} = \frac{0.250\,\cancel{L} \times \dfrac{0.20\,\text{mol}}{1\,\cancel{L}}}{0.200\,L + 0.250\,L} = 0.11\,\text{mol L}^{-1}$$

Construct an ICE table for the reaction and write down the initial concentrations of each species.

$$Cu^{2+}(aq) + 4\,NH_3(aq) \rightleftharpoons Cu(NH_3)_4^{2+}(aq)$$

	$[Cu^{2+}]$	$[NH_3]$	$[Cu(NH_3)_4^{2+}]$
Initial	6.7×10^{-4}	0.11	0
Change			
Equil			

Since the equilibrium constant is large, and the concentration of ammonia is much larger than the concentration of Cu^{2+}, we can assume that the reaction will be driven to the right so that most of the Cu^{2+} is consumed. Unlike previous ICE tables, where we let x represent the change in concentration in going to equilibrium, here we let x represent the small amount of Cu^{2+} that remains when equilibrium is reached.

$$Cu^{2+}(aq) + 4\,NH_3(aq) \rightleftharpoons Cu(NH_3)_4^{2+}(aq)$$

	$[Cu^{2+}]$	$[NH_3]$	$[Cu(NH_3)_4^{2+}]$
Initial	6.7×10^{-4}	0.11	0
Change	$\approx(-6.7 \times 10^{-4})$	$\approx 4(-6.7 \times 10^{-4})$	$\approx(+6.7 \times 10^{-4})$
Equil	x	0.11	6.7×10^{-4}

(continued)

EXAMPLE 16.15 (CONTINUED)

Substitute the expressions for the equilibrium concentrations into the expression for K_f and solve for x.	$K_f = \frac{[Cu(NH_3)_6{}^{2+}]}{[Cu^{2+}][NH_3]^4}$ $= \frac{6.7 \times 10^{-4}}{x(0.11)^4}$ $x = \frac{6.7 \times 10^{-4}}{K_f(0.11)^4}$ $= \frac{6.7 \times 10^{-4}}{1.7 \times 10^{13}(0.11)^4}$ $= 2.7 \times 10^{-13}$
Confirm that x is indeed small compared to the initial concentration of the metal cation. The remaining Cu^{2+} concentration is very small because the formation constant is very large.	Since $x = 2.7 \times 10^{-13} \ll 6.7 \times 10^{-4}$; the approximation is valid. The remaining $[Cu^{2+}] = 2.7 \times 10^{-13}$ mol L^{-1}.

FOR PRACTICE 16.15

A 125.0 mL sample of a solution that is 0.0117 mol L^{-1} in $NiCl_2$ is mixed with a 175.0 mL sample of a solution that is 0.250 mol L^{-1} in NH_3. After the solution reaches equilibrium, what concentration of $Ni^{2+}(aq)$ remains?

The Effect of Complex–Ion Equilibria on Solubility

Recall from Section 16.5 that the solubility of an ionic compound with a basic anion increases with increasing acidity because the acid reacts with the anion and drives the reaction to the right. Similarly, *the solubility of an ionic compound containing a metal cation that forms complex ions increases in the presence of Lewis bases that complex with the cation.* The most common Lewis bases that increase the solubility of metal cations are NH_3, CN^-, and OH^-. For example, silver chloride is only slightly soluble in pure water:

$$AgCl(s) \rightleftharpoons Ag^+(aq) + Cl^-(aq) \qquad K_{sp} = 1.77 \times 10^{-10}$$

However, adding ammonia increases its solubility dramatically because, as we saw previously in this section, the ammonia forms a complex ion with the silver cations:

$$Ag^+(aq) + 2\,NH_3(aq) \rightleftharpoons Ag(NH_3)_2{}^+(aq) \qquad K_f = 1.7 \times 10^7$$

The large value of K_f significantly lowers the concentration of $Ag^+(aq)$ in solution and therefore drives the dissolution of $AgCl(s)$. The two above reactions can be added together:

$$\begin{array}{rll} AgCl(s) & \rightleftharpoons Ag^+(aq) + Cl^-(aq) & K_{sp} = 1.77 \times 10^{-10} \\ Ag^+(aq) + 2\,NH_3(aq) & \rightleftharpoons Ag(NH_3)_2{}^+(aq) & K_f = 1.7 \times 10^7 \\ \hline AgCl(s) + 2\,NH_3(aq) & \rightleftharpoons Ag(NH_3)_2{}^+(aq) + Cl^-(aq) & K = K_{sp} \times K_f = 3.0 \times 10^{-3} \end{array}$$

As we learned in Section 14.3, the equilibrium constant for a reaction that is the sum of two other reactions is the product of the equilibrium constants for the two other reactions. Adding ammonia changes the equilibrium constant for the dissolution of $AgCl(s)$ by a factor of $3.0 \times 10^{-3}/1.77 \times 10^{-10} = 1.7 \times 10^7$ (17 million), which makes the otherwise relatively insoluble $AgCl(s)$ quite soluble, as shown in Figure 16.18 ▸.

CONCEPTUAL CONNECTION 16.5

Solubility and Complex-Ion Equilibria

Which compound, when added to water, is most likely to increase the solubility of CuS?

(a) NaCl **(b)** KNO_3 **(c)** NaCN **(d)** $MgBr_2$

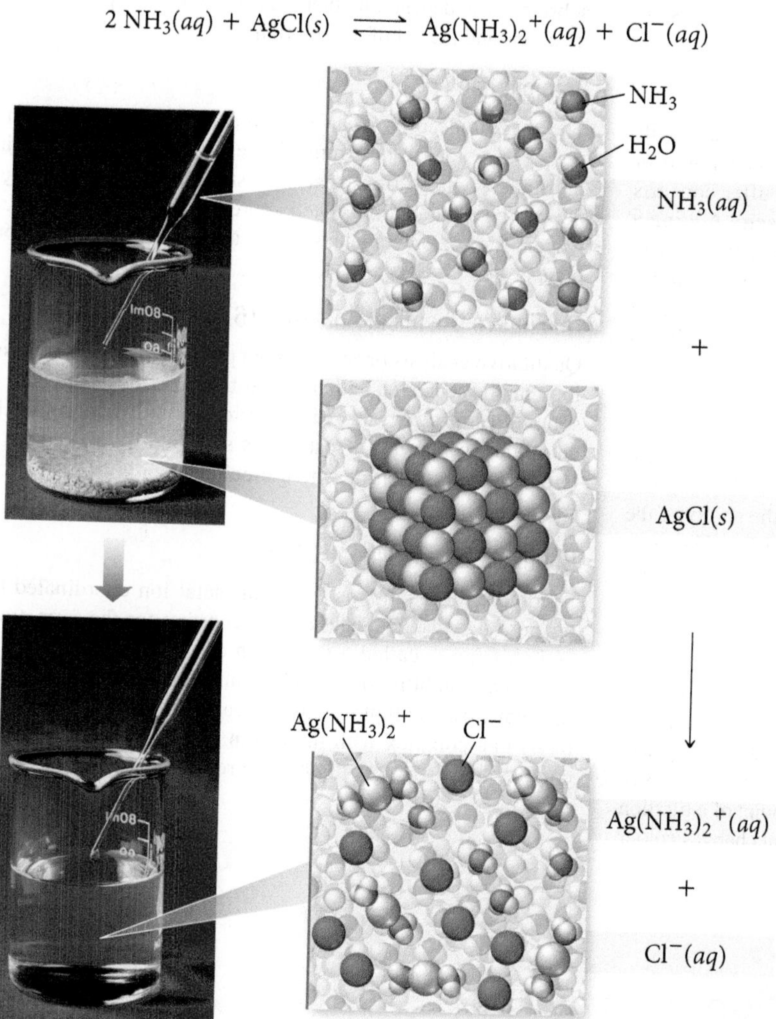

◀ **FIGURE 16.18 Complex-Ion Formation** Normally sparingly soluble AgCl is made soluble by the addition of NH_3, which forms a complex ion with Ag^+ and dissolves the AgCl.

CHAPTER IN REVIEW

Key Terms

Section 16.2
buffer (685)
common ion effect (686)
Henderson–Hasselbalch equation (688)
buffering action (692)

Section 16.3
buffer capacity (698)

Section 16.4
acid–base titration (698)
indicator (698)
equivalence point (698)
endpoint (709)

Section 16.5
solubility product constant (K_{sp}) (712)
molar solubility (712)

Section 16.6
selective precipitation (720)

Section 16.7
qualitative analysis (721)
quantitative analysis (721)

Section 16.8
complex ion (724)
ligand (724)
formation constant (K_f) (724)

Key Concepts

The Dangers of Antifreeze (16.1)

Although the pH of human blood is closely regulated by buffers, the capacity of these buffers to neutralize can be overwhelmed. Ethylene glycol, the main component of antifreeze, is metabolized by the liver into glycolic acid. The resulting acidity can exceed the buffering capacity of blood and cause acidosis, a serious condition that results in oxygen deprivation.

Buffers: Solutions That Resist pH Change (16.2)

Buffers contain significant amounts of both a weak acid and its conjugate base, enabling the buffer to neutralize added acid or added base. Adding a small amount of acid to a buffer converts a stoichiometric amount of base to the conjugate acid. Adding a small amount of base to a buffer converts a stoichiometric amount of the acid to the conjugate base. The pH of a buffer solution can be found either by solving an equilibrium problem, focusing on the common ion effect, or by using the Henderson–Hasselbalch equation.

Buffer Range and Buffer Capacity (16.3)

A buffer works best when the amounts of acid and conjugate base it contains are large and approximately equal. If the relative amounts of acid and base differ by more than a factor of 10, the ability of the buffer to neutralize added acid and added base diminishes. The maximum pH range at which a buffer is effective is one pH unit on either side of the acid's pK_a.

Titrations and pH Curves (16.4)

A titration curve is a graph of the change in pH versus added volume of acid or base during a titration. We covered three types of titration curves, representing three types of acid–base reactions: a strong acid with a strong base, a weak acid with a strong base (or vice versa), and a polyprotic acid with a base. The equivalence point of a titration can be made visible by an indicator, a compound that changes colour at a specific pH.

Solubility Equilibria and the Solubility Product Constant (16.5)

The solubility product constant (K_{sp}) is an equilibrium constant for the dissolution of an ionic compound in water. We can determine the molar solubility of an ionic compound from K_{sp} and vice versa. Although the value of K_{sp} is constant at a given temperature, the solubility of an ionic substance can depend on other factors, such as the presence of common ions and the pH of the solution.

Precipitation (16.6)

The magnitude of K_{sp} can be compared with the reaction quotient, Q, in order to determine the relative saturation of a solution. Substances with cations that have sufficiently different values of K_{sp} can be separated by selective precipitation, in which an added reagent forms a precipitate with one of the dissolved cations but not others.

Qualitative Chemical Analysis (16.7)

Qualitative analysis operates on the principle that a mixture of cations can be separated and analyzed based on the differences in the solubilities of their salts. In a classic qualitative analysis scheme, an unknown mixture of cations is sequentially treated with different reagents, each of which precipitates a known subgroup of cations.

Complex–Ion Equilibria (16.8)

A complex ion contains a central metal ion coordinated to two or more ligands. The equilibrium constant for the formation of a complex ion is called a formation constant and is usually quite large. The solubility of an ionic compound containing a metal cation that forms complex ions increases in the presence of Lewis bases that complex with the cation because the formation of the complex ion drives the dissolution reaction to the right.

Key Equations and Relationships

The Henderson–Hasselbalch Equation (16.2)

$$\text{pH} = \text{p}K_a + \log\frac{[\text{base}]}{[\text{acid}]}$$

Effective Buffer Range (16.3)

$$\text{pH range} = \text{p}K_a \pm 1$$

The Relation Between Q and K_{sp} (16.6)

If $Q < K_{sp}$, the solution is unsaturated. More of the solid ionic compound can dissolve in the solution.

If $Q = K_{sp}$, the solution is saturated. The solution is holding the equilibrium amount of the dissolved ions and additional solid will not dissolve in the solution.

If $Q > K_{sp}$, the solution is supersaturated. Under most circumstances, the solid will precipitate out of a supersaturated solution.

Key Skills

Calculating the pH of a Buffer Solution (16.2)

• Example 16.1 • For Practice 16.1 • For More Practice 16.1 • Exercises 29, 30, 33, 34

Using the Henderson–Hasselbalch Equation to Calculate the pH of a Buffer Solution (16.2)

• Example 16.2 • For Practice 16.2 • Exercises 37–42

Calculating the pH Change in a Buffer Solution After the Addition of a Small Amount of Strong Acid or Base (16.2)
• Example 16.3 • For Practice 16.3 • For More Practice 16.3 • Exercises 47–50

Using the Henderson–Hasselbalch Equation to Calculate the pH of a Buffer Solution Composed of a Weak Base and Its Conjugate Acid (16.2)
• Example 16.4 • For Practice 16.4 • For More Practice 16.4 • Exercises 37–40

Determining Buffer Range (16.3)
• Example 16.5 • For Practice 16.5 • Exercises 57, 58

Strong Acid–Strong Base Titration pH Curve (16.4)
• Example 16.6 • For Practice 16.6 • Exercises 67–70

Weak Acid–Strong Base Titration pH Curve (16.4)
• Example 16.7 • For Practice 16.7 • Exercises 65, 66, 71, 72, 75, 77–80

Calculating Molar Solubility from K_{sp} (16.5)
• Example 16.8 • For Practice 16.8 • Exercises 87, 88

Calculating K_{sp} from Molar Solubility (16.5)
• Example 16.9 • For Practice 16.9 • Exercises 89, 90, 92, 94

Calculating Molar Solubility in the Presence of a Common Ion (16.5)
• Example 16.10 • For Practice 16.10 • Exercises 95, 96

Determining the Effect of pH on Solubility (16.5)
• Example 16.11 • For Practice 16.11 • Exercises 97–100

Predicting Precipitation Reactions by Comparing Q and K_{sp} (16.6)
• Example 16.12 • For Practice 16.12 • Exercises 101–104

Finding the Minimum Required Reagent Concentration for Selective Precipitation (16.6)
• Example 16.13 • For Practice 16.13 • Exercises 105, 106

Finding the Concentrations of Ions Left in Solution After Selective Precipitation (16.6)
• Example 16.14 • For Practice 16.14 • Exercises 107, 108

Working with Complex–Ion Equilibria (16.8)
• Example 16.15 • For Practice 16.15 • Exercises 109–112

EXERCISES

Review Questions

1. What is the pH range of human blood? How is human blood maintained in this pH range?
2. What is a buffer? How does a buffer work? How does it neutralize added acid? Added base?
3. What is meant by buffer capacity? What factor(s) affect the buffer capacity?
4. What is the common ion effect?
5. What is the Henderson–Hasselbalch equation and why is it useful?
6. What is the pH of a buffer solution when the concentrations of both buffer components (the weak acid and its conjugate base) are equal? What happens to the pH when the buffer contains more of the weak acid than the conjugate base? More of the conjugate base than the weak acid?
7. Suppose that a buffer contains equal amounts of a weak acid and its conjugate base. What happens to the relative amounts of the weak acid and conjugate base when a small amount of strong acid is added to the buffer? What happens when a small amount of strong base is added?
8. How do you use the Henderson–Hasselbalch equation to calculate the pH of a buffer containing a base and its conjugate acid? Specifically, how do you determine the correct value for pK_a?
9. What factors influence the effectiveness of a buffer? What are the characteristics of an effective buffer?
10. What is the effective pH range of a buffer (relative to the pK_a of the weak acid component)?
11. Describe an acid–base titration. What is the equivalence point?
12. The pH at the equivalence point of the titration of a strong acid with a strong base is 7.0. However, the pH at the equivalence point of the titration of a *weak* acid with a strong base is above 7.0. Why?
13. The volume required to reach the equivalence point of an acid–base titration depends on the volume and concentration of the acid or base to be titrated and on the concentration of the acid or base used to do the titration. It does not, however, depend on the whether or not the acid or base being titrated is strong or weak. Explain why.

14. In the titration of a strong acid with a strong base, how would you calculate these quantities?
    a. initial pH
    b. pH before the equivalence point
    c. pH at the equivalence point
    d. pH beyond the equivalence point

15. In the titration of a weak acid with a strong base, how would you calculate these quantities?
    a. initial pH
    b. pH before the equivalence point
    c. pH at one-half the equivalence point
    d. pH at the equivalence point
    e. pH beyond the equivalence point

16. The titration of a polyprotic acid with sufficiently different pK_a's displays two equivalence points. Why?

17. In the titration of a polyprotic acid, the volume required to reach the first equivalence point is identical to the volume required to reach the second one. Why?

18. What is the difference between the endpoint and the equivalence point in a titration?

19. What is an indicator? How can an indicator signal the equivalence point of a titration?

20. What is the solubility product constant? Write a general expression for the solubility constant of a compound with the general formula A_mX_n.

21. What is molar solubility? How can you obtain the molar solubility of a compound from K_{sp}?

22. How does a common ion affect the solubility of a compound? More specifically, how is the solubility of a compound with the general formula AX different in a solution containing one of the common ions (A^+ or X^-) than it is in pure water? Explain.

23. Explain how the addition of an uncommon ion affects the solubility of a compound.

24. How is the solubility of an ionic compound with a basic anion affected by pH? Explain.

25. For a given solution containing an ionic compound, what is the relationship between Q, K_{sp}, and the relative saturation of the solution?

26. What is selective precipitation? What are the conditions under which selective precipitation may occur?

27. What is qualitative analysis? How does *qualitative* analysis differ from *quantitative* analysis?

28. What are the main groups in the general qualitative analysis scheme described in this chapter? Describe the steps and reagents necessary to identify each group.

Problems by Topic

The Common Ion Effect and Buffers

29. In which of these solutions will HNO_2 ionize less than it does in pure water?
    a. 0.10 mol L^{-1} NaCl
    b. 0.10 mol L^{-1} KNO_3
    c. 0.10 mol L^{-1} NaOH
    d. 0.10 mol L^{-1} $NaNO_2$

30. A methanoic acid solution has a pH of 3.25. Which of these substances will raise the pH of the solution upon addition? Explain.
    a. HCl
    b. NaBr
    c. HCOONa
    d. KCl

31. Solve an equilibrium problem (using an ICE table) to calculate the pH of each solution:
    a. a solution that is 0.20 mol L^{-1} in HCOOH and 0.15 mol L^{-1} in HCOONa
    b. a solution that is 0.16 mol L^{-1} in NH_3 and 0.22 mol L^{-1} in NH_4Cl

32. Solve an equilibrium problem (using an ICE table) to calculate the pH of each solution:
    a. a solution that is 0.195 mol L^{-1} in $HC_2H_3O_2$ and 0.125 mol L^{-1} in CH_3COOK
    b. a solution that is 0.255 mol L^{-1} in CH_3NH_2 and 0.135 mol L^{-1} in CH_3NH_3Br

33. Calculate the percent ionization of a 0.15 mol L^{-1} benzoic acid solution in pure water and also in a solution containing 0.10 mol L^{-1} sodium benzoate. Why does the percent ionization differ significantly in the two solutions?

34. Calculate the percent ionization of a 0.13 mol L^{-1} methanoic acid solution in pure water and also in a solution containing 0.11 mol L^{-1} potassium methanoate. Explain the difference in percent ionization in the two solutions.

35. Solve an equilibrium problem (using an ICE table) to calculate the pH of each solution:
    a. 0.30 mol L^{-1} HF
    b. 0.30 mol L^{-1} NaF
    c. a mixture that is 0.30 mol L^{-1} in HF and 0.30 mol L^{-1} in NaF

36. Solve an equilibrium problem (using an ICE table) to calculate the pH of each solution:
    a. 0.18 mol L^{-1} CH_3NH_2
    b. 0.18 mol L^{-1} CH_3NH_3Cl
    c. a mixture that is 0.18 mol L^{-1} in CH_3NH_2 and 0.18 mol L^{-1} in CH_3NH_3Cl

37. A buffer contains significant amounts of acetic acid and sodium acetate. Write equations showing how this buffer neutralizes added acid and added base.

38. A buffer contains significant amounts of ammonia and ammonium chloride. Write equations showing how this buffer neutralizes added acid and added base.

39. Use the Henderson–Hasselbalch equation to calculate the pH of each solution in Problem 31.

40. Use the Henderson–Hasselbalch equation to calculate the pH of each solution in Problem 32.

41. Use the Henderson–Hasselbalch equation to calculate the pH of each solution:
    a. a solution that is 0.135 mol L^{-1} in HClO and 0.155 mol L^{-1} in KClO
    b. a solution that contains 1.05% $C_2H_5NH_2$ by mass and 1.10% $C_2H_5NH_3Br$ by mass
    c. a solution that contains 10.0 g of CH_3COOH and 10.0 g of CH_3COONa in 150.0 mL of solution

42. Use the Henderson–Hasselbalch equation to calculate the pH of each solution:
    a. a solution that is 0.145 mol L^{-1} in propanoic acid and 0.115 mol L^{-1} in potassium propanoate
    b. a solution that contains 0.785% C_5H_5N by mass and 0.985% C_5H_5NHCl by mass
    c. a solution that contains 15.0 g of HF and 25.0 g of NaF in 125 mL of solution

43. Calculate the pH of the solution that results from each mixture:
   a. 50.0 mL of 0.15 mol L^{-1} HCOOH with 75.0 mL of 0.13 mol L^{-1} HCOONa
   b. 125.0 mL of 0.10 mol L^{-1} NH_3 with 250.0 mL of 0.10 mol L^{-1} NH_4Cl

44. Calculate the pH of the solution that results from each mixture:
   a. 150.0 mL of 0.25 mol L^{-1} HF with 225.0 mL of 0.30 mol L^{-1} NaF
   b. 175.0 mL of 0.10 mol L^{-1} $C_2H_5NH_2$ with 275.0 mL of 0.20 mol L^{-1} $C_2H_5NH_3Cl$

45. Calculate the mole ratio of NaF to HF required to create a buffer with pH = 4.00.

46. Calculate the mole ratio of CH_3NH_2 to CH_3NH_3Cl concentration required to create a buffer with pH = 10.24.

47. What mass of sodium benzoate should you add to 150.0 mL of a 0.15 mol L^{-1} benzoic acid solution to obtain a buffer with a pH of 4.25?

48. What mass of ammonium chloride should you add to 2.55 L of a 0.155 mol L^{-1} NH_3 to obtain a buffer with a pH of 9.55?

49. A 250.0 mL buffer solution is 0.250 mol L^{-1} in acetic acid and 0.250 mol L^{-1} in sodium acetate.
   a. What is the initial pH of this solution?
   b. What is the pH after addition of 0.0050 mol of HCl?
   c. What is the pH after addition of 0.0050 mol of NaOH?

50. A 100.0 mL buffer solution is 0.175 mol L^{-1} in HClO and 0.150 mol L^{-1} in NaClO.
   a. What is the initial pH of this solution?
   b. What is the pH after addition of 150.0 mg of HBr?
   c. What is the pH after addition of 85.0 mg of NaOH?

51. For each solution, calculate the initial and final pH after adding 0.010 mol of HCl.
   a. 500.0 mL of pure water
   b. 500.0 mL of a buffer solution that is 0.125 mol L^{-1} in CH_3COOH and 0.115 mol L^{-1} in CH_3COONa
   c. 500.0 mL of a buffer solution that is 0.155 mol L^{-1} in $C_2H_5NH_2$ and 0.145 mol L^{-1} in $C_2H_5NH_3Cl$

52. For each solution, calculate the initial and final pH after adding 0.010 mol of NaOH.
   a. 250.0 mL of pure water
   b. 250.0 mL of a buffer solution that is 0.195 mol L^{-1} in HCOOH and 0.275 mol L^{-1} in HCOOK
   c. 250.0 mL of a buffer solution that is 0.255 mol L^{-1} in $CH_3CH_2NH_2$ and 0.235 mol L^{-1} in $CH_3CH_2NH_3Cl$

53. A 350.0 mL buffer solution is 0.150 mol L^{-1} in HF and 0.150 mol L^{-1} in NaF. What mass of NaOH could this buffer neutralize before the pH rises above 4.00? If the same volume of the buffer was 0.350 mol L^{-1} in HF and 0.350 mol L^{-1} in NaF, what mass of NaOH could be handled before the pH rises above 4.00?

54. A 100.0 mL buffer solution is 0.100 mol L^{-1} in NH_3 and 0.125 mol L^{-1} in NH_4Br. What mass of HCl will this buffer neutralize before the pH falls below 9.00? If the same volume of the buffer were 0.250 mol L^{-1} in NH_3 and 0.400 mol L^{-1} in NH_4Br, what mass of HCl could be handled before the pH fell below 9.00?

55. Determine whether or not the mixing of the two solutions will result in a buffer.
   a. 100.0 mL of 0.10 mol L^{-1} NH_3; 100.0 mL of 0.15 mol L^{-1} NH_4Cl
   b. 50.0 mL of 0.10 mol L^{-1} HCl; 35.0 mL of 0.150 mol L^{-1} NaOH
   c. 50.0 mL of 0.15 mol L^{-1} HF; 20.0 mL of 0.15 mol L^{-1} NaOH
   d. 175.0 mL of 0.10 mol L^{-1} NH_3; 150.0 mL of 0.12 mol L^{-1} NaOH
   e. 125.0 mL of 0.15 mol L^{-1} NH_3; 150.0 mL of 0.20 mol L^{-1} NaOH

56. Determine whether or not the mixing of the two solutions will result in a buffer.
   a. 75.0 mL of 0.10 mol L^{-1} HF; 55.0 mL of 0.15 mol L^{-1} NaF
   b. 150.0 mL of 0.10 mol L^{-1} HF; 135.0 mL of 0.175 mol L^{-1} HCl
   c. 165.0 mL of 0.10 mol L^{-1} HF; 135.0 mL of 0.050 mol L^{-1} KOH
   d. 125.0 mL of 0.15 mol L^{-1} CH_3NH_2; 120.0 mL of 0.25 mol L^{-1} CH_3NH_3Cl
   e. 105.0 mL of 0.15 mol L^{-1} CH_3NH_2; 95.0 mL of 0.10 mol L^{-1} HCl

57. Blood is buffered by carbonic acid and the bicarbonate ion. Normal blood plasma is 0.024 mol L^{-1} in HCO_3^- and 0.0012 mol L^{-1} H_2CO_3 (pK_{a_1} for H_2CO_3 at body temperature is 6.1).
   a. What is the pH of blood plasma?
   b. If the volume of blood in a normal adult is 5.0 L, what mass of HCl can be neutralized by the buffering system in blood before the pH falls below 7.0 (which would result in death)?
   c. Given the volume from part (b), what mass of NaOH can be neutralized before the pH rises above 7.8?

58. The fluids within cells are buffered by $H_2PO_4^-$ and HPO_4^{2-}.
   a. Calculate the ratio of HPO_4^{2-} to $H_2PO_4^-$ required to maintain a pH of 7.1 within a cell.
   b. Could a buffer system employing H_3PO_4 as the weak acid and $H_2PO_4^-$ as the weak base be used as a buffer system within cells? Explain.

59. Which buffer system is the best choice to create a buffer with pH = 7.20? For the best system, calculate the ratio of the masses of the buffer components required to make the buffer.
   a. CH_3COOH/CH_3COOK
   b. NH_3/NH_4Cl
   c. $HClO_2/KClO_2$
   d. HClO/KClO

60. Which buffer system is the best choice to create a buffer with pH = 9.00? For the best system, calculate the ratio of the masses of the buffer components required to make the buffer.
   a. HF/KF
   b. NH_3/NH_4Cl
   c. HNO_2/KNO_2
   d. HClO/KClO

61. A 500.0 mL buffer solution is 0.100 mol L^{-1} in HNO_2 and 0.150 mol L^{-1} in KNO_2. Determine if each addition would exceed the capacity of the buffer to neutralize it.
   a. 250 mg NaOH
   b. 350 mg KOH
   c. 1.25 g HBr
   d. 1.35 g HI

62. A 1.0 L buffer solution is 0.125 mol L^{-1} in HNO_2 and 0.145 mol L^{-1} in $NaNO_2$. Determine the concentrations of HNO_2 and $NaNO_2$ after the addition of each substance:
   a. 1.5 g HCl b. 1.5 g NaOH c. 1.5 g HI

63. The organic compound below is abbreviated Tris and is basic. The conjugate acid ($TrisH^+$) has a pK_a of 8.10.

$$TrisH^+ + H_2O \rightleftharpoons Tris + H_3O^+$$

Tris is commonly used as a component in buffer solutions to study biochemical reactions.

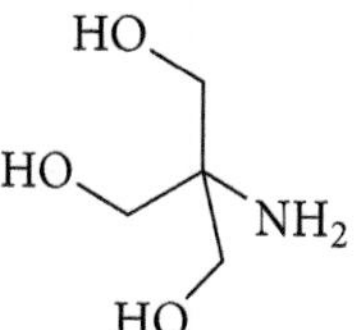

Trishydroxymethylaminomethane

a. A buffer solution is prepared by mixing 12.5 mL of 0.100 mol L^{-1} HCl with 25.0 mL of 0.100 mol L^{-1} Tris. What is the pH of this buffer?
b. The buffer was used to study an enzyme-catalyzed reaction in which 0.00020 mol of H_3O^+ was produced. What is the pH of the solution after the acid reacted with the buffer?

64. Cocodylic acid (dimethylarsinic acid, $HAsO_2(CH_3)_2$) is a common buffer used in biology to prepare and fix biological samples. The pK_a of cocodylic acid is 6.3.
a. What is the pH of a buffer solution prepared by mixing 20.0 mL of 0.0500 mol L^{-1} NaOH with 20 mL of 0.150 mol L^{-1} cocodylic acid?
b. What is the pH of the buffer solution in part (a) after 0.0002 moles of H_3O^+ was added to the mixture?

Titrations, pH Curves, and Indicators

65. The graphs labelled (i) and (ii) show the titration curves for two equal-volume samples of monoprotic acids, one weak and one strong. Both titrations were carried out with the same concentration of strong base.

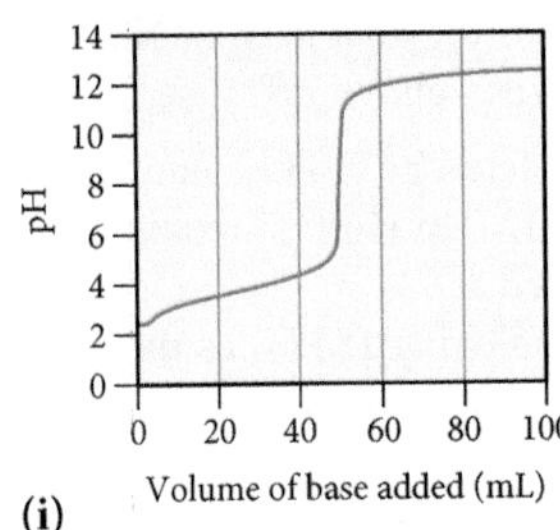

(i)

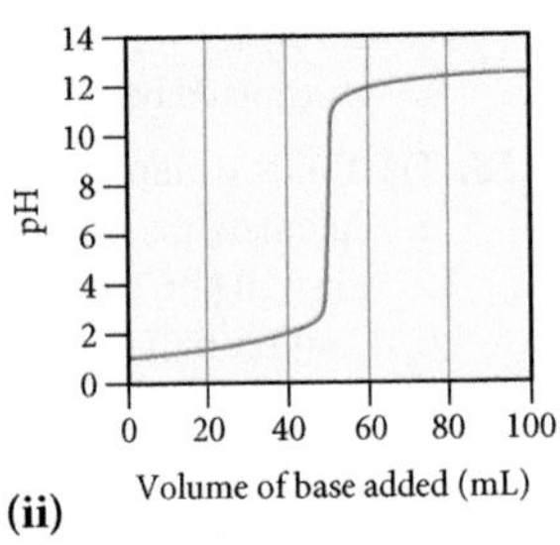

(ii)

a. What is the approximate pH at the equivalence point of each curve?
b. Which curve corresponds to the titration of the strong acid and which one to the titration of the weak acid?

66. Two 25.0 mL samples, one 0.100 mol L^{-1} HCl and the other 0.100 mol L^{-1} HF, were titrated with 0.200 mol L^{-1} KOH.
a. What is the volume of added base at the equivalence point for each titration?
b. Predict whether the pH at the equivalence point for each titration will be acidic, basic, or neutral.
c. Predict which titration curve will have the lower initial pH.
d. Make a rough sketch of each titration curve.

67. Two 20.0 mL samples, one 0.200 mol L^{-1} KOH and the other 0.200 mol L^{-1} CH_3NH_2 were titrated with 0.100 mol L^{-1} HI.
a. What is the volume of added acid at the equivalence point for each titration?
b. Predict whether the pH at the equivalence point for each titration will be acidic, basic, or neutral.
c. Predict which titration curve will have the lower initial pH.
d. Make a rough sketch of each titration curve.

68. The graphs labelled (i) and (ii) show the titration curves for two equal-volume samples of bases, one weak and one strong. Both titrations were carried out with the same concentration of strong acid.

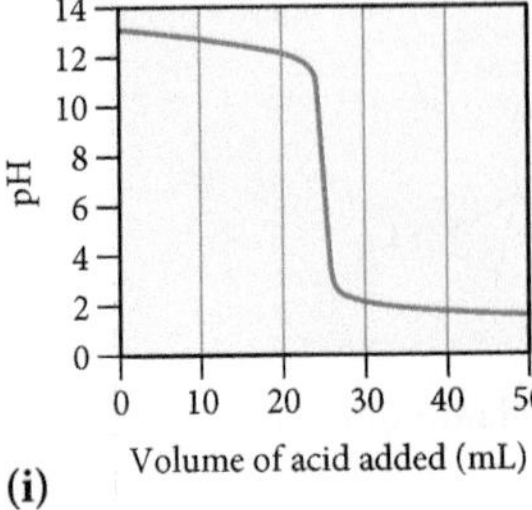

(i)

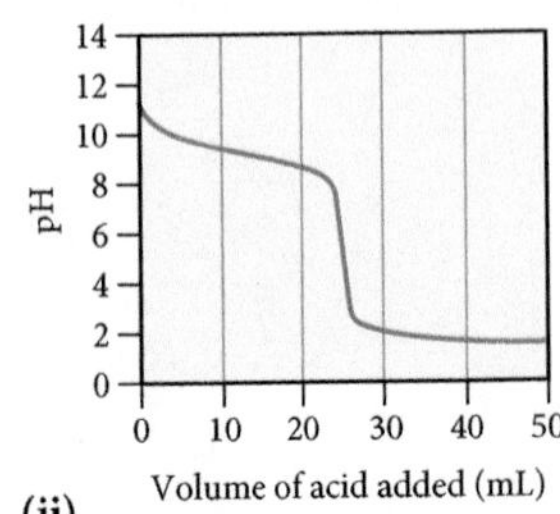

(ii)

a. What is the approximate pH at the equivalence point of each curve?
b. Which curve corresponds to the titration of the strong base and which one to the weak base?

69. Consider the curve for the titration of a weak monoprotic acid with a strong base and answer each question.

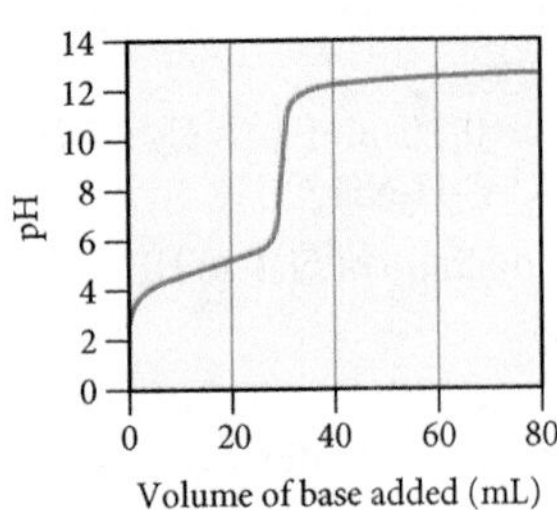

a. What is the pH and what is the volume of added base at the equivalence point?
b. At what volume of added base is the pH calculated by working an equilibrium problem based on the initial concentration and K_a of the weak acid?
c. At what volume of added base does pH = pK_a?
d. At what volume of added base is the pH calculated by working an equilibrium problem based on the concentration and K_b of the conjugate base?
e. Beyond what volume of added base is the pH calculated by focusing on the amount of excess strong base added?

70. Consider the curve for the titration of a weak base with a strong acid and answer each question.

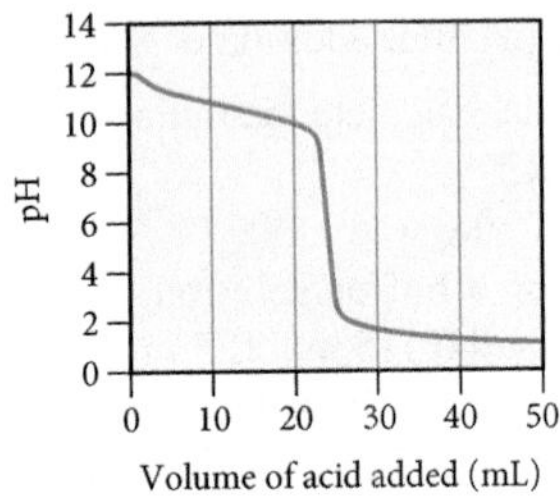

a. What is the pH and what is the volume of added acid at the equivalence point?
b. At what volume of added acid is the pH calculated by working an equilibrium problem based on the initial concentration and K_b of the weak base?
c. At what volume of added acid does pH = 14 − pK_b?
d. At what volume of added acid is the pH calculated by working an equilibrium problem based on the concentration and K_a of the conjugate acid?
e. Beyond what volume of added acid is the pH calculated by focusing on the amount of excess strong acid added?

71. Consider the titration of a 35.0 mL sample of 0.175 mol L^{-1} HBr with 0.200 mol L^{-1} KOH. Determine each quantity:
a. the initial pH
b. the volume of added base required to reach the equivalence point
c. the pH at 10.0 mL of added base
d. the pH at the equivalence point
e. the pH after adding 5.0 mL of base beyond the equivalence point

72. A 20.0 mL sample of 0.125 mol L^{-1} HNO_3 is titrated with 0.150 mol L^{-1} NaOH. Calculate the pH for at least five different points throughout the titration curve and make a sketch of the curve. Indicate the volume at the equivalence point on your graph.

73. Consider the titration of a 25.0 mL sample of 0.115 mol L^{-1} RbOH with 0.100 mol L^{-1} HCl. Determine each quantity:
a. the initial pH
b. the volume of added acid required to reach the equivalence point
c. the pH at 5.0 mL of added acid
d. the pH at the equivalence point
e. the pH after adding 5.0 mL of acid beyond the equivalence point

74. A 15.0 mL sample of 0.100 mol L^{-1} $Ba(OH)_2$ is titrated with 0.125 mol L^{-1} HCl. Calculate the pH for at least five different points throughout the titration curve and make a sketch of the curve. Indicate the volume at the equivalence point on your graph.

75. Consider the titration of a 20.0 mL sample of 0.105 mol L^{-1} CH_3COOH with 0.125 mol L^{-1} NaOH. Determine each quantity:
a. the initial pH
b. the volume of added base required to reach the equivalence point
c. the pH at 5.0 mL of added base
d. the pH at one-half of the equivalence point
e. the pH at the equivalence point
f. the pH after adding 5.0 mL of base beyond the equivalence point

76. A 30.0 mL sample of 0.165 mol L^{-1} propanoic acid is titrated with 0.300 mol L^{-1} KOH. Calculate the pH at each volume of added base: 0 mL, 5 mL, 10 mL, equivalence point, one-half equivalence point, 20 mL, 25 mL. Make a sketch of the titration curve.

77. Consider the titration of a 25.0 mL sample of 0.175 mol L^{-1} CH_3NH_2 with 0.150 mol L^{-1} HBr. Determine each quantity:
a. the initial pH
b. the volume of added acid required to reach the equivalence point
c. the pH at 5.0 mL of added acid
d. the pH at one-half of the equivalence point
e. the pH at the equivalence point
f. the pH after adding 5.0 mL of acid beyond the equivalence point

78. A 25.0 mL sample of 0.125 mol L^{-1} pyridine is titrated with 0.100 mol L^{-1} HCl. Calculate the pH at each volume of added acid: 0 mL, 10 mL, 20 mL, equivalence point, one-half equivalence point, 40 mL, 50 mL. Make a sketch of the titration curve.

79. Consider the titration curves for equal volumes of two weak acids, both titrated with 0.100 mol L^{-1} NaOH.

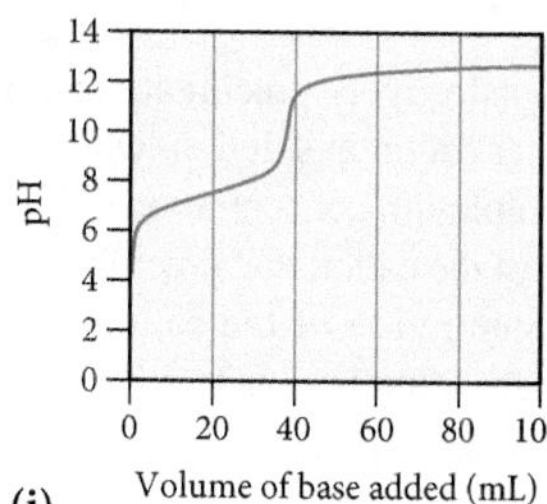

(i)

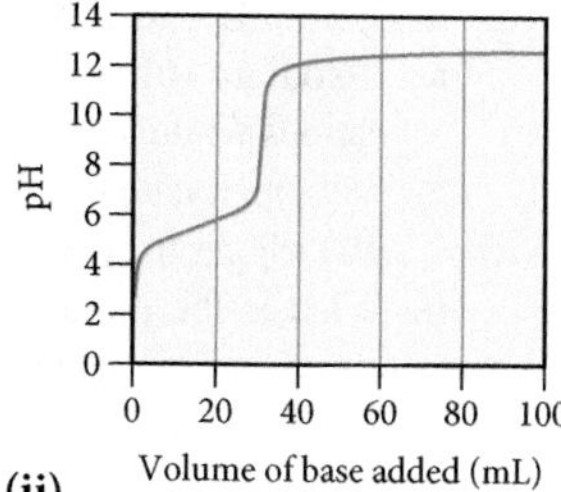

(ii)

a. Which acid solution is more concentrated?
b. Which acid has the larger K_a?

80. Consider the titration curves for equal volumes of two weak bases, both titrated with 0.100 mol L^{-1} HCl.

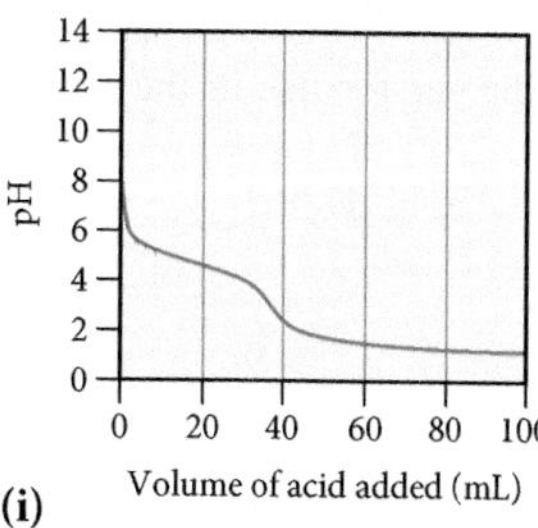

(i)

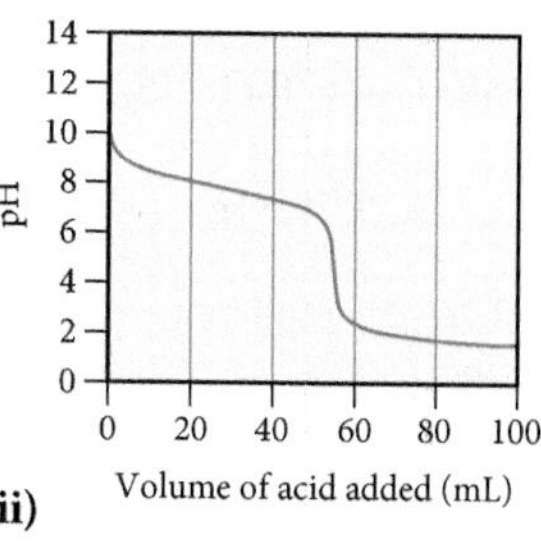

(ii)

a. Which base solution is more concentrated?
b. Which base has the larger K_b?

81. A 0.229 g sample of an unknown monoprotic acid is titrated with 0.112 mol L^{-1} NaOH. The resulting titration curve is shown here. Determine the molar mass and pK_a of the acid.

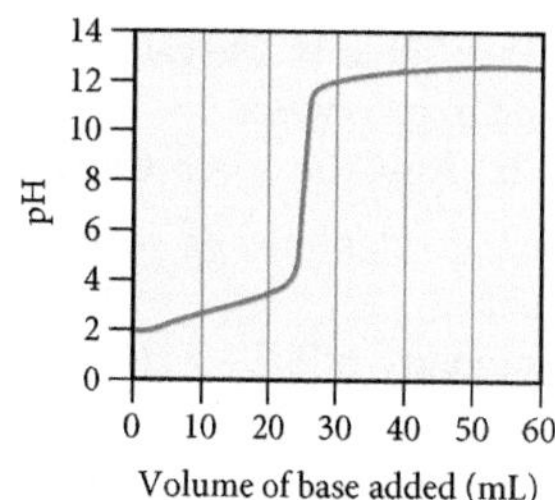

82. A 0.446 g sample of an unknown monoprotic acid is titrated with 0.105 mol L^{-1} KOH. The resulting titration curve is shown here. Determine the molar mass and pK_a of the acid.

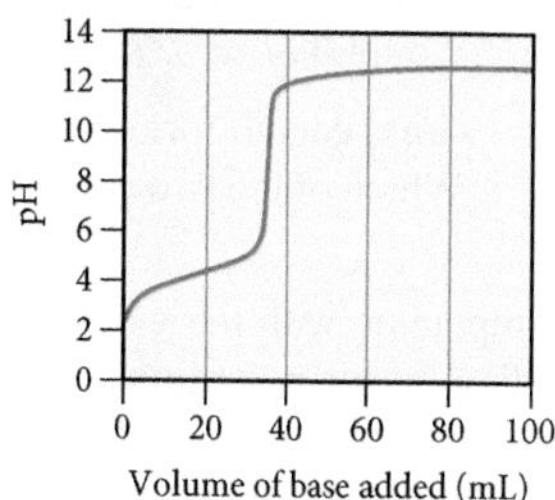

83. A 20.0 mL sample of 0.115 mol L^{-1} sulfurous acid (H_2SO_3) solution is titrated with 0.1014 mol L^{-1} KOH. At what added volume of base solution does each equivalence point occur?

84. A 20.0 mL sample of a 0.125 mol L^{-1} diprotic acid (H_2A) solution is titrated with 0.1019 mol L^{-1} KOH. The acid ionization constants for the acid are $K_{a_1} = 5.2 \times 10^{-5}$ and $K_{a_2} = 3.4 \times 10^{-10}$. At what added volume of base does each equivalence point occur?

85. Methyl red has a pK_a of 5.0 and is red in its acid form and yellow in its basic form. If several drops of this indicator are placed in a 25.0 mL sample of 0.100 mol L^{-1} HCl, what colour will the solution appear? If 0.100 mol L^{-1} NaOH is slowly added to the HCl sample, in what pH range will the indicator change colour?

86. Phenolphthalein has a pK_a of 9.7. It is colourless in its acid form and pink in its basic form. For each of the pH's listed, calculate $[In^-]/[HIn]$ and predict the colour of a phenolphthalein solution.
a. pH = 2.0
b. pH = 5.0
c. pH = 8.0
d. pH = 11.0

87. Using Table 16.1, pick an indicator for use in the titration of each acid with a strong base.
a. HF b. HCl c. HCN

88. Using Table 16.1, pick an indicator for use in the titration of each base with a strong acid.
a. CH_3NH_2 b. NaOH c. $C_6H_5NH_2$

Solubility Equilibria

89. Write balanced equations and expressions for K_{sp} for the dissolution of each ionic compound:
a. $BaSO_4$ b. $PbBr_2$ c. Ag_2CrO_4

90. Write balanced equations and expressions for K_{sp} for the dissolution of each ionic compound.
a. $CaCO_3$ b. $PbCl_2$ c. AgI

91. Use the K_{sp} values in Table 16.2 to calculate the molar solubility of each compound in pure water.
a. AgBr b. $Mg(OH)_2$ c. CaF_2

92. Use the K_{sp} values in Table 16.2 to calculate the molar solubility of each compound in pure water.
a. CuS b. Ag_2CrO_4 c. $Ca(OH)_2$

93. Use the given molar solubilities in pure water to calculate K_{sp} for each compound.
a. NiS; molar solubility $= 3.27 \times 10^{-11}$ mol L^{-1}
b. PbF_2; molar solubility $= 5.63 \times 10^{-3}$ mol L^{-1}
c. MgF_2; molar solubility $= 2.65 \times 10^{-4}$ mol L^{-1}

94. Use the given molar solubilities in pure water to calculate K_{sp} for each compound.
a. $BaCrO_4$; molar solubility $= 1.08 \times 10^{-5}$ mol L^{-1}
b. Ag_2SO_3; molar solubility $= 1.55 \times 10^{-5}$ mol L^{-1}
c. $Pd(SCN)_2$; molar solubility $= 2.22 \times 10^{-8}$ mol L^{-1}

95. Two compounds with general formulas AX and AX_2 have $K_{sp} = 1.5 \times 10^{-5}$. Which of the two compounds has the higher molar solubility?

96. Consider the compounds with the generic formulas listed and their corresponding molar solubilities in pure water. Which compound will have the smallest value of K_{sp}?
a. AX; molar solubility $= 1.35 \times 10^{-4}$ mol L^{-1}
b. AX_2; molar solubility $= 2.25 \times 10^{-4}$ mol L^{-1}
c. A_2X; molar solubility $= 1.75 \times 10^{-4}$ mol L^{-1}

97. Use the K_{sp} value from Table 16.2 to calculate the solubility of iron(II) hydroxide in pure water in grams per 100.0 mL of solution.

98. Based on the solubility product constants given below, which salt is the *least* soluble?
(i) $Fe(OH)_3$ $K_{sp} = 6.3 \times 10^{-38}$
(ii) $Pb_3(PO_4)_2$ $K_{sp} = 3.0 \times 10^{-44}$
(iii) $Ca_3(PO_4)_2$ $K_{sp} = 1.0 \times 10^{-26}$

99. Consider five different saturated solutions containing one of the following salts. Without using a calculator, determine which would have the lowest pH. (You may use a calculator if you wish, but a "back of the envelope" calculation—an estimate—should suffice.)
(i) KOH
(ii) $Pb(OH)_2$ $K_{sp} = 1.4 \times 10^{-20}$
(iii) $Be(OH)_2$ $K_{sp} = 6.9 \times 10^{-22}$
(iv) $Sc(OH)_3$ $K_{sp} = 4.2 \times 10^{-18}$
(v) $Y(OH)_3$ $K_{sp} = 1.0 \times 10^{-22}$

100. The solubility of copper(I) chloride is 3.91 mg per 100.0 mL of solution. Calculate K_{sp} for CuCl.

101. Calculate the molar solubility of barium fluoride in each liquid or solution.
a. pure water
b. 0.10 mol L^{-1} $Ba(NO_3)_2$
c. 0.15 mol L^{-1} NaF

102. Calculate the molar solubility of copper(II) sulfide in each liquid or solution.
a. pure water
b. 0.25 mol L^{-1} $CuCl_2$
c. 0.20 mol L^{-1} K_2S

103. Calculate the molar solubility of calcium hydroxide in a solution buffered at each pH.
a. pH = 4 b. pH = 7 c. pH = 9

104. Calculate the solubility (in grams per 1.00×10^2 mL of solution) of magnesium hydroxide in a solution buffered at pH = 10. How does this compare to the solubility of $Mg(OH)_2$ in pure water?

105. Determine whether or not each compound will be more soluble in acidic solution than in pure water. Explain.
a. $BaCO_3$ b. CuS c. AgCl d. PbI_2

106. Determine whether or not each compound will be more soluble in acidic solution than in pure water. Explain.
a. Hg_2Br_2 b. $Mg(OH)_2$ c. $CaCO_3$ d. AgI

Precipitation and Qualitative Analysis

107. A solution containing sodium fluoride is mixed with one containing calcium nitrate to form a solution that is 0.015 mol L^{-1} in NaF and 0.010 mol L^{-1} in $Ca(NO_3)_2$. Will a precipitate form in the mixed solution? If so, identify the precipitate.

108. A solution containing potassium bromide is mixed with one containing lead acetate to form a solution that is 0.013 mol L^{-1} in KBr and 0.0035 mol L^{-1} in $Pb(CH_3COO)_2$. Will a precipitate form in the mixed solution? If so, identify the precipitate.

109. Predict whether or not a precipitate will form if you mix 75.0 mL of a NaOH solution with pOH = 2.58 with 125.0 mL of a 0.018 mol L^{-1} $MgCl_2$ solution. Identify the precipitate, if any.

110. Predict whether or not a precipitate will form if you mix 175.0 mL of a 0.0055 mol L^{-1} KCl solution with 145.0 mL of a 0.0015 mol L^{-1} $AgNO_3$ solution. Identify the precipitate, if any.

111. Potassium hydroxide is used to precipitate each of the cations from their respective solution. Determine the minimum concentration of KOH required for precipitation to begin in each case.
a. 0.015 mol L^{-1} $CaCl_2$
b. 0.0025 mol L^{-1} $Fe(NO_3)_2$
c. 0.0018 mol L^{-1} $MgBr_2$

112. Determine the minimum concentration of the precipitating agent on the right to cause precipitation of the cation from the solution on the left.
a. 0.035 mol L^{-1} $BaNO_3$; NaF
b. 0.085 mol L^{-1} CaI_2; K_2SO_4
c. 0.0018 mol L^{-1} $AgNO_3$; RbCl

113. Consider a solution that is 0.010 mol L^{-1} in Ba^{2+} and 0.020 mol L^{-1} in Ca^{2+}.
a. If sodium sulfate is used to selectively precipitate one of the cations while leaving the other cation in solution, which cation will precipitate first? What minimum concentration of Na_2SO_4 will trigger the precipitation of the cation that precipitates first?
b. What is the remaining concentration of the cation that precipitates first, when the other cation begins to precipitate?

114. Consider a solution that is 0.022 mol L^{-1} in Fe^{2+} and 0.014 mol L^{-1} in Mg^{2+}.
a. If potassium carbonate is used to selectively precipitate one of the cations while leaving the other cation in solution, which cation will precipitate first? What minimum concentration of K_2CO_3 will trigger the precipitation of the cation that precipitates first?
b. What is the remaining concentration of the cation that precipitates first, when the other cation begins to precipitate?

Complex-Ion Equilbria

115. A solution is made that is 1.1×10^{-3} mol L^{-1} in $Zn(NO_3)_2$ and 0.150 mol L^{-1} in NH_3. After the solution reaches equilibrium, what concentration of $Zn^{2+}(aq)$ remains?

116. A 120.0 mL sample of a solution that is 2.8×10^{-3} mol L^{-1} in $AgNO_3$ is mixed with a 225.0 mL sample of a solution that is 0.10 mol L^{-1} in NaCN. After the solution reaches equilibrium, what concentration of $Ag^{+}(aq)$ remains?

117. Use the appropriate values of K_{sp} and K_f to find the equilibrium constant for the reaction:

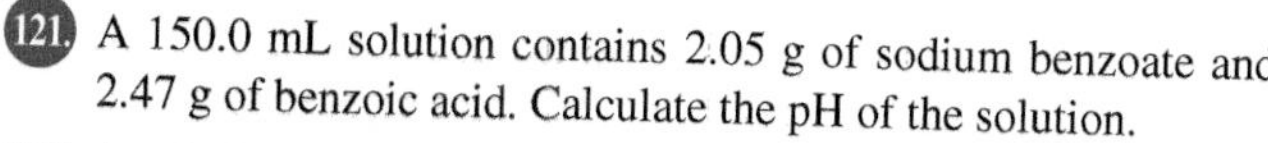

$$FeS(s) + 6\,CN^{-}(aq) \rightleftharpoons Fe(CN)_6^{4-}(aq) + S^{2-}(aq)$$

118. Use the appropriate values of K_{sp} and K_f to find the equilibrium constant for the reaction:

$$PbCl_2(s) + 3\,OH^{-}(aq) \rightleftharpoons Pb(OH)_3^{-}(aq) + 2\,Cl^{-}(aq)$$

119. Calculate the molar solubility of Ag_2S ($K_{sp} = 6.2 \times 10^{-51}$) solution that is also 5.0 mol L^{-1} in NH_3. (K_f $Ag(NH_3)_2^{+} = 1.6 \times 10^{7}$.)

120. Silver iodide has a K_{sp} of 8.51×10^{-17} and therefore is quite insoluble. $Ag(CN)_2^{-}$ has a formation constant of 1.0×10^{21}. What is the solubility of silver iodide in a 0.100 mol L^{-1} solution of NaCN?

Cumulative Problems

121. A 150.0 mL solution contains 2.05 g of sodium benzoate and 2.47 g of benzoic acid. Calculate the pH of the solution.

122. A solution is made by combining 10.0 mL of 17.5 mol L^{-1} acetic acid with 5.54 g of sodium acetate and diluting to a total volume of 1.50 L. Calculate the pH of the solution.

123. A buffer is created by combining 150.0 mL of 0.25 mol L^{-1} HCOOH with 75.0 mL of 0.20 mol L^{-1} NaOH. Determine the pH of the buffer.

124. A buffer is created by combining 3.55 g of NH_3 with 4.78 g of HCl and diluting to a total volume of 750.0 mL. Determine the pH of the buffer.

125. A 1.0 L buffer solution initially contains 0.25 mol of NH_3 and 0.25 mol of NH_4Cl. In order to adjust the buffer pH to 8.75, should you add NaOH or HCl to the buffer mixture? What mass of the correct reagent should you add?

126. A 250.0 mL buffer solution initially contains 0.025 mol of HCOOH and 0.025 mol of $NaCHO_2$. In order to adjust the buffer pH to 4.10, should you add NaOH or HCl to the buffer mixture? What mass of the correct reagent should you add?

127. In analytical chemistry, bases used for titrations must often be standardized; that is, their concentration must be precisely determined. Standardization of sodium hydroxide solutions can be accomplished by titrating potassium hydrogen phthalate ($KHC_8H_4O_4$), also known as KHP, with the NaOH solution to be standardized.

   a. Write an equation for the reaction between NaOH and KHP.
   b. The titration of 0.5527 g of KHP required 25.87 mL of an NaOH solution to reach the equivalence point. What is the concentration of the NaOH solution?

128. A 0.5224 g sample of an unknown monoprotic acid was titrated with 0.0998 mol L^{-1} NaOH. The equivalence point of the titration occurs at 23.82 mL. Determine the molar mass of the unknown acid.

129. A 0.25 mol sample of a weak acid with an unknown pK_a was combined with 10.0 mL of 3.00 mol L^{-1} KOH and the resulting solution was diluted to 1.500 L. The measured pH of the solution was 3.85. What is the pK_a of the weak acid?

130. A 5.55 g sample of a weak acid with $K_a = 1.3 \times 10^{-4}$ was combined with 5.00 mL of 6.00 mol L^{-1} NaOH and the resulting solution was diluted to 750 mL. The measured pH of the solution was 4.25. What is the molar mass of the weak acid?

131. A 0.552 g sample of ascorbic acid (vitamin C) was dissolved in water to a total volume of 20.0 mL and titrated with 0.1103 mol L^{-1} KOH. The equivalence point occurred at 28.42 mL. The pH of the solution at 10.0 mL of added base was 3.72. From this data, determine the molar mass and K_a for vitamin C.

132. Sketch the titration curve from Problem 131 by calculating the pH at the beginning of the titration, at one-half of the equivalence point, at the equivalence point, and at 5.0 mL beyond the equivalence point. Pick a suitable indicator for this titration from Table 16.1.

133. One of the main components of hard water is $CaCO_3$. When hard water evaporates, some of the $CaCO_3$ is left behind as a white mineral deposit. If a hard water solution is saturated with calcium carbonate, what volume of the solution has to evaporate to deposit 1.00×10^{2} mg of $CaCO_3$?

134. Gout—a condition that results in joint swelling and pain—is caused by the formation of sodium urate ($NaC_5H_3N_4$) crystals within tendons, cartilage, and ligaments. Sodium urate precipitates out of blood plasma when uric acid levels become abnormally high. This could happen as a result of eating too many rich foods and consuming too much alcohol, which is why gout is sometimes referred to as the "disease of kings." If the sodium concentration in blood plasma is 0.140 mol L^{-1}, and K_{sp} for sodium urate is 5.76×10^{-8}, what minimum concentration of urate would result in precipitation?

135. Pseudogout, a condition with symptoms similar to those of gout (see Problem 134), is caused by the formation of calcium diphosphate ($Ca_2P_2O_7$) crystals within tendons, cartilage, and ligaments. Calcium diphosphate will precipitate out of blood plasma when diphosphate levels become abnormally high. If the calcium concentration in blood plasma is 9.2 mg dL^{-1}, and K_{sp} for calcium diphosphate is 8.64×10^{-13}, what minimum concentration of diphosphate results in precipitation?

136. Calculate the solubility of silver chloride in a solution that is 0.100 mol L^{-1} in NH_3.

137. Calculate the solubility of copper(II) sulfide in a solution that is 0.150 mol L^{-1} in NaCN.

138. Aniline, abbreviated ϕNH_2, where ϕ is C_6H_5, is an important organic base used in the manufacture of dyes. It has $K_b = 7.5 \times 10^{-10}$. In a certain manufacturing process it is necessary to keep the concentration of ϕNH_3^{+} (aniline's conjugate acid, the anilinium ion) below 1.0×10^{-9} mol L^{-1} in a solution that is 0.10 mol L^{-1} in aniline. Find the concentration of NaOH necessary for this process.

139. The K_b of hydroxylamine, NH_2OH, is 1.10×10^{-8}. A buffer solution is prepared by mixing 100.0 mL of a 0.36 mol L^{-1}

hydroxylamine solution with 50.0 mL of a 0.26 mol L^{-1} HCl solution. Determine the pH of the resulting solution.

140. A 0.867 g sample of an unknown acid requires 32.2 mL of a 0.182 mol L^{-1} barium hydroxide solution for neutralization. Assuming the acid is diprotic, calculate the molar mass of the acid.

141. A 25.0 mL volume of a sodium hydroxide solution requires 19.6 mL of a 0.189 mol L^{-1} hydrochloric acid for neutralization. A 10.0 mL volume of a phosphoric acid solution requires 34.9 mL of the sodium hydroxide solution for complete neutralization. Calculate the concentration of the phosphoric acid solution.

142. Find the mass of sodium formate that must be dissolved in 250.0 cm^3 of a 1.4 mol L^{-1} solution of formic acid to prepare a buffer solution with pH = 3.36.

143. What relative masses of dimethyl amine and dimethyl ammonium chloride do you need to prepare a buffer solution of pH = 10.43?

144. You are asked to prepare 2.0 L of a HCN/NaCN buffer that has a pH of 9.8 and an osmotic pressure of 1.35 bar at 298 K. What masses of HCN and NaCN should you use to prepare the buffer? (Assume complete dissociation of NaCN.)

145. What should the molar concentrations of benzoic acid and sodium benzoate be in a solution that is buffered at a pH of 4.55 and has a freezing point of −2.0 °C? (Assume complete dissociation of sodium benzoate and a density of 1.01 g mL^{-1} for the solution.)

146. If two solutions of equal volume, one saturated with $CrPO_4$ ($K_{sp} = 2.4 \times 10^{-23}$) and the other saturated with $Ca(IO_3)_2$ ($K_{sp} = 1.0 \times 10^{-7}$), are mixed (no solids from either solution are mixed), will $Ca_3(PO_4)_2$ ($K_{sp} = 1.3 \times 10^{-32}$) precipitate?

147. A student measures the pH of a saturated solution of iron(II) hydroxide ($Fe(OH)_2$) to be 9.41. Based on this measurement, what is the K_{sp} of $Fe(OH)_2$?

Challenge Problems

148. Derive an equation similar to the Henderson–Hasselbalch equation for a buffer composed of a weak base and its conjugate acid. Instead of relating pH to pK_a and the relative concentrations of an acid and its conjugate base (as the Henderson–Hasselbalch equation does), the equation should relate pOH to pK_b and the relative concentrations of a base and its conjugate acid.

149. Since soap and detergent action is hindered by hard water, laundry formulations usually include water softeners—called builders—designed to remove hard water ions (especially Ca^{2+} and Mg^{2+}) from the water. A common builder used in North America is sodium carbonate. Suppose that the hard water used to do laundry contains 75 ppm $CaCO_3$ and 55 ppm $MgCO_3$ (by mass). What mass of Na_2CO_3 is required to remove 90.0% of these ions from 10.0 L of laundry water?

150. A 0.558 g sample of a diprotic acid with a molar mass of 255.8 g mol^{-1} is dissolved in water to a total volume of 25.0 mL. The solution is then titrated with a saturated calcium hydroxide solution.

a. Assuming that the pK_a values for each ionization step are sufficiently different to see two equivalence points, determine the volume of added base for the first and second equivalence points.

b. The pH after adding 25.0 mL of the base was 3.82. Find the value of K_{a_1}.

c. The pH after adding 20.0 mL past the first equivalence point was 8.25. Find the value of K_{a_2}.

151. When excess solid $Mg(OH)_2$ is shaken with 1.00 L of 1.0 mol L^{-1} NH_4Cl solution, the resulting saturated solution has pH = 9.00. Calculate the K_{sp} of $Mg(OH)_2$.

152. What amount of solid NaOH must be added to 1.0 L of a 0.10 mol L^{-1} H_2CO_3 solution to produce a solution with $[H^+] = 3.2 \times 10^{-11}$ mol L^{-1}? (There is no significant volume change as the result of the addition of the solid.)

153. Calculate the solubility of $Au(OH)_3$ in **(a)** water and **(b)** 1.0 mol L^{-1} nitric acid solution. ($K_{sp} = 5.5 \times 10^{-46}$)

154. Calculate the concentration of I^- in a solution obtained by shaking 0.10 mol L^{-1} KI with an excess of AgCl(*s*).

155. What volume of 0.100 mol L^{-1} sodium carbonate solution is required to precipitate 99% of the Mg from 1.00 L of 0.100 mol L^{-1} magnesium nitrate solution?

156. Find the solubility of CuI in 0.40 mol L^{-1} HCN solution. The K_{sp} of CuI is 1.1×10^{-12} and the K_f for the $Cu(CN)_2^-$ complex ion is 1×10^{24}.

157. Find the pH of a solution prepared from 1.0 L of a 0.10 mol L^{-1} solution of $Ba(OH)_2$ and excess $Zn(OH)_2(s)$. The K_{sp} of $Zn(OH)_2$ is 3×10^{-15} and the K_f of $Zn(OH)_4^{2-}$ is 2×10^{15}.

158. What amount of HCl gas must be added to 1.00 L of a buffer solution that contains [acetic acid] = 2.0 mol L^{-1} and [acetate] = 1.0 mol L^{-1} in order to produce a solution with pH = 4.00?

Conceptual Problems

159. Without doing any calculations, determine whether pH = pK_a, pH > pK_a, or pH < pK_a. Assume that HA is a weak monoprotic acid.

a. 0.10 mol HA and 0.050 mol of A^- in 1.0 L of solution

b. 0.10 mol HA and 0.150 mol of A^- in 1.0 L of solution

c. 0.10 mol HA and 0.050 mol of OH^- in 1.0 L of solution

d. 0.10 mol HA and 0.075 mol of OH^- in 1.0 L of solution

160. A buffer contains 0.10 mol of a weak acid and 0.20 mol of its conjugate base in 1.0 L of solution. Determine whether or not each addition exceeds the capacity of the buffer.

a. adding 0.020 mol of NaOH

b. adding 0.020 mol of HCl

c. adding 0.10 mol of NaOH

d. adding 0.010 mol of HCl

161. Consider three solutions:

(i) 0.10 mol L^{-1} solution of a weak monoprotic acid
(ii) 0.10 mol L^{-1} solution of strong monoprotic acid
(iii) 0.10 mol L^{-1} solution of a weak diprotic acid

Each solution is titrated with 0.15 mol L^{-1} NaOH. Which quantity will be the same for all three solutions?

a. the volume required to reach the final equivalence point
b. the volume required to reach the first equivalence point
c. the pH at the first equivalence point
d. the pH at one-half the first equivalence point

162. Two monoprotic acid solutions (A and B) are titrated with identical NaOH solutions. The volume to reach the equivalence point for solution A is twice the volume required to reach the equivalence point for solution B, and the pH at the equivalence point of solution A is higher than the pH at the equivalence point for solution B. Which statement is true?

a. The acid in solution A is more concentrated than in solution B and is also a stronger acid than that in solution B.
b. The acid in solution A is less concentrated than in solution B and is also a weaker acid than that in solution B.
c. The acid in solution A is more concentrated than in solution B and is also a weaker acid than that in solution B.
d. The acid in solution A is less concentrated than in solution B and is also a stronger acid than that in solution B.

163. Describe the solubility of CaF_2 in each solution compared to its solubility in water.

a. in a 0.10 mol L^{-1} NaCl solution
b. in a 0.10 mol L^{-1} NaF solution
c. in a 0.10 mol L^{-1} HCl solution

17 Gibbs Energy and Thermodynamics

Die Energie der Welt ist konstant. Die Entropie der Welt strebt einem Maximum zu. (The energy of the world is constant. The entropy of the world tends toward a maximum.)

—Rudolf Clausius (1822–1888)

In this clever illusion, it seems that the water can perpetually flow through the canal. However, perpetual motion is forbidden under the laws of thermodynamics.

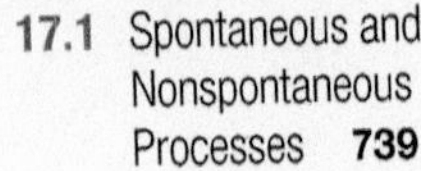

THROUGHOUT THIS TEXT, we have examined and learned much about chemical and physical changes. We have studied how fast chemical changes occur (kinetics) and how to predict how far they will go (through the use of equilibrium constants). We have learned that acids neutralize bases and that gases expand to fill their containers. We now turn to the following question: Why do these changes occur in the first place? What ultimately drives physical and chemical changes in matter? The answer may surprise you. The driving force behind chemical and physical change in the universe is a quantity called *entropy*, which is related to the dispersion (or spreading out) of energy. Nature tends toward that state in which energy is spread out to the greatest extent possible. Although it does not seem obvious at first glance, the freezing of water below 0°C, the dissolving of a solid into a solution, the neutralization of an acid by a base, and even the development of a person from an embryo all increase the entropy in the universe (they all result in greater energy dispersion). In our universe, entropy always increases.

17.1 Spontaneous and Nonspontaneous Processes

A fundamental goal of thermodynamics is to predict *spontaneity*. For example, will rust spontaneously form when iron comes into contact with oxygen? Will water spontaneously decompose into hydrogen and oxygen? A **spontaneous process** is one that occurs *without ongoing outside intervention* (such as the performance of work by some external force). For example, when you drop a book in a gravitational field, it spontaneously drops to the floor. When you place a ball on a slope, it spontaneously rolls down the slope. For simple mechanical systems, such as the dropping of a book or the rolling of a ball, predicting spontaneity is fairly intuitive. A mechanical system tends toward lowest potential energy, which is usually easy to see (at least in *simple* mechanical systems). However, the prediction of spontaneity for chemical systems is not so intuitively obvious. To do so, we need to develop a criterion for the spontaneity of chemical systems. In other words, we want to develop a *chemical potential* that predicts the direction of a chemical system, much as mechanical potential energy predicts the direction of a mechanical system (Figure 17.1 ▼).

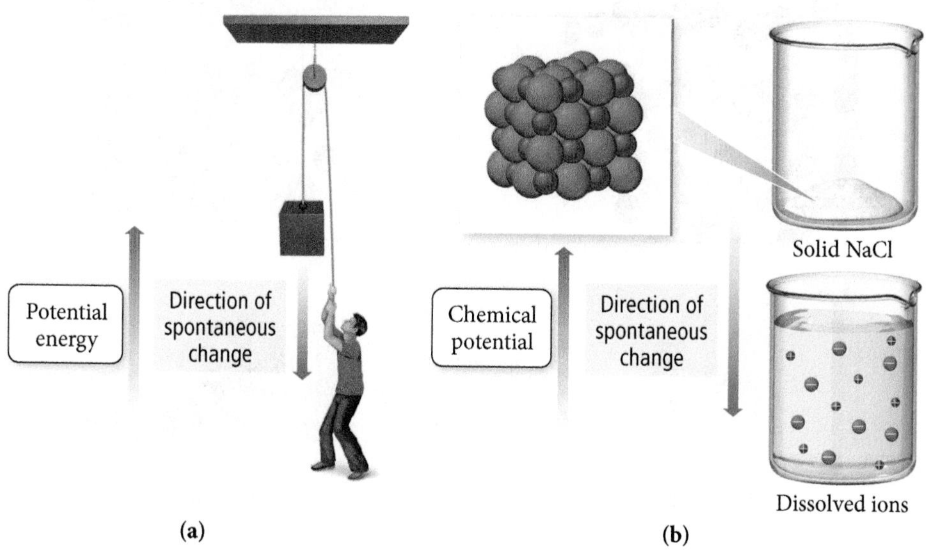

▲ **FIGURE 17.1 Mechanical Potential Energy and Chemical Potential** (**a**) Mechanical potential energy predicts the direction in which a mechanical system will spontaneously move. (**b**) We seek a chemical potential that predicts the direction in which a chemical system will spontaneously move.

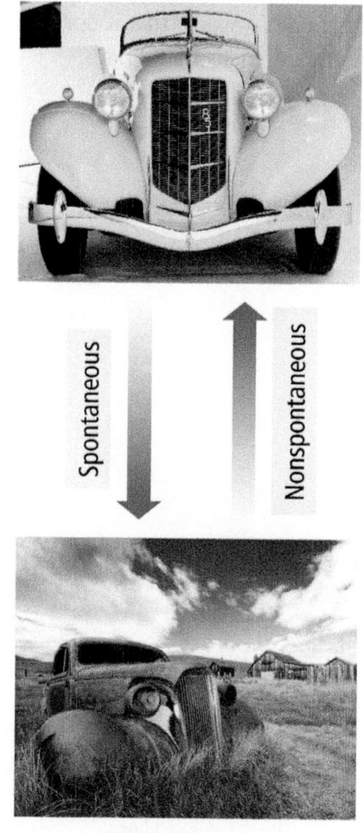

▲ Iron spontaneously rusts when it comes in contact with oxygen.

We must not confuse the *spontaneity* of a chemical reaction with the *speed* of a chemical reaction. In thermodynamics, we study the *spontaneity* of a reaction—the direction in which and extent to which a chemical reaction proceeds. In kinetics, we study the *speed* of the reaction—how fast a reaction takes place (Figure 17.2 ▼). A reaction

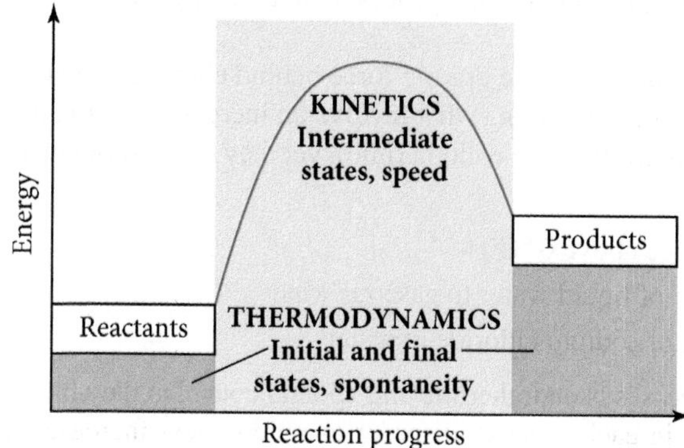

◀ **FIGURE 17.2 Thermodynamics and Kinetics** Thermodynamics deals with the relative chemical potentials of the reactants and products. It enables us to predict whether a reaction will be spontaneous, and to calculate how much work it can do. Kinetics deals with the chemical potential of intermediate states, and enables us to determine why a reaction is slow or fast.

may be thermodynamically spontaneous but kinetically slow at a given temperature. For example, the conversion of diamond to graphite is thermodynamically spontaneous. But your diamonds will not become worthless anytime soon because the process is extremely slow kinetically. Although the rate of a spontaneous process can be increased by the use of a catalyst (Section 13.7), a nonspontaneous process cannot be made spontaneous by the use of a catalyst. Catalysts affect only the rate of a reaction, not the spontaneity.

One last word about nonspontaneity—a nonspontaneous process is not *impossible.* The extraction of iron metal from iron ore is a nonspontaneous process; it does not happen if the iron ore is left to itself, but that does not mean it is impossible. As we will see later in this chapter, a nonspontaneous process can be made spontaneous by coupling it to another process that is spontaneous, or by supplying energy from an external source. Iron can be separated from its ore if external energy is supplied, usually by means of another reaction (that is itself highly spontaneous).

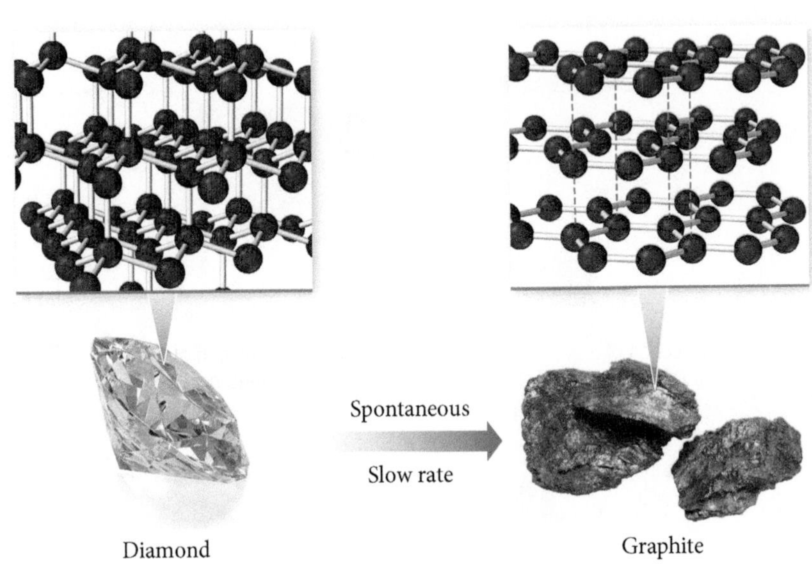

▶ Even though graphite is thermodynamically more stable than diamond, the conversion of diamond to graphite is kinetically so slow that it does not occur at any measurable rate.

17.2 Entropy and the Second Law of Thermodynamics

The first candidate in our search for a chemical potential might be enthalpy, which we defined in Chapter 6. Perhaps, just as a mechanical system proceeds in the direction of lowest potential energy, so a chemical system might proceed in the direction of lowest enthalpy. If this were the case, all exothermic reactions would be spontaneous and all endothermic reactions would not. However, although *most* spontaneous reactions are exothermic, some spontaneous reactions are *endothermic*. For example, above 0 °C, ice spontaneously melts (an endothermic process). So enthalpy must not be the sole criterion for spontaneity.

See Section 6.6 for the definition of enthalpy.

We can learn more about the driving force behind chemical reactions by considering several processes (like ice melting) that involve an increase in enthalpy. These processes are enthalpically uphill (they are endothermic), yet they occur spontaneously. What drives them?

- the melting of ice above 0 °C
- the evaporation of liquid water to gaseous water
- the dissolution of sodium chloride in water

The use of the word *disorder* here is analogous to our macroscopic notions of disorder. The definition of molecular disorder, which is covered shortly, is very specific.

Each of these processes is endothermic *and* spontaneous. Do they have anything in common? Notice that, in each process, disorder or randomness increases. In the melting of ice, the arrangement of the water molecules changes from a highly ordered one (in ice) to a somewhat disorderly one (in liquid water).

◀ When ice melts, the arrangement of water molecules changes from an orderly one to a more disorderly one.

During the evaporation of a liquid to a gas, the arrangement changes from a *somewhat* disorderly one (atoms or molecules in the liquid) to a *highly* disorderly one (atoms or molecules in the gas).

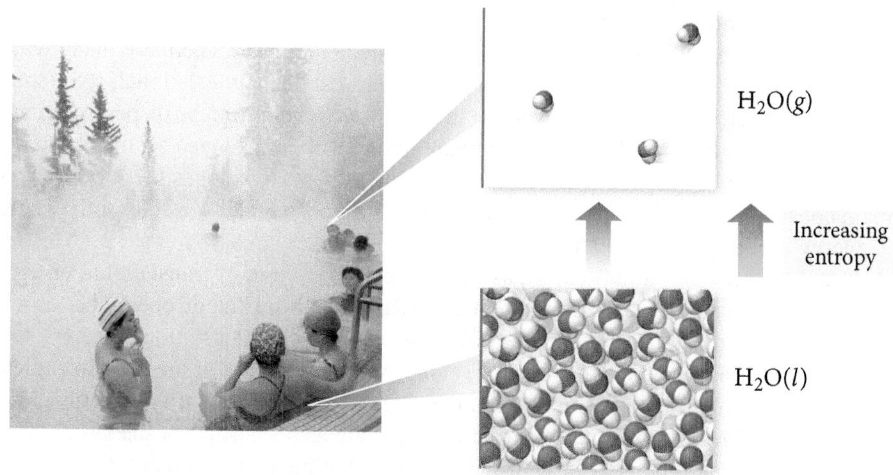

◀ When water evaporates, the arrangement of water molecules becomes still more disorderly.

In the dissolution of NaCl into water, the arrangement again changes from an orderly one (in which the ions in the salt occupy regular positions in the crystal lattice) to a more disorderly one (in which the ions are randomly dispersed throughout the liquid water).

◀ When salt dissolves in water, the arrangement of the molecules and ions becomes more disorderly.

▲ Boltzmann's equation is engraved on his tombstone.

In all three of these processes, a quantity called *entropy*—related to disorder or randomness at the molecular level—increases.

Entropy

We have now hit upon the criterion for spontaneity in chemical systems: entropy. Informally, we can think of entropy as disorder or randomness. But the concept of disorder or randomness on the macroscopic scale—such as the messiness of a drawer—is only *analogous* to the concept of disorder or randomness on the molecular scale. Formally, **entropy**, abbreviated by the symbol S, has the following definition:

> **Entropy (S) is a thermodynamic function that increases with the number of *equivalent* ways to arrange the energy among the components of a system to achieve a particular state.**

This definition was expressed mathematically by Ludwig Boltzmann in the 1870s as

$$S = k \ln W$$

where k is the Boltzmann constant (the gas constant divided by Avogadro's number, $R/N_A = 1.38 \times 10^{-23}$ J K^{-1}) and W is the number of equivalent ways to arrange the total energy in the system. Since W is unitless (it is simply a number), the units of entropy are joules per kelvin (J K^{-1}). We will talk about the significance of the units shortly. As you can see from the equation, as W increases, entropy increases.

The key to understanding entropy is the quantity W. What does W—the number of equivalent arrangements of the total energy in a system—signify? There are many ways that energy can be dispersed in a molecule. Molecules can have translational, rotational, vibrational, and electronic energy levels, or modes, where energy can be dispersed. Imagine a system of particles such as a fixed amount of an ideal gas. A given set of conditions (P, V, and T) defines the *state* (or *macrostate*) of the system. As long as these conditions remain constant, the energy of the system also remains constant. However, exactly where that energy is at any given instant is anything but constant.

At any one instant, a particular gas particle may have lots of translational energy. However, in the next instant, the particle might have only a little kinetic energy because it transferred some to another particle in a collision. Some of that translational energy may also have been transferred to rotational or even vibrational motion of the gas molecules. The exact energy distribution among the molecules at any one instant is sometimes referred to as a *microstate*. You can think of a microstate as a snapshot of the system at a given instant in time. The next instant, the snapshot (the microstate) changes. However, the *macrostate*—defined by P, V, and T—remains constant. A given macrostate can exist as a result of a large number of different microstates. In other words, the snapshot (or microstate) of a given macrostate is generally different from one moment to the next as the energy of the system is constantly redistributing itself among the molecules of the system.

We can now conceive of W in terms of microstates. The quantity, W, is the number of possible microstates that can result in a given macrostate. We can explore this concept further with a very simple example. Suppose we have two systems (call them System A and System B) that are each composed of two particles. Both systems have a total energy of 8 J of energy. System A has only three accessible energy levels and only two distinct ways to distribute the 8 J among the two molecules, as seen below. System A, therefore, has two microstates.

▶ With only 8 J of energy, one molecule cannot have all 8 J because that would leave the other molecule with 0 J (motionless), which violates Heisenberg's uncertainty principle. In these systems, there are only certain "allowed" energy levels because they are composed of atoms that are governed by the laws of quantum mechanics.

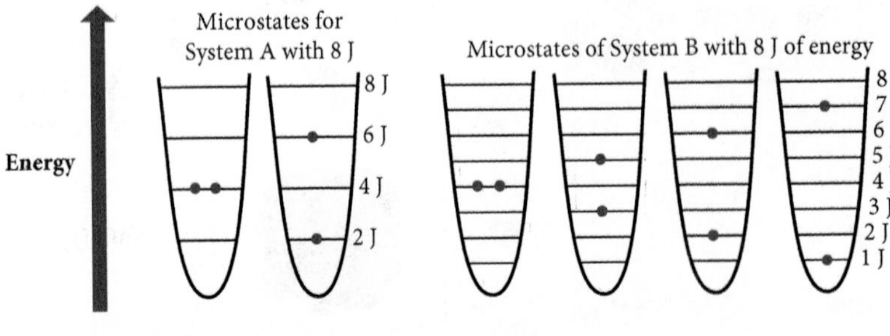

System B, however, is slightly more complex and its energy levels are more closely spaced. It can distribute its 8 J of energy in four different ways. For System A, $W = 2$, but for System B, $W = 4$. In other words, System B has more microstates that result in the same 8 J macrostate. Since W is larger for System B than for System A, System B has greater entropy; it has *more ways to distribute the total energy of the system among its particles.*

As a concrete example, let's consider two other systems, one containing a mole of ice and one containing a mole of liquid water, both at 0 °C. In ice, energy can be dispersed as intermolecular vibrations of the molecule in its lattice position. Clearly, in ice, the degree of translational motion is quite limited compared to liquid water and therefore liquid water is more complex. Energy in liquid water can be dispersed as translational motion of the water molecules around one another and it can be dispersed as rotational motion of the water molecules. The total energy can be dispersed in many more different ways in liquid water, resulting in many more microstates for liquid water than for ice. Since there are more microstates for liquid water, its entropy is higher than that of ice.

We can understand an important aspect of entropy by turning our attention to energy for a moment. The entropy of a state increases with the number of ways that the system has of dispersing energy within the energy levels of its molecules. This implies that a system with *high entropy has a larger number of accessible energy levels than a system with low entropy.* Returning to our previous example, the energy of liquid water can be dispersed many different ways compared to the energy of ice. At the heart of entropy is the concept of energy dispersal. *A system where a given amount of energy can be dispersed in many different ways has more entropy than a system whose energy can only be dispersed in a few ways.*

Although we have already alluded to the **second law of thermodynamics**, we can now formally define it:

> **For any spontaneous process, the entropy of the *universe* increases ($\Delta S_{univ} > 0$).**

The criterion for spontaneity is that the entropy of the universe increases. Processes that increase the entropy of the universe—those that result in greater dispersal or randomization of energy—occur spontaneously. Processes that decrease the entropy of the universe do not occur spontaneously.

Entropy, like enthalpy, is a *state function*—its value depends only on the state of the system, not on how the system arrived at that state. Therefore, for any process, *the change in entropy is the entropy of the final state minus the entropy of the initial state.*

See the discussion of state functions in Section 6.3.

$$\Delta S = S_{final} - S_{initial}$$

Entropy determines the direction of chemical and physical change. *A chemical system proceeds in a direction that increases the entropy of the universe*—it proceeds in a direction that has the largest number of *energetically equivalent* ways to arrange its components.

To better understand this tendency, let us examine the expansion of an ideal gas into a vacuum (a spontaneous process with no associated change in enthalpy). Consider a flask containing an ideal gas that is connected to another, evacuated, flask by a tube equipped with a stopcock. When the stopcock is opened, the gas spontaneously expands into the evacuated flask. Since the gas is expanding into a vacuum, the pressure against which it expands is zero, and therefore the work ($w = -P_{ext}\,\Delta V$) is also zero.

See the discussion of work done by an expanding gas in Section 6.4.

However, even though the total energy of the gas does not change during the expansion, the entropy does change. To picture this, consider our simple system that we described earlier, System B, which has 8 J of energy distributed among two particles. If we increase the volume of the system, each particle has more free space in which to move.

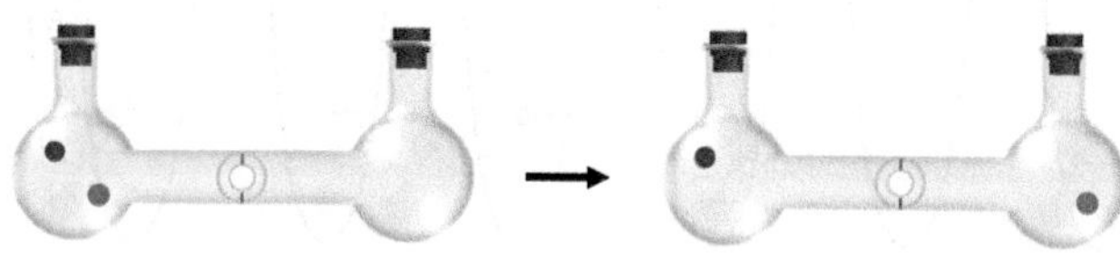

While it is beyond the scope of this text to provide a rigorous proof, the result of an increase in volume is that the energy levels for each of the molecules move closer together and increase in number:

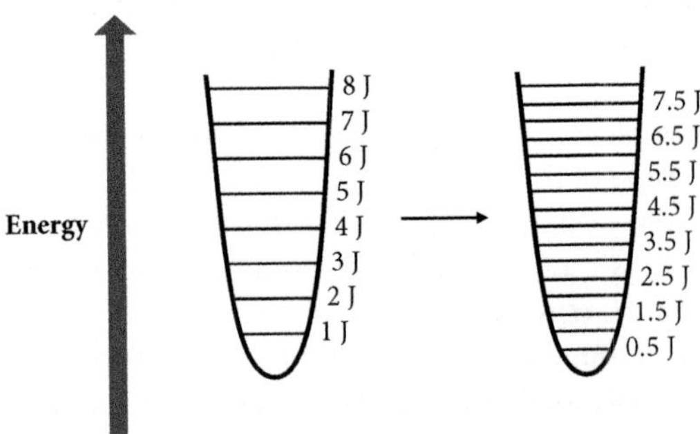

With this increase in the number of accessible energy levels comes an increase in the number of possible ways in which we can distribute 8 J of energy—an increase in the number of microstates:

Microstates of System B with 8 J after an increase in volume

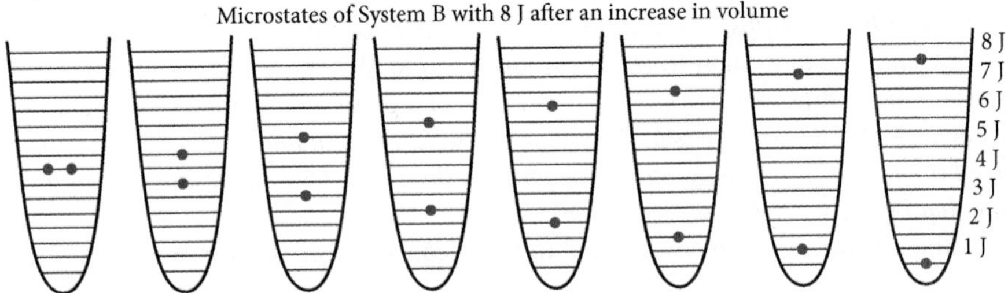

Since the number of microstates has increased—from four before the expansion to eight after the expansion—so too has the entropy of the system.

The *change in entropy* in transitioning to a state where the volume has increased is *positive* because the final state has a greater entropy than the initial state:

$$\Delta S = S_{\text{final}} - S_{\text{initial}}$$

Entropy of system after expansion (for S_{final})

Entropy of system before expansion (for S_{initial})

Since S_{final} is greater than S_{initial}, ΔS is positive and the process, expanding the gas into a vacuum, is spontaneous according to the second law of thermodynamics.

Let's consider a change in temperature of our system; what happens to the entropy of the system? If the temperature increases, then the total amount of energy in our system increases. Let's assume a temperature increase resulting in a change in the total energy of System B from 8 J to 12 J. With the increase in temperature there is more energy to be dispersed among the energy levels of the two atoms and there is an increase in the number of energy levels available to be populated. The number of microstates with a total energy equivalent to 12 J is six, an increase from the four microstates before the temperature change. The change in entropy is positive. A system at higher temperature has more entropy.

Microstates of System B after an increase in temperature: total energy increases from 8 J to 12 J

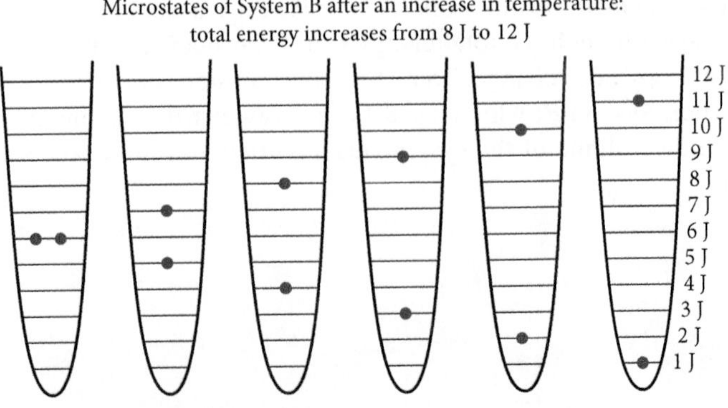

Let's also consider an increase in the number of atoms in our system. We saw that there were four microstates for our system of two atoms with a total of 8 J of energy. In order to maintain the same temperature, our new particle also brings with it an equal share of energy, 4J, so the energy of the system is now 12 J—on average 4 J per particle.

Microstates of System B after addition of a third atom with an average of 4 J per atom, 12 J total

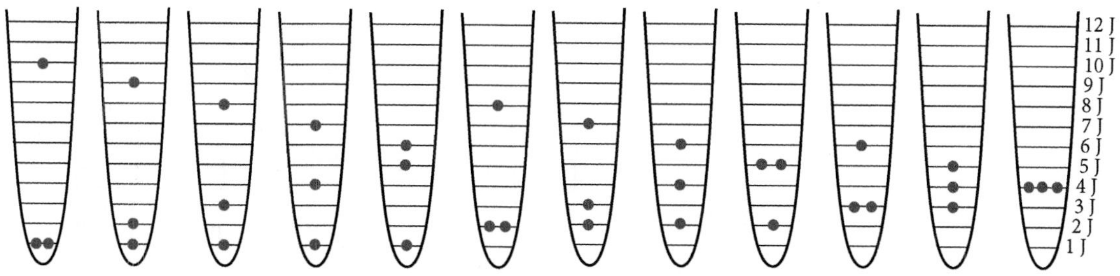

The total number of microstates increases from 6 to 12. The addition of a molecule will increase the entropy of the system at constant temperature.

What we have just seen—the effects of increasing the complexity of the system, increasing the volume of the system, increasing the temperature of the system, or adding more particles to the system—all result in an increase in the system's entropy or a positive S. The systems that we have looked at are very simplistic, with only two or three particles with only a few energy levels. Realistic systems contain on the order of a mole of particles (6.022×10^{23}) and the change in the numbers of microstates is equally enormous.

The second law also explains many phenomena not explained by the first law. In Chapter 6, we learned that heat travels from a substance at higher temperature to one at lower temperature. For example, if we drop an ice cube into water, heat travels from the water to the ice cube—the water cools and the ice warms (and eventually melts). Why? The first law does not prohibit some heat flowing the other way—from the ice to the water, leaving the ice colder and the water warmer. However, you have never seen this happen, nor will this ever happen. Heat flowing from a cold object to a warmer object would disobey the second law of thermodynamics. To show this, we will consider two systems that are identical except that one is at a higher temperature and one is at a lower temperature, and see what happens to the number of microstates (1) when the systems are brought together and they reach thermal equilibrium, and (2) when energy flows from the cooler system to the warmer system.

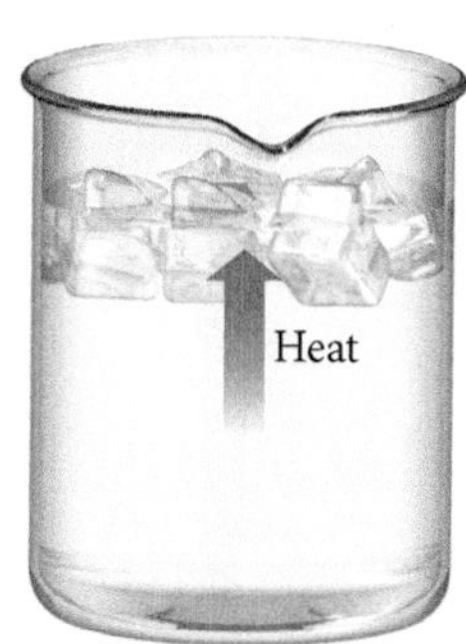

For simplicity, let's consider two System B's, each composed of two particles, but one with 8 J of energy and one at a higher temperature with 12 J of energy. As we just saw, together these two systems have ten microstates, four for the cooler one, and six for the warmer one. When we put these two systems together and they reach thermal equilibrium, they become one system with 20 J of energy distributed among all four particles. Counting the number of ways of distributing the 20 J of energy among the four particles—counting the microstates—is cumbersome, but not impossible. Below are 19 of the 64 ways that the energy can be distributed within our new system of four particles with 20 J of energy between them at thermal equilibrium:

19 of the 64 microstates after reaching thermal equilibrium of two System B's; one initially with 12 J and one initially with 8 J

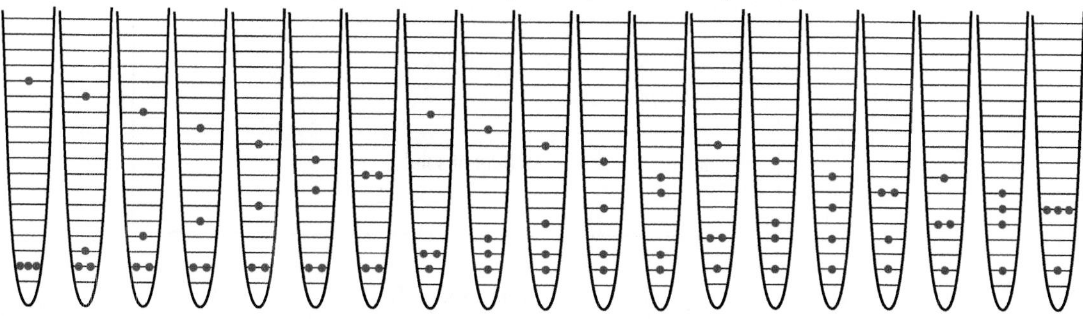

The number of microstates increased from 10 to 64 when the two systems come to thermal equilibrium. The entropy change is positive. The flow of energy from the warm system to the cooler system is spontaneous.

What happens when energy flows from the cooler system to the warmer system? Let's say we take 1 J of energy from the cool system and give it to the already warmer system. Now we have two systems, each with two particles, but one has 7 J of energy, the other 13 J. The microstates are shown below:

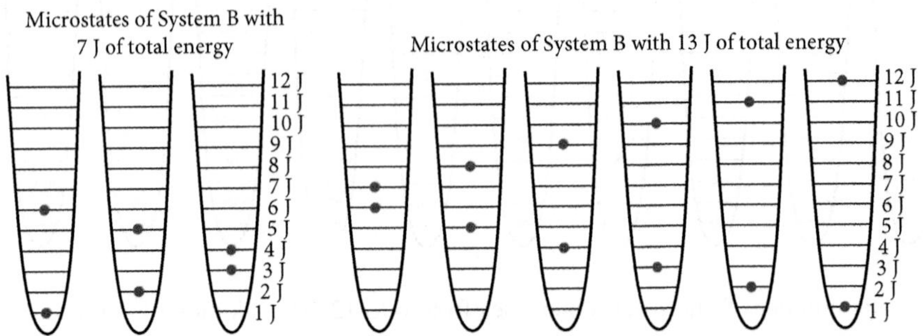

In total there are only nine microstates. Before the heat transfer, there were 10 microstates. The entropy decreased! This exchange of energy, where the cool system gets cooler by transferring heat to the warmer system, violates the second law of thermodynamics and is not spontaneous.

The Entropy Change Associated with a Change in State

The entropy of a sample of matter *increases* as it changes state from a solid to a liquid or from a liquid to a gas (Figure 17.3 ▼). As we just saw, the differences in entropy are related to the number of energetically equivalent ways of arranging energy among the particles in each state—more in the gas than in the liquid, and more in the liquid than in the solid.

A gas has more energetically equivalent configurations because it has more ways to distribute its energy than a solid. The energy in a molecular solid consists largely of the vibrations between its molecules. If the same substance is vaporized, however, the energy can take the form of straight-line motions of the molecules (called translational energy) and rotations of the molecules (called rotational energy). In other words, when a solid vaporizes, there are new "places" to put energy (Figure 17.4 ▶). The gas thus has more possible microstates (more energetically equivalent configurations) than the solid and therefore a greater entropy.

▶ FIGURE 17.3 Entropy and State Change Entropy increases in going from a solid to a liquid and in going from a liquid to a gas.

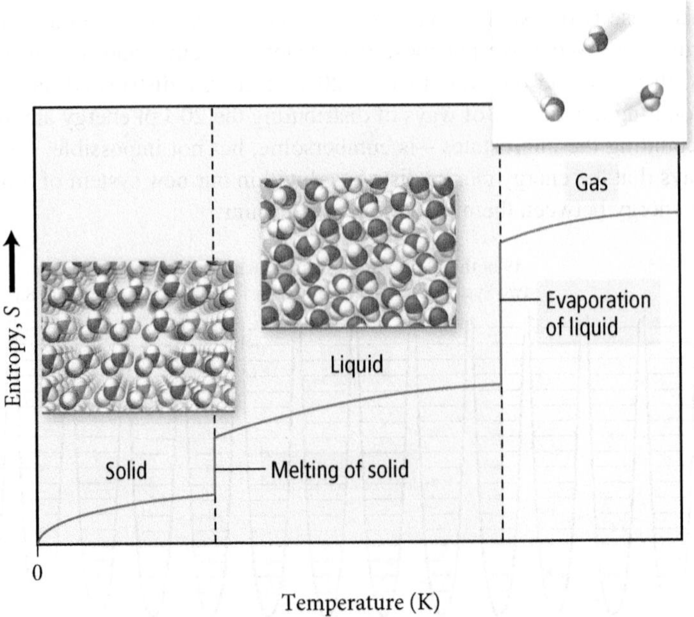

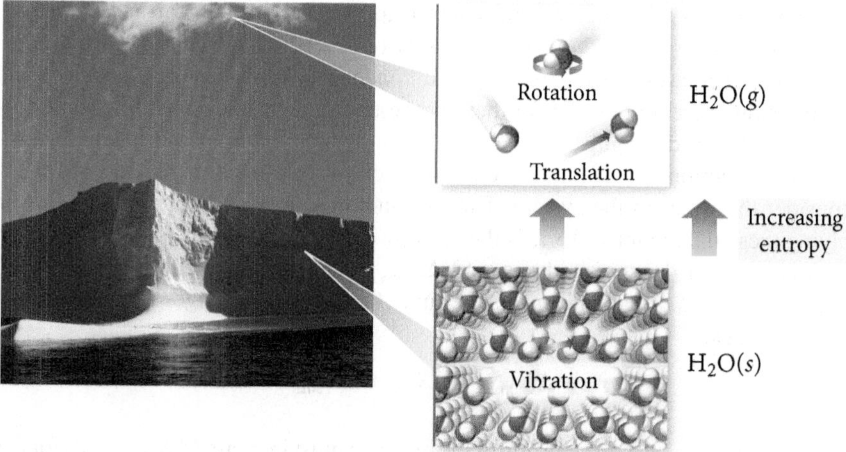

◀ **FIGURE 17.4 "Places" for Energy** In the solid state, energy is contained largely in the vibrations between molecules. In the gas state, energy can be contained in both the straight-line motion of molecules (translational energy) and the rotation of molecules (rotational energy).

We can now predict the sign of ΔS for processes involving changes of state (or phase). In general, entropy increases ($\Delta S > 0$) for each of the following:

- the phase transition from a solid to a liquid
- the phase transition from a solid to a gas
- the phase transition from a liquid to a gas
- an increase in the number of moles of a gas during a chemical reaction

EXAMPLE 17.1 PREDICTING THE SIGN OF ENTROPY CHANGE

Predict the sign of ΔS for each process:

(a) $H_2O(g) \longrightarrow H_2O(l)$

(b) Solid carbon dioxide sublimes.

(c) $2\ N_2O(g) \longrightarrow 2\ N_2(g) + O_2(g)$

SOLUTION

(a) Since a gas has a greater entropy than a liquid, the entropy decreases and ΔS is negative.

(b) Since a solid has a lower entropy than a gas, the entropy increases and ΔS is positive.

(c) Since the number of moles of gas increases, the entropy increases and ΔS is positive.

FOR PRACTICE 17.1

Predict the sign of ΔS for each process:

(a) the boiling of water

(b) $I_2(g) \longrightarrow I_2(s)$

(c) $CaCO_3(s) \longrightarrow CaO(s) + CO_2(g)$

17.3 Heat Transfer and Changes in the Entropy of the Surroundings

We have now seen that the criterion for spontaneity is an increase in the entropy of the universe. However, you can probably think of several spontaneous processes in which entropy seems to decrease. For example, when water freezes at temperatures below 0 °C, the entropy of the water decreases, yet the process is spontaneous. Similarly, when water vapour in air condenses into fog on a cold night, the entropy of the water also decreases. Why are these processes spontaneous?

To answer this question, we must return to the second law: for any spontaneous process, the entropy *of the universe* increases ($\Delta S_{univ} > 0$). Even though the entropy *of the water* decreases during freezing and condensation, the entropy *of the universe* must somehow increase in order for these processes to be spontaneous. In Chapter 6, we found it helpful to distinguish between a thermodynamic system and its surroundings. The same distinction is useful in our discussion of entropy. For the freezing of water, let us consider the water as the system. The surroundings are then the rest of the universe. Applying these distinctions, ΔS_{sys} is the entropy change for the water itself, ΔS_{surr} is the entropy change for the surroundings, and ΔS_{univ} is the entropy change for the universe. The entropy change for the universe is the sum of the entropy changes for the system and the surroundings:

$$\Delta S_{univ} = \Delta S_{sys} + \Delta S_{surr} \quad [17.1]$$

The second law states that the entropy of the universe must increase ($\Delta S_{univ} > 0$) for a process to be spontaneous. The entropy of the *system* can therefore decrease ($\Delta S_{sys} < 0$) as long as the entropy of the *surroundings* increases by a greater amount ($\Delta S_{surr} > -\Delta S_{sys}$), so that the overall entropy of the *universe* undergoes a net increase.

For liquid water freezing or water vapour condensing, we know that the change in entropy for the system (ΔS_{sys}) is negative because the water loses ways of storing energy (rotations and translations), resulting in fewer microstates for the particular macrostate. For ΔS_{univ} to be positive, therefore, ΔS_{surr} must be positive and greater in absolute value (or magnitude) than ΔS_{sys} as shown graphically here:

$$\Delta S_{univ} = \Delta S_{sys} + \Delta S_{surr}$$

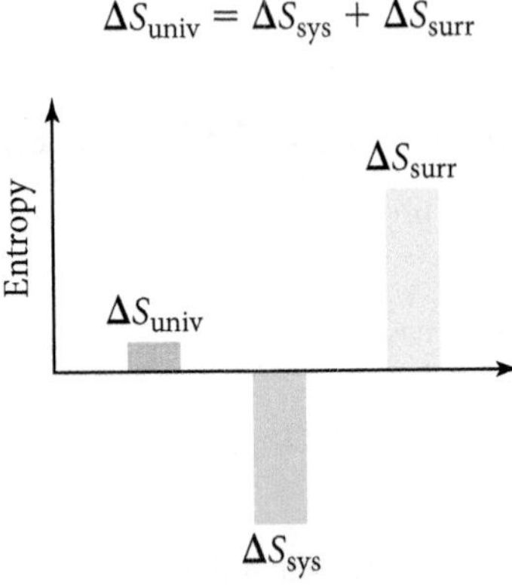

Even though (as we saw earlier) enthalpy by itself cannot determine spontaneity, the increase in the entropy of the surroundings caused by the release of heat explains why exothermic processes are so *often* spontaneous.

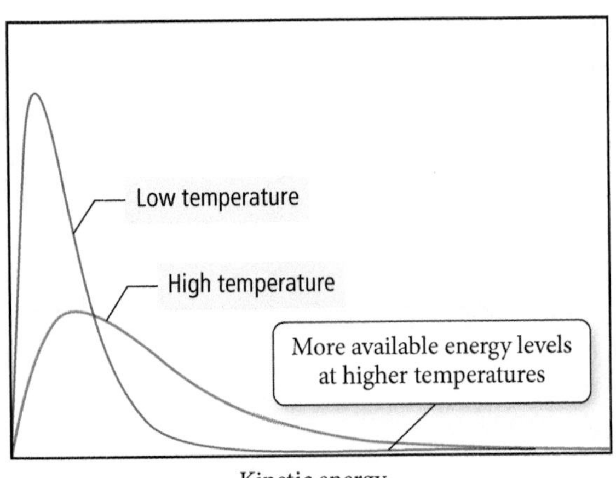

▲ **FIGURE 17.5 Maxwell-Boltzmann Distribution of Kinetic Energies for Two Different Temperatures**

But why does the freezing of ice or the condensation of water increase the entropy of the surroundings? The first clue in answering this question is that both processes, freezing and condensation, are *exothermic*: they give off heat to the surroundings which increases the temperature of the surroundings. If we look at a Maxwell-Boltzmann distribution of kinetic energies for two different temperatures, as in Figure 17.5 ◄, it is apparent that higher energy levels are accessible at higher temperatures. With more available energy levels, there are more possible microstates available that can describe the macrostate. Another way of saying this is that the energy can be dispersed over more possible energy levels. The freezing of water below 0 °C and the condensation of water vapour on a cold night both increase the entropy of the universe because the heat given off to the surroundings increases the entropy of the surroundings to a sufficient degree to overcome the entropy decrease in the water.

Summarizing Entropy Changes in the Surroundings:

- An exothermic process increases the entropy of the surroundings.
- An endothermic process decreases the entropy of the surroundings.

The Temperature Dependence of ΔS_{surr}

We have just seen how the freezing of water increases the entropy of the surroundings by dispersing heat energy into the surroundings. Yet we know that the freezing of water is not spontaneous at all temperatures. The freezing of water becomes *nonspontaneous* above 0 °C. Why? Because the magnitude of the increase in the entropy of the surroundings due to the dispersal of energy into the surroundings is *temperature dependent*.

The greater the temperature, the smaller the increase in entropy for a given amount of energy dispersed into the surroundings. Recall that the units of entropy are joules per kelvin: energy units divided by temperature units. *Entropy is a measure of energy dispersal (joules) per unit temperature (kelvins).* We can understand the temperature dependence of entropy changes due to heat flow with a simple analogy. Imagine that you have \$1000 to give away. If you gave the \$1000 to a rich person the impact on his net worth would be negligible (because they already have so much money). If you gave the same \$1000 to a poor person, however, their net worth would change substantially (because they have so little money). Similarly, if you disperse 1000 J of energy into surroundings that are hot, the entropy increase is small (because the impact of the 1000 J is small on surroundings that already contain a lot of energy). If you disperse the same 1000 J of energy into surroundings that are cold, however, the entropy increase is large (because the impact of the 1000 J is great on surroundings that contain little energy). For this same reason, the impact of the heat released to the surroundings by the freezing of water depends on the temperature of the surroundings—the higher the temperature, the smaller the impact.

Condensation is also spontaneous at temperatures below 100 °C, but nonspontaneous at higher temperatures. The positive entropy change in the surroundings is greater at lower temperature than at higher temperature.

We can now understand why water spontaneously freezes at low temperature but not at high temperature. For the freezing of liquid water into ice, the change in entropy of the system is negative at all temperatures.

$$\Delta S_{univ} = \Delta S_{sys} + \Delta S_{surr}$$

ΔS_{sys}: Negative

ΔS_{surr}: Positive and large at low temperature; Positive and small at high temperature

At low temperatures, the decrease in entropy of the system is overcome by the large increase in the entropy of the surroundings (a positive quantity), resulting in a positive ΔS_{univ} and a spontaneous process. At high temperatures, on the other hand, the decrease in entropy of the system is not overcome by the increase in entropy of the surroundings (because the magnitude of the positive ΔS_{surr} is smaller at higher temperatures), resulting in a negative ΔS_{univ}; therefore, the freezing of water is not spontaneous at high temperature as shown graphically here.

$$\Delta S_{univ} = \Delta S_{sys} + \Delta S_{surr} \quad \text{(for water freezing)}$$

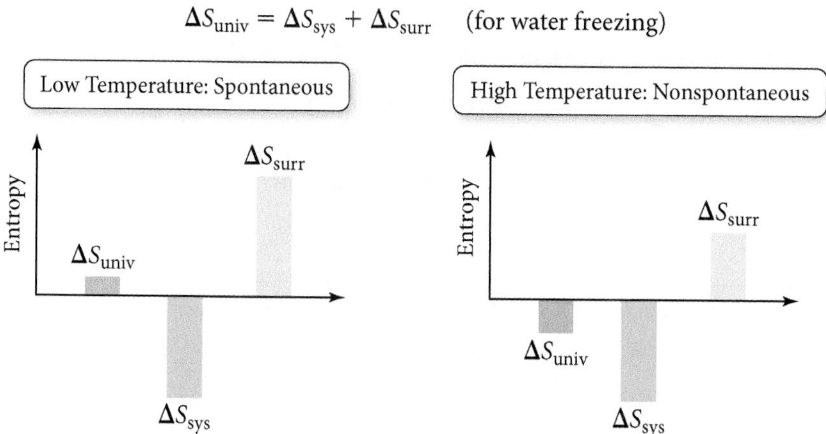

Quantifying Entropy Changes in the Surroundings

We have seen that when a system exchanges heat with the surroundings, it changes the entropy of the surroundings. At constant pressure, we can use q_{sys} to quantify the change in *entropy* for the surroundings (ΔS_{surr}). In general,

- A process that emits heat into the surroundings (q_{sys} negative) *increases* the entropy of the surroundings (positive ΔS_{surr}).

- A process that absorbs heat from the surroundings (q_{sys} positive) *decreases* the entropy of the surroundings (negative ΔS_{surr}).
- The magnitude of the change in entropy of the surroundings is proportional to the magnitude of q_{sys}.

We can summarize these three points with the proportionality:

$$\Delta S_{surr} \propto -q_{sys} \quad [17.2]$$

We have also seen that, for a given amount of heat exchanged with the surroundings, the magnitude of ΔS_{surr} is inversely proportional to the temperature. In general, the higher the temperature, the lower the magnitude of ΔS_{surr} for a given amount of heat exchanged:

$$\Delta S_{surr} \propto \frac{1}{T} \quad [17.3]$$

Combining the proportionalities in Equations 17.2 and 17.3, we get the following general expression at constant temperature:

$$\Delta S_{surr} = \frac{-q_{sys}}{T} \quad [17.4]$$

For any chemical or physical process occurring at constant temperature and pressure, the entropy change of the surroundings is equal to the energy dispersed into the surroundings ($-\Delta H_{sys}$) divided by the temperature of the surroundings in kelvin.

This equation provides insight into why exothermic processes have a tendency to be spontaneous at low temperatures—they increase the entropy of the surroundings. As temperature increases, however, a given negative ΔH produces a smaller positive ΔS_{surr}; thus, exothermicity becomes less of a determining factor for spontaneity as temperature increases.

Remember from Chapter 6 that the units for enthalpy of reaction are kJ mol^{-1}, where "mol^{-1}" means per mole of reaction. Similarly, the units for entropy of reaction are J K^{-1} mol^{-1}.

Under conditions of constant pressure $q_{sys} = \Delta H_{sys}$; therefore,

$$\Delta S_{surr} = \frac{-\Delta H_{sys}}{T} \quad \text{(constant } P, T) \quad [17.5]$$

EXAMPLE 17.2 CALCULATING ENTROPY CHANGES IN THE SURROUNDINGS

Consider the combustion of propane gas:

$$C_3H_8(g) + 5\ O_2(g) \longrightarrow 3\ CO_2(g) + 4\ H_2O(g) \quad \Delta_rH = -2044 \text{ kJ mol}^{-1}$$

(a) Calculate the entropy change in the surroundings associated with this reaction occurring at 100 °C.

(b) Determine the sign of the entropy change for the system.

(c) Determine the sign of the entropy change for the universe. Will the reaction be spontaneous?

SOLUTION

(a) The entropy change of the surroundings is given by Equation 17.5. Substitute the value of Δ_rH and the temperature in kelvins and calculate ΔS_{surr}.	$T = 273 + 100 = 373$ K $\Delta S_{surr} = \frac{-\Delta_rH}{T}$ $= \frac{-(-2044 \text{ kJ mol}^{-1})}{373 \text{ K}}$ $= +5.48 \text{ kJ K}^{-1}\text{mol}^{-1}$ $= 5.48 \times 10^3 \text{ J K}^{-1}\text{mol}^{-1}$
(b) Determine the number of moles of gas on each side of the reaction. An increase in the number of moles of gas implies a positive ΔS_{sys}.	$C_3H_8(g) + 5\ O_2(g)$ (6 mol gas) $\longrightarrow 3\ CO_2(g) + 4\ H_2O(g)$ (7 mol gas) ΔS_{sys} is positive.

(c) The change in entropy of the universe is the sum of the entropy changes of the system and the surroundings. If the entropy changes of the system and surroundings are both the same sign, the entropy change for the universe will also have the same sign.	$\Delta S_{univ} = \Delta S_{sys} + \Delta S_{surr}$ (Positive, Positive) Therefore, ΔS_{univ} is positive and the reaction is spontaneous.

FOR PRACTICE 17.2

Consider the reaction between nitrogen and oxygen to form dinitrogen monoxide:

$$2\ N_2(g) + O_2(g) \longrightarrow 2\ N_2O(g) \qquad \Delta_r H = +163.2\ kJ\ mol^{-1}$$

(a) Calculate the entropy change in the surroundings associated with this reaction occurring at 25 °C.

(b) Determine the sign of the entropy change for the system.

(c) Determine the sign of the entropy change for the universe. Will the reaction be spontaneous?

FOR MORE PRACTICE 17.2

A reaction has $\Delta_r H = -107\ kJ\ mol^{-1}$ and $\Delta_r S = 285\ J\ K^{-1} mol^{-1}$. At what temperature is the change in entropy for the reaction equal to the change in entropy for the surroundings?

CONCEPTUAL CONNECTION 17.1

Entropy and Biological Systems

Do biological systems contradict the second law of thermodynamics? By taking energy from their surroundings and synthesizing large, complex biological molecules, plants and animals tend to concentrate energy, not disperse it. How can this be so?

17.4 Entropy Changes for Phase Transitions

Let's return to the example of water freezing to ice. We said that at low temperatures, below 273.15 K (0 °C), S_{univ} is positive, and the process is spontaneous. At higher temperatures, S_{univ} is negative, and the freezing of water is nonspontaneous. What happens, though, at exactly 273.15 K? The process is neither spontaneous nor nonspontaneous. In fact, at 0 °C, if you have a mixture of water and ice, the system is at equilibrium. As long as no heat is added or removed, no more water freezes, and no more ice melts. When the system is at equilibrium, $S_{univ} = 0\ J\ K^{-1}\ mol^{-1}$.

Equation 17.1 can be written as follows:

$$0 = \Delta S_{sys} + \Delta S_{surr} \qquad [17.6]$$

While this system is at equilibrium, if we add a little bit of heat, a small amount of ice melts. On the other hand, if we remove a little bit of heat, some of the water will freeze. In both cases, the temperature remains at 0 °C, and the system is still at equilibrium. This process of melting ice by adding a little heat and freezing water by removing a little heat in an ice–water mixture at 0 °C is called a **reversible process** (we will return to the subject of a reversible process in Section 17.7). The small amount of energy added or removed from the system in this reversible process is called q_{rev}. We can write a similar equation to Equation 17.4 for the entropy change in the surroundings:

$$\Delta S_{surr} = \frac{-q_{rev}}{T} \qquad [17.7]$$

By combining Equations 17.6 and 17.7, we obtain the following expression for the entropy change of the system:

$$\Delta S_{sys} = \frac{q_{rev}}{T} \qquad [17.8]$$

Again, at constant pressure, $q = \Delta H$, so for any process occurring reversibly at constant temperature, we can determine the entropy change for the system by measuring the change in enthalpy for the system using the relationship in Equation 17.9:

$$\Delta_r S = \frac{\Delta_r H}{T} \tag{17.9}$$

Types of processes that can be considered to occur at constant temperature and reversibly are phase changes. For example, water freezes at 0 °C (273.15 K) and the enthalpy change associated with the freezing of water (enthalpy of fusion) is -6.02 kJ mol^{-1}. Using Equation 17.9, we calculate the entropy changes associated with freezing to be the following:

$$\Delta_r S = \frac{-6.02 \text{ kJ mol}^{-1}}{273.15 \text{ K}} = -0.0220 \text{ kJ K}^{-1} \text{ mol}^{-1} = -22.0 \text{ J K}^{-1} \text{ mol}^{-1}$$

Note that this entropy change corresponds to a loss of entropy, which is sensible for freezing.

17.5 Gibbs Energy

Equation 17.1 gives us a relationship between the enthalpy change in a system and the entropy change in the surroundings. Recall that for any process the entropy change of the universe is the sum of the entropy change of the system and the entropy change of the surroundings according to Equation 17.1:

$$\Delta S_{\text{univ}} = \Delta S_{\text{sys}} + \Delta S_{\text{surr}} \tag{17.1}$$

Combining Equation 17.1 with Equation 17.5 gives us the following relationship at constant temperature and pressure:

$$\Delta S_{\text{univ}} = \Delta S_{\text{sys}} - \frac{\Delta H_{\text{sys}}}{T} \tag{17.10}$$

Using Equation 17.10, we can calculate ΔS_{univ} while focusing only on the *system*. If we multiply Equation 17.10 by $-T$, we arrive at the expression:

$$\begin{aligned} -T\,\Delta S_{\text{univ}} &= -T\,\Delta S_{\text{sys}} + T\frac{\Delta H_{\text{sys}}}{T} \\ &= \Delta H_{\text{sys}} - T\,\Delta S_{\text{sys}} \end{aligned} \tag{17.11}$$

For a physical or chemical process, if we drop the subscript sys—from now on $\Delta_r H$ and $\Delta_r S$ without subscripts mean ΔH_{sys} and ΔS_{sys}—we get the expression:

$$-T\,\Delta S_{\text{univ}} = \Delta_r H - T\,\Delta_r S \tag{17.12}$$

The right-hand side of Equation 17.12 represents the change in a thermodynamic function called *Gibbs energy* (sometimes referred to as *Gibbs free energy* or simply *free energy*, but this is discouraged). The formal definition of **Gibbs energy (*G*)** is

$$G = H - TS \tag{17.13}$$

where H is enthalpy, T is the temperature in kelvins, and S is entropy. The *change* in Gibbs energy, symbolized by $\Delta_r G$, is expressed as follows (at constant temperature):

$$\Delta_r G = \Delta_r H - T\,\Delta_r S \tag{17.14}$$

If we combine Equations 17.12 and 17.14, we can understand the significance of $\Delta_r G$:

$$\Delta_r G = -T\,\Delta S_{\text{univ}} \quad \text{(constant } T, P) \tag{17.15}$$

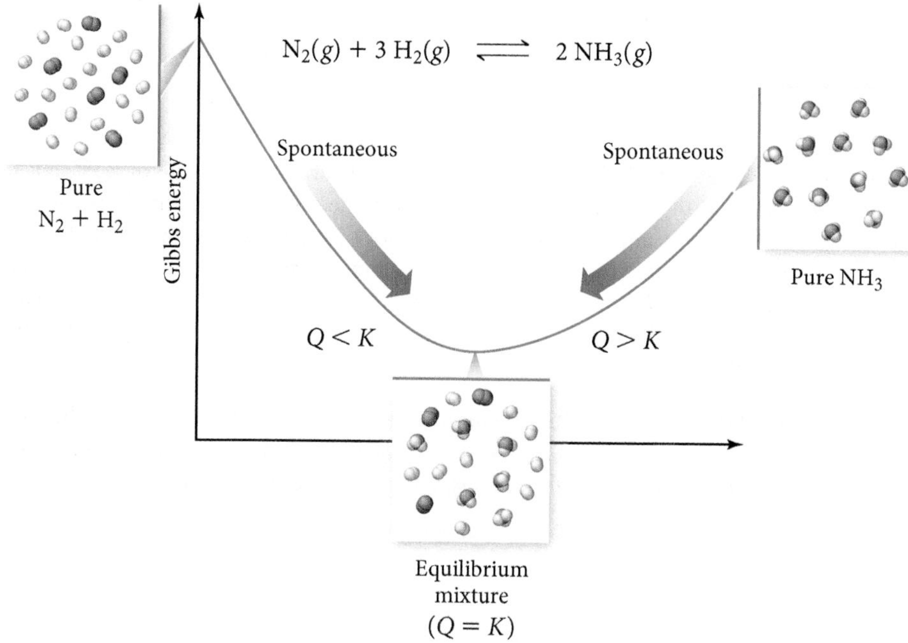

◀ **FIGURE 17.6 Gibbs Energy** Gibbs energy is also called chemical potential because it determines the direction of spontaneous change for chemical systems.

The change in Gibbs energy for a process occurring at constant temperature and pressure is proportional to the negative of ΔS_{univ}. Since a positive ΔS_{univ} is a criterion for a spontaneous process, a negative $\Delta_r G$ is also a criterion for a spontaneous process. In fact, Gibbs energy is also called *chemical potential*, because it is analogous to mechanical potential energy discussed earlier. Just as mechanical systems tend toward lower potential energy, so chemical systems tend toward lower Gibbs energy (toward lower chemical potential) (Figure 17.6 ▲).

Summarizing Gibbs Energy (at Constant Temperature and Pressure):

- ΔG is proportional to the negative of ΔS_{univ}.
- A decrease in Gibbs energy ($\Delta_r G < 0$) corresponds to a spontaneous process.
- An increase in Gibbs energy ($\Delta_r G > 0$) corresponds to a nonspontaneous process.

Notice that changes in Gibbs energy can be computed solely with reference to the system. So, to determine whether a process is spontaneous, we only have to find the change in *entropy* for the system ($\Delta_r S$) and the change in *enthalpy* for the system ($\Delta_r H$). We can then predict the spontaneity of the process at any temperature. In Chapter 6, we learned how to calculate changes in enthalpy ($\Delta_r H$) for chemical reactions. In Section 17.6, we learn how to calculate changes in entropy ($\Delta_r S$) for chemical reactions. We can then use those two quantities to calculate changes in Gibbs energy ($\Delta_r G$) for chemical reactions and predict their spontaneity (Section 17.7). Before we move on to these matters, however, let us examine some examples that demonstrate how $\Delta_r H$, $\Delta_r S$, and T affect the spontaneity of chemical processes.

The Effect of $\Delta_r H$, $\Delta_r S$, and T on Spontaneity

Case 1: $\Delta_r H$ Negative, $\Delta_r S$ Positive If a reaction is exothermic ($\Delta_r H < 0$), and if the change in entropy for the reaction is positive ($\Delta_r S > 0$), then the change in Gibbs energy will be negative at all temperatures and the reaction will be spontaneous at all temperatures.

$$\Delta_r G = \Delta_r H - T\,\Delta_r S$$

Negative at all temperatures — Negative — Positive

As an example, consider the dissociation of N_2O:

$$\underset{2\text{ mol gas}}{2\ N_2O(g)} \longrightarrow \underset{3\text{ mol gas}}{2\ N_2(g) + O_2(g)} \qquad \Delta_r H^\circ = -163.2\ \text{kJ mol}^{-1}$$

Recall from Chapter 6 that $\Delta_r H^\circ$ represents the standard enthalpy change. The definition of the standard state was first given in Section 6.9 and is summarized in Section 17.6.

The change in *enthalpy* is negative—heat is emitted, increasing the entropy of the surroundings. In Section 17.7, we will learn how to determine the value of $\Delta_r S^\circ$, but for now we can look at the reaction and at least determine whether $\Delta_r S^\circ$ might be positive or not. For the above example, the number of moles of gas increases, therefore there are more ways to disperse the given energy of the system, more translations, vibrations, and rotations. Therefore, $\Delta_r S^\circ$ is positive. Since the entropy of both the system and the surroundings increases, the entropy of the universe must also increase, making the reaction spontaneous at all temperatures.

Case 2: $\Delta_r H$ Positive, $\Delta_r S$ Negative If a reaction is endothermic $\Delta_r H$, and if the change in entropy for the reaction is negative $\Delta_r S$, then the change in Gibbs energy will be positive at all temperatures and the reaction will be nonspontaneous at all temperatures.

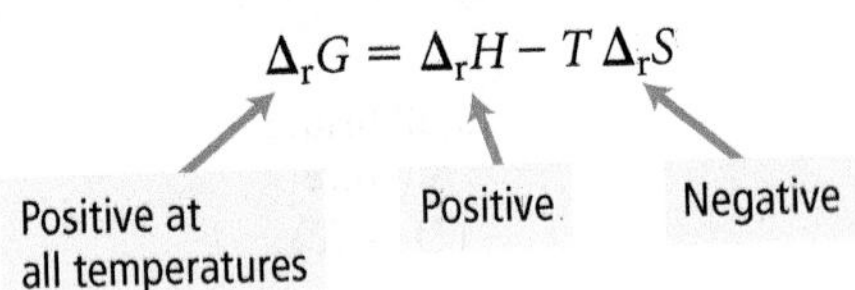

As an example, consider the formation of ozone from oxygen:

$$\underset{3\text{ mol gas}}{3\ O_2(g)} \longrightarrow \underset{2\text{ mol gas}}{2\ O_3(g)} \qquad \Delta_r H^\circ = 285.4\ \text{kJ mol}^{-1}$$

The change in *enthalpy* is positive—heat is therefore absorbed, *decreasing* the entropy of the surroundings. The change in *entropy* is negative, which means that the entropy of the system decreases. (We can see that the change in entropy is negative from the balanced equation—the number of moles of gas decreases.) Since the entropy of both the system and the surroundings decreases, the entropy of the universe must also decrease, making the reaction nonspontaneous at all temperatures.

Case 3: $\Delta_r H$ Negative, $\Delta_r S$ Negative If a reaction is exothermic $\Delta_r H$, and if the change in entropy for the reaction is negative $\Delta_r S$, then the change in Gibbs energy will depend on temperature. The reaction will be spontaneous at low temperature, but nonspontaneous at high temperature.

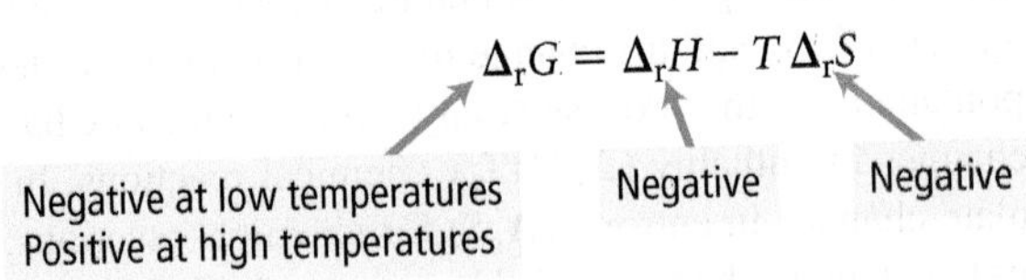

As an example, consider the freezing of liquid water to form ice:

$$H_2O(l) \longrightarrow H_2O(s) \qquad \Delta_r H^\circ = -6.01\ \text{kJ mol}^{-1}$$

The change in *enthalpy* is negative—heat is emitted, increasing the entropy of the surroundings. The change in *entropy* is negative, which means that the entropy of the system decreases. (We can see that the change in entropy is negative from the balanced equation—a liquid turns into a solid.)

Unlike the two previous cases, where the changes in *entropy* of the system and of the surroundings had the same sign, the changes here are opposite in sign. Therefore, the overall change in Gibbs energy depends on the relative magnitudes of the two changes. At a low enough temperature, the heat emitted into the surroundings causes a large entropy change in the surroundings, making the process spontaneous. At high temperature, the same amount of heat is dispersed into warmer surroundings, so the positive entropy change in the surroundings is smaller, resulting in a nonspontaneous process.

Case 4: $\Delta_r H$ Positive, $\Delta_r S$ Positive If a reaction is endothermic $\Delta_r H$, and if the change in entropy for the reaction is positive $\Delta_r S$, then the change in Gibbs energy will again depend on temperature. The reaction will be nonspontaneous at low temperature but spontaneous at high temperature.

$$\Delta_r G = \Delta_r H - T\,\Delta_r S$$

Positive at low temperatures
Negative at high temperatures

Positive

Positive

As an example, consider the vaporizing of liquid water to gaseous water:

$$H_2O(l) \longrightarrow H_2O(g) \qquad \Delta_r H° = 40.7 \text{ kJ mol}^{-1} \text{ (at 100 °C)}$$

In this example $\Delta_r H°$ is the same as $\Delta_{fus}H°$.

The change in *enthalpy* is positive—heat is absorbed from the surroundings, so the entropy of the surroundings decreases. The change in *entropy* is positive, which means that the entropy of the system increases. (We can see that the change in entropy is positive from the balanced equation—a liquid turns into a gas.) The changes in entropy of the system and the surroundings are again of opposite sign, only this time the entropy of the surroundings decreases while the entropy of the system increases. In cases such as this, high temperature favours spontaneity because the absorption of heat from the surroundings has less effect on the entropy of the surroundings as temperature increases.

The results of this section are summarized in Table 17.1. Notice that when $\Delta_r H$ and $\Delta_r S$ have opposite signs, the temperature will not affect whether or not the reaction is spontaneous. *When $\Delta_r H$ and $\Delta_r S$ have the same sign, however, the spontaneity does depend on temperature.* The temperature at which the reaction changes from being spontaneous to being nonspontaneous (or vice versa) is the temperature at which $\Delta_r G$ changes sign, which can be found by setting $\Delta_r G = 0$ and solving for T, as shown in part b of Example 17.3.

TABLE 17.1 The Effect of $\Delta_r H$, $\Delta_r S$, T on Spontaneity

$\Delta_r H$	$\Delta_r S$	Low Temperature	High Temperature	Example
−	+	Spontaneous ($\Delta_r G$ negative)	Spontaneous ($\Delta_r G$ negative)	$2\ N_2O(g) \longrightarrow 2\ N_2(g) + O_2(g)$
+	−	Nonspontaneous ($\Delta_r G$ positive)	Nonspontaneous ($\Delta_r G$ positive)	$3\ O_2(g) \longrightarrow 2\ O_3(g)$
−	−	Spontaneous ($\Delta_r G$ negative)	Nonspontaneous ($\Delta_r G$ positive)	$H_2O(l) \longrightarrow H_2O(s)$
+	+	Nonspontaneous ($\Delta_r G$ positive)	Spontaneous ($\Delta_r G$ negative)	$H_2O(l) \longrightarrow H_2O(g)$

EXAMPLE 17.3 COMPUTING GIBBS ENERGY CHANGES AND PREDICTING SPONTANEITY FROM $\Delta_r H$ AND $\Delta_r S$

Consider the reaction for the decomposition of carbon tetrachloride gas:

$$CCl_4(g) \longrightarrow C(s, \text{graphite}) + 2\ Cl_2(g) \qquad \Delta_r H = 95.7 \text{ kJ mol}^{-1}; \quad \Delta_r S = 142.2 \text{ J K}^{-1}\text{mol}^{-1}$$

(a) Calculate $\Delta_r G$ at 25 °C and determine whether the reaction is spontaneous.

(b) If the reaction is not spontaneous at 25 °C, determine at what temperature (if any) the reaction becomes spontaneous.

SOLUTION

(a) Use Equation 17.14 to calculate $\Delta_r G$ from the given values of $\Delta_r H$ and $\Delta_r S$. The temperature must be in kelvins. *Be sure to express both $\Delta_r H$ and $\Delta_r S$ in the same units (usually joules).*	$T = 273 + 25 = 298$ K $\Delta_r G = \Delta_r H - T\Delta_r S$ $= 95.7 \times 10^3 \text{ J mol}^{-1} - (298\cancel{K})142.2 \text{ J }\cancel{K^{-1}}\text{ mol}^{-1}$ $= 95.7 \times 10^3 \text{ J mol}^{-1} - 42.4 \times 10^3 \text{ J mol}^{-1}$ $= +53.3 \times 10^3 \text{ J mol}^{-1}$ The reaction is not spontaneous.

(continued)

EXAMPLE 17.3 (CONTINUED)

(b) Since $\Delta_r S$ is positive, $\Delta_r G$ will become more negative with increasing temperature. To determine the temperature at which the reaction becomes spontaneous, use Equation 17.14 to find the temperature at which $\Delta_r G$ changes from positive to negative (set $\Delta_r G = 0$ and solve for T). The reaction is spontaneous above this temperature.	$\Delta_r G = \Delta_r H - T\Delta_r S$ $0 = 95.7 \times 10^3 \text{ J mol}^{-1} - (T)142.2 \text{ J K}^{-1}\text{mol}^{-1}$ $T = \dfrac{95.7 \times 10^3 \text{ J mol}^{-1}}{142.2 \text{ J K}^{-1}\text{mol}^{-1}}$ $= 673 \text{ K}$

FOR PRACTICE 17.3

Consider the reaction:

$$C_2H_4(g) + H_2(g) \longrightarrow C_2H_6(g) \qquad \Delta_r H = -137.5 \text{ kJ mol}^{-1};\ \Delta_r S = -120.5 \text{ J K}^{-1}\text{mol}^{-1}$$

Calculate $\Delta_r G$ at 25 °C and determine whether the reaction is spontaneous. Does $\Delta_r G$ become more negative or more positive as the temperature increases?

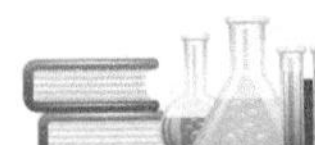

CONCEPTUAL CONNECTION 17.2

$\Delta_r H$, $\Delta_r S$, and $\Delta_r G$

Which statement is true regarding the sublimation of dry ice (solid CO_2)?

(a) $\Delta_r H$ is positive, $\Delta_r S$ is positive, and $\Delta_r G$ is positive at low temperature and negative at high temperature.

(b) $\Delta_r H$ is negative, $\Delta_r S$ is negative, and $\Delta_r G$ is negative at low temperature and positive at high temperature.

(c) $\Delta_r H$ is negative, $\Delta_r S$ is positive, and $\Delta_r G$ is negative at all temperatures.

(d) $\Delta_r H$ is positive, $\Delta_r S$ is negative, and $\Delta_r G$ is positive at all temperatures.

17.6 Entropy Changes in Chemical Reactions: Calculating $\Delta_r S^\circ$

In Chapter 6, we learned how to calculate standard changes in enthalpy ($\Delta_r H^\circ$) for chemical reactions. We now turn to calculating standard changes in *entropy* for chemical reactions. Recall from Section 6.9 that the standard enthalpy change for a reaction ($\Delta_r H^\circ$) is the change in enthalpy for a process in which all reactants and products are in their standard states. Recall also that the standard states of substances are defined as follows:

- *For a Gas:* The standard state for a gas is the pure gas at a pressure of exactly 1 bar.
- *For a Liquid or Solid:* The standard state for a liquid or solid is the pure substance at a pressure of 1 bar and at the temperature of interest (often taken to be 25 °C).
- *For a Substance in Solution:* The standard state for a substance in solution is a concentration of 1 mol L^{-1}.

We now define the **standard entropy change for a reaction ($\Delta_r S^\circ$)** as the change in *entropy* for a process in which all reactants and products are in their standard states. Since entropy is a function of state, the standard change in entropy is therefore the standard entropy of the products minus the standard entropy of the reactants.

$$\Delta_r S^\circ = S^\circ(\text{products}) - S^\circ(\text{reactants})$$

But how do we find the standard entropies of the reactants and products? Recall from Chapter 6 that we defined *standard molar enthalpies of formation* ($\Delta_f H^\circ$) to use in calculating $\Delta_r H^\circ$. We now need to define **standard molar entropies (S°)** to use in calculating $\Delta_r S^\circ$.

Standard Molar Entropies (S°) and the Third Law of Thermodynamics

In Chapter 6, we defined a *relative* zero for enthalpy. Recall that we assigned a value of zero to the standard enthalpy of formation for an element in its standard state. This was necessary because absolute values of enthalpy cannot be determined. In other words, for enthalpy, there is no absolute zero against which to measure all other values; therefore, we always have to rely on enthalpy changes from an arbitrarily assigned standard. For entropy, however, *there is an absolute zero*. The absolute zero of entropy is established by the **third law of thermodynamics**, which states that:

The entropy of a perfect crystal at absolute zero (0 K) is zero.

Earlier we learned that in any distribution of energy among molecules, no molecule can have 0 J of energy. Even at absolute zero, no particles can have 0 J of kinetic energy. If the particles did stop moving completely, this would disobey Heisenberg's uncertainty principle, which is stated in Equation 7.10:

$$\Delta x \times m\Delta v \geq \frac{h}{4\pi}$$

If any molecule stopped moving completely, the uncertainty in its velocity, Δv, would be 0 and the left-hand side would equate to 0, which is not greater than $h/4\pi$ as required by Heisenberg's uncertainty principle. So, even at 0 K, all substances have what we call **zero-point energy**, tiny vibrations with respect to one another (Figure 17.7 ▶). However, the zero-point energy is distributed evenly throughout the crystal and there is only one way to distribute the energy—the crystal's lowest energy state. The number of micro-states is one ($W = 1$), and therefore $S = 0$.

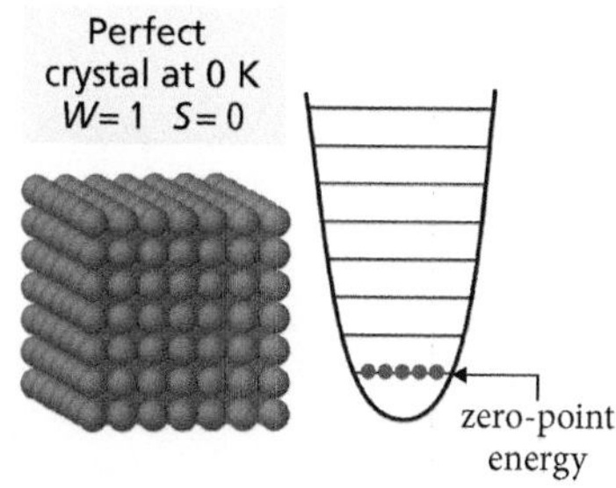

▲ **FIGURE 17.7** A perfect crystal at 0 K has only one way to distribute energy to the particles in the system. All particles have only zero-point energy.

We can measure all entropy values against the absolute zero of entropy as defined by the third law. Table 17.2 shows values of standard entropies at 25 °C for selected substances. A more complete list can be found in Appendix IIB. Standard entropy values are listed in units of joules per kelvin per mol (J K^{-1} mol^{-1}). The units of mole in the denominator is required because *entropy is an extensive property*—it depends on the amount of the substance.

At 25 °C, the standard entropy of any substance is the amount of energy dispersed into one mole of that substance at 25 °C. This amount of energy depends on the number of places or "energy levels" to disperse energy within the substance. The factors that affect the number of energy levels to disperse energy—and therefore the standard entropy—include the state of the substance, the molar mass of the substance, the particular allotrope, its molecular complexity, and its extent of dissolution. We examine each of these separately.

Some elements exist in two or more forms, called *allotropes*, within the same state.

TABLE 17.2 Standard Molar Entropy Values (S°) for Selected Substances at 298 K

Substance	S° (J K^{-1} mol^{-1})	Substance	S° (J K^{-1} mol^{-1})	Substance	S° (J K^{-1} mol^{-1})
Gases		**Liquids**		**Solids**	
$H_2(g)$	130.7	$H_2O(l)$	70.0	$MgO(s)$	27.0
$Ar(g)$	154.8	$CH_3OH(l)$	126.8	$Fe(s)$	27.3
$CH_4(g)$	186.3	$Br_2(l)$	152.2	$Li(s)$	29.1
$H_2O(g)$	188.8	$C_6H_6(l)$	173.4	$Cu(s)$	33.2
$N_2(g)$	191.6			$Na(s)$	51.3
$NH_3(g)$	192.8			$K(s)$	64.7
$F_2(g)$	202.8			$NaCl(s)$	72.1
$O_2(g)$	205.2			$CaCO_3(s)$	91.7
$C_2H_4(g)$	219.3			$FeCl_3(s)$	142.3
$Cl_2(g)$	223.1				

Relative Standard Entropies: Gases, Liquids, and Solids As we saw in Section 17.2, the entropy of a gas is generally greater than the entropy of a liquid, which is in turn greater than the entropy of a solid. We can see these trends in the tabulated values of standard entropies. For example, consider the relative standard entropies of liquid water and gaseous water at 25 °C.

	$S°(J\ K^{-1}\ mol^{-1})$
$H_2O(l)$	70.0
$H_2O(g)$	188.8

Gaseous water has a much greater standard entropy because, as we discussed in Section 17.2, it has more energy levels available to disperse energy at 25 °C.

Relative Standard Entropies: Molar Mass Consider the standard entropies of the noble gases at 25 °C:

	$S°(J\ K^{-1}\ mol^{-1})$
He(g)	126.2
Ne(g)	146.1
Ar(g)	154.8
Kr(g)	163.8
Xe(g)	169.4

The more massive the noble gas, the greater its entropy at 25 °C. A complete explanation of why entropy increases with increasing molar mass is beyond the scope of this text. Briefly, the energy states associated with the motion of heavy atoms are more closely spaced than those of lighter atoms. The more closely spaced energy states allow for greater dispersal of energy at a given temperature and therefore greater entropy. This trend holds only for elements in the same state. The effect of a state change—from a liquid to a gas, for example—is far greater than the effect of molar mass.

Relative Standard Entropies: Allotropes As mentioned previously, some elements can exist in two or more forms—called *allotropes*—in the same state of matter. For example, the allotropes of carbon include diamond and graphite—both solid forms of carbon. Since the arrangement of atoms within these forms is different, their standard molar entropies are different:

	$S°(J\ mol^{-1}\ K^{-1})$
C(s, diamond)	2.4
C(s, graphite)	5.7

In diamond the atoms are constrained by chemical bonds in a highly restricted three-dimensional crystal structure. In graphite the atoms bond together in sheets, but the sheets have freedom to slide past each other. The less constrained structure of graphite results in more energy levels into which energy can be dispersed and therefore greater entropy compared to diamond.

Relative Standard Entropies: Molecular Complexity For a given state of matter, entropy generally increases with increasing molecular complexity. Consider the standard entropies of the following two gases:

	Molar Mass (g mol^{-1})	S° (J K^{-1} mol^{-1})
Ar(*g*)	39.948	154.8
NO(*g*)	30.006	210.8

Ar has a greater molar mass than NO, yet it has less entropy at 25 °C. Why? Molecules generally have more energy levels to disperse energy than do atoms. In a gaseous sample of argon, the only form that energy can take is the translational motion of the atoms. In a gaseous sample of NO, on the other hand, energy can take the form of translational motion, rotational motion, and (at high enough temperatures) vibrational motions of (which we call "modes") the molecules (Figure 17.8 ▼). Therefore, for a given state, molecules will generally have a greater entropy than free atoms. Similarly, more complex molecules will generally have more entropy than simpler ones. For example, consider the standard entropies of CO and C_2H_4:

	Molar Mass (g mol^{-1})	S° (J K^{-1} mol^{-1})
CO(*g*)	28.01	197.7
C_2H_4(*g*)	28.05	219.3

These two substances have nearly the same molar mass, but the greater complexity of C_2H_4 results in a greater molar entropy. When molecular complexity and molar mass both increase (as is often the case), molar entropy also increases, as shown by the oxides of nitrogen:

	S° (J K^{-1} mol^{-1})
NO(*g*)	210.8
NO_2(*g*)	240.1
N_2O_4(*g*)	304.4

The increasing molecular complexity as you move down this list as well as the increasing molar mass results in greater entropy.

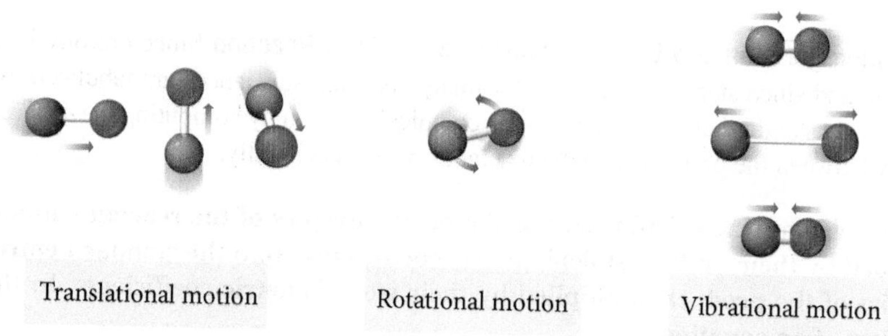

◀ **FIGURE 17.8 "Places" for Energy in Gaseous NO** Energy can be contained in translational motion, rotational motion, and (at high enough temperatures) vibrational motion.

Relative Standard Entropies: Dissolution The dissolution of a crystalline solid into solution usually results in an increase in entropy. Consider the standard entropies of solid and aqueous potassium chlorate:

The standard entropies for aqueous solutions are for the solution in its standard state, which is defined as having a concentration of 1 mol L^{-1}.

	S° (J K^{-1} mol^{-1})
$KClO_3$(*s*)	143.1
$KClO_3$(*aq*)	265.7

When solid potassium chlorate dissolves in water, the energy that was concentrated within the crystal becomes dispersed throughout the entire solution. The greater energy dispersal results in greater entropy.

When some ionic solids are dissolved, the entropy of the system *decreases.* Salts whose entropies decrease upon dissolution are usually composed of highly charged ions, such as $AlCl_3$. Compare the standard entropies of solid and aqueous aluminum chloride:

	$S°$ (J K^{-1} mol^{-1})
$AlCl_3(s)$	110.7
$AlCl_3(aq)$	−152.2

Despite having a negative entropy change, $AlCl_3$ is soluble in water due to the high exothermicity of dissolution. In order to understand why the entropy change is negative upon dissolution of $AlCl_3$, we must look at the solvent before and after dissolution. Prior to dissolution of $AlCl_3$ (Figure 17.9(a) ▼), the molecules of water store energy as vibrational, rotational, and translational energy. When $AlCl_3$ is dissolved, it dissociates into Al^{3+} and 3 Cl^- ions that are surrounded by water molecules. The Al^{3+} ions are very small and highly charged (high charge density) and have strong ion–dipole forces of attraction to the water molecules (Figure 17.9(b)).

The $Al^{3+}—H_2O$ interactions are so strong that they actually act as if there are Al—O bonds, and the Al^{3+} ion is better represented as $Al^{3+}(H_2O)_n$, meaning that there are a number of H_2O molecules bonded to the Al^{3+} ion. The water molecules that are attached to Al^{3+} lose some capability to store energy as translational and rotational energy. Furthermore, water molecules that are not directly attached to Al^{3+} are strongly attracted to the $Al^{3+}(H_2O)_n$ ion (called a *second solvation shell*), are oriented by the ion–dipole attraction and also lose freedom of motion. Despite $AlCl_3$ dissolving into four ions, the entropy of the entire system, water and $AlCl_3$, is lower.

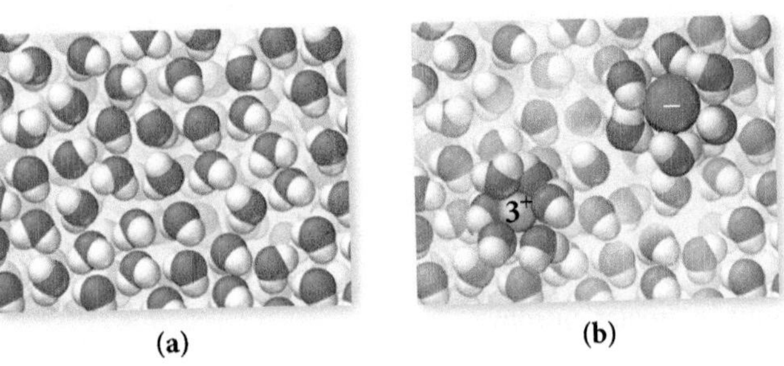

▶ **FIGURE 17.9 Water (a) Before and (b) After Dissolution of $AlCl_3$** For clarity, only one Cl^- is shown. The water molecules around Al^{3+}, even those not directly attached, are strongly oriented toward Al^{3+} and therefore have lost capability to store energy as translational and rotation energy. The entropy of the water/$AlCl_3$ system therefore decreases when $AlCl_3$ is dissolved.

Calculating the Standard Entropy Change ($\Delta_r S°$) for a Reaction Since entropy is a state function, and since standard entropies for many common substances are tabulated, we can calculate the standard entropy change for a chemical reaction by computing the difference in entropy between the products and the reactants. More specifically,

> **To calculate $\Delta_r S°$, subtract the standard entropies of the reactants multiplied by their unitless stoichiometric coefficients from the standard entropies of the products multiplied by their stoichiometric coefficients. In the form of an equation,**

$$\Delta_r S° = \sum \nu_p S°_{\text{products}} - \sum \nu_r S°_{\text{reactants}} \quad [17.16]$$

In Equation 17.16, ν_p represents the stoichiometric coefficients of the products, ν_r represents the stoichiometric coefficients of the reactants, and $S°$ represents the standard entropies. Keep in mind when using this equation that, *unlike enthalpies of formation, which are zero for elements in their standard states, standard entropies are always nonzero at 25 °C.* The following example demonstrates the application of Equation 17.16.

EXAMPLE 17.4 CALCULATING STANDARD ENTROPY CHANGES ($\Delta_r S^\circ$)

Calculate $\Delta_r S^\circ$ for the balanced chemical equation:

$$4\ NH_3(g) + 5\ O_2(g) \longrightarrow 4\ NO(g) + 6\ H_2O(g)$$

SOLUTION

Begin by looking up the standard entropy for each reactant and product in Appendix IIB. Be careful always to note the correct state—(g), (l), (aq), or (s)—for each reactant and product.

Reactant or Product	S° (J mol^{-1} K^{-1})
$NH_3(g)$	192.8
$O_2(g)$	205.2
$NO(g)$	210.8
$H_2O(g)$	188.8

Calculate $\Delta_r S^\circ$ by substituting the appropriate values into Equation 17.16.

Remember to include the stoichiometric coefficients in your calculation.

$$\begin{aligned}
\Delta_r S^\circ &= \sum \nu_p S^\circ_{\text{products}} - \sum \nu_r S^\circ_{\text{reactants}} \\
&= [4(S^\circ_{NO(g)}) + 6(S^\circ_{H_2O(g)})] - [4(S^\circ_{NH_3(g)}) + 5(S^\circ_{O_2(g)})] \\
&= [4(210.8\ \text{J K}^{-1}\,\text{mol}^{-1}) + 6(188.8\ \text{J K}^{-1}\,\text{mol}^{-1})] \\
&\quad - [4(192.8\ \text{J K}^{-1}\,\text{mol}^{-1}) + 5(205.2\ \text{J K}^{-1}\,\text{mol}^{-1})] \\
&= 1976.0\ \text{J K}^{-1}\text{mol}^{-1} - 1797.2\ \text{J K}^{-1}\text{mol}^{-1} \\
&= 178.8\ \text{J K}^{-1}\text{mol}^{-1}
\end{aligned}$$

CHECK Notice that $\Delta_r S^\circ$ is positive, as you would expect for a reaction in which the number of moles of gas increases.

FOR PRACTICE 17.4

Calculate $\Delta_r S^\circ$ for the balanced chemical equation:

$$2\ H_2S(g) + 3\ O_2(g) \longrightarrow 2\ H_2O(g) + 2\ SO_2(g)$$

17.7 Gibbs Energy Changes in Chemical Reactions: Calculating $\Delta_r G^\circ$

The previous section discussed how to calculate the standard change in entropy for a chemical reaction ($\Delta_r S^\circ$). However, the criterion for spontaneity is the **standard change in Gibbs energy ($\Delta_r G^\circ$)**. This section examines three methods to calculate the standard change in Gibbs energy for a reaction ($\Delta_r G^\circ$). In the first method, we calculate $\Delta_r H^\circ$ and $\Delta_r S^\circ$ from tabulated values of $\Delta_f H^\circ$ and S°, then use the relationship $\Delta_r G^\circ = \Delta_r H^\circ - T\Delta_r S^\circ$ to calculate $\Delta_r G^\circ$. In the second method, we use tabulated values of Gibbs energies of formation to calculate $\Delta_r G^\circ$ directly. In the third method, we determine the Gibbs energy change for a stepwise reaction from the Gibbs energies of each of the steps. Finally, we discuss what exactly the Gibbs energy is. Remember that $\Delta_r G^\circ$ is extremely useful because it tells us about the spontaneity of a process under standard conditions. The more negative $\Delta_r G^\circ$ is, the more spontaneous the process (the further it will go toward products to reach equilibrium).

Calculating Gibbs Energy Changes with $\Delta_r G^\circ = \Delta_r H^\circ - T\Delta_r S^\circ$

In Chapter 6 (Section 6.9), we learned how to use tabulated values of standard enthalpies of formation to calculate $\Delta_r H^\circ$. In the previous section, we learned how to use tabulated values of standard entropies to calculate $\Delta_r S^\circ$. We can use these calculated values of $\Delta_r H^\circ$ and $\Delta_r S^\circ$ to determine the standard Gibbs energy change for a reaction by using the equation:

$$\Delta_r G^\circ = \Delta_r H^\circ - T\Delta_r S^\circ \qquad [17.17]$$

Since tabulated values of standard enthalpies of formation and standard entropies (S°) are usually applicable at 25 °C, the equation should (strictly speaking) be valid only when $T = 298$ K (25 °C). However, the changes $\Delta_r H^\circ$ in $\Delta_r S^\circ$ over a limited temperature range are small when compared to the changes in the value of the temperature itself. For this reason, Equation 17.17 can be used to estimate changes in Gibbs energy at temperatures other than 25 °C.

EXAMPLE 17.5 CALCULATING THE STANDARD CHANGE IN GIBBS ENERGY FOR A REACTION USING $\Delta_r G^\circ = \Delta_r H^\circ - T\,\Delta_r S^\circ$

One of the possible initial steps in the formation of acid rain is the oxidation of the pollutant SO_2 to SO_3 by the reaction:

$$SO_2(g) + \tfrac{1}{2}O_2(g) \longrightarrow SO_3(g)$$

Calculate $\Delta_r G^\circ$ at 25 °C and determine whether the reaction is spontaneous.

SOLUTION

Begin by looking up (in Appendix IIB) the standard enthalpy of formation and the standard entropy for each reactant and product.

Reactant or product	$\Delta_f H^\circ$ (kJ mol^{-1})	S° (J mol^{-1} K^{-1})
$SO_2(g)$	−296.8	248.2
$O_2(g)$	0	205.2
$SO_3(g)$	−395.7	256.8

Calculate $\Delta_r H^\circ$ using Equation 6.17.

$$\begin{aligned}\Delta_r H^\circ &= \sum \nu_p \Delta_f H^\circ_{\text{products}} - \sum \nu_r \Delta_f H^\circ_{\text{reactants}} \\ &= [\Delta_f H^\circ_{SO_3(g)}] - [\Delta_f H^\circ_{SO_2(g)} + \tfrac{1}{2}\Delta_f H^\circ_{O_2(g)}] \\ &= -395.7 \text{ kJ mol}^{-1} - (-296.8 \text{ kJ mol}^{-1} + \tfrac{1}{2} \text{ x } 0 \text{ kJ mol}^{-1}) \\ &= -98.9 \text{ kJ mol}^{-1}\end{aligned}$$

Calculate $\Delta_r S^\circ$ using Equation 17.16.

$$\begin{aligned}\Delta_r S^\circ &= \sum \nu_p S^\circ_{\text{products}} - \sum \nu_r S^\circ_{\text{reactants}} \\ &= [\Delta S^\circ_{SO_3(g)}] - [\Delta S^\circ_{SO_2(g)} + \tfrac{1}{2}\Delta S^\circ_{O_2(g)}] \\ &= 256.8 \text{ J K}^{-1}\text{ mol}^{-1} - [248.2 \text{ J K}^{-1}\text{ mol}^{-1} + \tfrac{1}{2}(205.2 \text{ J K}^{-1}\text{ mol}^{-1})] \\ &= -94.0 \text{ J K}^{-1}\text{ mol}^{-1}\end{aligned}$$

Calculate $\Delta_r G^\circ$ using the calculated values of $\Delta_r H^\circ$ and $\Delta_r S^\circ$ and Equation 17.17. The temperature must be converted to kelvins.

$$\begin{aligned}T &= 25 + 273 = 298 \text{ K} \\ \Delta_r G^\circ &= \Delta_r H^\circ - T\,\Delta_r S^\circ \\ &= -98.9 \times 10^3 \text{ J mol}^{-1} - 298 \text{ K}(-94.0 \text{ J K}^{-1}\text{ mol}^{-1}) \\ &= -70.9 \times 10^3 \text{ J mol}^{-1} \\ &= -70.9 \text{ kJ mol}^{-1}\end{aligned}$$

The reaction is spontaneous at this temperature, because $\Delta_r G^\circ$ is negative.

FOR PRACTICE 17.5

Consider the oxidation of NO to NO_2:

$$NO(g) + \tfrac{1}{2}O_2(g) \longrightarrow NO_2(g)$$

Calculate $\Delta_r G^\circ$ at 25 °C and determine whether the reaction is spontaneous.

EXAMPLE 17.6 ESTIMATING THE STANDARD CHANGE IN GIBBS ENERGY FOR A REACTION AT A TEMPERATURE OTHER THAN 25 °C USING $\Delta_r G^\circ = \Delta_r H^\circ - T\,\Delta_r S^\circ$

For the reaction in Example 17.5, estimate the value of $\Delta_r G^\circ$ at 125 °C. Does the reaction become more or less spontaneous at this elevated temperature; that is, does the value of $\Delta_r G^\circ$ become more negative (more spontaneous) or more positive (less spontaneous)?

SOLUTION

Estimate $\Delta_r G^\circ$ at the new temperature using the calculated values of $\Delta_r H^\circ$ and $\Delta_r S^\circ$ from Example 17.5. For T, convert the given temperature to kelvins. Make sure to use the same units for $\Delta_r H^\circ$ and $\Delta_r S^\circ$ (usually joules).

$$\begin{aligned}T &= 125 \text{ K} + 273 \text{ K} = 398 \text{ K} \\ \Delta_r G^\circ &= \Delta_r H^\circ - T\,\Delta_r S^\circ \\ &= -98.9 \times 10^3 \text{ J mol}^{-1} - 398 \text{ K}(-94.0 \text{ kJ K}^{-1}\text{ mol}^{-1}) \\ &= -61.5 \times 10^3 \text{ J mol}^{-1} \\ &= -61.5 \text{ kJ mol}^{-1}\end{aligned}$$

	Since the value of $\Delta_r G°$ at this elevated temperature is less negative (or more positive) than the value of $\Delta_r G°$ at 25 °C (which is -70.9 kJ mol^{-1}), the reaction is less spontaneous.

FOR PRACTICE 17.6

For the reaction in For Practice 17.5, calculate the value of $\Delta_r G°$ at -55 °C. Does the reaction become more spontaneous (more negative $\Delta_r G°$) or less spontaneous (more positive $\Delta_r G°$) at the lower temperature?

Calculating $\Delta_r G°$ with Tabulated Values of Gibbs Energies of Formation

Because $\Delta_r G°$ is the *change* in Gibbs energy for a chemical reaction—the difference in Gibbs energy between the products and the reactants—and because Gibbs energy is a state function, we can calculate $\Delta_r G°$ by subtracting the Gibbs energies of the reactants of the reaction from the Gibbs energies of the products of the reaction. Also, since we are interested only in *changes* in Gibbs energy (and not in absolute values of Gibbs energy itself), we are free to define the *zero* of Gibbs energy as conveniently as possible. By analogy with our definition of enthalpies of formation, we define the **Gibbs energy of formation ($\Delta_f G°$)** as follows:

> **The Gibbs energy of formation ($\Delta_f G°$) is the change in Gibbs energy when 1 mol of a compound forms from its constituent elements in their standard states. The Gibbs energy of formation of pure elements in their standard states is zero.**

We can measure all changes in Gibbs energy relative to pure elements in their standard states. To calculate $\Delta_r G°$, we subtract the Gibbs energies of formation of the reactants multiplied by their stoichiometric coefficients from the Gibbs energies of formation of the products multiplied by their stoichiometric coefficients. In the form of an equation:

$$\Delta_r G° = \sum \nu_p \Delta_f G°_{\text{products}} - \sum \nu_r \Delta_f G°_{\text{reactants}} \qquad [17.18]$$

In Equation 17.18, ν_p are the unitless stoichiometric coefficients of the products, ν_r are the unitless stoichiometric coefficients of the reactants, and $\Delta_f G°$ represents the standard Gibbs energies of formation. Table 17.3 shows $\Delta_f G°$ values for selected substances. You can find a more complete list in Appendix IIB. Notice that, by definition, *elements* have standard Gibbs energies of formation of zero. Notice also that most *compounds* have negative standard Gibbs energies of formation. This means that those compounds spontaneously form from their elements in their standard states. Compounds with positive Gibbs energies of formation do not spontaneously form from their elements and are therefore less common.

Example 17.7 demonstrates the calculation of $\Delta_r G°$ from $\Delta_f G°$ values. This method of calculating $\Delta_r G°$ works only at the temperature for which the Gibbs energies of formation are tabulated, namely, 25 °C. Estimating $\Delta_r G°$ at other temperatures requires the use of $\Delta_r G° = \Delta_r H° - T\,\Delta_r S°$, as demonstrated previously.

TABLE 17.3 Standard Molar Gibbs Energies of Formation ($\Delta_f G°$) for Selected Substances at 298 K

Substance	$\Delta_f G°$(kJ mol^{-1})	Substance	$\Delta_f G°$(kJ mol^{-1})
$H_2(g)$	0	$CH_4(g)$	−50.5
$O_2(g)$	0	$H_2O(g)$	−228.6
$N_2(g)$	0	$H_2O(l)$	−237.1
C(*s*, graphite)	0	$NH_3(g)$	−16.4
C(*s*, diamond)	2.900	NO(*g*)	87.6
CO(*g*)	−137.2	$NO_2(g)$	51.3
$CO_2(g)$	−394.4	NaCl(*s*)	384.6

EXAMPLE 17.7 CALCULATING $\Delta_r G°$ FROM STANDARD GIBBS ENERGIES OF FORMATION

Ozone in the lower atmosphere is a pollutant that can be formed by the following reaction involving the oxidation of unburned hydrocarbons:

$$CH_4(g) + 8\ O_2(g) \longrightarrow CO_2(g) + 2\ H_2O(g) + 4\ O_3(g)$$

Use the standard Gibbs energies of formation to determine $\Delta_r G°$ for this reaction at 25 °C.

SOLUTION

Begin by looking up (in Appendix IIB) the standard free energies of formation for each reactant and product. Remember that the standard Gibbs energy of formation of a pure element in its standard state is zero.

Reactant or product	$\Delta_f G°$ (kJ mol^{-1})
$CH_4(g)$	−50.5
$O_2(g)$	0
$CO_2(g)$	−394.4
$H_2O(g)$	−228.6
$O_3(g)$	163.2

Calculate $\Delta_r G°$ by substituting into Equation 17.18.

$$\begin{aligned}\Delta_r G° &= \sum \nu_p \Delta_f G°_{\text{products}} - \sum \nu_r \Delta_f G°_{\text{reactants}} \\ &= [\Delta_f G°_{CO_2(g)} + 2(\Delta_f G°_{H_2O(g)}) + 4(\Delta_f G°_{O_3(g)})] - [\Delta_f G°_{CH_4(g)} + 8(\Delta_f G°_{O_2(g)})] \\ &= [-394.4\ \text{kJ mol}^{-1} + 2(-228.6\ \text{kJ mol}^{-1}) + 4(163.2\ \text{kJ mol}^{-1})] \\ &\quad - [-50.5\ \text{kJ mol}^{-1} + 8(0.0\ \text{kJ mol}^{-1})] \\ &= -198.8\ \text{kJ mol}^{-1} + 50.5\ \text{kJ mol}^{-1} \\ &= -148.3\ \text{kJ mol}^{-1}\end{aligned}$$

FOR PRACTICE 17.7

One of the reactions occurring within a catalytic converter in the exhaust pipe of a car is the simultaneous oxidation of carbon monoxide and reduction of NO (both of which are harmful pollutants).

$$2\ CO(g) + 2\ NO(g) \longrightarrow 2\ CO_2(g) + N_2(g)$$

Use standard Gibbs energies of formation to calculate $\Delta_r G°$ for this reaction at 25 °C. Is the reaction spontaneous?

FOR MORE PRACTICE 17.7

In For Practice 17.7, you calculated $\Delta_r G°$ for the simultaneous oxidation of carbon monoxide and reduction of NO using standard Gibbs energies of formation. Calculate $\Delta_r G°$ for that reaction again at 25 °C, only this time use $\Delta_r G° = \Delta_r H° - T\Delta_r S°$. How do the two values compare? Use your results to calculate $\Delta_r G°$ at 500.0 K and explain why you could not calculate $\Delta_r G°$ at 500.0 K using tabulated standard Gibbs energies of formation.

CHEMISTRY IN YOUR DAY Making a Nonspontaneous Process Spontaneous

A process that is nonspontaneous can be made spontaneous by coupling it with another process that is highly spontaneous. For example, hydrogen gas is a potential future fuel because it can be used in a fuel cell (a type of battery in which the reactants are constantly supplied—see Chapter 18) to generate electricity. The main problem with switching to hydrogen is securing a source. Where can we get the vast amounts of hydrogen gas that would be needed to meet our world's energy needs? Earth's oceans and lakes, of course, contain vast amounts of hydrogen. But that hydrogen is locked up in water molecules, and the decomposition of water into hydrogen and oxygen has a positive $\Delta_r G°$ and is therefore nonspontaneous.

$$H_2O(g) \longrightarrow H_2(g) + \tfrac{1}{2}O_2(g) \qquad \Delta_r G° = 228.6\ \text{kJ mol}^{-1}$$

To obtain hydrogen from water, we need to find another reaction with a highly negative $\Delta_r G°$ that might couple with the decomposition reaction to give an overall reaction with a negative $\Delta_r G°$. For example, the oxidation of carbon monoxide to carbon dioxide has a large negative $\Delta_r G°$ and is highly spontaneous.

$$CO(g) + \tfrac{1}{2}O_2(g) \longrightarrow CO_2(g) \quad \Delta_r G° = -257.2\ \text{kJ mol}^{-1}$$

If we add the two reactions together, we get a negative $\Delta_r G°$.

Nonspontaneous

$$H_2O(g) \longrightarrow H_2(g) + \tfrac{1}{2}O_2(g) \quad \Delta_r G° = 228.6 \text{ kJ mol}^{-1}$$

$$CO(g) + \tfrac{1}{2}O_2(g) \longrightarrow CO_2(g) \quad \Delta_r G° = -257.2 \text{ kJ mol}^{-1}$$

$$H_2O(g) + CO(g) \longrightarrow H_2(g) + CO_2(g) \quad \Delta_r G° = -28.6 \text{ kJ mol}^{-1}$$

Spontaneous

The reaction between water and carbon monoxide is thus a spontaneous way to generate hydrogen gas.

The coupling of nonspontaneous reactions with highly spontaneous ones is also important in biological systems. The synthesis reactions that create the complex biological molecules (such as proteins and DNA) needed by living organisms, for example, are themselves nonspontaneous. Living systems grow and reproduce by coupling these nonspontaneous reactions to highly spontaneous ones. The main spontaneous reaction that ultimately drives the nonspontaneous ones is the metabolism of food. The oxidation of glucose, for example, is highly spontaneous:

$$C_6H_{12}O_6(s) + 6\ O_2(g) \longrightarrow 6\ CO_2(g) + 6\ H_2O(l) \quad \Delta_r G° = -2880 \text{ kJ mol}^{-1}$$

Spontaneous reactions such as these ultimately drive the nonspontaneous reactions necessary to sustain life.

Calculating $\Delta_r G°$ for a Stepwise Reaction from the Changes in Gibbs Energy for Each of the Steps

Recall from Section 6.8 that, since enthalpy is a state function, we can calculate $\Delta_r H°$ for a stepwise reaction from the sum of the changes in enthalpy for each step (according to Hess's law). Since Gibbs energy is also a state function, the same relationships that we covered in Chapter 6 for enthalpy also apply to Gibbs energy:

1. If a chemical equation is multiplied by some factor, then $\Delta_r G°$ is also multiplied by the same factor.
2. If a chemical equation is reversed, then $\Delta_r G°$ changes sign.
3. If a chemical equation can be expressed as the sum of a series of steps, then $\Delta_r G°$ for the overall equation is the sum of the Gibbs energies of reactions for each step.

The following example illustrates the use of these relationships to calculate $\Delta_r G°$ for a stepwise reaction.

EXAMPLE 17.8 CALCULATING $\Delta_r G°$ FOR A STEPWISE REACTION

Find $\Delta_r G°$ for the following reaction:

$$3\ C(s) + 4\ H_2(g) \longrightarrow C_3H_8(g)$$

Use the following reactions with known $\Delta_r G°$'s:

$$C_3H_8(g) + 5\ O_2(g) \longrightarrow 3\ CO_2(g) + 4\ H_2O(g) \quad \Delta_r G° = -2074 \text{ kJ mol}^{-1}$$
$$C(s) + O_2(g) \longrightarrow CO_2(g) \quad \Delta_r G° = -394.4 \text{ kJ mol}^{-1}$$
$$2\ H_2(g) + O_2(g) \longrightarrow 2\ H_2O(g) \quad \Delta_r G° = -457.1 \text{ kJ mol}^{-1}$$

SOLUTION

To work this problem, manipulate the reactions with known $\Delta_r G°$'s in such a way as to get the reactants of interest on the left, the products of interest on the right, and other species to cancel.

Since the first reaction has C_3H_8 as a reactant, and the reaction of interest has C_3H_8 as a product, reverse the first reaction and change the sign of $\Delta_r G°$.	$3\ CO_2(g) + 4\ H_2O(g) \longrightarrow C_3H_8(g) + 5\ O_2(g) \quad \Delta_r G° = 2074 \text{ kJ mol}^{-1}$

(continued)

EXAMPLE 17.8 (CONTINUED)

The second reaction has C as a reactant and CO_2 as a product, just as required in the reaction of interest. However, the coefficient for C is 1, and in the reaction of interest, the coefficient for C is 3. Therefore, multiply this equation and its $\Delta_r G°$ by 3.	$3 \times [C(s) + O_2(g) \longrightarrow CO_2(g)]$ $\Delta_r G° = 3 \times (-394.4 \text{ kJ mol}^{-1}) = -1183 \text{ kJ mol}^{-1}$
The third reaction has $H_2(g)$ as a reactant, as required. However, the coefficient for H_2 is 2, and in the reaction of interest, the coefficient for H_2 is 4. Multiply this reaction and its $\Delta_r G°$ by 2.	$2 \times [2\ H_2(g) + O_2(g) \longrightarrow 2\ H_2O(g)]$ $\Delta_r G° = 2 \times (-457.1 \text{ kJ mol}^{-1}) = -914.2 \text{ kJ mol}^{-1}$
Lastly, rewrite the three reactions after multiplying through by the indicated factors and show how they sum to the reaction of interest. $\Delta_r G°$ for the reaction of interest is then the sum of the $\Delta_r G°$'s for the steps.	$3\ \cancel{CO_2(g)} + \cancel{4\ H_2O(g)} \longrightarrow C_3H_8(g) + \cancel{5\ O_2(g)}$ $\Delta_r G° = 2074 \text{ kJ mol}^{-1}$ $3\ C(s) + \cancel{3\ O_2(g)} \longrightarrow \cancel{3\ CO_2(g)}$ $\Delta_r G° = -1183 \text{ kJ mol}^{-1}$ $4\ H_2(g) + \cancel{2\ O_2(g)} \longrightarrow \cancel{4\ H_2O(g)}$ $\Delta_r G° = -914.2 \text{ kJ mol}^{-1}$ $3\ C(s) + 4\ H_2(g) \longrightarrow C_3H_8(g)$ $\Delta_r G° = -23 \text{ kJ mol}^{-1}$

FOR PRACTICE 17.8

Find $\Delta_r G°$ for the reaction:

$$N_2O(g) + NO_2(g) \longrightarrow 3\ NO(g)$$

Use the following reactions with known $\Delta_r G°$ values:

$$2\ NO(g) + O_2(g) \longrightarrow 2\ NO_2(g) \quad \Delta_r G° = -71.2 \text{ kJ mol}^{-1}$$
$$N_2(g) + O_2(g) \longrightarrow 2\ NO(g) \quad \Delta_r G° = 175.2 \text{ kJ mol}^{-1}$$
$$2\ N_2O(g) \longrightarrow 2\ N_2(g) + O_2(g) \quad \Delta_r G° = -207.4 \text{ kJ mol}^{-1}$$

What Is Gibbs Energy?

We often want to use the energy released by a chemical reaction to do work. For example, in an automobile, we want to use the energy released by the combustion of gasoline to move the car. The change in Gibbs energy of a chemical reaction represents the maximum amount of energy available to do work (if $\Delta_r G°$ is negative). For many reactions, the amount of Gibbs energy is less than the change in enthalpy for the reaction. Consider the combustion of octane at 25 °C:

$$C_8H_{18}(l) + \frac{25}{2} O_2(g) \longrightarrow 8\ CO_2(g) + 9\ H_2O(l)$$
$$\Delta_r H° = -5470.3 \text{ kJ mol}^{-1}$$
$$\Delta_r S° = -584.3 \text{ J K}^{-1} \text{mol}^{-1}$$
$$\Delta_r G° = -5296.2 \text{ kJ mol}^{-1}$$

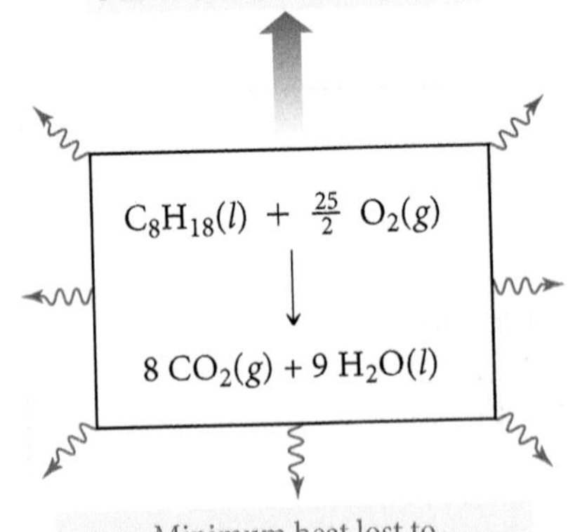

▲ **FIGURE 17.10 Gibbs Energy** Although the reaction produces 5470.3 kJ of energy, only 5296.2 kJ is available to do work. The rest of the energy is lost to the surroundings, increasing the entropy of the surroundings.

The reaction is exothermic and gives off 5470.3 kJ of heat energy. However, the maximum amount of energy available for useful work is 5296.2 kJ (Figure 17.10 ◀).

Why? We can see that the change in entropy of the system is negative. Nevertheless, the reaction is spontaneous. This is possible only if some of the emitted heat goes to increase the entropy of the surroundings by an amount sufficient to make the change in the entropy of the universe positive. The amount of energy available to do work (the Gibbs energy) is what is left after accounting for the heat that must go into the surroundings. The change in Gibbs energy for a chemical reaction represents a *theoretical limit* and is the maximum work that can be done by the reaction. In thermodynamics, a reaction that achieves the theoretical limit with respect to free energy is called a **reversible reaction**. A reversible reaction occurs infinitesimally slowly, and the free energy is drawn out in infinitesimally small increments that exactly match the amount of work that the reaction is being used to do during that increment (Figure 17.11 ▶).

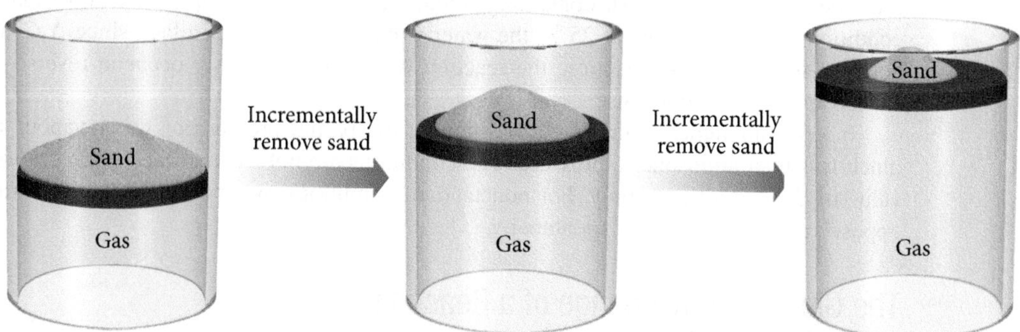

▲ **FIGURE 17.11 A Reversible Process** In a reversible process, the free energy is drawn out in infinitesimally small increments that exactly match the amount of energy that the process is producing in that increment. In this case, grains of sand are removed one at a time, resulting in a series of small expansions in which the weight of sand almost exactly matches the pressure of the expanding gas. This process is close to reversible—each sand grain would need to have an infinitesimally small mass for the process to be fully reversible.

Theoretically, burning octane in an internal combustion engine (like those in an automobile) would provide 5296.2 kJ of useful work. The combustion of octane in a *real* internal combustion engine is not done reversibly; it is done irreversibly. An amount of fuel is drawn into the cylinder and mixed with oxygen, and a spark initiates the combustion that is over extremely quickly. This results in far less work being done than the value of $\Delta_r G^\circ$ because additional energy produced by the reaction is lost to the surroundings as heat. Furthermore, the pistons on a real engine and the motion of the car parts are hindered by friction, and overcoming this friction produces heat that is energy lost to the surroundings. The effect of the reaction being done irreversibly and losses due to friction is to further reduce the efficiency of the reaction to do useful work.

More formally, a *reversible reaction is one that will change direction upon an infinitesimally small change in a variable (such as temperature or pressure) related to the reaction.*

Another way to convert the energy from a chemical reaction into useful work is to use a fuel cell, which can be much more efficient than an internal combustion engine, mainly because the Gibbs energy from the reaction is done so that it produces electricity directly, and this electricity is used to do work. There is no heat lost to friction in the engine, and the reaction, being done more slowly and in a more controlled manner, does not lose as much of the energy due to the reaction being done irreversibly. What is the same, whether a mole of octane is combusted in an internal combustion engine or in a fuel cell, is that the absolute maximum amount of work that can be done is 5296.2 kJ. The theoretical limit to the amount of useful work that can be done by any reaction is equal to the Gibbs energy.

If the change in Gibbs energy of a chemical reaction is positive, $\Delta_r G^\circ$ represents the minimum amount of energy required to make the reaction occur. Again, $\Delta_r G^\circ$ is a theoretical limit, and making a real nonspontaneous reaction occur always requires more energy than the theoretical limit.

17.8 Gibbs Energy Changes for Nonstandard States: The Relationship Between $\Delta_r G^\circ$ and $\Delta_r G$

We have learned how to calculate the *standard* Gibbs energy change for a reaction ($\Delta_r G^\circ$). However, the standard Gibbs energy change applies only to a very narrow set of conditions, namely, those conditions in which the reactants and products are in their standard states. Consider the standard Gibbs energy change for the evaporation of liquid water to gaseous water:

$$H_2O(l) \rightleftharpoons H_2O(g) \qquad \Delta_r G^\circ = 8.59 \text{ kJ mol}^{-1}$$

The standard Gibbs energy change for this process is positive, so the process is nonspontaneous. But you know that if you spill water onto the floor under ordinary conditions, it spontaneously evaporates. Why? *Because ordinary conditions are not standard conditions* and $\Delta_r G^\circ$ applies only to standard conditions. For a gas (such as the water vapour in the

▲ Spilled water spontaneously evaporates even though $\Delta_r G°$ for the vaporization of water is positive. Why?

above reaction), standard conditions are those in which the pure gas is present at a partial pressure of 1 bar. In a flask containing liquid water and water vapour under standard conditions (P_{H_2O} = 1 bar) at 25 °C the water would not vaporize. In fact, since $\Delta_r G°$ is negative for the reverse reaction, the reaction would spontaneously occur in reverse—water vapour would condense.

In open air under ordinary circumstances, the partial pressure of water vapour is much less than atmospheric pressure. The conditions are not standard and therefore the value of $\Delta_r G°$ does not apply. For nonstandard conditions, we must calculate $\Delta_r G$ (as opposed to $\Delta_r G°$) to predict spontaneity.

The Gibbs Energy Change of a Reaction Under Nonstandard Conditions

We can calculate the **Gibbs energy change of a reaction under nonstandard conditions** (**$\Delta_r G$**) from $\Delta_r G°$ using the following relationship, where Q is the reaction quotient (defined in Section 14.6), T is the temperature in kelvins, and R is the gas constant in the appropriate units (8.314 J K^{-1} mol^{-1}):

$$\Delta_r G = \Delta_r G° + RT \ln Q \qquad [17.19]$$

In all thermodynamic equations, remember that Q must be expressed in terms of pressures in bar for gases and concentrations in mol L^{-1} for solutes. We drop the units, as we did in Chapter 14, because we assume that the unitless activities are equal to the magnitudes of the pressures and concentrations. For liquids and solids, we assume that they are relatively pure and their amounts are not expressed in Q (their activities are equal to 1).

We can demonstrate the use of this equation by applying it to the liquid–vapour water equilibrium under several different conditions, as shown in Figure 17.12 ▼. Note that by the law of mass action, for this equilibrium, $Q = P_{H_2O}$.

$$H_2O(l) \longrightarrow H_2O(g) \quad Q = P_{H_2O}$$

Standard Conditions Under standard conditions, P_{H_2O} = 1 bar, and therefore Q = 1. Substituting, we get this expression:

$$\begin{aligned}\Delta_r G &= \Delta_r G° + RT \ln Q \\ &= 8.56 \text{ kJ mol}^{-1} + RT \ln(1) \\ &= 8.56 \text{ kJ mol}^{-1}\end{aligned}$$

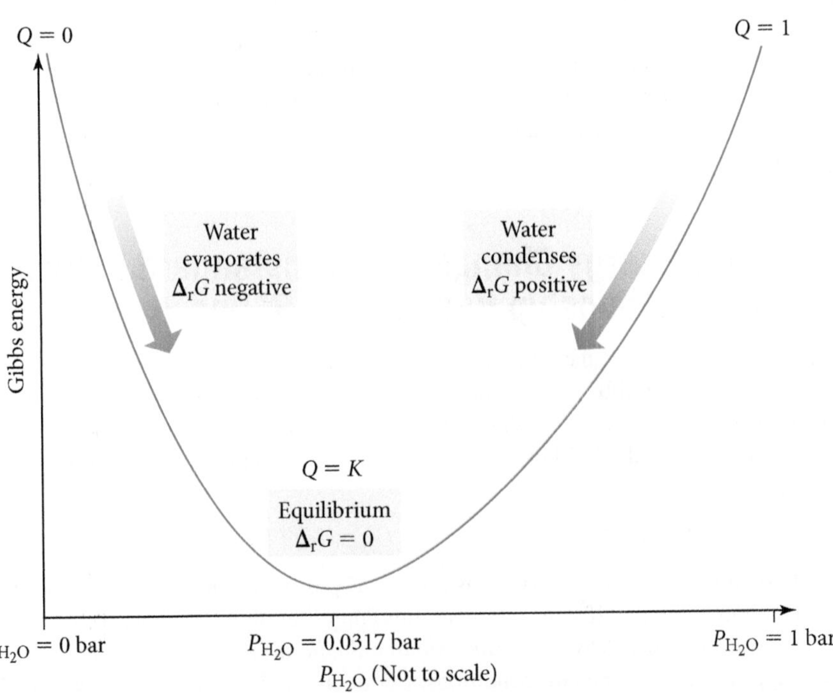

▶ **FIGURE 17.12 Gibbs Energy Versus Pressure for Water** The Gibbs energy change for the vaporization of water is a function of pressure.

Under standard conditions, Q will always be equal to 1, and since $\ln(1) = 0$, the value of $\Delta_r G$ will be equal to $\Delta_r G°$. For the liquid–vapour water equilibrium at 298 K, since $\Delta_r G° > 0$, the reaction is not spontaneous in the forward direction but is spontaneous in the reverse direction. As stated previously, under standard conditions at 298 K, water vapour condenses into liquid water.

Equilibrium Conditions At 25.00 °C, liquid water is in equilibrium with water vapour at a pressure of 0.0317 bar; therefore, $Q = P_{H_2O} = 0.0317$. Substituting, we get this expression:

$$\begin{aligned}\Delta_r G &= \Delta_r G° + RT\ln Q \\ &= 8.56 \text{ kJ mol}^{-1} + 8.314 \text{ J } \cancel{\text{K}^{-1}} \text{ mol}^{-1}\,(298\ \cancel{\text{K}})\ln(0.0317) \\ &= 8.56 \text{ kJ mol}^{-1} + (-8.56 \times 10^3 \text{ J mol}^{-1})\left(\frac{1 \text{ kJ}}{1000 \text{ J}}\right) \\ &= 0 \text{ kJ mol}^{-1}\end{aligned}$$

Under equilibrium conditions, the value of RT in Q will always be equal in magnitude but opposite in sign to the value of $\Delta_r G°$. Therefore, the value of $\Delta_r G$ will always be zero at equilibrium at any temperature. Since $\Delta_r G = 0$, the reaction is not spontaneous in either direction, as expected for a reaction at equilibrium.

Other Nonstandard Conditions To calculate the value of $\Delta_r G°$ under any other set of nonstandard conditions, calculate Q and substitute the value into the equation. For example, the partial pressure of water vapour in the air on a dry (nonhumid) day might be 5.00×10^{-3} bar, so $Q = 5.00 \times 10^{-3}$. Substituting, we get this expression:

A water partial pressure of 5.00×10^{-3} bar corresponds to a relative humidity of 16% at 25 °C.

$$\begin{aligned}\Delta_r G &= \Delta_r G° + RT\ln Q \\ &= 8.56 \text{ kJ mol}^{-1} + 8.314 \text{ J } \cancel{\text{K}^{-1}} \text{ mol}^{-1}\,(298\ \cancel{\text{K}})\ln(5.00 \times 10^{-3}) \\ &= 8.56 \text{ kJ mol}^{-1} + (-1.3\underline{1}2 \times 10^4\ \cancel{\text{J}} \text{ mol}^{-1})\left(\frac{1 \text{ kJ}}{1000\ \cancel{\text{J}}}\right) \\ &= -4.6 \text{ kJ mol}^{-1}\end{aligned}$$

Under these conditions, the value of $\Delta_r G < 0$, so the reaction is spontaneous in the forward direction, consistent with our experience of water evaporating when spilled on the floor.

EXAMPLE 17.9 CALCULATING $\Delta_r G°$ UNDER NONSTANDARD CONDITIONS

Consider the following reaction at 298 K:

$$2\,NO(g) + O_2(g) \longrightarrow 2\,NO_2(g) \qquad \Delta_r G° = -71.2 \text{ kJ mol}^{-1}$$

Calculate $\Delta_r G$ under the following conditions:

$$P_{NO} = 0.100 \text{ bar}; \quad P_{O_2} = 0.100 \text{ bar}; \quad P_{NO_2} = 2.00 \text{ bar}$$

Is the reaction more or less spontaneous under these conditions than under standard conditions?

SOLUTION

Use the law of mass action to calculate Q.	$Q = \dfrac{P^2_{NO_2}}{P^2_{NO}P_{O_2}} = \dfrac{(2.00)^2}{(0.100)^2(0.100)} = 4.00 \times 10^3$
Substitute Q, T, and $\Delta_r G°$ into Equation 17.15 to calculate $\Delta_r G$. (Since the units of R include joules, write $\Delta_r G°$ in joules.)	$\begin{aligned}\Delta_r G &= \Delta_r G° + RT\ln Q \\ &= -71.2 \times 10^3 \text{ J mol}^{-1} + 8.314\frac{\text{J}}{\text{mol}\cdot\cancel{\text{K}}}(298\ \cancel{\text{K}})\ln(4.00 \times 10^3) \\ &= -71.2 \times 10^3 \text{ J mol}^{-1} + 20.5 \times 10^3 \text{ J mol}^{-1} \\ &= -50.7 \times 10^3 \text{ J mol}^{-1} \\ &= -50.7 \text{ kJ mol}^{-1}\end{aligned}$ The reaction is spontaneous under these conditions, but less spontaneous than it was under standard conditions (because $\Delta_r G$ is less negative than $\Delta_r G°$).

(continued)

EXAMPLE 17.9 (CONTINUED)

CHECK The calculated result is consistent with what we would expect based on Le Châtelier's principle; increasing the concentration of the products and decreasing the concentration of the reactants relative to standard conditions should make the reaction less spontaneous than it was under standard conditions.

FOR PRACTICE 17.9

Consider the following reaction at 298 K:

$$2\ H_2S(g) + SO_2(g) \longrightarrow 3\ S(s,\ \text{rhombic}) + 2\ H_2O(g) \qquad \Delta_r G^\circ = -102\ \text{kJ mol}^{-1}$$

Compute $\Delta_r G$ under the following conditions:

$$P_{H_2S} = 2.00\ \text{bar};\quad P_{SO_2} = 1.50\ \text{bar};\quad P_{H_2O} = 0.0100\ \text{bar}$$

Is the reaction more or less spontaneous under these conditions than under standard conditions?

CONCEPTUAL CONNECTION 17.3

Gibbs Energy Changes and Le Châtelier's Principle

According to Le Châtelier's principle and the dependence of Gibbs energy on reactant and product concentrations, which statement is true? (Assume that both the reactants and products are gaseous.)

(a) A high concentration of reactants relative to products results in a more spontaneous reaction than one in which the reactants and products are in their standard states.

(b) A high concentration of products relative to reactants results in a more spontaneous reaction than one in which the reactants and products are in their standard states.

(c) A reaction in which the reactants are in standard states, but in which no products have formed, will have a $\Delta_r G$ that is more positive than $\Delta_r G^\circ$.

Equation 17.17 can be substituted into Equation 17.19 to compute the Gibbs energy change under nonstandard conditions and at temperatures other than 298 K:

$$\Delta_r G = \Delta_r H^\circ - T\Delta_r S^\circ + RT \ln Q \qquad [17.20]$$

This equation is valid under the assumption that the standard entropy and enthalpy changes for a reaction are independent of temperature, which is a satisfactory assumption for small temperature changes and that we use in this chapter.

EXAMPLE 17.10 CALCULATING $\Delta_r G$ UNDER NONSTANDARD CONDITIONS AND AT TEMPERATURES OTHER THAN 298 K

Consider the following reaction:

$$Ca(OH)_2(s) \rightleftharpoons Ca^{2+}(aq) + 2\ OH^-(aq) \qquad \Delta_r H^\circ = -17.6\ \text{kJ mol}^{-1}$$
$$\Delta_r S^\circ = -158.3\ \text{J K}^{-1}\ \text{mol}^{-1}$$

A saturated solution of $Ca(OH)_2$ contains 1.2×10^{-2} mol L^{-1} at 298 K and is at equilibrium with the solid in the container. The solution is quickly heated to 350 K. Calculate $\Delta_r G$ at 350 K with the 298 K concentrations and state whether $Ca(OH)_2$ will precipitate or more can be dissolved at the higher temperature.

SOLUTION

We can use Equation 17.20 to compute $\Delta_r G$ at nonstandard conditions and at temperatures other than 298 K. We are given the enthalpy and entropy changes for the reaction and the new temperature. We first need to use the concentration of the solution to compute Q. Due to stoichiometry, the concentration of OH^- is twice that of Ca^{2+}.	$[Ca^{2+}] = 1.2 \times 10^{-2}\ \text{mol L}^{-1}\ [OH^-] = 2.4 \times 10^{-2}$ $Q = [Ca^{2-}][OH^-]^2$ $= (1.2 \times 10^{-2})(2.4 \times 10^{-2})^2$ $= 6.91 \times 10^{-6}$

Now we can substitute Q, $\Delta_r H^\circ$, $\Delta_r S^\circ$, T, and R into Equation 17.20. Ensure the units are the same before adding terms; since $\Delta_r S^\circ$ and R are in J K^{-1} mol^{-1}, it is best to write $\Delta_r H^\circ$ in J mol^{-1} as well.	$\Delta_r G = \Delta_r H^\circ - T\Delta_r S^\circ + RT \ln Q$ $= -17.6 \times 10^3 \text{ J mol}^{-1} - (350 \text{ K})(-158.3 \text{ J K}^{-1} \text{ mol}^{-1})$ $+ (8.314 \text{ J K}^{-1} \text{ mol}^{-1})(350 \text{ K})(\ln 6.91 \times 10^{-6})$ $= -17.6 \times 10^3 \text{ J mol}^{-1} + 55.4 \times 10^3 \text{ J mol}^{-1}$ $-34.6 \times 10^3 \text{ J mol}^{-1}$ $= 3.2 \times 10^3 \text{ J mol}^{-1}$ The reaction is not spontaneous under these conditions, some $Ca(OH)_2$ will precipitate upon heating.

CHECK The reaction was saturated at 298 K and we increased the temperature. The reaction is exothermic (heat is a product of the reaction as written) so by Le Chatelier's principle, adding heat by increasing the temperature would cause the reaction to shift toward reactants, precipitating $Ca(OH)_2$. Similarly, we learned above that since $\Delta_r S^\circ$ is negative, an increase in temperature favours the reverse reaction. The positive $\Delta_r G$ we computed, therefore, seems reasonable.

FOR PRACTICE 17.10

Consider the dissolution of lead(II) chloride:

$$PbCl_2 \rightleftharpoons Pb^{2+}(aq) + 2\,Cl^-(aq) \qquad \Delta_r H^\circ = 26.12 \text{ kJ mol}^{-1}$$

$$\Delta_r S^\circ = -4.3 \text{ J K}^{-1} \text{ mol}^{-1}$$

Compute $\Delta_r G$ at 360 K when the concentration of Pb^{2+} is 0.0030 mol L^{-1} and the concentration of Cl^- is 0.0060 mol L^{-1}. Could more $PbCl_2$ be dissolved if some solid was present or will it precipitate under these conditions?

FOR MORE PRACTICE 17.10

Consider the dissolution of lead(II) chloride, the reaction and standard enthalpy and entropy changes for the reaction are provided above in For Practice 17.10. At what temperature would the concentrations provided above represent an equilibrium mixture if some solid were present?

17.9 Gibbs Energy and Equilibrium: Relating $\Delta_r G^\circ$ to the Equilibrium Constant (K)

We have learned throughout this chapter that $\Delta_r G^\circ$ determines the spontaneity of a reaction when the reactants and products are in their standard states. In Chapter 14, we learned that the equilibrium constant (K) determines how far a reaction goes toward products, a measure of spontaneity. Therefore, as you might expect, the standard Gibbs energy change of a reaction and the equilibrium constant are related—the equilibrium constant becomes larger as the Gibbs energy change becomes more negative. In other words, if the reactants in a particular reaction undergo a large *negative* Gibbs energy change as they become products, then the reaction will have a large equilibrium constant, with products strongly favoured at equilibrium. If, on the other hand, the reactants in a particular reaction undergo a large *positive* Gibbs energy change as they become products, then the reaction will have a small equilibrium constant, with reactants strongly favoured at equilibrium.

We can obtain a relationship between $\Delta_r G^\circ$ and K from Equation 17.19. We know that at equilibrium $Q = K$ and $\Delta_r G = 0$. Making these substitutions,

$$\Delta_r G = \Delta_r G^\circ + RT \ln Q$$

$$0 = \Delta_r G^\circ + RT \ln K$$

$$\Delta_r G^\circ = -RT \ln K \qquad [17.21]$$

We can better understand the relationship between $\Delta_r G^\circ$ and K by considering the following ranges of values for K, as summarized in Figure 17.13 ▼.

- When $K < 1$, $\ln K$ is negative and $\Delta_r G^\circ$ is positive. Under standard conditions (when $Q = 1$) the reaction is spontaneous in the reverse direction.

The relationship between $\Delta_r G^\circ$ and K is logarithmic—small changes in $\Delta_r G^\circ$ have a large effect on K.

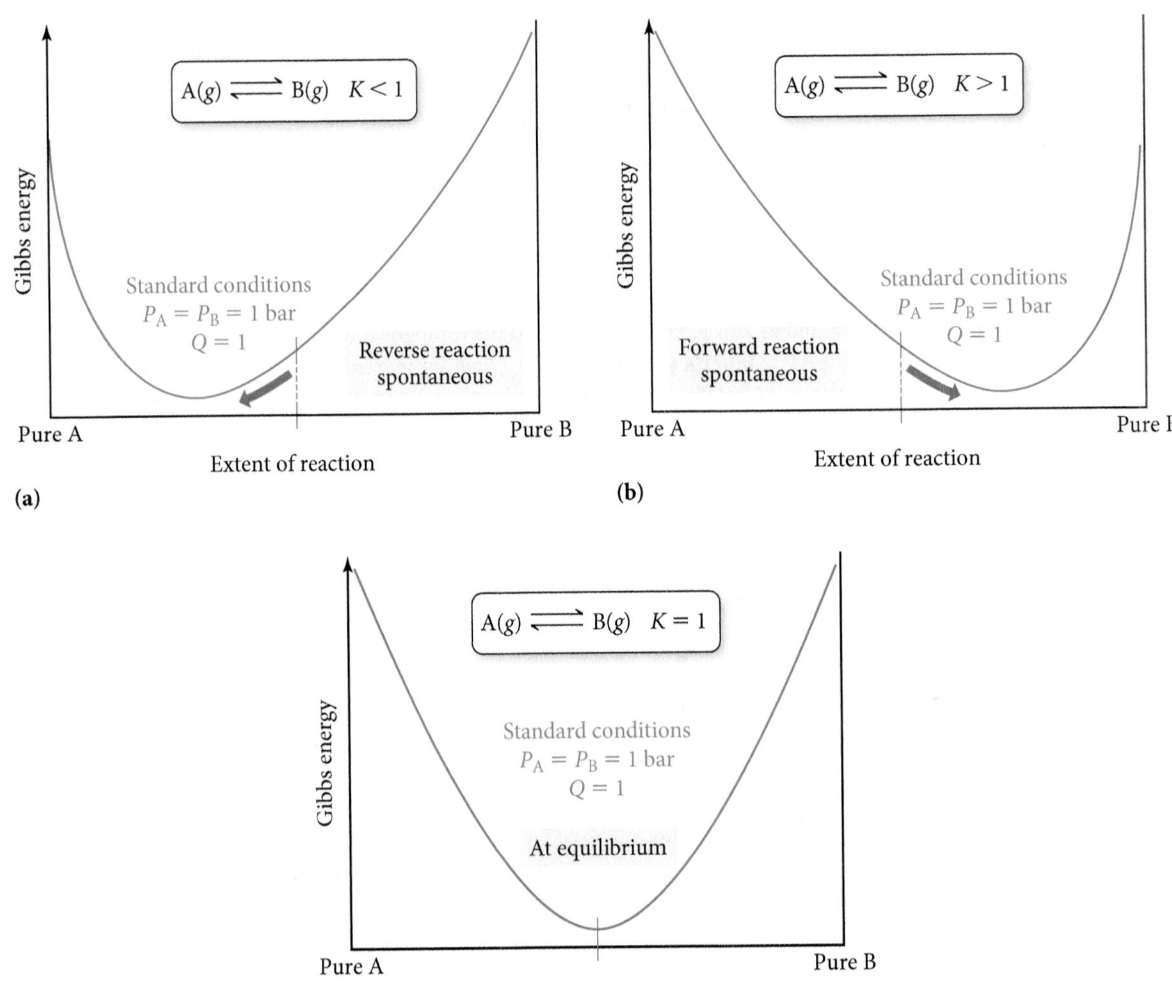

▲ **FIGURE 17.13 Gibbs Energy and the Equilibrium Constant** **(a)** Gibbs energy curve for a reaction with a small equilibrium constant. **(b)** Gibbs energy curve for a reaction with a large equilibrium constant. **(c)** Gibbs energy curve for a reaction in which $K = 1$.

- When $K > 1$, $\ln K$ is positive and $\Delta_r G°$ is negative. Under standard conditions (when $Q = 1$) the reaction is spontaneous in the forward direction.
- When $K = 1$, $\ln K$ is zero and $\Delta_r G°$ is zero. The reaction happens to be at equilibrium under standard conditions.

EXAMPLE 17.11 THE EQUILIBRIUM CONSTANT AND $\Delta_r G°$

Use tabulated Gibbs energies of formation to calculate the equilibrium constant for the following reaction at 298 K:

$$N_2O_4(g) \rightleftharpoons 2\ NO_2(g)$$

SOLUTION

Begin by looking up (in Appendix IIB) the standard Gibbs energies of formation for each reactant and product.

Reactant or product	$\Delta_f G°$ (kJ mol^{-1})
$N_2O_4(g)$	99.8
$NO_2(g)$	51.3

Calculate $\Delta_r G°$ by substituting into Equation 17.18.

$$\begin{aligned}\Delta_r G° &= \sum \nu_p \Delta_f G°_{products} - \sum \nu_r \Delta_f G°_{reactants}\\ &= 2[\Delta_f G°_{NO_2(g)}] - \Delta_f G°_{N_2O_4(g)}\\ &= 2(51.3\ \text{kJ mol}^{-1}) - 99.8\ \text{kJ mol}^{-1}\\ &= 2.8\ \text{kJ mol}^{-1}\end{aligned}$$

Calculate K from $\Delta_r G^\circ$ by solving Equation 17.21 for K and substituting the values of $\Delta_r G^\circ$ and temperature.	$\Delta_r G^\circ = -RT \ln K$ $\ln K = \dfrac{-\Delta_r G^\circ}{RT}$ $= \dfrac{-2.8 \times 10^3\, \text{J/mol}}{8.314 \frac{\text{J}}{\text{mol} \cdot \text{K}}(298\,\text{K})}$ $= -1.13$ $K = e^{-1.13}$ $= 0.32$

FOR PRACTICE 17.11

Calculate $\Delta_r G^\circ$ at 298 K for the following reaction:

$$I_2(g) + Cl_2(g) \rightleftharpoons 2ICl(g) \qquad K = 6.0 \times 10^5$$

The Temperature Dependence of the Equilibrium Constant

We now have an equation that relates the standard Gibbs energy change for a reaction ($\Delta_r G^\circ$) to the equilibrium constant for a reaction (K):

$$\Delta_r G^\circ = -RT \ln K \qquad [17.22]$$

We also have an equation for how the Gibbs energy change for a reaction ($\Delta_r G^\circ$) depends on temperature (T):

$$\Delta_r G^\circ = \Delta_r H^\circ - T\Delta_r S^\circ \qquad [17.23]$$

We can combine these two equations to obtain an equation for how the equilibrium constant depends on temperature. Combining Equation 17.22 and Equation 17.23, we get:

$$-RT \ln K = \Delta_r H^\circ - T\Delta_r S^\circ \qquad [17.24]$$

We can then divide both sides of Equation 17.24 by the quantity RT:

$$-\ln K = \frac{\Delta_r H^\circ}{RT} - \frac{T\Delta_r S^\circ}{RT}$$

Cancelling and rearranging, we get this important result:

$$\ln K = -\frac{\Delta_r H^\circ}{R}\frac{1}{T} + \frac{\Delta_r S^\circ}{R} \qquad [17.25]$$

$$y = \quad mx \quad + \quad b$$

The equation is in the form of a straight line and is called the van't Hoff equation. A plot of the natural log of the equilibrium constant ($\ln K$) versus the inverse of the temperature in kelvins ($1/T$) yields a straight line with a slope of $-\Delta_r H^\circ/R$ and a y-intercept of $\Delta_r S^\circ/R$. Such a plot is useful for obtaining thermodynamic data (namely, $\Delta_r H^\circ$ and $\Delta_r S^\circ$) from measurements of K as a function of temperature. However, since $\Delta_r H^\circ$ and $\Delta_r S^\circ$ can themselves be slightly temperature dependent, this analysis works only over a relatively limited temperature range.

Take some time to compare the equation with the Clausius–Clapeyron equation developed in Chapter 11 (Equation 11.5). In fact, the two equations are identical with $\ln \beta = \Delta_r S^\circ$ and $K = P_{vap}$. The intercept of a Clausius–Clapeyron equation yields the entropy of vaporization. The two-point versions of these equations (17.21 and 11.6) are also similar. It makes sense that the two equations are similar since the equilibrium constant for a phase change from liquid to gas (or solid to gas) is the vapour pressure.

EXAMPLE 17.12 USING THE VAN'T HOFF EQUATION TO DETERMINE THE STANDARD ENTHALPY AND ENTROPY OF REACTION

On the right is a van't Hoff plot for the isomerization of 1-pentene to cyclopentane.

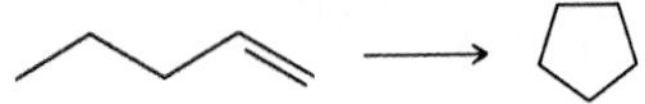

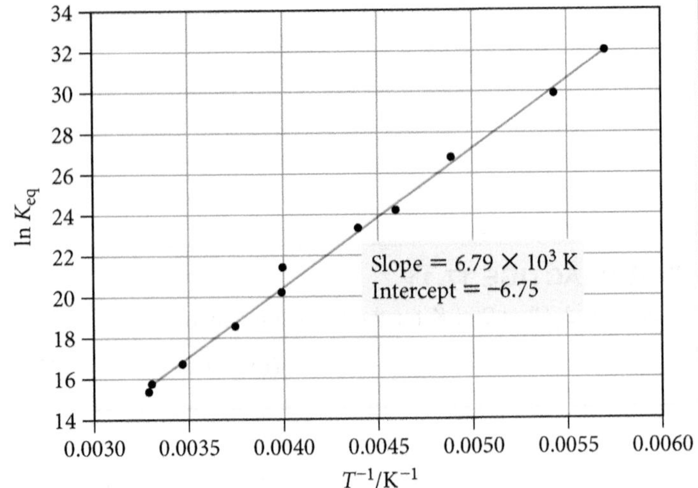

The values of both the slope and intercept are given on the plot. Determine the change in enthalpy and entropy for the isomerization reaction.

SOLUTION

To find the enthalpy of vaporization and the entropy of vaporization, we use the relationships developed above; the slope and intercept are given by the following relationships:

$$\text{slope} = -\Delta_r H°/R \qquad \text{intercept} = \Delta_r S°/R$$

which can be rearranged to

$$\Delta_r H° = -\text{slope} \times R \qquad \Delta_r S° = \text{intercept} \times R$$

Since we are given the values of the slope and intercept and we know the value of R, we substitute these values in and solve for the standard enthalpy and entropy of reaction:

$$\Delta_r H° = -6.79 \times 10^3 \text{ K} \times 8.314 \text{ J K}^{-1} \text{ mol}^{-1}$$

$$= -56450 \text{ J mol}^{-1} \times \frac{1 \text{ kJ}}{1000 \text{ J}}$$

$$= -56.5 \text{ kJ mol}^{-1}$$

$$\Delta_r S° = -6.75 \times 8.314 \text{ J K}^{-1} \text{mol}^{-1}$$

$$= -56.1 \text{ J K}^{-1} \text{mol}^{-1}$$

The standard enthalpy of reaction makes sense since two C—C bonds are being formed from one C=C bond. The negative entropy change also makes sense since freedom of rotation around all the C—C bonds is lost (fewer ways to store energy) on forming the cyclic alkane.

FOR PRACTICE 17.12

The temperature-dependent equilibrium constants for the gas phase clustering of chloride ion with acetonitrile are provided in the table on the right.

$$Cl^- + CH_3CN \longrightarrow Cl^-(CH_3CN)$$

Use a graphing program such as Excel to prepare a van't Hoff plot and determine the standard enthalpy and entropy changes for this reaction.

Temperature/K	K
492.7	629.4
466.7	1512
450.2	3112
433.2	5088
415.2	10400
395.2	28080
373.2	70610

Data from: Fridgen et al. J. Phys. Chem. A. 2005, 7, 2747.

Equation 17.21 can also be expressed in a two-point form:

$$\ln \frac{K_2}{K_1} = -\frac{\Delta_r H°}{R}\left(\frac{1}{T_2} - \frac{1}{T_1}\right) \qquad [17.26]$$

This equation can be used to find $\Delta_r H°$ from a measurement of the equilibrium constant at two different temperatures, or to find the equilibrium at some other temperature if you know the equilibrium constant at a given temperature and $\Delta_r H°$.

EXAMPLE 17.13 USING THE TWO-POINT FORM OF THE VAN'T HOFF EQUATION TO PREDICT THE EQUILIBRIUM CONSTANT AT A GIVEN TEMPERATURE

The standard Gibbs energy changes at 298 K for the dissolution of calcium hydroxide are these:

$$Ca(OH)_2(s) \xrightarrow{H_2O} Ca^{2+}(aq) + 2\,OH^-(aq) \qquad \Delta_r G^\circ = 30.0\,\text{kJ mol}^{-1}$$
$$\Delta_r H^\circ = -2.5\,\text{kJ mol}^{-1}$$

Using the two-point form of the van't Hoff equation to predict the equilibrium constant, determine the K_{sp} at 500 K.

SORT You are given the 298 K Gibbs energy and the enthalpy for the dissolution of calcium hydroxide. You are asked to find K_{sp} at 500 K.

GIVEN: $\Delta_r G^\circ\ (298\,\text{K}) = 30.0\,\text{kJ mol}^{-1}$

$\Delta_r H^\circ = -2.5\,\text{kJ mol}^{-1}$

FIND: K_{sp} at 500 K

STRATEGIZE There are two ways to solve this problem. We will focus on the two-point van't Hoff method as asked by the question and then check our answer by doing it another way. In order to use the two-point van't Hoff method, we need the 298 K equilibrium constant. We can use Equation 17.17 to determine this. Then the only unknown in the two-point van't Hoff equation is the 500 K equilibrium constant.

CONCEPTUAL PLAN

$$\Delta_r G^\circ = -RT \ln K$$

$$\ln \frac{K_2}{K_1} = -\frac{\Delta_r H^\circ}{R}\left(\frac{1}{T_2} - \frac{1}{T_1}\right)$$

SOLVE

First calculate the 298 K equilibrium constant.

SOLUTION

$$\Delta_r G^\circ = -RT \ln K$$
$$K = e^{-\Delta_r G^\circ/RT}$$
$$K = e^{-3.00 \times 10^5\ \cancel{\text{J}}\ \cancel{\text{mol}^{-1}} > 18.314\ \cancel{\text{J}}\ \cancel{\text{K}^{-1}}\ \cancel{\text{mol}^{-1}} \cdot 298\ \cancel{\text{K}}2}$$
$$= 5.512 \times 10^{-6}$$

Then use the van't Hoff equation to determine the 500 K equilibrium constant.

$$\ln \frac{K_2}{5.512 \times 10^{-6}} = -\frac{-2.5 \times 10^3\ \text{J}\ \cancel{\text{mol}^{-1}}}{8.314\ \text{J}\ \text{K}^{-1}\ \cancel{\text{mol}^{-1}}}\left(\frac{1}{500\,\text{K}} - \frac{1}{298\,\text{K}}\right)$$

$$\frac{K_2}{5.512 \times 10^{-6}} = e^{-0.40\underline{7}}$$

$$K_2 = 3.67 \times 10^{-6}$$

CHECK Since you are given $\Delta_r G^\circ$ at 298 K, and $\Delta_r H^\circ$, you can calculate $\Delta_r S^\circ$. Then you can use $\Delta_r H^\circ$ and $\Delta_r S^\circ$ to calculate $\Delta_r G^\circ$ at 500 K and then the equilibrium constant. The value should be the same as that computed above.

$$\Delta_r G^\circ = \Delta_r H^\circ - T\Delta_r S^\circ$$

$$\Delta_r S^\circ = \frac{\Delta_r H^\circ - \Delta_r G^\circ}{T}$$

$$= \frac{-2500\ \text{J mol}^{-1} - 30\,000\ \text{J mol}^{-1}}{298\ \text{K}} = -10\underline{9}.1\ \text{J K}^{-1}\ \text{mol}^{-1}$$

(The negative entropy change is due to the orientation of solvent primarily around the Ca^{2+} cations.)

$$\Delta_r G^\circ = \Delta_r H^\circ - T\Delta_r S^\circ$$

$$\Delta_r G^\circ\ (500\ \text{K}) = -2500\ \text{J mol}^{-1} - (500\ \text{K})(-109.1\ \text{J}\ \cancel{\text{K}^{-1}}\ \text{mol}^{-1})$$

$$\Delta_r G^\circ\ (500\ \text{K}) = 52\,\underline{0}50\ \text{J mol}^{-1}\ (=52.1\ \text{kJ mol}^{-1})$$

$$\Delta_r G^\circ = -RT \ln K$$

$$K = e^{-\Delta_r G^\circ/RT}$$

$$= e^{-(52050\ \cancel{\text{J}}\ \cancel{\text{mol}^{-1}})/(8.314\ \cancel{\text{J}}\ \cancel{\text{K}^{-1}}\ \cancel{\text{mol}^{-1}} \cdot 500\ \cancel{\text{K}})} = 3.65 \times 10^{-6}$$

FOR PRACTICE 17.13

Dry silver carbonate is used as a reagent in organic synthesis. It is typically dried in a stream of hot air. Silver carbonate can also decompose at high temperatures according to the following reaction, which produces carbon dioxide:

$$Ag_2CO_3(s) \longrightarrow Ag_2O(s) + CO_2(g) \qquad \Delta_r H^\circ = 80.8\ \text{kJ mol}^{-1}$$

(continued)

EXAMPLE 17.13 (CONTINUED)

At 298 K, the equilibrium constant for this reaction is 8.1×10^{-6}, which is also the pressure of CO_2 above the solid since $K = P_{CO_2}$. In order to prevent decomposition from occurring, the air used to dry the silver carbonate must have a partial pressure of CO_2 greater than the equilibrium constant. What is the partial pressure of CO_2 necessary to prevent decomposition of Ag_2CO_3 at 110 °C?

CHAPTER IN REVIEW

Key Terms

Section 17.1
spontaneous process (739)

Section 17.2
entropy (S) (742)
second law of thermodynamics (743)

Section 17.4
reversible process (751)

Section 17.5
Gibbs energy (G) (752)

Section 17.6
standard entropy change for a reaction ($\Delta_r S°$) (756)
standard molar entropies ($S°$) (756)
third law of thermodynamics (757)
zero-point energy (757)

Section 17.7
standard Gibbs energy change ($\Delta_r G°$) (761)
Gibbs energy of formation ($\Delta_f G°$) (763)
reversible reaction (766)

Key Concepts

Spontaneous and Nonspontaneous Processes (17.1)

Both spontaneous and nonspontaneous processes can occur, but only spontaneous processes can take place without outside intervention. Thermodynamics is the study of the *spontaneity* of reactions, *not* to be confused with kinetics, the study of the *rate* of reactions.

Entropy and the Second Law of Thermodynamics (17.2)

The second law of thermodynamics states that for *any* spontaneous process, the entropy of the universe increases. Entropy (S) is proportional to the number of ways in which energy can be distributed in a system and is a measure of energy dispersal per unit temperature. An example of a process in which entropy changes is a state change, such as a change from a solid to a liquid.

Heat Transfer and Changes in the Entropy of the Surroundings (17.3)

For a process to be spontaneous, the total entropy of the universe (system plus surroundings) must increase. The entropy of the surroundings increases when the change in *enthalpy* of the system (ΔH_{sys}) is negative (e.g., for exothermic reactions). The change in entropy of the surroundings for a given ΔH_{sys} depends inversely on temperature—the greater the temperature, the lower the magnitude of ΔS_{surr}.

Entropy Changes for Phase Transitions (17.4)

For a process carried out very slowly at constant temperature, such as a phase transition, the entropy change for the process can be computed from the measured enthalpy change for the process and the temperature at which it is carried out.

Gibbs Energy (17.5)

Gibbs energy, G, is a thermodynamic function that is proportional to the negative of the change in the entropy of the universe. A negative ΔG represents a spontaneous reaction and a positive ΔG represents a nonspontaneous reaction. We can calculate the value of $\Delta_r G$ for a reaction from the values of $\Delta_r H$ and $\Delta_r S$ for the *system* according to the equation $\Delta_r G = \Delta_r H - T\Delta_r S$.

Entropy Changes in Chemical Reactions: Calculating $\Delta_r S°$ (17.6)

We calculate the standard change in entropy for a reaction similarly to the way we calculate the standard change in enthalpy for a reaction: by subtracting the sum of the standard entropies of the reactants multiplied by their stoichiometric coefficients from the sum of the standard entropies of the products multiplied by their stoichiometric coefficients. In this equation, the standard entropies are *absolute*: an entropy of zero is determined by the third law of thermodynamics as the entropy of a perfect crystal at absolute zero. The absolute entropy of a substance depends on factors that affect the number of possible distributions of the energy of the system, or microstates; these include the state, size, and molecular complexity of the substance.

Gibbs Energy Changes in Chemical Reactions: Calculating $\Delta_r G°$ (17.7)

There are three ways to calculate $\Delta_r G°$: (1) from $\Delta_r H°$ and $\Delta_r S°$, (2) from Gibbs energies of formations (only at 25 °C), and (3) from the $\Delta_r G°$'s of reactions that sum to the reaction of interest. The magnitude of a negative $\Delta_r G°$ represents the extent to which the reaction will proceed toward products to reach equilibrium, and a positive $\Delta_r G°$ means that the reaction will not proceed very far toward products to reach equilibrium.

Gibbs Energy Changes for Nonstandard States: The Relationship Between $\Delta_r G°$ and $\Delta_r G$ (17.8)

The value of $\Delta_r G°$ applies only to standard conditions, and most real conditions are not standard. Under nonstandard conditions, we can calculate $\Delta_r G$ from the equation $\Delta_r G = \Delta_r G° + RT \ln Q$.

Gibbs Energy and Equilibrium: Relating $\Delta_r G°$ to the Equilibrium Constant (K) (17.9)

Under standard conditions, the Gibbs energy change for a reaction is directly proportional to the negative of the natural log of the equilibrium constant, K; the more negative the Gibbs energy change, the larger the equilibrium constant. The temperature dependence of $\Delta_r G°$, as given by $\Delta_r G° = \Delta_r H° - T\Delta_r S°$, can be used to derive an expression for the temperature dependence of the equilibrium constant.

Key Equations and Relationships

The Definition of Entropy (17.2)

$$S = k \ln W \qquad k = 1.38 \times 10^{-23}\ \mathrm{J\,K^{-1}}$$

Change in Entropy (17.2)

$$\Delta S = S_{\text{final}} - S_{\text{initial}}$$

Change in the Entropy of the Universe (17.3)

$$\Delta S_{\text{univ}} = \Delta S_{\text{sys}} + \Delta S_{\text{surr}}$$

Change in the Entropy of the Surroundings (17.3)

$$\Delta S_{\text{surr}} = \frac{-\Delta H_{\text{sys}}}{T} \quad \text{(constant } T, P\text{)}$$

Change in the Entropy of a System for a Phase Transition (17.4):

$$\Delta_r S = \frac{\Delta_r H}{T} \text{(constant } T \text{ and } P\text{)}$$

Change in Gibbs Energy (17.5)

$$\Delta_r G = \Delta_r H - T\Delta_r S$$

The Relationship Between Spontaneity and $\Delta_r H$, $\Delta_r S$, and T (17.5)

$\Delta_r H$	$\Delta_r S$	Low Temperature	High Temperature
−	+	Spontaneous	Spontaneous
+	−	Nonspontaneous	Nonspontaneous
−	−	Spontaneous	Nonspontaneous
+	+	Nonspontaneous	Spontaneous

Standard Change in Entropy (17.6)

$$\Delta_r S^\circ = \sum \nu_p S^\circ_{\text{products}} - \sum \nu_r S^\circ_{\text{reactants}}$$

Methods for Calculating the Gibbs Energy ($\Delta_r G^\circ$) (17.7)

1. $\Delta_r G^\circ = \Delta_r H^\circ - T\Delta_r S^\circ$
2. $\Delta_r G^\circ = \sum \nu_p \Delta_f G^\circ_{\text{products}} - \sum \nu_r \Delta_f G^\circ_{\text{reactants}}$
3. $\Delta_r G^\circ(\text{overall}) = \Delta_r G^\circ(\text{step 1}) + \Delta_r G^\circ(\text{step 2}) + \ldots$

The Relationship Between $\Delta_r G^\circ$ and $\Delta_r G$ (17.8)

$$\Delta_r G = \Delta_r G^\circ + RT \ln Q \qquad R = 8.314\ \mathrm{J\,mol^{-1}\,K^{-1}}$$

The Relationship Between $\Delta_r G^\circ$ and K (17.9)

$$\Delta_r G^\circ = -RT \ln K$$

The Temperature Dependence of the Equilibrium Constant (17.9)

$$\ln K = -\frac{\Delta_r H^\circ}{R}\frac{1}{T} + \frac{\Delta_r S^\circ}{R}$$

Equation 17.21 can also be expressed in a two-point form:

$$\ln \frac{K_2}{K_1} = -\frac{\Delta_r H^\circ}{R}\left(\frac{1}{T_2} - \frac{1}{T_1}\right)$$

Key Skills

Predicting the Sign of Entropy Change (17.2)
• Example 17.1 • For Practice 17.1 • Exercises 27, 28, 31–34, 37, 38

Calculating Entropy Changes in the Surroundings (17.3)
• Example 17.2 • For Practice 17.2 • For More Practice 17.2 • Exercises 33–36

Computing Gibbs Energy Changes and Predicting Spontaneity from $\Delta_r H$ and $\Delta_r S$ (17.5)
• Example 17.3 • For Practice 17.3 • Exercises 39–44

Calculating Standard Entropy Changes ($\Delta_r S^\circ$) (17.6)
• Example 17.4 • For Practice 17.4 • Exercises 51, 52

Calculating the Standard Change in Gibbs Energy for a Reaction Using $\Delta_r G^\circ = \Delta_r H^\circ - T\Delta_r S^\circ$ (17.7)
• Examples 17.5, 17.6 • For Practice 17.5, 17.6 • Exercises 55–58, 61, 62

Calculating $\Delta_r G^\circ$ from Standard Gibbs Energies of Formation (17.7)
• Example 17.7 • For Practice 17.7 • For More Practice 17.7 • Exercises 59, 60

Calculating $\Delta_r G^\circ$ for a Stepwise Reaction (17.7)
• Example 17.8 • For Practice 17.8 • Exercises 63, 64

Calculating $\Delta_r G$ Under Nonstandard Conditions (17.8)
• Example 17.9 • For Practice 17.9 • Exercises 65–72

Relating the Equilibrium Constant and ($\Delta_r G^\circ$) (17.9)
• Example 17.11 • For Practice 17.11 • Exercises 73–76

Calculating $\Delta_r G$ Under Nonstandard Conditions and at Temperatures Other than 298 K (17.10)
• Example 17.10 • For Practice 17.10 • Exercises 75, 76

EXERCISES

Review Questions

1. What is a perpetual motion machine? Is such a machine possible given the laws of thermodynamics?
2. What is a spontaneous process? Provide an example.
3. Explain the difference between the spontaneity of a reaction (which depends on thermodynamics) and the speed at which the reaction occurs (which depends on kinetics). Can a catalyst make a nonspontaneous reaction spontaneous?
4. What is the precise definition of entropy? What is the significance of entropy being a state function?
5. Why does the entropy of a gas increase when it expands into a vacuum?
6. Why is the following statement not correct? In any spontaneous process, the entropy of a system must increase.
7. Based on its fundamental definition, explain why entropy is a measure of energy dispersion.
8. Provide the definition of the second law of thermodynamics. How does the second law explain why heat travels from a substance at higher temperature to one at lower temperature?
9. What happens to the entropy of a sample of matter when it changes state from a solid to a liquid? From a liquid to a gas?
10. Explain why water spontaneously freezes to form ice below 0 °C even though the entropy of the water decreases during the state transition. Why is the freezing of water not spontaneous above 0 °C?
11. What is the significance of the change in Gibbs energy ($\Delta_r G$) for a reaction?
12. Predict the spontaneity of a reaction (and the temperature dependence of the spontaneity) for each possible combination of signs for $\Delta_r H$ and $\Delta_r S$ (for the system):
    a. $\Delta_r H$ negative, $\Delta_r S$ positive
    b. $\Delta_r H$ positive, $\Delta_r S$ negative
    c. $\Delta_r H$ negative, $\Delta_r S$ negative
    d. $\Delta_r H$ positive, $\Delta_r S$ positive
13. State the third law of thermodynamics and explain its significance.
14. Why is the standard entropy of a substance in the gas state greater than its standard entropy in the liquid state?
15. How does the standard entropy of a substance depend on its molar mass? On its molecular complexity?
16. How can you calculate the standard entropy change for a reaction from tables of standard entropies?
17. What are three different methods to calculate $\Delta_r G°$ for a reaction? Which method would you choose to calculate $\Delta_r G°$ for a reaction at a temperature other than 25 °C?
18. Explain the significance of the Gibbs energy change for a reaction.
19. Explain the difference between $\Delta_r G°$ and $\Delta_r G$.
20. Why does water spilled on the floor evaporate even though $\Delta_r G°$ for the evaporation process is positive at room temperature?
21. How do you calculate the change in Gibbs energy for a reaction under nonstandard conditions?
22. How does the value of $\Delta_r G°$ for a reaction relate to the equilibrium constant for the reaction? What does a negative $\Delta_r G°$ for a reaction imply about K for the reaction? A positive $\Delta_r G°$?

Problems by Topic

Entropy, the Second Law of Thermodynamics, and the Direction of Spontaneous Change

23. Which of these processes are spontaneous?
    a. the combustion of natural gas
    b. the extraction of iron metal from iron ore
    c. a hot drink cooling to room temperature
    d. drawing heat energy from the ocean's surface to power a ship
24. Which of these processes are nonspontaneous? Are the nonspontaneous processes impossible?
    a. a bike going up a hill
    b. a meteor falling to Earth
    c. obtaining hydrogen gas from liquid water
    d. a ball rolling down a hill
25. Suppose that two systems whose complexities are represented below, each composed of two particles represented by dots, have 20 J of total energy. Which system, A or B, has the greatest entropy? Why?

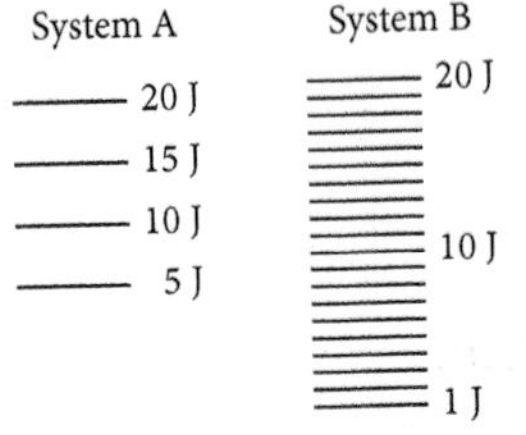

26. Suppose we have two systems at the same temperature, meaning that each particle in the system has the same average energy. The complexity of the system is represented below. One system is composed of two particles and 12 J of total energy and the other has three particles and 18 J of total energy. Which system has the greater entropy?

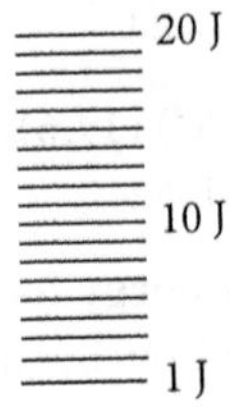

27. Without doing any calculations, determine the sign of ΔS_{sys} for each chemical reaction.
    a. $2\ KClO_3(s) \longrightarrow 2\ KCl(s) + 3\ O_2(g)$
    b. $CH_2{=}CH_2(g) + H_2(g) \longrightarrow CH_3CH_3(g)$
    c. $Na(s) + \frac{1}{2}\ Cl_2(g) \longrightarrow NaCl(s)$
    d. $N_2(g) + 3\ H_2(g) \longrightarrow 2\ NH_3(g)$
28. Without doing any calculations, determine the sign of ΔS_{sys} for each chemical reaction.
    a. $Mg(s) + Cl_2(g) \longrightarrow MgCl_2(s)$
    b. $2\ H_2S(g) + 3\ O_2(g) \longrightarrow 2\ H_2O(g) + 2\ SO_2(g)$
    c. $2\ O_3(g) \longrightarrow 3\ O_2(g)$
    d. $HCl(g) + NH_3(g) \longrightarrow NH_4Cl(s)$

29. Without doing any calculations, determine the sign of ΔS_{sys} and ΔS_{surr} for each chemical reaction. In addition, predict under what temperatures (all temperatures, low temperatures, or high temperatures), if any, the reaction will be spontaneous.

a. $C_3H_8(g) + 5O_2(g) \longrightarrow 3CO_2(g) + 4H_2O(g)$ $\quad \Delta_rH° = -2044\,kJ\,mol^{-1}$

b. $N_2(g) + O_2(g) \longrightarrow 2NO(g)$ $\quad \Delta_rH° = 182.6\,kJ\,mol^{-1}$

c. $2N_2(g) + O_2(g) \longrightarrow 2N_2O(g)$ $\quad \Delta_rH° = 163.2\,kJ\,mol^{-1}$

d. $4NH_3(g) + 5O_2(g) \longrightarrow 4NO(g) + 6H_2O(g)$ $\quad \Delta_rH° = -906\,kJ\,mol^{-1}$

30. Without doing any calculations, determine the sign of ΔS_{sys} and ΔS_{surr} for each chemical reaction. In addition, predict under what temperatures (all temperatures, low temperatures, or high temperatures), if any, the reaction will be spontaneous.

a. $2CO(g) + O_2(g) \longrightarrow 2CO_2(g)$ $\quad \Delta_rH° = -566.0\,kJ\,mol^{-1}$

b. $2\,NO_2(g) \longrightarrow 2\,NO(g) + O_2(g)$ $\quad \Delta_rH° = 113.1\,kJ\,mol^{-1}$

c. $2\,H_2(g) + O_2(g) \longrightarrow 2\,H_2O(g)$ $\quad \Delta_rH° = -483.6\,kJ\,mol^{-1}$

d. $CO_2(g) \longrightarrow C(s) + O_2(g)$ $\quad \Delta_rH° = 393.5\,kJ\,mol^{-1}$

31. Calculate ΔS_{surr} at the indicated temperature for each reaction.

a. $\Delta_rH° = -385\,kJ\,mol^{-1}$; 298 K

b. $\Delta_rH° = -385\,kJ\,mol^{-1}$; 77 K

c. $\Delta_rH° = 114\,kJ\,mol^{-1}$; 298 K

d. $\Delta_rH° = 114\,kJ\,mol^{-1}$; 77 K

32. A reaction has $\Delta_rH° = -112\,kJ\,mol^{-1}$ and $\Delta_rS° = 354\,J\,K^{-1}\,mol^{-1}$. At what temperature is the change in entropy for the reaction equal to the change in entropy for the surroundings?

33. Given the values of $\Delta_rH°$, $\Delta_rS°$ and T below, determine ΔS_{univ} and predict whether or not each reaction will be spontaneous.

a. $\Delta_rH° = 115\,kJ\,mol^{-1}$; $\Delta_rS° = -263\,J\,K^{-1}\,mol^{-1}$; $T = 298\,K$

b. $\Delta_rH° = -115\,kJ\,mol^{-1}$; $\Delta_rS° = 263\,J\,K^{-1}\,mol^{-1}$; $T = 298\,K$

c. $\Delta_rH° = -115\,kJ\,mol^{-1}$; $\Delta_rS° = -263\,J\,K^{-1}\,mol^{-1}$; $T = 298\,K$

d. $\Delta_rH° = -115\,kJ\,mol^{-1}$; $\Delta_rS° = -263\,J\,K^{-1}\,mol^{-1}$; $T = 615\,K$

34. Given the values of $\Delta_rH°$, $\Delta_rS°$, and T below, determine ΔS_{univ} and predict whether or not each reaction will be spontaneous.

a. $\Delta_rH° = -95\,kJ\,mol^{-1}$; $\Delta_rS° = -157\,J\,K^{-1}\,mol^{-1}$; $T = 298\,K$

b. $\Delta_rH° = -95\,kJ\,mol^{-1}$; $\Delta_rS° = -157\,J\,K^{-1}\,mol^{-1}$; $T = 855\,K$

c. $\Delta_rH° = 95\,kJ\,mol^{-1}$; $\Delta_rS° = -157\,J\,K^{-1}\,mol^{-1}$; $T = 298\,K$

d. $\Delta_rH° = -95\,kJ\,mol^{-1}$; $\Delta_rS° = 157\,J\,K^{-1}\,mol^{-1}$; $T = 398\,K$

35. The enthalpy change measured for the vaporization of water is $40.65\,kJ\,mol^{-1}$ at its boiling point. Determine the change in entropy for the vaporization of water.

36. The enthalpy change associated with the vaporization of ethanol is $38.6\,kJ\,mol^{-1}$ at its boiling point of 78 °C. Determine the change in entropy for the vaporization of ethanol and compare it to that computed for water in Problem 35.

Standard Entropy Changes and Gibbs Energy

37. Calculate the change in Gibbs energy for each of the sets of $\Delta_rH°$, $\Delta_rS°$, and T given in Problem 33. Predict whether or not each reaction will be spontaneous at the temperature indicated.

38. Calculate the change in Gibbs energy for each of the sets of $\Delta_rH°$, $\Delta_rS°$, and T given in Problem 34. Predict whether or not each reaction will be spontaneous at the temperature indicated.

39. Calculate the Gibbs energy change for this reaction at 25 °C. Is the reaction spontaneous?

$$C_3H_8(g) + 5\,O_2(g) \longrightarrow 3\,CO_2(g) + 4\,H_2O(g)$$
$$\Delta_rH° = -2217\,kJ\,mol^{-1};\ \Delta_rS° = 101.1\,J\,K^{-1}\,mol^{-1}$$

40. Calculate the Gibbs energy change for this reaction at 25 °C. Is the reaction spontaneous?

$$2\,Ca(s) + O_2(g) \longrightarrow 2\,CaO(s)$$
$$\Delta_rH° = -1269.8\,kJ\,mol^{-1};\ \Delta_rS° = -364.6\,J\,K^{-1}\,mol^{-1}$$

41. Fill in the blanks in the table. Both ΔH and ΔS refer to the system.

Δ_rH	Δ_rS	Δ_rG	Low Temperature	High Temperature
−	+	−	Spontaneous	______
−	−	Temperature dependent	______	______
+	+	______	______	Spontaneous
______	−	______	Nonspontaneous	Nonspontaneous

42. Predict the conditions (high temperature, low temperature, all temperatures, or no temperatures) under which each reaction is spontaneous.

a. $H_2O(g) \longrightarrow H_2O(l)$

b. $CO_2(s) \longrightarrow CO_2(g)$

c. $H_2(g) \longrightarrow 2\,H(g)$

d. $2\,NO_2(g) \longrightarrow 2\,NO(g) + O_2(g)$ (endothermic)

43. How does the molar entropy of a substance change with increasing temperature?

44. What is the molar entropy of a pure crystal at 0 K? What is the significance of the answer to this question?

45. For each pair of substances, choose the one that you expect to have the higher standard molar entropy ($S°$) at 25 °C. Explain the reasons for your choices.

a. $CO(g)$; $CO_2(g)$

b. $CH_3OH(l)$; $CH_3OH(g)$

c. $Ar(g)$; $CO_2(g)$

d. $CH_4(g)$; $SiH_4(g)$

e. $NO_2(g)$; $CH_3CH_2CH_3(g)$

f. $NaBr(s)$; $NaBr(aq)$

46. For each pair of substances, choose the one that you expect to have the higher standard molar entropy ($S°$) at 25 °C. Explain the reasons for your choices.

a. $NaNO_3(s)$; $NaNO_3(aq)$

b. $CH_4(g)$; $CH_3CH_3(g)$

c. $Br_2(l)$; $Br_2(g)$

d. $Br_2(g)$; $F_2(g)$

e. $PCl_3(g)$; $PCl_5(g)$

f. $CH_3CH_2CH_2CH_3(g)$; $SO_2(g)$

47. Rank each set of substances in order of increasing standard molar entropy ($S°$). Explain your reasoning.

a. $NH_3(g)$; $Ne(g)$; $SO_2(g)$; $CH_3CH_2OH(g)$; $He(g)$

b. $H_2O(s)$; $H_2O(l)$; $H_2O(g)$

c. $CH_4(g)$; $CF_4(g)$; $CCl_4(g)$

48. Rank each set of substances in order of increasing standard molar entropy ($S°$). Explain your reasoning.

a. $I_2(g)$; $F_2(g)$; $Br_2(g)$; $Cl_2(g)$

b. $H_2O(g)$; $H_2O_2(g)$; $H_2S(g)$

c. $C(s,$ graphite$)$; $C(s,$ diamond$)$; $C(s,$ amorphous$)$

49. Use data from Appendix IIB to calculate $\Delta_r S°$ for each of the reactions. In each case, try to rationalize the sign of $\Delta_r S°$.
a. $C_2H_4(g) + H_2(g) \longrightarrow C_2H_6(g)$
b. $C(s) + H_2O(g) \longrightarrow CO(g) + H_2(g)$
c. $CO(g) + H_2O(g) \longrightarrow H_2(g) + CO_2(g)$
d. $2\ H_2S(g) + 3\ O_2(g) \longrightarrow 2\ H_2O(l) + 2\ SO_2(g)$

50. Use data from Appendix IIB to calculate $\Delta_r S°$ for each of the reactions. In each case, try to rationalize the sign of $\Delta_r S°$.
a. $3\ NO_2(g) + H_2O(l) \longrightarrow 2\ HNO_3(aq) + NO(g)$
b. $Cr_2O_3(s) + 3\ CO(g) \longrightarrow 2\ Cr(s) + 3\ CO_2(g)$
c. $SO_2(g) + \frac{1}{2} O_2(g) \longrightarrow SO_3(g)$
d. $N_2O_4(g) + 4\ H_2(g) \longrightarrow N_2(g) + 4\ H_2O(g)$

51. Find $\Delta_r S°$ for the formation of $CH_2Cl_2(g)$ from its gaseous elements in their standard states. Rationalize the sign of $\Delta_r S°$.

52. Find $\Delta_r S°$ for the reaction between nitrogen gas and fluorine gas to form nitrogen trifluoride gas. Rationalize the sign of $\Delta_r S°$.

53. Methanol burns in oxygen to form carbon dioxide and water. Write a balanced equation for the combustion of liquid methanol and calculate $\Delta_r H°$, $\Delta_r S°$, and $\Delta_r G°$ at 25 °C. Is the combustion of methanol spontaneous?

54. In photosynthesis, plants form glucose ($C_6H_{12}O_6$) and oxygen from carbon dioxide and water. Write a balanced equation for photosynthesis and calculate $\Delta_r H°$, $\Delta_r S°$, and $\Delta_r G°$ at 25 °C. Is photosynthesis spontaneous?

55. For each reaction, calculate $\Delta_r H°$, $\Delta_r S°$, and $\Delta_r G°$ at 25 °C. and state whether or not the reaction is spontaneous. If the reaction is not spontaneous, would a change in temperature make it spontaneous? If so, should the temperature be raised or lowered from 25 °C?
a. $N_2O_4(g) \longrightarrow 2\ NO_2(g)$
b. $NH_4Cl(s) \longrightarrow HCl(g) + NH_3(g)$
c. $3\ H_2(g) + Fe_2O_3(s) \longrightarrow 2\ Fe(s) + 3\ H_2O(l)$
d. $N_2(g) + 3\ H_2(g) \longrightarrow 2\ NH_3(g)$

56. For each reaction, calculate $\Delta_r H°$, $\Delta_r S°$, and $\Delta_r G°$ at 25 °C and state whether or not the reaction is spontaneous. If the reaction is not spontaneous, would a change in temperature make it spontaneous? If so, should the temperature be raised or lowered from 25 °C?
a. $2\ CH_4(g) \longrightarrow C_2H_6(g) + H_2(g)$
b. $2\ NH_3(g) \longrightarrow N_2H_4(g) + H_2(g)$
c. $N_2(g) + O_2(g) \longrightarrow 2\ NO(g)$
d. $2\ KClO_3(s) \longrightarrow 2\ KCl(s) + 3\ O_2(g)$

57. Use standard Gibbs energies of formation to calculate $\Delta_r G°$ at 25 °C for each reaction in Problem 55. How do the values of $\Delta_r G°$ calculated this way compare to those calculated from $\Delta_r H°$ and $\Delta_r S°$? Which of the two methods could be used to determine how $\Delta_r G°$ changes with temperature?

58. Use standard Gibbs energies of formation to calculate $\Delta_r G°$ at 25 °C for each reaction in Problem 56. How well do the values of $\Delta_r G°$ calculated this way compare to those calculated from $\Delta_r H°$ and $\Delta_r S°$? Which of the two methods could be used to determine how $\Delta_r G°$ changes with temperature?

59. Consider the reaction:

$$2\ NO(g) + O_2(g) \longrightarrow 2\ NO_2(g)$$

Estimate $\Delta_r G°$ for this reaction at each temperature and predict whether or not the reaction will be spontaneous. (Assume that $\Delta_r H°$ and $\Delta_r S°$ do not change too much within the given temperature range.)
a. 298 K b. 715 K c. 855 K

60. Consider the reaction:

$$CaCO_3(s) \longrightarrow CaO(s) + CO_2(g)$$

Estimate $\Delta_r G°$ for this reaction at each temperature and predict whether or not the reaction will be spontaneous. (Assume that $\Delta_r H°$ and $\Delta_r S°$ do not change too much within the given temperature range.)
a. 298 K b. 1055 K c. 1455 K

61. Determine $\Delta_r G°$ for the reaction:

$$Fe_2O_3(s) + 3\ CO(g) \longrightarrow 2\ Fe(s) + 3\ CO_2(g)$$

Use the following reactions with known $\Delta_r G°$ values:

$$2\ Fe(s) + \tfrac{3}{2} O_2(g) \longrightarrow Fe_2O_3(s) \quad \Delta_r G° = -742.2 \text{ kJ mol}^{-1}$$
$$CO(g) + \tfrac{1}{2} O_2(g) \longrightarrow CO_2(g) \quad \Delta_r G° = -257.2 \text{ kJ mol}^{-1}$$

62. Calculate $\Delta_r G°$ for the reaction:

$$CaCO_3(s) \longrightarrow CaO(s) + CO_2(g)$$

Use the following reactions and given $\Delta_r G°$ values:

$$Ca(s) + CO_2(g) + \tfrac{1}{2} O_2(g) \longrightarrow CaCO_3(s) \quad \Delta_r G° = -734.4 \text{ kJ mol}^{-1}$$
$$2\ Ca(s) + O_2(g) \longrightarrow 2\ CaO(s) \quad \Delta_r G° = -1206.6 \text{ kJ mol}^{-1}$$

Gibbs Energy Changes, Nonstandard Conditions, and the Equilibrium Constant

63. Consider the sublimation of iodine at 25.0 °C:

$$I_2(s) \longrightarrow I_2(g)$$

a. Find $\Delta_r G°$ at 25.0 °C.
b. Find $\Delta_r G$ at 25.0 °C under the following nonstandard conditions:
(i) $P_{I_2} = 1.00$ mbar
(ii) $P_{I_2} = 0.100$ mbar
c. Explain why iodine spontaneously sublimes in open air at 25.0 °C.

64. Consider the evaporation of methanol at 25.0 °C.

$$CH_3OH(l) \longrightarrow CH_3OH(g)$$

a. Find $\Delta_r G°$ at 25.0 °C.
b. Find $\Delta_r G$ at 25.0 °C under the following nonstandard conditions:
(i) $P_{CH_3OH} = 150.0$ mbar
(ii) $P_{CH_3OH} = 100.0$ mbar
(iii) $P_{CH_3OH} = 10.0$ mbar
c. Explain why methanol spontaneously evaporates in open air at 25.0 °C.

65. Consider the reaction:

$$CH_3OH(g) \rightleftharpoons CO(g) + 2\ H_2(g)$$

Calculate $\Delta_r G$ for this reaction at 125 °C under the following conditions:

$P_{CH_3OH} = 0.855$ bar
$P_{CO} = 0.125$ bar
$P_{H_2} = 0.183$ bar

66. Consider the reaction:

$$CO_2(g) + CCl_4(g) \rightleftharpoons 2\ COCl_2(g)$$

Calculate $\Delta_r G$ for this reaction at 125 °C under the following conditions:

$P_{CO_2} = 0.112$ bar
$P_{CCl_4} = 0.174$ bar
$P_{COCl_2} = 0.744$ bar

67. Use data from Appendix IIB to calculate the equilibrium constants at 25 °C for each reaction.
a. $2\ CO(g) + O_2(g) \rightleftharpoons 2\ CO_2(g)$
b. $2\ H_2S(g) \rightleftharpoons 2\ H_2(g) + S_2(g)$

68. Use data from Appendix IIB to calculate the equilibrium constants at 25 °C for each reaction. $\Delta_f G°$ (298 K) for BrCl(g) is −1.0 kJ mol^{-1}.
a. $2\ NO_2(g) \rightleftharpoons N_2O_4(g)$
b. $Br_2(l) + Cl_2(g) \rightleftharpoons 2\ BrCl(g)$

69. Consider this reaction:

$$I_2(g) + Cl_2(g) \rightleftharpoons 2\ ICl(g) \quad K = 6.91 \times 10^3 \text{ at } 460\text{ K}$$

Calculate $\Delta_r G$ for the reaction at 460 K under each of the following conditions:
a. standard conditions
b. at equilibrium
c. $P_{I_2} = 0.325$ bar; $P_{Cl_2} = 0.221$ bar; $P_{ICl} = 2.55$ bar

70. Consider this reaction:

$$CO(g) + 2\ H_2(g) \rightleftharpoons CH_3OH(g) \quad K = 2.18 \times 10^2 \text{ at } 340\text{ K}$$

Calculate $\Delta_r G$ for the reaction at 340 K under each of the following conditions:
a. standard conditions
b. at equilibrium
c. $P_{CO} = P_{H_2} = 0.0010$ bar; $P_{CH_3OH} = 1.0$ bar

71. Estimate the value of the equilibrium constant at 525 K for each reaction in Problem 67.

72. Estimate the value of the equilibrium constant at 655 K for each reaction in Problem 68. ($\Delta_f H°$ for BrCl is 14.6 kJ mol^{-1}.)

73. Consider the reaction:

$$H_2(g) + I_2(g) \rightleftharpoons 2\ HI(g)$$

The data below show the equilibrium constant for this reaction measured at several different temperatures. Use the data to find $\Delta_r H°$ and $\Delta_r S°$ for the reaction.

Temperature/K	K
150	2.6×10^4
175	8.9×10^3
200	4.0×10^3
225	2.1×10^3
250	1.3×10^3

74. Consider the reaction:

$$2\ NO(g) + O_2(g) \rightleftharpoons 2\ NO_2(g)$$

The data below show the equilibrium constant for this reaction measured at several different temperatures. Use the data to find $\Delta_r H°$ and $\Delta_r S°$ for the reaction.

Temperature/K	K
400	1.9×10^7
425	2.5×10^6
465	1.6×10^5
515	8.8×10^3
600	2.0×10^2

75. The change in enthalpy ($\Delta_r H°$) for a reaction is −25.8 kJ mol^{-1}. The equilibrium constant for the reaction is 1.4×10^3 at 298 K. What is the equilibrium constant for the reaction at 655 K?

76. A reaction has an equilibrium constant of 8.5×10^3 at 298 K. At 755 K, the equilibrium constant is 0.65. Find $\Delta_r H°$ for the reaction.

Cumulative Problems

77. Determine the sign of ΔS_{sys} for each process:
a. water boiling
b. water freezing
c.

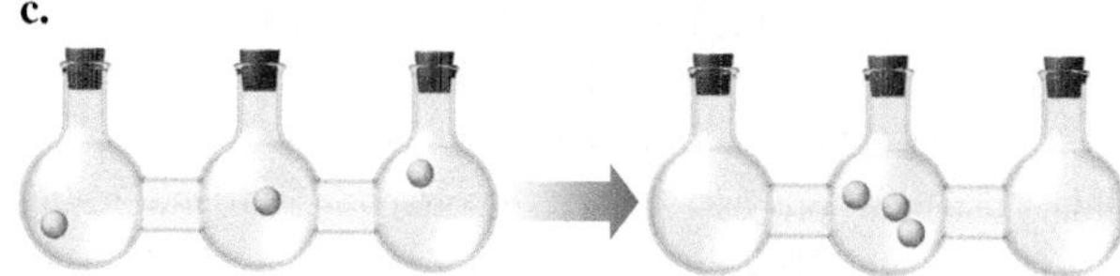

78. Determine the sign of ΔS_{sys} for each process:
a. dry ice subliming
b. dew forming
c.

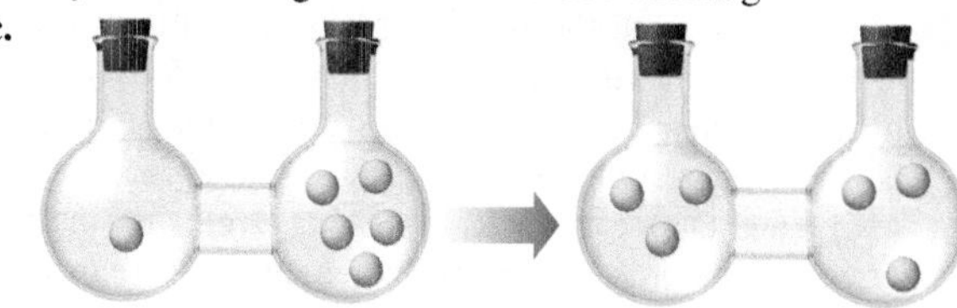

79. Our atmosphere is composed primarily of nitrogen and oxygen, which coexist at 25 °C without reacting to any significant extent. However, the two gases can react to form nitrogen monoxide according to the reaction:

$$N_2(g) + O_2(g) \rightleftharpoons 2\ NO(g)$$

a. Calculate $\Delta_r G°$ and K for this reaction at 298 K. Is the reaction spontaneous?
b. Estimate $\Delta_r G°$ at 2000 K. Does the reaction become more spontaneous as temperature increases?

80. Nitrogen dioxide, a pollutant in the atmosphere, can combine with water to form nitric acid. One of the possible reactions is shown here. Calculate $\Delta_r G°$ and K for this reaction at 25 °C and comment on the spontaneity of the reaction.

$$3\ NO_2(g) + H_2O(l) \longrightarrow 2\ HNO_3(aq) + NO(g)$$

81. Ethene (C_2H_4) can be halogenated by the reaction:

$$C_2H_4(g) + X_2(g) \rightleftharpoons C_2H_4X_2(g)$$

where X_2 can be Cl_2, Br_2, or I_2. Use the thermodynamic data given to calculate $\Delta_r H°$, $\Delta_r S°$, $\Delta_r G°$, and K for the halogenation reaction by each of the three halogens at 25 °C. Which reaction is most spontaneous? Least spontaneous? What is the main factor responsible for the difference in the spontaneity of the three reactions? Does higher temperature make the reactions more spontaneous or less spontaneous?

Compound	$\Delta_f H°$ (kJ mol^{-1})	$S°$(J mol^{-1} K^{-1})
$C_2H_4Cl_2(g)$	−129.7	308.0
$C_2H_4Br_2(g)$	38.3	330.6
$C_2H_4I_2(g)$	66.5	347.8

82. H_2 reacts with the halogens (X_2) according to the reaction:

$$H_2(g) + X_2(g) \rightleftharpoons 2\ HX(g)$$

where X_2 can be Cl_2, Br_2, or I_2. Use the thermodynamic data in Appendix IIB to calculate $\Delta_f H°$ and K for the reaction between hydrogen and each of the three halogens. Which reaction is most spontaneous? Least spontaneous? What is the main factor responsible for the difference in the spontaneity of the three reactions? Does higher temperature make the reactions more spontaneous or less spontaneous?

83. Consider this reaction occurring at 298 K:

$$N_2O(g) + NO_2(g) \rightleftharpoons 3\ NO(g)$$

a. Show that the reaction is not spontaneous under standard conditions by calculating $\Delta_r G°$.
b. If a reaction mixture contains only N_2O and NO_2 at partial pressures of 1.0 bar each, the reaction will be spontaneous until some NO forms in the mixture. What maximum partial pressure of NO builds up before the reaction ceases to be spontaneous?
c. Can the reaction be made more spontaneous by an increase or decrease in temperature? If so, what temperature is required to make the reaction spontaneous under standard conditions?

84. Consider this reaction occurring at 298 K:

$$BaCO_3(s) \rightleftharpoons BaO(s) + CO_2(g)$$

a. Show that the reaction is not spontaneous under standard conditions by calculating $\Delta_r G°$.
b. If $BaCO_3$ is placed in an evacuated flask, what partial pressure of CO_2 will be present when the reaction reaches equilibrium?
c. Can the reaction be made more spontaneous by an increase or decrease in temperature? If so, what temperature is required to produce a carbon dioxide partial pressure of 1.0 bar?

85. Living organisms use energy from the metabolism of food to create an energy-rich molecule called adenosine triphosphate (ATP). The ATP then acts as an energy source for a variety of reactions that the living organism must carry out to survive. ATP provides energy through its hydrolysis, which can be symbolized as follows:

$$ATP(aq) + H_2O(l) \longrightarrow ADP(aq) + P_i(aq) \quad \Delta_r G° = -30.5\ \text{kJ mol}^{-1}$$

where ADP represents adenosine diphosphate and P_i represents an inorganic phosphate group (such as HPO_4^{2-}).

a. Calculate the equilibrium constant, K, for the above reaction at 298 K.
b. The Gibbs energy obtained from the oxidation (reaction with oxygen) of glucose ($C_6H_{12}O_6$) to form carbon dioxide and water can be used to re-form ATP by driving the above reaction in reverse. Calculate the standard Gibbs energy change for the oxidation of glucose and estimate the maximum number of moles of ATP that can be formed by the oxidation of one mole of glucose.

86. The standard Gibbs energy change for the hydrolysis of ATP was given in Problem 85. In a particular cell, the concentrations of ATP, ADP, and P_i are 0.0031 mol L^{-1}, 0.0014 mol L^{-1}, and 0.0048 mol L^{-1}, respectively. Calculate the Gibbs energy change for the hydrolysis of ATP under these conditions. (Assume a temperature of 298 K.)

87. These reactions are important in catalytic converters in automobiles. Calculate $\Delta_r G°$. for each at 298 K. Predict the effect of increasing temperature on the magnitude of $\Delta_r G°$.

a. $2\ CO(g) + 2\ NO(g) \longrightarrow N_2(g) + 2\ CO_2(g)$
b. $5\ H_2(g) + 2\ NO(g) \longrightarrow 2\ NH_3(g) + 2\ H_2O(g)$
c. $2\ H_2(g) + 2\ NO(g) \longrightarrow N_2(g) + 2\ H_2O(g)$
d. $2\ NH_3(g) + 2\ O_2(g) \longrightarrow N_2O(g) + 3\ H_2O(g)$

88. Calculate $\Delta_r G°$. at 298 K for these reactions and predict the effect on $\Delta_r G°$. of lowering the temperature.

a. $NH_3(g) + HBr(g) \longrightarrow NH_4Br(s)$
b. $CaCO_3(s) \longrightarrow CaO(s) + CO_2(g)$
c. $CH_4(g) + 3\ Cl_2(g) \longrightarrow CHCl_3(g) + 3\ HCl(g)$
($\Delta_f G°$ for $CHCl_3(g)$ is –70.4 kJ mol^{-1}.)

89. All the oxides of nitrogen have positive values of $\Delta_f G°$ at 298 K, but only one common oxide of nitrogen has a positive $\Delta_r S°$. Identify that oxide of nitrogen without reference to thermodynamic data and explain.

90. The values of $\Delta_f G°$ for the hydrogen halides become less negative with increasing atomic number. The $\Delta_f G°$ of HI is slightly positive. On the other hand the trend in $S°$ is to become more positive with increasing atomic number. Explain.

91. Consider the reaction: $X_2(g) \longrightarrow 2\ X(g)$. When a vessel initially containing 755 Torr of X_2 comes to equilibrium at 298 K, the equilibrium partial pressure of X is 103 Torr. The same reaction is repeated with an initial partial pressure of 748 Torr of X_2 at 755 K; the equilibrium partial pressure of X is 532 Torr. Find $\Delta_r H°$ for the reaction.

92. Dinitrogen tetroxide decomposes to nitrogen dioxide:

$$N_2O_4(g) \longrightarrow 2\ NO_2(g) \quad \Delta_r H° = 55.3\ \text{kJ mol}^{-1}$$

At 298 K, a reaction vessel initially contains 0.100 bar of N_2O_4. When equilibrium is reached, 58% of the N_2O_4 has decomposed to NO_2. What percentage of N_2O_4 decomposes at 388 K? Assume that the initial pressure of N_2O_4 is the same (0.100 bar).

93. Indicate and explain the sign of ΔS_{univ} for each process.

a. $2\ H_2(g) + O_2(g) \longrightarrow 2\ H_2O(l)$ at 298 K
b. the electrolysis of $H_2O(l)$ to $H_2(g)$ and $O_2(g)$ at 298 K
c. the growth of an oak tree from a little acorn

94. The Haber process is very important for agriculture because it converts $N_2(g)$ from the atmosphere into bound nitrogen which can be taken up and used by plants. The reaction is $N_2(g) + 3\ H_2(g) \rightleftharpoons 2\ NH_3(g)$. This reaction is exothermic, but is carried out at relatively high temperatures. Why?

95. A metal salt with the formula MCl_2 crystallizes from water to form a solid with the composition $MCl_2 \cdot 6\ H_2O$. The equilibrium vapour pressure of water above this solid at 298 K is 18.3 mbar. What is the value of $\Delta_r G$ for the reaction $MCl_2 \cdot 6\ H_2O(s) \rightleftharpoons MCl_2(s) + 6\ H_2O(g)$ when the pressure of water vapour is 18.3 mbar? When the pressure of water vapour is 1 bar?

96. The solubility of AgCl(s) in water at 25 °C is 1.33×10^{-5} mol L^{-1} and its $\Delta_r H°$ of solution is 65.7 kJ mol^{-1}. What is its solubility at 50.0 °C?

97. The *normal boiling point* of a substance is defined as the temperature at which the vapour pressure above the liquid equals the external pressure, which is one atmosphere (1 atm) or simply the temperature at which the substance boils at 1 atm. Standard pressure is 1 bar, so the *standard boiling point* is the temperature at which the substance boils at 1 bar. The normal boiling point for water is 100.0 °C. Given that the heat of vaporization for water is 40.6 kJ mol^{-1} at 100 °C, determine the standard boiling point for water.

98. Given the following reaction at 298 K:

$$2\,H_2S(g) + SO_2(g) \longrightarrow \tfrac{3}{8}\,S_8(s) + 2\,H_2O(g) \qquad \Delta_r G^\circ = -102\,\text{kJ mol}^{-1}$$

a. Calculate $\Delta_r G$ under the following conditions:

$$P_{H_2S} = 2.00\,\text{bar};\ P_{SO_2} = 0.165\,\text{bar};\ P_{H_2O} = 1.162\,\text{bar}$$

b. Is this reaction more or less spontaneous than under standard conditions? Justify your answer.

c. Calculate the equilibrium constant for this reaction at 298 K.

Challenge Problems

99. Review the box in this chapter entitled *Chemistry in Your Day: Making a Nonspontaneous Process Spontaneous.* The hydrolysis of ATP, shown in Problem 85, is often used to drive nonspontaneous processes—such as muscle contraction and protein synthesis—in living organisms. The nonspontaneous process to be driven must be coupled to the ATP hydrolysis reaction. For example, suppose the nonspontaneous process is $A + B \longrightarrow AB$ ($\Delta_r G^\circ$ positive). The coupling of a nonspontaneous reaction such as this one to the hydrolysis of ATP is often accomplished by the mechanism:

$$A + ATP + H_2O \longrightarrow A{-}P_i + ADP$$
$$A{-}P_i + B \longrightarrow AB + P_i$$
$$\overline{A + B + ATP + H_2O \longrightarrow AB + ADP + P_i}$$

As long as $\Delta_r G^\circ$ for the nonspontaneous reaction is less than 30.5 kJ mol^{-1}, the reaction can be made spontaneous by coupling in this way to the hydrolysis of ATP. Suppose that ATP is to drive the reaction between glutamate and ammonia to form glutamine:

O^-–C(=O)–CH_2–CH_2–CH(NH_3^+)–C(=O)–O^- + NH_3 $\longrightarrow$

NH_2–C(=O)–CH_2–CH_2–CH(NH_3^+)–C(=O)–O^- + H_2O

a. Calculate K for the reaction between glutamate and ammonia. (The standard Gibbs energy change for the reaction is 14.2 kJ mol^{-1}. Assume a temperature of 298 K.)

b. Write a set of reactions such as those shown above showing how the glutamate and ammonia reaction can couple with the hydrolysis of ATP. What are $\Delta_r G^\circ$ and K for the coupled reaction?

100. Estimate the aqueous solubility of AgCl(s) at 320 K. Use thermodynamic data from Appendix II.

101. Suppose we redefine the standard state as $P = 2$ bar. Find the new standard $\Delta_f G^\circ$ values of each substance.

a. HCl(g) **b.** $N_2O(g)$ **c.** H(g)

Explain the results in terms of the relative entropies of reactants and products of each reaction.

102. The $\Delta_r G$ for the freezing of $H_2O(l)$ at −10 °C is −210 J mol^{-1} and the heat of fusion of ice at this temperature is 5610 J mol^{-1}. Find the entropy change of the universe when 1 mol of water freezes at −10 °C.

103. Consider the reaction that occurs during the Haber process:

$$N_2(g) + 3\,H_2(g) \longrightarrow 2\,NH_3(g)$$

The equilibrium constant is 3.9×10^5 at 300 K and 1.2×10^{-1} at 500 K. Calculate $\Delta_r H^\circ$ and $\Delta_r S^\circ$ for this reaction.

104. The salt ammonium nitrate can follow three modes of decomposition: **(a)** to $HNO_3(g)$ and $NH_3(g)$, **(b)** to $N_2O(g)$ and $H_2O(g)$, and **(c)** to $N_2(g)$, $O_2(g)$, and $H_2O(g)$. Calculate $\Delta_r G^\circ$ for each mode of decomposition at 298 K. Explain in light of these results how it is still possible to use ammonium nitrate as a fertilizer and the precautions that should be taken when it is used.

105. Given the data, calculate $\Delta_{vap}S$ for each of the first four liquids. ($\Delta_{vap}S = \Delta_{vap}H/R$, where T is in K.)

Compound	Name	BP(°C)*	$\Delta_{vap}H$ (kJ mol^{-1}) at BP
$C_4H_{10}O$	Diethyl ether	34.6	26.5
C_3H_6O	Acetone	56.1	29.1
C_6H_6	Benzene	79.8	30.8
$CHCl_3$	Chloroform	60.8	29.4
C_2H_5OH	Ethanol	77.8	38.6
H_2O	Water	100	40.7

*These are "normal boiling points" (i.e., the temperature at which the compound boils at 1 atm of pressure).

All four values should be close to each other. Predict whether the last two liquids in the table are expected to have $\Delta_{vap}S$ in this same range. If not, predict whether it should be larger or smaller and explain. Verify your prediction.

106. Consider the dissolution of the following two salts:

$$Pb(NO_3)_2(s) \longrightarrow Pb^{2+}(aq) + 2\,NO_3^-(aq)$$

$$\Delta_r H^\circ = 17.4 \text{ kJ mol}^{-1}$$
$$\Delta_r S^\circ = 233.1 \text{ J K}^{-1}\text{mol}^{-1}$$

$$PbCl_2(s) \longrightarrow Pb^{2+}(aq) + 2\,Cl^-(aq)$$

$$\Delta_r H^\circ = 26.2 \text{ kJ mol}^{-1}$$
$$\Delta_r S^\circ = -2.1 \text{ J K}^{-1}\text{mol}^{-1}$$

The enthalpies and entropies of these reactions are 298 K values.

a. Based on solubility rules, do you expect $Pb(NO_3)_2$ and/or $PbCl_2$ to be soluble? Explain.

b. Determine the solubility in mol L^{-1} of each of the two salts.

c. What thermodynamic property is driving the solubility of lead nitrate?

d. With the data provided in this question, determine whether a solution containing 1.0×10^{-2} mol L^{-1} Pb^{2+} and 2.0×10^{-2} Cl^- will precipitate or not at 298 K.

107. Given the following thermochemical data for the dissolution of sodium chloride:

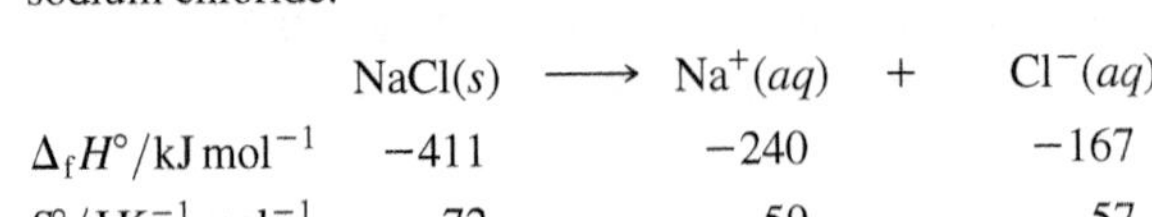

	$NaCl(s)$	$\longrightarrow$	$Na^+(aq)$	+	$Cl^-(aq)$
$\Delta_f H^\circ/\text{kJ mol}^{-1}$	−411		−240		−167
$S^\circ/\text{J K}^{-1}\text{mol}^{-1}$	72		59		57

Calculate the 298 K standard Gibbs energy change for this reaction, the equilibrium constant, and the solubility in mol L^{-1} of solid NaCl.

Conceptual Problems

108. Which is more efficient, a butane lighter or an electric lighter (such as can be found in most automobiles)? Explain.

109. Which statement is true?

a. A spontaneous reaction is always a fast reaction.

b. A spontaneous reaction is always a slow reaction.

c. The spontaneity of a reaction is not necessarily related to the speed of a reaction.

110. Which process is necessarily driven by an increase in the entropy of the surroundings?

a. the condensation of water

b. the sublimation of dry ice

c. the freezing of water

111. Which statement is true?

a. A reaction in which the entropy of the system increases can be spontaneous only if it is exothermic.

b. A reaction in which the entropy of the system increases can be spontaneous only if it is endothermic.

c. A reaction in which the entropy of the system decreases can be spontaneous only if it is exothermic.

112. Which process is spontaneous at 298 K?

a. $H_2O(l) \longrightarrow H_2O(g, 1 \text{ bar})$

b. $H_2O(l) \longrightarrow H_2O(g, 0.10 \text{ bar})$

c. $H_2O(l) \longrightarrow H_2O(g, 0.010 \text{ bar})$

113. The Gibbs energy change of the reaction $A(g) \longrightarrow B(g)$ is zero under certain conditions. The *standard* Gibbs energy change of the reaction is −42.5 kJ mol^{-1}. Which statement must be true about the reaction?

a. The concentration of the product is greater than the concentration of the reactant.

b. The reaction is at equilibrium.

c. The concentration of the reactant is greater than the concentration of the product.

Electrochemistry

18

One day sir, you may tax it.

—Michael Faraday (1791–1867)

[In response to William Gladstone, the British Chancellor of the Exchequer, when asked about the practical worth of electricity.]

The MP3 player shown here is powered by a hydrogen–oxygen fuel cell, a device that generates electricity from the reaction between hydrogen and oxygen to form water.

THIS CHAPTER'S OPENING QUOTE FROM MICHAEL FARADAY illustrates an important aspect of basic research (research for the sake of understanding how nature works). The Chancellor of the Exchequer (the British cabinet minister responsible for all financial matters) wanted to know how Michael Faraday's apparently esoteric investigations of electricity would ever be useful to the empire. Faraday responded in a way that the Chancellor would understand—he pointed out the eventual financial payoff. Today, of course, electricity is a fundamental form of energy, powering our entire economy. Although basic research does not always lead to useful applications, much of the technology our society relies on has grown out of basic research. The history of modern science shows that you must first understand nature (the goal of basic research) before you can harness its power. In this chapter, we seek to understand oxidation–reduction reactions (first introduced in Chapter 4) and how we can exploit them to generate electricity. The applications range from the batteries that power flashlights to the fuel cells that may one day power our homes and automobiles.

18.1 Pulling the Plug on the Power Grid

The power grid distributes centrally generated electricity throughout the country to homes and businesses. When you turn on a light or electrical appliance, electricity flows from the grid, through the wires in your home, to the light or appliance. The electrical energy is converted into light within the lightbulb or into work within the appliance. The average Canadian household consumes about 1000 kilowatt-hours (kWh) of electricity per month. The local electrical utility, of course, monitors your electricity use and bills you for it.

The kilowatt-hour is a unit of energy first introduced in Section 6.2.

In the future, you may have the option of disconnecting from the power grid. Several innovative companies are developing small, fuel-cell power plants—each no bigger than a refrigerator—to sit next to homes and quietly generate enough electricity to meet each household's power needs. The heat produced by a fuel cell's operation can be recaptured and used to heat water or the space within the home, eliminating the need for a hot-water heater and a furnace. Similar fuel cells could also be used to power cars. Fuel cells are highly efficient and, although some obstacles to their development and use must yet be overcome, one day they may supply a majority of our power while producing less pollution than fossil fuel combustion.

▲ The energy produced by this fuel cell can power an entire house.

Fuel cells are based on oxidation–reduction reactions (see Section 4.6). The most common type of fuel cell—called the hydrogen–oxygen fuel cell—is based on the reaction between hydrogen and oxygen.

$$2\,H(g) + O_2(g) \longrightarrow 2\,H_2O(l)$$

In this reaction, hydrogen and oxygen form covalent bonds with one another. Recall that, according to Lewis theory, a single covalent bond is a shared electron pair. However, since oxygen is more electronegative than hydrogen, the electron pair in a hydrogen–oxygen bond is not *equally* shared: oxygen gets the larger portion (see Section 9.7). In effect, oxygen has more electrons in H_2O than it does in elemental O_2—it has gained electrons in the reaction and has therefore been reduced.

In a direct reaction between hydrogen and oxygen, oxygen atoms gain electrons directly from hydrogen atoms. In a hydrogen–oxygen fuel cell, the same redox reaction occurs, but the hydrogen and oxygen are separated, forcing electrons to travel through an external wire to get from hydrogen to oxygen. These moving electrons constitute an electrical current. Fuel cells employ the electron-gaining tendency of oxygen and the electron-losing tendency of hydrogen to force electrons to move through a wire to create the electricity that can provide power for a home or an electric automobile. Smaller fuel cells can also replace batteries and be used to power consumer electronics such as laptop computers, cell phones, and MP3 players. The generation of electricity from spontaneous redox reactions (such as a fuel cell) and the use of electricity to drive nonspontaneous redox reactions (such as those that occur in gold or silver plating) are examples of electrochemistry, the subject of this chapter.

▲ BC Transit had 20 hydrogen fuel-cell buses in service in Whistler, BC, for the 2010 Winter Olympic games. These buses, which were manufactured in Winnipeg, MB, have top speeds of 90 km/h, a life expectancy of 20 years, and produce zero emissions. The only exhaust from running the bus is water vapour. While the buses themselves do not emit CO_2, since there are no terrestrial reservoirs of H_2, there may have been significant emissions in the production and transportation of the of H_2 fuel. Citing triple the operating costs of diesel buses, the hydrogen fuel cell buses have been put in storage and are being sold off.

18.2 Voltaic (or Galvanic) Cells: Generating Electricity from Spontaneous Chemical Reactions

Electrical current is the flow of electric charge. Electrons flowing through a wire or ions flowing through a solution both constitute electrical current. Since redox reactions involve the transfer of electrons from one substance to another, they have the potential to generate electrical current. For example, consider the spontaneous redox reaction:

$$Zn(s) + Cu^{2+}(aq) \longrightarrow Zn^{2+}(aq) + Cu(s)$$

When Zn metal is placed in a Cu^{2+} solution, the greater tendency of zinc to lose electrons results in Zn being oxidized and Cu^{2+} being reduced—electrons are transferred directly from the Zn to the Cu^{2+} (Figure 18.1 ▼). Although the actual process is more complicated, we can imagine that—on the atomic scale—a zinc atom within the zinc metal transfers two electrons to a copper ion in solution. The zinc atom then becomes a zinc ion dissolved in the solution. The copper ion accepts the two electrons and is deposited on the zinc as solid copper.

Suppose we could separate the zinc atoms and copper ions and force the electron transfer to occur another way—not directly from the zinc atom to the copper ion, but through a wire connecting the two half-reactions. The flowing electrons would constitute an electrical current and could be used to do electrical work.

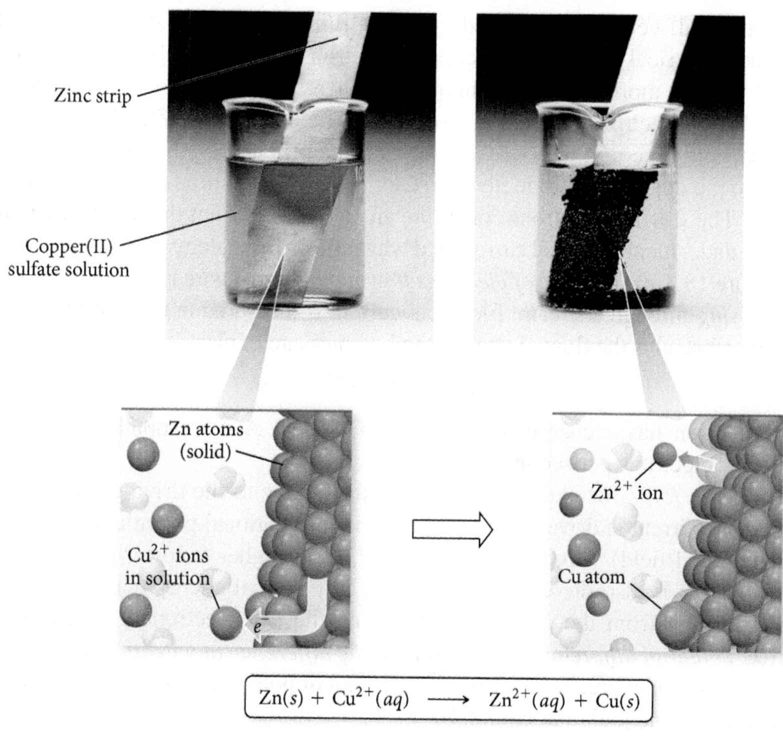

◀ **FIGURE 18.1 A Spontaneous Oxidation–Reduction Reaction** When zinc is immersed in a solution containing copper ions, the zinc atoms transfer electrons to the copper ions. The zinc atoms are oxidized and dissolve in the solution. The copper ions are reduced and are deposited on the electrode.

The generation of electricity through redox reactions is normally carried out in a device called an **electrochemical cell**. A **voltaic** (or **galvanic**) **cell** is an electrochemical cell that *produces* electrical current from a *spontaneous* chemical reaction. A second type of electrochemical cell, called an **electrolytic cell**, *consumes* electrical current to drive a *nonspontaneous* chemical reaction. We discuss voltaic cells in this section and electrolytic cells in Section 18.7.

In the voltaic cell in Figure 18.2 ▼, a solid strip of zinc is placed in a $Zn(NO_3)_2$ solution to form a **half-cell**. A solid strip of copper placed in a $Cu(NO_3)_2$ solution forms a second half-cell. The strips act as **electrodes**, conductive surfaces through which electrons can enter or leave the half-cells. Each metal strip reaches equilibrium with its ions in solution according to these half-reactions:

$$Zn(s) \rightleftharpoons Zn^{2+}(aq) + 2\,e^-$$
$$Cu^{2+}(aq) + 2\,e^- \rightleftharpoons Cu(s)$$

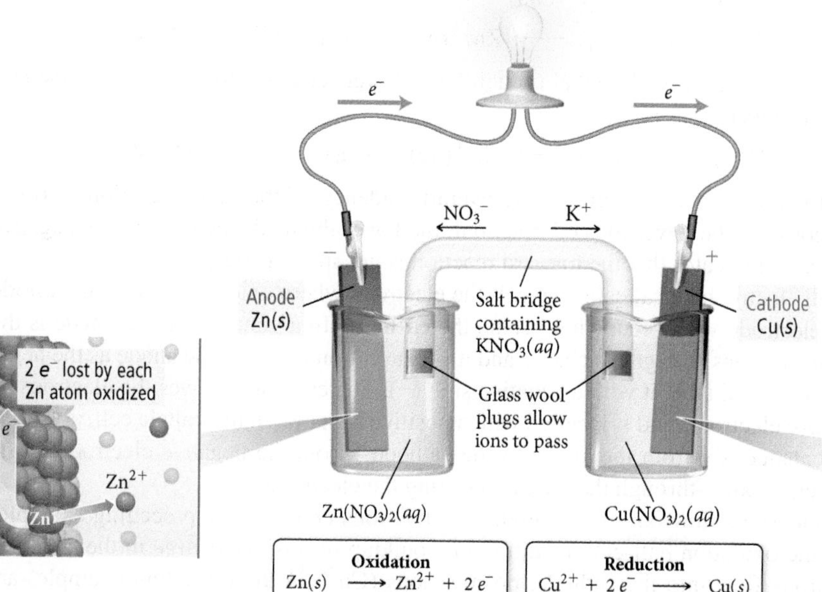

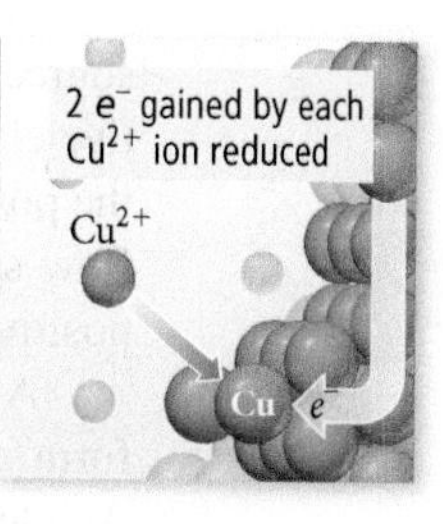

◀ **FIGURE 18.2 A Voltaic Cell** The tendency of zinc to transfer electrons to copper results in a flow of electrons through the wire that lights the bulb. The movement of electrons from the zinc anode to the copper cathode creates a positive charge buildup at the zinc half-cell and a negative charge buildup at the copper half-cell. The flow of ions within the salt bridge neutralizes this charge buildup, allowing the reaction to continue.

If the two half-cells are connected by a wire running from the zinc, through a lightbulb or other electrical device, to the copper, electrons spontaneously flow from the zinc electrode (which is more negatively charged and therefore repels electrons) to the copper electrode. As the electrons flow away from the zinc electrode, the Zn/Zn^{2+} equilibrium shifts to the right (according to Le Chatelier's principle) and oxidation occurs. As electrons flow to the copper electrode, the Cu/Cu^{2+} equilibrium shifts to the left, and reduction occurs. The flowing electrons constitute an electrical current that lights the bulb.

▲ **FIGURE 18.3 An Analogy for Electrical Current** Just as water flows downhill in response to a difference in gravitational potential energy, electrons flow through a conductor in response to an electrical potential difference, creating an electrical current.

We can understand electrical current and why it flows by analogy with water current in a stream (Figure 18.3 ◀). The *rate of electrons flowing* through a wire is analogous to the *rate of water moving* through a stream. Electrical current is measured in units of **amperes (A)**. One ampere represents the flow of one coulomb (a measure of electrical charge) per second:

$$1\ \text{A} = 1\ \text{C s}^{-1}$$

Since an electron has a charge of 1.602×10^{-19} C, 1 A corresponds to the flow of 6.242×10^{18} electrons per second.

The ampere is often abbreviated as amp.

The *driving force* for electrical current is analogous to the driving force for water current. Water current is driven by a difference in gravitational potential energy (caused by a gravitational field). Streams flow downhill, from higher to lower potential energy. Electrical current is also driven by a difference in potential energy (caused by an electric field resulting from the charge difference on the two electrodes) called **potential difference**. *Potential difference is a measure of the difference in potential energy (usually in joules) per unit of charge (coulombs).* The SI unit of potential difference is the **volt (V)**, which is equal to one joule per coulomb:

The *continual* flow of electrical current in a voltaic cell requires a pathway by which counterions can flow to neutralize charge buildup; this is discussed above.

$$1\ \text{V} = 1\ \text{J C}^{-1}$$

A large potential difference corresponds to a large difference in charge between the two electrodes and therefore a strong tendency for electron flow (analogous to a steeply descending streambed). Potential difference, since it gives rise to the force that results in the motion of electrons, is also referred to as **electromotive force (emf)**.

In a voltaic cell, the potential difference between the two electrodes is the **cell potential (E_{cell})** or **cell emf**. The cell potential depends on the relative tendencies of the reactants to undergo oxidation and reduction. Combining the oxidation of a substance with a strong tendency to undergo oxidation and the reduction of a substance with a strong tendency to undergo reduction produces a large difference in charge between the two electrodes and therefore a high positive cell potential.

The cell potential also depends on the concentrations of the reactants and products in the cell and the temperature (which we will assume to be 25 °C unless otherwise noted). Under standard conditions (1 mol L^{-1} concentration for reactants in solution and 1 bar pressure for gaseous reactants), the cell potential is called the **standard cell potential (E°_{cell})** or **standard emf**. For example, the standard cell potential in the zinc and copper cell described previously is 1.10 volts:

$$\text{Zn}(s) + \text{Cu}^{2+}(aq) \longrightarrow \text{Zn}^{2+}(aq) + \text{Cu}(s) \quad E^\circ_{\text{cell}} = 1.10\ \text{V}$$

If the zinc is replaced with nickel (which has a lower tendency to be oxidized) the cell potential is lower:

$$\text{Ni}(s) + \text{Cu}^{2+}(aq) \longrightarrow \text{Ni}^{2+}(aq) + \text{Cu}(s) \quad E^\circ_{\text{cell}} = 0.62\ \text{V}$$

The cell potential is a measure of the overall tendency of the redox reaction to occur spontaneously—the lower the cell potential, the lower the tendency to occur. A negative cell potential indicates that the forward reaction is not spontaneous.

In all electrochemical cells, we call the electrode where oxidation occurs the **anode** and the electrode where reduction occurs the **cathode**. In a voltaic cell, the anode is the source of electrons or negative charge and it is convention to assign the anode as the negative electrode and label it with a negative sign (−). The cathode receives the electrons, is the positive electrode, and is labelled with a positive sign (+). In the voltaic cell, electrons flow spontaneously from the anode to the cathode—from the negative electrode to the positive electrode—through the wire connecting the electrodes.

As electrons flow out of the anode, positive ions (Zn^{2+} in the preceding example) form in the oxidation half-cell, resulting in a buildup of *positive charge* in the *solution*. As electrons flow into the cathode, positive ions (Cu^{2+} in the preceding example) are reduced at the reduction half-cell, resulting in a buildup of *negative charge* in the *solution*.

If the movement of electrons from anode to cathode were the only flow of charge, the buildup of the opposite charge in the solution would stop electron flow almost immediately. The cell needs a pathway by which counterions can flow between the half-cells without the solutions in the half-cells totally mixing. One such pathway is a **salt bridge**, an inverted, U-shaped tube that contains a strong electrolyte such as KNO_3 and connects the two half-cells (see Figure 18.2). The electrolyte is usually suspended in a gel and held within the tube by permeable stoppers. The salt bridge allows a flow of ions that neutralizes the charge buildup in the solution. *The negative ions within the salt bridge flow to neutralize the accumulation of positive charge at the anode, and the positive ions flow to neutralize the accumulation of negative charge at the cathode.* In other words, the salt bridge completes the circuit, allowing electrical current to flow.

Electrochemical Cell Notation

Electrochemical cells are often represented with a compact notation called a *cell diagram* or *line notation*. For example, the electrochemical cell discussed on the previous page in which Zn is oxidized to Zn^{2+} and Cu^{2+} is reduced to Cu is represented as follows:

$$Zn(s)|Zn^{2+}(aq)||Cu^{2+}(aq)|Cu(s)$$

In this representation:

- We write the oxidation half-reaction on the left and the reduction on the right. A double vertical line, indicating the salt bridge, separates the two half-reactions.
- Substances in different phases are separated by a single vertical line, which represents the boundary between the phases.
- For some redox reactions, the reactants and products of one or both of the half-reactions may be in the same phase. In these cases (which are explained further below), the reactants and products are simply separated from each other with a comma in the line diagram. Such cells use an inert electrode, such as platinum (Pt) or graphite, as the anode or cathode (or both).

Consider the redox reaction in which Fe(*s*) is oxidized and $MnO_4^-(aq)$ is reduced:

$$5\,Fe(s) + 2\,MnO_4^-(aq) + 16\,H^+(aq) \longrightarrow 5\,Fe^{2+}(aq) + 2\,Mn^{2+}(aq) + 8\,H_2O(l)$$

The half-reactions for this overall reaction are as follows:

Oxidation: $Fe(s) \longrightarrow Fe^{2+}(aq) + 2\,e^-$

Reduction: $MnO_4^-(aq) + 8\,H^+(aq) + 5\,e^- \longrightarrow Mn^{2+}(aq) + 4\,H_2O(l)$

Notice that, in the reduction half-reaction, the principal species are all in the aqueous phase. In this case, the electron transfer needs an electrode on which to occur. An inert platinum electrode is employed, and the electron transfer takes place at its surface. Using line notation, we represent the electrochemical cell corresponding to the above reaction as follows:

$$Fe(s)|Fe^{2+}(aq)||MnO_4^-(aq), H^+(aq), Mn^{2+}(aq), H_2O(l)|Pt(s)$$

The Pt(*s*) on the far right indicates that an inert platinum electrode acts as the cathode in this reaction, as depicted in Figure 18.4 ▼.

18.3 Standard Electrode Potentials

As we have just seen, the standard cell potential (E°_{cell}) for an electrochemical cell depends on the specific half-reactions occurring in the half-cells, and is a measure of the potential energy difference (per unit charge) between the two electrodes. We can think of the electrode in each half-cell as having its own individual potential, called the **standard electrode potential**. The overall standard cell potential (E°_{cell}) is the difference between the two standard electrode potentials.

We can better understand this idea with an analogy. Consider two water tanks with different water levels connected by a common pipe, as shown in Figure 18.5 ▼. The water in each tank has its own level and corresponding potential energy. When the tanks are connected, water flows spontaneously from the tank with the higher level (higher potential energy) to the tank with a lower water level (lower potential energy).

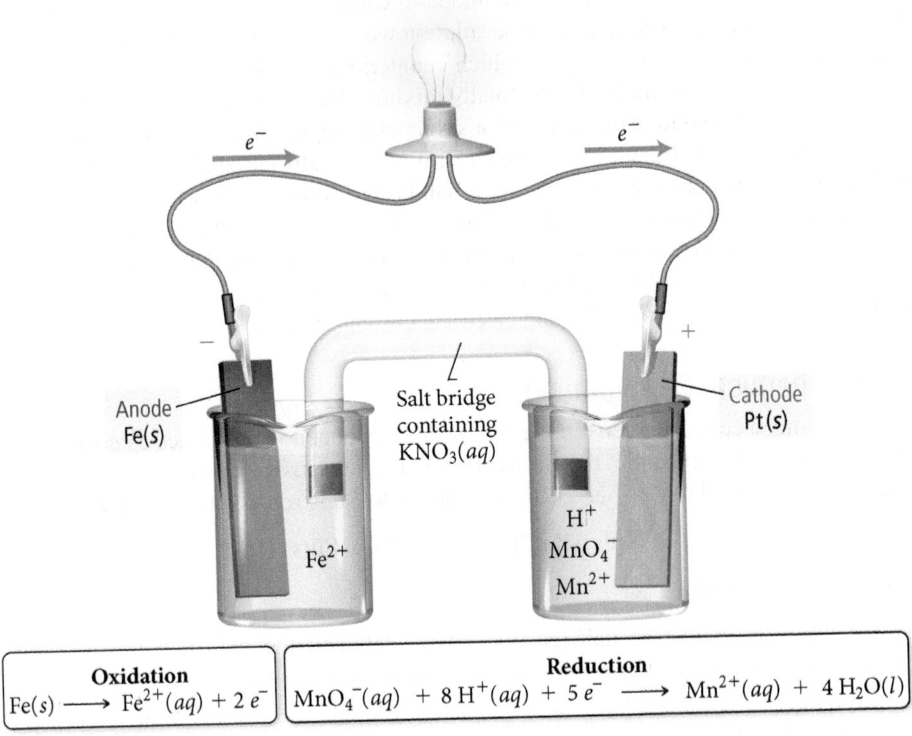

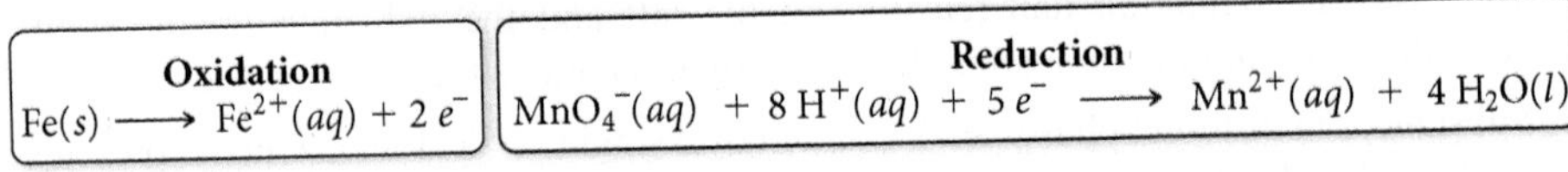

▶ **FIGURE 18.4 Inert Platinum Electrode** When the chemical species in a half-reaction are all in the aqueous phase, a conductive surface is needed for electron transfer to take place. In such cases, an inert electrode of graphite or platinum is often used. In this electrochemical cell, an iron strip acts as the anode and a platinum strip acts as the cathode. Iron is oxidized at the anode and MnO_4^- is reduced at the cathode.

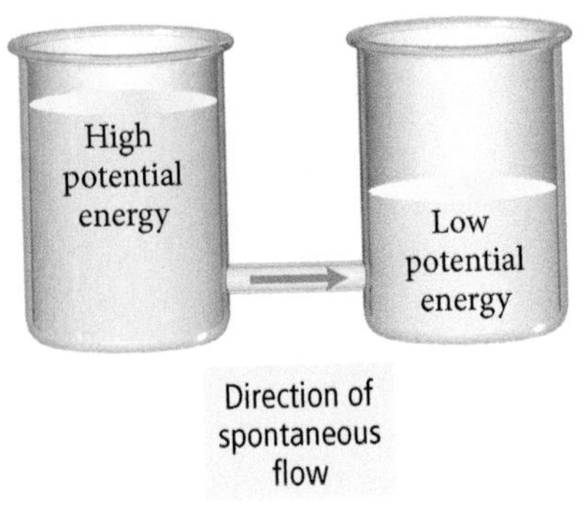

▲ **FIGURE 18.5 An Analogy for Electrode Potential**

Similarly, each half-cell in an electrochemical cell has its own electrode potential. *When the cells are connected, electrons flow spontaneously from the electrode with the higher potential for oxidation to the electrode with a higher potential for reduction.*

The half-cell electrode that is arbitrarily chosen to have a potential of zero is the **standard hydrogen electrode (SHE)**. This half-cell consists of an inert platinum electrode immersed in 1 mol L^{-1} HCl with hydrogen gas at 1 bar bubbling through the solution over the platinum electrode, as shown in Figure 18.6 ▶. When the SHE acts as the cathode, the following half-reaction occurs:

$$2\,H^+(aq) + 2\,e^- \longrightarrow H_2(g)$$

If we connect the standard hydrogen electrode to an electrode in another half-cell of interest, we can measure the potential difference (or voltage) between the two electrodes. Since the SHE is assigned a standard electrode potential of exactly zero volts, we can determine the standard electrode potential of the other half-cell.

For example, consider the electrochemical cell shown in Figure 18.7 ▶. In this electrochemical cell, Zn is oxidized to Zn^{2+}, so the Zn^{2+}/Zn electrode is the anode. At the SHE, H^+ is being reduced to produce gaseous H_2, as expected, since it must be the cathode. We have set up this electrochemical cell so that all solutes are present at a concentration of 1 mol L^{-1} and all gases are at 1 bar pressure (everything in their standard states). The measured cell potential for this cell is 0.76 V. The positive value for the standard cell potential means that the electrochemical cell runs spontaneously with the Zn^{2+}/Zn as the anode and the SHE as the cathode.

By convention, the standard electrode potentials are always written for *reduction* half-reactions. We write the standard electrode potentials for the two half-reactions in Figure 18.7 as follows:

$$2\,H^+(aq) + 2\,e^- \longrightarrow H_2(g) \qquad E^\circ = 0.00\text{ V}$$
$$Zn^{2+}(aq) + 2\,e^- \longrightarrow Zn(s) \qquad E^\circ = \ ?\text{ V},$$

even though the reverse reaction is occurring at the Zn^{2+}/Zn electrode and where we are trying to determine the standard electrode potential for the Zn^{2+}/Zn electrode. This convention allows us to write the standard cell potential, E°_{cell}, as the *difference between the standard electrode potentials of the cathode and the anode*:

$$E^\circ_{cell} = E^\circ_{cathode} - E^\circ_{anode} \qquad [18.1]$$

In Equation 18.1, remember that both $E^{\circ}_{\text{cathode}}$ and E°_{anode} are the standard electrode potentials for the half-reactions written as reductions (reduction potential). The negative sign in Equation 18.1 takes into account that at the anode the oxidation half-reaction is occurring and the oxidation potential is the negative of the reduction potential.

Since the SHE cathode has a potential of zero volts, we can determine the standard electrode potential for the Zn^{2+}/Zn half-cell (the anode) from the measured standard cell potential:

$$\begin{aligned} E^{\circ}_{\text{cell}} &= E^{\circ}_{\text{cathode}} - E^{\circ}_{\text{anode}} \\ 0.76\text{ V} &= 0.00\text{ V} - E^{\circ}_{Zn^{2+}/Zn} \\ E^{\circ}_{Zn^{2+}/Zn} &= -0.76\text{ V} \end{aligned}$$

The negative standard electrode potential means that the Zn^{2+}/Zn electrode will be the anode when it is paired with a SHE in a voltaic cell. In fact, we will see shortly that the Zn^{2+}/Zn electrode will be the anode in any voltaic cell when it is paired with an electrode with a more positive electrode potential.

Now let's consider an electrochemical cell composed of a SHE and a Cu^{2+}/Cu electrode with a Cu^{2+} concentration of 1 mol L^{-1}. When these two electrodes are paired as in Figure 18.8 ▼, the SHE is the anode, and the Cu^{2+}/Cu electrode is the cathode with electrons spontaneously flowing from the SHE anode to the Cu^{2+}/Cu cathode. The standard cell potential is measured to be 0.34 V. In the same way as before, we can determine the standard cell potential for the Cu^{2+}/Cu electrode:

$$\begin{aligned} E^{\circ}_{\text{cell}} &= E^{\circ}_{\text{cathode}} - E^{\circ}_{\text{anode}} \\ 0.34\text{ V} &= E^{\circ}_{Cu^{2+}/Cu}\text{ V} - 0.00\text{ V} \\ E^{\circ}_{Cu^{2+}/Cu} &= 0.34\text{ V} \end{aligned}$$

The positive standard electrode potential means that reduction is favoured at the Cu^{2+}/Cu electrode—it will be the cathode—when paired with an electrode with a more negative standard cell potential, such as the SHE.

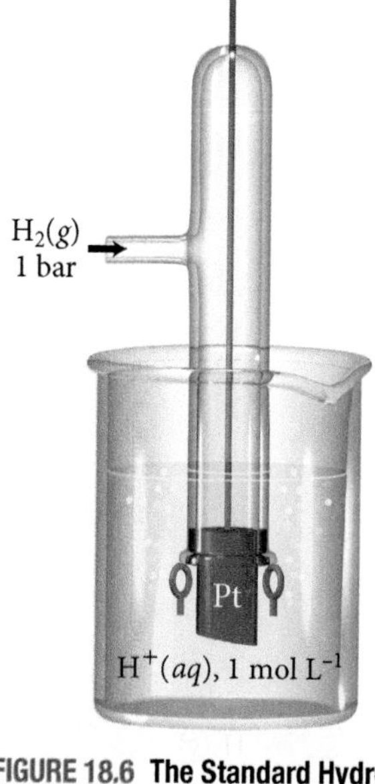

▲ **FIGURE 18.6 The Standard Hydrogen Electrode** The standard hydrogen electrode (SHE) is arbitrarily assigned an electrode potential of zero. All other electrode potentials are then measured relative to the SHE.

Summarizing Standard Electrode Potentials:

- The electrode potential of the standard hydrogen electrode (SHE) is exactly zero.
- The electrode in any half-cell with a greater tendency to undergo reduction is positively charged relative to the SHE and therefore has a positive E°.

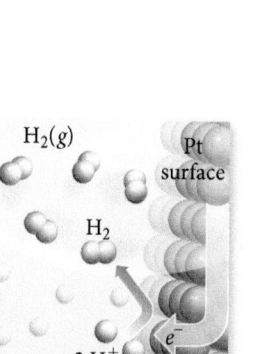

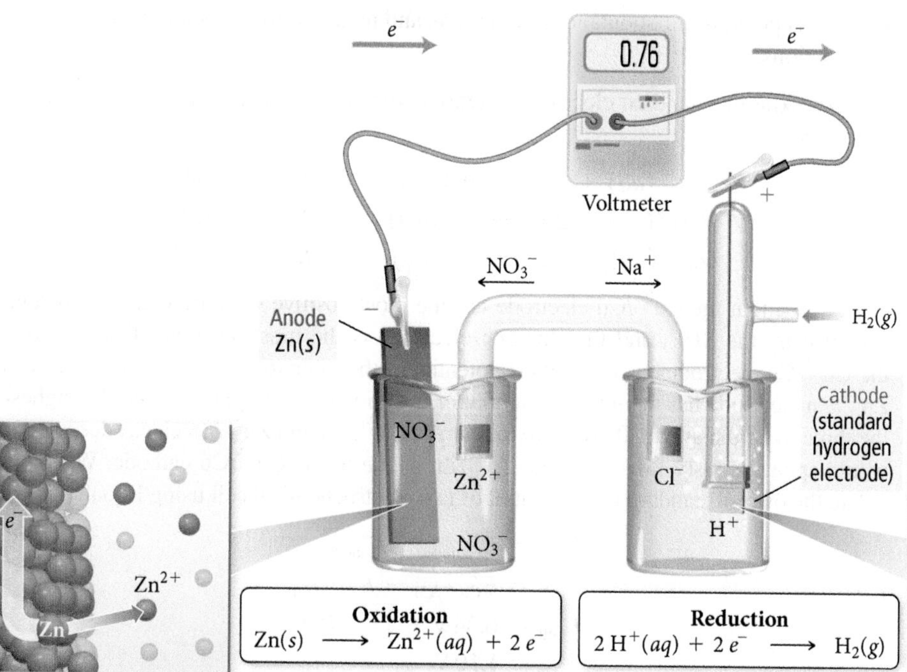

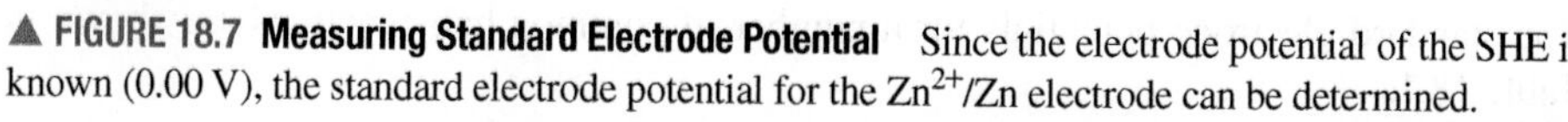

▲ **FIGURE 18.7 Measuring Standard Electrode Potential** Since the electrode potential of the SHE is known (0.00 V), the standard electrode potential for the Zn^{2+}/Zn electrode can be determined.

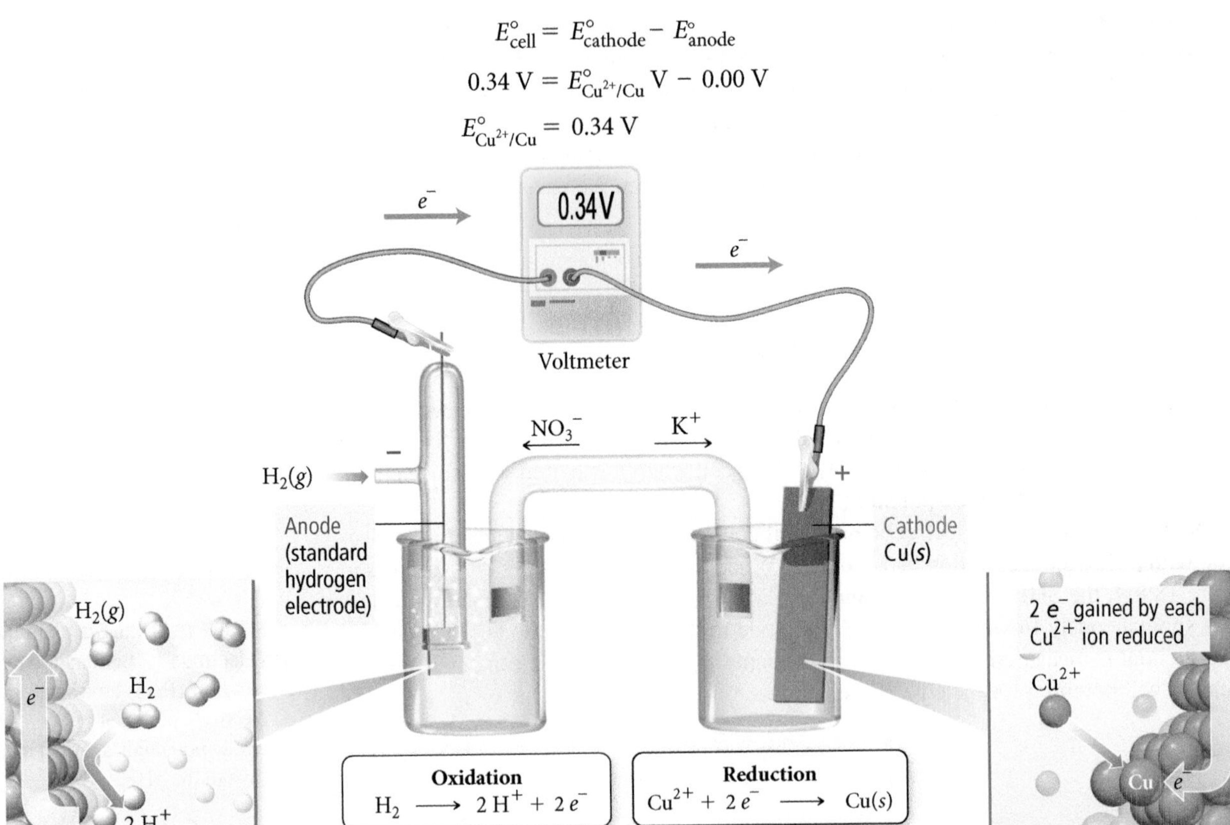

▲ **FIGURE 18.8 Electrochemical Cell with SHE as the Anode** In this pairing of electrodes, the potential for Cu^{2+} to be reduced is higher than for H^+ (as in Figure 18.7), so the SHE is the anode.

- The electrode in any half-cell with a lesser tendency to undergo reduction (or greater tendency to undergo oxidation) is negatively charged relative to the SHE and therefore has a negative E°.
- The cell potential of any electrochemical cell (E°_{cell}) is the difference between the electrode potentials of the cathode and the anode ($E^\circ_{cell} = E^\circ_{cat} - E^\circ_{an}$).
- E°_{cell} is positive for spontaneous reactions and negative for nonspontaneous reactions.

We write the standard electrode potentials for the three half-reactions just discussed as follows:

$$Cu^{2+}(aq) + 2\,e^- \longrightarrow Cu(s) \qquad E^\circ = 0.34\,V$$
$$2\,H^+(aq) + 2\,e^- \longrightarrow H_2(g) \qquad E^\circ = 0.00\,V$$
$$Zn^{2+}(aq) + 2\,e^- \longrightarrow Zn(s) \qquad E^\circ = -0.76\,V$$

We can see that the Cu^{2+}/Cu electrode has the most positive standard electrode potential, followed by the SHE, and the Zn^{2+}/Zn electrode is the most negative. This means that the Cu^{2+}/Cu electrode has the highest potential of the three to be the cathode, whereas the Zn^{2+}/Zn electrode has the lowest potential of the three to be the cathode and the highest of the three to be the anode. If we were to pair the Cu^{2+}/Cu and Zn^{2+}/Zn electrodes, electrons would spontaneously flow from the Zn^{2+}/Zn anode to the Cu^{2+}/Cu cathode. We can calculate the overall standard cell potential of this electrochemical cell using Equation 18.1:

$$E^\circ_{cell} = E^\circ_{cathode} - E^\circ_{anode}$$
$$E^\circ_{cell} = E^\circ_{Cu^{2+}/Cu} - E^\circ_{Zn^{2+}/Zn}$$
$$E^\circ_{cell} = 0.34\,V - (-0.76\,V)$$
$$= 1.10\,V$$

The standard electrode potentials for a number of common half-reactions are shown in Table 18.1.

TABLE 18.1 Standard Electrode Potentials at 25 °C

Stronger oxidizing agent

Weaker reducing agent

Reduction Half-Reaction		$E°$ (V)
$F_2(g) + 2\,e^-$	$\longrightarrow 2\,F^-(aq)$	2.87
$H_2O_2(aq) + 2\,H^+(aq) + 2\,e^-$	$\longrightarrow 2\,H_2O(l)$	1.78
$PbO_2(s) + 4\,H^+(aq) + SO_4^{2-}(aq) + 2\,e^-$	$\longrightarrow PbSO_4(s) + 2\,H_2O(l)$	1.69
$MnO_4^-(aq) + 4\,H^+(aq) + 3\,e^-$	$\longrightarrow MnO_2(s) + 2\,H_2O(l)$	1.68
$MnO_4^-(aq) + 8\,H^+(aq) + 5\,e^-$	$\longrightarrow Mn^{2+}(aq) + 4\,H_2O(l)$	1.51
$Au^{3+}(aq) + 3\,e^-$	$\longrightarrow Au(s)$	1.50
$PbO_2(s) + 4\,H^+(aq) + 2\,e^-$	$\longrightarrow Pb^{2+}(aq) + 2\,H_2O(l)$	1.46
$Cl_2(g) + 2\,e^-$	$\longrightarrow 2\,Cl^-(aq)$	1.36
$Cr_2O_7^{2-}(aq) + 14\,H^+(aq) + 6\,e^-$	$\longrightarrow 2\,Cr^{3+}(aq) + 7\,H_2O(l)$	1.33
$O_2(g) + 4\,H^+(aq) + 4\,e^-$	$\longrightarrow 2\,H_2O(l)$	1.23
$MnO_2(s) + 4\,H^+(aq) + 2\,e^-$	$\longrightarrow Mn^{2+}(aq) + 2\,H_2O(l)$	1.21
$IO_3^-(aq) + 6\,H^+(aq) + 5\,e^-$	$\longrightarrow \frac{1}{2}I_2(aq) + 3\,H_2O(l)$	1.20
$Br_2(l) + 2\,e^-$	$\longrightarrow 2\,Br^-(aq)$	1.09
$VO_2^+(aq) + 2\,H^+(aq) + e^-$	$\longrightarrow VO^{2+}(aq) + H_2O(l)$	1.00
$NO_3^-(aq) + 4\,H^+(aq) + 3\,e^-$	$\longrightarrow NO(g) + 2\,H_2O(l)$	0.96
$ClO_2(g) + e^-$	$\longrightarrow ClO_2^-(aq)$	0.95
$O_2(g) + 4\,H^+(aq) + 4\,e^-$	$\longrightarrow 2\,H_2O(l)$	$E = 0.82\,V\,(pH = 7)$
$Ag^+(aq) + e^-$	$\longrightarrow Ag(s)$	0.80
$Fe^{3+}(aq) + e^-$	$\longrightarrow Fe^{2+}(aq)$	0.77
$O_2(g) + 2\,H^+(aq) + 2\,e^-$	$\longrightarrow H_2O_2(aq)$	0.70
$MnO_4^-(aq) + e^-$	$\longrightarrow MnO_4^{2-}(aq)$	0.56
$I_2(s) + 2\,e^-$	$\longrightarrow 2\,I^-(aq)$	0.54
$Cu^+(aq) + e^-$	$\longrightarrow Cu(s)$	0.52
$O_2(g) + 2\,H_2O(l) + 4\,e^-$	$\longrightarrow 4\,OH^-(aq)$	0.40
$Cu^{2+}(aq) + 2\,e^-$	$\longrightarrow Cu(s)$	0.34
$SO_4^{2-}(aq) + 4\,H^+(aq) + 2\,e^-$	$\longrightarrow H_2SO_3(aq) + H_2O(l)$	0.20
$Cu^{2+}(aq) + e^-$	$\longrightarrow Cu^+(aq)$	0.16
$Sn^{4+}(aq) + 2\,e^-$	$\longrightarrow Sn^{2+}(aq)$	0.15
$2\,H^+(aq) + 2\,e^-$	$\longrightarrow H_2(g)$	0
$Fe^{3+}(aq) + 3\,e^-$	$\longrightarrow Fe(s)$	−0.036
$Pb^{2+}(aq) + 2\,e^-$	$\longrightarrow Pb(s)$	−0.13
$Sn^{2+}(aq) + 2\,e^-$	$\longrightarrow Sn(s)$	−0.14
$Ni^{2+}(aq) + 2\,e^-$	$\longrightarrow Ni(s)$	−0.23
$Cd^{2+}(aq) + 2\,e^-$	$\longrightarrow Cd(s)$	−0.40
$2\,H_2O(l) + 2\,e^-$	$\longrightarrow H_2(g) + 2\,OH^-(aq)$	$E = -0.41\,V\,(pH = 7)$
$Fe^{2+}(aq) + 2\,e^-$	$\longrightarrow Fe(s)$	−0.45
$Cr^{3+}(aq) + e^-$	$\longrightarrow Cr^{2+}(aq)$	−0.50
$Cr^{3+}(aq) + 3\,e^-$	$\longrightarrow Cr(s)$	−0.73
$Zn^{2+}(aq) + 2\,e^-$	$\longrightarrow Zn(s)$	−0.76
$2\,H_2O(l) + 2\,e^-$	$\longrightarrow H_2(g) + 2\,OH^-(aq)$	−0.83
$Mn^{2+}(aq) + 2\,e^-$	$\longrightarrow Mn(s)$	−1.18

(continued)

TABLE 18.1 (Continued)

	Reduction Half-Reaction		E° (V)	
↑	$Al^{3+}(aq) + 3\,e^-$	$\longrightarrow Al(s)$	−1.66	↓
	$Mg^{2+}(aq) + 2\,e^-$	$\longrightarrow Mg(s)$	−2.37	
	$Na^+(aq) + e^-$	$\longrightarrow Na(s)$	−2.71	
	$Ca^{2+}(aq) + 2\,e^-$	$\longrightarrow Ca(s)$	−2.76	
	$Ba^{2+}(aq) + 2\,e^-$	$\longrightarrow Ba(s)$	−2.90	
	$K^+(aq) + e^-$	$\longrightarrow K(s)$	−2.92	
Weaker oxidizing agent	$Li^+(aq) + e^-$	$\longrightarrow Li(s)$	−3.04	Stronger reducing agent

The highlighted reactions are for nonstandard state, but are more common. The electrode potentials are for the half-reactions at pH 7 ($[H^+] = 1 \times 10^{-7}$ or $[OH^-] = 1 \times 10^{-7}$). See Section 18.7 on electrolysis of aqueous solutions for the significance of these concentrations.

Example 18.1 shows how to calculate the potential of an electrochemical cell from the standard electrode potentials of the half-reactions.

EXAMPLE 18.1 CALCULATING STANDARD POTENTIALS FOR ELECTROCHEMICAL CELLS FROM STANDARD ELECTRODE POTENTIALS—I

Use tabulated standard electrode potentials to calculate the standard cell potential for the following reaction occurring in an electrochemical cell at 25 °C (the equation is balanced):

$$Al(s) + NO_3^-(aq) + 4\,H^+(aq) \longrightarrow Al^{3+}(aq) + NO(g) + 2\,H_2O(l)$$

SOLUTION

Begin by separating the reaction into oxidation and reduction half-reactions. In this case, it is apparent that $Al(s)$ is oxidized. In cases in which it is not as clear, you may want to assign oxidation states to help determine the correct half-reactions.

Oxidation: $Al(s) \longrightarrow Al^{3+}(aq) + \cancel{3e^-}$

Reduction: $NO_3^-(aq) + 4\,H^+(aq) + \cancel{3e^-} \longrightarrow NO(g) + 2\,H_2O(l)$

Overall: $Al(s) + NO_3^-(aq) + 4\,H^+(aq) \longrightarrow Al^{3+}(aq) + NO(g) + 2\,H_2O(l)$

Next, look up the standard electrode potential for each half-reaction. Remember, these reactions are written as reduction half-reactions. Use Equation 18.1 to calculate the standard cell potential.

(Cathode): $NO_3^-(aq) + 4\,H^+(aq) + 3\,e^- \longrightarrow NO(g) + 2\,H_2O(l) \quad E^\circ = 0.96\,V$

(Anode): $Al^{3+}(aq) + 3\,e^- \longrightarrow Al(s) \quad E^\circ = -1.66\,V$

$$E^\circ_{cell} = E^\circ_{cathode} - E^\circ_{anode}$$
$$E^\circ_{cell} = E^\circ_{NO_3^-/NO} - E^\circ_{Al^{3+}/Al}$$
$$E^\circ_{cell} = 0.96\,V - (-1.66\,V)$$
$$= 2.62\,V$$

FOR PRACTICE 18.1

Use tabulated standard electrode potentials to calculate the standard cell potential for the following reaction occurring in an electrochemical cell at 25 °C (the equation is balanced):

$$MnO_4^-(aq) + \tfrac{1}{2}\,I_2(aq) + 2\,H^+(aq) \longrightarrow Mn^{2+}(aq) + IO_3^-(aq) + H_2O(l)$$

In electrochemical cells where you must multiply one or both of the half-reactions by a constant in order to cancel out the electrons, you do not multiply the standard electrode potential. That is because E° is an *intensive quantity*—it doesn't depend on the amount of substance. Potential is a ratio of energy to charge; increasing the amount of substance increases both the energy content and the amount of charge by the same amount, so the ratio remains unchanged. Density (mass/volume) is also an intensive quantity. The following example is slightly more complicated than the previous one in that one or both of the half-reactions need to be multiplied by a factor in order to balance the equation.

EXAMPLE 18.2 CALCULATING STANDARD POTENTIALS FOR ELECTROCHEMICAL CELLS FROM STANDARD ELECTRODE POTENTIALS—II

Use tabulated standard electrode potentials to calculate the standard cell potential for the following reaction occurring in an electrochemical cell at 25 °C (the equation is balanced):

$$Cr_2O_7^{2-}(aq) + 3\,H_2O_2(aq) + 8\,H^+(aq) \longrightarrow 2\,Cr^{3+}(aq) + 3\,O_2(g) + 7\,H_2O(l)$$

SOLUTION

Again, begin by separating the reaction into oxidation and reduction half-reactions. The oxygen in H_2O_2 goes from an oxidation state of −1 to 0 and therefore is oxidized while Cr goes from +6 to +3 and is therefore reduced.	**Oxidation:** $3\,H_2O_2(aq) \longrightarrow 3\,O_2(g) + 6\,H^+(aq) + \cancel{6e^-}$ **Reduction:** $Cr_2O_7^{2-}(aq) + 14\,H^+(aq) + \cancel{6e^-} \longrightarrow 2\,Cr^{3+}(aq) + 7\,H_2O(l)$ **Overall:** $Cr_2O_7^{2-}(aq) + 3\,H_2O_2(aq) + 8\,H^+(aq) \longrightarrow 2\,Cr^{3+}(aq) + 3\,O_2(g) + 7\,H_2O(l)$
Next, look up the standard electrode potential for each half-reaction. These reactions are written as reduction half-reactions. Note that although the O_2/H_2O_2 cell is one-third of that used to balance the redox reaction, when using Equation 18.1 to calculate the standard cell potential, you do not multiply the standard cell potential by any factor.	*(Cathode):* $Cr_2O_7^{2-}(aq) + 14\,H^+(aq) + 6\,e^- \longrightarrow 2\,Cr^{3+}(aq) + 7\,H_2O(l)$ $E^\circ = 1.33\,V$ *(Anode):* $O_2(g) + 2\,H^+(aq) + 2\,e^- \longrightarrow H_2O_2(aq)$ $E^\circ = 0.70\,V$ $E^\circ_{cell} = E^\circ_{cathode} - E^\circ_{anode}$ $E^\circ_{cell} = E^\circ_{Cr_2O_7^{2-}/Cr^{3+}} - E^\circ_{O_2/H_2O_2}$ $E^\circ_{cell} = 1.33\,V - 0.70\,V$ $= 0.63\,V$

FOR PRACTICE 18.2

Use tabulated standard electrode potentials to calculate the standard cell potential for the following reaction occurring in an electrochemical cell at 25 °C (the equation is balanced):

$$Sn^{2+}(aq) + 2\,Cr^{2+}(aq) \longrightarrow Sn(s) + 2\,Cr^{3+}(aq)$$

Predicting the Spontaneous Direction of an Oxidation–Reduction Reaction

An oxidation–reduction reaction will proceed spontaneously in the direction that provides a positive cell potential. We can use Equation 18.1 and the standard electrode potentials of the two relevant half-reactions in Table 18.1. For example, consider an electrochemical cell composed of electrodes represented by the following two reduction half-reactions:

$$Ni^{2+}(aq) + 2\,e^- \longrightarrow Ni(s) \qquad E^\circ = -0.23\text{ V}$$
$$Mn^{2+}(aq) + 2\,e^- \longrightarrow Mn(s) \qquad E^\circ = -1.18\text{ V}$$

Equation 18.1 says:

$$E^\circ_{cell} = E^\circ_{cathode} - E^\circ_{anode}$$

In order to have an overall positive cell potential, the electrode with the more negative standard electrode potential must be the anode, and the one with the more positive standard electrode potential must be the cathode. We can confirm that this provides a positive cell potential:

$$\begin{aligned} E^\circ_{cell} &= E^\circ_{Ni^{2+}/Ni} - E^\circ_{Mn^{2+}/Mn} \\ &= -0.23\text{ V} - (-1.18\text{ V}) \\ &= 0.95\text{ V} \end{aligned}$$

We can write the overall reaction, remembering that the Mn^{2+}/Mn electrode is the anode and must be written in the opposite direction—as an oxidation:

Cathode (reduction): $Ni^{2+}(aq) + 2\,\cancel{e^-} \longrightarrow Ni(s)$

Anode (oxidation): $Mn(s) \longrightarrow Mn^{2+}(aq) + 2\,\cancel{e^-}$

$$Ni^{2+}(aq) + Mn(s) \longrightarrow Ni(s) + Mn^{2+}(aq)$$

The overall cell potential is positive, indicating a spontaneous reaction. The electrochemical cell corresponding to this spontaneous redox reaction is shown in Figure 18.9 ▼. We draw the manganese half-cell on the left as the anode and the nickel half-cell on the right as the cathode. Electrons flow from the anode to the cathode.

Another way to predict the spontaneity of a redox reaction is to note the relative positions of the two half-reactions in Table 18.1. Since the table lists reduction half-reactions in order of *decreasing* electrode potential, the half-reactions near the top of the table—those having large *positive* electrode potentials—tend to occur in the forward direction. The half-reactions near the bottom of the table—those having large *negative* electrode potentials—tend to occur in the reverse direction. In other words, as you move down Table 18.1, the half-reactions become less likely to occur in the forward direction and more likely to occur in the reverse direction. As a result, *any reduction half-reaction listed will be spontaneous when paired with the reverse of a half-reaction that appears below it in Table 18.1.*

Summarizing the Prediction of Spontaneous Direction for Redox Reactions:

▶ The half-reaction with the more *positive* electrode potential will undergo reduction (so substances listed at the top of Table 18.1 tend to undergo reduction; they are good oxidizing agents).

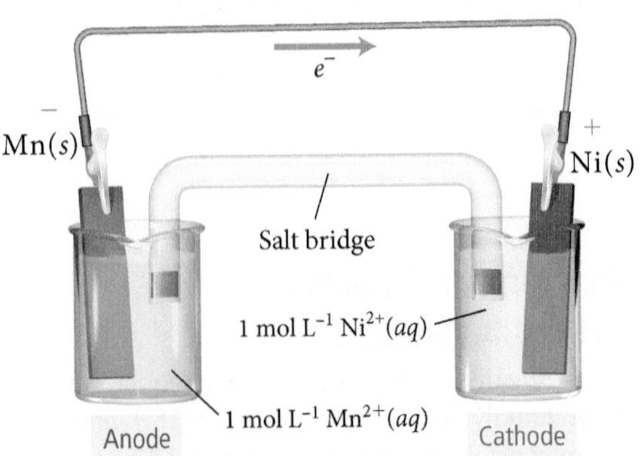

▶ **FIGURE 18.9 Mn/Ni^{2+} Electrochemical Cell** The reduction of Mn^{2+} is listed below the reduction of Ni^{2+} in Table 18.1; the reduction of Ni^{2+} is spontaneous when paired with the oxidation of Mn.

- The half-reaction with the more *negative* electrode potential will undergo oxidation (so substances listed near the bottom of Table 18.1 tend to undergo oxidation; they are good reducing agents).
- Any reduction reaction in Table 18.1 is spontaneous when paired with the *reverse* of the reaction listed below it.

EXAMPLE 18.3 PREDICTING SPONTANEOUS REDOX REACTIONS AND SKETCHING ELECTROCHEMICAL CELLS

Without calculating E°_{cell}, predict whether each of the following redox reactions is spontaneous. If the reaction is spontaneous as written, make a sketch of the electrochemical cell in which the reaction could occur. If the reaction is not spontaneous as written, write an equation for the spontaneous direction in which the reaction would occur and sketch the electrochemical cell in which the spontaneous reaction would occur. In your sketches, make sure to label the anode (which should be drawn on the left), the cathode, and the direction of electron flow.

(a) $Fe(s) + Mg^{2+}(aq) \longrightarrow Fe^{2+}(aq) + Mg(s)$

(b) $3\,Mg(s) + 2\,Cr^{3+}(aq) \longrightarrow 3\,Mg^{2+}(aq) + 2\,Cr(s)$

SOLUTION

(a) $Fe(s) + Mg^{2+}(aq) \longrightarrow Fe^{2+}(aq) + Mg(s)$

This reaction involves the reduction of Mg^{2+} and the oxidation of Fe. The reduction half-reactions along with the standard electrode potentials are:

$$Fe^{2+}(aq) + 2\,e^- \longrightarrow Fe(s) \qquad E^\circ = -0.45\ V$$
$$Mg^{2+}(aq) + 2\,e^- \longrightarrow Mg(s) \qquad E^\circ = -2.37\ V$$

The magnesium half-reaction has the more negative standard electrode potential and is the reaction that will occur as an oxidation (in the reverse). The reaction will not be spontaneous as written. However, the reverse reaction would be spontaneous:

$$Fe^{2+}(aq) + Mg(s) \longrightarrow Fe(s) + Mg^{2+}(aq)$$

The electrochemical cell is shown in Figure 18.10 ▶.

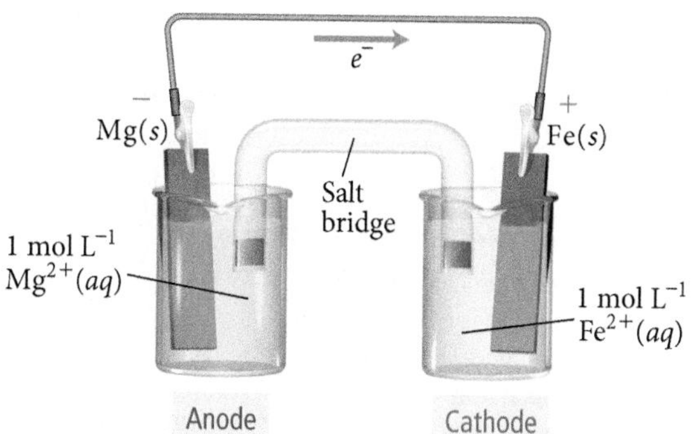

▲ **FIGURE 18.10 Electrochemical Cell Composed of Mg^{2+}/Mg and Fe^{2+}/Fe Electrodes**

(b) $3\,Mg(s) + 2\,Cr^{3+}(aq) \longrightarrow 3\,Mg^{2+}(aq) + 2\,Cr(s)$

This reaction involves the oxidation of Mg and the reduction of Cr^{3+}. From Table 18.1, the reduction half-reactions and standard electrode potentials are:

$$Cr^{3+}(aq) + 3\,e^- \longrightarrow Cr(s) \qquad E^\circ = -0.73\ V$$
$$Mg^{2+}(aq) + 2\,e^- \longrightarrow Mg(s) \qquad E^\circ = -2.37\ V$$

With this pairing of half-reactions, the Mg^{2+}/Mg half-reaction has the more negative standard electrode potential and will occur as an oxidation as written in the overall reaction. The reaction is spontaneous as written. Another way of saying this is that the reaction pairs the Cr^{3+}/Cr reduction with the reverse of a half-reaction below it in Table 18.1—such pairings are always spontaneous. The corresponding electrochemical cell is shown in Figure 18.11 ▶.

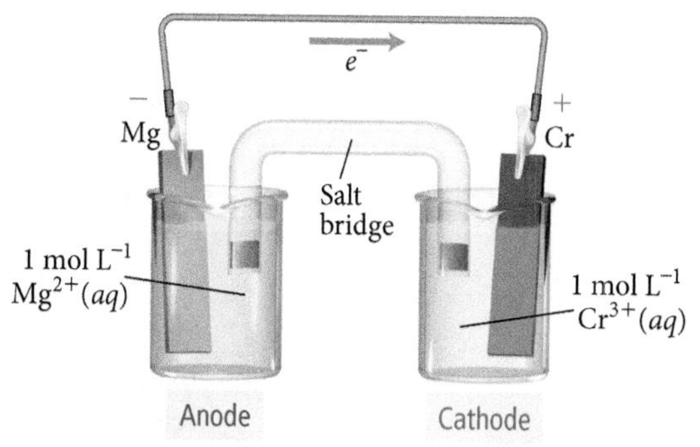

▲ **FIGURE 18.11 Electrochemical Cell Composed of Mg^{2+}/Mg and Cr^{3+}/Cr Electrodes**

FOR PRACTICE 18.3

Will the following redox reactions be spontaneous under standard conditions?

(a) $Zn(s) + Ni^{2+}(aq) \longrightarrow Zn^{2+}(aq) + Ni(s)$

(b) $3\,Zn(s) + 2\,Al^{3+}(aq) \longrightarrow 3\,Zn^{2+}(aq) + 2\,Al(s)$

CONCEPTUAL CONNECTION 18.1

Selective Oxidation

A solution contains both NaI and NaBr. Which oxidizing agent could you add to the solution to selectively oxidize $I^-(aq)$ but not $Br^-(aq)$?

(a) Cl_2 **(b)** H_2O_2 **(c)** $CuCl_2$ **(d)** HNO_3

Predicting Whether a Metal Will Dissolve in Acid

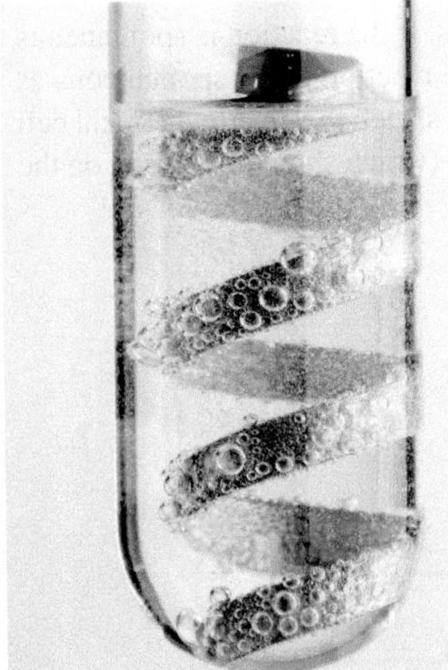

$Zn(s) + 2\,H^+(aq) \longrightarrow Zn^{2+}(aq) + H_2(g)$

▲ When zinc is immersed in hydrochloric acid, the zinc is oxidized, forming ions that become solvated in the solution. Hydrogen ions are reduced, forming bubbles of hydrogen gas.

In Chapter 15, we learned that acids dissolve metals. Most acids dissolve metals by the reduction of H^+ ions to hydrogen gas and the corresponding oxidation of the metal to its ion. For example, if solid Zn is dropped into hydrochloric acid, the following reaction occurs:

$$\begin{aligned} 2\,H^+(aq) + \cancel{2\,e^-} &\longrightarrow H_2(g) \\ Zn(s) &\longrightarrow Zn^{2+}(aq) + \cancel{2\,e^-} \\ \hline Zn(s) + 2\,H^+(aq) &\longrightarrow Zn^{2+}(aq) + H_2(g) \end{aligned}$$

We observe the reaction as the dissolving of the zinc and the bubbling of hydrogen gas. The zinc is oxidized and the H^+ ions are reduced. Notice that this reaction involves the pairing of a reduction half-reaction (the reduction of H^+) with the reverse of a half-reaction that falls below it in Table 18.1. Therefore, this reaction is spontaneous. What would happen, however, if we paired the reduction of H^+ with the oxidation of Cu? The reaction would not be spontaneous because it involves pairing the reduction of H^+ with the reverse of a half-reaction that is listed *above it* in the table. Consequently, copper does not react with H^+ and will not dissolve in acids such as HCl. In general, *metals whose reduction half-reactions are listed below the reduction of H^+ to H_2 in Table 18.1 will dissolve in acids, while metals listed above it will not.*

An important exception to this rule is nitric acid (HNO_3), which can oxidize metals and produces NO gas through the reduction half-reaction:

$$NO_3^-(aq) + 4\,H^+(aq) + 3\,e^- \longrightarrow NO(g) + 2\,H_2O(l) \quad E^\circ = 0.96\text{ V}$$

Since this half-reaction is above the reduction of H^+ in Table 18.1, HNO_3 can oxidize metals (such as copper) that can't be oxidized by HCl.

CONCEPTUAL CONNECTION 18.2

Metals Dissolving in Acids

Which metal dissolves in HNO_3 but not in HCl?

(a) Fe **(b)** Au **(c)** Ag

18.4 Cell Potential, Gibbs Energy, and the Equilibrium Constant

We have seen that a positive standard cell potential (E°_{cell}) corresponds to a spontaneous oxidation–reduction reaction. And we know (from Chapter 17) that the spontaneity of a reaction is determined by the sign of $\Delta_r G$, or under standard state condtions by the sign of $\Delta_r G^\circ$. Therefore, E°_{cell} and $\Delta_r G^\circ$ must be related. We also know from Section 17.9 that $\Delta_r G^\circ$ for a reaction is related to the equilibrium constant (K) for the reaction. Since E°_{cell} and $\Delta_r G^\circ$ are related, then E°_{cell} and K must also be related.

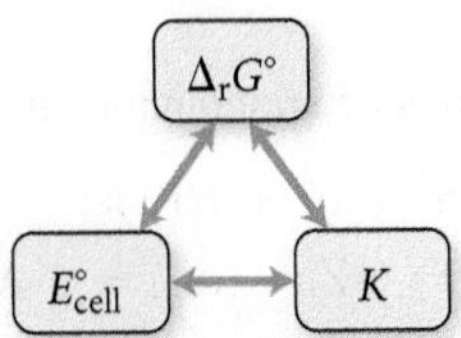

Before we look at the nature of each of these relationships in detail, let's consider the following generalizations.

For a spontaneous redox reaction (one that will proceed in the forward direction when all reactants and products are in their standard states):

- $\Delta_r G^\circ$ is negative (< 0)
- E°_{cell} is positive (> 0)
- $K > 1$

For a nonspontaneous reaction (one that will proceed in the reverse direction when all reactants and products are in their standard states):

- $\Delta_r G^\circ$ is positive (> 0)
- E°_{cell} is negative (< 0)
- $K < 1$

The Relationship Between $\Delta_r G^\circ$ and E°_{cell}

We can derive a relationship between $\Delta_r G^\circ$ and E°_{cell} by briefly returning to the definition of potential difference from Section 18.2—a potential difference is a measure of the difference of potential energy per unit charge (q):

Maximum work (w_{max})

$$E = \frac{\text{potential energy difference (in J)}}{\text{charge (in C)}}$$

Charge (q)

Since the potential energy difference represents the maximum amount of work that can be done by the system on the surroundings, we can write:

$$w_{max} = -qE^\circ_{cell} \qquad [18.2]$$

The negative sign follows the convention used throughout this text that work done by the system on the surroundings is negative.

We can quantify the charge (q) that flows in an electrochemical reaction by using **Faraday's constant (F)**, which represents the charge in coulombs of 1 mol of electrons.

$$F = 96485 \text{ C mol}^{-1}$$

The total charge is $q = nF$, where n is the number of electrons transferred in the balanced chemical equation (a unitless value) and F is Faraday's constant. Substituting $q = nF$ into Equation 18.2,

$$w_{max} = -qE^\circ_{cell}$$
$$= -nFE^\circ_{cell} \qquad [18.3]$$

Finally, recall from Chapter 17 that the standard change in Gibbs energy for a chemical reaction ($\Delta_r G^\circ$) represents the maximum amount of work that can be done by the reaction. Therefore, $w_{max} = \Delta_r G^\circ$. Making this substitution into Equation 18.3, we get the following important result:

$$\Delta_r G^\circ = -nFE^\circ_{cell} \qquad [18.4]$$

where $\Delta_r G^\circ$ is the standard change in Gibbs energy for an electrochemical reaction, n is the number of electrons transferred in the balanced equation, F is Faraday's constant, and E°_{cell} is the standard cell potential. The following example shows how to apply this equation to calculate the standard Gibbs energy change for an electrochemical cell.

EXAMPLE 18.4 **RELATING $\Delta_r G^\circ$ AND E°_{cell}**

Use the tabulated electrode potentials to calculate $\Delta_r G^\circ$ for the reaction between sodium metal and neutral water (pH = 7.0):

$$2\,Na(s) + 2\,H_2O(l) \longrightarrow H_2(g) + 2\,OH^-(aq) + 2\,Na^+(aq)$$

Is the reaction spontaneous?

SORT You are given a redox reaction and asked to find $\Delta_r G^\circ$.

GIVEN: $2\,Na(s) + 2\,H_2O(l) \longrightarrow H_2(g) + 2\,OH^-(aq) + 2\,Na^+(aq)$

FIND: $\Delta_r G^\circ$

STRATEGIZE Use the tabulated values of standard electrode potentials to calculate E°_{cell} using Equation 18.1. Then use Equation 18.4 to calculate $\Delta_r G^\circ$ from E°_{cell}.

CONCEPTUAL PLAN

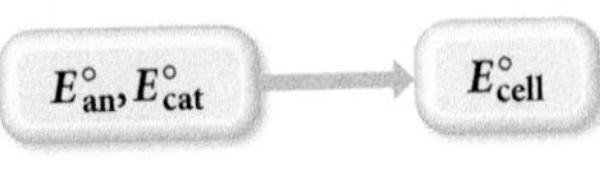

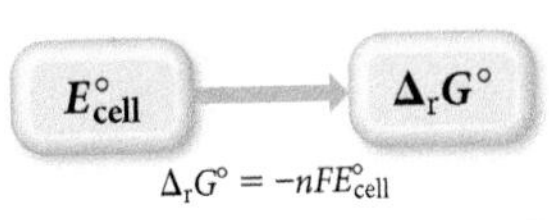

$\Delta_r G^\circ = -nFE^\circ_{cell}$

SOLVE Break the reaction up into oxidation and reduction half-reactions and find the standard electrode potentials for each from Table 18.1. Find E°_{cell} using Equation 18.1.

SOLUTION The way the reaction is written, Na is being oxidized, so the Na^+/Na reaction is the anodic reaction and water reduction is the cathodic reaction. The half-reactions and standard electrode potentials are as follows:

Cathode: $2\,H_2O(l) + 2\,e^- \longrightarrow H_2(g) + 2\,OH^-(aq)$ $E^\circ = -0.41$ V

Anode: $Na^+(aq) + e^- \longrightarrow Na(s)$ $E^\circ = -2.71$ V

$$E^\circ_{cell} = E^\circ_{cathode} - E^\circ_{anode}$$
$$E^\circ_{cell} = E^\circ_{H_2O/H_2,OH^-} - E^\circ_{Na^+/Na}$$
$$E^\circ_{cell} = -0.41\text{ V} - (-2.71\text{ V})$$
$$= 2.30\text{ V}$$

Calculate $\Delta_r G^\circ$ from E°_{cell} using Equation 18.4. Two electrons would be cancelled in the half-reaction to balance the overall reaction (the Na^+/Na half-reaction would be multiplied by two); therefore, $n = 2$. In order for units to cancel, 2.30 V should be expressed as 2.30 J C^{-1}.

$$\Delta_r G^\circ = -nFE^\circ_{cell}$$
$$= -2(96\,485\ \cancel{C}\ mol^{-1})(2.30\ J\ \cancel{C^{-1}})$$
$$= -4.44 \times 10^5\ \cancel{J}\ mol^{-1}(\times 1\ kJ/1000\ \cancel{J})$$
$$= -444\ kJ\ mol^{-1}$$

Since $\Delta_r G^\circ$ is negative, the reaction is spontaneous in the direction written.

CHECK The answer is in the correct units (kJ mol^{-1}) and seems reasonable in magnitude (sodium ignites when put in water and must be stored under oil). The sign is negative, which means the reaction is spontaneous and is consistent with a positive E°_{cell}.

FOR PRACTICE 18.4

Use tabulated electrode potentials to calculate $\Delta_r G^\circ$ for the reaction:

$$I_2(s) + 2\,Br^-(aq) \longrightarrow 2\,I^-(aq) + Br_2(l)$$

Is the reaction spontaneous?

CONCEPTUAL CONNECTION 18.3

Periodic Trends and the Direction of Spontaneity for Redox Reactions

When you do the For Practice Problem 18.4, you will see that the reaction of I_2 with Br^- to form I^- and Br_2 is not spontaneous. Based on conceptual reasoning, which of the following best explains why I_2 does not oxidize Br^-?

(a) Br has a larger electon affinity than I; therefore, we do not expect Br^- to give up an electron to I_2.

(b) I has a larger electron affinity than Br; therefore, we do not expect I_2 to give up an electron to Br^-.

(c) Br^- is in solution and I_2 is a solid. Solids do not gain electrons from substances in solution.

The Relationship Between E°_{cell} and K

We can derive a relationship between the standard cell potential (E°_{cell}) and the equilibrium constant for the redox reaction occurring in the cell (K) by returning to the relationship between $\Delta_r G^\circ$ and K that we learned in Chapter 17. Recall from Section 17.9 that

$$\Delta_r G^\circ = -RT \ln K \qquad [18.5]$$

By setting Equations 18.4 and 18.5 equal to each other, we get:

$$-nFE^\circ_{\text{cell}} = -RT \ln K$$

$$E^\circ_{\text{cell}} = \frac{RT}{nF} \ln K \qquad [18.6]$$

Equation 18.6 is usually simplified for use at 25 °C by making the following substitutions:

$$R = 8.314 \text{ J mol}^{-1}\text{ K}^{-1};\ T = 298.15 \text{ K};\ F = 96\,485 \text{ C mol}^{-1}$$

Substituting into Equation 18.6, we get the following important result:

$$E^\circ_{\text{cell}} = \frac{0.0257 \text{ V}}{n} \ln K \qquad [18.7]$$

where E°_{cell} is the standard cell potential, n is the number of electrons transferred in the redox reaction, and K is the equilibrium constant for the balanced redox reaction at 25 °C. The following example demonstrates how to use Equation 18.7.

EXAMPLE 18.5 RELATING E°_{cell} AND K

Use the tabulated electrode potentials to calculate K for the oxidation of copper by H^+ (at 25 °C).

$$\text{Cu}(s) + 2\,\text{H}^+(aq) \longrightarrow \text{Cu}^{2+}(aq) + \text{H}_2(g)$$

SORT You are given a redox reaction and asked to find K.

GIVEN: $\text{Cu}(s) + 2\,\text{H}^+(aq) \longrightarrow \text{Cu}^{2+}(aq) + \text{H}_2(g)$

FIND: K

STRATEGIZE Use the tabulated values of electrode potentials to calculate E°_{cell}. Then use Equation 18.7 to calculate K from E°_{cell}.

CONCEPTUAL PLAN

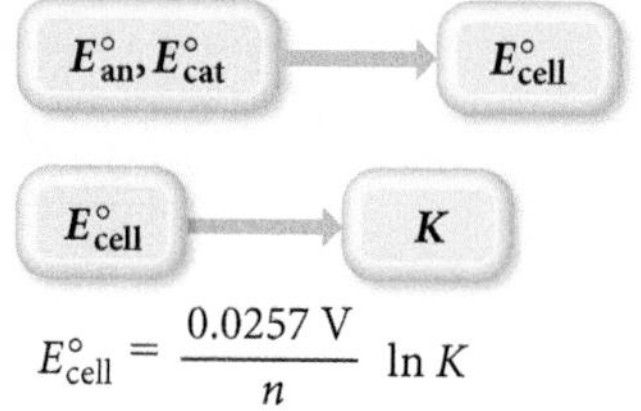

$$E^\circ_{\text{cell}} = \frac{0.0257 \text{ V}}{n} \ln K$$

SOLVE Break the reaction up into oxidation and reduction half-reactions and find the standard electrode potentials for each from Table 18.1. Find E°_{cell} using Equation 18.1.

SOLUTION

The way the reaction is written, Cu is being oxidized, so the Cu^{2+}/Cu reaction is the anodic reaction and the H^+ reduction is the cathodic reaction. The half-reactions and standard electrode potentials are as follows:

Cathode: $2\,\text{H}^+(s) + 2\,e^- \longrightarrow \text{H}_2(g) \qquad E^\circ = 0.00 \text{ V}$

Anode: $\text{Cu}^{2+}(aq) + 2\,e^- \longrightarrow \text{Cu}(s) \qquad E^\circ = 0.34 \text{ V}$

$$E^\circ_{\text{cell}} = E^\circ_{\text{cathode}} - E^\circ_{\text{anode}}$$

$$E^\circ_{\text{cell}} = E^\circ_{\text{H}^+/\text{H}_2} - E^\circ_{\text{Cu}^{2+}/\text{Cu}}$$

$$E^\circ_{\text{cell}} = 0.00 \text{ V} - 0.34 \text{ V}$$

$$= -0.34 \text{ V}$$

The reaction has a negative E°_{cell} and is not spontaneous under standard conditions.

(continued)

EXAMPLE 18.5 (CONTINUED)

Calculate K from E°_{cell} using Equation 18.7. Two electrons would be cancelled in the half-reaction to balance the overall reaction; therefore, $n = 2$.	$E^\circ_{cell} = \frac{0.0257\text{ V}}{n}\ln K$ $\ln K = \frac{nE^\circ_{cell}}{0.0257\text{ V}}$ $= \frac{2 \times (-0.34\text{ V})}{0.0257\text{ V}} = -2\underline{6}.46$ $K = e^{-2\underline{6}.46} = 3.2 \times 10^{-12}$

CHECK The answer has no units, as expected for an equilibrium constant. The K value is much less than one, indicating that the reaction lies far to the left at equilibrium, as expected for a reaction in which E°_{cell} is negative.

FOR PRACTICE 18.5
Use the tabulated electrode potentials to calculate K for the oxidation of iron by H^+ (at 25 °C):

$$2\,Fe(s) + 6\,H^+(aq) \longrightarrow 2\,Fe^{3+}(aq) + 3\,H_2(g)$$

Notice that the fundamental quantity in the above relationships is the standard change in Gibbs energy for a chemical reaction ($\Delta_r G^\circ$). From that quantity, we can calculate both E°_{cell} and K. The relationships between these three quantities is summarized with the following diagram:

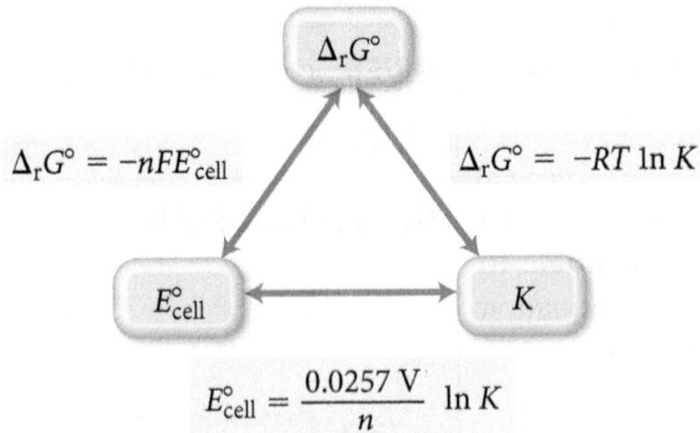

18.5 Cell Potential and Concentration

We have learned how to find E°_{cell} under standard conditions. For example, we know that when $[Cu^{2+}] = 1\text{ mol L}^{-1}$ and $[Zn^{2+}] = 1\text{ mol L}^{-1}$, the following reaction produces a potential of 1.10 V.

$$Zn(s) + Cu^{2+}(aq, 1\text{ mol L}^{-1}) \longrightarrow Zn^{2+}(aq, 1\text{ mol L}^{-1}) + Cu(s) \quad E^\circ_{cell} = 1.10\text{ V}$$

However, what if $[Cu^{2+}] > 1\text{ mol L}^{-1}$ and $[Zn^{2+}] < 1\text{ mol L}^{-1}$? For example, how would the cell potential for the following conditions be different from the potential under standard conditions?

$$Zn(s) + Cu^{2+}(aq, 2\text{ mol L}^{-1}) \longrightarrow Zn^{2+}(aq, 0.01\text{ mol L}^{-1}) + Cu(s) \quad E_{cell} = ?$$

Since the concentration of a reactant is greater than standard conditions, and since the concentration of product is less than standard conditions, we can use Le Châtelier's principle to predict that the reaction has an even stronger tendency to occur in the forward direction and that E_{cell} is therefore greater than 1.10 V (Figure 18.12 ▸).

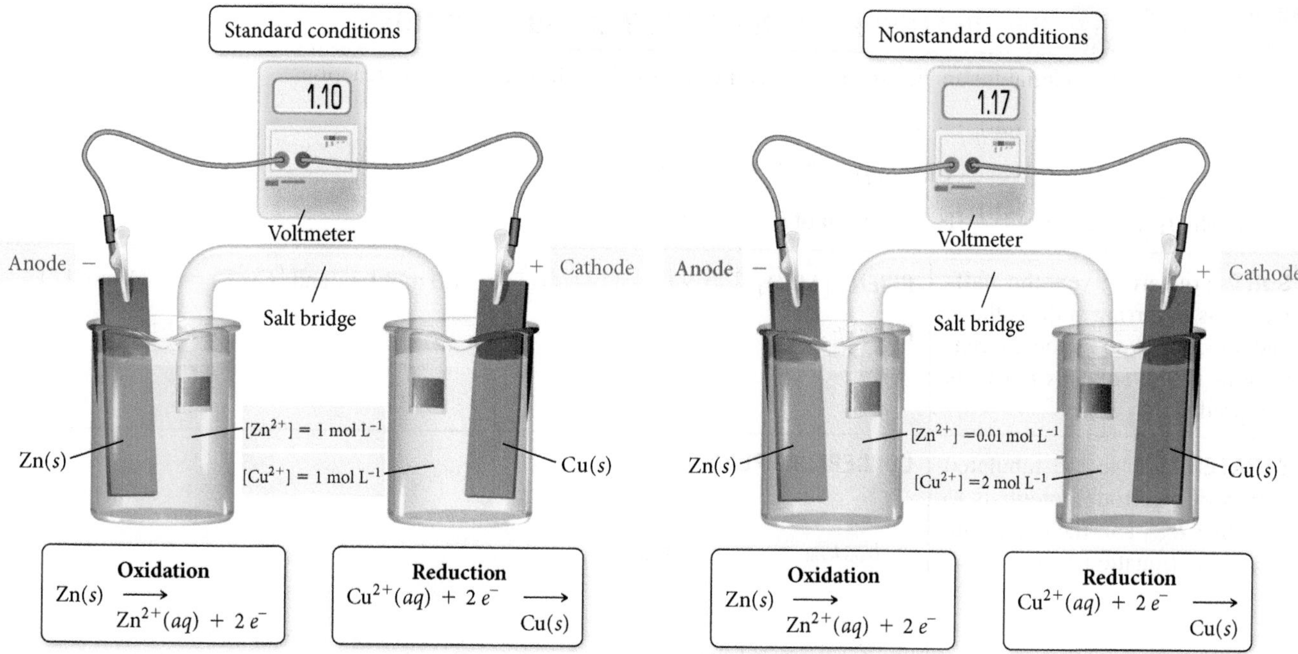

▲ **FIGURE 18.12 Cell Potential and Concentration** This figure compares the Zn/Cu^{2+} electrochemical cell under standard and nonstandard conditions. In this case, the nonstandard conditions consist of a higher Cu^{2+} concentration ($[Cu^{2+}] > 1$ mol L^{-1}) at the cathode and a lower Zn^{2+} concentration at the anode ($[Zn^{2+}] < 1$ mol L^{-1}). According to Le Châtelier's principle, the forward reaction has a greater tendency to occur, resulting in a greater overall cell potential than the potential under standard conditions.

We can derive an exact relationship between E_{cell} (under nonstandard conditions) and E°_{cell} by considering the relationship between the change in Gibbs energy ($\Delta_r G$) and the *standard* change in Gibbs energy ($\Delta_r G^{\circ}$) that we learned in Section 17.8:

$$\Delta_r G = \Delta_r G^{\circ} + RT \ln Q \qquad [18.8]$$

where R is the gas constant (8.314 J/mol · K), T is the temperature in kelvins, and Q is the reaction quotient corresponding to the nonstandard conditions. Since we know the relationship between $\Delta_r G$ and E_{cell} (Equation 18.4), we can substitute into Equation 18.8:

$$\Delta_r G = \Delta_r G^{\circ} + RT \ln Q$$

$$-nFE_{cell} = -nFE^{\circ}_{cell} + RT \ln Q$$

We can then divide each side by $-nF$ to arrive at:

$$E_{cell} = E^{\circ}_{cell} - \frac{RT}{nF} \ln Q \qquad [18.9]$$

As we have seen, R and F are constants; at $T = 25$ °C, $\dfrac{RT}{nF} = \dfrac{0.0257 \text{ V}}{n}$

Substituting into Equation 18.9, we arrive at the **Nernst equation**:

$$E_{cell} = E^{\circ}_{cell} - \frac{0.0257 \text{ V}}{n} \ln Q \qquad [18.10]$$

where E_{cell} is the cell potential in volts, E°_{cell} is the *standard* cell potential in volts, n is the number of electrons transferred in the redox reaction, and Q is the reaction quotient. Notice that, under standard conditions, $Q = 1$, and (since log 1 = 0) $E_{cell} = E^{\circ}_{cell}$, as expected. Example 18.6 shows how to calculate the cell potential under nonstandard conditions.

The Nernst equation is sometimes written in terms of the base 10 logarithm. Since $\ln Q = 2.303 \log Q$, the Nernst equation can be expressed as:

$$E_{cell} = E^{\circ}_{cell} - \frac{0.0592 \text{ V}}{n} \log Q$$

Both forms of the Nernst equation will give the same answer.

EXAMPLE 18.6 CALCULATING E_{cell} UNDER NONSTANDARD CONDITIONS

Determine the cell potential for an electrochemical cell based on the following two half-reactions:

Cathode: $MnO_4^-(aq) + 4\,H^+(aq) + 3\,e^- \longrightarrow MnO_2(s) + 2\,H_2O(l)$

Anode: $Cu^{2+}(aq) + 2\,e^- \longrightarrow Cu(s)$

when $[MnO_4^-] = 2.0\text{ mol L}^{-1}$, $[H^+] = 1.0\text{ mol L}^{-1}$, and $[Cu^{2+}] = 0.01\text{ mol L}^{-1}$.

SORT You are given the half-reactions occurring at the cathode and anode as well as the concentrations of the aqueous reactants and products.

GIVEN: $[MnO_4^-] = 2.0\text{ mol L}^{-1}$, $[H^+] = 1.0\text{ mol L}^{-1}$, and $[Cu^{2+}] = 0.01\text{ mol L}^{-1}$.

FIND: E_{cell}

STRATEGIZE Use the tabulated values of electrode potentials to calculate E°_{cell} and then calculate E_{cell} using Equation 18.10.

CONCEPTUAL PLAN

$E^\circ_{cell}, [MnO_4^-], [H^+], [Cu^{2+}] \longrightarrow E_{cell}$

$$E_{cell} = E^\circ_{cell} - \frac{0.0257\text{ V}}{n}\ln Q$$

SOLVE Using the tabulated values for the reduction reactions and Equation 18.1, compute the standard cell potential.

SOLUTION

Cathode: $MnO_4^-(aq) + 4H^+(aq) + 3\,e^- \longrightarrow MnO_2(s) + 2\,H_2O(l)$ $\quad E^\circ = 1.68\text{ V}$

Anode: $Cu^{2+}(aq) + 2\,e^- \longrightarrow Cu(s)$ $\quad E^\circ = 0.34\text{ V}$

$$E^\circ_{cell} = E^\circ_{cathode} - E^\circ_{anode}$$

$$E^\circ_{cell} = E^\circ_{MnO_4^-/MnO_2} - E^\circ_{Cu^{2+}/Cu}$$

$$E^\circ_{cell} = 1.68\text{ V} - 0.34\text{ V}$$

$$= 1.34\text{ V}$$

Equation 18.10 contains the reaction quotient, Q, which requires the balanced equation to write. Balance the equation by writing the anodic reaction in reverse and multiplying each reaction by a factor so that the electrons cancel.

$$MnO_4^-(aq) + 4\,H^+(aq) + 3\,e^- \longrightarrow MnO_2(s) + 2\,H_2O(l) \quad \times 2$$

$$Cu(s) \longrightarrow Cu^{2+}(aq) + 2\,e^- \quad \times 3$$

$$2\,MnO_4^-(aq) + 8\,H^+(aq) + \cancel{6e^-} \longrightarrow 2\,MnO_2(s) + 4\,H_2O(l)$$

$$3\,Cu(s) \longrightarrow 3\,Cu^{2+}(aq) + \cancel{6e^-}$$

$$2\,MnO_4^-(aq) + 3\,Cu(s) + 8\,H^+(aq) \longrightarrow 2\,MnO_2(s) + 3\,Cu^{2+}(aq) + 4\,H_2O(l)$$

Calculate E_{cell} from E°_{cell}. The value of n is the number of electrons transferred in the balanced equation, which is 6. The expression for Q can be determined from the balanced equation.

$$E_{cell} = E^\circ_{cell} - \frac{0.0257\text{ V}}{n}\ln Q$$

$$= E^\circ_{cell} - \frac{0.0257\text{ V}}{n}\ln\frac{[Cu^{2+}]^3}{[MnO_4^-]^2[H^+]^8}$$

$$= 1.34\text{ V} - \frac{0.0257\text{ V}}{6}\ln\frac{(0.010)^3}{(2.0)^2(1.0)^8}$$

$$= 1.34\text{ V} - (-0.065\text{ V})$$

$$= 1.41\text{ V}$$

CHECK The answer has the correct unit (V). The value of E_{cell} is larger than E°_{cell}, as expected based on Le Châtelier's principle because one of the aqueous reactants has a concentration greater than standard conditions, and the one aqueous product has a concentration less than standard conditions. Therefore, under the conditions given, the reaction has a greater tendency to proceed toward products than under standard conditions and has a greater cell potential.

FOR PRACTICE 18.6

Determine the cell potential for an electrochemical cell based on the following two half-reactions,

Cathode: $Ni^{2+}(aq) + 2\,e^- \longrightarrow Ni(s)$

Anode: $VO_2^{+}(aq) + 2\,H^+(aq) + e^- \longrightarrow VO^{2+}(aq) + H_2O(l)$

when $[VO_2^{+}] = 0.010\ \text{mol L}^{-1}$, $[VO^{2+}] = 2.0\ \text{mol L}^{-1}\,[H^+] = 1.0\ \text{mol L}^{-1}$, and $[Ni^{2+}] = 2.0\ \text{mol L}^{-1}$.

From the above examples, and from Equation 18.10, we can conclude the following:

- When a redox reaction within a voltaic cell occurs under standard conditions, $Q = 1$; therefore $E_{cell} = E^{\circ}_{cell}$.

$$E_{cell} = E^{\circ}_{cell} - \frac{0.0257\ \text{V}}{n}\ln Q$$

$$= E^{\circ}_{cell} - \frac{0.0257\ \text{V}}{n}\ln(1) \qquad \ln(1) = 0$$

$$= E^{\circ}_{cell}$$

- When a redox reaction within a voltaic cell occurs under conditions in which $Q < 1$, the greater concentration of reactants relative to products drives the reaction to the right, resulting in $E_{cell} > E^{\circ}_{cell}$.
- When a redox reaction within an electrochemical cell occurs under conditions in which $Q > 1$, the greater concentration of products relative to reactants drives the reaction to the left, resulting in $E_{cell} < E^{\circ}_{cell}$.
- When a redox reaction reaches equilibrium, $Q = K$. The redox reaction has no tendency to occur in either direction and $E_{cell} = 0$.

$$E_{cell} = E^{\circ}_{cell} - \frac{0.0257\ \text{V}}{n}\ln Q$$

$$= E^{\circ}_{cell} - \frac{0.0257\ \text{V}}{n}\ln K \qquad \left(\frac{0.0257\ \text{V}}{n}\ln K = E^{\circ}_{cell}\right)$$

(see Equation 18.7)

$$= 0\ \text{V}$$

This last point explains why batteries do not last forever—as the reactants are depleted, the reaction proceeds toward equilibrium and the potential tends toward zero.

CONCEPTUAL CONNECTION 18.4

Relating Q, K, E_{cell}, and E°_{cell}

In an electrochemical cell, $Q = 0.0010$ and $K = 0.10$. Which statement is true?

(a) E_{cell} is positive and E°_{cell} is negative.

(b) E_{cell} is negative and E°_{cell} is positive.

(c) Both E_{cell} and E°_{cell} are positive.

(d) Both E_{cell} and E°_{cell} are negative.

Concentration Cells

Since cell potential depends not only on the half-reactions occurring in the cell, but also on the *concentrations* of the reactants and products in those half-reactions, we can construct a voltaic cell in which both half-reactions are the same, but in which *a difference in concentration drives the current flow*. For example, consider the electrochemical cell shown in Figure 18.13 ▼, in which copper is oxidized at the anode and copper ions are reduced at the cathode. The second part of Figure 18.13 depicts this cell under nonstandard conditions, with $[Cu^{2+}] = 2.0 \text{ mol L}^{-1}$ in one half-cell and $[Cu^{2+}] = 0.010 \text{ mol L}^{-1}$ in the other:

$$Cu(s) + Cu^{2+}(aq, 2.0 \text{ mol L}^{-1}) \longrightarrow Cu^{2+}(aq, 0.010 \text{ mol L}^{-1}) + Cu(s)$$

The half-reactions are identical and the *standard* cell potential is therefore zero.

Cathode: $Cu^{2+}(aq) + 2\,e^- \longrightarrow Cu(s) \quad E^\circ = 0.34 \text{ V}$

Anode: $Cu^{2+}(aq) + 2\,e^- \longrightarrow Cu(s) \quad E^\circ = 0.34 \text{ V}$

$$E^\circ_{cell} = E^\circ_{cathode} - E^\circ_{anode}$$

$$E^\circ_{cell} = 0.34 \text{ V} - 0.34 \text{ V}$$

$$= 0.00 \text{ V}$$

The overall equation can be determined from the cathode and anode reactions, where *c* and *a* denote whether the species is in the anode or cathode:

Cathode: $Cu^{2+}(aq, c) + \cancel{2e^-} \longrightarrow Cu(s, c)$

Anode: $Cu(s, a) \longrightarrow Cu^{2+}(aq, a) + \cancel{2e^-}$

Overall $Cu^{2+}(aq, c) + Cu(s, a) \longrightarrow Cu(s, c) + Cu^{2+}(aq, a)$

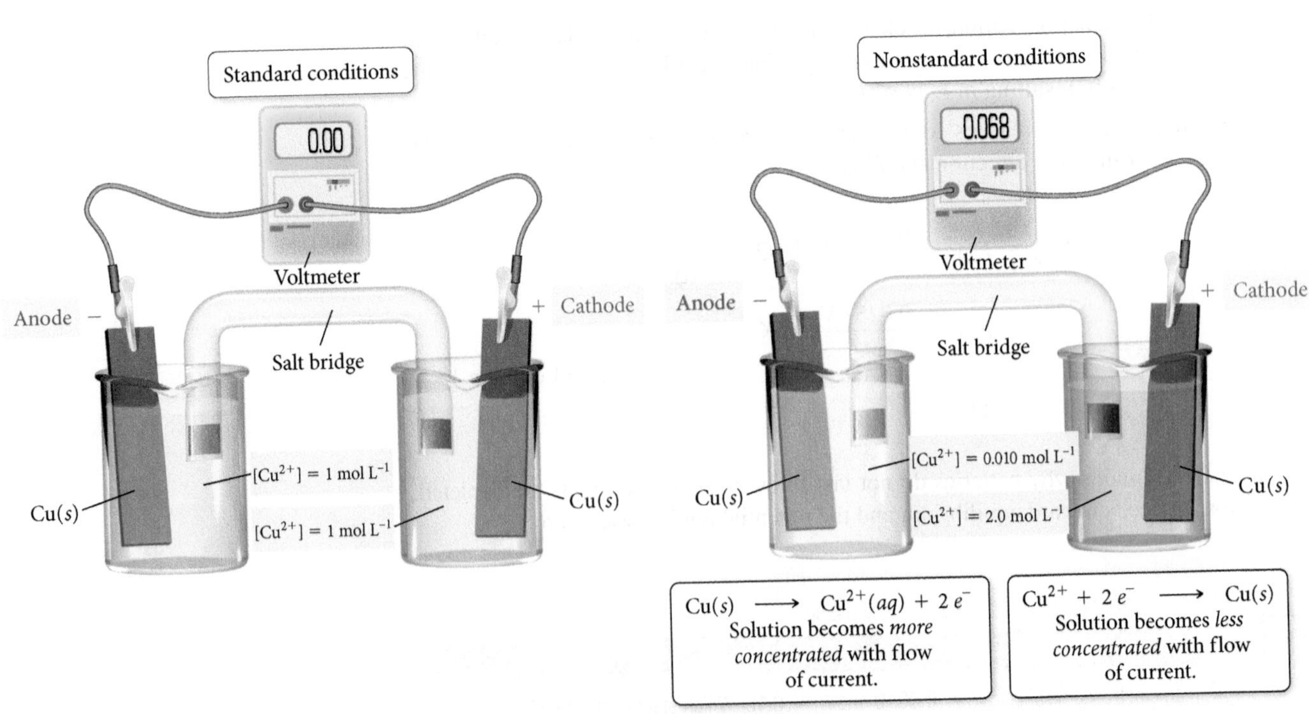

▲ **FIGURE 18.13 Cu/Cu^{2+} Concentration Cell** If two half-cells have the same Cu^{2+} concentration, the cell potential is zero. If one half-cell has a greater Cu^{2+} concentration than the other, a spontaneous reaction occurs. In the reaction, Cu^{2+} ions in the more concentrated cell are reduced (to solid copper), while Cu^{2+} ions in the more dilute cell are formed (from solid copper). The concentration of copper ions in the two half-cells tends toward equality.

Because of the different concentrations in the two half-cells, the cell potential must be calculated using the Nernst equation:

$$E_{cell} = E^{\circ}_{cell} - \frac{0.0257\text{ V}}{n}\ln Q$$

$$= E^{\circ}_{cell} - \frac{0.0257\text{ V}}{n}\ln\frac{[\text{Cu}\ (aq, a)]}{[\text{Cu}\ (aq, c)]}$$

$$= 0.000\text{ V} - \frac{0.0257\text{ V}}{2}\ln\frac{(0.010)}{(2.0)}$$

$$= 0.068\text{ V}$$

The cell produces a potential of 0.068 V. *Electrons spontaneously flow from the half-cell with the lower copper ion concentration to the half-cell with the higher copper ion concentration.* You can imagine a concentration cell in the same way you think about any concentration gradient. If you mix a concentrated solution of Cu^{2+} with a dilute solution, the Cu^{2+} ions flow from the concentrated solution to the dilute one. Similarly, in a concentration cell, the transfer of electrons *from* the dilute half-cell results in the forming of Cu^{2+} ions in the dilute half-cell. The electrons flow to the concentrated cell, where they react with Cu^{2+} ions and reduce them to Cu(s). Therefore, *the flow of electrons has the effect of increasing the concentration of Cu^{2+} in the dilute cell and decreasing the concentration of Cu^{2+} in the concentrated half-cell.*

EXAMPLE 18.7

DETERMINING THE K_{sp} OF A SLIGHTLY SOLUBLE SALT USING A CONCENTRATION CELL

A concentration cell is set up as in the diagram to the right. The cathode is a standard Zn^{2+} (i.e., $Zn(NO_3)_2$/Zn electrode), and the anode is composed of a Zn electrode immersed in a saturated solution of $Zn(OH)_2$. The cell potential is measured to be 0.169 V. Determine the K_{sp} for $Zn(OH)_2$.

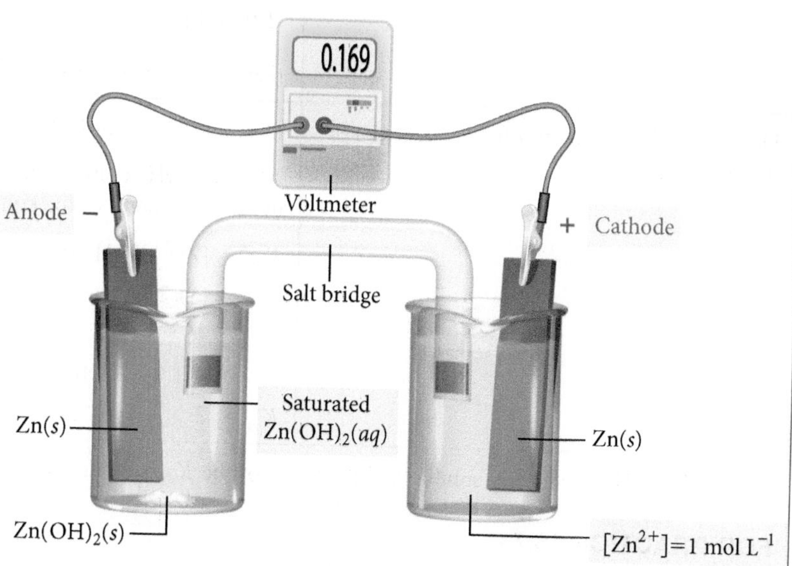

SORT You are given the cell potential and a concentration cell with an unknown Zn^{2+} concentration.	**GIVEN:** $E_{cell} = 0.169\text{ V}$ **FIND:** K_{sp}

(continued)

EXAMPLE 18.7 (CONTINUED)

STRATEGIZE Since it is a concentration cell $E^\circ_{cell} = 0$ V, determine the expression for Q from the balanced equation and calculate the $[Zn^{2+}]$ in the saturated $Zn(OH)_2$ solution using Equation 18.10. Then determine the expression for K_{sp} in terms of the solubility, S, and calculate K_{sp}.

CONCEPTUAL PLAN

$E_{cell} \rightarrow [Zn^{2+}]$

$$E_{cell} = E^\circ_{cell} - \frac{0.0257\text{ V}}{n}\ln Q$$

$[Zn^{2+}] = S \rightarrow K_{sp}$

SOLVE Determine the expression for the reaction quotient, Q, in terms of the concentrations of the solutes.

SOLUTION

Cathode: $Zn^{2+}(aq, c) + 2e^- \longrightarrow Zn(s, c)$

Anode: $Zn(s, a) \longrightarrow Zn^{2+}(aq, a) + 2e^-$

Overall $Zn^{2+}(aq, c) + Zn(s, a) \longrightarrow Zn(s, c) + Zn^{2+}(aq, a)$

$$Q = \frac{[Zn^{2+}(aq, a)]}{[Zn^{2+}(aq, c)]}$$

Use the Nernst equation (Equation 18.10) to determine $[Zn^{2+}(aq, a)]$.

$$E_{cell} = E^\circ_{cell} - \frac{0.0257\text{ V}}{n}\ln Q$$

$$= E^\circ_{cell} - \frac{0.0257\text{ V}}{n}\ln\frac{[Zn^{2+}(aq, a)]}{[Zn^{2+}(aq, c)]}$$

$$0.169\text{ V} = 0.000\text{ V} - \frac{0.0257\text{ V}}{2}\ln\frac{[Zn^{2+}(aq, a)]}{[1.0\text{ mol L}^{-1}]}$$

$$-13.\underline{1}5 = \ln\frac{[Zn^{2+}(aq, a)]}{1.0\text{ mol L}^{-1}}$$

$$\frac{[Zn^{2+}(aq, a)]}{1.0\text{ mol L}^{-1}} = e^{-13.\underline{1}5}$$

$$[Zn^{2+}(aq, a)] = 1.94 \times 10^{-6}\text{ mol L}^{-1}$$

Determine the expression for K_{sp} in terms of the solubility, S.

$$Zn(OH)_2(s) \longrightarrow Zn^{2+}(aq) + 2\,OH^-(aq)$$

All of the OH^- comes from the dissolution of $Zn(OH)_2$. Since $[Zn^{2+}] = S$, from the stoichiometry of the equilibrium $[OH^-] = 2S$.

$$\begin{aligned} K_{sp} &= [Zn^{2+}][OH^-]^2 \\ &= (S)(2S)^2 \\ &= 4S^3 \\ &= 4(\underline{1}.94 \times 10^{-6})^3 \\ K_{sp} &= 3 \times 10^{-17} \end{aligned}$$

CHECK $Zn(OH)_2$ is slightly soluble and the value of the K_{sp} is small, so the answer seems reasonable.

FOR PRACTICE 18.7

A concentration cell similar to the one in the diagram in Example 18.7 is constructed to measure the concentration of Fe^{3+}. The cathode is a standard Fe^{3+}/Fe electrode and the anode is composed of Fe electrode immersed in a saturated solution of $Fe(OH)_3$. The cell potential is measured to be 0.7887 V. Determine the K_{sp} for $Fe(OH)_3$.

CHEMISTRY AND MEDICINE Concentration Cells in Human Nerve Cells

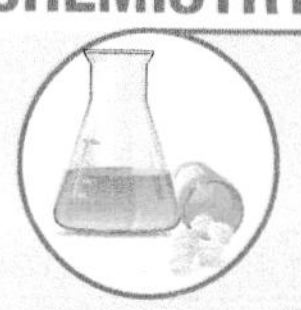

Recall from Section 8.1 that tiny pumps in the membranes of human nerve cells pump ions—especially sodium (Na^+) and potassium (K^+)—through those membranes establishing a concentration gradient for each ion: the concentration of sodium ions is higher outside the cell than within, while exactly the opposite is true for potassium ions. These concentration gradients result in an electrical potential across the cell membrane, called the resting potential, of about −70 mV. (The interior of the cell is negative with respect to the exterior.)

When the nerve cell is stimulated, certain channels in the membrane open, allowing Na^+ ions to rush into the cell and causing the potential to temporarily rise to about +30 mV (Figure 18.14 ▼). This is followed by the opening of other channels that allow K^+ ions to rush out of the cell, bringing the potential back down to near its resting potential. The result is a spike in the electrochemical potential across the membrane, which provides the stimulus for a similar spike in the neighbouring segment of the membrane (Figure 18.15 ▼). In this way, an electrical signal moves down the length of a nerve cell.

When the electrical signal reaches the end of the nerve cell, it triggers the release of a chemical neurotransmitter, which travels to the neighbouring nerve cell and stimulates the same kind of electrochemical spike. In this way, neural signals travel throughout the brain and nervous system of a human being.

▲ **FIGURE 18.14 Concentration Changes in Nerve Cells** In a nerve cell at rest, the concentration of sodium ions is higher outside the cell than inside. The reverse is true for potassium ions. When a nerve cell is stimulated, sodium channels open and Na^+ ions flood into the cell. A fraction of a second later, the sodium channels close and potassium channels open, allowing K^+ ions to leave the cell.

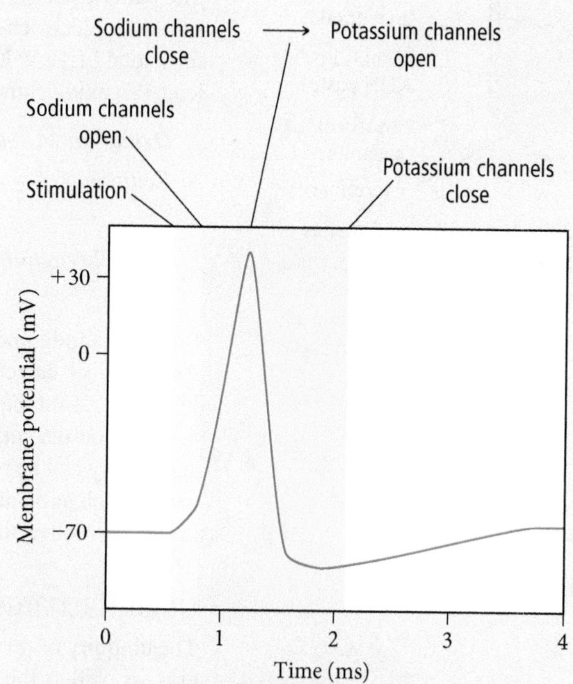

▲ **FIGURE 18.15 Potential Changes Across the Nerve Cell Membrane** The changes in ion concentrations that take place when a nerve cell is stimulated result in a spike in the electrochemical potential across the membrane.

18.6 Batteries: Using Chemistry to Generate Electricity

We have seen that we can combine the electron-losing tendency of one substance with the electron-gaining tendency of another to create electrical current in a voltaic cell. Batteries are simply voltaic cells conveniently packaged to act as portable sources of electricity. The actual oxidation and reduction reactions depend on the particular type of battery. In this section, we examine several different types.

Dry-Cell Batteries

Common batteries, such as the type you find in a flashlight, are called **dry-cell batteries** because they do not contain large amounts of liquid water. The most common dry cells are **alkaline batteries** (Figure 18.16 ▼). Alkaline batteries employ a Zn anode in a basic

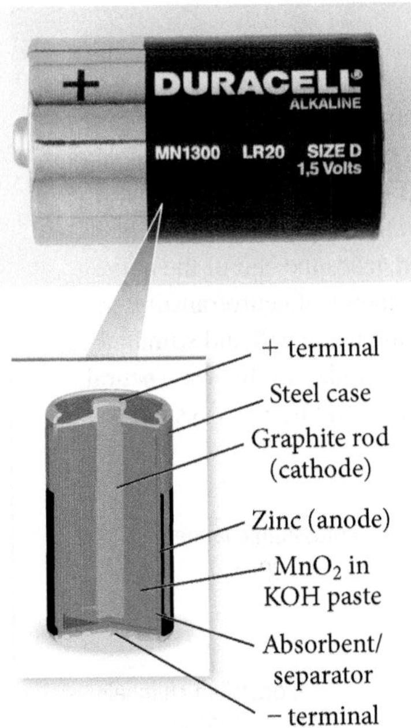

▲ **FIGURE 18.16 Alkaline Batteries** In the common dry-cell battery, zinc acts as the anode and a graphite rod immersed in a paste of MnO_2 and a base.

medium (therefore the name alkaline), where it is oxidized according to the following oxidation reaction:

$$\textbf{\textit{Oxidation}}\ \textit{(Anode):}\quad Zn(s) + \cancel{2\,OH^-}(aq) \longrightarrow Zn(OH)_2(s) + \cancel{2e^-}$$

$$\textbf{\textit{Reduction}}\ \textit{(Cathode):}\quad 2\,MnO_2(s) + 2\,H_2O(l) + \cancel{2e^-} \longrightarrow 2\,MnO(OH)(s) + \cancel{2\,OH^-}(aq)$$

$$\textbf{\textit{Overall reaction:}}\quad Zn(s) + 2\,MnO_2(s) + 2\,H_2O(l) \longrightarrow Zn(OH)_2(s) + 2\,MnO(OH)(s)$$

The two half-reactions produce a voltage of about 1.5 V. Alkaline batteries have a longer working life and a longer shelf life than their nonalkaline counterparts.

Lead–Acid Storage Batteries

The batteries in most automobiles are **lead–acid storage batteries**. These batteries consist of six electrochemical cells wired in series (Figure 18.17 ▼). Each cell produces 2 V for a total of 12 V. Each cell contains a porous lead anode where oxidation occurs and a lead(IV) oxide cathode where reduction occurs according to the reactions:

$$\textbf{\textit{Oxidation}}\ \textit{(Anode):}\quad Pb(s) + HSO_4^-(aq) \longrightarrow PbSO_4(s) + \cancel{H^+}(aq) + \cancel{2e^-}$$

$$\textbf{\textit{Reduction}}\ \textit{(Cathode):}\quad PbO_2(s) + HSO_4^-(aq) + 2\,\cancel{3}H^+(aq) + \cancel{2e^-} \longrightarrow PbSO_4(s) + 2\,H_2O(l)$$

$$\textbf{\textit{Overall reaction:}}\quad Pb(s) + PbO_2(s) + 2\,HSO_4^-(aq) + 2\,H^+(aq) \longrightarrow 2\,PbSO_4(s) + 2\,H_2O(l)$$

Both the anode and the cathode are immersed in aqueous sulfuric acid ($H_2SO_4(aq)$). As electrical current is drawn from the battery, both electrodes become coated with $PbSO_4(s)$. If the battery is run for a long time without recharging, too much $PbSO_4(s)$ develops on the surface of the electrodes and the battery goes dead. The lead–acid storage battery can be recharged by an electrical current (which must come from an external source such as an alternator in a car). The current causes the preceding reaction to occur in reverse, converting the $PbSO_4(s)$ back to $Pb(s)$ and $PbO_2(s)$.

Other Rechargeable Batteries

The ubiquity of power electronic products such as laptops, cell phones, and digital cameras, as well as the growth in popularity of hybrid electric vehicles, has driven the need for efficient, long-lasting, rechargeable batteries. The most common types include the **nickel–cadmium (NiCad) battery**, the **nickel–metal hydride (NiMH) battery**, and the **lithium–ion battery**.

The Nickel–Cadmium (NiCad) Battery Nickel–cadmium batteries consist of an anode composed of solid cadmium and a cathode composed of $NiO(OH)(s)$. The electrolyte is usually

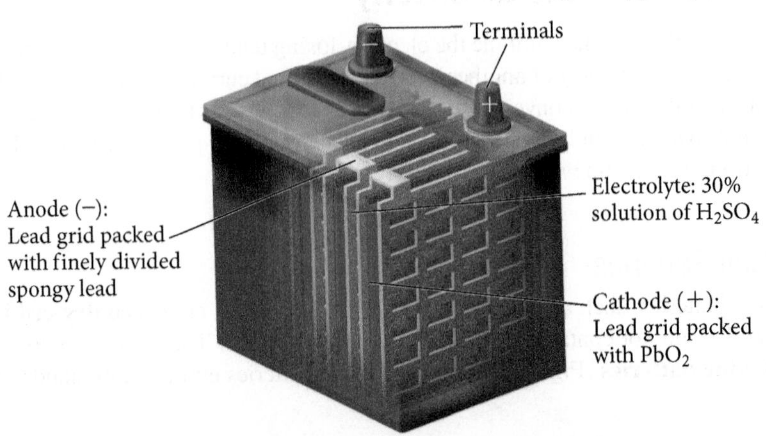

▶ **FIGURE 18.17 Lead–Acid Storage Battery** A lead–acid storage battery consists of six cells wired in series. Each cell contains a porous lead anode and a lead oxide cathode, both immersed in sulfuric acid.

$KOH(aq)$. During operation, the cadmium is oxidized and the NiO(OH) is reduced according to the equations:

$$\textit{Oxidation (Anode):} \quad Cd(s) + 2\,OH^-(aq) \longrightarrow Cd(OH)_2(s) + 2\,e^-$$

$$\textit{Reduction (Cathode):} \quad 2\,NiO(OH)(s) + 2\,H_2O(l) + 2\,e^- \longrightarrow 2\,Ni(OH)_2(s) + 2\,OH^-(aq)$$

The overall reaction produces about 1.30 V. As current is drawn from the NiCad battery, solid cadmium hydroxide accumulates on the anode and solid nickel(II) hydroxide accumulates on the cathode. But by running current in the opposite direction, the reactants can be regenerated from the products. A common problem in recharging NiCad and other rechargeable batteries is knowing when to stop. Once all of the products of the reaction are converted back to reactants, the charging process should ideally terminate—otherwise the electrical current will drive other, usually unwanted, reactions such as the electrolysis of water to form hydrogen and oxygen gas. These reactions typically damage the battery and may sometimes even cause an explosion. Consequently, most commercial battery chargers have sensors designed to measure when the charging is complete. These sensors rely on the small changes in voltage or increases in temperature that occur once the products have all been converted back to reactants.

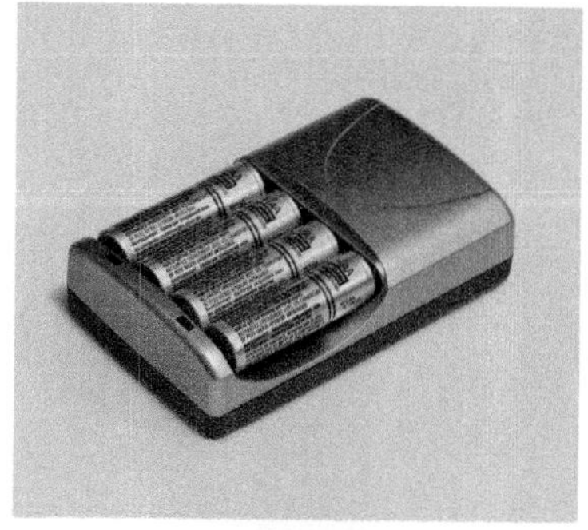

▲ Several types of batteries, including NiCad, NiMH, and lithium–ion batteries, are recharged by chargers that use household current.

The Nickel–Metal Hydride (NiMH) Battery Although NiCad batteries were the standard rechargeable battery for many years, they are being replaced by others, in part because of the toxicity of cadmium and the resulting disposal problems. One of these replacements is the nickel–metal hydride or NiMH battery. The NiMH battery employs the same cathode reaction as the NiCad battery but a different anode reaction. In the anode of a NiMH battery, hydrogen atoms held in a metal alloy are oxidized. If we let M represent the metal alloy, we can write the half-reactions as follows:

$$\textit{Oxidation (Anode):} \quad MH(s) + OH^-(aq) \longrightarrow M(s) + H_2O(l) + e^-$$

$$\textit{Reduction (Cathode):} \quad NiO(OH)(s) + H_2O(l) + e^- \longrightarrow Ni(OH)_2(s) + OH^-(aq)$$

In addition to being more environmentally friendly than NiCad batteries, NiMH batteries also have a greater energy density (energy content per unit battery mass), as we can see in Table 18.2. In some cases, a NiMH battery can carry twice the energy of a NiCad battery of the same mass, making NiMH batteries the most common choice for hybrid electric vehicles.

The Lithium–Ion Battery The most common type of rechargeable battery is the lithium–ion battery. Since lithium is the least dense metal ($0.53\ g\ cm^{-3}$), lithium batteries have high energy densities (see Table 18.2). The lithium battery works differently than the other batteries we have examined so far, and the details of its operation are beyond the scope of our current discussion. Briefly, you can think of the operation of the lithium battery as being due primarily to the motion of lithium ions from the anode to the cathode. The anode is composed of graphite into which lithium ions are incorporated between layers of carbon atoms. Upon discharge, the lithium ions spontaneously migrate to the cathode, which consists of a lithium transition–metal oxide such as $LiCoO_2$ or $LiMn_2O_4$. The transition metal is reduced during this process. Upon recharging, the transition metal is oxidized, forcing the lithium to migrate back into the graphite (Figure 18.18 ▼). The flow of lithium ions from the anode to the cathode causes a corresponding flow of electrons in the external circuit. Lithium–ion batteries are commonly used in applications

TABLE 18.2 Energy Density and Overcharge Tolerance of Several Rechargeable Batteries

Battery Type	Energy Density ($W\ h\ kg^{-1}$)	Overcharge Tolerance
NiCad	45–80	Moderate
NiMH	60–120	Low
Li ion	110–160	Low
Pb storage	30–50	High

where light weight and high energy density are important. These include cell phones, laptop computers, and digital cameras.

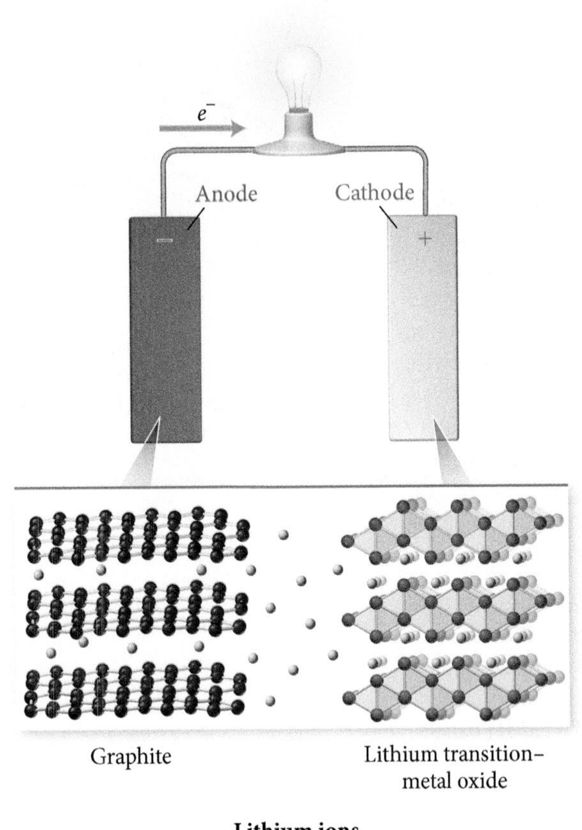

▲ **FIGURE 18.18 Lithium–Ion Battery** In the lithium–ion battery, the spontaneous flow of lithium ions from the graphite anode to the lithium–transition metal oxide cathode causes a corresponding flow of electrons in the external circuit.

Fuel Cells

We discussed the potential for *fuel cells* in the opening section of this chapter. Fuel cells may one day replace—or at least work in combination with—centralized power grid electricity. In addition, electric vehicles powered by fuel cells may one day usurp vehicles powered by internal combustion engines. Fuel cells are like batteries; the key difference is that a battery is self-contained, while in a fuel cell the reactants need to be constantly replenished from an external source. With use, normal batteries lose their ability to generate voltage because the reactants become depleted as electrical current is drawn from the battery. In a **fuel cell**, the reactants—the fuel provided from an external source—constantly flow through the battery, generating electrical current as they undergo a redox reaction.

The most common fuel cell is the hydrogen–oxygen fuel cell (Figure 18.19 ▼). In this cell, hydrogen gas flows past the anode (a screen coated with platinum catalyst) and undergoes oxidation:

***Oxidation** (Anode):* $2\,H_2(g) + 4\,OH^-(aq) \longrightarrow 4\,H_2O(l) + 4\,e^-$

Oxygen gas flows past the cathode (a similar screen) and undergoes reduction:

***Reduction** (Cathode):* $O_2(g) + 2\,H_2O(l) + 4\,e^- \longrightarrow 4\,OH^-(aq)$

The half-reactions sum to the following overall reaction:

Overall reaction: $2\,H_2(g) + O_2(g) \longrightarrow 2\,H_2O(l)$

Notice that the only product is water. In the space shuttle program, hydrogen–oxygen fuel cells consume hydrogen to provide electricity and astronauts drink the water that is produced by the reaction. In order for hydrogen-powered fuel cells to become more widely used, a more readily available source of hydrogen must be developed.

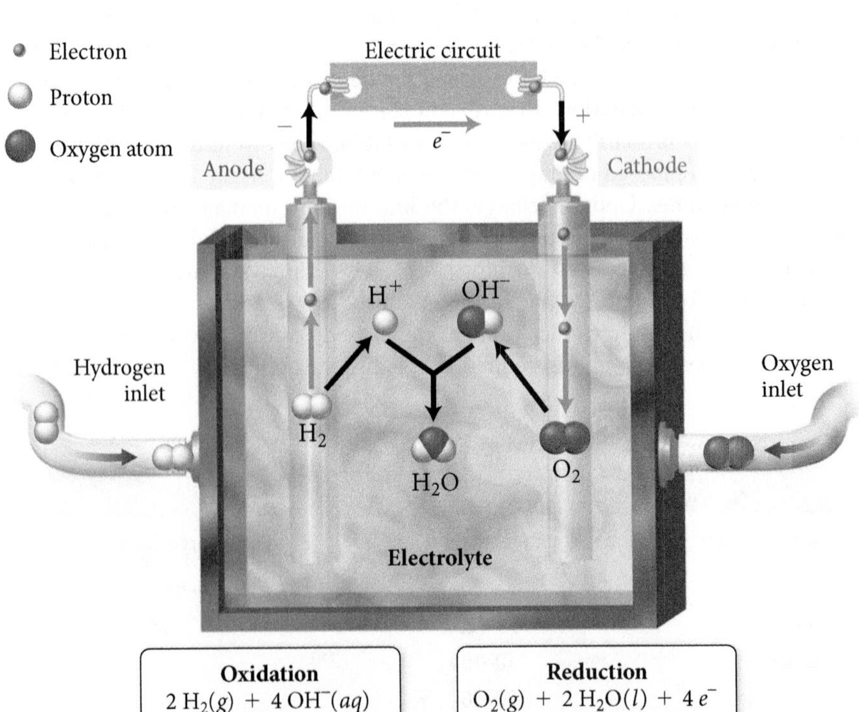

▶ **FIGURE 18.19 Hydrogen–Oxygen Fuel Cell** In this fuel cell, hydrogen and oxygen combine to form water.

CHEMISTRY IN YOUR DAY The Lithium-Ion Battery

Lithium-ion batteries are ubiquitous. They are found in all kinds of portable electronic devices, such as laptop computers, cameras, smartphones, power tools, and medical devices such as hearing aids and pacemakers. While they are more expensive than other types of batteries, their popularity is partly due to their large power densities, resulting in longer lifetimes, lack of a memory for rechargeable Li-ion batteries, and their light weight.

Li-ion batteries are manufactured on such a large scale that they can be considered to be a type of commodity, which is a marketable good that is priced solely according to supply and demand. An example of a commodity-priced Li-ion battery is the 18650 battery, which is 18 mm wide and 65 mm high, hence its name. 18650 batteries are produced by many different manufacturers. There is a plentiful supply of them, and this keeps the price down. 18650 batteries are commonly found in rechargeable flashlights and laptops. They are also used in some electric vehicles, such as the Tesla Model S.

The Tesla Model S battery is positioned at the bottom of the car, under the passenger compartment. On the surface, it looks like a large metallic slab. On the inside, this electric car battery consists of approximately 8000 18650 Li-ion batteries. Put together, these 8000 rechargeable batteries can store a total energy of 85 kWh, which is enough energy to give the car a range of over 400 km. In comparison, a typical laptop battery stores around 0.1 kWh.

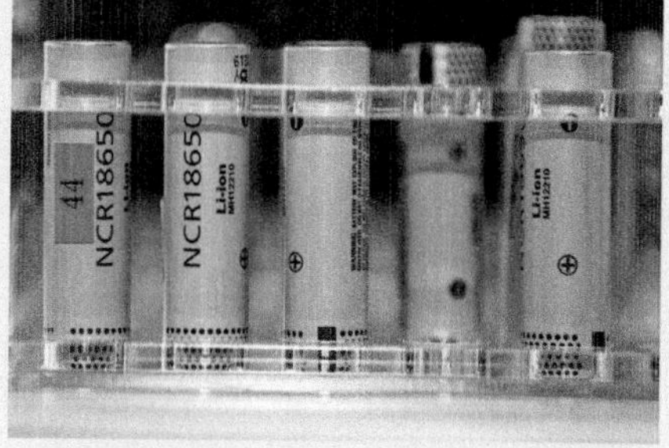

▲ 18650 Li-ion battery

▲ Chassis of a Tesla Model S electric car, showing the large, slab-like battery

18.7 Electrolysis: Driving Nonspontaneous Chemical Reactions with Electricity

In a voltaic cell, a spontaneous redox reaction produces electrical current. In an *electrolytic cell*, electrical current drives an otherwise nonspontaneous redox reaction through a process called **electrolysis**. We have seen that the reaction of hydrogen with oxygen to form water is spontaneous and can be used to produce an electrical current in a fuel cell. By supplying electrical current, we can cause the reverse reaction to occur, separating water into hydrogen and oxygen (Figure 18.20 ▼).

$$2\,H_2(g) + O_2(g) \longrightarrow 2\,H_2O(l)$$ (spontaneous—produces electrical current; occurs in a voltaic cell)

$$2\,H_2O(l) \longrightarrow 2\,H_2(g) + O_2(g)$$ (nonspontaneous—consumes electrical current; occurs in an electrolytic cell)

Recall from the last section that one of the problems associated with the widespread adoption of hydrogen fuel cells is the scarcity of hydrogen. Where will the hydrogen to power these fuel cells come from? One possible answer is to obtain hydrogen from water through solar-powered electrolysis. A solar-powered electrolytic cell can produce hydrogen from water when the sun is shining. The hydrogen made in this way can be converted back to water to generate electricity and could also be used to power fuel-cell vehicles.

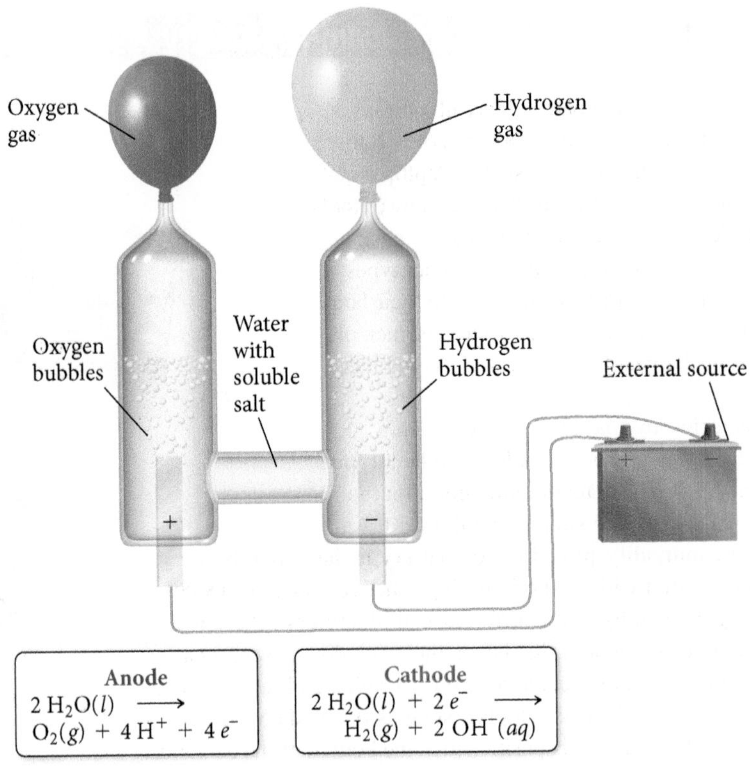

▶ **FIGURE 18.20 Electrolysis of Water** Electrical current can decompose water into hydrogen and oxygen gas.

Electrolysis also has numerous other applications. For example, most metals are found in Earth's crust as metal oxides. Converting an oxide to a pure metal requires that the cationic form of the metal be reduced, a nonspontaneous process. Electrolysis can be used to produce these metals. Thus, sodium is produced by the electrolysis of molten sodium chloride (discussed in the following subsection). Electrolysis is also used to plate metals onto other metals. For example, silver can be plated onto a less expensive metal using the electrolytic cell shown in Figure 18.21 ◀. In this cell, a silver electrode is placed in a solution containing silver ions. An electrical current causes the oxidation of silver at the anode (replenishing the silver ions in solution) and the reduction of silver ions at the cathode (coating the less expensive metal with solid silver).

***Oxidation** (Anode):* $Ag(s) \longrightarrow Ag^+(aq) + e^-$

***Reduction** (Cathode):* $Ag^+(aq) + e^- \longrightarrow Ag(s)$

Since the standard cell potential of the reaction is zero, the reaction is not spontaneous under standard conditions. An external power source can be used to drive current flow and cause the reaction to occur.

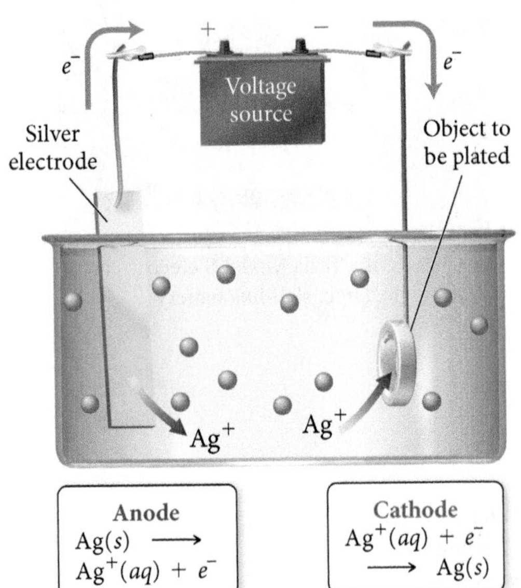

▲ **FIGURE 18.21 Silver Plating** Silver can be plated from a solution of silver ions onto metallic objects in an electrolytic cell.

The voltage required to cause electrolysis depends on the specific half-reactions. For example, we have seen that the oxidation of zinc and the reduction of Cu^{2+} produces a voltage of 1.10 V under standard conditions.

$$\text{(Cathode): } Cu^{2+}(aq) + 2\,e^- \longrightarrow Cu(s) \qquad E^\circ = 0.34\text{ V}$$

$$\text{(Anode): } Zn^{2+}(aq) + 2\,e^- \longrightarrow Zn(s) \qquad E^\circ = -0.76\text{ V}$$

$$E^\circ_{cell} = E^\circ_{cathode} - E^\circ_{anode}$$

$$E^\circ_{cell} = 0.34\text{ V} - (-0.76\text{ V}) = 1.10\text{ V}$$

If a power source producing *more than 1.10 V* is inserted into the Zn/Cu^{2+} voltaic cell, electrons can be forced to flow in the opposite direction, causing the reduction of Zn^{2+}

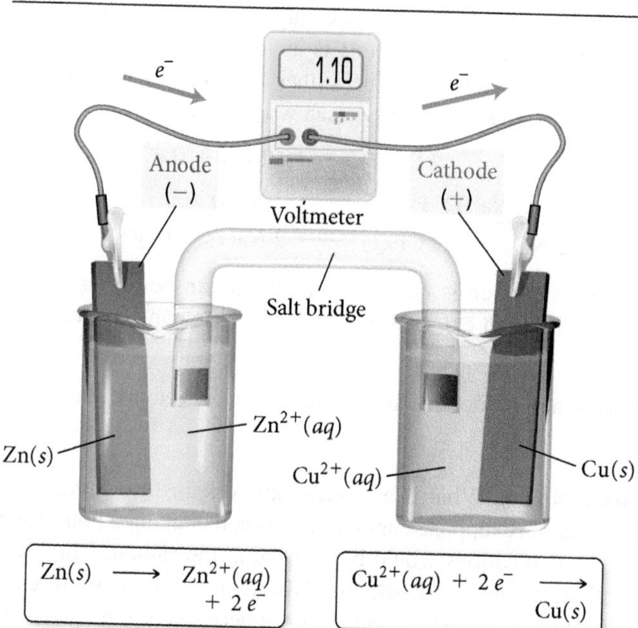

▲ **FIGURE 18.22 Voltaic Versus Electrolytic Cells** In a Zn/Cu^{2+} voltaic cell, the reaction proceeds in the spontaneous direction. In a Zn^{2+}/Cu electrolytic cell, electrical current drives the reaction in the nonspontaneous direction.

and the oxidation of Cu, as shown in Figure 18.22 ▲. Notice in Figure 18.22 that Zn is the anode in the voltaic cell and the cathode in the electrolytic cell. Recall that the anode and cathode are defined in terms of the reaction that occurs at their surface (oxidation always occurs at the anode).

In a *voltaic cell*, the anode is the source of electrons and is therefore labelled with a negative charge. The cathode draws electrons and is therefore labelled with a positive charge. In an *electrolytic cell*, however, the source of the electrons is the external power source. The external power source must *draw electrons away* from the anode; thus, the anode must be connected to the positive terminal of the battery (as shown in Figure 18.22). Similarly, the power source drives electrons toward the cathode (where they will be used in reduction), so the cathode must be connected to the *negative* terminal of the battery. The charge labels (+ and −) on an electrolytic cell are therefore opposite of what they are in a voltaic cell.

Summarizing Characteristics of Electrochemical Cell Types:

In all electrochemical cells:

- Oxidation occurs at the anode.
- Reduction occurs at the cathode.

In voltaic cells:

- The anode is the source of electrons and has a negative charge (anode −).
- The cathode draws electrons and has a positive charge (cathode +).

In electrolytic cells:

- Electrons are drawn away from the anode, which must be connected to the positive terminal of the external power source (anode +).
- Electrons are forced to the cathode, which must be connected to the negative terminal of the power source (cathode −).

Predicting the Products of Electrolysis

Predicting the products of an electrolysis reaction is in some cases relatively straightforward and in other cases more complex. We cover the simpler cases first and follow with the more complex ones.

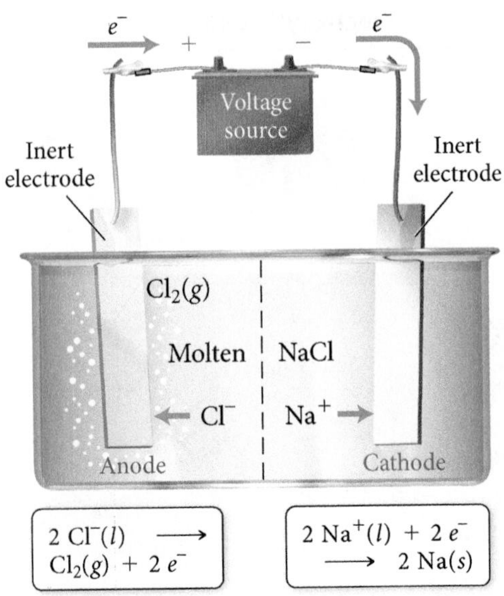

▲ **FIGURE 18.23 Electrolysis of Molten NaCl** In the electrolysis of a pure molten salt, the anion (in this case Cl^-) is oxidized and the cation (in this case Na^+) is reduced.

Pure Molten Salts Consider the electrolysis of a molten salt such as sodium chloride, shown in Figure 18.23 ◀. Na^+ and Cl^- are the only species present in the cell. The chloride ion cannot be further reduced (−1 is its lowest oxidation state), so it must be oxidized. The sodium ion cannot be further oxidized (+1 is its highest oxidation state), so it must be reduced. Thus we can write the half-reactions:

Oxidation (Anode):	$2\,Cl^-(l) \longrightarrow Cl_2(g) + \cancel{2e^-}$
Reduction (Cathode):	$2\,Na^+(l) + \cancel{2e^-} \longrightarrow 2\,Na(s)$
Overall:	$2\,Na^+(l) + 2\,Cl^-(l) \longrightarrow 2\,Na(s) + Cl_2(g)$

Although the reaction as written is not spontaneous, it can be driven to occur in an electrolytic cell by an external power source. We can generalize as follows:

- ▶ In the electrolysis of a pure molten salt, the anion is oxidized and the cation is reduced.

Mixtures of Cations or Anions What if a molten salt contains more than one anion or cation? For example, suppose our electrolysis cell contained both NaCl and KCl. Which of the two cations would be reduced at the cathode? In order to answer this question, we must ask which of the two cations is more easily reduced. Although the values of electrode potentials for aqueous solutions given in Table 18.1 do not apply to molten salts, the relative ordering of the electrode potentials does reflect the relative ease with which the metal cations are reduced. We can see from the table that the reduction of Na^+ is listed *above* the reduction of K^+; that is, Na^+ has a more positive electrode potential.

Throughout this discussion, more positive means the same thing as less negative.

$$Na^+(aq) + e^- \longrightarrow Na(s) \qquad E^\circ = -2.71 \text{ V (for aqueous solution)}$$
$$K^+(aq) + e^- \longrightarrow K(s) \qquad E^\circ = -2.92 \text{ V (for aqueous solution)}$$

Therefore, Na^+ is easier to reduce than K^+. Consequently, in a mixture of NaCl and KCl, Na^+ will have a greater tendency to be reduced at the cathode.

Similarly, what if a mixture of molten salts contained more than one anion? For example, in a mixture of NaBr and NaCl, which of the two anions would be oxidized at the cathode? The answer is similar: the anion that is more easily oxidized (the one with the more negative electrode potential).

Throughout this discussion, more negative means the same thing as less positive.

$$Cl_2(g) + 2\,e^- \longrightarrow 2\,Cl^-(aq) \qquad E^\circ = 1.36 \text{ V}$$
$$Br_2(g) + 2\,e^- \longrightarrow 2\,Br^-(aq) \qquad E^\circ = 1.09 \text{ V}$$

Since the standard electrode potential for the bromine half-reaction is more negative, the reverse reaction will proceed more easily. Therefore, electrons are more easily extracted from the bromide rather than the chloride.

We can generalize as follows:

- ▶ The cation that is most easily reduced (the one with the more positive electrode potential) is reduced first.
- ▶ The anion that is most easily oxidized (the one with the more negative electrode potential) is oxidized first.

Aqueous Solutions Electrolysis in an aqueous solution is complicated by the possibility of the electrolysis of water itself. Recall that water can be either oxidized or reduced according to the following half-reactions:

Anode: $O_2(g) + 4\,H^+(aq) + 4\,e^- \longrightarrow 2\,H_2O(l) \qquad E^\circ = 1.23 \text{ V}$
$E = 0.82 \text{ V (pH} = 7)$

Cathode: $2\,H_2O\,(l) + 2\,e^- \longrightarrow H_2(g) + 2\,OH^-(aq) \qquad E^\circ = -0.83 \text{ V}$
$E = -0.41 \text{ V (pH} = 7)$

The electrode potentials under standard conditions are shown to the right of each half-reaction. However, in pure water at room temperature, the concentrations of H^+ and OH^- are not standard. The electrode potentials for $[H^+] = 10^{-7}\text{ mol L}^{-1}$ and

$[OH^-] = 10^{-7}$ mol L^{-1} (at pH = 7) are shown in blue. Using those electrode potentials, we can calculate E_{cell} for the electrolysis of water as follows:

$$E_{cell} = E_{cat} - E_{an} = -0.41 \text{ V} - 0.82 \text{ V} = -1.23 \text{ V}$$

When a battery with a potential of several volts is connected to an electrolysis cell containing pure water, no reaction occurs because the concentration of ions in pure water is too low to conduct any significant electrical current. When an electrolyte such as Na_2SO_4 is added to the water, however, electrolysis occurs readily.

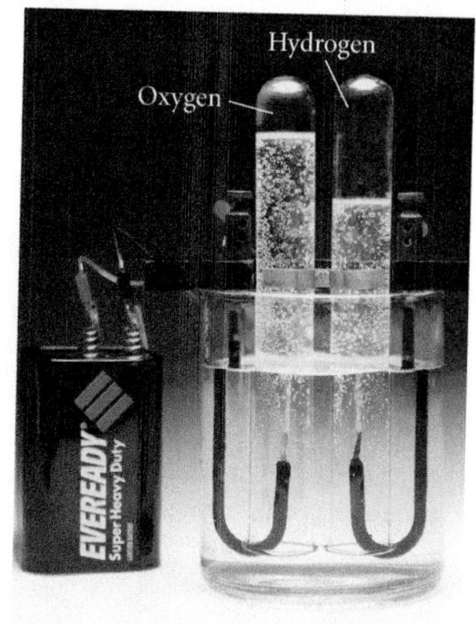

▲ Pure water is a poor conductor of electrical current, but the addition of an electrolyte allows electrolysis to take place, producing hydrogen and oxygen gas in a stoichiometric ratio.

In any aqueous solution in which electrolysis is to take place, the electrolysis of water at either electrode or at both electrodes is also possible. For example, consider the electrolysis of a sodium iodide solution, as shown in Figure 18.24 ▼. For the electrolysis of *molten* NaI, we can readily predict that I^- is oxidized at the anode and that Na^+ is reduced at the cathode. In an aqueous solution, however, two different reactions are possible at each electrode. At the cathode, it is possible to reduce either Na^+ or H_2O, according to the following:

$$2\,H_2O(l) + 2\,e^- \longrightarrow H_2(g) + 2\,OH^-(aq) \qquad E = -0.41 \text{ V (pH = 7)}$$
$$Na^+(aq) + e^- \longrightarrow Na(s) \qquad E^\circ = -2.71 \text{ V}$$

The reaction that occurs at the cathode is the one that has the most positive electrode potential. The reaction with the most positive electrode potential is the reduction of water; therefore, water will be reduced at the cathode, not sodium.

At the anode, it is possible to oxidize either H_2O or I^-, according to the reverse of the following:

$$O_2(g) + 4\,H^+(aq) + 4\,e^- \longrightarrow 2\,H_2O(l) \qquad E = 0.82 \text{ V (pH = 7)}$$
$$I_2(aq) + 2\,e^- \longrightarrow 2\,I^-(aq) \qquad E^\circ = 0.54 \text{ V}$$

The reaction that will occur at the anode is the one with the most negative standard electrode potential (because that will be the easiest to run in reverse). In this case, I^- will be oxidized to I_2 at the anode. The convention is to write the half-reactions as reductions and state the standard electrode (reduction) potential. However, saying that the reaction that occurs at the anode is the reverse of the reaction with the most negative standard electrode potential is the same as saying the reaction that occurs is the one with the most positive oxidation potential, which is the negative of the reduction potential:

$$2\,H_2O(l) \longrightarrow O_2(g) + 4\,H^+(aq) + 4\,e^- \qquad E = -0.82 \text{ V (pH = 7)}$$
$$2\,I^-(aq) \longrightarrow I_2(aq) + 2\,e^- \qquad E^\circ = -0.54 \text{ V}$$

Either way, the answer is the same: I^- will be oxidized at the anode rather than water.

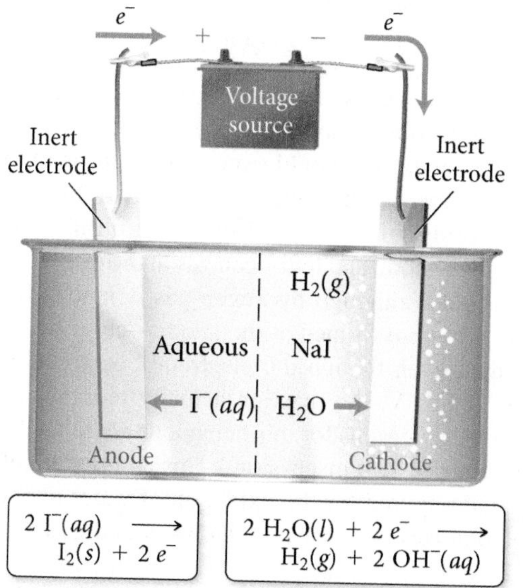

◀ **FIGURE 18.24 Electrolysis of Aqueous NaI** In this cell, I^- is oxidized to I_2 at the anode and H_2O is reduced to H_2 at the cathode. Sodium ions are not reduced because their electrode potential is more negative than the electrode potential of water.

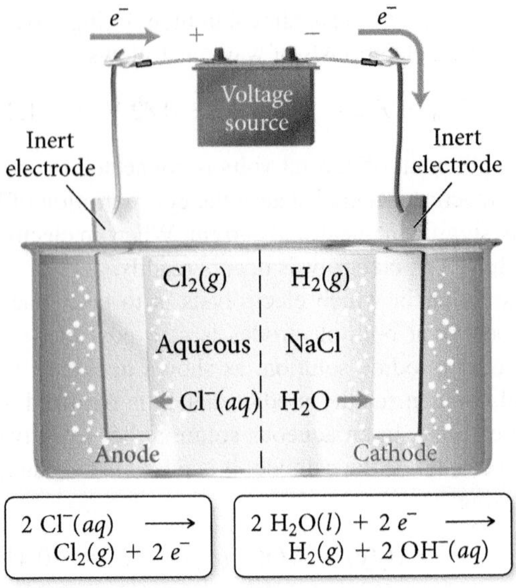

▶ **FIGURE 18.25 Electrolysis of Aqueous NaCl: The Effect of Overpotential** Because of overpotential, the anode reaction of this cell is the oxidation of Cl^- to Cl_2 gas rather than the oxidation of water to H^+ and O_2 gas.

Notice that Na^+ cannot be reduced in an aqueous solution—water will be reduced before Na^+. We can make the following generalization:

- ▶ The cations of active metals—those that are not easily reduced, such as Li^+, K^+, Na^+, Mg^{2+}, Ca^{2+}, and Al^{3+}—cannot be reduced from aqueous solutions by electrolysis because water is reduced at a lower voltage.

The Electrolysis of Aqueous Sodium Chloride and Overpotential An additional complication that we must consider when predicting the products of electrolysis is **overpotential**—an additional voltage that must be applied in order to get some nonspontaneous reactions to occur. We can demonstrate this concept by considering the electrolysis of a sodium chloride solution, shown in Figure 18.25 ▲. In order to predict the product of the electrolysis, we consider the two possible half-reactions that could occur at the cathode:

$$2\,H_2O(l) + 2\,e^- \longrightarrow H_2(g) + 2\,OH^-(aq) \qquad E = -0.41\text{ V (pH} = 7)$$
$$Na^+(aq) + e^- \longrightarrow Na(s) \qquad E^\circ = -2.71\text{ V}$$

At the anode, either water or chloride will be oxidized according to the reverse of the following two half-reactions:

$$Cl_2(aq) + 2\,e^- \longrightarrow 2\,Cl^-(aq) \qquad E^\circ = 1.36\text{ V}$$
$$O_2(g) + 4\,H^+(aq) + 4\,e^- \longrightarrow 2\,H_2O(l) \qquad E = 0.82\text{ V (pH} = 7)$$

As in the preceding example, because the reduction of water has a more positive electrode potential than the reduction of sodium ion, we expect water to be reduced at the cathode. Similarly, at the anode, we would expect water to be oxidized since the reaction involving water has a more negative electrode potential. In other words, we initially predict that a sodium chloride solution would simply result in the electrolysis of water, producing oxygen gas at the anode and hydrogen gas at the cathode. If we construct such a cell, however, we find that, although hydrogen gas is indeed formed at the cathode (as predicted), oxygen gas is *not* formed at the anode—chlorine gas is formed instead. Why? The answer is that, even though the electrode potential for the reaction at the anode involving water is 0.82 V, the reaction actually requires a voltage greater than 0.82 V in order to occur. (The reasons for this behaviour are related to kinetic factors that are beyond the scope of our current discussion.) This additional voltage, the *overpotential*, increases the voltage required for the oxidation of water to about 1.4 V. The result is that the chloride ion oxidizes more easily than water and $Cl_2(g)$ is therefore observed at the anode.

EXAMPLE 18.8 PREDICTING THE PRODUCTS OF ELECTROLYSIS REACTIONS

Predict the half-reaction occurring at the anode and the cathode for electrolysis for each reaction:

(a) a mixture of molten $AlBr_3$ and $MgCl_2$

(b) an aqueous solution of LiI and $CuBr_2$

SOLUTION

(a) In the electrolysis of a molten salt, the anion is oxidized and the cation is reduced. However, this mixture contains two cations and two anions. Start by writing the half-reactions that might occur at each electrode.

At the cathode, both the reduction of Al^{3+} and the reduction of $Mg^{2+}$are possible. The one that actually occurs is the one that occurs most easily or the one with the most positive standard electrode potential from Table 18.1.

At the anode, either chloride or bromide will be oxidized. The reaction that will occur at the anode is the reverse of the one with the more negative standard electrode potential.

Cathode Reactions:

$$Al^{3+}(l) + 3\,e^- \longrightarrow Al(s) \qquad E^\circ = -1.66\text{ V (aqueous)}$$
$$Mg^{2+}(l) + 2\,e^- \longrightarrow Mg(s) \qquad E^\circ = -2.37\text{ V (aqueous)}$$

▶ The reaction that occurs at the cathode is the one with the more positive electrode potential. Al^{3+} will be reduced at the cathode preferentially.

Anode Reactions:

$$Cl_2(aq) + 2\,e^- \longrightarrow 2\,Cl^-(aq) \qquad E^\circ = 1.36\text{ V (aqueous)}$$
$$Br_2(aq) + 2\,e^- \longrightarrow 2\,Br^-(aq) \qquad E^\circ = 1.09\text{ V (aqueous)}$$

▶ The reaction that occurs at the anode is the reverse of the one with the most negative electrode potential. Bromide will be oxidized at the anode preferentially.

(b) Since LiI and $CuBr_2$ are both in the same aqueous solution, there are three possible reactions at each the cathode and the anode.

At the cathode, either Li^+, Cu^{2+}, or H_2O will be reduced. Write all three half-reactions using Table 18.1 for the electrode potentials, but using the pH = 7 electrode potential for water.

At the anode, either I^-, Br^-, or water will be oxidized. The reaction that is going to occur at the anode is the reverse of the one with the most negative standard electrode potential.

Cathode Reactions:

$$Cu^{2+}(aq) + 2\,e^- \longrightarrow Cu(s) \qquad E^\circ = 0.52\text{ V}$$
$$2\,H_2O(l) + 2\,e^- \longrightarrow H_2(g) + 2\,OH^-(aq) \qquad E = -0.41\text{ V (pH = 7)}$$
$$Li^+(aq) + e^- \longrightarrow Li(s) \qquad E^\circ = -3.04\text{ V}$$

▶ The reaction that occurs at the cathode is the one with the more positive electrode potential. Cu^{2+} will be reduced at the cathode preferentially.

Anode Reactions:

$$Br_2(aq) + 2\,e^- \longrightarrow 2\,Br^-(aq) \qquad E^\circ = 1.09\text{ V}$$
$$O_2(g) + 4\,H^+(aq) + 4\,e^- \longrightarrow 2\,H_2O(l) \qquad E = 0.82\text{ V (pH = 7)}$$
$$I_2(aq) + 2\,e^- \longrightarrow 2\,I^-(aq) \qquad E^\circ = 0.54\text{ V}$$

▶ The reaction that occurs at the anode is the reverse of the one with the most negative electrode potential. I^- will be oxidized to I_2 at the anode preferentially.

FOR PRACTICE 18.8

Predict the half-reactions that will occur at the cathode and the anode for the electrolysis of an aqueous K_2SO_4 solution. (*Hint:* Both the anion and cation in this case might be reduced at the cathode).

Stoichiometry of Electrolysis

In an electrolytic cell, electrical current is used to drive a particular chemical reaction. In a sense, the electrons act as a reactant and therefore have a stoichiometric relationship with the other reactants and products. Unlike ordinary reactants, for which we usually measure quantity as mass, for electrons we measure quantity as charge. For example, consider an electrolytic cell used to coat copper onto metals, as shown in Figure 18.26 ▼. The half-reaction by which copper is deposited onto the metal is:

$$Cu^{2+}(aq) + 2\,e^- \longrightarrow Cu(s)$$

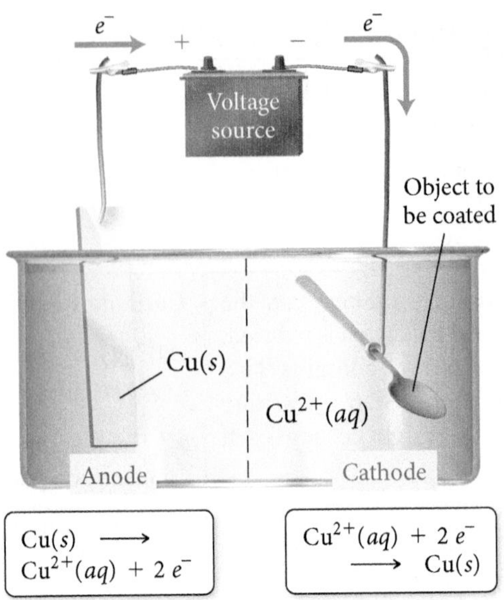

▶ **FIGURE 18.26 Electrolytic Cell for Copper Plating** In this cell, copper ions are plated onto other metals. It takes two moles of electrons to plate one mole of copper atoms.

For every 2 mol of electrons that flow through the cell, 1 mol of solid copper is plated. We can write the stoichiometric relationship:

$$2 \text{ mol } e^- : 1 \text{ mol Cu}(s)$$

We can determine the number of moles of electrons that have flowed in a given electrolysis cell by measuring the total charge that has flowed through the cell, which in turn depends on the *magnitude* of the current and on the *time* that the current runs. Recall from Section 18.2 that the unit of current is the ampere:

$$1 \text{ A} = 1 \text{ C s}^{-1}$$

If we multiply the amount of current (in A) flowing through the cell by the time (in s) that the current flowed, we find the total charge that passed through the cell in that time:

$$\text{Current C } \cancel{\text{s}}^{-1} \times \text{time } (\cancel{\text{s}}) = \text{charge (C)}$$

The relationship between charge and the number of moles of electrons is given by Faraday's constant, which, as we saw previously, corresponds to the charge in coulombs of 1 mol of electrons.

$$F = 96485 \text{ C mol}^{-1}$$

These relationships can be used to solve problems involving the stoichiometry of electrolytic cells, as shown in Example 18.9.

EXAMPLE 18.9 STOICHIOMETRY OF ELECTROLYSIS

Gold can be plated out of a solution containing Au^{3+} according to the half-reaction:

$$Au^{3+}(aq) + 3\,e^- \longrightarrow Au(s)$$

What mass of gold (in grams) is plated by a 25-minute flow of 5.5 A current?

SORT You are given the half-reaction for the plating of gold, which shows the stoichiometric relationship between moles of electrons and moles of gold. You are also given the current and time. You must find the mass of gold that will be deposited in that time.	**GIVEN:** 3 mol e^- : 1 mol Au 5.5 amps 25 min **FIND:** g Au

STRATEGIZE You need to find the amount of gold, which is related stoichiometrically to the number of electrons that have flowed through the cell. Begin with time in minutes and convert to seconds. Then, since current is a measure of charge per unit time, use the given current and the time to find the number of coulombs. You can use Faraday's constant to calculate the number of moles of electrons and the stoichiometry of the reaction to find the number of moles of gold. Finally, use the molar mass of gold to convert to mass of gold.	**CONCEPTUAL PLAN** 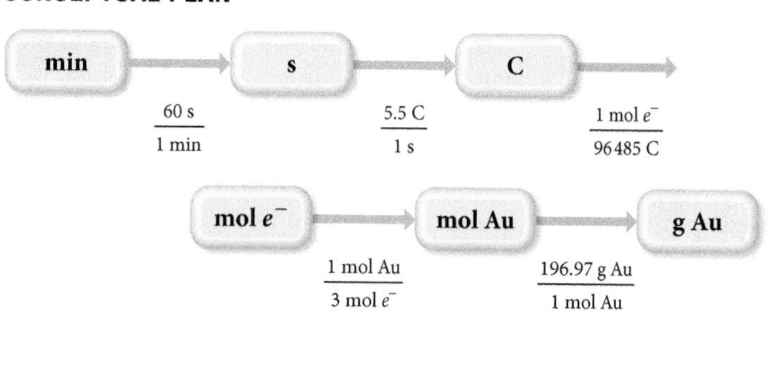
SOLVE Follow the conceptual plan to solve the problem, cancelling units to arrive at the mass of gold.	**SOLUTION** $25\ \text{min} \times \frac{60\ \text{s}}{1\ \text{min}} \times \frac{5.5\ \text{C}}{1\ \text{s}} \times \frac{1\ \text{mol}\ e^-}{96\,485\ \text{C}} \times \frac{1\ \text{mol Au}}{3\ \text{mol}\ e^-} \times \frac{196.97\ \text{g Au}}{1\ \text{mol Au}} = 5.6\ \text{g Au}$

CHECK The answer has the correct units (g Au). The magnitude of the answer is reasonable if we consider that 10 amps of current for one hour is the equivalent of about 1/3 mol of electrons (check for yourself), which would produce 1/9 mol (or about 20 g) of gold.

FOR PRACTICE 18.9

Silver can be plated out of a solution containing Ag^+ according to the half-reaction:

$$Ag^+(aq) + e^- \longrightarrow Ag(s)$$

How much time (in minutes) would it take to plate 12 g of silver using a current of 3.0 A?

18.8 Corrosion: Undesirable Redox Reactions

Corrosion is the (usually) gradual, nearly always undesired, oxidation of metals that occurs when they are exposed to oxidizing agents in the environment. From Table 18.1, we can see that the reduction of oxygen in the presence of water has a standard electrode potential of +0.40 V:

$$O_2(g) + 2\,H_2O(l) + 4\,e^- \longrightarrow 4\,OH^-(aq) \qquad E^\circ = 0.40\ \text{V}$$

In the presence of acid, the reduction of oxygen has an even more positive standard electrode potential of +1.23 V.

$$O_2(g) + 4\,H^+(aq) + 4\,e^- \longrightarrow 2\,H_2O(l) \qquad E^\circ = 1.23\ \text{V}$$

The reduction of oxygen, therefore, has a strong tendency to occur and can bring about the oxidation of other substances, especially metals. In other words, oxygen is a strong oxidizing agent, even stronger in the presence of acid. Notice that the half-reactions for the reduction of most metal ions are listed *below* the half-reactions for the reduction of oxygen in Table 18.1. Consequently, the oxidation (or corrosion) of those metals will be spontaneous when paired with the reduction of oxygen. Corrosion is the opposite of the process by which metals are extracted from their ores. In extraction, the free metal is reduced out from its ore. In corrosion, the metal is oxidized.

▲ The cationic form of a metal must usually be reduced to extract the metal from its ore. In corrosion, the metal is oxidized back to its more natural state.

Given the ease with which metals oxidize in the presence of oxygen, acid, and water, why are metals used so frequently as building materials in the first place? Many metals form oxides that coat the surface of the metal and prevent further corrosion. For example, bare aluminum metal, with an electrode potential of −1.66 V, is quickly oxidized in the

▲ Aluminum is stable because its oxide forms a protective film over the underlying metal, preventing further oxidation.

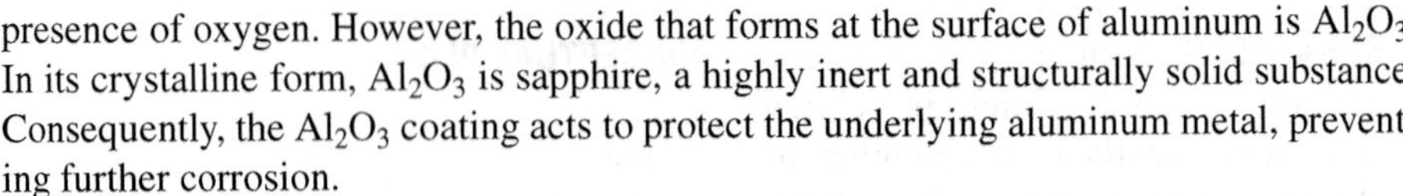

presence of oxygen. However, the oxide that forms at the surface of aluminum is Al_2O_3. In its crystalline form, Al_2O_3 is sapphire, a highly inert and structurally solid substance. Consequently, the Al_2O_3 coating acts to protect the underlying aluminum metal, preventing further corrosion.

The oxides of iron, however, are not structurally stable, and tend to flake away from the underying metal, exposing it to further corrosion. A significant part of the iron produced each year is used to replace rusted iron. Rusting is a redox reaction in which iron is oxidized from Fe to Fe^{2+}; according to the reverse of the following half-reaction:

$$Fe^{2+}(aq) + 2\,e^- \longrightarrow Fe(s) \qquad E^\circ = -0.45\text{ V}$$

This oxidation reaction tends to occur at defects on the surface of the iron—known as *anodic regions* because oxidation is occurring at these locations—as shown in Figure 18.27 ▼. The electrons produced at the anodic region, travel through the metal to areas called *cathodic regions*, where they react with oxygen and H^+ ions dissolved in moisture. (The H^+ ions come from carbonic acid, which naturally forms in water from carbon dioxide in air.)

$$O_2(g) + 4\,H^+(aq) + 4\,e^- \longrightarrow 2\,H_2O(l) \qquad E^\circ = 1.23\text{ V}$$

The overall reaction has a cell potential of +1.68 V and is highly spontaneous.

$$2\,Fe(s) + O_2(g) + 4\,H^+(aq) \longrightarrow 2\,H_2O(l) + 2\,Fe^{2+}(aq) \qquad E^\circ_{cell} = +1.68\text{ V}$$

The Fe^{2+} ions formed in the anodic regions can migrate through moisture on the surface of the iron to cathodic regions, where they are further oxidized by reaction with more oxygen:

$$4\,Fe^{2+}(aq) + O_2(g) + (4 + 2n)\,H_2O(l) \longrightarrow \underset{\text{Rust}}{2\,Fe_2O_3 \cdot nH_2O(s)} + 8\,H^+(aq)$$

Rust is a hydrated form of iron(III) oxide whose exact composition depends on the conditions under which it forms.

Consider each of the following important components in the formation of rust:

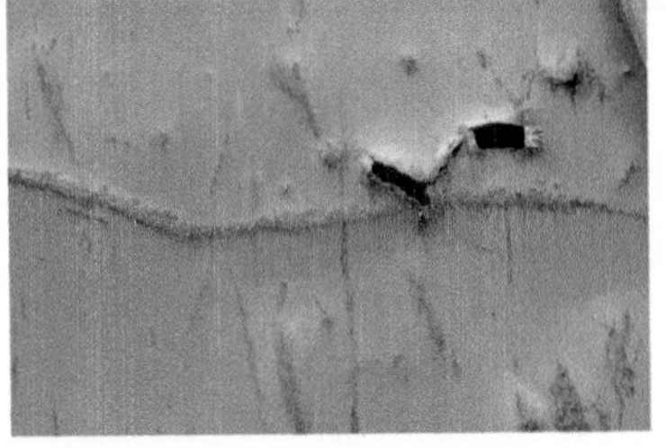

▲ A scratch in paint often allows the underlying iron to rust.

- *Moisture must be present for rusting to occur.* The presence of water is necessary because water is a reactant in the last reaction, and because charge (either electrons or ions) must be free to flow between the anodic and cathodic regions.
- *Additional electrolytes promote rusting.* The presence of an electrolyte (such as sodium chloride) on the surface of iron promotes rusting because it enhances current flow. This is why cars rust so quickly in cold climates where roads are salted, or in areas directly adjacent to beaches where salt water mist is present.
- *The presence of acids promotes rusting.* Since H^+ ions are involved in the reduction of oxygen, lower pH enhances the cathodic reaction and leads to faster rusting.

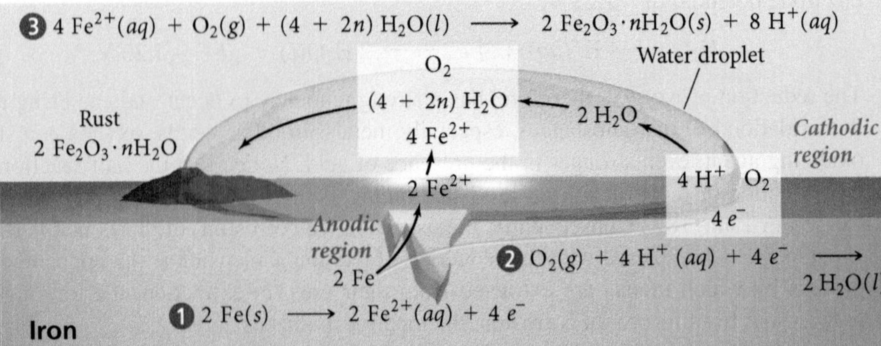

▲ **FIGURE 18.27 Corrosion of Iron: Rusting** The oxidation of iron occurs at anodic regions on the metal surface. The iron ions migrate to cathodic regions, where they react with oxygen and water to form rust.

Preventing Corrosion

Preventing the rusting of iron is a major industry. The most obvious way to prevent rust is to keep iron dry. Without water, the redox reaction cannot occur. Another way to prevent rust is to coat the iron with a substance that is impervious to water. Cars, for example, are painted and sealed to prevent rust. A scratch in the paint can lead to rusting of the underlying iron.

Rust can also be prevented by placing a **sacrificial anode** in electrical contact with the iron. The sacrificial anode must be composed of a metal that oxidizes more easily than iron (that is, it must be below iron in Table 18.1). The sacrificial anode oxidizes in place of the iron (just as the more easily oxidizable species in a mixture is the one to oxidize), protecting the iron from oxidation. A related way to protect iron from rusting is to coat it with a metal that oxidizes more easily than iron. Galvanized nails, for example, are coated with a thin layer of zinc. Since zinc has a more negative electrode potential than iron, it will oxidize in place of the underlying iron (just as a sacrificial anode does). The oxide of zinc is not crumbly and remains on the nail as a protective coating.

▲ In galvanized nails, a layer of zinc prevents the underlying iron from rusting. The zinc oxidizes in place of the iron, forming a protective layer of zinc oxide.

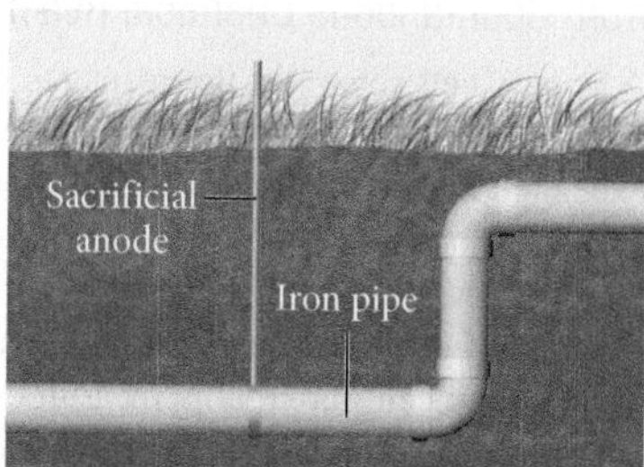

▲ If a metal more active than iron, such as magnesium or aluminum, is in electrical contact with iron, that metal rather than the iron will be oxidized. This principle underlies the use of sacrificial anodes to prevent the corrosion of iron.

CONCEPTUAL CONNECTION 18.5
Sacrificial Anodes

Which of the following metals does not act as a sacrificial anode for iron?

Zn, Mg, Mn, Cu

CHAPTER IN REVIEW

Key Terms

Section 18.2
electrical current (786)
electrochemical cell (787)
voltaic (galvanic) cell (787)
electrolytic cell (787)
half-cell (787)
electrode (787)
ampere (A) (788)
potential difference (788)
volt (V) (788)
electromotive force (emf) (788)
cell potential (cell emf) (E_{cell}) (788)
standard cell potential (standard emf) (E°_{cell}) (788)
anode (788)
cathode (788)
salt bridge (789)

Section 18.3
standard electrode potential (789)
standard hydrogen electrode (SHE) (790)

Section 18.4
Faraday's constant (F) (799)

Section 18.5
Nernst equation (803)

Section 18.6
dry-cell battery (809)
alkaline battery (809)
lead–acid storage battery (810)
nickel–cadmium (NiCad) battery (810)
nickel–metal hydride (NiMH) battery (810)
lithium–ion battery (810)
fuel cell (812)

Section 18.7
electrolysis (813)
overpotential (818)

Section 18.8
corrosion (821)
sacrificial anode (823)

Key Concepts

Pulling the Plug on the Power Grid (18.1)

Oxidation–reduction reactions are reactions in which electrons are transferred. If the reactants of a redox reaction are separated and connected by an external wire, electrons flow through the wire. In the most common form of fuel cell, an electrical current is created in this way as hydrogen is oxidized and oxygen is reduced; water is the only product.

Voltaic (or Galvanic) Cells: Generating Electricity from Spontaneous Chemical Reactions (18.2)

A voltaic cell separates the reactants of a spontaneous redox reaction into two half-cells that are connected by a wire and a means to exchange ions, so that electricity is generated. The electrode where oxidation occurs is the anode and the electrode where reduction occurs is the cathode; electrons flow from the anode to the cathode. The rate of electrons flowing through a wire is measured in amperes (A), and the cell potential is measured in volts (V). A salt bridge is commonly used to allow ions to flow between the half-cell solutions, thereby preventing the buildup of charge. Cell diagram or line notation provides a technique for writing redox reactions concisely by separating the components of the reaction using lines or commas.

Standard Electrode Potentials (18.3)

The electrode potentials of half-cells are measured in relation to that of a standard hydrogen electrode, which is assigned an electrode potential of zero at 25 °C and under standard conditions (solute concentrations of 1 mol L^{-1} and gas pressures of 1 bar). A species with a highly positive E° has a strong tendency to attract electrons and undergo reduction (and is therefore an excellent oxidizing agent). A species with a highly negative E° has a strong tendency to repel electrons and undergo oxidation (and is therefore an excellent reducing agent).

Cell Potential, Gibbs Energy, and the Equilibrium Constant (18.4)

For a reaction where all reactants and products are in their standard states, the reaction is spontaneous if E°_{cell} is positive, the change in Gibbs energy ($\Delta_r G^\circ$) is negative, and the equilibrium constant (K) is greater than one. On the contrary, if a reaction under standard conditions is nonspontaneous, E°_{cell} is negative, $\Delta_r G^\circ$ is positive, and K is less than one. Because E°_{cell}, $\Delta_r G^\circ$, and K all relate to spontaneity, we can derive equations relating all three quantities.

Cell Potential and Concentration (18.5)

Cells do not always operate under standard conditions. The standard cell potential (E°_{cell}) is related to the cell potential (E_{cell}) by the Nernst equation, $E_{cell} = E^\circ_{cell} - (0.0257\ V/n)\ln Q$. As shown by this equation, E_{cell} is related to the reaction quotient (Q); since E_{cell} equals zero when Q equals K, a battery is depleted as the reaction proceeds toward equilibrium. In a concentration cell, the reactions at both electrodes are identical and electrons flow because of a difference in concentration. Nerve cells are a biological example of concentration cells.

Batteries: Using Chemistry to Generate Electricity (18.6)

Batteries are packaged voltaic cells. Dry-cell batteries, including alkaline batteries, do not contain large amounts of water. The reactions in rechargeable batteries, such as lead–acid storage, nickel–cadmium, nickel–metal hydride, and lithium–ion batteries, can be reversed. Fuel cells are similar to batteries except that instead of being self-contained and having a finite amount of fuel in the form of reactants like batteries, fuel-cell reactants must be continually replenished from an external source.

Electrolysis: Driving Nonspontaneous Chemical Reactions with Electricity (18.7)

An electrolytic cell differs from a voltaic cell in that (1) an electrical charge is used to drive the reaction, and (2) although the anode is still the site of oxidation and the cathode the site of reduction, they are represented with signs opposite those of a voltaic cell (anode +, cathode −). In electrolysis reactions, the anion is oxidized; if there is more than one anion, the anion with the more negative E° will be oxidized. Stoichiometry can be used to calculate the quantity of reactants consumed or products produced in an electrolytic cell.

Corrosion: Undesirable Redox Reactions (18.8)

Corrosion is the undesired oxidation of metal by environmental oxidizing agents. When some metals, such as aluminum, oxidize they form a stable compound that prevents further oxidation. Iron, however, does not form a structurally stable compound when oxidized and therefore rust flakes off and exposes more iron to corrosion. Iron corrosion can be prevented by preventing water contact, minimizing the presence of electrolytes and acids, or using a sacrificial anode.

Key Equations and Relationships

Definition of an Ampere (18.2)

$$1\ A = 1\ C\ s^{-1}$$

Definition of a Volt (18.2)

$$1\ V = 1\ J\ C^{-1}$$

Standard Hydrogen Electrode (18.3)

$$2\ H^+(aq) + 2\ e^- \longrightarrow H_2(g) \qquad E^\circ = 0.00\ V$$

Equation for Cell Potential (18.3)

$$E^\circ_{cell} = E^\circ_{cathode} - E^\circ_{anode}$$

Relating $\Delta_r G^\circ$ and E°_{cell} (18.4)

$$\Delta_r G^\circ = -nFE^\circ_{cell} \qquad F = 96\,485\ C\ mol^{-1}$$

Relating E°_{cell} and K (18.4)

$$E^\circ_{cell} \quad \frac{0.0257\ \text{V}}{n} \ln K \qquad \text{(at 25 °C)}$$

The Nernst Equation (18.5)

$$E_{cell} = E^\circ_{cell} - \frac{0.0257\ \text{V}}{n} \ln Q \qquad \text{(at 25 °C)}$$

Key Skills

Calculating Standard Potentials for Electrochemical Cells from Standard Electrode Potentials (18.3)
• Examples 18.1, 18.2 • For Practice 18.1, 18.2 • Exercises 39–42, 55, 56

Predicting Spontaneous Redox Reactions and Sketching Electrochemical Cells (18.3)
• Example 18.3 • For Practice 18.3 • Exercises 37, 38, 45, 46

Relating $\Delta_r G^\circ$ and E°_{cell} (18.4)
• Example 18.4 • For Practice 18.4 • Exercises 59, 60

Relating E°_{cell} and K (18.4)
• Example 18.5 • For Practice 18.5 • Exercises 61–64

Calculating E_{cell} Under Nonstandard Conditions (18.5)
• Example 18.6 • For Practice 18.6 • Exercises 68–72

Determining the K_{sp} of a Slightly Soluble Salt Using a Concentration Cell (18.5)
• Example 18.7 • For Practice 18.7 • Exercises 75–78

Predicting the Products of Electrolysis Reactions (18.7)
• Example 18.8 • For Practice 18.8 • Exercises 85–92

Stoichiometry of Electrolysis (18.7)
• Example 18.9 • For Practice 18.9 • Exercises 95–98

EXERCISES

Review Questions

1. In electrochemistry, spontaneous redox reactions are used for what purpose?
2. In electrochemistry, what kind of reaction can be driven by electricity?
3. Give the basic definitions of oxidation and reduction and explain the basic procedure for balancing redox reactions.
4. Explain the difference between a voltaic (or galvanic) electrochemical cell and an electrolytic one.
5. What reaction (oxidation or reduction) occurs at the anode of a voltaic cell? What is the sign of the anode? Do electrons flow toward or away from the anode?
6. What reaction (oxidation or reduction) occurs at the cathode of a voltaic cell? What is the sign of the cathode? Do electrons flow toward or away from the cathode?
7. Explain the purpose of a salt bridge in an electrochemical cell.
8. What unit is used to measure the magnitude of electrical current? What unit is used to measure the magnitude of a potential difference? Explain how electrical current and potential difference differ.
9. What is the definition of the standard cell potential (E°_{cell})? What does a large positive standard cell potential imply about the spontaneity of the redox reaction occurring in the cell? What does a negative standard cell potential imply about the reaction?
10. Describe the basic features of a cell diagram (or line notation) for an electrochemical cell.
11. Why do some electrochemical cells employ inert electrodes such as platinum?
12. Describe the standard hydrogen electrode and explain its use in determining standard electrode potentials.

13. How is the standard cell potential of an electrochemical cell (E°_{cell}) related to the potentials of the half-cells?

14. Does a large positive electrode potential indicate a strong oxidizing agent or a strong reducing agent? What about a large negative electrode potential?

15. Can a spontaneous redox reaction be obtained by pairing any reduction half-reaction with one listed above it or with one listed below it in Table 18.1?

16. How can Table 18.1 be used to predict whether or not a metal will dissolve in HCl? In HNO_3?

17. Explain why E°_{cell}, $\Delta_r G^\circ$, and K are all interrelated.

18. Will a redox reaction with a small equilibrium constant ($K < 1$) have a positive or a negative E°_{cell}? Will it have a positive or a negative $\Delta_r G^\circ$?

19. How does E_{cell} depend on the concentrations of the reactants and products in the redox reaction occurring in the cell? What effect does increasing the concentration of a reactant have on E_{cell}? Increasing the concentration of a product?

20. Use the Nernst equation to show that $E_{cell} = E^\circ_{cell}$ under standard conditions.

21. What is a concentration electrochemical cell?

22. What are the anode and cathode reactions in a common dry-cell battery?

23. What are the anode and cathode reactions in a lead–acid storage battery? What happens when the battery is recharged?

24. What are the three common types of portable rechargeable batteries and how does each one work?

25. What is a fuel cell? What is the most common type of fuel cell and what reactions occur at its anode and cathode?

26. What currently limits the widespread use of the hydrogen–oxygen fuel cell?

27. What are some applications of electrolysis?

28. The anode of an electrolytic cell must be connected to which terminal, positive or negative, of the power source?

29. What species is oxidized and what species is reduced in the electrolysis of a pure molten salt?

30. If an electrolytic cell contains a mixture of species that can be oxidized, how do you determine which species will actually be oxidized? If it contains a mixture of species that can be reduced, how do you determine which one will actually be reduced?

31. Why does the electrolysis of an aqueous sodium chloride solution produce hydrogen gas at the cathode?

32. What is overpotential in an electrochemical cell? Why is it important?

33. How is the amount of current flowing through an electrolytic cell related to the amount of product produced in the redox reaction?

34. What is corrosion? Why is corrosion only a problem for some metals (such as iron)?

35. Explain the role of each of the following in promoting corrosion: moisture, electrolytes, and acids.

36. How can the corrosion of iron be prevented?

Problems by Topic

Voltaic Cells, Standard Cell Potentials, and Direction of Spontaneity

37. Sketch a voltaic cell for each redox reaction. Label the anode and cathode and indicate the half-reaction that occurs at each electrode and the species present in each solution. Also indicate the direction of electron flow.

a. $2\ Ag^+(aq) + Pb(s) \longrightarrow 2\ Ag(s) + Pb^{2+}(aq)$
b. $2\ ClO_2(g) + 2\ I^-(aq) \longrightarrow 2\ ClO_2^-(aq) + I_2(s)$
c. $O_2(g) + 4\ H^+(aq) + 2\ Zn(s) \longrightarrow 2\ H_2O(l) + 2\ Zn^{2+}(aq)$

38. Sketch a voltaic cell for each redox reaction. Label the anode and cathode and indicate the half-reaction that occurs at each electrode and the species present in each solution. Also indicate the direction of electron flow.

a. $Ni^{2+}(aq) + Mg(s) \longrightarrow Ni(s) + Mg^{2+}(aq)$
b. $2\ H^+(aq) + Fe(s) \longrightarrow H_2(g) + Fe^{2+}(aq)$
c. $2\ NO_3^-(aq) + 8\ H^+(aq) + 3\ Cu(s) \longrightarrow 2\ NO(g) + 4\ H_2O(l) + 3\ Cu^{2+}(aq)$

39. Calculate the standard cell potential for each of the electrochemical cells in Problem 37.

40. Calculate the standard cell potential for each of the electrochemical cells in Problem 38.

41. Consider the voltaic cell:

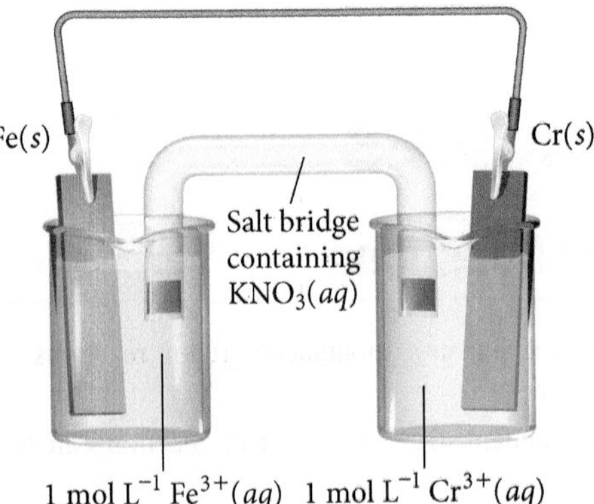

a. Determine the direction of electron flow and label the anode and the cathode.
b. Write a balanced equation for the overall reaction and calculate E°_{cell}.
c. Label each electrode as negative or positive.
d. Indicate the direction of anion and cation flow in the salt bridge.

42. Consider the voltaic cell:

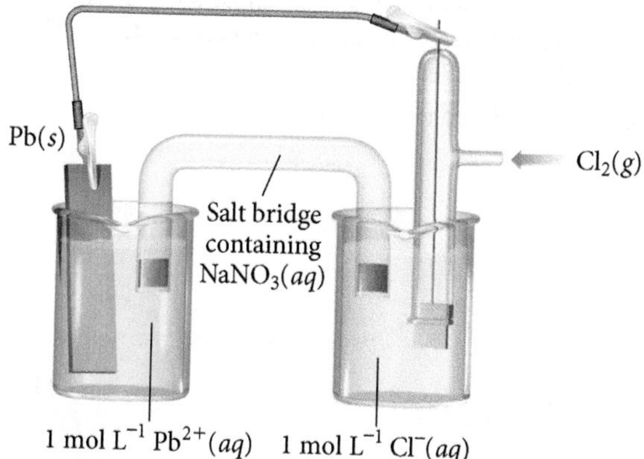

a. Determine the direction of electron flow and label the anode and the cathode.
b. Write a balanced equation for the overall reaction and calculate E°_{cell}.
c. Label each electrode as negative or positive.
d. Indicate the direction of anion and cation flow in the salt bridge.

43. Use line notation to represent each electrochemical cell in Problem 37.

44. Use line notation to represent each electrochemical cell in Problem 38.

45. Make a sketch of the voltaic cell represented by the following line notation. Write the overall balanced equation for the reaction and, assuming standard conditions, calculate E°_{cell}.

$$Sn(s)\,|\,Sn^{2+}(aq)\,||\,NO_3^-(aq), H^+(aq), H_2O(l)\,|\,NO(g)\,|\,Pt(s)$$

46. Make a sketch of the voltaic cell represented by the following line notation. Write the overall balanced equation for the reaction and, assuming standard conditions, calculate E°_{cell}.

$$Mn(s)\,|\,Mn^{2+}(aq)\,||\,ClO_2(g)\,|\,ClO_2^-(aq)\,|\,Pt(s)$$

47. Which of these redox reactions do you expect to occur spontaneously in the forward direction?
a. $Ni(s) + Zn^{2+}(aq) \longrightarrow Ni^{2+}(aq) + Zn(s)$
b. $Ni(s) + Pb^{2+}(aq) \longrightarrow Ni^{2+}(aq) + Pb(s)$
c. $Al(s) + 3\,Ag^+(aq) \longrightarrow Al^{3+}(aq) + 3\,Ag(s)$
d. $Pb(s) + Mn^{2+}(aq) \longrightarrow Pb^{2+}(aq) + Mn(s)$

48. Which of these redox reactions do you expect to occur spontaneously in the reverse direction?
a. $Ca^{2+}(aq) + Zn(s) \longrightarrow Ca(s) + Zn^{2+}(aq)$
b. $2\,Ag^+(aq) + Ni(s) \longrightarrow 2\,Ag(s) + Ni^{2+}(aq)$
c. $Fe(s) + Mn^{2+}(aq) \longrightarrow Fe^{2+}(aq) + Mn(s)$
d. $2\,Al(s) + 3\,Pb^{2+}(aq) \longrightarrow 2\,Al^{3+}(aq) + 3\,Pb(s)$

49. Which metal could you use to reduce Mn^{2+} ions but not Mg^{2+} ions?

50. Which metal can be oxidized with an Sn^{2+} solution but not with an Fe^{2+} solution?

51. Decide whether or not each metal dissolves in 1 mol L^{-1} HCl(*aq*). For those metals that do dissolve, write a balanced redox reaction showing what happens when the metal dissolves.
a. Al b. Ag c. Pb

52. Decide whether or not each metal dissolves in 1 mol L^{-1} HCl(*aq*). For those metals that do dissolve, write a balanced redox reaction showing what happens when the metal dissolves.
a. Cu b. Fe c. Au

53. Decide whether or not each metal dissolves in 1 mol L^{-1} $HIO_3(aq)$. For those metals that do dissolve, write a balanced redox reaction showing what happens when the metal dissolves.
a. Cu b. Au

54. Decide whether or not each metal dissolves in 1 mol L^{-1} $HIO_3(aq)$. For those metals that do dissolve, write a balanced redox equation for the reaction that occurs.
a. Au b. Cr

55. Calculate E°_{cell} for each balanced redox reaction and determine whether the reaction is spontaneous as written.
a. $2\,Cu(s) + Mn^{2+}(aq) \longrightarrow 2\,Cu^+(aq) + Mn(s)$
b. $MnO_2(s) + 4\,H^+(aq) + Zn(s) \longrightarrow Mn^{2+}(aq) + 2\,H_2O(l) + Zn^{2+}(aq)$
c. $Cl_2(g) + 2\,F^-(aq) \longrightarrow F_2(g) + 2\,Cl^-(aq)$

56. Calculate E°_{cell} for each balanced redox reaction and determine whether the reaction is spontaneous as written.
a. $O_2(g) + 2\,H_2O(l) + 4\,Ag(s) \longrightarrow 4\,OH^-(aq) + 4\,Ag^+(aq)$
b. $Br_2(l) + 2\,I^-(aq) \longrightarrow 2\,Br^-(aq) + I_2(s)$
c. $PbO_2(s) + 4\,H^+(aq) + Sn(s) \longrightarrow Pb^{2+}(aq) + 2\,H_2O(l) + Sn^{2+}(aq)$

57. Which metal cation is the best oxidizing agent?
a. Pb^{2+} b. Cr^{3+} c. Fe^{2+} d. Sn^{2+}

58. Which metal is the best reducing agent?
a. Mn b. Al c. Ni d. Cr

Cell Potential, Gibbs Energy, and the Equilibrium Constant

59. Use tabulated electrode potentials to calculate $\Delta_r G^\circ$ for each reaction at 25 °C.
a. $Pb^{2+}(aq) + Mg(s) \longrightarrow Pb(s) + Mg^{2+}(aq)$
b. $Br_2(l) + 2\,Cl^-(aq) \longrightarrow 2\,Br^-(aq) + Cl_2(g)$
c. $MnO_2(s) + 4\,H^+(aq) + Cu(s) \longrightarrow Mn^{2+}(aq) + 2\,H_2O(l) + Cu^{2+}(aq)$

60. Use tabulated electrode potentials to calculate $\Delta_r G^\circ$ for each reaction at 25 °C.
a. $2\,Fe^{3+}(aq) + 3\,Sn(s) \longrightarrow 2\,Fe(s) + 3\,Sn^{2+}(aq)$
b. $O_2(g) + 2\,H_2O(l) + 2\,Cu(s) \longrightarrow 4\,OH^-(aq) + 2\,Cu^{2+}(aq)$
c. $Br_2(l) + 2\,I^-(aq) \longrightarrow 2\,Br^-(aq) + I_2(s)$

61. Calculate the equilibrium constant for each of the reactions in Problem 59.

62. Calculate the equilibrium constant for each of the reactions in Problem 60.

63. Calculate the equilibrium constant for the reaction between $Ni^{2+}(aq)$ and Cd(*s*) (at 25 °C).

64. Calculate the equilibrium constant for the reaction between $Fe^{2+}(aq)$ and Zn(*s*) (at 25 °C).

65. Calculate $\Delta_r G^\circ$ and E°_{cell} for a redox reaction with $n = 2$ that has an equilibrium constant of $K = 25$ (at 25 °C).

66. Calculate $\Delta_r G^\circ$ and E°_{cell} for a redox reaction with $n = 3$ that has an equilibrium constant of $K = 0.050$ (at 25 °C).

Nonstandard Conditions and the Nernst Equation

67. A voltaic cell employs the following redox reaction:

$$Sn^{2+}(aq) + Mn(s) \longrightarrow Sn(s) + Mn^{2+}(aq)$$

Calculate the cell potential at 25 °C under each set of conditions:
a. standard conditions
b. $[Sn^{2+}] = 0.0100\ mol\ L^{-1}$; $[Mn^{2+}] = 2.00\ mol\ L^{-1}$
c. $[Sn^{2+}] = 2.00\ mol\ L^{-1}$; $[Mn^{2+}] = 0.0100\ mol\ L^{-1}$

68. A voltaic cell employs the redox reaction:

$$2\ Fe^{3+}(aq) + 3\ Mg(s) \longrightarrow 2\ Fe(s) + 3\ Mg^{2+}(aq)$$

Calculate the cell potential at 25 °C under each set of conditions:
a. standard conditions
b. $[Fe^{3+}] = 1.0 \times 10^{-3}\ mol\ L^{-1}$; $[Mg^{2+}] = 2.50\ mol\ L^{-1}$
c. $[Fe^{3+}] = 2.00\ mol\ L^{-1}$; $[Mg^{2+}] = 1.5 \times 10^{-3}\ mol\ L^{-1}$

69. An electrochemical cell is based on these two half-reactions:

$$\text{Ox: } Pb(s) \longrightarrow Pb^{2+}(aq,\ 0.10\ mol\ L^{-1}) + 2\ e^-$$
$$\text{Red: } MnO_4^-(aq, 1.50\ mol\ L^{-1}) + 4\ H^+(aq, 2.0\ mol\ L^{-1}) + 3\ e^- \longrightarrow MnO_2(s) + 2\ H_2O(l)$$

Compute the cell potential at 25 °C.

70. An electrochemical cell is based on these two half-reactions:

$$\text{Ox: } Sn(s) \longrightarrow Sn^{2+}(aq,\ 2.00\ mol\ L^{-1}) + 2\ e^-$$
$$\text{Red: } ClO_2(g,\ 0.100\ bar) + e^- \longrightarrow ClO_2^-(aq,\ 2.00\ mol\ L^{-1})$$

Calculate the cell potential at 25 °C.

71. A voltaic cell consists of a Zn/Zn^{2+} half-cell and a Ni/Ni^{2+} half-cell at 25 °C. The initial concentrations of Ni^{2+} and Zn^{2+} are $1.50\ mol\ L^{-1}$ and $0.100\ mol\ L^{-1}$, respectively.
a. What is the initial cell potential?
b. What is the cell potential when the concentration of Ni^{2+} has fallen to $0.500\ mol\ L^{-1}$?
c. What are the concentrations of Ni^{2+} and Zn^{2+} when the cell potential falls to 0.45 V?

72. A voltaic cell consists of a Pb/Pb^{2+} half-cell and a Cu/Cu^{2+} half-cell at 25 °C. The initial concentrations of Pb^{2+} and Cu^{2+} are $0.0500\ mol\ L^{-1}$ and $1.50\ mol\ L^{-1}$, respectively.
a. What is the initial cell potential?
b. What is the cell potential when the concentration of Cu^{2+} has fallen to $0.200\ mol\ L^{-1}$?
c. What are the concentrations of Pb^{2+} and Cu^{2+} when the cell potential falls to 0.35 V?

73. The following reaction is nonspontaneous as written when the components are in their standard states:

$$Cd(s) + Fe^{2+}(aq) \longrightarrow Cd^{2+}(aq) + Fe(s)$$

What is the ratio of $[Cd^{2+}]/[Fe^{2+}]$ above which the reaction will be spontaneous?

74. The following reaction is spontaneous as written when the components are in their standard states:

$$3\ Zn(s) + 2\ Cr^{3+}(aq) \longrightarrow 3\ Zn^{2+}(aq) + 2\ Cr(s)$$

If the $[Zn^{2+}]$ is $1\ mol\ L^{-1}$, determine the value of $[Cr^{3+}]$ below which the reaction will be spontaneous in the opposite direction.

75. Make a sketch of a concentration cell employing two Zn/Zn^{2+} half-cells. The concentration of Zn^{2+} in one of the half-cells is $2.0\ mol\ L^{-1}$ and the concentration in the other half-cell is $1.0 \times 10^{-3}\ mol\ L^{-1}$. Label the anode and the cathode and indicate the half-reaction occurring at each electrode. Also indicate the direction of electron flow.

76. Consider the concentration cell:

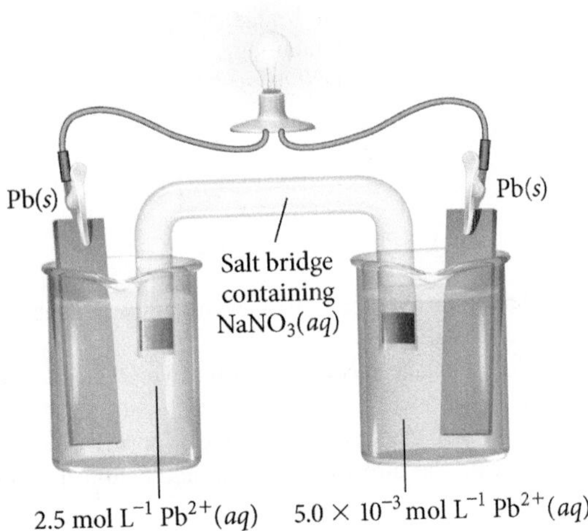

a. Label the anode and cathode.
b. Indicate the direction of electron flow.
c. Indicate what happens to the concentration of Pb^{2+} in each half cell.

77. A concentration cell consists of two Sn/Sn^{2+} half-cells. The cell has a potential of 0.10 V at 25 °C. What is the ratio of the Sn^{2+} concentrations in the two half-cells?

78. A Cu/Cu^{2+} concentration cell has a voltage of 0.22 V at 25 °C. The concentration of Cu^{2+} in the cathode is $1.5 \times 10^{-3}\ mol\ L^{-1}$. What is the concentration of Cu^{2+} in the anode?

Batteries, Fuel Cells, and Corrosion

79. Determine the optimum mass ratio of Zn to MnO_2 in an alkaline battery.

80. What mass of lead sulfate is formed in a lead–acid storage battery when 1.00 g of Pb undergoes oxidation?

81. Refer to the tabulated values of $\Delta_f G°$ in Appendix IIB to calculate $E°_{cell}$ for a fuel cell that employs the reaction between methane gas (CH_4) and oxygen to form carbon dioxide and gaseous water.

82. Refer to the tabulated values of $\Delta_f G°$ in Appendix IIB to calculate the standard cell potential for the dry cell discussed in Section 18.6 based on the following half-reactions:

$$\text{Cathode: } 2\ MnO_2(s) + 2\ NH_4^+(aq) + 2\ e^- \longrightarrow Mn_2O_3(s) + 2\ NH_3(g) + H_2O(l)$$

$$\text{Anode: } Zn^{2+}(aq) + 2\ e^- \longrightarrow Zn(s)$$

$$\Delta_f G°(Mn_2O_3) = -882.1\ kJ\ mol^{-1}$$

83. Which metal(s), if coated onto iron, would prevent the corrosion of iron?
a. Zn **b.** Sn **c.** Mn

84. Which metal(s), if coated onto iron, would prevent the corrosion of iron?
a. Mg **b.** Cr **c.** Cu

Electrolytic Cells and Electrolysis

85. Consider the electrolytic cell:

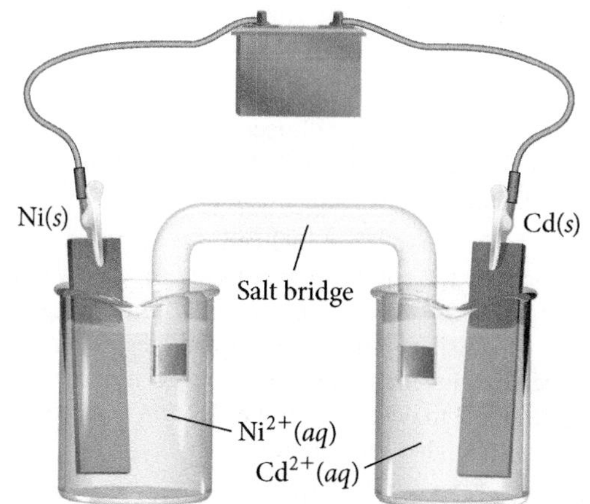

a. Label the anode and the cathode and indicate the half-reactions occurring at each.
b. Indicate the direction of electron flow.
c. Label the terminals on the battery as positive or negative and calculate the minimum voltage necessary to drive the reaction.

86. Draw an electrolytic cell in which Mn^{2+} is reduced to Mn and Sn is oxidized to Sn^{2+}. Label the anode and cathode, indicate the direction of electron flow, and write an equation for the half-reaction occurring at each electrode. What minimum voltage is necessary to drive the reaction?

87. Write equations for the half-reactions that occur in the electrolysis of molten potassium bromide.

88. What products are obtained in the electrolysis of molten NaI?

89. Write equations for the half-reactions that occur in the electrolysis of a mixture of molten potassium bromide and molten lithium bromide.

90. What products are obtained in the electrolysis of a molten mixture of KI and KBr?

91. Write equations for the half-reactions that occur at the anode and cathode for the electrolysis of each aqueous solution:
a. $NaBr(aq)$ **b.** $PbI_2(aq)$ **c.** $Na_2SO_4(aq)$

92. Write equations for the half-reactions that occur at the anode and cathode for the electrolysis of each aqueous solution:
a. $Ni(NO_3)_2(aq)$ **b.** $KCl(aq)$ **c.** $CuBr_2(aq)$

93. Make a sketch of an electrolysis cell that electroplates copper onto other metal surfaces. Label the anode and the cathode and indicate the reactions that occur at each.

94. Make a sketch of an electrolysis cell that electroplates nickel onto other metal surfaces. Label the anode and the cathode and indicate the reactions that occur at each.

95. Copper can be electroplated at the cathode of an electrolysis cell by the half-reaction:

$$Cu^{2+}(aq) + 2\,e^- \longrightarrow Cu(s)$$

How much time would it take for 325 mg of copper to be plated at a current of 5.6 A?

96. Silver can be electroplated at the cathode of an electrolysis cell by the half-reaction:

$$Ag^+(aq) + e^- \longrightarrow Ag(s)$$

What mass of silver would plate onto the cathode if a current of 6.8 A flowed through the cell for 72 min?

97. A major source of sodium metal is the electrolysis of molten sodium chloride. What magnitude of current produces 1.0 kg of sodium metal in one hour?

98. What mass of aluminum metal can be produced per hour in the electrolysis of a molten aluminum salt by a current of 25 A?

Cumulative Problems

99. Consider the unbalanced redox reaction:

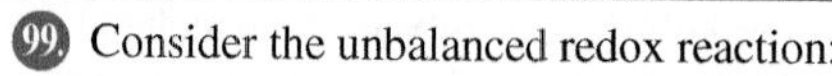

$$MnO_4^-(aq) + Zn(s) \longrightarrow Mn^{2+}(aq) + Zn^{2+}(aq)$$

Balance the equation and determine the volume of a 0.500 mol L^{-1} $KMnO_4$ solution required to completely react with 2.85 g of Zn.

100. Consider the unbalanced redox reaction:

$$Cr_2O_7^{2-}(aq) + Cu(s) \longrightarrow Cr^{3+}(aq) + Cu^{2+}(aq)$$

Balance the equation and determine the volume of a 0.850 mol L^{-1} $K_2Cr_2O_7$ solution required to completely react with 5.25 g of Cu.

101. Consider the molecular views of an Al strip and Cu^{2+} solution. Draw a similar sketch showing what happens to the atoms and ions after the Al strip is submerged in the solution for a few minutes.

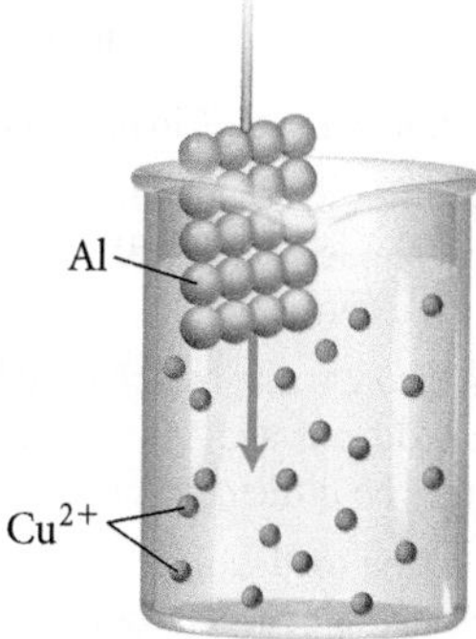

102. Consider the molecular view of an electrochemical cell involving the overall reaction:

$$Zn(s) + Ni^{2+}(aq) \longrightarrow Zn^{2+}(aq) + Ni(s)$$

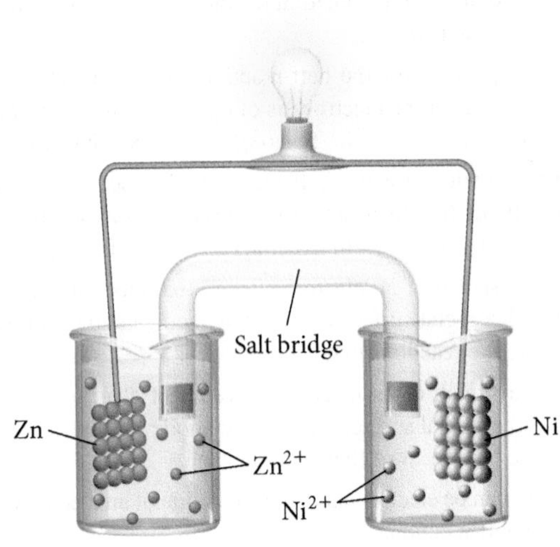

Draw a similar sketch showing how the cell might appear after it has generated a substantial amount of electrical current.

103. Determine whether $HI(aq)$ can dissolve each metal sample. If so, write a balanced chemical reaction showing how the metal dissolves in $HI(aq)$ and determine the minimum volume of 3.5 mol L^{-1} $HI(aq)$ required to completely dissolve the sample.
a. 2.15 g Al **b.** 4.85 g Cu **c.** 2.42 g Ag

104. Determine if $HNO_3(aq)$ can dissolve each metal sample. If it can, write a balanced chemical reaction showing how the metal dissolves in $HNO_3(aq)$ and determine the minimum volume of 6.0 mol L^{-1} $HNO_3(aq)$ required to completely dissolve the sample.
a. 5.90 g Au **b.** 2.55 g Cu **c.** 4.83 g Sn

105. The cell potential of this electrochemical cell depends on the pH of the solution in the anode half-cell:

$$Pt(s)|H_2(g,\ 1\ bar)|H^+(aq,\ ?\ mol\ L^{-1})||Cu^{2+}(aq,\ 1.0\ mol\ L^{-1})|Cu(s)$$

What is the pH of the solution if E_{cell} is 355 mV?

106. The cell potential of this electrochemical cell depends on the gold concentration in the cathode half-cell:

$$Pt(s)|H_2(g,\ 1.0\ bar)|H^+(aq,\ 1.0\ mol\ L^{-1})||Au^{3+}(aq,\ ?\ mol\ L^{-1})|Au(s)$$

What is the concentration of Au^{3+} in the solution if E_{cell} is 1.22 V?

107. A friend wants you to invest in his newly designed battery that produces 24 V in a single voltaic cell. Why should you be wary of investing in such a battery?

108. What voltage can theoretically be achieved in a battery in which lithium metal is oxidized and fluorine gas is reduced? Why might such a battery be difficult to produce?

109. A battery relies on the oxidation of magnesium and the reduction of Cu^{2+}. The initial concentrations of Mg^{2+} and Cu^{2+} are 1.0×10^{-4} mol L^{-1} and 1.5 mol L^{-1}, respectively, in 1.0 litre half-cells.
a. What is the initial voltage of the battery?
b. What is the voltage of the battery after delivering 5.0 A for 8.0 h?
c. How long can the battery deliver 5.0 A before going dead?

110. A rechargeable battery is constructed based on a concentration cell constructed of two Ag/Ag^+ half-cells. The volume of each half-cell is 2.0 L and the concentrations of Ag^+ in the half-cells are 1.25 mol L^{-1} and 1.0×10^{-3} mol L^{-1}.
a. How long can this battery deliver 2.5 A of current before it goes dead?
b. What mass of silver is plated onto the cathode by running at 3.5 A for 5.5 h?
c. Upon recharging, how long would it take to redissolve 1.00×10^2 g of silver at a charging current of 10.0 amps?

111. If a water electrolysis cell operates at a current of 7.8 A, how long will it take to generate 25.0 L of hydrogen gas at a pressure of 25.0 atm and a temperature of 25 °C?

112. For a hydrogen–oxygen fuel cell, use standard cell potentials to compute the equilibrium constant for the overall reaction. Compare this value of the equilibrium constant with that computed using standard Gibbs energies of formations from Appendix II. Finally, use the standard molar entropies from Appendix II to determine if the reaction is more or less spontaneous at higher temperatures.

113. The K_{sp} of CuI is 1.1×10^{-12}. Find E_{cell} for the cell:

$$Cu(s)|CuI(s)|I^-(aq,\ 1.0\ mol\ L^{-1})||Cu^+(aq,\ 1.0\ mol\ L^{-1})|Cu(s)$$

114. The K_{sp} of $Zn(OH)_2$ is 1.8×10^{-14}. Find E_{cell} for the half-reaction:

$$Zn(OH)_2(s) + 2\ e^- \rightleftharpoons Zn(s) + 2\ OH^-(aq)$$

115. Calculate Δ_rG° and K for each reaction:
a. The disproportionation of $Mn^{2+}(aq)$ to $Mn(s)$ and $MnO_2(s)$ in acid solution at 25 °C.
b. The disproportionation of $MnO_2(s)$ to $Mn^{2+}(aq)$ and $MnO_4^-(aq)$ in acid solution at 25 °C.

116. Calculate Δ_rG° and K for each reaction:
a. The reaction of $Cr^{2+}(aq)$ with $Cr_2O_7^{2-}(aq)$ in acid solution to form $Cr^{3+}(aq)$.
b. The reaction of $Cr^{3+}(aq)$ and $Cr(s)$ to form $Cr^{2+}(aq)$. [The electrode potential of $Cr^{2+}(aq)$ to $Cr(s)$ is −0.91 V.]

117. The molar mass of a metal (M) is 50.9 g mol^{-1}; it forms a chloride of unknown composition. Electrolysis of a sample of the molten chloride with a current of 6.42 A for 23.6 minutes produces 1.20 g of the metal at the cathode. Determine the empirical formula of the chloride.

118. A metal forms the fluoride MF_3. Electrolysis of the molten fluoride by a current of 3.86 A for 16.2 minutes deposits 1.25 g of the metal. Calculate the molar mass of the metal.

119. A sample of impure tin of mass 0.535 g is dissolved in strong acid to give a solution of Sn^{2+}. The solution is then titrated with a 0.0448 mol L^{-1} solution of $NO_3^-(aq)$, which is reduced to $NO(g)$. The equivalence point is reached upon the addition of 0.0344 L of the $NO_3^-(aq)$ solution. Find the percent by mass of tin in the original sample, assuming that it contains no other reducing agents.

120. A 0.0251 L sample of a solution of $Cu^+(aq)$ requires 0.0322 L of 0.129 mol L^{-1} $KMnO_4(aq)$ solution to reach the equivalence point. The products of the reaction are Cu^{2+} and Mn^{2+}. What is the concentration of the resulting $Cu^{2+}(aq)$ solution?

121. A current of 11.3 A is applied to 1.25 L of a solution of 0.552 mol L^{-1} aqueous HBr, converting some of the $H^+(aq)$ to $H_2(g)$, which bubbles out of solution. What is the pH of the solution after 73 minutes?

122. A 215 mL sample of a 0.500 mol L^{-1} aqueous NaCl solution with an initial pH of 7.00 is subjected to electrolysis. After 15.0 minutes, a 10.0 mL portion (or aliquot) of the solution was removed from the cell and titrated with 0.100 mol L^{-1} $HCl(aq)$

solution. The endpoint in the titration was reached upon addition of 22.8 mL of HCl. Assuming constant current, what was the current (in A) running through the cell?

123. An $MnO_2(s)/Mn^{2+}(aq)$ electrode in which the pH is 10.24 is prepared. Find the $[Mn^{2+}]$ necessary to lower the potential of the half-cell to 0.00 V (at 25 °C).

124. To what pH should you adjust a standard hydrogen electrode to get an electrode potential of −0.122 V? (Assume that the partial pressure of hydrogen gas remains at 1 bar.)

Challenge Problems

125. Suppose a hydrogen–oxygen fuel-cell generator produces electricity for a house. Use the balanced redox reactions and the standard cell potential to predict the volume of hydrogen gas (at STP) required each month to generate the electricity needed for a typical house. Assume the home uses 1.2×10^3 kWh of electricity per month.

126. A voltaic cell designed to measure $[Cu^{2+}]$ is constructed of a standard hydrogen electrode and a copper metal electrode in the Cu^{2+} solution of interest. If you wanted to construct a calibration curve for how the cell potential varies with the concentration of copper(II), what would you plot in order to obtain a straight line? What would be the slope of the line?

127. The surface area of an object to be gold plated is 49.8 cm^2 and the density of gold is 19.3 g cm^{-3}. A current of 3.25 A is applied to a solution that contains gold in the +3 oxidation state. Calculate the time required to deposit an even layer of gold 1.00×10^{-3} cm thick on the object.

128. To electrodeposit all the Cu and Cd from a solution of $CuSO_4$ and $CdSO_4$ required 1.20 F of electricity (1 F = 1 mol e^-). The mixture of Cu and Cd that was deposited had a mass of 50.36 g. What mass of $CuSO_4$ was present in the original mixture?

129. Sodium oxalate, $Na_2C_2O_4$, in solution is oxidized to $CO_2(g)$ by MnO_4^- which is reduced to Mn^{2+} in excess of an acid. A 50.1 mL volume of a solution of MnO_4^- is required to titrate a 0.339 g sample of sodium oxalate. This solution of MnO_4^- is used to analyze uranium-containing samples. A 4.62 g sample of a uranium-containing material requires 32.5 mL of the solution for titration. The oxidation of the uranium can be represented by the change $UO^{2+} \longrightarrow UO_2^{2+}$. Calculate the percentage of uranium in the sample.

130. Three electrolytic cells are connected in a series. The electrolytes in the cells are aqueous copper(II) sulfate, gold(III) sulfate, and silver nitrate. A current of 2.33 A is applied and after some time 1.74 g Cu is deposited. How long was the current applied? What mass of gold and silver were deposited?

131. The cell $Pt(s)|Cu^+(1\ mol\ L^{-1}),\ Cu^{2+}(1\ mol\ L^{-1})||Cu^+(1\ mol\ L^{-1})|Cu(s)$ has $E° = 0.364$ V. The cell $Cu(s)|Cu^{2+}(1\ mol\ L^{-1})||Cu^+(1\ mol\ L^{-1})|Cu(s)$ has $E° = 0.182$ V.

Write the cell reaction for each cell and explain the differences in $E°$. Calculate $\Delta_r G°$ for each cell reaction to help explain these differences.

Conceptual Problems

132. An electrochemical cell has a positive standard cell potential but a negative cell potential. What is true of Q and K for the cell?

a. $K > 1;\ Q > K$
b. $K < 1;\ Q > K$
c. $K > 1;\ Q < K$
d. $K < 1;\ Q < K$

133. Which oxidizing agent will oxidize Br^- but not Cl^-?

a. $K_2Cr_2O_7$ (acidic aqueous solution)
b. $KMnO_4$ (acidic aqueous solution)
c. $HNO_3(aq)$

134. A redox reaction employed in an electrochemical cell has a negative $\Delta_r G°$. Which statement is true?

a. $E°_{cell}$ is positive; $K < 1$
b. $E°_{cell}$ is positive; $K > 1$
c. $E°_{cell}$ is negative; $K > 1$
d. $E°_{cell}$ is negative; $K < 1$

19 Radioactivity and Nuclear Chemistry

I am among those who think that science has great beauty. A scientist in his laboratory is not only a technician; he is also a child placed before natural phenomena which impress him like a fairy tale.

—Marie Curie (1867–1934)

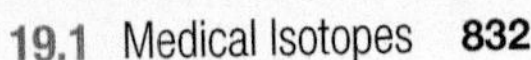

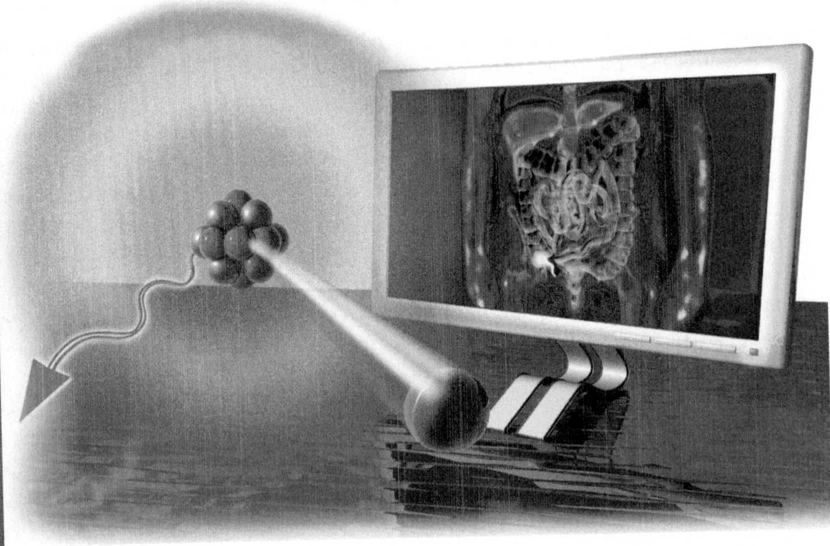

Antibodies labelled with radioactive atoms can be used to diagnose an infected appendix.

IN THIS CHAPTER, WE EXAMINE RADIOACTIVITY and nuclear chemistry, both of which involve changes within the *nuclei* of atoms. Unlike ordinary chemical processes, in which elements retain their identity, nuclear processes often result in one element changing into another, frequently emitting tremendous amounts of energy. Radioactivity has numerous applications, including the diagnosis and treatment of medical conditions such as cancer, thyroid disease, abnormal kidney and bladder function, and heart disease. Naturally occurring radioactivity also allows us to estimate the age of fossils, rocks, and ancient artifacts. And radioactivity, perhaps most famously, led to the discovery of nuclear fission, used for electricity generation and nuclear weapons. In this chapter, we learn about radioactivity—how it was discovered, what it is, and how we use it.

19.1 Medical Isotopes

In Chapter 2, we discussed isotopes—atoms of the same element whose nuclei contain different numbers of neutrons. Some isotopes exhibit the property of radioactivity. **Radioactivity** is the emission of subatomic particles or high-energy electromagnetic radiation by the nuclei of certain atoms. Such atoms are said to be **radioactive**.

In medicine, radioactive isotopes are used to diagnose or treat millions of patients every year. An example of this is radiation therapy, which is used to treat several forms of cancer. The radioactive isotope ^{60}Co emits a type of radiation called gamma radiation. Gamma radiation from ^{60}Co is aimed and focused on the tumour, killing the malignant tissue. There is no need for a doctor to make an incision in the patient because the radiation passes through healthy tissue. Radiation therapy is noninvasive and painless.

Radioactive isotopes can also be used in diagnostic techniques. When some isotopes are administered intravenously, they are circulated through the bloodstream and can be absorbed to different degrees by different tissues. Radiation from the isotope passes outward from the body. Then, the concentrations of radioactivity in different tissues are determined using three-dimensional cameras. The resulting scan is interpreted by a radiologist to diagnose the patient's condition or disease. ^{99}Tc is the most commonly used isotope for this kind of diagnostic procedure.

▲ The Chalk River Laboratories near Chalk River, ON, produce a large fraction of the world's medical isotopes.

Medical isotopes are a Canadian innovation. They were first produced in the 1950s at a nuclear research reactor at Chalk River Laboratories, near Chalk River, Ontario. The production of medical isotopes has continued there. The Chalk River facility produces 75% of the world's supply of ^{60}Co. It also produces over half of the ^{99}Tc used in nuclear medicine scans worldwide. There are only five reactors in the world that produce medical isotopes.

19.2 The Discovery of Radioactivity

Radioactivity was discovered in 1896 by a French scientist named Antoine Henri Becquerel (1852–1908). Becquerel was interested in the newly discovered X-rays (see Chapter 7), which were a hot topic of physics research in his time. He hypothesized that X-rays were emitted in conjunction with **phosphorescence**, the long-lived *emission* of light that sometimes follows the absorption of light by certain atoms and molecules. Phosphorescence is probably most familiar to you as the *glow* in glow-in-the-dark products (such as toys or stickers). After such a product is exposed to light, it re-emits some of that light, usually at slightly longer wavelengths. If you turn off the room lights or put the glow-in-the-dark-product in the dark, you see the greenish glow of the emitted light. Becquerel hypothesized that this visible greenish glow was associated with the emission of X-rays (which are invisible).

▲ The greenish light emitted from glow-in-the-dark toys is phosphorescence.

To test his hypothesis, Becquerel placed crystals—composed of potassium uranyl sulfate, a compound known to phosphoresce—on top of a photographic plate wrapped in black cloth (Figure 19.1 ▾). He then exposed the crystals to sunlight. He knew the crystals had phosphoresced because he could see the emitted light when he brought them back into the dark. If the crystals had also emitted X-rays, the X-rays would have passed through the black cloth and exposed the underlying photographic plate. Becquerel performed the

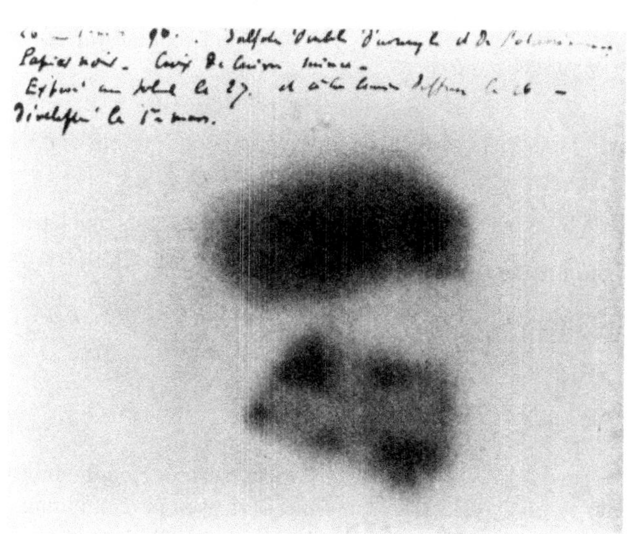

◀ **FIGURE 19.1 The Discovery of Radioactivity** This photographic plate (with Becquerel's original comments at top) played a key role in the discovery of radioactivity. Becquerel placed a uranium-containing compound on the plate (which was wrapped in black cloth to shield it from visible light). He found that the plate was darkened by some unknown form of penetrating radiation that was produced continuously, independently of phosphorescence.

▲ Marie Curie, one of the first women in France to pursue a doctoral degree, was twice awarded the Nobel Prize, in 1903 and 1911. She is seen here with her daughters, in about 1905. Irène (left) became a distinguished nuclear physicist in her own right, winning a Nobel Prize in 1935. Eve (right) wrote a highly acclaimed biography of her mother.

experiment several times and always got the same result—the photographic plate showed a dark exposure spot where the crystals had been. Becquerel believed his hypothesis was correct and presented the results—that phosphorescence and X-rays were linked—to the French Academy of Sciences.

Becquerel later retracted his results, however, when he discovered that a photographic plate with the same crystals showed a dark exposure spot even when the plate and the crystals were stored in a drawer and not exposed to sunlight. Becquerel realized that the crystals themselves were constantly emitting something that exposed the photographic plate, regardless of whether or not they phosphoresced. Becquerel concluded that it was the uranium within the crystals that was the source of the emissions, and he named the emissions *uranic rays*.

Soon after Becquerel's discovery, a young graduate student named Marie Sklodowska-Curie (1867–1934) (one of the first women in France to pursue doctoral work) decided to study uranic rays for her doctoral thesis. Her first task was to determine whether any other substances besides uranium (the heaviest known element at the time) emitted these rays. In her search, Curie discovered two new elements, both of which also emitted uranic rays. Curie named one of her newly discovered elements polonium, after her home country of Poland. The other element she named radium, because of its high level of radioactivity. Radium is so radioactive that it gently glows in the dark and emits significant amounts of heat. Since it was clear that these rays were not unique to uranium, Curie changed the name of uranic rays to radioactivity. In 1903, Curie and her husband, Pierre Curie, as well as Becquerel, were all awarded the Nobel Prize in physics for the discovery of radioactivity. In 1911, Curie received a second Nobel Prize, this time in chemistry, for her discovery of the two new elements.

19.3 Types of Radioactivity

While Curie focused her work on discovering the different kinds of radioactive elements, Ernest Rutherford and others focused on characterizing the radioactivity itself. These scientists found that the emissions are produced by the nuclei of radioactive atoms. Such nuclei are unstable and spontaneously decompose, emitting small pieces of themselves to gain stability. These fragments are the radioactivity that Becquerel and Curie detected. Natural radioactivity can be categorized into several different types, including *alpha* (α) *decay*, *beta* (β) *decay*, *gamma* (γ) *ray emission*, and *positron emission*. In addition, some unstable atomic nuclei can attain greater stability by absorbing an electron from one of the atom's own orbitals, a process called *electron capture*.

Element 96 is named curium in honor of Marie Curie and her contributions to our understanding of radioactivity.

In order to understand these different types of radioactivity, we must briefly review the notation for symbolizing isotopes that we first saw in Section 2.4. Recall that we can represent any isotope with the following notation:

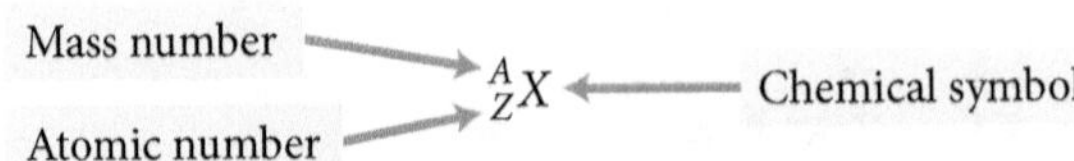

▲ Radium, discovered by Marie Curie, is so radioactive that it glows visibly and emits heat.

Mass number (A) = the sum of the number of protons and the number of neutrons in the nucleus

Atomic number (Z) = the number of protons in the nucleus

Thus, the number of neutrons in the nucleus (N) is $A - Z$.

$$N = A - Z$$

↑ Number of neutrons

For example, the symbol $^{21}_{10}Ne$ represents the neon isotope containing 10 protons and 11 neutrons. The symbol $^{20}_{10}Ne$ represents the neon isotope containing 10 protons and 10 neutrons. Remember that most elements have several different isotopes. When we are discussing nuclear properties, we often refer to a particular isotope (or species) of an element as a **nuclide**.

We can represent the main subatomic particles—protons, neutrons, and electrons—with similar notation.

Proton symbol $^{1}_{1}\text{p}$ Neutron symbol $^{1}_{0}\text{n}$ Electron symbol $^{0}_{-1}e$

The 1 in the lower left of the proton symbol represents 1 proton, and the 0 in the lower left corner of the neutron symbol represents 0 protons. The −1 in the lower left corner of the electron symbol is a bit different from the other atomic numbers, but it will make sense when we see it in the context of nuclear decay a bit later in this section.

Alpha (α) Decay

Alpha (α) decay occurs when an unstable nucleus emits a particle composed of two protons and two neutrons (Figure 19.2 ▶) Since two protons and two neutrons combined are identical to a helium-4 nucleus, the symbol for alpha radiation is the symbol for helium-4:

Alpha (α) particle $^{4}_{2}\text{He}$ 

When an element emits an alpha particle, the number of protons in its nucleus changes, transforming the element into a different element. We symbolize this phenomenon with a **nuclear equation**, an equation that represents nuclear processes such as radioactivity. For example, the nuclear equation for the alpha decay of uranium-238 is

Parent nuclide → $^{238}_{92}\text{U}$; Daughter nuclide → $^{234}_{90}\text{Th}$

$$^{238}_{92}\text{U} \longrightarrow {}^{234}_{90}\text{Th} + {}^{4}_{2}\text{He}$$

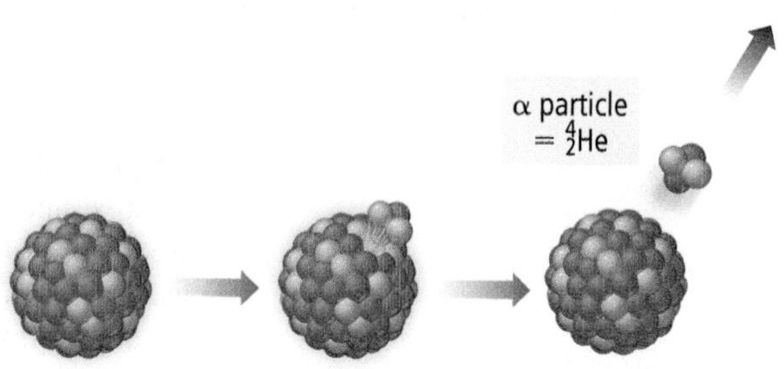

▲ **FIGURE 19.2 Alpha Decay** In alpha decay, a nucleus emits a particle composed of two protons and two neutrons (a helium-4 nucleus).

The original atom is called the *parent nuclide* and the product of the decay is called the *daughter nuclide*. In this case, uranium-238 (the parent nuclide) becomes thorium-234 (the daughter nuclide). Unlike a chemical reaction, in which elements retain their identity, a nuclear reaction often results in elements changing their identity. Like a chemical equation, a nuclear equation must also be balanced. However, balancing a nuclear equation is slightly different. *The sum of the atomic numbers on both sides of a nuclear equation must be equal, and the sum of the mass numbers on both sides must also be equal.*

As will be discussed in Section 19.4, nuclei are unstable when they are too large or when they contain an unbalanced ratio of neutrons to protons.

In nuclear chemistry, we are primarily interested in changes within the nucleus; therefore, the 2+ charge that we would normally write for a helium nucleus is omitted for an alpha particle.

$$^{238}_{92}\text{U} \longrightarrow {}^{234}_{90}\text{Th} + {}^{4}_{2}\text{He}$$

Reactants	Products
Sum of mass numbers = 238	Sum of mass numbers = 234 + 4 = 238
Sum of atomic numbers = 92	Sum of atomic numbers = 90 + 2 = 92

The identity and symbol of the daughter nuclide in any alpha decay can be deduced from the mass and atomic number of the parent nuclide. During alpha decay, the mass number decreases by 4 and the atomic number decreases by 2, as shown in Example 19.1.

EXAMPLE 19.1 WRITING NUCLEAR EQUATIONS FOR ALPHA DECAY

Write a nuclear equation for the alpha decay of Ra-224.

SOLUTION

Begin with the symbol for Ra-224 on the left side of the equation and the symbol for an alpha particle on the right side.	$^{224}_{88}\text{Ra} \longrightarrow {}^{?}_{?}? + {}^{4}_{2}\text{He}$

(continued)

EXAMPLE 19.1 (CONTINUED)

Equalize the sum of the mass numbers and the sum of the atomic numbers on both sides of the equation by writing the appropriate mass number and atomic number for the unknown daughter nuclide.	$^{224}_{88}\text{Ra} \longrightarrow {}^{220}_{86}? + {}^{4}_{2}\text{He}$
Using the periodic table, deduce the identity of the unknown daughter nuclide from its atomic number and write its symbol. Since the atomic number is 86, the daughter nuclide is radon (Rn).	$^{224}_{88}\text{Ra} \longrightarrow {}^{220}_{86}\text{Rn} + {}^{4}_{2}\text{He}$

FOR PRACTICE 19.1
Write a nuclear equation for the alpha decay of Po-216.

Alpha radiation is the 18-wheeler truck of radioactivity. Of all particles emitted by radioactive nuclei, the alpha particle is the most massive and it carries a +2 charge. Consequently, alpha radiation has the most potential to interact with and damage other molecules, including biological ones. Highly energetic radiation interacts with other molecules and atoms by ionizing them. When radiation ionizes molecules within the cells of living organisms, those molecules may undergo damaging chemical reactions, and the cells can die or begin to reproduce abnormally. The ability of radiation to ionize other molecules and atoms is called its **ionizing power**. Of all types of radioactivity, alpha radiation has the highest ionizing power.

However, alpha particles, because of their large size, have the lowest **penetrating power**—the ability to penetrate matter. (Imagine a semi truck trying to get through a traffic jam.) In order for radiation to damage important molecules within living cells, it must penetrate into the cell. Alpha radiation does not easily penetrate into cells because it can be stopped by a sheet of paper, by clothing, or even by air. Consequently, a low-level alpha emitter that remains outside the body is relatively safe. If an alpha emitter is ingested, or inhaled however, it becomes very dangerous because the alpha particles then have direct access to the molecules that compose organs and tissues.

Beta (β) Decay

This kind of beta radiation is also called beta minus (β^-) radiation due to its negative charge.

Beta (β) decay occurs when an unstable nucleus emits an electron (Figure 19.3 ◀). How does a nucleus, which contains only protons and neutrons, emit an electron? The electron forms in some unstable nuclei when a neutron changes into a proton and emits an electron in the process:

Beta decay Neutron $\longrightarrow$ proton + emitted electron

The symbol for a beta (β) particle in a nuclear equation is

Beta (β) particle $^{0}_{-1}e$

We can represent beta decay with the nuclear equation:

$$^{1}_{0}\text{n} \longrightarrow {}^{1}_{1}\text{p} + {}^{0}_{-1}e$$

The −1 reflects the charge of the electron, which is equivalent to an atomic number of −1 in a nuclear equation. When an atom emits a beta particle, its atomic number increases by 1 because it now has an additional proton. For example, the nuclear equation for the beta decay of radium-228 is

$$^{228}_{88}\text{Ra} \longrightarrow {}^{228}_{89}\text{Ac} + {}^{0}_{-1}e$$

Notice that the nuclear equation is balanced—the sum of the mass numbers on both sides is equal and the sum of the atomic numbers on both sides is equal.

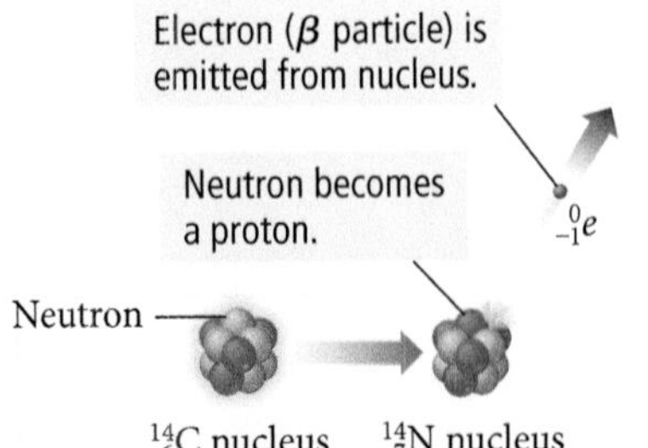
Electron (β particle) is emitted from nucleus.
Neutron becomes a proton.
$^{0}_{-1}e$
Neutron
$^{14}_{6}$C nucleus
$^{14}_{7}$N nucleus

▲ **FIGURE 19.3 Beta Decay** In beta decay, a neutron emits an electron and becomes a proton.

Beta radiation is the four-door sedan of radioactivity. Beta particles are much less massive than alpha particles and consequently have a lower ionizing power. However, because of their smaller size, beta particles have a higher penetrating power and only something as substantive as a sheet of metal or a thick piece of wood will stop them. Consequently, a beta emitter outside of the body poses a higher risk than an alpha emitter. Inside the body, however, the beta emitter does less damage than an alpha emitter. Even still, one does not want to ingest a beta emitter.

Gamma (γ) Ray Emission

Gamma (γ) ray emission is significantly different from alpha or beta radiation. Gamma radiation is a form of *electromagnetic* radiation (see Section 7.2). Gamma rays are high-energy (short-wavelength) photons. The symbol for a gamma ray is

See Section 7.2 for a review of electromagnetic radiation.

Gamma (γ) ray $\quad {}^{0}_{0}\gamma$

A gamma ray has no charge and no mass. When a gamma-ray photon is emitted from a radioactive atom, it does not change the mass number or the atomic number of the element. Gamma rays, however, are often emitted in conjunction with other types of radiation. For example, the alpha emission of U-238 (discussed previously) is also accompanied by the emission of a gamma ray.

$$ {}^{238}_{92}\text{U} \longrightarrow {}^{234}_{90}\text{Th} + {}^{4}_{2}\text{He} + {}^{0}_{0}\gamma $$

Gamma rays are the motorbikes of radioactivity. They have the lowest ionizing power, but the highest penetrating power. (Imagine a motorbike zipping through a traffic jam.) Stopping gamma rays requires several inches of lead shielding or thick slabs of concrete.

Positron Emission

Positron emission occurs when an unstable nucleus emits a positron (Figure 19.4 ▶). A **positron** is the *antiparticle* of the electron: it has the same mass as an electron, but the opposite charge. If a positron collides with an electron, the two particles annihilate each other, releasing energy in the form of gamma rays. In positron emission, a proton is converted into a neutron and emits a positron:

Positron emission can be thought of as a type of beta emission and is sometimes referred to as beta plus emission (β^+).

Positron emission $\quad$ Proton $\longrightarrow$ neutron + emitted positron

The symbol for a positron in a nuclear equation is

Positron $\quad {}^{0}_{+1}e$

We can represent positron emission with the nuclear equation:

$$ {}^{1}_{1}\text{p} \longrightarrow {}^{1}_{0}\text{n} + {}^{0}_{+1}e $$

When an atom emits a positron, its atomic number *decreases* by 1 because it has one fewer proton after emission. For example, the nuclear equation for the positron emission of phosphorus-30 is

$$ {}^{30}_{15}\text{P} \longrightarrow {}^{30}_{14}\text{Si} + {}^{0}_{+1}e $$

We can determine the identity and symbol of the daughter nuclide in any positron emission in a manner similar to that used for alpha and beta decay, as shown in Example 19.2. Positrons are similar to beta particles in their ionizing and penetrating power.

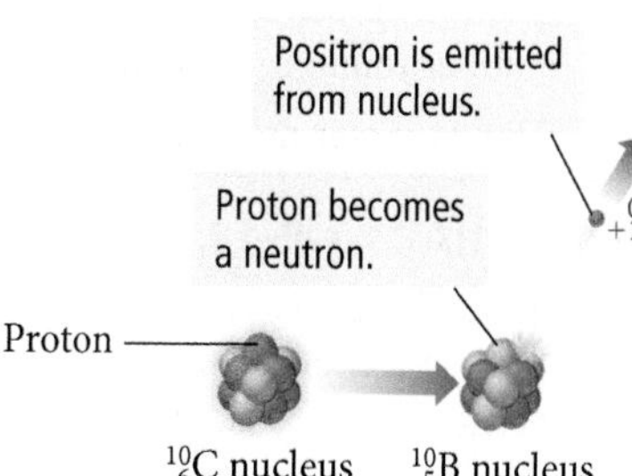
Positron is emitted from nucleus.
Proton becomes a neutron.
$^{0}_{+1}e$
Proton
$^{10}_{6}$C nucleus
$^{10}_{5}$B nucleus

▲ **FIGURE 19.4 Positron Emission** In positron emission, a proton emits a positron and becomes a neutron.

Electron Capture

Unlike the forms of radioactive decay that we have discussed so far, electron capture involves a particle being *absorbed by* instead of *ejected from* an unstable nucleus. **Electron capture** occurs when a nucleus assimilates an electron from an inner orbital of its electron cloud. Like positron emission, the net effect of electron capture is the conversion of a proton into a neutron:

Electron capture $\quad$ Proton + electron $\longrightarrow$ neutron

We can represent electron capture with the nuclear equation:

$$^{1}_{1}\text{p} + {}^{0}_{-1}e \longrightarrow {}^{1}_{0}\text{n}$$

When an atom undergoes electron capture, its atomic number decreases by 1 because it has one less proton. For example, when Ru-92 undergoes electron capture, its atomic number changes from 44 to 43:

$$^{92}_{44}\text{Ru} + {}^{0}_{-1}e \longrightarrow {}^{92}_{43}\text{Tc}$$

In electron capture decay, the electron that is captured by the nucleus is usually one of the inner core electrons. The capture results in a partially vacant core electron shell. Subsequently, there is a cascade of electron transitions from higher shells to fill the vacancy. These transitions result in the emissions of X-rays.

The different kinds of radiation are summarized in Table 19.1.

EXAMPLE 19.2 WRITING NUCLEAR EQUATIONS FOR BETA DECAY, POSITRON EMISSION, AND ELECTRON CAPTURE

Write a nuclear equation for each type of decay:

(a) beta decay in Bk-249

(b) positron emission in O-15

(c) electron capture in I-111

SOLUTION

(a) In beta decay, the atomic number *increases* by 1 and the mass number remains unchanged. The daughter nuclide is element number 98, californium.	$^{249}_{97}\text{Bk} \longrightarrow {}^{249}_{98}? + {}^{0}_{-1}e$ $^{249}_{97}\text{Bk} \longrightarrow {}^{249}_{98}\text{Cf} + {}^{0}_{-1}e$
(b) In positron emission, the atomic number *decreases* by 1 and the mass number remains unchanged. The daughter nuclide is element number 7, nitrogen.	$^{15}_{8}\text{O} \longrightarrow {}^{15}_{7}? + {}^{0}_{+1}e$ $^{15}_{8}\text{O} \longrightarrow {}^{15}_{7}\text{N} + {}^{0}_{+1}e$
(c) In electron capture, the atomic number also *decreases* by 1 and the mass number remains unchanged. The daughter nuclide is element number 52, tellurium.	$^{111}_{53}\text{I} + {}^{0}_{-1}e \longrightarrow {}^{111}_{52}?$ $^{111}_{53}\text{I} + {}^{0}_{-1}e \longrightarrow {}^{111}_{52}\text{Te}$

FOR PRACTICE 19.2

(a) Write three nuclear equations to represent the nuclear decay sequence that begins with the alpha decay of U-235 followed by a beta decay of the daughter nuclide and then another alpha decay.

(b) Write a nuclear equation for the positron emission of Na-22.

(c) Write a nuclear equation for electron capture in Kr-76.

FOR MORE PRACTICE 19.2

Potassium-40 decays to produce Ar-40. What is the method of decay? Write the nuclear equation for this decay.

CONCEPTUAL CONNECTION 19.1

Alpha and Beta Decay

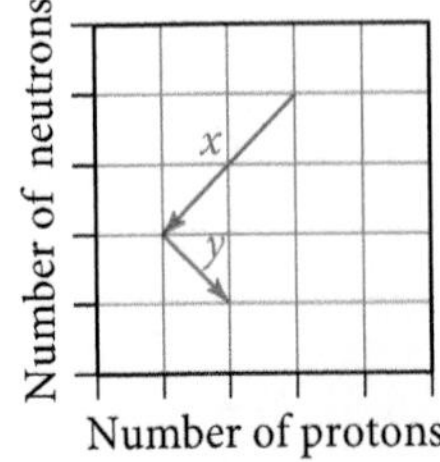

Consider the graphical representation of a series of decays shown at left. The arrow labelled *x* and the arrow labelled *y* each correspond to what kind of decay?

(a) *x* corresponds to alpha decay and *y* corresponds to positron emission.

(b) *x* corresponds to positron emission and *y* corresponds to alpha decay.

(c) *x* corresponds to alpha decay and *y* corresponds to beta decay.

(d) *x* corresponds to beta decay and *y* corresponds to alpha decay.

TABLE 19.1 Modes of Radioactive Decay

Decay Mode	Process	Change in: A	Z	N/Z*	Example
α	Parent nuclide → Daughter nuclide + ^4_2He (α particle)	−4	−2	Increase	$^{238}_{92}U \longrightarrow {}^{234}_{90}Th + {}^4_2He$
β	Neutron; Parent nuclide → Daughter nuclide (Neutron becomes a proton.) + $^0_{-1}e$ (β particle)	0	+1	Decrease	$^{228}_{88}Ra \longrightarrow {}^{228}_{89}Ac + {}^0_{-1}e$
γ	Excited nuclide → Stable nuclide + $^0_0\gamma$ (Photon)	0	0	None	$^{234}_{90}Th \longrightarrow {}^{234}_{90}Th + {}^0_0\gamma$
Positron emission	Proton; Parent nuclide → Daughter nuclide (Proton becomes a neutron.) + $^0_{+1}e$ (Positron)	0	−1	Increase	$^{30}_{15}P \longrightarrow {}^{30}_{14}Si + {}^0_{+1}e$
Electron capture	Proton; Parent nuclide + $^0_{-1}e$ → Daughter nuclide (Proton becomes a neutron.)	0	−1	Increase	$^{92}_{44}Ru + {}^0_{-1}e \longrightarrow {}^{92}_{43}Tc$

*Neutron-to-proton ratio

19.4 The Valley of Stability: Predicting the Type of Radioactivity

So far, we have described various types of radioactivity. But what causes a particular nuclide to be radioactive in the first place? And why do some nuclides decay via alpha decay, while others decay via beta decay or positron emission? The answers to these questions are not simple, but we can get a basic idea of the factors that influence the stability of the nucleus and the nature of its decay.

A nucleus is a collection of protons (positively charged) and neutrons (uncharged). We know that positively charged particles such as protons repel one another. So what binds the nucleus together? The binding is provided by a fundamental force of physics known as the **strong force**. All *nucleons*—protons and neutrons—are attracted to one another by the strong force. However, the strong force acts only at very short distances. So we can think of the stability of a nucleus as a balance between the *repulsive* coloumbic force among protons and the *attractive* strong force among all nucleons. The neutrons in a nucleus, therefore, play an important role in stabilizing the nucleus because they attract other nucleons (through the strong force) but lack the repulsive force associated with positive charge. (It might seem that adding more neutrons would *always* lead to greater stability, so that the more neutrons the better. This is not the case, however, because

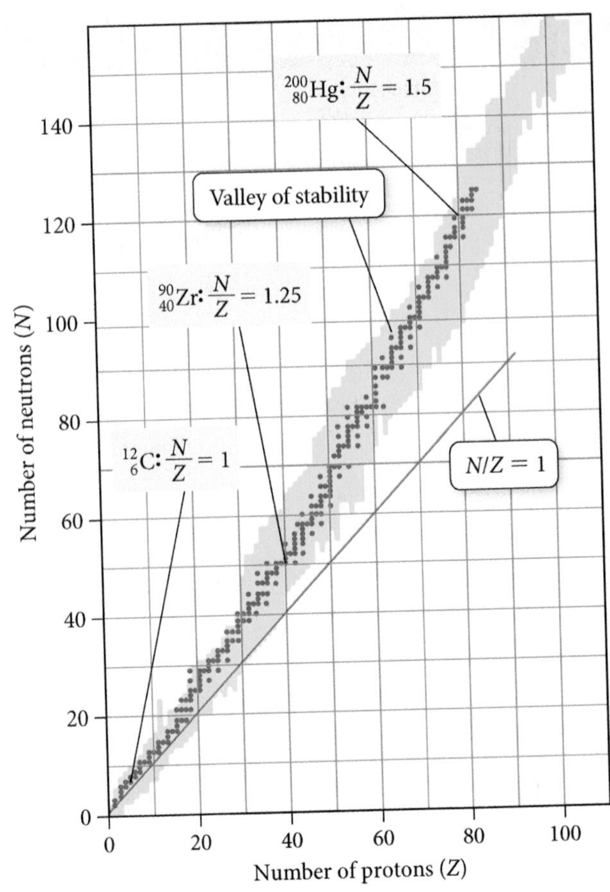

▲ **FIGURE 19.5 Stable and Unstable Nuclei** A plot of N (the number of neutrons) versus Z (the number of protons) for all known stable nuclei—represented by green dots on this graph—shows that these nuclei cluster together in a region known as the valley (or island) of stability. Nuclei with an N/Z ratio that is too high tend to undergo beta decay. Nuclei with an N/Z ratio that is too low tend to undergo positron emission or electron capture.

protrons and neutrons occupy energy levels in a nucleus that are similar to those occupied by electrons in an atom. As you add more neutrons, they must occupy increasingly higher energy levels within the nucleus. At some point, the energy payback from the strong nuclear force is not enough to compensate for the high energy state that the neutron must occupy.)

An important number in determining nuclear stability is the *ratio* of neutrons to protons (N/Z). Figure 19.5 ◂ shows a plot of the number of neutrons versus the number of protons for all known nuclei. The green dots along the diagonal of the graph represent stable nuclei, and this region is known as the *valley* (or *island*) *of stability*. Notice that for the lighter elements, the N/Z ratio of stable isotopes is about one (equal numbers of neutrons and protons). For example, the most abundant isotope of carbon ($Z = 6$) is carbon-12, which contains 6 protons and 6 neutrons. However, beyond about $Z = 20$, the N/Z ratio of stable nuclei begins to get larger. For example, at $Z = 40$, stable nuclei have an N/Z ratio of about 1.25 and at $Z = 80$, the N/Z ratio reaches about 1.5. Above $Z = 83$, stable nuclei do not exist—bismuth ($Z = 83$) is the heaviest element with stable (nonradioactive) isotopes.

The type of radioactivity emitted by a nuclide depends in part on the N/Z ratio:

N/Z too high: Nuclides that lie above the valley of stability have too many neutrons and tend to convert neutrons to protons via beta decay.

N/Z too low: Nuclides that lie below the valley of stability have too many protons and tend to convert protons to neutrons via positron emission or electron capture. (Alpha decay also raises the N/Z ratio for nuclides in which $N/Z > 1$, but the effect is smaller than for positron emission or electron capture.)

One way to decide whether a particular nuclide has an N/Z that is too high, too low, or about right, is to consult Figure 19.5. Those nuclides that lie within the valley of stability are stable. Alternatively, we can also compare the mass number of the nuclide to the atomic mass listed in the periodic table for the corresponding element. The atomic mass is an average of the masses of the stable nuclides for an element and thus represents an N/Z that is about right. For example, suppose we want to evaluate the N/Z ratio for Ru-112. Ruthenium has an atomic mass of 101.07 so we know that the nuclide with a mass number of 112 must contain too many neutrons and therefore have an N/Z that is too high. The following example shows how to apply these considerations in predicting the mode of decay for a nucleus.

EXAMPLE 19.3 PREDICTING THE TYPE OF RADIOACTIVE DECAY

Predict whether each nuclide is more likely to decay via beta decay or positron emission.

(a) Mg-28 **(b)** Mg-22 **(c)** Mo-102

SOLUTION

(a) Magnesium-28 has 16 neutrons and 12 protons, so $N/Z = 1.33$. However, for $Z = 12$, you can see from Figure 19.5 that stable nuclei should have an N/Z ratio of about 1. Alternatively, if you consult the periodic table you find that the atomic mass of magnesium is 24.31 and you can determine that a nuclide with a mass number of 28 is too heavy to be stable because the N/Z ratio is too high. Therefore, Mg-28 undergoes *beta decay*, resulting in the conversion of a neutron to a proton.

(b) Magnesium-22 has 10 neutrons and 12 protons, so $N/Z = 0.83$ (too low). Alternatively you can determine from the periodic table that the atomic mass of magnesium is 24.31. A nuclide with a mass number of 22 is too light; the N/Z ratio is too low. Therefore, Mg-22 undergoes *positron emission*, resulting in the conversion of a proton to a neutron. (Electron capture would accomplish the same thing as positron emission, but in Mg-22, positron emission is the only decay mode observed.)

(c) Molybdenum-102 has 60 neutrons and 42 protons, so $N/Z = 1.43$. However, for $Z = 42$, you can see from Figure 19.5 that stable nuclei should have an N/Z ratio of about 1.3. Alternatively you can determine from the periodic table that the atomic mass of molybdenum is 95.94. A nuclide with a mass number of 102 is too heavy to be stable; the N/Z ratio is too high. Therefore, Mo-102 undergoes *beta decay*, resulting in the conversion of a neutron to a proton.

FOR PRACTICE 19.3

Predict whether each nuclide is more likely to decay via beta decay or positron emission.

(a) Pb-192 **(b)** Pb-212 **(c)** Xe-114

Magic Numbers

In addition to the N/Z ratio, the *actual number* of protons and neutrons also affects the stability of the nucleus. Table 19.2 shows the number of nuclei with different possible combinations of even or odd nucleons. Notice that a large number of stable nuclides have both an even number of protons and an even number of neutrons. Only five stable nuclides have an odd and odd combination.

The reason for this is that nucleons occupy energy levels within the nucleus much as electrons occupy energy levels within an atom. Just as atoms with certain numbers of electrons have unique stability (in particular, the number of electrons associated with the noble gases: 2, 10, 18, 36, 54, etc.), so atoms with certain numbers of nucleons (N or $Z = 2, 8, 20, 28, 50, 82$, and $N = 126$) have unique stability. These numbers are often referred to as **magic numbers**. Nuclei containing a magic number of protons or neutrons are particularly stable. Since the magic numbers are even, this in part accounts for the abundance of stable nuclides with even numbers of nucleons. Moreover, nucleons also have a tendency to pair together (much as electrons pair together). This tendency and the resulting stability of paired nucleons also contribute to the abundance of stable nuclides with even numbers of nucleons.

TABLE 19.2 Number of Stable Nuclides with Even and Odd Numbers of Nucleons

Z	*N*	Number of Nuclides
Even	Even	157
Even	Odd	53
Odd	Even	50
Odd	Odd	5

Radioactive Decay Series

Atoms with $Z > 83$ are radioactive and decay in one or more steps involving primarily alpha and beta decay (with some gamma decay to carry away excess energy). For example, uranium (atomic number 92) is the heaviest naturally occurring element. Its most common isotope is U-238, an alpha emitter that decays to Th-234:

$$^{238}_{92}\text{U} \longrightarrow {}^{234}_{90}\text{Th} + {}^{4}_{2}\text{He}$$

The daughter nuclide, Th-234, is itself radioactive—it is a beta emitter that decays to Pa-234:

$$^{234}_{90}\text{Th} \longrightarrow {}^{234}_{91}\text{Pa} + {}^{0}_{-1}e$$

Protactinium-234 is also radioactive, decaying to U-234 via beta emission. Radioactive decay continues until a stable nuclide, Pb-206, is reached. The entire uranium-238 decay series is shown in Figure 19.6 ▶.

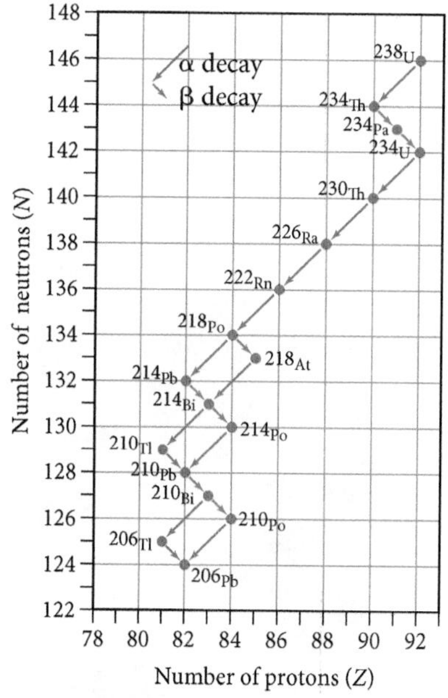

▲ **FIGURE 19.6 The Uranium-238 Radioactive Decay Series** Uranium-238 decays via a series of steps ending in Pb-206, which is stable. Each diagonal line to the left represents an alpha decay and each diagonal line to the right represents a beta decay.

19.5 Measurements and Units of Radioactivity

The particles emitted by radioactive nuclei have a lot of energy and can therefore be readily detected. In a radiation detector, the particles are detected through their interactions with atoms or molecules. The simplest radiation detectors are pieces of

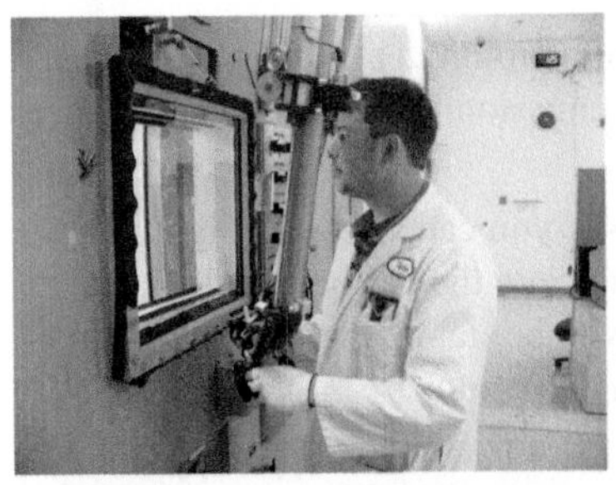

▲ **FIGURE 19.7 Film-Badge Dosimeter** A film-badge dosimeter simply consists of a piece of photographic film in a light-resistant container usually worn in the pocket or as a badge of radiation scientists or technicians. The film's exposure in a given time is proportional to the amount of radiation it receives.

photographic film that become exposed when radiation passes through them. **Film-badge dosimeters**—which consist of photographic film held in a small case that is pinned to clothing—are issued to most people working with or near radioactive substances (Figure 19.7 ◀). These badges are collected and processed (or developed) regularly as a way to monitor a person's exposure. The more exposed the film has become in a given period of time, the more radioactivity the person has been exposed to during that time.

Radioactivity can be instantly detected with devices such as a **Geiger-Müller counter** (Figure 19.8 ▼). In this instrument (commonly referred to simply as a Geiger counter), particles emitted by radioactive nuclei pass through an argon-filled chamber. The energetic particles create a trail of ionized argon atoms. High voltage applied between a wire within the chamber and the chamber itself causes these newly formed ions to produce an electrical signal that can be displayed on a meter or turned into an audible click. Each click corresponds to a radioactive particle passing through the argon gas chamber. This clicking is the stereotypical sound most people associate with a radiation detector.

A second type of device commonly used to detect radiation instantly is a **scintillation counter**. In a scintillation counter, the radioactive emissions pass through a material (such as NaI or CsI) that emits ultraviolet or visible light in response to excitation by energetic particles. The radioactivity excites the atoms to a higher energy state. The atoms release this energy as light, which is then detected and turned into an electrical signal that can be read on a meter. Scintillation counters usually give radioactivity in units of counts per minute, which is directly related to the number of nuclear disintegrations per minute that are detected.

In nuclear chemistry, radioactivity is measured on a particle or event basis. The SI unit of radioactivity is the **becquerel (Bq)**, which is equal to one decay event per second ($1\ \text{Bq} = 1\ \text{s}^{-1}$). An older, but commonly used, unit of radioactivity is the curie (Ci), which is equal to 3.7×10^{10} decay events per second.

19.6 The Kinetics of Radioactive Decay and Radiometric Dating

Radioactivity is a natural component of our environment. The ground beneath you most likely contains radioactive atoms that emit radiation. The food you eat contains a residual quantity of radioactive atoms that are absorbed into your body fluids and incorporated

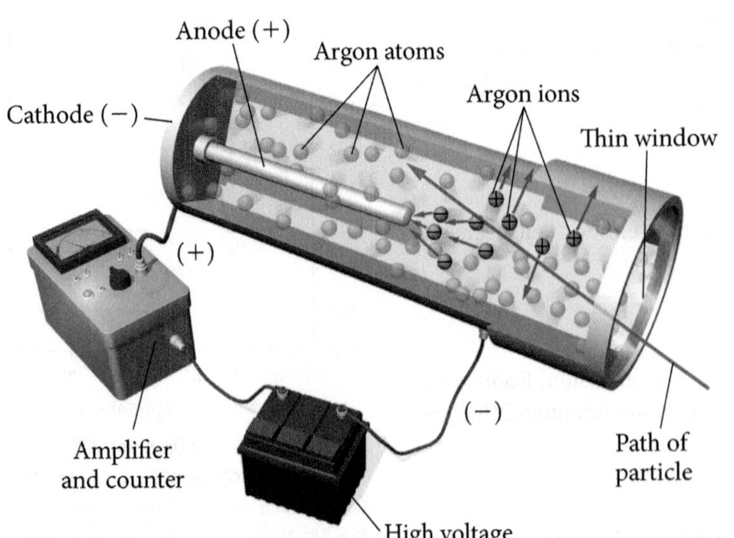

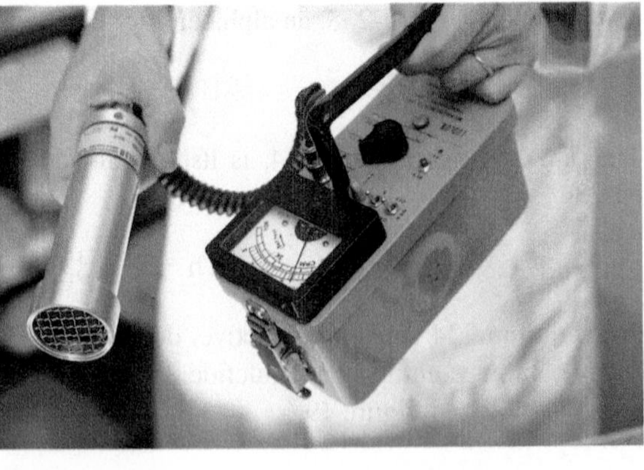

▲ **FIGURE 19.8 Geiger-Müller Counter** When ionizing radiation passes through the argon-filled chamber, it ionizes the atoms, giving rise to a brief, tiny pulse of electrical current that is transduced onto a meter or into an audible click.

into tissues. Small amounts of radiation from space make it through our atmosphere and constantly bombard Earth. Humans and other living organisms have evolved in this environment and have adapted to survive in it.

One reason for the radioactivity in our environment is the instability of all atomic nuclei beyond atomic number 83 (bismuth). Every known element with more than 83 protons in its nucleus is unstable and therefore radioactive. In addition, some isotopes of elements with fewer than 83 protons are also unstable and radioactive. Radioactive nuclides *persist* in our environment because new ones are constantly being formed, and because many of the existing ones decay away only very slowly.

All radioactive nuclei decay via first-order kinetics, so the rate of decay in a particular sample is directly proportional to the number of nuclei present:

You may find it useful to review the discussion of first-order kinetics in Section 13.3.

$$\text{Rate} = kN$$

where N is the number of radioactive nuclei and k is the rate constant. Different radioactive nuclides decay into their daughter nuclides with different rate constants. Some nuclides decay quickly (large rate constant) while others decay slowly (small rate constant).

The time it takes for one-half of the parent nuclides in a radioactive sample to decay to the daughter nuclides is the *half-life*, and is identical to the concept of half-life for chemical reactions that we covered in Chapter 13. Thus, the relationship between the half-life of a nuclide and its rate constant is given by the same expression (Equation 13.19a) that we derived for a first-order reaction in Section 13.4:

$$t_{1/2} = \frac{0.693}{k} \qquad [19.1]$$

Nuclides that decay quickly have short half-lives and large rate constants—they are considered very active (many decay events per unit time). Nuclides that decay slowly have long half-lives and are less active (fewer decay events per unit time). For example, thorium-232 is an alpha emitter with a half-life of 1.4×10^{10} years, or 14 billion years. If we start with a sample of Th-232 containing one million atoms, the sample would decay to $\frac{1}{2}$ million atoms in 14 billion years and then to $\frac{1}{4}$ million in another 14 billion years and so on. Notice that a radioactive sample does *not* decay to *zero* atoms in two half-lives—you can't add two half-lives together to get a "whole" life. The amount that remains after one half-life is always one-half of what was present at the start. The amount that remains after two half-lives is one-quarter of what was present at the start, and so on.

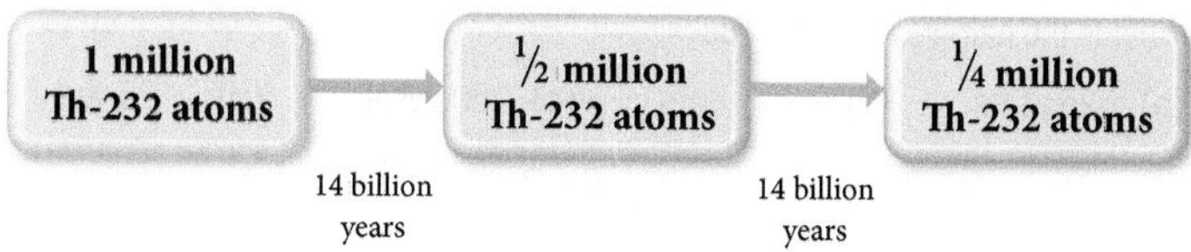

Some nuclides have very short half-lives. For example, radon-220 has a half-life of approximately 1 minute (Figure 19.9 ▼). If we had a 1-million-atom sample of radon-220, it would be diminished to $\frac{1}{4}$ million radon-220 atoms in just 2 minutes and to approximately 1000 atoms in 10 minutes. Table 19.3 lists several nuclides and their half-lives.

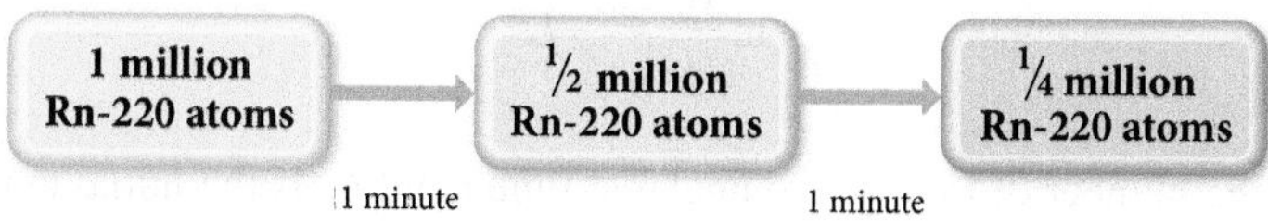

TABLE 19.3 Selected Nuclides and Their Half-Lives

Nuclide	Half-Life	Type of Decay
$^{232}_{90}Th$	1.4×10^{10} y	Alpha
$^{238}_{92}U$	4.5×10^{9} y	Alpha
$^{14}_{6}C$	5730 y	Beta
$^{220}_{86}Rn$	55.6 s	Alpha
$^{219}_{90}Th$	1.05×10^{-6} s	Alpha

The Integrated Rate Law

In Chapter 13, we learned that for first-order chemical reactions, the concentration of a reactant (A) as a function of time is given by the integrated rate law:

$$\ln \frac{[A]_t}{[A]_0} = -kt \qquad [19.2]$$

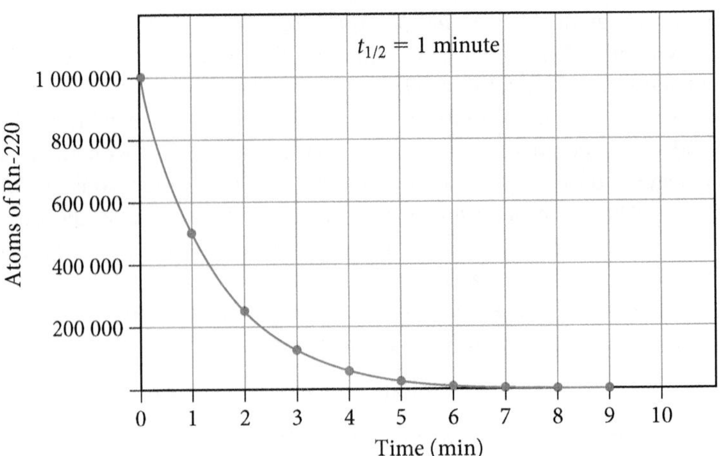

▶ **FIGURE 19.9 The Decay of Radon-220** Radon-220 decays with a half-life of approximately 1 minute.

CONCEPTUAL CONNECTION 19.2
Half-Life

Consider this graph representing the decay of a radioactive nuclide:

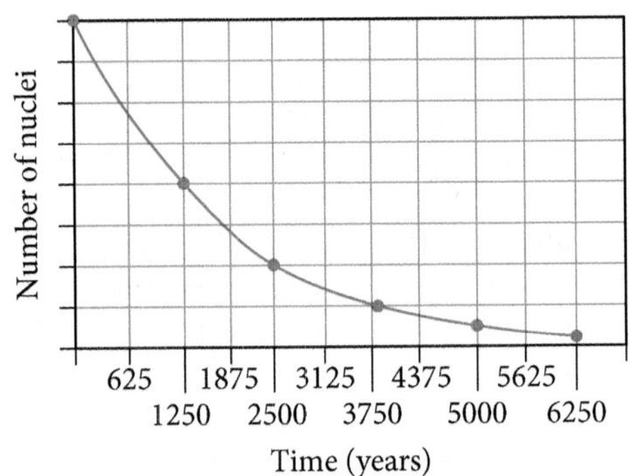

What is the half-life of the nuclide?

(a) 625 years **(b)** 1250 years **(c)** 2500 years **(d)** 3125 years

Since nuclear decay follows first-order kinetics, we can substitute the number of nuclei for concentration to arrive at the equation

$$\ln \frac{N_t}{N_0} = -kt \qquad [19.3]$$

where N_t is the number of radioactive nuclei at time t and N_0 is the initial number of radioactive nuclei.

Since radioactivity is a first-order process, the rate of decay is linearly proportional to the number of nuclei in the sample. Therefore the initial rate of decay (rate$_0$) and the rate of decay at time t (rate$_t$) can also be used in the integrated rate law.

$$\text{Rate}_t = kN_t \qquad \text{Rate}_0 = kN_0$$

$$\frac{N_t}{N_0} = \frac{\text{rate}_t/\cancel{k}}{\text{rate}_0/\cancel{k}} = \frac{\text{rate}_t}{\text{rate}_0}$$

Substituting into Equation 19.3, we get the following result:

$$\ln \frac{\text{rate}_t}{\text{rate}_0} = -kt \qquad [19.4]$$

We can use Equation 19.4 to predict how the rate of decay of a radioactive sample will change with time or how much time has passed based on how the rate has changed (see Examples 19.4–19.6).

EXAMPLE 19.4 RADIOACTIVE DECAY KINETICS

Plutonium-236 is an alpha emitter with a half-life of 2.86 years. If a sample of Pu-236 initially contains 135 Bq, how much radioactivity is present after 5.00 years?

SORT You are given the initial radioactivity of Pu-236 in a sample and asked to find the radioactivity after 5.00 years.

GIVEN: Initial radioactivity = 135 Bq; $t = 5.00\ \text{y}$; $t_{1/2} = 2.86\ \text{y}$

FIND: Final radioactivity

STRATEGIZE Use the integrated rate law (Equation 19.4) to solve this problem. To do so, you must determine the value of the rate constant (k) from the half-life expression (Equation 19.1).

CONCEPTUAL PLAN

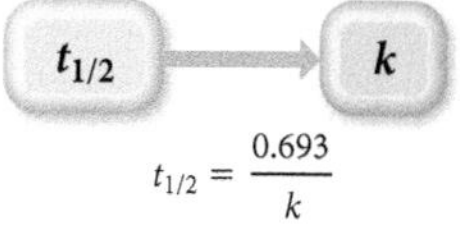

Use the value of the rate constant, the initial radioactivity (rate_0) of Pu-236, and the time along with integrated rate law to find the final radioactivity (rate_t) of Pu-236.

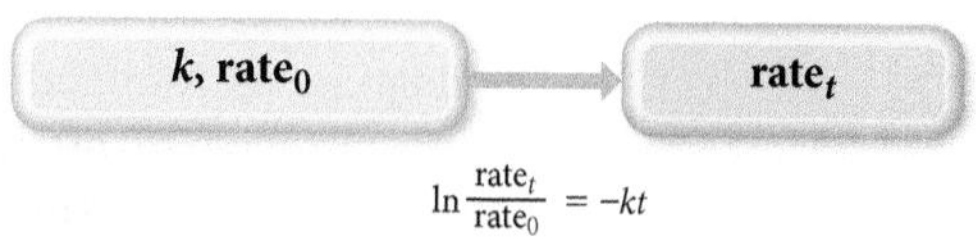

SOLVE Follow your plan. Begin by finding the rate constant from the half-life.

SOLUTION

$$t_{1/2} = \frac{0.693}{k}$$

$$k = \frac{0.693}{t_{1/2}} = \frac{0.693}{2.86\ \text{y}}$$

$$= 0.2423\ \text{y}^{-1}$$

Solve the integrated rate law for rate_t and substitute the values of the rate constant, the initial radioactivity (rate_0) of Pu-236, and the time into the solved equation. Calculate the final radioactivity of Pu-236.

$$\ln \frac{\text{rate}_t}{\text{rate}_0} = -kt$$

$$\frac{\text{rate}_t}{\text{rate}_0} = e^{-kt}$$

$$\text{rate}_t = \text{rate}_0\, e^{-kt}$$

$$\text{rate}_t = 135\ \text{Bq}\,[e^{-(0.2423\cancel{\text{y}^{-1}})(5.00\ \cancel{\text{y}})}]$$

$$\text{rate}_t = 40.2\ \text{Bq}$$

CHECK The units of the answer (Bq) are correct. The magnitude of the answer (40.2 Bq) is about one-third of the original radioactivity (135 Bq) which seems reasonable given that the amount of time is between one and two half-lives. (One half-life would result in one-half of the original mass and two half-lives would result in one-fourth of the original mass.)

FOR PRACTICE 19.4

How long will it take for the 135 Bq sample of Pu-236 in Example 19.4 to decay to 10.0 Bq?

The presence of radioactive isotopes in our environment, and their predictable decay with time, can therefore be used to estimate the age of rocks or artifacts containing those isotopes. The technique is known as **radiometric dating**, and we examine two different types individually.

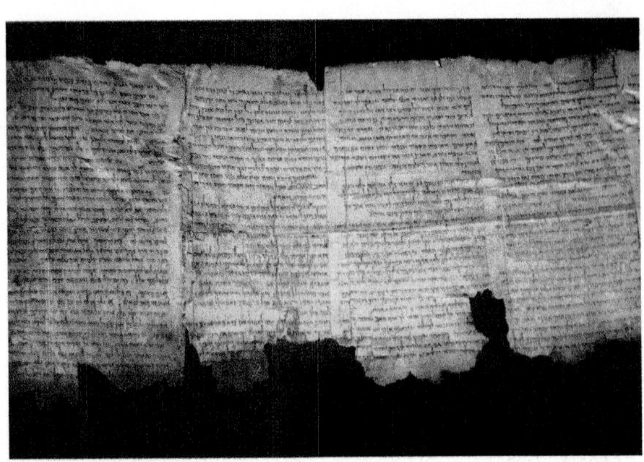

▲ The Dead Sea Scrolls are 2000-year-old biblical manuscripts. Their age was determined by radiocarbon dating.

Radiocarbon Dating: Using Radioactivity to Measure the Age of Fossils and Artifacts

Archeologists, geologists, anthropologists, and other scientists use **radiocarbon dating**, a technique devised in 1949 by Willard Libby at the University of Chicago, to estimate the ages of fossils and artifacts. For example, in 1947, young shepherds searching for a stray goat near the Dead Sea (east of Jerusalem) entered a cave and discovered ancient scrolls that had been stuffed into jars. These scrolls—now named the Dead Sea Scrolls—are 2000-year-old texts of the Hebrew Bible, predating other previously discovered manuscripts by almost a thousand years.

The Dead Sea Scrolls, like other ancient artifacts, contain a radioactive signature that reveals their age. This signature results from the presence of carbon-14 (which is radioactive) in the environment. Carbon-14 is constantly formed in the upper atmosphere by the neutron bombardment of nitrogen:

$$^{14}_{7}\text{N} + ^{1}_{0}\text{n} \longrightarrow ^{14}_{6}\text{C} + ^{1}_{1}\text{H}$$

Libby received the Nobel Prize in 1960 for the development of radiocarbon dating.

After it forms, carbon-14 decays back to nitrogen by beta emission with a half-life of 5730 years.

$$^{14}_{6}\text{C} \longrightarrow ^{14}_{7}\text{N} + ^{0}_{-1}e \qquad t_{1/2} = 5730 \text{ y}$$

The continuous formation of carbon-14 in the atmosphere and its continuous decay back to nitrogen-14 produces a nearly constant equilibrium amount of atmospheric carbon-14, which is oxidized to carbon dioxide and incorporated into plants by photosynthesis. The C-14 then makes its way up the food chain and ultimately into all living organisms. As a result, the tissue in all living plants, animals, and humans contain the same ratio of carbon-14 to carbon-12 ($^{14}\text{C} : ^{12}\text{C}$) as that found in the atmosphere. When a living organism dies, however, it stops incorporating new carbon-14 into its tissues. The $^{14}\text{C} : ^{12}\text{C}$ ratio then begins to decrease with a half-life of 5730 years. Since many artifacts, including the Dead Sea Scrolls, are made from materials that were once living—such as papyrus, wood, or other plant and animal derivatives—the $^{14}\text{C} : ^{12}\text{C}$ ratio in these artifacts indicates their age. For example, suppose an ancient artifact has a $^{14}\text{C} : ^{12}\text{C}$ ratio that is 25% of that found in living organisms. How old is the artifact? Since it contains one-quarter as much carbon-14 as a living organism, it must be two half-lives or 11 460 years old.

The accuracy of carbon-14 dating can be checked against objects whose ages are known from historical sources. These kinds of comparisons have revealed that ages obtained from C-14 dating may deviate from the actual ages by up to about 5%. For a 6000-year-old object, that would result in an error of about 300 years. The reason for the deviations is the variance of atmospheric C-14 levels over time.

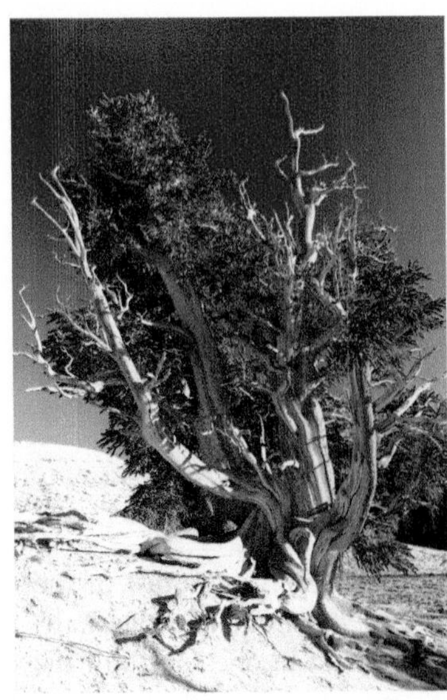

▲ Western bristlecone pine trees can live up to 5000 years, and their age can be precisely determined by counting the annual rings in their trunks. They can therefore be used to calibrate the timescale for radiocarbon dating.

In order to make C-14 dating more accurate, scientists have studied the carbon-14 content of western bristlecone pine trees, which can live up to 5000 years. Each tree trunk contains growth rings corresponding to each year of the tree's life, and the wood laid down in each ring incorporates carbon derived from the carbon dioxide in the atmosphere at that time. The rings thus provide a record of the historical atmospheric carbon-14 content. In addition, the rings of living trees can be correlated with the rings of dead trees, allowing the record to be extended back about 11 000 years. Using the data from the bristlecone pine, the 5% deviations from historical dates can be corrected. In effect, the known ages of bristlecone pine trees are used to calibrate C-14 dating, resulting in more accurate results. The maximum age that can be estimated from carbon-14 dating is about 50 000 years—beyond that, the amount of carbon-14 becomes too low to measure accurately.

EXAMPLE 19.5 RADIOCARBON DATING

A skull believed to belong to an ancient human being is found to have a carbon-14 decay rate of 7.5×10^{-2} disintegrations per second per gram of carbon ($7.50 \times 10^{-2}\ s^{-1}g^{-1}$). If living organisms have a decay rate of $2.55 \times 10^{-1}\ s^{-1}g^{-1}$, how old is the skull? (The decay rate is directly proportional to the amount of carbon-14 present.)

SORT You are given the current rate of decay for the skull and the assumed initial rate. You are asked to find the age of the skull, which is the time that passed in order for the rate to have reached its current value.

GIVEN: $\text{rate}_t = 7.50 \times 10^{-2}\ s^{-1}g^{-1}$

$\text{rate}_0 = 2.55 \times 10^{-1}\ s^{-1}g^{-1}$

FIND: t

STRATEGIZE Use the expression for half-life (Equation 19.1) to find the rate constant (k) from the half-life for C-14, which is 5730 y (Table 19.3).

CONCEPTUAL PLAN

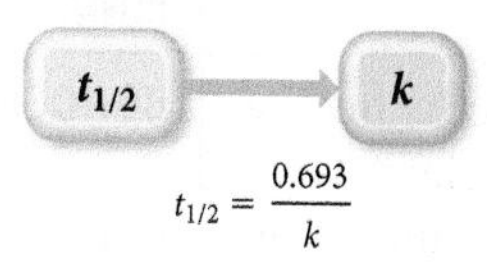

$$t_{1/2} = \frac{0.693}{k}$$

Use the value of the rate constant and the initial and current rates to find t from the integrated rate law (Equation 19.4).

$k, \text{rate}_t, \text{rate}_0$ → t

$$\ln\frac{\text{rate}_t}{\text{rate}_0} = -kt$$

SOLVE Follow your plan. Begin by finding the rate constant from the half-life.

SOLUTION

$$t_{1/2} = \frac{0.693}{k}$$

$$k = \frac{0.693}{t_{1/2}} = \frac{0.693}{5730\ \text{y}}$$

$$= 1.209 \times 10^{-4}\ \text{y}^{-1}$$

Substitute the rate constant and the initial and current rates into the integrated rate law and solve for t.

$$\ln\frac{\text{rate}_t}{\text{rate}_0} = -kt$$

$$t = -\frac{\ln\dfrac{\text{rate}_t}{\text{rate}_0}}{k} = -\frac{\ln\dfrac{7.50 \times 10^{-2}s^{-1}g^{-1}}{2.55 \times 10^{-1}s^{-1}g^{-1}}}{1.209 \times 10^{-4}y^{-1}}$$

$$= 1.0 \times 10^{4}\text{y}$$

CHECK The units of the answer (y) are correct. The magnitude of the answer is about 10000 years, which is a little less than two half-lives. This value is reasonable given that two half-lives would result in a decay rate of about $6.3 \times 10^{-2}\ s^{-1}g^{-1}$.

FOR PRACTICE 19.5

An ancient scroll is claimed to have originated from Greek scholars in about 500 B.C.E. A measure of its carbon-14 decay rate gives a value that is 89% of that found in living organisms. How old is the scroll and could it be authentic?

Uranium/Lead Dating

Radiocarbon dating is limited to measuring the ages of objects that were once living and that are relatively young (<50000 years). Other radiometric dating techniques can measure the ages of prehistoric objects that were never alive. The most dependable technique for these purposes relies on the ratio of uranium-238 to lead-206 within igneous rocks (rocks of volcanic origin). This technique measures the time that has passed since the rock solidified (at which point the "radiometric clock" was reset).

Since U-238 decays into Pb-206 with a half-life of 4.5×10^9 years, the relative amounts of U-238 and Pb-206 in a uranium-containing rock reveal its age. For example, if a rock originally contained U-238 and currently contains equal amounts of U-238 and Pb-206, it would be 4.5 billion years old, assuming that the rock did not contain any Pb-206 when it was formed. The latter assumption can be tested because the lead that results from the decay of uranium has a different isotopic composition than the lead that was deposited in rocks at the time of their formation. Example 19.6 shows how the relative amounts of Pb-206 and U-238 in a rock can be used to estimate its age.

EXAMPLE 19.6 URANIUM/LEAD DATING TO ESTIMATE THE AGE OF A ROCK

A meteor contains 0.556 g of Pb-206 to every 1.00 g of U-238. Assuming that the meteor did not contain any Pb-206 at the time of its formation, determine the age of the meteor. Uranium-238 decays to lead-206 with a half-life of 4.5 billion years.

SORT You are given the current masses of Pb-206 and U-238 in a rock and asked to find its age. You are also given the half-life of U-238.

GIVEN: $m_{U\text{-}238} = 1.00\text{ g}$; $m_{Pb\text{-}206} = 0.556\text{ g}$;

$t_{1/2} = 4.5 \times 10^9\text{ y}$

FIND: t

STRATEGIZE Use the integrated rate law (Equation 19.3) to solve this problem. To do so, you must first determine the value of the rate constant (k) from the half-life expression (Equation 19.1).

CONCEPTUAL PLAN

$t_{1/2} \rightarrow k$

$$t_{1/2} = \frac{0.693}{k}$$

Before substituting into the integrated rate law, you will also need the ratio of the current amount of U-238 to the original amount (N_t/N_0). The current mass of uranium is simply 1.00 g. The initial mass includes the current mass (1.00 g) plus the mass that has decayed into lead-206, which can be found from the current mass of Pb-206.

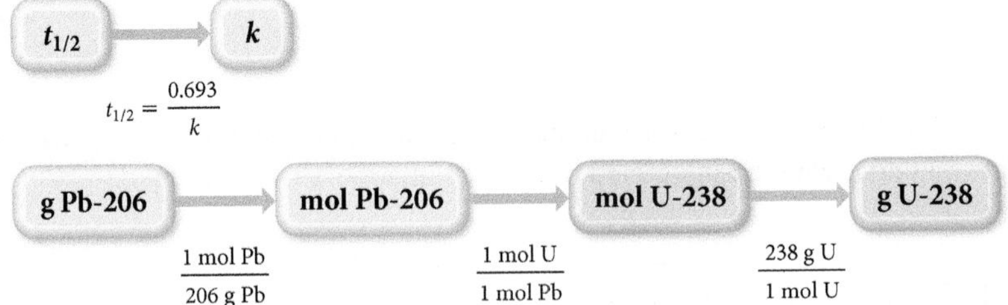

Use the value of the rate constant and the initial and current amounts of U-238 along with the integrated rate law to find t.

$k, N_t, N_0 \rightarrow t$

$$\ln\frac{N_t}{N_0} = -kt$$

SOLVE Follow your plan. Begin by finding the rate constant from the half-life.

SOLUTION

$$t_{1/2} = \frac{0.693}{k}$$

$$k = \frac{0.693}{t_{1/2}} = \frac{0.693}{4.5 \times 10^9\text{ y}} = 1.5\underline{4} \times 10^{-10}\text{ y}^{-1}$$

Determine the mass in grams of U-238 that would have been required to form the given mass of Pb-206.

$$0.556\text{ g Pb-206} \times \frac{1\text{ mol Pb-206}}{206\text{ g Pb-206}} \times \frac{1\text{ mol U-238}}{1\text{ mol Pb-206}} \times \frac{238\text{ g U-238}}{1\text{ mol U-238}} = 0.64\underline{2}4\text{ g U-238}$$

Substitute the rate constant and the initial and current masses of U-238 into the integrated rate law and solve for t. (The initial mass of U-238 is the sum of the current mass and the mass that would have been required to form the given mass of Pb-206.)

$$\ln\frac{N_t}{N_0} = -kt$$

$$t = -\frac{\ln\frac{N_t}{N_0}}{k} = -\frac{\ln\frac{1.00\text{ g}}{1.00\text{ g} + 0.64\underline{2}4\text{ g}}}{1.5\underline{4} \times 10^{-10}\text{ y}^{-1}}$$

$$= 3.2 \times 10^9\text{ y}$$

CHECK The units of the answer (y) are correct. The magnitude of the answer is about 3.2 billion years, which is less than one half-life. This value is reasonable given that less than half of the uranium in the meteor has decayed into lead.

FOR PRACTICE 19.6

A rock contains a Pb-206 to U-238 mass ratio of 0.145:1.00. Assuming that the rock did not contain any Pb-206 at the time of its formation, determine its age.

The Age of Earth The uranium/lead radiometric dating technique as well as other radiometric dating techniques (such as the decay of potassium-40 to argon-40) have been widely used to measure the ages of rocks on Earth and have produced highly consistent results. Rocks with ages greater than 3.5 billion years have been found on every continent. The oldest rocks have an age of approximately 4.0 billion years, establishing a lower limit for Earth's age (Earth must be at least as old as its oldest rocks). The ages of about 70 meteorites that have struck Earth have also been extensively studied and have been found to be about 4.5 billion years old. Since the meteorites were formed at the same time as our solar system (which includes Earth), the best estimate for Earth's age is therefore about 4.5 billion years. That age is consistent with the estimated age of our universe—about 13.7 billion years.

The age of the universe is estimated from its expansion rate, which can be measured by examining changes in the wavelength of light from distant galaxies.

19.7 The Discovery of Fission: The Atomic Bomb and Nuclear Power

In the mid-1930s Enrico Fermi (1901–1954), an Italian physicist, attempted to synthesize a new element by bombarding uranium—the heaviest known element at that time—with neutrons. Fermi speculated that if a neutron were to be incorporated into the nucleus of a uranium atom, the nucleus might undergo beta decay, converting a neutron into a proton. If that happened, a new element, with atomic number 93, would be synthesized for the first time. The nuclear equation for the process is

The element with atomic number 100 is named fermium in honour of Enrico Fermi.

$$^{238}_{92}\text{U} + {}^{1}_{0}\text{n} \longrightarrow {}^{239}_{92}\text{U} \longrightarrow {}^{239}_{93}\text{X} + {}^{0}_{-1}e$$

Neutron (points to ${}^{1}_{0}\text{n}$) — Newly synthesized element (points to ${}^{239}_{93}\text{X}$)

Fermi performed the experiment and detected the emission of beta particles. However, his results were inconclusive. Had he synthesized a new element? Fermi never chemically examined the products to determine their composition and therefore could not say with certainty that he had.

The element with atomic number 109 is named meitnerium in honor of Lise Meitner.

Three researchers in Germany—Lise Meitner (1878–1968), Fritz Strassmann (1902–1980), and Otto Hahn (1879–1968)—repeated Fermi's experiments, and then performed careful chemical analysis of the products. What they found in the products—several elements *lighter* than uranium—would change the world forever. On January 6, 1939, Meitner, Strassmann, and Hahn reported that the neutron bombardment of uranium resulted in **nuclear fission**—the splitting of the uranium atom. The nucleus of the neutron-bombarded uranium atom had been split into barium, krypton, and other smaller products. They also realized that the process emits enormous amounts of energy. A nuclear equation for a fission reaction, showing how uranium breaks apart into the daughter nuclides, is shown here.

$$^{235}_{92}\text{U} + {}^{1}_{0}\text{n} \longrightarrow {}^{140}_{56}\text{Ba} + {}^{93}_{36}\text{Kr} + 3\,{}^{1}_{0}\text{n} + \text{energy}$$

▲ Lise Meitner in Otto Hahn's Berlin laboratory. Together with Hahn and Fritz Strassmann, Meitner determined that U-235 could undergo nuclear fission.

Notice that the initial uranium atom is the U-235 isotope, which constitutes less than 1% of all naturally occurring uranium. U-238, the most abundant uranium isotope, does not undergo fission. Notice also that the process produces three neutrons, which have the potential to initiate fission in three other U-235 atoms.

Scientists quickly realized that a sample rich in U-235 could undergo a **chain reaction** in which neutrons produced by the fission of one uranium nucleus would induce fission in other uranium nuclei (Figure 19.10 ▾). This self-amplifying reaction is capable of

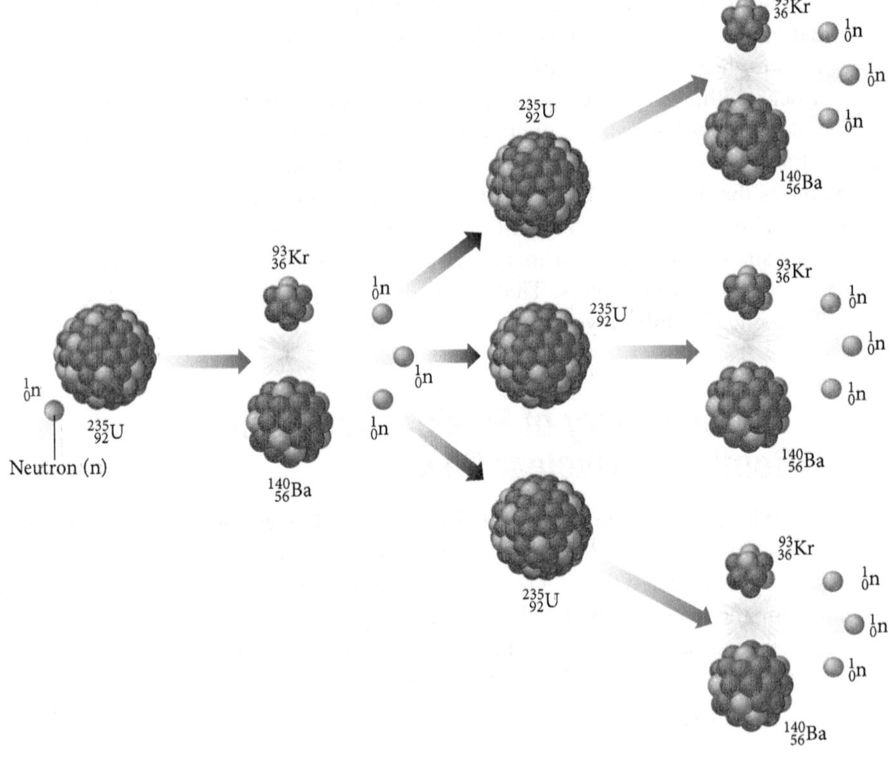

▶ **FIGURE 19.10 A Self-Amplifying Chain Reaction** The fission of one U-235 nucleus emits neutrons which can then initiate fission in other U-235 nuclei, resulting in a chain reaction that releases enormous amounts of energy.

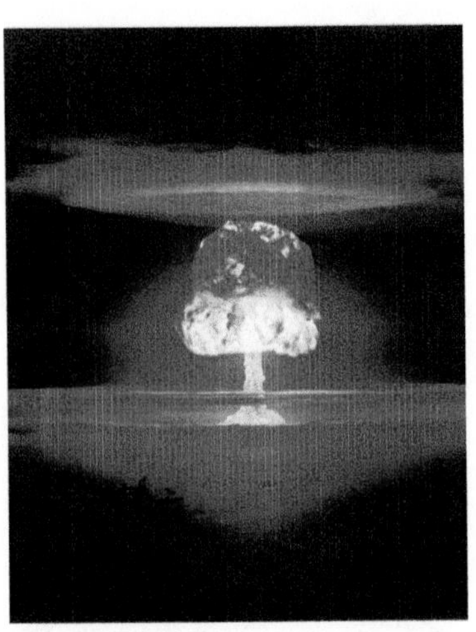

▲ On July 16, 1945, in the New Mexico desert, the world's first atomic bomb was detonated. It had the power of 18 000 tons of dynamite.

producing an enormous amount of energy—an atomic bomb. However, to make a bomb, a **critical mass** of U-235—enough U-235 to produce a self-sustaining reaction—is necessary. The first atomic bomb was constructed by scientists and engineers in the *Manhattan Project* during World War II. The *Manhattan Project* cost about US$2 billion (1945 dollars), which is equivalent to more than US$30 billion in 2015 dollars, and involved around 125 000 people. Most of the effort went into producing fissile materials. Canadians were part of this work. For example, uranium ore came from a mine in the Northwest Territories, and the Chalk River Laboratories in Ontario was the site of the first nuclear reactor outside of the United States.

Nuclear Power: Using Fission to Generate Electricity

Nuclear reactions, such as fission, generate enormous amounts of energy. In a nuclear bomb, the energy is released all at once. The energy can also be released more slowly and used for peaceful purposes such as electricity generation. In Canada, nuclear fission generates about 16% of our electricity. A number of other countries use nuclear fission to produce much larger fractions of their electricity (Table 19.4). To get an idea of the amount of energy released during fission, imagine a hypothetical nuclear-powered car. Suppose the fuel for such a car was a uranium cylinder about the size of a pencil. How often would you have to refuel the car? The energy content of the uranium cylinder would be equivalent to about 1000 twenty-gallon tanks of gasoline. If you refuel your gasoline-powered car once a week, your nuclear-powered car could go 1000 weeks—almost 20 years—before refuelling.

Similarly, a nuclear-powered electricity generation plant can produce a lot of electricity from a small amount of fuel. Such plants exploit the heat created by fission, using it to boil water and make steam, which then turns the turbine on a generator to produce electricity (Figure 19.11 ▶). The fission reaction occurs in the nuclear core of the power plant. The core consists of uranium fuel rods—enriched to about 3.5% U-235—interspersed between retractable neutron-absorbing control rods. When the control rods are fully retracted from the fuel rod assembly, the chain reaction can occur. When the control rods are fully inserted into the fuel assembly, however, they absorb the neutrons that would otherwise induce fission, shutting down the chain reaction. By retracting or inserting the control rods, the operator can increase or decrease the rate of fission. In this way, the fission reaction is controlled to produce the right amount of heat needed for electricity generation. In case of a power failure, the control rods automatically drop into the fuel rod assembly, shutting down the fission reaction.

TABLE 19.4 Selected Countries That Use Nuclear Power

Country	Percentage of Domestic Electricity Generated by Nuclear Power (2013)
France	73.3
Ukraine	43.6
Korea	27.6
United States	19.4
United Kingdom	18.3
Russian Federation	17.5
Canada	16.0
Germany	15.4
China	2.1
Japan	1.7

Source: International Atomic Energy Agency (IAEA): http://www.iaea.org/PRIS/WorldStatistics/NuclearShareofElectricityGeneration.aspx

A typical nuclear power plant generates enough electricity for a city of about 1 million people and uses about 50 kg of fuel per day. In contrast, a coal-burning power plant uses about 2 000 000 kg of fuel to generate the same amount of electricity. Furthermore, a nuclear power plant generates no air pollution and no greenhouse gases. A coal-burning power plant emits pollutants such as carbon monoxide, nitrogen oxides, and sulfur oxides. Coal-burning power plants also emit carbon dioxide, a greenhouse gas. Of course, mining and enriching uranium, as well as other processes, does produce greenhouse gases, but the amount of greenhouse gases per kWh is much less from a nuclear power plant than a coal-burning power plant.

Nuclear power generation, however, is not without problems. Foremost among them is the danger of nuclear accidents. In spite of safety precautions, the fission reaction occurring in a nuclear power plant can overheat. Infamous examples of this include the 1986 vapour burst explosion of the nuclear power station in Chernobyl, in the former Soviet Union, and the nuclear meltdown at the Fukushima I Nuclear Power Plant, in Japan, that followed the March 11, 2011 tsunami. These catastrophes resulted in the release of radioactive material into the environment, making surrounding land uninhabitable. As bad as these events were, however, they did not involve nuclear detonations. A nuclear power plant *cannot* become a nuclear bomb. The uranium fuel used in electricity generation is not sufficiently enriched in U-235 to produce a nuclear detonation.

A second problem associated with nuclear power is waste disposal. Although the amount of nuclear fuel used in electricity generation is small compared with other fuels, the products of the reaction are radioactive and have long half-lives. What do we do with this waste? In Canada, the spent nuclear fuel rods are first cooled for up to ten years in water. When cool enough, they are placed in lead casks that are stored in concrete silos or vaults.

Reactor cores in North America are not made of graphite and cannot burn in the way that the Chernobyl core did.

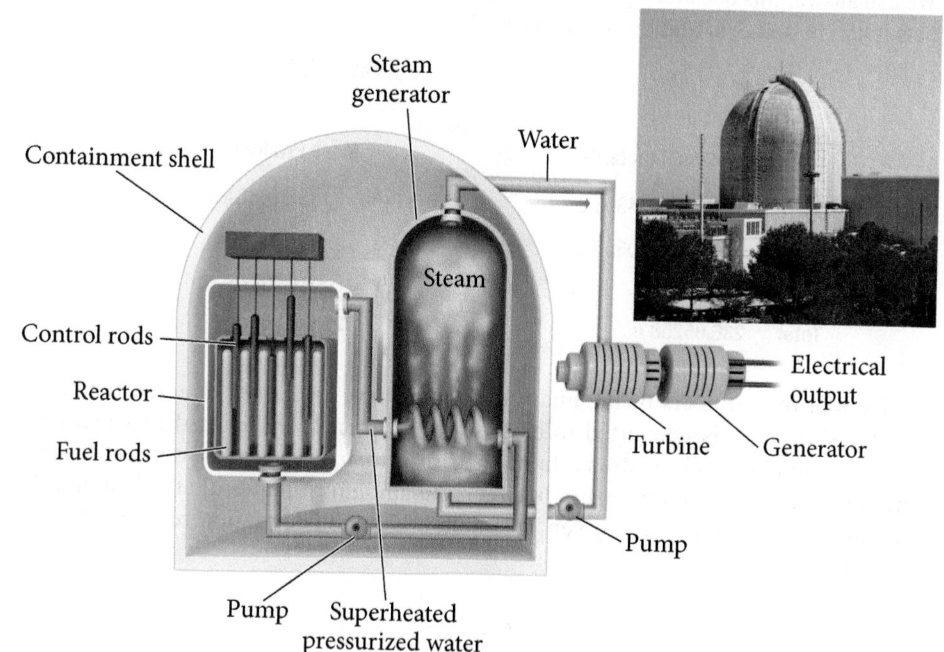

FIGURE 19.11 A Nuclear Reactor The fission of U-235 in the core of a nuclear power plant generates heat that creates steam and turns a turbine on an electrical generator. Control rods are raised or lowered to control the fission reaction. (Note that the water carrying heat away from the reactor core is contained within its own pipes and does not come into direct contact with the steam that drives the turbines.)

CHEMISTRY IN YOUR DAY Uranium Isotopes and the CANDU Reactor

The two major naturally occurring uranium isotopes are U-235 (0.71% abundance) and U-238 (99.28% abundance). Both isotopes decay via alpha decay. U-235 is important in nuclear energy because it is fissile. That is, the U-235 nucleus can be broken into smaller nuclei when struck by neutrons, releasing a large amount of energy. U-238 is not fissile.

In nuclear fuel, the concentration of U-235 must be high enough to sustain a chain reaction. The fission of each U-235 nucleus produces neutrons. For the reaction to be self-sustaining, a fraction of these produced neutrons must collide with other U-235 nuclei, leading to more nuclear fission. If the U-235 concentration is higher, you would expect that more collisions would take place and the rate of fission would be higher. If the concentration of U-235 was too low, fewer collisions would take place, and the nuclear reaction would eventually stop. For most nuclear reactor designs, uranium fuel is enriched to 3.5% U-235. Uranium enrichment is technically challenging and expensive.

▲ CANDU nuclear power plant in Qinshan, People's Republic of China.

The Canadian Deuterium Uranium (CANDU) reactor is a type of reactor that was developed by Atomic Energy Canada, Ltd. (AECL). The CANDU design is unique because, unlike other reactor designs, it can operate with natural uranium. That is, U-235 enriched uranium fuel is not necessary. This feature significantly reduces the cost of nuclear fuel.

All of Canada's nuclear power stations use CANDU reactors. AECL has sold CANDU reactors in many countries, including Argentina, India, the People's Republic of China, Romania, and South Korea.

▲ In 1986, the reactor core at Chernobyl (in what is now Ukraine) overheated, exploded, and destroyed part of the containment structure. The release of radioactive nuclides into the environment forced the government to relocate over 335000 people. It is estimated that there may eventually be several thousand additional cancer deaths among the exposed populations.

In a chemical reaction, there are also mass changes associated with the emission or absorption of energy. Because the energy involved in chemical reactions is so much smaller than that of nuclear reactions, however, these mass changes are completely negligible.

19.8 Converting Mass to Energy in Nuclear Reactions and Nuclear Binding Energy

Nuclear fission produces large amounts of energy. But where does the energy come from? We can answer this question by carefully examining the masses of the reactants and products in the fission equation from Section 19.7.

$$^{235}_{92}U + ^{1}_{0}n \longrightarrow ^{140}_{56}Ba + ^{93}_{36}Kr + 3\,^{1}_{0}n$$

	Mass Reactants		Mass Products
$^{235}_{92}U$	235.04392 u	$^{140}_{56}Ba$	139.910581 u
$^{1}_{0}n$	1.00866 u	$^{93}_{36}Kr$	92.931130 u
		$3\,^{1}_{0}n$	3(1.00866) u
Total	**236.05258 u**		**235.86769 u**

Notice that the products of the nuclear reaction have *less mass* than the reactants. The missing mass is converted to energy. In Chapter 2, we learned that matter is conserved in chemical reactions. In nuclear reactions, however, matter can be converted to energy. The relationship between the amount of matter that is lost and the amount of energy formed is given by Einstein's famous equation relating the two quantities,

$$E = mc^2$$

where E is the energy produced, m is the mass lost, and c is the speed of light. For example, in the above fission reaction, we calculate the quantity of energy produced as follows:

$$\begin{aligned}\text{Mass lost } (m) &= 236.05258 \text{ u} - 235.86769 \text{ u}\\ &= 0.18489 \cancel{\text{u}} \times \frac{1.66054 \times 10^{-27} \text{ kg}}{1 \cancel{\text{u}}}\\ &= 3.0702 \times 10^{-28} \text{ kg}\end{aligned}$$

$$\begin{aligned}\text{Energy produced } (E) &= mc^2\\ &= 3.0702 \times 10^{-28} \text{ kg } (2.9979 \times 10^8 \text{ m s}^{-1})^2\\ &= 2.7593 \times 10^{-11} \text{ J}\end{aligned}$$

The result (2.7593×10^{-11} J) is the energy produced when one nucleus of U-235 undergoes fission.

Although chemists typically report energies in joules, nuclear scientists often use the electron volt (eV) or megaelectron volt (MeV): 1 eV $= 1.602 \times 10^{-19}$ J; 1 MeV $= 1.602 \times 10^{-13}$ J. Unlike energy in joules, which is usually reported per mole, energy in electron volts is usually reported per nucleus. A particularly useful conversion for calculating and reporting nuclear energies is the relationship between u (unified atomic mass units) and MeV (energy units):

An electron volt is defined as the kinetic energy of an electron that has been accelerated through a potential difference of 1 V.

$$1 \text{ u} = 931.5 \text{ MeV}$$

In other words, a mass defect of 1 u, when substituted into the equation $E = mc^2$, gives an energy of 931.5 MeV.

In the fission reaction of U-235, the mass lost was 0.1849 u. Using the conversion factor, this lost mass corresponds to an energy per U-235 atom of:

$$\text{Energy} = 0.1849 \cancel{\text{u}} \times \frac{931.5 \text{ MeV}}{1 \cancel{\text{u}}} = 172.2 \text{ MeV}$$

CONCEPTUAL CONNECTION 19.3

Comparing the Energies of Nuclear Reactions to Chemical Reactions

For the nuclear fission reaction just discussed,

$$^{235}_{92}\text{U} + ^{1}_{0}\text{n} \longrightarrow ^{140}_{56}\text{Ba} + ^{93}_{36}\text{Kr} + 3\,^{1}_{0}\text{n}$$

the energy produced per U-235 nucleus is 2.7893×10^{-11} J. What is the energy produced *per mole* of U-235? How does this compare to a highly exothermic chemical reaction that produces 1000 kJ per mole of reactant?

Nuclear Binding Energy

We can consider the formation of a stable nucleus from its component particles as a nuclear reaction in which mass is converted to energy. For example, consider the formation of helium-4 from its components:

$$2\,^{1}_{1}\text{H} + 2\,^{1}_{0}\text{n} \longrightarrow ^{4}_{2}\text{He}$$

	Mass Reactants		Mass Products
$2\,^{1}_{1}\text{H}$	2(1.00783) u	$^{4}_{2}\text{He}$	4.00260 u
$2\,^{1}_{0}\text{n}$	2(1.00866) u		
Total	**4.03298 u**		**4.00260 u**

The hydrogen atom, $^{1}_{1}\text{H}$, is used rather than the proton, $^{1}_{1}\text{P}$, to account for the mass of electrons present in the helium atom. If you write the equation using only two protons on the left ($^{1}_{1}\text{p}$), you must also add two electrons to the left.

A helium-4 atom has less mass than the sum of the masses of its separate components. This difference in mass, known as the **mass defect**, exists in all stable nuclei. The energy corresponding to the mass defect—obtained by substituting the mass defect into the equation $E = mc^2$—is known as the **nuclear binding energy**.

Using the conversion factor between u and MeV, we can use the mass defect to readily calculate the binding energy of the helium nucleus:

$$\text{Mass defect} = 4.03298\text{ u} - 4.00260\text{ u}$$
$$= 0.03038\text{ u}$$
$$\text{Nuclear binding energy} = 0.03038\text{ u} \times \frac{931.5\text{ MeV}}{1\text{ u}}$$
$$= 28.30\text{ MeV}$$

So the binding energy of the helium nucleus is 28.30 MeV. In order to compare the binding energy of one nucleus to that of another, we calculate the *binding energy per nucleon*, which is the nuclear binding energy of a nuclide divided by the number of nucleons in the nuclide. For helium-4, we calculate the binding energy per nucleon as follows:

$$\text{Binding energy per nucleon} = \frac{28.30\text{ MeV}}{4\text{ nucleons}}$$
$$= 7.075\text{ MeV per nucleon}$$

We can calculate the binding energy per nucleon for other nuclides in the same way. For example, the nuclear binding energy of carbon-12 is 7.680 MeV per nucleon. Since the binding energy per nucleon of carbon-12 is greater than that of helium-4, we conclude the carbon-12 nuclide is more *stable* (it has lower potential energy).

EXAMPLE 19.7 MASS DEFECT AND NUCLEAR BINDING ENERGY

Calculate the mass defect and nuclear binding energy per nucleon (in MeV) for C-16, a radioactive isotope of carbon with a mass of 16.014701 u.

SOLUTION

Calculate the mass defect as the difference between the mass of one C-16 atom and the sum of the masses of 6 hydrogen atoms and 10 neutrons.	$\text{Mass defect} = 6(\text{mass } {}^{1}_{1}\text{H}) + 10(\text{mass } {}^{1}_{0}\text{n}) - \text{mass } {}^{16}_{6}\text{C}$ $= 6(1.00783)\text{ u} + 10(1.00866)\text{ u} - 16.014701\text{ u}$ $= 0.118879\text{ u}$
Calculate the nuclear binding energy by converting the mass defect (in u) into MeV. (Use 1 u = 931.5 MeV.)	$0.118879\text{ u} \times \frac{931.5\text{ MeV}}{\text{u}} = 110.74\text{ MeV}$
Determine the nuclear binding energy per nucleon by dividing by the number of nucleons in the nucleus.	$\text{Nuclear binding energy per nucleon} = \frac{110.74\text{ MeV}}{16\text{ nucleons}}$ $= 6.921\text{ MeV per nucleon}$

FOR PRACTICE 19.7

Calculate the mass defect and nuclear binding energy per nucleon (in MeV) for U-238, which has a mass of 238.050784 u.

Figure 19.12 ▶ shows the binding energy per nucleon plotted as a function of mass number (*A*). The binding energy per nucleon is relatively low for small mass numbers and increases until about $A = 60$, where it reaches a maximum. Nuclides with mass numbers of about 60, therefore, are among the most stable. Beyond $A = 60$, the binding energy per nucleon decreases again. Figure 19.12 illustrates why nuclear fission is a highly **exoergic** process, which means that the standard Gibbs energy change is negative. When a heavy nucleus, such as U-235, breaks up into smaller nuclei, such as Ba-140 and Kr-93, the binding energy per nucleon increases. This is analogous to a chemical reaction in which weak bonds break and strong bonds form. In both cases, the process is exoergic.

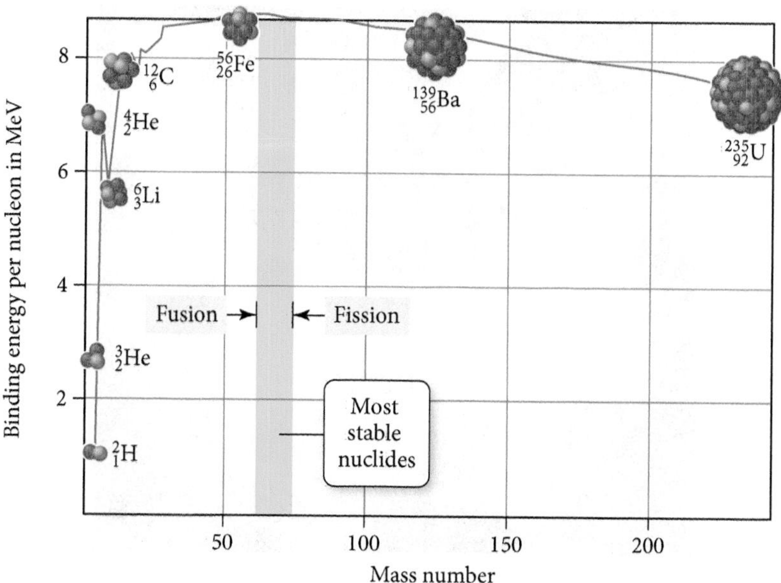

FIGURE 19.12 Nuclear Binding Energy per Nucleon The nuclear binding energy per nucleon (a measure of the stability of a nucleus) reaches a maximum at Fe-56. Consequently, energy can be obtained either by breaking a heavy nucleus up into lighter ones (fission) or by combining lighter nuclei into heavier ones (fusion).

Figure 19.12 also reveals that the *combining* of two lighter nuclei (below $A = 60$) to form a heavier nucleus should be exoergic as well. This process is called *nuclear fusion*.

19.9 Nuclear Fusion: The Power of the Sun

Nuclear fission is the *splitting* of a heavy nucleus to form two or more lighter ones. **Nuclear fusion**, by contrast, is the *combination* of two light nuclei to form a heavier one. Both fusion and fission emit large amounts of energy because, as we have just seen, they both form daughter nuclides with greater binding energies per nucleon than the parent nuclides. Nuclear fusion is the energy source of stars, including our sun. In stars, hydrogen atoms fuse together to form helium atoms, emitting energy in the process:

$$^{2}_{1}\text{H} + ^{3}_{1}\text{H} \longrightarrow ^{4}_{2}\text{He} + ^{1}_{0}\text{n}$$

In this reaction, deuterium (the isotope of hydrogen with one neutron) and tritium (the isotope of hydrogen with two neutrons) combine to form helium-4 and a neutron (Figure 19.13 ▶). Because fusion reactions require two positively charged nuclei (which repel each other) to fuse together, extremely high temperatures are required. In a hydrogen bomb, a small fission bomb is detonated first, providing temperatures high enough for fusion to proceed.

Nuclear fusion has been intensely investigated as a way to produce electricity. Because of the higher energy density—fusion provides about 10 times more energy per gram of fuel than does fission—and because the products of the reaction are less problematic than those of fission, fusion holds promise as a future energy source. However, in spite of concerted efforts, the generation of electricity by fusion remains elusive. One of the main problems is the high temperature required for fusion to occur—no material can withstand those temperatures. Using powerful magnetic fields or laser beams, scientists have succeeded in compressing and heating nuclei to the point where fusion has been initiated, and even sustained for brief periods of time (Figure 19.14 ▼). To date, however, the amount of energy generated by fusion reactions has been less than the amount required to get it to occur.

The International Thermonuclear Experimental Reactor (ITER) is a multinational project for the design and construction of a nuclear fusion reactor. The ITER member countries are China, the European Union, India, Japan, Russia, and the United States. The ITER reactor is currently under construction in France. The ITER reactor design involves a "tokamak" reactor (Figure 19.14), in which strong magnetic

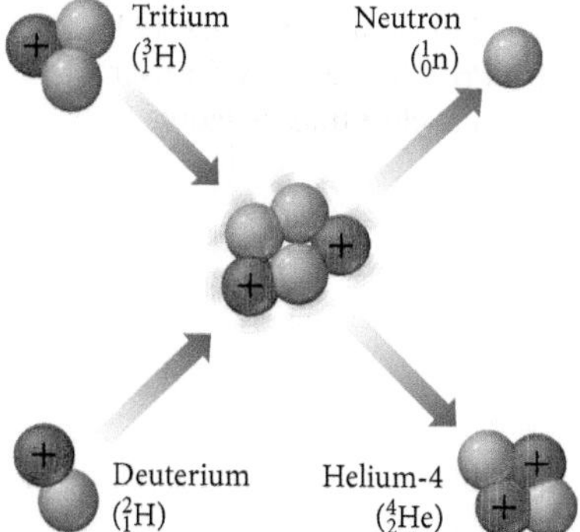

▲ **FIGURE 19.13 A Nuclear Fusion Reaction** In this reaction, two heavy isotopes of hydrogen, deuterium (hydrogen-2) and tritium (hydrogen-3), fuse to form helium-4 and a neutron.

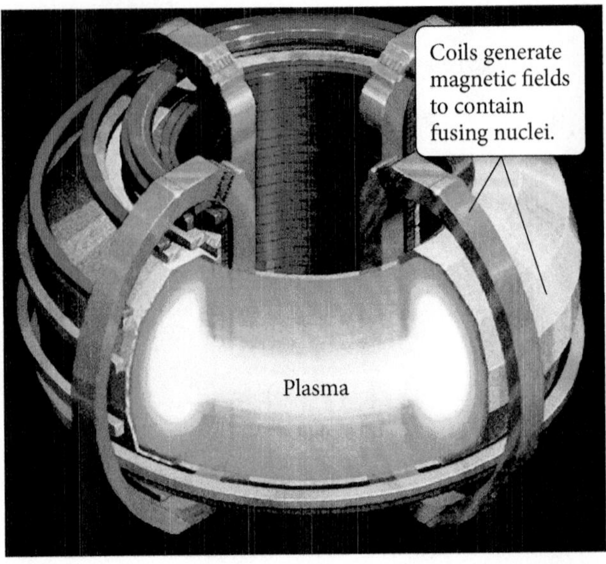
Coils generate magnetic fields to contain fusing nuclei.
Plasma

▶ **FIGURE 19.14 Tokamak Fusion Reactor** A tokamak uses powerful magnetic fields to confine nuclear fuel at the enormous temperatures needed for fusion.

fields are used to confine the nuclear fuel at the enormous temperature and pressures needed for fusion. The ITER experimental reactor is projected to start operations in the early 2030s. If successful, the project may lead to the ultimate widespread use of fusion power to generate electricity.

19.10 Nuclear Transmutation and Transuranium Elements

One of the goals of the early chemists of the Middle Ages, who were known as *alchemists*, was the transformation of ordinary metals into gold. Many alchemists hoped to turn low-cost metals, such as lead or tin, into precious metals, and in this way become wealthy. These alchemists were never successful because their attempts were merely chemical—they mixed different metals together or tried to get them to react with other substances in order to turn them into gold. In a chemical reaction, an element retains its identity, so a less valuable metal—such as lead—will always remain lead, even when it forms a compound with another element.

▲ The Joliot-Curies won the 1935 Nobel Prize in chemistry for their work on nuclear transmutation.

Nuclear reactions, by contrast, result in the transformation of one element into another, a process known as **transmutation**. We have already seen how this occurs in radioactive decay, in fission, and in fusion. In addition, other nuclear reactions that transmute elements are possible. For example, in 1919, Ernest Rutherford bombarded nitrogen-14 with alpha particles to form oxygen:

$$^{14}_{7}\text{N} + ^{4}_{2}\text{He} \longrightarrow ^{17}_{8}\text{O} + ^{1}_{1}\text{H}$$

Irène Joliot-Curie (daughter of Marie Curie) and her husband Frédéric bombarded aluminum-27 with alpha particles to form phosphorus:

$$^{27}_{13}\text{Al} + ^{4}_{2}\text{He} \longrightarrow ^{30}_{15}\text{P} + ^{1}_{0}\text{n}$$

In the 1930s, scientists began building devices that accelerate particles to high velocities, opening the door to even more possibilities. These devices are generally of two types, the **linear accelerator** and the **cyclotron**.

In a single-stage linear accelerator, a charged particle such as a proton is accelerated in an evacuated tube. The accelerating force is provided by a potential difference (or voltage) between the ends of the tube. In multistage linear accelerators, such as the Stanford Linear Accelerator (SLAC) at Stanford University, a series of tubes of increasing length are connected to a source of alternating voltage, as shown in Figure 19.15 ▶. The voltage

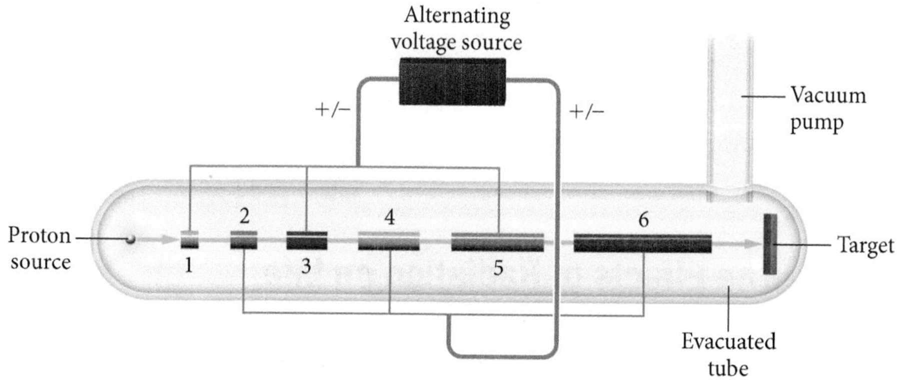

◀ **FIGURE 19.15 The Linear Accelerator** In a multistage linear accelerator, the charge on successive tubes is rapidly alternated in such a way that as a positively charged particle leaves a particular tube, that tube becomes positively charged, repelling the particle toward the next tube. At the same time, the tube that the particle is now approaching becomes negatively charged, pulling the particle toward it. This process repeats through a number of tubes until the particle has been accelerated to a high velocity.

alternates in such a way that, as a positively charged particle leaves a particular tube, that tube becomes positively charged, repelling the particle to the next tube. At the same time, the tube that the particle is now approaching becomes negatively charged, pulling the particle toward it. This continues throughout the linear accelerator, allowing the particle to be accelerated to velocities up to 90% of the speed of light. When particles of this speed collide with a target, they produce a shower of subatomic particles that can be studied. For example, researchers using the Stanford Linear Accelerator were awarded the 1990 Nobel Prize in physics for discovering evidence that protons and neutrons were composed of still smaller subatomic particles called quarks.

In a cyclotron, a similarly alternating voltage is used to accelerate a charged particle, only this time the alternating voltage is applied between the two semicircular halves of the cyclotron (Figure 19.16 ▼). A charged particle originally in the middle of the two semicircles is accelerated back and forth between them. Additional magnets cause the particle to move in a spiral path. As the charged particle spirals out from the centre, it gains speed and eventually exits the cyclotron aimed at the target.

With linear accelerators or cyclotrons, all sorts of nuclear transmutations can be achieved. In this way, scientists have made nuclides that don't normally exist in nature. For example, uranium-238 can be made to collide with carbon-12 to form an element with atomic number 98:

$$^{238}_{92}\text{U} + ^{12}_{6}\text{C} \longrightarrow ^{244}_{98}\text{Cf} + 6\,^{1}_{0}\text{n}$$

This element was named californium (Cf) because it was first produced (by a slightly different nuclear reaction) at the University of California at Berkeley. Many other nuclides with atomic numbers larger than that of uranium have been synthesized since the 1940s. These synthetic elements—called transuranium elements—have been added to modern versions of the periodic table.

▲ The Stanford Linear Accelerator (top) is located at Stanford University in California. The Fermi National Accelerator Laboratory complex in Batavia, Illinois (bottom), includes two cyclotrons in a figure-8 configuration.

Most synthetic elements are unstable and have very short half-lives. Some exist for only fractions of a second after they are made.

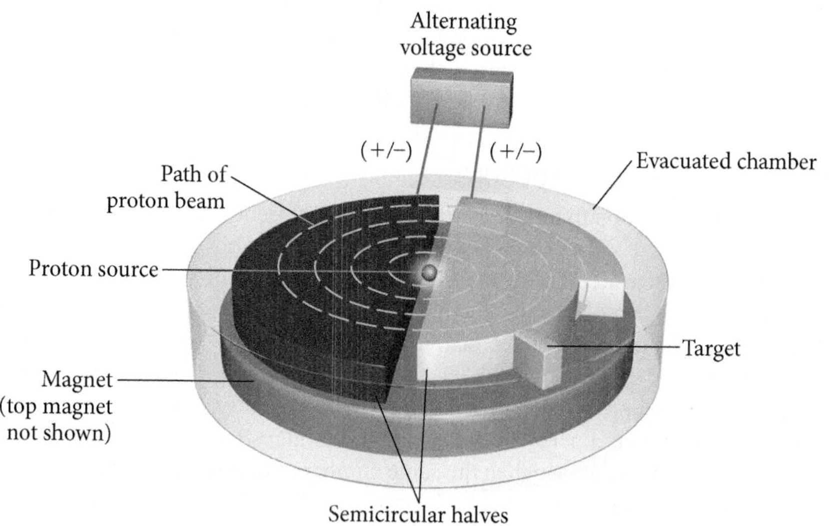

◀ **FIGURE 19.16 The Cyclotron** In a cyclotron, two semicircular D-shaped structures are subject to an alternating voltage. A charged particle, starting from a point between the two, is accelerated back and forth between them, while additional magnets cause the particle to move in a spiral path.

CONCEPTUAL CONNECTION 19.4

Nuclear Transformations

Californium-252 is bombarded with a boron-10 nucleus to produce another nuclide and six neutrons. What nuclide forms?

19.11 The Effects of Radiation on Life

As we discussed in Section 19.2, the energy associated with radioactivity can ionize molecules. When radiation ionizes important molecules in living cells, problems can develop. The ingestion of radioactive materials—especially alpha and beta emitters—is particularly dangerous because the radioactivity once inside the body can do even more damage. The effects of radiation can be divided into three different types: acute radiation damage, increased cancer risk, and genetic effects.

Acute Radiation Damage

Acute radiation damage results from exposure to large amounts of radiation in a short period of time. The main sources of this kind of exposure are nuclear bombs and exposed nuclear reactor cores. These high levels of radiation kill large numbers of cells. Rapidly dividing cells, such as those in the immune system and the intestinal lining, are most susceptible. Consequently, people exposed to high levels of radiation have weakened immune systems and a lowered ability to absorb nutrients from food. In milder cases, recovery is possible with time. In more extreme cases, death results, often from infection.

Increased Cancer Risk

DNA and its function in the body are explained in more detail in Chapter 22.

Lower doses of radiation over extended periods of time can increase cancer risk. Radiation increases cancer risk because it can damage DNA, the molecules in cells that carry instructions for cell growth and replication. When the DNA within a cell is damaged, the cell normally dies. Occasionally, however, changes in DNA cause cells to grow abnormally and to become cancerous. These cancerous cells grow into tumours that can spread and, in some cases, cause death. Cancer risk increases with increasing radiation exposure. However, cancer is so prevalent and has so many convoluted causes that determining an exact threshold for increased cancer risk from radiation exposure is difficult.

Genetic Defects

Another possible effect of radiation exposure is genetic defects in future generations. If radiation damages the DNA of reproductive cells—such as eggs or sperm—then the offspring that develop from those cells may have genetic abnormalities. Genetic defects of this type have been observed in laboratory animals exposed to high levels of radiation. However, such genetic defects—with a clear causal connection to radiation exposure—have yet to be verified in humans, even in studies of Hiroshima survivors.

Measuring Radiation Exposure

We can measure radiation exposure in a number of different ways. For example, we can measure the number of decay events to which a person is exposed. The unit used for this type of exposure measurement is the same as for radioactivity, the becquerel (Bq). A person exposed to 1 Bq (1 becquerel) of radiation from an alpha emitter is being bombarded with 1 alpha particle per second. However, we already know that different kinds of radiation produce different effects. For example, we know that alpha radiation has a much greater ionizing power than beta radiation. Consequently, a certain number of alpha decays occurring within a person's body (due to the ingestion or inhalation of an alpha emitter) would do more damage than the same number of beta decays. If the alpha emitter and beta emitter were external to the body, however, the radiation from the alpha emitter would largely be stopped by clothing or the skin (due to the low penetrating power of alpha radiation), while the radiation from the beta emitter could penetrate the skin and cause more damage. For this reason, the becquerel is not an effective measure of how much biological tissue damage the radiation actually does.

A better way to assess radiation exposure is to measure the **absorbed dose**, the amount of energy actually absorbed by body tissue. The SI unit for radiation dose is the **gray (Gy)**, which corresponds to 1 J of energy absorbed per kilogram of material (such as body tissue).

$$1 \text{ gray (Gy)} = 1 \text{ J/kg body tissue}$$

Although these units measure the actual energy absorbed by bodily tissues, they still do not account for the amount of damage to biological molecules caused by that energy absorption, which differs from one type of radiation to another and from one type of biological tissue to another. For example, when a gamma ray passes through biological tissue, the energy absorbed is spread out over the long distance that the radiation travels through the body, resulting in a low ionization density within the tissue. When an alpha particle passes through biological tissue, in contrast, the energy is absorbed over a much shorter distance, resulting in a much higher ionization density. The higher ionization density results in greater damage, even though the amount of energy absorbed by the tissue might be the same.

Consequently, the absorbed dose is usually multiplied by a dimensionless **radiation weighting factor (W_R)** to obtain the **equivalent dose**. Weighting factors are given in Table 19.5. The SI unit for equivalent dose is the **sievert (Sv)**. The sievert has the same base units as the gray (J/kg) because the weighting factor is dimensionless.

$$\text{Equivalent dose in Sv} = \text{absorbed dose in Gy} \times \text{radiation weighting factor } (W_R)$$

The equivalent dose for alpha radiation, for example, is much higher than that for gamma radiation.

On average, each of us is exposed to 3.6 mSv of radiation per year. The majority of this exposure comes from natural sources, especially radon, one of the products in the uranium decay series. However, some medical procedures involve exposure levels similar to those received from natural sources. For example, a thallium heart scan has a typical equivalent dose of 5.0 mSv.

It takes much more than the average equivalent dose to produce significant health effects in humans. The first measurable effect, a decreased white blood cell count, occurs at instantaneous exposures of approximately 0.2 Sv (Table 19.6). Exposures of 1 Sv produce a definite increase in cancer risk, and exposures over 5 Sv often result in death.

TABLE 19.5 Radiation Weighting Factors

Radiation Type	W_R
alpha	20
beta	1
gamma	1
positron	2

Source: European Nuclear Society

The rad and the rem are older units for absorbed dose and equivalent dose, respectively. 1 rad = 0.01 Gy and 1 rem = 0.01 Sv.

TABLE 19.6 Effects of Instantaneous Radiation Exposure

Approximate Equivalent Dose (Sv)	Probable Outcome(s)
0.20–1.0	Decreased white blood cell count; possible increase in cancer risk
1–4	Radiation sickness, including vomiting and diarrhea; skin lesions; increase in cancer risk
5	Death (often within 2 months)
10	Death (often within 2 weeks)
20	Death (within hours)

CONCEPTUAL CONNECTION 19.5

Radiation Exposure

Suppose a person ingests an equal number of atoms of two nuclides, both of which are beta emitters (of roughly equal energy). Nuclide A has a half-life of 8.5 hours and Nuclide B has a half-life of 15.0 hours. Both nuclides are eliminated from the body within 24 hours of ingestion. Which of the two nuclides produces the greater radiation exposure?

19.12 Radioactivity in Medicine and Other Applications

Radioactivity is often perceived as dangerous; however, it is also immensely useful to physicians in the diagnosis and treatment of disease and has numerous other valuable applications. The use of radioactivity in medicine can be broadly divided into *diagnostic techniques* (used to diagnose disease) and *therapeutic techniques* (used to treat disease).

Diagnosis in Medicine

The use of radioactivity in diagnosis usually involves a **radiotracer**, a radioactive nuclide attached to a compound or introduced into a mixture in order to track the movement of the compound or mixture within the body. Tracers are useful in the diagnosis of disease because of two main factors: (1) the sensitivity with which radioactivity can be detected, and (2) the identical chemical behaviour of a radioactive nucleus and its nonradioactive counterpart. For example, the thyroid gland naturally concentrates iodine. When a patient is given small amounts of iodine-131 (a radioactive isotope of iodine), the radioactive iodine accumulates in the thyroid, just as nonradioactive iodine does. However, the radioactive iodine emits radiation, which can then be detected with great sensitivity and used to measure the rate of iodine uptake by the thyroid, and thus to image the gland.

Since different elements are taken up preferentially by different organs or tissues, various radiotracers are used to monitor metabolic activity and image a variety of organs and structures, including the kidneys, heart, brain, gallbladder, bones, and arteries, as shown in Table 19.7. Radiotracers can also be employed to locate infections or cancers within the body. To locate an infection, antibodies are labelled (or tagged) with a radioactive nuclide, such as technetium-99m (where "m" means metastable), and administered to the patient. The tagged antibodies aggregate at the infected site, as described in the opening section of this chapter. Cancerous tumours can be detected because they naturally concentrate phosphorus. When a patient is given phosphorus-32 (a radioactive isotope of phosphorus) or a phosphate compound incorporating another radioactive isotope such as Tc-99m, the tumours concentrate the radioactive substance and become sources of radioactivity that can be detected (Figure 19.17 ◀).

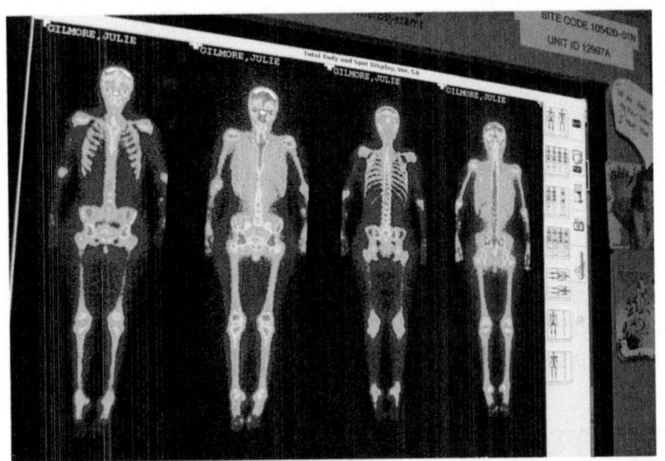

▲ **FIGURE 19.17 A Bone Scan** These images, front and rear views of the human body, were created by the gamma ray emissions of Tc-99m. Such scans are often used to locate cancer that has metastasized to the bones from a primary tumour elsewhere.

A specialized imaging technique known as **positron emission tomography (PET)** employs positron-emitting nuclides, such as fluorine-18, synthesized in cyclotrons. The fluorine-18 is attached to a metabolically active substance such as glucose and administered to the patient. As the glucose travels through the bloodstream and to the heart and brain, it carries the radioactive fluorine, which decays with a half-life of just under 2 hours. When a fluorine-18 nuclide decays, it emits a positron which immediately combines with any nearby electrons. Since a positron and an electron are antiparticles, they annihilate one other, producing two gamma rays that travel in exactly opposing directions. The gamma rays are detected

TABLE 19.7 Common Radiotracers

Nuclide	Type of Emission	Half-Life	Part(s) of Body Studied
Technetium-99m	Gamma (primarily)	6.01 hours	Various organs, bones
Iodine-131	Beta	8.0 days	Thyroid
Iron-59	Beta	44.5 days	Blood, spleen
Thallium-201	Electron capture	3.05 days	Heart
Fluorine-18	Positron emission	1.83 hours	PET studies of heart, brain
Phosphorus-32	Beta	14.3 days	Tumours in various organs

by an array of detectors that can locate the point of origin of the rays with great accuracy. The result is a set of highly detailed images that show both the rate of glucose metabolism and structural features of the imaged organ (Figure 19.18 ►).

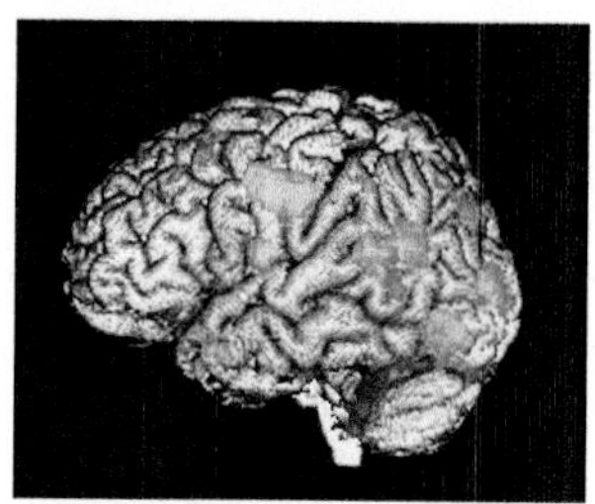

▲ **FIGURE 19.18 A PET Scan** The coloured areas indicate regions of high metabolic activity in the brain of a schizophrenic patient experiencing hallucinations.

Radiotherapy in Medicine

Because radiation kills cells, and because it is particularly effective at killing rapidly dividing cells, it is often used as a therapy for cancer (cancer cells reproduce much faster than normal cells). Gamma rays are focused on internal tumours to kill them. The gamma ray beam is usually moved in a circular path around the tumour (Figure 19.19 ▼), maximizing the exposure of the tumour while minimizing the exposure of the surrounding healthy tissue. Nonetheless, cancer patients receiving such treatment usually develop the symptoms of radiation sickness, which include vomiting, skin burns, and hair loss.

You may wonder why radiation—which is known to cause cancer—is also used to treat cancer. The answer lies in risk analysis. A cancer patient is normally exposed to radiation doses of about 1 Sv. Such a dose increases cancer risk by about 1%. However, if the patient has a 100% chance of dying from the cancer that he already has, such a risk becomes acceptable, especially since there is a significant chance of curing the cancer.

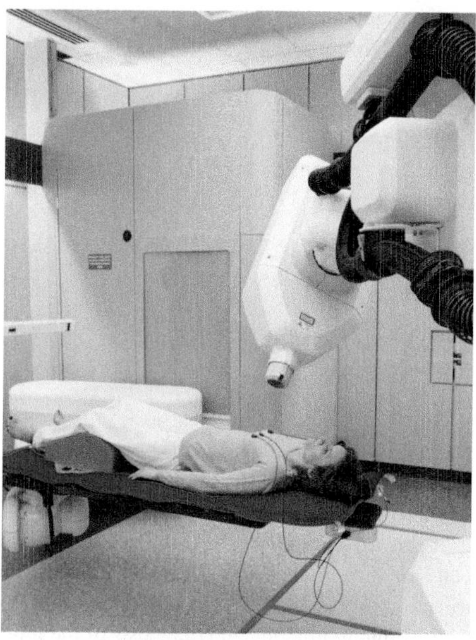

▲ **FIGURE 19.19 Radiotherapy for Cancer** This treatment involves exposing a malignant tumour to gamma rays generated by nuclides such as cobalt-60. The beam is moved in a circular pattern around the tumour to maximize exposure of the tumour to radiation while minimizing the exposure of healthy tissues.

Other Applications

Radioactivity is often used to kill microorganisms. For example, physicians use radiation to sterilize medical devices that are to be surgically implanted. The radiation kills bacteria that might otherwise lead to infection. Similarly, radiation is used to kill bacteria and parasites in foods. Like the pasteurization of milk, the irradiation of foods makes them safer to consume and gives them a longer shelf life (Figure 19.20 ▼). The irradiation of raw meat and poultry kills *E. coli* and *Salmonella*, bacteria that can lead to serious illness and even death when consumed. The irradiation of food does not, however, make the food itself radioactive, nor does it decrease the nutritional value of the food. In Canada, the Canadian Food Inspection Agency has approved the irradiation of a limited number of foods such as potatoes, onions, flour, and spices. In the United States, the irradiation of other types of foods is allowed. These include beef, poultry, and fruit.

Radioactivity is also used to control the populations of harmful insects. For example, fruit flies can be raised in large numbers in captivity and sterilized with radiation. When these fruit flies are released, they mate with wild fruit flies but do not produce offspring. The efforts of the wild fruit flies, which might otherwise lead to reproduction, are wasted and the next generation of flies is smaller than it would otherwise have been. Similar strategies have been employed to control the populations of disease-carrying mosquitoes.

► **FIGURE 19.20 Irradiation of Food** Irradiation kills microbes that cause food to decay, allowing for longer and safer storage. The food is not made radioactive and its properties are unchanged in the process. These strawberries were picked at the same time, but those on the bottom were irradiated before storage.

CHAPTER IN REVIEW

Key Terms

Section 19.1
radioactivity (832)
radioactive (832)

Section 19.2
phosphorescence (833)

Section 19.3
nuclide (835)
alpha (α) decay (835)
alpha (α) particle (835)
nuclear equation (835)
ionizing power (836)
penetrating power (836)
beta (β) decay (836)
beta (β) particle (836)
gamma (γ) ray emission (837)
gamma (γ) ray (837)
positron emission (837)
positron (837)
electron capture (837)

Section 19.4
strong force (839)
magic numbers (841)

Section 19.5
film-badge dosimeter (842)
Geiger-Müller counter (842)
scintillation counter (842)
becquerel (Bq) (842)

Section 19.6
radiometric dating (846)
radiocarbon dating (846)

Section 19.7
nuclear fission (849)
chain reaction (849)
critical mass (850)

Section 19.8
mass defect (853)
nuclear binding energy (854)
exoergic (854)

Section 19.9
nuclear fusion (855)

Section 19.10
transmutation (856)
linear accelerator (856)
cyclotron (856)

Section 19.11
absorbed dose (859)
gray (Gy) (859)
radiation weighting factor (W_R) (859)
equivalent dose (859)
sievert (Sv) (859)

Section 19.12
radiotracer (860)
positron emission tomography (PET) (860)

Key Concepts

Medical Isotopes (19.1)

Radioactivity is the emission of subatomic particles or energetic electromagnetic radiation by the nuclei of certain atoms. Because some of these emissions can pass through matter, radioactivity is useful in medicine and many other areas of study. For example, antibodies can be radioactively labelled and injected into a person's body; if an infection is present, the radioactivity accumulates at the site of infection, allowing imaging and diagnosis of the infected organ.

The Discovery of Radioactivity (19.2)

Radioactivity was discovered by Antoine Henri Becquerel when he found that uranium causes a photographic exposure in the absence of light. Marie Sklodowska-Curie later determined that this phenomenon was not unique to uranium, and she began calling the rays that produced the exposure radioactivity. Curie also discovered two new elements, polonium and radium.

Types of Radioactivity (19.3)

The major types of natural radioactivity are alpha (α) decay, beta (β) decay, gamma (γ) ray emission, and positron emission. Alpha radiation is helium nuclei. Beta particles are electrons. Gamma rays are electromagnetic radiation of very high energy. Positrons are the antiparticles of electrons. In addition, a nucleus may absorb one of its orbital electrons (electron capture). We can represent each radioactive process with a nuclear equation that illustrates how the parent nuclide changes into the daughter nuclide. In a nuclear equation, although the specific types of atoms may not balance, the atomic numbers and mass numbers must. Each type of radioactivity has a different ionizing and penetrating power. These values are inversely related; a particle with a higher ionizing power has a lower penetrating power. Alpha particles are the most massive and they have the highest ionizing power, followed by beta particles and positrons, which are equivalent in their ionizing power. Gamma rays have the lowest ionizing power.

The Valley of Stability: Predicting the Type of Radioactivity (19.4)

The stability of a nucleus, and therefore the probability that it will undergo radioactive decay, depends largely on two factors. The first is the ratio of neutrons to protons (N/Z), because neutrons provide a strong force which overcomes the electromagnetic repulsions between the positive protons. This ratio is one for smaller elements, but becomes greater than one for larger elements. The second factor related to nuclei stability is a concept known as magic numbers; certain numbers of nucleons are more stable than others.

Measurements and Units of Radioactivity (19.5)

Radiation detectors are used to determine the quantity of radioactivity in an area or sample. Film-badge dosimeters utilize photographic film for that purpose; however, such detectors do not provide an instantaneous response. Two detectors that instantly register the amount of radiation are the Geiger-Müller counter, which uses the ionization of argon by radiation to produce an electrical signal, and the scintillation counter, which uses the emission of light induced by radiation.

The Kinetics of Radioactive Decay and Radiometric Dating (19.6)

All radioactive elements decay according to first-order kinetics (Chapter 13); the half-life equation and the integrated rate law for radioactive decay are derived from the first-order rate laws. The kinetics of radioactive decay is used to date objects and artifacts. The age of materials that were once part of living organisms can be measured by carbon-14 dating. The age of ancient rocks and even Earth itself is determined by uranium/lead dating.

The Discovery of Fission: The Atomic Bomb and Nuclear Power (19.7)

Fission is the splitting of an atom, such as uranium-235, into two atoms of lesser atomic weight. Because the fission of one uranium-235 atom releases enormous amounts of energy, and produces neutrons that can split other uranium-235 atoms, the energy from these collective reactions can be harnessed in an atomic bomb or nuclear reactor. Nuclear power produces no pollution and requires little mass to release lots of energy; however, there is always a danger of accidents, and it is difficult to dispose of nuclear waste.

Converting Mass to Energy in Nuclear Reactions and Nuclear Binding Energy (19.8)

In a nuclear fission reaction, a substantial amount of mass is converted into energy. The difference in mass between the products and the reactants is called the mass defect and the corresponding energy, calculated from Einstein's equation $E = mc^2$, is the nuclear binding energy. The stability of the nucleus is determined by the binding energy per nucleon, which increases up to mass number 60 and then decreases.

Nuclear Fusion: The Power of the Sun (19.9)

Stars produce their energy by a process that is the opposite of fission: nuclear fusion, the combination of two light nuclei to form a heavier one. Modern nuclear weapons employ fusion. Although fusion has been examined as a possible method to produce electricity, experiments with hydrogen fusion have thus far been more costly than productive.

Nuclear Transmutation and Transuranium Elements (19.10)

Nuclear transmutation, the changing of one element to another element, has been used to create the transuranium elements, elements with atomic numbers greater than that of uranium. Two devices are most commonly used to accelerate particles to the high speeds necessary for transmutation reactions: the linear accelerator and the cyclotron. Both use alternating voltage to propel particles by electromagnetic forces.

The Effects of Radiation on Life (19.11)

The effects of radiation can be grouped into three categories. Acute radiation damage is caused by a large exposure to radiation for a short period of time. Lower radiation exposures may result in increased cancer risk because of damage to DNA. Genetic defects are caused by damage to the DNA of reproductive cells. The most effective unit of measurement for the amount of radiation absorbed is the gray, which takes into account the different penetrating and ionizing powers of the various types of radiation.

Radioactivity in Medicine (19.12)

Radioactivity is central to the diagnosis of medical problems by means of radiotracers and positron emission tomography (PET). Both of these techniques can provide data about the appearance and metabolic activity of an organ, or help locate a tumour. Radiation is also used to treat cancer because it can kill cells. Although this treatment has unpleasant side effects and increases the risk of a new cancer developing, the risk is usually acceptable compared to the risk of death from an established cancer. Radiation can also be used to kill bacteria in foods and to control harmful insect populations.

Key Equations and Relationships

The First-Order Rate Law (19.6)

$$\text{Rate} = kN$$

The Half-Life Equation (19.6)

$$t_{1/2} = \frac{0.693}{k} \qquad k = \text{rate constant}$$

The Integrated Rate Law (19.6)

$$\ln \frac{N_t}{N_0} = -kt \qquad N_t = \text{number of radioactive nuclei at time } t$$

$$N_0 = \text{initial number of radioactive nuclei}$$

Einstein's Energy–Mass Equation (19.8)

$$E = mc^2$$

Key Skills

Writing Nuclear Equations for Alpha Decay (19.3)
• Example 19.1 • For Practice 19.1 • Exercises 31–36

Writing Nuclear Equations for Beta Decay, Positron Emission, and Electron Capture (19.3)
• Example 19.2 • For Practice 19.2 • For More Practice 19.2 • Exercises 31–36

Predicting the Type of Radioactive Decay (19.4)
• Example 19.3 • For Practice 19.3 • Exercises 41, 42

Using Radioactive Decay Kinetics (19.6)
• Example 19.4 • For Practice 19.4 • Exercises 45–52

Using Radiocarbon Dating (19.6)
• Example 19.5 • For Practice 19.5 • Exercises 53, 54

Using Uranium/Lead Dating to Estimate the Age of a Rock (19.6)
• Example 19.6 • For Practice 19.6 • Exercises 55, 56

Determining the Mass Defect and Nuclear Binding Energy (19.8)
• Example 19.7 • For Practice 19.7 • Exercises 65–72

EXERCISES

Review Questions

1. What is radioactivity? Who discovered it? How was it discovered?
2. Explain the role of Marie Curie in the discovery of radioactivity.
3. Define *A*, *Z*, and *X* in the following notation used to specify a nuclide: ${}^{A}_{Z}X$.
4. Use the notation from Question 3 to write symbols for a proton, a neutron, and an electron.
5. What is an alpha particle? What happens to the mass number and atomic number of a nuclide that emits an alpha particle?
6. What is a beta particle? What happens to the mass number and atomic number of a nuclide that emits a beta particle?
7. What is a gamma ray? What happens to the mass number and atomic number of a nuclide that emits a gamma ray?
8. What is a positron? What happens to the mass number and atomic number of a nuclide that emits a positron?
9. Describe the process of electron capture. What happens to the mass number and atomic number of a nuclide that undergoes electron capture?
10. Rank alpha particles, beta particles, positrons, and gamma rays in terms of: **(a)** increasing ionizing power; **(b)** increasing penetrating power.
11. Explain why the ratio of neutrons to protons (N/Z) is important in determining nuclear stability. How can you use the N/Z ratio of a nuclide to predict the kind of radioactive decay that it might undergo?
12. What are magic numbers? How are they important in determining the stability of a nuclide?
13. Explain the basic way that each device detects radioactivity: **(a)** film-badge dosimeter; **(b)** Geiger-Müller counter; and **(c)** scintillation counter.
14. Explain the concept of half-life with respect to radioactive nuclides. What rate law is characteristic of radioactivity?
15. Explain the main concepts behind the technique of radiocarbon dating. How can radiocarbon dating be corrected for changes in atmospheric concentrations of C-14? What range of ages can be reliably determined by C-14 dating?
16. How is the uranium to lead ratio in a rock used to estimate its age? How does this dating technique provide an estimate for Earth's age? How old is Earth according to this dating method?
17. Describe fission. Include the concepts of chain reaction and critical mass in your description. How and by whom was fission discovered?
18. Explain how fission can be used to generate electricity.
19. Describe the advantages and disadvantages of using fission to generate electricity.
20. The products of a nuclear reaction usually have a different mass than the reactants. Why?
21. Explain the concepts of mass defect and nuclear binding energy. At what mass number does the nuclear binding energy per nucleon peak? What is the significance of this?
22. What is fusion? Why can fusion and fission both produce energy? Explain.
23. What are some of the problems associated with using fusion to generate electricity?
24. Explain transmutation and give one or two examples.
25. How does a linear accelerator work? For what purpose is it used?
26. Explain the basic principles by which a cyclotron functions.
27. How does radiation affect living organisms?
28. Explain why different kinds of radiation affect biological tissues differently, even though the amount of radiation exposure may be the same.
29. Explain the significance of the biological effectiveness factor in measuring radiation exposure. What types of radiation would you expect to have the highest biological effectiveness factor?
30. Describe some of the medical uses, both in diagnosis and in treatment of disease, of radioactivity.

Problems by Topic

Radioactive Decay and Nuclide Stability

31. Write a nuclear equation for the indicated decay of each nuclide:
   a. U-234 (alpha)
   b. Th-230 (alpha)
   c. Pb-214 (beta)
   d. N-13 (positron emission)
   e. Cr-51 (electron capture)

32. Write a nuclear equation for the indicated decay of each nuclide:
   a. Po-210 (alpha)
   b. Ac-227 (beta)
   c. Tl-207 (beta)
   d. O-15 (positron emission)
   e. Pd-103 (electron capture)

33. Write a partial decay series for Th-232 undergoing the sequential decays: $\alpha, \beta, \beta, \alpha$.

34. Write a partial decay series for Rn-220 undergoing the sequential decays: $\alpha, \alpha, \beta, \alpha$.

35. Fill in the missing particles in each nuclear equation.
   a. $\_\_\_\_ \longrightarrow {}^{217}_{85}\text{At} + {}^{4}_{2}\text{He}$
   b. ${}^{241}_{94}\text{Pu} \longrightarrow {}^{241}_{95}\text{Am} + \_\_\_\_$
   c. ${}^{19}_{11}\text{Na} \longrightarrow {}^{19}_{10}\text{Ne} + \_\_\_\_$
   d. ${}^{75}_{34}\text{Se} + \_\_\_\_ \longrightarrow {}^{75}_{33}\text{As}$

36. Fill in the missing particles in each nuclear equation.
   a. ${}^{241}_{95}\text{Am} \longrightarrow {}^{237}_{93}\text{Np} + \_\_\_\_$
   b. $\_\_\_\_ \longrightarrow {}^{233}_{92}\text{U} + {}^{0}_{-1}e$
   c. ${}^{237}_{93}\text{Np} \longrightarrow \_\_\_\_ + {}^{4}_{2}\text{He}$
   d. ${}^{75}_{35}\text{Br} \longrightarrow \_\_\_\_ + {}^{0}_{+1}e$

37. Determine whether or not each nuclide is likely to be stable. State your reasons.
   a. Mg-26 **b.** Ne-25 **c.** Co-51 **d.** Te-124

38. Determine whether or not each nuclide is likely to be stable. State your reasons.
a. Ti-48 **b.** Cr-63 **c.** Sn-102 **d.** Y-88

39. The first six elements of the first transition series have the following number of stable isotopes:

Element	Number of Stable Isotopes
Sc	1
Ti	5
V	1
Cr	3
Mn	1
Fe	4

Explain why Sc, V, and Mn each has only one stable isotope while the other elements have several.

40. Neon and magnesium each has three stable isotopes while sodium and aluminum each has only one. Explain why this might be so.

41. Predict a likely mode of decay for each unstable nuclide.
a. Mo-109 **b.** Ru-90 **c.** P-27 **d.** Rn-196

42. Predict a likely mode of decay for each unstable nuclide.
a. Sb-132 **b.** Te-139 **c.** Fr-202 **d.** Ba-123

43. Which one of each pair of nuclides would you expect to have the longest half-life?
a. Cs-113 or Cs-125 **b.** Fe-62 or Fe-70

44. Which one of each pair of nuclides would you expect to have the longest half-life?
a. Cs-149 or Cs-139 **b.** Fe-45 or Fe-52

The Kinetics of Radioactive Decay and Radiometric Dating

45. One of the nuclides in spent nuclear fuel is U-235, an alpha emitter with a half-life of 703 million years. How long will it take for the amount of U-235 to reach 10.0% of its initial amount?

46. A patient is given 0.050 Bq of technetium-99m, a radioactive isotope with a half-life of about 6.0 hours. How long does it take for the radioactive isotope to decay to 1.0×10^{-3} mg Bq? (Assume no excretion of the nuclide from the body.)

47. A radioactive sample contains 1.55 MBq of an isotope with a half-life of 3.8 days. How much radioactivity of the isotope remains after 5.5 days?

48. At 8:00 a.m., a patient receives a 580 MBq dose of I-131 to obtain an image of her thyroid. If the nuclide has a half-life of 8 days, how much radioactivity of the nuclide remains in the patient at 5:00 p.m. the next day?

49. A sample of F-18 has an initial decay rate of 1.5×10^5 Bq. How long will it take for the decay rate to fall to 2.5×10^3 Bq? (F-18 has a half-life of 1.83 hours.)

50. A sample of Tl-201 has an initial decay rate of 5.88×10^4 Bq. How long will it take for the decay rate to fall to 287 Bq? (Tl-201 has a half-life of 3.042 days.)

51. A wooden boat discovered just south of the Great Pyramid in Egypt has a carbon-14/carbon-12 ratio that is 72.5% of that found in living organisms. How old is the boat?

52. A layer of peat beneath the glacial sediments of the last ice age has a carbon-14/carbon-12 ratio that is 22.8% of that found in living organisms. How long ago was this ice age?

53. An ancient skull has a carbon-14 decay rate of 1.4×10^{-2} Bq per gram of carbon ($1.4 \times 10^{-2}\ s^{-1}g^{-1}$). How old is the skull? (Assume that living organisms have a carbon-14 decay rate of $2.55 \times 10^{-1}\ s^{-1}g^{-1}$ and that carbon-14 has a half-life of 5730 y.)

54. A mammoth skeleton has a carbon-14 decay rate of 8.0×10^{-3} Bq per gram of carbon (8.0×10^{-3} Bq g^{-1}). When did the mammoth live? (Assume that living organisms have a carbon-14 decay rate of 2.55×10^{-1} Bq g^{-1} and that carbon-14 has a half-life of 5730 y.)

55. A rock from Australia contains 0.438 g of Pb-206 to every 1.00 g of U-238. Assuming that the rock did not contain any Pb-206 at the time of its formation, how old is the rock?

56. A meteor has a Pb-206: U-238 mass ratio of 0.855:1.00. What is the age of the meteor? (Assume that the meteor did not contain any Pb-206 at the time of its formation.)

Fission, Fusion, and Transmutation

57. Write a nuclear reaction for the neutron-induced fission of U-235 to form Xe-144 and Sr-90. How many neutrons are produced in the reaction?

58. Write a nuclear reaction for the neutron-induced fission of U-235 to produce Te-137 and Zr-97. How many neutrons are produced in the reaction?

59. Write a nuclear equation for the fusion of two H-2 atoms to form He-3 and one neutron.

60. Write a nuclear equation for the fusion of H-3 with H-1 to form He-4.

61. A breeder nuclear reactor is a reactor in which nonfissionable (or nonfissile) U-238 is converted into fissionable (or fissile) Pu-239. The process involves bombardment of U-238 by neutrons to form U-239 which then undergoes two sequential beta decays. Write nuclear equations to represent this process.

62. Write a series of nuclear equations to represent the bombardment of Al-27 with a neutron to form a product that subsequently undergoes an alpha decay followed by a beta decay.

63. Rutherfordium-257 was synthesized by bombarding Cf-249 with C-12. Write a nuclear equation for this reaction.

64. Element 107, now named bohrium, was synthesized by German researchers by colliding bismuth-209 with chromium-54 to form a bohrium isotope and one neutron. Write a nuclear equation to represent this reaction.

Energetics of Nuclear Reactions, Mass Defect, and Nuclear Binding Energy

65. If 1.0 g of matter is converted to energy, how much energy is formed?

66. A typical home uses approximately 1.0×10^3 kWh of energy per month. If the energy came from a nuclear reaction, what mass would have to be converted to energy per year to meet the energy needs of the home?

67. Calculate the nuclear binding energy in MeV per nucleon of each nuclide.
a. O-16 (atomic mass = 15.994915 u)
b. Ni-58 (atomic mass = 57.935346 u)
c. Xe-129 (atomic mass = 128.904780 u)

68. Calculate the nuclear binding energy in MeV per nucleon of each nuclide.
a. Li-7 (atomic mass = 7.016003 u)
b. Ti-48 (atomic mass = 47.947947 u)
c. Ag-107 (atomic mass = 106.905092 u)

69. Calculate the quantity of energy produced per gram of U-235 (atomic mass = 235.043922 u) for the neutron-induced fission of U-235 to form Xe-144 (atomic mass = 143.9385 u) and Sr-90 (atomic mass = 89.907738 u) (discussed in Problem 57).

70. Calculate the quantity of energy produced per mole of U-235 (atomic mass = 235.043922 u) for the neutron-induced fission of U-235 to produce Te-137 (atomic mass = 136.9253 u) and Zr-97 (atomic mass = 96.910950 u) (discussed in Problem 58).

71. Calculate the quantity of energy produced per gram of reactant for the fusion of two H-2 (atomic mass = 2.014102 u) atoms to form He-3 (atomic mass = 3.016029 u) and one neutron (discussed in Problem 59).

72. Calculate the quantity of energy produced per gram of reactant for the fusion of H-3 (atomic mass = 3.016049 u) with H-1 (atomic mass = 1.007825 u) to form He-4 (atomic mass = 4.002603 u) (discussed in Problem 60).

Effects and Applications of Radioactivity

73. A 75 kg human is exposed to 0.328 Gy of radiation. How much energy is absorbed by the person's body? Compare this energy to the amount of energy absorbed by a person's body if they jumped from a chair to the floor (assume that the chair is 0.50 m from the ground and that all of the energy from the fall is absorbed by the person).

74. If a 55 g laboratory mouse is exposed to 0.205 Gy of radiation, how much energy is absorbed by the mouse's body?

75. PET studies require fluorine-18, which is produced in a cyclotron and decays with a half-life of 1.83 hours. Assuming that the F-18 can be transported at 60.0 km/h, how close must the hospital be to the cyclotron if 65% of the F-18 produced is to make it to the hospital?

76. Suppose a patient is given 155 mg of I-131, a beta emitter with a half-life of 8.0 days. Assuming that none of the I-131 is eliminated from the person's body in the first 4.0 hours of treatment, what is the exposure (in Bq) during those first four hours?

Cumulative Problems

77. Complete each nuclear equation and calculate the energy change (in MeV per decay) associated with each. (Be-9 = 9.012182 u, Bi-209 = 208.980384 u, He-4 = 4.002603 u, Li-6 = 6.015122 u, Ni-64 = 63.927969 u, Rg-272 = 272.1535 u, Ta-179 = 178.94593 u, and W-179 = 178.94707 u)

a. $\_\_\_\_ + {}^{9}_{4}\text{Be} \longrightarrow {}^{6}_{3}\text{Li} + {}^{4}_{2}\text{He}$

b. ${}^{209}_{83}\text{Bi} + {}^{64}_{28}\text{Ni} \longrightarrow {}^{272}_{111}\text{Rg} + \_\_\_\_$

c. ${}^{179}_{74}\text{W} + \_\_\_\_ \longrightarrow {}^{179}_{73}\text{Ta}$

78. Complete each nuclear equation and calculate the energy change (in MeV per decay) associated with each. (Al-27 = 26.981538 u, Am-241 = 241.056822 u, He-4 = 4.002603 u, Np-237 = 237.048166 u, P-30 = 29.981801 u, S-32 = 31.972071 u, and Si-29 = 28.976495 u.)

a. ${}^{27}_{13}\text{Al} + {}^{4}_{2}\text{He} \longrightarrow {}^{30}_{15}\text{P} + \_\_\_\_$

b. ${}^{32}_{16}\text{S} + \_\_\_\_ \longrightarrow {}^{29}_{14}\text{Si} + {}^{4}_{2}\text{He}$

c. ${}^{241}_{95}\text{Am} \longrightarrow {}^{237}_{93}\text{Np} + \_\_\_\_$

79. Write a nuclear equation for the most likely mode of decay for each unstable nuclide:

a. Ru-114 b. Ra-216 c. Zn-58 d. Ne-31

80. Write a nuclear equation for the most likely mode of decay for each unstable nuclide:

a. Kr-74 b. Th-221 c. Ar-44 d. Nb-85

81. Bismuth-210 is a beta emitter with a half-life of 5.0 days. If a sample contains 1.2 mg of Bi-210 (atomic mass = 209.984105u), how many beta emissions occur in 13.5 days? If the average beta particle has an energy of 1.16 MeV, and a person's 80 kg body intercepts 0.55% of those emissions, to what dose of radiation (in Gy) is the person exposed?

82. Polonium-218 is an alpha emitter with a half-life of 3.0 minutes. If a sample contains 55 mg of Po-218 (atomic mass = 218.008965 u), how many alpha emissions occur in 25.0 minutes?

83. Radium-226 (atomic mass = 226.025402 u) decays to radon-222 (a radioactive gas) with a half-life of 1.6×10^3 years. Assuming that radon gas does not decay, what volume of radon gas (at 25.0 °C and 1.0 bar) does 25.0 g of radium produce in 5.0 days? (Report your answer to two significant digits.)

84. In one of the neutron-induced fission reactions of U-235 (atomic mass = 235.043922 u), the products are Ba-140 and Kr-93 (a radioactive gas). What volume of Kr-93 (at 25.0 °C and 1.0 bar) is produced when 1.00 g of U-235 undergoes this fission reaction?

85. When a positron and an electron annihilate one another, the resulting mass is completely converted to energy. Calculate the energy associated with this process in MeV.

86. A typical nuclear reactor produces about 1.0 MW of power per day. What is the minimum rate of mass loss required to produce this much energy?

87. Find the binding energy in an atom of ${}^{3}\text{He}$, which has a mass of 3.016030 u.

88. The overall hydrogen burning reaction in stars can be represented as the conversion of four protons to one α particle. Use the data for the mass of H-1 and He-4 to calculate the energy released by this process.

89. The nuclide ${}^{247}\text{Es}$ can be made by bombardment of ${}^{238}\text{U}$ in a reaction that emits five neutrons. Identify the bombarding particle.

90. The nuclide ${}^{6}\text{Li}$ reacts with ${}^{2}\text{H}$ to form two identical particles. Identify the particles.

91. The half-life of ${}^{238}\text{U}$ is 4.5×10^9 y. A sample of rock of mass 1.6 g produces 29 Bq. Assuming all the radioactivity is due to ${}^{238}\text{U}$, find the percent by mass of ${}^{238}\text{U}$ in the rock.

92. The half-life of ${}^{232}\text{Th}$ is 1.4×10^{10} y. Find the number of disintegrations emitted by 1.0 mol of ${}^{232}\text{Th}$ in 1 minute.

93. A 1.50 L gas sample at 0.980 bar and 25.0 °C contains 3.55% radon-220 by volume. Radon-220 is an alpha emitter with a half-life of 55.6 s. How many alpha particles are emitted by the gas sample in 5.00 minutes?

94. A 228 mL sample of an aqueous solution contains 2.35% $MgCl_2$ by mass. Exactly one-half of the magnesium ions are Mg-28, a beta emitter with a half-life of 21 hours. What is the decay rate of Mg-28 in the solution after 4.00 days? (Assume a density of 1.02 g mL^{-1} for the solution.)

95. When a positron and an electron collide and annihilate each other, two photons of equal energy are produced. Find the wavelength of these photons.

96. The half-life of ^{235}U, an alpha emitter, is 7.1×10^8 y. Calculate the number of alpha particles emitted by 1.0 mg of this nuclide in 1.0 minute.

97. Given that the energy released in the fusion of two deuterons to a ^{3}He and a neutron is 3.3 MeV and in the fusion to tritium and a proton it is 4.0 MeV, calculate the energy change for the process $^{3}He + {}^{1}n \longrightarrow {}^{3}H + {}^{1}p$. Suggest an explanation for why this process occurs at much lower temperatures than either of the first two.

98. The nuclide ^{18}F decays by both electron capture and β^+ decay. Find the difference in the energy released by these two processes. The atomic masses are $^{18}F = 18.000950$ u and $^{18}O = 17.9991598$ u.

Challenge Problems

99. Before the retirement of the space shuttle in 2011, it carried about 72 500 kg of solid aluminum fuel, which is oxidized with ammonium perchlorate according to the reaction:

$$10\ Al(s) + 6\ NH_4ClO_4(s) \longrightarrow 4\ Al_2O_3(s) + 2\ AlCl_3(s) + 12\ H_2O(g) + 3\ N_2(g)$$

The space shuttle also carried about 608 000 kg of oxygen (which reacts with hydrogen to form gaseous water).

a. Assuming that aluminum and oxygen are the limiting reactants, determine the total energy produced by these fuels. ($\Delta_f H^\circ$ for solid ammonium perchlorate is -295 kJ mol^{-1}.)

b. Suppose that a future space shuttle is powered by matter–antimatter annihilation. The matter could be normal hydrogen (containing a proton and an electron) and the antimatter could be antihydrogen (containing an antiproton and a positron). What mass of antimatter is required to produce the energy equivalent of the aluminum and oxygen fuel previously carried on the space shuttle?

100. When BF_3 is bombarded with neutrons, the boron undergoes an alpha decay, but the F is unaffected. A 0.20 mol sample of BF_3 contained in a 3.0 L container at 298 K is bombarded with neutrons until half of the BF_3 has reacted. What is the pressure in the container at 298 K?

101. In addition to the natural radioactive decay series that begins with U-238 and ends with Pb-206, there are natural radioactive decay series that begin with U-235 and Th-232. Both of these series end with nuclides of Pb. Predict the likely end product of each series and the number of α decay steps that occur.

102. The hydride of an unstable nuclide of a group 2 metal, $MH_2(s)$, decays by α-emission. A 0.025 mol sample of the hydride is placed in an evacuated 2.0 L container at 298 K. After 82 minutes, the pressure in the container is 0.55 atm. Find the half-life of the nuclide.

103. The nuclide ^{38}Cl decays by beta emission with a half-life of 40.0 minutes. A sample of 0.40 mol of $H^{38}Cl$ is placed in a 6.24 L container. After 80.0 minutes, the pressure is 1650 mmHg. What is the temperature of the container?

Conceptual Problems

104. Approximately how many half-lives must pass for the amount of radioactivity in a substance to decrease to below 1% of its initial level?

105. Closely examine the diagram representing the beta decay of fluorine-21 and draw in the missing nucleus.

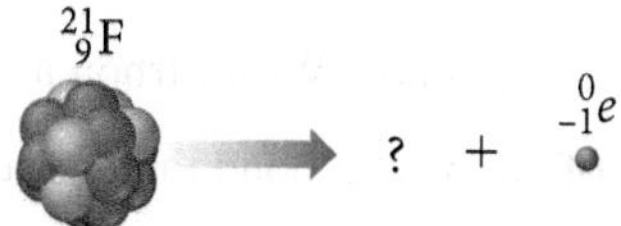

106. Identical amounts of two different nuclides, an alpha emitter and a gamma emitter, with roughly equal half-lives are spilled in a building adjacent to your bedroom. Which of the two nuclides poses the greater health threat to you while you sleep in your bed? If you accidentally wander into the building and ingest equal amounts of the two nuclides, which one poses the greater health threat?

107. A person is exposed for three days to identical amounts of two different nuclides that emit positrons of roughly equal energy. The half-life of nuclide A is 18.5 days and the half-life of nuclide B is 255 days. Which of the two nuclides poses the greater health risk?

20 Organic Chemistry I: Structures

Organic chemistry just now is enough to drive one mad. It gives one the impression of a primeval, tropical forest full of the most remarkable things. . . .

—Friedrich Wöhler (1800–1882)

About half of all men's colognes contain at least some patchouli alcohol ($C_{15}H_{26}O$)*, an organic compound (pictured here) derived from the patchouli plant. Patchouli alcohol has a pungent, musty, earthy fragrance.*

ORGANIC CHEMISTRY IS THE STUDY of carbon-containing compounds. Since life has organized itself around organic compounds, organic chemistry is critical to the study of life. Carbon is unique in the sheer number of compounds that it forms. Millions of organic compounds are known, and researchers discover new ones every day. Carbon is also unique in the diversity of compounds that it forms. In most cases, a fixed number of carbon atoms can combine with a fixed number of atoms of another element to form many different compounds. For example, 10 carbon atoms and 22 hydrogen atoms can form 75 distinctly different compounds. With carbon as the backbone, nature can take the same combination of atoms and bond them together in slightly different ways to produce a huge diversity of substances. It is not surprising that life is based on the chemistry of carbon because life needs diversity to exist, and organic chemistry is nothing if not diverse. In this chapter, we peer into Friedrich Wöhler's "primeval tropical forest" (see chapter-opening quotation) and discover the most remarkable things.

20.1 Fragrances and Odours

Have you ever ridden an elevator with someone wearing too much perfume? Or found yourself too close to a skunk? Or been overwhelmed by a whiff of rotting fish? What causes these fragrances and odours? When we inhale certain molecules called odourants, they bind with olfactory receptors in our noses. This interaction sends a nerve signal to the brain that we experience as a smell. Some smells, such as that of perfume, are pleasant (when not overdone). Other smells, such as that of the skunk or rotting fish, are unpleasant. Our sense of smell helps us identify food, people, and other organisms, and alerts us to dangers such as polluted air or spoiled food. Smell (olfaction) is one way we probe the environment around us.

Odourants, if they are to reach our noses, must be volatile. However, many volatile substances have no scent at all. Nitrogen, oxygen, water, and carbon dioxide molecules, for example, are constantly passing through our noses, yet they produce no smell because they do not bind to olfactory receptors. Most common smells are caused by **organic molecules**, molecules containing carbon combined with several other elements, such as hydrogen, nitrogen, oxygen, and sulfur. Organic molecules are responsible for the smells of roses, vanilla, cinnamon, almond, jasmine, body odour, and rotting fish. When you wander into a rose garden, you experience the sweet smell caused in part by geraniol, an organic compound emitted by roses. Men's colognes often contain patchouli alcohol, an earthy-smelling organic compound extracted from the patchouli plant. If you have been in the vicinity of skunk spray (or have been unfortunate enough to be sprayed yourself), you are familiar with the unpleasant smell of but-2-en-1-thiol and 3-methylbutan-1-thiol, two particularly odouriferous compounds present in the secretion that skunks use to defend themselves.

The study of compounds containing carbon combined with one or more of the elements mentioned previously (hydrogen, nitrogen, oxygen, and sulfur), including their properties and their reactions, is known as **organic chemistry**. Besides composing much of what we smell, organic compounds are prevalent in foods, drugs, petroleum products, and pesticides. Organic chemistry is also the basis for living organisms. Life has evolved based on carbon-containing compounds, making organic chemistry of utmost importance to any person interested in understanding living organisms.

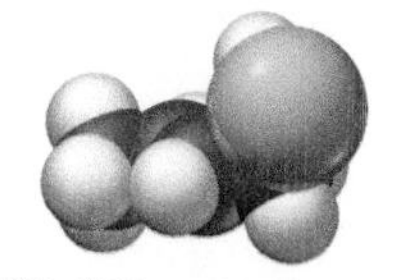

$CH_3CH{=}CHCH_2SH$

But-2-en-1-thiol

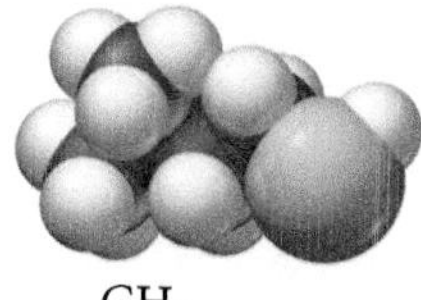

$CH_3CH(CH_3)CH_2CH_2SH$

3-Methylbutan-1-thiol

▲ The smell of skunk is caused primarily by the molecules shown here.

20.2 Carbon: Why It Is Unique

Why did life evolve based on the chemistry of carbon? Why is life not based on some other element? The answer may not be simple, but we know that life—in order to exist—must entail complexity, and carbon chemistry is certainly complex. The number of compounds containing carbon is greater than the number of compounds containing all of the other elements combined. The reasons for carbon's unique and versatile behaviour include its ability to form four covalent bonds, its ability to form double and triple bonds, and its tendency to **catenate** (that is, to form chains).

Carbon's Tendency to Form Four Covalent Bonds Carbon—with its four valence electrons—forms four covalent bonds. Consider the Lewis structure and space-filling models of two simple carbon compounds, methane and ethane.

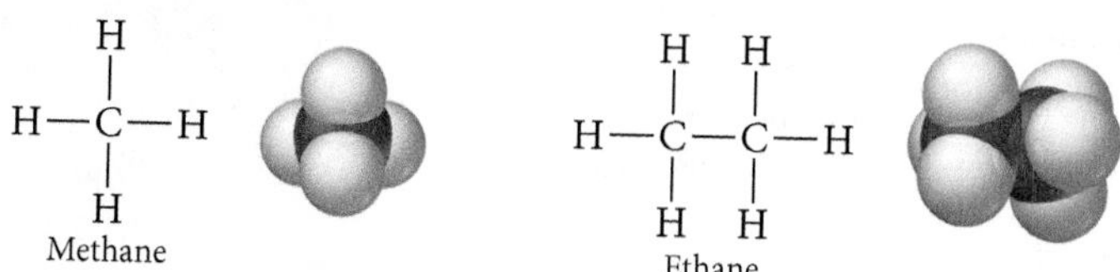

The geometry about a carbon atom forming four single bonds is tetrahedral, as shown above for methane. Carbon's ability to form four bonds, and to form those bonds with a number of different elements, results in the potential to form many different compounds. As you learn to draw structures for organic compounds, always remember to draw carbon with four bonds.

Carbon's Ability to Form Double and Triple Bonds Carbon atoms also form double bonds (trigonal planar geometry) and triple bonds (linear geometry), adding even more diversity to the number of compounds that carbon forms.

Ethene

$H-C\equiv C-H$

Ethyne

In contrast, silicon (the element in the periodic table with properties closest to that of carbon) does not readily form double or triple bonds because the greater size of silicon atoms results in a Si—Si bond that is too long for much overlap between nonhybridized *p* orbitals.

Carbon's Tendency to Catenate Carbon, more than any other element, can bond to itself to form chain, branched, and ring structures.

Propane

2-Methylpropane

Cyclohexane

THE NATURE OF SCIENCE Vitalism and the Perceived Difference Between Organic and Inorganic

By the end of the eighteenth century, chemists had learned that compounds could be broadly categorized as either organic or inorganic. It was believed that organic compounds came from living things while inorganic compounds came from the nonliving things on Earth. Sugar—obtained from sugarcane or the sugar beet—is a common example of an organic compound. Salt—mined from the ground or extracted from ocean water—is a common example of an inorganic compound.

Organic and inorganic compounds are different, not only in their origin, but also in their properties. Organic compounds are easily decomposed. Sugar, for example, readily decomposes into carbon and water when heated. (Think of the last time while cooking you burned something sugary in the pan or in the oven.) Inorganic compounds are more difficult to decompose. Salt decomposes only when heated to very high temperatures. Even more curious to these early chemists was their inability to synthesize a single organic compound in the laboratory. Although they were able to synthesize many inorganic compounds, despite concerted efforts, they were not able to synthesize any organic compounds.

The origin and properties of organic compounds led early chemists to postulate that organic compounds were unique to living organisms. They hypothesized that living organisms contained a *vital force*—a mystical or supernatural power—that allowed them to produce organic compounds. They thought that producing an organic compound outside of a living organism was impossible because the vital force was not present. This belief—which became known as *vitalism*—explained why no chemist had succeeded in synthesizing an organic compound in the laboratory.

An experiment performed in 1828 by German chemist Friedrich Wöhler (1800–1882) marked the beginning of the end of vitalism. Wöhler heated ammonium cyanate (an inorganic compound) and formed urea (an organic compound).

$$\underset{\text{Ammonium cyanate}}{NH_4OCN} \xrightarrow{\text{heat}} \underset{\text{Urea}}{H_2NCONH_2}$$

Urea was a known organic compound that had previously been isolated only from urine. Although it was not realized at the time, Wöhler's simple experiment was a key step in opening all of life to scientific investigation. He showed that the compounds composing living organisms—like all compounds—follow scientific laws and can be studied and understood. Today, known organic compounds number in the millions, and modern organic chemistry is a vast field that produces substances as diverse as drugs, petroleum products, and plastics and many other compounds that are not found in nature.

Friedrich Wöhler

▶ The synthesis of urea in 1828 by German chemist Friedrich Wöhler marked the beginning of the end for vitalism.

Urea

Although other elements can form chains, none beats carbon at this ability. Silicon, for example, can form chains with itself. However, silicon's affinity for oxygen (the Si—O bond is 142 kJ mol^{-1} stronger than the Si—Si bond) coupled with the prevalence of oxygen in our atmosphere means that silicon–silicon chains are readily oxidized to form silicates (the silicon–oxygen compounds that compose a significant proportion of minerals). By contrast, the C—C bond (347 kJ mol^{-1}) and the C—O bond (359 kJ mol^{-1}) are nearly the same strength, allowing carbon chains to exist relatively peacefully in an oxygen-rich environment. Silicon's affinity for oxygen robs it of the rich diversity that catenation provides to carbon.

20.3 Hydrocarbons

Hydrocarbons are compounds that contain only carbon and hydrogen. They are the simplest type of organic compounds and are commonly used as fuels. Candle wax, oil, gasoline, and natural gas are all composed of hydrocarbons. Hydrocarbons provide the structural backbone for all organic compounds, which makes them good starting materials in the synthesis of many different products such as dyes, pharmaceuticals, plastics, and rubber.

Drawing Hydrocarbon Structures

Before we examine the different types of hydrocarbons, it is useful to discuss how we usually draw their structures. We will use these representations throughout the rest of this chapter and the next.

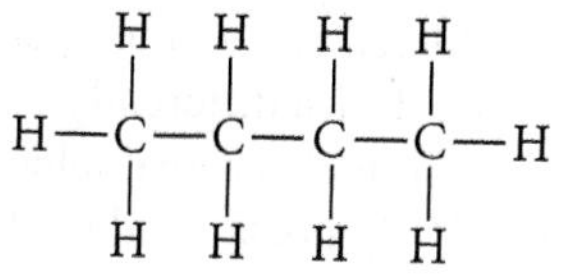

```
                                           H
                                           |
    H   H   H   H                    H H—C—H H
    |   |   |   |                    |     |     |
H—C—C—C—C—H                 H—C———C———C—H
    |   |   |   |                    |     |     |
    H   H   H   H                    H     H     H
      Butane                        2-Methylpropane
```

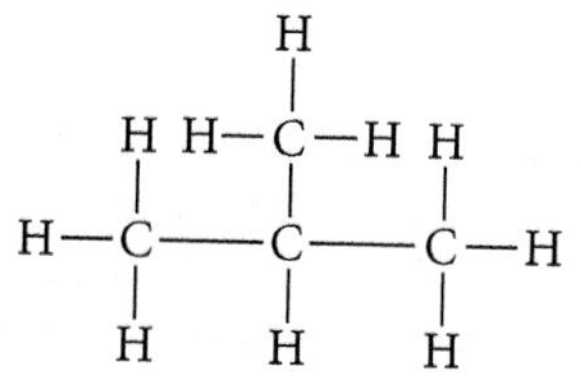

Butane and isobutane are **structural isomers**, molecules with the same molecular formula but different structures. Because of their different structures, they have different properties—they are indeed different compounds. Isomerism is ubiquitous in organic chemistry. Butane has two structural isomers. Pentane (C_5H_{12}) has three, hexane (C_6H_{14}) has five, and decane ($C_{10}H_{22}$) has 75!

The structure of a particular hydrocarbon is represented with a **structural formula**, a formula that shows not only the numbers of each kind of atoms, but also how the atoms are bonded together. Organic chemists use several different kinds of structural formulas. For example, we can represent butane and 2-methylpropane in each of the following ways:

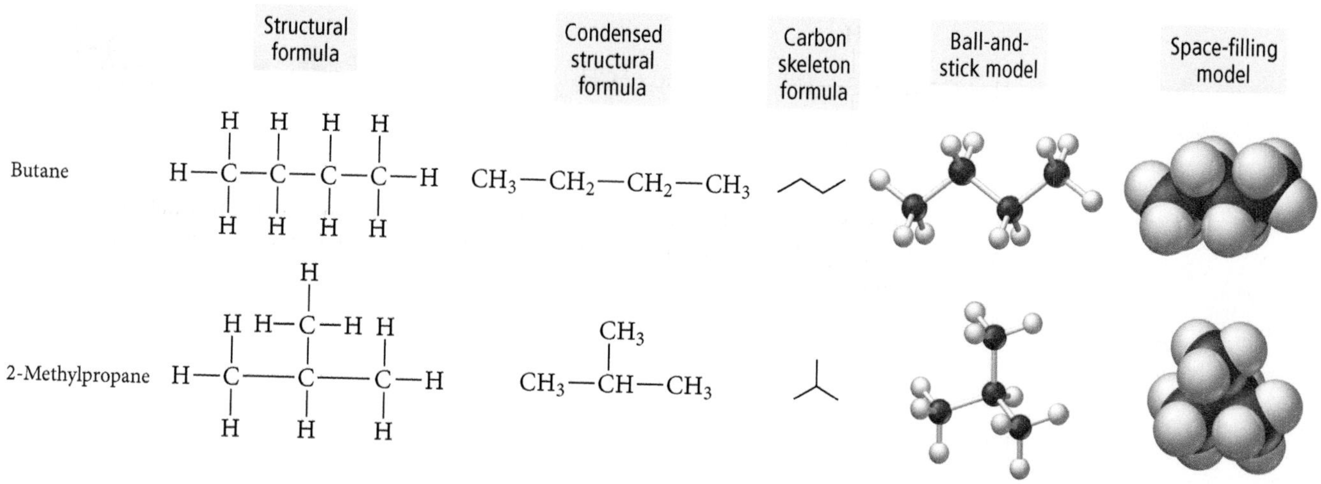

	Structural formula	Condensed structural formula	Carbon skeleton formula	Ball-and-stick model	Space-filling model
Butane	H—C(H)(H)—C(H)(H)—C(H)(H)—C(H)(H)—H	$CH_3—CH_2—CH_2—CH_3$			
2-Methylpropane	H—C(H)(H)—C(H)(CH₃)—C(H)(H)—H	$CH_3—CH(CH_3)—CH_3$			

The structural formula shows all of the carbon and hydrogen atoms in the molecule and how they are bonded together. The *condensed structural formula* groups the hydrogen atoms with the carbon atom to which they are bonded. Condensed structural formulas may show some of the bonds (as on the previous page) or none at all. The condensed structural formula for butane can also be written as $CH_3CH_2CH_2CH_3$. The *carbon skeleton formula* (also called a line formula) shows the carbon–carbon bonds only as lines. Each end or bend of a line represents a carbon atom bonded to as many hydrogen atoms as necessary to form a total of four bonds. Carbon skeleton formulas allow you to draw complex structures quickly.

A carbon skeleton formula is called a *line* formula because it uses lines to represent a molecule.

Note that structural formulas are generally not three-dimensional representations of the molecule—as space-filling or ball-and-stick models are—but rather two-dimensional representations that show how atoms are bonded together. As such, the most important feature of a structural formula is the *connectivity* of the atoms, not the exact way the formula is drawn. For example, consider the following two condensed structural formulas for butane and the corresponding space-filling models below them:

$CH_3—CH_2—CH_2—CH_3$ $CH_3—CH_2—CH_2$ (with CH_3 bonded below the last CH_2)

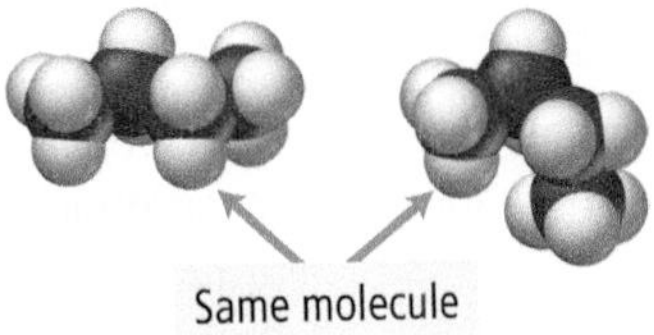

Same molecule

Since rotation about single bonds is relatively unhindered at room temperature, the two structural formulas are identical, even though they are drawn differently.

We represent double and triple bonds in structural formulas with double or triple lines. For example, we draw the structural formulas for C_3H_6 (propene) and C_3H_4 (propyne) as follows:

	Structural formula	Condensed structural formula	Carbon skeleton formula	Ball-and-stick model	Space-filling model
Propene	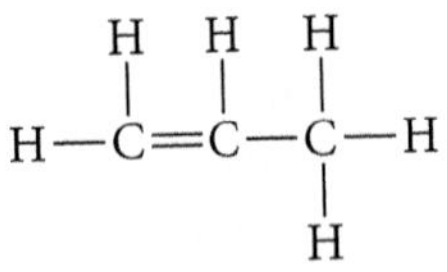 H—C(H)=C(H)—C(H)(H)—H	$CH_2=CH—CH_3$	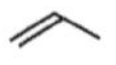	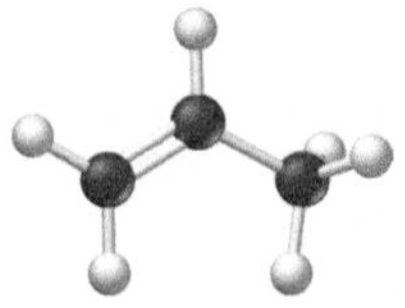	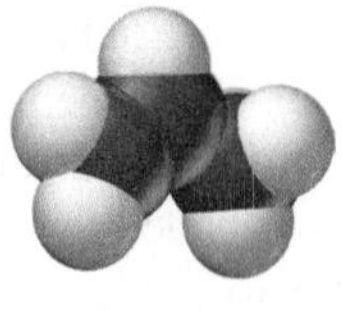
Propyne	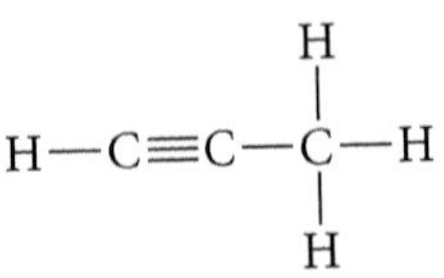 H—C≡C—C(H)(H)—H	$CH≡C—CH_3$	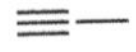 ≡—		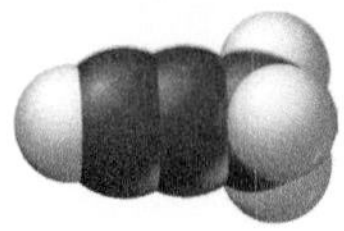

The kind of structural formula we use depends on how much information we want to portray. The following example illustrates how to write structural formulas for a compound.

EXAMPLE 20.1 WRITING STRUCTURAL FORMULAS FOR HYDROCARBONS

Write the structural formulas and carbon skeleton formulas for the five isomers of C_6H_{14} (hexane).

SOLUTION

To start, draw the carbon backbone of the straight-chain isomer.

```
C—C—C—C—C—C
```

Next, determine the carbon backbone structure of the other isomers by arranging the carbon atoms in four other unique ways.

```
C—C—C—C—C     C—C—C—C—C
      |             |
      C             C

     C           C
     |           |
C—C—C—C      C—C—C—C
     |              |
     C              C
```

Fill in all the hydrogen atoms so that each carbon forms four bonds.

```
   H  H  H  H  H  H
   |  |  |  |  |  |
H—C—C—C—C—C—C—H
   |  |  |  |  |  |
   H  H  H  H  H  H

   H  H  H  H  H              H  H  H  H  H
   |  |  |  |  |              |  |  |  |  |
H—C—C—C—C—C—H          H—C—C—C—C—C—H
   |  |  |  |  |              |  |  |  |  |
   H  H  H  |  H              H  H  |  H  H
         H—C—H                  H—C—H
            |                      |
            H                      H

          H                     H
          |                     |
        H—C—H                 H—C—H
   H  H   |   H               H   |      H  H
   |  |   |   |               |   |      |  |
H—C—C—C—C—H               H—C—C——C—C—H
   |  |   |   |               |   |      |  |
   H  H   |   H               H   H      |  H
        H—C—H                          H—C—H
          |                              |
          H                              H
```

Write the carbon skeleton formulas by using lines to represent each carbon–carbon bond. Remember that each end or bend represents a carbon atom.

FOR PRACTICE 20.1

Write the structural and condensed structural formulas for each of the following carbon skeleton formulas:

(a) 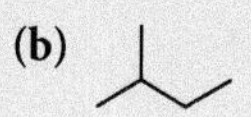 (b) 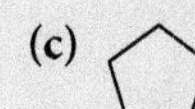 (c)

TABLE 20.1 Alkanes, Alkenes, Alkynes

Type of Hydrocarbon	Type of Bonds	Generic Formula*	Example	Average Carbon-Carbon Bond Energy (kJ mol^{-1})	Typical Bond Length (pm)
Alkane	All single	C_nH_{2n+2}	H H H—C—C—H H H Ethane	347	154
Alkene	One double	C_nH_{2n}	H H C=C H H Ethene	611	134
Alkyne	One triple	C_nH_{2n-2}	H—C≡C—H Ethyne	837	120

*n is the number of carbon atoms. These formulas apply only to noncyclic structures containing no more than one multiple bond.

Section 20.3 makes use of valence bond theory and molecular orbital theory, which were covered in Chapter 10. We recommend that you review this material.

Types of Hydrocarbons

Hydrocarbons can be classified as **open chain hydrocarbons** or **cyclic hydrocarbons.** Open chain hydrocarbons consist of open chains of carbon atoms. For example, butane and 2-methylpropane are open chain hydrocarbons. Cyclic hydrocarbons involve carbon atoms that are arranged to form one or more ring structures (e.g., cyclohexane).

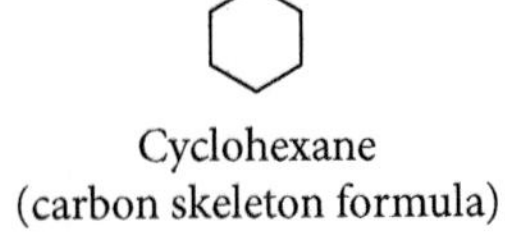

Cyclohexane
(carbon skeleton formula)

Hydrocarbons are also classified according to the type of bonds between carbon atoms. **Alkanes** have only single bonds between carbon atoms, **alkenes** have a double bond, and **alkynes** have a triple bond. These categories are outlined in Table 20.1. **Saturated hydrocarbons** are hydrocarbons with the maximum number of hydrogen atoms for the number of carbon atoms present. **Unsaturated hydrocarbons** have fewer hydrogen atoms than the maximum for that number of carbon atoms. Unsaturation occurs whenever rings or π bonds are present in the structure.

Alkanes

The simplest alkane is methane, CH_4. In Chapter 10, we saw that the carbon atom in methane is sp^3 hybridized and the four C—H bonds are σ bonds, arranged in a tetrahedron.

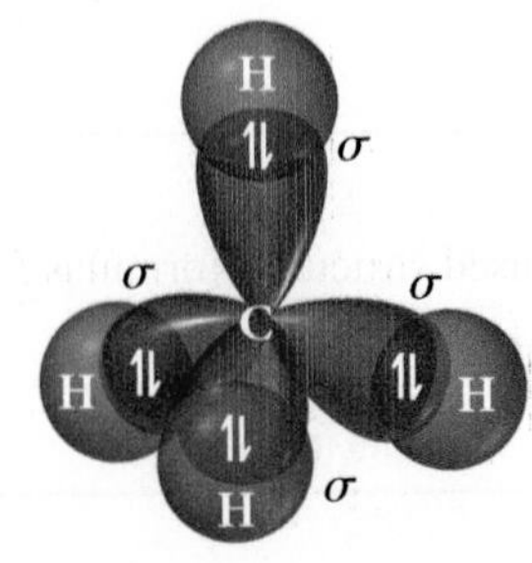

In higher alkanes with two or more carbon atoms, each carbon atom is sp^3 hybridized and the C—C and C—H bonds are all σ bonds with tetrahedral geometry.

Sigma bonds are symmetrical around the imaginary axis connecting the two atoms. This symmetry gives largely unrestricted rotation about the C—C single bonds in an alkane. Alkanes are "flexible" molecules because rotation can occur around each C—C bond. The rotation is not entirely free, as we will see in Section 20.6.

Alkenes

The simplest alkene is ethene, C_2H_4. The structure and bonding of C—C double bonds was also presented in Chapter 10. The carbon atoms involved in a double bond are sp^2 hybridized. Two of the sp^2 orbitals on each carbon form σ bonds with a hydrogen or another atom, and one sp^2 orbital from each carbon atom overlap to form a σ bond, which is part of the double bond. The p orbitals on each carbon atom overlap to form a π bond.

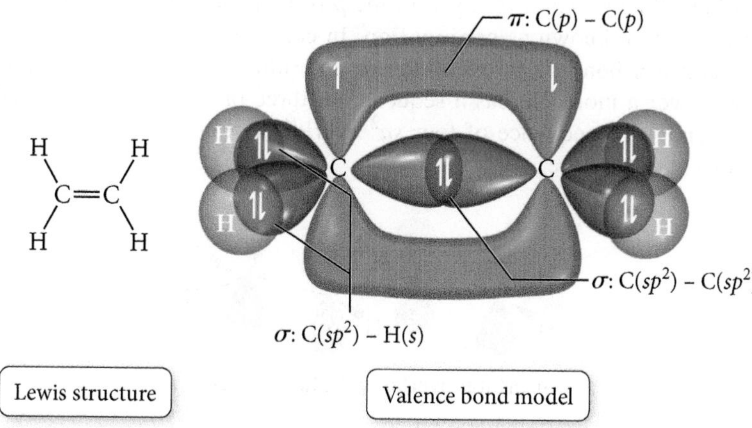

As we will discuss in Section 20.6, there is only a small energy barrier associated with C—C bond rotation in alkanes. On the other hand, rotation around C═C double bonds requires significant energy in the form of heat or light. The reason is that the π bond locks the molecule in place around the two carbons of the double bond, with approximate bond angles of 120° to fit the sp^2 hybridization. Note the difference in bond energies of C—C single (347 kJ mol^{-1}) and double bonds (611 kJ mol^{-1}) in Table 20.1. The difference (263 kJ mol^{-1}) can be seen as the activation energy required to break the π bond and allow for rotation around the sigma bond. Rotation around a double bond is possible if the alkene is strongly heated or if the molecule absorbs a photon of appropriate energy.

Alkynes

The carbon–carbon triple bond in alkynes is made up of one σ bond and two π bonds:

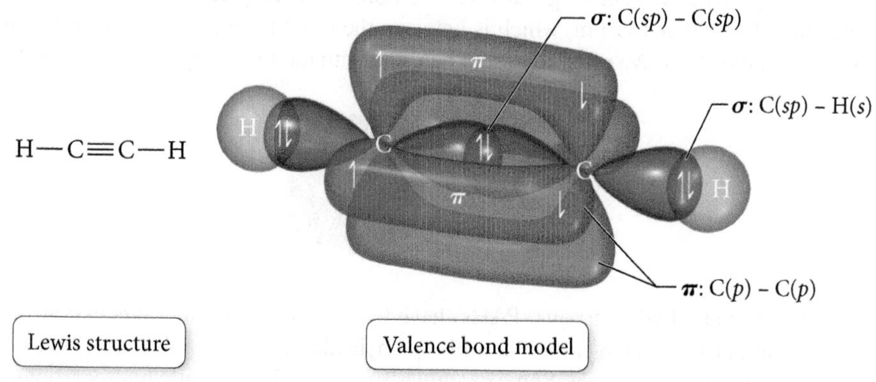

▲ The acetylene torches used in metalworking burn ethyne (commonly called "acetylene") to produce the very hot flame needed for cutting through steel.

Alkynes have a linear geometry due to the sp hybridization of the carbon atoms. The C—C triple bond has a very high bond energy (837 kJ mol^{-1}).

Conjugated Alkenes and Aromatics

In alkenes with two or more C—C double bonds, the relative location of the double bonds can affect the properties of the molecule. Consider the following molecule:

Buta-1,3-diene

In buta-1,3-diene, carbons 1 through 4 are all sp^2 hybridized. Each of these carbon atoms has a *p* orbital that can overlap with a neighbouring *p* orbital. The *p* orbitals on carbons 2 and 3 can overlap with the *p* orbitals on either side. This leads to a bonding interaction known as **conjugation**. In conjugation, the *p* orbitals overlap to give delocalized π bonding across all the sp^2 hybridized carbons that are linked. This occurs whenever a molecule has a sequence of three or more sp^2 hybridized atoms. Buta-1,3-diene has a sequence of four sp^2 hybridized atoms. Conjugation leads to a planar molecular structure.

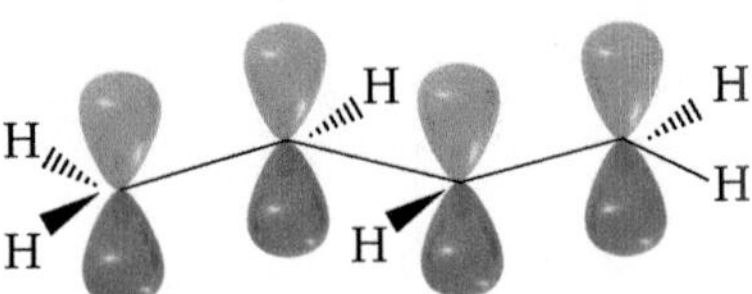

p-orbital overlap in buta-1,3-diene

Under current definitions, any organic compound that is not aromatic is considered to be an *aliphatic* compound.

Aromatic hydrocarbons are a class of organic compounds that are closely related to conjugated alkenes. The most important type of aromatic structure is the benzene ring. Recall from Chapter 10 that the Lewis structures of benzene rings have alternating single and double bonds, which gives two resonance forms:

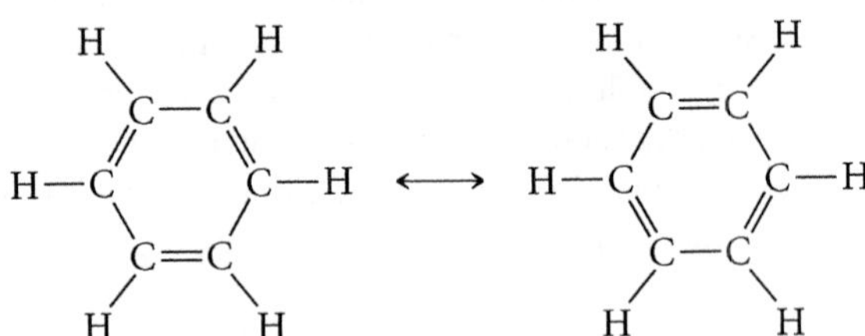

Resonance structures are defined in Section 9.8. Recall that the actual structure of a molecule represented by resonance structures is intermediate between the two resonance structures and is called a *resonance hybrid.*

Aromatic hydrocarbons are often referred to as *arenes.* When an arene unit is a substituent on another group, it is called an *aryl group.*

What is really happening here is that the six *p* orbitals (one from each carbon atom) are overlapping to form π molecular orbitals over the entire ring. This π delocalization confers extra stability to the benzene ring. Each C—C bond is actually equivalent, and the bond lengths are identical at 139 pm, which is between the bond lengths for single and double bonds (see Table 20.1). We often represent benzene with the following shorthand notation.

Polycyclic aromatic hydrocarbons (PAHs) have two or more benzene rings that are connected. As in benzene, each carbon atom is sp^2 hybridized and π molecular orbitals are shared over the entire molecule. Some examples of polycyclic aromatic hydrocarbons are shown in Figure 20.1 ▶. Naphthalene is the substance that composes mothballs. Pyrene is a carcinogen found in cigarette smoke.

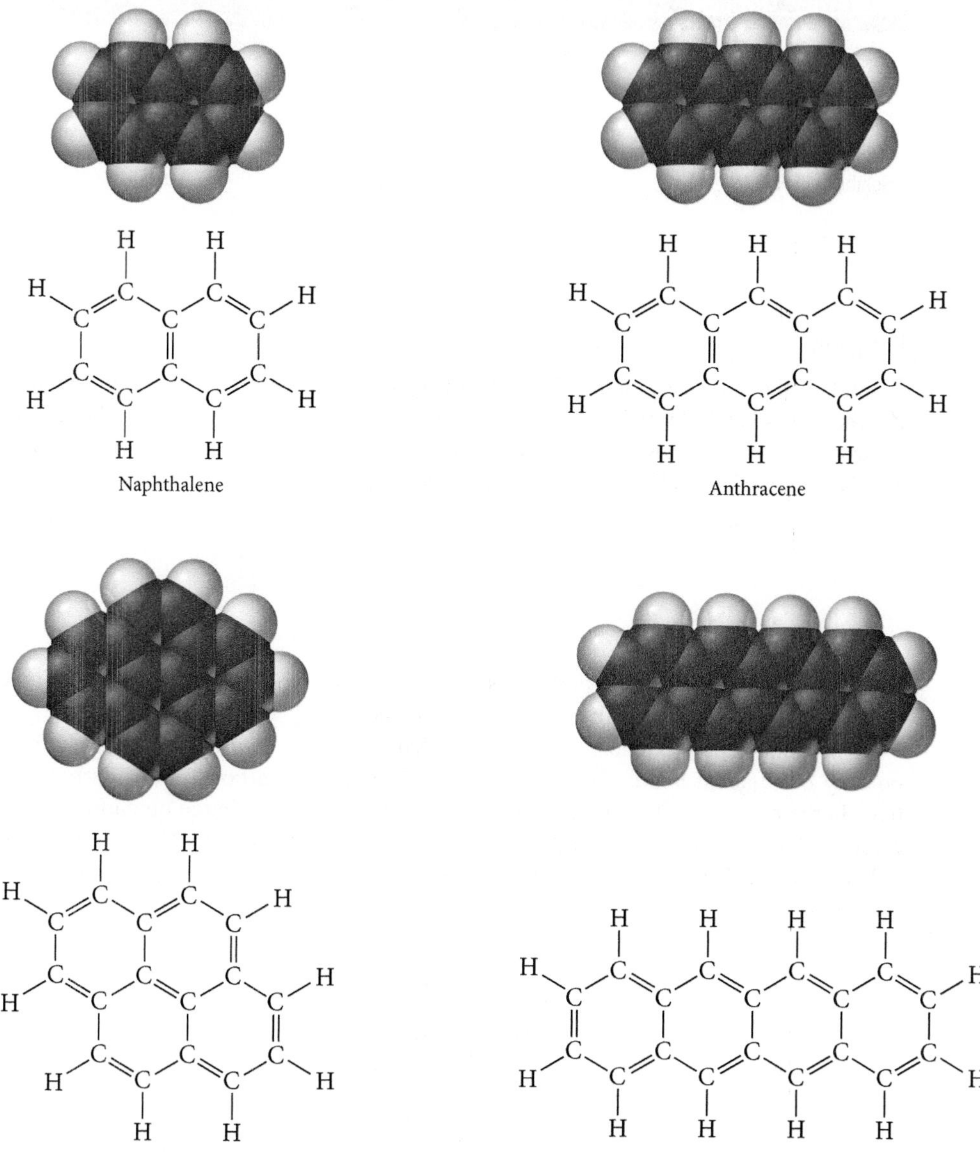

▲ **FIGURE 20.1 Polycyclic Aromatic Compounds** The structures of some common polycyclic aromatic compounds contain fused rings.

20.4 Functional Groups

Most other families of organic compounds can be thought of as hydrocarbons with one or more **functional group(s)**—a characteristic atom or group of atoms—inserted into the hydrocarbon. A group of organic compounds with the same functional group forms a **family**. For example, alcohols are a family of compounds that have an —OH group.

The insertion of a functional group into a hydrocarbon alters the properties of the compound significantly. For example, methanol—which can be thought of as methane with an —OH group substituted for one of the hydrogen atoms—is a polar, hydrogen-bonded liquid at room temperature. Methane, in contrast, is a nonpolar gas. The —OH group gives methanol a completely different set of physical and chemical properties from its parent hydrocarbon methane (Table 20.2).

Although each member of a family is unique, their common functional group also gives them some similarities in both their physical and chemical properties. This will emerge as we discuss a variety of important functional groups.

The term *functional group* derives from the functionality or chemical character that a specific atom or group of atoms imparts to an organic compound. Even a carbon–carbon double bond can justifiably be called a "functional group."

TABLE 20.2 Properties of Methane and Methanol		
	CH_4	CH_3OH
Melting point (°C)	−187	−98
Boiling point (°C)	−161	65
Solubility in H_2O (g L^{-1})	0.00227 (at 101 kPa partial pressure CH_4)	Miscible

Halides

A halide is the simplest functional group. It is simply a halogen atom, usually denoted as X, where X is F, Cl, Br, or I. Halogen atoms are more electronegative than carbon, which means that C—X bonds are polar. The carbon bonded to a halogen atom has a partial positive charge. The halogen has a partial negative charge.

$$\overset{\delta+}{C}-\overset{\delta-}{X}$$

All organic halides are polar molecules except in cases where individual bond dipoles cancel out, as in a molecule like tetrachloromethane.

In tetrachloromethane, CCl_4, the C—Cl bonds are in a tetrahedral geometry, and the bond dipoles cancel each other out.

The bond dipole between carbon and a halogen atom can in turn affect the bond polarity of adjacent bonds. For example, in chloroethane, carbon 1 has a partial positive charge because of the chlorine atom. The partial positive charge on carbon 1 pulls electron density from the second carbon atom, which polarizes the C—C bond. This is known as an **inductive effect**, and can occur in bonds that are adjacent to a polar functional group.

Chloroethane

We know from Chapter 8 that the atomic sizes of the halogens increase down the group (F < Cl < Br < I). Similarly, C—X bond lengths also vary, with C—F bonds being shortest and C—I bonds being longest. These trends are shown in Table 20.3.

▲ Teflon tape is used to seal metal threads, as in pipe fittings. Teflon is a polymer consisting of long straight chains of carbon atoms with two fluorine atoms bonded to each carbon. Polymers are covered in Section 21.10.

Amines

An amine group is simply a nitrogen atom that has three single bonds to H atoms or **R groups**. Amines can be thought of as derivatives of ammonia, with one H atom replaced

TABLE 20.3 Bonds in Organic Halides		
Bond	Average Bond Energy (kJ mol^{-1})	C—X Bond Length in CH_3X (pm)
C—F	485	138
C—Cl	339	179
C—Br	284	193
C—I	213	213

by R (a primary amine), two H atoms replaced by R (a secondary amine), or three H atoms replaced by R (a tertiary amine).

R designates a hydrocarbon group (Section 3.5).

H—N̈—H, with H below	H—N̈—R, with H below	H—N̈—R, with R′ below	R″—N̈—R, with R′ below
Ammonia	Primary (1°) amine	Secondary (2°) amine	Tertiary (3°) amine

Quaternary ammonium ions have four R groups bonded to the N atom. This gives the nitrogen a positive charge, just as in the ammonium ion NH_4^+.

$$R'''—\overset{R}{\underset{R''}{N^+}}—R'$$

In simple, alkyl amines, the N atom is sp^3 hybridized, giving tetrahedral geometries. Due to the electronegativity of nitrogen, amines are polar molecules with a partial negative charge on the N atom:

$$—\overset{\delta+}{C}—\overset{\delta-}{\ddot{N}H_2}$$

In amines that are next to a benzene ring, the lone pair on a nitrogen atom can become part of the delocalized π bonding. This would suggest that the nitrogen atom should be sp^2 hybridized. As it turns out, the structure of aniline suggests that the hybridization of nitrogen is somewhere in between sp^2 and sp^3. Aniline is not planar—the angle between the ring plane and the NH_2 plane is 37.3°. The H—N—H bond angle is 113.1°, which is in between the angles expected for sp^2 or sp^3 hybridization (120° and 109.5°). For arylamines (an amine with an aromatic group like aniline in Figure 20.2 ▼), the nitrogen atom has a hybridization between sp^2 and sp^3.

▲ Sockeye salmon on ice, for sale at the Granville Island Market in Vancouver. Freshly caught fish are kept cold to prevent the formation of chemicals such as trimethylamine in the meat. Amines are responsible for the fishy smell of rotting seafood.

▶ **FIGURE 20.2 The Structure of Aniline** The N atom hybridization is between sp^2 and sp^3. This gives a bent, as opposed to planar, molecular structure.

Alcohols

As we discussed at the beginning of this section, alcohols are organic compounds containing the —OH group, or hydroxyl group, and they have the general formula R—OH. The oxygen atom is sp^3 hybridized, giving C—O—H bond angles that are close to the ideal tetrahedral bond angle of 109.5°. For example, the C—O—H bond angle in methanol is 108.5°. The slightly smaller angle is due to the effect of lone pair repulsions, which we discussed in Chapter 10.

Oxygen atoms are very electronegative, whereas carbon atoms are not. The difference in electronegativity leads to a very polar C—O bond. The O—H bond is also very polar, which leads to strong hydrogen bonding between alcohol molecules. Hydrogen bonding can also occur with water molecules, which makes many alcohols soluble in water even with the presence of nonpolar hydrocarbon components. However, as the size of the nonpolar hydrocarbon component increases, aqueous solubility decreases dramatically, as shown in Table 20.4.

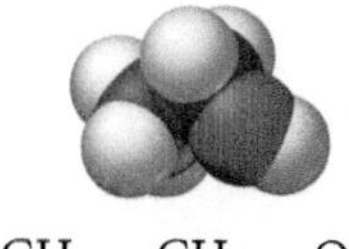

$CH_3—CH_2—OH$

Ethanol

▲ Ethanol can be blended with nonpolar organic liquids like gasoline as well as polar liquids like water.

$$\mathrm{H{-}\overset{\overset{R}{|}}{\underset{\underset{H}{|}}{C}}{-}OH}$$

Primary (1°) alcohol

$$\mathrm{R'{-}\overset{\overset{R}{|}}{\underset{\underset{H}{|}}{C}}{-}OH}$$

Secondary (2°) alcohol

$$\mathrm{R'{-}\overset{\overset{R}{|}}{\underset{\underset{R''}{|}}{C}}{-}OH}$$

Tertiary (3°) alcohol

▲ Alcohols can be primary, secondary, or tertiary, depending on the number of R groups attached to the carbon atom attached to the OH group.

TABLE 20.4 Solubilities of Alcohols

Alcohol	Solubility in H_2O (g L^{-1})
Methanol	miscible
Ethanol	miscible
Propan-1-ol	miscible
Butan-1-ol	80
Pentan-1-ol	22.4
Hexan-1-ol	6.0
Heptan-1-ol	1.74
Octan-1-ol	0.54

Source: David R. Lide (ed.). (2005). *CRC Handbook of Chemistry and Physics*, Boca Raton, FL: CRC Press.

Ethers

An ether has the general formula R — O — R′, where R and R′ may or may not be different hydrocarbon groups. The oxygen atom is sp^3 hybridized. In dimethyl ether, the C — O — C bond angle is 112°.

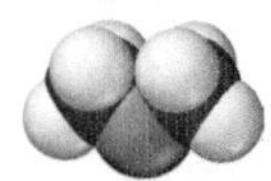

$CH_3{-}O{-}CH_3$

Dimethyl ether

The difference in electronegativities of oxygen and carbon means that ethers are slightly polar. However, this slight dipole is not enough to make simple alkyl ethers soluble in water. The boiling points of ethers are usually higher than the corresponding hydrocarbons. For example, the boiling points of dimethyl ether and propane are −25 and −45 °C, respectively. This is due to the small dipole–dipole interactions that are present between ether molecules but not between propane molecules. Dimethyl ether and ethanol have the same molecular formula (C_2H_6O), and yet ethanol has a boiling point of 78 °C, which is 103 °C higher than the boiling point of dimethyl ether. The reason is that alcohols exhibit hydrogen bonding, which is absent between molecules of dimethyl ether.

The C — O — C linkage is important in chemistry because it can function as a connector between molecules. For example, in Chapter 22 we will see how it is used to connect glucose molecules together to form the polysaccharides starch and cellulose.

Carbonyls: Aldehydes and Ketones

Aldehydes and **ketones** have the following general formulas:

$$\mathrm{R{-}\overset{\overset{O}{\|}}{C}{-}H} \qquad \mathrm{R{-}\overset{\overset{O}{\|}}{C}{-}R}$$

Aldehyde Ketone

The condensed structural formula for aldehydes is RCHO and that for ketones is RCOR.

Both aldehydes and ketones contain the **carbonyl group**:

$$\mathrm{{\diagup}\overset{\overset{O}{\|}}{C}{\diagdown}}$$

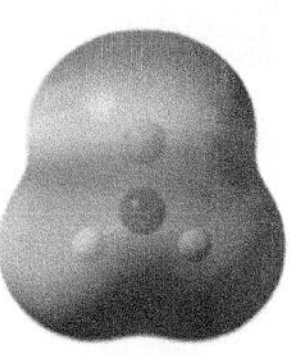

Formaldehyde

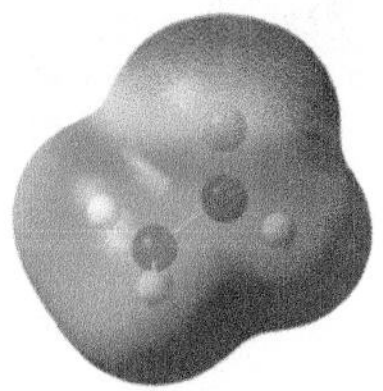

Acetaldehyde

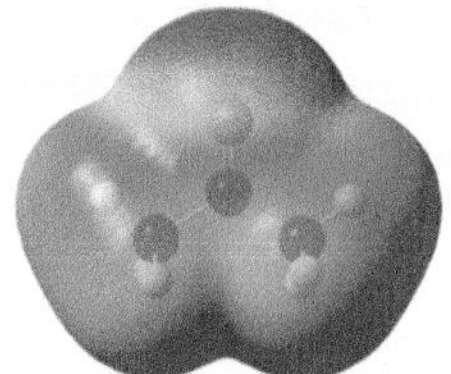

Acetone

◀ **FIGURE 20.3 Electrostatic Potential Maps of the Carbonyl Group** The carbonyl group is highly polar, as shown in these plots of electrostatic potential.

Ketones have an R group attached to both sides of the carbonyl, while aldehydes have one R group and a hydrogen atom. (An exception is methanal, which is an aldehyde with two H atoms attached to the carbonyl group.)

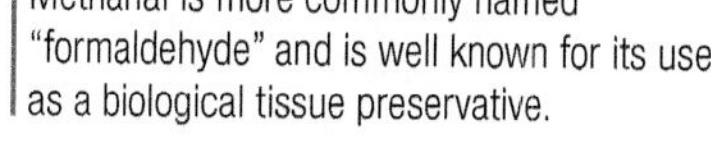

Methanal is more commonly named "formaldehyde" and is well known for its use as a biological tissue preservative.

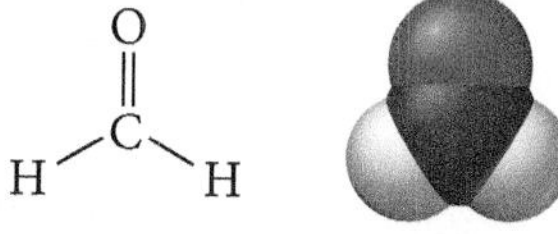

Formaldehyde (methanal)

The bonding in formaldehyde was discussed in Section 10.7. The carbon atom is sp^2 hybridized. The C—O double bond consists of a σ bond and a π bond.

The C—O bond is polar due to the difference in electronegativities of carbon and oxygen (Figure 20.3 ▲). Furthermore, carbonyls have an important resonance structure in which the carbon atom has a formal positive charge. In the next chapter, we will see how this bond polarity and partial positive charge on carbon results in an important class of chemical reactions involving the carbonyl group.

$$\ddot{\text{O}}\!=\!\text{C} \longleftrightarrow {:}\ddot{\text{O}}{:}^{-}\!-\!\text{C}^{+}$$

The Carboxylic Acid Family

A carboxylic acid has the general formula:

$$\text{R—C(=O)—OH}$$

Carboxylic acid

The structure and bonding of a carboxylic acid group is very similar to that of carbonyls, except that the additional —OH group modifies the chemical behaviour. Several other functional groups can be viewed as being derived from carboxylic acids. All of these groups share what is called an **acyl group**, RCO:

$$\text{R—C(=O)—}$$

Acyl group

The difference between the various acyl functional groups and an aldehyde or ketone is that a substituent that is not hydrogen or an alkyl group is bonded to the central carbon. Rather, the substituent is a polar group that is often displaced during reactions. The reactions of acyl groups will be covered in the next chapter. Table 20.5 gives a list of acyl functional groups.

TABLE 20.5 Acyl Functional Groups

Acyl Group	Structure
Acyl halide (X = Cl, Br)	R—C(=O)—X
Acid anhydride	R—C(=O)—O—C(=O)—R
Ester	R—C(=O)—O—R
Carboxylic acid	R—C(=O)—O—H
Amide	R—C(=O)—N̈(H)—H

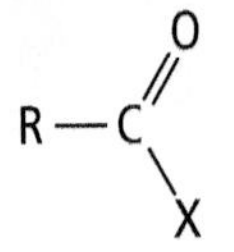

▲ Many ester compounds have strong, fruity odours. For example, pentyl ethanoate smells like bananas. Bananas contain this and several other compounds that combine to give them their distinctive, pleasant odour.

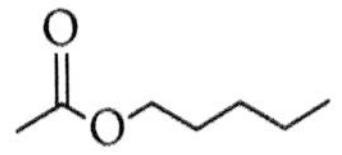

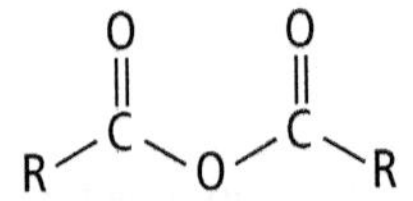

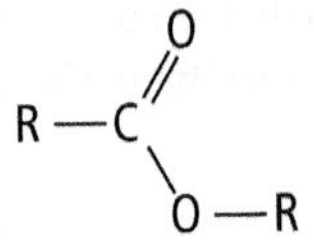

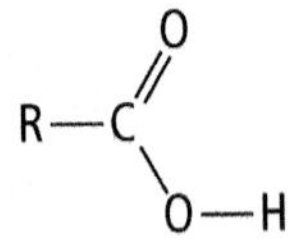

$CH_3C(=O)O(CH_2)_4CH_3$

Pentyl ethanoate

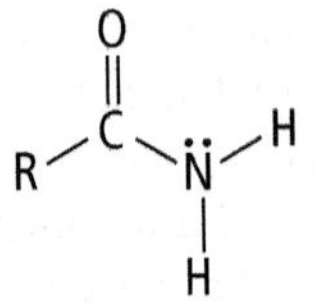

Amides are very unreactive in comparison to the other members of this family. The stability comes from the following resonance structures:

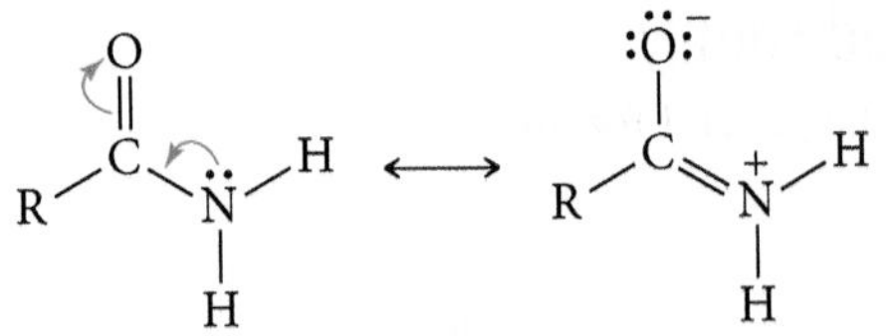

R—C(=O)—N̈H—H ⟷ R—C(—Ö:$^-$)=N$^+$H—H

Another way of looking at this is that the p orbital on the N atom becomes part of a delocalized π system over the O—C—N bonds. As a consequence, the amide group is planar. The relative unreactivity of amides comes from the partial double bond between carbon and nitrogen, which is difficult to break. The C=N character that arises from the resonance structures adds rigidity to the group. This is very important biologically because proteins are made of amino acids that are connected together by amide groups, which are called peptide bonds in biochemistry. The rigidity of peptide bonds is one factor that allows proteins to maintain their three-dimensional structure. Also, if amide groups were very reactive, proteins would not exist because they would hydrolyze in water. Hydrolysis of acyl groups will be discussed in the next chapter.

The carboxylate anion, $RCOO^-$, is like the amide group in its low reactivity. Again, this is due to its resonance stabilization:

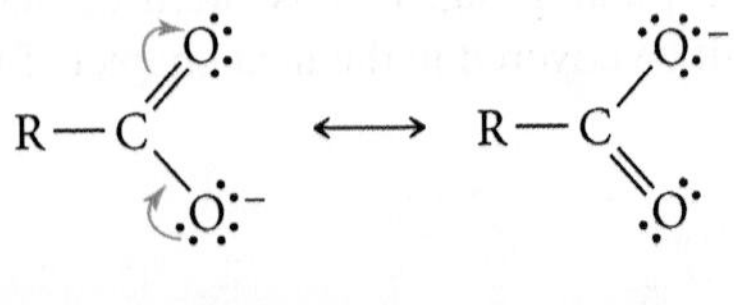

R—C(=Ö:)—Ö:$^-$ ⟷ R—C(—Ö:$^-$)=Ö:

20.5 Constitutional Isomerism

Molecular formulas are generally the simplest way to represent compounds. In organic chemistry, however, molecular formulas are insufficient because the same atoms can bond together in different ways to form different compounds. For example, consider an alkane with 4 carbon atoms and 10 hydrogen atoms. Two different structures are possible: butane and 2-methylpropane.

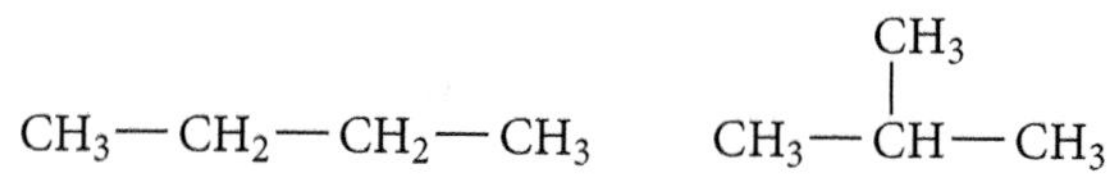

$CH_3—CH_2—CH_2—CH_3$

Butane

$CH_3—CH(CH_3)—CH_3$

2-Methylpropane

Butane and 2-methylpropane are **constitutional isomers**: molecules with the same molecular formula but different structures. Because of their different structures, they have different properties—they are indeed different compounds. Constitutional isomerism is ubiquitous in organic chemistry. The more carbon atoms you have in a molecular formula, the more constitutional isomers are possible.

The number and variety of constitutional isomers for a given molecular formula become more complicated when rings, double bonds, or triple bonds can be present. For example, in Section 20.3, we showed that the formula of a cycloalkane is C_nH_{2n}, which is the same as the formula for an alkene with one double bond. Consider the molecular formula C_4H_8. Of the possible constitutional isomers, two are cycloalkanes and three are alkenes:

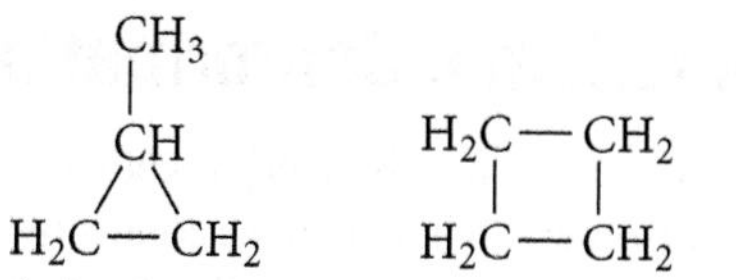

Methylcyclopropane

Cyclobutane

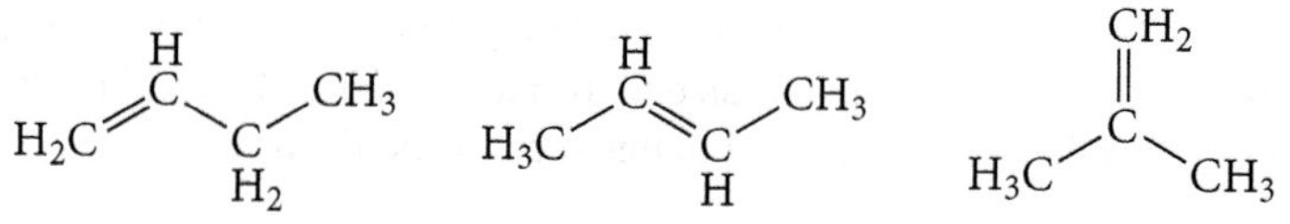

But-1-ene

But-2-ene

2-Methylpropene

CONCEPTUAL CONNECTION 20.1
Constitutional Isomers

Which of the following is/are a constitutional isomer(s) of this molecule? (*Hint:* Which structures have the same molecular formula?)

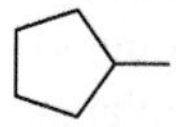

(a) **(b)** **(c)** **(d)**

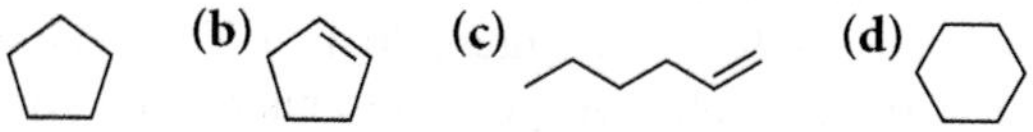

So far, we have discussed isomers that involve differences in the branching of hydrocarbon components of molecules—that is, cases in which the carbon skeletons are different. It is also possible for compounds to share the same molecular formula but have different functional groups. For example, consider the molecular formula C_2H_6O. Ethanol and dimethyl ether share this formula, and are therefore isomers:

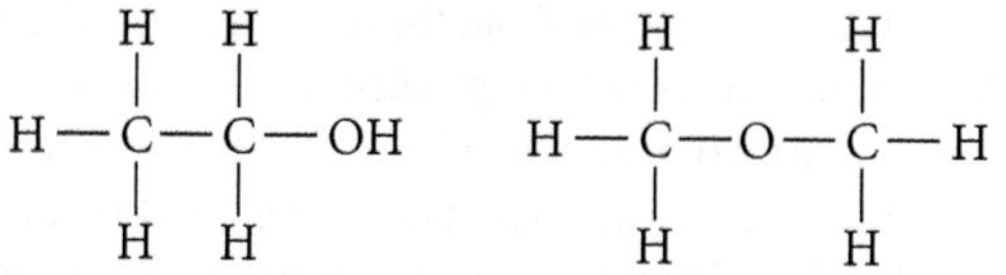

Ethanol

Dimethyl ether

Another variation of constitutional isomerism involving functional groups is when the same functional group can be located in different positions in different molecules (e.g.,

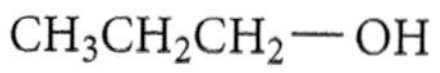

$CH_3CH_2CH_2—OH$

Propan-1-ol

$CH_3CH(OH)CH_3$

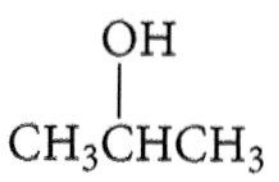

Propan-2-ol

propan-1-ol vs. propan-2-ol). Another example is the case of amines that can be primary, secondary, or tertiary, giving rise to isomers with different R groups.

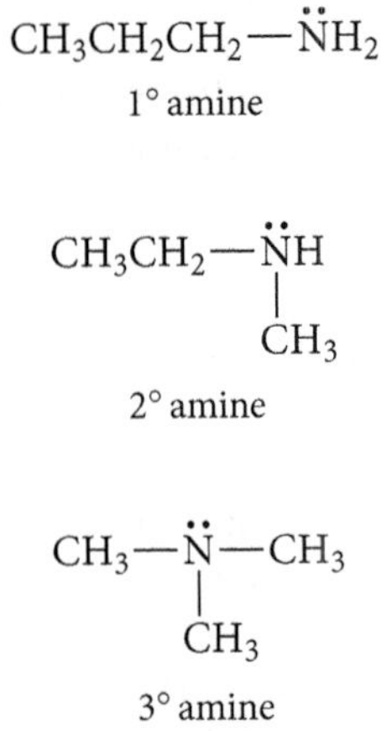

$$CH_3CH_2CH_2-\ddot{N}H_2$$

1° amine

$$CH_3CH_2-\ddot{N}H-CH_3$$

2° amine

$$CH_3-\ddot{N}(CH_3)-CH_3$$

3° amine

▲ These amines have the same molecular formula, C_3H_9N.

The task of determining the actual structure of a molecule from its molecular formula often requires additional information. In Section 20.8, we will discuss how to do this.

20.6 Stereoisomerism I: Conformational Isomerism

In constitutional isomerism, atoms are bonded together with different connectivities. **Stereoisomerism** is a type of isomerism in which the connectivity between atoms is identical, but the spatial arrangements of atoms are different. Stereoisomerism can be **conformational** or **configurational**. Conformational isomerism is the result of bond rotations. Conformational isomers can be interconverted simply by rotating around single bonds, without breaking any bonds. Configurational isomers can only be interconverted by breaking bonds. These two types of stereoisomerism are covered in this section and the next.

Conformational Isomerism: Rotation About Single Bonds

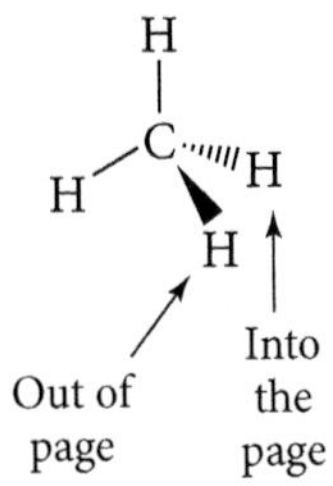

From our discussion of bonding in alkanes, we know that rotation about a single bond is to be expected because of the axial symmetry of sigma bonds. The unlimited rotation about every single bond in a molecule leads to a continuum of possible molecular shapes that vary only by the amount of rotation around each single bond in the molecule. This variety of shapes is called conformational isomerism. The various molecular shapes that result from the rotation about single bonds are known as **conformers** (from conformational isomers) or **rotamers** (from rotational isomers).

In order to represent different molecular shapes in three dimensions, chemists use a **three-dimensional formula**, which is similar to a structural formula except that some of the bonds are drawn as wedges (see Figure 20.4 ▸). This type of representation was introduced in Section 10.4. A solid wedge represents a bond coming out of the page, toward the viewer. A hashed wedge represents a bond going into the page, away from the viewer. This allows you to picture the molecule in three dimensions.

H, C, H, H, H
Out of page
Into the page

When representing a molecular conformation, three-dimensional formulas provide a side view of the entire molecule. To show the molecular conformation around one C—C bond, chemists use a **Newman projection formula**. In a Newman projection, we look directly down the C—C bond of interest. The carbon atom in front is represented by a point from which three bonds emerge, representing three single bonds. The rear carbon atom is represented by a circle. Three lines emerge from the rear carbon, indicating the three groups bonded to it. Figure 20.4 shows the Newman projections for two important conformations of ethane. In the **staggered conformation**, the C—H bonds on different carbons are as far apart as possible. The dihedral angle (the angle between C—H bonds on the different carbon atoms as seen down the C—C bond) is 60°. In the **eclipsed conformation**, the C—H bonds on different carbon atoms are aligned with each other and the dihedral angle is 0°. The amount of bond rotation needed to go from staggered to eclipsed conformations is 60°.

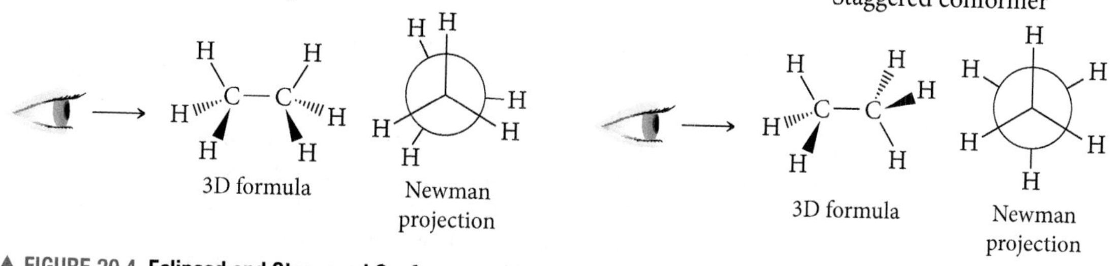

Eclipsed conformer

3D formula

Newman projection

Staggered conformer

3D formula

Newman projection

▲ **FIGURE 20.4 Eclipsed and Staggered Conformers of Ethane** Three-dimensional formulas and Newman projection formulas are shown for these conformations. In the Newman projection, the molecule is viewed down the C—C bond. The "front" carbon atom is represented by the intersection of the three lines representing C—H bonds. The circle represents the "rear" carbon atom. The C—H bonds of the rear carbon atom are obscured by the rear carbon atom.

From experiments, we know that rotation about the C—C bond in alkanes is extremely fast at room temperature—it is on the order of picoseconds ($1\ \text{ps} = 10^{-12}\ \text{s}$). When the temperature is decreased, bond rotation slows down. This allows for the measurement of the activation energy for bond rotation. In the case of ethane, the energy barrier to rotation is $12\ \text{kJ mol}^{-1}$. This energy corresponds to the difference in potential energy of staggered and eclipsed conformations. This difference in energy is known as the **torsional strain**. One explanation for the energy difference is that it arises from the stabilization of the staggered conformer by favourable interactions between sigma bonding orbitals and adjacent sigma antibonding orbitals, which are aligned in the staggered conformation. Figure 20.5 ▼ shows the potential energies for ethane conformations with bond rotations.

When we examine the rotation about the central C—C bond in butane, we observe the different staggered and eclipsed conformations shown in Figure 20.6 ▼. Just as in ethane, torsional strain limits bond rotation. However, the methyl groups around the C2—C3 bond in butane give rise to another type of strain. To understand the energies of butane conformations, we need to look at the relative positions of the methyl groups as

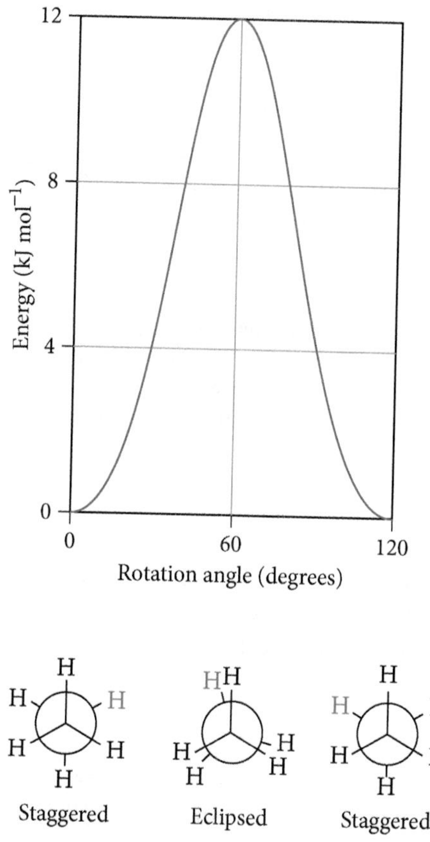

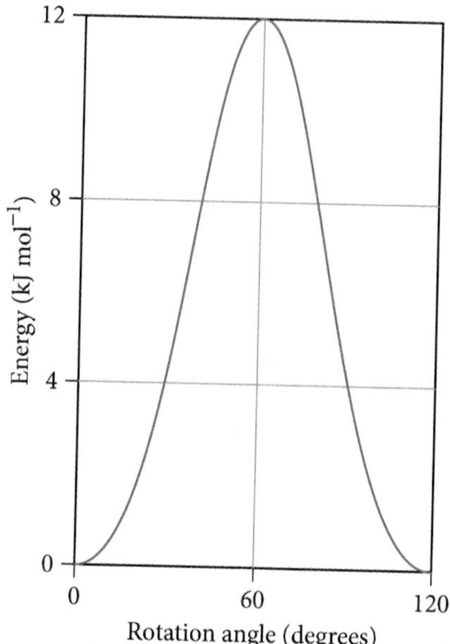

Staggered

Eclipsed

Staggered

◀ **FIGURE 20.5 Energy Versus Rotation Angle for Ethane** Starting in the staggered conformation, the C—C bond is rotated. A rotation of 60° gives the eclipsed conformation, which is higher in energy than the staggered conformation. A further bond rotation of 60° returns the molecule to the staggered conformation.

they rotate about the middle C2—C3 bond. The angle that the C—CH_3 bonds make with each other is the dihedral angle. Conformations where the methyl groups are closer to each other are less stable than those where they are farther apart. This is due to the interactions of the methyl groups. The hydrogen atoms on the methyl groups can come close enough that the atomic radii of the hydrogen atoms begin to overlap. This produces a repulsive interaction known as **steric strain**. The lowest-energy conformation is the **antistaggered conformation** in which the methyl groups are farthest apart at 180° to each other. The next-lowest-energy conformation is the **gauche-staggered conformation** in which the methyl groups are 60° to each other. Out of the two eclipsed conformations, the least favourable is the one in which the methyl groups are closest to each other when 0° apart, which has the largest steric strain. The relative energies of these butane conformations are shown in Figure 20.6.

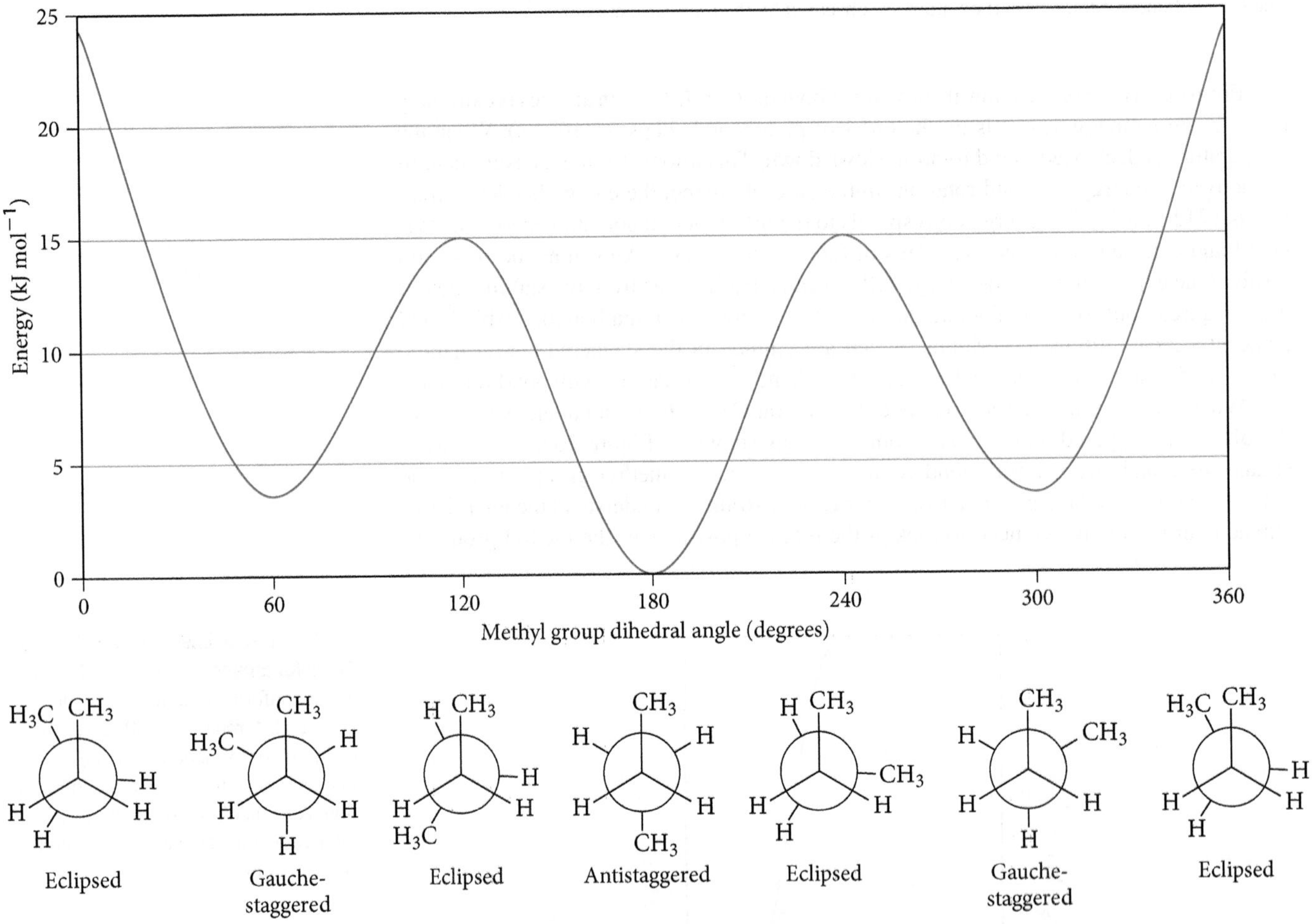

Energy (kJ mol^{-1})

Methyl group dihedral angle (degrees)

Eclipsed | Gauche-staggered | Eclipsed | Antistaggered | Eclipsed | Gauche-staggered | Eclipsed

▲ **FIGURE 20.6 Energies of Butane Conformations** Starting with the two methyl groups in the highest-energy eclipsed conformation, the C2—C3 bond is rotated through 360°. A rotation of 60° gives the gauche-staggered conformation. At 120° of bond rotation the methyl groups are eclipsed with H atoms. At 180° is the lowest-energy conformation (antistaggered) in which the two methyl groups are as far apart as possible.

Ring Conformations of Cycloalkanes

Organic chemists in the nineteenth century thought that cycloalkanes existed as planar structures in which the carbon atoms in the ring shared the same plane. In this model, the ring structures were all simple geometrical figures:

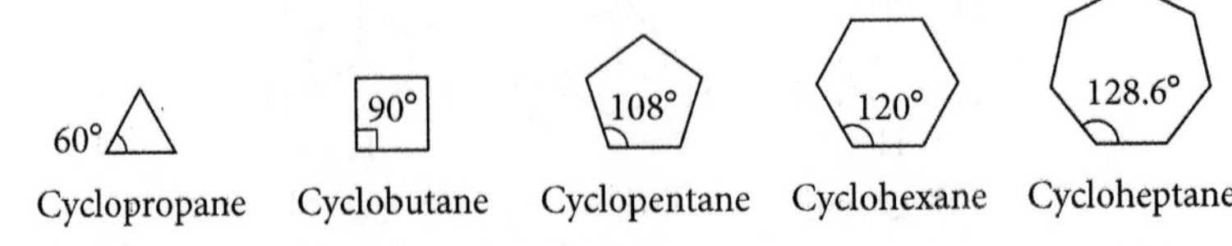

Most of the internal angles in simple polygons are very different from the ideal C—C—C bond angle of 109.5° that is expected for an sp^3 hybridized carbon. The difference between the bond angle in the ring and the ideal 109.5° is known as **angle strain**. For example, the angle strain in cyclopropane is 109.5° − 60° = 49.5°. In cyclopentane, the angle strain is much smaller at 1.5°. Also, note that in planar cycloalkanes, C—H and C—C bonds on adjacent carbon atoms are eclipsed:

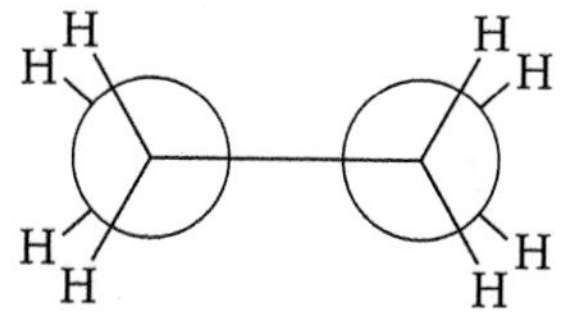

Newman projection of cyclobutane

In 1895, the German chemist Hermann Sachse proposed that ring strain could disappear if rings were nonplanar. This idea was initially rejected by the chemical community, but was later shown to be correct. Cycloalkane rings are quite flexible due to C—C bond rotation, which leads to a twisting of the ring. In cyclobutane and cyclopentane, the rings buckle to give "puckered" conformations that reduce the angle strain:

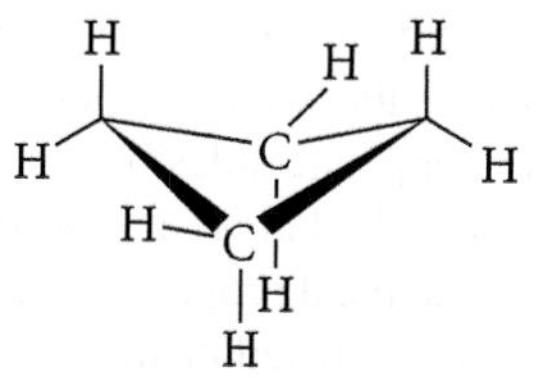

Cyclobutane

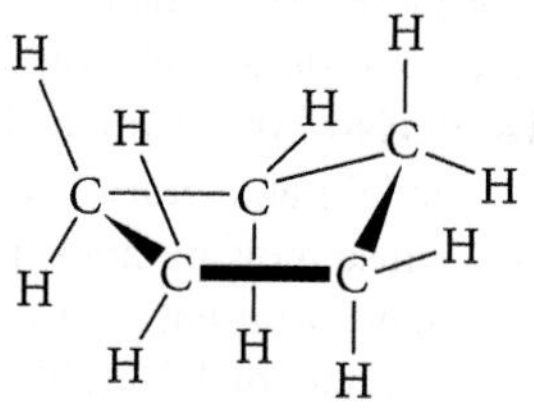

Cyclopentane

In cyclohexane, the most favourable conformer is known as the **chair conformation**. In this conformation, all C—C—C bond angles in the ring are 111.4°, so there is minimal angle strain. In addition, the chair conformation has staggered C—H and C—C bonds all around the ring. C—H bonds that are arranged around the plane of the ring pointing outward are described as **equatorial bonds**, and those pointed vertically up and down, perpendicular to the ring, are called **axial bonds**.

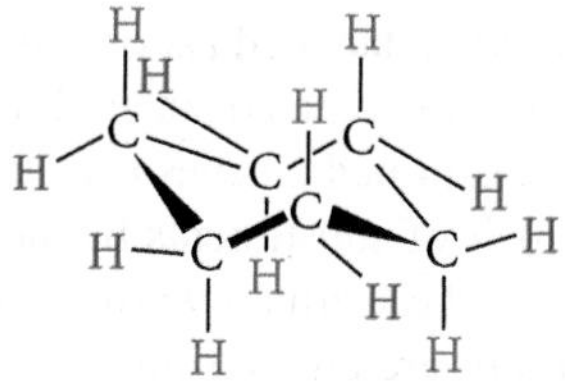

◀ Chair conformation of cyclohexane. Equatorial hydrogen atoms are blue. Axial hydrogen atoms are red.

CONCEPTUAL CONNECTION 20.2

Staggered Conformations in Rings

In the chair conformation of cyclohexane, the C—H and C—C bonds are in staggered conformations all the way around the ring. Compare these with the conformations of butane (Figure 20.6). Are the cyclohexane conformations antistaggered or gauche-staggered?

20.7 Stereoisomerism II: Configurational Isomerism

Configurational isomerism occurs when atoms and functional groups are connected in the same sequence, but there is a difference in the spatial locations of atoms or groups. The only way to interconvert configurational isomers is to break covalent bonds.

Configurational isomers can be divided into two categories: **Enantiomers** are molecules that are nonsuperimposable mirror images. **Diastereomers** are molecules that are nonsuperimposable but are not mirror images.

Cis–Trans Isomerism in Alkenes

A major difference between a single bond and a double bond is the degree to which rotation occurs about the bond. As discussed in Section 20.3, rotation about a double bond is highly restricted. Consider the following two isomers of 1,2-dichloroethene:

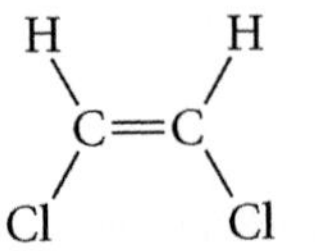

H H
C=C
Cl Cl

cis-1,2-Dichloroethene

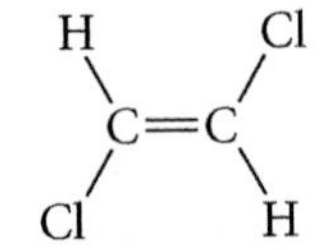

H Cl
C=C
Cl H

trans-1,2-Dichloroethene

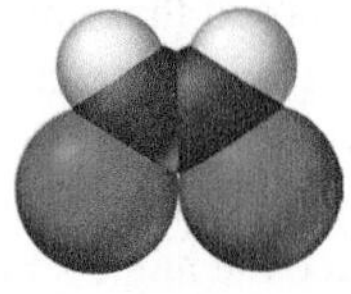

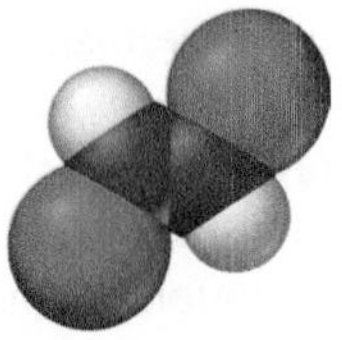

There is no way for these two isomers to interconvert without breaking the double bond. Therefore, these are configurational isomers. Specifically, this kind of stereoisomerism is called ***cis–trans*** **isomerism**. We distinguish between the two isomers with the designations *cis* (meaning "same side") and *trans* (meaning "opposite sides"). *Cis* and *trans* isomers are diastereomers because they are nonsuperimposable, but are not mirror images of each other. Diastereomers have different physical and chemical properties. The physical properties of the two stereoisomers of 1,2-dichloroethene are listed in Table 20.6.

The *cis–trans* labels work well for disubstituted alkenes and are commonly used. However, for alkenes in which there are three or four different substituents, these labels become ambiguous. For example, consider the configurational isomers of 1-bromo-1-chloropropene:

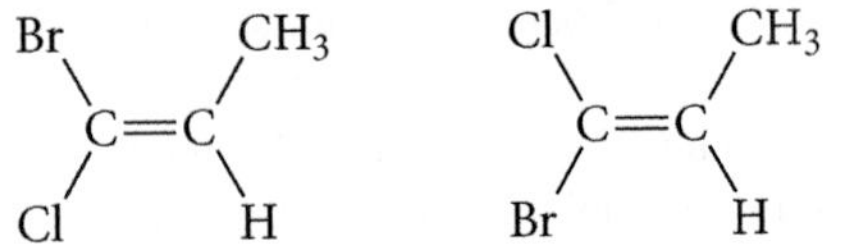

Br CH_3
C=C
Cl H

Cl CH_3
C=C
Br H

1-Bromo-2-chloropropene
configurational isomers

It is not clear which isomer should be labelled *cis* or *trans* because there is ambiguity as to which halogen atom (Cl or Br) should be considered relative to the methyl group. The IUPAC convention for naming substituted alkenes is called the ***E,Z*** **system**, and is based on assigning priorities to each pair of substituents bonded to each carbon of the double bond. A configuration of Z (from the German word *zusammen*, meaning "together") is assigned if the high-priority groups are on the same side of the bond; a configuration of

TABLE 20.6 Physical Properties of *cis*- and *trans*-1,2-Dichloroethene

Name	Structure	Space-Filling Model	Density (g mL^{-1})	Melting Point (°C)	Boiling Point (°C)
cis-1,2-Dichloroethene	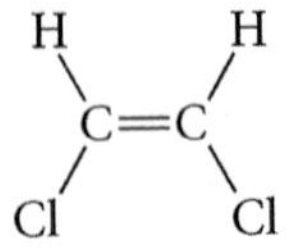 H H C=C Cl Cl	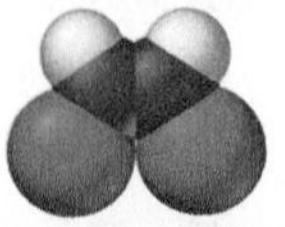	1.284	−80.5	60.1
trans-1,2-Dichloroethene	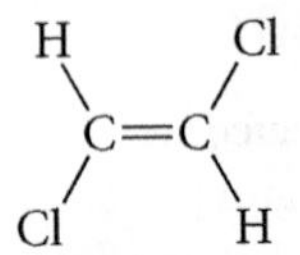 H Cl C=C Cl H		1.257	−49.4	47.5

E (from the German word *entgegen*, meaning "opposite") is assigned if the high-priority groups are on different sides:

A useful memory trick is that *zusammen* has the "word" samme embedded within: "same" side.

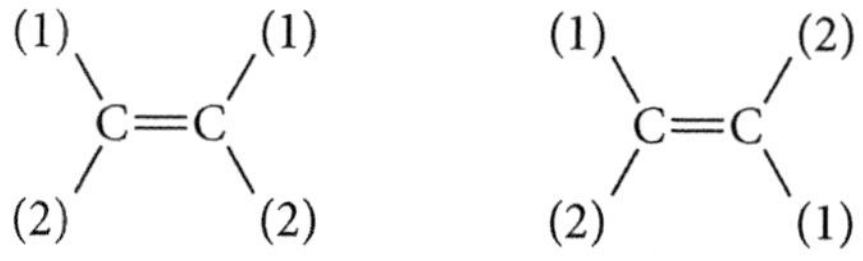

(1) (1) C=C (2) (2)
Z configuration

(1) (2) C=C (2) (1)
E configuration

The priorities of substituents are determined using what are known as the Cahn–Ingold–Prelog rules:

Rule 1: Priority is first determined on the basis of the atomic mass of the atoms that are directly bonded to the carbons in the double bond. In our example above, Br is a higher priority than Cl, and the methyl carbon atom is a higher priority than H, so we can assign the following names:

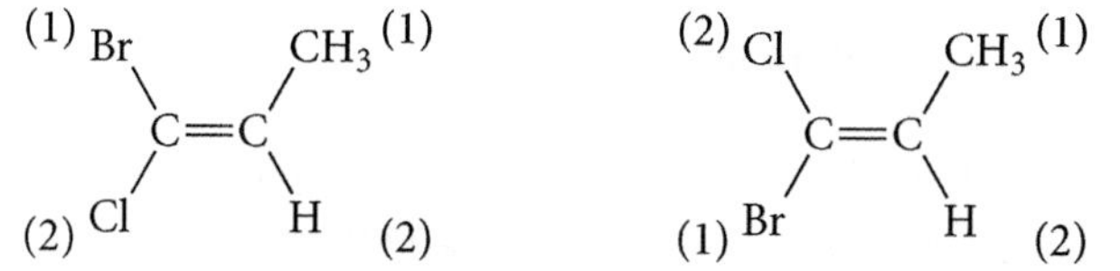

(1) Br, CH_3 (1), C=C, (2) Cl, H (2)
Z-1-Bromo-1-chloropropene

(2) Cl, CH_3 (1), C=C, (1) Br, H (2)
E-1-Bromo-1-chloropropene

Rule 2: If the atoms directly attached to a double-bonded carbon atom are the same, then the second atoms of the substituents are compared. Again, priority is assigned on the basis of atomic mass. If there is no difference in priority among the second atoms, then the third atoms are considered, and so on. Consider ethyl and propyl substituents, where the first point of difference occurs at the third atom. The propyl group is a higher-priority group because the third atom is a carbon whereas in the ethyl group the third atom is hydrogen.

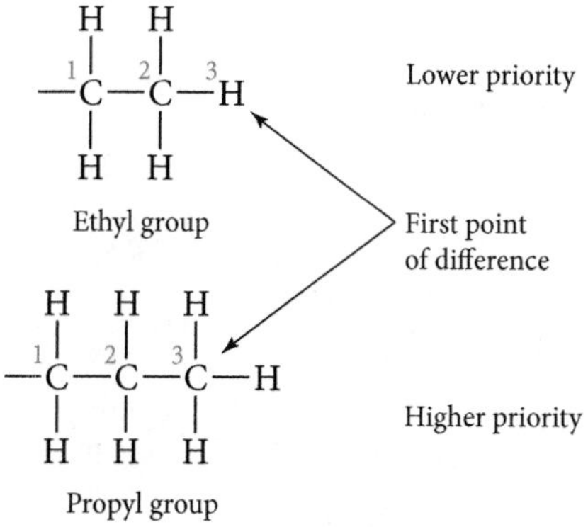

Ethyl group: $-\overset{1}{C}H_2-\overset{2}{C}H_2-\overset{3}{H}$ — Lower priority

First point of difference

Propyl group: $-\overset{1}{C}H_2-\overset{2}{C}H_2-\overset{3}{C}H_2-H$ — Higher priority

Rule 3: If a substituent contains a double or triple bond, the multiply bonded atom is treated as if it were two or three atoms bonded to the same carbon atom. For example,

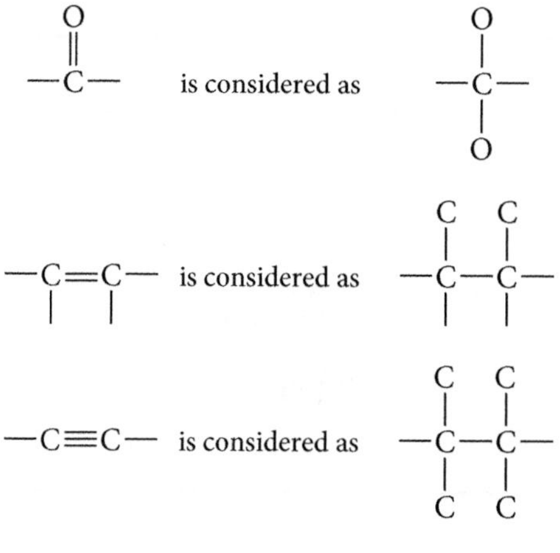

$-C(=O)-$ is considered as $-C(O)(O)-$

$-C=C-$ is considered as $-C(C)-C(C)-$

$-C\equiv C-$ is considered as $-C(C)(C)-C(C)(C)-$

EXAMPLE 20.2 ASSIGNING THE CONFIGURATIONS OF ALKENES

As appropriate, assign a configuration of *E*/*Z* to the following compounds:

(a) H(Cl)C=C(Cl)(CH$_3$) (b) (c)

SORT You are given the molecular structure, or configuration of groups around an alkene. You are asked to assign the configuration as *E* or Z.	**GIVEN:** Alkene configuration **FIND:** *E*/*Z* configuration
STRATEGIZE Assign priorities of groups bonded to each carbon atom of the alkene unit, using the Cahn–Ingold–Prelog rules. If same-priority groups are on opposite sides, the configuration is *E*. If on the same side, it is *Z*.	**CONCEPTUAL PLAN** **Assign Priority to Each Group ⟶ Determine Configuration** **Definitions and Rules Used:** Cahn–Ingold–Prelog Rules *E* configuration = priority groups opposite sides *Z* configuration = priority groups same side
SOLVE **(a) 1.** On the left-hand side of the double bond, Cl has priority over H. On the right-hand side, Cl has priority over the methyl group. **2.** The priority groups are on opposite sides, so this is an *E* configuration.	(2) H, Cl (1), (1) Cl, CH$_3$ (2) ***E* configuration**
(b) 1. On the left-hand side of the double bond, the methyl group has priority over H. On the right-hand side, the ethyl group has priority over the methyl group. **2.** The priority groups are on the same side, so this is a *Z* configuration.	(1) (1) (2) (2) ***Z* configuration**
(c) 1. On the left-hand side of the double bond, the methyl group has priority over H. On the right-hand side, *Rule 3* must be used. The C—C double bond is counted as extra C atoms. The first point of difference is shown. The extra C atom takes priority, thus the alkene group has priority over the ethyl group. **2.** The priority groups are on the same side, so this is a *Z* configuration.	(1) (2) (1) (2) First point of difference ***Z* configuration**
CHECK Confirm that priorities were assigned correctly.	

FOR PRACTICE 20.2

As appropriate, assign a configuration of *E*/*Z* to the following compounds:

(a) I(Br)C=C(Br)(Cl) (b) H(HOOC)C=C(COOH)(H) (c) H(H$_3$C)C=C(C(=O)—CH$_3$)(H)

Enantiomers: Chirality

Enantiomers are molecules that are nonsuperimposable mirror images of each other. For example, consider the molecule shown here:

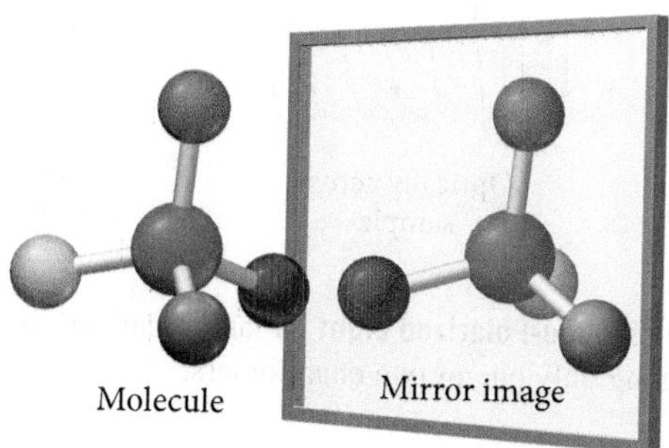

The molecule cannot be superimposed onto its mirror image. If we swing the mirror image around to try to superimpose the two, we find that there is no way to get all four substituent atoms to align together.

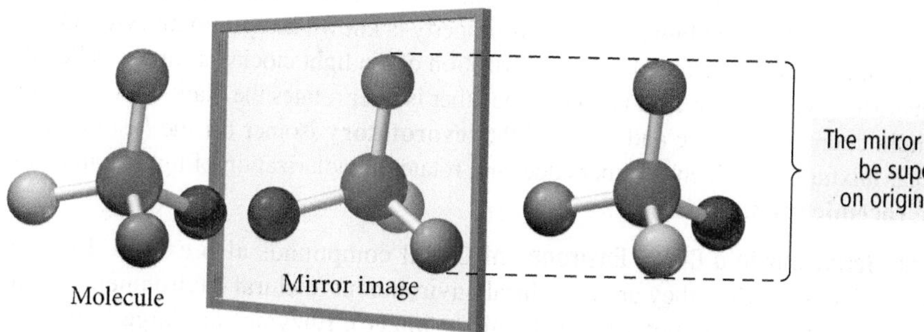

Enantiomers are similar to your right and left hands (Figure 20.7 ▸). The two are mirror images of one another, but you cannot superimpose one on the other. For this reason, a right-handed glove does not fit on your left hand and vice versa. This type of isomerism is known as **chirality**. The word derives from the Greek word *cheir*, which means "hand."

Any carbon atom with four different substituents in a tetrahedral arrangement is a **chirality centre**. Consider 3-methylhexane below. The molecules on the left and right are nonsuperimposable mirror images and are enantiomers of one another.

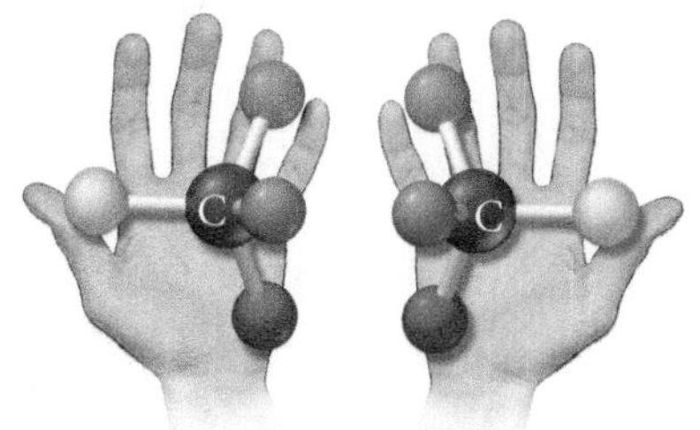

▲ **FIGURE 20.7 Mirror Images** The left and right hand are nonsuperimposable mirror images, just as are optical isomers.

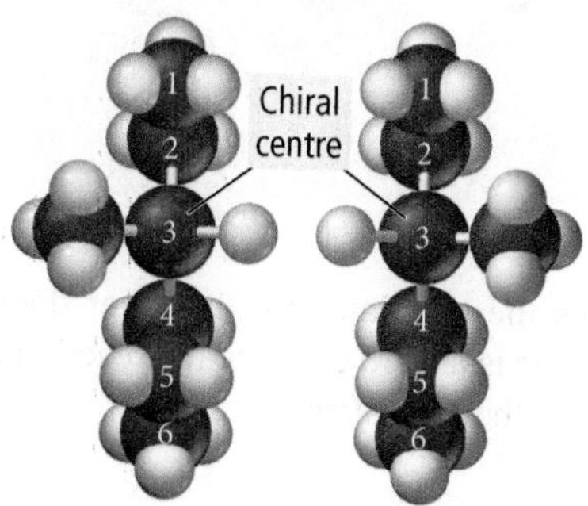

Optical isomers of 3-methylhexane

Chirality is important, not only to organic chemistry, but also to biology and biochemistry. Most biological molecules are chiral and usually only one or the other enantiomer is active in biological systems. For example, glucose, the primary fuel of cells, is chiral. Only one of the enantiomers of glucose has that familiar sweet taste and only that enantiomer can fuel our cellular functioning; the other enantiomer is not even metabolized by the body.

Some of the physical and chemical properties of enantiomers are indistinguishable from one another. For example, both of the optical isomers of 3-methylhexane have identical melting points, boiling points, and densities. However, the properties of enantiomers

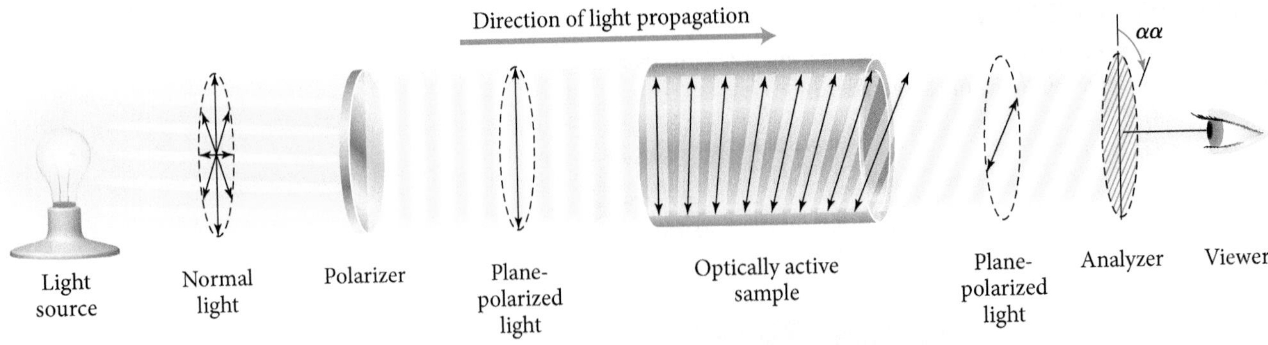

▲ **FIGURE 20.8 Rotation of Plane-Polarized Light** Plane-polarized light rotates as it passes through a sample containing only one of two enantiomers.

differ from one another in two important ways: (1) the direction in which they rotate plane-polarized light and (2) in their chemical behaviour in a chiral environment.

Optical Activity *Plane-polarized light* is light in which electric field waves oscillate in only one plane, as shown in Figure 20.8 ▲. When a beam of plane-polarized light is directed through a sample containing only one of two enantiomers, the plane of polarization of the light is rotated, as shown in Figure 20.8. This property is known as **optical activity**. One of the two enantiomers rotates the plane of polarization of the light clockwise and is called the **dextrorotatory isomer** (or the *d* isomer). The other isomer rotates the plane of polarization of the light counterclockwise and is called the **levorotatory** isomer (or the *l* isomer). An equimolar mixture of both enantiomers does not rotate the polarization of light at all and is called a **racemic mixture**.

Dextrorotatory means turning clockwise, or to the right. Levorotatory means turning counterclockwise, or to the left.

Chemical Behaviour in a Chiral Environment Chiral compounds also exhibit different chemical behaviour when they are in a chiral environment (a chiral environment is simply one that is not superimposable on its mirror image). Enzymes are large biological molecules that catalyze reactions in living organisms and provide chiral environments. Consider the following simplified picture of two enantiomers in a chiral environment.

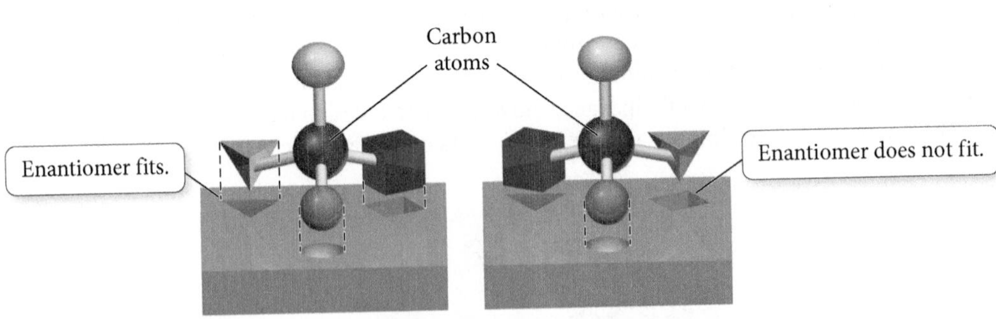

One of the enantiomers fits the template, but the other does not, no matter how it is rotated. In this way, an enzyme is able to catalyze the reaction of one enantiomer because that particular enantiomer fits the "template."

CONCEPTUAL CONNECTION 20.3

Chirality

Which structure is chiral?

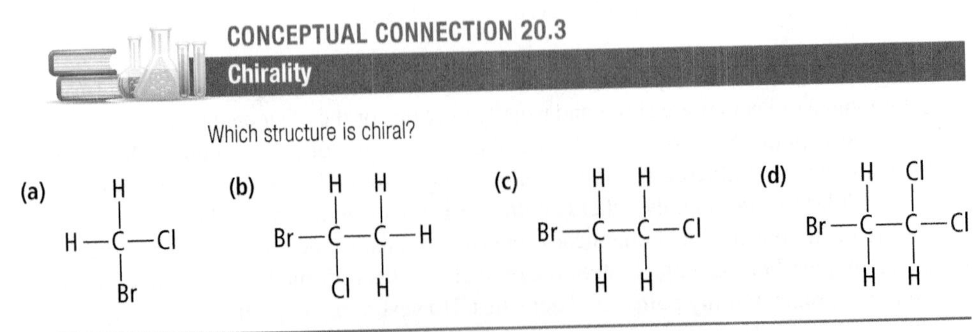

Absolute Configurations

Enantiomers have identical physical properties except in the way that they interact with plane-polarized light. Thus, it is difficult to determine experimentally the actual structure of an enantiomer. How does a chemist determine whether an enantiomer is one configuration or its mirror image? The actual configuration of atoms at a chirality centre is known as the **absolute configuration**. There was no way to know the absolute configuration of stereoisomers until 1951, when the Dutch chemist Johannes Martin Bijvoet and coworkers used an X-ray crystallography technique to determine the absolute configuration of sodium rubidium *d*-tartrate.

Sodium rubidium *d*-tartrate

Once the absolute configuration is known, it is labelled according to the ***R,S*** **system**. In this system, each group around the chirality centre is assigned a priority according to the Cahn–Ingold–Prelog rules that are used in the *E,Z* system for alkenes. Priorities are assigned as the numbers 1, 2, 3, and 4, with 1 being the highest-priority group and 4 the lowest. The molecule is "viewed" from the opposite side as the lowest-priority group. (This is similar to a Newman projection, where we look along the bond.) If the other three groups are arranged in a clockwise sequence from 1–3, then the configuration is *R* (from the Latin *rectus*, meaning right). If the sequence is counterclockwise, then the configuration is *S* (from the Latin *sinister*, meaning left). The *R* and *S* configurations of butan-2-ol are shown in Figure 20.9 ▼.

1,2,3 Clockwise

(*R*)-Butan-2-ol

1,2,3 Counterclockwise

(*S*)-Butan-2-ol

◀ **FIGURE 20.9 Absolute Configurations of Butan-2-ol Enantiomers** With the lowest-priority group (H) positioned into the page, the group priorities 1, 2, and 3 are clockwise in the *R* enantiomer and counterclockwise in the *S* enantiomer.

EXAMPLE 20.3 ASSIGNING *R,S* CONFIGURATIONS

Determine the absolute configurations of the following compounds:

(a)

(b)

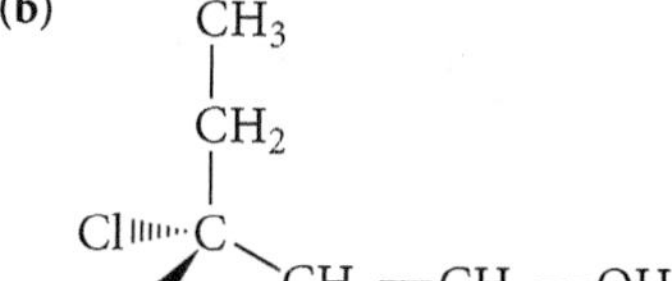

(c)

SOLUTION

SORT You are given the molecular structure at a chirality centre, and you are asked to determine the absolute configuration.

GIVEN: Molecular structure

FIND: Absolute configuration (*R,S*)

STRATEGIZE Using the Cahn–Ingold–Prelog rules, assign priorities to groups at each chirality centre.

Rotate the molecule so that you can view it along the bond from the central carbon atom to the fourth-priority group. If the priority groups 1–3 are arranged in a clockwise manner, the configuration is *R*. If counterclockwise, it is *S*.

CONCEPTUAL PLAN

Assign Priority to Each Group ⟶ Determine Configuration

Definitions and Rules Used:

Cahn–Ingold–Prelog Rules

R configuration = groups arranged clockwise

S configuration = groups arranged counterclockwise

SOLVE

(a) 1. The group with highest priority is $—NH_2$ because the N has the highest atomic number. The —COOH group is higher in priority than $—CH_3$ because the C is bonded to two O atoms, which have higher atomic number than the H atoms on the methyl group. The lowest-priority group is H.

(continued)

EXAMPLE 20.3 (CONTINUED)

2. When the molecule is rotated so that the C—H bond is into the page, the groups with priorities 1, 2, and 3 are in a counterclockwise arrangement. The absolute configuration is *S*.	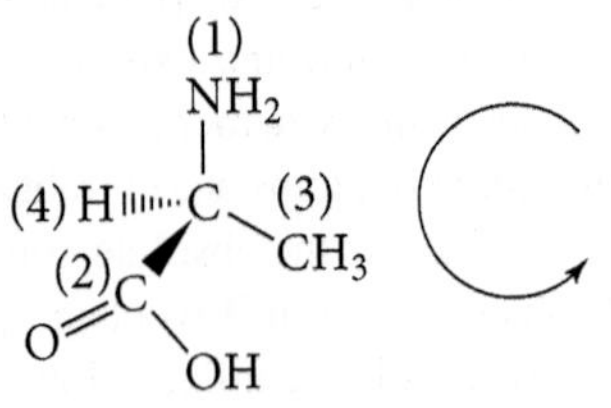 (1) NH_2; (4) H; (3) CH_3; (2) C; O; OH ***S* configuration**
(b) 1. The Cl atom has the highest priority, followed by the $—CH_2—CH_2—OH$ group, then the $—CH_2—CH_3$ group (because the first point of difference is the —OH group). The H atom has the lowest priority.	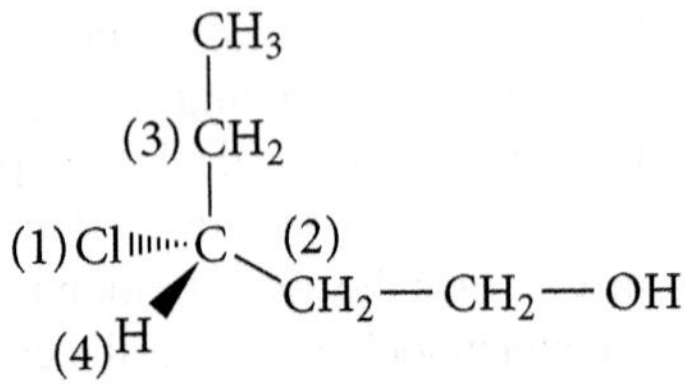 CH_3; (3) CH_2; (1) Cl; C; (2) $CH_2—CH_2—OH$; (4) H
2. By rotating the structural formula, we can move the groups into positions that are more convenient to view their arrangement.	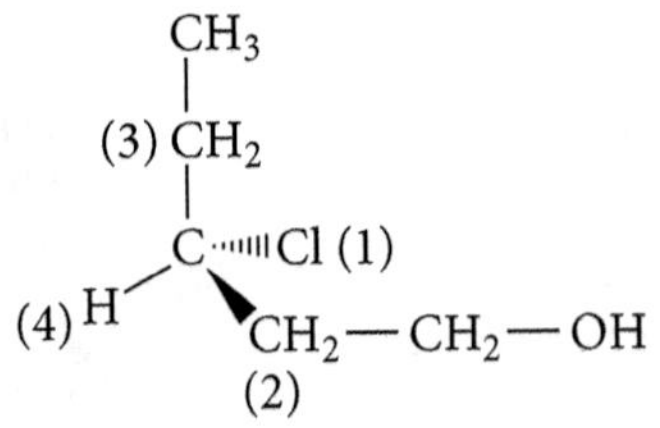 CH_3; (3) CH_2; C; Cl (1); (4) H; $CH_2—CH_2—OH$ (2)
3. When the molecule is rotated so that the C—H bond is into the page, the groups with priorities 1, 2, and 3 are in a clockwise arrangement. The absolute configuration is *R*.	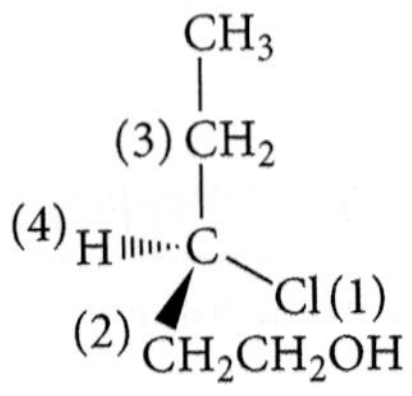 CH_3; (3) CH_2; (4) H; C; Cl (1); (2) CH_2CH_2OH ***R* configuration**
(c) 1. The group with the highest priority is Cl. In the ring, the C=C double bond is treated according to Cahn–Ingold–Prelog *Rule 3*. It is equivalent to an extra C atom on each of the alkene carbon atoms. The first point of difference is shown in red. The side of the ring with the C=C double bond takes priority over the other side of the ring, because of the extra C atom, and is therefore the second-priority group. The third-priority group is the "alkane" side of the ring. The lowest-priority group is H.	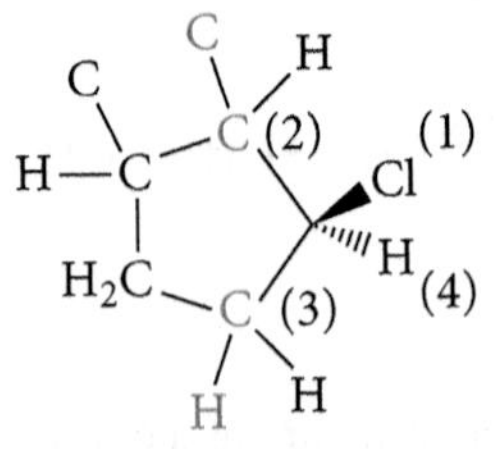 C; C; H; H—C; C (2); (1) Cl; H (4); H_2C; C (3); H; H
2. The structure is already oriented so that the lowest-priority group is into the page. The groups with priorities 1, 2, and 3 are in a counterclockwise arrangement. The absolute configuration is *S*.	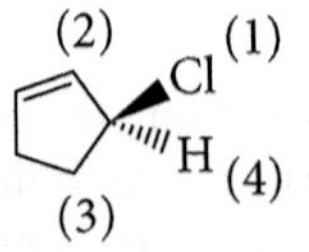 (2); (1) Cl; H (4); (3) ***S* configuration**

CHECK Confirm that the priorities of different groups are correct.

FOR PRACTICE 20.3

Determine the absolute configurations of the following compounds:

(a) 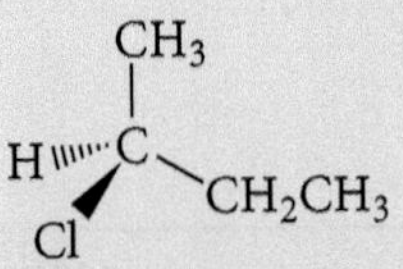 CH_3; H; C; CH_2CH_3; Cl

(b) 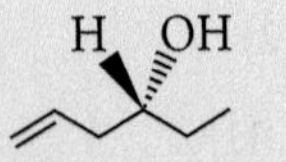 H; OH

(c) CH_3; H; O

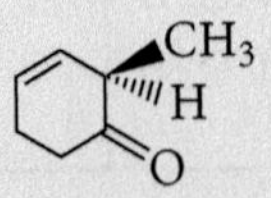

CHEMISTRY AND MEDICINE Anesthetics and Alcohol

When someone has a surgery, they are usually given a general anesthetic so that they do not feel pain or discomfort during the procedure. The anesthetist usually gives the patient an intravenous injection of an **induction agent**, which quickly sends the patient to sleep. After this, the anesthetist "intubates" the patient and administers a mixture of gases that maintains the unconscious state.

An example of an induction agent is the drug *etomidate*, shown below. Etomidate binds to a receptor protein called a **GABA receptor**. (GABA stands for ***gamma*-aminobutanoic acid**, which is a neurotransmitter.) Several different GABA receptors are known, such as $GABA_A$ and $GABA_B$. When etomidate binds to a GABA receptor on a neuron, that neuron is less likely to "fire," or transmit a signal. When neurotransmission in general is inhibited like this, the result is a sedative effect on the nervous system. Etomidate is a chiral molecule, and is used as a racemic mixture. However, the $GABA_A$ receptor is ten times more responsive to the *R* enantiomer of etomidate than to the *S* enantiomer. The reason is that the $GABA_A$ receptor is also chiral, and reacts differently with different enantiomers.

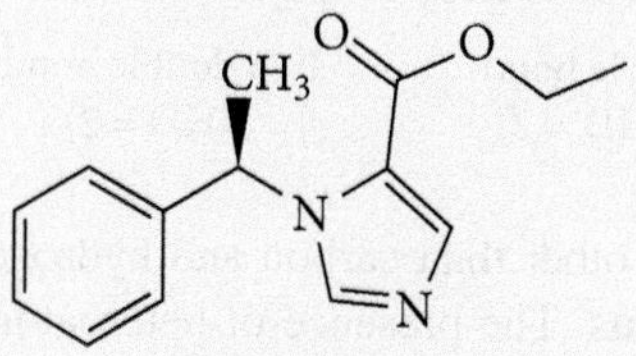

Many other compounds can bind to GABA receptors and consequently produce sedative effects. Many of these compounds are not chiral. One example is ethanol. When ethanol binds to the $GABA_A$ receptor, neurotransmission is inhibited, and mental functions slow down. This explains some of the effects of drinking alcohol!

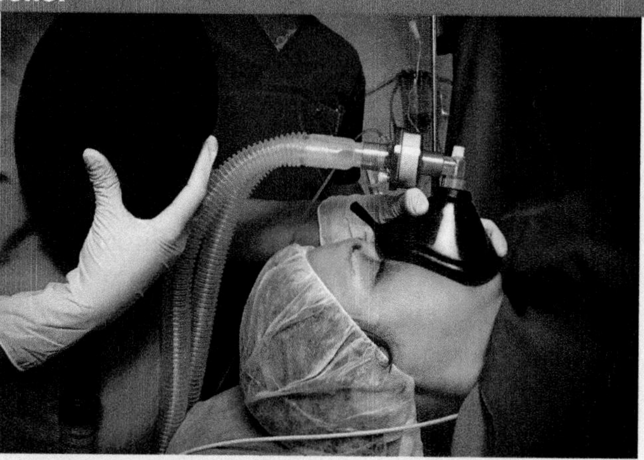

▲ A patient receives oxygen while an induction agent is administered intravenously.

Etomidate (*R* enantiomer)

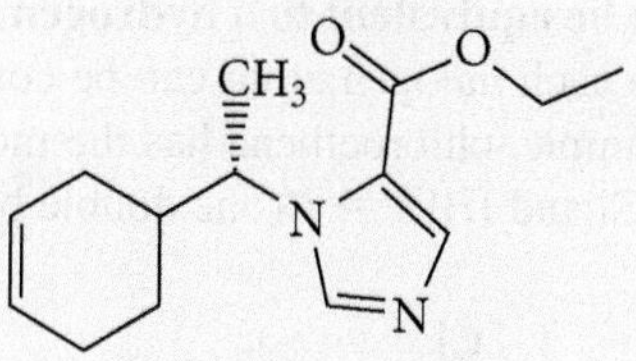

Etomidate (*S* enantiomer)

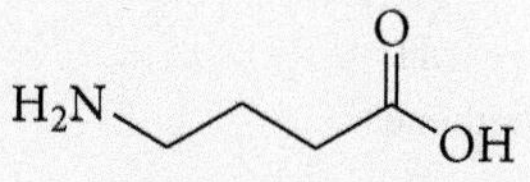

Gamma-aminobutanoic acid (GABA)

20.8 Structure Determination

How do we determine the molecular structures of organic molecules? Suppose a chemist is given an unknown, pure organic compound and is asked to find out what it is. What tools are available to the chemist? The chemist could obtain the molecular formula by combustion analysis and mass spectrometry—methods which were discussed in Chapters 2 and 3. Let's say that the molecular formula determined in this way is C_6H_6O. This molecular formula has a lot of chemical information hidden in it, and the chemist can use this information to narrow down the possible structures. The chemist can also use various spectroscopic methods to determine details about the actual molecular structure.

Using the Molecular Formula: The Index of Hydrogen Deficiency

In previous sections, we saw that saturated alkanes have the general formula C_nH_{2n+2}. We consider this formula to be the **parent formula** for a compound having n carbon atoms. Recall that the general formula of an alkene is C_nH_{2n}, which is two hydrogen atoms less than the parent alkane because of the C—C double bond. The missing hydrogen atoms indicate that there are units of unsaturation in the molecule due to the presence of rings or multiple bonds. The **index of hydrogen deficiency (IHD**, sometimes also called the unsaturation number) is the number of missing hydrogen atoms divided by two (i.e., the number of missing H_2 molecules). Every double bond means that there are two fewer hydrogen atoms than the parent formula (IHD = 1 per double bond). Every triple bond means that there are four fewer hydrogen atoms (IHD = 2 per triple bond). And every cyclic structure means that there are two fewer hydrogen atoms (IHD = 1 per ring). The IHD is therefore a count of the number of π bonds and rings (i.e., units of unsaturation) that are present within a structure.

Consider a hydrocarbon with the molecular formula C_3H_4. The parent formula for 3 carbon atoms is C_3H_8. The number of missing hydrogen atoms is $8 - 4 = 4$. The number of missing hydrogen atoms (4) divided by two gives IHD = 2. Therefore, the molecule has two units of unsaturation, which could mean that there is a triple bond, two double bonds, or a ring and a double bond. The following structures are the only possibilities that fit the formula C_3H_4:

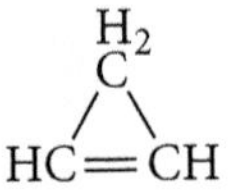

H_2C ring with HC=CH	HC≡C—CH_3	H_2C=C=CH_2
Ring, double bond (IHD = 2)	Triple bond (IHD = 2)	Two double bonds (IHD = 2)

Many organic compounds contain atoms other than carbon and hydrogen. Collectively, these atoms are referred to as **heteroatoms**. The presence of heteroatoms changes how the parent formula is determined:

1. **Each halogen atom is considered to be equivalent to a hydrogen atom.** Halogens form a single bond like hydrogen, so each halogen atom can be considered to have replaced one hydrogen atom. For example, chloroethene has the molecular formula C_2H_3Cl. The parent formula is C_2H_5Cl and IHD = 1 (one double bond).

   H(H)C=C(Cl)H

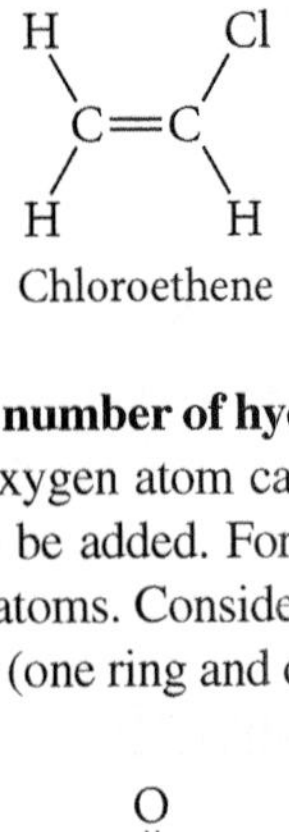

   Chloroethene

2. **Oxygen atoms do not change the number of hydrogen atoms in the parent formula.** Oxygen forms two bonds, so an oxygen atom can be inserted into a molecule without requiring extra hydrogen atoms to be added. For example, methane, CH_4, and methanol, CH_3OH, each contain four H atoms. Consider cyclohexanone, $C_6H_{10}O$. The parent formula is $C_6H_{14}O$ and IHD = 2 (one ring and one double bond).

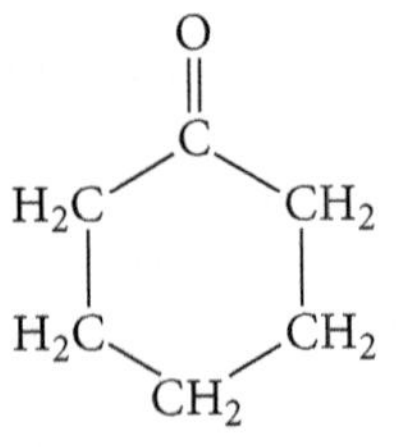

   Cyclohexanone

3. **Each nitrogen atom requires one additional hydrogen atom in the parent formula.** Nitrogen forms three bonds, so if a nitrogen atom is inserted into a molecule, one extra hydrogen must also be added. For example, methylamine, CH_3NH_2, has one extra H atom compared to methane, CH_4. Consider 3-aminopropene, C_3H_7N. The parent formula is C_3H_9N and IHD = 1 (one double bond).

   H_2C=CH—CH_2—NH_2

   3-Aminopropene

We can use these three rules to write an equation for IHD. Let's say we have an organic compound with the molecular formula $C_cH_hN_nO_oX_x$. The maximum number of hydrogen atoms in the parent formula is equal to $2c + 2 + n$. This is because $2c + 2$ is the number of hydrogens in a saturated alkane with c carbon atoms, and one extra hydrogen atom is needed for each n atom. To obtain the IHD, we subtract the actual number of hydrogen atoms, h, and halogen atoms, x, from number of hydrogens in the parent formula $(2c + 2 + n)$, and then divide by 2:

$$\text{IHD} = \frac{(2c + 2 + n) - h - x}{2} \qquad [20.1]$$

This equation is used in the following example.

EXAMPLE 20.4 INDEX OF HYDROGEN DEFICIENCY

Determine the IHD and the possible combinations of multiple bonds and rings required for compounds with the following molecular formulas:

(a) C_4H_6O **(b)** C_6H_9N

SOLUTION

SORT You are given a molecular formula. You are asked to calculate the IHD and determine the possible combinations of multiple bonds and rings.	**GIVEN:** Molecular formula **FIND:** Possible combinations of multiple bonds and rings
STRATEGIZE Calculate the IHD using the IHD equation. The IHD is the total number of multiple bonds and rings. Determine which combinations of multiple bonds and rings add up to the IHD.	**CONCEPTUAL PLAN** **Calculate IHD ⟶ Determine Possible Combinations of Multiple Bonds and Rings**
SOLVE **(a)** In the molecular formula, $c = 4$, $h = 6$, and the oxygen atom does not affect IHD calculation. Using the IHD equation: $\text{IHD} = \frac{(2c + 2 + n) - h - x}{2} = \frac{(2(4) + 2 + 0) - (6) - 0}{2} = 2$	IHD = 2 Possible combinations: • Two rings • One ring, one double bond • Two double bonds • One triple bond
(b) In the molecular formula, $c = 6$, $h = 9$, and $n = 1$. Using the IHD equation: $\text{IHD} = \frac{(2c + 2 + n) - h - x}{2} = \frac{(2(6) + 2 + 1) - (9) - 0}{2} = 3$	IHD = 3 Possible combinations: • Three rings • Two rings, one double bond • One ring, two double bonds • One ring, one triple bond • One double bond, one triple bond

CHECK The numbers of multiple bonds and rings in each combination all add up to the IHD value.

FOR PRACTICE 20.4

Determine the IHD and the possible combinations of multiple bonds and rings required for compounds with the following molecular formulas:

(a) $C_6H_{10}O_2$ **(b)** C_5H_8NCl

FOR MORE PRACTICE 20.4

What is the IHD for the following structures? (*Hint:* The formula is not needed to determine the IHD.)

(a) 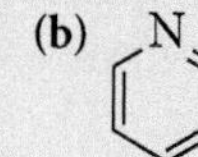

(b) N

Spectroscopic Methods for Structure Determination

In the case of the unknown compound C_6H_6O at the start of this section, we now know that the IHD is 4. While this narrows down the number of possible structures, to select which of these structures is the right one, we need more information than the molecular formula can give us. The IHD = 4 implies that we can have rings, double bonds, or triple bonds. The presence of a single oxygen atom in the formula indicates that there is an oxygen-containing functional group. Since IHD is not zero, a carbonyl group, C=O, may be present. However, carboxylic acid or ester groups are not possible because only one oxygen atom is present. The molecule may contain an alcohol, aldehyde, ketone, or ether functional group.

Infrared Absorption Spectroscopy A common method for identifying functional groups is **infrared (IR) absorption spectroscopy**, which was introduced in Section 9.6. This technique makes use of the fact that bond vibrations are associated with frequencies in the infrared region of the electromagnetic spectrum (400–4000 cm^{-1}). Different functional groups absorb different frequencies of infrared radiation because of the different strengths of the bonds (single, double, or triple) and the atoms involved in the bond (e.g., C—H versus O—H). The intensity (strength) of the absorption typically depends on the polarity of the bond, where a more polar bond gives a stronger absorption. The resulting graph of absorption versus frequency (called the spectrum) can be used to identify which functional groups are present in a compound. Table 20.7 lists wavenumber ranges that various functional groups typically absorb. Figure 20.10 ▼ shows the infrared absorption spectrum of butan-2-one. The strong absorption around 1700 cm^{-1} is characteristic of the carbonyl group, and is one of the most important absorptions in an IR spectra.

NMR Spectroscopy **Nuclear magnetic resonance (NMR) spectroscopy** is a widely used technique for structure determination. It works because certain atomic nuclei generate small magnetic dipoles, or magnetic spins. These spins have some similarities to electron spin states discussed in Chapter 7. Several different atomic nuclei, including ^{1}H and ^{13}C, have two nuclear spin states with different energies under an applied magnetic field. The different

The units of wavenumber are cm^{-1} (reciprocal centimetres). The wavenumber is related to frequency and wavelength, and is a convenient measure for infrared spectroscopy. It is calculated by taking the inverse of the wavelength in centimetres. The wavenumber value in cm^{-1} can be converted to frequency in Hertz by multiplying by the speed of light in $cm \cdot s^{-1}$.

TABLE 20.7 Infrared Absorptions of Selected Bonds

Bond	Wavenumber Range (cm^{-1})	Intensity
C—O	1050–1250	Strong
C=C	1600–1680	Weak
C=O	1630–1800	Strong
C—H	2850–3300	Strong
N—H	3100–3500	Medium
O—H	3200–3500	Strong, broad

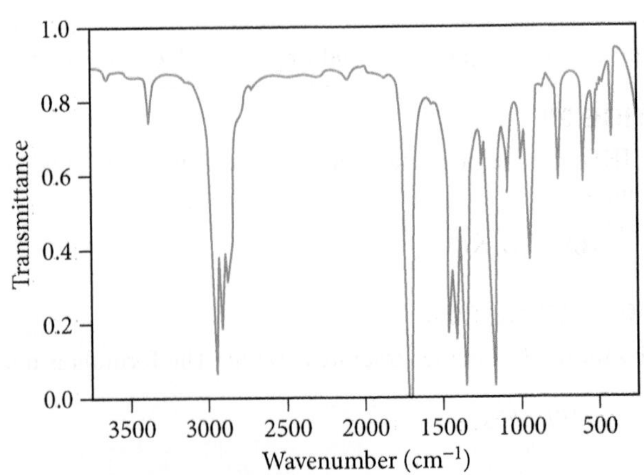

▶ **FIGURE 20.10 Infrared Absorption Spectrum of Butan-2-one** The strong absorption near 1700 cm^{-1} is characteristic of the carbonyl group.

energies arise because the magnetic spin can either be aligned with the applied magnetic field (lower energy) or aligned opposite to the magnetic field (higher energy). The energy difference between the two spin states depends on the strength of the magnetic field that is present at the nucleus. The stronger the external applied magnetic field, the greater the energy difference between spin states. An NMR scan measures the energy required to flip the nucleus between the spin states. This energy difference between the two nuclear spin states, ΔE, corresponds to the energy of photons being absorbed ($E = h\nu$). In a magnetic field, the energy difference between the two nuclear spin states corresponds to the energies of photons ($E = h\nu$) in the radio frequency region of the electromagnetic spectrum. The relationship between electromagnetic frequency, ν, and the magnetic field strength, B in Tesla, is:

$$\nu = \frac{\gamma B}{2\pi}$$

The constant γ is called the magnetogyric ratio, a constant that depends on the specific nucleus.

The unit tesla (T) is the SI unit of magnetic field strength, B.

The energy difference between spin states also depends on the chemical environment around each nucleus. Every nucleus is surrounded by an electron cloud, which varies in density throughout a molecule. A region of high electron density around a nucleus will "shield" it from the external magnetic field, and the energy difference between spin states is small. When the electron density is low, the nucleus is "deshielded" from the external magnetic field, and the energy difference between states is large. Thus, nuclei that are located in different positions in a molecule have different absorption frequencies. The difference in absorption frequency of a particular nucleus from the absorption of a reference nucleus is called the **chemical shift**. A common reference compound for ^{1}H and ^{13}C NMR spectra is tetramethylsilane (TMS).

$Si(CH_3)_4$ (structure: CH_3 groups on Si: H_3C—Si—CH_3 with CH_3 above and below)

Tetramethylsilane (TMS)

In an NMR spectrometer, chemical samples are placed in a strong magnetic field and radio frequency absorptions are measured. NMR spectra are recorded in units that are frequency independent, in order to correct for the different magnetic field strengths of different NMR spectrometers. Chemical shift values are measured on what is known as the delta (δ) scale, in units of parts per million (ppm).

$$\delta = \frac{\nu(\text{sample}) - \nu(\text{reference})}{\nu(\text{spectrometer})} \times 10^6 \text{ ppm}$$

In the numerator, ν(sample) $-$ ν(reference) is the difference in absorption frequency relative to the reference nucleus. The denominator, ν(spectrometer), is the frequency of the NMR spectrometer (e.g., 60 MHz).

Figure 20.11 ▼ shows the ^{13}C NMR spectrum of cyclohexanone. This molecule has six carbon atoms, but because of the symmetry of the molecule, it has only four unique

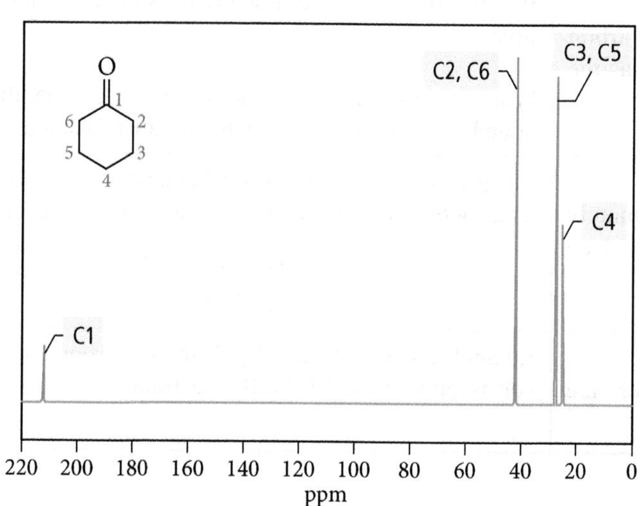

◀ **FIGURE 20.11** ^{13}**C NMR Spectrum of Cyclohexanone**

chemical environments (i.e., there are four types of carbon) and only four absorptions occur in the spectrum. Carbon atom 1 is sp^2 hybridized and is bonded to an oxygen atom. This carbon atom has a partial positive charge, and a low electron density. Therefore, this ^{13}C nucleus is strongly deshielded, with a chemical shift of 211.6 ppm. Carbon atoms 2 and 6 are **chemically equivalent**; the molecular structure is the same around each of these atoms. This means that the electron cloud density surrounding these nuclei is identical, and will have the same chemical shift. Being further removed from the oxygen atom, these nuclei are more shielded than carbon 1, and the chemical shift is much smaller at 42.0 ppm. Carbon atoms 3 and 5 are also chemically equivalent and more shielded, with a chemical shift of 27.1 ppm. Carbon atom 4 has a chemical shift of 25.1 ppm.

^{13}C NMR spectroscopy can identify the number of unique types of carbon atoms in a molecule, and also provides information about the chemical environment of the atoms. ^{1}H NMR spectroscopy can identify the number of unique hydrogen atoms, but also provides information about the number and type of *neighbouring* hydrogen atoms next to each one.

EXAMPLE 20.5 DETERMINING THE STRUCTURE OF AN UNKNOWN ORGANIC COMPOUND

An unknown organic compound has the molecular formula C_2H_6O. The ^{13}C NMR spectrum shows only two absorptions, at 17.3 and 57.0 ppm. The compound has the following IR spectrum. Identify the compound.

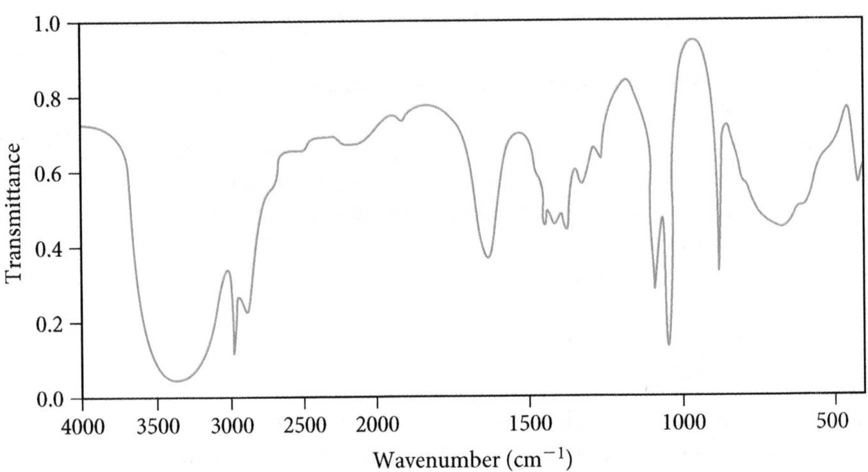

SOLUTION

Information	Conclusion about the structure
Molecular formula: The parent formula for a compound with two carbon atoms and one oxygen atom is C_2H_6O, the same as the molecular formula. Thus, IHD = 0.	Because IHD = 0, the structure does not contain rings or multiple bonds. From the oxygen atom in the formula, we know that the compound contains either an alcohol or ether functional group.
IR spectrum: A broad, strong absorption is centred at approximately 3400 cm^{-1}. This is consistent with the presence of an O—H bond.	The presence of an O—H bond indicates that this compound is an alcohol. There is only one alcohol with the formula C_2H_6O: $CH_3—CH_2—OH$ Ethanol
^{13}C NMR spectrum: There are only two absorptions, which means there are two types of carbon atoms in the structure.	Ethanol has two chemically different carbon atoms, which is consistent with the ^{13}C NMR spectrum.

FOR PRACTICE 20.5

An unknown organic compound has the molecular formula C_3H_6O. The ^{13}C NMR spectrum shows only two absorptions, at 29.9 and 206.7 ppm. The compound has the following IR spectrum. Identify the compound.

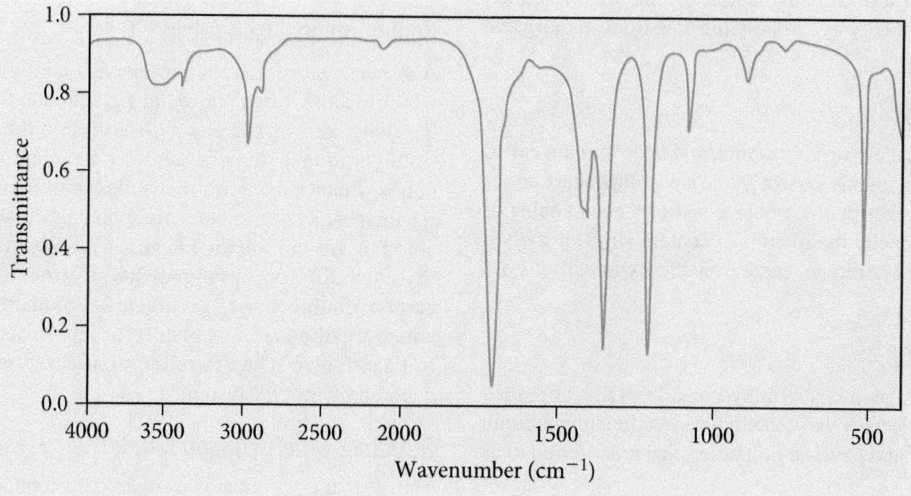

CHAPTER IN REVIEW

Key Terms

Section 20.1
organic molecule (869)
organic chemistry (869)

Section 20.2
catenation (869)

Section 20.3
structural isomers (871)
structural formula (871)
open chain hydrocarbon (874)
cyclic hydrocarbon (874)
alkane (874)
alkene (874)
alkyne (874)
saturated hydrocarbon (874)
unsaturated hydrocarbon (874)
conjugation (876)
aromatic hydrocarbon (876)

Section 20.4
functional group (877)
family (877)
inductive effect (878)
R group (878)
aldehyde (880)
ketone (880)
carbonyl group (880)
acyl group (881)

Section 20.5
constitutional isomer (883)

Section 20.6
stereoisomerism (884)
conformational isomerism (884)
configurational isomerism (884)
conformer (884)
rotamer (884)
three-dimensional formula (884)
Newman projection formula (884)
staggered conformation (884)
eclipsed conformation (884)
torsional strain (885)
steric strain (886)
antistaggered conformation (886)
gauche-staggered conformation (886)
angle strain (887)
chair conformation (887)
equatorial bond (887)
axial bond (887)

Section 20.7
enantiomers (888)
diastereomers (888)
cis–trans isomerism (888)
E,Z system (888)
chirality (891)
chirality centre (891)
optical activity (892)
dextrorotatory isomer (892)
levorotatory (892)
racemic mixture (892)
absolute configuration (893)
R,S system (893)
induction agent (895)
GABA (*gamma*-aminobutanoic acid) receptor (895)

Section 20.8
parent formula (895)
index of hydrogen deficiency (IHD) (895)
heteroatom (896)
infrared (IR) absorption spectroscopy (898)
nuclear magnetic resonance (NMR) spectroscopy (898)
chemical shift (899)
chemical equivalence (900)

Key Concepts

Fragrances and Odours (20.1)

Organic chemistry is the study of organic compounds, which contain carbon and other elements, including hydrogen, oxygen, and nitrogen. These compounds produce many odours.

Carbon (20.2)

Carbon forms more compounds than all the other elements combined for several reasons. Its four valence electrons (combined with its size) allow carbon to form four bonds (in the form of single, double, or triple bonds). Carbon also has the capacity to catenate (forming long chains) because of the strength of the carbon–carbon bond.

Before the properties of carbon were studied, some scientists believed that organic compounds had a vital force and could therefore never be synthesized in the laboratory. In 1828, Friedrich Wöhler disproved this theory by synthesizing urea from an inorganic compound.

Hydrocarbons (20.3)

Organic compounds containing only carbon and hydrogen are called hydrocarbons, most commonly known as the key components of our world's fuels. Open chain hydrocarbons consist of open chains of carbon atoms, while cyclic hydrocarbons contain rings of carbon atoms. Alkanes, alkenes, alkynes, and aromatic hydrocarbons are types of hydrocarbons.

Functional Groups (20.4)

Characteristic groups of atoms, such as hydroxyl (—OH), are called functional groups. Molecules that contain the same functional group have similar chemical and physical properties, and are referred to as families.

Constitutional Isomerism (20.5)

Isomerism is the phenomenon of compounds having the same chemical formula, but different structures. Constitutional isomerism occurs when the bonding sequences between atoms are different. Functional-group isomerism is a type of constitutional isomerism.

Conformational Isomerism (20.6)

Stereoisomerism is different from constitutional isomerism in that the bonding sequences between atoms in stereoisomers are the same. Stereoisomerism arises from different spatial arrangements of atoms. Conformational isomerism comes from the rotation of single bonds to give different structures. Conformational isomers are interconvertible through bond rotation.

Configurational Isomerism (20.7)

Another type of stereoisomerism is configurational isomerism, which occurs when the bonding sequences between atoms are the same, and yet there is a difference in the spatial arrangement. Configurational isomers can only be interconverted by breaking bonds. Enantiomers are molecules with nonsuperimposable mirror images. Diastereomers are molecules that are nonsuperimposable but are not mirror images. *Cis–trans* isomerism in alkenes involves different arrangements of groups around the carbon–carbon double bond, giving diastereomers. Chirality centres, where a carbon atom is bonded to four different groups, give rise to enantiomers. The absolute configurations of enantiomers is denoted by the *R,S* system.

Structure Determination (20.8)

The structures of unknown organic compounds can be determined using information derived from the chemical formula and spectroscopic data. The index of hydrogen deficiency (IHD) uses the chemical formula to give the number of rings and multiple bonds in the molecule. Infrared absorption spectroscopy helps identify any functional groups that may be present. ^{13}C NMR spectroscopy provides information about the number of chemically equivalent carbon atoms in the structure.

Key Equations and Relationships

Common Functional Groups (20.4)

Functional Group	General Formula	Condensed General Formula
Halides (X = F, Cl, Br, I)	R—X	RX
Amines	R—N(—R)—R	R_3N
Alcohols	R—OH	ROH
Ethers	R—O—R	ROR
Aldehydes	R—C(=O)—H	RCHO
Ketones	R—C(=O)—R	RCOR

Functional Group	General Formula	Condensed General Formula
Carboxylic acids	R—C(=O)—OH	RCO_2H
Acyl halides (X = Cl, Br)	R—C(=O)—X	RCOX
Acid anhydrides	R—C(=O)—O—C(=O)—R	RC(O)OC(O)R
Esters	R—C(=O)—O—R	RC(O)OR
Amides	R—C(=O)—N(R)—R	$RC(O)NR_2$

Index of Hydrogen Deficiency (20.8)

$$\text{IHD} = \frac{(2c + 2 + n) - h - x}{2}$$

Key Skills

Writing Structural Formulas for Hydrocarbons (20.3)
• Example 20.1 • For Practice 20.1 • Exercises 46–49

Assigning the Configurations of Alkenes (20.7)
• Example 20.2 • For Practice 20.2 • Exercises 61, 62

Assigning *R,S* Configurations (20.7)
• Example 20.3 • For Practice 20.3 • Exercises 66–69

Using the Index of Hydrogen Deficiency (20.8)
• Example 20.4 • For Practice 20.4 • For More Practice 20.4 • Exercises 70–73

Determining the Structure of an Unknown Organic Compound (20.8)
• Example 20.5 • For Practice 20.5 • Exercises 95–99

EXERCISES

Review Questions

1. What is organic chemistry?
2. What is unique about carbon and carbon-based compounds? Why did life evolve around carbon?
3. Why does carbon form such a large diversity of compounds?
4. Why does silicon not exhibit the great diversity of compounds that carbon does?
5. Describe the geometry and hybridization about a carbon atom that forms:
   a. four single bonds
   b. two single bonds and one double bond
   c. one single bond and one triple bond
6. What are hydrocarbons? What are their main uses?

7. What are the main classifications of hydrocarbons? What are their generic molecular formulas?
8. Explain the differences between a structural formula, a condensed structural formula, a carbon skeleton formula, a ball-and-stick model, and a space-filling model.
9. What is the structure of benzene? What are the different ways in which this structure is represented?
10. What is conjugation? How can you tell if there is conjugation in a molecule?
11. What is a functional group? What functional groups contain oxygen atoms? Nitrogen atoms?
12. What is the generic structure of alkyl halides? What is the generic structure of an acyl halide?
13. What are the generic structures of primary, secondary, and tertiary amines? Write the structures for specific primary, secondary, and tertiary amines that have the formula C_3H_9N.
14. What is the generic structure of alcohols? Write the structures for specific primary, secondary, and tertiary alcohols that have the formula $C_4H_{10}O$.
15. What is the generic structure of ethers? Write the structures of two specific ethers that have the formula $C_4H_{10}O$.
16. What are the generic structures of aldehydes and ketones? Write the structures for a specific aldehyde and a specific ketone that have the formula C_3H_6O.
17. What is the generic structure of an acyl group? What are the structures of various acyl groups?
18. Draw important resonance structures of the carbonyl group.
19. Draw important resonance structures of the carboxylate anion.
20. What are constitutional isomers? How do the properties of constitutional isomers differ from one another?
21. What is functional-group isomerism?
22. What is stereoisomerism? How is stereoisomerism different from constitutional isomerism?
23. What is conformational isomerism? What are eclipsed and staggered conformers?
24. What is configurational isomerism?
25. Explain *cis–trans* isomerism in alkenes. How do the properties of *cis–trans* isomers differ from one another?
26. What are the Cahn–Ingold–Prelog rules for determining priority of substituents?
27. What is chirality? What are enantiomers?
28. What is optical activity? Define the terms dextrorotatory, levorotatory, and racemic mixture.
29. What are the similarities and differences in physical and chemical properties of chiral compounds?
30. What is an absolute configuration?
31. What is the index of hydrogen deficiency? How can it be used in structure determination?
32. What information about molecular structure can be obtained from an infrared spectrum?
33. What information about molecular structure can be obtained from a ^{13}C NMR spectrum?

Problems by Topic

Hydrocarbons

34. Based on the molecular formula, determine whether each of the following compounds is an alkane, alkene, or alkyne. (Assume that the hydrocarbons are acyclic and there is no more than one multiple bond.)

a. C_8H_{16} b. C_4H_6 c. C_7H_{16} d. C_2H_2

35. Based on the molecular formula, determine whether each of the following compounds is an alkane, alkene, or alkyne. (Assume that the hydrocarbons are acyclic and there is no more than one multiple bond.)

a. C_5H_{12} b. C_3H_6 c. C_7H_{12} d. $C_{11}H_{22}$

36. What are the hybridizations of each carbon atom in the following molecules?

a. $CH_3—CH_2—CH{=}CH_2$

b. H_2C bonded to both carbons of $HC{=}CH$ (ring)

c. $H—C{\equiv}C—CH_3$

d. $H_2C{=}CH—CH{=}CH_2$

37. What are the hybridizations of each carbon atom in the following molecules?

a. $CH_3—C{\equiv}C—CH_3$

b.
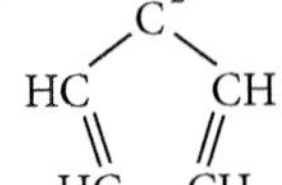

c. $CH_3—CH(CH_3)—CH{=}CH_2$

d. $CH_3—CH{=}CH_2$

38. Draw resonance structures for the following molecules:

a. 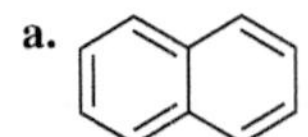

b. 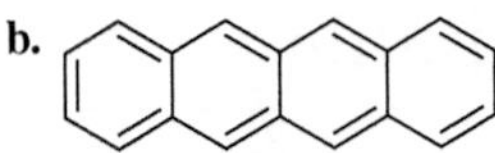

39. Draw resonance structures for the following molecules:

a. 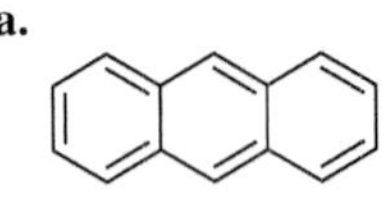

b. 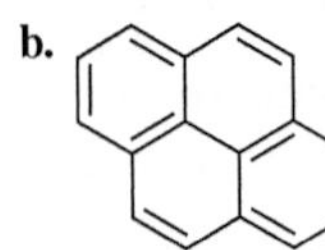

Functional Groups

40. What is the hybridization of each atom in the following molecules? (Do not include hydrogen atoms.)

a. $CH_3—CH_2—OH$

b. $CH_2{=}CH—CH_3$

c. $HO—CH_2—CH_2—SH$

d. $CH_3—C({=}O)—OH$

41. What is the hybridization of each atom in the following molecules? (Do not include hydrogen atoms.)

a. $NH_2—CH_3$

b. $CH_3—C({=}O)—O—CH_2—CH_3$

c. $CH_3—C({=}O)—CH_3$

d. 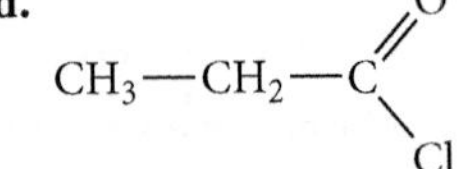

42. For all of the molecules in Problem 40, draw the bond dipole(s) between each heteroatom and any carbon atoms it is bonded to.

43. For all of the molecules in Problem 41, draw the bond dipole(s) between each heteroatom and any carbon atoms it is bonded to.

44. List the following compounds in order of increasing boiling point: CH_3CH_2OH, CH_3CH_3, CH_3OCH_3

45. List the following compounds in order of increasing boiling point: $CH_3CHOHCH_3$, $CH_3CH_2CH_3$, CH_3COCH_3

Constitutional Isomerism

46. Write structural formulas for all of the possible isomers of pent-1-yne that can be formed by moving the position of the triple bond.

47. Write structural formulas for all of the possible isomers of hex-1-ene that can be formed by moving the position of the double bond.

48. Write structural formulas for any 6 of the 18 constitutional isomers of octane.

49. Write structural formulas for each of the nine constitutional isomers of heptane.

50. Determine whether or not the following pairs are constitutional isomers:

a.

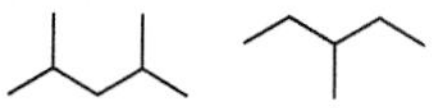

b.

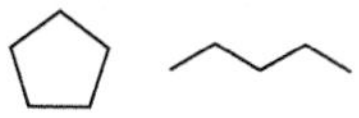

c. 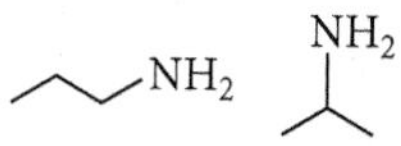 NH_2 NH_2

51. Determine whether or not the following pairs are constitutional isomers:

a.

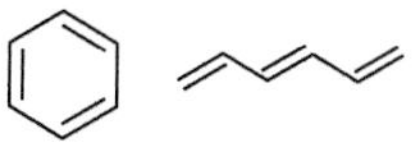

b.

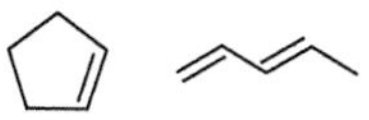

c. 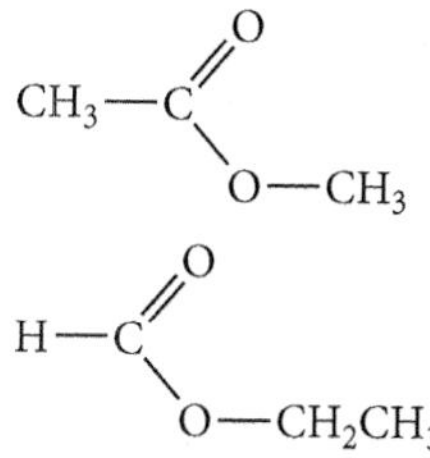 $CH_3—C(=O)—O—CH_3$ $H—C(=O)—O—CH_2CH_3$

52. Draw five constitutional isomers with the formula C_6H_{12} that are open chain hydrocarbons.

53. Draw five constitutional isomers with the formula C_6H_{12} that are cyclic hydrocarbons.

54. Draw three constitutional isomers with the formula C_3H_8O.

55. Draw three constitutional isomers with the formula $C_4H_8O_2$, each with different functional groups.

Conformational Isomerism

56. Draw Newman projections for the eclipsed and staggered conformers of propane, looking down the C1—C2 bond.

57. Draw Newman projections for the eclipsed and staggered conformers of chloroethane.

58. Draw Newman projections for all eclipsed and staggered conformers of 1,2-dichloroethane.

59. Draw Newman projections for all eclipsed and staggered conformers of 1-chloropropane.

60. Draw a Newman projection for cyclopropane.

Configurational Isomerism

61. As appropriate, assign a configuration of *cis* or *trans*, or *E* or *Z* to the following compounds:

a. 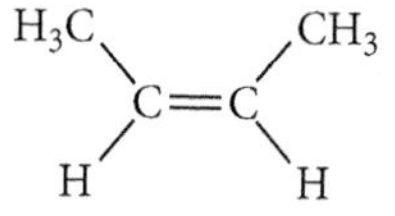 H_3C, H / C=C / CH_3, H

b. H, Cl / C=C / CH_3, H

c. Cl, H_3C / C=C / CH_2CH_3, H

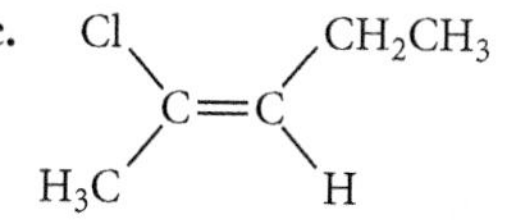

d. 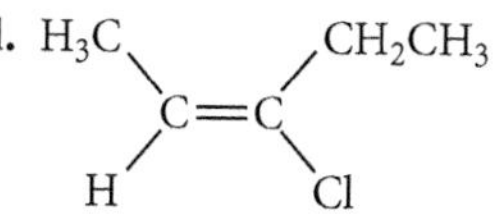 H_3C, H / C=C / CH_2CH_3, Cl

62. As appropriate, assign a configuration of *cis* or *trans*, or *E* or *Z* to the following compounds:

a. 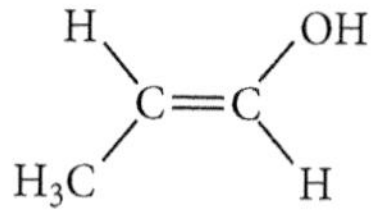 H, H_3C / C=C / OH, H

b. H_3C, H / C=C / $CH=CH_2$, H

c. H_3C, H / C=C / CH_3, CH_2CH_3

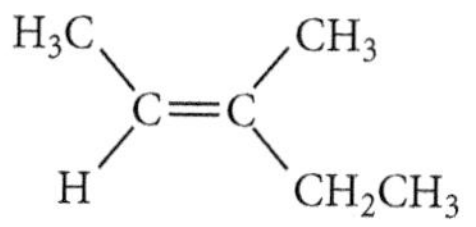

d. 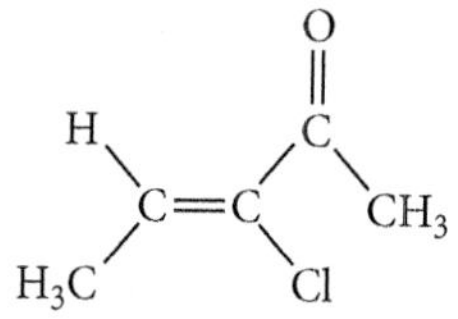 H, H_3C / C=C / C(=O)CH_3, Cl

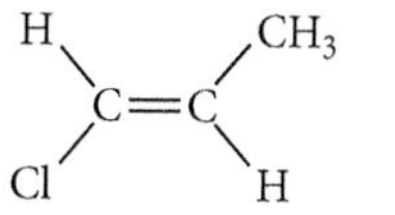

63. Determine whether the following pairs are the same molecules or enantiomers:

a. 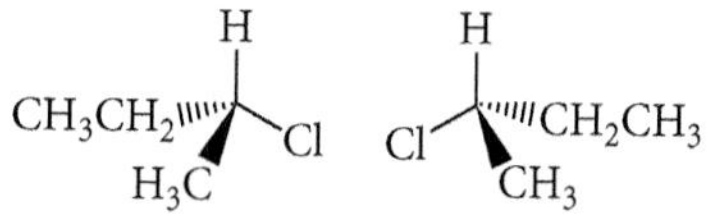 H, CH_3CH_2, Cl, H_3C H, Cl, CH_2CH_3, CH_3

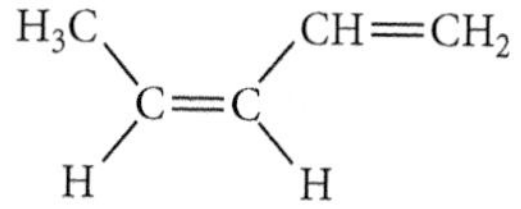

b. 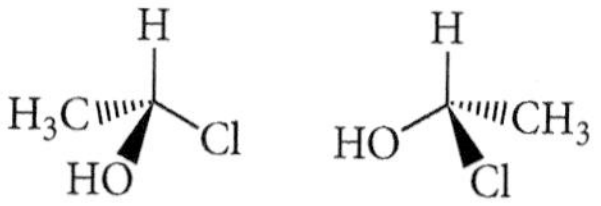 H, H_3C, Cl, HO   H, HO, CH_3, Cl

c. 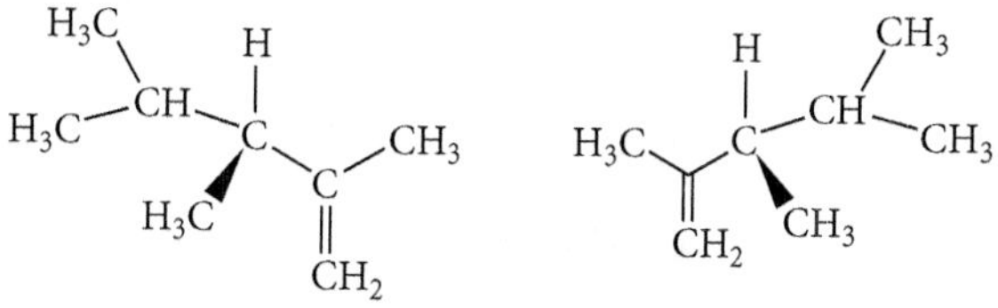 H_3C, $H_3C—CH$, H, C, CH_3, H_3C, C, CH_2 H, CH_3, H_3C, C, CH, CH_3, CH_2, CH_3

64. Determine whether or not the following molecules are chiral:

a. $CH_3CH_2CHClCH_3$

b. $CH_3CCl_2CH_3$

c. 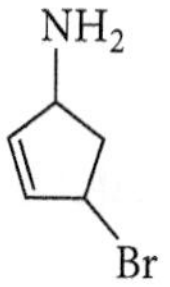 NH_2, Br

d. 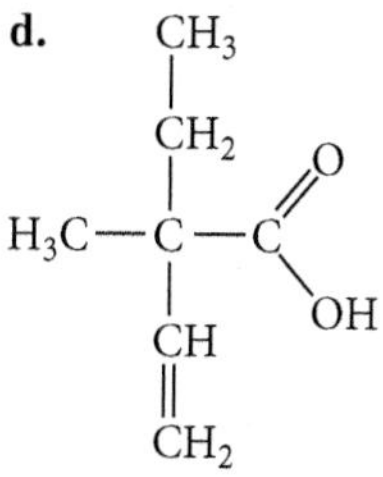 CH_3, CH_2, $H_3C—C—C(=O)OH$, CH, CH_2

65. Determine whether the following pairs are the same molecules or enantiomers:

a. CH_3 / H_3C / Cl / HO and CH_3 / Cl / CH_3 / OH

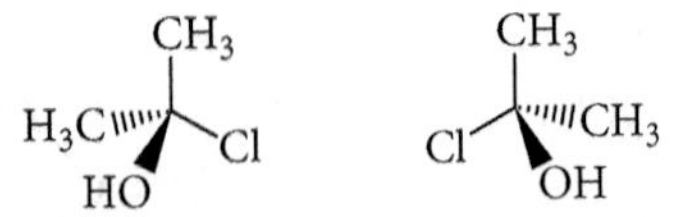

b. H / H_3C / Br / H_2N and H / Br / CH_3 / NH_2

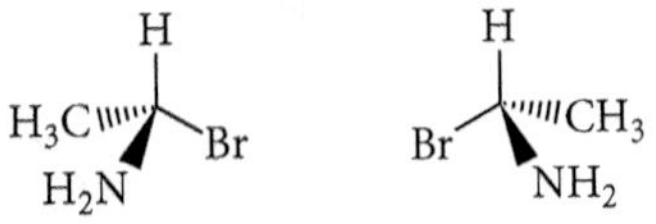

c. H / H_3C–C / CCl_3 / CH / H_3C / CH_3 and H / CH_3 / C–CH / Cl_3C / CH_3 / CH_3

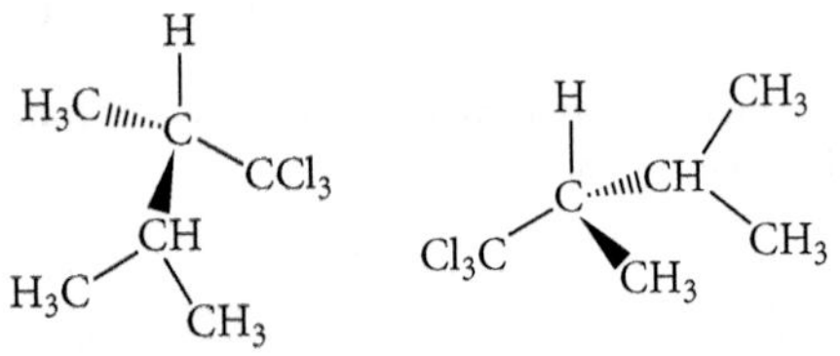

66. Assign *R* or *S* configurations to the molecules in Problem 64.

67. Assign *R* or *S* configurations to the molecules in Problem 65.

68. Assign *R* or *S* configurations to each of the following molecules:

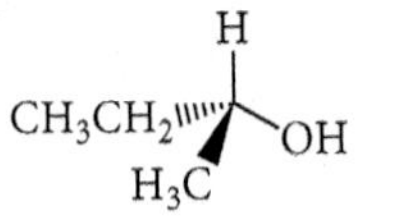

a. H / CH_3CH_2 / OH / H_3C

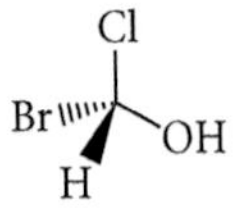

b. $CH{=}CH_2$ / CH_3CH_2 / OH / H_3C

c. Cl / Br / OH / H

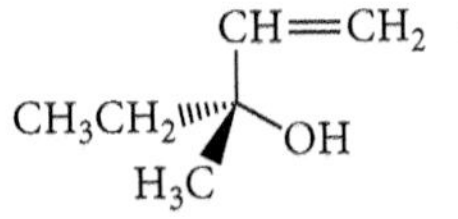

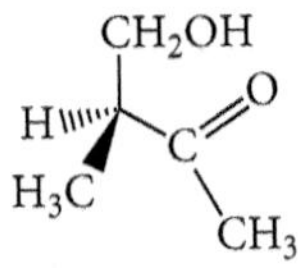

d. $CH{=}CH_2{-}CH_3$ / $CH_2{=}CH$ / OH / H_3C

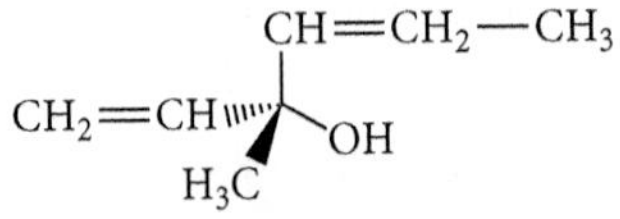

69. Assign *R* or *S* configurations to each of the following molecules:

a. CH_2OH / H / C=O / H_3C / CH_3

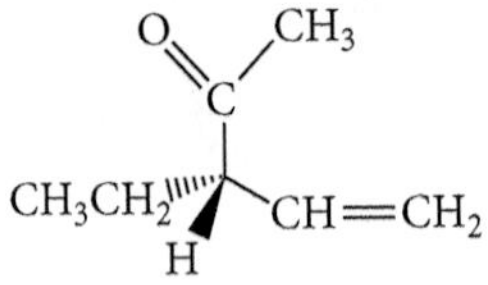

b. CH_2CH_2OH / CH_3CH_2 / $CH_2{-}C$(=O)Cl / H_3C

c. O=C–CH_3 / CH_3CH_2 / $CH{=}CH_2$ / H

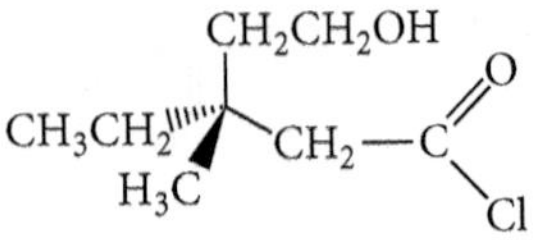

d. CH_3 / Br / H / I

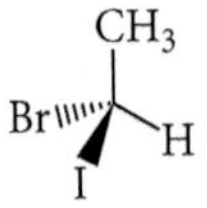

Structure Determination

70. Determine the index of hydrogen deficiency and the possible combinations of multiple bonds and rings required for the following molecular formulas:

a. $C_3H_8O_2$ b. $C_3H_8O_3$ c. C_3H_7Cl d. C_5H_4FN

71. Determine the index of hydrogen deficiency and the possible combinations of multiple bonds and rings required for the following molecular formulas:

a. $C_4H_4O_2$ b. $C_4H_4O_4$ c. $C_5H_4O_3$ d. $C_6H_4N_2O_5$

72. Using the index of hydrogen deficiency, what functional groups could be present in molecules with the following formulas?

a. C_3H_7OClO b. C_2H_7N

73. Using the index of hydrogen deficiency, what functional groups could be present in molecules with the following formulas?

a. $C_4H_8O_2$ b. C_3H_8O

74. Predict the frequency range of strong absorptions in the IR spectra of the following molecules:

a. $CH_3CH_2CH_2OH$ b. (cyclic lactone, =O, O)

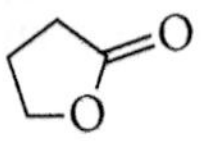

75. Predict the frequency range of strong absorptions in the IR spectra of the following molecules:

a. $CH_3CH_2NH_2$ b. CH_3CO_2H

76. Determine the number of different sets of chemically equivalent carbon atoms in the following molecules:

a. (benzene ring)–CH_3 b. (zigzag chain)

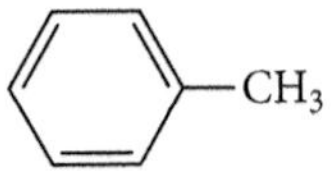

77. Determine the number of different sets of chemically equivalent carbon atoms in the following molecules:

a. (cyclopentadienone, =O) b. (branched chain)

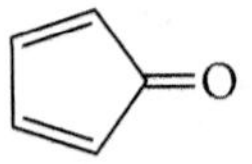

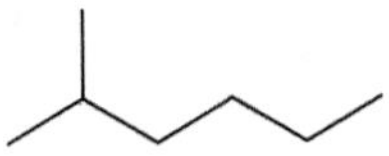

Cumulative Problems

78. For each of the following molecules, determine the orbital hybridization of each nonhydrogen atom, draw any resonance structures, and draw bond dipoles for each bond between carbon and a heteroatom.

a. $HOCH_2COOH$

b. H / HO / O / OH

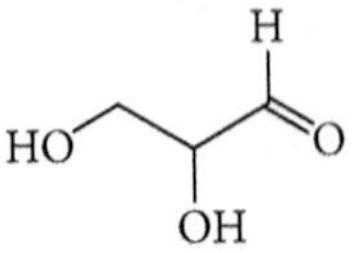

c. (cyclopentenone, =O)

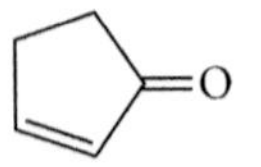

79. For each of the following molecules, determine the orbital hybridization of each nonterminal, nonhydrogen atom, draw any resonance structures, and draw bond dipoles for each bond between carbon and a heteroatom.

a. $H_2C{=}CH{-}\overset{O}{\overset{\|}{C}}{-}NH_2$

b. (pyridine ring, N)

c. H / Cl / H / H (C=C)

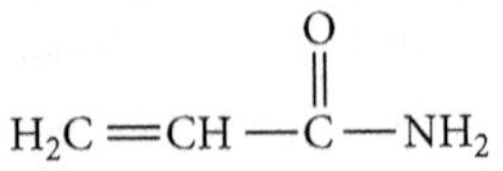

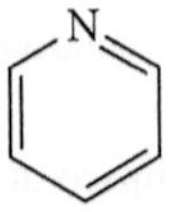

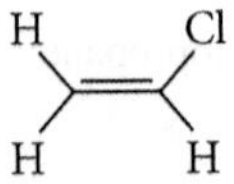

80. For each of the following molecules, draw two constitutional isomers that contain different functional groups:

a. CH_3CH_2COOH

b. O

CH_2OH

c. O

81. For each of the following molecules, draw two constitutional isomers that contain different functional groups:

a.
CH_3
|
CH_2
|
$H_2N—CH—COOH$

b. $CH_3—CH_2—CH_2—C(=O)—Cl$

c. OH

OH

82. Two of the following names correspond to structures that display stereoisomerism. Identify the two compounds and draw their structures.

a. 3-methylpentan-3-ol
b. 2-methylpentan-2-ol
c. 3-methylpentan-2-ol
d. 2-methylpentan-3-ol
e. 2,4-dimethylpentan-3-ol

83. Draw a structure corresponding to each of the following names and indicate those structures that can exist as stereoisomers.

a. 3-methylpent-1-ene
b. 3,5-dimethylhex-2-ene
c. 3-propylhex-2-ene

84. There are seven structures with the formula C_3H_7NO in which the O is part of a carbonyl group. Draw the structures and identify the functional groups in each.

85. Draw seven structures of alcohols with the formula C_4H_8O.

86. For each of the following molecular formulas, calculate IHD and draw three constitutional isomers with that formula.

a. C_3H_9N b. C_3H_7ClO c. C_5H_{10}

87. For each of the following molecular formulas, calculate IHD and draw three constitutional isomers with that formula.

a. C_3H_6O b. $C_5H_{10}O_3$ c. $C_6H_2BrF_3$

88. Predict the frequencies of absorption peaks in the IR spectra, and number of absorptions in ^{13}C NMR spectra, for the following molecules:

a. $CH_3—CH_2—CH_2—C(=O)—CH_2—CH_3$

b. $CH_3CH_2CH_2NH_2$

89. Predict the frequencies of absorption peaks in the IR spectra, and number of absorptions in ^{13}C NMR spectra, for the following molecules:

a.
CH_3
|
$CH_3—CH_2—CH—CH_2—CH_2OH$

b. $CH_3—CH_2—C(=O)—H$

Challenge Problems

90. Tetrodotoxin is a powerful neurotoxin that is found in several animal species, including puffer fish.

a. Identify all chirality centres in tetrodotoxin.
b. Determine the absolute configuration of each chirality centre.

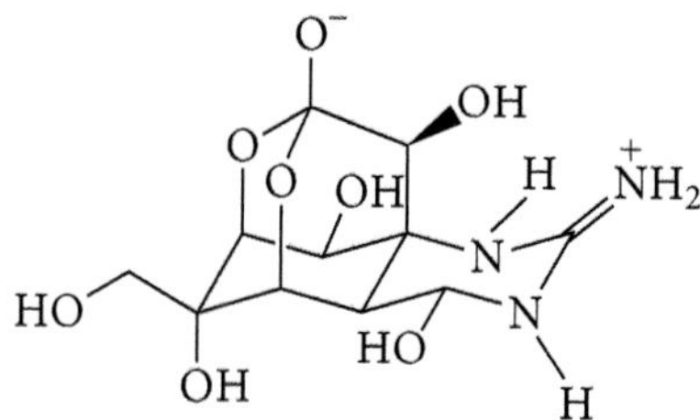

Tetrodotoxin

91. Vitamin D_3 is made in the skin when exposed to UV light. This vitamin helps the body regulate calcium and phosphorus, which are important in maintaining healthy bones and teeth.

a. Identify all chirality centres in vitamin D_3.
b. Determine the absolution configuration of each chirality centre.
c. Determine the *E* or *Z* or *cis* or *trans* configuration around each double bond.

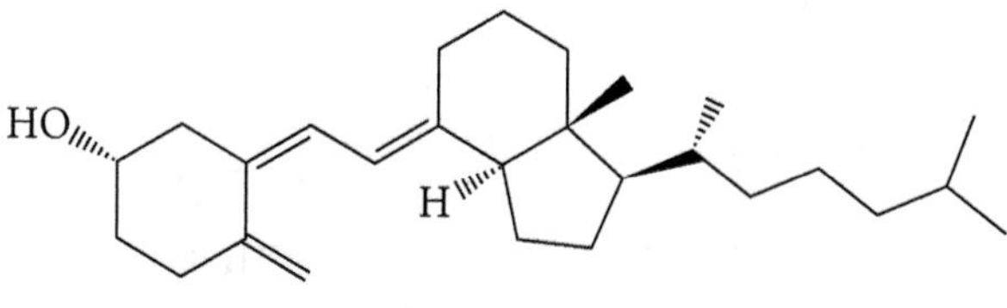

Vitamin D_3

92. Quinine and quinidine are stereoisomers. Quinine is an important antimalarial drug. Quinidine is an antiarrhythmic drug, which means that it prevents heart arrhythmias. Are quinine and quinidine enantiomers? Why or why not?

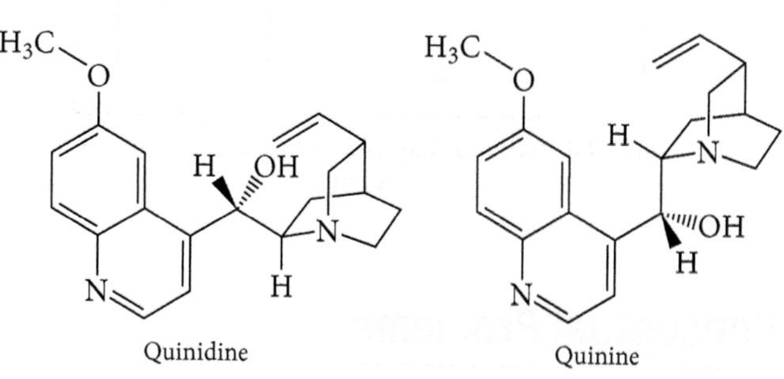

93. Indigo is a naturally occurring, blue-coloured dye. How many different sets of chemically equivalent carbon atoms are present in indigo?

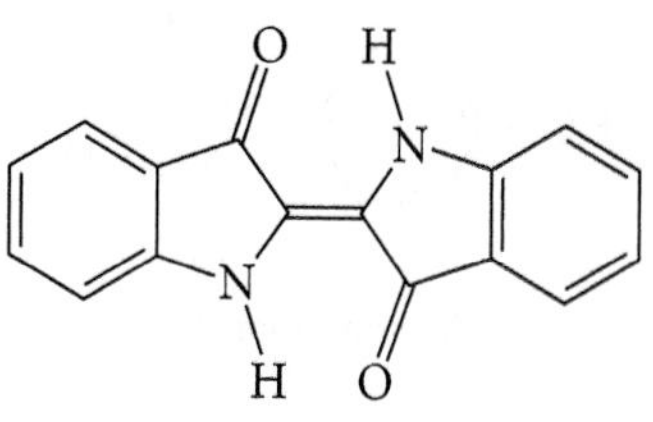

Indigo

94. Draw all possible configurational isomers for each of the three compounds shown below. How many chirality centres are present in each molecule? How many configurational isomers are possible for each? What is a simple mathematical formula for the number of configurational isomers, using only the number of chirality centres?

a.

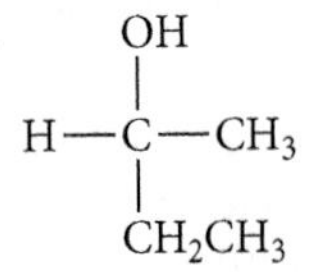

```
       OH
       |
   H—C—CH3
       |
     CH2CH3
```

c.

```
          OH  OH  OH
          |   |   |
   H3C—C—C—C—CH3
          |   |   |
          H   H   CH2CH3
```

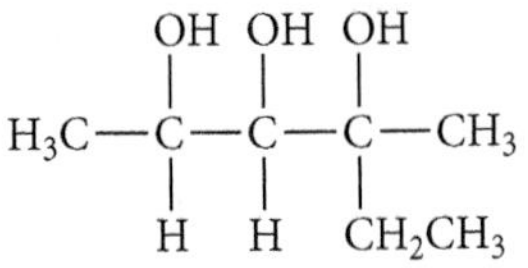

b.

```
          OH  OH
          |   |
   H3C—C—C—CH3
          |   |
          H   H
```

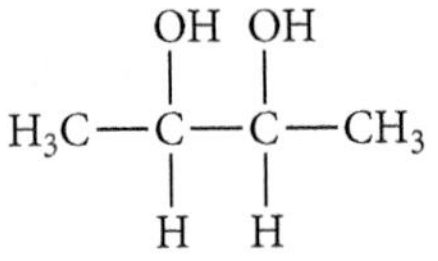

95. An unknown organic compound has the molecular formula C_3H_8O. The infrared and ^{13}C NMR spectra are shown below. Identify the compound.

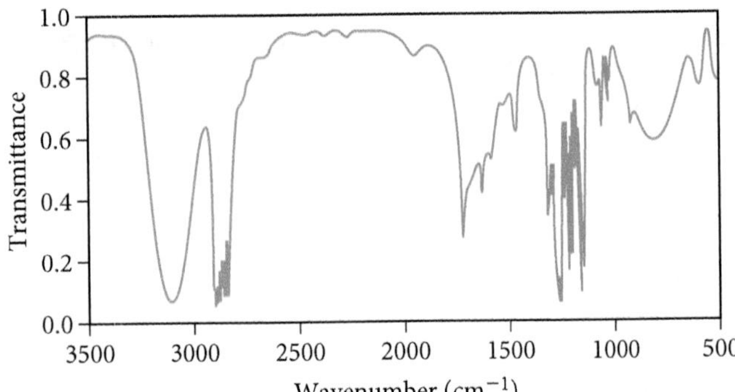

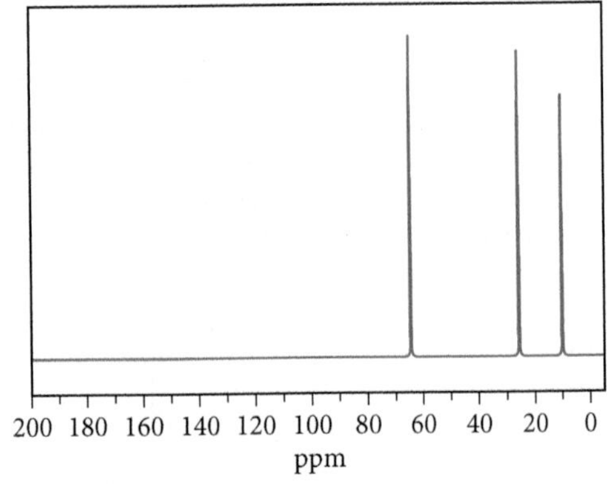

96. An unknown organic compound has the molecular formula $C_3H_{15}N$. The ^{13}C NMR spectrum has two peaks, at 44.5 and 11.8 ppm. The infrared absorption spectrum is shown below. Identify the compound.

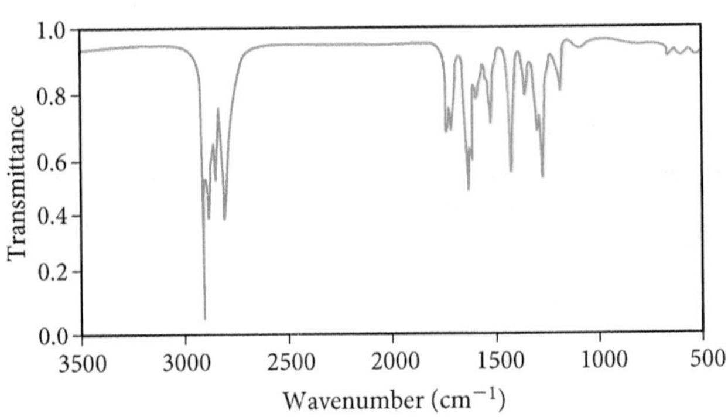

97. An unknown organic liquid has a boiling point of 35 °C. Elemental analysis gives the formula $C_4H_{10}O$. The infrared absorption spectrum has a strong absorption at 1126 cm^{-1}. The ^{13}C NMR spectrum has two peaks, at 65.97 and 15.35 ppm. Identify the compound.

98. A chemist is asked to determine the structure of an unknown organic compound. The compound is a clear liquid at room temperature. In combustion analysis, 24.0 mg of the compound gives 81.1 mg CO_2 and 16.5 mg H_2O. Mass spectrometry gives a molecular mass of 78 g mol^{-1}. The ^{13}C NMR spectrum has a single peak at 128.5 ppm. What is the structure of the unknown compound?

99. An unknown compound has the molecular formula C_8H_8. The ^{13}C NMR spectrum shows a single peak. Suggest a structure for this molecule that does not have any double or triple bonds. (*Hint:* This compound is known as "cubane.")

Conceptual Problems

100. Acetominophen is a widely used analgesic. Draw resonance structures of acetaminophen. What is the orbital hybridization of each atom (excluding hydrogen)? What is the orientation of the amide group with respect to the benzene ring?

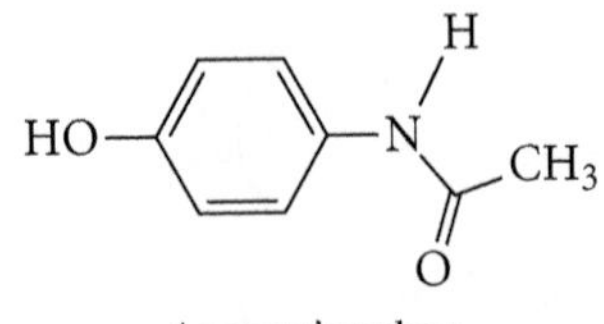

Acetominophen

101. Determine whether each of the following structures is chiral.

a.

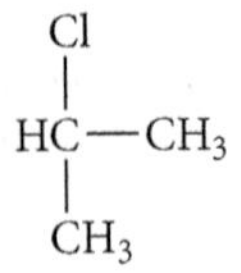

```
     Cl
     |
     HC—CH3
     |
     CH3
```

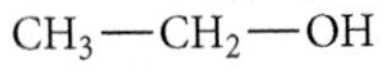

b.

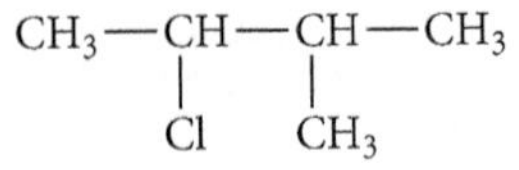

```
   CH3—CH—CH—CH3
        |    |
        Cl   CH3
```

c. $CH_3—CH_2—OH$

d.

```
     Cl
     |
     HC—CH2
     |    |
     CH3  Br
```

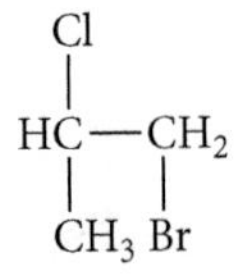

102. Determine whether the following molecule is chiral. If it is chiral, draw its enantiomer. If it is not chiral, draw a stereoisomer of the compound that is chiral.

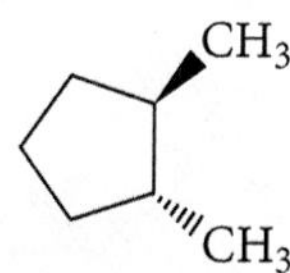

103. How many different sets of chemically equivalent carbon atoms are present in the molecule shown in Problem 102?

104. Determine whether or not the following molecule is chiral. If it is chiral, draw its enantiomer. If it is not chiral, draw a stereoisomer of the compound that is chiral.

HOOC COOH
H H
HO OH

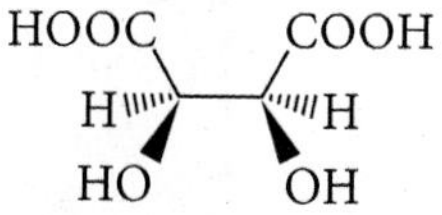

21 Organic Chemistry II: Reactions

Where nature finishes producing its own species, man begins, using natural things and with the help of this nature, creating an infinity of species.

—Leonardo da Vinci

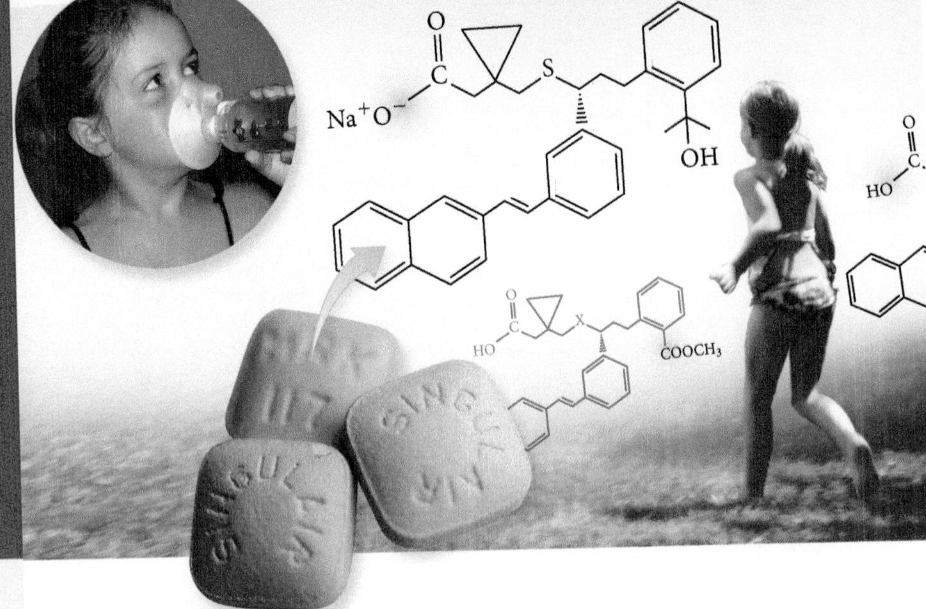

Montelukast sodium is a prescription drug that treats chronic asthma. It was discovered and developed in Canada.

CREATING NEW, structurally complex organic molecules requires extensive knowledge of organic chemical reactivity. Approximately one thousand organic reactions are known, and many of these have variations that involve similar reactants, or reagents. Fortunately for us, however, organic reactions can be classified into a relatively small number of basic types. The process of making an organic compound is known as *synthesis*. It usually involves a sequence of chemical reactions that convert a starting compound to the final product. Often, the synthetic sequence is quite long. For example, montelukast sodium is a complex organic molecule that is used as a prescription drug to help control asthma. Every structural component is important for its proper function. The synthesis of montelukast sodium involves 23 separate reactions. In this chapter, we build upon what we learned about organic chemistry in Chapter 20 and see how organic compounds are synthesized.

21.1 Discovering New Drugs

Chances are that you have been prescribed medicine by a doctor at one time or another to help you with a particular condition or illness. We often take for granted that a drug exists to help us with a health problem. However, discovering new drugs to cure diseases is not easy. Every year, hundreds of clinical drug trials are conducted in order to find out if new drugs are safe and effective. Ultimately, only a small fraction of new drugs are successful. Drug discovery is usually a long process involving the efforts of hundreds of scientists, including molecular biologists, biochemists, and in particular, chemists.

Modern drug discovery often begins with new knowledge into the biochemical origins of diseases. An example of this is asthma, a respiratory condition, which affects approximately 5% of the adult population in Canada. In 1979, it was discovered that asthma is mediated by compounds known as leukotrienes. Leukotrienes are formed in white blood cells (leukocytes) in response to an inflammatory stimulus such as airborne dust or pollen. The essential fatty acid arachidonic acid is converted to leukotrienes by enzymes, including 5-lipoxygenase. Leukotrienes are a substrate for a protein, called the target receptor, that is located on the surfaces of cells in airway tissues. The binding of leukotrienes to the target receptors triggers mucus secretion, constriction of the bronchi, and swelling of tissues. That is, it triggers an asthma attack.

Scientists at Merck Frosst in Montreal searched for a compound that could act as an antagonist to the leukotriene receptor that initiates the asthmatic response. An antagonist is a compound that binds to a receptor, but does not induce the normal biological response. Rather, the antagonist blocks or diminishes the response because it prevents the active substrate from binding to its receptor.

Over several years, Merck Frosst scientists screened over 14 000 compounds as leukotriene receptor antagonists. Only a few of these compounds were effective antagonists. Chemists went on to synthesize hundreds of new compounds based on the structures that were known to be effective. Eventually, they found one that was many times more effective than all the other antagonists. This compound was developed into the drug montelukast sodium, marketed as Singulair®. (In honour of the city in which it was discovered, the "mont" in the name stands for Montreal.) With a prescription, chronic asthma sufferers can take Singulair on a daily basis, as a pill. Once in the body, the drug binds to leukotriene receptors and thus prevents the onset of an asthma attack. Clinical trials have shown that Singulair is so safe that it has been approved for the treatment of asthma in six-month-old infants.

The **synthesis** of montelukast sodium involves 23 different chemical reactions. These reactions fall into several different categories which are covered in this chapter, including substitution reactions and oxidation reactions. The knowledge of organic reactions allows chemists to synthesize compounds such as new pharmaceuticals.

21.2 Organic Acids and Bases

Acid–base reactivity in organic compounds is very common, and is not limited to the acid–base reactions of carboxylic acids. For example, alcohols and amines can act as proton donors (i.e., acids). In addition, there are many organic molecules that contain "acidic" hydrogen atoms that are bonded to carbon atoms.

The Range of Organic Acidities

In Chapters 15 and 16, we studied acids and bases and acid–base equilibria in aqueous systems. As such, we were limited to the pH range of 0–14. In organic chemistry, water is only one of many solvents in which reactions occur. Thus, organic acid–base reactivity covers a larger range of K_a values than what is possible in water. Recall that K_a is a measure of acid strength. Note that since organic acid–base equilibria are not restricted to aqueous media, H_2O does not appear in the following general equilibrium expression for K_a:

$$HA \rightleftharpoons H^+ + A^-$$

$$K_a = \frac{[H^+][A^-]}{[HA]}$$

$$pK_a = -\log K_a$$

pK_a values for a range of organic and inorganic acids are shown in Table 21.1. You will immediately notice the very large range of pK_a's. These pK_a values are determined by measuring the equilibrium concentrations of acids and their conjugate bases in various acid–base reactions, generally in organic solvents.

In Section 15.10, we explained the relative acidities of simple inorganic acids. Recall from that discussion that if an acidic proton is bonded to a generic atom or group Y, the

TABLE 21.1 pK_a Values for Selected Acids

Acid	pK_a	Conjugate Base
$CH_3—CH_3$	51	$CH_3—\ddot{C}H_2^-$
CH_4	48	$:CH_3^-$
$C_6H_5—CH_3$ (toluene)	41	$C_6H_5—\ddot{C}H_2^-$
$:NH_3$	38	$\ddot{N}H_2^-$
$CH_3C(=O)OCH_3$	25	$^-:CH_2C(=O)OCH_3$
$HC \equiv CH$	25	$HC \equiv C:^-$
$CH_3C(=O)CH_3$	20	$CH_3C(=O)\ddot{C}H_2^-$
$(CH_3)_3COH$	18	$(CH_3)_3CO:^-$
CH_3CH_2OH	16	$CH_3CH_2O:^-$
cyclopentadiene	16	cyclopentadienyl anion
$H_2\ddot{O}$	15.74	$H\ddot{O}:^-$
RNH_3^+ $R_2NH_2^+$ R_3NH^+	10–11	$R\dot{N}H_2$ $R_2\ddot{N}H$ $R_3N:$
HCO_3^-	10.2	CO_3^{2-}
$C_6H_5—OH$ (phenol)	9.88	$C_6H_5—\ddot{O}:^-$
NH_4^+	9.25	$:NH_3$
HCN	9.31	$:CN^-$

TABLE 21.1 (*continued*)

Acid	pK_a	Conjugate Base
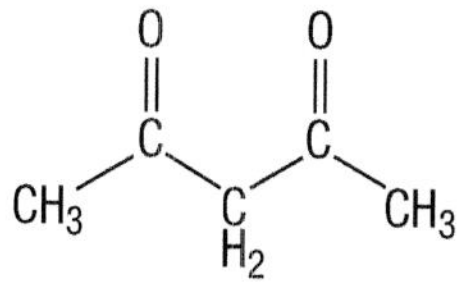 $CH_3C(=O)CH_2C(=O)CH_3$	8.99	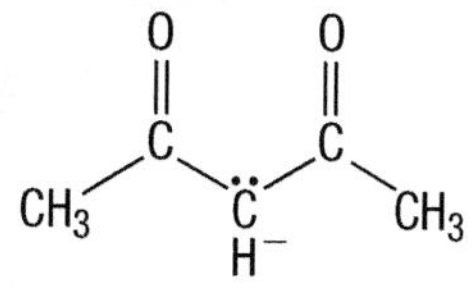 $CH_3C(=O)\ddot{C}H^-C(=O)CH_3$
CH_3CO_2H	4.74	$CH_3CO_2^-$
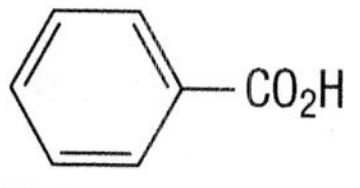 $C_6H_5CO_2H$	4.18	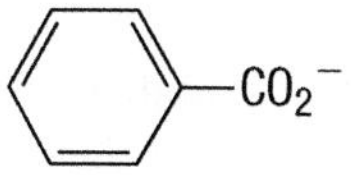 $C_6H_5CO_2^-$
HF	3.46	$:\ddot{F}:^-$
CF_3CO_2H	0.23	$CF_3CO_2^-$
$H_3\ddot{O}^+$	−1.74	$H_2\ddot{O}$
$CH_3CH_2\ddot{O}H_2^+$	−2.4	CH_3CH_2OH
H_2SO_4	−5.2	HSO_4^-
HCl	−7.0	$:\ddot{Cl}:^-$
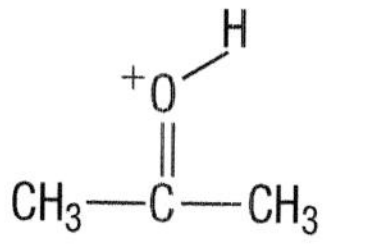 $CH_3C(=O^+H)CH_3$	−7.2	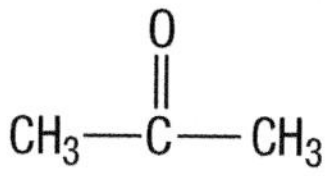 $CH_3C(=O)CH_3$
HBr	−9.0	$:\ddot{Br}:^-$
HI	−10.0	$:\ddot{I}:^-$

Note: pK_a values can vary significantly depending on the solvent.

acidity depends on the H—Y heterolytic bond dissociation energy. This, in turn, is a function of the H—Y homolytic bond dissociation energy, the ionization energy of H, and the electron affinity of Y. For example, compare the acidities of CH_4, NH_3, H_2O, and HF. The pK_a's are listed in Table 21.1, and are in the order $CH_4 > NH_3 > H_2O > HF$. The order of acid strengths is $CH_4 < NH_3 < H_2O < HF$, which is the same order as the general trend for increasing electron affinities across this group.

Organic compounds have much more structural variation than simple inorganic acids. To explain the acidity of organic compounds, we also need to consider **inductive effects** (introduced in Chapter 20) and **resonance effects**.

Inductive Effects: Withdrawal of Electron Density

An inductive effect results from bond polarization due to adjacent, electronegative atoms. An example is the case of hydrogen cyanide, HCN. The nitrogen atom is more electronegative than the carbon atom, and this induces a C—N bond dipole. The dipole, in turn, polarizes the bond:

$$\overset{\delta-}{:N}\equiv\overset{\delta+}{C}-H$$

Hydrogen cyanide
pK_a = 9.31

Ethyne is analogous to HCN in that it also contains a triple bond adjacent to the H atom. However, there is no adjacent electronegative atom and the ethyne has much lower acidity:

$$HC\equiv CH$$

pK_a = 25

Inductive effects can occur even when electronegative atoms are several bonds away. Compare acetic acid with trifluoroacetic acid, in which all of the methyl hydrogen atoms have been replaced with fluorine atoms:

$F_3C{-}C({=}O){-}O{-}H$ Trifluoroacetic acid $pK_a = 0.23$

$H_3C{-}C({=}O){-}O{-}H$ Acetic acid $pK_a = 4.74$

The electronegative fluorine atoms are three bonds away from the O—H bond that releases H^+, yet there is a large inductive effect that gives trifluoroacetic acid a much lower pK_a. Each C—F bond is very polar, creating a large positive partial charge on the methyl carbon. This induces further polarization of electron density in the carboxylic acid group and gives a more polarized O—H bond, which promotes ionization. Furthermore, the negative charge on the conjugate base is stabilized because electron density can be shifted throughout the molecule to electronegative atoms. Figure 21.1 ▼ shows the electrostatic potential surfaces for the conjugate bases of acetic acid and trifluoroacetic acid.

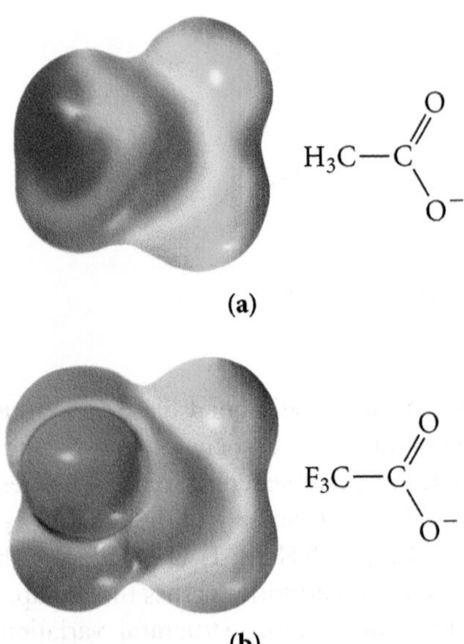

▲ **FIGURE 21.1 Electrostatic Potential Surfaces** of **(a)** acetate ion and **(b)** trifluoroacetate ion. The carboxylate (COO^-) units are on the right and the CX_3 ($X = H, F$) units are on the left. Colour indicates charge: Red is negative charge and green is partially negative; blue is positive charge and yellow is partially positive. In the acetate ion, the methyl group hydrogen atoms have a significant positive charge. The carboxylate group has a strong electron-withdrawing effect and "pulls" negative charge from the C—H bond. In trifluoroacetate, the effect of the electronegative F atoms can be seen: the F atoms are partially negative and the carboxylate group is more positive compared to the carboxylate group in acetate. In other words, the negative charge in trifluoroacetate is more stabilized.

Resonance Effects: Charge Delocalization in the Conjugate Base

Most alkyl alcohols (e.g., ethanol) have pK_a values in the range of 15–18. However, consider the acidity of phenol:

$$C_6H_5{-}OH \rightleftharpoons C_6H_5{-}\ddot{\underset{..}{O}}{:}^- + H^+ \qquad pK_a = 9.88$$

Phenol   Phenoxide ion

The conjugate base, the phenoxide ion, is resonance stabilized. (Lewis resonance structures were introduced in Section 9.8.) As shown below, the negative charge of the phenoxide ion is distributed, or shared, in the benzene ring. Another way to describe this is to say that the negative charge is *delocalized* over the ring because of the following resonance structures:

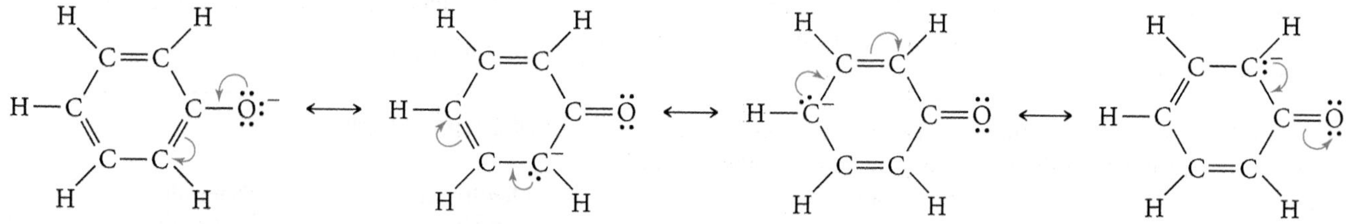

Acidic Hydrogen Atoms Bonded to Carbon

Table 21.1 lists many examples of molecules in which a C—H hydrogen atom is acidic. The loss of a hydrogen ion, or proton, from a carbon atom leads to a carbon with a localized, formal negative charge, known as a **carbanion**.

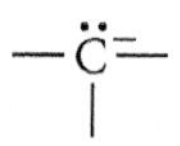

Carbanion

Carbanions are stabilized to different degrees by the surrounding molecular structure. In simple alkyl carbanions, such as CH_3^- and $CH_3CH_2^-$, the charge is completely localized on a carbon atom and there is no additional stabilization of the charge. Thus, the pK_a values of alkanes are very high.

$$H_3C—CH_3 \longrightarrow H_3C—\ddot{C}H_2^- + H^+ \qquad pK_a = 51$$

Ethane

In other molecules, the charge can be distributed throughout the molecule through resonance effects. For example, in pentan-2,4-dione, the loss of a hydrogen atom from the central carbon atom gives a carbanion with the resonance structures shown below. This compound has a much lower pK_a value (8.8), and is even more acidic than the ammonium ion (pK_a = 9.2).

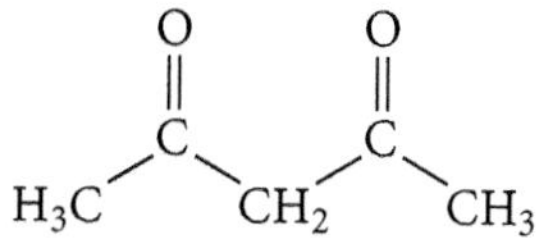

Pentan-2,4-dione

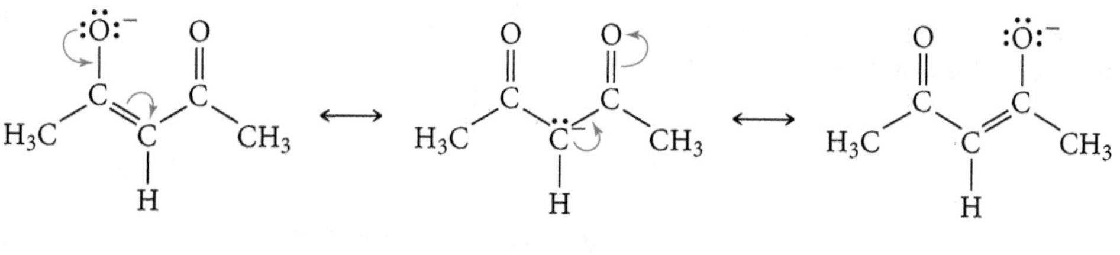

Mechanisms in Organic Chemistry

A mechanism is an attempt to represent a reaction at a molecular level, in a step-by-step manner, including any intermediates or transition states that are part of the mechanism. Organic mechanisms indicate the movement of electrons, which is inherent in bond formation and bond breaking. The movement of pairs of electrons is shown using a curved arrow, just as in resonance structures.

Consider the case of the bond dissociation of HCl. The two bonding electrons end up as a lone pair on the chlorine atom. An arrow from the H—Cl bond toward the Cl atom shows that the bond is breaking:

$$H—\ddot{C}l: \longrightarrow H^+ + :\ddot{C}l:^-$$

In the reverse reaction, a lone pair of electrons on the Cl atom becomes the bonding pair in H—Cl:

$$:\ddot{C}l:^- + H^+ \longrightarrow H—\ddot{C}l:$$

In mechanisms, curved arrows must start where electrons are, and end where they are going. Example 21.1 shows how to draw a mechanism for an acid–base reaction.

EXAMPLE 21.1 MECHANISMS FOR ACID–BASE REACTIONS

Draw a mechanism for the following acid–base reaction:

$$CH_3CO_2H + NH_3 \longrightarrow NH_4^+ + CH_3CO_2^-$$

SORT You are given a chemical equation that shows the reaction of an acid and a base. You are asked to draw the mechanism, which means to show the flow of electrons.

GIVEN: Equation for an acid–base reaction

FIND: Mechanism

STRATEGIZE Identify the movement of atoms in the reaction. In acid–base reactions, protons are donated and accepted. Another definition of acids and bases is that of electron acceptors and electron donors. By identifying the acid and the base, the movement of electrons can be determined.

CONCEPTUAL PLAN:

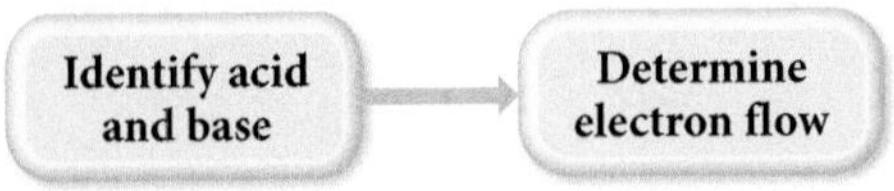

Identify acid and base → Determine electron flow

DEFINITIONS USED:

Acid = electron pair acceptor

Base = electron pair donor

SOLVE Draw the structural formulas for all reactants and products. A proton is transferred from acetic acid to ammonia. Acetic acid is the acid, and ammonia is the base. This means that ammonia is the electron donor, and acetic acid is the electron acceptor.

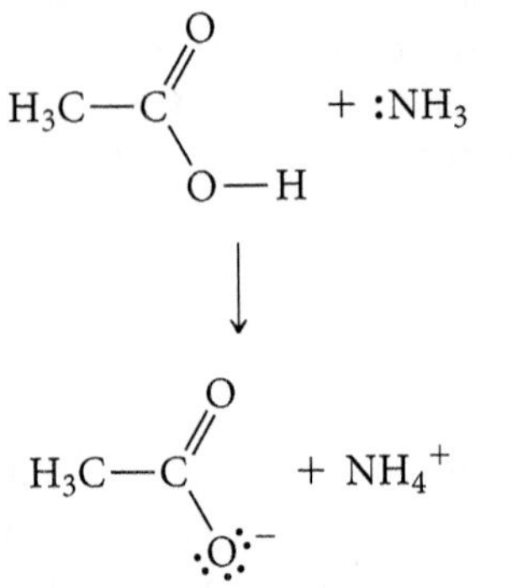

$H_3C{-}C(=O){-}O{-}H$ + :NH_3

↓

$H_3C{-}C(=O){-}\ddot{O}:^-$ + NH_4^+

Draw a curved arrow from the lone pair on NH_3 to the acidic hydrogen on acetic acid.

The O—H bond must break, and the two electrons in the O—H bond must go to the oxygen atom. Draw a curved arrow from the O—H bond to the oxygen atom.

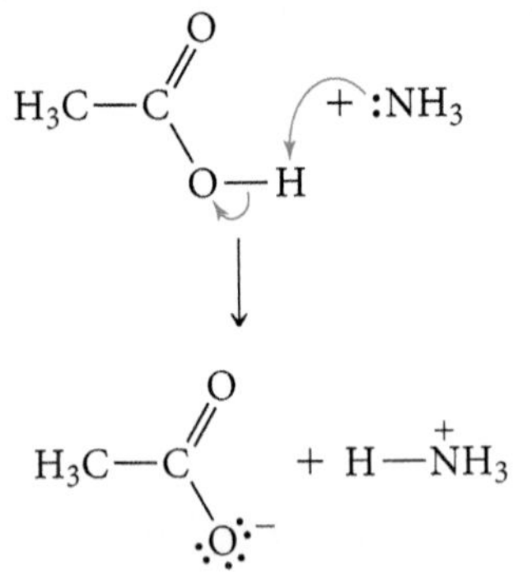

$H_3C{-}C(=O){-}O{-}H$ + :NH_3

↓

$H_3C{-}C(=O){-}\ddot{O}:^-$ + $H{-}\overset{+}{N}H_3$

CHECK One curved arrow shows the donation of two electrons to the H atom, which forms an N—H bond. The other curved arrow shows the breaking of the O—H bond, and the two electrons are transferred to the oxygen atom as a lone pair.

The overall charge remains constant, and the total number of electrons remains constant.

FOR PRACTICE 21.1

Draw a mechanism for the following acid–base reaction:

$$H_3O^+ + OH^- \longrightarrow 2\ H_2O$$

Acid and Base Reagents

The acid–base reactions of organic compounds are common in the laboratory and in industry. When chemists wish to perform a given acid–base reaction, they consider the pK_a values of different reactants to determine which combinations of acids and bases will react. Other concerns are cost and safety. Strong acids and bases can be hazardous to work with because they can cause damage to eyes and skin. Also, they may react violently with other chemicals. Generally speaking, the stronger the acid or base, the more expensive it is. Chemists try to choose acid and base reagents that are just strong enough to take a reaction to completion while minimizing the cost and safety risk. Some common Brønsted–Lowry acid and base reagents are listed to the right.

As an example, suppose you need to convert phenol ($pK_a = 9.88$) into its conjugate base. You have several possible bases from which to choose for this reaction, including sodium hydroxide (NaOH), sodium ethoxide ($NaOCH_2CH_3$), and sodium amide ($NaNH_2$). In order to choose the most appropriate base, let's compare the pK_a values of the conjugate acids of each of these bases. In Table 21.1, NH_3 ($pK_a = 38$) is the conjugate acid of NH_2^-; CH_3CH_2OH ($pK_a = 16$) is the conjugate acid of $CH_3CH_2O^-$; and H_2O ($pK_a = 15.7$) is the conjugate acid of OH^-. The conjugate acid with the highest pK_a value corresponds to the strongest base. NaOH is the best option because while it is the weakest base of the three, it is still strong enough to react completely with phenol. This minimizes the cost and safety risk. One further advantage is that the by-product, water, is nontoxic.

$$C_6H_5OH + NaOH \longrightarrow C_6H_5O^-Na^+ + H_2O$$

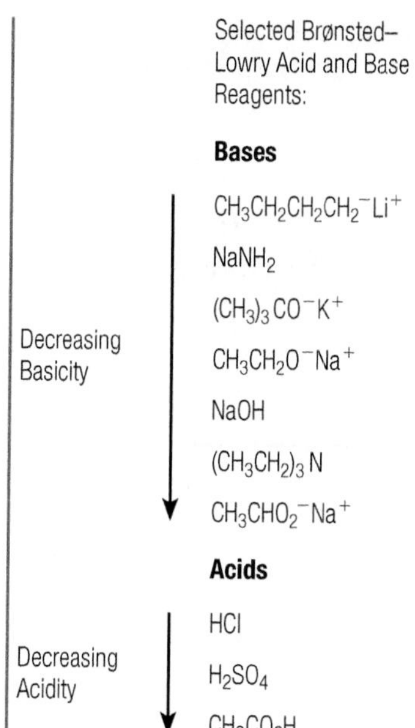

Selected Brønsted–Lowry Acid and Base Reagents:
Bases
Decreasing Basicity
$CH_3CH_2CH_2CH_2^-Li^+$
$NaNH_2$
$(CH_3)_3CO^-K^+$
$CH_3CH_2O^-Na^+$
NaOH
$(CH_3CH_2)_3N$
$CH_3CHO_2^-Na^+$
Acids
Decreasing Acidity
HCl
H_2SO_4
CH_3CO_2H

EXAMPLE 21.2 SELECTING AN APPROPRIATE ACID–BASE REAGENT

Use Table 21.1 and the list of selected acid–base reagents (above) to select an appropriate base, B^-, for the following reaction:

+ $B:^-$ ⟶ + B—H

SORT You are given an incomplete chemical equation for an acid–base reaction. The acid is cylcopenta-1,3-diene.

GIVEN: The acid is cyclopenta-1,3-diene.

You are asked to find a base that would remove an H atom from cylcopenta-1,3-diene.

FIND: A base that would remove an H atom to give

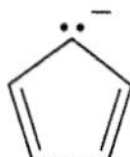

STRATEGIZE Determine the pK_a of the acid in Table 21.1. To react with this acid, a base must have a conjugate acid that has a pK_a higher than that of the reactant. The pK_a of cylcopenta-1,3-diene is 16.

CONCEPTUAL PLAN:
Find a base that has a conjugate acid with a pK_a higher than 16, which is the pK_a of the reactant.

RELATIONSHIP USED
Higher pK_a corresponds to higher basicity.

SOLVE From Table 21.1 and the list of selected acid-base reagents, the base $(CH_3)_3CO^-$ would be appropriate. The conjugate acid, $(CH_3)_3COH$, has a pK_a of 18, which is larger than 16.

From the list of selected acid–base reagents, this base corresponds to $(CH_3)_3CO^-$ K^+.

An appropriate base is:

$(CH_3)_3CO^-$ K^+

The balanced reaction is:

+ $(CH_3)_3CO^-$ K^+

↓

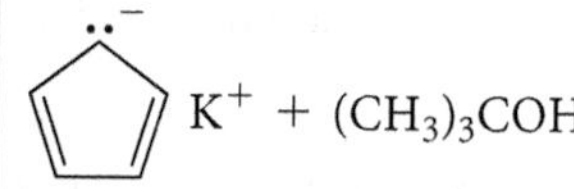

K^+ + $(CH_3)_3COH$

(continued)

EXAMPLE 21.2 (CONTINUED)

CHECK The acid cylcopenta-1,3-diene is more acidic than $(CH_3)_3COH$, which means that the reverse reaction will not take place to any appreciable extent.

FOR PRACTICE 21.2
Use Table 21.1 and the list of selected acid–base reagents to select an appropriate base, B^-, for the following reaction:

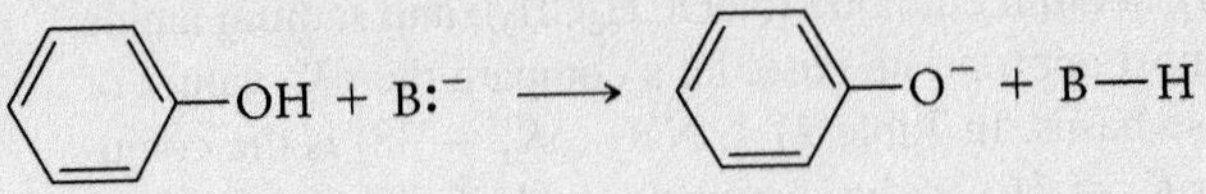

$$C_6H_5{-}OH + B{:}^- \longrightarrow C_6H_5{-}O^- + B{-}H$$

21.3 Oxidation and Reduction

Another broad class of organic reactions are oxidation–reduction (redox) reactions. Oxidation reactions involve the loss of electrons, while reduction reactions involve the gain of electrons. To determine whether or not electrons have been lost or gained, we examine the changes in oxidation states of the atoms in the reaction. We discussed how to do this for inorganic, binary compounds in Chapter 4. To determine the oxidation states of atoms in organic molecules, which are characterized by covalent bonds in many different arrangements, we use a slightly different approach. When determining the oxidation state of an atom, we examine the relative electronegativity of every atom it is bonded to:

- Each bond to an atom that is less electronegative is counted as -1 toward the oxidation state.
- Each bond to an atom that is more electronegative is counted as $+1$ toward the oxidation state.
- Bonds to the same type of atom are not counted.

EXAMPLE 21.3 OXIDATION STATES IN ORGANIC MOLECULES

Determine the oxidation state of each carbon atom in the following molecules:

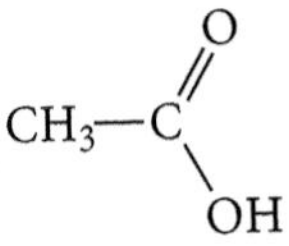

(a) $CH_3{-}C({=}O){-}OH$

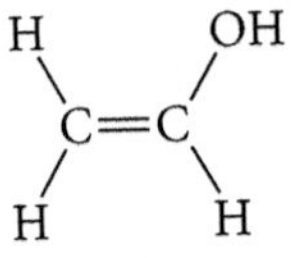

(b) $H_2C{=}CH{-}OH$ (H, H on left carbon; OH, H on right carbon)

(c) $H_2N{-}CH_2{-}C({=}O){-}OH$

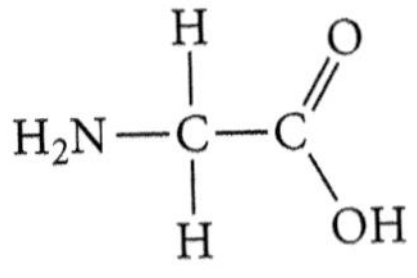

SOLUTION

(a) The methyl carbon atom is bonded to 3 H atoms (less electronegative) and 1 C atom (no effect). The oxidation state $= 3(-1) + 0 = -3$. The carboxylic acid carbon atom has three bonds to O atoms (more electronegative) and one bond to a C atom (no effect). The oxidation state $= 3(+1) + 0 = +3$.	$\overset{-3}{CH_3}{-}C^{+3}({=}O){-}OH$
(b) The carbon on the left is bonded to 2 H atoms (less electronegative) and has two bonds to the other C atom (no effect). The oxidation state $= 2(-1) + 2(0) = -2$. The other carbon is bonded to 1 H atom (less electronegative), 1 O atom (more electronegative), and has two bonds to the first C atom. The oxidation state $= 1(-1) + 1(+1) + 2(0) = 0$.	$H_2\overset{-2}{C}{=}\overset{0}{C}H{-}OH$
(c) The central carbon atom is bonded to 2 H atoms (less electronegative), 1 N atom (more electronegative), and 1 C atom (no effect). The oxidation state $= 2(-1) + 1(+1) + 1(0) = -1$. The carboxylic acid carbon atom has three bonds to O atoms (more electronegative) and one bond to a C atom (no effect). The oxidation state $= 3(+1) + 0 = +3$.	$H_2N{-}\overset{-1}{C}H_2{-}C^{+3}({=}O){-}OH$

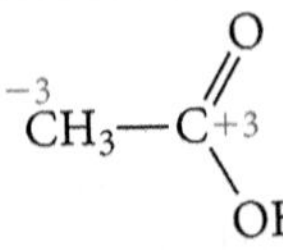

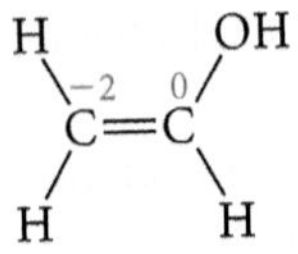

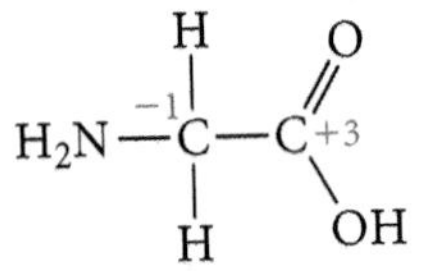

FOR PRACTICE 21.3

Determine the oxidation state of each carbon atom in the following molecules:

(a) $CH_3{-}C{\equiv}N$

(b) CH_3Cl

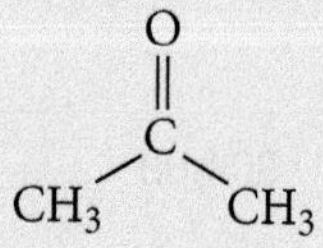

(c) $CH_3{-}C({=}O){-}CH_3$

Redox Reactions

The reduction of organic molecules usually involves the addition of hydrogen. An example of this is **hydrogenation** of alkenes or alkynes.

$$\overset{-3}{CH_3}{-}\overset{-1}{CH}{=}\overset{-2}{CH_2} + H_2 \xrightarrow{Pd/C} \overset{-3}{CH_3}{-}\overset{-2}{CH_2}{-}\overset{-3}{CH_3}$$

Propene → Propane

In this reaction, the oxidation states of the double-bonded carbon atoms have each decreased by 1. The total change in oxidation state of carbon is −2, which means a gain of two electrons. In other words, carbon has been reduced. Hydrogenation and reduction are equivalent terms. Hydrogenation reactions are usually performed in the presence of a hydrogenation catalyst like palladium metal supported on activated carbon, written as "Pd/C."

The oxidation of organic molecules usually involves the addition of oxygen. Combustion is the most common oxidation reaction of organic compounds:

$$\overset{-4}{CH_4} + 2\,O_2 \longrightarrow \overset{+4}{CO_2} + 2\,H_2O$$

Methane → Carbon dioxide

The combustion of methane leads to a total change of oxidation state of carbon of +8, which means a loss of eight electrons. We can also say that carbon has gained oxygen.

Functional groups can often be transformed into other functional groups through redox reactions. An important set of **interconversions** occurs among alcohols, carbonyls, and carboxylic acids, as shown in the following sequences.

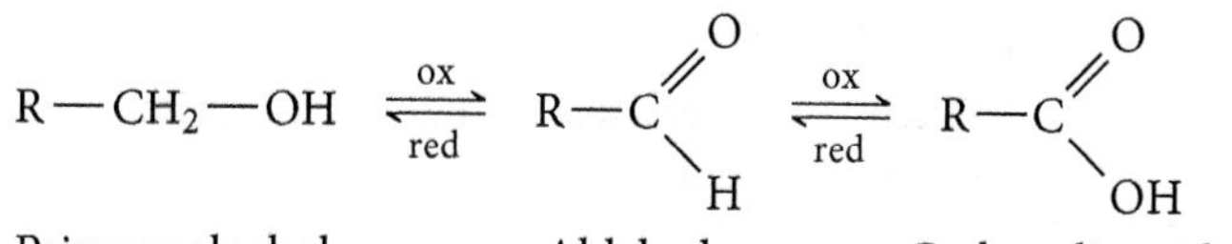

$$R{-}CH_2{-}OH \underset{red}{\overset{ox}{\rightleftharpoons}} R{-}C({=}O){-}H \underset{red}{\overset{ox}{\rightleftharpoons}} R{-}C({=}O){-}OH$$

Primary alcohol → Aldehyde → Carboxylic acid

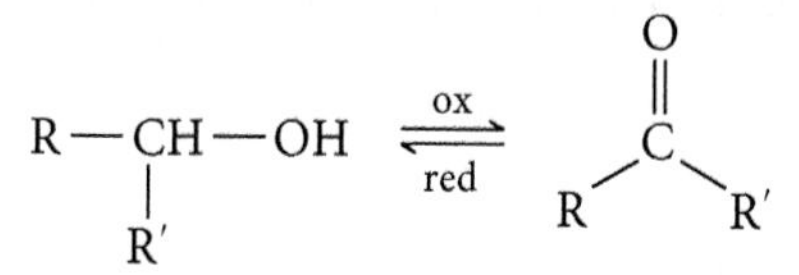

$$R{-}CH(R'){-}OH \underset{red}{\overset{ox}{\rightleftharpoons}} R{-}C({=}O){-}R'$$

Secondary alcohol → Ketone

Primary alcohols are oxidized to aldehydes, not ketones, because they have only one R group. Similarly, secondary alcohols are oxidized to ketones, not aldehydes. It is not possible to oxidize tertiary alcohols to carbonyls. Table 21.2 lists reagents that can be used for these interconversions.

TABLE 21.2 Reagents for Selected Oxidations and Reductions

Reactant	Reagent	Product
	Oxidations	
RCH_2OH	PCC (pyridinium chlorochromate) (pyridinium N^+–H CrO_3Cl^-)	RCHO
RCH_2OH	$K_2Cr_2O_7$, H_2SO_4 (Jones reagent)	RCOOH
RCHO	CrO_3, H_3O^+	RCOOH
R_2CHOH	$K_2Cr_2O_7$, H_2SO_4	R_2CO
RNH_2	$KMnO_4$	RNO_2
	Reductions	
RCOOH	$LiAlH_4$	RCH_2OH
RCHO	$NaBH_4$	RCH_2OH
R_2CO	$NaBH_4$	R_2CHOH
RNO_2	$LiAlH_4$ or H_2, Pd/C	RNH_2
C=C	H_2, Pd/C	H–C–C–H

EXAMPLE 21.4 CHOOSING REAGENTS FOR OXIDATIONS AND REDUCTIONS

Choose an appropriate reagent that can be used to convert the following reactant into the product shown:

$$\text{CH}_3\text{CH}_2\text{CH}_2\text{CH}_2\text{OH} \longrightarrow \text{CH}_3\text{CH}_2\text{CH}_2\text{C(=O)OH}$$

SORT You are asked to find a reagent that can be used to convert the reactant into the desired product.

GIVEN: The reactant is a primary alcohol. The product is a carboxylic acid.

FIND: A reagent that can convert a primary alcohol into a carboxylic acid.

STRATEGIZE Use Table 21.2 to identify the reagent.

CONCEPTUAL PLAN
Find the formula for a primary alcohol in Table 21.2 and select the reagent that will give a carboxylic acid product.

SOLVE From Table 21.2, primary alcohols can react with PCC or Jones reagent to give an aldehyde or carboxylic acid, respectively. The appropriate reagent must be Jones reagent, $K_2Cr_2O_7$, H_2SO_4.

The reaction may be written as:

$$\text{CH}_3\text{CH}_2\text{CH}_2\text{CH}_2\text{OH} \xrightarrow{K_2Cr_2O_7,\ H_2SO_4} \text{CH}_3\text{CH}_2\text{CH}_2\text{C(=O)OH}$$

CHECK The reaction is an oxidation. The reagent used is a strong oxidizing agent.

FOR PRACTICE 21.4

Choose an appropriate reagent that can be used to convert the following reactant into the product shown:

(cyclohexane)$-NO_2 \longrightarrow$ (cyclohexane)$-NH_2$

CONCEPTUAL CONNECTION 21.1

Oxidation and Reduction

Confirm that all of the conversions in Table 21.2 are in fact oxidation and reduction reactions.

CHEMISTRY IN YOUR DAY Hydrogen and the Oil Sands

The oil sands industry in Alberta is a source of economic prosperity. The oil sands is a large, naturally occurring deposit of tar-like hydrocarbons known as bitumen, mixed with sand. The bitumen is separated from the sand by mixing the oil sands with warm water at a basic pH. Once separated, the raw bitumen is upgraded to a "synthetic crude" that is similar to conventional crude oil. The synthetic crude is transported to oil refineries, where it is processed into liquid fuels such as gasoline.

Oil sands bitumen is a complex mixture of hydrocarbons, including high concentrations of polycyclic aromatic hydrocarbons (PAHs) and saturated polycyclic hydrocarbons known as naphthenes. Upgrading the bitumen is a very complex process, involving multiple stages. Bitumen is chemically transformed in processes called *hydrocracking* and *hydrotreating*, which require hydrogen.

▲ Syncrude's Mildred Lake Upgrader, near Fort McMurray, Alberta.

In *hydrocracking*, the bitumen is heated above 350 °C, at high pressure, in the presence of hydrogen and catalysts. A simplified description of hydrocracking is that PAHs are hydrogenated to the corresponding naphthenes. "Ring scission," or ring opening, of the naphthenes also takes place. These steps require different catalysts. The end result of hydrocracking is a complex mixture of branched, saturated hydrocarbons, and partially transformed PAHs and naphthenes. These reactions all involve hydrogenation, and are therefore reductions.

In *hydrotreating*, sulphur is removed by reducing sulphur-containing compounds with hydrogen in the presence of yet another catalyst. The removal of sulphur from synthetic crude is important because sulphur is undesirable in fuels. For example, Canada has strict regulations on the sulphur content of gasoline. This minimizes dangerous sulphur dioxide emissions from vehicles. Hydrotreating is a type of reduction reaction:

$$RSH + H_2 \xrightarrow{\text{catalyst}} RH + H_2S$$

The hydrogen used in upgrading is obtained from natural gas, which is composed primarily of methane, through a process called *steam-methane reforming*. The first reaction is highly endothermic, and must be carried out at 700 °C.

Hydrocracking

A PAH $\xrightarrow[\text{Heat, catalyst}]{H_2}$ A naphthene $\xrightarrow[\text{Heat, catalyst}]{H_2}$ A branched hydrocarbon

(continued)

CHEMISTRY IN YOUR DAY (CONTINUED)

The second reaction is exothermic and takes place at a lower temperature. These are oxidation–reduction reactions:

$$CH_4 + H_2O \xrightarrow[\text{catalyst}]{700\ °C} CO + 3\ H_2$$

$$CO + H_2O \longrightarrow CO_2 + H_2$$

The oil sands industry has been criticized on several environmental issues. The separation of bitumen from sand produces large quantities of untreatable waste water, which is placed in massive tailings ponds that are dangerous to wildlife. In June 2010, Syncrude Canada Ltd. was found guilty of failing to prevent the deaths of 1600 ducks that landed in Syncrude's Aurora tailings pond in the spring of 2008. There is evidence that the industry is responsible for polluting the Athabasca River with heavy metals such as mercury and lead. The oil sands industry is also responsible for massive CO_2 emissions, due to the large amount of energy required by the extraction and upgrading processes. Industry scientists and engineers are continually working on ways to improve these processes to make them more efficient and reduce the environmental impact.

21.4 Nucleophilic Substitution Reactions at Saturated Carbon

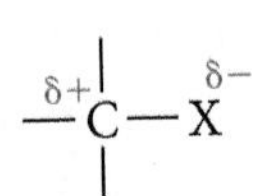

A **substitution reaction** is the replacement of one functional group with another. Groups can be replaced at saturated carbon atoms under certain conditions. Consider a saturated carbon that is bonded to a more electronegative heteroatom, such as a halogen atom. Recall from Chapter 20 that a partial positive charge resides on the carbon atom.

A carbon atom with a partial positive charge may react with a **nucleophile** (literally, "nucleus lover"), which is a molecule or ion that can donate a lone pair of electrons to the carbon atom and form a new covalent bond. In nucleophilic substitutions, a nucleophile replaces another atom or group (called the **leaving group**). The organic molecule in which the substitution is taking place is called the **substrate**. The substrate has a partial positive charge on the C atom, and is an **electrophile** ("electron lover"). The nucleophile reacts with the electrophilic substrate. The general reaction scheme looks like this:

$$\underset{\text{Nucleophile}}{Nu:^-} + \underset{\text{Substrate}}{-\overset{|}{\underset{|}{C}}{}^{\delta+}\!-\!L^{\delta-}} \longrightarrow \underset{\text{Product}}{-\overset{|}{\underset{|}{C}}-Nu} + \underset{\text{Leaving group}}{:L^-}$$

For example, in the reaction below, hydroxide is the nucleophile, bromomethane is the substrate, and bromide is the leaving group.

$$\underset{\substack{\text{Hydroxide}\\\text{(nucleophile)}}}{H\ddot{\underset{\cdot\cdot}{O}}:^-} + \underset{\substack{\text{Bromomethane}\\\text{(substrate)}}}{CH_3Br} \longrightarrow \underset{\substack{\text{Methanol}\\\text{(product)}}}{CH_3OH} + \underset{\substack{\text{Bromide ion}\\\text{(leaving group)}}}{:\ddot{\underset{\cdot\cdot}{Br}}:^-}$$

In this section, we will examine the two principal mechanisms for nucleophilic substitutions at saturated carbon: the S_N1 and S_N2 mechanisms. Then, we will discuss how various nucleophiles, leaving groups, and substrate structures affect the reactivity.

The S_N1 Mechanism

In the S_N1 mechanism, the bond between the carbon atom and the leaving group is broken first. This is known as a dissociation. This step produces an intermediate that has a carbon atom with a formal positive charge, known as a **carbocation**. (This is different from a carbanion, which is a carbon atom with a formal negative charge.) A carbocation is highly electrophilic. Energy is required to break the C—L bond, and the carbocation intermediate has a relatively high potential energy (see Figure 21.2 ▶). The formation

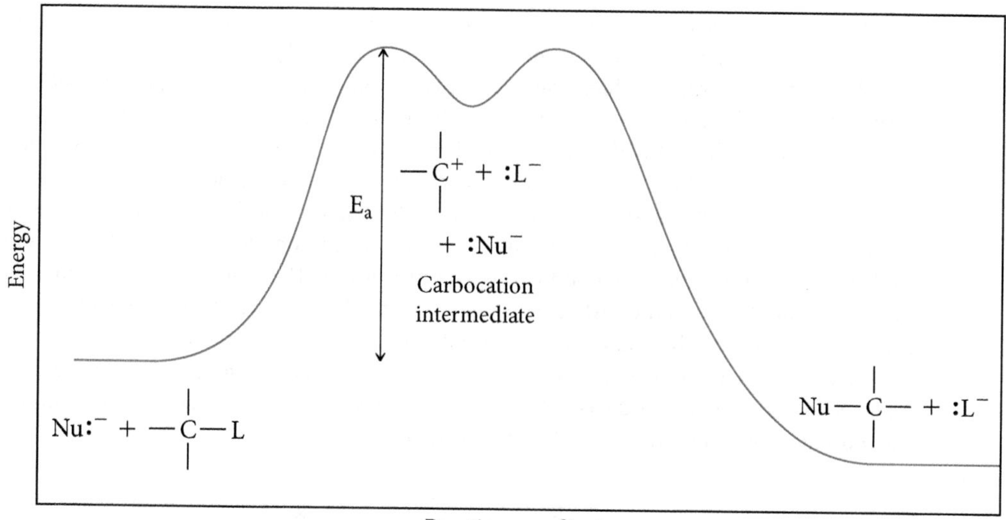

▲ **FIGURE 21.2 Energy Profile for S_N1 Mechanism** The rate-determining step is the formation of the carbocation intermediate (the first step). The activation energy for this step is labelled on the figure. The activation energy for the second step is small in comparison. The second step does not affect the overall rate of reaction.

of a carbocation intermediate is most likely to occur if the carbocation is stabilized by the structure of the substrate. The second step in this mechanism is the formation of a covalent bond between the nucleophile and the carbocation.

Step 1

$$-\overset{|}{\underset{|}{C}}-L \xrightleftharpoons{\text{Rate-determining step}} -\overset{|}{\underset{|}{C^+}} \quad + \quad :L^-$$

Substrate — Carbocation intermediate — Leaving group

Step 2

$$-\overset{|}{\underset{|}{C^+}} \quad + \quad :Nu^- \xrightarrow{\text{Fast}} -\overset{|}{\underset{|}{C}}-Nu$$

Carbocation intermediate — Nucleophile — Product

The dissociation step is much slower than the second step. Thus, the first step is rate limiting and the reaction is first order. Because the rate depends only on the substrate concentration, the reaction is "unimolecular." The designation "S_N1" means substitution, nucleophilic, and unimolecular.

The rate law for an S_N1 substitution reaction is: rate = k[substrate]

An example of an S_N1 mechanism is the reaction between 2-chloro-2-methylpropane and iodide ions:

Step 1

$$(CH_3)_3C-Cl \rightleftharpoons (CH_3)_3C^+ \quad + \quad :\ddot{\underset{..}{Cl}}:^-$$

2-Chloro-2-methylpropane (substrate) — Carbocation intermediate — Chloride ion (leaving group)

Step 2

$$(CH_3)_3C^+ \quad + \quad :\ddot{\underset{..}{I}}:^- \rightleftharpoons (CH_3)_3C-\ddot{\underset{..}{I}}:$$

Carbocation intermediate — Iodide ion (nucleophile) — 2-Iodo-2-methylpropane (product)

The rate law for this reaction is first order because the rate-determining step is the dissociation of the leaving group from the substrate: rate $= k[(CH_3)_3CCl]$

When the substrate is chiral, an S_N1 substitution reaction affects the stereochemistry of the substitution product. This is due to the molecular geometry of the carbocation intermediate. From VSEPR theory in Chapter 10, we know that the geometry at the positively charged carbon atom is trigonal planar (it has only three bonds). A nucleophile can approach the carbocation from either side of the plane. Consider the case of an S_N1 substitution at a chiral carbon. The four groups at the carbon atom are R_1, R_2, R_3, and the leaving group L. Let's say that the order of priorities is $R_1 > R_2 > R_3 > L$, and the substrate is the *S* enantiomer. After dissociation of the leaving group, the stereochemical configuration of the substrate is lost because the intermediate now has a planar geometry. Nucleophilic attack can occur from either side of the carbocation, giving a mixture of *R* and *S* enantiomers as products. The process of converting a single enantiomer into an equal mixture of enantiomers is called **racemization**.

Step 1

R_1, C, L, R_2, R_3 ⇌ R_1, C^+, R_2, R_3 + L^-

S enantiomer — Trigonal planar

Step 2

R_1, C^+, R_2, R_3 + $:Nu^-$ → R_1, C, R_2, R_3, Nu — *S* enantiomer

or

$Nu:^-$ + R_1, C^+, R_2, R_3 → R_1, C, L, Nu, R_3 — *R* enantiomer

Racemic mixture

The S_N2 Mechanism

The S_N2 mechanism involves a single step. The nucleophile "attacks" the substrate from the side opposite the leaving group. The reaction proceeds through a transition state with simultaneous bond formation and bond breaking.

$$Nu:^- + -\overset{|}{\underset{|}{C}}-L \longrightarrow \left[\overset{\delta-}{Nu}\cdots C \cdots \overset{\delta-}{L}\right] \longrightarrow Nu-\overset{|}{\underset{|}{C}}- + :L^-$$

Nucleophile Substrate — Transition state — Product Leaving group

The substitution reaction of bromomethane with hydroxide follows an S_N2 mechanism. Figure 21.3 ▶ shows the energy profile for this reaction mechanism.

$$H\ddot{O}:^- + CH_3Br \longrightarrow CH_3OH + :\ddot{Br}:^-$$

Hydroxide (nucleophile)	Bromomethane (substrate)	Methanol (product)	Bromide ion (leaving group)

The "2" in the S_N2 designation means bimolecular. The single step in the mechanism is bimolecular and therefore the rate law for a S_N2 substitution reaction is second order. In this case, rate $= k[CH_3Br][OH^-]$.

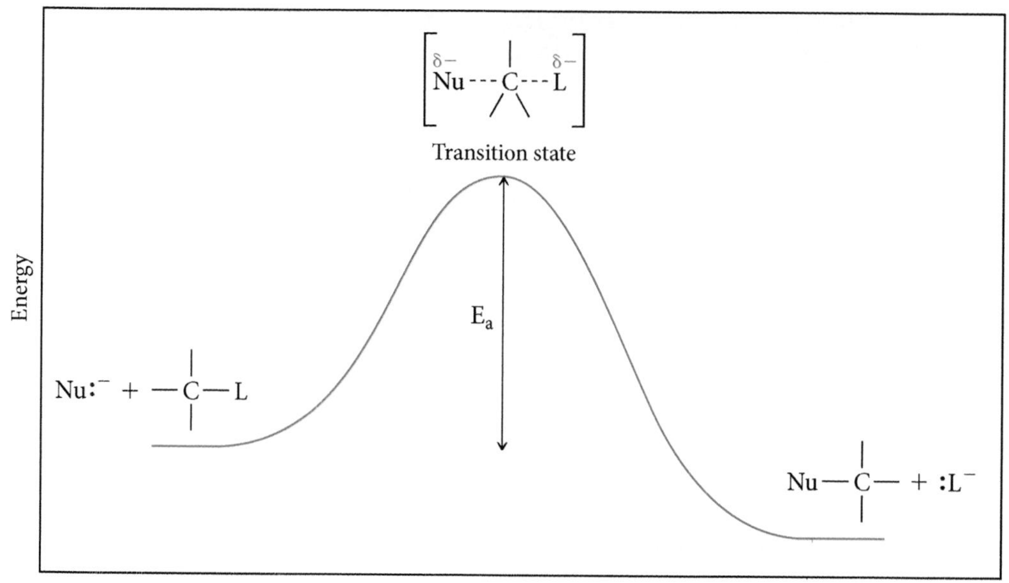

▲ **FIGURE 21.3 Energy Profile for S_N2 Mechanism** The rate of reaction depends on the activation energy for the formation of the unstable transition state.

If the carbon atom at the site of substitution is a chirality centre, the S_N2 mechanism results in stereochemical **inversion**. This means that the substitution product has the opposite absolute configuration to the initial substrate. Inversion occurs because the nucleophile attacks from the opposite side from the leaving group. As the molecule passes through the transition state, the other three groups must "flip" away from the direction of nucleophilic attack. This is a lot like an umbrella being inverted in high winds. In the figure below, you can see how the absolute configuration of the product must be opposite from that of the substrate.

▲ The inversion of an umbrella in high winds is similar to the stereochemical inversion that occurs in S_N2 substitution reactions.

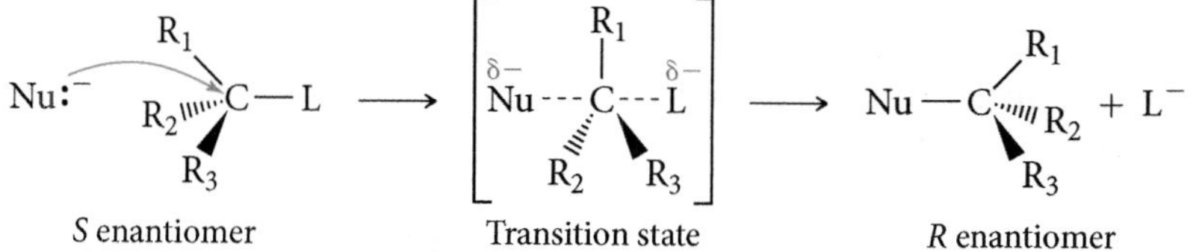

Factors Affecting Nucleophilic Substitution Reactions

The Nucleophile In S_N1 reactions, the rate-limiting step is the formation of the carbocation intermediate. The nucleophile is only involved in the second step. Therefore, the nucleophile has no effect on rates of S_N1 reactions. On the other hand, in S_N2 reactions, the nature of the nucleophile is very important because it "displaces" the leaving group by forming a new bond at the site of substitution.

The effectiveness of a nucleophile, or **nucleophilicity**, in S_N2 reactions varies depending on the substrate and reaction conditions. The nucleophile appears in the rate law, so changes in the choice of nucleophile affect the rate of an S_N2 reaction. An S_N2 substitution with a good nucleophile will take place much faster than with a poor nucleophile. In fact, a poor nucleophile will often not react with a substrate via an S_N2 pathway to any appreciable extent. Table 21.3 lists some common nucleophiles and their relative strengths.

The Leaving Group The leaving group is important in both S_N1 and S_N2 mechanisms. In both mechanisms, as the bond with the carbon atom is broken, the leaving group must develop and accept a negative charge. Therefore, the stability of the corresponding anion is the most important criterion for the effectiveness of the leaving group. A convenient way to assess the relative stabilities of anions is to compare the pK_a values of the corresponding acids. The best leaving groups are the conjugate bases of strong acids.

TABLE 21.3 Selected Nucleophiles and Their Relative Effectiveness

Good	I^-, Br^-, CN^- RS^- (e.g., CH_3S^-) OH^-, RO^- (e.g., CH_3O^-)
Moderate	$RCOO^-$ (e.g., CH_3COO^-) RSH (e.g., CH_3SH) NH_3 RNH_2, R_2NH, R_3N
Poor	H_2O ROH (e.g., CH_3OH) RCOOH (e.g., CH_3COOH)

Common leaving groups:

$$I^- > Br^- > Cl^- >> F^- > CH_3COO^- > HO^- > CH_3O^- > NH_2^-$$

The leaving group is always part of the substrate, which is part of the rate law for both S_N1 and S_N2 substitutions. The leaving group directly affects the rate of substitution.

CONCEPTUAL CONNECTION 21.2

Leaving Groups and Base Strength

Look up the pK_a values of the conjugate acid of each of the common leaving groups listed above. Confirm that the best leaving groups are conjugate bases of strong acids. Is a good leaving group a weak base or a strong base?

Substrate Structure In S_N1 reactions, the rate of reaction is strongly affected by the stability of the carbocation intermediate. The stability of a carbocation depends on the number of alkyl groups it is bonded to.

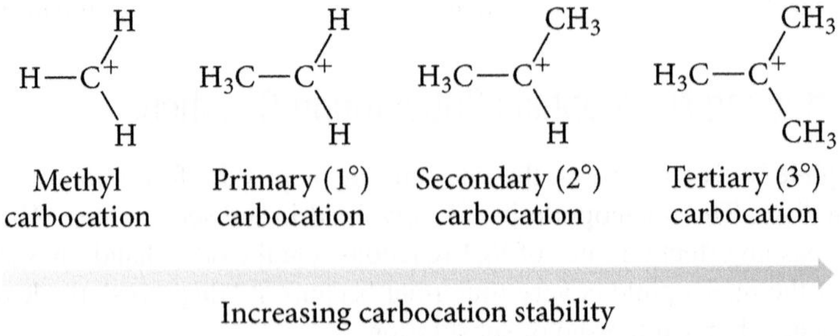

$H-C^+(H)(H)$	$H_3C-C^+(H)(H)$	$H_3C-C^+(CH_3)(H)$	$H_3C-C^+(CH_3)(CH_3)$
Methyl carbocation	Primary (1°) carbocation	Secondary (2°) carbocation	Tertiary (3°) carbocation

Increasing carbocation stability →

The order of carbocation stabilities is due to inductive effects. However, it is not as straightforward as the inductive effects discussed in Section 21.2. The carbocation species shown above do not contain any highly electronegative atoms bonded to carbon atoms, which would result in bond dipoles. In these carbocations, the positive charge on the carbon atom *induces dipoles* in adjacent sigma bonds and draws electron density toward it. This somewhat delocalizes the charge over nearby atoms. With more adjacent sigma bonds, the charge can be better delocalized. This explains the order of carbocation stability—the number of adjacent sigma bonds increases from methyl to primary, secondary, and tertiary carbocations.

S_N1 reactions only occur with secondary and teritiary substrates because of the stability of the carbocations. Methyl and primary substrates never undergo S_N1 substitutions because of the very low stability of methyl and primary carbocations.

In S_N2 reactions, the rate is affected by the amount of **steric hindrance** at the substitution site. Consider two substrates: bromomethane and 2-bromo-2-methylpropane. When a nucleophile attacks the carbon atom in bromomethane, it must come in close proximity with the three hydrogen atoms, which is not energetically favourable. However, if the same nucleophile attacks the carbon in 2-bromo-2-methylpropane, it must experience even closer contact with all of the atoms on the three methyl groups. The degree of steric hindrance is so unfavourable at tertiary carbons that S_N2 substitution does not occur. Instead, S_N1 substitution occurs because of the stability of the tertiary carbocation. S_N2 substitution only occurs in methyl, primary, and secondary substrates.

Bromomethane	Bromoethane (1° halide)	2-Bromopropane (2° halide)	2-Bromo-2-methylpropane (3° halide)
S_N2 only	S_N2 only	S_N1 or S_N2	S_N1 only

In the substitution of methyl and primary substrates, the mechanism is always S_N2. In tertiary substrates, the mechanism is always S_N1. With secondary substrates, substitution can be either S_N1 or S_N2, and the mechanism depends on the other factors that affect nucleophilic substitution: the nucleophile and the leaving group. The prediction of which substitution mechanism occurs in secondary substrates is often difficult. In some cases, both substitution mechanisms take place simultaneously.

EXAMPLE 21.5 PREDICTING NUCLEOPHILIC SUBSTITUTIONS

Predict the substitution product for the following reaction, and predict whether the mechanism is S_N1 or S_N2. Draw the mechanism.

$$CH_3CH_2Br + CN^- \longrightarrow ?$$

SOLUTION

SORT You are given a substitution reaction. You are asked to predict the mechanism and then draw the mechanism.

GIVEN: The reactants CH_3CH_2Br and CN^-

FIND: Predict the mechanism of substitution and draw the mechanism.

STRATEGIZE To predict the mechanism, identify the substrate and nucleophile, and determine whether the substrate is primary, secondary, or tertiary. Determine whether it is a strong or weak nucleophile. Once all of this is known, the mechanism can be predicted and drawn.

CONCEPTUAL PLAN

Determine Nature of Substrate and Nucleophile ⟶ Predict Mechanism ⟶ Draw Mechanism

RELATIONSHIPS USED

- ▶ 1° substrate gives S_N2
- ▶ 2° substrate gives S_N1 or S_N2, depending on Nu and L
- ▶ 3° substrate gives S_N1

SOLVE The substrate, CH_3CH_2Br, is a 1° substrate. The substitution will occur by an S_N2 mechanism.

The mechanism can be drawn by comparing with the general S_N2 mechanism in this section.

The reaction will proceed by an S_N2 mechanism:

$$:N{\equiv}C:^- + H_3C{-}CH_2{-}Br$$

$$\downarrow$$

$$H_3C{-}CH_2{-}CN + Br^-$$

(*continued*)

EXAMPLE 21.5 (CONTINUED)

CHECK The mechanism gives a balanced chemical reaction. Charges are balanced.

FOR PRACTICE 21.5

Predict the substitution product for the following reaction, and predict whether the mechanism is S_N1 or S_N2.

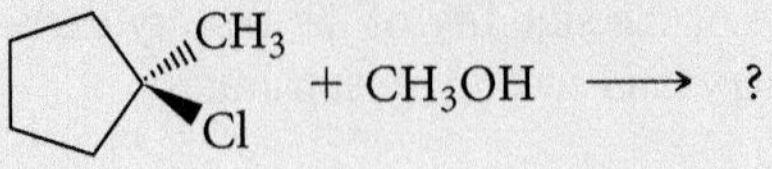

$$\text{(1-chloro-1-methylcyclopentane: ring C bearing } CH_3 \text{ (hashed) and Cl (wedged))} + CH_3OH \longrightarrow ?$$

21.5 Elimination Reactions

Elimination reactions occur when atoms are removed from a molecule. In organic chemistry, an important type of elimination is the loss of two atoms or groups from adjacent carbon atoms in a molecule. These reactions are therefore often referred to as **1,2-eliminations**. The removal of atoms leads to the formation of multiple bonds in the molecule:

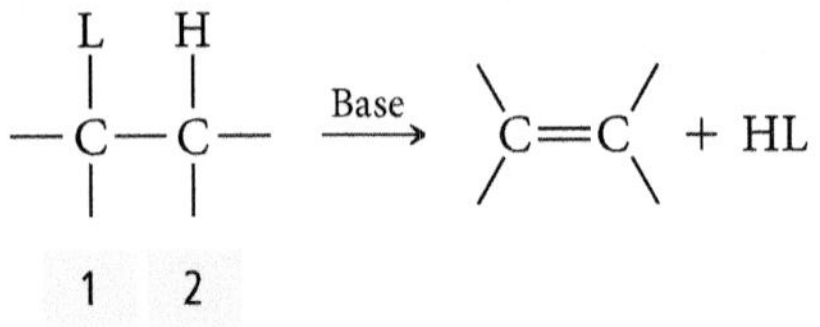

$$-\overset{L}{\underset{1}{C}}-\overset{H}{\underset{2}{C}}- \xrightarrow{\text{Base}} >C{=}C< + HL$$

In this section, we will focus on two types of elimination reaction—**dehydration** and **dehydrohalogenation**. Dehydration is the loss of water from an alcohol. This reaction occurs in the presence of a strong acid and heat.

$$\underset{\text{Butan-1-ol}}{CH_3CH_2CH_2CH_2OH} \xrightarrow[\text{Heat}]{H_3PO_4} \underset{\text{But-1-ene}}{CH_3CH_2CH{=}CH_2} + H_2O$$

Dehydrohalogenation is the loss of HX (X = Cl, Br, I) from an alkyl halide. This reaction often requires the presence of a strong base and heat.

$$\underset{\text{1-Bromopropane}}{CH_3CH_2CH_2Br} + \underset{\text{Sodium ethoxide}}{CH_3CH_2O^-Na^+} \xrightarrow[\text{Heat}]{CH_3CH_2OH} \underset{\text{Propene}}{CH_3CH{=}CH_2} + \underset{\text{Ethanol}}{CH_3CH_2OH} + \underset{\text{Sodium bromide}}{NaBr}$$

Many elimination reactions give mixtures of products because there are often two or more elimination sites around the −X or −OH groups. For example, 2-bromo-3-methylbutane yields two alkene products. The more substituted alkene, 2-methylbut-2-ene, is the major product.

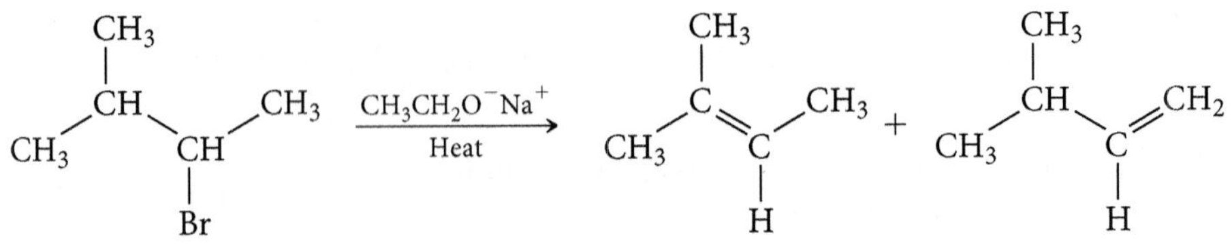

$$\underset{\text{2-Bromo-3-methylbutane}}{CH_3CH(CH_3)CH(Br)CH_3} \xrightarrow[\text{Heat}]{CH_3CH_2O^-Na^+} \underset{\substack{\text{2-Methylbut-2-ene}\\ \text{Major product}}}{(CH_3)_2C{=}CHCH_3} + \underset{\text{2-Methylbut-1-ene}}{CH_3CH(CH_3)CH{=}CH_2}$$

An exception to Zaitsev's rule occurs when large, bulky bases, such as $(CH_3)_3CO^-$, are used. The bulky base extracts an H atom from a less-substituted carbon atom, which leads to a less-substituted alkene.

Whenever isomeric alkenes are produced in an elimination reaction, the major product is usually the most substituted alkene. This is known as **Zaitsev's rule**.

The E1 Mechanism

The E1 mechanism for elimination is similar to the S_N1 mechanism for substitution in that they share the same initial, rate-determining step, the dissociation of an atom or group to give a carbocation intermediate. Similarly, the designation "E1" means elimination, unimolecular. For example, the elimination of HBr from 2-bromo-2-methylpropane in methanol follows an E1 mechanism. The initial step is:

Step 1

$$(CH_3)_3C{-}Br \xrightarrow[\text{determining}]{\text{Rate}} CH_3{-}\overset{CH_3}{\overset{|}{C^+}}{-}CH_3 + :\ddot{Br}:^-$$

In the second step, a hydrogen atom adjacent to the carbocation is removed by a base, leaving a C—C double bond. In this particular reaction, the solvent methanol can act as the base:

Step 2

$$CH_3{-}\overset{CH_3}{\overset{|}{C^+}}{-}CH_2{-}H + :\ddot{O}(H)CH_3 \longrightarrow CH_3{-}\overset{CH_3}{\overset{|}{C}}{=}CH_2 + H{-}\overset{+}{\ddot{O}}(H)CH_3$$

In the previous section, we saw that —OH is a poor leaving group. Thus, in dehydration reactions, the leaving group is not —OH. A much better leaving group is formed in the presence of a strong acid like H_2SO_4. The —OH becomes protonated to give an **oxonium ion**, which is an ion in which oxygen has a positive charge because it is bonded to three other atoms. Recall from Table 21.1 that H_2SO_4 is a stronger acid than $CH_3CH_2OH_2^+$. So, in concentrated sulfuric acid, virtually all of the —OH groups are protonated. This creates a very good leaving group, namely H_2O.

Step 1

$$H^+ + CH_3{-}\overset{CH_3}{\overset{|}{C}}{-}CH_3 \ (\text{with } :\ddot{O}{-}H) \longrightarrow CH_3{-}\overset{CH_3}{\overset{|}{C}}{-}CH_3 \ (\text{with } \overset{+}{\ddot{O}}H_2) \longrightarrow CH_3{-}\overset{CH_3}{\overset{|}{C^+}}{-}CH_3 + H_2O$$

Oxonium ion

The conjugate base of H_2SO_4, HSO_4^-, removes a hydrogen atom from the carbocation and thus generates the alkene.

Step 2

$$CH_3{-}\overset{CH_3}{\overset{|}{C^+}}{-}CH_2{-}H + :\ddot{O}^-{-}S(=O)_2{-}OH \longrightarrow CH_3{-}\overset{CH_3}{\overset{|}{C}}{=}CH_2 + H_2SO_4$$

CONCEPTUAL CONNECTION 21.3

Can a Strong Acid React Like a Base?

In Step 1 of the dehydration mechanism above, H_2O is produced. In concentrated H_2SO_4, what species is H_2O converted to? Write a chemical equation. Use Table 21.1 to confirm that HSO_4^- is the strongest base in the reaction mixture. What does this tell you about the pK_a of a carbocation?

Just like the S_N1 mechanism, the E1 mechanism generally does not occur in primary alcohols or primary alkyl halides, due to the instability of primary carbocations. The strength of the base is not a concern in E1 reactions because it is only involved in the second step, which does not affect the rate. If a weak base is used, the elimination will probably proceed via an E1 mechanism. This is different from the E2 mechanism on the next page, which generally requires a strong base.

The E2 Mechanism

The E2 mechanism involves a single step and is bimolecular. A base removes a hydrogen atom, the C—C double bond is formed, and the leaving group dissociates. All of this occurs in a single step. The removal of the hydrogen atom is integral to the E2 mechanism. Therefore, this pathway is strongly favoured when a strong base, B^-, such as an alkoxide (e.g., $CH_3CH_2O^-Na^+$) is used. E2 eliminations can occur at primary, secondary, and tertiary carbon centres.

$$B:^- + -\overset{H}{\underset{|}{\overset{|}{C}}}-\underset{|}{\overset{|}{C}}-L \longrightarrow \;\rangle C{=}C\langle\; + BH + L:^-$$

Elimination Versus Substitution

We already know that elimination reactions can produce mixtures of isomeric alkene products. Another complication is that bases, which promote elimination, are also nucleophiles. This opens up the possibility of competing elimination and substitution reactions. For example, when 2-bromopropane reacts with a weak base (ethanol) versus a strong base (sodium ethoxide), the yields of elimination and substitution products are very different:

2-Bromopropane ($CH_3CHBrCH_3$) → $CH_3CH{=}CH_2$ (Elimination product) + $CH_3CH(OCH_2CH_3)CH_3$ (Substitution product)

Reagent	Elimination product	Substitution product
CH_3CH_2OH	3%	97%
$CH_3CH_2O^-Na^+$, CH_3CH_2OH	80%	20%

The reagent $CH_3CH_2O^-Na^+$, sodium ethoxide, is a very strong base (see Table 21.1). As a reagent, it is often listed with CH_3CH_2OH because $CH_3CH_2O^-Na^+$ is prepared by reacting sodium metal, Na, with an excess of CH_3CH_2OH:

$2\,CH_3CH_2OH(l) + 2\,Na(s) \rightarrow 2\,CH_3CH_2O^-Na^+ + H_2(g)$

The general rule is that strong bases favour the elimination pathway over substitution.

21.6 Electrophilic Additions to Alkenes

In Section 21.4, we defined a nucleophile as an atom or group that could form new bonds by donating a lone pair of electrons to an atom with a partial positive charge. Nucleophiles are Lewis bases in that they are electron donors. The opposite of a nucleophile is an electrophile. An electrophile forms a new bond by accepting a lone pair of electrons. Electrophiles are Lewis acids, or electron acceptors. In the previous two sections, we saw how carbocations are intermediates in S_N1 and E1 pathways. In each of these pathways, the carbocations were electrophiles in that they formed new bonds with nucleophiles by accepting a lone pair of electrons. This is really a sort of acid–base reaction.

Electrophiles are not limited to reactions with typical nucleophiles. In this section, we will describe the reactions of electrophiles with alkenes. Carbon–carbon double bonds are high in electron density, and can donate electrons to an electrophile, which leads to an **electrophilic addition** reaction.

Hydrohalogenation

Hydrohalogenation is the addition of HX to an alkene to give an alkyl halide. It is the reverse reaction of the elimination of HX, covered in the preceding section. The addition of HX is a two-step process. The first step is the reaction of the electrophile (HX) and the alkene to form a carbocation intermediate:

Step 1 $$\rangle C{=}C\langle \; + H{-}X \longrightarrow -\overset{+}{\underset{|}{C}}-\underset{|}{\overset{H}{\overset{|}{C}}}- + :\ddot{\underset{..}{X}}:^-$$

Alkene Electrophile Carbocation intermediate

The second step is the same as what we saw in the S_N1 mechanism—the reaction of the carbocation with X^-.

$$\text{Step 2}\quad :\ddot{X}:^- + -\overset{+}{C}(H)-C- \longrightarrow -C(X)-C(H)-$$

Many alkenes are unsymmetrical in that there are different groups on each end of the double bond. In such cases, we would normally expect to see two different addition products, where the halogen atom is bonded to either of the two carbon atoms. In reality, there is usually only one addition product, the one in which the halogen atom is bonded to the most substituted carbon. For example, when propene reacts with HCl, the only product observed is 2-chloropropane:

$$\underset{\text{Propene}}{CH_3CH{=}CH_2} + HCl \longrightarrow \underset{\text{2-Chloropropane}}{CH_3CH(Cl)-CH_2(H)} + \left[\underset{\text{1-Chloropropane not observed}}{CH_3CH(H)-CH_2(Cl)}\right]$$

This product selectivity arises from the stabilities of carbocation intermediates. As we have seen, carbocation stabilities are in the order 3° > 2° > 1°. In the first step of the addition mechanism, the hydrogen atom adds to the double bond in such a way as to generate the most stable carbocation, which subsequently reacts to form a C—X bond. This pattern of reactivity is known as **Markovnikov's rule**, after the Russian chemist who first proposed it.

CONCEPTUAL CONNECTION 21.4

H—X as an Electrophile

Draw the bond dipole of HX (e.g., HCl) to show why it is the electrophile in the first step of the hydrohalogenation mechanism.

Other Addition Reactions

Several other addition reactions involve alkenes. A selection is listed in Table 21.4. It is worth noting that many addition reactions can be formally considered to be oxidation

TABLE 21.4 Selected Additions to Alkenes for the Reaction:

$$>C{=}C< \xrightarrow{\text{Reagent}}$$

Reaction	Reagent	Product(s)
Hydrogenation	H_2, Pd/C	$-C(H)-C(H)-$
Halogenation	Cl_2 or Br_2	$-C(Cl)-C(Cl)-$ or $-C(Br)-C(Br)-$
Epoxidation	RCO_3H (peroxy acid) $R-C(=O)-O-O-H$	$-C-O-C-$ (three-membered ring), an epoxide
Dihydroxylation	$KMnO_4$, NaOH	$-C(OH)-C(OH)-$

or reduction reactions. For example, we have previously shown that hydrogenation is a reduction reaction. In halogenation, epoxidation, and hydroxylation reactions, the formal charges of the carbon atoms become more positive (i.e., oxidation). In contrast, hydration (the addition of water) is not formally a reduction or oxidation reaction.

CONCEPTUAL CONNECTION 21.5

Mechanism of Hydration

Follow the mechanistic steps for hydrohalogenation to write a similar mechanism for the hydration of alkenes with H_2O, H^+.

21.7 Nucleophilic Additions to Aldehydes and Ketones

In Chapter 20, we saw that the carbonyl group is highly polarized. The carbon atom in a carbonyl group has a large partial positive charge due to the double bond to the more electronegative oxygen. Carbonyl groups are subject to nucleophilic attack at the electrophilic carbon atom. Unlike at a saturated carbon, where nucleophilic attack leads to substitution, nucleophilic attack on a carbonyl group gives an addition product. As we will see, this is due to the carbon–oxygen double bond.

The general mechanism is as follows. The first step in the reaction is the formation of a bond between the nucleophile and the carbon atom of the aldehyde or ketone. The intermediate formed contains a negatively charged oxygen, which reacts with a proton, H^+, to give the —OH group.

$$\mathrm{C{=}O} + :\mathrm{Nu}^- \longrightarrow -\overset{:\ddot{O}:^-}{\underset{|}{C}}-\mathrm{Nu} \quad H^+ \longrightarrow -\overset{OH}{\underset{|}{C}}-\mathrm{Nu}$$

Addition of Alcohols

$$R'-\overset{OH}{\underset{H}{C}}-OR'' \qquad R'-\overset{OH}{\underset{R}{C}}-OR''$$

Hemiacetal Hemiketal

An example of **nucleophilic addition** to aldehydes and ketones is the formation of **hemiacetals** and **hemiketals**, which are compounds with an —OH and an —OR group on the same carbon atom. Hemiacetals are produced from the reaction between an aldehyde and an alcohol. Hemiketals are produced from the reaction between a ketone and an alcohol. These reactions are reversible and are usually catalyzed by acid.

$$\underset{\text{Propanal}}{CH_3CH_2CHO} + \underset{\text{Methanol}}{CH_3OH} \overset{H^+}{\rightleftharpoons} \underset{\text{1-Methoxypropan-1-ol (a hemiacetal)}}{CH_3CH_2\overset{OH}{\overset{|}{C}H}-OCH_3}$$

$$\underset{\text{Propanone}}{CH_3\overset{O}{\overset{\|}{C}}CH_3} + CH_3OH \overset{H^+}{\rightleftharpoons} \underset{\text{2-Methoxypropan-2-ol (a hemiketal)}}{H_3C-\overset{OH}{\underset{CH_3}{C}}-OCH_3}$$

In IUPAC nomenclature, all compounds with the general structure RR′C(OH)(OR″) are known as hemiacetals. The class term "hemiketal" is considered a subclass of hemiacetals.

The mechanisms for formation of hemiacetals and hemiketals are identical, so we will only present the mechanism for hemiacetals. In acidic conditions, the oxygen atom in the carbonyl group can be protonated to give a type of oxonium ion (step 1). The protonated carbonyl has a resonance structure in which the carbon atom is positively charged. This carbon atom is very electrophilic and is attacked by the nucleophilic oxygen atom of the alcohol (step 2). The final step is the release of a proton, regenerating the acid catalyst (step 3).

Resonance structures for protonated carbonyl oxonium ion

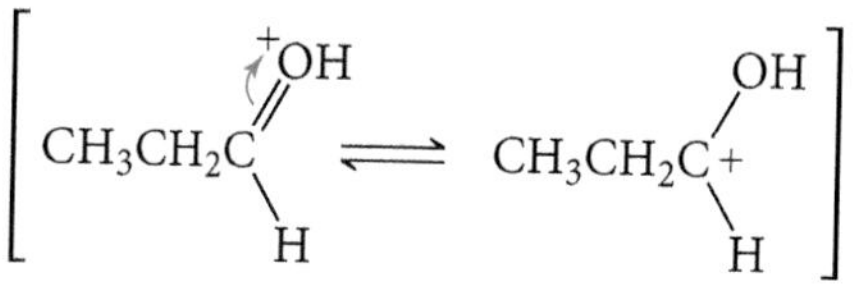

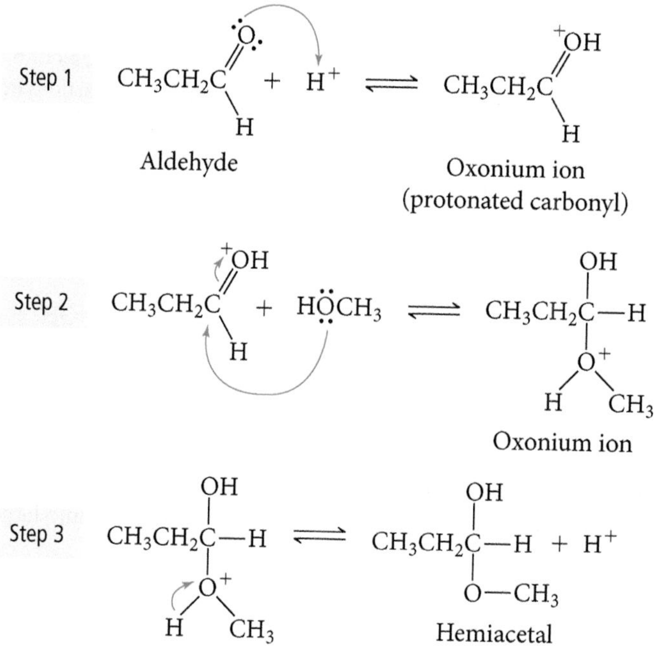

$$\left[CH_3CH_2CH{=}\overset{+}{O}H \rightleftharpoons CH_3CH_2\overset{+}{C}H{-}OH \right]$$

Step 1 $CH_3CH_2CHO + H^+ \rightleftharpoons CH_3CH_2CH{=}\overset{+}{O}H$

Aldehyde; Oxonium ion (protonated carbonyl)

Step 2 $CH_3CH_2CH{=}\overset{+}{O}H + HOCH_3 \rightleftharpoons CH_3CH_2CH(OH){-}\overset{+}{O}(H)CH_3$

Oxonium ion

Step 3 $CH_3CH_2CH(OH){-}\overset{+}{O}(H)CH_3 \rightleftharpoons CH_3CH_2CH(OH){-}O{-}CH_3 + H^+$

Hemiacetal

Hemiacetals are important in biological systems because many monosaccharides (e.g., glucose) primarily exist in the hemiacetal form:

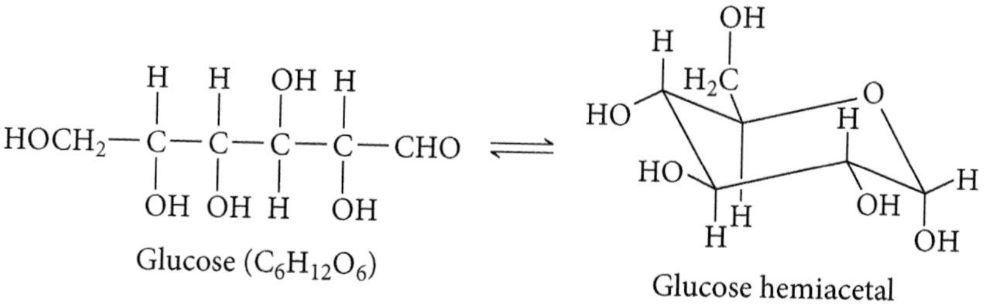

$HOCH_2{-}CH(OH){-}CH(OH){-}CH(OH){-}CH(OH){-}CHO \rightleftharpoons$ (cyclic glucose hemiacetal)

Glucose ($C_6H_{12}O_6$) Glucose hemiacetal

The Grignard Reaction

A very useful reaction involving nucleophilic addition to aldehydes and ketones is the **Grignard reaction**. This reaction involves a carbon-centred nucleophile, called a Grignard reagent, having the general formula RMgX (X = I, Br, Cl). The Grignard reagent is typically prepared by reacting a halogenated compound with magnesium metal in anhydrous ether. Anhydrous conditions are important because water reacts with the Grignard reagent.

Anhydrous = "no water"

$$CH_3CH_2Br + Mg \xrightarrow{\text{Diethyl ether}} CH_3CH_2MgBr$$

Ethylmagnesium bromide (a Grignard reagent)

Grignard reagents are "organometallic compounds," meaning that they contain a metal–carbon bond. The Mg—C bond has significant ionic character. Carbon is more electronegative than magnesium, so the carbon atom has a large partial negative charge and can act as a nucleophile. For example,

$$\overset{\delta-}{CH_3CH_2}-\overset{\delta+}{MgBr}$$

Grignard reagents (RMgX) react with aldehydes and ketones to give alcohols. The mechanism involves transfer of the R group from the Mg atom to the carbonyl carbon atom. Once all of the Grignard reagent is consumed, the reaction mixture is "worked up" (i.e., neutralized) with dilute acid, which converts the alkoxide salt to the alcohol.

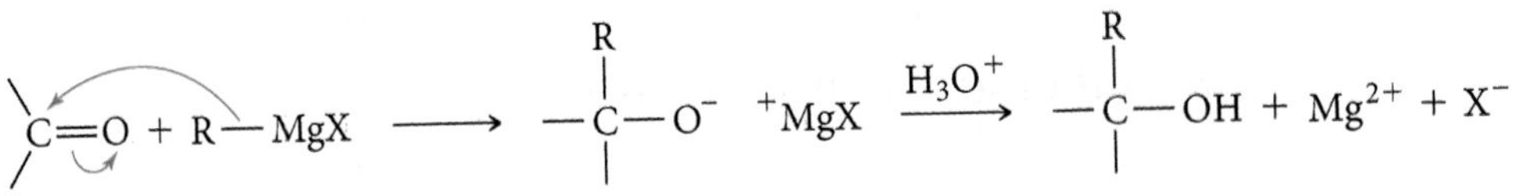

$$>C{=}O + R{-}MgX \longrightarrow -\overset{R}{\underset{|}{\overset{|}{C}}}-O^- \; {}^+MgX \xrightarrow{H_3O^+} -\overset{R}{\underset{|}{\overset{|}{C}}}-OH + Mg^{2+} + X^-$$

Alkoxide salt

The Grignard reaction is useful in organic synthesis because it results in new C—C bonds. Thus, it provides a way to join smaller organic units together into larger molecules.

EXAMPLE 21.6 GRIGNARD REACTIONS

Predict the organic products for the following Grignard reactions:

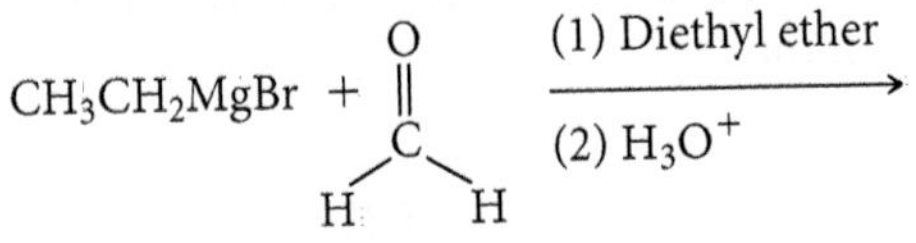

$$CH_3CH_2MgBr + H{-}\overset{O}{\overset{\|}{C}}{-}H \xrightarrow[\text{(2) } H_3O^+]{\text{(1) Diethyl ether}}$$

(a)

$$CH_3MgI + C_5H_9{-}\overset{O}{\overset{\|}{C}}{-}CH_3 \xrightarrow[\text{(2) } H_3O^+]{\text{(1) Diethyl ether}}$$

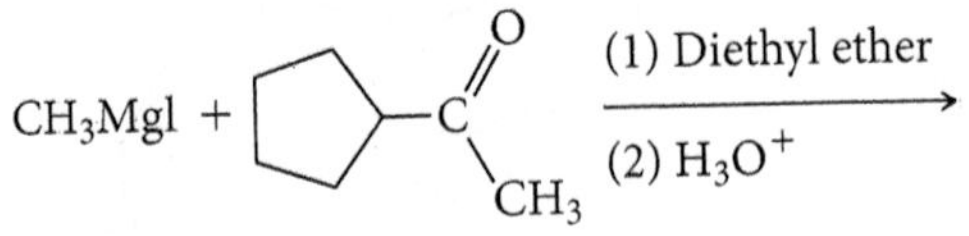

(b)

SOLUTION

(a) The R group in the Grignard reagent is an ethyl group. This transfers to the carbonyl carbon to give the alcohol. Since the two other groups on the carbonyl carbon are hydrogen atoms, the alcohol must be primary.	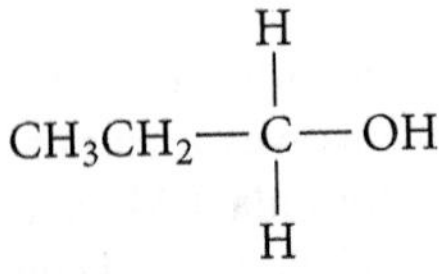 $CH_3CH_2{-}\overset{H}{\underset{H}{C}}{-}OH$
(b) The R group in the Grignard reagent is a methyl group, which transfers to the carbonyl carbon to give the alcohol. Since the carbonyl is a ketone, the final product must be a tertiary alcohol.	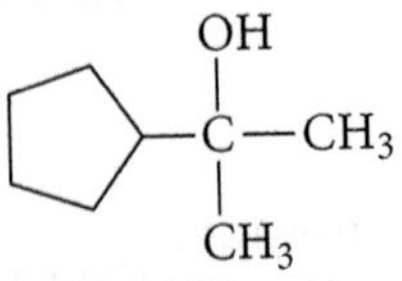 $C_5H_9{-}\overset{OH}{\underset{CH_3}{C}}{-}CH_3$

FOR PRACTICE 21.6

Predict the organic products for the following Grignard reactions:

$$C_6H_5MgBr + CH_3CHO \xrightarrow[(2)\ H_3O^+]{(1)\ \text{Diethyl ether}}$$

(a)

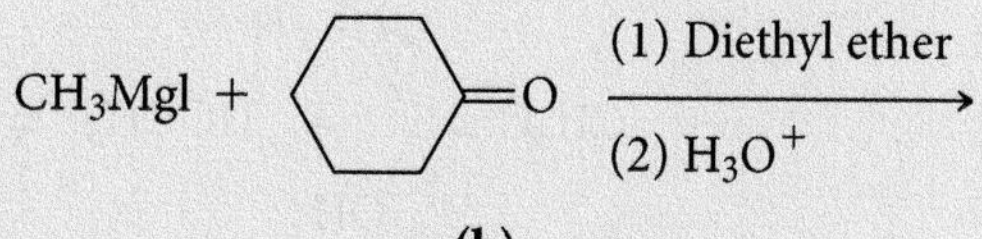

$$CH_3MgI + \text{(cyclohexanone)}{=}O \xrightarrow[(2)\ H_3O^+]{(1)\ \text{Diethyl ether}}$$

(b)

21.8 Nucleophilic Substitutions of Acyl Compounds

The acyl compounds described in Chapter 20 are very similar to aldehydes and ketones, in that they all contain a C=O bond. However, unlike carbonyl compounds, acyl compounds react with nucleophiles to give substitution reactions. Why the difference? In aldehydes and ketones, the carbon atom of the carbonyl unit is bonded to hydrogen and/or carbon atoms, which are not good leaving groups. In contrast, in acyl compounds, the carbon atom is bonded to a potentially good leaving group such as an alkoxy group and this changes the reactivity. Substitution is the predominant reaction observed in acyl compounds.

Consider the general case of a nucleophile reacting with an acyl group. The first step of the reaction is the same as the addition step that occurs with carbonyls, forming an alkoxide intermediate in which the central carbon atom is sp^3 hybridized. Subsequent to this addition step, the leaving group departs, giving the substitution product.

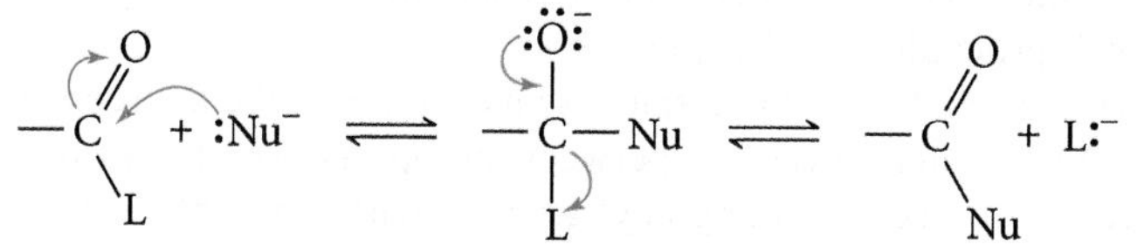

$$-C(=O)L + :Nu^- \rightleftharpoons -C(:\ddot{O}:^-)(L)-Nu \rightleftharpoons -C(=O)Nu + L:^-$$

An example of acyl substitution is **Fischer esterification**, the reaction of carboxylic acids with alcohols to give esters. The reaction is reversible, which means that esters can be hydrolyzed by water. Both reactions are catalyzed by acid.

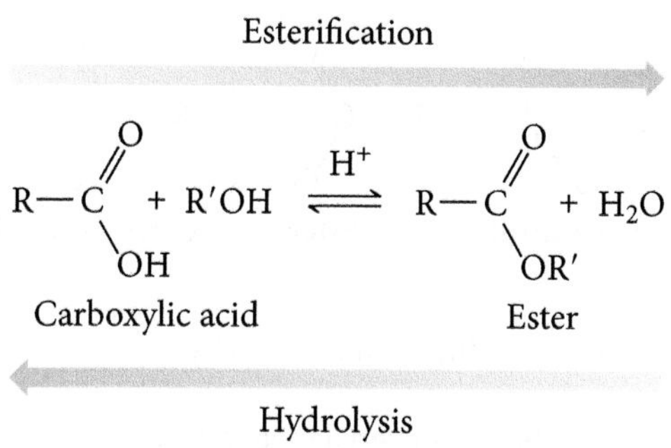

Esterification

$$R-C(=O)OH + R'OH \underset{}{\overset{H^+}{\rightleftharpoons}} R-C(=O)OR' + H_2O$$

Carboxylic acid — Ester

Hydrolysis

The mechanism of esterification has similarities to the mechanism for the formation of hemiacetals and hemiketals, discussed in the previous section. For example, the first step involves the double-bonded oxygen atom reacting with H^+ to form an oxonium ion. Also similarly, the next step is nucleophilic attack by the alcohol. After this, the mechanisms diverge. The next steps in esterification involve movements of H^+ to ultimately generate an H_2O leaving group. The loss of H_2O completes the substitution. Each step in the esterification mechanism can proceed in either direction.

The Mechanism of Fischer Esterification

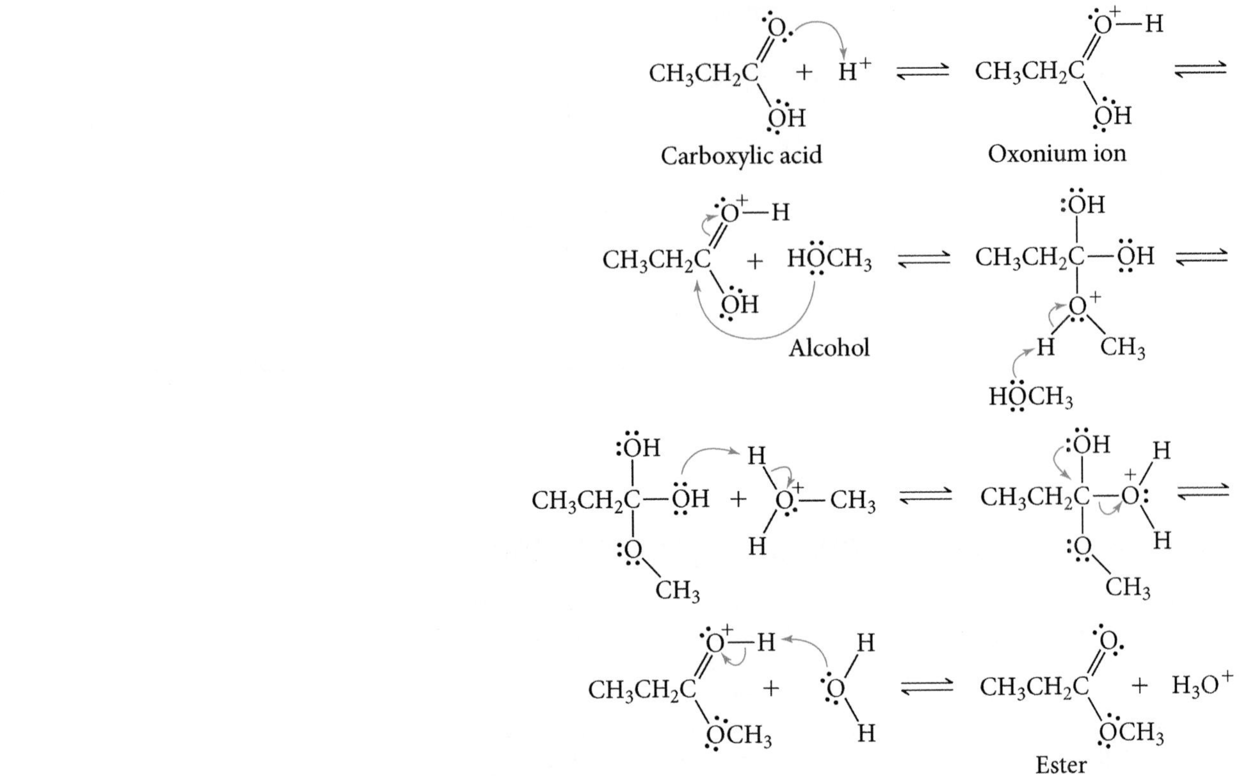

$$CH_3CH_2C(=O)OH + H^+ \rightleftharpoons CH_3CH_2C(=O^+\!-\!H)OH \rightleftharpoons$$

Carboxylic acid — Oxonium ion

$$CH_3CH_2C(=O^+\!-\!H)OH + HOCH_3 \rightleftharpoons CH_3CH_2C(OH)(OH)\!-\!O^+(H)CH_3 \rightleftharpoons$$

Alcohol — $HOCH_3$

$$CH_3CH_2C(OH)(OH)OCH_3 + H_2O^+\!-\!CH_3 \rightleftharpoons CH_3CH_2C(OH)(OCH_3)\!-\!O^+H_2 \rightleftharpoons$$

$$CH_3CH_2C(=O^+\!-\!H)OCH_3 + H_2O \rightleftharpoons CH_3CH_2C(=O)OCH_3 + H_3O^+$$

Ester

Esterification is a reversible equilibrium process, and the equilibrium constants are usually small. K is typically between 1 and 10 when the alcohol is primary or secondary, and $K < 1$ when the alcohol is tertiary. In order to obtain practical yields of ester, the equilibrium must be shifted toward products. This can be done by using an excess of the alcohol or by removing the ester and/or water through distillation. This is a practical application of Le Châtelier's principle from Chapter 14.

The esterification of carboxylic acids is an example of the interconversion between acyl groups. Direct interconversion between groups is not always possible because an order of reactivity exists among acyl groups, with acyl chlorides being the most reactive and amides being the least reactive. For the most part, this can be explained by the ability of various groups to function as leaving groups, which was discussed in Section 21.4.

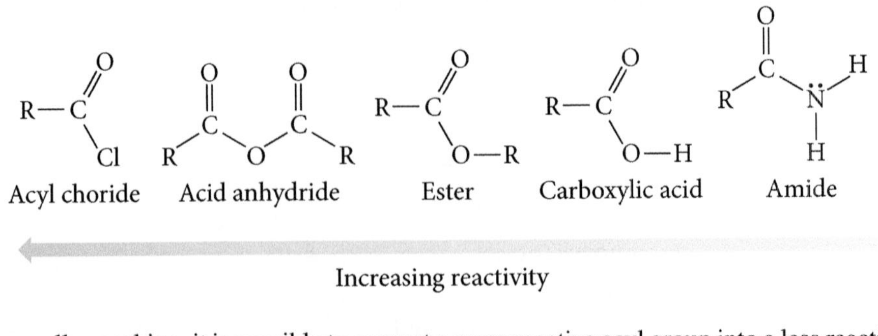

R—C(=O)Cl — Acyl choride; RC(=O)OC(=O)R — Acid anhydride; R—C(=O)O—R — Ester; R—C(=O)O—H — Carboxylic acid; RC(=O)NH₂ — Amide

Increasing reactivity (←)

Generally speaking, it is possible to convert a more reactive acyl group into a less reactive acyl group. Interconversions of acyl groups are summarized in Table 21.5. It is possible to convert acyl chlorides (most reactive) to any of the other groups. This is important because conversion to the acyl chloride allows for an indirect way to convert carboxylic acids into any of the other groups. That is, once the acyl chloride is made, it is possible to generate any of the other acyl groups in high yields. Acyl chlorides can be prepared by reacting the corresponding carboxylic acid with either $SOCl_2$ (**thionyl chloride**) or $(COCl)_2$ (**oxalyl chloride**). A disadvantage of using $SOCl_2$ is that one of the by-products is SO_2, a very toxic gas. $(COCl)_2$ is considered a milder reagent, and the by-products include CO and CO_2, which are not as toxic as SO_2.

$$\underset{\text{Carboxylic acid}}{R{-}C({=}O){-}O{-}H} + \underset{\text{Thionyl chloride}}{SOCl_2} \longrightarrow \underset{\text{Acyl chloride}}{R{-}C({=}O){-}Cl} + HCl + SO_2$$

$$\underset{\text{Carboxylic acid}}{R{-}C({=}O){-}O{-}H} + \underset{\text{Oxalyl chloride}}{Cl{-}C({=}O){-}C({=}O){-}Cl} \longrightarrow \underset{\text{Acyl chloride}}{R{-}C({=}O){-}Cl} + HCl + CO_2 + CO$$

TABLE 21.5 Reagents for Common Interconversions of Acyl Groups

The reagent for an interconversion is found where the reactant and product acyl groups meet in the table.

Reactant Acyl Group	Product Acyl Group: $R{-}C({=}O){-}Cl$	$R{-}C({=}O){-}O{-}C({=}O){-}R$	$R{-}C({=}O){-}O{-}R$	$R{-}C({=}O){-}O{-}H$	$R{-}C({=}O){-}NH_2$
$R{-}C({=}O){-}Cl$	—	$R'{-}C({=}O){-}O^-$	R′OH	H_2O	2 NH_3
$R{-}C({=}O){-}O{-}C({=}O){-}R$	—	*	R′OH	H_2O, H^+	2 NH_3
$R{-}C({=}O){-}O{-}R$	—	—	R′OH, H^+	H_2O, H^+	NH_3
$R{-}C({=}O){-}O{-}H$	$SOCl_2$ or (COCl)2	*	R′OH, H^+	—	†
$R{-}C({=}O){-}NH_2$	—	—	—	H_2O, H^+, heat	—

**Anhydride exchange* is a means of generating symmetrical acid anhydrides. Two moles of carboxylic acid react with acetic anhydride to give the new anhydride and 2 moles of acetic acid: $2\ RCOOH + (CH_3CO)_2O \rightarrow (RCO)_2O + 2\ CH_3COOH$.

†The reaction between a carboxylic acid and an ammonia is an acid–base reaction, and the product is an ammonium carboxylate ($NH_4^+RCOO^-$), which does not have a good nucleophile or electrophile. At high temperatures, the ammonium carboxylate can be converted to the amide. This is an industrially important reaction, but is not used in the laboratory.

The conversion of one ester into another is called **transesterification**. This equilibrium reaction is entirely analogous to Fischer esterification, with the first ester reacting with an alcohol to give an ester with a different alkoxy group. The reaction is catalyzed by acid, and follows the same basic mechanism as for esterification:

$$R{-}C({=}O){-}O{-}R + R'OH \xrightarrow{H^+} R{-}C({=}O){-}O{-}R' + ROH$$

EXAMPLE 21.7 ACYL GROUP INTERCONVERSIONS

Suggest appropriate reagents for the following interconversion. (*Hint:* This interconversion requires more than one step.)

$$C_6H_{11}{-}C({=}O){-}OH \longrightarrow C_6H_{11}{-}C({=}O){-}NHCH_3$$

SOLUTION

Step 1: Interconvert the carboxylic acid group into a more reactive acyl group. This can be done by reacting the acid with thionyl chloride to give the acyl chloride.

$$C_6H_{11}{-}C({=}O){-}OH \xrightarrow{SOCl_2} C_6H_{11}{-}C({=}O){-}Cl$$

Step 2: Interconvert to the amide: this amide could be made from the reaction between methylamine (CH_3NH_2) and an acyl chloride.

$$C_6H_{11}{-}C({=}O){-}Cl + NH_2CH_3 \longrightarrow C_6H_{11}{-}C({=}O){-}NHCH_3$$

FOR PRACTICE 21.7

Suggest appropriate reagents for the following interconversion. (*Hint:* This interconversion requires only one step.)

$$C_6H_5{-}C({=}O){-}OH \longrightarrow C_6H_5{-}C({=}O){-}O{-}C({=}O){-}CH_3$$

CONCEPTUAL CONNECTION 21.6

The Reaction Between an Acyl Chloride and NH_3

Write a balanced equation for the reaction between a generic acid chloride and NH_3. What are the products? In Table 21.5, "2 NH_3" is listed as a reagent. What will the extra mole of NH_3 react with?

21.9 Electrophilic Aromatic Substitutions

In Section 21.6, we examined electrophilic additions to alkenes. In those reactions, an electrophile reacts with the π bond of the alkene, forming a carbocation intermediate that subsequently reacts with a nucleophile. You might expect to observe similar addition reactions with aromatic compounds. However, the reactivity of aromatic compounds is very different: *in aromatic compounds, electrophilic substitution is almost always preferred over electrophilic addition.* This is due to the stability of aromatic rings.

In the following mechanism, benzene reacts as a nucleophile with an electrophile to generate a carbocation. This is the same as the first step in electrophilic addition to alkenes. The carbocation intermediate is resonance stabilized, but not aromatic. In the next step, however, the carbocation quickly loses H^+ to a base and the aromatic ring is recovered. *The carbocation does not react with the base to give the addition product.*

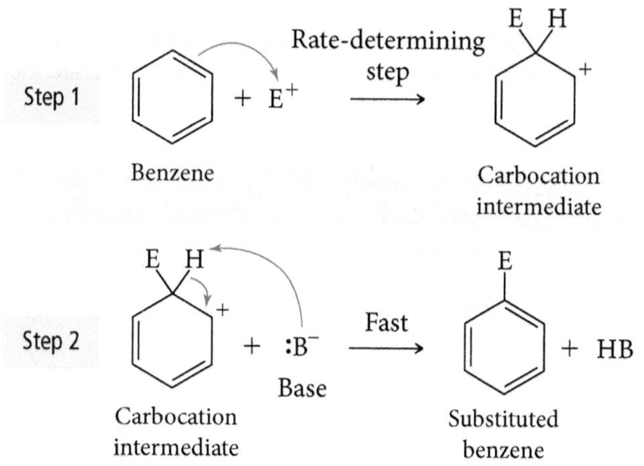

Step 1 Benzene + E^+ $\xrightarrow{\text{Rate-determining step}}$ Carbocation intermediate (E, H)

Step 2 Carbocation intermediate (E, H) + $:B^-$ (Base) $\xrightarrow{\text{Fast}}$ Substituted benzene (E) + HB

CONCEPTUAL CONNECTION 21.7

Resonance Structures

Draw the resonance structures for the carbocation intermediate in electrophilic substitution of benzene.

An example of electrophilic aromatic substitution is **nitration**, in which a hydrogen atom is substituted with a nitro group (NO_2). The electrophile in this reaction is the nitronium ion (NO_2^+), which is generated from the reaction between sulfuric acid and nitric acid. Recall from Table 21.1 that sulfuric acid is stronger than nitric acid.

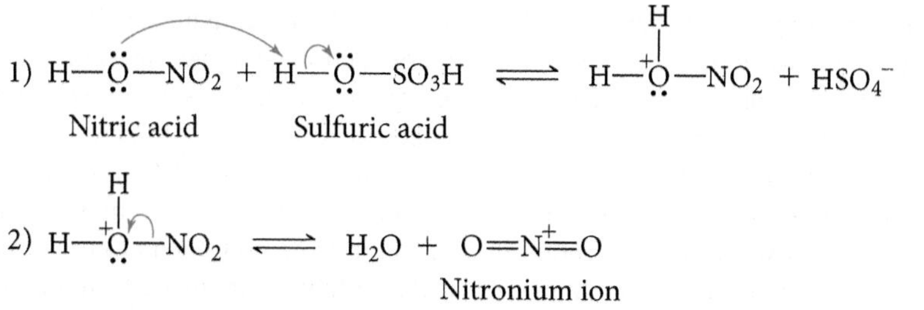

1) $H{-}\ddot{O}{-}NO_2$ (Nitric acid) + $H{-}\ddot{O}{-}SO_3H$ (Sulfuric acid) $\rightleftharpoons$ $H{-}\overset{+}{\underset{|}{O}}(H){-}NO_2 + HSO_4^-$

2) $H{-}\overset{+}{O}(H){-}NO_2 \rightleftharpoons H_2O + O{=}\overset{+}{N}{=}O$ (Nitronium ion)

The nitration mechanism follows the general mechanism for electrophilic aromatic substitution shown above.

Step 1: Benzene + $O{=}\overset{+}{N}{=}O$ (Nitronium ion) —Rate-determining step→ Carbocation intermediate (O_2N, H, +)

Step 2: Carbocation intermediate (O_2N, H, +) + $H_2\ddot{O}$ —Fast→ NO_2-benzene + H_3O^+

Common electrophilic aromatic substitutions are presented in Table 21.6. All of these reactions employ either a Brønsted or Lewis acid catalyst to generate the electrophile.

TABLE 21.6 Common Electrophilic Aromatic Substitution Reactions

Reaction	Reagent	Product
Chlorination	Cl_2, $FeCl_3$	C_6H_5–Cl
Bromination	Br_2, $FeBr_3$	C_6H_5–Br
Nitration	HNO_3, H_2SO_4	C_6H_5–NO_2
Friedel-Crafts Acylation	R–C(=O)–Cl, $AlCl_3$	C_6H_5–C(=O)–R
Friedel-Crafts Alkylation	R—X, AlX_3 (X = Cl, Br)	C_6H_5–R

21.10 Polymerization

Polymers are long, chain-like molecules composed of repeating units called **monomers**. In Chapter 22, we will study natural polymers such as starches, proteins, and DNA, which are fundamental components of living organisms. In this section, we apply some of the reactions we discussed earlier in this chapter to making synthetic polymers. We encounter synthetic polymers daily in plastic products such as PVC tubing, Styrofoam coffee cups, nylon rope, and shatter-resistant acrylic windows. Polymer materials are common in our everyday lives, found in everything from computers to toys to packaging materials to clothing. For example, polar fleece fabrics are made from polyethylene terephthalate.

Most polymers are durable, partly because of the length of their molecules. In order to break or tear a polymeric material, the intermolecular forces between molecules must be broken. Because polymers are hundreds or even thousands of atoms in length, the intermolecular forces between molecules are very strong.

Step-Growth Polymers

One type of polymerization involves substitution reactions between **difunctional monomers** to produce the polymer. Difunctional means that the monomers have two different functional groups that react together. This process is known as **condensation** or **step-growth polymerization**. This type of polymerization always generates a by-product such as water; hence the name "condensation."

Consider the possible substitution reactions between two monomers: One monomer is a **diol**, with two alcohol groups. The second monomer is a **diacid**, with two carboxylic acid groups. We know from Section 21.8 that carboxylic acids react with alcohols to give esters. With large numbers of these two molecules, an ester group can be formed on both ends of each molecule. The result is a polymer chain in which the monomers are connected by ester groups. This type of polymer is a **polyester**.

$$\underset{\text{Diacid}}{n\text{HO}\overset{\text{O}}{\overset{\|}{\text{C}}}(\text{CH}_2)_4\overset{\text{O}}{\overset{\|}{\text{C}}}\text{OH}} + \underset{\text{Diol}}{n\text{HOCH}_2\text{CH}_2\text{OH}} \longrightarrow \underset{\text{Polyester}}{\left[\overset{\text{O}}{\overset{\|}{\text{C}}}(\text{CH}_2)_4\overset{\text{O}}{\overset{\|}{\text{C}}}\text{OCH}_2\text{CH}_2\text{O}\right]_n} + 2n\text{H}_2\text{O}$$

Another way to make polyesters is by reacting diester and diol monomers, which produces transesterification reactions. For example, **poly(ethylene terephthalate), PET**, is made this way. The stiff plastic bottles that hold carbonated beverages are made of PET (Figure 21.4 ▾). The reason for the stiffness of PET polymer is that the molecular polymer structure itself is somewhat resistant to bond rotations along polymer strands, due to the conjugation of the benzene ring and ester groups.

In polymer notation, the repeating unit of the polymer is placed within square brackets. The letter *n* refers to the number of repeating units.

$$\underset{\text{Dimethyl terephthalate}}{n\text{CH}_3\text{O}{-}\overset{\text{O}}{\overset{\|}{\text{C}}}{-}\text{C}_6\text{H}_4{-}\overset{\text{O}}{\overset{\|}{\text{C}}}{-}\text{OCH}_3} + \underset{\text{Ethan-1,2-diol}}{n\text{HOCH}_2\text{CH}_2\text{OH}} \longrightarrow \underset{\text{Poly(ethylene terephthalate)}}{\left[\overset{\text{O}}{\overset{\|}{\text{C}}}{-}\text{C}_6\text{H}_4{-}\overset{\text{O}}{\overset{\|}{\text{C}}}{-}\text{OCH}_2\text{CH}_2\text{O}\right]_n} + 2n\text{CH}_3\text{OH}$$

Another example of step-growth polymerization is the formation of **polyamides**. As the name implies, in polyamides, the monomers are connected by amide groups. Polyamides are usually made by reacting diacids and diamines. The first step is an acid–base reaction to give a dicarboxylate, diammonium salt. When this salt is heated to 250 °C, the amide groups form and water is lost. In the example below, the polyamide that forms is nylon 6,6. The "6,6" refers to the numbers of carbon atoms in each of the monomers. By changing the numbers of carbon atoms, the properties of the nylon polymers can be altered. Nylon polymers can be drawn into fibres and used to make consumer products such as pantyhose, carpet fibres, and fishing line.

▲ **FIGURE 21.4 Poly(ethylene terephthalate)** These beverage bottles are made from PET.

$$\underset{\text{Diacid}}{n\text{HO}\overset{\text{O}}{\overset{\|}{\text{C}}}(\text{CH}_2)_4\overset{\text{O}}{\overset{\|}{\text{C}}}\text{OH}} + \underset{\text{Diamine}}{n\text{H}_2\text{N}(\text{CH}_2)_6\text{NH}_2} \longrightarrow \underset{\text{Dicarboxylate, diammonium salt}}{n\left[\left({}^{-}\text{O}\overset{\text{O}}{\overset{\|}{\text{C}}}(\text{CH}_2)_6\overset{\text{O}}{\overset{\|}{\text{C}}}\text{O}^{-}\right)(\text{H}_3\overset{+}{\text{N}}(\text{CH}_2)_6\overset{+}{\text{N}}\text{H}_3)\right]}$$

$$\xrightarrow{250\ ^\circ\text{C}} \underset{\text{Nylon 6,6}}{\left[\overset{\text{O}}{\overset{\|}{\text{C}}}(\text{CH}_2)_4\overset{\text{O}}{\overset{\|}{\text{C}}}\text{NH}(\text{CH}_2)_6\text{NH}\right]_n} + 2n\text{H}_2\text{O}$$

Addition Polymers

Addition polymers are formed by monomers that simply link together without the elimination of any atoms. The simplest addition polymer is polyethylene. The monomer is ethene (also called ethylene). When ethene monomers react with each other, the double

CHEMISTRY IN YOUR DAY Kevlar

In 1965, Stephanie Kwolek, working for DuPont to develop new polymer fibres, noticed an odd cloudy product from a polymerization reaction. Some researchers might have rejected the product, but Kwolek insisted on examining its properties more carefully. The results were astonishing—when the polymer was spun into a fibre, it was stronger than any fibre known before. Kwolek had discovered Kevlar, a material that is pound for pound five times stronger than steel.

Kevlar is a condensation polymer featuring aromatic rings and amide linkages:

[Structure: Kevlar repeat unit, $-[C(=O)-C_6H_4-C(=O)-NH-C_6H_4-NH]_n-$, labelled "Aromatic ring" and "Amide linkage"]

▲ **FIGURE 21.5 Kevlar** Kevlar is used to make bullet-proof vests.

The polymeric chains within Kevlar crystallize in a parallel arrangement (like dry spaghetti noodles in a box), with strong cross-linking between neighbouring chains resulting from hydrogen bonding. The hydrogen bonding occurs between the N—H groups on one chain and the C=O groups on neighbouring chains:

[Structure: neighbouring Kevlar chains with N—H···O=C hydrogen bonds between them]

This structure is responsible for Kevlar's high strength and its other properties, including fire resistance and chemical resistance (for example, resistance to acids).

Today, DuPont sells hundreds of millions of dollars' worth of Kevlar every year. Kevlar is particularly well-known for its use in bulletproof vests (Figure 21.5 ▲). This application of Kwolek's discovery has saved thousands of lives. In addition, Kevlar is used to make helmets, radial tires, brake pads, racing sails, suspension bridge cables, skis, and high-performance hiking and camping gear.

Question

Examine the structure of the Kevlar polymer to the left. Knowing that the polymer is a condensation polymer, draw the structures of its monomers before the condensation reaction.

bonds between carbon atoms are broken and C—C single bonds are formed between monomer units. Catalysts are used for this type of polymerization. The result is a long hydrocarbon polymer chain:

$$nCH_2{=}CH_2 \xrightarrow{\text{Catalyst}} \left[CH_2CH_2 \right]_n$$

Polyethylene is a plastic that has a wide range of uses, including plastic shopping bags and liquid containers such as the wash bottles found in chemistry laboratories.

Substituted polyethylenes make up an entire class of polymers. For example, **poly(vinyl chloride)**, or **PVC**—the plastic used to make certain kinds of pipes and plumbing fixtures (Figure 21.6 ▼)—is composed of monomers of chloroethene (also known as vinyl chloride).

$$n\text{HC}(\text{Cl})\!=\!\text{CH}_2 \longrightarrow \left[\!-\text{CH}(\text{Cl})\text{CH}_2-\!\right]_n$$

Chloroethene → Polyvinyl chloride

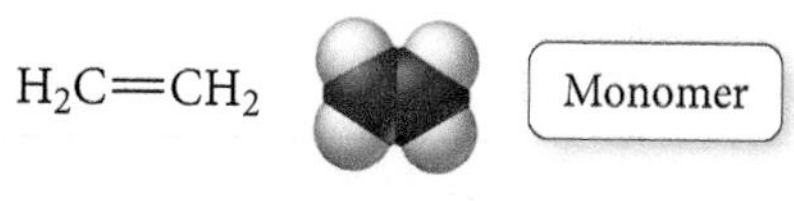

Ethene or ethylene

$\cdots CH_2-CH_2-CH_2-CH_2-CH_2-CH_2-CH_2-CH_2-CH_2\cdots$

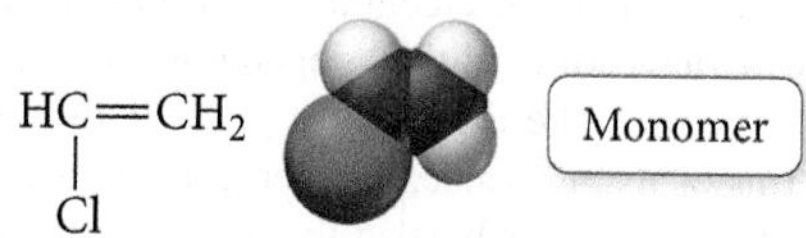

Polyethylene

$HC(Cl)\!=\!CH_2$ Monomer

Chloroethene or vinyl chloride

$\cdots CH(Cl)-CH_2-CH(Cl)-CH_2-CH(Cl)-CH_2-CH(Cl)-CH_2-CH(Cl)\cdots$

Polymer

Poly(vinyl chloride) (PVC)

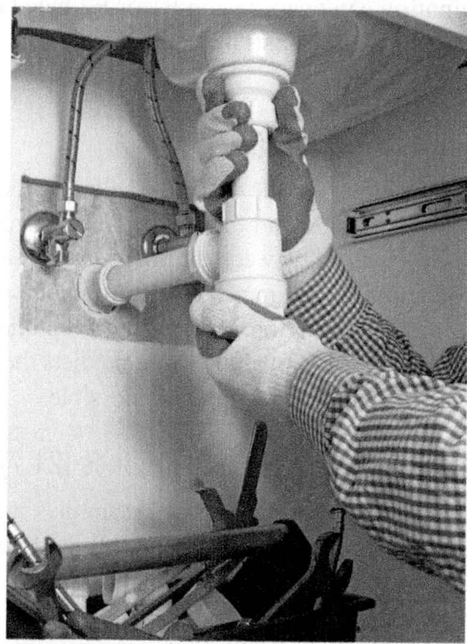

▲ **FIGURE 21.6 Poly(vinyl chloride)** PVC is used for many plastic plumbing supplies, such as pipes and connectors.

CHAPTER IN REVIEW

Key Terms

Section 21.1
synthesis (911)

Section 21.2
inductive effect (913)
resonance effect (913)
carbanion (915)

Section 21.3
hydrogenation (919)
interconversion (919)

Section 21.4
substitution reaction (922)
nucleophile (922)
leaving group (922)
substrate (922)
electrophile (922)
carbocation (922)
racemization (924)
inversion (925)
nucleophilicity (925)
steric hindrance (927)

Section 21.5
1,2-elimination (928)
dehydration (928)
dehydrohalogenation (928)
Zaitsev's rule (928)
oxonium ion (929)

Section 21.6
electrophilic addition (930)
Markovnikov's rule (931)

Section 21.7
nucleophilic addition (932)
hemiacetal (932)
hemiketal (932)
Grignard reaction (933)

Section 21.8
Fischer esterification (935)
thionyl chloride (936)
oxalyl chloride (936)
transesterification (938)

Section 21.9
nitration (939)

Section 21.10
polymer (940)
monomer (940)
difunctional monomer (941)
condensation (step-growth) polymerization (941)
diol (941)
diacid (941)
polyester (941)
poly(ethylene terephthalate), PET (941)
polyamide (941)
addition polymer (941)
polyethylene (942)
poly(vinyl chloride), PVC (943)

Key Concepts

Discovering New Drugs (21.1)

Drug discovery is typically a long process that involves scientists from several disciplines. Many clinical drug trials are held every year but only a few drugs are found to be safe and effective. Montelukast sodium is an asthma drug, developed in Canada, whose synthesis requires a long sequence of separate reactions.

Organic Acids and Bases (21.2)

Organic compounds exhibit a large range of acidities. Acidic hydrogen atoms can be bonded to heteroatoms in functional groups such as carboxylic acid groups and alcohols. Hydrogen atoms bonded to carbon show a range of acidities, depending on the surrounding molecular structure. The acidity of a given hydrogen atom is expressed in terms of its pK_a value, and depends on factors such as the atom the hydrogen atom is bonded to, and inductive and resonance effects within the molecule.

Acid–base reagents have a range of pK_a values. To select an appropriate acid–base reagent for a desired reaction, the chemist compares the pK_a value of the reactant with pK_a values of the acid–base reagents.

Oxidation and Reduction (21.3)

Oxidation and reduction reactions involve the loss or gain of electrons, respectively. Whether there has been a loss or gain of electrons in organic compounds can be determined by calculating the relative oxidation states of atoms. For any given atom, the relative oxidation state is determined by comparing the electronegativity values of the atoms it is bonded to.

Common reduction reactions are the hydrogenation of alkenes, and the reductions of carboxylic acids, ketones, and aldehydes to alcohols. Oxidation reactions include combustion, and the oxidations of alcohols to carboxylic acids, aldehydes, and ketones.

Nucleophilic Substitution Reactions at Saturated Carbon (21.4)

A substitution reaction is the replacement of one functional group with another. In nucleophilic substitutions, a new bond is formed between a carbon atom and a nucleophile, and a bond is broken between the carbon atom and a leaving group. Nucleophilic substitutions at saturated carbon atoms can occur by one of two mechanisms: S_N1 and S_N2. In the S_N1 mechanism, the leaving group dissociates first, giving a carbocation intermediate that subsequently reacts with the nucleophile. In the S_N2 mechanism, the nucleophile attacks the carbon atom, giving rise to a transition state in which the nucleophile and leaving group are partially bonded to the carbon atom, and the leaving group dissociates. When the substrate is chiral, S_N1 reactions lead to racemization, whereas S_N2 reactions lead to stereochemical inversion.

Nucleophilic substitution reactions depend on the effectiveness of the nucleophile, the stability of the leaving group, and the structure of the substrate. The stablility of the leaving group correlates well with the pK_a values of the corresponding conjugate acid—good leaving groups tend to be the conjugates bases of strong acids. When the substrate can stabilize a carbocation, an S_N1 mechanism is favoured. Steric hindrance in the substrate can also hinder the attack of a nucleophile.

Elimination Reactions (21.5)

Elimination reactions involve the loss of two adjacent atoms or groups, in the presence of a base, to give an alkene. Dehydration is the loss of a hydroxyl group and an adjacent hydrogen atom, which produces H_2O. Dehydrohalogenation is the loss of adjacent halogen (X) and hydrogen atoms, which produces HX. When isomeric alkene elimination products are possible, the major product tends to be the more substituted alkene. This tendency is known as Zaitsev's rule, and arises from the stability of carbocation intermediates. Elimination can occur via an E1 or E2 mechanism, depending on the nature of the substrate and the strength of the base used.

Electrophilic Additions to Alkenes (21.6)

Electrophilic addition reactions are the reverse of elimination reactions. The carbon–carbon double bond of the alkene is broken, and two new single bonds are formed between the carbon atoms and the components of the electrophile. Examples of electrophilic addition are hydrohalogenation, hydrogenation, halogenation, epoxidation, hydroxylation, and hydration. Markovnikov's rule predicts the major product whenever isomeric addition products are possible.

Nucleophilic Additions to Aldehydes and Ketones (21.7)

The carbonyl carbon atom in an aldehyde or ketone has a partial positive charge and can react with nucleophiles to yield addition products. When alcohols react with aldehydes and ketones in the presence of acid, the products are hemiacetals and hemiketals, respectively. A Grignard reagent is a carbon-centred nucleophile that can react with aldehydes and ketones to create a new carbon–carbon bond, which is useful in organic synthesis.

Nucleophilic Substitutions of Acyl Compounds (21.8)

Nucleophilic substitutions of acyl compounds take place because the carbon atom in acyl groups has a large partial positive charge, and is bonded to groups that are also stable leaving groups. Acyl compounds can be interconverted through nucleophilic substitutions. Fischer esterification is the equilibrium conversion of a carboxylic acid into an ester. Acyl halides, carboxylic anhydrides, esters, carboxylic acids, and amides can be interconverted through single or multiple nucleophilic substitutions.

Electrophilic Aromatic Substitutions (21.9)

Aromatic compounds are very stable and tend to react with electrophiles as substitutions rather than addition reactions. Electrophilic aromatic substitutions include nitration, chlorination, bromination, Friedel-Crafts acylation, and Friedel-Crafts alkylation.

Polymerization (21.10)

Polymers are long molecules consisting of repeating units called monomers. Monomers that are difunctional, meaning that they contain two reactive functional groups, react to form step-growth polymers. Step-growth polymerization involves the elimination of atoms through substitution. Addition polymers involve monomers that link together without the elimination of atoms. Addition polymers tend to involve addition reactions between alkene monomers.

Key Equations and Relationships

Summary of Reaction Mechanisms

Nucleophilic Substitution at Saturated Carbon (21.4)

S_N1 Mechanism

Step 1 $$-\overset{|}{\underset{|}{C}}-L \underset{\text{step}}{\overset{\text{Rate-determining}}{\rightleftharpoons}} -\overset{|}{\underset{|}{C}}^{+} + :L^-$$

Step 2 $$-\overset{|}{\underset{|}{C}}^{+} + :Nu^- \xrightarrow{\text{Fast}} -\overset{|}{\underset{|}{C}}-Nu$$

S_N2 Mechanism

$$Nu:^- + -\overset{|}{\underset{|}{C}}-L \longrightarrow \left[\overset{\delta-}{Nu}\cdots C \cdots \overset{\delta-}{L}\right] \longrightarrow Nu-\overset{|}{\underset{|}{C}}- + :L^-$$

Elimination Reactions (21.5)

E1 Mechanism

Step 1 $$-\overset{L}{\underset{|}{C}}-\overset{H}{\underset{|}{C}}- \xrightarrow[\text{step}]{\text{Rate-determining}} -\underset{|}{C}^{+}-\overset{H}{\underset{|}{C}}- + :L^-$$

Step 2 $$-\underset{|}{C}^{+}-\overset{H}{\underset{|}{C}}- + :B^- \longrightarrow \;\rangle C{=}C\langle\; + HB$$

E2 Mechanism

$$B:^- \quad -\overset{H}{\underset{|}{C}}-\overset{|}{\underset{|}{C}}-L \longrightarrow \;\rangle C{=}C\langle\; + BH + :L^-$$

Electrophilic Additions to Alkenes (21.6)

Hydrohalogenation

Step 1 $$\rangle C{=}C\langle \quad H-X \longrightarrow -\underset{|}{C}^{+}-\overset{H}{\underset{|}{C}}- + :\ddot{X}:^-$$

Step 2 $$:\ddot{X}:^- \quad -\underset{|}{C}^{+}-\overset{H}{\underset{|}{C}}- \longrightarrow -\overset{X}{\underset{|}{C}}-\overset{H}{\underset{|}{C}}-$$

Nucleophilic Additions to Aldehydes and Ketones (21.7)

$$\overset{O}{\overset{\|}{C}} + :Nu^- \longrightarrow -\overset{:\ddot{O}:^-}{\underset{|}{C}}-Nu + H^+ \longrightarrow -\overset{OH}{\underset{|}{C}}-Nu$$

Nucleophilic Substitutions of Acyl Compounds (21.8)

$$-\overset{O}{\overset{\|}{C}}-L + :Nu^- \rightleftharpoons -\overset{:\ddot{O}:^-}{\underset{L}{C}}-Nu \rightleftharpoons -\overset{O}{\overset{\|}{C}}-Nu + :L^-$$

Electrophilic Aromatic Substitutions (21.9)

Step 1 $$\text{benzene} + \underset{\text{Electrophile}}{E^+} \xrightarrow[\text{step}]{\text{Rate-determining}} \text{(E, H)-cyclohexadienyl cation}^{+}$$

Step 2 $$\text{(E, H)-cyclohexadienyl cation}^{+} + :B^- \xrightarrow{\text{Fast}} \text{E-substituted benzene} + HB$$

$:B^-$ = Base

Key Skills

Writing Mechanisms of Acid–Base Reactions (21.2)
• Example 21.1 • For Practice 21.1 • Exercises 33, 34

Selecting an Appropriate Acid–Base Reagant (21.2)
• Example 21.2 • For Practice 21.2 • Exercises 35, 36

Determining Oxidation States in Organic Molecules (21.3)
• Example 21.3 • For Practice 21.3 • Exercises 39, 40

Choosing Reagents for Oxidations and Reductions (21.3)
• Example 21.4 • For Practice 21.4 • Exercises 45, 46

Predicting Nucleophilic Substitution Mechanisms and Products (21.4)
• Example 21.5 • For Practice 21.5 • Exercises 47–54

Predicting Products of Elimination Reactions (21.5)
• Exercises 55–58

Predicting Products of Electrophilic Addition Reactions (21.6)
• Exercises 63–68

Predicting Products of Nucleophilic Additions to Aldehydes and Ketones (21.7)
• Example 21.6 • For Practice 21.6 • Exercises 71–76

Predicting Products of Nucleophilic Substitutions of Acyl Compounds (21.8)
• Exercises 77–81

Choosing Appropriate Reagents for Acyl Group Interconversions (21.8)
• Example 21.7 • For Practice 21.7 • Exercises 82–83

Predicting Products of Electrophilic Aromatic Substitutions (21.9)
• Exercises 84–85

Predicting the Structure of Polymers (21.10)
• Exercises 88, 89, 92, 93

EXERCISES

Review Questions

1. Describe inductive and resonance effects on the acidities of organic acids.
2. What is a carbanion? How can carbanions be stabilized by the surrounding molecular structure?
3. Describe how to choose an appropriate acid or base reagent for a desired organic acid–base reaction.
4. Explain oxidation and reduction with respect to organic compounds.
5. What are hydrocarbon combustion reactions? Give an example.
6. What is a hydrogenation reaction? Give an example.
7. What are the products of the oxidation of primary and secondary alcohols? What reagents are used?
8. What are the products of the reduction of ketones and carboxylic acids? What reagents are used?
9. What is a nucleophilic substitution reaction? Give an example.
10. What is a leaving group? What makes a leaving group effective?
11. What is a nucleophile? Give three examples of good nucleophiles.
12. How does substrate structure affect the mechanism of nucleophilic substitution reactions?
13. Describe the mechanisms of S_N1 and S_N2 reactions.
14. What is a 1,2-elimination reaction? Give an example.
15. Explain Zaitsev's rule and give an example of a reaction to which it applies.
16. How does substrate structure affect the mechanism of elimination?
17. What is an oxonium ion and why is it important in several reaction mechanisms?
18. What is an electrophilic addition reaction? Give three examples.
19. How are elimination reactions and electrophilic addition reactions mechanistically similar?
20. Explain Markovnikov's rule and give an example of a reaction to which it applies.
21. Describe nucleophilic addition to aldehydes and ketones.
22. Draw the mechanism for the formation of a hemiacetal from an aldehyde and alcohol.
23. What is a Grignard reaction? What type of nucleophile is involved in a Grignard reaction?
24. Draw the mechanism for Fischer esterification.
25. Describe the interconversions of acyl groups.

26. What is the general mechanism for the electrophilic substitution of aromatics? Why is electrophilic substitution of aromatics more commonly observed than electrophilic addition?

27. What is a polymer? What is a monomer?

28. What is the difference between step-growth polymerization and addition polymerization?

29. Name two well-known examples each of step-growth polymers and addition polymers.

30. How are nucleophilic substitution reactions used to make step-growth polymers?

Problems by Topic

Organic Acids and Bases

31. For each of the following acids, write the Lewis structural formula for the conjugate base formed by its reaction with NaOH.

a. 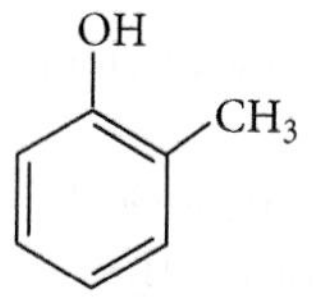 OH, CH_3 (benzene ring)

b. 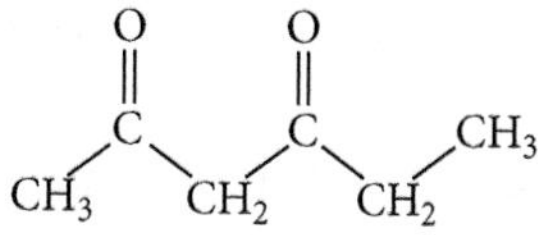 O, O, C, C, CH_3, CH_3, CH_2, CH_2

c. $CH_3CH_2NH_3^+Cl^-$

d. $CH_3CH_2CO_2H$

32. For each of the following acids, write the Lewis structural formula for the conjugate base formed by its reaction with $NaNH_2$.

a. $CH_3{\equiv}CH$

b. 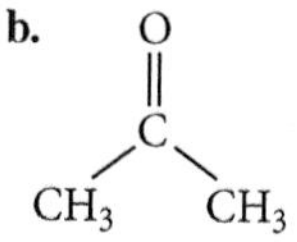 O, C, CH_3, CH_3

c. OH, CH_3—C—CH_3, CH_3

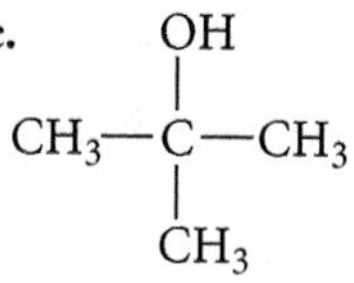

d. H_2O

33. Each of the following molecules can function as a base. Write the mechanism for the reaction with H_2SO_4, including the Lewis structural formula for the conjugate acid.

a. CH_3OH b. $CH_3CH_2NH_2$ c. HCO_3^- d. CH_3O^-

34. Each of the following molecules can function as a base. Write the mechanism for the reaction with HCl, including the Lewis structural formula for the conjugate acid.

a. 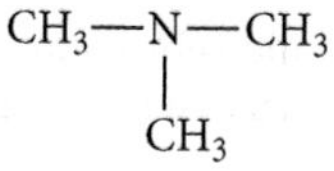 CH_3—N—CH_3, CH_3

b. 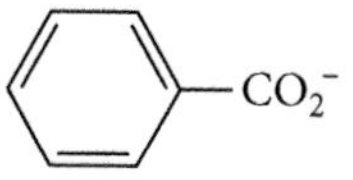 (benzene ring)—CO_2^-

c. 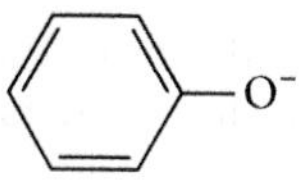 (benzene ring)—O^-

d. H_2O

35. Identify an appropriate acid or base reagent for each of the following reactions:

a. 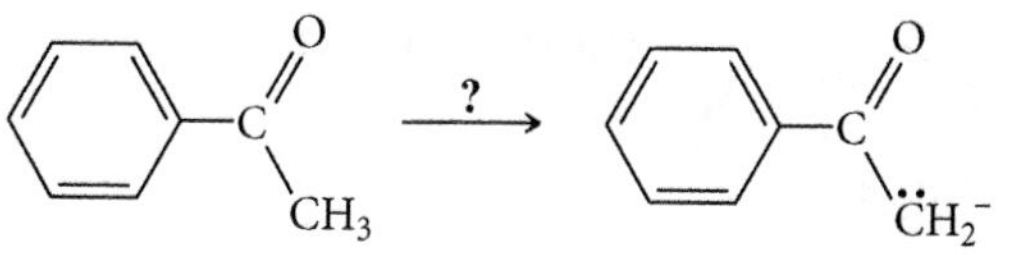 (benzene ring)—C(=O)—CH_3 $\xrightarrow{?}$ (benzene ring)—C(=O)—$\ddot{C}H_2^-$

b. 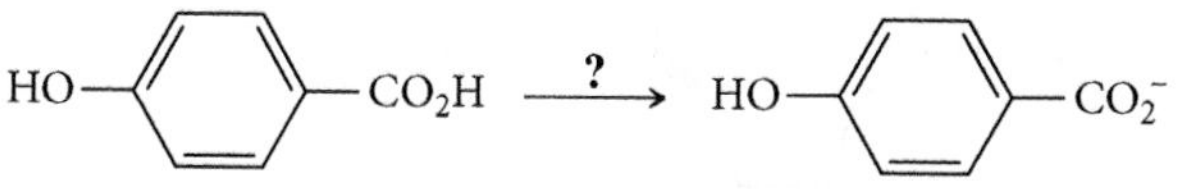 HO—(benzene ring)—CO_2H $\xrightarrow{?}$ HO—(benzene ring)—CO_2^-

c. $CH_3CH_2NH_2$ $\xrightarrow{?}$ $CH_3CH_2NH_3^+Cl^-$

36. Identify an appropriate acid or base reagent for each of the following reactions:

a.  (benzene ring)—CO_2H $\xrightarrow{?}$ (benzene ring)—CO_2^-

b. 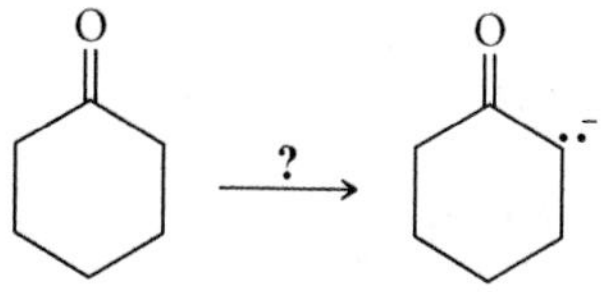 O (cyclohexanone) $\xrightarrow{?}$ O (cyclohexanone enolate carbanion)

c. $CH_3CH_3CH_2CH_2OH$ $\xrightarrow{?}$ $CH_3CH_2CH_2OH_2^+$

37. Draw resonance structures for the conjugate bases of:

a.  O_2N—(benzene ring)—OH

b. 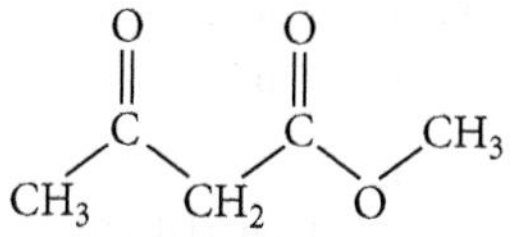 O, O, C, C, CH_3, CH_3, CH_2, O

38. Draw resonance structures for the conjugate bases of:

a. 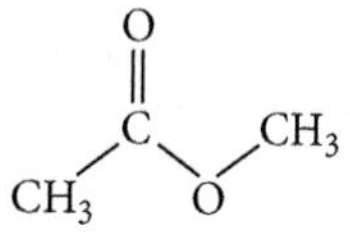 O, C, CH_3, CH_3, O

b. 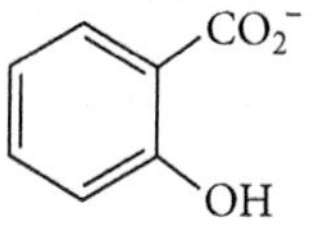 (benzene ring) CO_2^-, OH

Oxidation and Reduction

39. Determine the oxidation state of each carbon atom in the following molecules or ions:

a. 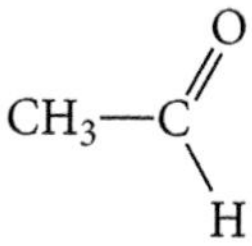 CH_3—C(=O)—H

b. CH_3—C≡C—CH_3

c. 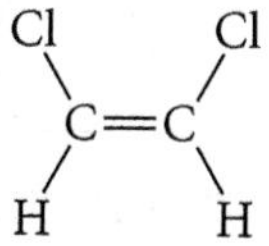 Cl, Cl, C=C, H, H

40. Determine the oxidation state of each carbon atom in the following molecules or ions:

a. 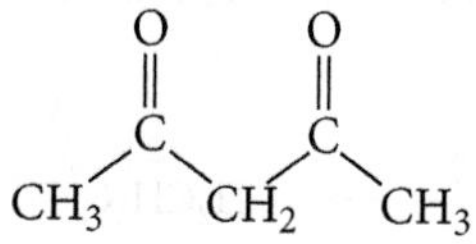 O, O, C, C, CH_3, CH_2, CH_3

b. CH_3, CH_3—C—OH, CH_3

c. CH_2=CH—C(=O)—NH_2

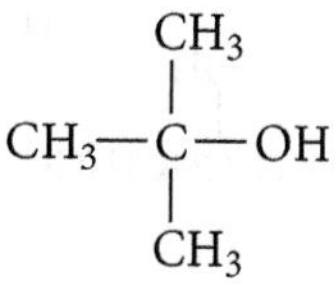

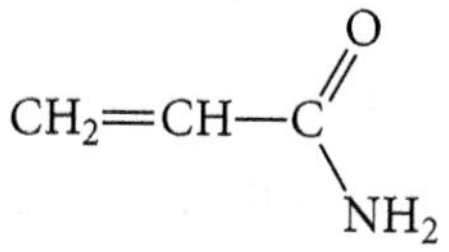

41. Complete and balance each combustion reaction.

a. $CH_3CH_2CH_3 + O_2 \longrightarrow$

b. $CH_3CH_2CH{=}CH_2 + O_2 \longrightarrow$

c. $HC{\equiv}CH + O_2 \longrightarrow$

42. Complete and balance each combustion reaction.

a. $CH_3CH_2CH_2CH_3 + O_2 \longrightarrow$

b. $H_2C{=}CHCH_3 + O_2 \longrightarrow$

c. $HC{\equiv}CCH_2CH_3 + O_2 \longrightarrow$

43. What are the organic products for each oxidation or reduction reaction?

a. $CH_3{-}CH(OH){-}CH_2CH_3 \xrightarrow{K_2Cr_2O_7,\ H_2SO_4}$

b. $CH_3CH_2CH{=}CHCH_3 \xrightarrow{H_2,\ Pd/C}$

c. 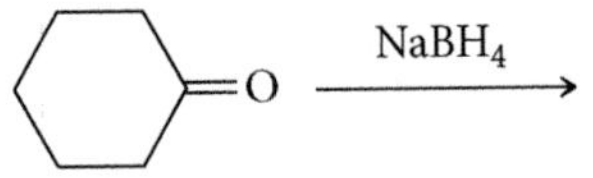 cyclohexanone (ring)=O $\xrightarrow{NaBH_4}$

d. $CH_3CH_2CH_2NH_2 \xrightarrow{KMnO_4}$

44. What are the organic products for each oxidation or reduction reaction?

a. $HOCH_2CH_2CH_2CH_2CH_2OH \xrightarrow{K_2Cr_2O_7,\ H_2SO_4}$

b. $CH_3CH_2CH_2CH_2OH \xrightarrow{PCC}$

c. $CH_3CH{=}CHCH_2CH_2CH_2CO_2H \xrightarrow{LiAlH_4}$

d. $CH_3CH_2C({=}O)CH_3 \xrightarrow{NaBH_4}$

45. What reagents can be used for each of the following reactions?

a. 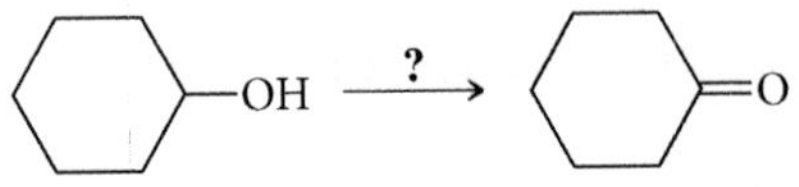 cyclohexane–OH $\xrightarrow{?}$ cyclohexane=O

b. $CH_2CH{=}CHCH_2CH_2CH_2CO_2H \xrightarrow{?} CH_3CH_2CH_2CH_2CH_2CH_2CO_2H$

46. What reagents can be used for each of the following reactions?

a. $CH_2CH_2CH_2OH \xrightarrow{?} CH_2CH_2C({=}O)H$

b. $CH_3C({=}O)CH_2CH_3 \xrightarrow{?} CH_3CH(OH)CH_2CH_3$

Nucleophilic Substitution Reactions

47. Complete and balance each nucleophilic substitution reaction:

a. 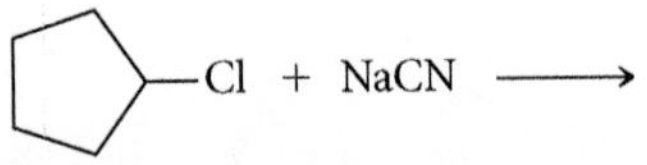 cyclopentane–Cl + NaCN $\longrightarrow$

b. $CH_3CH_2CH(Br)CH_3 + NaI \longrightarrow$

c. $(CH_3CH_2)_2NH + ClCH_2CH_2OH \xrightarrow{NaOH}$

48. Complete and balance each nucleophilic substitution reaction:

a. 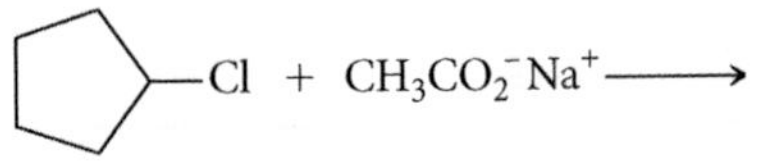 cyclopentane–Cl + $CH_3CO_2^-Na^+ \longrightarrow$

b. $CH_3I + NaOH \longrightarrow$

c. $(CH_3)_3N + CH_3I \longrightarrow$

49. Predict the mechanism, S_N1 or S_N2, by which the following substitution reactions take place:

a. $(CH_3)_3CBr + CH_3CH_2OH \longrightarrow (CH_3)_3COCH_2CH_3 + HBr$

b. $CH_3CH_2CH_2OH + NH_3 \longrightarrow CH_3CH_2CH_2NH_2 + H_2O$

50. Predict the mechanism, S_N1 or S_N2, by which the following substitution reactions take place:

a. $(CH_3)_3CBr + H_2O \longrightarrow (CH_3)_3COH + HBr$

b. $(CH_3)_2C(Cl)CH_2CH_3 + H_2O \longrightarrow (CH_3)_2C(OH)CH_2CH_3 + HCl$

51. Draw mechanisms for each of the reactions in Problem 49.

52. Draw mechanisms for each of the reactions in Problem 50.

53. Complete and balance each nucleophilic substitution reaction and predict whether inversion or racemization takes place:

a. 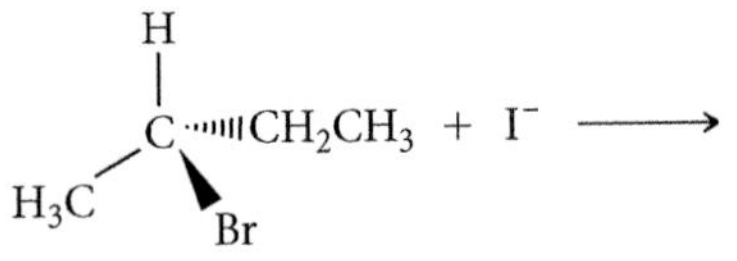 H–C(H$_3$C)(Br)····CH_2CH_3 + $I^- \longrightarrow$

b. 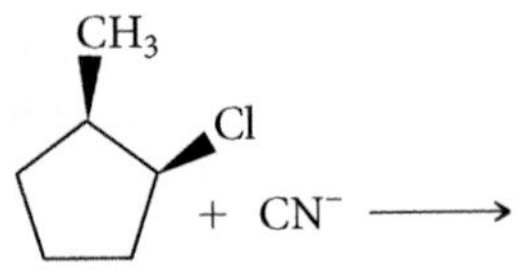 cyclopentane with wedged CH_3 and wedged Cl + $CN^- \longrightarrow$

c. cyclopentane with hashed H_3C and wedged Br + $H_2O \longrightarrow$

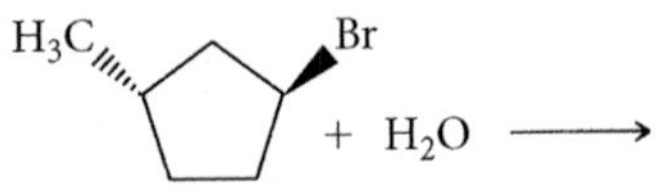

54. Complete and balance each nucleophilic substitution reaction and predict whether inversion or racemization takes place:

a. 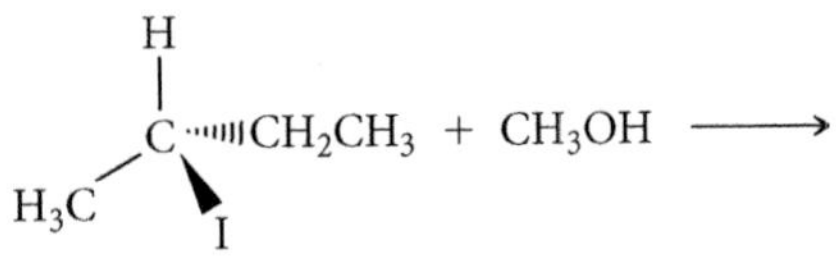 H–C(H$_3$C)(I)····CH_2CH_3 + $CH_3OH \longrightarrow$

b. CH_3–C(phenyl)(I)····CH_2CH_3 + $CH_3OH \longrightarrow$

c. cyclopentane with hashed H_3C and wedged I + $Br^- \longrightarrow$

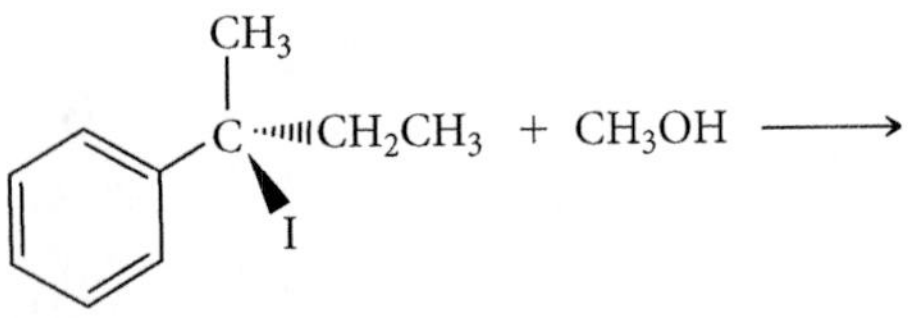

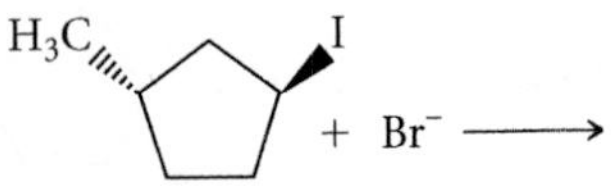

Elimination Reactions

55. Complete and balance each dehydration and dehydrohalogenation reaction. Identify major and minor elimination products, where appropriate.

a. $CH_3CH_2CH_2CH_2CH_2OH \xrightarrow[\text{Heat}]{H_2SO_4}$

b. 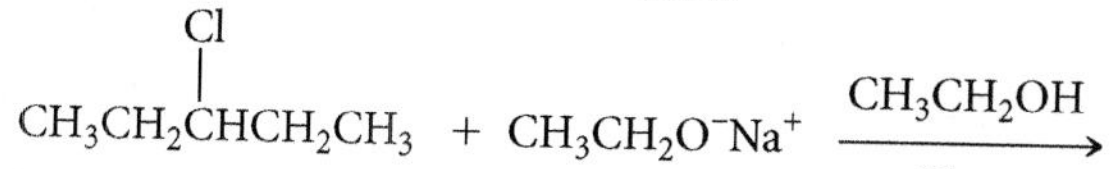 $CH_3CH_2CH(Cl)CH_2CH_3 + CH_3CH_2O^-Na^+ \xrightarrow[\text{Heat}]{CH_3CH_2OH}$

c. 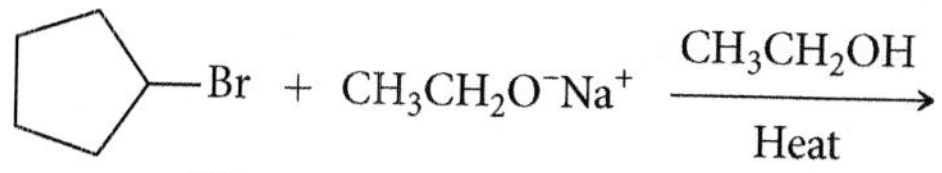 (cyclopentyl)–Br $+ CH_3CH_2O^-Na^+ \xrightarrow[\text{Heat}]{CH_3CH_2OH}$

d. 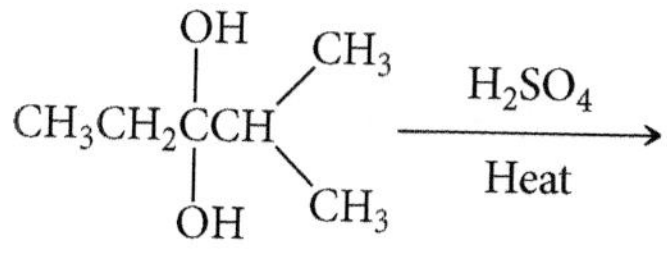 $CH_3CH_2C(OH)_2CH(CH_3)_2 \xrightarrow[\text{Heat}]{H_2SO_4}$

56. Complete and balance each dehydration and dehydrohalogenation reaction. Identify major and minor elimination products, where appropriate.

a. 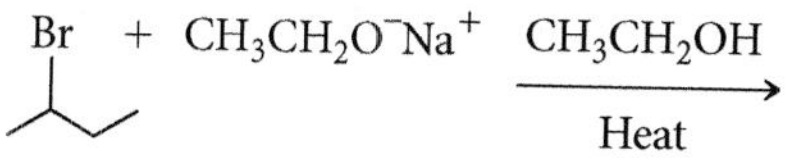 (2-bromobutane, skeletal) Br $+ CH_3CH_2O^-Na^+ \xrightarrow[\text{Heat}]{CH_3CH_2OH}$

b. 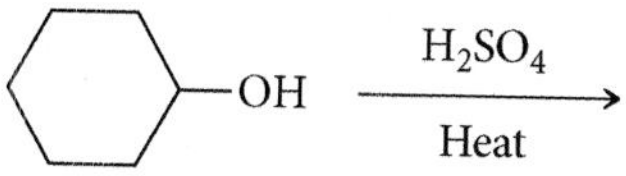 (cyclohexyl)–OH $\xrightarrow[\text{Heat}]{H_2SO_4}$

c. 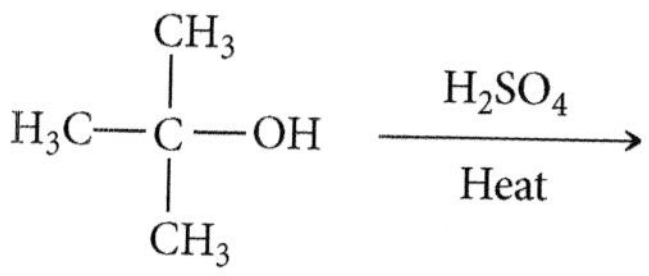 $H_3C{-}C(CH_3)_2{-}OH \xrightarrow[\text{Heat}]{H_2SO_4}$

d. 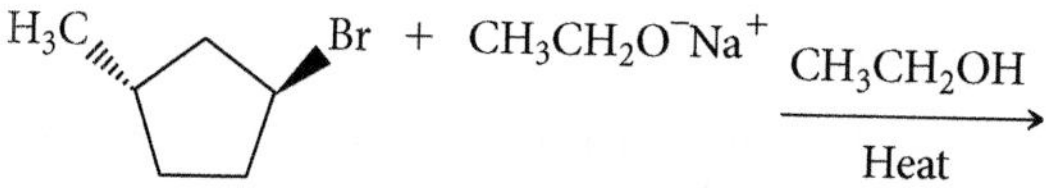 H_3C (hashed)–cyclopentane–(wedged) Br $+ CH_3CH_2O^-Na^+ \xrightarrow[\text{Heat}]{CH_3CH_2OH}$

57. Predict the major and minor elimination products for each of the following reactions:

a. 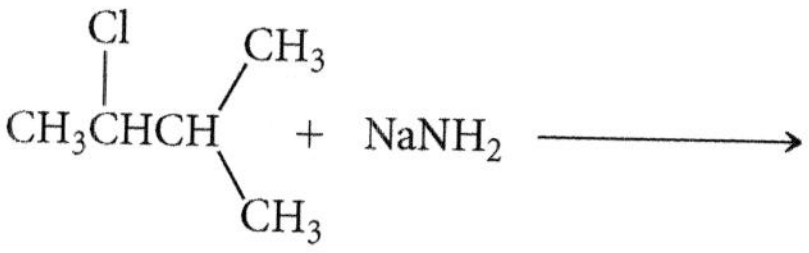 $CH_3CH(Cl)CH(CH_3)_2 + NaNH_2 \longrightarrow$

b. 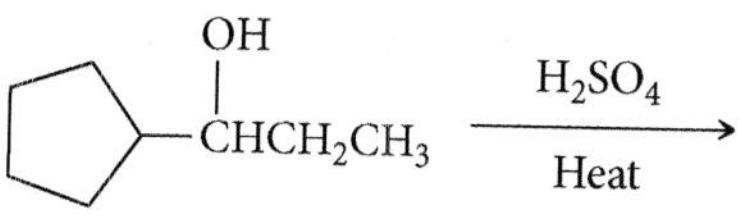 (cyclopentyl)–$CH(OH)CH_2CH_3 \xrightarrow[\text{Heat}]{H_2SO_4}$

c. 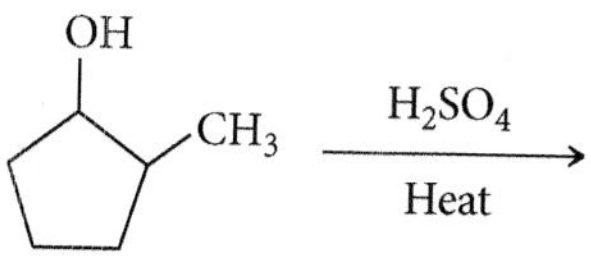 2-methylcyclopentanol (OH, CH_3 on ring) $\xrightarrow[\text{Heat}]{H_2SO_4}$

58. Predict the major and minor elimination products for each of the following reactions:

a. 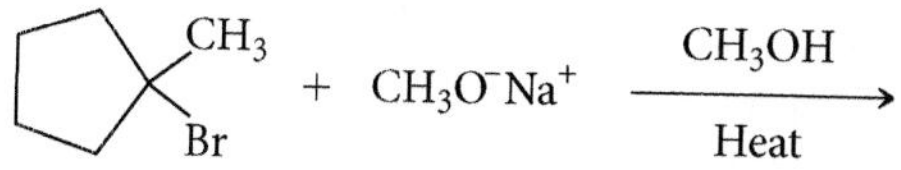 1-bromo-1-methylcyclopentane (CH_3, Br) $+ CH_3O^-Na^+ \xrightarrow[\text{Heat}]{CH_3OH}$

b. 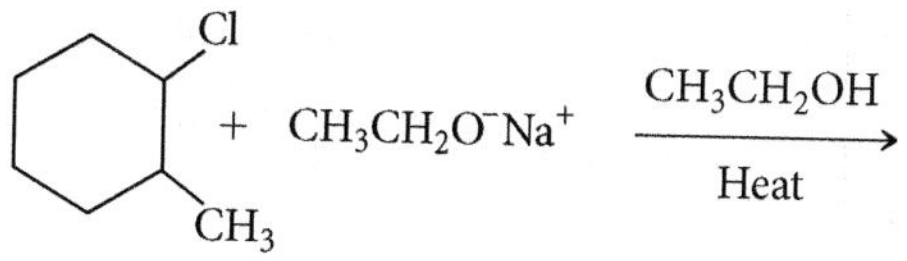 1-chloro-2-methylcyclohexane (Cl, CH_3) $+ CH_3CH_2O^-Na^+ \xrightarrow[\text{Heat}]{CH_3CH_2OH}$

c. 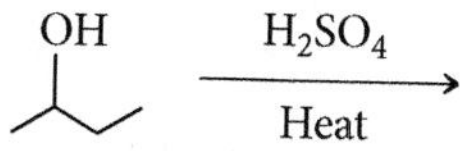 (2-butanol, skeletal) OH $\xrightarrow[\text{Heat}]{H_2SO_4}$

59. Predict whether the following elimination reactions proceed via an E1 or E2 mechanism.

a. 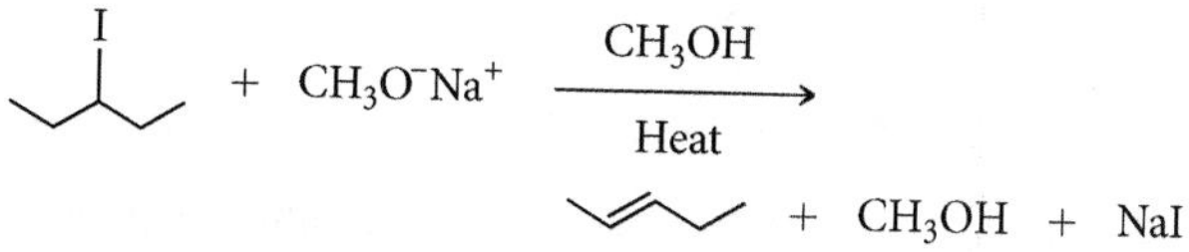 (3-iodopentane, skeletal) I $+ CH_3O^-Na^+ \xrightarrow[\text{Heat}]{CH_3OH}$ (2-pentene, skeletal) $+ CH_3OH + NaI$

b. 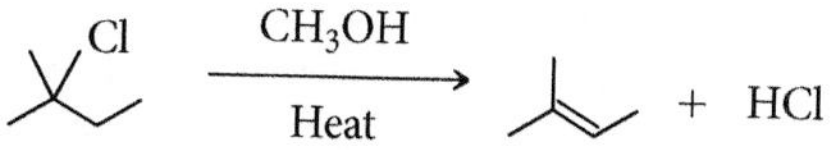 (2-chloro-2-methylbutane, skeletal) Cl $\xrightarrow[\text{Heat}]{CH_3OH}$ (2-methyl-2-butene, skeletal) $+ HCl$

60. Predict whether the following elimination reactions proceed via an E1 or E2 mechanism.

a. 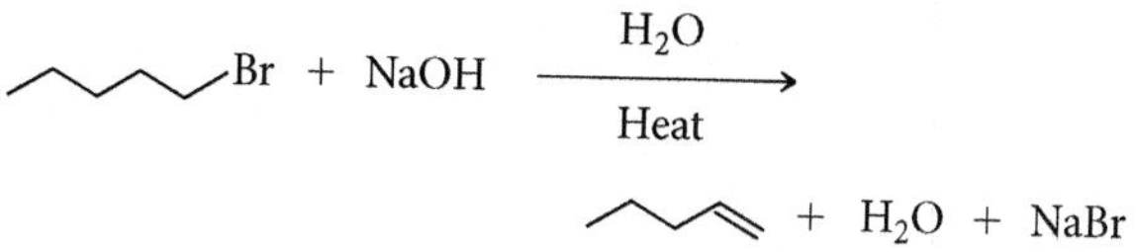 (1-bromopentane, skeletal) Br $+ NaOH \xrightarrow[\text{Heat}]{H_2O}$ (1-pentene, skeletal) $+ H_2O + NaBr$

b. 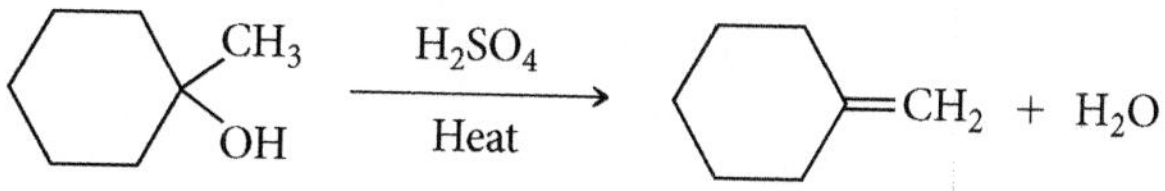 1-methylcyclohexanol (CH_3, OH) $\xrightarrow[\text{Heat}]{H_2SO_4}$ (cyclohexyl)$=CH_2 + H_2O$

61. Draw mechanisms for each of the reactions in Problem 59.

62. Draw mechanisms for each of the reactions in Problem 60.

Electrophilic Additions to Alkenes

63. What are the products of the following addition reactions?

a. $CH_3{-}CH{=}CH{-}CH_3 + HCl \longrightarrow$

b. 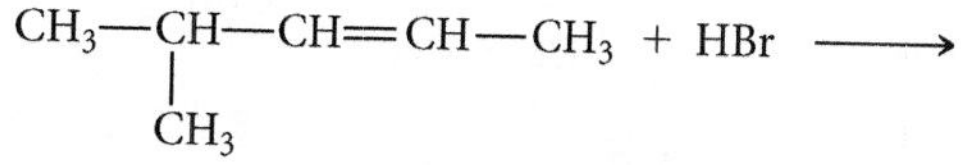 $CH_3{-}CH(CH_3){-}CH{=}CH{-}CH_3 + HBr \longrightarrow$

c. $CH_3{-}CH_2{-}CH{=}CH{-}CH_3 + Br_2 \longrightarrow$

d. 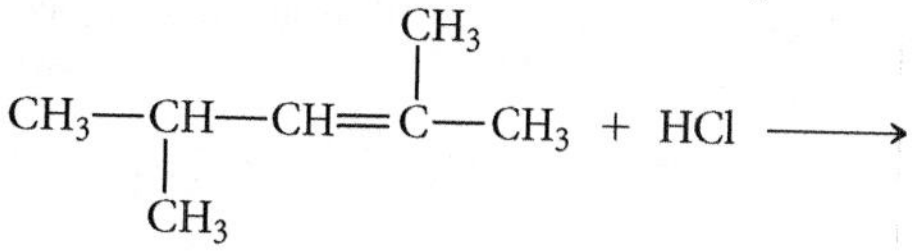 $CH_3{-}CH(CH_3){-}CH{=}C(CH_3){-}CH_3 + HCl \longrightarrow$

64. What are the products of the following addition reactions?

a. 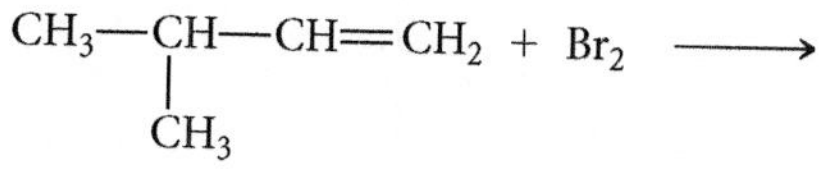 $CH_3{-}CH(CH_3){-}CH{=}CH_2 + Br_2 \longrightarrow$

b. $CH_2{=}CH{-}CH_3 + Cl_2 \longrightarrow$

c. 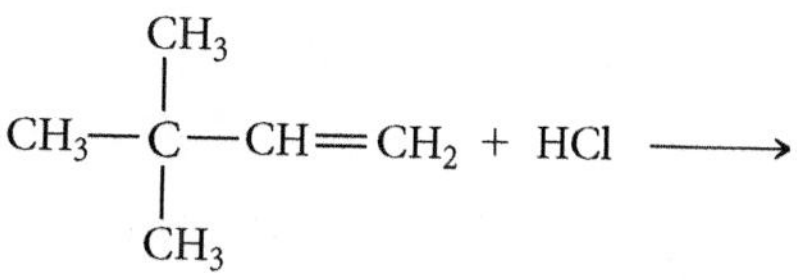 $CH_3{-}C(CH_3)_2{-}CH{=}CH_2 + HCl \longrightarrow$

d. 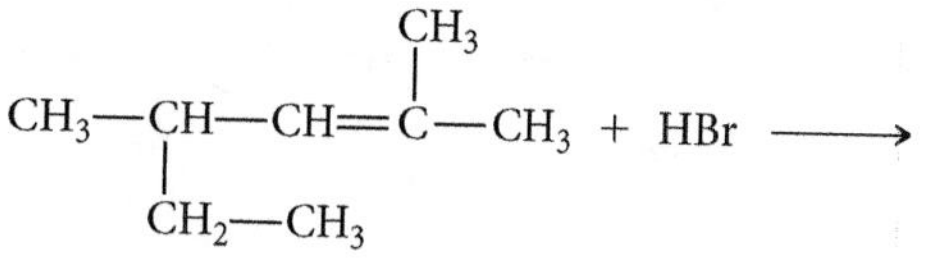 $CH_3{-}CH(CH_2{-}CH_3){-}CH{=}C(CH_3){-}CH_3 + HBr \longrightarrow$

65. Complete the following hydrogenation reactions:

a. $CH_3-\underset{\large CH_3}{\underset{|}{CH}}-CH{=}CH_2 + H_2 \xrightarrow{Pd/C}$

b. $CH_2{=}CH-CH_3 + H_2 \xrightarrow{Pd/C}$

66. Complete the following hydrogenation reactions:

a. $CH_3-CH_2-CH{=}CH_2 + H_2 \xrightarrow{Pd/C}$

b. $CH_3-CH_2-\overset{CH_3}{\overset{|}{C}}{=}\overset{CH_3}{\overset{|}{C}}-CH_3 + H_2 \xrightarrow{Pd/C}$

67. What are the products of the following addition reactions?

a. $CH_3-\underset{\large CH_3}{\underset{|}{CH}}-CH{=}CH_2 \xrightarrow{H^+, H_2O}$

b. cyclohexene + 3-chloroperoxybenzoic acid (Cl–C$_6$H$_4$–C(=O)–O–O–H) $\longrightarrow$

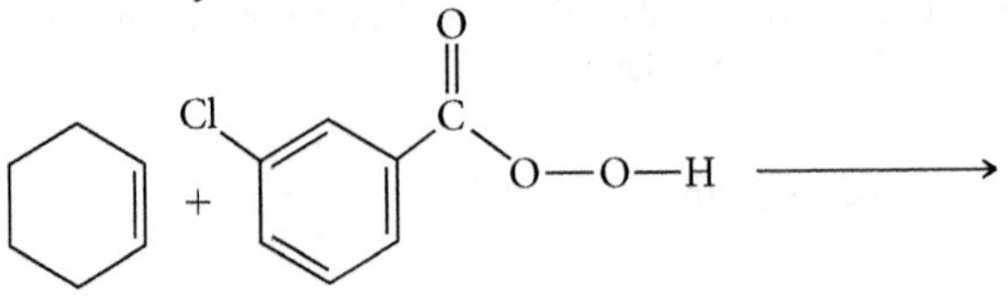

c. $CH_3-\underset{\large CH_3}{\underset{|}{\overset{OH}{\overset{|}{C}}}}-CH{=}CH_2 \xrightarrow{KMnO_4}$

68. What are the products of the following addition reactions?

a. $CH_3-CH{=}\overset{CH_3}{\overset{|}{C}}-CH_3 \xrightarrow{H^+, H_2O}$

b. $CH_3-CH_2-CH{=}CH-CH_3 \xrightarrow{RCO_3H}$

c. $CH_3-CH_2-\underset{\large CH_3}{\underset{|}{C}}{=}CH-CH_3 \xrightarrow{KMnO_4}$

69. Choose an appropriate reagent with which to complete each of the following reactions:

a. $CH_3-CH_2-CH{=}CH-CH_2 \longrightarrow CH_3-CH_2-\overset{OH}{\overset{|}{CH}}-CH_2-CH_3$

b. 1-methylcyclohexene (ring with CH$_3$) $\longrightarrow$ 1-chloro-1-methylcyclohexane (ring with CH$_3$ and Cl)

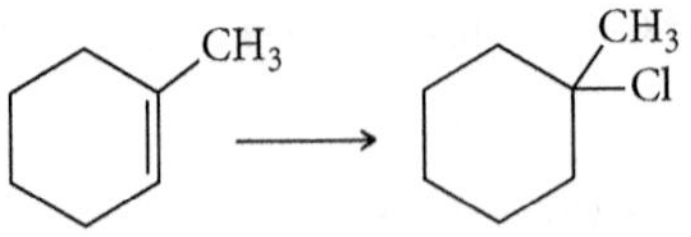

c. $CH_2{=}CH-CH_2-CH_2-CH{=}CH_2 \longrightarrow CH_3CH_2CH_2CH_2CH_2CH_3$

d. $CH_3-CH_2{=}C(CH_3)(CH_3) \longrightarrow CH_3-\overset{Br}{\overset{|}{CH}}-\underset{\large Br}{\underset{|}{\overset{CH_3}{\overset{|}{C}}}}-CH_2$

70. Choose an appropriate reagent with which to complete each of the following reactions:

a. cyclopentene $\longrightarrow$ cyclopentane

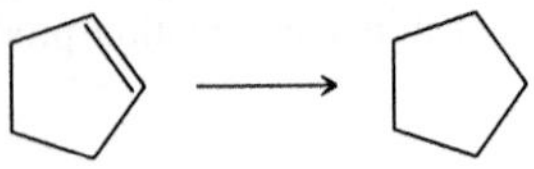

b. $(H_3C)_2C{=}C(CH_3)_2 \longrightarrow H_3C-\overset{O}{C}(H_3C)-C(CH_3)-CH_3$ (epoxide: O bridging the two central carbons)

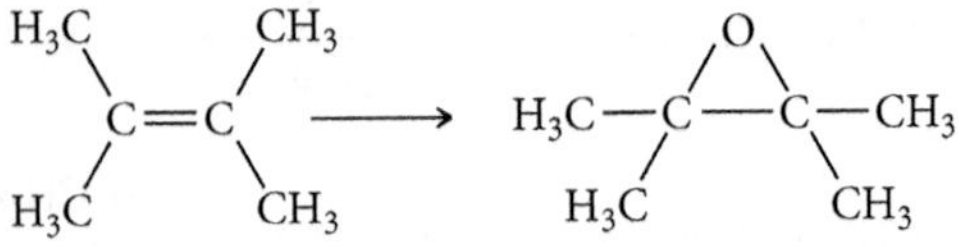

c. $CH_3-\underset{\large CH_3}{\underset{|}{CH}}-\underset{\large CH_3}{\underset{|}{C}}{=}CH_2 \longrightarrow CH_3-\underset{\large CH_3}{\underset{|}{CH}}-\underset{\large CH_3}{\underset{|}{\overset{OH}{\overset{|}{C}}}}-CH_3$

d. $CH_3-CH_2-CH{=}CH-CH_2-CH_3 \longrightarrow CH_3-CH_2-\overset{OH}{\overset{|}{CH}}-\overset{OH}{\overset{|}{CH}}-CH_2-CH_3$

Nucleophilic Additions to Aldehydes and Ketones

71. Complete the following nucleophilic addition reactions:

a. $CH_3-CH_2-CH_2-\overset{O}{\overset{\|}{C}}-H + CH_3CH_2OH \overset{H^+}{\rightleftharpoons}$

b. $CH_3-CH_2-\overset{O}{\overset{\|}{C}}-CH_3 + CH_3-\overset{OH}{\overset{|}{CH}}-CH_3 \overset{H^+}{\rightleftharpoons}$

c. cyclopentyl–C(=O)H + $CH_3OH \overset{H^+}{\rightleftharpoons}$

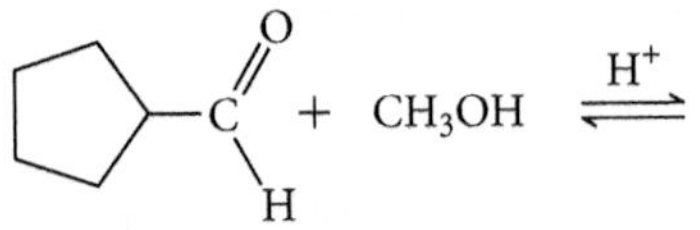

72. Complete the following nucleophilic addition reactions:

a. $CH_3-CH_2-\overset{O}{\overset{\|}{C}}-H + CH_3CH_2OH \overset{H^+}{\rightleftharpoons}$

b. cyclohexanone (ring=O) + $CH_3OH \overset{H^+}{\rightleftharpoons}$

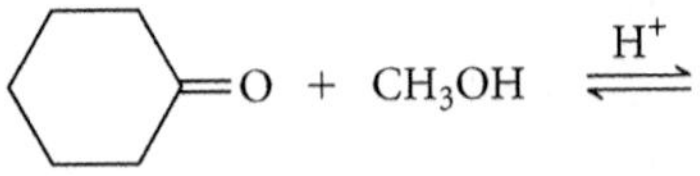

c. $CH_3-\overset{O}{\overset{\|}{C}}-CH_3$ + cyclohexanol (ring–OH) $\overset{H^+}{\rightleftharpoons}$

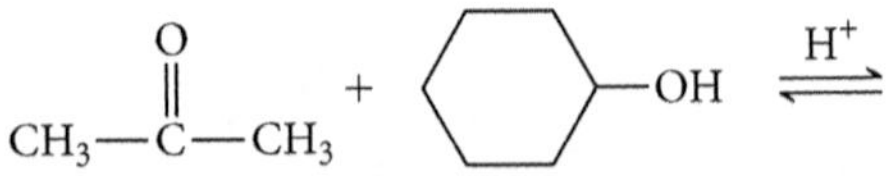

73. Complete the following Grignard reactions:

a. phenyl–MgBr + $CH_3CHO \xrightarrow[(2)\ H_3O^+]{(1)\ \text{Diethyl ether}}$

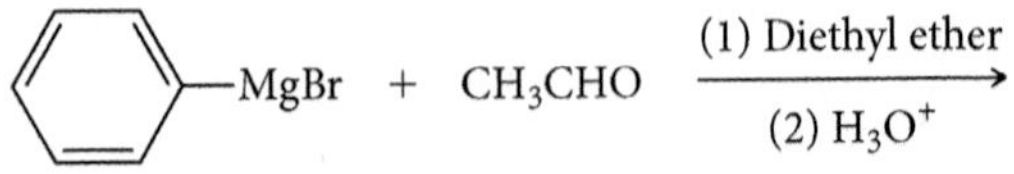

b. $CH_3-\underset{\large CH_3}{\underset{|}{CH}}-MgBr + H-\overset{O}{\overset{\|}{C}}-H \xrightarrow[(2)\ H_3O^+]{(1)\ \text{Diethyl ether}}$

c. $CH_3MgI + CH_3CH_2\overset{O}{\overset{\|}{C}}CH_2CH_3 \xrightarrow[(2)\ H_3O^+]{(1)\ \text{Diethyl ether}}$

74. Complete the following Grignard reactions:

a. 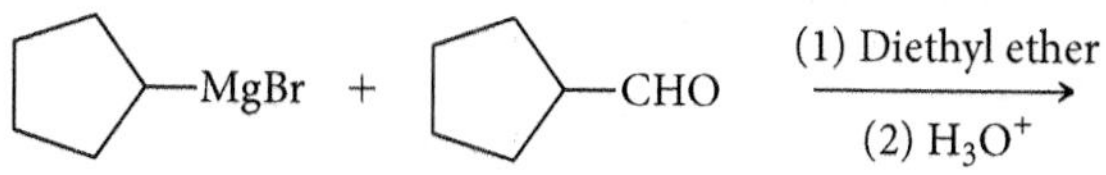 (cyclopentyl)–MgBr + (cyclopentyl)–CHO $\xrightarrow[\text{(2) } H_3O^+]{\text{(1) Diethyl ether}}$

b. 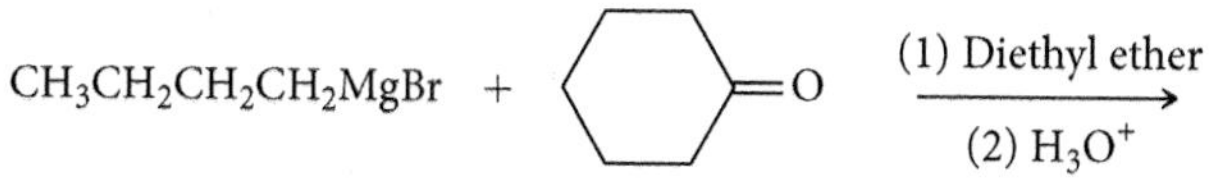 $CH_3CH_2CH_2CH_2MgBr$ + (cyclohexanone, =O) $\xrightarrow[\text{(2) } H_3O^+]{\text{(1) Diethyl ether}}$

c. $CH_3CH_2CH_2MgBr + CH_3\overset{O}{\overset{\|}{C}}CH_2CH_3 \xrightarrow[\text{(2) } H_3O^+]{\text{(1) Diethyl ether}}$

75. What Grignard reagent, RMgX, could be used to complete the following reactions?

a. 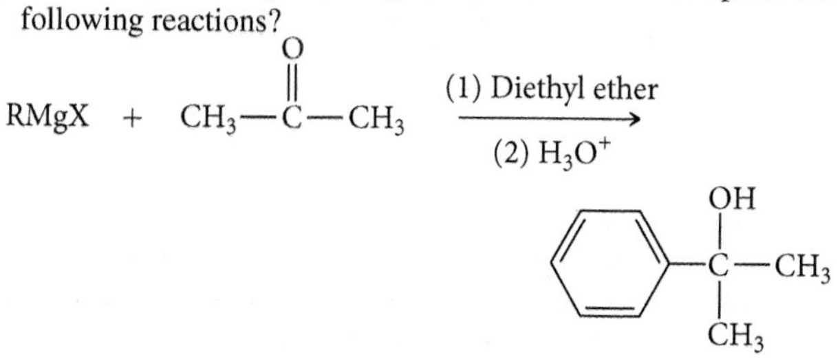 $RMgX + CH_3-\overset{O}{\overset{\|}{C}}-CH_3 \xrightarrow[\text{(2) } H_3O^+]{\text{(1) Diethyl ether}}$ (phenyl)–C(OH)(CH$_3$)–CH$_3$

b. 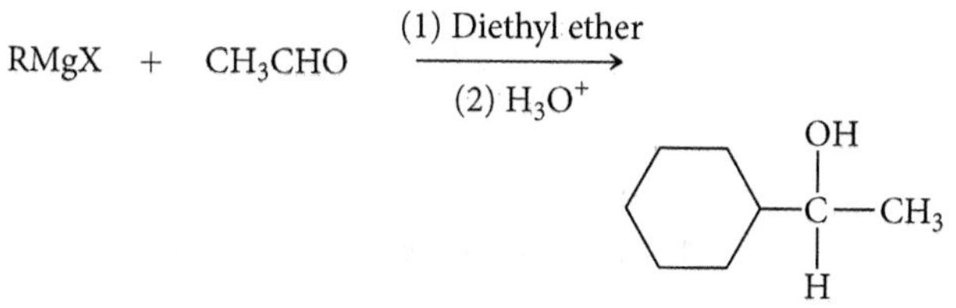 $RMgX + CH_3CHO \xrightarrow[\text{(2) } H_3O^+]{\text{(1) Diethyl ether}}$ (cyclohexyl)–C(OH)(H)–CH$_3$

76. What Grignard reagent, RMgX, could be used to complete the following reactions?

a. $RMgX + CH_3CHO \xrightarrow[\text{(2) } H_3O^+]{\text{(1) Diethyl ether}} CH_3CH_2CH_2CH_2\overset{OH}{\overset{|}{C}}HCH_3$

b. 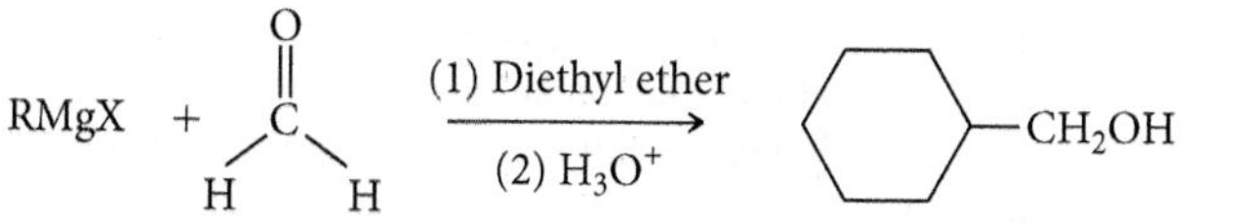 RMgX + H–C(=O)–H $\xrightarrow[\text{(2) } H_3O^+]{\text{(1) Diethyl ether}}$ (cyclohexyl)–CH_2OH

Nucleophilic Substitutions of Acyl Compounds

77. What are the products of the following esterification reactions?

a. $CH_3-CH_2-CH_2-CH_2-\overset{O}{\overset{\|}{C}}-OH + CH_3CH_2OH \xrightarrow{H^+}$

b. 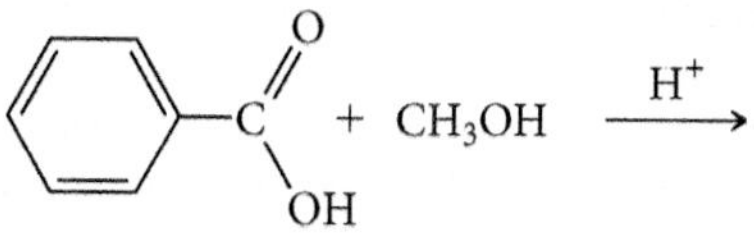 (phenyl)–C(=O)–OH + $CH_3OH \xrightarrow{H^+}$

78. What are the products of the following esterification reactions?

a. HO–C(=O)–CH_2-CH_2–C(=O)–OH + $2\ CH_3CH_2OH \xrightarrow{H^+}$

b. H–C(=O)–OH + $CH_3CH_2OH \xrightarrow{H^+}$

79. Complete the following acyl group interconversions:

a. $CH_3-CH_2-CH_2-CH_2-CH_2-$C(=O)–OH + Cl–C(=O)–C(=O)–Cl $\longrightarrow$

b. CH_3-CH_2-C(=O)–O–CH_3 + $CH_3CH_2OH \xrightarrow{H^+}$

c. CH_3-C(=O)–O–CH_3 + $NH_3 \longrightarrow$

d. 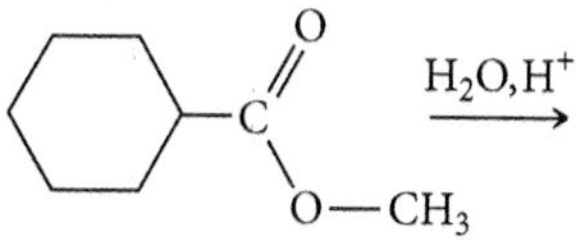 (cyclohexyl)–C(=O)–O–CH_3 $\xrightarrow{H_2O, H^+}$

80. Complete the following acyl group interconversions:

a. 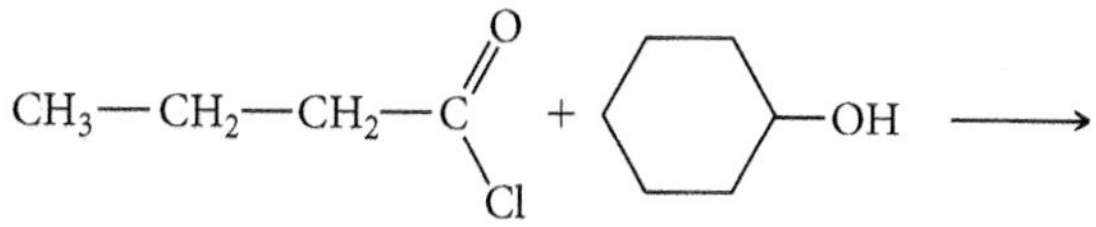 $CH_3-CH_2-CH_2-$C(=O)–Cl + (cyclohexyl)–OH $\longrightarrow$

b. CH_3–C(=O)–O–C(=O)–CH_3 + $CH_3-\overset{OH}{\overset{|}{C}H}-CH_3 \longrightarrow$

c. 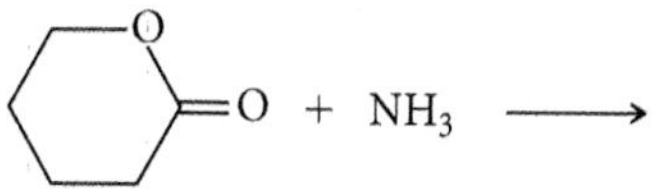 (six-membered cyclic ester, δ-lactone, =O) + $NH_3 \longrightarrow$

d. 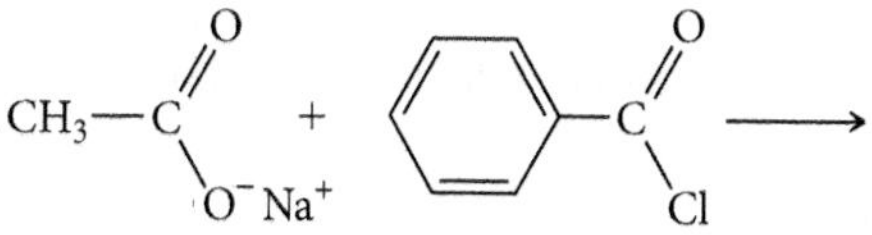 CH_3-C(=O)–O^-Na^+ + (phenyl)–C(=O)–Cl $\longrightarrow$

81. What are the cyclic products of each of the following reactions?

a. $HO-CH_2-CH_2-CH_2-\overset{O}{\overset{\|}{C}}-OH \xrightarrow{H^+}$

b. HO–C(=O)–$CH_2-CH_2-CH_2$–C(=O)–OH $\xrightarrow{\text{Heat}}$

82. Suggest appropriate reagents and reactants for the following acyl group interconversions. More than one step may be required.

a. $CH_3-CH_2-\overset{O}{\overset{\|}{C}}-NH_2 \longrightarrow CH_3-CH_2-\overset{O}{\overset{\|}{C}}-Cl$

b. 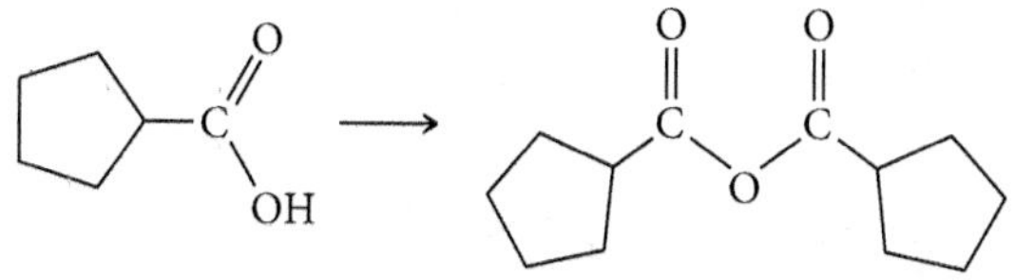 (cyclopentyl)–C(=O)–OH $\longrightarrow$ (cyclopentyl)–C(=O)–O–C(=O)–(cyclopentyl)

83. Suggest appropriate reagents and reactants for the following acyl group interconversions. More than one step may be required.

a. Cyclohexyl–C(=O)–Cl → Cyclohexyl–C(=O)–O–C(=O)–CH_3

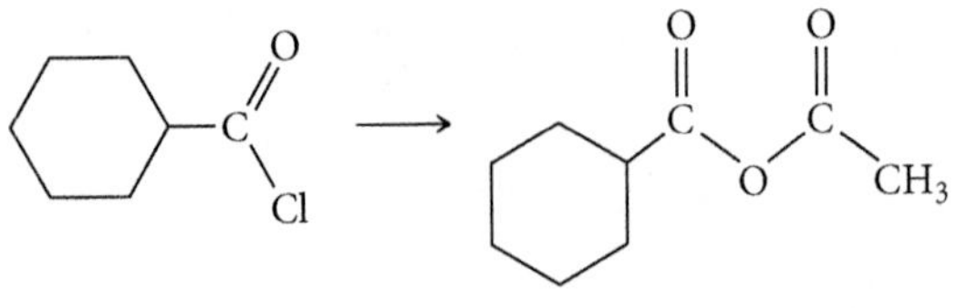

b. $CH_3—CH_2—CH_2—C(=O)OH$ → $CH_3—CH_2—CH_2—C(=O)—N(CH_3)—CH_3$

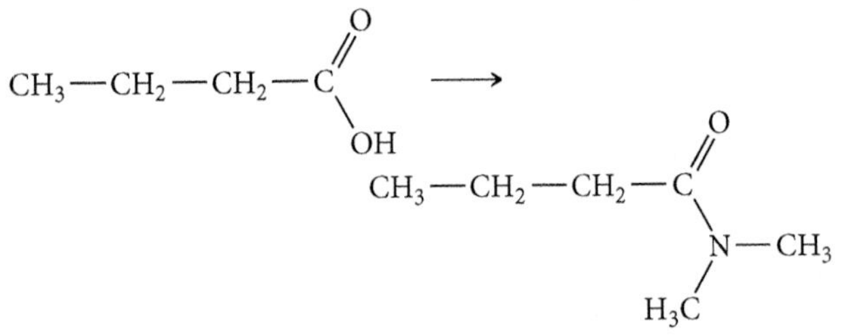

Electrophilic Aromatic Substitutions

84. What are the products of the following aromatic substitution reactions?

a. Benzene + Br_2 $\xrightarrow{FeBr_3}$

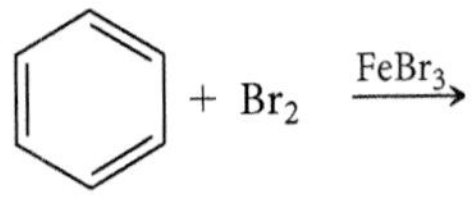

b. Benzene + $CH_3—CH(CH_3)—Cl$ $\xrightarrow{AlCl_3}$

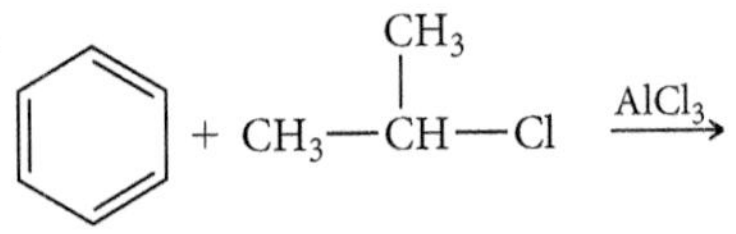

c. Benzene + HNO_3 $\xrightarrow{H_2SO_4}$

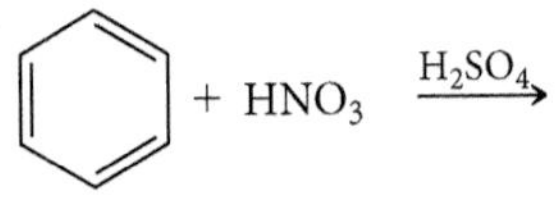

85. What are the products of the following aromatic substitution reactions?

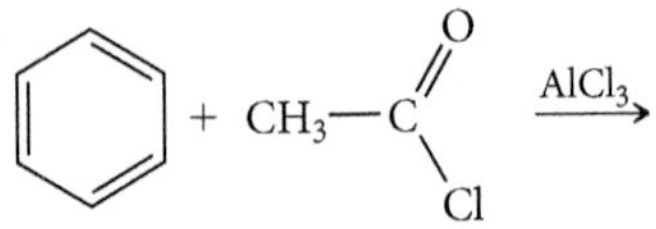

a. Benzene + Cl_2 $\xrightarrow{FeCl_3}$

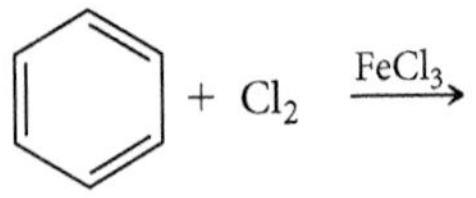

b. Benzene + $CH_3—C(=O)—Cl$ $\xrightarrow{AlCl_3}$

c. Benzene + $CH_3—C(CH_3)_2—Cl$ $\xrightarrow{AlCl_3}$

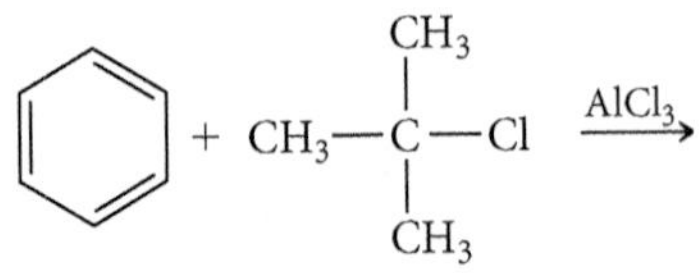

86. Choose an appropriate reagent with which to complete each of the following reactions:

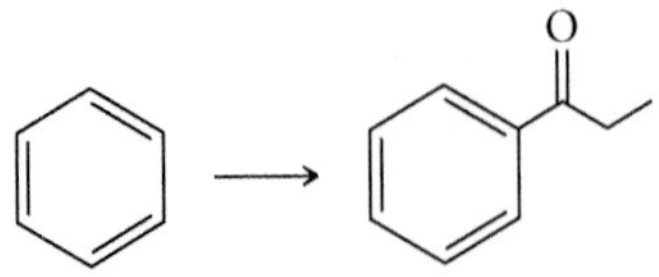

a. Benzene → Nitrobenzene (NO_2)

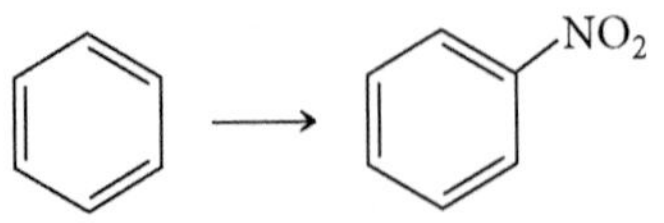

b. Benzene → Phenyl–C(=O)–CH_2CH_3

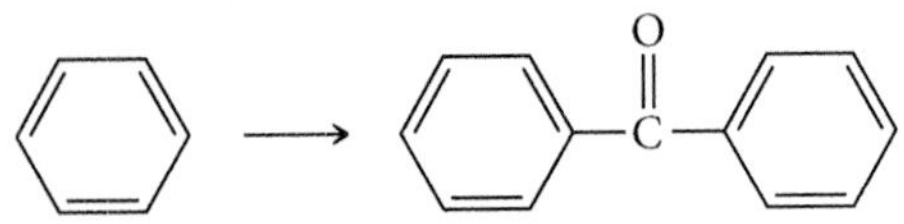

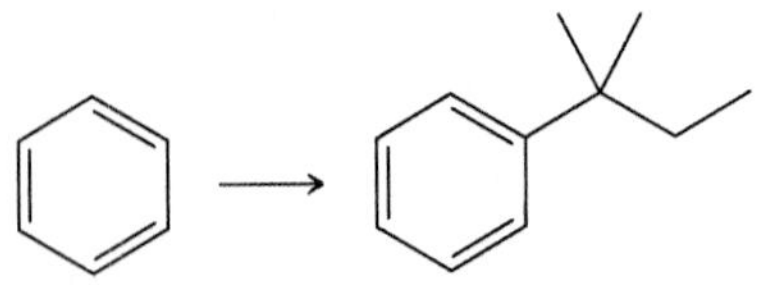

c. Benzene → Bromobenzene (Br)

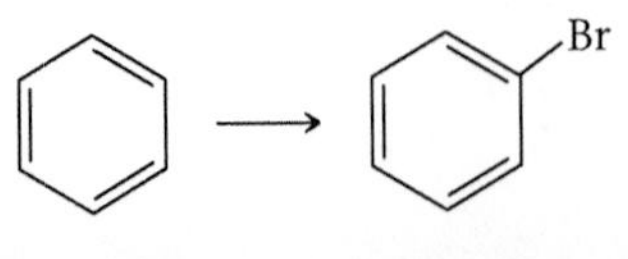

87. Choose an appropriate reagent with which to complete each of the following reactions:

a. Benzene → Phenyl–C(=O)–Phenyl

b. Benzene → Phenyl–C(CH_3)$_2$–CH_2CH_3

c. Benzene → Chlorobenzene (Cl)

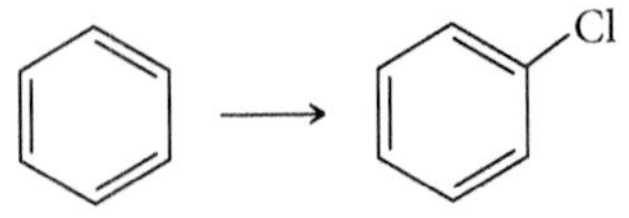

Polymerization

88. Saran, the polymer used to make saran wrap, is an addition polymer formed from the following two monomers: 1,1-dichloroethene and chloroethene. Draw the structure of the polymer. (*Hint:* The monomers alternate.)

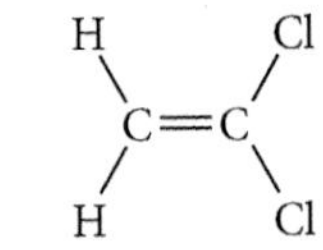

$H_2C=CCl_2$ — 1,1,-Dichloroethene

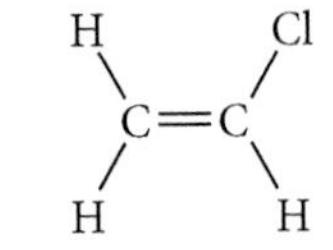

$H_2C=CHCl$ — Chloroethene

89. Teflon is an addition polymer formed from the following monomer. Draw the structure of the polymer.

$F_2C=CF_2$

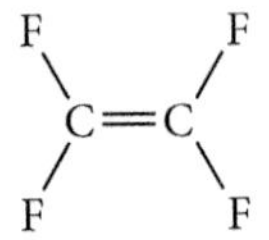

90. Nomex, a condensation polymer used by firefighters because of its flame-resistant properties, is formed in a reaction between isophthalic acid and 3-aminoaniline. Draw the structure of the dimer. (*Hint:* Water is eliminated when the bond between the monomers forms.)

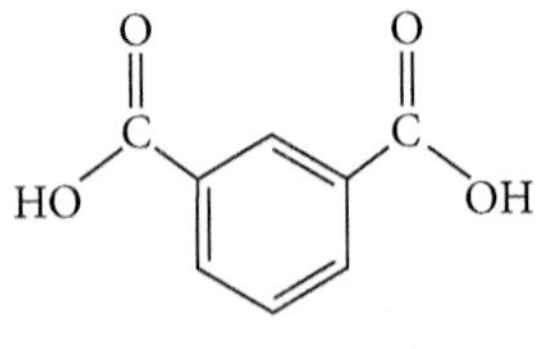

HO–C(=O)–C_6H_4–C(=O)–OH (meta) — Isophthalic acid

H_2N–C_6H_4–NH_2 (meta) — 3-Aminoaniline

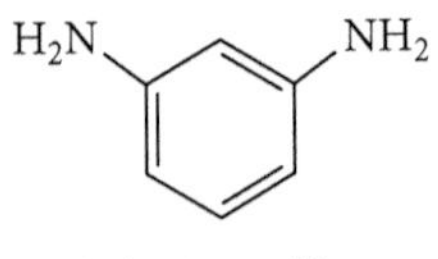

91. One kind of polyester is a condensation copolymer formed in a reaction between terephthalic acid and ethylene glycol. Draw the structure of the dimer and circle the ester functional group. (*Hint:* Water is eliminated when the bond between the monomers forms.)

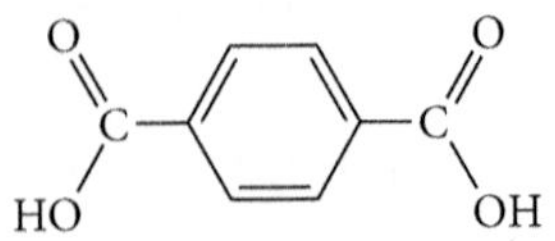

HO–C(=O)–C_6H_4–C(=O)–OH (para) — Terephthalic acid

$HO—CH_2—CH_2—OH$ — Ethylene glycol

92. What polymer is formed in each of the following reactions? Draw each polymer in polymer notation.

a. $n\,H_2NCH_2CH_2NH_2 + n\,ClC(=O)-C_6H_4-C(=O)Cl \xrightarrow{\text{Base}}$

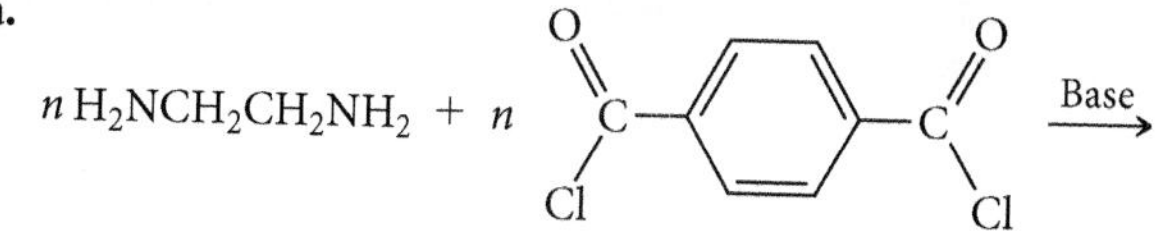

b. $n\,C_6H_5-CH{=}CH_2 \xrightarrow{\text{Catalyst}}$

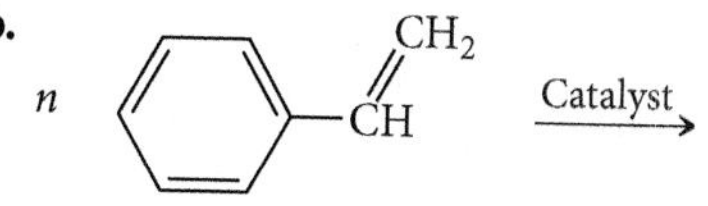

93. What polymer is formed in each of the following reactions? Draw each polymer in polymer notation.

a. $n\,H_2C{=}C(CH_3)_2 \xrightarrow{\text{Catalyst}}$

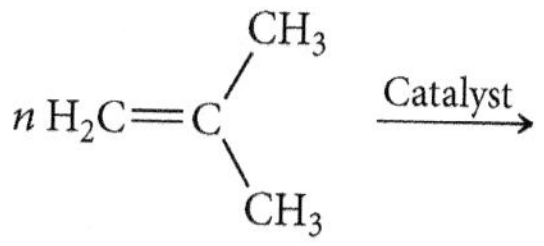

b. $n\,H_2C{=}C(CN)H \xrightarrow{\text{Catalyst}}$

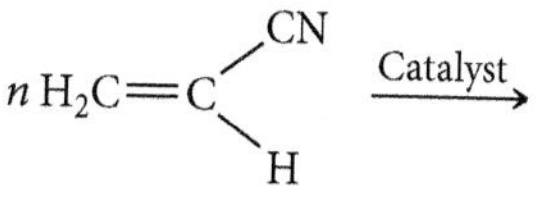

Cumulative Problems

94. Classify the following organic reactions as acid–base, oxidation–reduction, nucleophilic substitution, elimination, electrophilic addition, nucleophilic addition, or electrophilic aromatic substitution:

a. $2\,CH_3CH{=}CH_2 + 9\,O_2 \longrightarrow 6\,CO_2 + 6\,H_2O$

b. $CH_3CH{=}CH_2 + Cl_2 \longrightarrow CH_3-CH(Cl)-CH_2Cl$

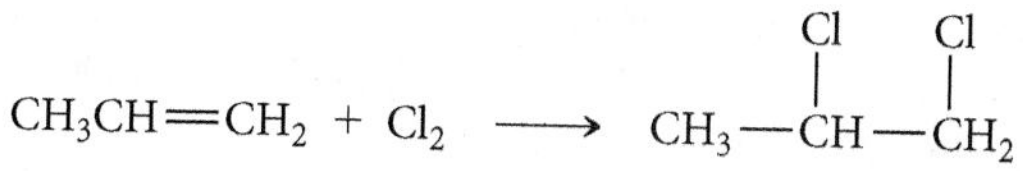

c. $CH_3-CH_2-CH(CH_3)-CH_2-OH \xrightarrow{H_2SO_4} CH_3-CH_2-C(CH_3){=}CH_2$

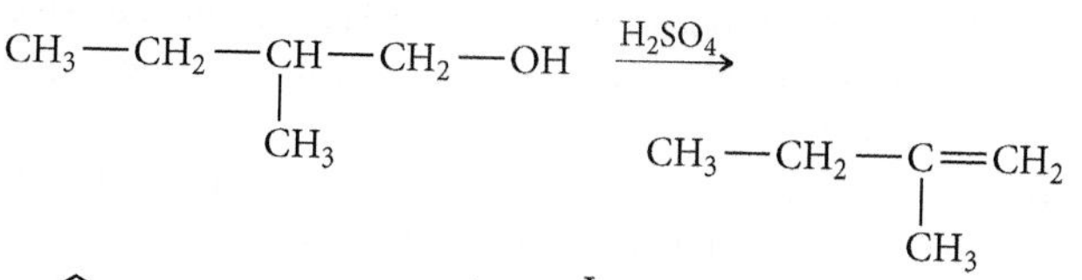

d. $C_6H_6 + I_2 \xrightarrow{FeI_3} C_6H_5I$

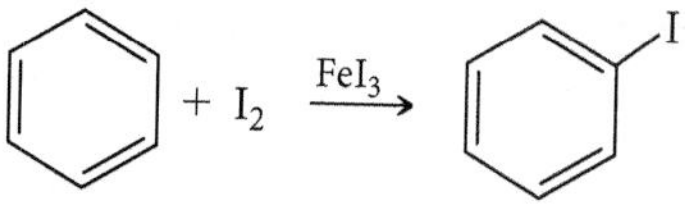

95. Classify the following organic reactions as acid–base, oxidation–reduction, nucleophilic substitution, elimination, electrophilic addition, nucleophilic addition, or electrophilic aromatic substitution:

a. $CH_3-C(=O)OH + NaOH \longrightarrow CH_3-C(=O)O^- \; Na^+ + H_2O$

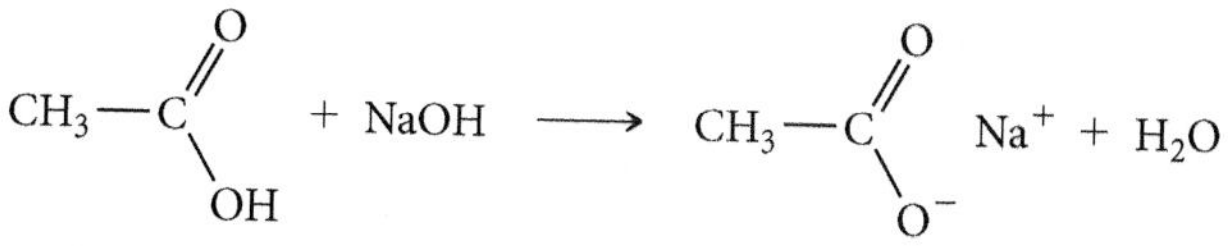

b. $CH_3CH_2CH_2CH_2Cl + NaCN \longrightarrow CH_3CH_2CH_2CH_2CN + NaCl$

c. $CH_3-CH(CH_3)-CH_2-CH(=O) + CH_3OH \xrightarrow{H^+} CH_3-CH(CH_3)-CH_2-CH(OH)-OCH_3$

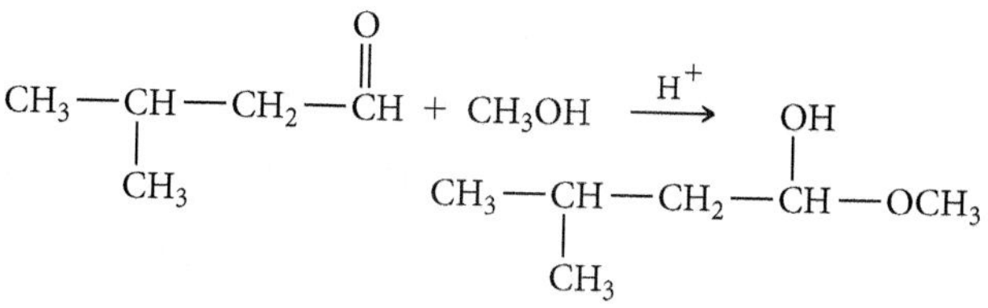

d. $CH_3-CH(CH_3)-CH_2-C(=O)OH + CH_3OH \overset{H^+}{\rightleftharpoons} CH_3-CH(CH_3)-CH_2-C(=O)OCH_3 + H_2O$

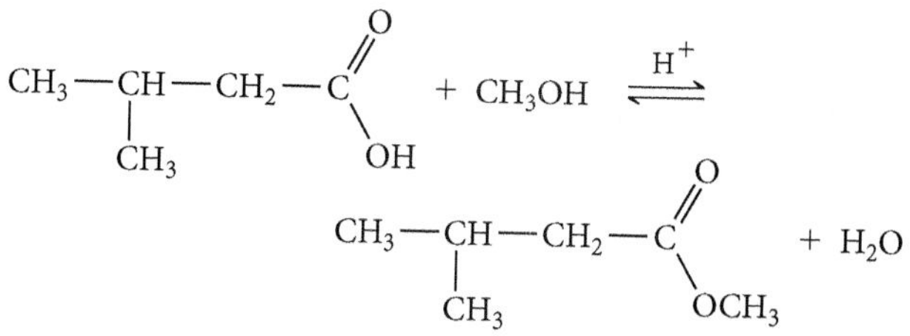

96. In the Williamson ether synthesis, ethers can be prepared as in the following example reactions:

a. $CH_3CH_2OH + Na \longrightarrow CH_3CH_2O^- + Na^+ + \tfrac{1}{2}H_2$

b. $CH_3CH_2O^- + CH_3CH_2CH_2Br \longrightarrow CH_3CH_2OCH_2CH_2CH_3 + Br^-$

Classify reactions (a) and (b) as acid–base, oxidation–reduction, substitution, elimination, or addition. Write the balanced chemical equation for the overall reaction. Draw a mechanism for step 2.

97. What are the products of the following reactions? What are the absolute configurations of the products (*R*, *S*, or a racemic mixture)?

a. $C_6H_5-C(Br)(CH_2CH_3)(CH_3) \xrightarrow{H_2O}$

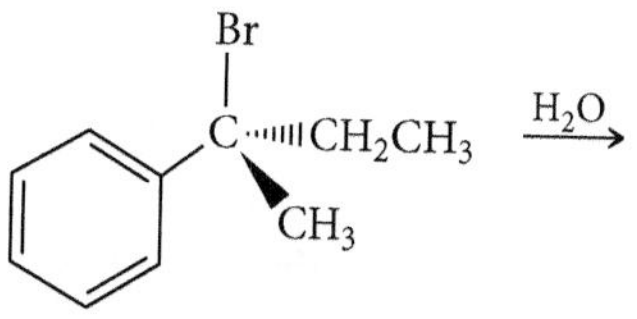

b. $CH_3-CH_2-C(H)(CH_3)(I) + NaCN \longrightarrow$

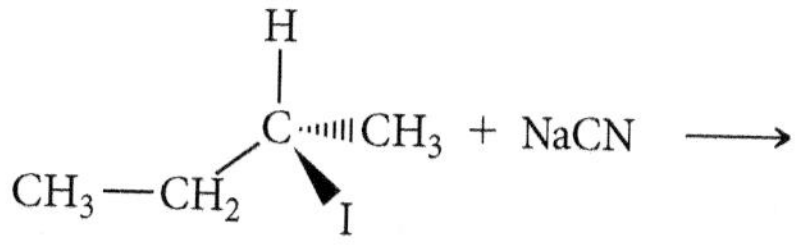

98. What are the products of the following reactions?

a. $CH_3-CH_2-C(CH_3){=}CH_2 + H_2 \xrightarrow{Pd/C}$

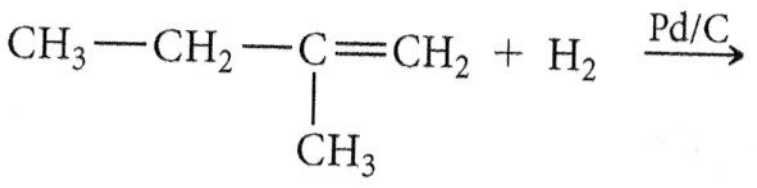

b. $CH_3-CH_2-CH(CH_3)-CH_2-C(=O)-OH + CH_3CH_2OH \xrightarrow{H^+}$

c. $CH_3-C(=O)-CH_3 + CH_3CH_2CH_2CH_2CH_2MgBr \xrightarrow[(2)\ H_3O^+]{(1)\ \text{Diethyl ether}}$

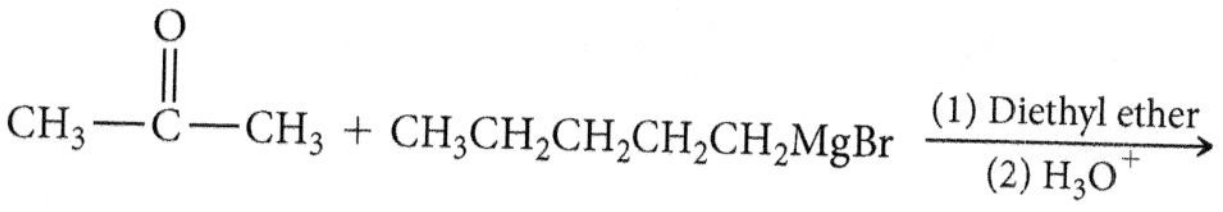

d. $C_6H_6 + HNO_3 \xrightarrow{H_2SO_4}$

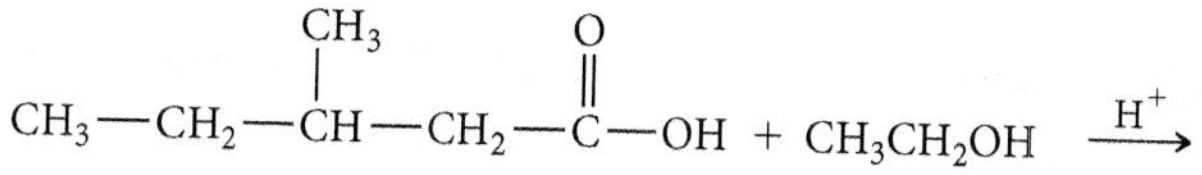

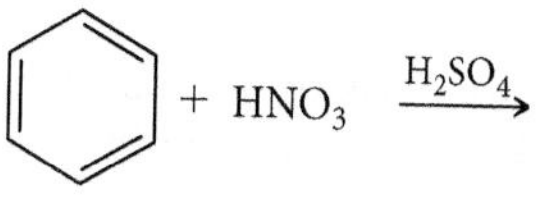

99. What are the products of the following reactions?

a. $CH_3-CH_2-CH(CH_3)-C(=O)OH \xrightarrow{SOCl_2}$

b. 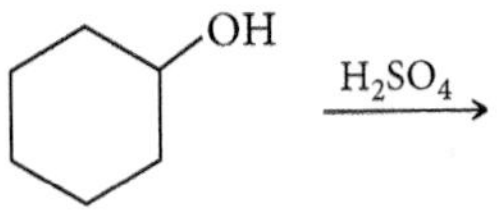 Cyclohexanol $\xrightarrow{H_2SO_4}$

c. 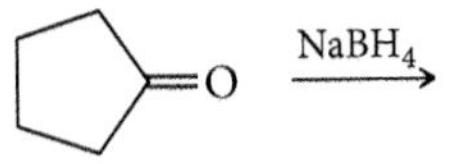 Cyclopentanone $\xrightarrow{NaBH_4}$

d. $H_3C-C(=O)-O-CH_2CH_3 \xrightarrow{NaNH_2}$

100. What are the products of each step in the following reaction sequences?

a. 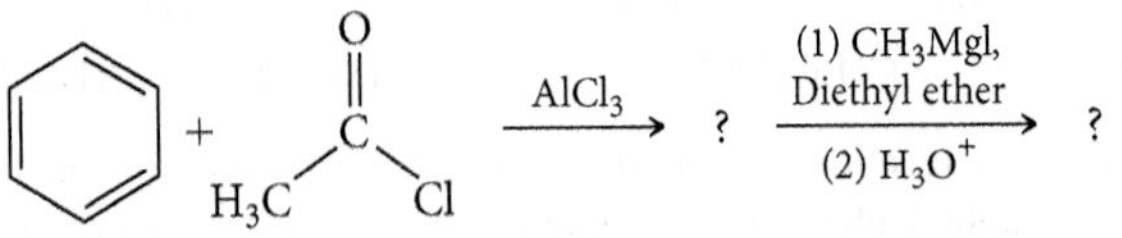 Benzene + $H_3C-C(=O)-Cl \xrightarrow{AlCl_3}$? $\xrightarrow[(2)\ H_3O^+]{(1)\ CH_3MgI,\ \text{Diethyl ether}}$?

b. $CH_3-CH_2-CH(I)-CH_2-CH_3 \xrightarrow{H_2O}$? $\xrightarrow{K_2Cr_2O_7,\ H_2SO_4}$?

101. What are the products of each step in the following reaction sequences?

a. 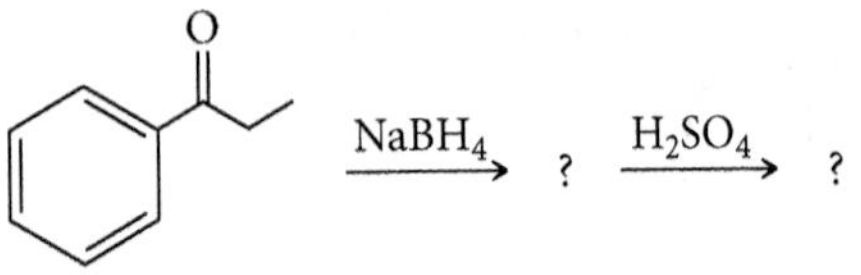 $C_6H_5-C(=O)-CH_2CH_3 \xrightarrow{NaBH_4}$? $\xrightarrow{H_2SO_4}$?

b. $CH_3-CH_2-C(=O)OH \xrightarrow{NaOH}$? $\xrightarrow{H_3C-C(=O)-Cl}$?

102. The compound 2-hydroxybenzoic acid can be converted into methyl salicylate (oil of wintergreen) or acetylsalicylic acid (aspirin), each in a single step. What reagents and other reactants are needed for these conversions?

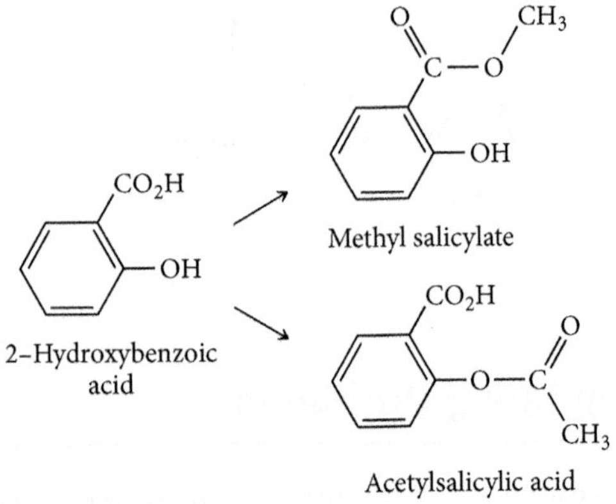

2-Hydroxybenzoic acid → Methyl salicylate ($C_6H_4(OH)-C(=O)-O-CH_3$)

2-Hydroxybenzoic acid → Acetylsalicylic acid ($C_6H_4(CO_2H)-O-C(=O)-CH_3$)

103. What is the minimum amount of hydrogen gas, in grams, required to completely hydrogenate 15.5 kg of but-2-ene?

104. How many kilograms of CO_2 are produced by the complete combustion of 3.8 kg of octane?

105. Acetyl chloride can be prepared by reacting acetic acid with either thionyl chloride, $SOCl_2$, or oxalyl chloride, $(COCl)_2$. In order to make 1.2 kg of acetyl chloride,

a. What is the minimum amount, in kg, of acetic acid required?

b. If both reactions are used to make acetyl chloride, what are the amounts, in kg, of each by-product generated by each reaction?

106. Vinyl acetate can be polymerized to give poly(vinyl acetate), which is used in glues. This polymer can be hydrolyzed with sodium hydroxide in water to give poly(vinyl alcohol). Draw the repeating units of poly(vinyl acetate) and poly(vinyl alcohol).

$CH_3-C(=O)-O-CH=CH_2$ Vinyl acetate

$HO-CH=CH_2$ Vinyl alcohol

Challenge Problems

107. Write a mechanism that explains the mixture of products in this reaction:

$$(CH_3)_2C(Cl)-CH=CH_2 \xrightarrow[Na_2CO_3]{H_2O} (CH_3)_2C(OH)-CH=CH_2 + (CH_3)_2C=CHCH_2OH$$

85% 15%

108. Determine the one or two steps it would take to get from the starting material to the product using the reactions found in this chapter.

a. 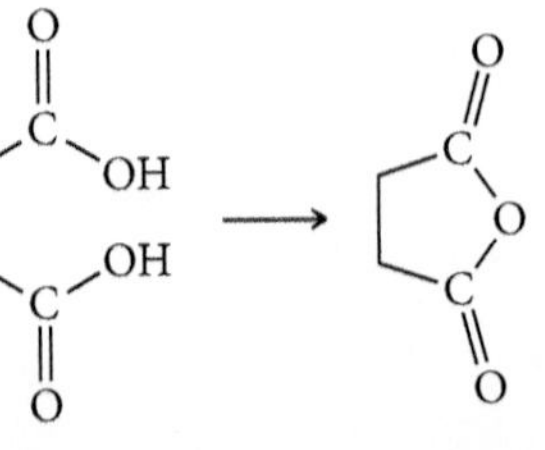 $HO-C(=O)-CH_2-CH_2-C(=O)-OH \longrightarrow$ cyclic anhydride (five-membered ring: $C(=O)-O-C(=O)$)

b. $CH_3-CH(CH_2-CH_3)-CH_2-CH(CH_2-OH)-CH_3 \longrightarrow CH_3-CH(CH_2-CH_3)-CH_2-C(=CH_2)-CH_3$

c. $CH_3-CH_2-C(CH_3)=CH_2 \longrightarrow CH_3-CH_2-C(Br)(CH_3)-CH_3$

109. Given the following synthesis of ethyl 3-methylbutanoate, fill in the missing intermediates or reactants.

$$CH_3{-}\underset{\displaystyle CH_3}{\underset{|}{CH}}{-}CH_2{-}CH_2{-}OH \xrightarrow{\text{a.}} \text{b.} \xrightarrow{\text{c.}} CH_3{-}\underset{\displaystyle CH_3}{\underset{|}{CH}}{-}CH_2{-}\overset{\displaystyle O}{\overset{\|}{C}}{-}O{-}CH_2{-}CH_3$$

110. The drug captopril is synthesized according to the following reaction sequence:

(1) 3-chloro-2-methylproprionyl chloride + L-proline →

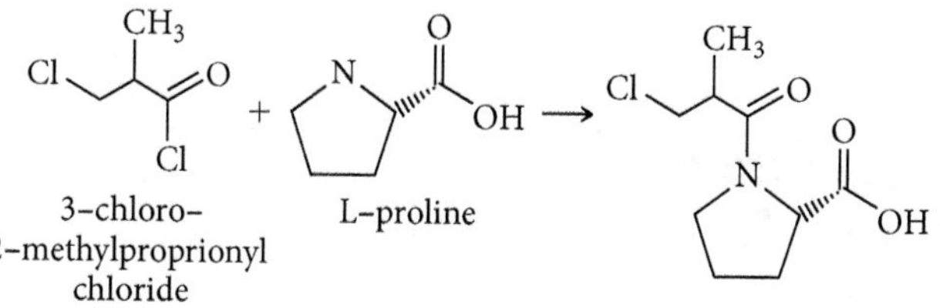

(2) $\xrightarrow{NH_4SH}$ Captopril

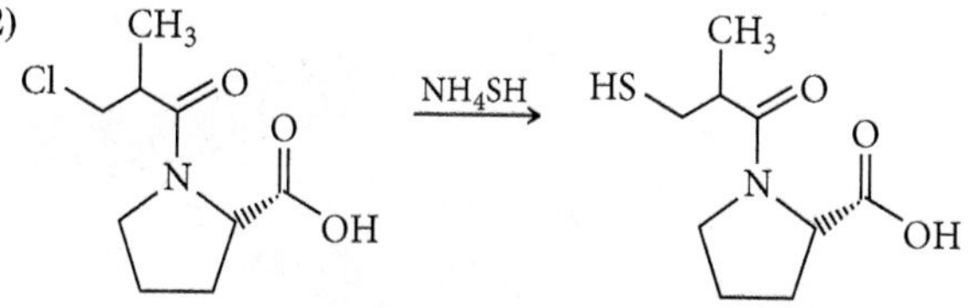

a. Write a mechanism for each of the two steps.
b. One of the starting materials, 3-chloro-2-methylproprionyl chloride, has two enantiomers. Draw the two enantiomers.
c. A racemic mixture of 3-chloro-2-methylproprionyl chloride is typically used for reaction (1). Draw the two stereoisomers produced by reaction (1) when racemic 3-chloro-2-methylproprionyl chloride is used.
d. Enantiomers cannot be separated using physical or chemical properties. Show that the two products of reaction (1) are not enantiomers, meaning that they can be separated.

111. Polyanhydrides are polymers with repeating carboxylic anhydride groups. Two reactions for making polyanhydrides are shown below. What are the products and by-products of each reaction? Draw each polymer in polymer notation.

a. $$n\ HO{-}\overset{\displaystyle O}{\overset{\|}{C}}{-}R{-}\overset{\displaystyle O}{\overset{\|}{C}}{-}OH \xrightarrow{(CH_3CO)_2O}$$

b. $$n\ HO{-}\overset{\displaystyle O}{\overset{\|}{C}}{-}R{-}\overset{\displaystyle O}{\overset{\|}{C}}{-}OH + n\ Cl{-}\overset{\displaystyle O}{\overset{\|}{C}}{-}R'{-}\overset{\displaystyle O}{\overset{\|}{C}}{-}Cl \xrightarrow{\text{Base}}$$

112. An unknown hydrocarbon has the formula C_8H_{14}. There are four peaks in the ^{13}C NMR spectrum of the hydrocarbon. When the unknown hydrocarbon is treated with H_2 over a palladium catalyst, a product with the formula C_8H_{16} is formed. The C_8H_{16} product has a single peak in the ^{13}C NMR spectrum. When the unknown hydrocarbon is treated with HBr, only one product with the formula $C_8H_{15}Br$ is formed. The $C_8H_{15}Br$ product has five distinct peaks in the ^{13}C NMR spectrum. Draw the structure of the unknown compound and the products of each reaction.

Conceptual Problems

113. In the following reaction, an excess of ammonia is usually added. Why is this necessary?

$$CH_3Cl + NH_3 \longrightarrow CH_3NH_2 + HCl$$

114. Pick the more oxidized structure from each pair:

a. $CH_3{-}\overset{O}{\overset{\|}{C}}H$ or $CH_3{-}CH_2{-}OH$

b. $CH_3{-}CH_2{-}OH$ or $CH_3{-}CH_3$

c. $CH_3{-}CH_2{-}\overset{O}{\overset{\|}{C}}H$ or $CH_3{-}CH_2{-}\overset{O}{\overset{\|}{C}}{-}OH$

115. The strong base butyl lithium, $CH_3CH_2CH_2CH_2^-Li^+$, is prepared according to the reaction below. What class of reaction, covered in this chapter, is this?

$$CH_3CH_2CH_2CH_2Br + 2\,Li \longrightarrow CH_3CH_2CH_2CH_2^-Li^+ + LiBr$$

116. Use inductive and resonance effects to explain the relative pK_a values of propanone and ethane, shown below.

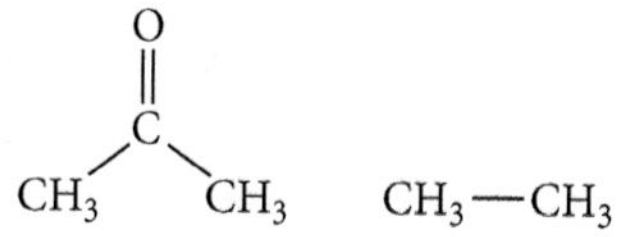

Propanone ($CH_3{-}\overset{O}{\overset{\|}{C}}{-}CH_3$) $pK_a = 20$

Ethane ($CH_3{-}CH_3$) $pK_a = 51$

22 Biochemistry

We've discovered the secret of life.

—Francis H. C. Crick (1916–2004)

The above image depicts a timeline marking the important events in the treatment of diabetes.

IN CHAPTERS 20 AND 21, we examined organic chemistry and learned about the different types of organic compounds and their structures and chemistry. In this chapter, we turn to biochemical compounds, those organic compounds important in living organisms. Biochemistry—the area of study at the interface between chemistry and biology that strives to understand living organisms at the molecular level—exploded in the second half of the twentieth century. That explosion began with the discovery of the structure of DNA in 1953 by James D. Watson and Francis H. C. Crick and continues to this day, including the 2003 completion of the Human Genome Project, which succeeded in mapping the 3 billion base pairs within the DNA of humans. The benefits of biochemistry to humankind are numerous, ranging from a better understanding of illnesses and better drugs to cure them to a better understanding of ourselves and our origins.

22.1 Diabetes and the Synthesis of Human Insulin

Diabetes is a serious disease afflicting approximately one out of every 20 people in Canada. Today, it is a chronic but generally manageable ailment. At the beginning of the twentieth century, however, it was often fatal. The most dangerous form of this condition, type 1 diabetes, develops when the pancreas does not make enough *insulin*, a protein that promotes the absorption of glucose from the blood into cells, where glucose is used for energy. Consequently, diabetics have high blood-sugar levels that can lead to a number of complications, including heart disease, blindness, and kidney failure. Before 1922, diabetics could control their blood-sugar levels only through diet, but this was often not enough to overcome the disease.

Important advances throughout the twentieth century dramatically changed the prognosis for diabetics. The initial breakthrough came in 1922, when Frederick Banting and Charles Best at the University of Toronto first injected insulin from animal sources into a hospitalized diabetic. The insulin worked, resulting in a nearly complete recovery for the patient. Within a year, insulin harvested from the pancreases of slaughtered pigs became widely available, and, for many patients, diabetes became a long-term, manageable disease. However, insulin taken from pigs and cattle is not identical to human insulin, and some patients do not tolerate the animal insulin as well as others.

▲ Frederick Banting (right) and his research assistant Charles Best, who isolated insulin from the pancreases of dogs. Banting shared the 1923 Nobel Prize in physiology or medicine with University of Toronto Professor J. J. R. Macleod, who provided laboratory space and resources for Banting's experiments. Banting shared his prize money with Best.

In 1955, Frederick Sanger discovered the detailed chemical structure of human insulin. As we will see later in this chapter, insulin is a *protein*, a biological molecule composed of repeating units called amino acids (of which there are 20 different types in humans). Sanger was able to determine the specific sequence of amino acids in human insulin, work for which he received the 1958 Nobel Prize in chemistry. Knowing the amino acid sequence allowed researchers to synthesize human insulin in the laboratory by 1963. Unfortunately, they could not make sufficient amounts to meet the needs of diabetics.

The growing field of biotechnology, however, allowed a fledgling company called Genentech to synthesize human insulin on a large scale by the early 1980s. Researchers at Genentech were able to insert the human *gene* for insulin—the blueprint that determines how insulin is synthesized in humans—into the DNA of bacterial cells. When the bacteria reproduced in culture, they made copies of the inserted human insulin gene and passed it on to their offspring. Furthermore, as the growing bacterial culture synthesized the bacterial proteins that they needed to grow and survive, they also synthesized human insulin. In other words, researchers at Genentech were able to get bacteria to produce human insulin for them! The ability to synthesize human insulin in this way revolutionized the treatment of diabetes, resulting in better health and extended lives for hundreds of millions of people who suffer from this disease.

The study of the chemistry occurring in living organisms is **biochemistry**, the topic of this chapter. Many biologically important molecules are very large and complex—they are *macromolecules*. However, understanding their structures is not as difficult as you might imagine, because most of them consist of much smaller, simpler components linked together into long chains (polymers). We divide our study of biochemistry along the lines of the major chemical components of cells: lipids, carbohydrates, proteins, and nucleic acids.

22.2 Lipids

Lipids are the chemical components of the cell that are insoluble in water but soluble in nonpolar solvents. Fatty acids, fats, oils, phospholipids, glycolipids, and steroids are all lipids. Their insolubility in water makes it possible for lipids to function as the structural components of cell membranes, which separate the aqueous interior of the cell from its aqueous environment in the body. Lipids also play a role in long-term energy storage and insulation.

Fatty Acids

One type of lipid is the **fatty acid**, a carboxylic acid (see Section 20.4) with a long hydrocarbon tail. The general structure for a fatty acid is

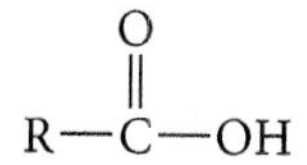

Fatty acid general structure

where R represents a hydrocarbon chain containing 3 to 19 carbon atoms. Fatty acids differ only in their R group.

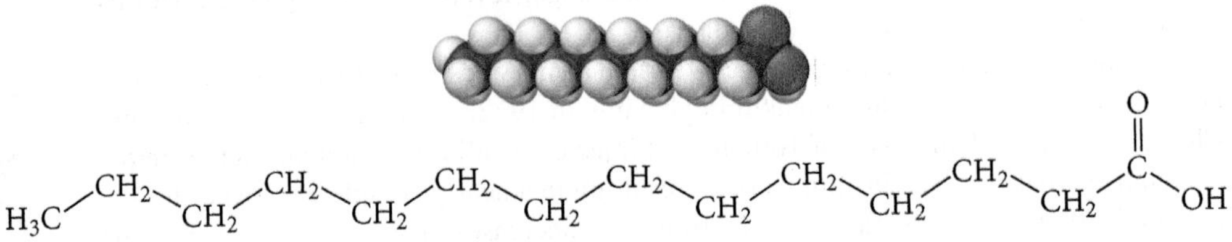

Myristic acid

Myristic acid, which occurs in butterfat and in coconut oil, has the R group $CH_3(CH_2)_{12}$. Myristic acid is a *saturated* fatty acid: its carbon chain has no double bonds. Other fatty acids—called *monounsaturated* or *polyunsaturated* fatty acids—have one or more double bonds in their carbon chains. For example, oleic acid—found in olive oil, peanut oil, and human fat—is a monounsaturated fatty acid.

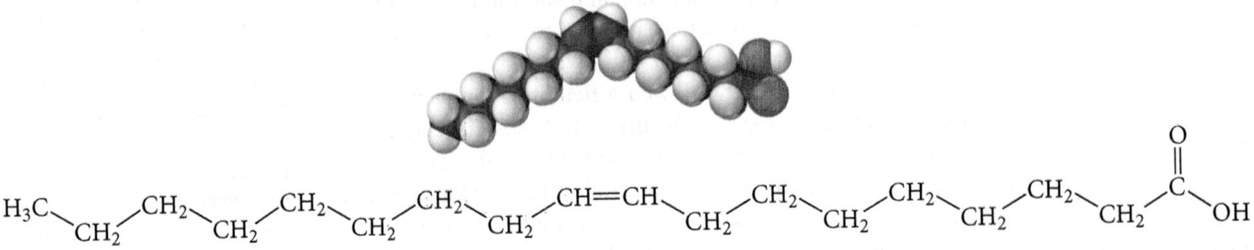

Oleic acid

The long hydrocarbon tails of fatty acids make them insoluble in water. Table 22.1 lists several different fatty acids, some common sources for each, and their melting points. Notice that the melting points of the fatty acids *increase* as their carbon chain lengths increase. The longer the chains, the greater the dispersion forces between adjacent molecules in the solid state, and the higher the melting point. Notice also that the melting points *decrease* with the presence of double bonds. For example, stearic acid and oleic acid have the same number of carbon atoms, but stearic acid melts at 70 °C and oleic acid

Dispersion forces were discussed in Section 11.3.

TABLE 22.1 Fatty Acids

Saturated Fatty Acids

Name	Number of Carbons	mp (°C)	Structure	Source(s)
Butyric acid	4	−7.9	$CH_3CH_2CH_2COOH$	Milk fat
Caproic acid	10	31	$CH_3(CH_2)_8COOH$	Milk fat, whale oil
Myristic acid	14	59	$CH_3(CH_2)_{12}COOH$	Butterfat, coconut oil
Palmitic acid	16	64	$CH_3(CH_2)_{14}COOH$	Beef fat, butterfat
Stearic acid	18	70	$CH_3(CH_2)_{16}COOH$	Beef fat, butterfat

Unsaturated Fatty Acids

Name	Number of Carbons	Number of Double Bonds	mp (°C)	Structure	Source(s)
Oleic acid	18	1	4	$CH_3(CH_2)_7CH{=}CH(CH_2)_7COOH$	Olive oil, peanut oil
Linoleic acid	18	2	−5	$CH_3(CH_2)_4(CH{=}CHCH_2)_2(CH_2)_6COOH$	Linseed oil, corn oil
Linolenic acid	18	3	−11	$CH_3CH_2(CH{=}CHCH_2)_3(CH_2)_6COOH$	Linseed oil, corn oil

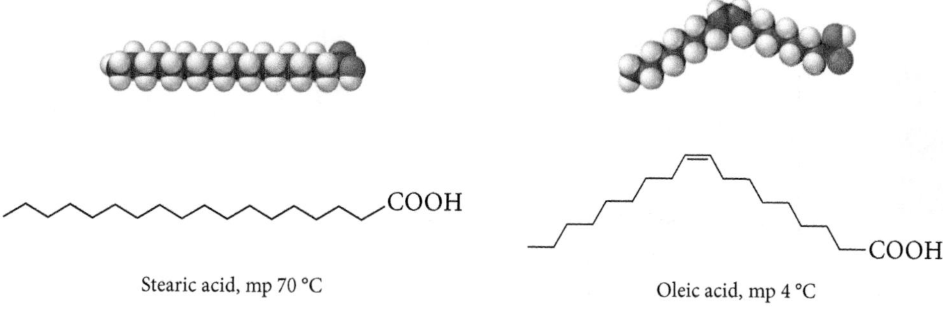

◀ FIGURE 22.1 The Effect of Unsaturation A double bond results in a bend in the carbon chain of a fatty acid or fat that makes it more difficult for neighbouring molecules to interact over the entire length of the carbon chain, thus lowering the melting point.

melts at 4 °C. The double bond puts a "kink" in the carbon chain that makes it more difficult for neighbouring molecules to interact over the entire length of the chain (Figure 22.1 ▲), thus lowering the melting point.

Fats and Oils

Fats and oils are **triglycerides**, triesters composed of glycerol with three fatty acids attached. Triglycerides form when a glycerol molecule reacts with three fatty acids:

The general structure of esters was discussed in Section 20.4.

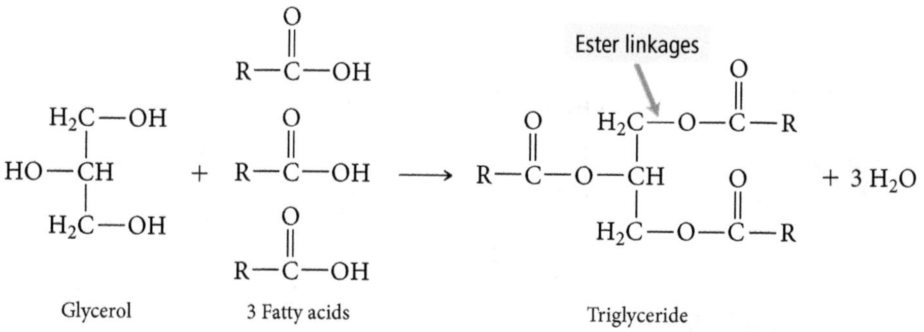

$$\underset{\text{Glycerol}}{H_2C(OH)-CH(OH)-H_2C(OH)} + \underset{\text{3 Fatty acids}}{3\ R-C(=O)-OH} \longrightarrow \underset{\text{Triglyceride}}{H_2C(-O-C(=O)-R)-CH(-O-C(=O)-R)-H_2C(-O-C(=O)-R)} + 3\,H_2O$$

Ester linkages

The bonds that join the glycerol to the fatty acids are called **ester linkages**. The reaction between glycerol and fatty acids (i.e., an alcohol and a carboxylic acid) is an esterification reaction (see Section 21.8). For example, tristearin—the main component of beef fat—forms from the reaction of glycerol and three stearic acid molecules (Figure 22.2 ▼). If the fatty acids in a triglyceride are saturated, the triglyceride is a **saturated fat** and tends to be

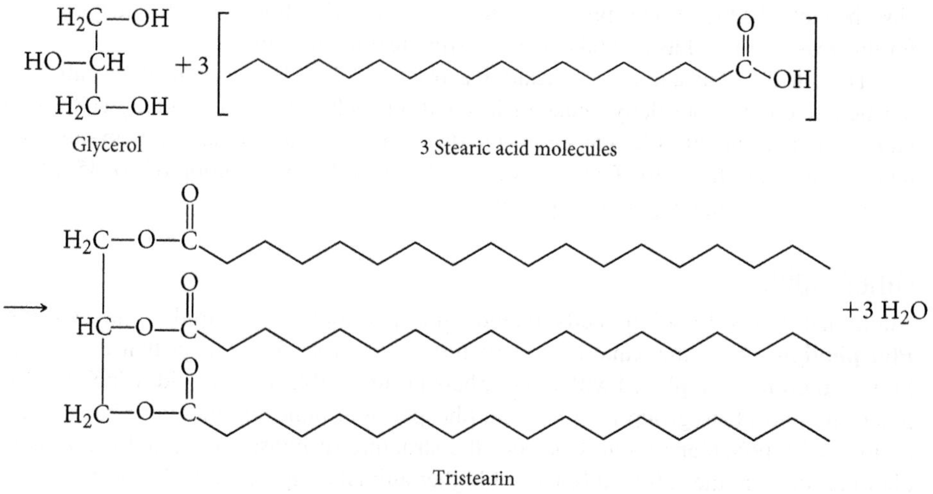

$$\underset{\text{Glycerol}}{H_2C(OH)-CH(OH)-H_2C(OH)} + 3\left[\underset{\text{3 Stearic acid molecules}}{C_{17}H_{35}-C(=O)-OH}\right] \longrightarrow \underset{\text{Tristearin}}{H_2C(-O-C(=O)C_{17}H_{35})-HC(-O-C(=O)C_{17}H_{35})-H_2C(-O-C(=O)C_{17}H_{35})} + 3\,H_2O$$

◀ FIGURE 22.2 The Formation of Tristearin The reaction between glycerol and stearic acid forms tristearin.

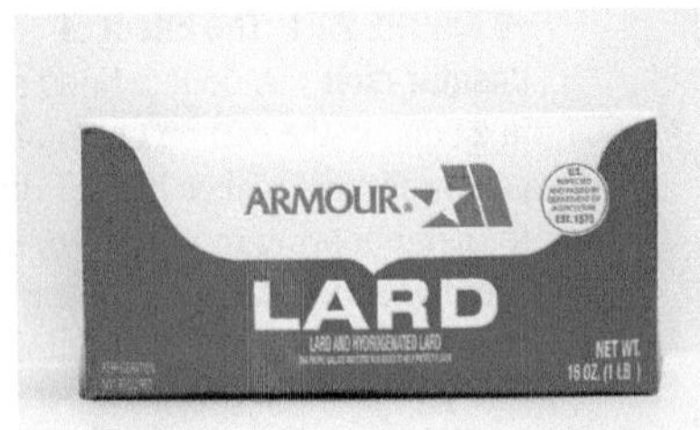

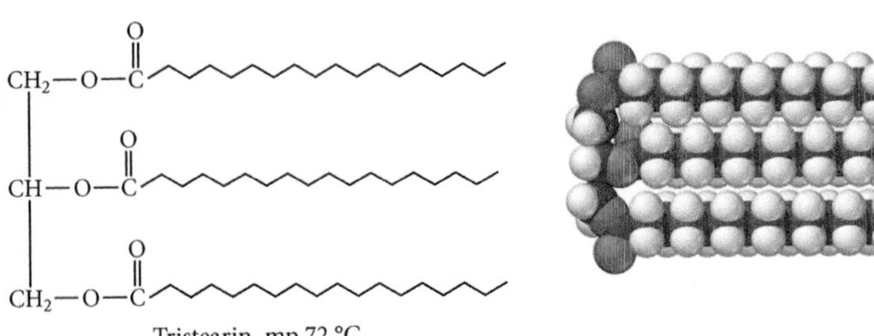

Tristearin, mp 72 °C

▲ Tristearin is a triglyceride found in lard—it is a saturated fat.

solid at room temperature. Triglycerides from warm-blooded animals (for example, lard) are generally saturated.

If the fatty acids in a triglyceride are unsaturated, the triglyceride is called an **unsaturated fat**, or an oil, and tends to be liquid at room temperature. Triglycerides from plants (olive oil, corn oil, canola oil, etc.) or from cold-blooded animals (fish oil) are generally unsaturated.

▶ Triolein is a triglyceride found in olive oil—it is a monounsaturated fat.

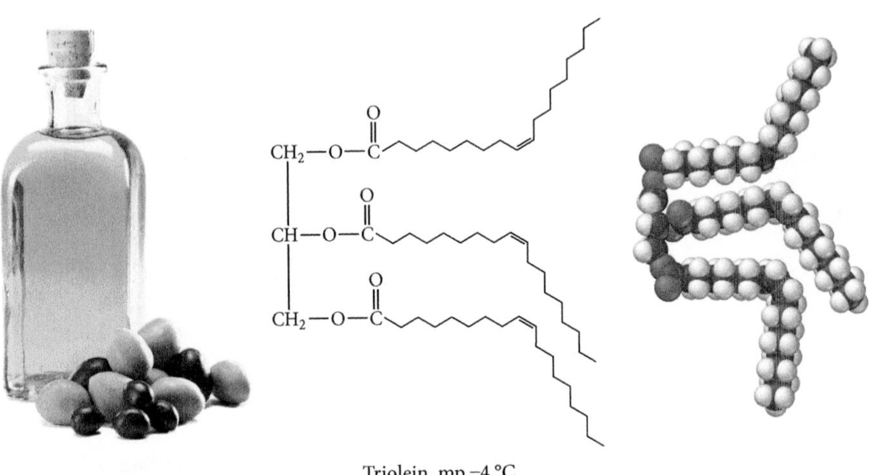

Triolein, mp −4 °C

Most of the fats and oils in our diet are triglycerides. During digestion, triglycerides are broken down into fatty acids, glycerol, monoglycerides, and diglycerides. These products pass through the intestinal wall and reassemble into triglycerides before they are absorbed into the blood. This process is slower than the digestion of other food types, and for this reason eating fats and oils gives a lasting feeling of fullness.

The effect of fats and oils on health has been widely debated. Some diets call for a drastic reduction of our daily intake of fats and oils, whereas others actually call for an *increase* in fats and oils. Canada's Food Guide recommends a diet that is low in saturated fats. On the other hand, the Guide recommends the daily consumption of 30–45 mL of unsaturated fat (e.g., margarine, vegetable oils).

Other Lipids

Additional lipids found in cells include phospholipids, glycolipids, and steroids. **Phospholipids** have the same basic structure as triglycerides, except that one of the fatty acid groups is replaced with a phosphate group. Unlike a fatty acid, which is nonpolar, the phosphate group is polar. The phospholipid molecule therefore has a polar region and a nonpolar region. Consider the structure of phosphatidylcholine, a phospholipid found in the cell membranes of higher animals (Figure 22.4 ▶). The polar part of the molecule is *hydrophilic* (has a strong affinity for water) while the nonpolar part is

CHEMISTRY AND MEDICINE Dietary Fat: The Good, the Bad, and the Ugly

Today, the debate about fat focuses as much on the *kind* of fats that should be included in a healthy diet as on their quantity. Nutrition experts generally agree that unsaturated fats from plants and fish are better for you than the saturated fats from warm-blooded animals. However, unsaturated fats are liquids at room temperature and do not have the creamy, melt-in-your-mouth feel of saturated fats (try making chocolate chip cookies with vegetable oil). Consequently, food producers in the mid-twentieth century developed ways of using hydrogenation reactions (see Section 21.6) to convert polyunsaturated vegetable oil into a saturated fat (known as vegetable shortening) that was added to many of our processed foods. The hydrogenated vegetable shortening, even though it was highly saturated, was originally believed to be better for our health than lard or butter because it comes from plant sources and does not contain cholesterol.

Nutrition Facts
Per 2 crackers (50 g)

Amount	% Daily Value
Calories 210	
Fat 6 g	9 %
Saturated 1.5 g + Trans 0 g	8 %
Cholesterol 15 mg	
Sodium 170 mg	7 %
Carbohydrate 34 g	11 %
Fibre 1 g	4 %
Sugars 12 g	
Sorbitol 2 g	
Protein 3 g	

Vitamin A	0 %	Vitamin C	0 %
Calcium	0 %	Iron	6 %

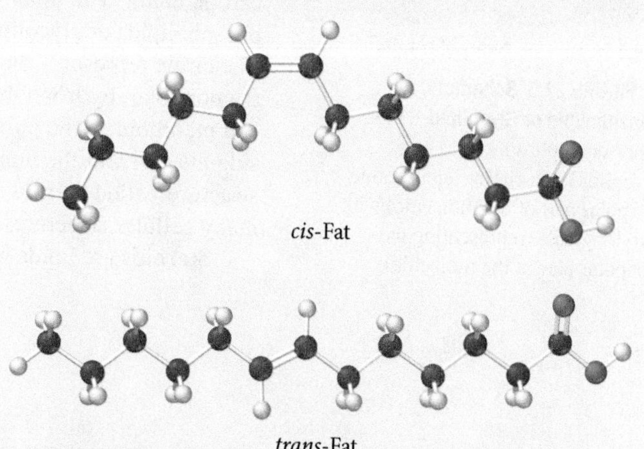

▲ **FIGURE 22.3 *Cis* and *Trans* Fats** The hydrogenation process introduces some *trans* double bonds into fats. The double bonds in naturally occurring oils are normally *cis*.

Later research, however, raised serious concerns about saturated fats in general (regardless of their source) and in particular about the presence of *trans* fats in hydrogenated vegetable shortening. The hydrogenation process converts *cis* double bonds (see Section 21.6) between carbon atoms in oils into single bonds. However, the catalyst and the temperatures employed by manufacturers also trigger small amounts of the reverse reaction, the conversion of single bonds into double bonds. The double bonds that form in this way can be either the naturally occurring *cis* double bond or an unnatural *trans* double bond (Figure 22.3 ▲). So hydrogenated vegetable oil not only has fewer double bonds overall, but some of the double bonds are *trans* (which is why the fats are called "trans fats"). Consumption of too much trans fat, even more than consumption of too much saturated fat, raises the risk of coronary artery disease. Thus *trans* fat has become the target of many health scientists and consumer groups, including Health Canada.

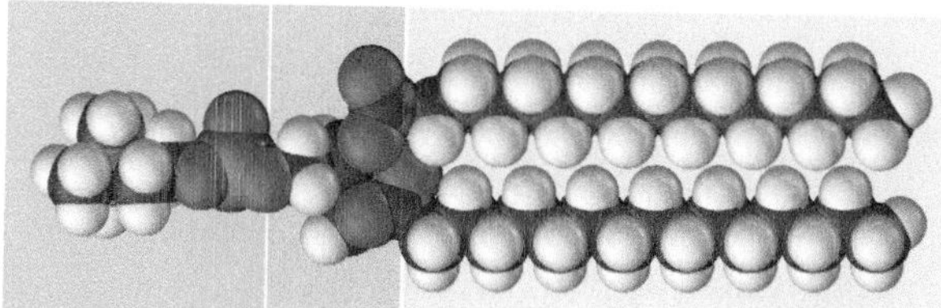

Polar head | Glycerol | Nonpolar tail
Choline | Phosphate

$H_3C-\overset{+}{N}(CH_3)_2-CH_2-CH_2-O-P(=O)(O^-)-O-CH_2-CH(-O-C(=O)-CH_2\text{∼∼∼})-CH_2-O-C(=O)-CH_2\text{∼∼∼}$

◀ **FIGURE 22.4 Phosphatidylcholine** Phosphatidylcholine is a phospholipid. The structure is similar to a triglyceride except that one of the fatty acid groups is replaced with a phosphate group.

▲ **FIGURE 22.5 Schematic for Phospholipid or Glycolipid** We represent a phospholipid or a glycolipid as a circle (representing the polar part of the molecule) with two long tails (representing the nonpolar part of the molecule).

hydrophobic (is repelled by water). **Glycolipids** have similar structures and properties. The nonpolar section of a glycolipid is composed of a fatty acid chain and a hydrocarbon chain. The polar section is a sugar molecule such as glucose. We often portray phospholipids or glycolipids schematically as a circle with two long tails (Figure 22.5 ◄). The circle represents the polar, hydrophilic part of the molecule and the tails represent the nonpolar, hydrophobic parts. Phospholipids and glycolipids are key components of cell membranes; the polar parts interact with the aqueous environments inside and outside the cell and the nonpolar parts interact with each other, forming a double-layered structure called a **lipid bilayer** (Figure 22.6 ▼). Lipid bilayers encapsulate cells and many cellular structures.

Steroids are lipids with a four-ring structure:

Cholesterol, testosterone, and β-estradiol are common steriods:

Cholesterol

Testosterone

β-Estradiol

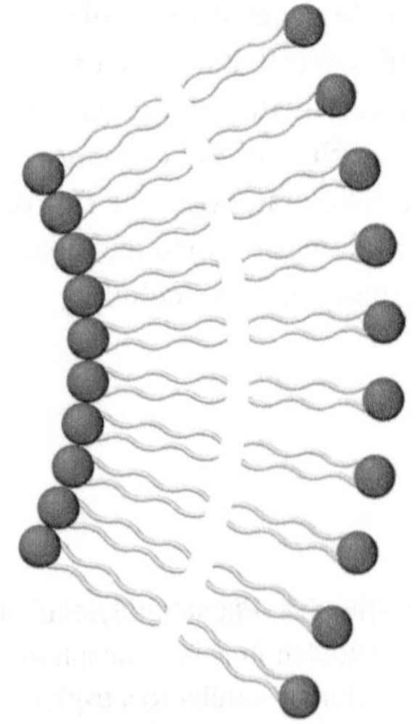

▲ **FIGURE 22.6 Lipid Bilayer** Lipid bilayers are composed of phospholipids or glycolipids arranged in a structure that encapsulates cells and many cellular structures.

Although cholesterol has a bad reputation, it serves many important functions in the body. Like phospholipids and glycolipids, cholesterol is part of cell membranes. Cholesterol also serves as a starting material (or precursor) for the body's synthesis of other steroids such as testosterone, a principal male hormone, and β-estradiol, a principal female hormone.

22.3 Carbohydrates

Carbohydrates are responsible for short-term storage of energy in living organisms, and they make up the main structural components of plants. Carbohydrates often have the general formula $(CH_2O)_n$. Structurally, we identify **carbohydrates** as polyhydroxy aldehydes or ketones. For example, glucose, with the formula $C_6H_{12}O_6$, has the following structure:

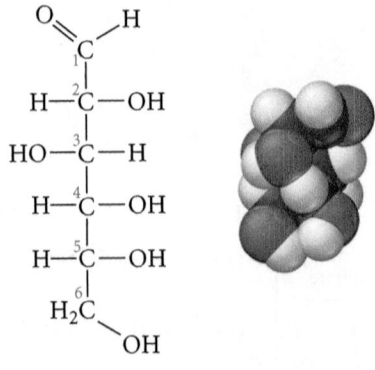

Glucose

Glucose is a six-carbon aldehyde (that is, it contains the —CHO group) with —OH groups on five of the six carbon atoms. The many —OH groups make glucose soluble in water (and therefore, in blood), which is crucial to glucose's role as the primary fuel of cells. Glucose is easily transported in the bloodstream and is soluble within the aqueous interior of a cell. Carbohydrates can be broadly classified as simple carbohydrates (or simple sugars) and complex carbohydrates.

Simple Carbohydrates: Monosaccharides and Disaccharides

Monosaccharides—meaning "one sugar"—are the simplest carbohydrates. Monosaccharides contain between three and eight carbon atoms and have only one aldehyde or ketone functional group. The general names for monosaccharides have a prefix that indicates the number of carbon atoms, followed by the suffix *-ose*. The most common carbohydrates in living organisms are pentoses and hexoses.

3-carbon sugar: triose
4-carbon sugar: tetrose
5-carbon sugar: pentose
6-carbon sugar: hexose
7-carbon sugar: heptose
8-carbon sugar: octose

Glucose, whose structure we saw previously, is an example of a **hexose**, a six-carbon sugar. Glucose is also an example of an **aldose**, a sugar with an aldehyde group. Often, these two ways of designating sugars are combined, so we say that glucose is an *aldohexose* (*aldo-* indicates that it is an aldehyde; *-hex-* indicates that it has six carbon atoms; and *-ose* indicates that it is a carbohydrate).

Another common carbohydrate is fructose, a polyhydroxy *ketone* with the following structure:

As we learned in Section 20.4, aldehydes have the general structure RCHO, and ketones have the general structure RCOR.

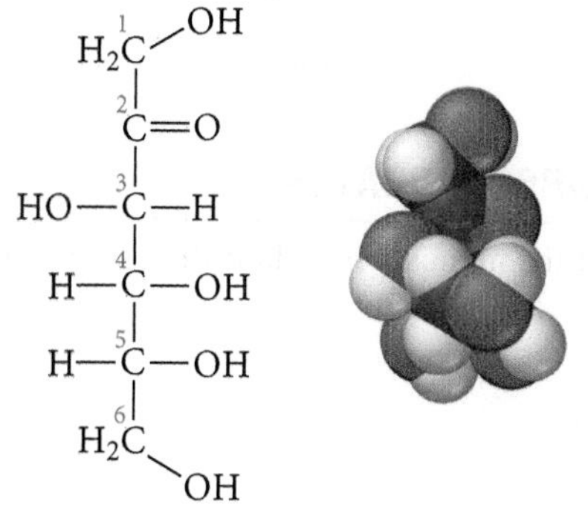

$$\begin{array}{c} {}^{1}H_2C{-}OH \\ | \\ {}^{2}C{=}O \\ | \\ HO{-}{}^{3}C{-}H \\ | \\ H{-}{}^{4}C{-}OH \\ | \\ H{-}{}^{5}C{-}OH \\ | \\ {}^{6}H_2C{-}OH \end{array}$$

Fructose

Glucose and fructose are constitutional (or structural) isomers—they both have the same formula ($C_6H_{12}O_6$), but they have different structures. Fructose is a **ketose**, a sugar that is a ketone. Since fructose has six carbon atoms, it is a *ketohexose*. Fructose, often called fruit sugar, is in many fruits and vegetables and is a major component of honey.

Monosaccharides contain one or more chirality centres. The simplest aldose, glyceraldehyde, has a single chirality centre at carbon 2. Thus, there are two stereoisomers of glyceraldehyde:

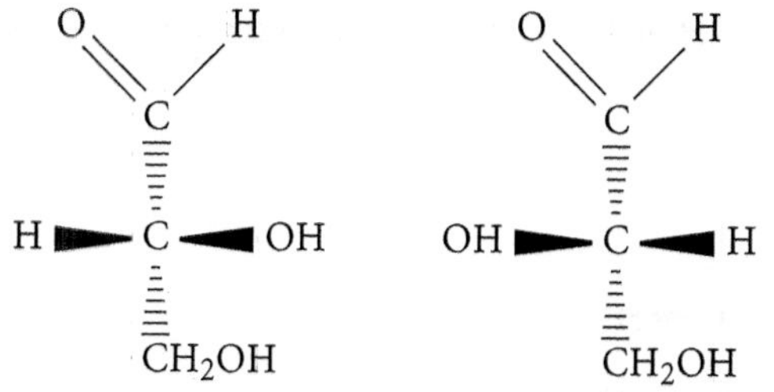

$$\begin{array}{c} O{=}C{-}H \\ | \\ H \blacktriangleright C \blacktriangleleft OH \\ | \\ CH_2OH \end{array} \qquad \begin{array}{c} O{=}C{-}H \\ | \\ OH \blacktriangleright C \blacktriangleleft H \\ | \\ CH_2OH \end{array}$$

D-Glyceraldehyde L-Glyceraldehyde

In biochemistry, absolute configurations are usually labelled as D or L. These labels go back to Emil Fischer, who arbitrarily assigned absolute configurations to dextrorotatory and laevorotatory isomers of monosaccharides in 1891. Fischer had no way of actually knowing the absolute configurations because the experimental techniques that are used for this were not available at the time. Fischer had a 50% chance of assigning the correct absolute configuration and he guessed correctly. The D and L configurations of monosaccharides refer to the absolute configuration of the chirality centre that is farthest from the aldehyde or ketone group, and respectively correspond to *R* and *S* absolute configurations. So, in D-glyceraldehyde, the absolute configuration at carbon 2 is *R*. In D-glucose, the farthest chirality centre is at carbon 5, and the absolute configuration is also *R*.

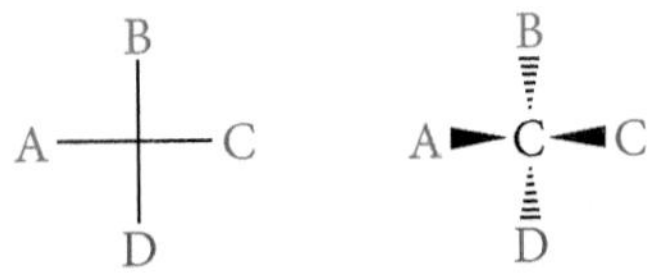

B, A, C, D — Fischer projection; B, A, C, D — Absolute configuration

▲ **FIGURE 22.7** The Fischer projection of a carbon atom with four different substituents (letters A, B, C, and D) and the corresponding absolute configuration.

Absolute configurations of monosaccharides can be drawn using **Fischer projections**, which are a type of skeleton formula in which horizontal bonds are projected toward the viewer, and vertical bonds are projected away from the viewer (Figure 22.7 ◀). Typically, these are drawn so that the aldehyde or ketone group is at the top. The Fischer projection of D-glucose is:

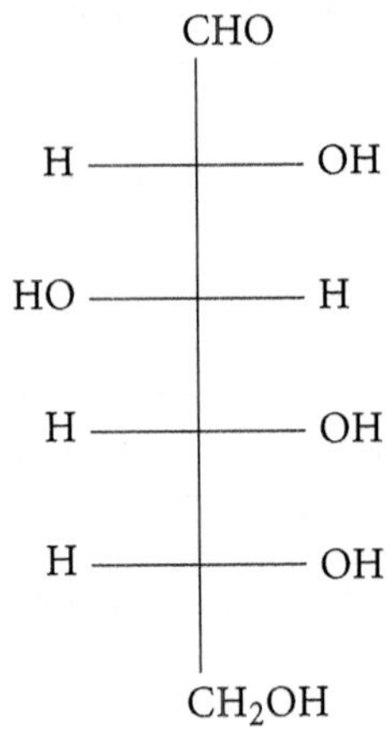

CHO
H — OH
HO — H
H — OH
H — OH
CH_2OH

D-Glucose

EXAMPLE 22.1 ABSOLUTE CONFIGURATIONS OF CARBOHYDRATES

Assign absolute configurations (*R*, *S*) to the chiral carbon atoms of the monosaccharide D-threose (an aldotetrose), given the Fischer projection.

1 CHO
HO —2— H
H —3— OH
4 CH_2OH

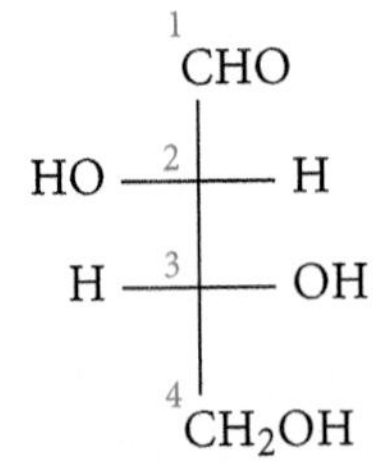

D-Threose

SOLUTION

Carbon atoms 2 and 3 are chiral because they have four different substituents. The first step is to interpret the Fischer projection. If we look at carbon atom 2, the horizontal bonds (to —H and —OH) are projected out toward the viewer, while the vertical bonds are projected away, as shown here.

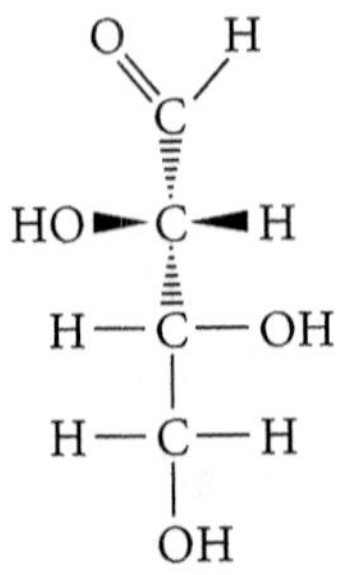

O=C—H
HO—C—H
H—C—OH
H—C—H
OH

The substituents around carbon 2 are prioritized according to the Cahn–Ingold–Prelog rules covered in Section 20.7. The hydroxide is first priority, followed by the aldehyde group, then the —CH(OH)CH_2OH unit, and the fourth priority is the hydrogen atom. When looking through the C—H bond, the substituents are arranged in a counterclockwise order, which is an *S* configuration (see below). In a similar manner, carbon 3 can be shown to have an *R* configuration.

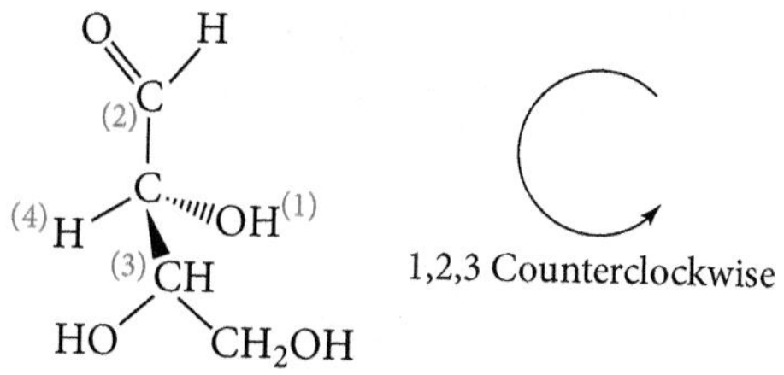

(4)H, (3)CH, HO, CH₂OH, (2)C, O, H, C, OH(1)

1,2,3 Counterclockwise

FOR PRACTICE 22.1

Assign absolute configurations (*R, S*) to the chiral carbon atoms of the monosaccharide fructose, given the Fischer projection in Example 22.1.

Most five- and six-carbon monosaccharides undergo intramolecular reactions that convert their straight carbon chain into a ring. An intramolecular reaction occurs between one of the alcohol groups and the aldehyde or ketone group of the monosaccharide. This forms a ring, and gives the corresponding hemiacetal or hemiketal (see Section 21.7). For example, in glucose, the alcohol group on C5 reacts with the aldehyde to form a ring, which is a hemiacetal (Figure 22.8 ▼).

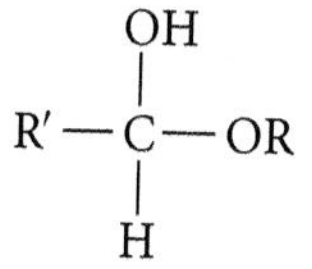

Hemiacetal

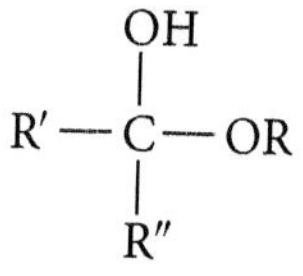

Hemiketal

In an aqueous glucose solution, the vast majority of molecules are in ring form. However, the molecules in ring form exist in equilibrium with a small fraction in the open-chain form. Other common monosaccharides, in their ring form, include fructose (discussed previously in its straight-chain form) and galactose. The ring form of fructose is a hemiketal.

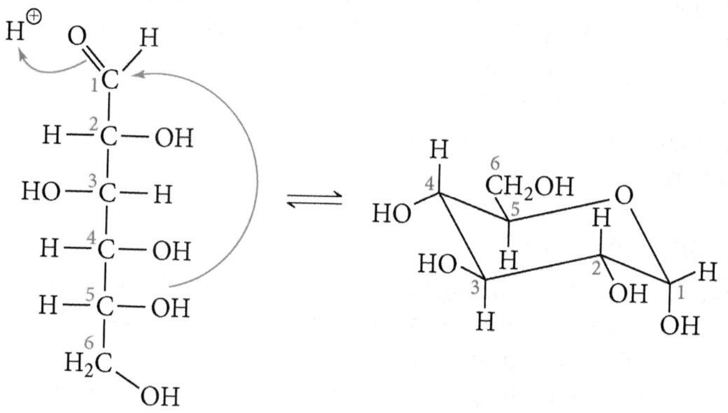

◀ **FIGURE 22.8 Intramolecular Reaction of Glucose to Form a Ring** The alcohol group on C5 in glucose reacts with the aldehyde (C1) to form a closed ring. The ring form is a hemiacetal because C1 has —H, —OH, —OR, and —R substituents. The blue arrow shows how the alcohol group on C5 reacts with C1 to form the hemiacetal. The mechanism for hemiacetal formation was discussed in section 21.7.

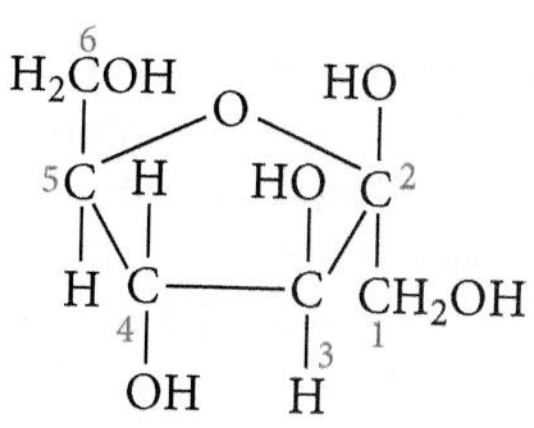

Fructose

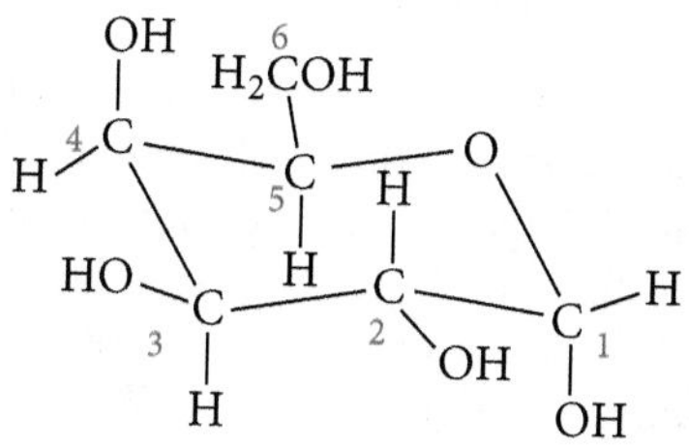

Galactose

Galactose, also known as brain sugar, is a hexose usually found combined with other monosaccharides in disaccharides such as lactose (see next paragraph). Galactose also occurs within the brain and nervous system of most animals. Galactose and glucose differ only in the stereochemistry at C4. Notice that in galactose, the —OH group is roughly perpendicular to the plane of the ring while in glucose it is roughly in the same plane as the ring.

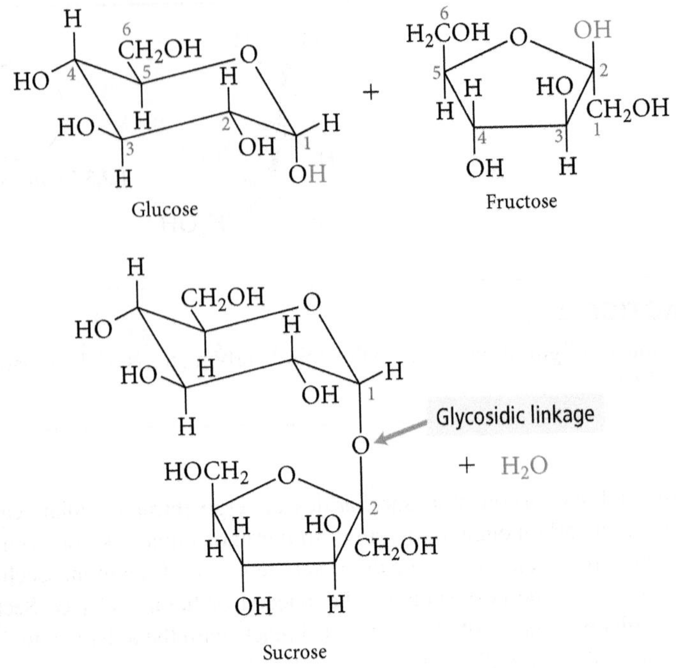

▶ **FIGURE 22.9 Formation of a Glycosidic Linkage** Glucose and fructose can join, eliminating water and forming a glycosidic linkage that results in the disaccharide sucrose, commonly known as table sugar.

Two monosaccharides can link together via a **glycosidic linkage** to form a **disaccharide**, a carbohydrate that can be decomposed into two simpler sugars. For example, glucose and fructose join to form sucrose, commonly known as table sugar (Figure 22.9 ▲). When we eat disaccharides, the link between individual monosaccharides is broken during digestion by **hydrolysis**, the splitting of a chemical bond with water that results in the addition of H and OH to the products.

The resultant monosaccharides readily pass through the intestinal wall and enter the bloodstream to become fuel for cells (Figure 22.10 ◀).

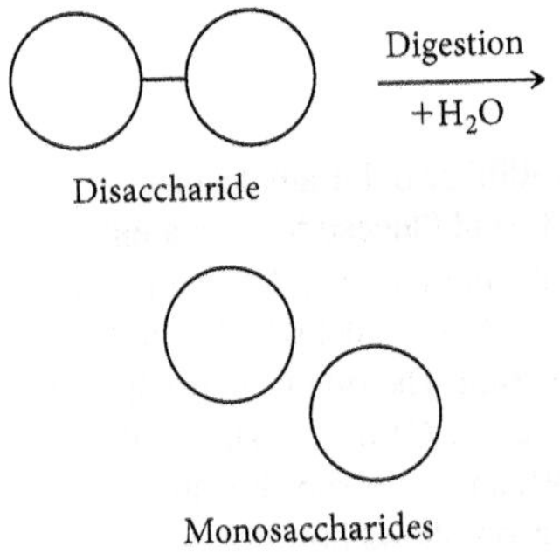

▲ **FIGURE 22.10 Hydrolysis of Disaccharides** A disaccharide is hydrolyzed during digestion. The resultant monosaccharides pass through the intestinal wall and enter the bloodstream.

Complex Carbohydrates

Monosaccharides can also link together to form a type of natural polymer (or biopolymer) called a **polysaccharide**, a long, chainlike molecule composed of many monosaccharide units bonded together. Polysaccharides are known as **complex carbohydrates** because of their long chains of sugars. The most common polysaccharides are *cellulose*, *starch*, and *glycogen*, all three of which are composed of repeating glucose units. The main difference among them lies in the way the units are bonded together. In cellulose, the oxygen atoms are roughly parallel with the planes of the rings. This is referred to as a β-glycosidic linkage. In starch and glycogen, the oxygen atoms joining neighbouring glucose units point down relative to the planes of the rings. This is an α-glycosidic linkage.

Cellulose The main structural component of plants, **cellulose** is the most abundant organic substance on Earth and consists of glucose units bonded together by β-glycosidic linkages. The resulting linear structure allows neighbouring cellulose molecules to form multiple hydrogen bonds with one another, resulting in the rigid and structurally stable properties we associate with wood and fibre. Humans lack the enzyme required to digest cellulose. When we eat cellulose (usually called fibre when it is present in foods), it passes right through our intestines, providing bulk to stools and preventing constipation. Some bacteria have the enzyme required to metabolize cellulose into its component glucose units. These bacteria are common in the guts of termites and ruminants such as cows, allowing them to extract caloric content from cellulose.

Starch The main energy storage medium for plants is **starch**, the soft, pliable substance abundant in potatoes and grains. Starch is composed of two slightly different polysaccharides, *amylose* and *amylopectin*. Both are made up of glucose units bonded together by α-glycosidic linkages, but amylopectin contains branches in the chains.

Cellulose

β-Glycosidic linkages

Starch

α-Glycosidic linkages

◀ The primary difference between starch and cellulose is in the way the units are bonded together.

When animals digest starch, the link between individual glucose units is broken by hydrolysis, allowing glucose molecules to pass through the intestinal wall and into the bloodstream (Figure 22.11 ▼).

Glycogen The structure of **glycogen** is similar to that of amylopectin, but the chain is even more highly branched. Animals use glycogen to store glucose in the muscles. Glycogen's highly branched structure leaves many end groups that can be quickly hydrolyzed to meet energy needs. When muscles become depleted of glycogen, muscle movement and exercise become much more difficult. Marathon runners often "hit the wall" at about 30 km because they have depleted most of the glycogen from their muscles.

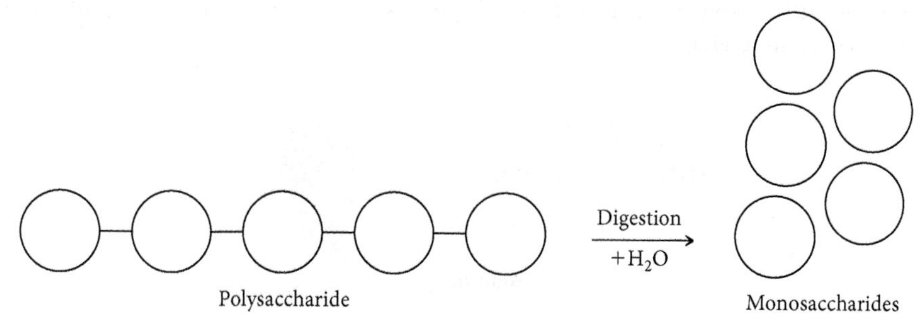

◀ **FIGURE 22.11 Hydrolysis of Polysaccharides** A polysaccharide is hydrolyzed during digestion. The resultant monosaccharides pass through the intestinal wall and enter the bloodstream.

22.4 Proteins and Amino Acids

Proteins are the workhorse molecules in living organisms; they are involved in virtually every facet of cell structure and function. For example, most of the chemical reactions that occur in living organisms are enabled by **enzymes**, proteins that act as catalysts in biochemical reactions. Without enzymes, life would be impossible. Proteins are also the structural elements of muscle, skin, and cartilage. They transport oxygen in the blood, act as antibodies to fight disease, and function as hormones to regulate metabolic processes. Proteins reign supreme as the working molecules of life. Table 22.2 summarizes some of the important classes of proteins and lists examples of each.

TABLE 22.2 Protein Functions

Class of Protein	Primary Function(s)	Example(s)
Structural proteins	Compose structures within living organisms	Collagen (skin, tendon, cartilage), keratin (hair, fingernails)
Enzymes	Catalyze and control biochemical reactions	DNA polymerase (involved in replication of DNA)
Hormones	Regulate metabolic processes	Insulin (regulates glucose metabolism)
Transport proteins	Transport substances from one place to another	Hemoglobin (transports oxygen)
Storage proteins	Provide source of essential nutrients	Casein (protein in mammalian milk)
Contractile and motile proteins	Mediate motion and muscle contraction	Actin and myosin (provide muscle contraction)
Protective proteins	Protect and defend cells	Antibodies (neutralize infectious agents)

Amino Acids: The Building Blocks of Proteins

In a protein, the presence of an R group does not necessarily indicate a pure alkyl group. See Table 22.3 for possible R groups.

Proteins are polymers of amino acids. Each **amino acid** molecule consists of a carbon atom—called the α-carbon—bonded to four different groups: an amine group, an R group (also called a side chain), a carboxylic acid group, and a hydrogen atom:

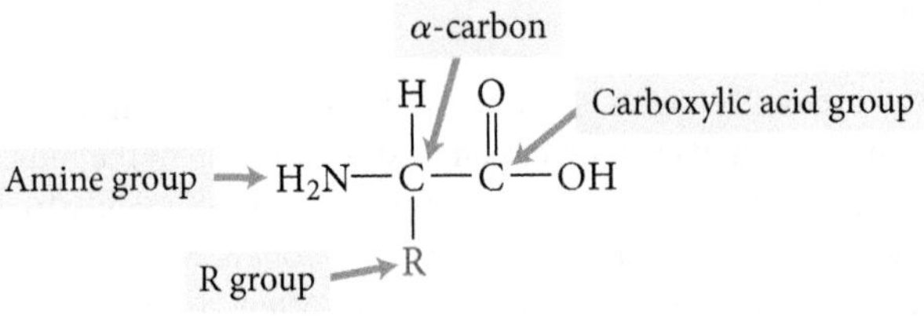

α-carbon
Carboxylic acid group
Amine group → $H_2N-C(H)(R)-C(=O)-OH$
R group → R

Amino acid general structure

Amino acids differ from each other in their R groups. For example, the R group in alanine is a methyl group (CH_3):

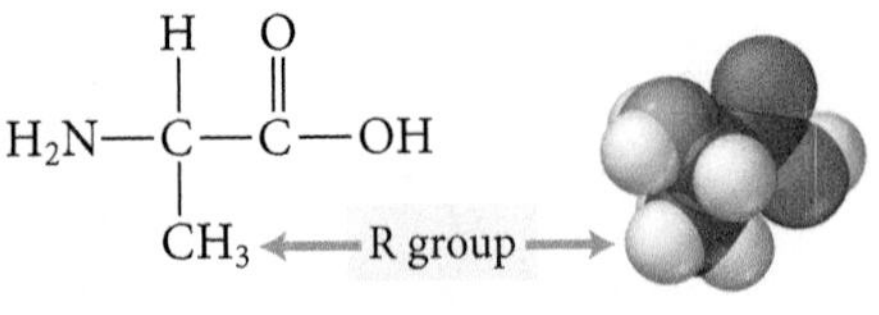

$H_2N-C(H)(CH_3)-C(=O)-OH$
R group

Alanine

Other amino acids are glycine (R = H), phenylalanine (R = $CH_2C_6H_5$), serine (R = CH_2OH), aspartic acid (R = CH_2COOH), and lysine (R = $CH_2CH_2CH_2CH_2NH_2$).

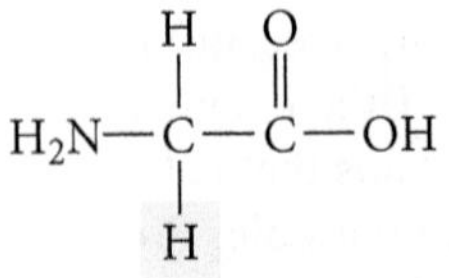

$H_2N-C(H)(H)-C(=O)-OH$

Glycine

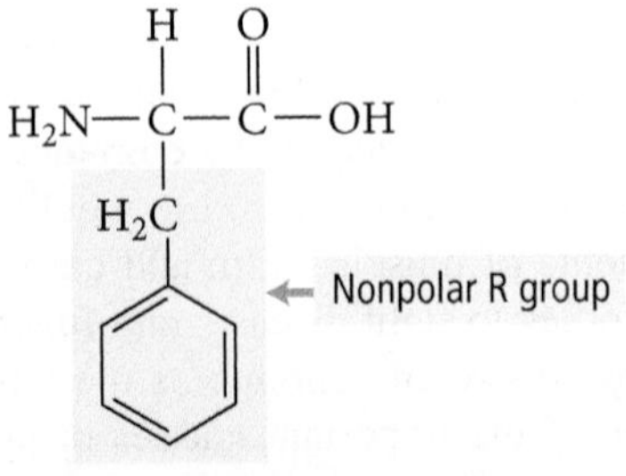

$H_2N-C(H)(H_2C-C_6H_5)-C(=O)-OH$
Nonpolar R group

Phenylalanine

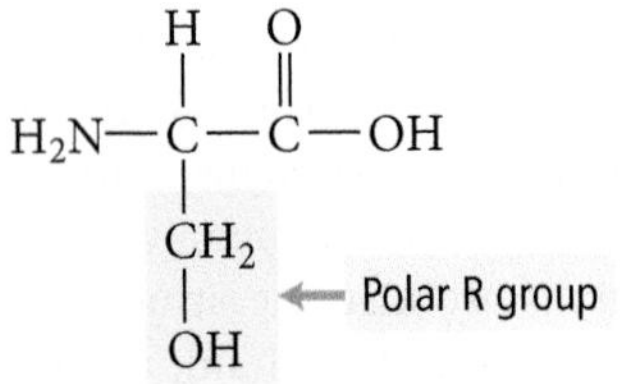

$H_2N-C(H)(CH_2-OH)-C(=O)-OH$
Polar R group

Serine

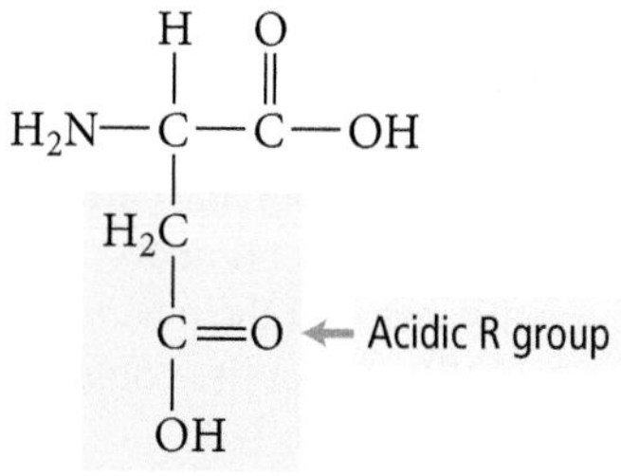

Acidic R group

Aspartic acid

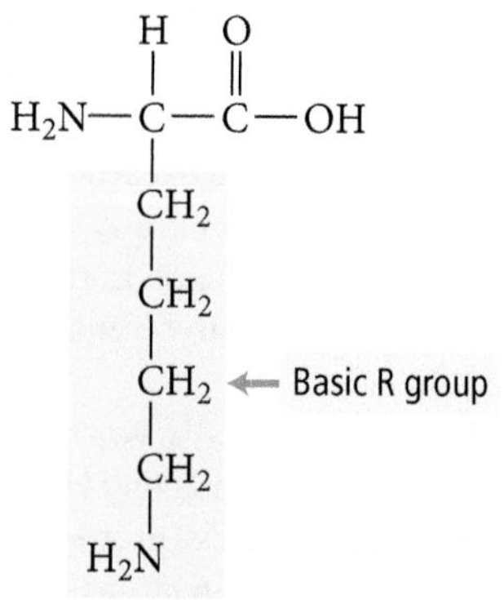

Basic R group

Lysine

The R groups, or side chains, differ chemically. For example, phenylalanine has a large nonpolar R group, whereas serine has a polar one. Aspartic acid has an acidic R group, whereas lysine, since it contains nitrogen, has a basic one. When amino acids are strung together to make a protein, the chemical properties of the R groups determine the structure and properties of the protein. Table 22.3 shows the most common amino acids

TABLE 22.3 Common Amino Acids

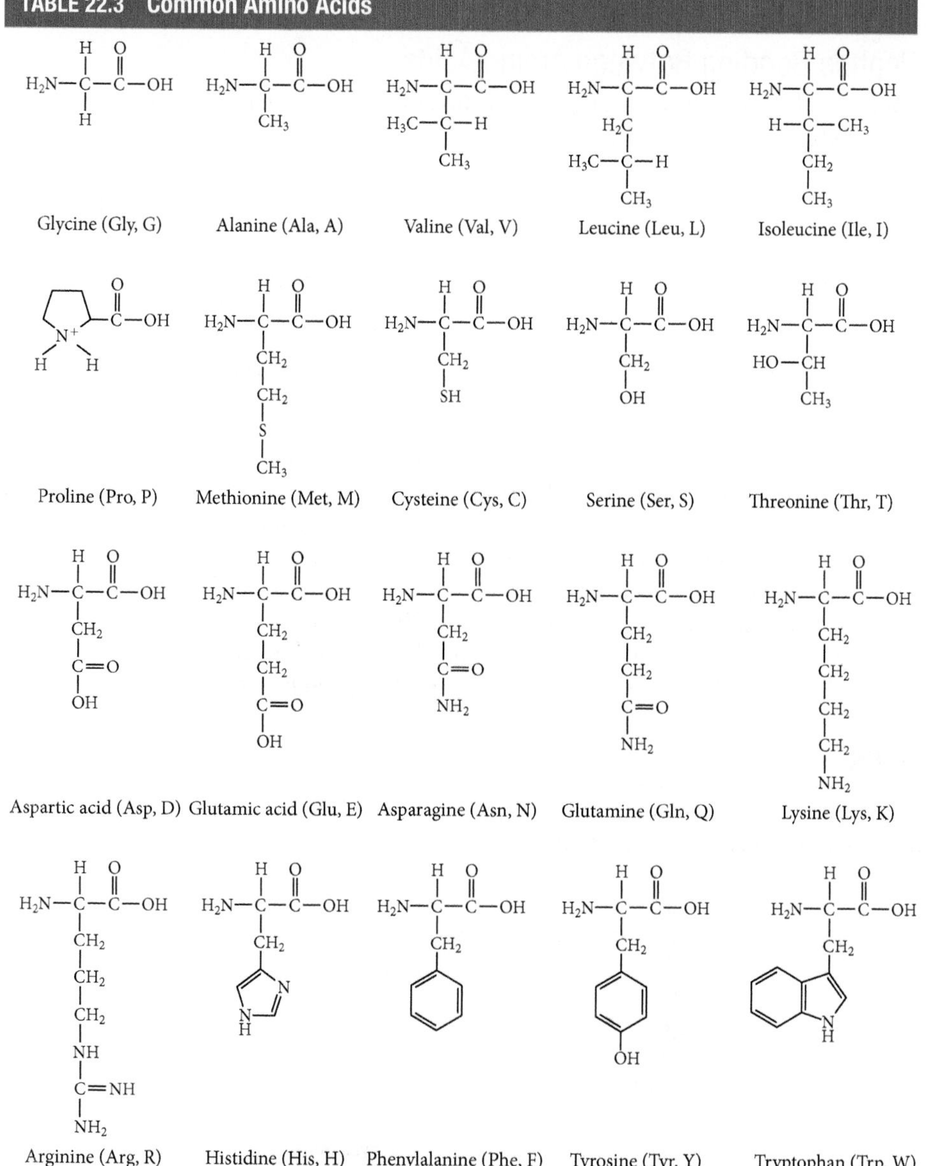

in proteins and both their three- and one-letter abbreviations. The diversity of amino acids creates the possibility for an even larger diversity of proteins.

Since all amino acids (except glycine) contain four different groups attached to a tetrahedral carbon (the α-carbon), all amino acids are chiral about that carbon. The amino acids that compose naturally occurring proteins are the L enantiomers, and are called L-amino acids. Why life on Earth is based on this enantiomer over the other is an interesting question that remains to be answered. (It seems just as likely that life could have used the D enantiomer.)

Although we usually write the structures of amino acids as neutral, their actual structure is ionic and depends on pH. At physiological pH, the carboxylic acid is deprotonated, and the amine group is protonated. This form is known as a **zwitterion**. Even though formal charges exist on atoms within a zwitterion, it has no overall charge:

$$H_3N^+—C(H)(CH_3)—C(=O)O^-$$

Zwitterion

Since one side of the dipolar ion is positively charged and the other negatively charged, amino acids are highly polar and soluble in water. They also have fairly high melting points (usually >200 °C).

Peptide Bonding Between Amino Acids

Amino acids link together through the reaction of the amine end of one amino acid with the carboxylic end of another.

$$H—N(H)—C(H)(R_1)—C(=O)—OH + H—N(H)—C(H)(R_2)—C(=O)—OH \longrightarrow H—N(H)—C(H)(R_1)—C(=O)—N(H)—C(H)(R_2)—C(=O)—OH + H_2O$$

N-terminal end

C-terminal end

Peptide bond

The reaction between amine and carboxylic acid groups to form an amide is an example of a nucleophilic substitution of acyl compounds (see Section 21.8). In biochemistry, the amide group is known as a peptide bond. For the structure and bonding of amide groups, see Section 20.4.

The resulting bond is a **peptide bond**, and the resulting molecule—two amino acids linked together—is a **dipeptide**. When two or more amino acids link in this way, the molecule they form has two distinct ends: an amino terminal (or N-terminal end) and a carboxyl terminal (or C-terminal end). A *tripeptide* is three amino acids joined by peptide bonds; a *tetrapeptide* is four, and so on. Short chains of amino acids are generally called *oligopeptides*, and longer chains (more than 20) are called **polypeptides**. Functional proteins usually contain one or more polypeptide chains with each chain consisting of hundreds or even thousands of amino acids joined by peptide bonds.

EXAMPLE 22.2 PEPTIDE BONDS

Show the reaction by which valine, cysteine, and phenylalanine (in that order) link via peptide bonds. Designate valine as the N-terminal and label the N-terminal and C-terminal ends in the resulting tripeptide.

$$H_2N—C(H)(CH(CH_3)_2)—C(=O)—OH$$

Valine

$$H_2N—C(H)(CH_2SH)—C(=O)—OH$$

Cysteine

$$H_2N—C(H)(CH_2C_6H_5)—C(=O)—OH$$

Phenylalanine

SOLUTION

Peptide bonds form when the carboxylic end of one amino acid reacts with the amine end of another amino acid.

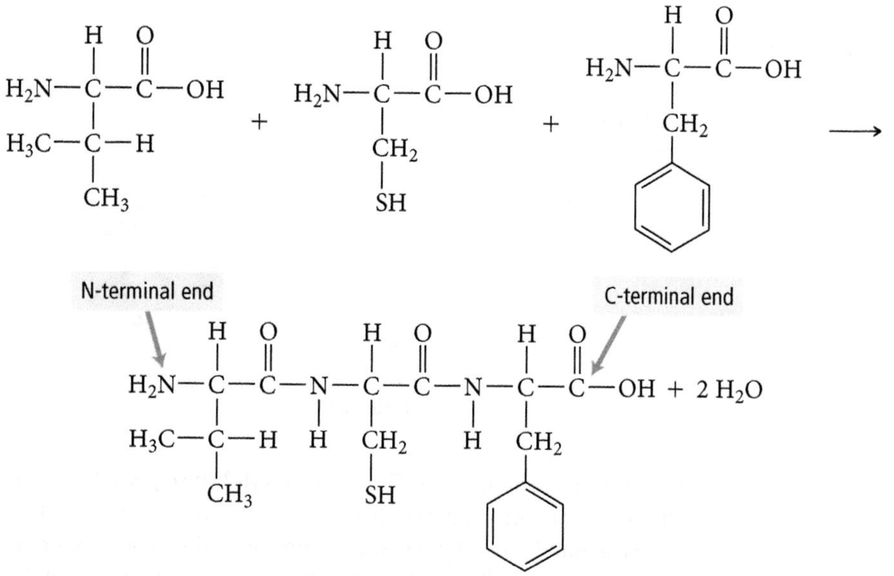

$$H_2N{-}CH(CH(CH_3)_2){-}COOH + H_2N{-}CH(CH_2SH){-}COOH + H_2N{-}CH(CH_2C_6H_5){-}COOH \longrightarrow$$

N-terminal end

C-terminal end

$$H_2N{-}CH(CH(CH_3)_2){-}CO{-}NH{-}CH(CH_2SH){-}CO{-}NH{-}CH(CH_2C_6H_5){-}COOH + 2\,H_2O$$

FOR PRACTICE 22.2

Show the reaction by which alanine, threonine, and serine (in that order) link via peptide bonds. Designate alanine as the N-terminal and label the N-terminal and C-terminal ends in the resulting tripeptide.

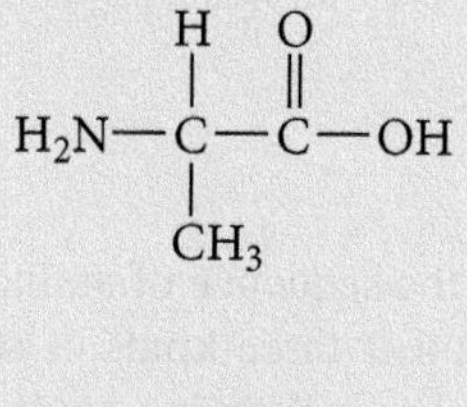

$$H_2N{-}CH(CH_3){-}COOH \qquad H_2N{-}CH(CH(OH)CH_3){-}COOH \qquad H_2N{-}CH(CH_2OH){-}COOH$$

Alanine 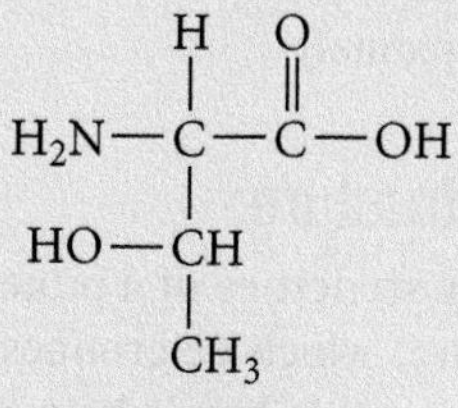 Threonine 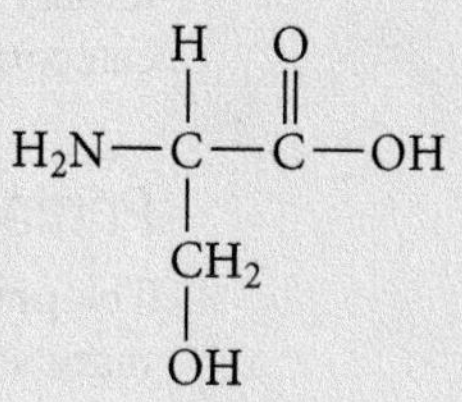 Serine

CONCEPTUAL CONNECTION 22.1

Peptides

How many different tripeptides can form from the three amino acids listed here? (The amino acids are indicated using the three-letter amino acid abbreviations in Table 22.3.)

Ser, Ala, Gly

22.5 Protein Structure

A protein's structure is critical to its function. For example, we have learned that insulin is a protein that promotes the absorption of glucose out of the blood and into muscle cells where the glucose is needed for energy. Insulin recognizes muscle cells because muscle cell surfaces contain *insulin receptors*, molecules that fit a specific portion of the insulin protein. If insulin were a different shape, it would not latch onto insulin receptors on muscle cells and could not do its job. Thus the shape or *conformation* of a protein is crucial to its function.

We can broadly classify proteins into two main structural categories: fibrous proteins and globular proteins (Figure 22.12 ▾). **Fibrous proteins** tend to have relatively simple linear structures and be insoluble in aqueous solutions. They serve primarily structural functions within living organisms. Collagen and keratin, for example, are

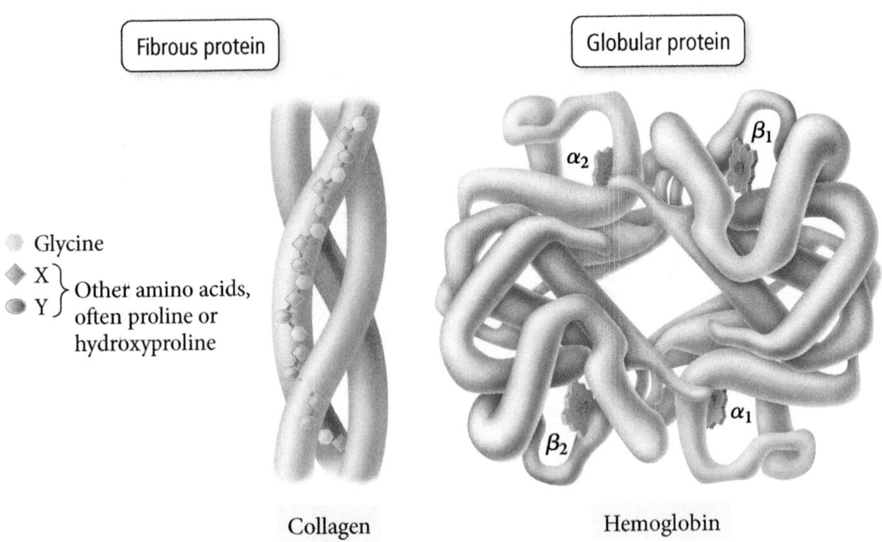

▶ **FIGURE 22.12 Fibrous and Globular Proteins** Proteins are broadly divided into fibrous proteins (which have relatively simple linear structures) and globular proteins (which have more complex three-dimensional structures).

both fibrous proteins (see Table 22.2). **Globular proteins** tend to have more complex structures, but are often roughly spherical in overall shape. Globular proteins are generally structured so that polar side chains on amino acids are oriented toward the exterior of the protein, while nonpolar side chains are oriented toward the interior of the protein. Consequently, globular proteins tend to be soluble in water, but they maintain a nonpolar environment within the protein that excludes water. Hemoglobin and insulin are both globular proteins.

Protein structure is analyzed at four levels: primary structure, secondary structure, tertiary structure, and quaternary structure (Figure 22.13 ▼). We examine each of these categories separately.

Primary Structure

The **primary structure** of a protein is the sequence of amino acids in its chain(s). Primary structure, which determines the other three kinds of structure, is maintained by the covalent peptide bonds between individual amino acids. The primary structure of

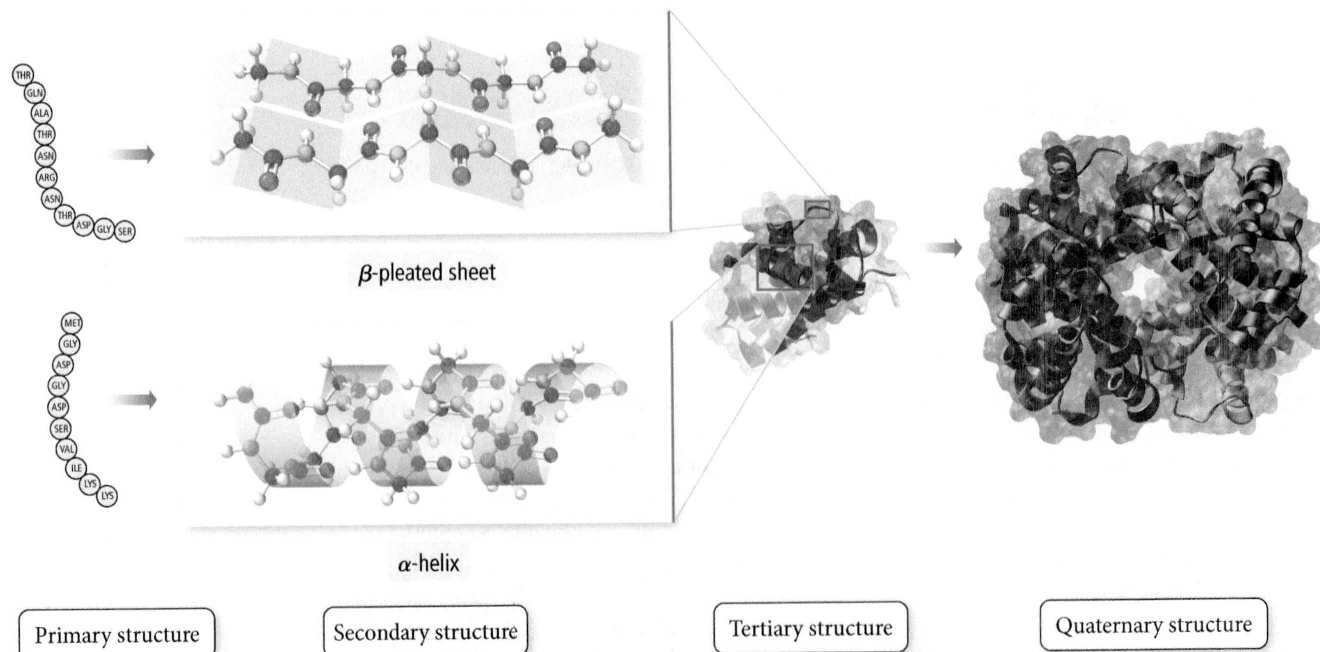

▲ **FIGURE 22.13 Levels of Protein Structure** Protein structure is analyzed at four levels: primary, secondary, tertiary, and quaternary.

CHEMISTRY AND MEDICINE The Essential Amino Acids

Of the 20 amino acids necessary for protein synthesis in humans, our bodies can synthesize about half. The other 10, called *essential amino acids* (Table 22.4), must be ingested from food, and we must eat them in the proportions that allow for protein synthesis. Many animal proteins, especially those in dairy products such as eggs and milk, contain all the essential amino acids in proportions that closely match human needs. These are known as high-quality, or complete, proteins. Most plant proteins, however, do not contain the 10 essential amino acids in the right proportions. For example, grains are short on lysine, and beans or lentils are short on methionine. Since different types of plants are generally deficient in different amino acids, a vegetarian can obtain complete protein by pairing foods lacking in one amino acid with foods that lack a different one. The best-known combination of this sort is rice and beans—rice lacks lysine and beans lack methionine, but together they provide a complete protein.

Table 22.4 Essential Amino Acids

Phenylalanine	Valine
Tryptophan	Threonine
Isoleucine	Methionine
Histidine	Arginine
Lysine	Leucine

egg-white lysozyme—a protein that helps fight infection—is shown in Figure 22.14 ▼. The figure illustrates the amino acid sequence, the N-terminal and C-terminal ends, and the presence of *disulfide linkages*, covalent cross-links between cysteine amino acids in the polymer. We discuss disulfide linkages in more detail later, in the section on tertiary structure. Researchers determined the first amino acid sequences for proteins in the 1950s. Today, the amino acid sequences for thousands of proteins are known.

Changes in the amino acid sequence of a protein, even minor ones, can destroy the function of a protein. Hemoglobin, as we saw in Chapter 14, is a protein that transports oxygen in the blood. It is composed of four polypeptide chains made up of a total of 574 amino acid units. If valine is replaced by glutamic acid in just one position on two

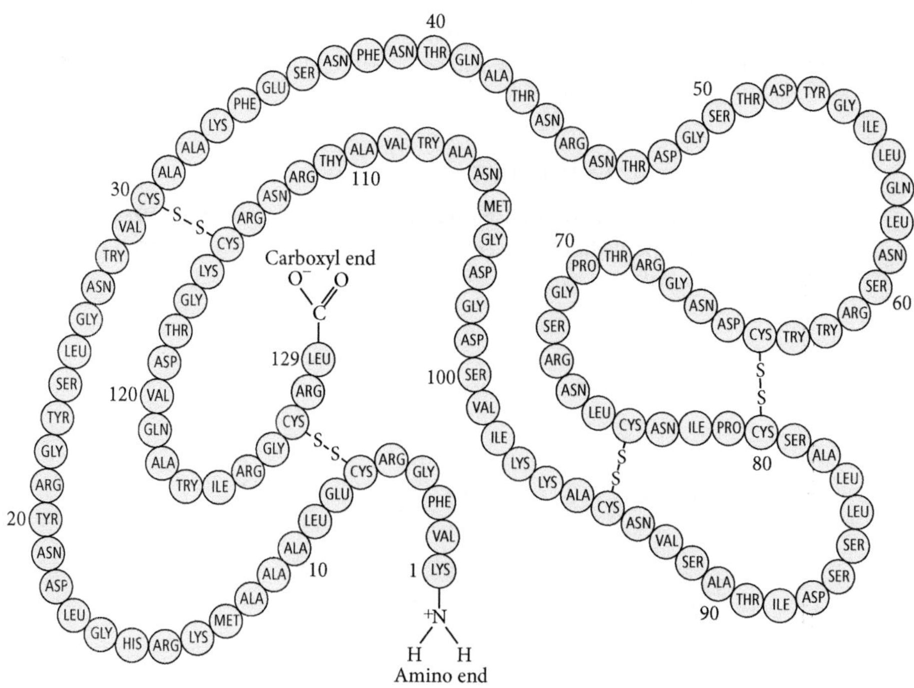

◀ **FIGURE 22.14 Primary Structure of Egg-White Lysozyme** Primary structure refers to the sequence of amino acids in a protein.

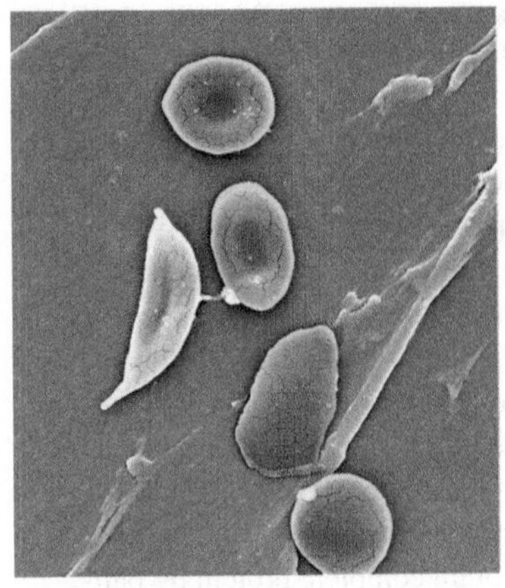

▲ The genetic disease known as sickle-cell anemia results in red blood cells with a sickle shape. These cells impede circulation of blood, causing damage to major organs.

of these chains, the disease known as sickle-cell anemia results. The red blood cells of people with sickle-cell anemia take on a sickle shape that impedes circulation, causing damage to major organs. In the past, sickle-cell anemia was fatal, often resulting in death before age 30—all due to a change in a few atoms of 2 amino acids out of 574. Modern therapies have extended the lifespan of sickle-cell anemia patients so they now live into their 40s and 50s.

Secondary Structure

The **secondary structure** of a protein refers to certain regular periodic or repeating patterns in the arrangement of protein chains. Secondary structure is maintained by interactions between amino acids that are fairly close together in the linear sequence of the protein chain or that are adjacent to each other on neighbouring chains or chains which fold back on themselves. The most common of these patterns is the ***α*-helix**, shown in Figure 22.15 ▼. In the α-helix structure, the amino acid chain wraps into a tight coil from which side chains extend. The structure is maintained by hydrogen-bonding interactions between NH and CO groups along the peptide backbone of the protein. Some proteins—such as keratin, which composes human hair—have the α-helix pattern throughout their entire chain. Other proteins have very little or no α-helix pattern in their chain. It depends on the particular protein.

A second common pattern in the secondary structure of proteins is the ***β*-pleated sheet** (Figure 22.16 ▼). In this structure, the chain is extended (as opposed to coiled) and forms a zigzag pattern. The peptide backbones of neighbouring chains interact with one another through hydrogen bonding to form zigzag-shaped sheets. Some proteins—such as silk—have the β-pleated sheet structure throughout their entire chain. Since the protein chains in the β-pleated sheet are fully extended, silk is inelastic. Many proteins have some sections that are β-pleated sheets, other sections that are α-helical, and still other sections that have less regular patterns referred to as **random coils**.

▼ **FIGURE 22.15 The *α*-Helix Structure** The α-helix is an example of secondary protein structure.

α-Helix protein structure

Tertiary Structure

The **tertiary structure** of a protein consists of the large-scale bends and folds resulting from interactions between the R groups of amino acids that are separated by large distances in the linear sequence of the protein chain. These interactions, shown in Figure 22.17 ▶, include hydrogen bonding, disulfide linkages (covalent bonds between cysteine amino acids), hydrophobic interactions (attractions between large, nonpolar side chains), and salt bridges (acid–base interactions between acidic and basic side chains). Fibrous proteins generally lack tertiary structure; they simply extend in a long continuous chain with some secondary structure. Globular proteins, by contrast, fold in on themselves, forming complex globular shapes rich in tertiary structure.

Quaternary Structure

Some proteins—called *monomeric* proteins—are composed of only one polypeptide chain. However, *multimeric* proteins are composed of several polypeptide chains, called subunits. We just saw, for

▶ **FIGURE 22.16 The *β*-Pleated Sheet Structure** The β-pleated sheet is a secondary protein structure.

β-Pleated sheet protein structure

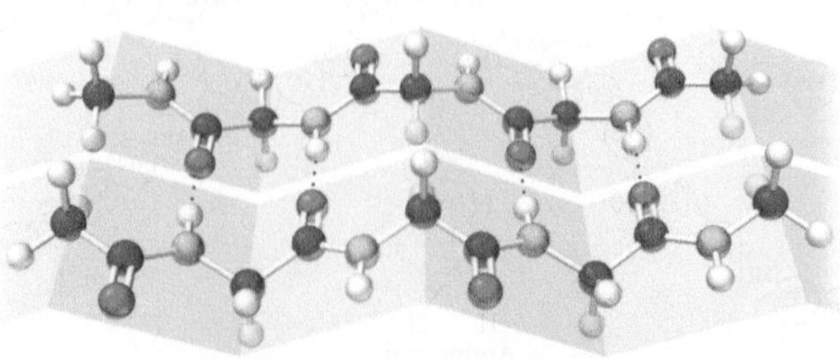

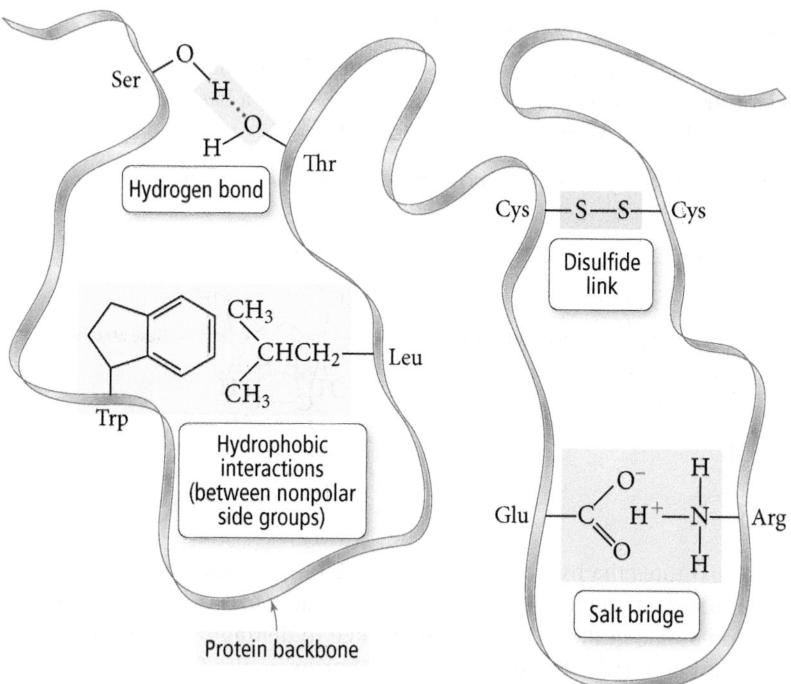

◀ **FIGURE 22.17 Interactions Within Proteins** The tertiary structure of a protein is maintained by interactions between the R groups of amino acids that are separated by large distances in the linear sequence of the protein chain.

example, that hemoglobin is composed of four such subunits. The way that subunits fit together in a multimeric protein is referred to as the **quaternary structure** of the protein. Quaternary structure is maintained by the same types of interactions that maintain tertiary structure, but the interactions are between amino acids on different subunits.

Summarizing Protein Structure:

- Primary structure is simply the amino acid sequence. It is maintained by the peptide bonds that hold amino acids together.
- Secondary structure refers to the repeating patterns in the arrangement of protein chains. These are maintained by interactions between the peptide backbones of amino acids that are close together in the chain sequence or adjacent to each other on neighbouring chains. Secondary structure is characteristic of fibrous proteins, but globular proteins also frequently feature regions of α-helix, β-pleated sheet, and random coil secondary structure.
- Tertiary structure refers to the large-scale twists and folds of globular proteins. These are maintained by interactions between the R groups of amino acids that are separated by long distances in the chain sequence.
- Quaternary structure refers to the arrangement of subunits in proteins that have more than one polypeptide chain. Quaternary structure is maintained by interactions between amino acids on different subunits.

22.6 Nucleic Acids: Blueprints for Proteins

We have seen that the amino acid sequence in a protein determines that protein's structure and function. If the amino acid sequence is incorrect, the protein is unlikely to function properly. How do cells in living organisms synthesize the many thousands of different required proteins, each with the correct amino acid sequence? The answer lies in nucleic acids, molecules that serve as blueprints for protein synthesis. Nucleic acids employ a chemical code to specify the correct amino acid sequences for proteins. Nucleic acids are broadly divided into two types: deoxyribonucleic acid, or DNA, which exists primarily in the nucleus of the cell; and ribonucleic acid, or RNA, which exists throughout the cell.

The Basic Structure of Nucleic Acids

Like proteins, nucleic acids are polymers. The individual units composing nucleic acids are **nucleotides**. Each nucleotide has three parts: a sugar, a base, and a phosphate group that serves as a link between sugars (Figure 22.18 ▼).

Sugars In DNA, the sugar is deoxyribose, whereas in RNA, the sugar is ribose.

The difference between ribose and deoxyribose is that in the latter, the —OH group has been replaced by a —H, hence the prefix "deoxy."

Base attaches here.

Deoxyribose

Base attaches here.

Ribose

The base substitutes the hydroxyl (—OH) on C1, and phosphate groups connect C3 and C5 on different sugar units. When a base is attached to the sugar, the numbers of the carbon atoms in the sugar ring are primed to distinguish them from the carbon atoms on the bases (which are not primed). For example, C5 becomes C5′ and C3 becomes C3′.

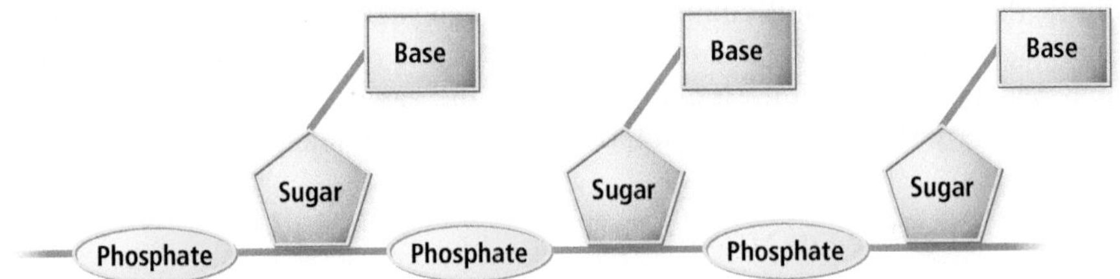

▶ **FIGURE 22.18 DNA Structure** DNA is composed of repeating units called nucleotides. Each nucleotide contains a sugar, a base, and a phosphate group.

Bases Every nucleotide in DNA has the same sugar, but each nucleotide has just one of four different bases. In DNA, the four bases are adenine (A), cytosine (C), guanine (G), and thymine (T). Each of these bases bonds to the sugar via the nitrogen atom circled in the illustrations shown here.

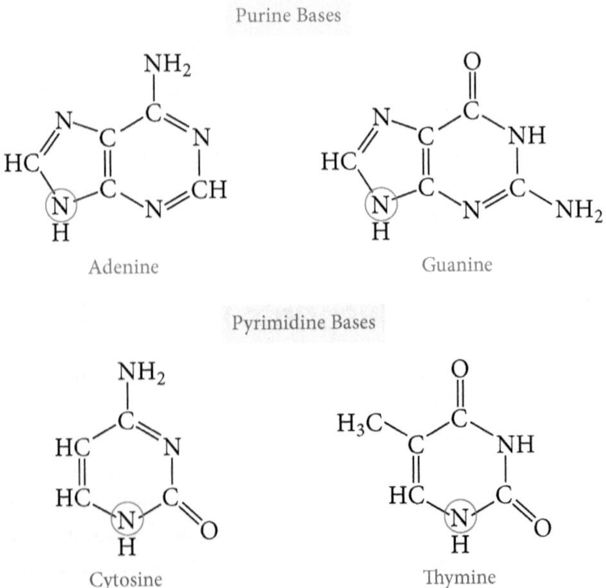

Adenine and guanine are called *purine* bases because they resemble the bicyclic compound purine. Cytosine and thymine are called *pyrimidine* bases because they resemble the monocyclic compound pyrimidine.

Purine

Pyrimidine

In RNA, the base uracil (U), also a pyrimidine base, replaces thymine. Uracil and thymine differ only in a methyl ($-CH_3$) group.

No methyl group on uracil

Uracil

The bases in nucleic acids are **complementary**—that is, they precisely pair with another base. Each pyrimidine base pairs with only one purine base via specific hydrogen bonds that occur between the two bases. More specifically, guanine pairs only with cytosine through three hydrogen bonds and adenine pairs only with thymine through two hydrogen bonds, as shown in Figure 22.19 ▼. In other words, guanine is complementary

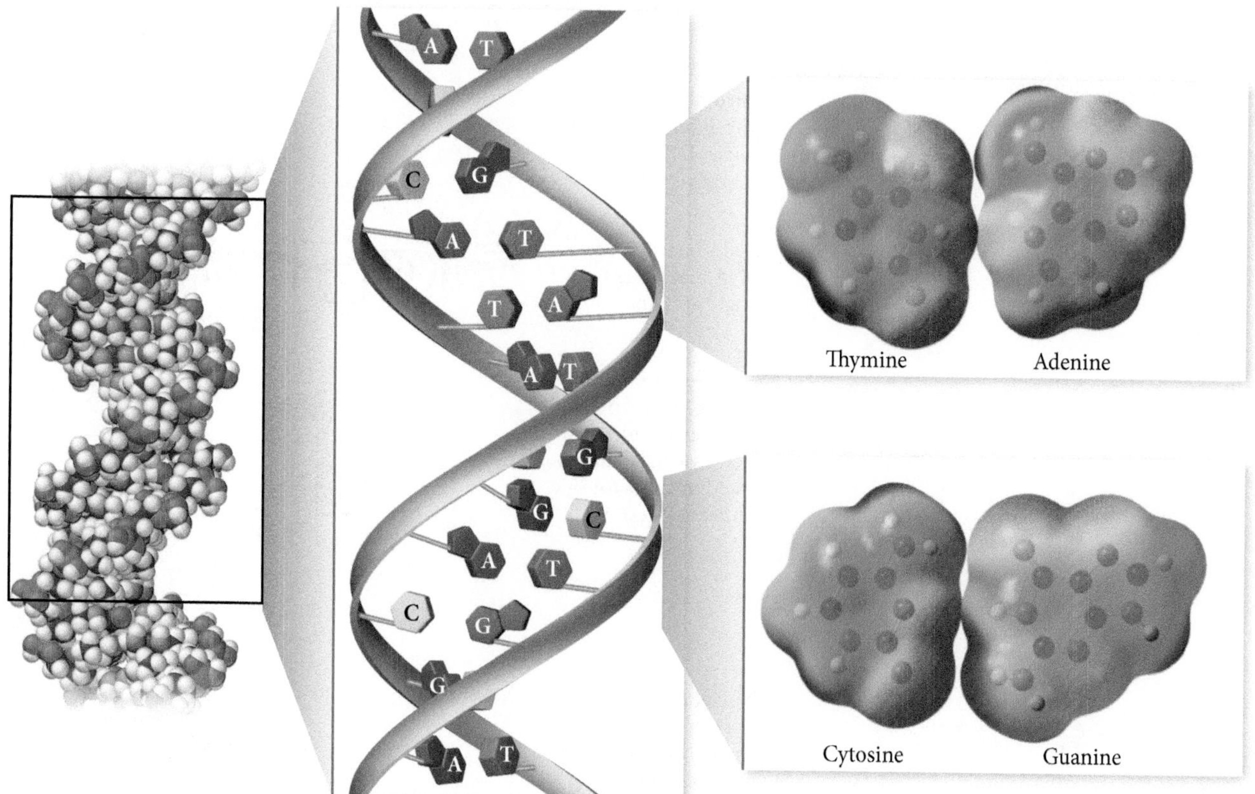

▲ **FIGURE 22.19 Base Pairing in DNA** The bases in nucleic acids are complementary. Each pyrimidine base pairs with only one purine base (G with C, A with T) via specific hydrogen bonds that occur between the two bases.

to cytosine and adenine is complementary to thymine. This base pairing is central to DNA replication, as we discuss in Section 22.7.

Phosphate Links The sugar units in nucleic acids link together by phosphate groups, which bind to C5′ and C3′ of the sugar as shown in Figure 22.20 ◄. Note that a nucleic acid molecule has two distinct ends, which we call the 5′ end and the 3′ end.

5′ end

Base (A or G or C or T)

Base (A or G or C or T)

Base (A or G or C or T)

Base (A or G or C or T)

Base (A or G or C or T)

3′ end

▲ **FIGURE 22.20 Short Strand of DNA** DNA contains alternating sugar and phosphate groups with bases attached to each sugar. The end of the molecule missing an attachment at the number 3 position in the sugar ring is called the 3′ end, and the end missing an attachment at the number 5 position is called the 5′ end.

The Genetic Code

The order of bases in a nucleic acid chain determines the order of amino acids in a protein. However, since there are only four bases, and since together they must have the ability to code for 20 different amino acids, a single base cannot code for a single amino acid. We need a sequence of three bases—called a **codon**—to code for one amino acid (Figure 22.21 ▼). The genetic code—the code that identifies the amino acid specified by a particular codon—was worked out in 1961. It is nearly universal—the same codons specify the same amino acids in nearly all organisms. For example,

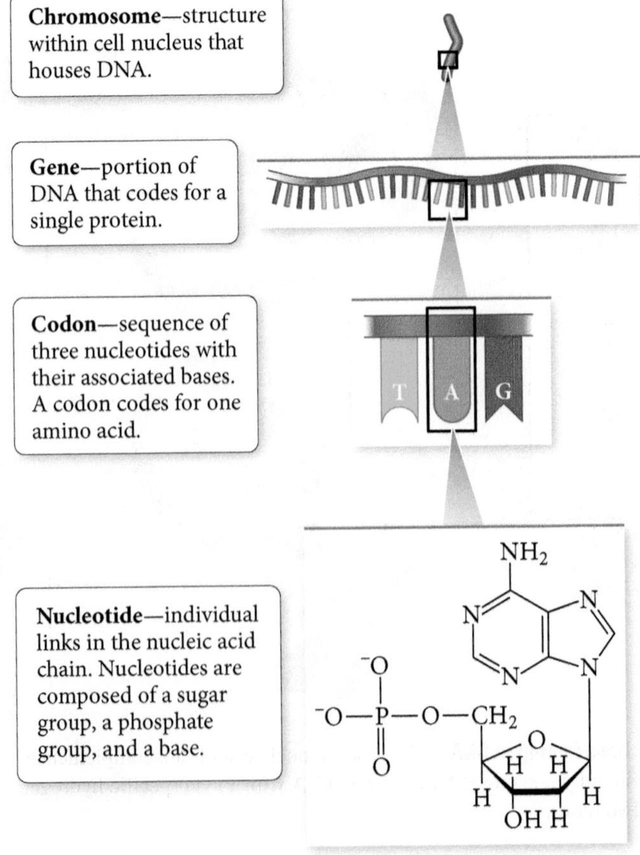

Chromosome—structure within cell nucleus that houses DNA.
Gene—portion of DNA that codes for a single protein.
Codon—sequence of three nucleotides with their associated bases. A codon codes for one amino acid.
T
A
G
Nucleotide—individual links in the nucleic acid chain. Nucleotides are composed of a sugar group, a phosphate group, and a base.
NH_2
N
N
N
N
^-O
^-O—P—O—CH_2
O
O
H H
H H
OH H

► **FIGURE 22.21 Genetic Structure** The hierarchical structure of genetic information is: chromosome, gene, codon, and nucleotide.

in DNA, the sequence AGT codes for the amino acid serine and the sequence ACC codes for the amino acid threonine. It does not matter if you are a rat, a bacterium, or a human—the code is the same.

A **gene** is a sequence of codons within a DNA molecule that codes for a single protein. Since proteins vary in size from a few dozen to thousands of amino acids, genes vary in length from dozens to thousands of codons. For example, egg-white lysozyme (Figure 22.14) is composed of 129 amino acids. So the lysozyme gene contains 129 codons—one for each amino acid in the lysozyme protein. Each codon is like a three-letter word that specifies one amino acid. String the correct number of codons together in the correct sequence, and you have a gene, the instructions for the amino acid sequence in a protein. Genes are contained in structures called **chromosomes** (Figure 22.22 ▼). There are 46 chromosomes in the nuclei of human cells.

In addition to having a codon for each amino acid, genes also contain additional coding that signals, for example, where the gene begins and where it ends.

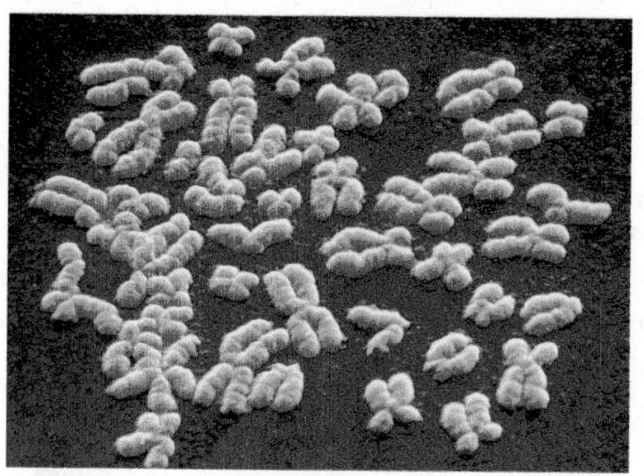

◀ **FIGURE 22.22 Chromosomes**
Genes are contained in structures called chromosomes. Most human cells contain 46 chromosomes.

CONCEPTUAL CONNECTION 22.2
The Genetic Code

Assuming you have four different bases, how many amino acids can you code for with two-base sequences? Three-base sequences?

22.7 DNA Replication, the Double Helix, and Protein Synthesis

Most of the cells in our bodies contain all of the genes required to make all of the proteins that we need—the DNA within any one cell is *complete*. However, any particular cell does not express all those genes; it does not synthesize all those proteins. Cells synthesize only the proteins that are important to their function. For example, a pancreatic cell expresses the insulin gene within its nucleus to synthesize insulin. Pancreatic cells do not express the gene for keratin (the protein in hair), even though the keratin gene is also contained in their nuclei. The cells in our scalp, in contrast, which also have both insulin and keratin genes in their nuclei, synthesize keratin but not insulin.

DNA Replication and the Double Helix

The human body contains on the order of 10^{13} cells, most of which have complete copies of the DNA that originally was present in a single cell (the fertilized egg). When a cell divides, it makes complete copies of its DNA for each daughter cell. The ability of DNA to copy itself is related to its structure, discovered in 1953 by James D. Watson and Francis H. C. Crick. Watson and Crick, aided by evidence from X-ray diffraction photos (see Section 11.10), determined that DNA exists as two complementary strands wound around each other in a double helix (Figure 22.23 ▶). The strands are antiparallel, so that one runs $3' \longrightarrow 5'$ while the other runs $5' \longrightarrow 3'$. The bases on each DNA strand are directed

▲ **FIGURE 22.23 Watson and Crick** James Watson and Francis Crick discovered the structure of DNA, including the double helix and the pairing of complementary bases.

toward the interior of the helix, where they hydrogen bond to their complementary bases on the other strand. For example, if a section of DNA contains the bases

the complementary strand would have the sequence

T A C T T A G G C T G

As we saw earlier, A pairs only with T, and C pairs only with G. The two complementary strands are tightly wrapped into a helical coil, the famous DNA double helix structure (Figure 22.24 ▼).

When a cell is about to divide, the DNA unwinds and the hydrogen bonds joining the complementary bases break (Figure 22.25 ▼), forming two daughter strands. With the help of the enzyme DNA polymerase, a complement to each daughter strand—with the correct complementary bases in the correct sequence—forms. The hydrogen bonds between the old strands and the new

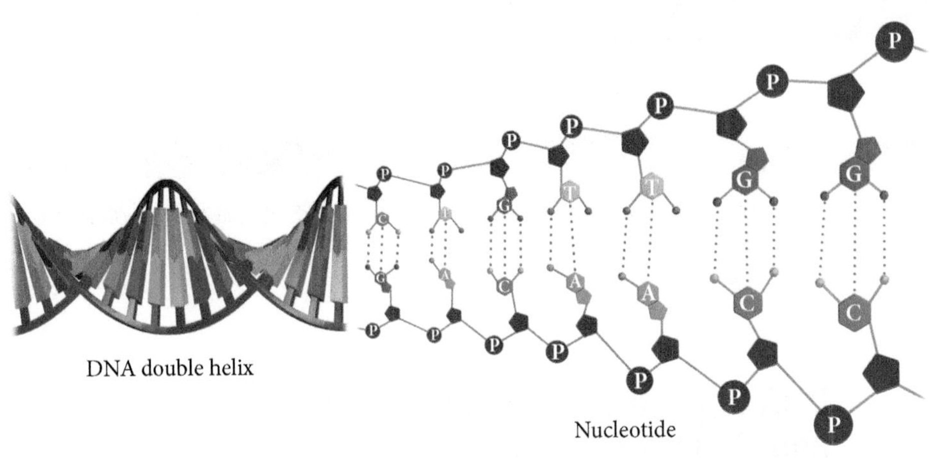

▶ **FIGURE 22.24 DNA Double Helix** Two complementary strands of DNA wrap around one another to form a double helix.

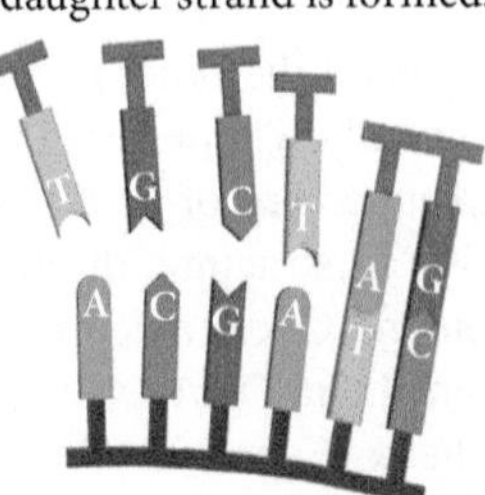

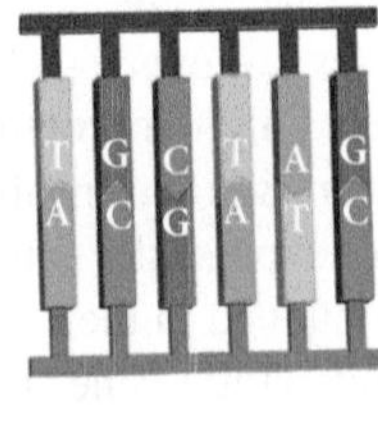

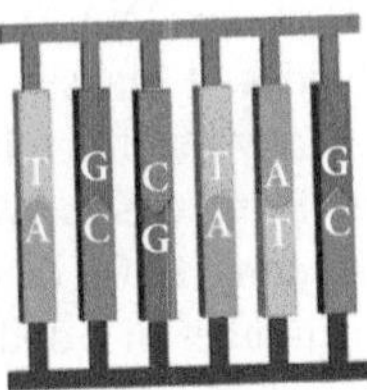

▶ **FIGURE 22.25 DNA Replication** When a cell is about to divide, its DNA unwinds. With the help of the enzyme DNA polymerase, a complement to each daughter strand is formed, resulting in two complete copies of the original DNA.

complementary strands then re-form, resulting in two complete copies of the original DNA, one for each daughter cell.

Protein Synthesis

Living organisms must continually synthesize thousands of proteins to survive, each when it is needed, and in the quantities required. When a cell needs to make a particular protein, the gene—the section of the DNA that codes for that particular protein—unravels. Complementary copies of that gene are then synthesized (or transcribed) as single strands of messenger RNA (or mRNA). The mRNA moves out of the cell's nucleus to structures in the cytoplasm called *ribosomes*. At the ribosome, protein synthesis occurs. The ribosome (which has a large subunit and a small subunit) moves along the mRNA chain that codes for the protein, "reading" the sequence of codons. At each codon, the specified amino acid is brought into place and a peptide bond forms with the previous amino acid (Figure 22.26 ▼). As the ribosome moves along the mRNA, the protein is formed. All of this is orchestrated by enzymes that catalyze the necessary reactions.

The "central dogma" of molecular biology is that DNA sequences are codes for the amino acid sequences of proteins. In cells, DNA is transcribed into a complementary RNA sequence, which is then translated into the amino acid sequence of a protein.

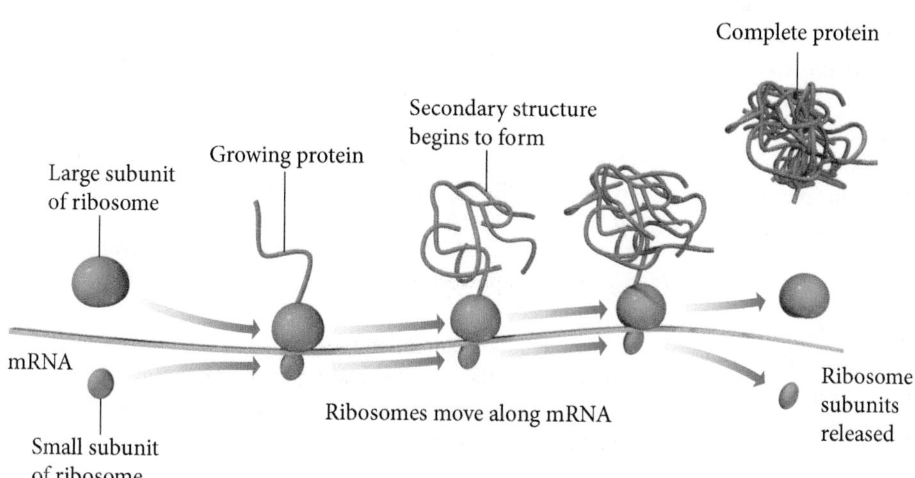

▲ **FIGURE 22.26 Protein Synthesis** A ribosome moves along a strand of mRNA, joining amino acids to form a protein.

Summarizing DNA Coding:

- DNA contains the code for the sequence of amino acids in proteins.
- A codon—three nucleotides with their bases—codes for one amino acid.
- A gene—a sequence of codons—codes for one protein.
- Genes are contained in structures called chromosomes that occur within cells. Humans have 46 chromosomes in the nuclei of their cells.
- When a human cell divides, each daughter cell receives a complete copy of the DNA—all 46 chromosomes.
- When a cell synthesizes a protein, the base sequence of the gene which codes for that protein is transferred to mRNA. mRNA then moves to a ribosome, where the amino acids are linked in the correct sequence to synthesize the protein. The general sequence of information flow is

$$\text{DNA} \longrightarrow \text{RNA} \longrightarrow \text{Protein}$$

CHEMISTRY AND MEDICINE The Human Genome Project

The Human Genome Project was an international project in which all of the genetic material of a human being was mapped. Beginning in 1990, it involved more than 2500 researchers from 18 countries. An initial draft of the map was completed in 2001 and the final draft was completed in 2003. Here, we highlight some of what has been learned through this massive undertaking.

- The human genome contains 3165 million nucleotide base pairs.
- The average gene contains about 3000 base pairs. The largest gene is for the protein dystrophin (whose deficiency is the root cause of muscular dystrophy); it contains 2.4 million base pairs.
- The human genome contains about 30 000 genes. The function of over half of these is still unknown. Before the Human Genome Project, researchers had estimated that humans had about 100 000 genes. The number of genes in humans is not much larger than the number found in many simpler organisms. For example, the number of genes in a roundworm is nearly 20 000. Whatever makes humans unique, it is not the number of genes in our genome.
- Less than 2% of human DNA actually consists of genes. These genes are aggregated in seemingly random areas within the genome, with vast expanses of noncoding DNA between the coding regions. This stands in contrast to other organisms, which tend to have more uniform distribution of genes throughout their genome.
- The order of DNA base pairs is 99.9% identical in all humans.
- About 1.4 million single base-pair differences (called SNPs for single-nucleotide polymorphisms) have been identified in the human genome. Understanding SNPs can help in identifying individuals who are susceptible to certain diseases. Knowledge of SNPs may also allow physicians to tailor drugs to match individuals.

Knowledge of the human genome is expected to lead to the development of new therapies in several ways. First, knowledge of genes can lead to smart drug design. Instead of developing drugs by trial and error (the current procedure for many drugs), knowledge of a specific gene will allow scientists to design drugs to carry out a specific function related to that gene or its protein product. Second, human genes themselves can provide the blueprint for the production of certain types of drugs, either in the laboratory or by other organisms. For example, we have seen that insulin can be made by inserting the insulin gene into bacteria, which then synthesize the needed drug. Intriguingly, it may even be possible to replace abnormal or missing genes in the cells of diseased patients. Such gene therapies are still in the early stages of development, but they may eventually give us a powerful new tool for combating inherited diseases.

Although the completion of the Human Genome Project may seem like the end, it is really just the beginning. Thousands of studies in the coming years will rely on the data obtained through this endeavour.

CHAPTER IN REVIEW

Key Terms

Section 22.1
biochemistry (957)

Section 22.2
lipid (957)
fatty acid (957)
triglyceride (959)
ester linkage (959)
saturated fat (959)
unsaturated fat (960)
phospholipid (960)
glycolipid (962)
lipid bilayer (962)
steroid (962)

Section 22.3
carbohydrate (962)
monosaccharide (963)
hexose (963)
aldose (963)
ketose (963)
Fischer projection (964)
glycosidic linkage (966)
disaccharide (966)
hydrolysis (966)
polysaccharide (966)
complex carbohydrate (966)
cellulose (966)
starch (966)
glycogen (967)

Section 22.4
enzyme (967)
amino acid (968)
zwitterion (970)
peptide bond (970)
dipeptide (970)
polypeptide (970)

Section 22.5
fibrous protein (971)
globular protein (972)
primary structure (972)
secondary structure (974)
α-helix (974)
β-pleated sheet (974)
random coil (974)
tertiary structure (974)
quaternary structure (975)

Section 22.6
nucleotide (976)
complementary (977)
codon (978)
gene (979)
chromosome (979)

Key Concepts

Diabetes and the Synthesis of Human Insulin (22.1)

Diabetes is a chronic illness that occurs when the pancreas cannot make enough insulin, a protein that promotes the absorption of glucose into cells. The chemical structure of insulin was discovered in 1955 by Frederick Sanger, who made it possible for insulin to be synthesized in the laboratory. Eventually, scientists inserted the human gene that codes for the production of insulin into bacteria, which were then able to produce enough insulin to supply diabetics. This example demonstrates the usefulness of biochemistry, the study of the chemicals that compose living organisms.

Lipids (22.2)

Lipids are biological chemicals that are nonpolar and, therefore, insoluble in water. In our bodies, they compose cell membranes, store energy, and provide insulation. A type of lipid called a fatty acid is a carboxylic acid with a long hydrocarbon chain. Fatty acids can be saturated, meaning they contain the maximum number of hydrogen atoms, or unsaturated, meaning they contain one or more carbon–carbon double bond. Saturated fatty acids experience greater molecular forces, making them solid at room temperature, while unsaturated fatty acids are liquids. Fats and oils are triglycerides, triesters composed of glycerol bonded by ester linkages to three fatty acids. Like fatty acids, triglycerides can be saturated (fats) or unsaturated (oils). Other lipids include phospholipids, made up of a glycerol bonded to two nonpolar fatty acids and a polar phosphate group, used in animal cell membranes; glycolipids, similar to phospholipids but with a sugar molecule as their polar head; and steroids, four-ringed lipids that include cholesterol and sex hormones.

Carbohydrates (22.3)

Carbohydrates are polyhydroxy aldehydes or ketones and generally have the formula $(CH_2O)_n$. They are important to short-term energy storage and plant structure composition. Monosaccharides, the simplest carbohydrates, contain three to eight carbons with one aldehyde or ketone functional group. Glucose, an example of a hexose, can exist both in a linear form and a ring form. Two monosaccharides can combine to form a disaccharide. For example, glucose and fructose can combine to form sucrose. The glycosidic linkages that connect the two monosaccharides are broken during digestion by hydrolysis. Polysaccharides are polymers of monosaccharides known as complex carbohydrates. They include cellulose, also called fibre, the main structural component of plants; starch, an energy storage compound found in potatoes and grains; and glycogen, used by animals to store glucose in the muscles.

Proteins and Amino Acids (22.4)

Proteins are polymers of amino acids and serve a variety of biological functions including structure composition, metabolic regulation, and muscle contraction. Enzymes are particularly important proteins that catalyze biochemical reactions in cells. Each amino acid contains a carbon atom bonded to an amine group, a carboxylic acid group, a hydrogen atom, and an R group. There are 20 amino acids in humans and they all differ only in their R group. Amino acids form peptide bonds between the amine end of one amino acid with the carboxylic end of another, creating dipeptides, tripeptides, etc., or polypeptides, large examples of which are called proteins.

Protein Structure (22.5)

Protein structure and shape are critical to protein function. Proteins can be broadly divided into two structural categories. Fibrous proteins are generally linear, insoluble structures that serve structural functions. Globular proteins fold into roughly spherical conformations with nonpolar side chains oriented to the interior and polar side chains oriented to the exterior; this structure makes them soluble in water. Protein structure can be analyzed at four levels. The primary structure is the sequence of the amino acid chain. The secondary structure refers to certain regular repeating patterns in the arrangement of protein chains, such as α-helix and β-pleated sheet patterns. The tertiary structure refers to large-scale bends and folds due to interactions between the R groups of amino acids such as hydrogen bonding, disulfide linkages, hydrophobic interactions, and salt bridges. Quaternary structure shows the way that monomeric subunits fit together in multimeric proteins that have more than one polypeptide chain.

Nucleic Acids (22.6)

Nucleic acids, such as DNA and RNA, are the chemical blueprints used to synthesize proteins. They are polymers of nucleotides, which are each composed of a sugar, a base, and a phosphate group. The bases of DNA are adenine (A), cytosine (C), guanine (G), and thymine (T), which are subject to complementary pairing: each pyrimidine base combines with only one purine base. Phosphate links bind the C5′ carbon of one sugar with the C3′ carbon of another sugar to make the polymeric chain. The order of the bases in a nucleic acid chain specifies the order of amino acids in a protein. Each amino acid is coded by a codon, a sequence of three bases. A gene is a sequence of codons that codes for a specific protein. Genes, in turn, make up structures called chromosomes.

DNA Replication, the Double Helix, and Protein Synthesis (22.7)

Though the DNA code is complete in any cell in the body, only certain cells express certain genes. DNA is two complementary strands wound around each other in a double helix. The strands are antiparallel: the bases of each strand face the interior and hydrogen bond to their complements on the other strand. A always binds to T and C always binds to G. In order to replicate, a DNA strand divides and an enzyme called DNA polymerase creates the complement of each of the divided strands, thereby making two copies of the original DNA molecule. To synthesize proteins, the section of DNA that codes for that gene unravels. Messenger RNA (mRNA) is synthesized as a copy of the gene. The mRNA then combines with ribosomes, structures that "read" the mRNA code and synthesize the correct sequence of amino acids.

Key Skills

Recognizing and Working with the Basic Structures of Lipids (22.2)

- Exercises 31–34

Recognizing and Working with the Basic Structures of Carbohydrates (22.3)

- Exercises 37–40

Identifying Chiral Carbon Atoms in Carbohydrates (22.3)
- Example 22.1 • For Practice 22.1 • Exercises 41, 42, 86

Drawing Structures for Amino Acids and Peptide Bonds (22.4)
- Example 22.2 • For Practice 22.2 • Exercises 49–58

Recognizing Levels of Protein Structure (22.5)
- Exercises 59–62

Recognizing Nucleic Acids and Nucleotides (22.6)
- Exercises 63, 64

EXERCISES

Review Questions

1. What is biochemistry? What significant advances in biochemistry have helped diabetics?
2. What is a lipid? What roles do lipids play in living organisms?
3. What is a fatty acid? Draw the general structure of a fatty acid.
4. What effect do double bonds have within the hydrocarbon chain of a fatty acid?
5. What are triglycerides? Draw a general structure of a triglyceride.
6. Explain the difference, both in terms of structure and in terms of properties, between a saturated fat and an unsaturated fat.
7. Describe the basic structure of phospholipids and glycolipids. What functions do these lipids have in living organisms?
8. What is a steroid? What are some functions of steroids?
9. What are carbohydrates? What role do they play in living organisms?
10. How do monosaccharides and disaccharides differ? Aldoses and ketoses?
11. How do simple and complex carbohydrates differ?
12. How do cellulose, starch, and glycogen differ? Describe the function of each.
13. What roles do proteins play in living organisms? List specific examples.
14. Describe the basic structure of an amino acid. How are amino acids linked together to form proteins?
15. How do the properties of the R groups in amino acids relate to the properties of proteins?
16. Why are amino acids chiral?
17. Draw the structure of a neutral amino acid and its dipolar ion.
18. Draw the structure of any two amino acids, showing how they link together to form a dipeptide.
19. List the ten essential amino acids. What does it mean for an amino acid to be essential?
20. How do fibrous proteins and globular proteins differ?
21. Describe the various levels of protein structure (primary, secondary, tertiary, and quaternary).
22. What types of interactions or bonds maintain each of the structures listed in the previous problem?
23. Describe the secondary structures known as α-helix and β-pleated sheet.
24. What is the function of nucleic acids in living organisms?
25. What is the general structure of a nucleic acid?
26. The bases in nucleic acids are *complementary*. What does this mean?
27. What is a codon? A gene? A chromosome?
28. Do most cells contain complete copies of an organism's DNA? Do most cells express all of the genes contained in their DNA?
29. Explain the mechanism by which DNA is replicated.
30. Explain the mechanism by which proteins are synthesized from the information contained within DNA.

Problems by Topic

Lipids

31. Determine whether or not each molecule is a lipid. If the molecule is a lipid, indicate the kind of lipid. If it is a fatty acid or a triglyceride, classify it as saturated or unsaturated.

a. $CH_3-CH_2-CH_2-CH_2-CH_2-CH_2-CH_2-CH_2-CH_2-CH_3$

b. $H_2N-CH(CH_2CH_2CH_2CH_2NH_2)-C(=O)-OH$

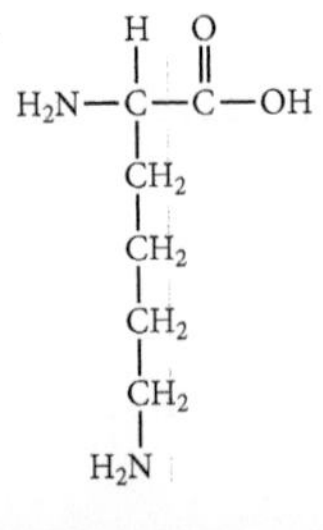

H O
H₂N—C—C—OH
CH₂
CH₂
CH₂
CH₂
H₂N

c. $H_3C-CH_2-CH_2-CH_2-CH_2-CH_2-CH_2-CH_2-CH_2-C(=O)OH$

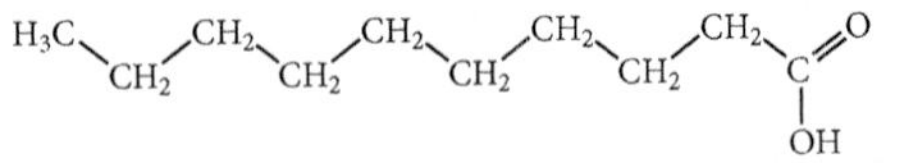

d. H₃C, CH₃, CH₃, CH₃, H₃C, HO

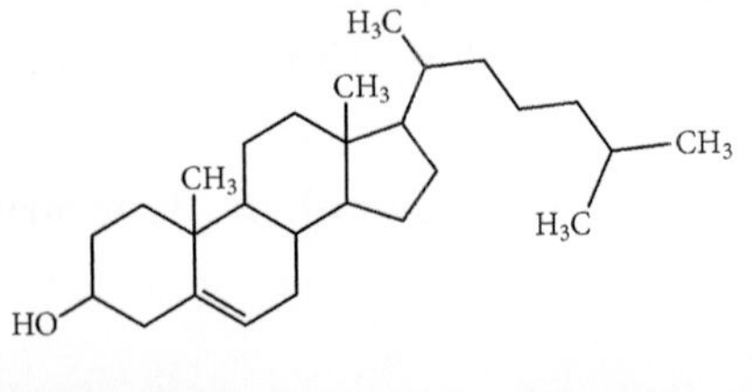

32. Determine whether or not each molecule is a lipid. If the molecule is a lipid, state the kind of lipid. If it is a fatty acid or a triglyceride, classify it as saturated or unsaturated.

a.

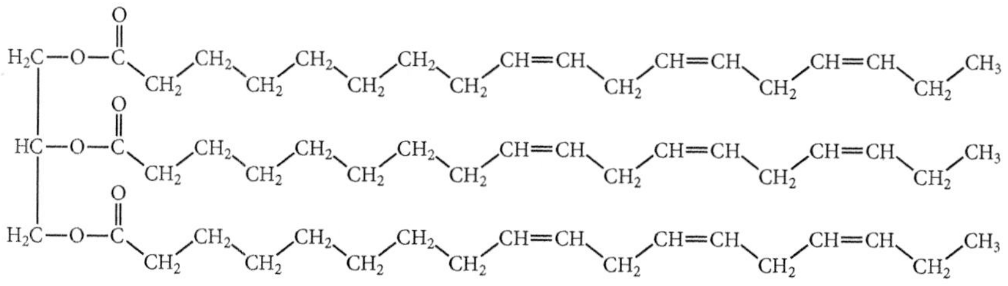

$H_2C-O-C(=O)-CH_2-CH_2-CH_2-CH_2-CH_2-CH_2-CH_2-CH=CH-CH_2-CH=CH-CH_2-CH=CH-CH_2-CH_3$

$HC-O-C(=O)-CH_2-CH_2-CH_2-CH_2-CH_2-CH_2-CH_2-CH=CH-CH_2-CH=CH-CH_2-CH=CH-CH_2-CH_3$

$H_2C-O-C(=O)-CH_2-CH_2-CH_2-CH_2-CH_2-CH_2-CH_2-CH=CH-CH_2-CH=CH-CH_2-CH=CH-CH_2-CH_3$

b. $CH_3-CH_2-CH_2-CH_2-CH_2-CH_2-CH_2-CH_2-CH_2-CH_2-CH_2-CH_3$

c.

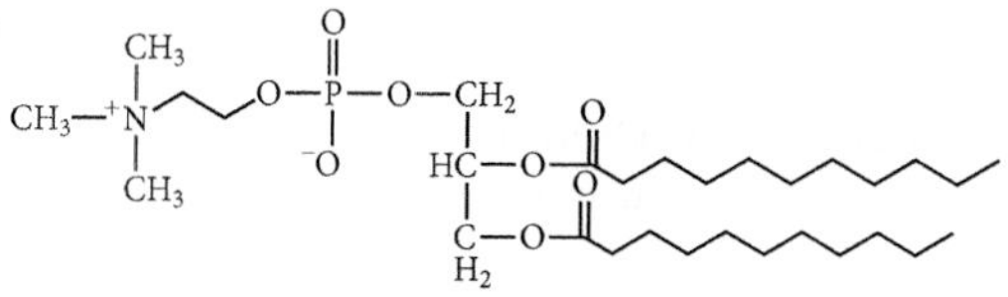

$CH_3-{}^{+}N(CH_3)(CH_3)-CH_2CH_2-O-P(=O)(O^-)-O-CH_2-HC(-O-C(=O)-R)-H_2C-O-C(=O)-R$

d.

$H_2N-C(H)(C(H)(CH_3)-CH_2-CH_3)-C(=O)-N(H)-C(H)(CH_2-SH)-C(=O)-OH$

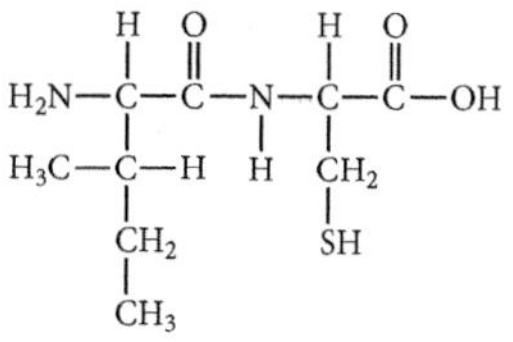

33. Determine whether or not each molecule is a fatty acid. If it is a fatty acid, classify it as saturated, monounsaturated, or polyunsaturated.

a. $CH_3-CH_2-CH_2-CH_2-CH_2-CH_2-CH_2-CH_2-CH_2-CH_2-CH_2-CH_2-CH_2-CH_2-CH_2-C(=O)-OH$

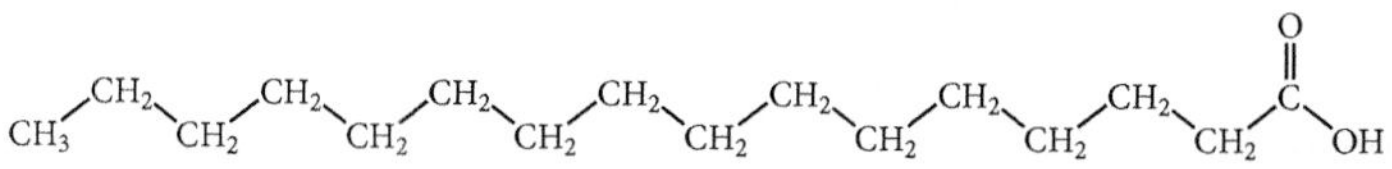

b. $CH_3-CH_2-CH_2-CH_2-CH_2-CH_2-CH_2-CH_2-CH_2-CH_2-CH_2-CH_2-CH_2-CH_3$

c. $CH_3-CH_2-CH_2-CH_2-O-CH_2-CH_2-CH_2-CH_3$

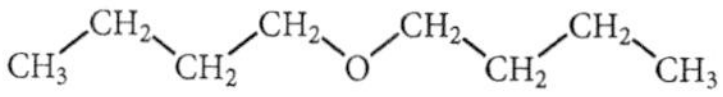

d. $CH_3-CH_2-CH_2-CH_2-CH_2-CH_2-CH_2-CH_2-CH=CH-CH_2-CH_2-CH_2-CH_2-CH_2-CH_2-CH_2-C(=O)-OH$

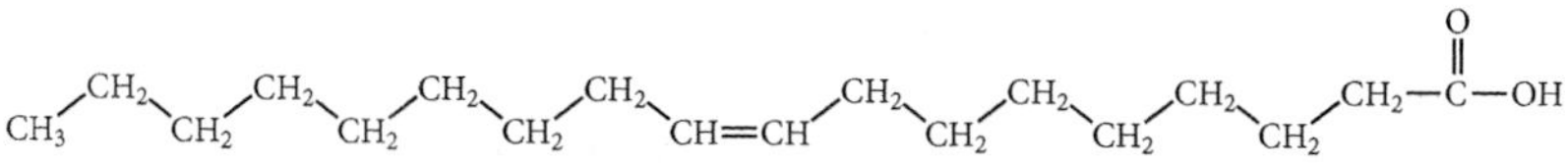

34. Which fatty acid is most likely to be a solid at room temperature?

a. $CH_3-CH_2-CH_2-C(=O)-OH$

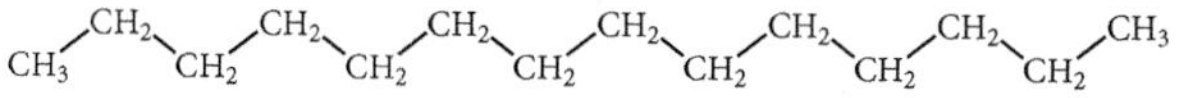

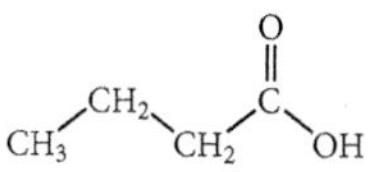

b. $CH_3-CH_2-CH_2-CH_2-CH_2-CH_2-CH_2-CH_2-CH_2-CH_2-CH_2-CH_2-CH_2-C(=O)-OH$

c. $CH_3-CH_2-CH_2-CH_2-CH_2-CH_2-CH_2-CH_2-CH=CH-CH_2-CH_2-CH_2-CH_2-CH_2-CH_2-CH_2-C(=O)-OH$

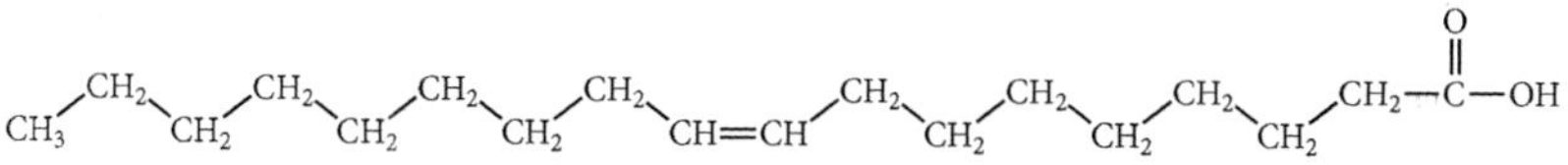

d. $CH_3-CH_2-CH_2-CH_2-CH_2-CH=CH-CH_2-CH=CH-CH_2-CH_2-CH_2-CH_2-CH_2-CH_2-CH_2-C(=O)-OH$

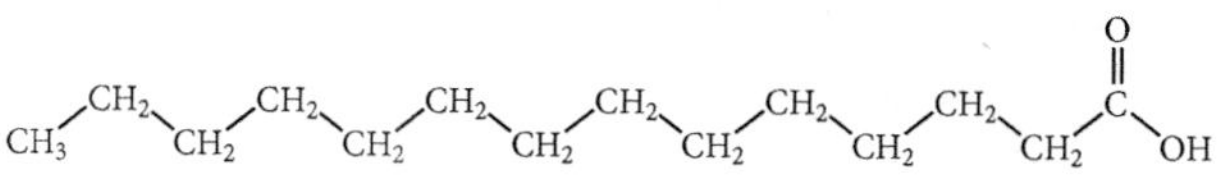

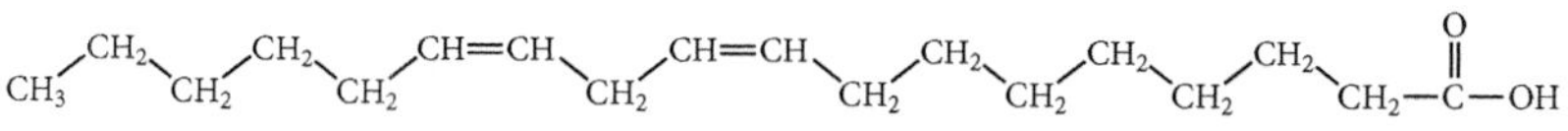

35. Draw structures showing the reaction of glycerol with linoleic acid to form the triglyceride trilinolean. Would you expect this triglyceride to be a fat or an oil?

36. Draw structures showing the reaction of glycerol with myristic acid to form the triglyceride trimyristin. Would you expect this triglyceride to be a fat or an oil?

Carbohydrates

37. Determine whether or not each structure is a carbohydrate. If the molecule is a carbohydrate, classify it as a monosaccharide, disaccharide, or trisaccharide.

a.

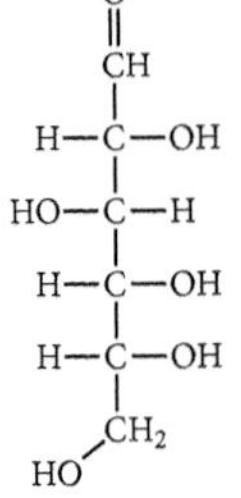

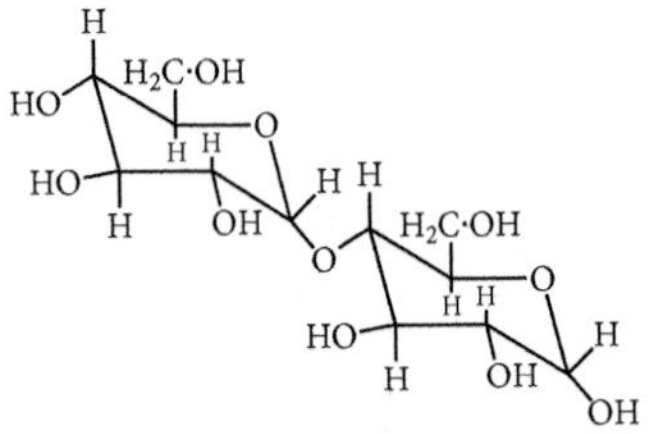

b.

c.

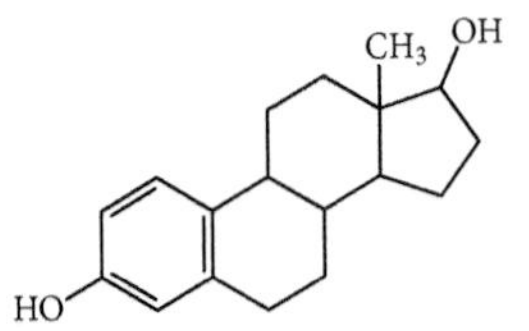

d.

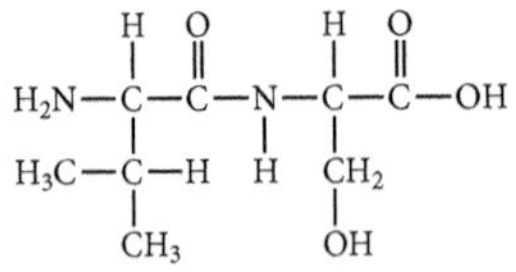

38. Determine whether or not each structure is a carbohydrate. If the molecule is a carbohydrate, classify it as a monosaccharide, disaccharide, or trisaccharide.

a.

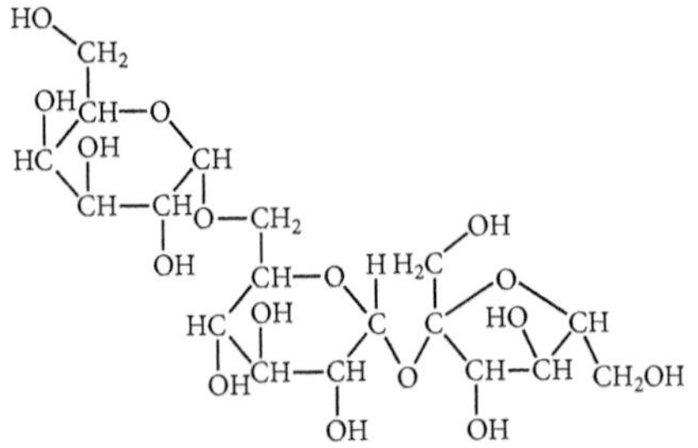

b.

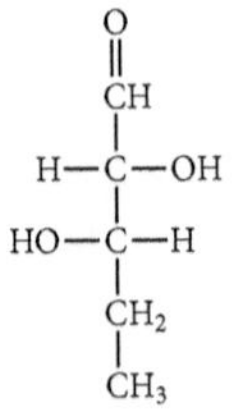

c.

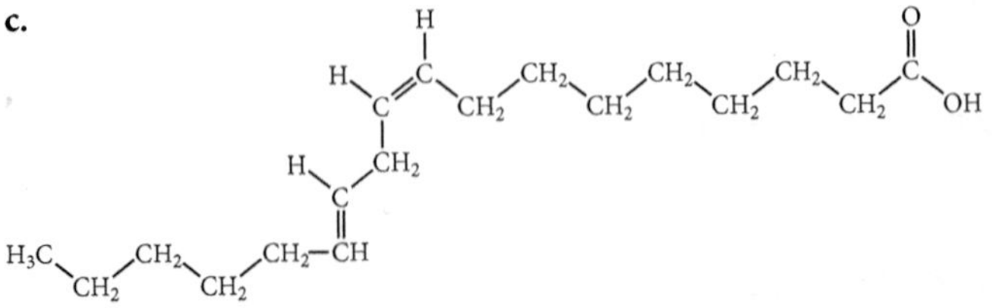

d.

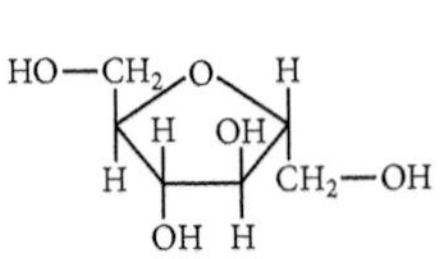

39. Classify each saccharide as an aldose or a ketose. Also classify each as a triose, tetrose, pentose, etc.

a.

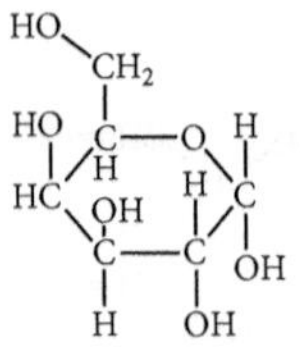

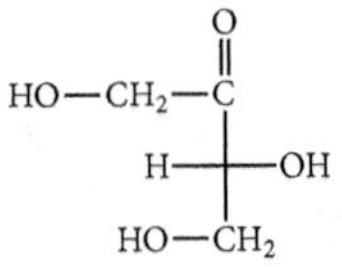

b.

c.

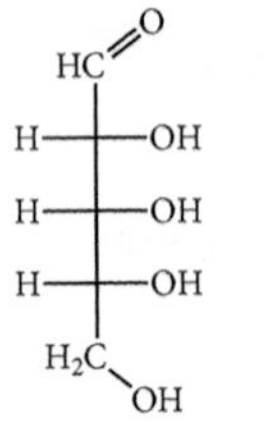

d.

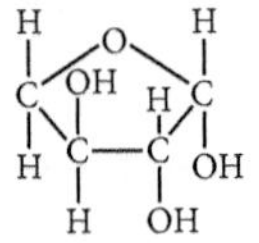

40. Classify each saccharide as an aldose or a ketose. Also classify each as a triose, tetrose, pentose, etc.

a.

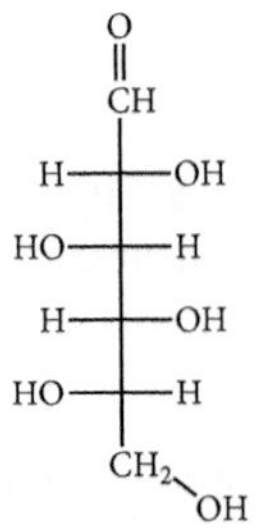

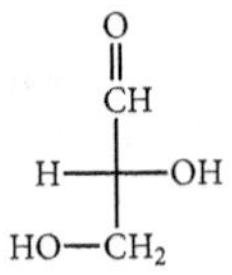

b.

c.

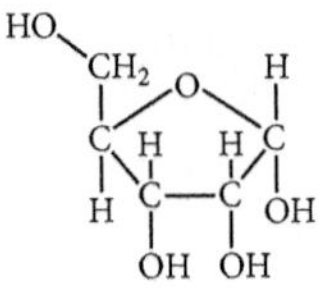

d.

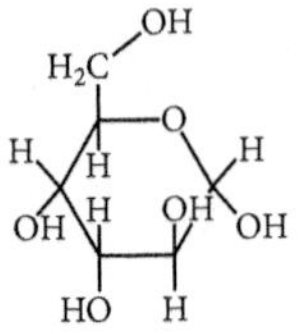

41. For each of the structures in Problem 39, identify all the chiral carbon atoms and assign an absolute configuration (*R*, *S*) to each.

42. For each of the structures in Problem 40, identify all the chiral carbon atoms and assign an absolute configuration (*R*, *S*) to each.

43. Draw structures for the straight-chain and ring forms of glucose.

44. Draw structures for the straight-chain and ring forms of fructose.

45. Draw the products that result from the hydrolysis of the carbohydrate:

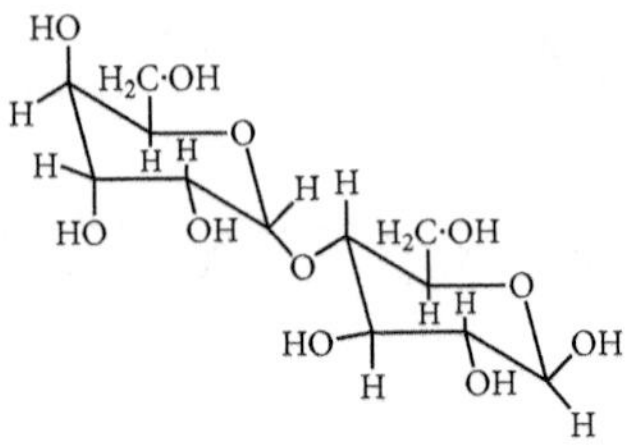

46. Draw the products that result from the hydrolysis of the carbohydrate:

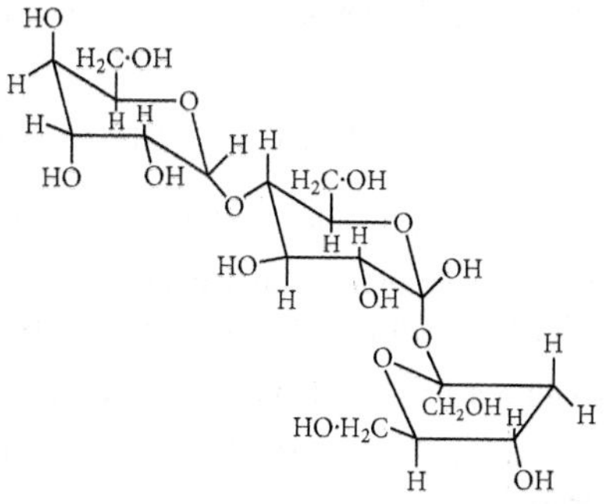

47. Draw the structure of sucrose. Label the glucose and fructose rings in this disaccharide.

48. Lactose is a disaccharide of glucose and galactose. Draw the structure of lactose.

Amino Acids and Proteins

49. Draw each amino acid in its dipolar ion, or zwitterion, form:
a. Thr b. Ala c. Leu d. Lys

50. Draw each amino acid in its dipolar ion, or zwitterion, form:
a. Val b. Phe c. Tyr d. Cys

51. Draw the structures of the two enantiomers of alanine.

52. Draw the structures of the two enantiomers of cysteine.

53. How many different tripeptides can form from serine, glycine, and cysteine? Give the amino acid sequence of each one.

54. How many dipeptides can form from leucine and serine? Give the amino acid sequence for each one.

55. Draw the reaction by which serine and tyrosine form a peptide bond.

56. Draw the reaction by which valine and asparagine form a peptide bond.

57. Draw a structure for each tripeptide.
a. Gln-Met-Cys b. Ser-Leu-Cys
c. Cys-Leu-Ser

58. Draw a structure for each tetrapeptide.
a. Ser-Ala-Leu-Cys b. Gln-Met-Cys-Gly
c. Gly-Cys-Met-Gln

59. A phenylalanine amino acid on a protein strand undergoes hydrophobic interactions with another phenylalanine amino acid that is 26 amino acid units away. The resulting fold in the protein is an example of what kind of structure (primary, secondary, tertiary, or quaternary)?

60. An amino acid on a protein strand forms a hydrogen bond to another amino acid that is four amino acid units away. The next amino acid on the chain does the same, hydrogen bonding to an amino acid that is four amino acids away from it. This pattern repeats itself over a significant part of the protein chain. The resulting pattern in the protein is an example of what kind of structure (primary, secondary, tertiary, or quaternary)?

61. The amino acid sequence in one section of a protein is shown here. It represents what kind of structure (primary, secondary, tertiary, or quaternary)?

-Lys-Glu-Thr-Ala-Ala-Ala-Lys-Phe-Glu-

62. A dimeric protein is composed of two individual chains of amino acids. The way these two chains fit together is an example of what kind of structure (primary, secondary, tertiary, or quaternary)?

Nucleic Acids

63. Determine whether or not each structure is a nucleotide. For each nucleotide, identify the base as A, T, C, or G.

a.

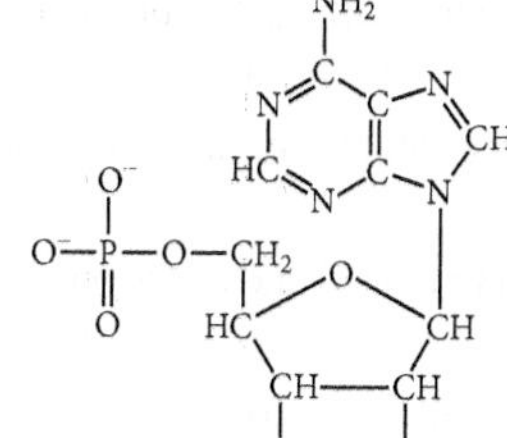

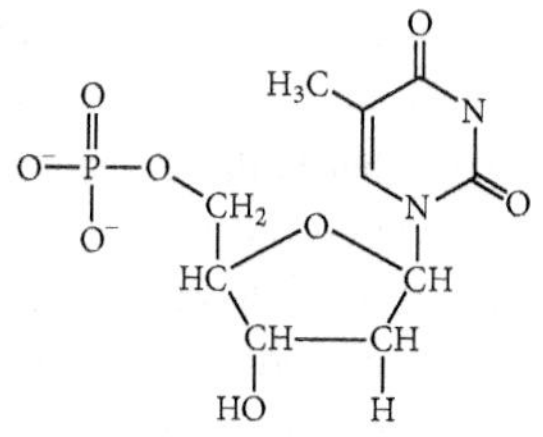

b.

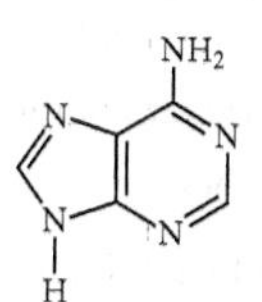

c.

d.

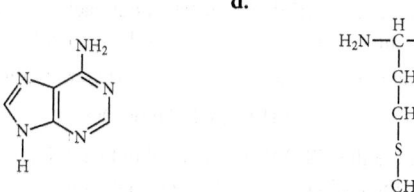

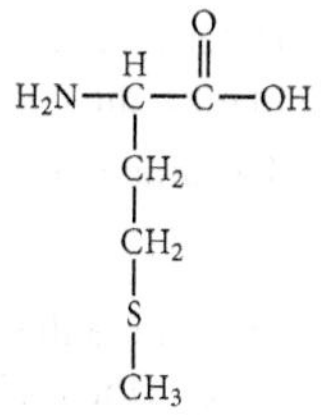

64. Determine whether or not each structure is a nucleotide. For each nucleotide, identify the base as A, T, C, or G.

a.

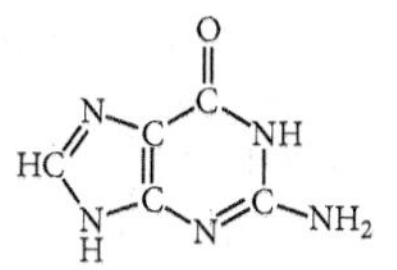

b.

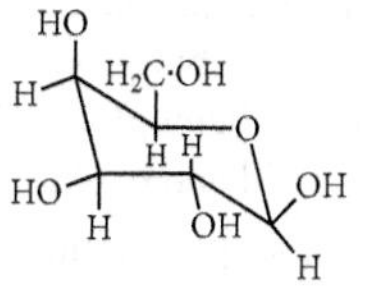

c.

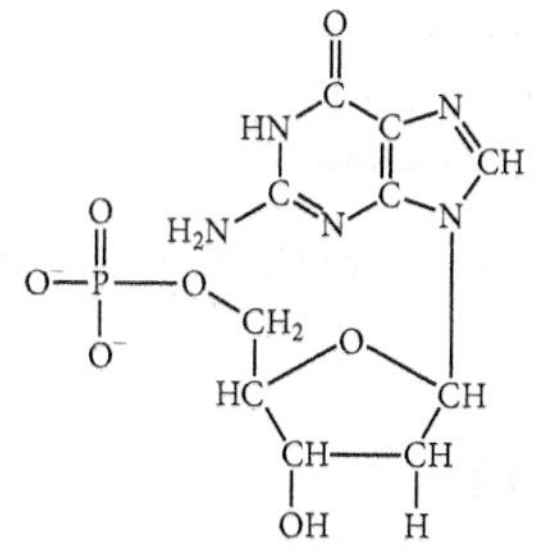

d.

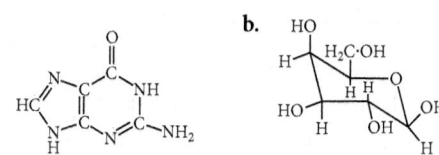

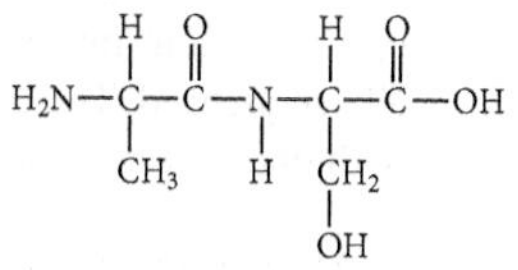

65. Draw the structures of the two purine bases in nucleic acids.

66. Draw the structures of the three pyrimidine bases in nucleic acids.

67. Draw the DNA strand that is complementary to the DNA strand shown here.

T G T A C G C

68. Draw the DNA strand that is complementary to the DNA strand shown here.

A T G A C T G

69. A monomeric protein contains 154 amino acids. How many codons code for these amino acids? How many nucleotides?

70. A dimeric protein contains 142 amino acids in one strand and 148 in the other. How many codons code for these amino acids? How many nucleotides?

Cumulative Problems

71. Determine the class of biochemical compound that contains each type of linkage.
    a. peptide bonds
    b. glycosidic linkage
    c. ester linkage

72. Name the type of polymer associated with each monomer.
    a. nucleotide b. amino acid c. saccharide

73. What is the difference between a codon and a nucleotide? A codon and a gene?

74. What is the difference between a fatty acid and a triglyceride? A triglyceride and a phospholipid?

75. The amino acid alanine has the condensed structural formula:

$$NH_2CH(CH_3)COOH$$

Determine the VSEPR geometry about each internal atom and make a three-dimensional sketch of the molecule.

76. The amino acid serine has the condensed structural formula:

$$NH_2CH(CH_2OH)COOH$$

Determine the VSEPR geometry about each internal atom and make a three-dimensional sketch of the molecule.

77. Which amino acids in Table 22.3 are most likely to be involved in hydrophobic interactions?

78. Sickle-cell anemia is caused by a genetic defect that substitutes valine for glutamic acid at one position in two of the four chains of the hemoglobin protein. The result is a decrease in the water solubility of hemoglobin. Examine the structures of valine and glutamic acid and explain why this might be so.

79. Determining the amino acid sequence in a protein usually involves treating the protein with various reagents that break up the protein into smaller fragments which can be individually sequenced. Treating a particular 11-amino acid polypeptide with one reagent produced the fragments:

Ala-Leu-Phe-Gly-Asn-Lys   Trp-Glu-Cys   Gly-Arg

Treating the same polypeptide with a different reagent produced the fragments:

Glu-Cys   Gly-Asn-Lys-Trp   Gly-Arg-Ala-Leu-Phe

What is the amino acid sequence of the polypeptide?

80. Treating a particular polypeptide with one reagent (as described in the previous problem) produced the fragments:

Gly-Glu-Ser-Lys   Trp-Arg   Leu-Thr-Ala-Trp

Treating the same polypeptide with a different reagent produced the fragments:

Gly-Glu   Thr-Ala-Trp   Ser-Lys-Trp-Arg-Leu

What is the amino acid sequence of the polypeptide?

81. Naturally occurring D-glucose is one of a pair of enantiomers. Its mirror image is L-glucose. Draw the two cyclic six-membered isomers of L-glucose that differ in the configuration around C1 and indicate which is α and which is β.

82. Calculate the mass percent of phosphorus in a strand of DNA that consists of equal amounts of each of the four N-bases.

83. The double helical structure of DNA disrupts on heating but reforms on cooling. Use thermodynamic reasoning to account for these observations.

84. From the structural formula of cholesterol shown on page 962, determine **(a)** the composition, and **(b)** the number of chirality centres.

85. Biologically occurring amino acids are all L enantiomers, which means that they rotate plane polarized light counterclockwise. For amino acids, the L enantiomers correspond to the *S* absolute configuration at the chiral carbon atom. Draw the correct absolute stereochemistry for the following amino acids:
    a. alanine
    b. cysteine
    c. serine
    d. aspartic acid

86. Identify the amino acid in Table 22.3 that contains two chirality centres.

Challenge Problems

87. One way to fight viral infections is to prevent a virus from replicating its DNA. Without DNA replication, the virus cannot multiply. Some viral drug therapies cause the introduction of *fake* nucleotides into cells. When the virus uses one of these fake nucleotides in an attempt to replicate its DNA, the fake nucleotide doesn't work and viral DNA replication is halted. For example, azidothymidine (AZT), a drug used to fight the human immunodeficiency virus (HIV) that causes AIDS, results in the introduction of the following fake thymine-containing nucleotide into cells. Examine the structures of the real nucleotide and the AZT fake nucleotide. Can you propose a mechanism for how this fake nucleotide might halt DNA replication?

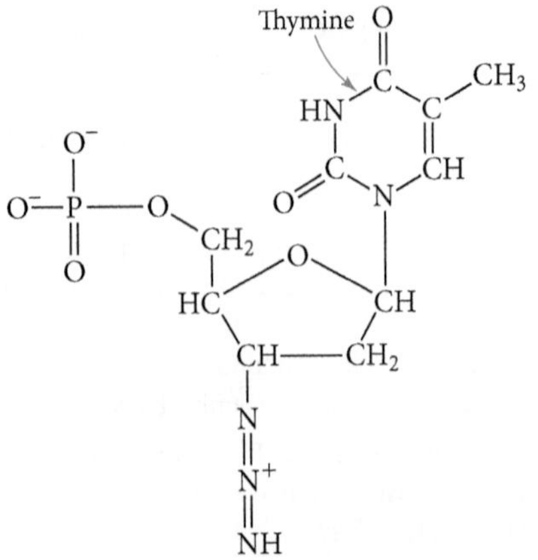

Thymine

AZT nucleotide

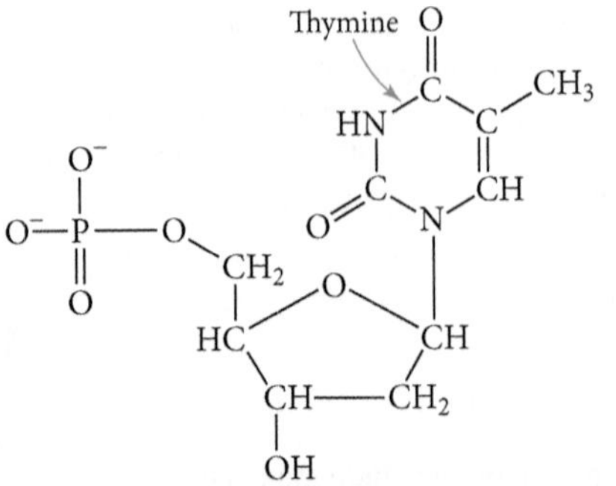

Thymine

Actual nucleotide

88. Draw each molecule and identify the chirality centres within them.
   a. ribose
   b. galactose
   c. 5-deoxyribose (*Hint:* The 5 indicates that the oxygen is removed from the fifth carbon.)

89. Glucose transport across the red blood cell membranes (erythrocyte membrane) is a well-studied system. One laboratory project obtained the data shown here for glucose transport.

$[\text{Glucose}]_{\text{outside}}$ (mM)	Rate of Glucose Entry (μM/min^{-1})
0.5	12
1.0	19
2.0	27
3.0	32
4.0	35

The kinetics of glucose transport through the membrane follows the Michaelis–Menten equation:

$$V_0 = \frac{V_{max}[\text{glucose}]}{K_t + [\text{glucose}]}$$

V_0 = rate of glucose entry

V_{max} = maximum rate (the point at which addition of glucose has no effect on the rate)

K_t = transport constant

The Michaelis–Menten equation can be rearranged so that a plot $1/V_0$ versus 1/[glucose] produces a straight line. Rearrange the equation and plot the data in order to determine K_t and V_{max} for glucose transport across the erythrocyte membrane.

90. Eukaryotic DNA is equipped with special ends called telomers. Telomers are made up of hexanucleotide sequences that repeat at the ends of the DNA. For example, human DNA features repeating AGGGTT sequences. Functionally, telomers protect the ends of chromosomes from being treated as a broken piece of DNA needing repair. Interestingly, telomers are cut off each time the DNA is replicated, indicating a possible cellular clock that allows only a certain number of cellular replications. Telomerase is the enzyme which catalyzes the synthesis of telomers. Telomerase is found in limited quantities within certain cells such as fetal tissue, adult male germ cells, and stem cells. It is also found in over 85% of tumour cells. Researchers speculate that the telomerase activity may be linked to cancer. Give an explanation for why telomerase activity could be associated with cancer and speculate on ways in which cancer treatments in the future may capitalize on research on this enzyme.

91. Write the major equilibrium that is established in a solution of glycine at pH = 2.0 and at pH = 10.0. The pK_a of the COOH group is 2.3 and the pK_a of the NH_3^+ group is 9.6. Determine the relative concentrations of each member of the relevant conjugate acid–base pair at pH = 2.0 and pH = 10.0. Calculate the pH at which glycine is neutral.

Conceptual Problems

92. How many different tetrapeptides can form from four different amino acids?

93. Could the genetic code have been based on just three bases and three-base codons? Explain why or why not. (Assume that the code must accommodate 20 different amino acids.)

94. The genetic code is random, which means that a particular codon could have coded for a different amino acid. The genetic code is also nearly universal, meaning that it is the same code in nearly all organisms (and in the few where it differs, it does so only slightly). If scientists ever find life on another planet, they will be curious to know its genetic code. What would a completely different genetic code indicate about the origin of the life-form? What would a genetic code identical to terrestrial life indicate?

23 Chemistry of the Nonmetals

What one learns in chemistry is that Nature wrote all the rules of structuring; man does not invent chemical structuring rules; he only discovers the rules. All the chemist can do is find out what Nature permits, and any substances that are thus developed or discovered are inherently natural.

—R. Buckminster Fuller (1895–1983)

Scientists have been able to synthesize carbon nanotubes that each have an insulating boron nitride sheath. These structures are like electrical wires 100 000 times thinner than a human hair.

THROUGHOUT THIS TEXT, YOU HAVE been introduced to many chemical topics, but you still may not know the composition of some everyday objects such as a drinking glass, a computer chip, or even rocks and soil. In this chapter and the following two chapters, we explore the descriptive chemistry of the nonmetals and metals. These descriptions are part of a branch of chemistry called inorganic chemistry. We begin our exploration of descriptive inorganic chemistry in this chapter by looking at the chemistry of some of the main-group elements. The main-group elements are grouped together because their valence electrons occupy only *s* or *p* orbitals; however, their properties vary greatly. The main-group elements include metals, nonmetals, and semimetals, and they may be solids, liquids, or gases at room temperature. This great diversity of properties, bonding, and structures cannot be adequately described in a single chapter. Therefore, this chapter focuses on only a few main-group elements (silicon, boron, carbon, nitrogen, phosphorus, oxygen, sulfur, and the halogens) and their compounds in an effort to illustrate the diversity within the group.

23.1 Insulated Nanowires

In 1991, scientists discovered carbon nanotubes, the long, thin, hollow cylinders of carbon atoms that we discuss in some detail in Section 23.5. In the late 1990s, scientists discovered that they could make similar tubes from boron nitride. Boron nitride contains BN units that are isoelectronic with carbon in the sense that each BN unit contains eight valence electrons, or four per atom (just like carbon). The size and electronegativity of a carbon atom are also almost equal to the average of those properties for a boron atom and a nitrogen atom, as shown in Table 23.1. Because of this, BN forms a number of structures that are similar to those formed by carbon, including nanotubes.

TABLE 23.1 Properties of BN and C

Element	Atomic Radius (pm)	Ionization Energy (kJ mol^{-1})	Electronegativity
B	85	800	2
BN	77.5 average	1101 average	2.5 average
N	70	1402	3
C	77	1086	2.5

An important difference between boron nitride nanotubes and carbon nanotubes is their conductivity. Carbon nanotubes conduct electrical current but boron nitride tubes act as insulators. In 2003, scientists were able to combine these two sorts of nanotubes into one structure: a conducting carbon nanotube with an insulating boron nitride sheath, shown in Figure 23.1 ▶. The result is an insulated conducting wire that is 100 000 times thinner than a human hair. Such thin wires may someday be used in computers and other electronic devices, allowing these devices to continue to become smaller and more efficient.

The more we learn about the structures and reactivities of known materials, the better equipped we are to discover new materials and applications. Even though it may seem that most inorganic compounds have already been discovered and analyzed, new materials, with immense impacts on our society, are constantly being discovered. As Buckminster Fuller states in this chapter's opening quote, we continue to find "what Nature permits." In some cases, what nature permits turns out to be extremely useful to society.

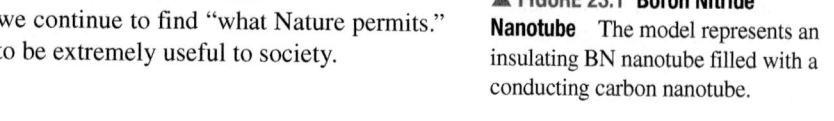

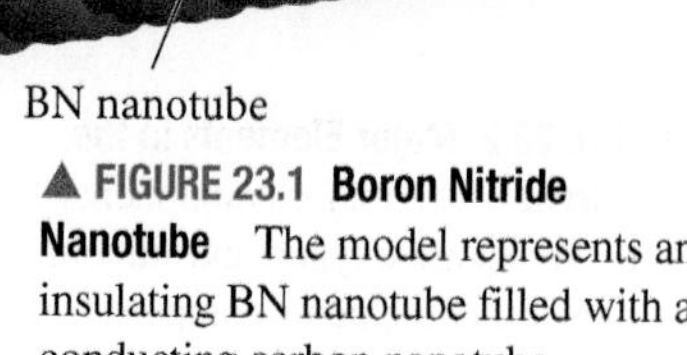

▲ **FIGURE 23.1 Boron Nitride Nanotube** The model represents an insulating BN nanotube filled with a conducting carbon nanotube.

23.2 The Main-Group Elements: Bonding and Properties

We identify the **main-group elements** by their valence electrons and their electron configurations. In this chapter, we focus on groups 13–17, the major part of the *p* block in the periodic table. The *p* orbitals fill incrementally across any row of this section of the periodic table; they contain from one electron in group 13 to five electrons in group 17 (the halogens). The physical properties of the elements, such as atomic size and electronegativity, also change across each period, and this affects their reactivity and the types of compounds they form.

Atomic Size and Types of Bonds

Recall from Section 8.5 that the effective nuclear charge of the main-group elements becomes greater as we move to the right across any row in the periodic table. This increasing effective charge results in smaller radii, increasing electronegativity, and increasing ionization energy as we move to the right across the periods. Consequently, as we have

See Chapter 8 for a more thorough discussion of the periodic trends and exceptions in these properties of the elements.

seen since the early chapters of this book, the nonmetals on the right side of the periodic table tend to form anions in ionic compounds. They are easily reduced, gaining electrons to completely fill their *p* orbitals and attain noble gas electron configurations. These elements act in reactions as *oxidizing agents*—they oxidize other substances while they are themselves reduced. The smallest halogens and the elements in the oxygen group are the strongest oxidizing agents in the *p* block.

Elements near the centre of the *p* block have fewer *p* electrons and do not usually fill the *p* orbitals by forming anions; instead they share electrons, forming covalent bonds. We see this type of reactivity in the vast array of molecular compounds formed by the smaller elements in the carbon and nitrogen groups. The main-group elements on the far left of the *p* block have only one *p* electron and form cations in ionic compounds and electron-deficient species (species with an incomplete octet) in covalent compounds.

13	14	15	16	17	18
					2 He
5 B	6 C	7 N	8 O	9 F	10 Ne
13 Al	14 Si	15 P	16 S	17 Cl	18 Ar
31 Ga	32 Ge	33 As	34 Se	35 Br	36 Kr
49 In	50 Sn	51 Sb	52 Te	53 I	54 Xe
81 Tl	82 Pb	83 Bi	84 Po	85 At	86 Rn

▲ The *p*-block elements.

Notice that as we move to the right across any row in the *p* block, the type of bonding changes as the elements become less metallic. Recall from Section 8.8 that metallic character increases as you go down each column. The diagonal group of metalloid elements stretching from boron to astatine divides the main-group elements: to the left of this diagonal, the elements are metals that form cations and metallic compounds; to the right, the elements are nonmetals that form anions and covalent compounds.

The vast range in elemental properties, from those of metallic elements such as thallium and lead that have very low electronegativities of 1.8 and 1.9 (respectively) to those of the nonmetallic elements such as oxygen and fluorine that have the highest electronegativities of 3.5 and 4.0 (respectively), provides for the great chemical diversity of the elements in the *p* block. These elements include metals, alloys, simple covalent compounds, enormous covalent network compounds, simple binary ionic compounds, and complex chain and layered ionic compounds.

23.3 Silicates: The Most Abundant Matter in Earth's Crust

The most abundant elements in the Earth's crust are oxygen (45–50% by mass) and silicon (about 28% by mass). The few other elements that individually comprise more than 1% of the crust's mass are aluminum, iron, calcium, magnesium, sodium, and potassium (as shown in Figure 23.2 ▼), and most of these are found in silicon and oxygen compounds. In order to understand most of the matter on the Earth's surface, we must understand silicon and oxygen compounds.

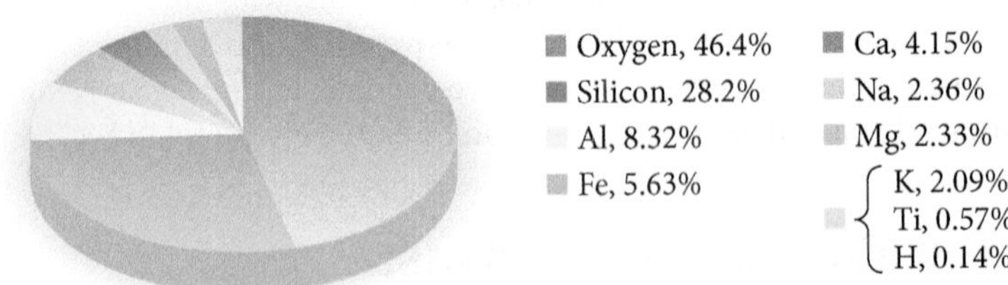

▶ **FIGURE 23.2 Major Elements in the Earth's Crust** The major components of Earth's crust are oxygen and silicon. Only a few other elements compose more than 1% of the crust.

Silicates are covalent atomic solids (see Section 11.2) that contain silicon, oxygen, and various metal atoms. Rocks, clays, and soils contain silicates. Their great diversity illustrates again a theme that we have encountered since Chapter 1 of this text: the properties of substances are determined by their atomic and molecular structures. The structures of silicates, therefore, determine their properties—and since these structures are varied, their properties are also varied. Some silicates form strong three-dimensional materials, while others break into sheets, and still others are highly fibrous. Let's examine more closely several of these structures.

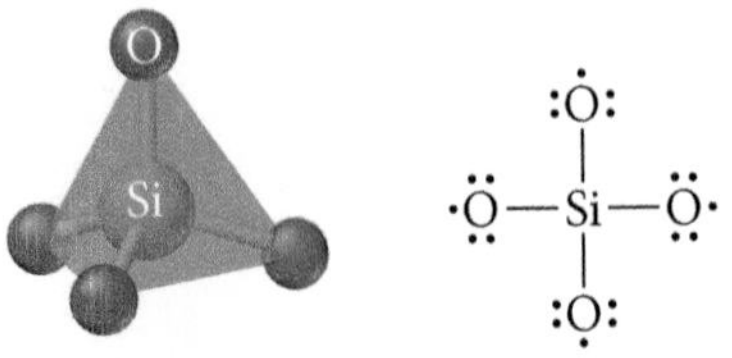

▲ **FIGURE 23.3 SiO_4 Tetrahedron** In an SiO_4 tetrahedron, silicon occupies the centre of the tetrahedron and one oxygen atom occupies each corner.

Quartz and Glass

Silicon and oxygen form a network covalent structure in which a silicon atom bonds to four oxygen atoms, forming a tetrahedral shape with the silicon atom in the middle and the four oxygen atoms at the corners of the tetrahedron, as shown in Figure 23.3 ◀. In this structure, the silicon atom bonds to each oxygen atom with a single covalent sigma bond. In contrast to carbon, which often bonds to oxygen with a double bond (one sigma and one pi bond), silicon forms only a single bond with oxygen, because the silicon atom is too large to allow substantial overlap between the *p* orbitals on the two atoms. The silicon atom in this structure, by bonding to four oxygen atoms, obtains a complete octet. However, each oxygen atom is one electron short of an octet. Therefore, each O atom forms a second covalent bond to a different Si atom, forming the three-dimensional structure of **quartz**. Quartz has a formula unit of SiO_2 and is generally called **silica**. Each Si atom is in a tetrahedron surrounded by four O atoms, and each O atom acts as a bridge connecting the corners of two tetrahedrons, as shown in Figure 23.4 ▶. Silica melts when heated above 1500 °C. After melting, if cooled quickly, silica does not crystallize back into the quartz structure. Instead, the Si atoms and O atoms form a randomly ordered or amorphous structure called a glass. Indeed, common glass is amorphous SiO_2.

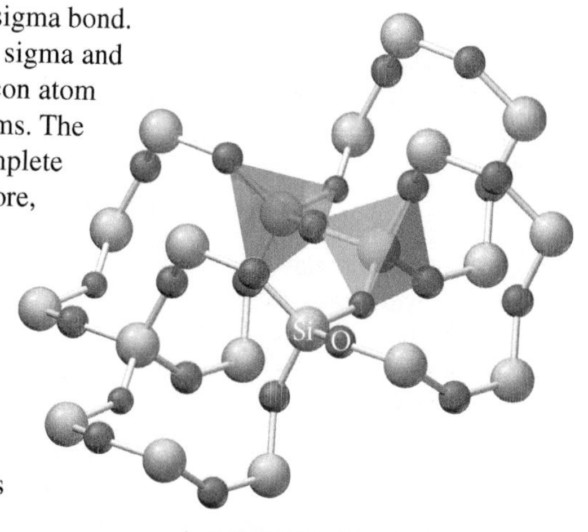

▲ **FIGURE 23.4 Structure of Quartz** In the quartz structure, each Si atom is in a tetrahedron surrounded by four O atoms, and each O atom is a bridge connecting the corners of two tetrahedrons.

Aluminosilicates

Aluminosilicates are a family of compounds in which aluminum atoms substitute for silicon atoms in some of the lattice sites of the silica structure. Since the aluminum ion has only three valence electrons (in contrast to the four valence electrons of silicon), a SiO_2 unit becomes AlO_2^- upon substitution of aluminum. The negative charge is balanced by a positive counterion. A common group of aluminosilicates are the feldspars, an example of which is the mineral albite. In albite, one-fourth of the Si atoms are replaced by Al atoms. Na^+ ions provide the necessary balancing positive charge. The formula for albite is $Na(AlSi_3O_8)$, but it may be written as $Na(AlO_2)(SiO_2)_3$ to illustrate the substitution of Al for Si.

EXAMPLE 23.1 DETERMINING THE COMPOSITION OF AN ALUMINOSILICATE

Write the formula for anorthite, an aluminosilicate crystal in which Al atoms substitute for one-half of the Si atoms and the charge is balanced by Ca^{2+} ions.

SOLUTION

The AlO_2^- unit substitutes for one-half of the SiO_2 units; therefore, the formula has equal numbers of AlO_2^- and SiO_2 units. Every AlO_2^- ion in the formula must be balanced by a corresponding positive charge. Since Ca^{2+} has a 2+ charge, it can balance two AlO_2^- units. Thus, the formula for anorthite is $Ca(Al_2Si_2O_8)$ or $Ca(AlO_2)_2(SiO_2)_2$.

FOR PRACTICE 23.1

Orthoclase is a crystal in which Al^{3+} substitutes for one-fourth of the Si^{4+} ions. K^+ ions balance the charge. Write the formula for orthoclase.

Individual Silicate Units, Silicate Chains, and Silicate Sheets

In many silicate compounds, the oxygen atoms are not connected to two silicon atoms to form the neutral compound that is found in quartz. Instead, the oxygen atoms gain electrons from metal atoms and form polyatomic anions, such as SiO_4^{4-}. The positively charged metal ions then bond to the negatively charged silicon oxide. In these minerals, the SiO_4 tetrahedrons occur singly, in chains, or in sheets.

When a tetrahedron occurs singly (not bonded to other tetrahedrons), it forms the SiO_4^{4-} polyatomic anion (which has four extra electrons that satisfy the octet rule for the four oxygen atoms). These types of silicates are **orthosilicates** (or nesosilicates) and require cations that have a sum total charge of 4+ to neutralize the negative charge. The cations can be of a single metal, such as Zn^{2+} in Zn_2SiO_4 (the mineral willemite), or they can be a mixture of different metals, such as the family of crystals called olivines

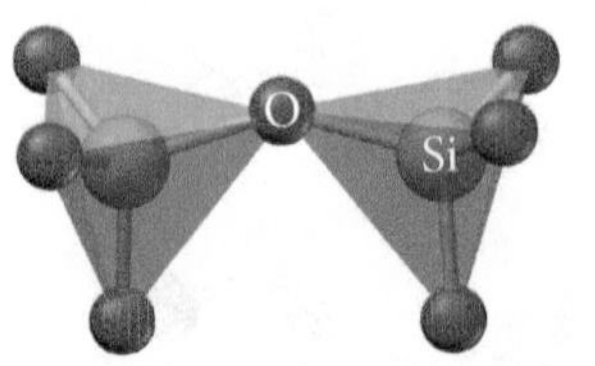

$^-O-Si(O^-)_2-O-Si(O^-)_2-O^-$

Formula unit: $Si_2O_7^{6-}$

▲ **FIGURE 23.5 Pyrosilicate Structure** In pyrosilicates, the silicate tetrahedrons share one corner, forming $Si_2O_7^{6-}$ units. Pyrosilicates are also called sorosilicates.

$[(Mg,Fe)_2SiO_4]$ where the Mg^{2+} and Fe^{2+} ions can exist in variable proportions, providing a total charge of 4+. All of these compounds are held together by the ionic bonding between the metal cations and SiO_4^{4-} polyatomic anions.

The silicate tetrahedrons can also form structures called **pyrosilicates** (or sorosilicates) in which two tetrahedrons share one corner (as shown in Figure 23.5 ◀), forming the disilicate ion, which has the formula $Si_2O_7^{6-}$. This group requires cations that balance the 6− charge on $Si_2O_7^{6-}$. Again, these cations can be the same metal ions or a mixture of different metal ions. For example, in the mineral hardy stonite ($Ca_2ZnSi_2O_7$), two Ca^{2+} ions and one Zn^{2+} ion together provide the 6+ charge.

The silicon tetrahedron also forms structures called **pyroxenes** (or inosilicates) in which many of the tetrahedrons bond together creating chains, shown in Figure 23.6 ▼. The formula unit for these chains is the SiO_3^{2-} unit, and the repeating unit in the structure is two formula units ($Si_2O_6^{4-}$). Two of the oxygen atoms are bonded to two silicon atoms (and thus to two other tetrahedrons) at two of the four corners of each tetrahedron. The silicate chains are held together by ionic bonding to metal cations that lie between the chains. For example, in the crystal diopside, $CaMg(SiO_3)_2$, Ca^{2+} and Mg^{2+} ions bond with the silicate chains.

▶ **FIGURE 23.6 Pyroxene Structure** In pyroxenes, chains of silicate tetrahedrons are formed. Pyroxenes are also called inosilicates.

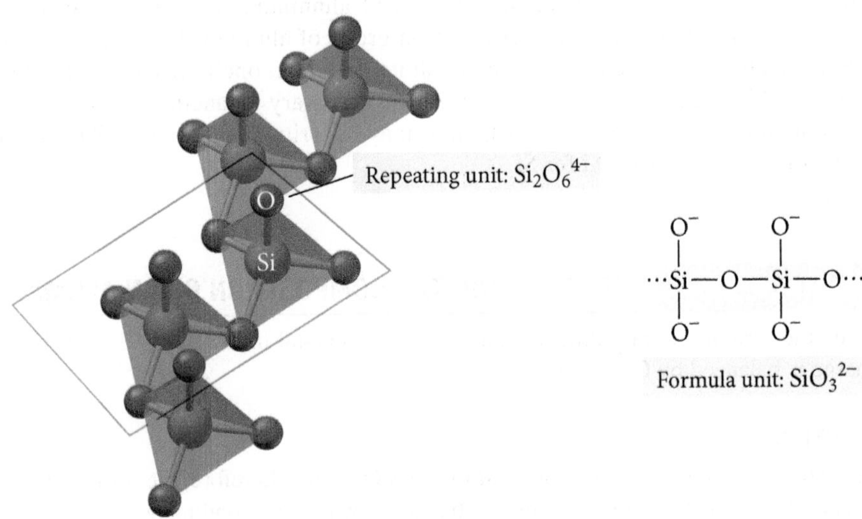

▲ The fibrous texture of asbestos results from the silicate double chains of the amphibole structure.

▲ The flaky texture of mica is due to silicate sheets of the phyllosilicate structure.

Some silicate structures feature *double chains* in which half of the tetrahedrons of one chain are bonded to tetrahedrons in another chain through oxygen atoms. The minerals with double silicate chains are called **amphiboles**, and the repeating unit in the crystal is $Si_4O_{11}^{6-}$, as shown in Figure 23.7 ▶. Half of the tetrahedrons are bonded by two of the four corner O atoms, and half of the tetrahedrons are bonded by three of the four corners, joining the two chains together. The bonding within the double chains is very strong, but the bonding between the double chains is not so strong. This structure often results in fibrous minerals such as asbestos. An example of an asbestos-type mineral is tremolite, $Ca_2(OH)_2Mg_5(Si_4O_{11})_2$. In this crystal, hydroxide ions bonded to some of the metal cations help balance the charge between the cations and the anionic silicate chains.

When three of the four oxygen atoms are bonded between the silicate tetrahedrons, the sheet structure shown in Figure 23.8 ▶ results. These compounds are called **phyllosilicates** and have a formula unit of $Si_2O_5^{2-}$. Sheets of tetrahedral silicates are bonded together by metal cations that lie between the sheets. For example, the mineral talc, $Mg_3(Si_2O_5)_2(OH)_2$ is a phyllosilicate. The weak interactions between silicate sheets gives talc its slippery feel (this is similar to the way the weak interactions between sheets of carbon atoms give graphite its slippery feel). Table 23.2 summarizes the different kinds of silicate structures.

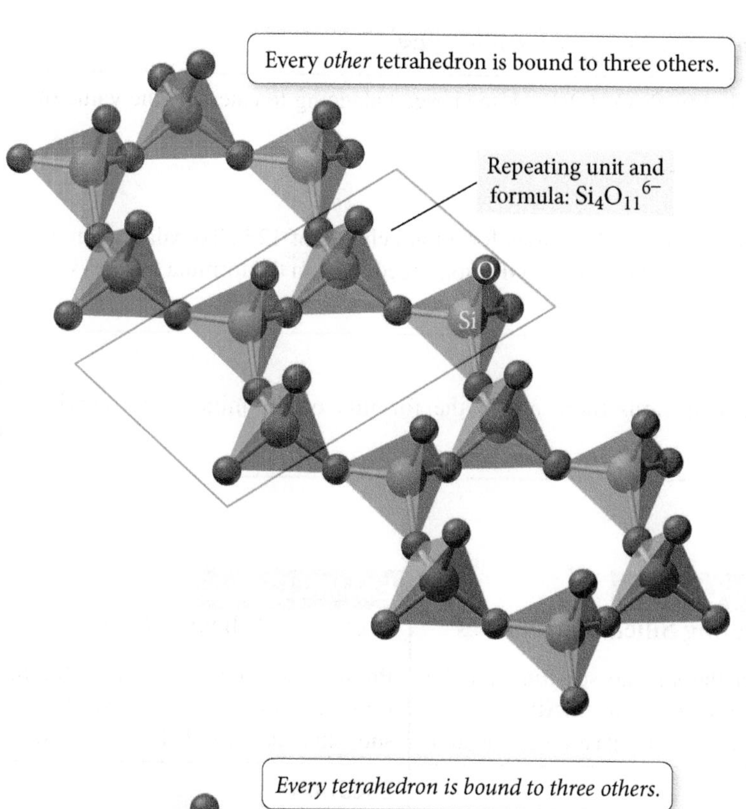

◀ **FIGURE 23.7 Amphibole Structure** Amphiboles contain double chains of silica tetrahedrons.

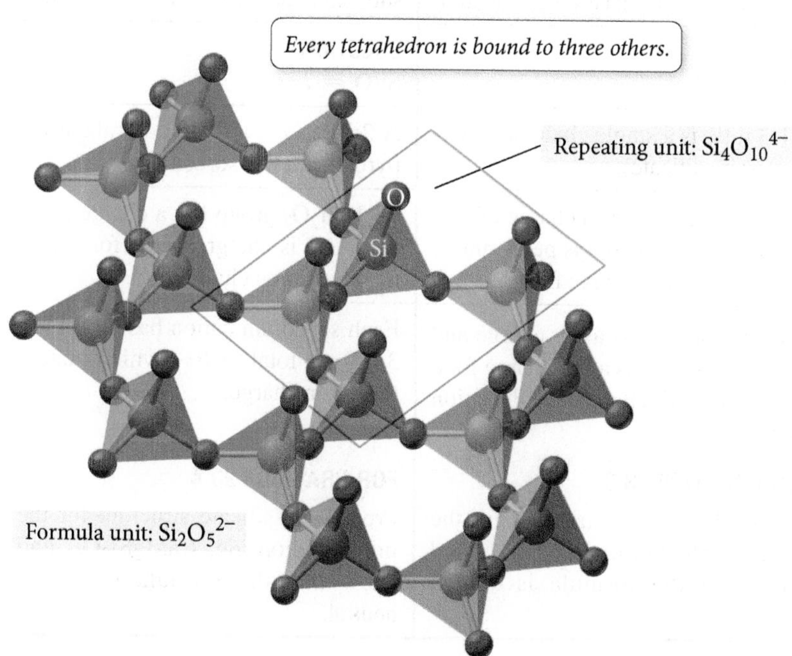

◀ **FIGURE 23.8 Phyllosilicate Structure** In phyllosilicates, three of the four oxygens are bonded to two silicon atoms, forming sheets of silica tetrahedrons.

TABLE 23.2 Types of Silicate Structures

Tetrahedrons	Shared Vertices	Formula Unit	Si:O Ratio	Class Name(s)	Example
Single tetrahedron	0	SiO_4^{4-}	1:4	Orthosilicates, nesosilicates	Olivine, Mg_2SiO_4
Double tetrahedron	1	$Si_2O_7^{6-}$	2:7	Pyrosilicates, sorosilicates	Hardystonite, $Ca_2ZnSi_2O_7$
Single chain	2	SiO_3^{2-}	1:3	Pyroxenes, inosilicates	Jadeite, $NaAl(SiO_3)_2$
Double chain	2 and 3	$Si_4O_{11}^{6-}$	4:11	Amphiboles	Tremolite, $Ca_2(OH)_2Mg_5(Si_4O_{11})_2$
Sheet	3	$Si_2O_5^{2-}$	2:5	Phyllosilicates	Talc, $Mg_3(Si_2O_5)_2(OH)_2$
Network covalent	4	SiO_2	1:2	Silicas, tectosilicates	Quartz, SiO_2
Network covalent	4	$AlSi_3O_8^-$ or $Al_2Si_2O_8^{2-}$	Variable	Feldspars	Albite, $NaAlSi_3O_8$

EXAMPLE 23.2 COMPOSITION AND CHARGE BALANCE OF SILICATES

The silicate chrysotile is an amphibole with the formula $Mg_6Si_4O_{11}(OH)_x$. Use charge balancing to calculate the value of x in the formula.

SOLUTION

The silicate unit for amphiboles is $Si_4O_{11}^{6-}$. The formula has six Mg^{2+} ions for a total charge of 12+. To balance, another 6− charge needs to be added to the 6− charge for the silicate. Therefore, 6 OH^- ions need to be in the formula for chrysotile, giving a formula of $Mg_6Si_4O_{11}(OH)_6$.

FOR PRACTICE 23.2

Use charge balancing to calculate how many hydroxide ions there are in the formula of the mineral pyrophyllite, $Al_2(Si_2O_5)_2(OH)_x$.

PROCEDURE FOR... Predicting Types of Silicate Structure and Accounting for Charge Balance	**EXAMPLE 23.3 Predicting Silicate Structures** Predict the silicate structure for the mineral spudomene, $LiAlSi_2O_6$, and show that the formula is charge neutral.	**EXAMPLE 23.4 Predicting Silicate Structures** Predict the silicate structure for the mineral thortveitite, $Sc_2Si_2O_7$, and show that the formula is charge neutral.
Determine the ratio of Si to O in the formula.	**SOLUTION** Si:O = 1:3	**SOLUTION** Si:O = 2:7
Match the Si:O ratio to the type of silicate in Table 23.2.	A 1:3 ratio is a single chain, a pyroxene (or inosilicate).	A 2:7 ratio is a double tetrahedron, a pyrosilicate (or sorosilicate).
Determine the total anion charge.	Each SiO_3 group has a charge of 2−, and there are two groups per formula, so the total anion charge is 4−.	Each Si_2O_7 group has a charge of 6−, and there is one group per formula, so the total anion charge is 6−.
Determine the total cation charge and show that it matches the total anion charge.	The Li^+ cation has a 1+ charge and the Al^{3+} cation has a 3+ charge for a total of 4+, which matches the anion charge.	Each scandium cation has a charge of 3+ for a total of 6+, which matches the anion charge.
	FOR PRACTICE 23.3 Predict the silicate structure for the mineral phenakite, Be_2SiO_4, and show that the formula is charge neutral.	**FOR PRACTICE 23.4** Predict the silicate structure for the mineral diopside, $CaMgSi_2O_6$, and show that the formula is charge neutral.

23.4 Boron and Its Remarkable Structures

The group 13 elements each have a filled *s* sublevel and one electron in the *p* sublevel. This electron configuration does not allow these main-group elements, especially boron, to easily attain a full octet. Most of the elements in the group are metals; however, because of its small size and higher electronegativity, boron behaves as a semimetal. These characteristics endow boron with some special properties and result in a wide array of different structures not common to most elements.

Elemental Boron

The structure of elemental boron is complex. Boron has at least five different allotropes (different structures with the same elemental composition). The structure of each allotrope is based on an icosahedron (Figure 23.9 ▶), a geometrical shape containing 20 triangular faces joined at 12 vertices that is very roughly spherical. Twelve boron atoms occupy the 12 vertices. Each different allotrope connects the icosahedrons in different ways. They all have boron atoms outside the icosahedrons that bridge the icosahedrons together.

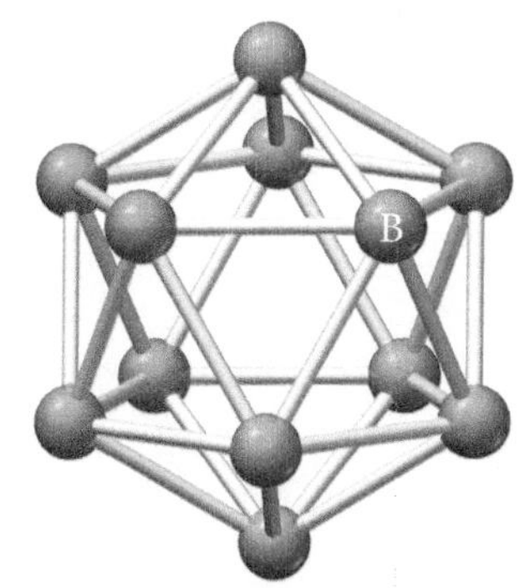

▲ **FIGURE 23.9 B_{12} Icosahedron** An icosahedron contains 20 triangular faces that are connected at 12 vertices. Elemental boron forms several different structures, each based on the basic icosahedral unit.

Boron is rare in Earth's crust, making up less than 0.001% by mass. Yet, because it is highly concentrated at various deposits around the world, it can be mined in large quantities. The largest deposit occurs at an old, volcanically active site in Boron, California. Naturally occurring boron always occurs in compounds, and it is almost always bonded to oxygen. Among the major sources of boron are the sodium borates, which include borax, $Na_2[B_4O_5(OH)_4] \cdot 8\,H_2O$, and kernite, $Na_2[B_4O_6(OH)_2] \cdot 3\,H_2O$. Another major source of boron is calcium borate, or colemanite, $Ca_2B_6O_{11} \cdot 5\,H_2O$. In all of these compounds, boron is bonded in polyatomic anions.

The primary use for boron today is in glass manufacture. Adding boron oxide to silicon oxide glass alters the thermal expansion of the glass, which is important for glassware intended for heating. When glass is heated, the outer edge of the glass warms and expands more quickly than the inner edge, creating stress that can result in cracking. Adding boron oxide to glass reduces its thermal expansion, allowing the glass (called borosilicate glass or Pyrex) to be heated without cracking.

Elemental boron is also used in the nuclear energy industry. Boron readily absorbs neutrons and is used in the control rods of nuclear reactors. When the nuclear reaction needs to be slowed down, the rods are inserted into the reactor to absorb the neutrons (see Section 19.7).

Boron–Halogen Compounds: Trihalides

Boron forms many covalently bonded compounds in which boron atoms bond to each other. In some ways, these compounds are similar to those in which carbon covalently bonds to itself; however, the structures are different because boron is less electronegative and has only three valence electrons. Recall from earlier in this section that elemental boron has a tendency to form polyhedral cluster structures. Boron also tends to form compounds in which boron has an incomplete octet (see Section 9.9).

Boron halides have the general formula BX_3 and have a trigonal planar structure.

:Ẍ̤:
120°
B
:Ẍ̤ :Ẍ̤:

The bonds in the boron trihalides are stronger and shorter than a typical single bond, which we can explain using valence bond theory and hybridization. The boron atom uses sp^2 hybridized orbitals to form sigma bonds with the three halogen atoms. Because boron's three valence electrons are used to form the sigma bonds, the third *p* orbital of boron is an empty orbital that is perpendicular to the trigonal plane of the molecule. Each halogen atom has a filled *p* orbital, also perpendicular to the trigonal plane of the molecule. The empty *p* orbital on the boron atom can overlap with the full *p* orbitals on the halogens, forming a coordinate-covalent type second bond. In BCl_3, for example, the boron and chlorine are joined by bonds resembling a double bond. Like normal double bonds, the boron–chlorine bond is shorter and stronger than a single bond.

The boron trihalides are strong Lewis acids. For example, BF_3 reacts with NH_3 according to the following Lewis acid–base reaction:

$$BF_3(g) \;+\; :NH_3(g) \longrightarrow F_3B{:}NH_3(s)$$

Boron trihalides act as Lewis acids in many organic reactions, such as those in which alcohols or acids are converted into esters. In water, the trihalides hydrolyze to form acidic solutions according to these reactions:

$$BF_3(g) + H_2O(l) \longrightarrow BF_3 \cdot H_2O(s) \longrightarrow BF_3OH^-(aq) + H^+(aq)$$

$$4\,BF_3(g) + 3\,H_2O(l) \longrightarrow 3\,H^+(aq) + 3\,BF_4^-(aq) + B(OH)_3(aq)$$

$$BCl_3(g) + 3\,H_2O(l) \longrightarrow B(OH)_3(aq) + 3\,H^+(aq) + 3\,Cl^-(aq)$$

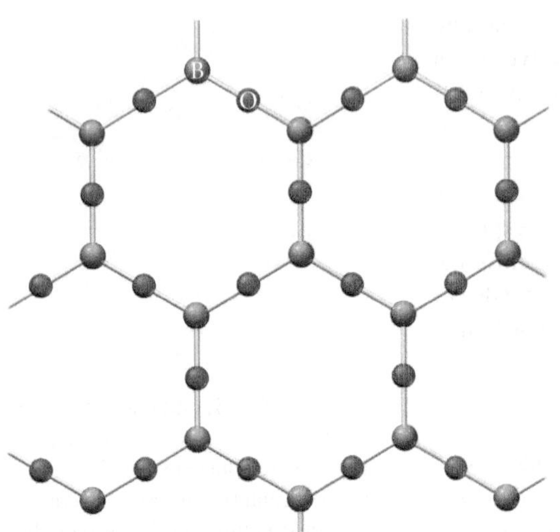

▲ **FIGURE 23.10 B_2O_3 Structure** Crystalline B_2O_3 consists of BO_3 trigonal structures that form hexagonal rings of B_6O_6.

Boron–Oxygen Compounds

Boron forms very strong bonds with oxygen in structures that contain trigonal BO_3 structures. The formula for the crystalline structure of boron and oxygen is B_2O_3. In this compound, the trigonal BO_3 structures hook together to form interlocking B_6O_6 hexagonal rings, as shown in Figure 23.10 ◄. Each hexagonal ring has a boron atom at each of its six corners and an oxygen atom in the middle of each of the six sides. The compound B_2O_3 melts at 450 °C. If the molten B_2O_3 cools quickly, it forms a glass (an amorphous solid). The glass still contains many interlocking B_6O_6 hexagonal rings but lacks the long-range order of the crystal. Molten boron oxide dissolves many metal oxides and silicon oxide to form glasses of many different compositions.

Boron–Hydrogen Compounds: Boranes

Compounds composed of boron and hydrogen, called **boranes**, form many unique cluster, cagelike, and netlike structures. The ***closo*-boranes** have the formula $B_nH_n^{2-}$ and form fully closed polyhedrons with triangular sides; two of these structures are shown in Figure 23.11 ▼. A boron atom, with an attached hydrogen atom, occupies each of the vertices in the polyhedrons. The *closo*-borane with the formula $B_{12}H_{12}^{2-}$ forms the full icosohedral shape, as does elemental boron, but with the added hydrogen atoms.

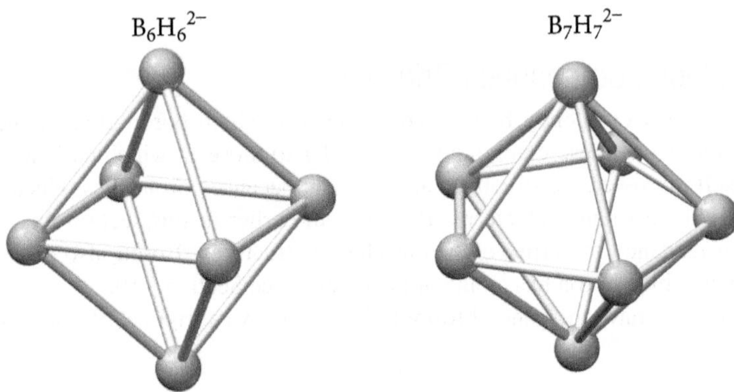

► **FIGURE 23.11 *closo*-Borane Structures** *closo*-Borane structures form closed polyhedrons with triangular faces. In this figure, each sphere represents a BH unit. $B_6H_6^{2-}$ has an octahedral (square bipyramidal) shape. $B_7H_7^{2-}$ has a pentagonal bipyramidal shape.

If the borane polyhedron is missing one or more boron atoms, extra hydrogen atoms attach to the structure to make the borane neutral. Researchers have identified over 35 structurally different neutral boranes, ranging from B_2H_6 to $B_{20}H_{26}$. We can classify these neutral boranes on the basis of their different chemical formulas. The ***nido*-boranes**, named from the Latin word for *net*, have the formula B_nH_{n+4}. They consist of a cage of boron atoms missing one corner. The ***arachno*-boranes**, named from the Greek word for *spiderweb*, have the formula B_nH_{n+6}. They consist of a cage of boron atoms that is missing two or three corners. Examples of a *nido-* and an *arachno*-borane are shown in Figure 23.12 ▼.

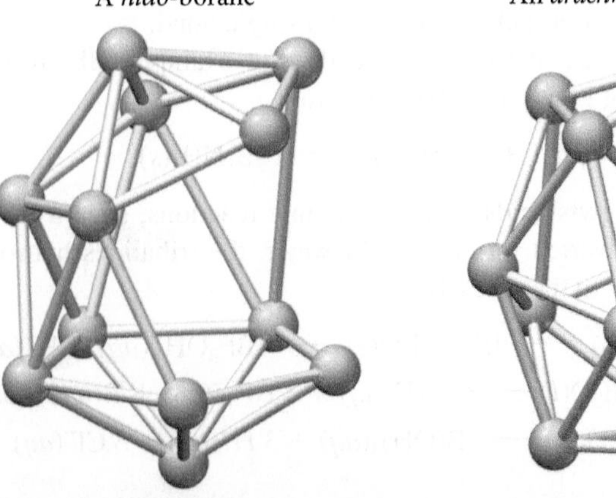

► **FIGURE 23.12 *nido-* and *arachno-*Boranes** The *nido*-borane structure forms a cage missing one boron atom from a corner. The *arachno*-borane structure forms a net missing more than one boron from a corner.

Boranes not only form interesting structures, but are also valuable as reagents in organic reactions. For example, adding an alkene to a diborane forms an alkane bonded to the boron atom. The alkane can be cleaved from the boron, resulting in a net hydrogenation reaction that can be carried out under mild (lower temperature) conditions.

$$B_2H_6(g) + 6\ CH_2{=}CHCH_3(g) \longrightarrow 2\ B(CH_2CH_2CH_3)_3(l)$$

23.5 Carbon, Carbides, and Carbonates

The group 14 elements exhibit the most versatile bonding of all elements. As we saw in Chapters 20 and 21, carbon has the ability to bond with other carbon atoms and with a few other elements to form a great variety of organic compounds. From these come the molecules of life that we examined in Chapter 22. Here we focus on elemental carbon and those compounds of carbon which are known as *inorganic* (rather than organic).

Carbon

Elemental carbon exists in several different forms. Two well-known naturally occurring crystalline forms of carbon are **graphite** and **diamond**. Graphite deposits occur mostly in mines in East Asia. Graphite's structure, shown in Figure 23.13 ▼, consists of flat sheets of carbon atoms bonded together as interconnected hexagonal rings. Although the covalent bonds *within* the sheets are strong, the interactions *between* the sheets are weak, allowing the layers of graphite to slip easily past each other and making graphite a good lubricant. The electrons in the extended pi bonding network within a sheet make graphite a good electrical conductor in the direction of the plane of the sheets. Because of its relative stability and electrical properties, graphite is used for electrodes in electrochemical applications and for heating elements in furnaces.

The density of graphite is 2.2 g cm^{-3}. Under high pressure, the carbon atoms in graphite rearrange to form diamond, which has a higher density of 3.5 g cm^{-3}. Diamonds form naturally when carbon is exposed to high pressures deep underground. Through movements in Earth's crust, the diamonds rise toward the surface. Most diamonds are found in Africa, mainly in the Congo region and in South Africa. The first synthetic diamonds were produced in the 1940s, using pressures of 5 million kPa and a temperature of 1600 °C. The diamond structure, shown in Figure 23.14 ▼, consists of carbon atoms connected to four other carbon atoms at the corners of a tetrahedron. This bonding extends throughout three dimensions, making giant molecules described as network covalent solids (see Section 11.12).

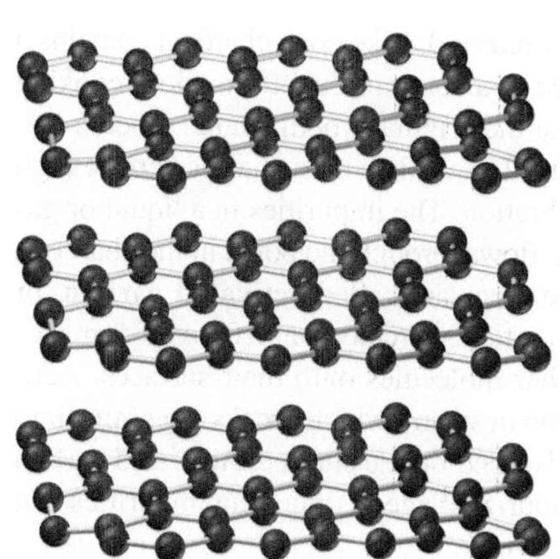

▲ **FIGURE 23.13 Graphite Structure** The carbon atoms in graphite bond strongly within the plane of the carbon atoms but bond weakly between the sheets.

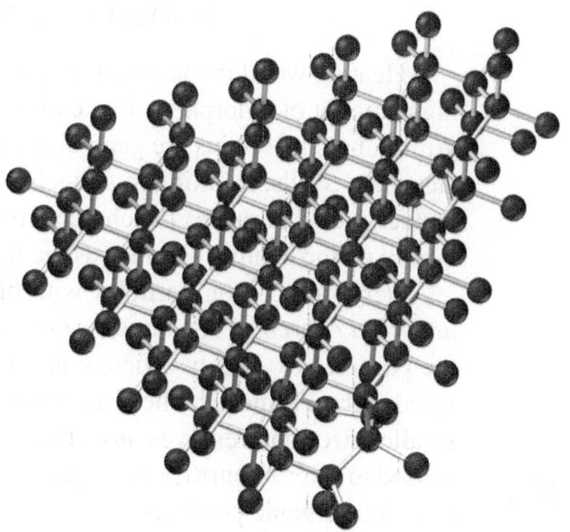

▲ **FIGURE 23.14 Diamond Structure** The diamond structure has carbon atoms at the corners of a tetrahedron, each connected to four other carbon atoms.

CONCEPTUAL CONNECTION 23.1

Phase Changes and Pressure

Why do high pressures favour the formation of diamond from graphite?

TABLE 23.3 Approximate Composition of the Main Types of Coal

Type of Coal	Free C (mol %)	Total C (mol %)	H (mol %)	O (mol %)	S (mol %)
Lignite	22	71	4	23	1
Bituminous	60	80	6	8	5
Anthracite	88	93	3	3	1

Diamond is very hard and is an excellent conductor of heat. Consequently, the largest use of diamonds is for abrasives and cutting tools. Small diamonds are used at the cutting edge of the tools, making the edges much harder and giving them a longer life. Natural diamonds are valued as gems for their brilliance and relative inertness.

Carbon also occurs naturally in noncrystalline forms. **Coal** forms from the decomposition of ancient plant material that has been buried for millions of years, during which time it undergoes a process called carbonization. The reaction, which occurs under high pressure in the presence of water and the absence of air, removes most of the hydrogen and oxygen (which are lost as volatile gases such as methane and water) from the original organic compounds that composed the plant. The resulting coal contains a mixture of various hydrocarbons and carbon-rich particles. It is extensively mined and employed as an energy source throughout the world. Coal types are classified by the amount of carbon and other elements that they contain, as shown in Table 23.3.

Among the types of coal listed in Table 23.3, anthracite has the highest carbon content and consequently yields the most energy per mass when burned. Bituminous coal also contains a relatively high amount of carbon but has in addition high levels of sulfur, which results in increased formation of sulfur oxides when this type of coal is burned. Sulfur oxides are the pollutants that create acid rain (see Section 15.12).

Heating coal in the absence of air forms a solid called **coke** that is composed mainly of carbon and ash. Coke is used in the steel industry for the reduction of iron ore to iron. In a blast furnace, the carbon in the coke is oxidized to form carbon monoxide, which reduces the iron in iron oxide according to these reactions:

$$O_2(g) + \underset{\text{coke}}{C(s)} \longrightarrow CO_2(g)$$

$$CO_2(g) + \underset{\text{coke}}{C(s)} \longrightarrow 2\,CO(g)$$

$$Fe_2O_3(s) + 3\,CO(g) \longrightarrow 2\,Fe(s) + 3\,CO_2(g)$$

Heating wood in the absence of air produces **charcoal**. Like coal, charcoal contains a high amount of amorphous free carbon and is used as a common fuel for outdoor cooking grills. Charcoal retains the general overall shape of the original wood, but the process creates many voids, resulting in a much lower density. The voids within charcoal create high surface area that makes the charcoal useful for filtration. The impurities in a liquid or gas adsorb on the charcoal surface as the liquid or gas flows through the pores in the charcoal.

Very fine carbon particles with high surface areas are called **activated carbon**, or *activated charcoal*. The large surface area of the particles, greater than $10^3\,m^2\,g^{-1}$, makes the particles extremely efficient at adsorbing other molecules onto their surfaces. Activated carbon is made by heating amorphous carbon in steam, which breaks the grains into smaller sizes and removes any other materials adsorbed on the surface. Activated carbon is used to filter impurities from gas and as a decolourizing agent, removing impurities that discolour organic products such as sugar or wheat flour.

Soot is an amorphous form of carbon that forms during the incomplete combustion of hydrocarbons; its presence is indicated by blue or black smoke. Toxic carbon monoxide also forms in the process.

$$H_xC_y(s) + O_2(g) \longrightarrow H_2O(g) + CO_2(g) + CO(g) + \underset{\text{soot}}{C(s)}$$

Carbon black, a fine, powdered form of carbon, is a component of soot. Over a million tons of carbon black, a strengthener for rubber tires, are used in manufacturing each day. The black colour of automobile tires is due to the several kilograms of carbon black within each tire, over 25% of the mass of the typical tire.

▲ Automobile tires are black because of the carbon black that is added to strengthen the tires and maintain flexibility.

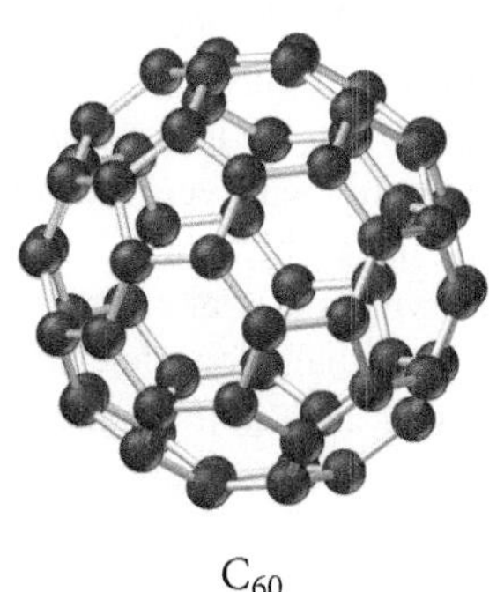

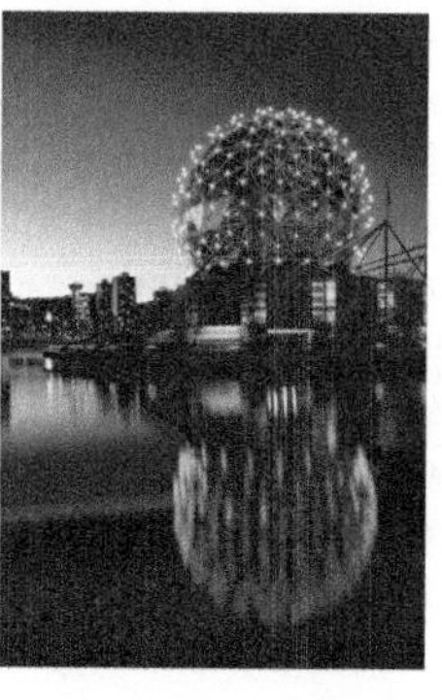

◀ **FIGURE 23.15 C_{60} and a Geodesic Dome** The C_{60} structure resembles Buckminster Fuller's geodesic dome. This geodesic dome was built for Expo 86 in Vancouver, BC.

In the 1980s, researchers discovered a new form of carbon when they aimed a powerful laser at a graphite surface. This new form of carbon occurs as soccer-ball-shaped clusters of 60 carbon atoms (C_{60}). The atoms form five- and six-membered carbon rings wrapped into a 20-sided icosahedral structure, as shown in Figure 23.15 ▲. The compound was named *buckminsterfullerene*, honouring R. Buckminster Fuller, a twentieth-century engineer and architect who advocated the construction of buildings using a structurally strong geodesic dome shape that he patented.

Researchers have since identified carbon clusters similar to C_{60} but containing from 36 to over 100 carbon atoms. As a class, all of these carbon clusters are called **fullerenes**, and nicknamed *buckyballs*. At room temperature, all fullerenes are black solids—the individual clusters are held together by dispersion forces. Fullerenes are somewhat soluble in nonpolar solvents, and the different fullerenes form solutions of different colours.

Nanotubes

Researchers synthesize long carbon structures called **nanotubes**, which consist of sheets of interconnected C_6 rings that assume the shape of a cylinder (like a roll of chicken wire). The first nanotubes discovered consisted of tubes with double walls of C_6 rings with closed ends. The ends of the tubes can be opened when they are heated under the proper conditions. Researchers have also introduced salts and organometallic compounds into the nanotubes, and have been able to form some generally not stable compounds inside nanotubes. The discovery of these materials opens a new synthetic route to making novel chemicals.

Today, two general types of nanotubes can be produced: (1) single-walled nanotubes (SWNT), which have one layer of interconnected C_6 rings forming the walls, and (2) multiwalled nanotubes (MWNT), which have concentric layers of interconnected C_6 rings forming the walls. Both types of nanotubes are shown in Figure 23.16 ▼.

(a) Single-walled nanotube (SWNT)

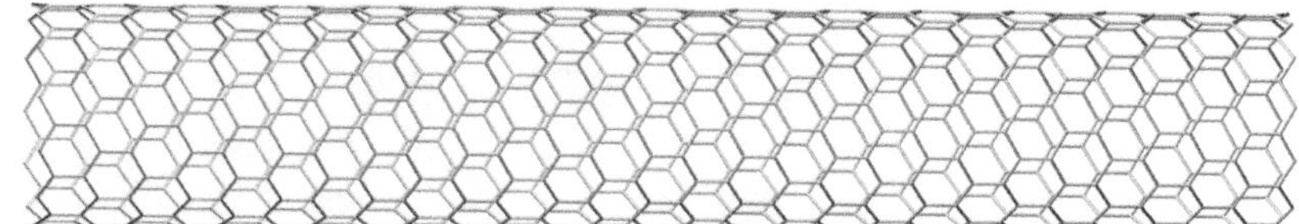

(b) Multiwalled nanotube (MWNT)

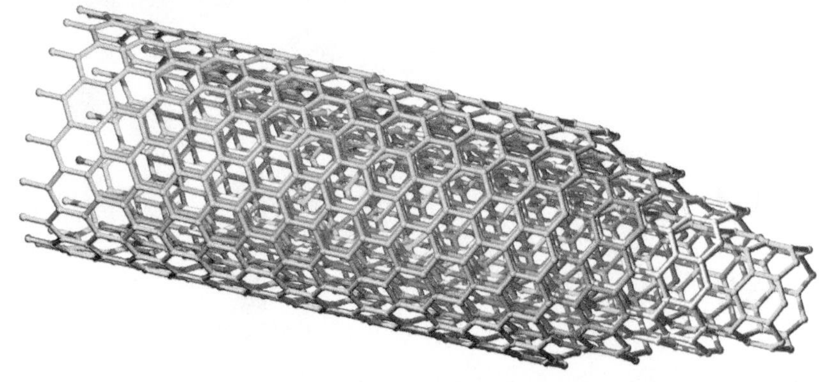

◀ **FIGURE 23.16 Carbon Nanotubes** Carbon nanotubes can be formed with **(a)** a single wall of carbon atoms or **(b)** multiple walls of carbon atoms.

▲ **FIGURE 23.17 The Nanocar** This nanocar has buckyballs for wheels. Researchers, then at Rice University (Shirai, Osgood, Zhao, Kelly, and Tour), showed that the wheels actually roll across an atomic surface.

Nanotubes are 100 times stronger than steel and only one-sixteenth as dense. Consequently, carbon nanotubes are used commercially for lightweight applications that require strength, such as golf clubs and bicycle frames. When the nanotubes are lined up parallel to one another, a bundle of the tubes form a "wire" with very low electrical resistance. These tiny wires raise the possibility of making incredibly small electronic devices. Other applications include using nanotubes and buckyballs to make nanomachines. For example, Figure 23.17 ◀ shows a nanocar that has buckyballs for wheels. The car can actually roll across an atomic surface and is so small that 20000 of them laid end to end would span the thickness of a human hair.

Carbides

Binary compounds composed of carbon combined with less electronegative elements are called **carbides**. We classify carbides into three general categories: ionic, covalent, and metallic. All three types of carbides have some shared properties; they are extremely hard materials with high melting points.

Ionic Carbides Compounds composed of carbon and a low-electronegativity metal such as an alkali metal or an alkaline earth metal are **ionic carbides**. Most of the ionic carbides contain the dicarbide ion, C_2^{2-}, commonly called the *acetylide ion*. For example, calcium carbide has the formula CaC_2 and a structure similar to that of NaCl, shown in Figure 23.18 ▼.

Calcium carbide forms by the reaction of calcium oxide with coke in an electric furnace.

$$CaO(s) + 3\,C(s) \longrightarrow CaC_2(s) + CO(g)$$

Ionic carbides react with water, forming acetylene. For example, sodium carbide reacts with water according to the reaction:

$$Na_2C_2(s) + 2\,H_2O(l) \longrightarrow 2\,NaOH(aq) + C_2H_2(g)$$

In the past, calcium carbide was used as a source of acetylene (which is highly flammable) for lighting. The solid CaC_2 reacts with water, releasing acetylene gas, which was burned in applications such as automobile headlights and lamps for mines. Transporting solid calcium carbide was more convenient than transporting the flammable gas.

Covalent Carbides Compounds composed of carbon and low-electronegativity *nonmetals* or *metalloids* are **covalent carbides**. The most important covalent carbide is silicon carbide (SiC), a very hard material. Over 500000 tons of silicon carbide are produced annually,

▶ **FIGURE 23.18 Calcium Carbide Structure** In the NaCl-type structure for CaC_2, the dicarbide ions are in the positions of the chloride ions, making the structure slightly noncubic.

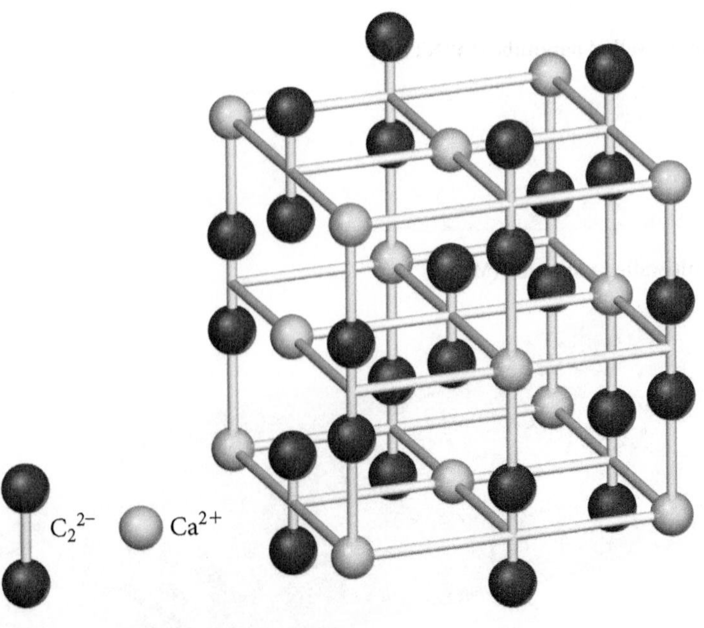

mostly for use as an abrasive material in the cutting and polishing of metals. In a process analogous to the formation of calcium carbide, silicon carbide forms by the reaction of silicon oxide with coke at high temperatures.

$$SiO_2(s) + 3\,C(s) \longrightarrow SiC(s) + 2\,CO(g)$$

Moissanite is a gem quality form of SiC. It is described as being more brilliant than all other gems, including diamonds. Yet moissanite costs much less than diamond and is consequently sold as a diamond substitute (like the more common diamond substitute cubic zirconia, ZrO_2). Moissanite was first identified in small particles at the Diablo Canyon meteorite impact crater in Arizona, and is therefore sometimes advertised as a gift from the stars.

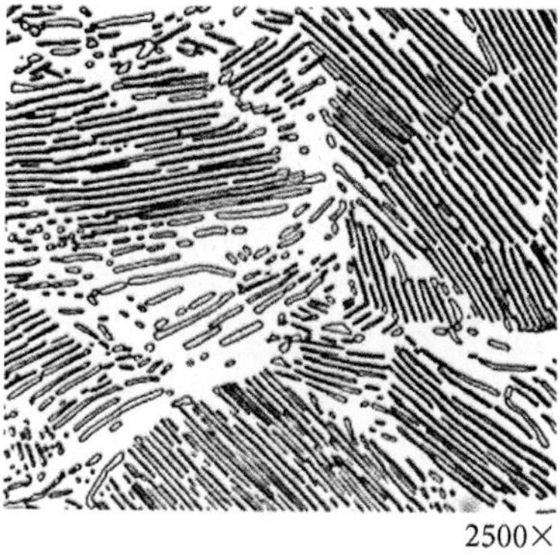

▲ This micrograph shows cementite (dark regions) in steel.

Metallic Carbides Compounds composed of carbon and metals that have a metallic lattice with holes small enough to fit carbon atoms are **metallic carbides**. Metallic carbides retain many of their metallic properties, such as high electrical conductivity, but they are stronger, harder, and less malleable than their corresponding metals. Adding carbon to steel, for example, increases its hardness by forming regions of cementite (Fe_3C) in the steel matrix. Tungsten carbide (WC) is a metallic carbide used in cutting tools.

Carbon Oxides

Carbon forms two stable oxides, carbon monoxide and carbon dioxide. Our atmosphere contains about 0.04% carbon dioxide by volume. Plants use atmospheric carbon dioxide to produce sugars during photosynthesis.

$$6\,CO_2(g) + 6\,H_2O(g) \longrightarrow C_6H_{12}O_6(s) + 6\,O_2(g)$$

Carbon dioxide returns to the atmosphere via animal respiration, plant and animal decay, and (in modern history) fossil fuel combustion. Because carbon dioxide is highly soluble in water, the oceans of the world act as a reservoir for CO_2, keeping the amount of CO_2 in the atmosphere generally stable. As we saw in Section 6.10, however, the increase in the combustion of fossil fuels in the last century has increased the amount of CO_2 in the atmosphere by over 25%.

Recall from Section 11.8 that CO_2 has a triple point at -57 °C and 5.2 bar. At atmospheric pressure, therefore, the liquid phase of CO_2 does not exist. Solid carbon dioxide sublimes directly to the gas phase when heated, which is why solid CO_2 is called "dry ice."

Carbon monoxide (CO) is a colourless, odourless, and tasteless gas. The boiling point of carbon monoxide is -192 °C at atmospheric pressure, and CO is only very slightly soluble in water. Carbon monoxide is toxic because it interferes with the ability of hemoglobin to bind oxygen. Unlike carbon dioxide, which is very stable, carbon monoxide is relatively reactive and can be used as a reducing agent. For example, carbon monoxide reacts with oxygen and metal oxides to form carbon dioxide.

$$2\,CO(g) + O_2(g) \longrightarrow 2\,CO_2(g)$$

$$CO(g) + CuO(s) \longrightarrow CO_2(g) + Cu(s)$$

Carbonates

When carbon dioxide dissolves in water, it forms carbonic acid (H_2CO_3). As a weak acid, carbonic acid partially ionizes into hydrogen carbonate (or bicarbonate) and carbonate.

$$CO_2(aq) + H_2O(l) \rightleftharpoons \underset{\text{carbonic acid}}{H_2CO_3(aq)}$$

$$H_2CO_3(aq) \rightleftharpoons H^+(aq) + \underset{\text{hydrogen carbonate}}{HCO_3^-(aq)} \rightleftharpoons 2\,H^+(aq) + \underset{\text{carbonate}}{CO_3^{2-}(aq)}$$

Recall from Section 12.2 that the solubility of carbon dioxide, like that of other gases, increases with increasing pressure. Carbon dioxide under high pressure is used to carbonate soft drinks. Under most conditions, less than 0.5% of the dissolved carbon dioxide reacts with water to form carbonic acid. This leaves most of the carbon dioxide as dissolved gas molecules so the soft drink does not acquire much of a sour acidic taste.

The hydrated crystal of sodium carbonate, $Na_2CO_3 \cdot 10\ H_2O$, is known as **washing soda**. When washing soda is heated, the waters of hydration are released, forming the stable anhydrous sodium carbonate, Na_2CO_3. All of the alkali metal ions form stable carbonates that remain stable even when heated. The carbonates all make basic solutions when added to water because the carbonate ions readily ionize water (as described more fully in Section 15.8).

▲ Alka-Seltzer contains sodium bicarbonate mixed with citric acid and aspirin. When put in water, the acid and carbonate react to produce the fizz.

$$Na_2CO_3(s) \xrightarrow{H_2O(l)} 2\ Na^+(aq) + CO_3^{2-}(aq)$$

$$CO_3^{2-}(aq) + H_2O(l) \longrightarrow HCO_3^-(aq) + OH^-(aq)$$

Sodium bicarbonate ($NaHCO_3$) is *baking soda*. When heated, baking soda gives off carbon dioxide gas, which is why its use in baking helps raise dough.

$$2\ NaHCO_3(s) \longrightarrow Na_2CO_3(s) + H_2O(l) + CO_2(g)$$

Baking *powder* is a mixture of $NaHCO_3$ and an acid. The two components of the mixture are kept from reacting by a starch filler. When water is added to the mixture, however, the two components dissolve and react, producing the carbon dioxide that forms pockets of gas in baked products. You can perform a simple test to determine if baking powder is still active (that is, whether the acid has not already slowly reacted with the sodium bicarbonate) by pouring some boiling water over a small sample of the baking powder. If the hot water produces bubbles, then the baking powder is still active. Alka-Seltzer is another common consumer product that employs sodium bicarbonate, in this case mixed with citric acid and aspirin. When immersed in water, the acid and carbonate react to produce carbon dioxide, producing the familiar fizz.

CONCEPTUAL CONNECTION 23.2

Carbonate Solubility

As we saw in Chapter 4, the carbonates of metal ions other than group 1 are insoluble in water. Which action would increase their solubility?

(a) adding acid to the solution

(b) adding base to the solution

(c) increasing the amount of the solid carbonate in the solution

23.6 Nitrogen and Phosphorus: Essential Elements for Life

The group 15 elements range from nonmetallic nitrogen and phosphorus to metallic bismuth. Both nitrogen and phosphorus are nonmetals; they do not conduct electricity and they form acidic oxides. They both have s^2p^3 electron configurations, and yet their chemical properties are very different.

Elemental Nitrogen and Phosphorus

Nitrogen was identified in 1772 and phosphorus in 1669. Elemental nitrogen is a diatomic gas that composes about 78% of Earth's atmosphere by volume. To obtain elemental nitrogen, air is cooled below −196 °C, which causes it to liquefy. When the liquid air is warmed slightly, the nitrogen boils off, leaving liquid oxygen (which boils at the higher temperature of −183 °C). Passing the vaporized gas over hot copper metal purifies the nitrogen by removing residual oxygen (which reacts with the copper to form CuO). Nitrogen gas can also be separated from the other atmospheric gases by passing air through certain silicate materials called zeolites, which have channels of just the right diameter to separate gas molecules of different size. Some mineral sources for nitrogen are saltpeter (KNO_3) and Chile saltpeter ($NaNO_3$).

As we first saw in Section 9.5, nitrogen molecules have a triple bond between the two N atoms. The strength of the triple bond makes N_2 very stable, and attempts to break the bond have not been commercially successful. When nitrogen gas is heated with oxygen or hydrogen, nitric oxide (NO) or ammonia (NH_3), respectively, form with low yields. When nitrogen gas is heated with active metals, metal nitrides form. Beyond this, however, nitrogen gas is relatively unreactive.

The stability of elemental nitrogen makes it useful in creating a protective atmosphere to prevent oxidation in many industrial processes. For example, industrial furnaces employ a nitrogen atmosphere to anneal (hold at elevated temperature below the melting point) products made of metal, and chemical reactions sensitive to oxygen are carried out in a nitrogen atmosphere. Nitrogen is also used to preserve a variety of foods.

Elemental phosphorus was first isolated by accident from urine when Hennig Brand, a seventeenth-century physician and alchemist from Hamburg, Germany, was distilling urine in an ill-informed attempt to obtain gold from the golden liquid. The elemental form of phosphorus that he obtained instead was a white, waxy, flammable solid called **white phosphorus**. White phosphorus is highly toxic to humans. For over a hundred years, the phosphorus-containing compounds in urine were the main source for elemental phosphorus. Today, however, phosphorus is obtained from a calcium phosphate mineral called apatite [$Ca_3(PO_4)_2$]. The mineral is heated with sand and coke in an electric furnace.

$$\underset{\text{apatite}}{2\ Ca_3(PO_4)_2(s)} + \underset{\text{sand}}{6\ SiO_2(s)} + \underset{\text{coke}}{10\ C(s)} \longrightarrow \underset{\text{white phosphorus}}{P_4(g)} + 6\ CaSiO_3(l) + 10\ CO(g)$$

The desired product, white phosphorus, spontaneously burns in air so it is normally stored under water to prevent contact with air.

White phosphorus consists of P_4 molecules in a tetrahedral shape, with the phosphorus atoms at the corners of the tetrahedron, as shown in Figure 23.19 ►. The bond angles between the three P atoms on any one face of the tetrahedron is small (60°) and strained, making the P_4 molecule unstable and reactive.

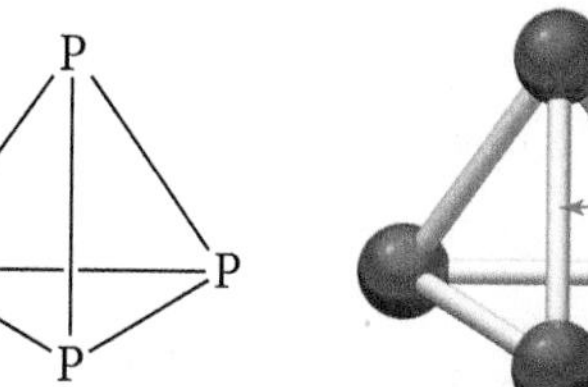

▲ **FIGURE 23.19 White Phosphorus** The small bond angle of 60° between the phosphorus atoms at the corners of the tetrahedron puts a great strain on the structure and makes the P_4 molecule unstable.

When heated to about 300 °C in the absence of air, white phosphorus slightly changes its structure to a different allotrope called **red phosphorus**, which is amorphous. The general structure of red phosphorus is similar to that of white phosphorus, except that one of the bonds between two phosphorus atoms in the tetrahedron is broken, as shown in Figure 23.20 ▼. The two phosphorus atoms then link to other phosphorus atoms, making chains that vary in structure.

Red phosphorus is neither as reactive nor as toxic as white phosphorus, and even though it is also flammable, it can be stored in air. Red phosphorus is used commercially in applications such as match heads. Rubbing the match head onto a surface produces enough heat (through friction) to ignite the phosphorus. Today, most strike-anywhere matches feature the phosphorus compound tetraphosphorus trisulfide (P_4S_3) and an oxidizing agent, potassium chlorate ($KClO_3$).

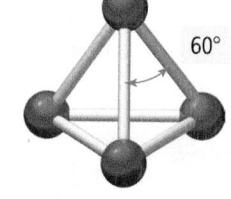

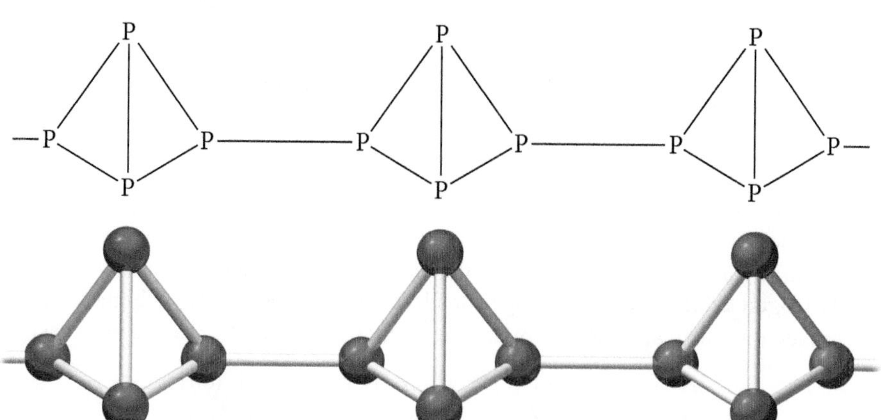

◄ **FIGURE 23.20 Red Phosphorus** Red phosphorus consists of chains of phosphorus atoms that form amorphous structures.

A third allotrope of phosphorus is **black phosphorus**. Black phosphorus is obtained by heating white phosphorus under pressure. This form of phosphorus is the most thermodynamically stable form, and therefore the least reactive. Black phosphorus has a layered structure similar to that of graphite.

TABLE 23.4 Oxidation States of Various Nitrogen Compounds

Nitrogen-Containing Compound(s)	Oxidation State
NH_3	−3
N_2H_4	−2
H_2NOH	−1
HN_3	$-\frac{1}{3}$
N_2	0
N_2O	+1
NO	+2
N_2O_3, NF_3	+3
NO_2, N_2O_4	+4
N_2O_5, HNO_3	+5

Nitrogen Compounds

Nitrogen, with a valence electron configuration of $2s^2 2p^3$, can gain three electrons or lose five electrons to obtain an octet. Nitrogen forms many covalent compounds with oxidation states from −3 to +5, as shown in Table 23.4.

Nitrogen Hydrides The most common nitrogen hydride is **ammonia** (NH_3), the strong-smelling compound in which nitrogen displays its lowest oxidation state (−3). Ammonia is important to humans because it reacts with sulfuric acid (or phosphoric acid) to produce ammonium salts for fertilizers.

$$2\,NH_3(g) + H_2SO_4(aq) \longrightarrow (NH_4)_2SO_4(aq)$$

For hundreds of years, natural biological materials such as animal manure were used as nitrogen-containing fertilizers. In the 1800s, however, the nitrogen-bearing nitrate mineral $NaNO_3$ was discovered in Chile (and named Chile saltpeter). This nitrate mineral became an important source of fertilizer and made the country of Chile very wealthy; yet it was a limited source, so chemists were continually striving to develop a new source.

The obvious *unlimited* source of nitrogen is the atmosphere, but the strong triple bond in elemental nitrogen renders it unusable by plants. In order to be used as fertilizer, elemental nitrogen has to be *fixed*, which means that it has to be converted into a nitrogen-containing compound such as NH_3. However, the direct reaction of nitrogen gas with hydrogen gas to form ammonia is very slow and produces low yields of ammonia under normal conditions.

$$N_2(g) + 3\,H_2(g) \rightleftharpoons 2\,NH_3(g)$$

In the early 1900s, German chemist Fritz Haber studied the equilibrium conditions for this reaction and showed that high pressures and lower temperatures favoured the product. Carrying out the reaction at a higher pressure, and using a catalyst to increase the reaction rate, the industrial process for producing ammonia from nitrogen gas and hydrogen gas—now called the **Haber–Bosch process**—became practical by the middle 1930s. This process is now the main industrial process for making ammonia and fixing nitrogen for many uses, including fertilizers and explosives.

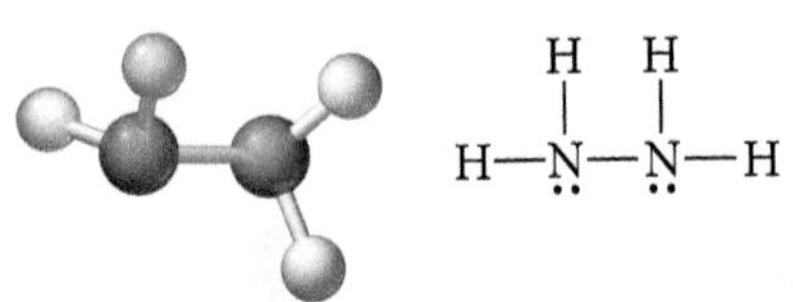

Hydrazine

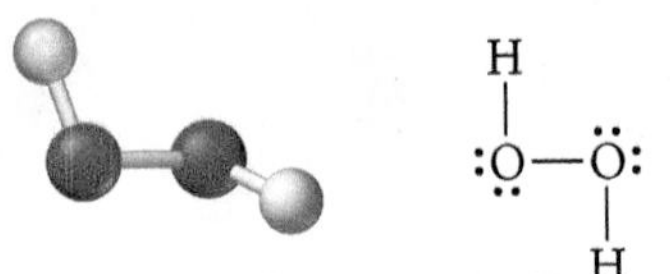

Hydrogen peroxide

▲ **FIGURE 23.21 Hydrazine and Hydrogen Peroxide** Hydrazine forms a structure similar to hydrogen peroxide with an N—N bond in the place of the O—O bond.

Hydrazine (N_2H_4) is another nitrogen and hydrogen compound in which nitrogen has a negative oxidation state (−2). Hydrazine is the nitrogen analog of hydrogen peroxide; it has a bond between nitrogen atoms that is similar to the bond between oxygen atoms in hydrogen peroxide, as shown in Figure 23.21 ◄. Hydrazine, like hydrogen peroxide, is a colourless liquid. However, while hydrogen peroxide is a powerful oxidizing agent, hydrazine is a powerful reducing agent, as shown in each of the following reactions:

$$\underset{-2\ +1}{N_2H_4}(l) + 2\,\underset{+1\ -1}{H_2O_2}(l) \longrightarrow \underset{0}{N_2}(g) + 4\,\underset{+1\ -2}{H_2O}(g)$$

Reduction: H_2O_2 (−1) → H_2O (−2); Oxidation: N_2H_4 (−2) → N_2 (0)

$$\underset{-2\ +1}{N_2H_4}(aq) + 2\,\underset{0}{I_2}(aq) \longrightarrow \underset{0}{N_2}(g) + 4\,\underset{+1\ -1}{HI}(aq)$$

Reduction: I_2 (0) → HI (−1); Oxidation: N_2H_4 (−2) → N_2 (0)

$$\underset{-2\ +1}{N_2H_4}(aq) + 2\,\underset{+2}{Pb^{2+}}(aq) \longrightarrow \underset{0}{N_2}(g) + 2\,\underset{0}{Pb}(s) + 4\,\underset{+1}{H^+}(aq)$$

Reduction: Pb^{2+} (+2) → Pb (0); Oxidation: N_2H_4 (−2) → N_2 (0)

The oxidation state of each atom is shown directly below its symbol. Notice that in each reaction, nitrogen is oxidized and causes the reduction of the other reactant.

Hydrogen azide (HN_3) is a nitrogen and hydrogen compound with a higher nitrogen-to-hydrogen ratio than ammonia or hydrazine. Ammonia and hydrazine are both basic:

$$N_2H_4(aq) + H_2O(l) \longrightarrow N_2H_5^+(aq) + OH^-(aq)$$
$$NH_3(aq) + H_2O(l) \longrightarrow NH_4^+(aq) + OH^-(aq)$$

Hydrogen azide, by contrast, is acidic, ionizing in water to form the azide ion (N_3^-):

$$HN_3(aq) + H_2O(l) \longrightarrow H_3O^+(aq) + N_3^-(aq)$$

The N_3^- ion can be represented with the resonance structures (formal charges indicated in red):

$$\left[:N{\equiv}N{-}\ddot{\underset{..}{N}}:\right]^- \leftrightarrow \left[:\ddot{N}{=}N{=}\ddot{N}:\right]^- \leftrightarrow \left[:\ddot{\underset{..}{N}}{-}N{\equiv}N:\right]^-$$

$$0 \quad +1 \quad -2 \qquad\qquad -1 \quad +1 \quad -1 \qquad\qquad -2 \quad +1 \quad 0$$

Since the centre structure has the least amount of formal charge, it contributes most to the hybrid structure.

Hydrogen azide is thermodynamically unstable compared to its constituent elements and reacts explosively to produce hydrogen and nitrogen gas.

$$2\ HN_3(l) \longrightarrow H_2(g) + 3\ N_2(g)$$

The sodium azide salt is a stable solid at room temperature, but at elevated temperatures, or with a spark, it quickly forms elemental sodium and nitrogen gas.

$$2\ NaN_3(s) \longrightarrow 2\ Na(l) + 3\ N_2(g)$$

The large volume of N_2 gas that forms from a small volume of $NaN_3(s)$ is the basis for air bags in automobiles. However, pure sodium azide also forms liquid sodium, which is dangerous because of its high reactivity. Therefore, other components, such as KNO_3 and SiO_2, are added to the mixture in air bags to react with the liquid sodium:

$$10\ Na(l) + 2\ KNO_3(s) \longrightarrow K_2O(s) + 5\ Na_2O(s) + N_2(g)$$
$$2\ K_2O(s) + SiO_2(s) \longrightarrow K_4SiO_4(s)$$
$$2\ Na_2O(s) + SiO_2(s) \longrightarrow Na_4SiO_4(s)$$

The overall reaction thus produces the large volume of nitrogen gas required to fill the air bag quickly, along with harmless potassium and sodium silicates.

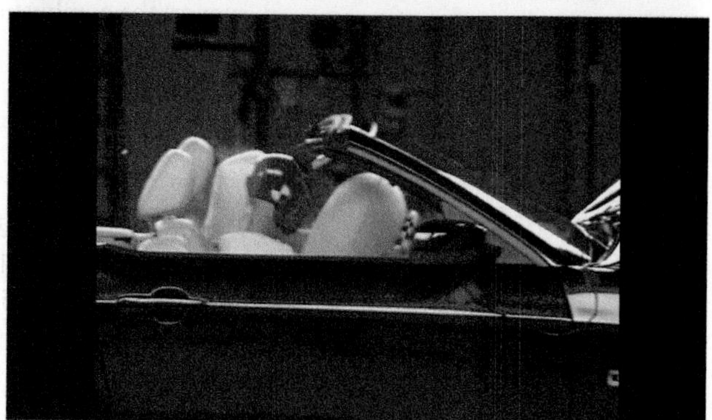

▲ Vehicle crash test with an air bag.

Nitrogen Oxides Under certain conditions, especially high temperatures, nitrogen is oxidized by oxygen to form a number of different oxides. For example, during lightning storms, nitrogen monoxide (NO) gas forms in the upper atmosphere.

$$N_2(g) + O_2(g) \xrightarrow{\text{lightning}} 2\ NO(g)$$

Other nitrogen oxides, such as nitrogen dioxide and dinitrogen trioxide, form from the further oxidation of nitrogen monoxide.

$$2\ NO(g) + O_2(g) \longrightarrow 2\ NO_2(g)$$
$$NO(g) + NO_2(g) \longrightarrow N_2O_3(l)$$

All nitrogen oxides are thermodynamically unstable and eventually decompose into their constituent elements or react to form more stable compounds. However, many of these reactions are kinetically slow, allowing some nitrogen oxides to persist for long periods of time.

The most important nitrogen oxide, because of its significance in biological systems, is probably nitrogen monoxide (NO), also called nitric oxide. In 1987, nitrogen monoxide was named molecule of the year by the journal *Science* because of several discoveries related to its biological functions. For example, NO helps control blood pressure through blood vessel dilation; it is important in memory and digestion; and it plays major roles in inducing male erections and female uterine contractions. The ability to adjust NO levels is a key role of the medications that treat erectile dysfunction (such as Viagra).

Earlier in this section, we learned that lightning forms NO in the atmosphere. In Section 15.12, we saw that NO and NO_2, formed as by-products of fossil fuel combustion, are among the important precursors of acid rain.

Nitrogen monoxide and nitrogen dioxide are both reactive free radicals (they contain unpaired electrons). At low temperature, two NO_2 molecules dimerize to form N_2O_4, pairing their two lone electrons. If N_2O_4 is heated, it decomposes back to NO_2. Consequently, the equilibrium between NO_2 and N_2O_4 is highly temperature-dependent, as we saw in Section 14.8.

$$\underset{\text{colourless}}{N_2O_4(g)} \xrightleftharpoons{\text{heat}} \underset{\text{reddish brown}}{2\,NO_2(g)}$$

Dinitrogen monoxide (N_2O), also called nitrous oxide, is a good oxidizing agent. It can support the combustion of active metals.

$$Mg(s) + N_2O(g) \longrightarrow MgO(s) + N_2(g)$$

Dinitrogen monoxide is unstable when heated, decomposing into nitrogen and oxygen gas.

$$2\,N_2O(g) \xrightarrow{\text{heat}} 2\,N_2(g) + O_2(g)$$

Dinitrogen monoxide (often referred to as "nitrous" or laughing gas) is used as an anesthetic by dentists and to pressurize food dispensers (such as whipped-cream dispensers). Commercially, N_2O is produced by the decomposition of ammonium nitrate.

$$NH_4NO_3(aq) \xrightarrow{\text{heat}} N_2O(g) + 2\,H_2O(l)$$

Nitric Acid, Nitrates, and Nitrites Nitric acid is an important commercial product of nitrogen. In an electric furnace, nitric acid forms from nitrogen and oxygen gas.

$$2\,N_2(g) + 5\,O_2(g) + 2\,H_2O(g) \longrightarrow 4\,HNO_3(g)$$

This reaction is thermodynamically favoured, but it is kinetically slow. (What would happen to our atmosphere if this reaction were thermodynamically *and* kinetically favoured?) Because of the slow speed of this reaction, a more efficient process, called the **Ostwald process**, is used to commercially produce nitric acid.

The first step of the Ostwald process involves passing ammonia gas over hot metal gauze at 600–700 °C to form NO gas. The gauze is made from metals such as platinum and rhodium that are good catalysts for this reaction.

$$4\,NH_3(g) + 5\,O_2(g) \xrightarrow{\text{catalyst}} 4\,NO(g) + 6\,H_2O(g)$$

Next, additional oxygen is added to oxidize the NO to NO_2 gas, which is then passed through a water spray to form nitric acid.

$$3\,NO_2(g) + H_2O(l) \longrightarrow 2\,HNO_3(l) + NO(g)$$

These steps are similar to the natural process that forms acid rain from NO and NO_2 gas in the atmosphere. The NO gas made during this last step can be recycled back to form more NO_2 and eventually more HNO_3.

Nitric acid is a strong acid that ionizes virtually completely in water. Concentrated nitric acid is 70% nitric acid by mass, or 16 mol L^{-1}. A small fraction of the HNO_3 in a bottle of concentrated nitric acid will react with water to form NO_2, a reddish brown gas that, in small amounts, gives the acid its characteristic pale yellow colour.

$$4\,HNO_3(aq) \longrightarrow 4\,NO_2(g) + O_2(g) + 2\,H_2O(l)$$

The main commercial uses of nitric acid are in the production of fertilizers and explosives. Over a million tons of ammonium nitrate fertilizer is produced annually by the reaction between ammonia and nitric acid.

$$NH_3(g) + HNO_3(aq) \longrightarrow NH_4NO_3(aq)$$

Besides being a good fertilizer, ammonium nitrate (as well as some other nitrates) are also good explosives. Ammonium nitrate explodes according to the following reaction:

$$2\,NH_4NO_3(s) \xrightarrow{\text{heat}} 2\,N_2O(g) + 4\,H_2O(g) \longrightarrow 2\,N_2(g) + O_2(g) + 4\,H_2O(g)$$

Metal nitrates are responsible for the various colours seen in fireworks displays. The different metal ions emit different colours as the nitrate explodes in air. For example, copper nitrate produces a green-coloured light according to the reaction:

$$2\ Cu(NO_3)_2(s) \xrightarrow{\text{heat}} 2\ CuO(s) + 4\ NO_2(g) + O_2(g) + \text{green light}$$

As we learned in Chapter 4, nitrates are very soluble in water. For reactions that need soluble metal cations, a nitrate compound is a good source for the cation without interference from the anion.

Nitrites are compounds containing the nitrite ion (NO_2^-). Sodium nitrite is used as a food preservative because it kills *Clostridium botulinum* bacteria, the cause of botulism, and because it keeps meat from discolouring when the meat is exposed to air. Recently, the public has raised concern over this practice, both because it hides the true age of the meat and because the nitrites can react with amines in the meat to form compounds called nitrosamines, which are suspected cancer-causing agents. However, no evidence exists to support the idea that nitrites at levels currently used in meats increase cancer risk in humans.

Phosphorus Compounds

Phosphorus has a valence electron configuration of $3s^2 3p^3$, similar to that of nitrogen. Phosphorus also forms many compounds with oxidation states ranging from −3 through +5. The most stable compounds have the +5 oxidation state.

Phosphine **Phosphine** (PH_3) is a colourless, poisonous gas that smells like decaying fish in which phosphorus has an oxidation state of −3. Since phosphorus is less electronegative than nitrogen, phosphine is less polar than ammonia. Phosphine forms from the hydrolysis of metal phosphides:

$$Ca_3P_2(s) + 6\ H_2O(l) \longrightarrow 2\ PH_3(g) + 3\ Ca(OH)_2(aq)$$

The disproportionation of white phosphorus in a basic solution can also produce phosphine:

$$2\ P_4(s) + 3\ OH^-(aq) + 9\ H_2O(l) \longrightarrow 5\ PH_3(g) + 3\ H_2PO_4^-(aq)$$

Disproportionation is a reaction in which an element is both reduced and oxidized during the same reaction (see Section 4.6). In this equation, the phosphorus in P_4 is both oxidized and reduced. Phosphorus has an oxidation number of 0 in P_4 and is reduced to −3 in PH_3 and oxidized to +5 in $H_2PO_4^-$.

When heated, phosphine decomposes to phosphorus and hydrogen:

$$4\ PH_3(g) \xrightarrow{\text{heat}} P_4(s) + 6\ H_2(g)$$

Like ammonia, phosphine can form phosphonium compounds such as PH_4Cl and PH_4I. Unlike ammonia, phosphine is not basic in aqueous solution.

Phosphorus Halides When phosphorus reacts with the halogens, it forms phosphorus halides, the most important of which generally have the formulas PX_3 and PX_5.

$$P_4(s) + 6\ Cl_2(g) \longrightarrow 4\ PCl_3(l)$$
$$P_4(s) + 10\ Cl_2(g) \longrightarrow 4\ PCl_5(s) \qquad \text{(with excess chlorine)}$$

Phosphorus halides react with water to form phosphoric acid and the corresponding hydrogen halide. For example, PCl_3 reacts with water:

$$PCl_3(l) + 3\ H_2O(l) \longrightarrow H_3PO_3(aq) + 3\ HCl(aq)$$

Reaction of PCl_3 with oxygen at room temperature forms phosphorus oxychloride:

$$2\ PCl_3(l) + O_2(g) \longrightarrow 2\ POCl_3(l)$$

Other phosphorus oxyhalides form as a result of the reactions of $POCl_3$ with metal fluorides or iodides:

$$POCl_3(l) + 3\ NaI(s) \longrightarrow POI_3(s) + 3\ NaCl(s)$$

The phosphorus halides and oxyhalides are important compounds in organic chemistry and serve as starting materials for the production of many phosphorus-containing compounds. Many of the key compounds in pesticides, oil additives, fire retardants for clothing, and surfactants (agents that act at surfaces), for example, are commercially made from phosphorus oxyhalides.

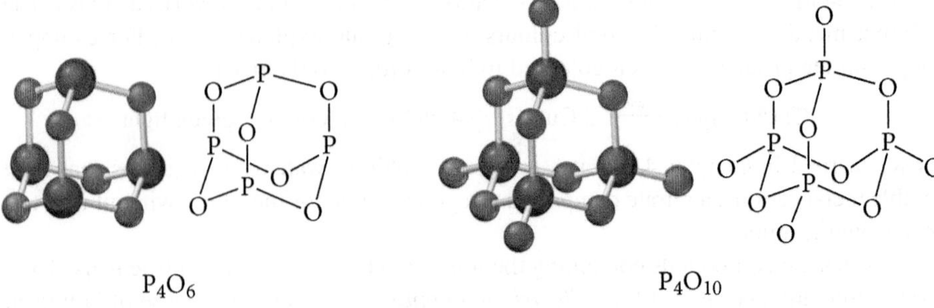

▶ **FIGURE 23.22 Tetraphosphorus Hexaoxide and Decaoxide, P_4O_6 and P_4O_{10}** The P_4O_6 structure has the P atoms at the corners of a tetrahedron and the O atoms on the edges. The P_4O_{10} structure has O atoms also bonded to the P atoms at the corners.

Phosphorus Oxides White phosphorus reacts directly with oxygen to form phosphorus oxides, as in this reaction:

$$P_4(s) + 5\ O_2(g) \longrightarrow P_4O_{10}(s)$$

The product depends upon the amount of oxygen. Tetraphosphorus hexoxide, $P_4O_6(s)$, forms when oxygen is limited, and tetraphosphorus decaoxide, $P_4O_{10}(s)$, forms when greater amounts of oxygen are available, as shown above.

Phosphorus oxides form interesting cage structures, as shown in Figure 23.22 ▲. You can visualize the P_4O_6 structure as a tetrahedron with a phosphorus atom at each of the vertices and an oxygen atom between each pair of phosphorus atoms. The P_4O_{10} structure has four additional oxygen atoms bonded to each phosphorus atom at the vertices of each tetrahedron.

Phosphoric Acid and Phosphates Phosphoric acid and phosphates are among the most important phosphorus-containing compounds. Phosphoric acid is a colourless solid that melts at 42 °C. Concentrated phosphoric acid is 85% phosphoric acid by mass, or 14.7 mol L^{-1}. Phosphoric acid is produced from the oxidation of white phosphorus to tetraphosphorus decoxide (see reaction above), which is then reacted with water.

$$P_4O_{10}(s) + 6\ H_2O(l) \longrightarrow 4\ H_3PO_4(aq)$$

This method produces a very pure phosphoric acid. A less pure product forms from the reaction of calcium phosphate (a mineral source of phosphate) with concentrated sulfuric acid.

$$Ca_3(PO_4)_2(s) + 3\ H_2SO_4(aq) \longrightarrow 3\ CaSO_4(s) + 2\ H_3PO_4(aq)$$

One direct use of phosphoric acid is rust removal. In steel production, thick steel slabs must be heated and rolled into thinner ones. During this process, the hot steel is exposed to air, which oxidizes the surface. To remove this rust, the thin steel sheets pass through phosphoric or hydrochloric acid baths, which dissolve the rust from the metal.

A major use of phosphoric acid is fertilizer production. In the past, phosphorus-containing materials such as fish, bones, and bat guano were used as fertilizer. Sulfuric acid decomposes bones to make phosphorus compounds that are more readily taken up by plants. Today many different phosphorus compounds have been developed specifically as fertilizers for various types of plants.

Detergent manufacturers use sodium phosphate compounds as additives. Compounds such as sodium pyrophosphate ($Na_4P_2O_7$) and sodium tripolyphosphate ($Na_5P_3O_{10}$) remove metal ions such as Ca^{2+} and Mg^{2+} from hard water, increasing the effectiveness of the detergent and preventing scum rings on sinks and tubs. However, phosphate compounds in detergents are being replaced by other compounds because of the ecological problems—primarily the overfertilization of algae in bodies of water—associated with the phosphates.

Phosphoric acid and phosphates are also important chemicals in the food industry. Phosphoric acid is a soft drink additive. At a low concentration, phosphoric acid is non-toxic and adds a tart, acidic taste to soft drinks. It also prevents bacterial growth in the soda. Table 23.5 summarizes the uses of phosphates in the food industry.

TABLE 23.5 Uses of Phosphates in the Food Industry

Phosphoric acid, H_3PO_4	Flavour agent in soda, yeast nutrient
Sodium dihydrogen phosphate (also sodium phosphate monobasic), NaH_2PO_4	Emulsifier, pH buffering agent
Sodium hydrogen phosphate (also sodium phosphate dibasic), Na_2HPO_4	Baking powder, fermentation auxiliary
Sodium hexametaphosphate, $(NaPO_3)_6$	Preservative, pH buffering agent
Sodium trimetaphosphate, $(NaPO_3)_3$	Starch modifier, juice dispersant
Iron(III) pyrophosphate nonahydrate, $Fe_4(P_2O_7)_3 \cdot 9\ H_2O$	Nutritional supplement
Sodium monofluorophosphate, Na_2PO_3F	Fluoride source for toothpaste
Pyrophosphate, $P_2O_7^{4-}$	Tartar control for toothpaste

23.7 Oxygen

The group 16 elements have an s^2p^4 valence electron configuration and a strong attraction for electrons. They can obtain a full octet by gaining only two more electrons. Because of its small size, oxygen is a much stronger oxidizing agent than the rest of the group 16 elements. Oxygen has the second highest electronegativity of any element (3.5), while the rest of the group 16 elements range from 2.5 to 2.0. Because of its high abundance (almost half the mass of Earth's crust is composed of oxygen) and its high reactivity, oxygen occurs in many common compounds, including metal oxides, carbonates, silicates, hydrates, and water. Oxygen is also critical for life; the oxidation of biomolecules by oxygen provides energy for most living systems on Earth.

Elemental Oxygen

Oxygen exists naturally as a colourless, odourless, diatomic, nonpolar gas. It condenses to a pale blue liquid at −183 °C. Oxygen is slightly soluble in water (0.04 g in 1 L or 0.001 mol L^{-1} at 25 °C). This rather low concentration of oxygen is enough to support life in aquatic environments. A few types of living systems that dwell deep in the ocean near vents that exude sulfur-containing fumes base their life processes on sulfur chemistry rather than oxygen chemistry.

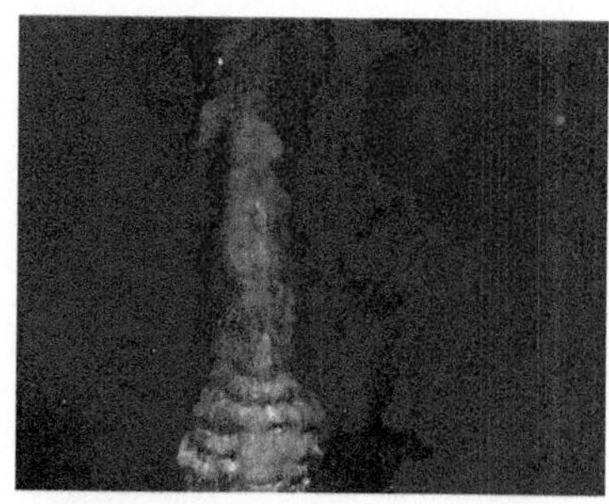

▲ Black smokers are vents found under the ocean that provide energy based on sulfur chemistry for life dwelling near the vents.

Today, about 21% of the Earth's atmosphere is composed of O_2, but this was not always the case. Earth's early atmosphere was reducing (rather than oxidizing) and contained nitrogen, hydrogen, methane, ammonia, and carbon dioxide. About 2.7 billion years ago, cyanobacteria (blue-green algae) began to convert the carbon dioxide and water to oxygen by photosynthesis. It took hundreds of millions of years to reach the present oxygen composition.

Joseph Priestley, an English scientist and minister, is credited with discovering oxygen. In 1774, he isolated oxygen by focusing sunlight on mercury(II) oxide and collecting the gas that was released as the red powder oxide formed liquid mercury. He tested the gas by using it to make a candle burn more brightly. He carried out a number of experiments with oxygen over the years, including bravely breathing his newfound gas. Antoine Lavoisier is credited with recognizing that oxygen is necessary for combustion. He described combustion as the reaction of a substance with oxygen (and not the loss of a substance). These discoveries and explanations were important steps in the development of modern chemistry.

Oxygen is one of the most abundantly produced industrial chemicals. The major production method is the fractionation of air. Fractionation involves cooling air until its components liquefy. Then the air is warmed, and components such as N_2 and Ar are separated out, leaving oxygen behind. Most commercial oxygen is stored and transported as a gas in tanks under high pressure. Another method for the production of oxygen is the electrolysis of water. Passing an electric current through water containing a small amount of an electrolyte will form hydrogen gas at the cathode and oxygen gas at the anode (see Section 18.8). Because of the large amount of electricity needed, however, electrolysis is not a cost-efficient method for oxygen production.

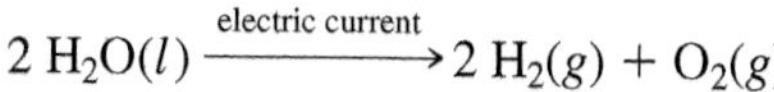

$$2\ H_2O(l) \xrightarrow{\text{electric current}} 2\ H_2(g) + O_2(g)$$

In the laboratory, oxygen can be produced by heating and decomposing metal oxides and other oxygen-containing compounds. The oxides of mercury, silver, and gold lose all their oxygen when heated, while the oxides of other metals, such as barium, lose only some of their oxygen.

$$2\,HgO(s) \xrightarrow{\text{heat}} 2\,Hg(l) + O_2(g)$$

$$2\,BaO_2(s) \xrightarrow{\text{heat}} 2\,BaO(s) + O_2(g)$$

Metal nitrates and chlorates also yield oxygen when heated. Use of a catalyst, such as manganese(IV) oxide or iron(III) oxide, can make these reactions very fast and dangerous.

$$2\,NaNO_3(s) \xrightarrow{\text{heat}} 2\,NaNO_2(s) + O_2(g)$$

$$2\,KClO_3(s) \xrightarrow[\text{catalyst}]{\text{heat}} 2\,KCl(s) + 3\,O_2(g)$$

Uses for Oxygen

The greatest industrial use for oxygen is the enrichment of the air in a blast furnace for the conversion of high-carbon iron to steel. Large quantities of oxygen are also used in oxyhydrogen or oxyacetylene torches for the cutting of metals. Oxygen is also used to create artificial air for use underwater, during high-altitude travel, and in safety equipment.

Oxygen plays an important role in the treatment of a number of medical conditions, such as acute and chronic lung diseases and heart disorders. Generally, patients use masks or nasal catheters to receive oxygen from a tank of compressed oxygen. New technology, however, has developed portable oxygen concentrators that use molecular sieves to separate and concentrate oxygen from air. Hyperbaric oxygen therapy is the application of high oxygen levels to patients with skin wounds, such as those with skin grafts or hard-to-heal wounds associated with diabetes. The high oxygen level kills anaerobic bacteria that can infect such wounds.

Oxides

As a strong oxidizing agent, oxygen reacts with most other elements to form oxides. We classify oxides according to the oxidation state of oxygen in the oxide, as shown in Table 23.6. The type of oxide that forms depends on the size and oxidation state of the metal. Regular oxides are more stable for the smaller ions with a higher charge. Superoxides are more stable for the larger ions with a smaller charge.

Oxygen also reacts with many nonmetals to form covalent compounds. Many of these nonmetals form several different binary oxides. For example, we have already seen that carbon forms CO and CO_2 and that nitrogen forms N_2O, NO, N_2O_3, NO_2, N_2O_4, and N_2O_5.

Ozone

Ozone (O_3), an allotrope of oxygen, is a toxic blue diamagnetic gas with a strong odour. People can detect the smell at levels as low as 0.01 ppm and the odour is often noticed in electrical storms or near electrical equipment because the gas forms from O_2 by an electrical discharge. Ozone is denser than O_2 and condenses to a deep blue liquid at

TABLE 23.6 Types of Oxides

Class	Ion	Oxidation State of O	Example
Oxide	O^{2-}	-2	Li_2O, MgO
Peroxide	O_2^{2-}	-1	Na_2O_2, BaO_2
Superoxide	O_2^{-}	$-\frac{1}{2}$	RbO_2, CsO_2

−112 °C. Ozone is naturally made by the irradiation of O_2 with ultraviolet light in the upper atmosphere.

$$3\,O_2(g) \xrightarrow{\text{UV radiation}} 2\,O_3(g)$$

Ozone is also produced by passing O_2 gas through an electric field. The volume of gas decreases as the O_2 is converted to O_3. Ozone is produced industrially by the electrolysis of cold concentrated sulfuric acid.

Thermodynamically unstable, ozone decomposes spontaneously to oxygen.

$$2\,O_3(g) \longrightarrow 3\,O_2(g)$$

Ozone is used commercially as a strong oxidizing agent. For example, ozone can oxidize NO_2 to N_2O_5 or PbS to $PbSO_4$.

$$2\,NO_2(g) + O_3(g) \longrightarrow N_2O_5(g) + O_2(g)$$
$$PbS(s) + 4\,O_3(g) \longrightarrow PbSO_4(s) + 4\,O_2(g)$$

Ozone kills bacteria and is an environmentally safe replacement for chlorine in water-purification plants because the only by-product is O_2. However, since ozone naturally decomposes, it must constantly be replenished, an economic drawback that limits its use.

The air we breathe contains ozone because it forms as a by-product of fossil fuel combustion. Since it is a strong oxidizing agent, it is a harmful substance. In the lower atmosphere, ozone damages the lungs and skin, stings the eyes, and damages most plant and animal tissues. Ozone also reacts with many types of plastic and rubber materials, causing them to become brittle and to crack.

The layer of ozone in the upper atmosphere plays an important role in the absorption of harmful ultraviolet radiation from the sun. It absorbs the UV radiation and breaks apart to O_2 and O. This oxygen atom will often react with another O_2 molecule to re-form as ozone. During this cycle, each ozone molecule absorbs many ultraviolet photons. The ozone layer has been depleted by the emission of chlorofluorocarbons (CFCs) into the atmosphere. However, legislation has banned CFCs, in the hope that the reduction of CFCs will help the ozone layer to recover.

23.8 Sulfur: A Dangerous but Useful Element

Like oxygen, sulfur is a nonmetal that belongs to the 16 family. However, sulfur's 3*p* orbitals extend farther out from the nucleus than do oxygen's 2*p* orbitals. Consequently, sulfur is larger and is a much weaker oxidizing agent than oxygen. Unlike oxygen, which forms compounds with *only* negative oxidation states, sulfur forms compounds with both negative and positive oxidation states. Sulfur, selenium, and tellurium generally form covalent compounds with a +4 or +6 oxidation state, forming anions only when bonding with highly electropositive metals. Sulfur is also much less abundant than oxygen, yet still composes about 0.06% of the mass of Earth's crust.

Elemental Sulfur

Sulfur has several allotropes; the most common naturally occurring allotrope is composed of an S_8 ring structure called cyclooctasulfur. Most of the different allotropes of sulfur have ring structures with rings ranging in size from S_6 to S_{20}. When heated above its melting point of 112 °C, cyclooctasulfur forms a straw-yellow liquid with low viscosity. Above 150 °C, the rings begin to break, and the sulfur becomes a darker, more viscous liquid as the broken rings entangle one another. The colour is darkest at 180 °C when the liquid becomes very viscous and pours very slowly, as can be seen in the photo at right. Above this temperature, however, the intermolecular forces between the S_8 chains weaken, and the liquid becomes less viscous again. If the hot liquid is poured into cold water, the sulfur will quench into an amorphous solid, as shown in Figure 23.23 ▼. Initially, this amorphous material is flexible like a plastic, but it hardens into a brittle solid.

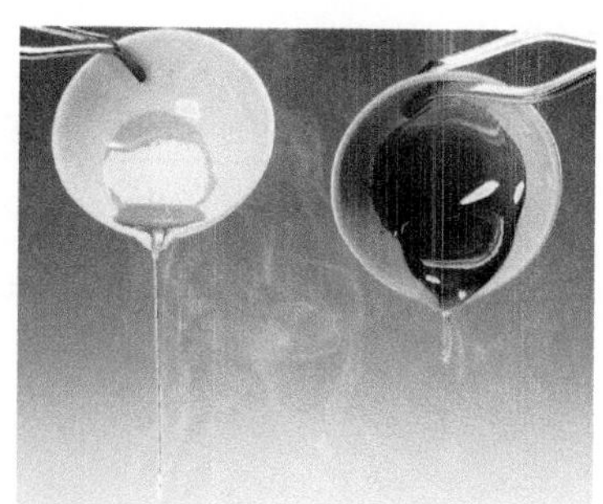

▲ Molten sulfur below 150 °C (left) and nearing 180 °C (right).

Sulfur can be found in natural deposits located underground or close to the Earth's surface where volcanic activity has brought the element to the surface. The most

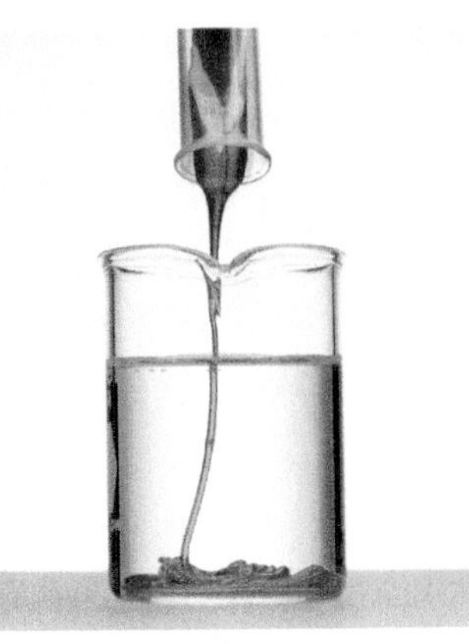

▲ **FIGURE 23.23 Quenching Liquid Sulfur** When hot liquid sulfur is poured into cold water, the sulfur quenches into an amorphous solid.

important industrial source of sulfur is "sour" natural gas, which contains a large percentage of dihydrogen sulfide (H_2S). The H_2S can be separated from the other components by passing the gas through organic solvents such as ethanolamine. The H_2S dissolves in the organic solvent:

$$\underset{\text{ethanolamine}}{HOC_2H_4NH_2(l)} + H_2S(g) \longrightarrow HOC_2H_4NH_3^+(\text{solvent}) + HS^-(\text{solvent})$$

The H_2S is recovered and oxidized to elemental sulfur through a two-step process—the **Claus process**—that accounts for over 50% of all sulfur produced.

$$2\,H_2S(g) + 3\,O_2(g) \longrightarrow 2\,SO_2(g) + 2\,H_2O(g)$$

$$4\,H_2S(g) + 2\,SO_2(g) \longrightarrow \frac{6}{8}\,S_8(s) + 4\,H_2O(g)$$

Throughout western Canada, there are many natural gas plants that employ the Claus process to remove H_2S from natural gas. Sulfur is stored on site (Figure 23.24 ▼) until it can be transported, initially by rail, to industrial customers. Most sulfur is converted into sulfuric acid for various industrial processes.

▲ **FIGURE 23.24 Natural Gas Plant** Sulfur extracted from natural gas is stored in large piles.

Hydrogen Sulfide and Metal Sulfides

Hydrogen sulfide, a component of natural gas, is toxic and forms by the reactions of anaerobic bacteria on organic substances. Rotting vegetation and bogs are natural sources of H_2S for the atmosphere. Fortunately, we can detect the odour of H_2S (a rotten egg smell) at concentrations as low as 0.02 ppm, which pose no threat to our health. Levels as low as 10 ppm can cause nausea, and 100 ppm can cause death. The smell of H_2S becomes more difficult to detect at high levels because H_2S also has an anesthetic effect that dulls the sense of smell. Consequently, the sudden onset of strong H_2S odour is a reason to move quickly to fresh air.

It might initially seem that hydrogen sulfide (H_2S) might share chemical properties with water (H_2O), but it does not. Water has a larger bond angle (104.5°) than hydrogen sulfide (92.5°) and is much more polar. Because of its polarity, water forms strong hydrogen bonds, but hydrogen sulfide does not. In addition, the O—H bond is much stronger than the S—H bond. These differences result in a much lower boiling point and greater reactivity for hydrogen sulfide compared to water. Water is a stable molecule in the presence of air and oxygen. Hydrogen sulfide burns in air, reacting with oxygen to form elemental sulfur or sulfur oxides.

EXAMPLE 23.5 BALANCING OF AND ASSIGNING OXIDATION STATES TO SULFUR REACTIONS

Write a balanced equation for the reaction of O_2 and H_2S to form elemental S (in the form of S_8). Identify the change of the oxidation state for S.

SOLUTION

Write the skeletal equation. The products are elemental S_8 and H_2O.	$H_2S(g) + O_2(g) \longrightarrow H_2O(g) + S_8(s)$
Since hydrogen is initially balanced, balance S first, followed by H and O.	$8\,H_2S(g) + 4\,O_2(g) \longrightarrow 8\,H_2O(g) + S_8(s)$
Assign oxidation states to each element (see Section 4.6).	$\underset{+1\ -2}{8\,H_2S(g)} + \underset{0}{4\,O_2(g)} \longrightarrow \underset{+1\ -2}{8\,H_2O(g)} + \underset{0}{S_8(s)}$ Oxidation (S: −2 → 0) The oxidation state of S changes from −2 in H_2S to 0 in S_8; therefore, S is oxidized.

FOR PRACTICE 23.5

Write a balanced equation for the reaction of oxygen with H_2S to form SO_2. Identify the change of the oxidation state for S.

TABLE 23.7 Common Metal Sulfides

Sulfide	Formula	Common Name	K_{sp} (at 25 °C)
Iron(II) disulfide	FeS_2	Pyrite	3.72×10^{-19}
Zinc sulfide	ZnS	Sphalerite	2.0×10^{-25}
Lead(II) sulfide	PbS	Galena	9.04×10^{-29}
Mercury(II) sulfide	HgS	Cinnabar	1.6×10^{-54}

Hydrogen sulfide forms from the reactions of metal sulfides with hydrochloric acid.

$$FeS(s) + 2\,HCl(aq) \longrightarrow FeCl_2(s) + H_2S(g)$$

Only a few of the metal sulfides, those with group 1 and 2 metals and Al, are very soluble in water. Some common metal sulfides and their solubility product constants are listed in Table 23.7. The low solubility of these sulfides allows the use of H_2S as a good analytical method to determine whether metal ions are present in a solution. Sodium sulfide is used to precipitate toxic metals from industrial waste sources.

Metal sulfides have a number of industrial uses, mostly because they are toxic to bacteria. For example, SeS_2 is a shampoo additive that kills bacteria and controls dandruff, and As_2S_3 kills parasites.

Sulfur Dioxide

Sulfur dioxide is another toxic sulfur compound. Under standard conditions, it is a colourless, dense gas that has an acidic taste. The acidic taste results from the reaction of the gas with the water in your mouth.

$$SO_2(g) + H_2O(l) \longrightarrow H_2SO_3(aq)$$

Sulfur dioxide forms naturally during volcanic activity when sulfides oxidize in the high volcanic temperatures. Sulfur dioxide is also a pollutant that forms during many industrial processes, such as coal and oil combustion and metal extraction. As we have seen, when the sulfur dioxide is emitted into the air, it reacts with oxygen and water to produce acid rain:

$$2\,SO_2(g) + 2\,H_2O(g) + O_2(g) \longrightarrow 2\,H_2SO_4(aq)$$

Sulfuric acid as a pollutant is destructive to plants, animals, and man-made structures (see Section 15.12).

To prevent the emission of SO_2 into the atmosphere, industrial processes "scrub" the gas to remove the SO_2. The exhaust gas flows through stacks lined with calcium carbonate that, when heated, capture sulfur oxides in the form of calcium sulfate dust:

$$CaCO_3(s) \xrightarrow{\text{heat}} CaO(s) + CO_2(g)$$
$$2\,CaO(s) + 2\,SO_2(g) + O_2(g) \longrightarrow 2\,CaSO_4(s)$$

The $CaSO_4$ dust is collected and disposed of. New uses for the tons of waste $CaSO_4$, such as fireproof insulation, are needed.

Sulfuric Acid

The most important use of sulfur and its compounds is the production of sulfuric acid. In fact, sulfuric acid is the most abundantly produced chemical in the world because it is a strong acid, a strong oxidizing agent, and a good dehydrating agent. It is also plentiful and inexpensive. Sulfuric acid is used in the manufacture of fertilizers, colour dyes, petrochemicals, paints, plastics, explosives, batteries, steel, and detergents, to name just a few.

▲ **FIGURE 23.25 Dehydration of Sucrose** Sulfuric acid dehydrates sucrose by removing the hydrogen and oxygen as water molecules and leaving carbon behind. The porous carbon foam forms because the reaction is very exothermic.

Pure H_2SO_4 melts at 10.4 °C and boils at 337 °C. At room temperature, it is an oily, dense liquid. Sulfuric acid reacts vigorously and exothermically with water. Pure or concentrated H_2SO_4 must be added to water slowly to avoid rapid heating, boiling, and splattering.

$$H_2SO_4(l) \xrightarrow{H_2O(l)} H_2SO_4(aq) \quad \text{highly exothermic}$$

The strong attraction between sulfuric acid and water makes sulfuric acid a very strong dehydrating agent. As shown in Figure 23.25 ◄, its affinity for water is strong enough to decompose some organic materials, such as sucrose.

$$C_{12}H_{22}O_{11}(s) + H_2SO_4(l) \longrightarrow 12\,C(s) + 11\,H_2O(g) + H_2SO_4(aq)$$

Sulfuric acid is produced industrially by a method known as the **contact process**, developed in the early twentieth century. In this method, molten, elemental sulfur is first sprayed into a furnace with air to form SO_2 gas, which is then heated in contact with a V_2O_5 catalyst to form SO_3 gas.

$$S(l) + O_2(g) \xrightarrow{\text{heat}} SO_2(g)$$

$$2\,SO_2(g) + O_2(g) \xrightarrow{V_2O_5 \text{ catalyst}} 2\,SO_3(g)$$

The SO_3 gas is absorbed into concentrated sulfuric acid, producing a dense form of sulfuric acid called oleum, $H_2S_2O_7$, which produces H_2SO_4 when dissolved in water.

$$SO_3(g) + H_2SO_4(l) \longrightarrow H_2S_2O_7(l)$$

$$H_2S_2O_7(l) + H_2O(l) \longrightarrow 2\,H_2SO_4(aq)$$

As we have already seen, sulfuric acid is used in fertilizer production, which consumes a significant amount of the sulfuric acid produced.

23.9 Halogens: Reactive Elements with High Electronegativity

The halogens are all one electron short of a noble gas electron configuration. They are the most electronegative elements in their respective periods and are therefore very reactive. They do not naturally occur in their elemental form. The source of most of the halogens (except fluorine) is the dissolved salts present in seawater. The major sources for fluorine are several different minerals, including fluorspar (CaF_2) and fluoroapatite [$Ca_{10}F_2(PO_4)_6$].

We have already seen some of the properties of the halogens, especially those that exhibit periodic trends, in Chapter 8. For example, the atomic radius of the halogens increases regularly from fluorine to iodine, as shown in Table 23.8. Due partly to its small size, fluorine has the highest electronegativity of all elements, and is always found in oxidation states of −1 or 0. The other halogens can be found with oxidation states ranging from −1 to +7. The positive oxidation states occur when the halogen bonds to more electronegative elements such as fluorine or oxygen.

TABLE 23.8 Selected Properties of the Halogens

Element	Melting Point (°C)	Boiling Point (°C)	Atomic Radius (pm)	Electronegativity
Fluorine	−219	−188	72	4.0
Chlorine	−101	−34	99	3.0
Bromine	−7	60	113	2.8
Iodine	114	185	133	2.5

EXAMPLE 23.6 DETERMINING THE OXIDATION STATE OF HALOGENS IN COMPOUNDS

Calculate the oxidation state for Cl in each compound.

(a) ClO_3^- **(b)** HClO **(c)** Cl_2

SOLUTION

(a) For ClO_3^-, each O atom has an oxidation state of −2 for a total of −6 for all three O atoms. Therefore, the Cl atom has to be +5 for the sum of the oxidation states to equal the charge of the ion (5 − 6 = −1).

(b) For HClO, the O atom has an oxidation state of −2 and the H atom has an oxidation state of +1. Therefore, the Cl atom has to be +1 to have a neutral charge (1 + 1 − 2 = 0).

(c) For Cl_2, the Cl atoms are in their elemental state, so they have an oxidation state of 0.

FOR PRACTICE 23.6

Calculate the oxidation state of Cl in ClO_4^- and Cl^-.

Elemental Fluorine and Hydrofluoric Acid

Fluorine is the most reactive element and forms binary compounds with all elements except He, Ne, and Ar. Fluorine even forms compounds with some of the noble gases, producing compounds such as XeF_2, XeF_6, and $XeOF_4$. The high reactivity of fluorine is related to several factors. First, the F—F bond is among the weakest halogen–halogen bonds, as shown in Table 23.9. In order for a halogen to react with other substances, the halogen–halogen bond must break. The energy required to break that bond is small for F_2, allowing the resulting reaction to be more exothermic. Second, the small size of fluorine results in a high lattice energy for the ionic compounds that it forms. The high lattice energy means the compounds are very stable.

TABLE 23.9 Comparison of Halogen X X Bond Energy

Halogen	F—F	Cl—Cl	Br—Br	I—I
Bond energy (kJ mol^{-1})	159	243	193	151

The high reactivity of fluorine is illustrated by its ability to burn (or quickly oxidize) many substances, such as iron and sulfur, that do not readily burn with oxygen.

$$Fe(s) + F_2(g) \longrightarrow FeF_2(s)$$

$$\frac{1}{8}S_8(s) + 3\,F_2(g) \longrightarrow SF_6(g)$$

Fluorine gas even reacts with asbestos and glass, two materials commonly used as containers for reactive substances. Consequently, fluorine is normally held in metal containers made of iron, copper, or nickel. These metals also initially react with fluorine, but then a thin layer of the product coats the surface of the metal, protecting the underlying metal from further reaction.

Elemental fluorine is produced from the electrolysis of anhydrous hydrofluoric acid or hydrogen fluoride gas, forming F_2 and H_2 gases.

Oxidation: $$2\,F^-(g) \longrightarrow F_2(g) + 2\,e^-$$

Reduction: $$2\,H^+(g) + 2\,e^- \longrightarrow H_2(g)$$

Gaseous hydrogen fluoride can be obtained from the reaction of the mineral fluorspar (CaF_2) with sulfuric acid.

$$CaF_2(s) + H_2SO_4(l) \longrightarrow 2\,HF(g) + CaSO_4(s)$$

In its solid form, HF has a crystal structure that contains zigzag chains of alternating H and F atoms. In aqueous solutions, HF is a weak acid ($K_a = 3.5 \times 10^{-4}$ for HF at 298 K). Like all anions in aqueous solution, the F^- ions from ionized HF are solvated by water molecules. However, the F^- ions can also associate with other HF molecules to form HF_2^-:

$$F^-(aq) + HF(aq) \longrightarrow HF_2^-(aq)$$

The structure of HF_2^-, shown here, is unique because it contains a bridging hydrogen atom (a hydrogen atom that essentially forms two bonds) and can be considered the strongest hydrogen bond known:

Hydrofluoric acid is extremely corrosive and reacts with glass according to the following reactions:

$$SiO_2(s) + 4\,HF(aq) \longrightarrow SiF_4(g) + 2\,H_2O(l)$$

or

$$SiO_2(s) + 6\,HF(aq) \longrightarrow SiF_6^{2-}(aq) + 2\,H^+(aq) + 2\,H_2O(l)$$

As a result, hydrofluoric acid cannot be held in a glass container and is generally stored in plastic. The ability of HF to react with glass makes it useful in etching glass. The parts of the glass to be etched are left exposed, and the rest is masked with a nonreactive substance such as plastic. The surface is then exposed to hydrofluoric acid and the non-masked glass etches away, leaving the desired pattern. Hydrofluoric acid is particularly dangerous because it quickly penetrates into tissues, damaging internal organs and bones. Direct exposure of just 2% of body surface area to concentrated hydrofluoric acid can be fatal.

Elemental Chlorine

Historically, the primary source for chlorine has been seawater. Electrolysis of NaCl in seawater produces Cl_2 gas and H_2 gas:

$$2\,NaCl(aq) + 2\,H_2O(l) \xrightarrow{\text{electricity}} Cl_2(g) + 2\,NaOH(aq) + H_2(g)$$

Today much Cl_2 gas is produced and collected as a by-product of the various metal processing methods, such as in reduction of metal chlorides to form metals:

$$MgCl_2(l) \xrightarrow{\text{electricity}} Mg(s) + Cl_2(g)$$

Halogen Oxides

Most halogen oxides are unstable and many are explosive. A unique halogen oxide is OF_2; oxygen usually has a negative oxidation state in its compounds but has a +2 oxidation state in OF_2 (due to the high electronegativity of fluorine).

A number of different chlorine oxides are known, including Cl_2O, ClO_2, Cl_2O_6, and Cl_2O_7. Chlorine dioxide is a powerful oxidizing agent used to bleach flour and wood pulp (to make white paper). Because ClO_2 is explosive, the gas is diluted with CO_2 or N_2 for safety. Some water treatment plants are now using ClO_2 for water disinfection in place of Cl_2. ClO_2 is produced by the oxidation of sodium chlorite with Cl_2 or by the reduction of sodium chlorate with hydrochloric acid.

$$2\,NaClO_2(aq) + Cl_2(g) \longrightarrow 2\,NaCl(aq) + 2\,ClO_2(g)$$
$$2\,NaClO_3(aq) + 4\,HCl(aq) \longrightarrow 2\,ClO_2(g) + Cl_2(g) + 2\,H_2O(l) + 2\,NaCl(aq)$$

EXAMPLE 23.7 IDENTIFYING CHANGES IN OXIDATION STATES

Identify the change of oxidation state for Cl in the production of chlorine dioxide from sodium chlorite. Identify the oxidizing agent and the reducing agent.

SOLUTION

First determine the oxidation state of Cl in each compound.

$$\underset{+1\,+3\,-2}{2\,NaClO_2(aq)} + \underset{0}{Cl_2(g)} \longrightarrow \underset{+1\,-1}{2\,NaCl(aq)} + \underset{+4\,-2}{2\,ClO_2(g)}$$

The Cl in the $NaClO_2$ was oxidized from +3 to +4 by the oxidizing agent Cl_2, which was reduced from 0 to −1 by the reducing agent $NaClO_2$.

FOR PRACTICE 23.7

Identify the change of oxidation state for Cl in the production of chlorine dioxide from sodium chlorate. Identify the oxidizing agent and the reducing agent.

CHAPTER IN REVIEW

Key Terms

Section 23.2
main-group elements (991)

Section 23.3
silicates (992)
quartz (993)
silica (993)
aluminosilicate (993)
orthosilicate (993)
pyrosilicate (994)
pyroxene (994)
amphibole (994)
phyllosilicate (994)

Section 23.4
borane (998)
closo-borane (998)
nido-borane (998)
arachno-borane (998)

Section 23.5
graphite (999)
diamond (999)
coal (1000)
coke (1000)
charcoal (1000)
activated carbon (1000)
soot (1000)
carbon black (1000)
fullerene (1001)
nanotube (1001)
carbide (1002)
ionic carbide (1002)
covalent carbide (1002)
metallic carbide (1003)
washing soda (1004)

Section 23.6
white phosphorus (1005)
red phosphorus (1005)
black phosphorus (1006)
ammonia (1006)
Haber–Bosch process (1006)
hydrazine (1006)
hydrogen azide (1006)
Ostwald process (1008)
phosphine (1009)

Section 23.7
ozone (1012)

Section 23.8
Claus process (1014)
contact process (1016)

Key Concepts

Bonding and Properties (23.2)

Main-group elements are defined by their electron configurations and their location in the periodic table. The properties of the main-group elements show great diversity. Metals, nonmetals, and metalloids are all found among the main-group elements. Some of the main-group elements form covalent bonds while others form ionic bonds.

The Most Common Matter: Silicates (23.3)

Silicates are covalent atomic solids that contain silicon, oxygen, and various metal atoms. Silicates are found in rocks, clays, and soils. Four oxygen atoms bond to silicon, forming a negatively charged polyatomic anion that has a structure with a tetrahedral shape. Various metal ions within the structure balance the charge of the compound. The SiO_4 tetrahedrons can link to form chains, double chains, sheets, or even extended three-dimensional structures. The properties of the silicates depend on the connections between the silicate tetrahedrons. Because of the wide variety of combinations of tetrahedron connections and the many different metal ions that fit within the structure, an enormous variety of different silicate minerals exist in nature, making the silicate materials the most common structures found on Earth.

Boron (23.4)

Because of its small size and high electronegativity, boron behaves as a metalloid. The structure of elemental boron consists of icosahedron structures bonded together in various ways. Boron tends to form electron-deficient compounds. Compounds of boron and hydrogen form cluster compounds resembling spheres, cages, and nets.

Carbon (23.5)

Organic chemistry is based on the chemistry of carbon, yet carbon is also very important in many inorganic compounds and applications. Graphite and diamond are two well-known structures of elemental carbon, but many other forms of elemental carbon, such as carbon black, coke, and the newly discovered fullerenes have many industrial applications. Important types of inorganic carbon compounds include carbides and carbonates. Carbon can form carbides with metallic, covalent, or ionic properties. Carbon and its oxygen compounds are intimately involved in the functions of life.

Nitrogen and Phosphorus (23.6)

Nitrogen and phosphorus have been known for over 200 years. Nitrogen and phosphorus both form compounds with oxidation numbers ranging from −3 to +5. Both nitrogen and phosphorus compounds are very important for plant growth and their most important use is as fertilizers. The strong triple bond between nitrogen atoms in N_2 makes nitrogen from the atmosphere inaccessible to most plants, so ingenious chemical processes have been devised to make nitrogen compounds that are more readily available to plants.

Oxygen (23.7)

Oxygen is the most common element on Earth. It is found in the atmosphere as the elemental gas and as many oxide gases. Oxygen is found in ocean water and in Earth's crust as silicate and oxide compounds. Oxygen is a strong oxidizing agent and forms compounds with $-\frac{1}{2}$, −1, or −2 oxidation states. Ozone, O_3, is a helpful molecule in the upper atmosphere, where it absorbs harmful ultraviolet radiation, but a harmful molecule at Earth's surface.

Sulfur (23.8)

More sulfuric acid is produced than any other chemical. Most of the sulfuric acid is used to make fertilizers. Other uses take advantage of its strong oxidation and dehydration properties. Elemental sulfur has several allotropes, ranging from ring structures to chain structures and amorphous materials, depending on temperature.

Halogens (23.9)

The halogens are the most electronegative elements, so they are always found as compounds, usually ionic. When they bond with other electronegative elements, however, they can form covalent compounds. Fluorine has special chemical properties because it is the most electronegative element and is very small, making it a very strong oxidizing agent.

Key Skills

Determining the Composition, Charge Balance, and Type of Silicates and Aluminosilicates (23.3)
• Examples 23.1, 23.2, 23.3, 23.4 • For Practice 23.1, 23.2, 23.3, 23.4 • Exercises 17–26

Writing Equations for Reactions and Assigning Oxidation States (23.8, 23.9)
• Examples 23.5, 23.6, 23.7 • For Practice 23.5, 23.6, 23.7 • Exercises 43–46, 55–58, 73, 74, 77, 78

EXERCISES

Review Questions

1. Why does BN form compounds similar to those of elemental carbon?
2. What is the main characteristic that determines whether or not an element is a main-group element?
3. Does the metallic characteristic of a main-group element increase or decrease as we move down a family? Explain why.
4. Why does silicon form only single bonds with oxygen but carbon, which is in the same family as silicon, form double bonds with oxygen in many compounds?
5. What is the difference between SiO_2 that is cooled slowly and SiO_2 that is cooled quickly?
6. What is the difference between a rock and a mineral?
7. Briefly define each term:
   a. orthosilicate b. amphibole c. pyroxene
   d. pyrosilicate e. feldspar
8. Why is boron oxide often added to silica glass?
9. Why does boron form electron-deficient bonds? Provide an example.
10. List three allotropes of crystalline carbon.
11. Explain why solid CO_2 is referred to as dry ice.
12. Nitric acid and phosphoric acid are two major products of the chemical industry. Describe some of their uses.
13. What is the typical concentration of oxygen in dry air?
14. Describe how nitrogen can be separated from the other components of air.
15. Earth's atmosphere originally did not contain oxygen. Explain how the atmosphere gained oxygen.
16. Name a benefit, a hazard, and a useful commercial application of ozone.

Problems by Topic

Silicates: The Most Abundant Matter in Earth's Crust

17. Silicon bonds to oxygen to form a tetrahedral shape in both the network covalent silica compound, SiO_2, and in ionic silicate compounds. What is the oxidation state of Si in each of these structures?
    a. silica compound, SiO_2 c. pyrosilicates, $Si_2O_7^{6-}$
    b. orthosilicates, SiO_4^{4-}
18. What is the oxidation state of Si in each of these structures?
    a. pyroxenes, SiO_3^{2-} c. phyllosilicates, $Si_2O_5^{2-}$
    b. amphiboles, $Si_4O_{11}^{6-}$
19. In the orthosilicate garnet, the formula unit has three SiO_4^{4-} units and is balanced by Ca^{2+} and Al^{3+} cations. Determine the formula unit of garnet.

20. In the pyroxene kanoite, the formula unit has two SiO_3^{2-} units and is balanced by manganese and magnesium ions. Determine the formula unit of kanoite. Assume that the oxidation state of Mn is +2.

21. Kaolin is a clay material that is a phyllosilicate. Use charge balancing to determine how many hydroxide ions are in the formula for kaolin, $Al_2Si_2O_5(OH)_x$.

22. Tremolite is a double-chain silicate in the amphibole class. Use charge balancing to determine how many hydroxide ions are in the formula for tremolite, $Ca_2Mg_5Si_8O_{23}(OH)_x$.

23. How are the silica tetrahedrons linked for $ZrSiO_4$? To what class of silicates does this compound belong?

24. How are the silica tetrahedrons linked for $CaSiO_3$? To what class of silicates does this compound belong?

25. Predict the structure and give the charges on the cations in one of the minerals in the hornblende family, $Ca_2Mg_4FeSi_7AlO_{22}(OH)_2$.

26. Predict the structure and label the charges on the cations in the mineral hedenbergite, $CaFeSi_2O_6$.

Boron and Its Remarkable Structures

27. A major source of boron is the mineral kernite, $Na_2[B_4O_5(OH)_4] \cdot 3\ H_2O$. Calculate how many grams of boron can be produced from 1.0×10^3 kg of a kernite-bearing ore if the ore contains 0.98% kernite by mass and the process has a 65% yield.

28. An uncommon mineral of boron is ulexite, $NaCaB_5O_9 \cdot 8\ H_2O$. How many grams of boron can be produced from 5.00×10^2 kg of ulexite-bearing ore if the ore contains 0.032% ulexite by mass and the process has an 88% yield?

29. Explain why the bond angles in BCl_3 and NCl_3 are different.

30. Explain why the bond between boron and Cl in the molecule BCl_3 is shorter than would be expected from a single B—Cl bond.

31. Predict the number of vertices and faces on each *closo*-borane:
a. $B_6H_6^{2-}$ **b.** $B_{12}H_{12}^{2-}$

32. Predict the number of vertices and faces on each *closo*-borane:
a. $B_4H_4^{2-}$ **b.** $B_9H_9^{2-}$

33. Describe the differences between a *closo*-borane, a *nido*-borane, and an *arachno*-borane.

34. Describe how boron is used in the nuclear industry.

Carbon, Carbides, and Carbonates

35. Explain why the graphite structure of carbon allows graphite to be used as a lubricant, but the diamond structure of carbon does not.

36. Explain why graphite can conduct electricity, but diamond does not.

37. Describe the difference between regular charcoal and activated charcoal.

38. Explain why the structure of charcoal allows carbon to act as a good filter while the diamond structure does not.

39. Describe the difference between an ionic carbide and a covalent carbide. Which types of atoms will form these carbides with carbon?

40. Silicon carbide is produced by heating silicone polymers, forming methane gas, hydrogen gas, and silicon carbide. Balance the reaction of heating $[(CH_3)_2Si]_8$ to form silicon carbide.

41. Using the phase diagram given in Section 11.8, describe what happens to the phase of CO_2 during each process.
a. reducing the pressure on solid CO_2 that is at −80 °C
b. decreasing the temperature on CO_2 gas that is held at a pressure of 20 atm
c. increasing the temperature on solid CO_2 that is held at a pressure of 0.8 atm

42. Using the phase diagram given in Section 11.8, describe what happens to the phase of CO_2 during each process.
a. reducing the temperature from the critical point
b. increasing the pressure on CO_2 gas that is held at a temperature of −50 °C
c. increasing the temperature on solid CO_2 that is held at a pressure of 20 bar

43. Predict the products for each reaction and write a balanced equation.
a. $CO(g) + CuO(s)$ **b.** $SiO_2(s) + C(s)$

44. Predict the products for each reaction and write a balanced equation.
a. $\frac{1}{8}\ S_8(s) + C(s)$ **b.** $CO_2(g) + Mg(s)$

45. Give the oxidation state for carbon in:
a. CO **b.** CO_2 **c.** C_3O_2

46. Write a balanced reaction for the gas release reaction of Alka-Seltzer, sodium bicarbonate with citric acid, $C_6H_8O_7$. (The acid is a triprotic acid and consists of a chain of three carbon atoms each with a carboxylic acid group, COOH.)

Nitrogen and Phosphorus: Essential Elements for Life

47. Explain what is meant by fixing nitrogen.

48. Explain why the diatomic nitrogen atom is unusable by most plants. Where do plants get nitrogen?

49. Describe the differences in the allotropes of white and red phosphorus. Explain why red phosphorus is more stable.

50. Describe how red and black phosphorus can be made from white phosphorus.

51. Saltpeter and Chile saltpeter are two important mineral sources for nitrogen. Calculate the mass percent of nitrogen in both minerals.

52. Apatite is a main mineral source for the production of phosphorus. Calculate the atomic and mass percent of P in the mineral apatite.

53. Using the tables in Appendix IIB, determine whether or not hydrogen azide is unstable at room temperature compared to its elements, H_2 and N_2. Is hydrogen azide stable at any temperature?

54. Using the tables in Appendix IIB, determine if dinitrogen monoxide is unstable at room temperature compared to its elements, O_2 and N_2. Is dinitrogen monoxide stable at any temperature?

55. Predict the products for each reaction and write a balanced equation.
a. $NH_4NO_3(aq)$ + heat **c.** $PCl_3(l) + O_2(g)$
b. $NO_2(g) + H_2O(l)$

56. Predict the products for each reaction and write a balanced equation.
a. $NO(g) + NO_2(g)$ **c.** $P_4(s) + 5\ O_2(g)$
b. heating PH_3 gas

57. Rank the nitrogen ions from the one with N in the highest oxidation state to the one with N in the lowest.

$$N_3^-, N_2H_5^+, NO_3^-, NH_4^+, NO_2^-$$

58. Determine the oxidation state of N in the compounds in the reaction for the formation of nitric acid. Identify the oxidizing agent and the reducing agent.

$$3\ NO_2(g) + H_2O(l) \longrightarrow 2\ HNO_3(l) + NO(g)$$

59. Draw Lewis structures for the phosphorus halides PCl_3 and PCl_5. Describe their VSEPR shape.

60. Dinitrogen pentoxide is an ionic compound formed from the ions NO_2^+ and NO_3^-. Give the oxidation state of N in each ion and the VSEPR shape for each of the ions.

61. Ammonium carbonate is produced from the reaction of urea, $CO(NH_2)_2$, with water. Write a balanced equation for this reaction and determine how much urea is needed to produce 23 g of ammonium carbonate.

62. Explain why phosphine, PH_3, is less polar than ammonia.

63. Reacting oxygen with white phosphorus can form either P_4O_6 or P_4O_{10}. State the conditions that determine which product is formed.

64. P_4O_{10} is one of the most effective drying agents, having the ability to extract water from other molecules. The P_4O_{10} forms phosphoric acid. Write balanced reactions for the reaction of P_4O_{10} with:

a. HNO_3, forming N_2O_5 **b.** H_2SO_4, forming SO_3

Oxygen

65. Name the major source for the element oxygen and describe how it is produced.

66. Explain why either greatly decreasing or increasing the percentage of oxygen in the atmosphere is dangerous.

67. Identify each compound as an oxide, peroxide, or superoxide:

a. LiO_2 **b.** CaO **c.** K_2O_2

68. Identify each compound as an oxide, peroxide, or superoxide:

a. MgO **b.** Na_2O_2 **c.** CsO_2

Sulfur: A Dangerous but Useful Element

69. Explain why the viscosity of liquid sulfur increases with increasing temperature initially, but then decreases upon further increases in temperature.

70. Sulfur dioxide is a toxic sulfur compound. List one natural source and one industrial source that produces SO_2.

71. Calculate the maximum mass (in grams) of each metal sulfide that will dissolve in 1.0 L of a solution that is 5.00×10^{-5} mol L^{-1} in Na_2S.

a. PbS **b.** ZnS

72. A coal source contains 1.1% sulfur by mass. If 2.0×10^4 kg of coal is burned and forms oxides, calculate the mass of $CaSO_4(s)$ that is produced from "scrubbing" the SO_2 pollutant out of the exhaust gas. Assume that all of the sulfur in the coal is converted to calcium sulfate.

73. Write the equation for roasting iron pyrite in the absence of air to form elemental sulfur. Calculate the volume of S_2 gas that can be produced from roasting 5.5 kg of iron pyrite. Assume that all of the sulfur in the iron pyrite is converted to S_2 gas. (Assume STP to calculate the gas volume.)

74. Write an overall reaction from the two steps in the Claus process. Calculate the volume of H_2S gas needed to produce 1.0 kg of $S_8(s)$. (Assume STP to calculate the gas volume.)

Halogens

75. Carbon tetrachloride is produced by passing chlorine gas over carbon disulfide in the presence of a catalyst. The reaction also produces S_2Cl_2. Write a balanced reaction and identify which element is oxidized and which element is reduced.

76. If 55 g of $SiO_2(s)$ glass is placed into 111 L of 0.032 mol L^{-1} HF, is there enough HF to dissolve all of the glass? Determine which substance is the limiting reagent and calculate how much of the other reagent is left if the reaction proceeds to completion.

Cumulative Problems

77. From the compositions of lignite and bituminous coal, calculate the mass of sulfuric acid that could potentially form as acid rain from burning 1.00×10^2 kg of each type of coal.

78. Calculate the volume of CO_2 released from heating and decomposing 88 g of sodium bicarbonate. (Assume standard pressure and temperature.)

79. With the exception of fluorine, all of the halogens form oxyacids. The perhalic acids have the general formula of HXO_4. Explain why $HClO_4$ is a much stronger acid than HIO_4.

80. The halogens (except fluorine) form oxoacids with different amounts of oxygen. Explain why $HClO_4$ is a stronger acid than $HClO_2$.

81. Determine the ratio of effusion rates of HCl compared to each gas:

a. Cl_2 **b.** HF **c.** HI

82. A current of 3.00 A is passed through a tank of seawater for 24.0 h. How many grams of $Cl_2(g)$ are generated?

83. Sodium peroxide is a very powerful oxidizing agent. Balance the reaction of sodium peroxide with elemental iron to give sodium oxide and Fe_3O_4.

84. Sulfur dioxide is a reducing agent. When it is bubbled through an aqueous solution containing Br_2, a red-coloured solution, it reduces the bromine to colourless bromide ions and forms sulfuric acid. Write a balanced equation for this reaction and identify the oxidizing agent and the reducing agent.

85. Using the molecular orbital model for a diatomic molecule, explain the different bond lengths for the ions of oxygen. Also, state which ion is diamagnetic.

Ion	O—O Bond Length (pm)
O_2^+	112
O_2	121
O_2^-	133
O_2^{2-}	149

86. The *closo*-borane with the formula $B_6H_6^{2-}$ has the six B atoms at vertices, forming an octahedron structure with eight faces. The formula for the number of sides is $2n - 4$, where n is the number of boron atoms. Determine the number of vertices and faces for each *closo*-borane.

a. $B_4H_4^{2-}$ **b.** $B_{12}H_{12}^{2-}$

87. Find the amount (in moles) of C—C bonds that must be broken when 1.0 mol of C(g) is formed from C(diamond). Calculate the

ΔH of sublimation of diamond from the data in Appendix II. Then do the calculation using the C—C bond energy in Table 9.1 (see page 345). Suggest a reason for the difference between the two values.

88. Breathing air that contains 0.13% CO by volume for 30 minutes will cause death. CO can form by incomplete combustion of carbon-containing compounds. Calculate the minimum volume of octane (C_8H_{18}, a component of gasoline, which has a density of 0.70 g mL^{-1}) that must burn to produce this composition of CO in a garage of volume 40 m^3 at 298 K and 1.0 bar.

89. Given that the $\Delta_f H°$ of aqueous H_2SO_3 is −633 kJ mol^{-1}, use the data in Appendix IIB to calculate the $\Delta_f H°$ for an aqueous solution of H_2SO_3 from $SO_2(g)$ and water.

90. Use the data in Appendix IIB to calculate $\Delta_f H°$ for the formation of an aqueous solution of H_2SO_4 from $SO_3(g)$ and water.

Challenge Problems

91. Calculate the standard enthalpy of reaction for reducing the different forms of iron oxide to iron metal and CO_2 from the reaction of the oxide with CO. Identify which reaction is the most exothermic per mole of iron and explain why.

a. Fe_3O_4 **b.** FeO **c.** Fe_2O_3

92. Balance the equation for the production of acetylene (C_2H_2) from the reaction of calcium carbide with water. If the acetylene is burned to form water and carbon dioxide, how many kilojoules of energy are produced from the complete reaction of 18 g of calcium carbide?

93. Carbon suboxide, C_3O_2, is a linear molecule with oxygen atoms at each end and double bonds between each carbon and oxygen atom.

a. Draw the Lewis structure for C_3O_2.

b. State the type of hybridization of each carbon atom.

c. Calculate the heat of reaction for the reaction of carbon suboxide with water to form malonic acid ($HO_2CCH_2CO_2H$). (*Hint:* Each end of malonic acid has a carbon double bonded to an oxygen and bonded to a hydroxide.)

94. Calcium carbonate is insoluble in water. Yet, it readily dissolves in an acidic solution. Calculate the standard enthalpy, entropy, and Gibbs energy change for the reaction between solid calcium carbonate and hydrochloric acid. What drives the reaction, the enthalpy change or the entropy change?

95. When hydrazine is dissolved in water it acts like a base:

$$N_2H_4(aq) + H_2O(l) \rightleftharpoons N_2H_5^+(aq) + OH^-(aq) \qquad K_{b_1} = 8.5 \times 10^{-7}$$

$$N_2H_5^+(aq) + H_2O(l) \rightleftharpoons N_2H_6^{2+}(aq) + OH^-(aq) \qquad K_{b_2} = 8.9 \times 10^{-16}$$

a. Calculate the K_b for the overall reaction of hydrazine forming $N_2H_6^{2+}$.

b. Calculate K_{a_1} for $N_2H_5^+$.

c. Calculate the concentration of hydrazine and both cations in a solution buffered at a pH of 8.5 for a solution that was made by dissolving 0.012 mol of hydrazine in 1 L of water.

96. Solid fuel in the booster rockets for spacecraft consists of aluminum powder as the fuel and ammonium perchlorate as the oxidizing agent:

$$3\ NH_4ClO_4(s) + 3\ Al(s) \longrightarrow Al_2O_3(s) + AlCl_3(s) + 6\ H_2O(g) + 3\ NO(g)$$

If a rocket launch burns 2.200×10^3 kg of aluminum, calculate the energy produced in joules. Calculate the volume of the gas produced assuming it was cooled back to 298 K at 1 bar. The standard enthalpy of formation of solid ammonium perchlorate is −295.3 kJ mol^{-1}.

97. Two compounds are known with the formula $H_2N_2O_2$. One of them is a weak acid and one is a weak base. The acid, called hyponitrous acid, has two O—H bonds. The base, called nitramide, has no O—H bonds. Draw Lewis structures for these compounds. Predict whether the acid is stronger or weaker than nitrous acid and whether the base is stronger or weaker than ammonia.

Conceptual Problems

98. Explain why fine particles of activated charcoal can absorb more (as a filter) than large briquettes of charcoal.

99. The two major components of the atmosphere are the diatomic molecules of nitrogen and oxygen. Explain why pure nitrogen is used as a protective atmosphere and pure oxygen is much more reactive.

100. Explain why nitrogen can form compounds with many different oxidation numbers.

101. Describe how sodium dihydrogen phosphate can be used as a pH buffering agent.

102. Explain why H_2S has a different bond angle and is much more reactive than H_2O.

103. Explain why fluorine is found only with the oxidation state of −1 or 0, while the other halogens are found in compounds with other oxidation states.

104. Why do some substances burn in fluorine gas even if they do not burn in oxygen gas?

105. Explain why SO_2 is used as a reducing agent but SO_3 is not.

24 Metals and Metallurgy

The metals are not presented immediately to the hand of man . . . but they are, for the most part, buried in darkness, in the bowels of the Earth, where they are so much disguised, by combination and mixture with other substances, that they often appear entirely unlike themselves.

—William Henry (1774–1836)

Oil can be contaminated with vanadium, which is thought to have been the metal used for oxygen transport by some ancient life forms.

IF YOU LOOK AROUND YOUR HOUSE, classroom, or neighbourhood, much of what you see is made of metal or at least has some metal parts. Can you imagine life without metals? Without metals, we would have no skyscrapers with their rigid framework of steel beams, no automobiles with their metal engines and bodies, and no electricity transmitted through copper and aluminum wire. Metallurgy is in some ways both a very old and a very new science. We find the roots of chemistry in the distant past, when our primitive ancestors began to search for and process metals. Of the three prehistoric ages of humankind—the Stone Age, the Bronze Age, and the Iron Age—two are named after our quest for metals. But we do not commonly find metals as elements on Earth; instead we find them in compounds, often scattered within other compounds. The mining, separating, and refining of the vast array of metals is a fairly new science. Many modern metals were not available even as recently as 200 years ago. In the middle of the nineteenth century, gold was cheaper than aluminum because aluminum was so difficult to refine, and titanium, which today is important in the aerospace industry, could not even be manufactured. In this chapter, we cover the area of chemistry known as metallurgy.

24.1 Vanadium: A Problem and an Opportunity

Recently, members of a university's chemistry and engineering departments met with representatives of an oil company to discuss how the faculty and students could cooperate on some industrial research. A major topic was vanadium contamination in oil, a serious problem of continuing concern. Because vanadium is toxic, governments regulate the quantity of vanadium that can be emitted by industrial processes, so oil companies have to figure out environmentally acceptable ways to remove vanadium from oil.

Vanadium is a rare element, making up only about 0.015% of Earth's crust (by mass). It is a soft, silvery grey metal with high ductility and malleability, which means that it can be easily drawn into narrow wires or rolled into thin sheets. Because of the high reactivity of pure vanadium, this element naturally occurs within compounds. However, vanadium compounds are not normally found in the rocks or soils near oil fields, so why does this rare, reactive metal occur in oil? The answer lies in the biology of ancient life-forms. Most modern animals use iron in hemoglobin to transport oxygen through their bloodstreams (see Section 14.1), and a few (such as lobsters) use copper for this function. It appears that some extinct animals used vanadium. Even today, one group of simple marine organisms, the tunicates or sea squirts, are believed to employ vanadium compounds for oxygen transport. Therefore, the source of vanadium in some crude oil may be the very animals from which the oil was formed.

▲ Vanadium is a soft, silvery grey metal.

During refining, crude oil is heated to carry out the reactions that form the different petroleum products. If some of the vanadium-containing oil burns during heating, the vanadium forms vanadate compounds, ionic compounds with vanadium oxide polyatomic ions such as VO_4^{3-} and VO_3^{-}. These compounds, which have low melting points, can dissolve the protective oxide coatings on stainless steel containers, causing the steel to corrode and ruining the containers in which the oil is stored. If the vanadium compounds are not removed from the oil before storage, the customer inherits the problem. In addition, vanadium and many of its compounds are toxic, so oil companies cannot simply dump the extracted vanadium compounds into the environment.

The presence of vanadium in crude oil may, however, turn out to be profitable for the oil companies. If vanadium can be economically recovered from oil, then oil could become a major source of vanadium, a valuable metal with several important industrial uses including the production of iron alloys and sulfuric acid.

The recovery of vanadium from oil involves metallurgy, the topic of this chapter. **Metallurgy** includes all the processes associated with mining, separating, and refining metals and the subsequent production of pure metals and mixtures of metals called *alloys* (which we define in Section 24.4). In this chapter, we explore the general properties and natural distribution of metals; several different categories of metallurgical processes, including pyrometallurgy, hydrometallurgy, electrometallurgy, and powder metallurgy; the structures and alloys formed by metals; and the metallic products and applications for several selected materials.

24.2 The General Properties and Natural Distribution of Metals

Metals share several common properties. All metals are opaque (you cannot see through them), and they are good conductors of heat and electricity. They generally have high malleability (the ability to be bent or hammered into desired forms) and ductility (the ability to be drawn into wires). We can explain these properties by the bonding theories that we have already introduced for metals: the electron sea model and band theory. In the electron sea model, each metal atom within a metal sample donates one or more electrons to an *electron sea*, which then flows within the metal. In band theory, the atomic orbitals of the metal atoms are combined, forming *bands* that are delocalized over the entire crystalline solid; electrons move freely within these bands. The mobile electrons in both of these models endow metals with many of their shared properties.

Each metal, however, is also unique, and even their shared properties may vary within a range. For example, some metals, such as copper, silver, and aluminum, have

TABLE 24.1 Thermal Conductivity and Electrical Resistivity of Several Metals

Metal	Thermal Conductivity ($W\ cm^{-1}\ K^{-1}$)	Electrical Resistivity ($\mu\Omega \cdot cm$)
Ag, silver	4.29	1.59
Cu, copper	4.01	1.67
Fe, iron	0.804	9.71
V, vanadium	0.307	24.8

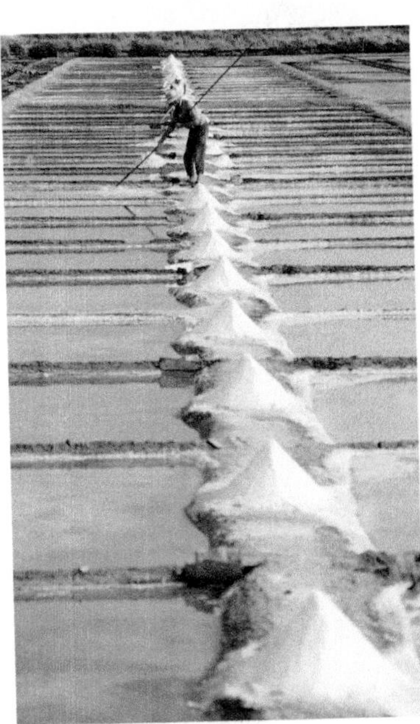

▲ Most NaCl salt is produced by trapping ocean water in shallow basins and letting the water evaporate, leaving salt.

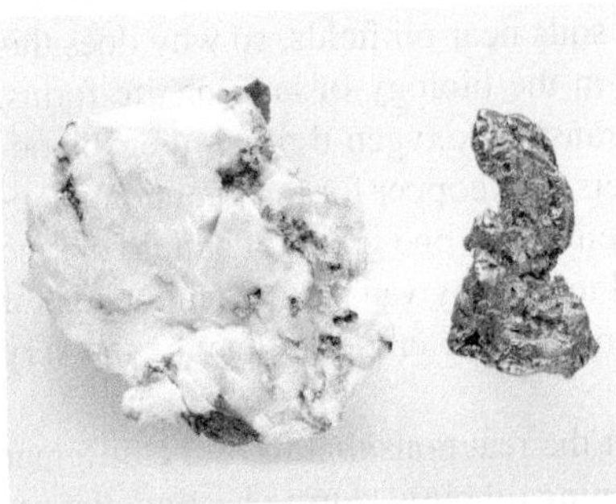

▲ Gold is one of the few metals that can be found as an element in nature, often in veins like the one shown here.

much higher thermal and electrical conductivities than do other metals. Table 24.1 lists the thermal conductivity and electrical resistivity (a low resistivity corresponds to a high conductivity) of a few metals. Notice that both properties can vary by factors of 10 or more. Most metals are very strong, malleable, and ductile. But lead is a soft, weak metal, and chromium is a brittle metal that will not bend without breaking. When we think about the shared properties of metals, we must allow for a range of properties, as well as some unique ones.

Over 75% of the elements in the periodic table are metals, yet metals make up only about 25% of the mass of Earth's crust (see Figure 23.2 for the composition of Earth's crust). Earth's core is thought to be composed of iron and nickel, but because the core is so far from the surface, these metals are not accessible. The most abundant metal on Earth is aluminum, a main-group metal. Several alkali and alkaline earth metals (calcium, sodium, potassium, and magnesium) make up more than 1% of Earth's crust. Iron, which makes up about 5% of the crust, is the only transition metal that accounts for more than 0.1% of the crust. Of the first-row transition metals, titanium, chromium, iron, nickel, copper, and zinc are all plentiful enough to be important industrial materials.

Only a few metals occur naturally as elements; these include nickel, copper, palladium, silver, platinum, and gold. Because of their low reactivity, these metals are often called the "noble metals." They are usually concentrated within mountainous or volcanic regions in small isolated veins within a rock matrix.

Most of the rest of the metals occur naturally in positive oxidation states within mineral deposits. **Minerals** are homogeneous, naturally occurring, crystalline inorganic solids. A rock that contains a high concentration of a specific mineral is called an **ore**. Metallurgical processes separate useful minerals from other, nonuseful material.

The main sources for the alkali metals are chloride minerals, such as halite (sodium chloride) and sylvite (potassium chloride). Halite occurs in large deposits from dried ancient oceans or it can be precipitated by evaporating ocean water. The main source for some other metals are oxide minerals, such as hematite (Fe_2O_3), rutile (TiO_2), and cassiterite (SnO_2). The ores containing these minerals are unevenly distributed throughout the Earth. For example, North America has large deposits of hematite, but no substantial deposits of cassiterite. Sulfides are the most important minerals for many metals, such as galena (PbS), cinnabar (HgS), sphalerite (ZnS), and molybdenite (MoS_2).

The main mineral source for some other metals can be complex. For example, the main *mineral* sources for vanadium are vanadinite [$Pb_5(VO_4)_3Cl$] and carnotite [$K_2(UO_2)_2(VO_4)_2 \cdot 3\ H_2O$], which is also a main mineral source for uranium. Vanadium, as we have seen, is also found in crude oil. No specific minerals contain the metal radium. Yet radium sometimes substitutes for uranium within uranium-containing minerals. The small amount of radium that replaces uranium in carnotite is also the major source of radium. Tantalum and niobium, named after the Greek god Tantalus and his daughter Niobe, always occur together in mixed deposits of columbite [$Fe(NbO_3)_2$] and tantalite [$Fe(TaO_3)_2$]. The minerals are mined together and the elements are later separated by recrystallization.

24.3 Metallurgical Processes

Mined ores are first physically *separated* into their metal-containing and nonmetal-containing components. Then, the elemental metal is extracted from the compounds in which it is found, a process called **extractive metallurgy**. In this section, we look at several metallurgical processes, including pyrometallurgy, hydrometallurgy, electrometallurgy, and powder metallurgy. After separation and extraction, the crude material is purified through **refining**.

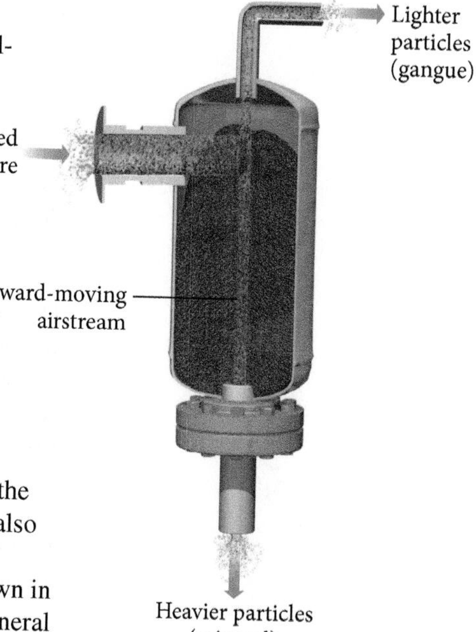

▲ **FIGURE 24.1 Separation by Air** An industrial cyclone separates the crushed light particles of gangue from the heavier metal-bearing particles.

Separation

The first step in processing metal-containing ores is to crush the ore into smaller particles. The particles that contain the minerals are then separated from the undesired material, called **gangue** (pronounced "gang"), usually by physical methods. For example, in some cases, a cyclone of wind is used to lift the gangue away from the metal-containing particles, as shown in Figure 24.1 ▸. If the minerals are magnetic, magnets can separate the minerals. Electrostatic forces are also used to separate polar minerals from nonpolar gangue.

Sometimes solutions are used to separate the minerals from the gangue, as shown in Figure 24.2 ▾. A wetting agent (or detergent) that preferentially attaches to the mineral surfaces is added to a mixture of the mined material and water. Air is then blown through the mixture, forming bubbles and a froth. Because they are attached to the wetting agent, the minerals segregate into the froth where they can be collected. The gangue separates into the solution.

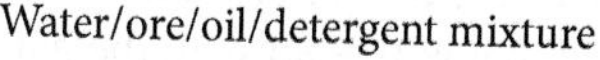

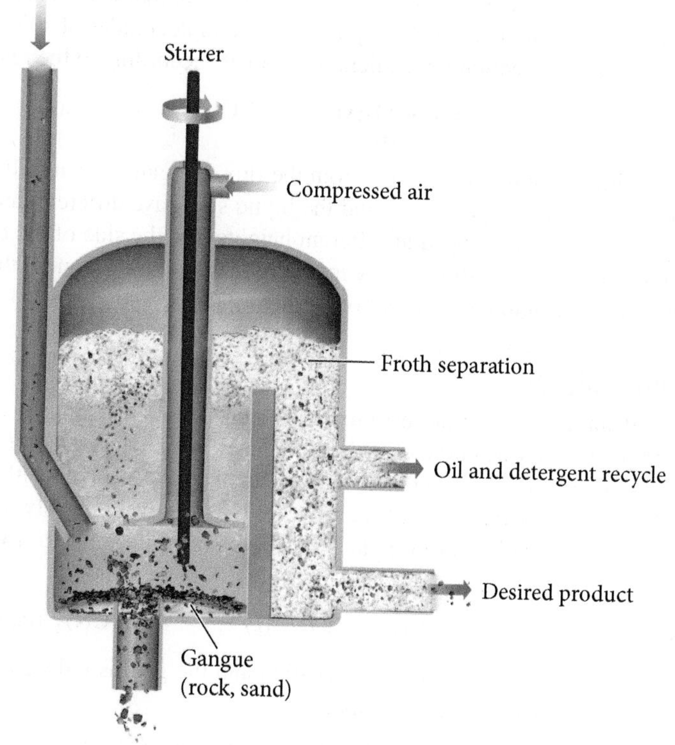

◂ **FIGURE 24.2 Separation by Using a Solution** A wetting agent helps the minerals attach to the froth in a bubbled solution. The minerals in the froth are separated from the gangue remaining in the solution.

Pyrometallurgy

Pyrometallurgy contains the Greek stem *pyro*, meaning fire or heat.

Once the mineral is separated from the gangue, the elemental metal is extracted from the mineral. Several different techniques can be used to achieve this separation. In **pyrometallurgy**, heat is employed to extract a metal from its mineral. Different heating conditions have different effects on the mineral.

Calcination is the heating of an ore in order to decompose it and drive off a volatile product. For example, when carbonate minerals are heated, carbon dioxide is driven off, as shown in these examples:

$$PbCO_3(s) \xrightarrow{\text{heat}} PbO(s) + CO_2(g)$$

$$4\ FeCO_3(s) + O_2(g) \xrightarrow{\text{heat}} 2\ Fe_2O_3(s) + 4\ CO_2(g)$$

Hydrated compounds are discussed in Section 3.4.

Many minerals occur in a hydrated form (that is, they contain water). Calcination can also drive off water:

$$Fe_2O_3 \cdot 2\ Fe(OH)_3(s) \xrightarrow{\text{heat}} 2\ Fe_2O_3(s) + 3\ H_2O(g)$$

Heating that causes a chemical reaction between the furnace atmosphere (the gases in the furnace) and the mineral is called **roasting**. Roasting is particularly important in processing sulfide ores. The ores are heated in the presence of oxygen, thereby converting the sulfide into an oxide and emitting sulfur dioxide. For example, the roasting of lead(II) sulfide occurs by the reaction:

$$2\ PbS(s) + 3\ O_2(g) \xrightarrow{\text{heat}} 2\ PbO(s) + 2\ SO_2(g)$$

In some cases, especially with the less active metals such as mercury, roasting the sulfide produces the pure metal.

$$HgS(s) + O_2(g) \xrightarrow{\text{heat}} Hg(g) + SO_2(g)$$

Smelting is a process in which pure metals are formed in the liquid phase, which makes separation easier. Consider, for example, the smelting of zinc oxide:

$$ZnO(s) + C(s) \xrightarrow{\text{heat}} Zn(l) + CO(g)$$

The gaseous carbon monoxide separates from the liquid zinc, allowing the metal to be readily recovered. In some cases, a *flux* must be added to the mixture during smelting to help separate the two materials. The **flux** is a material that will react with the gangue to form a substance with a low melting point. For example, oxides of silicon within gangue can be liquefied by reaction with calcium carbonate according to the reaction:

$$\underset{\text{gangue}}{SiO_2(s)} + \underset{\text{flux}}{CaCO_3(s)} \longrightarrow CO_2(g) + \underset{\text{slag}}{CaSiO_3(l)}$$

The waste liquid solution that forms from the flux and gangue is usually a silicate material called a **slag**. The liquid metal and the liquid slag have different densities and therefore separate. Holes are tapped at different heights into the side of the container holding the liquid metal and slag, allowing the more dense liquid to flow out of the lower tap holes and the less dense liquid to flow out of the higher tap holes.

Hydrometallurgy

The use of an aqueous solution to extract metals from their ores is known as **hydrometallurgy**. An early example of hydrometallurgy is a process used to obtain gold. Gold occurs in its elemental state, but often as very small particles mixed with other substances. The gold can be separated out of the mixture by selectively dissolving it into solution, a process called **leaching**. Solid gold reacts with sodium cyanide to form a soluble gold complex.

$$4\ Au(s) + 8\ CN^-(aq) + O_2(g) + 2\ H_2O(l) \longrightarrow 4\ Au(CN)_2^-(aq) + 4\ OH^-(aq)$$

The impurities are filtered out of the solution and the gold is reduced back to elemental gold with a reactive metal such as zinc:

$$2\ Au(CN)_2^-(aq) + Zn(s) \longrightarrow Zn(CN)_4^{2-}(aq) + 2\ Au(s)$$

This process for obtaining gold has been practiced for many years and often results in the contamination of streams and rivers with cyanide. New alternatives, using the thiosulfate ion ($S_2O_3^{2-}$), are being investigated to replace it.

Different acid, base, and salt solutions are sometimes used to selectively separate out metal-bearing minerals. For example, sulfuric acid is used to separate the copper and iron from the mineral chalcopyrite, $CuFeS_2$, and a sodium chloride solution is used to separate the lead from the insoluble mineral anglesite, $PbSO_4$.

$$2\ CuFeS_2(s) + H_2SO_4(aq) + 4\ O_2(g) \longrightarrow 2\ CuSO_4(aq) + Fe_2O_3(s) + \frac{3}{8}\,S_8(s) + H_2O(l)$$

$$PbSO_4(s) + 4\ NaCl(aq) \longrightarrow Na_2[PbCl_4](aq) + Na_2SO_4(aq)$$

Hydrometallurgy is often more economical than pyrometallurgy, due to the high energy costs associated with reaching the elevated temperatures needed for calcination and roasting.

Electrometallurgy

In **electrometallurgy**, electrolysis is used to produce metals from their compounds. For example, the *Hall process* is an electrometallurgical process crucial to aluminum production. The main source of aluminum is bauxite, $Al_2O_3 \cdot n\,H_2O$. A hydrometallurgical process, the *Bayer process*, separates bauxite from the iron and silicon oxide with which it is usually found. In this process, the bauxite is heated in a concentrated aqueous NaOH solution under high pressure. The aluminum oxide dissolves, leaving the other oxides behind in solid form.

See Section 18.7 for a description of electrolysis.

$$Al_2O_3 \cdot n\,H_2O(s) + 2\ OH^-(aq) + 2\ H_2O(l) \longrightarrow 2\ Al(OH)_4^-(aq)$$

The basic aluminum solution is separated from the oxide solids, and then the aluminum oxide is precipitated out of solution by neutralizing it [recall the pH dependence of the solubility of $Al(OH)_3$ from Section 16.8]. Calcination of the precipitate at temperatures greater than 1000 °C yields anhydrous alumina (Al_2O_3). Electrolysis is then used to reduce the aluminum out of the aluminum oxide. Because Al_2O_3 melts at such a high temperature (greater than 2000 °C), however, the electrolysis is not carried out on molten Al_2O_3. Instead, in the Hall process the Al_2O_3 is dissolved into molten cryolite (Na_3AlF_6), and graphite rods are used as electrodes to carry out the electrolysis in the liquid mixture, as illustrated in Figure 24.3 ▼. The carbon that composes the graphite electrodes is oxidized by the dissolved oxygen ions in the molten salt and converted to carbon dioxide. The aluminum ions dissolved in the molten salt reduce to molten aluminum, which sinks down to the bottom of the cell and is removed.

$$\text{Oxidation:}\quad C(s) + 2\ O^{2-}(\text{dissolved}) \longrightarrow CO_2(g) + 4\ e^-$$

$$\text{Reduction:}\quad 3\ e^- + Al^{3+}(\text{dissolved}) \longrightarrow Al(l)$$

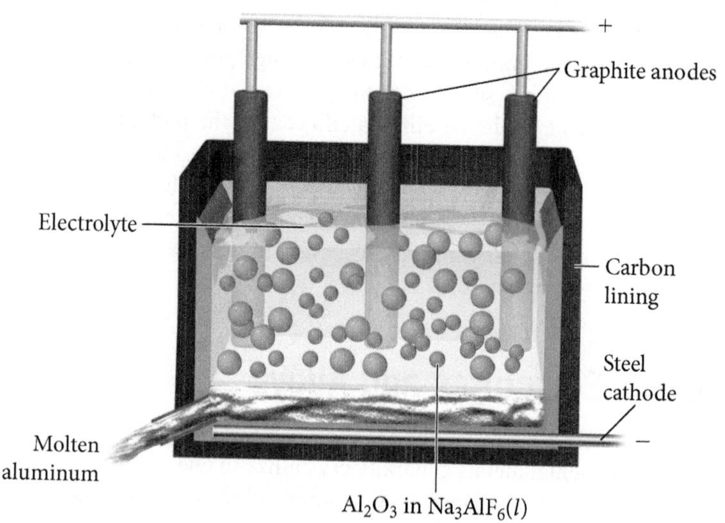

◀ **FIGURE 24.3 The Hall Process** The Hall process produces aluminum metal by reducing the aluminum ions in alumina. Graphite electrodes act as reducing agents. Dissolved oxygen ions in the molten cryolite oxidize the carbon in the graphite electrodes to form carbon dioxide.

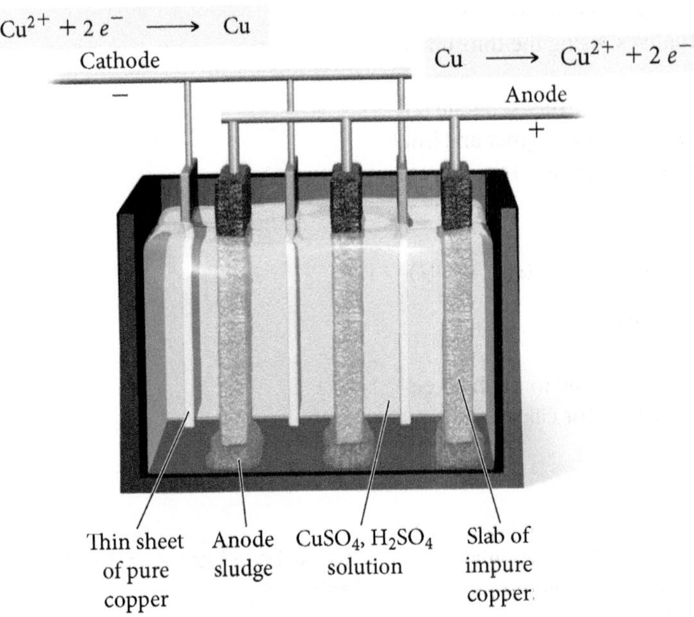

▲ **FIGURE 24.4 Copper Electrolysis Cell** Copper is refined by electrolysis. The impure copper is oxidized at the anode and then reduced to form pure metal on the cathode. Many precious metals from the impure copper collect in the sludge at the bottom of the electrolysis cell.

Another important use of metallurgy is the refinement of copper. The most abundant copper source is the mineral chalcopyrite, $CuFeS_2$. First, the chalcopyrite is converted to CuS by roasting. During this process, the iron also forms oxides and sulfides. Silica is added to form an iron silicate slag, which is then removed. The remaining copper sulfide is reacted with oxygen to form sulfur dioxide gas and copper metal, but the metal is not very pure. Electrolysis is employed to refine (or purify) the copper.

In the electrolysis cell used to purify copper, both the anode and the cathode are made of copper, as shown in Figure 24.4 ◄. The anode is the impure copper (to be purified) and the cathode is a thin sheet of pure copper. As the current flows through the cell, the copper from the anode oxidizes and dissolves in a copper sulfate solution. It then plates out as pure copper on the cathode. The impurities in the copper anode separate from the copper during electrolysis because, even though the more active metals also oxidize from the anode, they stay in solution and do not plate out on the cathode. The less active metals do not oxidize at all and simply fall to the bottom of the cell as the copper is dissolved from the anode. The sludge at the bottom of the electrolysis cell contains many precious metals, including gold and silver. About one-quarter of the U.S. production of silver is from the impurities recovered from the refinement of copper.

Powder Metallurgy

Powder metallurgy, first developed in the 1920s, is used to make metallic components from powdered metal. In powder metallurgy, micron-sized metal particles are pressed together under high pressures to form the desired component. The component is then heated (sintered). The sintering process occurs below the melting point of the powder, but at a temperature high enough to cause the metal particles to fuse together, strengthening the metal and increasing its density.

▲ These metal products were all made by powder metallurgy.

Originally, iron powder from mill scrap was used in powder metallurgy. The scrap was primarily iron oxide that would fall off the steel as it was being milled. The iron oxide dust was heated in a hydrogen atmosphere to reduce the oxide to iron particles. Manufacturers named the powdered metal *iron sponge* because numerous holes form in the particles when the oxygen escapes.

In the 1960s, the A. O. Smith Company in the United States introduced a new method for the development of powdered metal, called water atomization. The pure metal is melted and a small stream of the liquid is allowed to flow from the bottom of the container of molten metal. A high-pressure blast of cold water hits the stream, breaking it into small droplets that quickly solidify. The powdered metal particles made in this way are more smooth and dense than the sponge powder particles from oxide scrap. Beyond powdered iron metal, many copper, bronze, carbide, and brass parts are made through powder metallurgical processes.

Powder metallurgy offers several advantages over traditional casting or milling of metal. For example, waste is almost eliminated because the part can be pressed directly into the desired shape. Intricate teeth on gears and multiple holes can be designed into the press and therefore do not have to be machined after production. Making cast metal objects from metals with high melting points, such as molybdenum and tungsten, can be difficult because of the high temperatures necessary to melt the metal. Using the powder avoids the need for high temperatures.

24.4 Metal Structures and Alloys

The structures of metals can be described as the closest packing of spheres, first discussed in Section 11.11. Elemental metals generally crystallize in one of the basic types of crystal lattices, including face-centred cubic, body-centred cubic, and hexagonal closest packed.

TABLE 24.2 The Crystal Structures of the 3*d* Elements

Metal	Natural Crystal Structure at 298 K and 1 bar	Other Crystal Structures at Different Temperatures and Pressures
Sc	Hexagonal closest packed	Face-centred cubic, body-centred cubic
Ti	Hexagonal closest packed	Body-centred cubic above 882 °C
V	Body-centred cubic	
Cr	Body-centred cubic	Hexagonal closest packed
Mn	Alpha complex body-centred cubic form	Beta simple cubic form above 727 °C Face-centred cubic above 1095 °C Body-centred cubic above 1133 °C
Fe	Body-centred cubic	Face-centred cubic above 909 °C Body-centred cubic above 1403 °C
Co	Hexagonal closest packed	Face-centred cubic above 420 °C
Ni	Face-centred cubic	
Cu	Face-centred cubic	
Zn	Hexagonal closest packed	

The crystal structure of a metal may change, however, as a function of temperature and pressure. Table 24.2 shows the crystal structures for the 3*d* transition metals under different conditions.

Alloys

An **alloy** is a metallic material that contains more than one type of element. Some alloys are simply solid solutions, while others are specific compounds with definite ratios of the component elements. Alloys have metallic properties, but they can consist of either two or more metals or a metal and a nonmetal. Alloys can be broadly classified as substitutional or interstitial. In a **substitutional alloy**, one metal atom substitutes for another in the crystal structure. The crystal structure may either stay the same upon the substitution, or it may change to accommodate the differences between the atoms. In an **interstitial alloy**, small, usually nonmetallic atoms fit in between the metallic atoms of a crystal. The alloy maintains its metallic properties with these interstitial atoms in the structure.

Substitutional Alloys For two metals to form a substitutional alloy, the radii of the two metal atoms must be similar, usually within 15% of each other. For example, the atomic radii of copper and nickel are both 135 pm and both of the elements form the face-centred cubic structure. Thus, either metal can easily replace the other in the metal crystal structure.

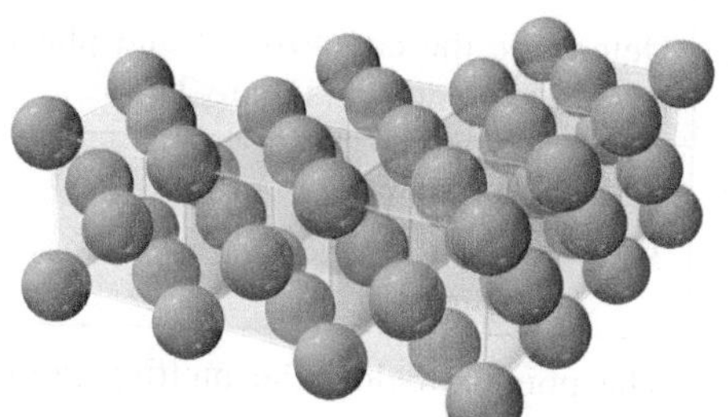

▲ Copper crystallizes in the face-centred structure shown here.

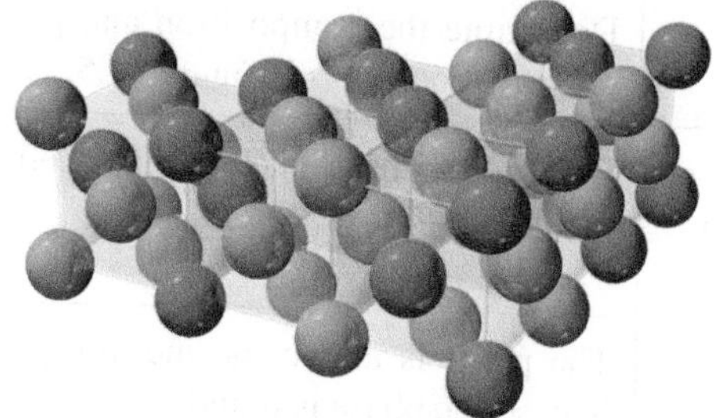

▲ In a nickel and copper alloy, nickel atoms simply substitute for some of the copper atoms.

Figure 24.5 ▼ shows a phase diagram for a copper and nickel alloy. This phase diagram, called a *binary* phase diagram, is different from those that we discussed in Section 11.8, which show the phases of a pure substance at different pressures and

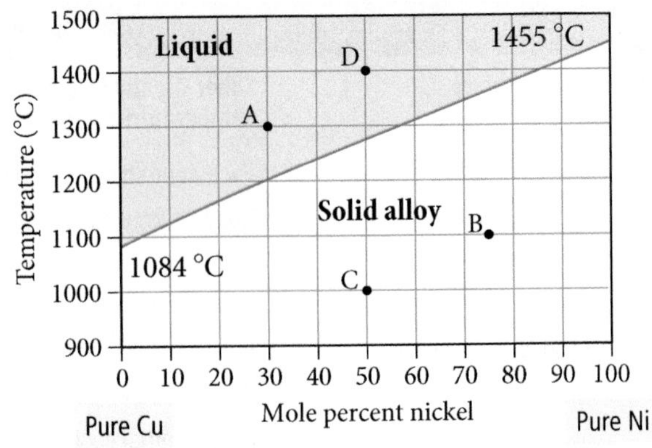

▶ **FIGURE 24.5 Cu–Ni Phase Diagram** Because copper and nickel have similar crystal structures and similar size, they can form a solid solution. A solution forms at all compositions from pure copper to pure nickel.

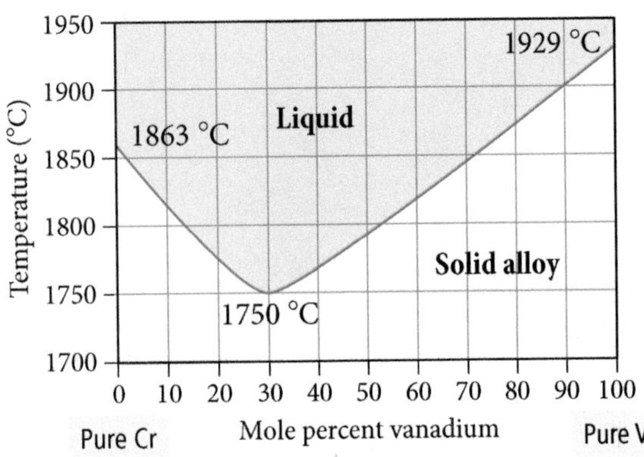

▲ **FIGURE 24.6 Cr–V Phase Diagram** In a binary phase diagram of two metals that form a solid solution, an intermediate composition can have either the highest or lowest melting point. In the chromium and vanadium phase diagram an intermediate composition has the lowest melting point.

temperatures. This diagram shows the different phases for a mixture at different *compositions* and temperatures. The *x*-axis indicates the composition (in this case, the mole percent of nickel in the alloy, with the left side representing pure copper and the right side representing pure nickel). The *y*-axis indicates the temperature.

Pure copper melts at 1084 °C, as indicated by the change from solid to liquid at 0% nickel. Pure nickel melts at 1455 °C, as indicated by the change from solid to liquid at 100% nickel. The area on the diagram above the line connecting the melting points of copper and nickel represents a liquid solution of the two metals. The area below that line represents a solid solution of the two metals. Any ratios of copper and nickel can form the face-centred cubic structure.

The phase diagrams of some alloys can be more complex. Consider the phase diagram for Cr and V, shown in Figure 24.6 ◀. Both Cr and V form the body-centred cubic crystal, and the atoms are close in size. Yet this phase diagram reveals an important difference compared to the Cu and Ni alloy: the melting temperature does not vary in a uniform way from the lower melting point of Cr to the higher melting point of V. Instead we see that the alloys with intermediate compositions melt at lower temperatures than either pure metal. The lowest melting point is 1750 °C at a composition of 30 mol % vanadium. Solid compositions that melt at temperatures lower than either of the pure metals, as well as compositions that melt at temperatures higher than either of the two metals, are common in these types of alloys.

GUIDELINES FOR... **Interpreting a Binary Phase Diagram**	EXAMPLE 24.1 **Determining Alloy Compositions from a Phase Diagram** Determine the composition and phase present at point A on Figure 24.5.	EXAMPLE 24.2 **Determining Alloy Compositions from a Phase Diagram** Determine the composition and phase present at point B on Figure 24.5.
Locate the temperature and composition of the alloy on the binary phase diagram.	Point A represents 30 mol % Ni at 1300 °C.	Point B represents 75 mol % Ni at 1100 °C.
Identify the phase.	The point is above the melting point line, so the phase is liquid.	The point is below the melting point line, so the phase is solid.
Identify the amount of copper and nickel in the phase.	This liquid phase is made up of 30 mol % Ni, so it is 70 mol % Cu.	This solid phase is made up of 75 mol % Ni, so it is 25 mol % Cu.
	FOR PRACTICE 24.1 Determine the composition and phase present at point C on Figure 24.5.	**FOR PRACTICE 24.2** Determine the composition and phase present at point D on Figure 24.5.

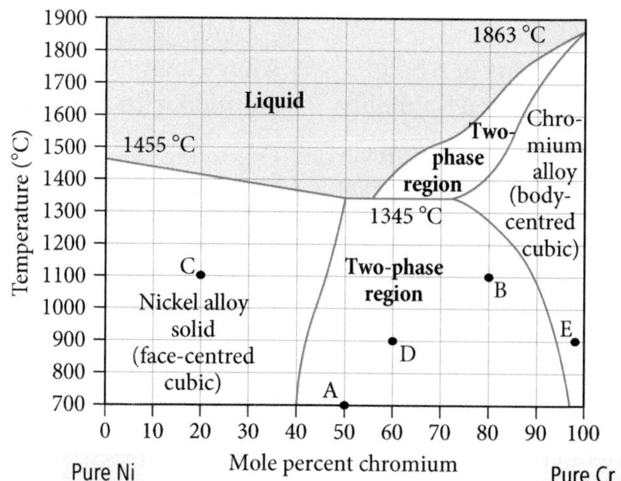

◀ **FIGURE 24.7 Cr–Ni Phase Diagram** Because chromium and nickel form solids with crystal structures that differ from each other, an alloy mixture of the two metals does not form a solid solution at all compositions. A two-phase region exists at compositions between the possible compositions of the two different structures. In the two-phase region, both crystal structures coexist in equilibrium.

Alloys with Limited Solubility Some alloys are composed of metals with different crystal structures. For example, nickel crystallizes in the face-centred cubic structure and chromium in the body-centred cubic structure. Because of their different structures, these two metals do not form a miscible solid solution throughout the entire composition range. At some intermediate composition, the structure has to change. Figure 24.7 ▲ shows the nickel and chromium phase diagram from about 700 °C up to 1900 °C. Notice that the diagram has two different solid phases: face-centred cubic and body-centred cubic. From pure nickel (0 mol % chromium) to about 40–50 mol % chromium, the structure is face-centred cubic. In this structure, Cr atoms substitute for Ni atoms in the face-centred cubic structure of nickel. However, beyond a certain percentage of chromium (which depends on temperature), that structure is no longer stable. At 700 °C, about 40 mol % Cr can fit in the crystal and at 1200 °C, about 50 mol % Cr can fit in. Adding additional Cr beyond these points results in a different phase.

At the other end of the diagram (nearly pure chromium), and at 700 °C, only a small amount of nickel can be substituted into the body-centred cubic structure of the chromium. As the temperature rises to 1300 °C, however, about 20 mol % nickel can be accommodated into the chromium structure. The region in between the two phases is called a **two-phase region**. At these compositions, the two phases (nickel-rich face-centred cubic and chromium-rich body-centred cubic) exist together. The amount of each phase depends upon the composition of the alloy.

We can determine the composition and relative amounts of the two different phases that coexist in a two-phase region from a phase diagram. Point A on Figure 24.7 in the Cr–Ni phase diagram represents 50% composition at 700 °C, and both of the phases are present. Some of the Cr atoms have substituted into the nickel-rich face-centred cubic structure, but there is too much Cr to all fit into the crystal. So the leftover Cr atoms form the chromium-rich body-centred cubic structure with a small number of Ni atoms in the crystal.

The two crystals that exist at 700 °C are (1) the nickel-rich face-centred cubic structure with 40 mol % Cr; and (2) the chromium-rich body-centred cubic structure with 5 mol % Ni. The 50% composition on the phase diagram has just slightly more Cr atoms than can fit into the nickel structure. Thus most of the crystals in the two-phase region are the nickel-rich, face-centred cubic structure with only a small amount of the chromium-rich, body-centred cubic structure, as determined by a method called the *lever rule*. The **lever rule** tells us that in a two-phase region, whichever phase is closest to the composition of the alloy is the more abundant phase. In this example, the 50 mol % Cr composition on the phase diagram is closer to the 40 mol % Cr composition of the nickel-rich face-centred cubic phase than the 95 mol % Cr composition of the chromium-body-centred cubic phase, so more face-centred cubic crystals are present than body-centred cubic crystals.

Interstitial Alloys Recall that in contrast to substitutional alloys, where one metal atom substitutes for another in the lattice, interstitial alloys contain atoms of one kind that fit into the holes, or interstitial sites, of the crystal structure of the other. In metals with the interstitial elements hydrogen, boron, nitrogen, or carbon, the alloy that results retains its metallic properties.

GUIDELINES FOR... **Interpreting the Phases and Compositions in a Binary Phase Diagram as Described by the Lever Rule**	EXAMPLE 24.3 **Alloy Compositions in a Solid Solution with Limited Solubility** Determine the composition, relative amounts, and phases present at point B on Figure 24.7.	EXAMPLE 24.4 **Alloy Compositions in a Solid Solution with Limited Solubility** Determine the composition, relative amounts, and phases present at point C on Figure 24.7.
Locate the temperature and composition of the alloy on the binary phase diagram.	Point B represents 80 mol % Cr at 1100 °C.	Point C represents 20 mol % Cr at 1100 °C.
Identify the phase(s).	Point B is located in the two-phase region, consisting of the nickel-rich face-centred cubic structure and the chromium-rich body-centred cubic structure.	Point C is located in the one-phase region of the nickel-rich face-centred cubic structure.
Identify the amount of Ni and Cr in the phases.	At 1100 °C, at the phase boundaries, the nickel-rich face-centred cubic structure has 45 mol % Cr and 55 mol % Ni and the chromium rich body-centred cubic structure has 90 mol % Cr and 10 mol % Ni.	The nickel-rich face-centred cubic structure at this temperature has 20 mol % Cr and 80 mol % Ni.
Identify the relative amounts of the phases.	At a composition of 80 mol % Cr, the composition is closer to the Cr-rich body-centred cubic phase, so there is more of this phase than there is of the Ni-rich face-centred cubic phase.	There is only one phase. It is 100 mol % of the Ni face-centred cubic phase.
	FOR PRACTICE 24.3 Determine the composition, relative amounts, and phases present at point D on Figure 24.7.	**FOR PRACTICE 24.4** Determine the composition, relative amounts, and phases present at point E on Figure 24.7.

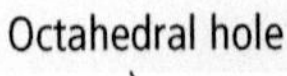

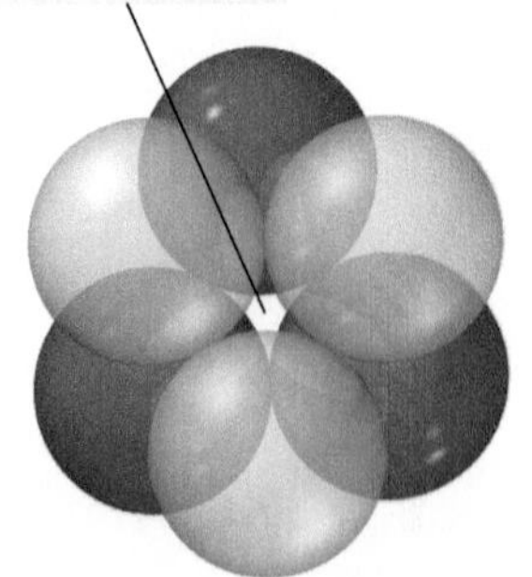

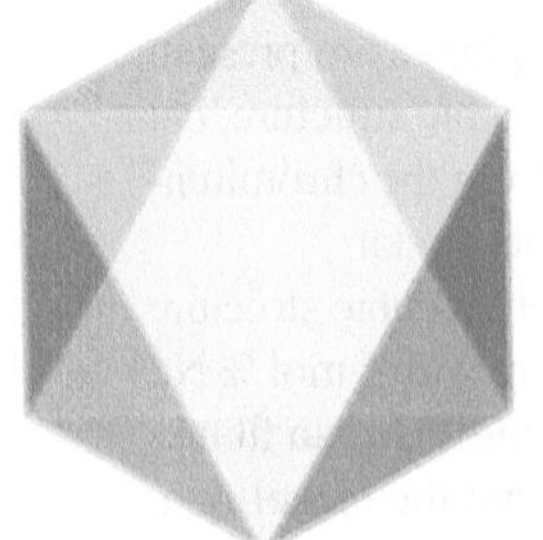

▲ **FIGURE 24.8 Octahedral Holes in Closest Packed Crystals** Octahedral holes are found in a closest packed structure. The octahedral hole is surrounded by six of the atoms in the closest packed structure.

Closest packed crystal structures have two different types of holes between the atoms in the crystalline lattice. An **octahedral hole**, shown in Figure 24.8 ◀, exists in the middle of six atoms on two adjacent closest packed sheets of metal atoms. The hole is located directly above the centre of three closest packed metal atoms in one sheet and below the three metal atoms in the adjacent sheet. This configuration of metal atoms is identical to a regular octahedral configuration that consists of four atoms in a square plane with one atom above and one atom below the square. Therefore, the size of an octahedral hole can be calculated by determining the size of a hole on a square of four atoms in a plane, as shown in Figure 24.9 ▶. Any of the four corners of the square is the 90° angle of a right triangle formed from the adjacent two sides and the diagonal line that runs across the centre of the square. According to the Pythagorean theorem, the length of the diagonal line (c) is related to the length of the sides (a and b) as follows:

$$c^2 = a^2 + b^2 \quad [24.1]$$

If we let r_m equal the metal atom radius, the lengths of the sides are $2r_m$. We can then substitute $2r_m$ for both a and b:

$$c^2 = (2r_m)^2 + (2r_m)^2$$
$$c^2 = 8r_m^{\,2}$$
$$c = 2.828r_m \quad [24.2]$$

We can see from Figure 24.9 that the length of the diagonal (c) is twice the radius of the atoms plus twice the radius of the hole:

$$c = 2r_m + 2r_{hole} \qquad [24.3]$$

Combining Equations 24.2 and 24.3, we get the important result:

$$2.828r_m = 2r_m + 2r_{hole}$$
$$0.828r_m = 2r_{hole}$$
$$r_{hole} = 0.414r_m \qquad [24.4]$$

The octahedral hole, surrounded by six metal atoms, has a radius that is 41.4% of the metal atom radius. By contrast, the hole in the centre of a cube in the *simple cubic* structure has a radius that is 73% of the metal atom radius. The *number* of octahedral holes in a closest packed structure is equal to the number of metal atoms.

The second type of interstitial hole in a closest packed structure is a **tetrahedral hole** (first introduced in Section 11.12), which is formed directly above the centre point of three closest packed metal atoms in one plane and below a fourth metal atom located directly above the centre point in the adjacent plane, as shown in Figure 24.10 ▼. The number of tetrahedral holes in a closest packed structure is equal to *twice* the number of metal atoms. Because this hole is surrounded by only four atoms, the hole is smaller than the octahedral interstitial hole. We can apply geometric considerations similar to those used previously for the octahedral hole to determine that the tetrahedral hole has a radius that is 23% of the metal atom radius.

Interstitial alloys form when small nonmetallic atoms fit within the octahedral or tetrahedral holes of the crystalline lattice of the metal. The formulas for these alloys depend both on the type of hole occupied by the nonmetallic atom and on the fraction of holes occupied. For example, titanium and carbon form an alloy with a closest packed structure for titanium in which all of the octahedral holes are filled with carbon atoms. Since the number of octahedral holes in a closest packed structure is equal to the number of atoms in the structure, the ratio of carbon atoms to titanium atoms must be 1:1 and the corresponding formula is therefore TiC. In the compound formed between molybdenum and nitrogen, by contrast, only one-half of the octahedral holes in the closest packed structure of Mo are filled with N. Therefore, the formula for this compound is Mo_2N. Table 24.3 shows the formulas and relative number of holes filled for several different interstitial alloys.

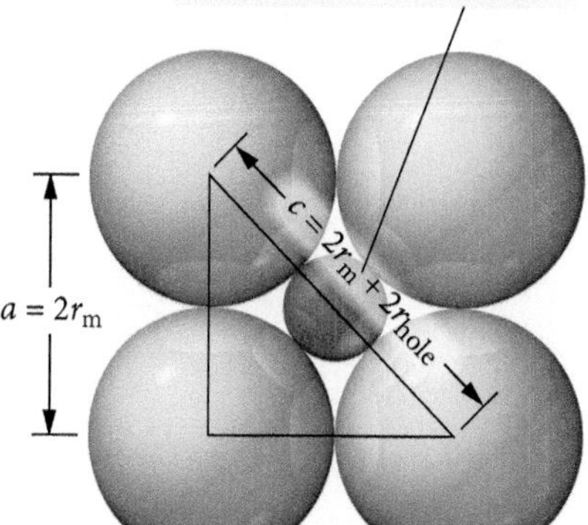

▲ **FIGURE 24.9 A Different View of an Octahedral Hole** An octahedral hole can be viewed as the area in the middle of a square plane of atoms, with one additional atom above the hole and one additional atom below the hole, accounting for the six close atoms. The diagonal of the square is equal to the radius of the two corner atoms plus the diameter of the hole. The length of the diagonal is related to the lengths of the sides of the square by the Pythagorean theorem.

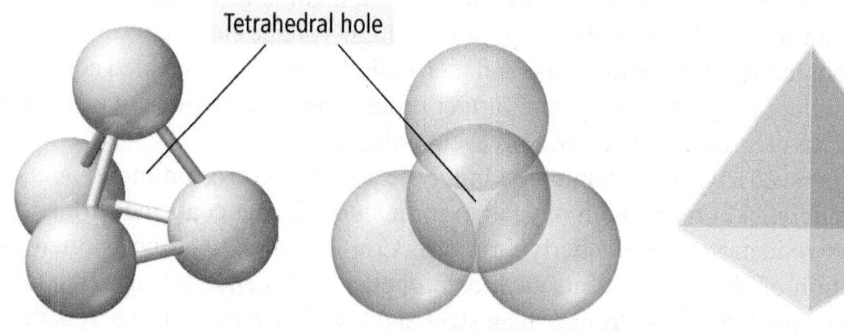

◀ **FIGURE 24.10 A Tetrahedral Hole in a Closest Packed Crystal** Tetrahedral holes are found in a closest packed structure. The tetrahedral hole is surrounded by four of the atoms in the closest packed structure.

TABLE 24.3 Formulas of Several Interstitial Alloys

Compound	Type of Interstitial Hole Occupied	Fraction of Holes Occupied	Formula
Titanium carbide	Octahedral	All	TiC
Molybdenum nitride	Octahedral	One-half	Mo_2N
Tungsten nitride	Octahedral	One-half	W_2N
Manganese nitride	Octahedral	One-quarter	Mn_4N
Palladium hydride	Tetrahedral	One-quarter	Pd_2H
Titanium hydride	Tetrahedral	All	TiH_2

CONCEPTUAL CONNECTION 24.1

Interstitial Alloys

An interstitial alloy contains a nonmetal (X) that occupies one-eighth of the tetrahedral holes of the closest packed structure of the metal (M). What is its formula?

24.5 Sources, Properties, and Products of Some of the 3*d* Transition Metals

In this section, we examine major sources, interesting properties, and important products of several of the 3*d* transition metals, specifically, titanium, chromium, manganese, cobalt, copper, nickel, and zinc. We also survey the different metallurgical methods used to separate and refine them. The variety of uses for these metals reflects their varied properties.

Titanium

Titanium is the ninth most abundant element in Earth's crust, and the fourth most abundant metal. Titanium was discovered in 1791, but the pure metal was not isolated until 1910. The principal minerals of titanium are rutile (TiO_2) and ilmenite ($FeTiO_3$). Another source of titanium is coal ash, the residue from burned coal. Black shiny ilmenite is found in granite deposits along the North Atlantic coast, often within silica sand. The mineral is magnetic due to the presence of Fe^{2+} ions, so it can be separated with a magnet from the nonmagnetic silica. The separated mineral is heated in the presence of carbon under an atmosphere of chlorine gas, forming $TiCl_4$, a volatile gas that can be isolated.

$$FeTiO_3(s) + 3\,Cl_2(g) + 3\,C(s) \longrightarrow 3\,CO(g) + FeCl_2(s) + TiCl_4(g)$$

The $TiCl_4$ gas is reacted with hot magnesium metal turnings (shaved pieces of magnesium), forming elemental titanium—a solid sponge material.

$$TiCl_4(g) + 2\,Mg(s) \longrightarrow 2\,MgCl_2(l) + Ti(s)$$

Titanium is very reactive, readily oxidizing in the presence of oxygen and even nitrogen. Consequently, the elemental titanium is **arc-melted**—a method in which the solid metal is melted with an arc (an electrical discharge) from a high-voltage electric source in a controlled atmosphere to prevent oxidation—and then collected in a water-cooled copper pot. Because of titanium's high reactivity, any further processing must be done in a protective atmosphere of an inert gas, such as Ar, to prevent oxidation.

Despite its reactivity, solid titanium is highly resistant to corrosion in air, acid, and seawater since it quickly reacts with oxygen to form an oxide that coats the surface, preventing further oxidation of the underlying metal. Consequently, titanium is often used in the production of ship components such as propeller shafts and rigging. Titanium is also very strong and light; it is stronger than steel and less than half as dense. It is denser than aluminum but it is twice as strong. For these reasons, titanium is used in the airline industry for the production of jet engine parts. When titanium is alloyed with 5% aluminum and trace amounts of Fe, Cr, and Mo, the resulting metal retains its strength under higher temperature.

The largest use of titanium, however, is as titanium dioxide (TiO_2), which forms a clear crystal but a brilliant white powder. Most white paints use TiO_2 as the pigment, which is far less toxic than older paints that used PbO_2 as the pigment. Titanium dioxide is made by reacting sulfuric acid with ilmenite, which dissolves the titanium into solution.

$$FeTiO_3(s) + 3\,H_2SO_4(l) \longrightarrow FeSO_4(aq) + Ti(SO_4)_2(aq) + 3\,H_2O(l)$$

Neutralizing the solution with a strong base forms titanium oxide.

$$Ti^{4+}(aq) + 4\,OH^-(aq) \longrightarrow TiO_2(s) + 2\,H_2O(l)$$

Calcination of the oxide dries it to form TiO_2 rutile crystals. Large rutile crystals are sometimes used as gems because they resemble diamonds.

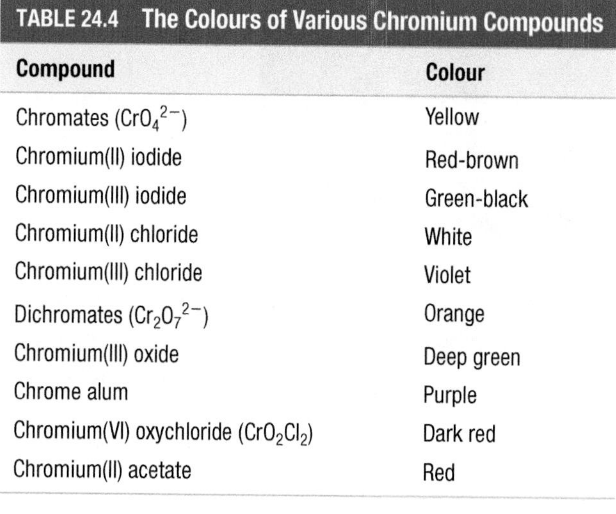

TABLE 24.4 The Colours of Various Chromium Compounds

Compound	Colour
Chromates (CrO_4^{2-})	Yellow
Chromium(II) iodide	Red-brown
Chromium(III) iodide	Green-black
Chromium(II) chloride	White
Chromium(III) chloride	Violet
Dichromates ($Cr_2O_7^{2-}$)	Orange
Chromium(III) oxide	Deep green
Chrome alum	Purple
Chromium(VI) oxychloride (CrO_2Cl_2)	Dark red
Chromium(II) acetate	Red

Chromium

The name chromium comes from the Greek root *chroma*, which means colour. The different compounds of chromium are brightly coloured, as tabulated in Table 24.4 and shown in Figure 24.11 ▼. The main ore source of chromium is chromite, $FeCr_2O_4$. No appreciable sources of chromium ores exist in North America. Chromium metal is produced by reducing chromium ore with aluminum.

$$3\ FeCr_2O_4(s) + 8\ Al(s) \longrightarrow 4\ Al_2O_3(s) + 6\ Cr(s) + 3\ Fe(s)$$

Metallic chromium is a white, hard, lustrous, and brittle metal. The metal readily dissolves in acids such as hydrochloric acid and sulfuric acid, but does not dissolve in nitric acid. The main use of chromium is in the production of steel alloys called *stainless steels*. Reducing chromite with carbon produces ferrochrome, an alloy that is added to steel.

$$FeCr_2O_4(s) + 4\ C(s) \xrightarrow{\text{heat}} Fe_xCr_y(s) + 4\ CO(g)$$

▲ **FIGURE 24.11 Chromium Compounds** Chromium compounds tend to be brightly coloured.

The chromium reacts with oxygen to form a protective chromium oxide layer on the surface. This protects the iron from rusting. Chromium compounds were also used extensively in metal coatings such as paints, because the chromium helps to rustproof the underlying metal, and in wood preservatives, because these compounds kill many of the bacteria and moulds that rot wood. Chromium compounds are finding less use today, however, because of their toxicity and potential carcinogenicity. Nonetheless, because of their great corrosion resistance, chromate coatings are still used on large outdoor steel structures such as bridges, and chromate paints are used to mark streets (on the pavement) and street signs.

Because chromium has the electron configuration [Ar] $4s^1 3d^5$, with six orbitals available for bonding, it can have oxidation states from +1 to +6. Low-oxidation-state chromium exists primarily as the *cation* in salt compounds such as $Cr(NO_3)_3$ and $CrCl_3$. High-oxidation-state chromium occurs within the polyatomic *anions* of salts. The most important compounds with chromium in the +6 oxidation state are the chromates and dichromates. In an acidic solution (below pH 6), the orange-red dichromate ion $Cr_2O_7^{2-}$ is more stable. In more basic solutions (above pH 6), the yellow chromate ion CrO_4^{2-} dominates. Adding acid to a solution containing the chromate ion produces the dichromate ion.

$$2\ H^+(aq) + 2\ CrO_4^{2-}(aq) \longrightarrow Cr_2O_7^{2-}(aq) + H_2O(l)$$

The chromate ion has a tetrahedral arrangement of oxygen atoms around a chromium atom. The dichromate ion has one bridging oxygen between the two tetrahedrons surrounding the chromium ions.

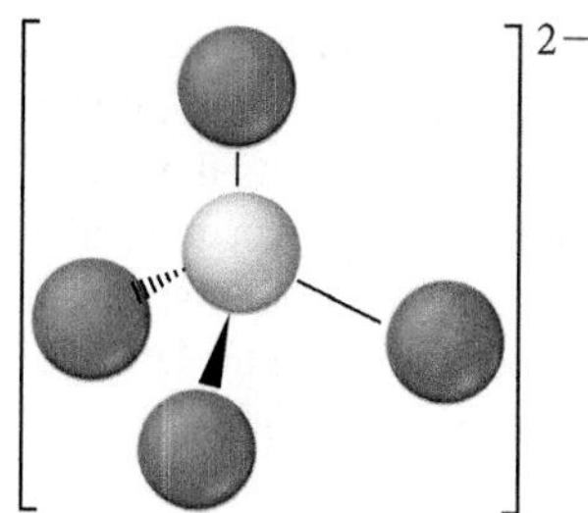

Chromate (CrO_4^{2-})

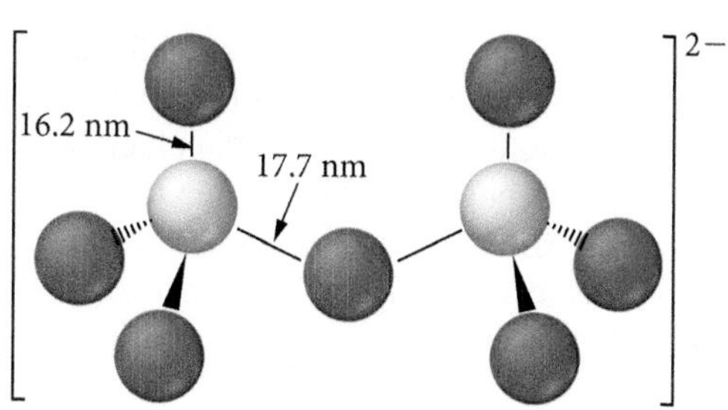

Dichromate ($Cr_2O_7^{2-}$)

The high-oxidation-state chromates and dichromates are very strong oxidizing agents (that is, they are easily reduced). Consequently, they are used as coatings on other metal

▲ Ammonium dichromate does not require additional oxygen to burn.

surfaces to prevent oxidation. The chromates react with the atoms on the surface of the other metals, forming a strongly bonded gel-like film. The film is nonmetallic and bonds very effectively with paint and resins that are applied over the film. We can see evidence of the oxidizing power of dichromate in the ability of ammonium dichromate to sustain combustion without any additional oxygen. Once ignited, ammonium dichromate burns with visible flames, giving off a smoke of green chromium oxide dust.

$$(NH_4)_2Cr_2O_7(s) \xrightarrow{\text{heat}} 4\ H_2O(g) + N_2(g) + Cr_2O_3(s)$$

Manganese

Of all the first-row transition metals, manganese, with the electron configuration [Ar] $4s^23d^5$, exhibits the widest range of oxidation states, from +1 to +7. The most common natural sources of manganese are pyrolusite (MnO_2), hausmannite (Mn_3O_4), and rhodochrosite ($MnCO_3$) minerals. Calcination of rhodochrosite produces manganese(IV) oxide.

$$MnCO_3(s) + \frac{1}{2}O_2(g) \xrightarrow{\text{heat}} MnO_2(s) + CO_2(g)$$

The manganese(IV) oxide or pyrolusite minerals can react with active metals such as Al or Na to produce the elemental metal.

$$3\ MnO_2(s) + 4\ Al(s) \longrightarrow 3\ Mn(s) + 2\ Al_2O_3(s)$$

Pyrolusite, however, is often found as an impure mineral, containing mixtures of MnO and Fe_2O_3. Heating the mineral in the presence of carbon can reduce the mineral, forming an alloy of manganese and iron called ferromanganese.

$$MnO_2(s) + MnO(s) + Fe_2O_3(s) + n\ C(s) \xrightarrow{\text{heat}} Mn_xFe_yC_z(s) + n\ CO(g)$$

Ferromanganese generally contains about 5–6% carbon and is used as an alloying material in steel. Manganese is added to steel alloys to change the physical properties of the steel. For example, manganese makes the steel easier to deform at high temperatures. Therefore, adding manganese to steel helps the rolling and forging steps of steel production. Steel alloys containing about 12% manganese are used for military armour and industrial applications such as bulldozer blades. Manganese also strengthens copper, aluminum, and magnesium alloys.

Manganese is a reactive metal that dissolves in most acids. When heated in the presence of air, it forms the various manganese oxides, including MnO, Mn_3O_4, and MnO_2. When heated in pure oxygen, the high-oxidation-state oxide Mn_2O_7 is also formed. At high oxidation states, the manganese compounds are good oxidizing agents. Dissolving MnO_2 into a solution of hydrochloric acid oxidizes the chloride and produces chlorine gas.

$$MnO_2(s) + 4\ HCl(aq) \longrightarrow Cl_2(g) + 2\ H_2O(l) + MnCl_2(aq)$$

The permanganate ion (MnO_4^-) has an oxidation state of +7 for Mn and is also an important oxidizing agent. The permanganate ion can even oxidize hydrogen peroxide, which is itself used as an oxidizing agent.

$$2\ MnO_4^-(aq) + 3\ H_2O_2(aq) + 2\ H^+(aq) \longrightarrow 2\ MnO_2(s) + 3\ O_2(g) + 4\ H_2O(g)$$

The compound MnO_2 is a glass additive. By itself, MnO_2 is either a brown or black crystal, depending on the degree of hydration. Yet, when added to a silica glass, it imparts a pink colour to the glass. The pink colour is useful because it counteracts the green colour often seen in glass, which is due to small concentrations of impure iron oxides. In other words, MnO_2 is added to glass to "decolourize" it. Old manganese-containing glass that has been exposed to UV light for over 100 years develops a slight purple tint. This purple colour is due to the oxidation of MnO_2 in the glass to Mn(VII) oxides.

Cobalt

Cobalt ore is often found within the ores of other metals, such as iron, nickel, lead, and silver. Cobalt's most common ores are sulfide minerals, such as cobaltite (CoAsS), which is collected as a by-product in the extraction processes of the other metal ores. North American production of cobalt is mainly in Ontario and in Cuba.

Cobalt, like iron and nickel, is **ferromagnetic** and is important in the production of magnets. Like the paramagnetic materials described in Section 7.7, the atoms in ferromagnetic materials contain unpaired electrons. In ferromagnetic materials, however, these electrons can all align with their spins oriented in the same direction, creating a permanent magnetic field.

Magnets are becoming increasingly important in space, health, industrial, and military applications. In the United States in particular, concerns have arisen over the lack of domestic sources of cobalt for these applications. New and stronger magnetic materials that do not require cobalt have been developed, but these require neodymium, which is found mostly in China.

Cobalt is also an important additive for high-strength steels. Carbaloy, a mixture composed primarily of cobalt metal with grains of tungsten carbide, is a very tough material. The strength of the cobalt and hardness of the carbides make this a good material for industrial cutting and abrasion. In addition, cobalt forms many compounds with brilliant blue colours and is used in making pigments and inks. Cobalt compounds are also essential for health, because cobalt is the metal in vitamin B_{12}, which is necessary to avoid anemia.

▲ Copper wiring is used to transmit electricity throughout the world.

Copper

Copper, which can be found in its elemental form, was one of the first elements to be isolated and used by humans—copper products have been known for over 10 000 years. Ancient civilizations used copper to form tools. The earliest known artifacts produced by the smelting of copper are at a site in Tepe Yahya, Iran, dating from about 3800 B.C.E. The discovery of **bronze**, a copper and tin alloy, improved toolmaking because copper's bronze alloys are stronger, and they resist wear and corrosion better than pure copper.

The most important copper ores are chalcopyrite ($CuFeS_2$) and malachite [$Cu_2(OH)_2CO_3$]. Copper ores often occur near deposits of elemental copper, providing early humans with an easy way to locate copper ores. The electrometallurgical production of pure copper from chalcopyrite is described in Section 24.3.

The high natural abundance and generally high concentration of copper and copper ores makes copper an economical choice for many industrial applications. Today over 40% of copper products are made from recycled copper. The ease and low cost of recycling copper has allowed copper to remain an important industrial metal.

The high conductivity of copper is second only to that of silver, making copper the most important metal for electrical wires. Along with iron in steel, copper is now among the most widely used metals; it is used in electrical motors and devices, the electrical wiring that snakes though the walls of houses, and the electrical transmission network linking power sources to homes and industries all over the world. Because of its high heat conductivity, copper is also used as a heat exchange material—for example, in car radiators. In addition, copper is used to make pipes for water distribution. Copper pipes can be easily connected to each other with watertight seals by soldering. Copper displaced lead for use as water pipes because of the toxicity of lead; however, advancing technology keeps presenting new options. Today, because of its lower price and lighter weight, plastic is used for many water pipes.

Copper has a distinctive reddish colour that can be polished to a beautiful metallic luster; therefore it has been used in architecture, as a decorative metal in jewellery, and as a material for sculpture. Copper composes the decorative sheathings on many domes and roof-top art works. When exposed to the atmosphere and rain, some of the copper oxidizes, forming a number of different compounds, such as malachite and brochanite [$Cu_4SO_4(OH)_6$], that have beautiful blue or green colours. Copper roofing shingles can be bought as polished copper sheets or as sheets that have already been oxidized and exhibit a beautiful weathered *patina* (a coating that comes with age and use). Chemical compounds are used to speed up the aging process and produce the desired patina, which takes 20 or more years to develop naturally.

Even though copper has many useful properties, it is not a very strong metal; therefore, alloys of copper with improved strength have been developed. Bronze was one of

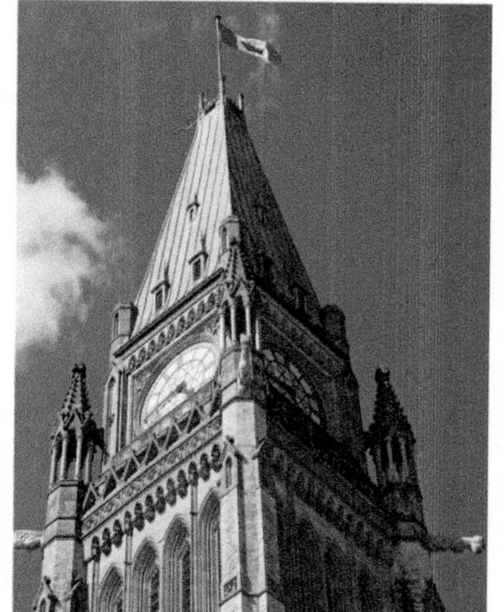

▲ Copper is used in a variety of applications.

the first alloys ever produced. This alloy of copper and tin has been used for thousands of years because it could be made even in the low heat of a Stone Age campfire. **Brass**, another widely used alloy, contains copper and zinc. Many brass and bronze alloys also contain other metals to achieve certain physical properties. Some of the most important applications of bronze and brass are for plumbing fixtures, bearings, and art decorations. In addition, the tendency of brass and bronze alloys (unlike those of iron) not to spark when struck make them useful in applications where a spark could be dangerous.

Nickel

Most of the world's nickel comes from deposits in Ontario. These deposits are believed to have formed from a meteorite impact (most meteorites have high nickel content). The nickel occurs as a sulfide compound mixed with copper and iron sulfides. To produce nickel, the sulfides are roasted in air to form metal oxides, and then they are reduced to the elemental metals with carbon. The metal mixture is heated in the presence of carbon monoxide, forming nickel carbonyl, which has a boiling point of 43 °C and can therefore be collected as a gas.

$$Ni(s) + 4\,CO(g) \xrightarrow{\text{heat}} Ni(CO)_4(g)$$

When the nickel carbonyl is heated past 200 °C, it decomposes back to nickel metal and carbon monoxide. This method of refining nickel is called the *Mond process*.

Nickel metal is fairly unreactive and resistant to corrosion, characteristics that it shares with platinum and palladium. Consequently, nickel is used as an alloying metal in the production of stainless steels. Many nickel alloys are used for applications where corrosion resistance is important. For example, the alloy Monel contains 72% Ni, 25% Cu, and 3% Fe and is resistant to reaction with most chemicals. Monel does not react even with fluorine gas at room temperature. Nickel–steel alloys are used for armour plates, and elemental nickel is often plated onto other metals as a protective coating.

Zinc

Elemental zinc was officially discovered in Europe in 1746 when calamine (zinc silicate) was reduced with charcoal to produce the metal. However, zinc had been used for many hundreds of years before this discovery because zinc ores and copper ores were used to form copper–zinc brass alloys. The main sources of zinc are ores composed of sphalerite (ZnS), smithsonite ($ZnCO_3$), and an oxide mixture of zinc, iron, and manganese called franklinite. These ores are roasted to form the oxides of the metals and then reduced with carbon to produce the elemental metals. Zinc combines with many different metals to form useful alloys. As we have seen, the combination of zinc and copper produces the brass family of alloys. The combination of zinc and nickel with copper produces alloys with a silver colour called German or silver brass. Zinc is also used in solder alloys with low melting points.

Galvanizing a steel object (such as a nail) involves dipping the object into a molten bath of zinc. The zinc, which is more reactive than the iron in steel, preferentially oxidizes, forming a tough protective coating. Zinc compounds are also used to coat steel before applying other coatings. The zinc compounds, such as zinc phosphate, adhere strongly to the steel surface, forming rough crystals onto which other coatings, such as paint, adhere very well. If a painted steel surface is scratched, the underlying exposed metal is susceptible to rust, but the added zinc ions prevent this by migrating toward the defect and forming a protective zinc oxide coating.

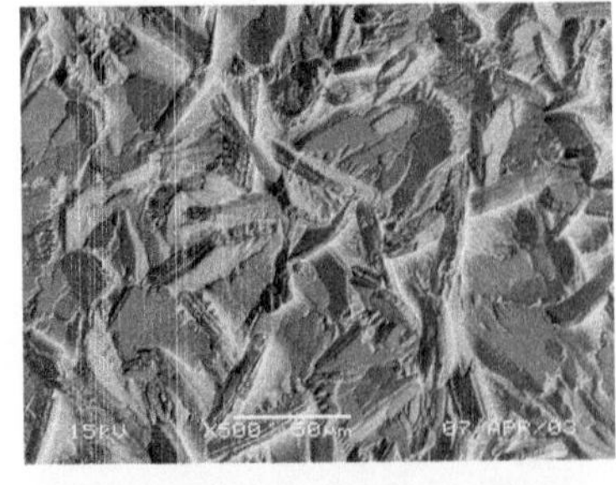

▲ Zinc phosphate adheres strongly to steel surfaces, forming rough crystals onto which other coatings, such as paint, can be applied.

Zinc and its compounds have generally been considered safe. Zinc additives in coatings have replaced many of the chromium and lead additives (both of which are toxic) that were previously used. Today, however, even zinc additives in coatings are being studied for environmental hazards. In Europe, all substances that contain zinc compounds must be labelled as potential polluters of environmental water. More environmentally safe organic compounds have been developed to replace the metallic anticorrosion additives, but these compounds are more expensive to produce. Opportunities abound for chemists to develop needed products that are both environmentally safe and economically viable.

CHAPTER IN REVIEW

Key Terms

Section 24.1
metallurgy (1025)

Section 24.2
minerals (1026)
ore (1026)

Section 24.3
extractive metallurgy (1027)
refining (1027)
gangue (1027)
pyrometallurgy (1028)
calcination (1028)
roasting (1028)
smelting (1028)
flux (1028)
slag (1028)
hydrometallurgy (1028)
leaching (1028)
electrometallurgy (1029)
powder metallurgy (1030)

Section 24.4
alloy (1031)
substitutional alloy (1031)
interstitial alloy (1031)
two-phase region (1033)
lever rule (1033)
octahedral hole (1034)
tetrahedral hole (1035)

Section 24.5
arc-melting (1036)
ferromagnetic (1039)
bronze (1039)
brass (1040)

Key Concepts

General Properties (24.2)

Metals have many common physical properties, such as high conductivity of electricity and heat, and high malleability and ductility. However, these properties vary among the different metals. For example, some metals are very malleable, while other metals are more brittle.

Natural Distribution of Metals (24.2)

Metals are unevenly distributed throughout Earth's crust. All the metals together are responsible for 25% of the mass of Earth's crust, but just a few key metals are abundant enough to each individually make up more than 1% of the crust. Few metals exist naturally in their elemental state; most are found in ores, rocks that contain a high concentration of metal-containing minerals. Most metal-containing minerals are oxides, sulfides, chlorides, carbonates, or more complex compounds.

Metallurgical Processes (24.3)

To be useful, metals have to be separated from the gangue, the non-useful part of the ores, reduced to the elemental metals, and refined to reach higher purity. Extractive metallurgy is the general term for the processes such as pyrometallurgy, hydrometallurgy, and electrometallurgy that are used to separate the metal from the ore. A new method of forming metal components from micron-sized metal particles is called powder metallurgy.

Phase Diagrams (24.4)

The structure of metals can be described as the packing of spheres, including body-centred cubic and the closest packed types—face-centred cubic and hexagonal closest packed. When two types of metal atoms bond together, they form an alloy. A binary phase diagram is a graphical representation of the phases and crystal types of alloys present at different compositions and temperatures. If the two metals are similar in size and crystallize with the same crystal structure, they will most likely form a miscible solid solution, which means that they can form an alloy at any composition ratio. If the two metals are dissimilar in size or crystal structure, the solubility of one atom in the other's crystal structure is often limited. At certain compositions two different crystals can coexist in equilibrium; this is called a two-phase region. The lever rule determines which phase is present in a greater proportion.

Types of Alloys (24.4)

There are generally two different types of alloys, substitutional and interstitial. A substitutional alloy is a mixture in which one type of metal atom replaces another type of metal atom in the crystal structure. In an interstitial alloy, one type of atom (either a metal or nonmetal) fits into the interstitial holes within the crystal structure of the metal. Interstitial alloys can be made with different atoms filling different fractions of the different types of holes.

Key Skills

Using a Phase Diagram to Determine the Composition, Relative Amounts, and Phases Present (24.4)
• Examples 24.1, 24.2, 24.3, 24.4 • For Practice 24.1, 24.2, 24.3, 24.4 • Exercises 35–38

Determining the Composition of an Interstitial Alloy from the Occupancy of the Interstitial Holes (24.4)
• Exercises 41, 42

EXERCISES

Review Questions

1. How can we account for the presence of vanadium in oil sources?
2. Name three categories of metallurgical processes.
3. Why is Ni not considered a common metal even though it composes over 2% of the total mass of Earth? Only Fe and Mg have a higher percent composition of Earth's total mass.
4. Metal elements are found in both minerals and ores. Describe the difference between a mineral and an ore.
5. Ores contain minerals and gangue. Describe the difference between a mineral and gangue.
6. Calcination, roasting, and smelting are three pyrometallurgical processes. Describe the differences among the processes.
7. What compound has been historically used to leach gold from gold ores? Why should this process be discontinued?
8. Name three benefits of making metal components from the powder metallurgical process.
9. Describe the difference between body-centred cubic and face-centred cubic structures.
10. Describe the difference between a substitutional alloy and an interstitial alloy.
11. Why was copper one of the first metals that humans used?
12. Describe why bronze was one of the first alloys that humans used.
13. Both brass and bronze contain copper. Describe the difference between these two alloys.
14. Name the properties of copper that make it appropriate for electric wires and the properties that make it appropriate for water pipes.

Problems by Topic

The General Properties and Natural Distribution of Metals

15. Describe three typical properties of metals.
16. Describe whether each of the following are generally higher or lower for metals compared to nonmetals.
    a. thermal conductivity
    b. electrical resistivity
    c. transparency
    d. ductility
17. List four metal elements that each individually compose more than 1% of Earth's crust.
18. List four metals that occur as elements in their natural state.
19. List the name and formula of one important mineral source for each of these metals: Fe, Hg, V, and Nb.
20. List the name and formula of one important mineral source for each of these metals: Ti, Zn, U, and Ta.

Metallurgical Processes

21. Two ores of magnesium are $MgCO_3$ and $Mg(OH)_2$. Write balanced equations for the calcination of these two minerals to form MgO.
22. Two ores of copper are CuO and CuS. Write balanced equations for the roasting of CuO with C to form Cu metal and the roasting of CuS with O_2 to form CuO.
23. Give the definition of a flux and identify the flux in the reaction:

$$SiO(s) + MgO(s) \xrightarrow{\text{heat}} MgSiO_3(l)$$

24. Give the definition of a slag and identify the slag in the reaction:

$$SiO_2(s) + MgO(s) \xrightarrow{\text{heat}} MgSiO_3(l)$$

25. Provide a general description of how hydrometallurgy is used to extract metals from ores.
26. Provide a general description of how electrometallurgy is used to extract metals from ores.
27. How is Al_2O_3 separated from other oxides using the Bayer process? What soluble form of aluminum forms from Al_2O_3 during the Bayer process?
28. When copper is purified using an electrochemical cell, which electrode has the pure copper and which electrode has the impure copper? Explain how gold is obtained from this process.
29. Describe the difference between sponge powdered iron and water-atomized powdered iron.
30. Describe the difference in the processing of sponge powdered iron and water-atomized powdered iron.

Metal Structures and Alloys

31. Determine the composition of each vanadium alloy.
    a. One-half of the V atoms are replaced by Cr atoms.
    b. One-fourth of the V atoms are replaced by Fe atoms.
    c. One-fourth of the V atoms are replaced by Cr atoms and one-fourth of the V atoms are replaced by Fe atoms.
32. Determine the composition of each cobalt alloy.
    a. One-third of the Co atoms are replaced by Zn atoms.
    b. One-eighth of the Co atoms are replaced by Ti atoms.
    c. One-third of the Co atoms are replaced by Zn atoms and one-sixth of the Co atoms are replaced by Ti atoms.
33. Using Table 24.2, explain why you might expect Cr and Fe to form miscible alloys.
34. Using Table 24.2, explain why you might expect Co and Cu to not form miscible alloys.

35. Determine the composition and phases present at points A and B on the Cr–Fe phase diagram.

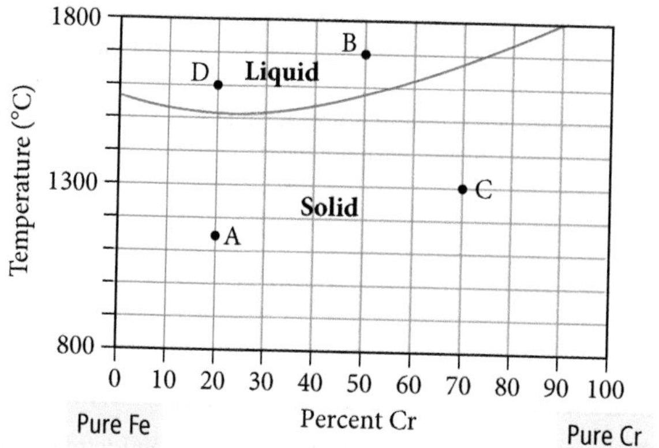

36. Determine the composition and phases, present at points C and D on the Cr–Fe phase diagram (see previous problem for diagram).

37. Determine the composition, relative amounts, and phases present at points A and B on the Co–Cu phase diagram.

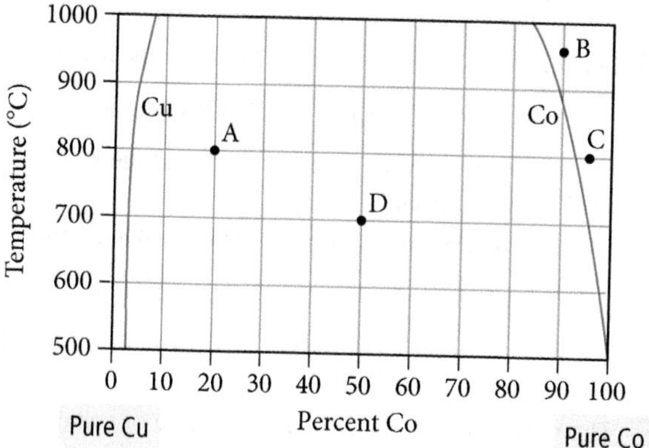

38. Determine the composition, relative amounts, and phases present at points C and D on the Co–Cu phase diagram (see previous problem for phase diagram).

39. The elements Mn and Si are added to steel to improve its properties in electric motors, and some C is often found as a detrimental impurity. Which of these elements fills interstitial holes in the Fe lattice and which substitutes for the Fe in the lattice?

40. The elements Si and P are added to steel to improve its properties in electric motors, and some N is often found as a detrimental impurity. Which of these elements fills interstitial holes in the Fe lattice and which substitutes for the Fe in the lattice?

41. Determine the formula for each interstitial alloy:
   a. Nitrogen occupies one-half of the octahedral sites of a closest packed Mo structure.
   b. Hydrogen occupies all of the tetrahedral sites of a Cr closest packed structure.

42. Determine the formula for each interstitial alloy:
   a. Nitrogen occupies one-fourth of the octahedral sites of a closest packed Fe structure.
   b. Hydrogen occupies one-half of the tetrahedral sites of a Ti closest packed structure.

Sources, Properties, and Products of Some of the 3*d* Transition Metals

43. Identify the metal found in each mineral:
   a. sphalerite **b.** malachite **c.** hausmannite

44. Name at least one important mineral that is a source for each metal:
   a. Fe **b.** Co **c.** Cr

45. Calculate the heat of reaction ($\Delta_r H°$) for the calcination of rhodochrosite. ($\Delta_f H°$ for rhodochrosite is -894.1 kJ mol^{-1}.)

46. The extraction of Mn from pyrolusite with aluminum produces pure Mn metal and Al_2O_3. Calculate the heat of reaction ($\Delta_r H°$).

47. Describe the effects of adding Cr to steel and give a use for chromium–steel alloys.

48. Describe the effects of adding Mn to steel and give a use for manganese–steel alloys.

49. Calculate the mole percent and mass percent of Ti in the minerals rutile and ilmenite.

50. Calculate the mole percent and mass percent of Mn in the minerals pyrolusite and rhodochrosite.

51. Why is it important to use an inert atmosphere to surround the metal when arc-melting titanium?

52. Titanium is a very reactive metal. Explain why titanium has a high corrosion resistance to seawater and can be used for the production of ship components.

53. Which compound of Ti is the most important industrial product of titanium metal? Describe an application for this compound.

54. Describe how Zn is used to protect the surface of steel products. What is the name of this process?

55. Describe the Bayer process.

56. Describe the Mond process.

57. Which metals are found in carbaloy steel?

58. Which metals are found in Monel steel?

Cumulative Problems

59. After 2.0×10^4 kg of an ore that contains 0.051% ilmenite is mined, the percent yield from extracting and refining the metals from the mineral is 87% for the iron and 63% for the titanium. Calculate the mass of iron and titanium produced from the ore.

60. Calculate the mass of aluminum metal that is needed to produce Cr metal from 5.00×10^2 g of chromite. Calculate how many grams of Cr metal are produced from 5.00×10^2 g of chromite.

61. How many lattice atoms surround a tetrahedral hole and an octahedral hole in a closest packed structure? Describe which hole site is larger and explain why.

62. Explain why the crystal structure and atomic size of the two elements are important factors in a two-component phase diagram.

63. Why does Mn form compounds with higher oxidation states than Cr?

64. When MnO_2 is added to silica glass, the glass has a pink colour. Why is MnO_2 added to the glass?

65. Co, Fe, and Ni are ferromagnetic. What is the difference between ferromagnetic and paramagnetic?

66. Is the chromate ion or dichromate ion more stable in an acidic solution? Which ion has a higher Cr : O ratio? Which ion has a higher oxidation state for Cr?

67. The first ionization energies of iron, cobalt, nickel, and the first three platinum metals are all about the same, but the first ionization energies of osmium, iridium, and platinum are substantially greater. Suggest an explanation for this observation.

68. Although both the group 1 and 11 metals have a half-filled *s* subshell, the group 11 metals have markedly higher first ionization energies, densities, and melting points, and markedly lower second and third ionization energies than the corresponding group 1 metals. Explain these observations.

Challenge Problems

69. Iron powder is placed into a tall cylinder-shaped die and pressed from the top and bottom to make a cylinder-shaped pressed part with a height of 5.62 cm and radius of 4.00 cm. The density of the iron powder before it was pressed was 2.41 g mL^{-1}. The density of a pressed iron part is 6.85 g mL^{-1}. The density of pure solid iron is 7.78 g mL^{-1}.

a. Calculate the original height of the powder before it was pressed.

b. Calculate the theoretical height of the pressed component if it could be pressed to the same density as pure iron.

c. What percentage of the component is composed of voids between the iron particles?

70. When a part is made by pressing together powdered metal, no metal is wasted, whereas metal is typically scrapped after a metal part is cut from a solid metal plate. If a circular part with a diameter of 10.0 cm is made from an original shape of a square with a side length of 10.0 cm, calculate the percentage of the metal that is thrown away as scrap. If the circular shape also has a circular hole with a diameter of 6.0 cm, calculate the percentage of the metal that is thrown away as scrap.

71. Hydrogen can be in both the octahedral and tetrahedral holes for lanthanum. Determine the percentage of the holes that are filled if the formula is $LaH_{2.76}$.

72. Tin exists in two allotropic forms. Gray tin has a diamond structure and white tin has a closest packed structure. Predict which allotrope is **(a)** denser, and **(b)** a conductor of electricity. Predict the valence electronic configuration of tin in each allotrope.

73. Find the equilibrium constant at 298 K for the reaction

$$[Ag(CN)_2]^-(aq) + Cu(s) \rightleftharpoons [Cu(CN)_2]^-(aq) + Ag(s)$$

The K_f for $[Cu(CN)_2]^- = 1.0 \times 10^{24}$ and the rest of the data needed are in Appendix II.

74. Find the equilibrium constant at 298 K for the reaction

$$2[Cu(NH_3)_2]^+(aq) \rightleftharpoons [Cu(NH_3)_4]^{2+}(aq) + Cu(s)$$

The K_f for $[Cu(NH_3)_2]^+ = 6.3 \times 10^{10}$ and the rest of the data needed are in Appendix II.

75. The mineral cobaltite, CoAsS, is a source of cobalt. Propose a chemical procedure to extract cobalt from this mineral. What are some of the hazards of such a procedure?

Conceptual Problems

76. Why are metals such as Ni and Co economical to mine and use in industrial processes even though they have a very low natural abundance in Earth's crust?

77. Explain why metals such as Au and Ag are found in their elemental states in nature, but metals like Na and Ca are always found in compounds in nature.

Transition Metals and Coordination Compounds

Chemistry must become the astronomy of the molecular world.

—Alfred Werner (1866–1919)

The red colour of ruby is caused by a splitting of the d*-orbital energy levels in Cr^{3+} by the host crystal.*

IN THIS CHAPTER, WE EXAMINE the chemistry of the transition metals and an important class of their compounds called coordination compounds. In doing so, we will see that coordination compounds form all of the types of isomers that we have studied so far, as well as some new types. In our examination of the transition metals, we draw on much of what we learned in Chapter 7 and Chapter 8 about electronic structure and periodicity. We will also briefly revisit valence bond theory to explain bonding in coordination compounds, but we will quickly shift to a different theory—called ligand field theory—that better explains many of the properties of these compounds. Transition metals and coordination compounds are important, not only because of their interesting chemistry, but because of their numerous applications. Coordination compounds are the basis for a number of therapeutic drugs, chemical sensors, and colouring agents. In addition, many biological molecules contain transition elements in arrangements that are similar to their arrangements of coordination compounds. For example, the oxygen-carrying site on hemoglobin is an iron ion bonded partly to an amino acid in the hemoglobin molecule and partly to a flat molecule called a porphyrin. An oxygen molecule reversibly bonds to the iron and is transported throughout the body by blood flow.

▲ **Ruby and Emerald** The red colour of ruby and the green colour of emerald are both caused by Cr^{3+}.

25.1 The Colours of Rubies and Emeralds

Rubies are deep red and emeralds are brilliant green, yet the colour of both gemstones is caused by the same ion, Cr^{3+}. The difference lies in the crystal that hosts the ion. Rubies are crystals of aluminum oxide (Al_2O_3) in which about 1% of the Al^{3+} ions are replaced by Cr^{3+} ions. Emeralds, by contrast, are crystals of beryllium aluminum silicate [$Be_3Al_2(SiO_3)_6$] in which a similar percentage of the Al^{3+} ions are replaced by Cr^{3+}. The imbedded Cr^{3+} ion is red in the aluminum oxide crystal, but green in the beryllium aluminum silicate crystal. Why?

The answer to this question lies in the effect that the host crystal has on the energies of the atomic orbitals in Cr^{3+}. Atoms in the crystal create a field around the ion—sometimes called the *crystal field*—that splits the five normally degenerate *d* orbitals into two or more levels. The colour of the gemstone is caused by electron transitions between these levels. In rubies, the crystal field is stronger (and the corresponding splitting of the *d* orbitals greater) than it is in emeralds. Recall from Chapter 7 that the colour of a substance depends on the colours *absorbed* by that substance, which in turn depends on the energy differences between the orbitals involved in the absorption. The greater splitting in ruby results in a greater energy difference between the *d* orbitals of Cr^{3+}, and consequently the absorption of a different colour of light than in emerald.

The colours of several other gemstones are also caused by the splitting of the *d* orbitals in transition metal ions imbedded within host crystals. For example, the red in garnet, which has $Mg_3Al_2(SiO_4)_3$ as a host crystal, and the yellow-green of peridot, which has Mg_2SiO_4 as a host crystal, are both caused by electron transitions between *d* orbitals in Fe^{2+}. Similarly, the blue in turquoise, which has $[Al_6(PO_4)_4(OH)_8 \cdot 4\,H_2O]^{2-}$ as a host crystal, is caused by transitions between the *d* orbitals in Cu^{2+}.

In this chapter, we examine the properties of the transition metals and their ions more closely. We also examine the properties of coordination compounds in some detail. You will recall that we first encountered this common type of transition metal compound in Chapter 16 (see Section 16.8). In a coordination compound, bonds to a central metal ion split the *d* orbitals much as they are split in the crystals of gemstones. The theory that explains these splittings and the corresponding colours is called **ligand field theory**, which we also explore in this chapter.

▲ **Garnet, Peridot, and Turquoise** The red in garnet and the yellow-green of peridot are both caused by Fe^{2+}. The blue of turquoise is caused by Cu^{2+}.

25.2 Electron Configurations of Transition Metals

Transition metals, the elements in the *d* block of the periodic table, are a study in similarities and differences. When we compare their properties with the varied properties of the main-group elements, they seem markedly similar. For example, almost all transition metals have moderate to high densities, good electrical conductivity, high melting points, and moderate to extreme hardness. Their similar properties are related to their similar electron configurations: they all have electrons in *d* orbitals that can be involved in metallic bonding. In spite of their similarities, however, each element is also unique, and they exhibit a wide variety of chemical behaviour. Before we examine some of the periodic properties of the transition metals, let's review the electron configurations of these elements, first discussed in Chapter 7.

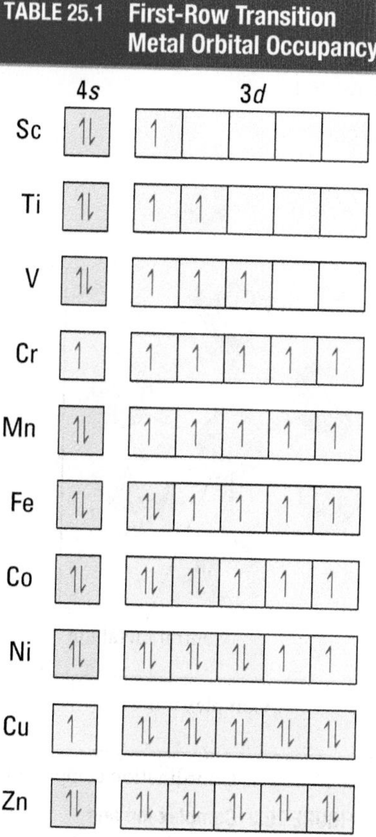

TABLE 25.1 First-Row Transition Metal Orbital Occupancy

	4s	3d				
Sc	↑↓	↑				
Ti	↑↓	↑	↑			
V	↑↓	↑	↑	↑		
Cr	↑	↑	↑	↑	↑	↑
Mn	↑↓	↑	↑	↑	↑	↑
Fe	↑↓	↑↓	↑	↑	↑	↑
Co	↑↓	↑↓	↑↓	↑	↑	↑
Ni	↑↓	↑↓	↑↓	↑↓	↑	↑
Cu	↑	↑↓	↑↓	↑↓	↑↓	↑↓
Zn	↑↓	↑↓	↑↓	↑↓	↑↓	↑↓

Electron Configurations

Recall from Section 7.7 that, as we move to the right across a row of transition elements, electrons are added to $(n - 1)d$ orbitals (where n is the row number in the periodic table and also the quantum number of the highest occupied principal level). For example, as we move across the fourth-period transition metals, electrons are added to the $3d$ orbitals, as shown in Table 25.1.

In general, the ground state electron configuration for the first two rows of transition elements is [noble gas] $ns^2(n - 1)d^x$ and for the third and fourth rows is [noble gas] $ns^2(n - 2)f^{14}(n - 1)d^x$, where x ranges from 1 to 10. Recall from Section 7.7, however, that because the ns and $(n - 1)d$ sublevels are close in energy, many exceptions occur. For example, in the first transition series of the d block, the outer configuration is $4s^2 3d^x$ with two exceptions: Cr is $4s^1 3d^5$ and Cu is $4s^1 3d^{10}$. This behaviour is related to the closely spaced $3d$ and $4s$ energy levels.

Recall from Section 7.7 that the transition metals form ions by losing electrons from the ns orbital *before* losing electrons from the $(n - 1)d$ orbitals. For example, Fe^{2+} has an electron configuration of [Ar] $3d^6$ because it has lost both of the $4s$ electrons to form the 2+ charge.

Oxidation States

Unlike main-group metals, which tend to exhibit predominantly one oxidation state, the transition metals often exhibit a variety of oxidation states, as shown in Figure 25.1 ▼. The highest oxidation state for a first-row transition metal is +7 for manganese (Mn). The electron configuration of manganese in this oxidation state corresponds to the loss of all the electrons in the $4s$ and $3d$ orbitals, leaving a noble gas electron configuration ([Ar]). This is the same configuration we see for all of the highest oxidation states of the elements to the left of Mn. To the right of manganese, the oxidation states are all lower, mostly +2 or +3. A +2 oxidation state for a transition metal is not surprising, since $4s$ electrons are readily lost.

Metals in high oxidation states, such as +7, exist only when the metal is bound to a highly electronegative element, such as oxygen; they do not exist as bare ions.

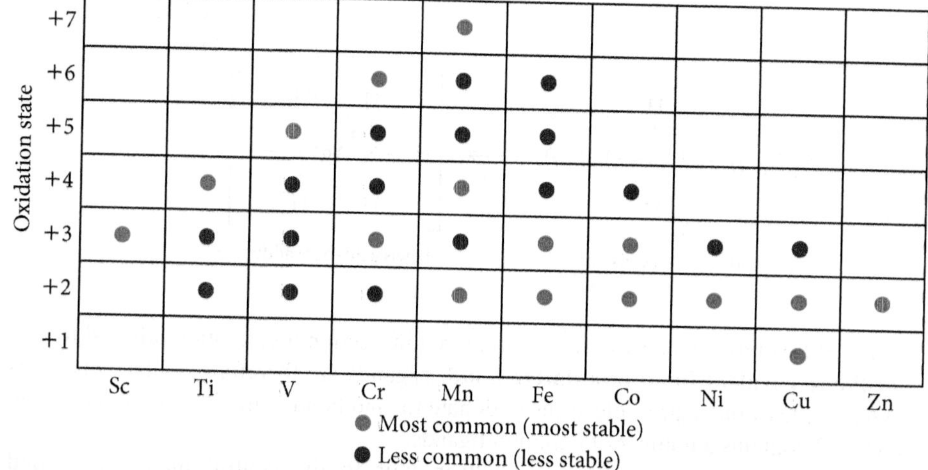

▲ **FIGURE 25.1 First-Row Transition Metal Oxidation States** The transition metals exhibit many more oxidation states than the main-group elements. These oxidation states range from +7 to +1.

25.3 Coordination Compounds

Lewis acid and base theory are covered in Section 15.10.

We discussed at the end of Chapter 16 that transition metals tend to form *complex ions*. A **complex ion** contains a central metal ion bound to one or more *ligands*. A **ligand** is a Lewis base (or electron donor) that forms a bond with the metal. When a complex ion combines with one or more *counterions* (ions of opposite charge that are not acting as ligands), the resulting neutral compound is called a **coordination compound**. The first coordination compounds were discovered in the early eighteenth century, but their nature was not understood until nearly 200 years later. Swiss chemist Alfred Werner studied coordination compounds extensively—especially a series of cobalt(III) compounds with ammonia, whose formulas were then written as $CoCl_3 \cdot 6\,NH_3$, $CoCl_3 \cdot 5\,NH_3$ and, $CoCl_3 \cdot 4\,NH_3$. In 1893, he proposed that the central metal ion has two types of interactions that he named **primary valence** and **secondary valence**. The primary valence is the oxidation state on the central metal atom, and the secondary valence is the number of molecules or ions directly bound to the metal atom, called the **coordination number**. In $CoCl_3 \cdot 6\,NH_3$ the primary valence is +3, and it was discovered that the ammonia molecules are directly bound to the central cobalt, giving a coordination number of 6. Today we write the formula of this compound as $[Co(NH_3)_6]Cl_3$ to better represent the coordination compound as the combination of a complex ion, $Co(NH_3)_6{}^{3+}$, and three Cl^- counterions (Figure 25.2 ◀).

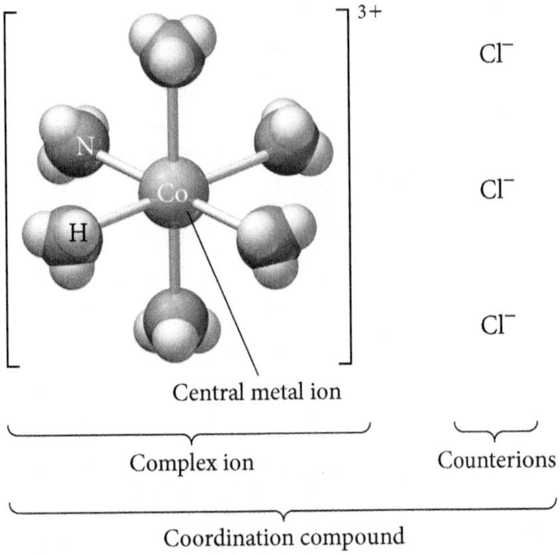

Complex ion: $[Co(NH_3)_6]^{3+}$ (Central metal ion: Co; N; H) — Counterions: Cl^- Cl^- Cl^- — Coordination compound

▲ **FIGURE 25.2 Complex Ion and Coordination Compound** A coordination compound contains a complex ion and corresponding counterions. The complex ion contains a central metal atom coordinated to several ligands. The particular compound shown here is $[Co(NH_3)_6]Cl_3$.

The formulas of the other cobalt(III) compounds studied by Werner are now written as $[Co(NH_3)_5Cl]Cl_2$ and $[Co(NH_3)_4Cl_2]Cl$. In these two cases, the complex ions are $Co(NH_3)_5Cl^{2+}$ (with two Cl^- counterions) and $Co(NH_3)_4Cl_2{}^+$ (with one Cl^- counterion), respectively. With this series of compounds, Werner demonstrated that the Cl^- can replace NH_3 in the secondary valence. In other words, Cl^- can act as a counterion, or it can bond directly to the metal as part of the complex ion.

The complex ion itself contains the metal ion in the centre and the ligands—which can be neutral molecules or ions—arranged around it. We can think of the metal–ligand complex as a Lewis acid–base adduct (see Section 15.10) because the bond is formed when the ligand donates a pair of electrons to an empty orbital on the metal. For example, consider the reaction between the silver ion and ammonia:

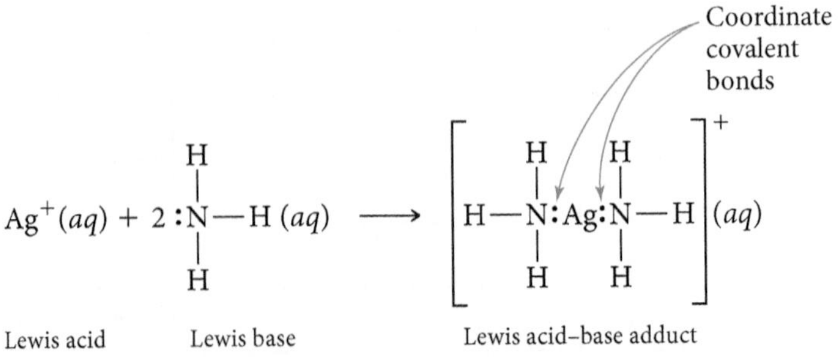

$$\underset{\text{Lewis acid}}{Ag^+(aq)} + \underset{\text{Lewis base}}{2\,:NH_3(aq)} \longrightarrow \underset{\text{Lewis acid–base adduct}}{[H_3N\!:\!Ag\!:\!NH_3]^+(aq)}$$

Coordinate covalent bonds

A bond of this type, which we first encountered in Section 9.9, is often referred to as a **coordinate covalent bond** or a **dative bond**. Ligands are therefore good Lewis bases and have at least one pair of electrons to donate to, and bond with, the central metal ion. Table 25.2 contains a number of common ligands.

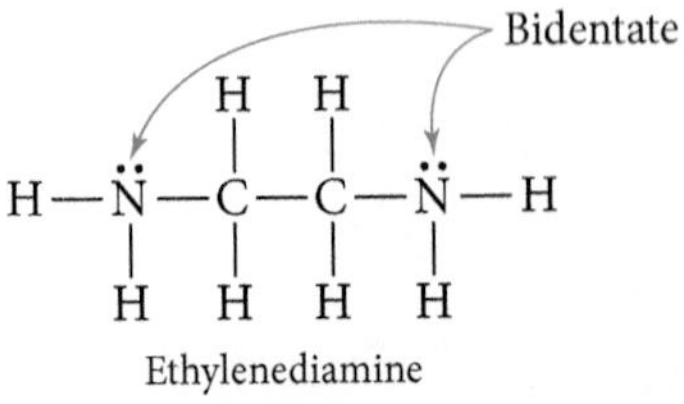

Ligands that donate only one electron pair to the central metal are called **monodentate**. Some ligands, however, have the ability to donate two pairs of electrons (from two different atoms) to the metal; these are called **bidentate**. Examples of bidentate ligands include the oxalate ion (abbreviated ox) and the ethylenediamine molecule (abbreviated en). The ethylenediamine ligand bonded to Co^{3+} is shown in Figure 25.3(a) ▶.

$H_2\ddot{N}{-}CH_2{-}CH_2{-}\ddot{N}H_2$ (Bidentate)

Ethylenediamine

TABLE 25.2 Common Ligands

Name	Lewis Diagram
Water	$H-\ddot{\underset{..}{O}}-H$
Ammonia	$H-\ddot{N}(H)-H$
Chloride ion	$:\ddot{\underset{..}{Cl}}:^{-}$
Carbon monoxide	$:C{\equiv}O:$
Cyanide ion	$[:C{\equiv}N:]^{-}$
Thiocyanate ion	$[:\ddot{S}{=}C{=}\ddot{N}:]^{-}$
Oxalate ion (ox)	$\left[\begin{matrix} .\ddot{O}. & & .\ddot{O}. \\ \Vert & & \Vert \\ C & - & C \\ \vert & & \vert \\ :\ddot{O}. & & .\ddot{O}: \end{matrix}\right]^{2-}$
Ethylenediamine (en)	$H-\ddot{N}(H)-CH_2-CH_2-\ddot{N}(H)-H$
Ethylenediaminetetraacetate (EDTA)	$\left[(^{-}:\ddot{O}-C({=}\ddot{O}:)CH_2)_2\ddot{N}CH_2CH_2\ddot{N}(CH_2C({=}\ddot{O}:)-\ddot{O}:^{-})_2\right]^{4-}$

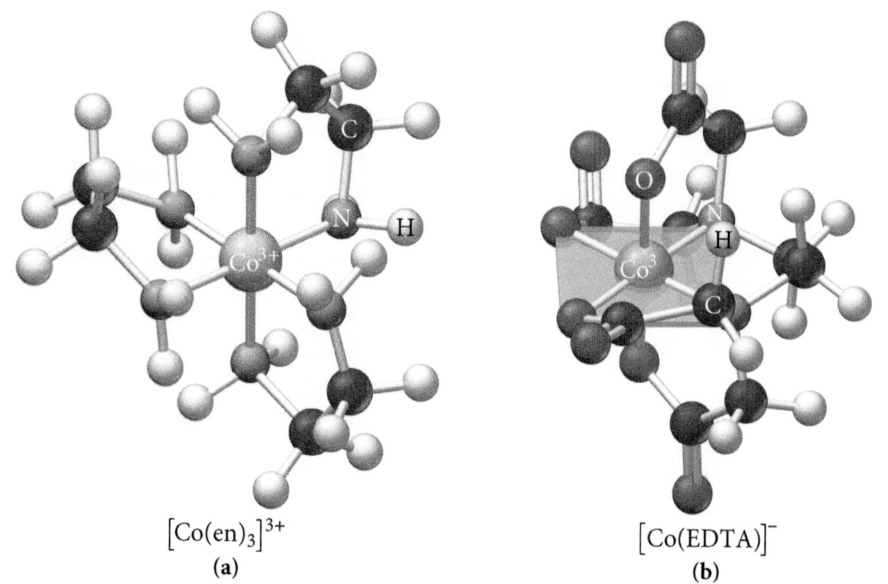

▲ **FIGURE 25.3 Bidentate and Polydentate Ligands Coordinated to Co(III)** (**a**) Ethylenediamine is a bidentate ligand; (**b**) EDTA is a hexadentate ligand.

Some ligands, called **polydentate** ligands, can donate even more than two electron pairs (from more than two atoms) to the metal. A very common polydentate ligand is the ethylenediaminetetraacetate ion ($EDTA^{4-}$).

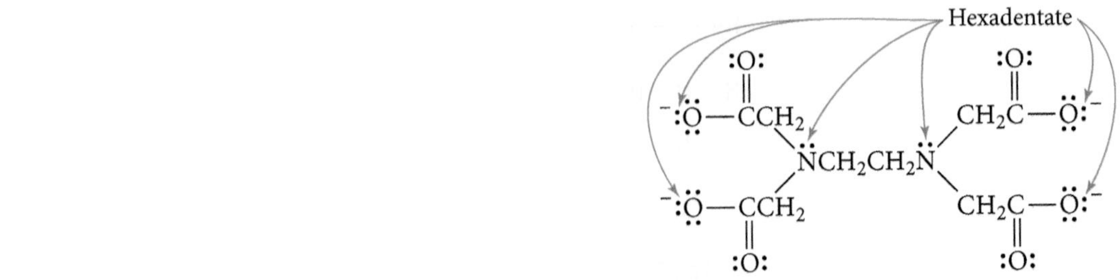

Hexadentate

$$\begin{array}{c} {}^{-}:\ddot{O}-C(=O)CH_2 \quad\quad CH_2C(=O)-\ddot{O}:^{-} \\ \diagdown\quad\quad\quad\diagup \\ \ddot{N}CH_2CH_2\ddot{N} \\ \diagup\quad\quad\quad\diagdown \\ {}^{-}:\ddot{O}-C(=O)CH_2 \quad\quad CH_2C(=O)-\ddot{O}:^{-} \end{array}$$

$EDTA^{4-}$

The EDTA ligand wraps itself completely around the metal, donating up to six pairs of electrons, as shown in Figure 25.3(b) ▲. A complex ion that contains either a bidentate or polydentate ligand is a **chelate** (pronounced "key-late"), and the coordinating ligand is known as a **chelating agent**.

A survey of many coordination compounds shows that coordination numbers can vary from as low as 2 to as high as 12. The most common coordination numbers are 6, as occurs in $[Co(NH_3)_6]^{3+}$, and 4, as occurs in $[PdCl_4]^{2-}$. Coordination numbers greater than 6 are rarely observed for the first-row transition metals. Typically, only 1+ metal ions have a coordination number as low as 2, as occurs in $[Ag(NH_3)_2]^{+}$. Odd coordination numbers exist, but they are rare.

The common geometries of complex ions, shown in Table 25.3, depend in part on their coordination number. A coordination number of 2 results in a linear geometry, and a coordination number of 6 results in an octahedral geometry. A coordination number of 4 can have either a tetrahedral geometry or a square planar geometry, depending on the number of d electrons in the metal ion. Metal ions with a d^8 electron configuration (such

TABLE 25.3 Common Geometrics of Complex Ions

Coordination Number	Shape	Model	Example
2	Linear	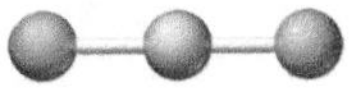	$[Ag(NH_3)_2]^{+}$
4	Square planar	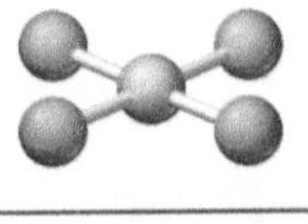	$[PdCl_4]^{2-}$
4	Tetrahedral	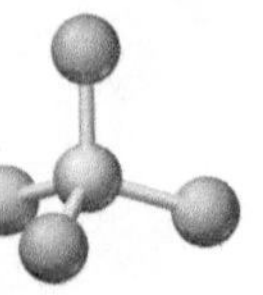	$[Zn(NH_3)_4]^{2+}$
6	Octahedral	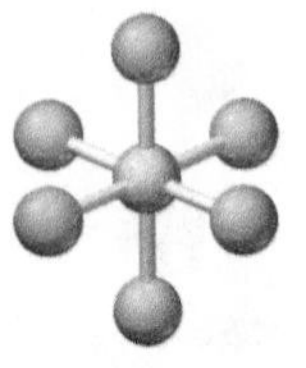	$[Fe(H_2O)_6]^{3+}$

as $[PdCl_4]^{2-}$) exhibit square planar geometry, and metal ions with a d^{10} electron configuration (such as $[Zn(NH_3)_4]^{2+}$) exhibit tetrahedral geometry.

Naming Coordination Compounds

To name coordination compounds, we follow a series of general rules based on the system originally proposed by Werner. As with all salts (see Section 3.4), the name of the cation goes before the name of the anion.

Guidelines for Naming Complex Ions	Examples
1. Name the ligands. • Name neutral ligands as molecules with the following notable exceptions. H_2O (aqua) NH_3 (ammine) CO (carbonyl) • Name anionic ligands with the name of the ion plus an ending modified as follows: *-ide* becomes -o *-ate* becomes -ato *-ite* becomes -ito *Table 25.4 lists the names of some common ligands.*	$NH_2CH_2CH_2NH_2$ is ethylenediamine. H_2O is aqua. Cl^- is chloro. SO_4^{2-} is sulfato. SO_3^{2-} is sulfito.
2. List the names of the ligands in alphabetical order before the name of the metal cation.	Ammine (NH_3) is listed before chloro (Cl^-) which is listed before nitrito/nitro (NO_2^-).
3. Use a prefix to indicate the number of ligands (when there is more than one of a particular type): *di-* (2), *tri-* (3), *tetra-* (4), *penta-* (5), or *hexa-* (6). If the name of the ligand already contains a prefix, such as ethylenediamine, place parentheses around the ligand name and use *bis-* (2), *tris-* (3), or *tetrakis-* (4) to indicate the number. Prefixes do not affect the order in which you list the ligands.	Trichloro indicates three Cl^- ligands. Tetraammine indicates four NH_3 ligands. Tris(ethylenediamine) indicates three ethylenediamine ligands.
4. Name the metal. **a.** When the complex ion is a cation, use the name of the metal followed by the oxidation state written with a Roman numeral. **b.** If the complex ion is an anion, drop the ending of the metal and add *-ate* followed by the oxidation state written with a Roman numeral. Some metals use the Latin root with the *-ate* ending. Table 25.5 lists the names for some common metals in anionic complexes.	In cations: Co^{3+} is cobalt(III). Pt^{2+} is platinum(II). Cu^+ is copper(I). In anions: Co^{3+} is cobaltate(III). Pt^{2+} is platinate(II). Cu^+ is cuprate(I).
5. Write the entire name of the complex ion by listing the ligands first followed by the metal.	$[Pt(NH_3)_2Cl_4]^{2-}$ is diamminetetrachloroplatinate(II). $[Co(NH_3)_6]^{3+}$ is hexaamminecobalt(III).

TABLE 25.4 Names and Formulas of Common Ligands

Ligand	Name in Complex Ion
Anions	
Bromide, Br^-	Bromo
Chloride, Cl^-	Chloro
Hydroxide, OH^-	Hydroxo
Cyanide, CN^-	Cyano
Nitrite, NO_2^-	Nitro
Oxalate, $C_2O_4^{2-}$ (ox)	Oxalato
Neutral molecules	
Water, H_2O	Aqua
Ammonia, NH_3	Ammine
Carbon monoxide, CO	Carbonyl
Ethylenediamine (en)	Ethylenediamine
Ethylenediaminetetraacetate (EDTA)	Ethylenediaminetetraacetato

TABLE 25.5 Names of Common Metals When Found in Anionic Complex Ions

Metal	Name in Anionic Complex
Chromium	Chromate
Cobalt	Cobaltate
Copper	Cuprate
Gold	Aurate
Iron	Ferrate
Lead	Plumbate
Manganese	Manganate
Molybdenum	Molybdate
Nickel	Nickelate
Platinum	Platinate
Silver	Argentate
Tin	Stannate
Zinc	Zincate

When you write the *formula* of a complex ion, write the symbol for the metal first, followed by neutral molecules, and then anions. If there is more than one anion or neutral molecule acting as a ligand, list them in alphabetical order based on the chemical symbol.

PROCEDURE FOR... Naming Coordination Compounds	**EXAMPLE 25.1 Naming Coordination Compounds** Name the following: $[Cr(H_2O)_5Cl]Cl_2$	**EXAMPLE 25.2 Naming Coordination Compounds** Name the following: $K_3[Fe(CN)_6]$
Identify the cation and anion and first name the simple ion (i.e., not the complex one).	**SOLUTION** $[Cr(H_2O)_5Cl]^{2+}$ is a complex cation. Cl^- is chloride.	**SOLUTION** K^+ is potassium. $[Fe(CN)_6]^{3-}$ is a complex anion.
Give each ligand a name and list them in alphabetical order.	H_2O is aqua. Cl^- is chloro.	CN^- is cyano.

Name the metal ion.	Cr^{3+} is chromium(III).	Fe^{3+} is ferrate(III) because the complex is anionic.
Name the complex ion by adding prefixes to indicate the number of each ligand, followed by the name of each ligand, followed by the name of the metal ion.	$[Cr(H_2O)_5Cl]^{2+}$ is pentaaquachlorochromium(III).	$[Fe(CN)_6]^{3-}$ is hexacyanoferrate(III).
Name the compound by writing the name of the cation before the anion. The only space is between ion names.	$[Cr(H_2O)_5Cl]Cl_2$ is pentaaquachlorochromium(III) chloride.	$K_3[Fe(CN)_6]$ is potassium hexacyanoferrate(III).
	FOR PRACTICE 25.1 Name the following: $[Mn(CO)(NH_3)_5]SO_4$	**FOR PRACTICE 25.2** Name the following: $Na_2[PtCl_4]$

25.4 Structure and Isomerization

Isomerism is common in coordination compounds. Just like isomerism in organic compounds (Chapter 20), we can broadly divide the isomerism observed in coordination compounds into two categories: **structural isomers** and **stereoisomers**. Structural isomers are those in which atoms are connected to one another in different ways, whereas stereoisomers are those in which atoms are connected by the ligands and have different spatial arrangements.

Structural Isomerism

We can subdivide the broad category of structural isomers into two types: coordination isomers and linkage isomers. **Coordination isomers** occur when a coordinated ligand exchanges places with the uncoordinated counterion. For example, two different compounds have the general formula $Co(NH_3)_5BrCl$. In one of them, the bromine coordinates to the metal and chloride is a counterion, pentaamminebromocobalt(II) chloride, $[Co(NH_3)_5Br]Cl$, in the other one, the chlorine coordinates to the metal and bromide is the counterion, pentaamminechlorocobalt(II) bromide ($[Co(NH_3)_5Cl]Br$).

Linkage isomers have ligands that can coordinate to the metal in different orientations. For example, the nitrite ion (NO_2^-) has a lone pair on the N atom as well as lone pairs on the O atoms—either of the two atoms can form coordinate covalent bonds with the metal. When the nitrite ion coordinates through the N atom it is a *nitro* ligand and is represented as NO_2^-, but when it coordinates through the O atom, it is a *nitrito* ligand and is usually represented as ONO^-. An example of linkage isomerization can be seen in the yellow-orange complex ion pentaamminenitrocobalt(III), $[Co(NH_3)_5NO_2]^{2+}$, which contrasts with the red-orange complex ion pentaamminenitritocobalt(III), $[Co(NH_3)_5ONO]^{2+}$, as shown in Figure 25.4 ▼. Other ligands capable of linkage isomerization, as well as their names, are listed in Table 25.6.

TABLE 25.6 Ligands Capable of Linkage Isomerization

nitro
$[:\ddot{O}-\ddot{N}=\ddot{O}]^-$
nitrito

isocyanato
$[:\ddot{O}=C=\ddot{N}:]^-$
cyanato

isothiocyanato
$[:\ddot{S}=C=\ddot{N}:]^-$
thiocyanato

Stereoisomerism

In coordination compounds, stereoisomers are the result of ligands bonding to the metal in different spatial arrangements. One type of stereoisomerism (see Section 20.7) is *cis–trans* isomerism, which in complex ions occurs in square planar complexes of the general formula MA_2B_2 or octahedral complexes of the general formula MA_4B_2. For example, *cis–trans* isomerism occurs in the square planar complex $Pt(NH_3)_2Cl_2$. Figure 25.5(a) ▼ shows the two distinct ways in which the ligands can be oriented around the metal. In one complex, the Cl^- ligands are next to each other on one side of the molecule—this is the *cis* isomer. In the other complex, the Cl^- ligands are on opposite sides of the molecule—this is the *trans* isomer. *Cis–trans* isomerism also exists in the octahedral complex ion $[Co(NH_3)_4Cl_2]^+$. As

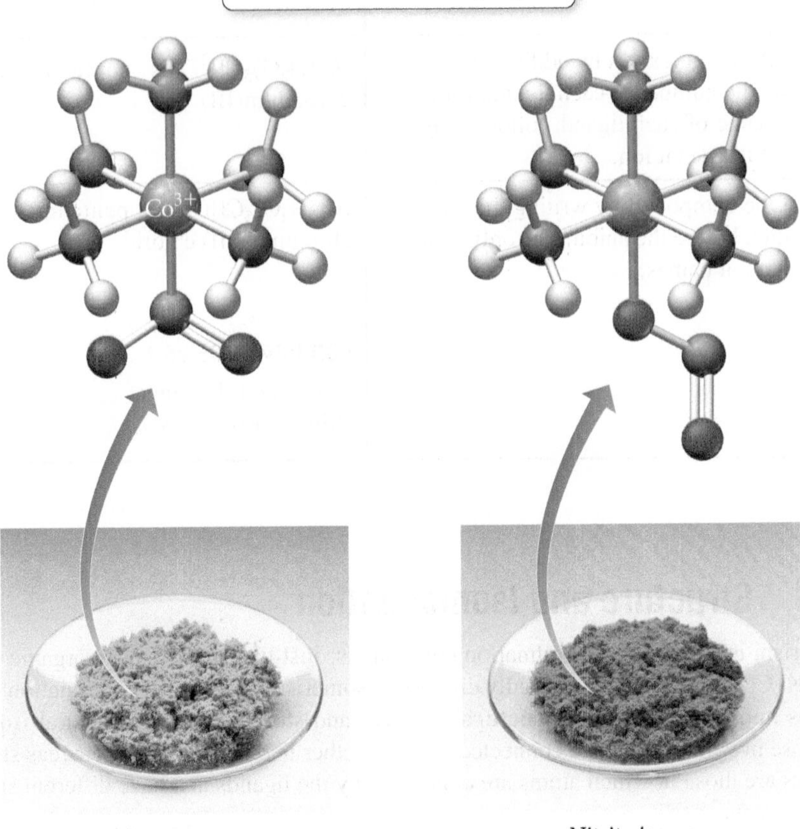

▶ **FIGURE 25.4 Linkage Isomers** In $[Co(NH_3)_5NO_2]^{2+}$, the NO_2 ligand bonds to the central metal atom through the nitrogen atom. In $[Co(NH_3)_5ONO]^{2+}$, the NO_2 ligand bonds through the oxygen atoms. The different isomers have different colours.

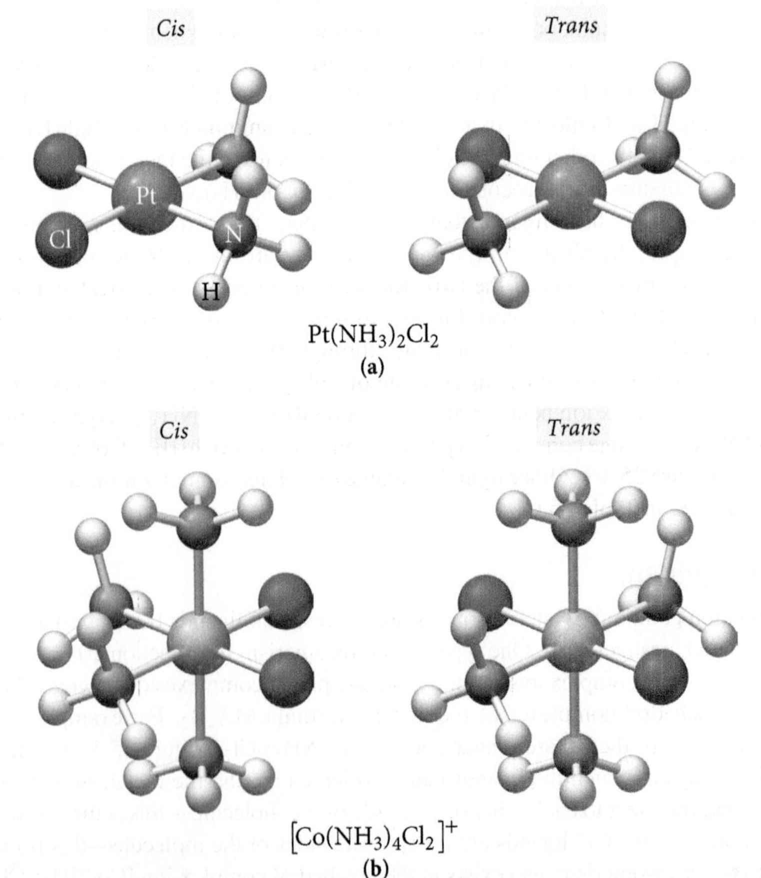

▶ **FIGURE 25.5 *Cis–trans* Isomerism** (a) *Cis–trans* isomerism in square planar $Pt(NH_3)_2Cl_2$. In the *cis* isomer, the Cl^- ligands are next to each other on one side of the molecule. In the *trans* isomer, the Cl^- ligands are on opposite sides of the molecule. (b) *Cis–trans* isomerism in octahedral $[Co(NH_3)_4Cl_2]^+$. In the *cis* isomer, the Cl^- ligands are on the same side. In the *trans* isomer, the Cl^- ligands are on opposite sides.

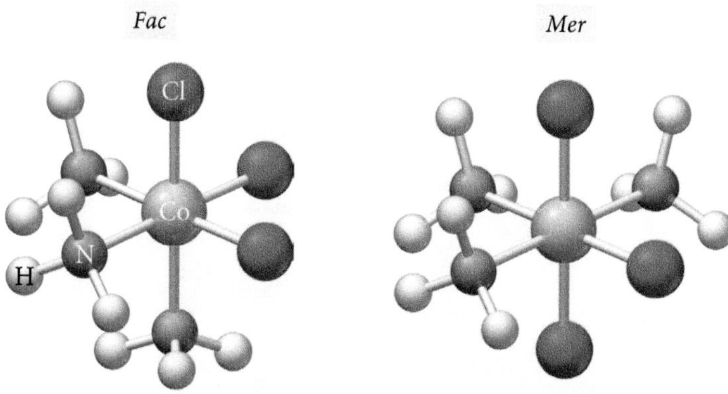

▲ **FIGURE 25.6** ***Fac–mer* Isomerism in $Co(NH_3)_3Cl_3$** In the *fac* isomer, the three Cl^- ligands are all on one side of the molecule and make up one face of the octahedron. In the *mer* isomer, the three ligands inscribe an arc around the middle (or meridian) of the octahedron.

shown in Figure 25.5(b) ◄, the ligands arrange themselves around the metal in two ways, one with the Cl^- ligands on the same side (the *cis* isomer) and another with the Cl^- ligands on opposite sides of the metal (the *trans* isomer). Note that *cis–trans* isomerism does not occur in tetrahedral complexes because all bond angles around the metal are 109.5°, and each corner of a tetrahedron is considered to be adjacent to all three other corners.

Another type of stereoisomerism is *fac–mer* isomerism, which occurs in octahedral complexes of the general formula MA_3B_3. For example, in $Co(NH_3)_3Cl_3$, the ligands arrange themselves around the metal in two ways (Figure 25.6 ▲). In the *fac* isomer, the three Cl^- ligands are all on one side of the molecule and make up one face of the octahedron (*fac* is short for facial). In the *mer* isomer, the three ligands form an arc around the middle of the octahedron (*mer* is short for meridional).

PROCEDURE FOR... Identifying and Drawing Stereoisomers	**EXAMPLE 25.3 Identifying and Drawing Stereoisomers** Draw the structures and label the type for all the isomers of $[Co(en)_2Cl_2]^+$.	**EXAMPLE 25.4 Identifying and Drawing Stereoisomers** Draw the structures and label the type for all the isomers of $[Ni(CN)_2Cl_2]^{2-}$.
Identify the coordination number and the geometry around the metal.	**SOLUTION** The ethylenediamine (en), $NH_2CH_2CH_2NH_2$, ligand is bidentate so each occupies two coordination sites. Each Cl^- is monodentate, occupying one site. The total coordination number is 6 so this must be an octahedral complex.	**SOLUTION** All the ligands are monodentate so the total coordination number is 4. Ni^{2+} is a d^8 electronic configuration so we expect a square planar complex.
Identify if this is *cis–trans* or *fac–mer* isomerism.	With ethylenediamine occupying four sites and Cl^- occupying two sites, we fit the general formula MA_4B_2, leading to *cis–trans* isomers.	Square planar complexes can only have *cis–trans* isomers.
Draw and label the two isomers.	$[Co(en)_2Cl_2]^+$: NH₂, H₂N, Co, Cl, H₂N, Cl, NH₂ — *Cis*; H₂ Cl H₂, N, Co, N, N, N, H₂ Cl H₂ — *Trans*	$[Ni(CN)_2Cl_2]^{2-}$: Cl, CN, Ni, Cl, CN — *Cis*; Cl, CN, Ni, NC, Cl — *Trans*
	FOR PRACTICE 25.3 Draw the structures and label the type for all the isomers of $[Cr(H_2O)_3Cl_3]^+$.	**FOR PRACTICE 25.4** Draw the structures and label the type for all the isomers of $[Co(NH_3)_2Cl_2(ox)]^-$.

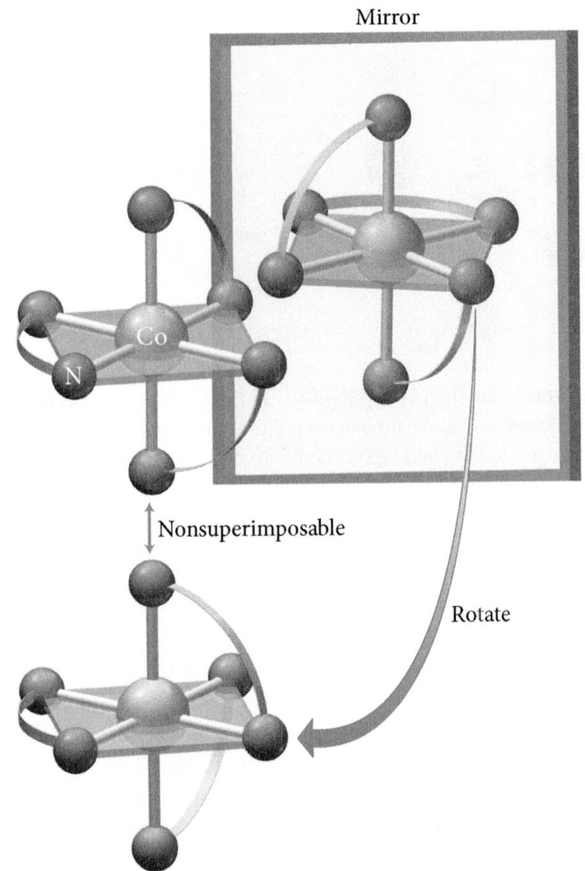

▶ **FIGURE 25.7 Stereoisomerism in $[Co(en)_3]^{3+}$** The mirror images of $[Co(en)_3]^{3+}$ are not superimposable. (The connected nitrogen atoms represent the ethylenediamine ligand.)

The second category of stereoisomerism is optical isomerism. As we discussed in Section 20.7, **enantiomers** are nonsuperimposable mirror images of one another. If you hold your right hand up to a mirror, the image in the mirror looks like your left hand. No matter how you rotate or flip your left hand, you cannot superimpose it on your right hand. Molecules or ions that exhibit this quality are *chiral*. The isomers are *enantiomers*, and they exhibit the property of optical activity (the rotation of polarized light). As shown in Figure 25.7 ▲, the complex ion $[Co(en)_3]^{3+}$ is nonsuperimposable on its mirror image, so it is a chiral complex.

EXAMPLE 25.5 RECOGNIZING AND DRAWING ENANTIOMERS

Determine whether the *cis* or *trans* isomers shown in Example 25.3 are optically active (demonstrate optical isomerism).

SOLUTION

Draw the *trans* isomer of $[Co(en)_2Cl_2]^+$ and its mirror image. Check to see if they are superimposable by rotating one isomer 180°.

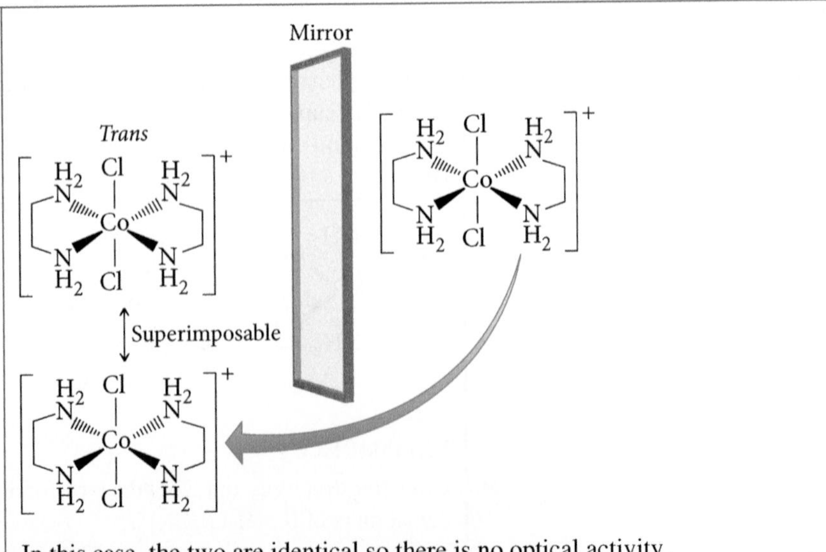

In this case, the two are identical so there is no optical activity.

Draw the *cis* isomer and its mirror image. Check to see if they are superimposable by rotating one isomer 180°.

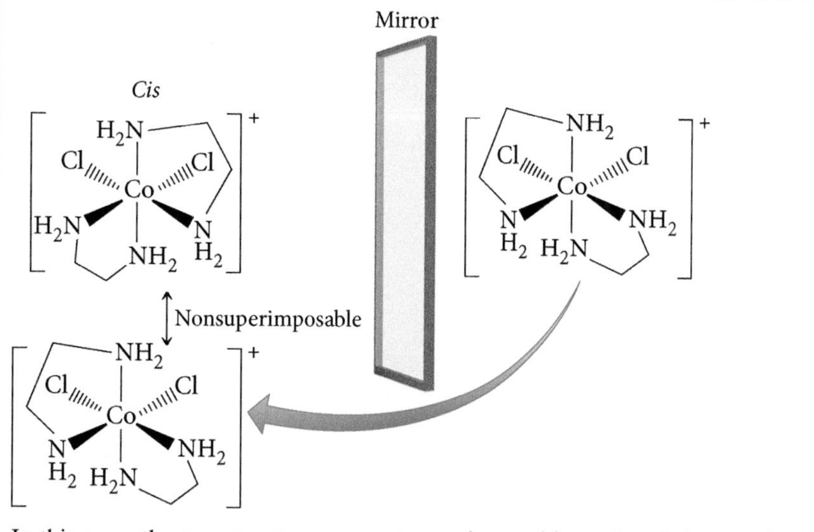

In this case, the two structures are not superimposable so the *cis* isomer does exhibit optical activity.

FOR PRACTICE 25.5

Determine whether the *fac* or *mer* isomers of $[Cr(H_2O)_3Cl_3]^+$ are optically active.

The previous examples demonstrate optical isomerism in octahedral complexes. Tetrahedral complexes can also exhibit chirality, but only if all four coordination sites are occupied by different ligands, just like in organic compounds (Section 20.7). Square planar complexes do not normally exhibit optical isomerism as they are superimposable on their mirror images.

25.5 Bonding in Coordination Compounds

Ligand Field Theory

Valence bond theory, while useful for describing the geometries of the complex ions, cannot explain other properties such as colour and magnetism. Ligand field theory (LFT), a bonding model for transition metal complexes, accounts for the properties of colour and magnetism observed in these compounds. To illustrate the basic principles of LFT, we examine the central metal atom's *d* orbitals in an octahedral complex.

Octahedral Complexes

The basic premise of LFT is that complex ions form because of attractions between the electrons on the ligands and the positive charge on the metal ion. However, the electrons on the ligands also repel the electrons in the *unhybridized* metal *d* orbitals. LFT focuses on these repulsions. Figure 25.8 ▼ shows how the ligand positions superimpose on the *d* orbitals in an octahedral complex. Notice that the ligands in an octahedral complex are located in the same space as the lobes of the $d_{x^2-y^2}$ and d_{z^2} orbitals. The repulsions between electron pairs in the ligands and any potential electrons in the *d* orbitals result in an increase in the energies of these orbitals. In contrast, the d_{xy}, d_{xz}, and d_{yz} orbitals lie *between* the axes and have nodes directly on the axes, which results in less repulsion and lower energies for these three orbitals. In other words, the *d* orbitals—which are degenerate in the bare metal ion—are split into higher and lower energy levels because of the spatial arrangement of the ligands (as shown in Figure 25.9 ▼). The difference in energy between these split *d* orbitals is known as the crystal field splitting energy (Δ). The magnitude of the splitting depends on the particular complex. In **strong-field complexes**, the splitting is large; in **weak-field complexes**, the splitting is small.

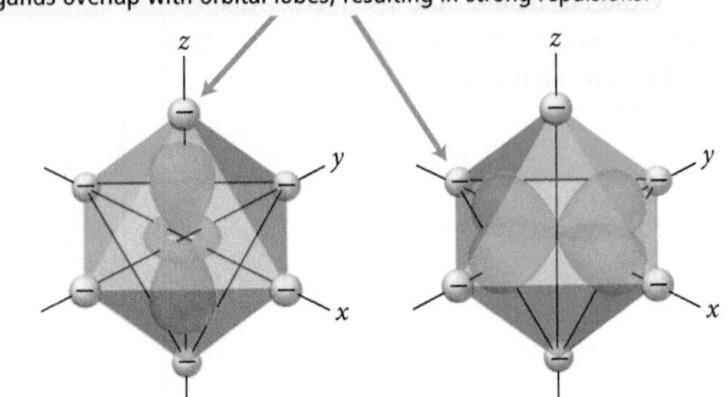

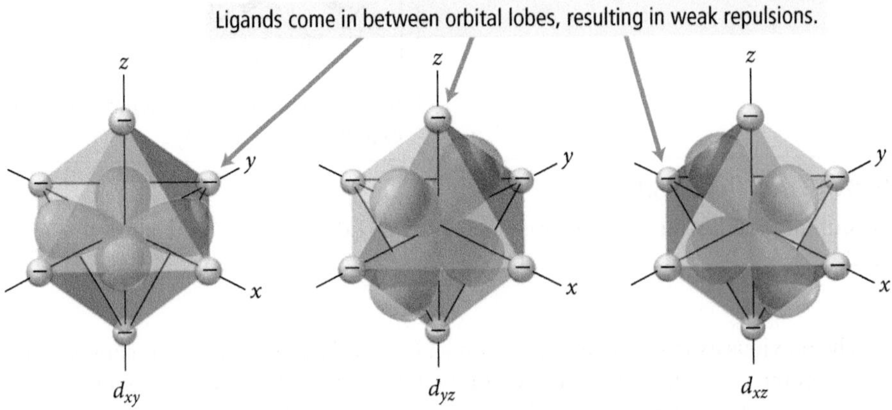

▶ **FIGURE 25.8 Relative Positions of *d* Orbitals and Ligands in an Octahedral Complex** The ligands in an octahedral complex (represented here as spheres of negative charge) interact most strongly with the d_{z^2} and $d_{x^2-y^2}$ orbitals.

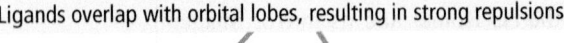

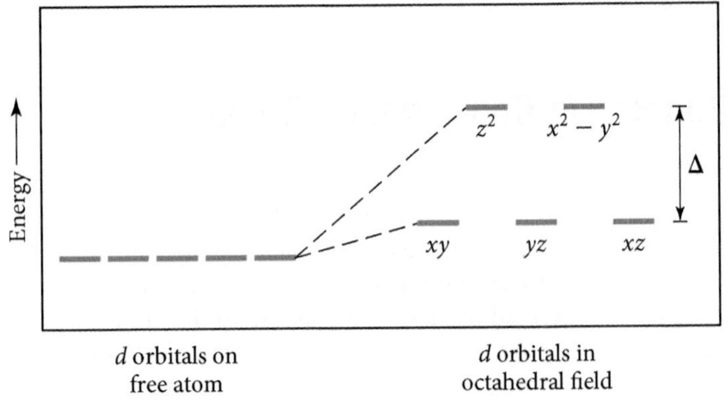

▶ **FIGURE 25.9 *d* Orbital Splitting in an Octahedral Field** The otherwise degenerate *d* orbitals are split into two energy levels by the ligands in an octahedral complex ion.

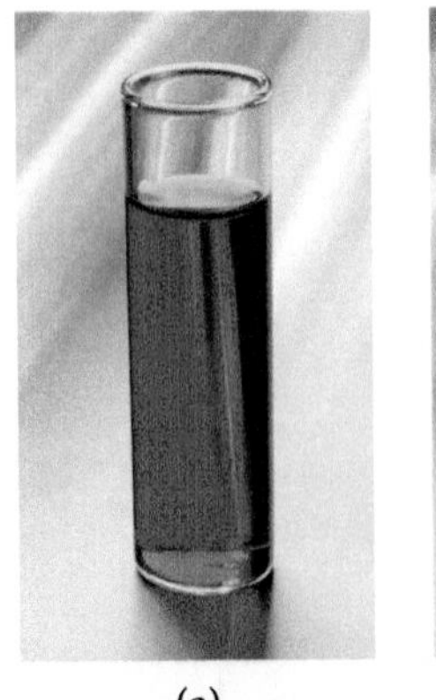

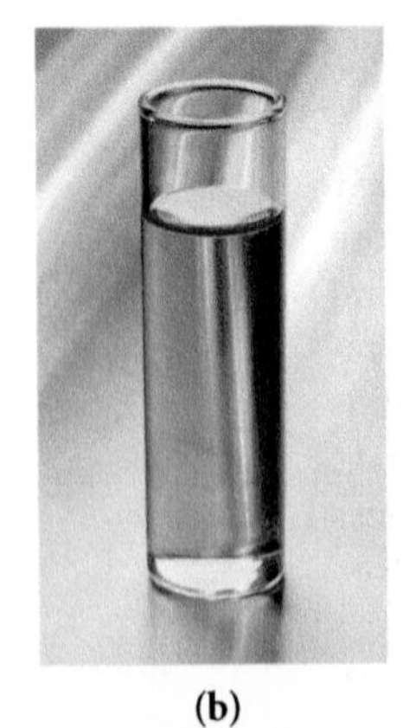

(a) (b)

▲ **FIGURE 25.10 Colours of Complex Ions** (**a**) The complex ion $[Fe(CN)_6]^{3-}$ forms a deep red solution, and (**b**) $[Ni(NH_3)_6]^{2+}$ is blue.

The Colour of Complex Ions and Ligand Field Strength

We saw in the opening section of this chapter that transition metals in host crystals often show brilliant colours because of the ligand field splitting of their *d* orbitals. Solutions of complex ions display brilliant colours because of similar splittings. For example, an $[Fe(CN)_6]^{3-}$ solution is deep red, and an $[Ni(NH_3)_6]^{2+}$ solution is blue (see Figure 25.10 ◀). Recall from Section 7.2 that the colour of an object is related to the absorption of light energy by its electrons. If a substance absorbs all of the visible wavelengths, it appears black. If it transmits (or reflects) all the wavelengths (absorbs no light), it appears colourless. A substance appears to be a particular colour if it absorbs some visible light but also transmits (or reflects) the wavelengths associated with that colour. A substance also appears to be a given colour if it transmits (or reflects) most wavelengths but absorbs the *complementary colour* on a colour wheel (Figure 25.11 ▶). For example, a substance that absorbs green light (the complement of red) will appear red. A solution of $[Ti(H_2O)_6]^{3+}$ is purple because it absorbs strongly between 490 and 580 nm, the yellow-green region of the visible spectrum.

The easiest way to measure the energy difference between the *d* orbitals in a complex ion is to use spectroscopy to determine the wavelength of light absorbed when an electron makes a transition from the lower energy *d* orbitals to the higher energy ones. With that information we can calculate the ligand field splitting energy, Δ:

$$E_{photon} = h\nu = \frac{hc}{\lambda} = \Delta$$

Consider the $[Ti(H_2O)_6]^{3+}$ absorption spectrum shown in Figure 25.12 ▼. The maximum absorbance is at 498 nm. Using this wavelength, we calculate Δ:

$$\begin{aligned}\Delta &= hc/\lambda \\ &= (6.626 \times 10^{-34}\ \text{J} \cdot \cancel{\text{s}})(3.00 \times 10^{8}\ \cancel{\text{m}}\ \cancel{\text{s}^{-1}})/ \\ &\quad (498\ \cancel{\text{nm}} \times 1 \times 10^{-9}\ \cancel{\text{m}}\ \cancel{\text{nm}^{-1}}) \\ \Delta &= 3.99 \times 10^{-19}\ \text{J}\end{aligned}$$

This energy corresponds to a single $[Ti(H_2O)_6]^{3+}$ ion. We can convert to kilojoules per mole:

$$\begin{aligned}\Delta &= (3.99 \times 10^{-19}\ \cancel{\text{J}}\ \cancel{\text{ion}^{-1}})(6.02 \times 10^{23}\ \cancel{\text{ion}}\ \text{mol}^{-1})(1\ \text{kJ}/1000\ \cancel{\text{J}}) \\ &= 240\ \text{kJ mol}^{-1}\end{aligned}$$

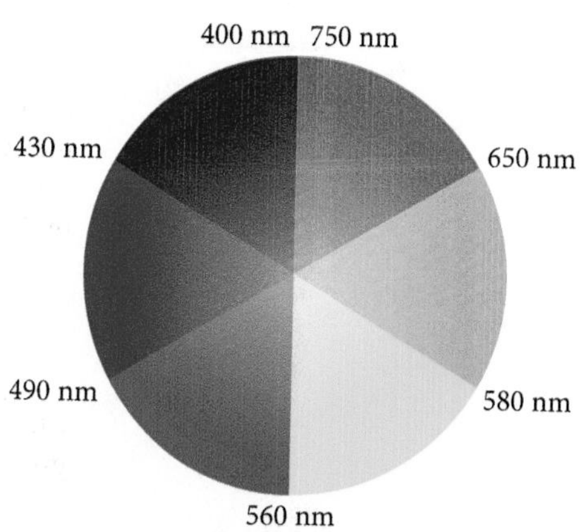

▲ **FIGURE 25.11 The Colour Wheel** Colours across from one another on the colour wheel are said to be complementary. A substance that absorbs a colour on the wheel will appear to be its complementary colour.

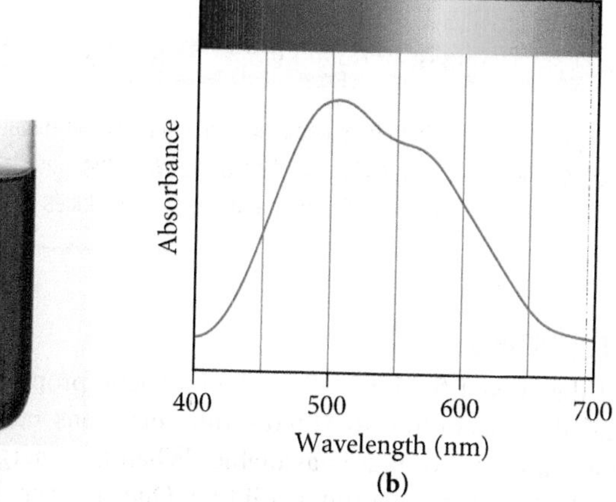

◀ **FIGURE 25.12 The Colour and Absorption Spectrum of $[Ti(H_2O)_6]^{3+}$** **(a)** A solution containing $[Ti(H_2O)_6]^{3+}$ is purple. **(b)** The absorption spectrum of $[Ti(H_2O)_6]^{3+}$ extends across the green-yellow region of the spectrum.

EXAMPLE 25.6 **CALCULATING CRYSTAL FIELD SPLITTING ENERGY**

The complex ion $[Cu(NH_3)_6]^{2+}$ is blue in aqueous solution. Estimate the crystal field splitting energy (in kJ mol^{-1}) for this ion.

SOLUTION

Begin by consulting the colour wheel to determine approximately what wavelength is being absorbed.	Since the solution is blue, we can deduce that orange light is absorbed since orange is the complementary colour to blue.
Estimate the absorbed wavelength.	The colour orange ranges from 580 to 650 nm, so we estimate the average wavelength as 615 nm.
Calculate the energy corresponding to this wavelength, using $E = hc/\lambda$. This energy corresponds to Δ.	$E = \frac{(6.626 \times 10^{-34}\ \text{J} \cdot \cancel{\text{s}})(3.00 \times 10^{8}\ \cancel{\text{m}}\ \cancel{\text{s}^{-1}})}{(615\ \cancel{\text{nm}})(1 \times 10^{-9}\ \cancel{\text{m}}\ \cancel{\text{nm}^{-1}})}$ $E = 3.23 \times 10^{-19}\ \text{J} = \Delta$
Convert J ion^{-1} into kJ mol^{-1}.	$\Delta = \frac{(3.23 \times 10^{-19}\ \cancel{\text{J}}\ \cancel{\text{ion}^{-1}})(6.02 \times 10^{23}\ \cancel{\text{ion}}\ \text{mol}^{-1})}{(1000\ \cancel{\text{J}}\ \text{kJ})}$ $\Delta = 195\ \text{kJ mol}^{-1}$

FOR PRACTICE 25.6

The complex ion $[Co(NH_3)_5NO_2]^{2+}$ is yellow. Estimate the crystal field splitting energy (in kJ mol^{-1}) for this ion.

The magnitude of the crystal field splitting in a complex ion—and, therefore whether it is a strong-field or a weak-field complex—depends in large part on the ligands attached to the central metal ion. Spectroscopic studies of various ligands attached to the same metal allow us to arrange different ligands in order of their ability to split the *d* orbitals. This list is known as the *spectrochemical series* and is arranged from ligands that result in the largest Δ to those that result in the smallest:

$$CN^- > NO_2^- > en > NH_3 > H_2O > OH^- > F^- > Cl^- > Br^- > I^-$$

large Δ — small Δ

typically strong-field ligands — typically weak-field ligands

Ligands that produce large values of Δ are known as *strong-field ligands* and those that give small values of Δ are known as *weak-field ligands*.

The metal ion also has an effect on the magnitude of Δ. If we examine different metal ions with the same ligand, we find that Δ increases as the charge on the metal ion increases. The greater charge on the metal draws the ligands closer, causing greater repulsion with the *d* orbitals and therefore a larger Δ. An example of this behaviour occurs in the complex ions between NH_3 (a ligand in the middle of the spectrochemical series) and the +2 or +3 oxidation states of Co. Hexaamminecobalt(II) ion, $[Co(NH_3)_6]^{2+}$, has a weak crystal field (small Δ) and hexaamminecobalt(III) ion, $[Co(NH_3)_6]^{3+}$, has a strong field (large Δ).

CONCEPTUAL CONNECTION 25.1

Weak- and Strong-Field Ligands

Two ligands, A and B, both form complexes with a particular metal ion. When the metal ion complexes with ligand A, the resulting solution is red. When the metal ion complexes with ligand B, the resulting solution is yellow. Which of the two ligands produces the larger Δ?

Magnetic Properties

Recall from Section 7.7 that a paramagnetic species contains unpaired electrons and a diamagnetic one does not.

The strength of the crystal field can affect the magnetic properties of a transition metal complex. Recall that, according to Hund's rule, electrons occupy degenerate orbitals singly as long as an empty orbital is available. When the energies of the *d* orbitals are split by ligands, the lower energy orbitals fill first. Once they are half-filled, the next electron can either (1) pair with an electron in one of the lower energy half-filled orbitals by overcoming the electron–electron repulsion associated with having two electrons in the same orbital, or (2) go into an empty orbital of higher energy by overcoming the energy difference between the orbitals—in this case, the crystal field splitting energy, Δ. The magnitude of Δ compared to the electron–electron repulsions determines which of these two actually occurs.

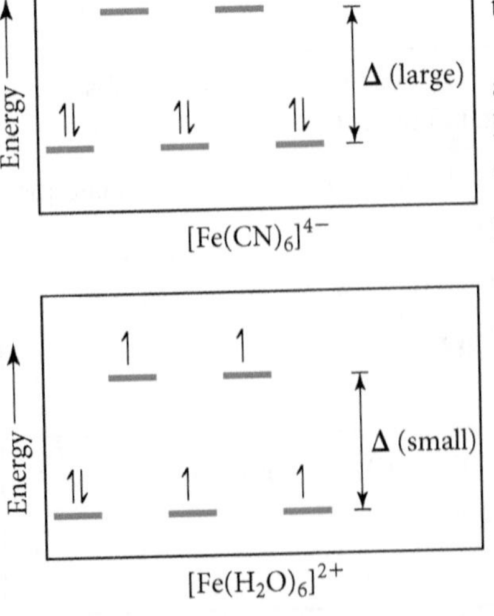

Let's compare two iron(II) complexes to see the difference in behaviour under strong- and weak-field conditions. $[Fe(CN)_6]^{4-}$ is known to be diamagnetic and $[Fe(H_2O)_6]^{2+}$ is known to be paramagnetic. Both of these complexes contain Fe^{2+}, which has an electron configuration of [Ar] $3d^6$. In the case of $[Fe(CN)_6]^{4-}$, CN^- is a strong-field ligand that generates a large Δ, so it takes more energy to occupy the higher energy level than it does to pair the electrons in the lower energy level. The result is that all six electrons are paired and the compound is diamagnetic, as shown at left.

In $[Fe(H_2O)_6]^{2+}$, H_2O is a weak-field ligand that generates a small Δ, so the electron pairing energy is greater than Δ. Consequently, the first five electrons occupy the five *d* orbitals singly and only the sixth pairs up, resulting in a paramagnetic compound with four unpaired electrons, as shown at left.

In general, complexes with strong-field ligands have fewer unpaired electrons relative to the free metal ion, and are therefore called **low-spin complexes**. Complexes with weak-field ligands, by contrast, have the same number of unpaired electrons as the free metal ion and are called **high-spin complexes**.

When we examine the orbital diagrams of the d^1 through d^{10} metal ions in octahedral complexes, we find that only d^4, d^5, d^6, and d^7 metal ions have low- and high-spin possibilities. Since there are three lower energy *d* orbitals, the d^1, d^2, and d^3 metal ions always have unpaired electrons, independent of Δ. In the d^8, d^9, and d^{10} metal ions, the three lower energy orbitals are completely filled, so the remaining electrons fill the two higher orbitals (as expected by Hund's rule), also independent of Δ.

PROCEDURE FOR... **Determining the Number of Unpaired Electrons in Octahedral Complexes**	EXAMPLE 25.7 **High- and Low-Spin Octahedral Complexes** How many unpaired electrons are there in the complex ion $[CoF_6]^{3-}$?	EXAMPLE 25.8 **High- and Low-Spin Octahedral Complexes** How many unpaired electrons are there in the complex ion $[Co(NH_3)_5NO_2]^{2+}$?
Begin by determining the charge and number of *d* electrons of the metal.	**SOLUTION** The metal is Co^{3+} and has a d^6 electronic configuration.	**SOLUTION** The metal is Co^{3+} and has a d^6 electronic configuration.
Look at the spectrochemical series to determine whether the ligand is a strong-field or a weak-field ligand.	F^- is a weak-field ligand, so Δ is relatively small.	NH_3 and NO_2^- are both strong-field ligands, so Δ is relatively large.
Decide if the complex is high- or low-spin and draw the electron configuration.	Weak-field ligands yield high-spin configurations. Energy; Δ (small)	Strong-field ligands yield low-spin configurations. Energy; Δ (large)
Count the unpaired electrons.	This configuration has four unpaired electrons.	This configuration has no unpaired electrons.
	FOR PRACTICE 25.7 How many unpaired electrons are there in the complex ion $[FeCl_6]^{3-}$?	**FOR PRACTICE 25.8** How many unpaired electrons are there in the complex ion $[Co(CN)_6]^{4-}$?

Tetrahedral and Square Planar Complexes

So far, we have examined the *d* orbital energy changes only for octahedral complexes, but transition metal complexes can have other geometries, such as tetrahedral and square planar. We use crystal field theory to determine the *d* orbital splitting pattern for these geometries as well. For a tetrahedral complex, the *d* orbital splitting pattern is the opposite of the octahedral splitting pattern: three *d* orbitals (d_{xy}, d_{xz}, and d_{yz}) are higher in energy and two *d* orbitals ($d_{x^2-y^2}$ and d_{z^2}) are lower in energy, as shown in Figure 25.13 ▼. Almost all

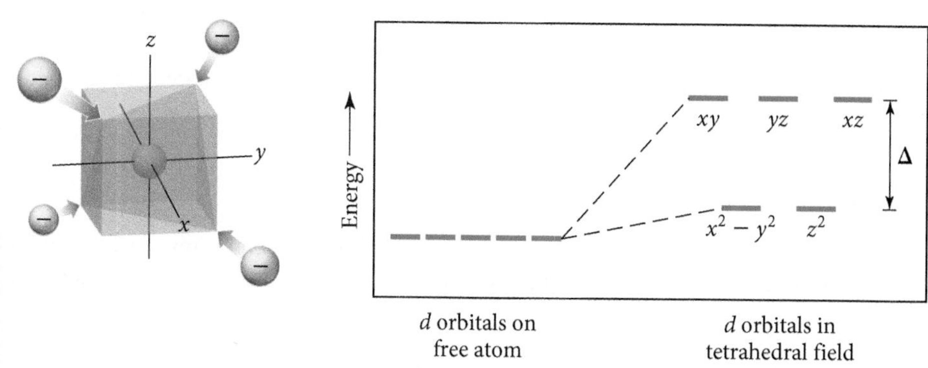

◀ **FIGURE 25.13 Splitting of *d* Orbitals by a Tetrahedral Ligand Geometry** In tetrahedral complexes, the splitting of the *d* orbitals has a pattern that is the opposite of the octahedral splitting pattern. The d_{xy}, d_{yz}, and d_{xz} orbitals are higher in energy than the d_{z^2} and $d_{x^2-y^2}$ orbitals.

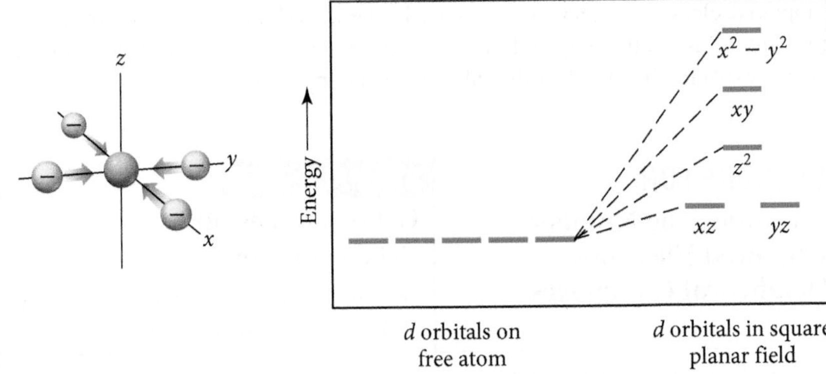

▶ **FIGURE 25.14 Splitting of *d* Orbitals by a Square Planar Ligand Geometry** Square planar complexes produce the *d* orbital energy pattern shown here.

tetrahedral complexes are high-spin because of reduced ligand–metal interactions. The *d* orbitals in a tetrahedral complex interact with only four ligands, as opposed to six in the octahedral complex, so the value of Δ is generally smaller.

A square planar complex gives us the most complex splitting pattern of the three geometries, as shown in Figure 25.14 ▲. As we discussed previously, square planar complexes occur in d^8 metal ions, such as Pt^{2+}, Pd^{2+}, Ir^+, or Au^{3+}, and in nearly all cases they are low-spin.

25.6 Applications of Coordination Compounds

Coordination compounds are commonly found in living systems, in industry, and even in household products. In Chapter 24, we saw how both silver and gold metals are extracted from their respective ores using cyanide complexes and how nickel metal is extracted by forming the gaseous carbonyl complex, $Ni(CO)_4$. In this section, we describe a few other applications of coordination compounds.

Chelating Agents

Earlier in this chapter, we saw the chelating agent ethylenediaminetetraacetate ion ($EDTA^{4-}$). This ligand has lone pairs on six different donor atoms that can interact with a metal ion to form very stable metal complexes. EDTA is used to treat the victims of heavy metal poisoning such as lead poisoning. The patient is given $[Ca(EDTA)]^{2-}$ and since the lead complex ($K_f = 2 \times 10^{18}$) is more stable than the calcium complex ($K_f = 4 \times 10^{10}$), the lead displaces the calcium. The body excretes the lead complex and leaves behind the calcium, which is nontoxic (and is, in fact, a nutrient).

Chemical Analysis

Some ligands are selective in their binding, preferring specific metal ions, so they can be used in chemical analysis. For example, dimethylglyoxime is used to chemically analyze a sample for Ni^{2+} or Pd^{2+}. In the presence of Ni^{2+}, an insoluble red precipitate forms, and in the presence of Pd^{2+}, an insoluble yellow precipitate forms. Another ligand used in chemical analysis is the SCN^- ligand, which is used to test for Co^{2+} or Fe^{3+}. In the presence of Co^{2+} a blue solution forms, and in the presence of Fe^{3+} a deep red solution forms (Figure 25.15 ◀).

(a) (b)

▲ **FIGURE 25.15 Chemical Analysis with SCN^-** (a) Blue indicates Co^{2+}. (b) Red indicates Fe^{3+}.

Colouring Agents

Because of the wide variety of colours found in coordination complexes, they are often used as colouring agents. For example, a commercially available agent, iron blue, is a mixture of the hexacyano complexes of iron(II) and iron(III). Iron blue is used in ink, paint, cosmetics (eye shadow), and blueprints.

Biomolecules

Living systems contain many molecules based on metal complexes. Hemoglobin (involved in oxygen transport), cytochrome c (involved in electron transport), carbonic anhydrase (involved in respiration), and chlorophyll (involved in photosynthesis) all have coordinated metal ions that are critical to their structure and function. Table 25.7 summarizes the biological significance of many of the first-row transition metals.

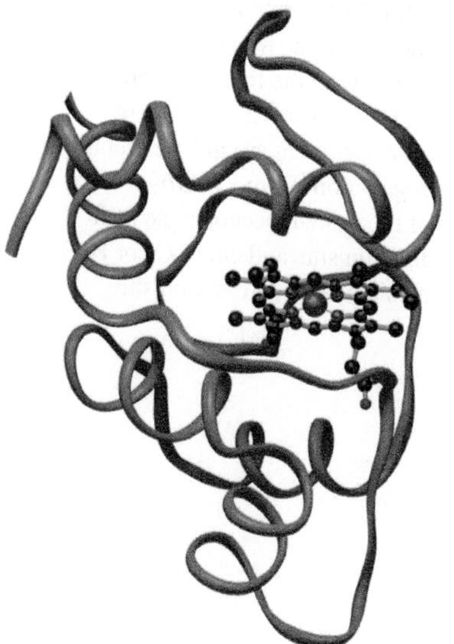

Cytochrome c

TABLE 25.7 Transition Metals and Some of Their Functions in the Human Body

Transition Metal	Biological Function
Chromium	Works with insulin to control utilization of glucose
Manganese	Fat and carbohydrate synthesis
Molybdenum	Involved in hemoglobin synthesis
Iron	Oxygen transport
Copper	Involved in hemoglobin synthesis
Zinc	Involved in cell reproduction and tissue growth; part of more than 70 enzymes; assists in the utilization of carbohydrate, protein, and fat

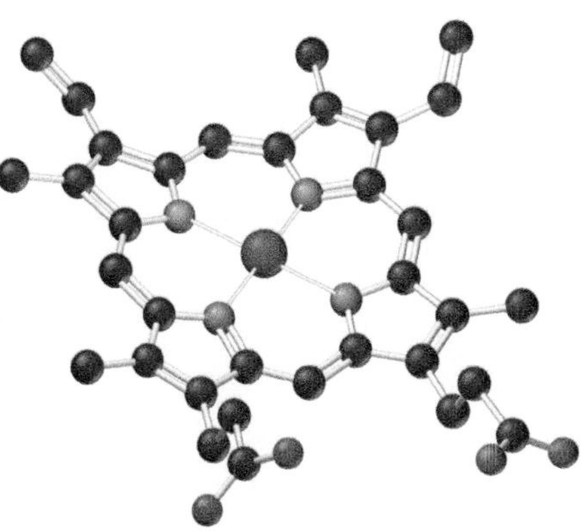

Heme (H atoms omitted for clarity)

Hemoglobin and Cytochrome c In hemoglobin and in cytochrome c, an iron complex called a heme is connected to a protein, as shown here. A heme is an iron ion coordinated to a flat, polydentate ligand called a porphyrin (Figure 25.16 ▼). The porphyrin ligand has a planar ring structure with four nitrogen atoms that can coordinate to the metal ion. Different porphyrins have different substituent groups connected around the outside of the ring.

In hemoglobin, the iron complex is octahedral, with the four nitrogen atoms of the porphyrin in a square planar arrangement around the metal. A nitrogen atom from a nearby amino acid of the protein occupies the fifth coordination site, and either O_2 or H_2O occupies the last coordination site (Figure 25.17 ▼). In the lungs, where the

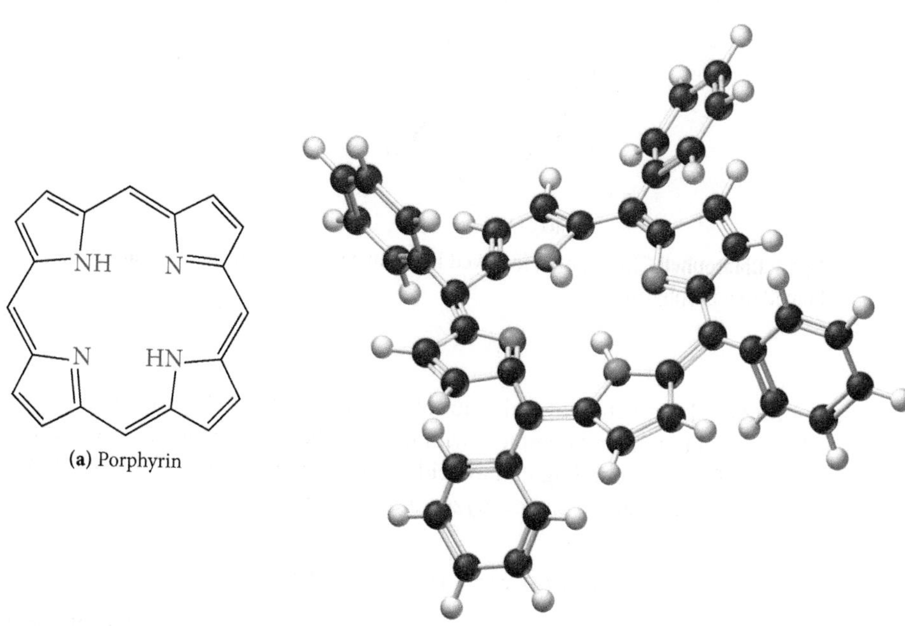

(a) Porphyrin

(b) Tetraphenylporphyrin

◀ **FIGURE 25.16 Porphyrin Structures** (a) Porphyrin has a planar ring structure. (b) Tetraphenylporphyrin (TPP) has four phenyl groups bonded around the outside of the porphyrin ring.

▶ FIGURE 25.17 Hemoglobin
In hemoglobin, the iron complex is octahedral, with the four nitrogen atoms of the porphyrin in a square planar arrangement around the metal. A nitrogen atom from a nearby amino acid of the protein occupies the fifth coordination site, and either O_2 or H_2O occupies the last coordination site.

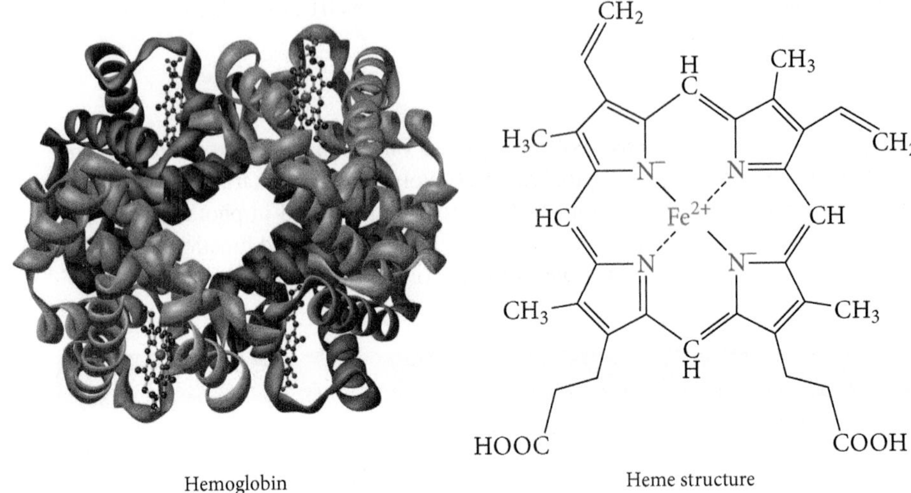

Hemoglobin

Heme structure

Hemoglobin is discussed in Section 14.1.

oxygen content is high, the hemoglobin coordinates to an O_2 molecule. The oxygen-rich hemoglobin is carried by the bloodstream to areas throughout the body that are depleted in oxygen, where oxygen is released and replaced by a water molecule. The hemoglobin then travels back to the lungs to repeat the cycle.

Chlorophyll Chlorophyll, shown in Figure 25.18 ▼, is another porphyrin-based biomolecule, but in chlorophyll the porphyrin is not surrounded by a protein, and the coordinated metal is magnesium (which is a main-group metal, not a transition metal). Chlorophyll is essential for the process of photosynthesis performed by plants, in which light energy from the sun is converted to chemical energy to fuel the plant's growth.

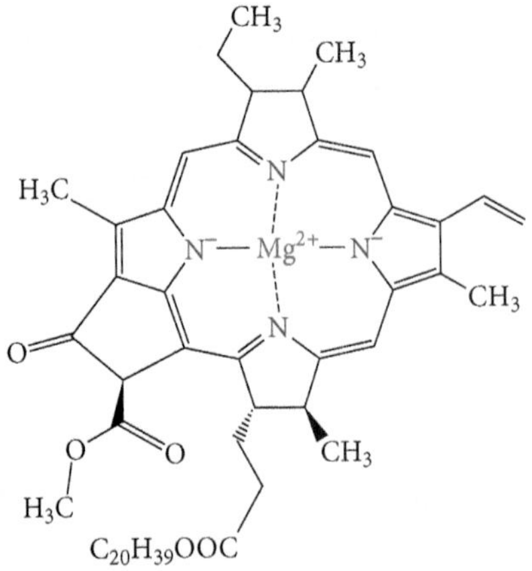

▲ FIGURE 25.18 Chlorophyll Chlorophyll, involved in photosynthesis in plants, contains magnesium coordinated to a porphyrin.

Carbonic Anhydrase The structure of carbonic anhydrase is shown in Figure 25.19 ▶. The zinc ion is bound in a tetrahedral complex, with three of the coordination sites occupied by nitrogen atoms from surrounding amino acids and the fourth site available to bind a water molecule. Carbonic anhydrase catalyzes the reaction between water and CO_2 in respiration:

$$H_2O(l) + CO_2(g) \rightleftharpoons H^+(aq) + HCO_3^-(aq)$$

A water molecule alone is not acidic enough to react with a CO_2 molecule at a sufficient rate. When the water molecule is bound to the zinc ion in carbonic anhydrase, the positive

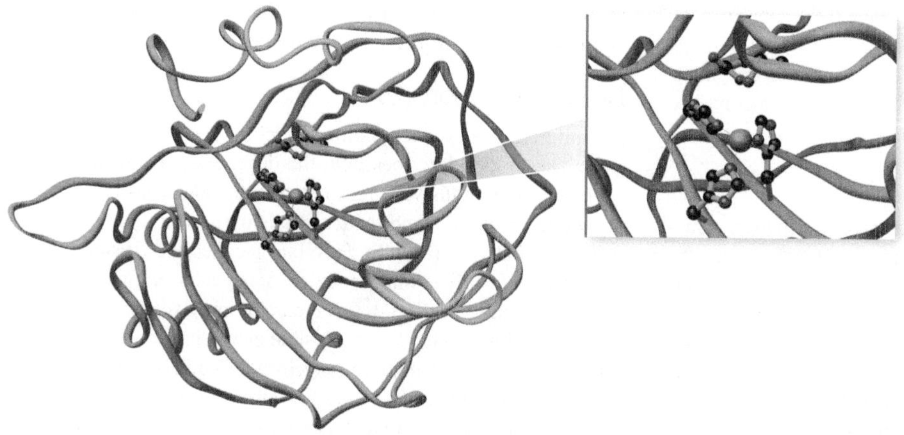

◀ **FIGURE 25.19 Carbonic Anhydrase** Carbonic anhydrase contains a zinc ion that is bound in a tetrahedral complex, with three of the coordination sites occupied by nitrogen atoms from surrounding amino acids and the fourth site available to bind a water molecule.

charge on the metal draws electron density from the O—H bond and the H_2O becomes more acidic—sufficiently so to readily lose a proton. The resulting bound OH^- easily reacts with a CO_2 molecule, and the reaction is much faster than the uncatalyzed version.

Drugs and Therapeutic Agents In the mid-1960s, researchers found that the platinum(II) complex *cis*-$[Pt(NH_3)_2Cl_2]$, known as cisplatin and shown in Figure 25.20 ▶, is an effective anticancer agent. Interestingly, the closely related geometric isomer *trans*-$[Pt(NH_3)_2Cl_2]$ has little or no effect on cancer tumours. Cisplatin is believed to function by attaching itself to the cancer cell's DNA and replacing the Cl^- ligands with donor atoms from the DNA strands. The *cis* arrangement of the Cl^- ligands corresponds to the geometry required to bind to the DNA strands. The *trans* isomer, although closely related, cannot bind properly due to the *trans* arrangement of the Cl^- ligands and is therefore not an effective agent. Cisplatin and other closely related platinum(II) complexes are still used today in chemotherapy for certain types of cancer and are among the most effective anticancer agents available for these cases.

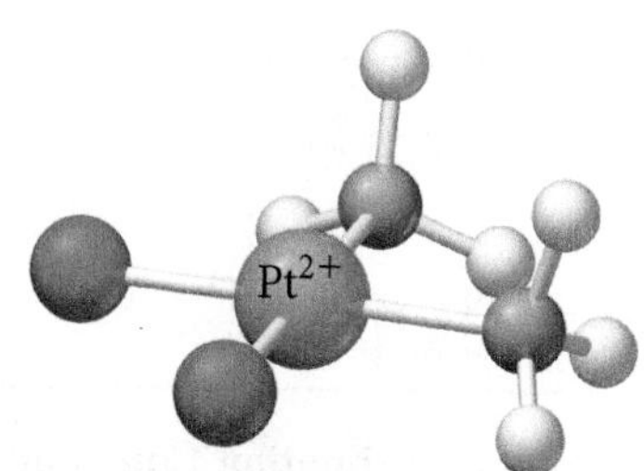

▲ **FIGURE 25.20 Cisplatin** Cisplatin is an effective anticancer agent.

CHAPTER IN REVIEW

Key Terms

Section 25.1
ligand field theory (1046)

Section 25.3
complex ion (1048)
ligand (1048)
coordination compound (1048)
primary valence (1048)
secondary valence (1048)
coordination number (1048)
coordinate covalent bond (dative bond) (1048)
monodentate (1048)
bidentate (1048)
polydentate (1050)
chelate (1050)
chelating agent (1050)

Section 25.4
structural isomer (1053)
stereoisomer (1053)
coordination isomer (1053)
linkage isomer (1053)
enantiomer (1056)

Section 25.5
strong-field complex (1057)
weak-field complex (1057)
low-spin complex (1060)
high-spin complex (1060)

Key Concepts

Electron Configurations (25.2)

As we work across a row of transition elements, we add electrons to the $(n - 1)d$ orbitals, resulting in a general electron configuration for first- and second-row transition elements of [noble gas] $ns^2(n - 1)d^x$ and for the third and fourth rows of [noble gas] $ns^2(n - 2)f^{14}(n - 1)d^x$, where x ranges from 1 to 10. A transition element forms a cation by losing electrons from the ns orbitals before losing electrons from the $(n - 1)d$ orbitals.

Composition and Naming of Coordination Compounds (25.3)

A coordination compound is made up of a complex ion and a counterion. A complex ion contains a central metal ion bound to one or more ligands. The number of ligands directly bound to the metal ion is called the coordination number. The ligand forms a coordinate covalent bond to the metal ion by donating a pair of electrons to an empty orbital on the metal. Ligands that donate a single pair of electrons are monodentate, a ligand that donates two pairs of electrons is bidentate, and a ligand that donates more than two pairs is polydentate. In naming coordination compounds, we use the name of the cation followed by the name of the anion. To name a complex ion we use the guidelines outlined in Section 25.3.

Types of Isomers (25.4)

We broadly divide the isomerism observed in coordination compounds into two categories: structural isomers, in which atoms are connected differently to one another, and stereoisomers, in which atoms are connected in the same way but the ligands have a different spatial arrangement about the metal atom. These broad categories are each further broken down into two groups. Structural isomers are either coordination isomers (a coordinated ligand exchanges places with an uncoordinated counterion) or linkage isomers (a particular ligand has the ability to coordinate to the metal in different ways). In stereoisomers, the ligands bonded to the metal have a different spatial arrangement relative to each other. This gives rise to *cis–trans* isomers, *fac–mer* isomers, and enantiomers.

Ligand Field Theory (25.5)

Ligand field theory is a bonding model for transition metal complex ions. The model describes how the degeneracy of the *d* orbitals is broken by the repulsive forces between the electrons on the ligands around the metal ion and the *d* orbitals in the metal ion. The energy difference between the split *d* orbitals is called the crystal field splitting energy (Δ). The magnitude of Δ depends in large part on the ligands bound to the metal. Octahedral complexes with a d^4, d^5, d^6, or d^7 metal ion can have two possible electronic configurations with different numbers of unpaired electrons. The first, called high-spin, has the same number of unpaired electrons as the free metal ion and is usually the result of a weak crystal field. The second, called low-spin, has fewer unpaired electrons than the free metal ion and is usually the result of a strong crystal field.

Key Equations and Relationships

Crystal Field Splitting Energy (25.5)

$\Delta = hc/\lambda$ (where λ is the wavelength of maximum absorption)

Key Skills

Naming Coordination Compounds (25.3)
• Examples 25.1, 25.2 • For Practice 25.1, 25.2 • Exercises 21–26

Identifying and Drawing Stereoisomers (25.4)
• Examples 25.3, 25.4 • For Practice 25.3, 25.4 • Exercises 33–38, 59, 60

Recognizing and Drawing Enantiomers (25.4)
• Example 25.5 • For Practice 25.5 • Exercises 37, 38, 59, 60

Calculating Crystal Field Splitting Energy (25.5)
• Example 25.6 • For Practice 25.6 • Exercises 41–44

Recognizing and Predicting High-Spin and Low-Spin Octahedral Complex Ions (25.5)
• Examples 25.7, 25.8 • For Practice 25.7, 25.8 • Exercises 47–50, 63

EXERCISES

Review Questions

1. When a transition metal atom forms an ion, which electrons are lost first?

2. Explain why transition metals exhibit multiple oxidation states instead of a single oxidation state (like most of the main-group metals).

3. Why is the +2 oxidation state so common for transition metals?

4. Briefly define each term:
- **a.** coordination number
- **b.** ligand
- **c.** bidentate and polydentate
- **d.** complex ion
- **e.** chelating agent

5. Using the Lewis acid–base definition, how would you categorize a ligand? How would you categorize a transition metal ion?

6. Explain the differences between each pair of isomer types:
- **a.** structural isomer and stereoisomer
- **b.** linkage isomer and coordination isomer
- **c.** *cis–trans* isomer and *fac–mer* isomer

7. Which complex ion geometry has the potential to exhibit *cis–trans* isomerism: linear, tetrahedral, square planar, octahedral?

8. How can you tell whether a complex ion is optically active?

9. Explain the differences between weak-field and strong-field metal complexes.

10. Explain why compounds of Sc^{3+} are colourless, but compounds of Ti^{3+} are coloured.

11. Explain why compounds of Zn^{2+} are white, but compounds of Cu^{2+} are often blue or green.

12. Explain the differences between high-spin and low-spin metal complexes.

13. Why are almost all tetrahedral complexes high-spin?

14. Many transition metal compounds are coloured. How does ligand field theory account for this?

Problems by Topic

Properties of Transition Metals

15. Write the ground state electron configuration for each atom or ion:
a. Ni, Ni^{2+} b. Mn, Mn^{4+} c. Y, Y^{+} d. Ta, Ta^{2+}

16. Write the ground state electron configuration for each atom or ion:
a. Zr, Zr^{2+} b. Co, Co^{2+} c. Tc, Tc^{3+} d. Os, Os^{4+}

17. Determine the highest possible oxidation state for each element:
a. V b. Re c. Pd

18. Which first-row transition metal(s) has the following highest possible oxidation state?
a. +3 b. +7 c. +4

Coordination Compounds

19. Determine the oxidation state and coordination number of the metal ion in each complex ion:
a. $[Cr(H_2O)_6]^{3+}$
b. $[Co(NH_3)_3Cl_3]^{-}$
c. $[Cu(CN)_4]^{2-}$
d. $[Ag(NH_3)_2]^{+}$

20. Determine the oxidation state and coordination number of the metal ion in each complex ion:
a. $[Co(NH_3)_5Br]^{2+}$
b. $[Fe(CN)_6]^{4-}$
c. $[Co(ox)_3]^{4-}$
d. $[PdCl_4]^{2-}$

21. Name each complex ion or coordination compound:
a. $[Cr(H_2O)_6]^{3+}$
b. $[Cu(CN)_4]^{2-}$
c. $[Fe(NH_3)_5Br]SO_4$
d. $[Co(H_2O)_4(NH_3)(OH)]Cl_2$

22. Name each complex ion or coordination compound:
a. $[Cu(en)_2]^{2+}$
b. $[Mn(CO)_3(NO_2)_3]^{2+}$
c. $Na[Cr(H_2O)_2(ox)_2]$
d. $[Co(en)_3][Fe(CN)_6]$

23. Write the correct formula for each complex ion or coordination compound:
a. hexaamminechromium(III)
b. potassium hexacyanoferrate(III)
c. ethylenediaminedithiocyanatocopper(II)
d. tetraaquaplatinum(II) hexachloroplatinate(IV)

24. Write the correct formula for each complex ion or coordination compound:
a. hexaaquanickel(II) chloride
b. pentacarbonylchloromanganese(I)
c. ammonium diaquatetrabromovanadate(III)
d. tris(ethylenediamine)cobalt(III) trioxalatoferrate(III)

25. Write the formula and give the name of each complex ion:
a. a complex ion with Co^{3+} as the central ion and three NH_3 molecules and three CN^- ions as ligands
b. a complex ion with Cr^{3+} as the central ion and a coordination number of 6 with ethylenediamine ligands

26. Write the formula and give the name of each complex ion or coordination compound:
a. a complex ion with four water molecules and two ONO^- ions connected to an Fe(III) ion
b. a coordination compound made of two complex ions: one a complex of V(III) with two ethylenediamine molecules and two Cl^- ions as ligands and the other a complex of Ni(II) having a coordination number of 4 with Cl^- ions as ligands

Structure and Isomerism

27. Draw two linkage isomers of $[Mn(NH_3)_5(NO_2)]^{2+}$.

28. Draw two linkage isomers of $[PtCl_3(SCN)]^{2-}$.

29. Write the formulas and names for the coordination isomers of $[Fe(H_2O)_6]Cl_2$.

30. Write the formulas and names for the coordination isomers of $[Co(en)_3][Cr(ox)_3]$.

31. Which complexes exhibit stereoisomerism?
a. $[Cr(NH_3)_5(OH)]^{2+}$
b. $[Cr(en)_2Cl_2]^{+}$
c. $[Cr(H_2O)(NH_3)_3Cl_2]^{+}$
d. $[Pt(NH_3)Cl_3]^{-}$
e. $[Pt(H_2O)_2(CN)_2]$

32. Which complexes exhibit stereoisomerism?
a. $[Co(H_2O)_2(ox)_2]^{-}$
b. $[Co(en)_3]^{3+}$
c. $[Co(H_2O)_2(NH_3)_2(ox)]^{+}$
d. $[Ni(NH_3)_2(en)]^{2+}$
e. $[Ni(CO)_2Cl_2]$

33. If W, X, Y, and Z are different monodentate ligands, how many stereoisomers are there for each ion?
a. square-planar $[NiWXYZ]^{2+}$
b. tetrahedral $[ZnWXYZ]^{2+}$

34. How many stereoisomers are there for each species?
a. $[Fe(CO)_3Cl_3]$ b. $[Mn(CO)_2Cl_2Br_2]^{+}$

35. Draw the structures and label the type for all the isomers of each ion:
a. $[Cr(CO)_3(NH_3)_3]^{3+}$ b. $[Pd(CO)_2(H_2O)Cl]^{+}$

36. Draw the structures and label the type for all the isomers of each species:
a. $[Fe(CO)_4Cl_2]^{+}$ b. $[Pt(en)Cl_2]$

37. Determine if either isomer of $[Cr(NH_3)_2(ox)_2]^{-}$ is optically active.

38. Determine if either isomer of $[Fe(CO)_3Cl_3]$ is optically active.

Bonding in Coordination Compounds

39. Draw the octahedral crystal field splitting diagram for each metal ion:
a. Zn^{2+}
b. Fe^{3+} (high- and low-spin)
c. V^{3+}
d. Co^{2+} (high-spin)

40. Draw the octahedral crystal field splitting diagram for each metal ion:
a. Cr^{3+}
b. Cu^{2+}
c. Mn^{3+} (high- and low-spin)
d. Fe^{2+} (low-spin)

41. The $[CrCl_6]^{3-}$ ion has a maximum in its absorption spectrum at 735 nm. Calculate the crystal field splitting energy (in kJ mol^{-1}) for this ion.

42. The absorption spectrum of the complex ion $[Rh(NH_3)_6]^{3+}$ has maximum absorbance at 295 nm. Calculate the crystal field splitting energy (in kJ mol^{-1}) for this ion.

43. Three complex ions of cobalt(III), $[Co(CN)_6]^{3-}$, $[Co(NH_3)_6]^{3+}$, and $[CoF_6]^{3-}$, absorb light at wavelengths of (in no particular order) 290 nm, 440 nm, and 770 nm. Match each complex ion to the appropriate wavelength absorbed. What colour would you expect each solution to be?

44. Three bottles of aqueous solutions are discovered in an abandoned lab. The solutions are green, yellow, and purple. It is known that three complex ions of chromium(III) were commonly used in that lab: $[Cr(H_2O)_6]^{3+}$, $[Cr(NH_3)_6]^{3+}$, and $[Cr(H_2O)_4Cl_2]^+$. Determine the likely identity of each of the solutions.

45. The $[Mn(NH_3)_6]^{2+}$ ion is paramagnetic with five unpaired electrons. The NH_3 ligand is usually a strong field ligand. Is NH_3 acting as a strong field ligand in this case?

46. The complex $[Fe(H_2O)_6]^{2+}$ is paramagnetic. Is the H_2O ligand inducing a strong or weak field?

47. How many unpaired electrons would you expect for each complex ion?
a. $[RhCl_6]^{3-}$
b. $[Co(OH)_6]^{4-}$
c. *cis*-$[Fe(en)_2(NO_2)_2]^+$

48. How many unpaired electrons would you expect for each complex ion?
a. $[Cr(CN)_6]^{4-}$
b. $[MnF_6]^{4-}$
c. $[Ru(en)_3]^{2+}$

49. How many unpaired electrons would you expect for the complex ion $[CoCl_4]^{2-}$ if it is a tetrahedral shape?

50. The complex ion $[PdCl_4]^{2-}$ is known to be diamagnetic. Use this information to determine if it is a tetrahedral or square planar structure.

Applications of Coordination Compounds

51. What structural feature do hemoglobin, cytochrome c, and chlorophyll have in common?

52. Identify the central metal atom in each complex:
a. hemoglobin
b. carbonic anhydrase
c. chlorophyll
d. iron blue

53. Hemoglobin in our bodies exists in two predominant forms. One form, known as oxyhemoglobin, has O_2 bound to the iron and the other, known as deoxyhemoglobin, has a water molecule bound instead. Oxyhemoglobin is a low-spin complex that gives arterial blood its red colour, and deoxyhemoglobin is a high-spin complex that gives venous blood its darker colour. Explain these observations in terms of crystal field splitting. Would you categorize O_2 as a strong- or weak-field ligand?

54. Carbon monoxide and the cyanide ion are both toxic because they bind more strongly than oxygen to the iron in hemoglobin (Hb).

$$Hb + O_2 \rightleftharpoons HbO_2 \quad K_1 = 2 \times 10^{12}$$
$$Hb + CO \rightleftharpoons HbCO \quad K_2 = 1 \times 10^{14}$$

Calculate the equilibrium constant value for the reaction:

$$HbO_2 + CO \rightleftharpoons HbCO + O_2$$

Does the equilibrium favour reactants or products?

Cumulative Problems

55. In Chapter 7, we learned that Cr and Cu were exceptions to the normal orbital filling, resulting in a [Ar] $4s^13d^x$ configuration. Write the ground state electron configuration for each species:
a. Cr, Cr^+, Cr^{2+}, Cr^{3+}
b. Cu, Cu^+, Cu^{2+}

56. Most of the second row transition metals do not follow the normal orbital filling pattern. Five of them—Nb, Mo, Ru, Rh, and Ag—have a [Kr] $5s^14d^x$ configuration and Pd has a [Kr] $4d^{10}$ configuration. Write the ground state electron configuration for each species:
a. Mo, Mo^+, Ag, Ag^+
b. Ru, Ru^{3+}
c. Rh, Rh^{2+}
d. Pd, Pd^+, Pd^{2+}

57. Draw the Lewis diagrams for each ligand. Indicate the lone pair(s) that may be donated to the metal. Indicate any you expect to be bidentate or polydentate.
a. NH_3
b. SCN^-
c. H_2O

58. Draw the Lewis diagrams for each ligand. Indicate the lone pair(s) that may be donated to the metal. Indicate any you expect to be bidentate or polydentate.
a. CN^-
b. bipyridyl (bipy), which has the following structure:

N N

c. NO_2^-

59. List all the different formulas for an octahedral complex made from a metal (M) and three different ligands (A, B, and C). Describe any isomers for each complex.

60. Amino acids, such as glycine (gly), form complexes with the trace metal ions found in the bloodstream. Glycine, whose structure is shown below, acts as a bidentate ligand coordinating with the nitrogen atom and one of the oxygen atoms.

$$H_2N-\overset{H}{\underset{H}{\overset{|}{\underset{|}{C}}}}-\overset{O}{\overset{\|}{C}}-OH$$

Draw all the possible isomers of
a. square planar $[Ni(gly)_2]$
b. tetrahedral $[Zn(gly)_2]$
c. octahedral $[Fe(gly)_3]$

61. Oxalic acid solutions remove rust stains. Draw a complex ion that is likely responsible for this effect. Does it have any isomers?

62. W, X, Y, and Z are different monodentate ligands.
a. Will the square planar $[NiWXYZ]^{2+}$ be optically active?
b. Will the tetrahedral $[ZnWXYZ]^{2+}$ be optically active?

63. Hexacyanomanganate(III) ion is a low-spin complex. Draw the crystal field splitting diagram with electrons filled in appropriately. Is this complex paramagnetic or diamagnetic?

64. Determine the colour and approximate wavelength absorbed most strongly by each solution.
   a. blue solution
   b. red solution
   c. yellow solution

65. Draw the structures of all the stereoisomers of $[Ru(H_2O)_2(NH_3)_2Cl_2]^+$. Draw the mirror images of any that are chiral.

66. A 0.32 mol amount of NH_3 is dissolved in 0.47 L of a 0.38 mol L^{-1} silver nitrate solution. Calculate the equilibrium concentrations of all species in the solution.

Challenge Problems

67. When a solution of $PtCl_2$ reacts with the ligand trimethylphosphine, $P(CH_3)_3$, two compounds are produced. The compounds share the same elemental analysis: 46.7% Pt; 17.0% Cl; 14.8% P; 17.2% C; 4.34% H. Determine the formulas, draw the structures, and give the systematic names for each compound.

68. Draw a crystal field splitting diagram for a trigonal planar complex ion. Assume the plane of the molecule is perpendicular to the *z*-axis.

69. Draw a crystal field splitting diagram for a trigonal bipyramidal complex ion. Assume the axial positions are on the *z*-axis.

70. Explain why $[Ni(NH_3)_4]^{2+}$ is paramagnetic, while $[Ni(CN)_4]^{2-}$ is diamagnetic.

71. Sulfide (S^{2-}) salts have notoriously low solubilities in aqueous solution.
   a. Calculate the molar solubility of nickel(II) sulfide in water. $K_{sp}(NiS) = 3 \times 10^{-16}$
   b. Nickel(II) ions form a complex ion in the presence of ammonia with a formation constant (K_f) of 2.0×10^8: $Ni^{2+}(aq) + 6\,NH_3(aq) \rightleftharpoons [Ni(NH_3)_6]^{2+}(aq)$. Calculate the molar solubility of NiS in 3.0 mol L^{-1} NH_3.
   c. Explain any differences in the answers to parts (**a**) and (**b**).

72. Calculate the solubility of $Zn(OH)_2(s)$ in 2.0 mol L^{-1} aqueous NaOH solution. (*Hint:* You must take into account the formation of $Zn(OH)_4^{2-}$, which has a $K_f = 2 \times 10^{15}$.)

73. Halide complexes of metal M of the form $[MX_6]^{3-}$ are found to be stable in aqueous solution. But it is possible that they undergo rapid ligand exchange with water (or other ligands) that is not detectable because the complexes are less stable. This property is referred to as their lability. Suggest an experiment to measure the lability of these complexes that does not employ radioactive labels.

74. The K_f for $[Cu(en)_2]^{2+}$ is much larger than the one for $[Cu(NH_3)_4]^{2+}$. This difference is primarily an entropy effect. Explain why and calculate the difference between the $\Delta_r S°$ values at 298 K for the complete dissociation of the two complex ions. (*Hint:* The value of $\Delta_r H°$ is about the same for both systems.)

75. When solid $Cd(OH)_2$ is added to a solution of 0.10 mol L^{-1} aqueous NaI, some of it dissolves. Calculate the pH of the solution at equilibrium.

Conceptual Problems

76. The complexes of Fe^{3+} have magnetic properties that depend on whether the ligands are strong- or weak-field. Explain why this observation supports the idea that electrons are lost from the 4*s* orbital before the 3*d* orbitals in the transition metals.

77. Two ligands, A and B, both form complexes with a particular metal ion. When the metal ion complexes with ligand A, the solution is green. When the metal ion complexes with ligand B, the solution is violet. Which of the two ligands results in the largest Δ?

Appendix I:

Common Mathematical Operations in Chemistry

A. Scientific Notation

A number written in scientific notation consists of a **decimal part**, a number that is usually between 1 and 10, and an **exponential part**, 10 raised to an **exponent**, *n*.

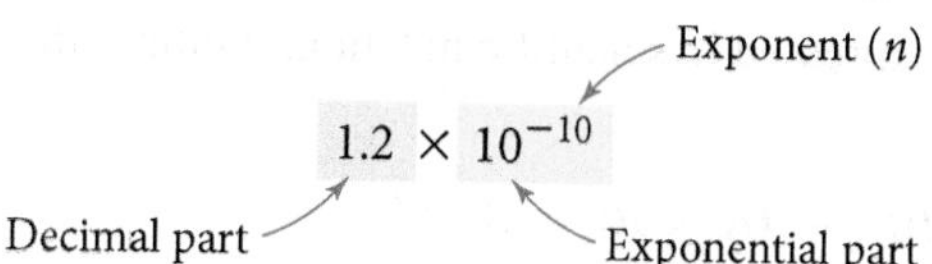

Each of the following numbers is written in both scientific and decimal notation.

$1.0 \times 10^5 = 100\,000 \qquad 1.0 \times 10^{-5} = 0.000\,001$

$6.7 \times 10^3 = 6700 \qquad 6.7 \times 10^{-3} = 0.0067$

A positive exponent means 1 multiplied by 10 *n* times.

$10^0 = 1$

$10^1 = 1 \times 10$

$10^2 = 1 \times 10 \times 10 = 100$

$10^3 = 1 \times 10 \times 10 \times 10 = 1000$

A negative exponent $(-n)$ means 1 divided by 10 *n* times.

$$10^{-1} = \frac{1}{10} = 0.1$$

$$10^{-2} = \frac{1}{10 \times 10} = 0.01$$

$$10^{-3} = \frac{1}{10 \times 10 \times 10} = 0.001$$

To convert a number to scientific notation, we move the decimal point to obtain a number between 1 and 10 and then multiply by 10 raised to the appropriate power. For example, to write 5983 in scientific notation, we move the decimal point to the left three places to get 5.983 (a number between 1 and 10) and then multiply by 1000 to make up for moving the decimal point.

$5983 = 5.983 \times 1000$

Since 1000 is 10^3, we write

$5983 = 5.983 \times 10^3$

We can do this in one step by counting how many places we move the decimal point to obtain a number between 1 and 10 and then writing the decimal part multiplied by 10 raised to the number of places we moved the decimal point.

$5983 = 5.983 \times 10^3$

If the decimal point is moved to the left, as in the previous example, the exponent is positive. If the decimal is moved to the right, the exponent is negative.

$0.00034 = 3.4 \times 10^{-4}$

To express a number in scientific notation:

1. **Move the decimal point to obtain a number between 1 and 10.**
2. **Write the result from step 1 multiplied by 10 raised to the number of places you moved the decimal point.**
   - *The exponent is positive if you moved the decimal point to the left.*
   - *The exponent is negative if you moved the decimal point to the right.*

Consider the following additional examples:

$$290\ 809\ 000 = 2.90809 \times 10^8$$

$$0.000\ 000\ 000\ 070\ \text{m} = 7.0 \times 10^{-11}\ \text{m}$$

Multiplication and Division

To multiply numbers expressed in scientific notation, multiply the decimal parts and add the exponents.

$$(A \times 10^m)(B \times 10^n) = (A \times B) \times 10^{m+n}$$

To divide numbers expressed in scientific notation, divide the decimal parts and subtract the exponent in the denominator from the exponent in the numerator.

$$\frac{(A \times 10^m)}{(B \times 10^n)} = \left(\frac{A}{B}\right) \times 10^{m-n}$$

Consider the following example involving multiplication:

$$(3.5 \times 10^4)(1.8 \times 10^6) = (3.5 \times 1.8) \times 10^{4+6}$$
$$= 6.3 \times 10^{10}$$

Consider the following example involving division:

$$\frac{(5.6 \times 10^7)}{(1.4 \times 10^3)} = \left(\frac{5.6}{1.4}\right) \times 10^{7-3}$$
$$= 4.0 \times 10^4$$

Addition and Subtraction

To add or subtract numbers expressed in scientific notation, rewrite all the numbers so that they have the same exponent, then add or subtract the decimal parts of the numbers. The exponents remained unchanged.

$$\begin{array}{r} A \times 10^n \\ \pm B \times 10^n \\ \hline (A \pm B) \times 10^n \end{array}$$

Notice that the numbers *must have* the same exponent. Consider the following example involving addition:

$$\begin{array}{r} 4.82 \times 10^7 \\ + 3.4 \times 10^6 \\ \hline \end{array}$$

First, express both numbers with the same exponent. In this case, we rewrite the lower number and perform the addition as follows:

$$\begin{array}{r} 4.82 \times 10^7 \\ + 0.34 \times 10^7 \\ \hline 5.16 \times 10^7 \end{array}$$

Consider the following example involving subtraction.

$$\begin{array}{r} 7.33 \times 10^5 \\ -1.9 \times 10^4 \\ \hline \end{array}$$

First, express both numbers with the same exponent. In this case, we rewrite the lower number and perform the subtraction as follows:

$$\begin{array}{r} 7.33 \times 10^5 \\ -0.19 \times 10^5 \\ \hline 7.14 \times 10^5 \end{array}$$

Powers and Roots

To raise a number written in scientific notation to a power, raise the decimal part to the power and multiply the exponent by the power:

$$\begin{aligned}(4.0 \times 10^6)^2 &= 4.0^2 \times 10^{6\times 2} \\ &= 16 \times 10^{12} \\ &= 1.6 \times 10^{13}\end{aligned}$$

To take the *n*th root of a number written in scientific notation, take the *n*th root of the decimal part and divide the exponent by the root:

$$\begin{aligned}(4.0 \times 10^6)^{1/3} &= 4.0^{1/3} \times 10^{6/3} \\ &= 1.6 \times 10^2\end{aligned}$$

B. Logarithms

Common (or Base 10) Logarithms

The common or base 10 logarithm (abbreviated log) of a number is the exponent to which 10 must be raised to obtain that number. For example, the log of 100 is 2 because 10 must be raised to the second power to get 100. Similarly, the log of 1000 is 3 because 10 must be raised to the third power to get 1000. The logs of several multiples of 10 are shown below.

$$\begin{aligned}&\log 10 = 1 \\ &\log 100 = 2 \\ &\log 1000 = 3 \\ &\log 10\,000 = 4\end{aligned}$$

Because $10^0 = 1$ by definition, $\log 1 = 0$.

The log of a number smaller than one is negative because 10 must be raised to a negative exponent to get a number smaller than one. For example, the log of 0.01 is -2 because 10 must be raised to -2 to get 0.01. Similarly, the log of 0.001 is -3 because 10 must be raised to -3 to get 0.001. The logs of several fractional numbers are shown below.

$$\begin{aligned}&\log 0.1 = -1 \\ &\log 0.01 = -2 \\ &\log 0.001 = -3 \\ &\log 0.0001 = -4\end{aligned}$$

The logs of numbers that are not multiples of 10 can be computed on your calculator. See your calculator manual for specific instructions.

Inverse Logarithms

The inverse logarithm or invlog function is exactly the opposite of the log function. For example, the log of 100 is 2 and the inverse log of 2 is 100. The log function and the invlog function undo one another.

$$\begin{aligned}&\log 100 = 2 \\ &\text{invlog } 2 = 100 \\ &\text{invlog}(\log 100) = 100\end{aligned}$$

The inverse log of a number is simply 10 raised to that number.

$$\text{invlog } x = 10^x$$
$$\text{invlog } 3 = 10^3 = 1000$$

The inverse logs of numbers can be computed on your calculator. See your calculator manual for specific instructions.

Natural (or Base *e*) Logarithms

The natural (or base *e*) logarithm (abbreviated ln) of a number is the exponent to which *e* (which has the value of 2.71828 . . .) must be raised to obtain that number. For example, the ln of 100 is 4.605 because *e* must be raised to 4.605 to get 100. Similarly, the ln of 10.0 is 2.303 because *e* must be raised to 2.303 to get 10.0.

The inverse natural logarithm or invln function is exactly the opposite of the ln function. For example, the ln of 100 is 4.605 and the inverse ln of 4.605 is 100. The inverse ln of a number is simply *e* raised to that number.

$$\text{invln } x = e^x$$
$$\text{invln } 3 = e^3 = 20.1$$

The invln of a number can be computed on your calculator. See your calculator manual for specific instructions.

Mathematical Operations Using Logarithms

Because logarithms are exponents, mathematical operations involving logarithms are similar to those involving exponents as follows:

$$\log(a \times b) = \log a + \log b \qquad \ln(a \times b) = \ln a + \ln b$$
$$\log \frac{a}{b} = \log a - \log b \qquad \ln \frac{a}{b} = \ln a - \ln b$$
$$\log a^n = n \log a \qquad \ln a^n = n \ln a$$

C. Quadratic Equations

A quadratic equation contains at least one term in which the variable x is raised to the second power (and no terms in which x is raised to a higher power). A quadratic equation has the following general form:

$$ax^2 + bx + c = 0$$

A quadratic equation can be solved for x using the quadratic formula:

$$x = \frac{-b \pm \sqrt{b^2 - 4ac}}{2a}$$

Quadratic equations are often encountered when solving equilibrium problems. Below we show how to use the quadratic formula to solve a quadratic equation for x.

$$3x^2 - 5x + 1 = 0 \quad \textit{(quadratic equation)}$$
$$x = \frac{-b \pm \sqrt{b^2 - 4ac}}{2a}$$
$$= \frac{-(-5) \pm \sqrt{(-5)^2 - 4(3)(1)}}{2(3)}$$
$$= \frac{5 \pm 3.606}{6}$$
$$x = 1.43 \quad \text{or} \quad x = 0.233$$

As you can see, the solution to a quadratic equation usually has two values. In any real chemical system, one of the values can be eliminated because it has no physical significance. (For example, it may correspond to a negative concentration, which does not exist.)

D. Graphs

Graphs are often used to visually show the relationship between two variables. For example, in Chapter 5, we show the following relationship between the volume of a gas and its pressure:

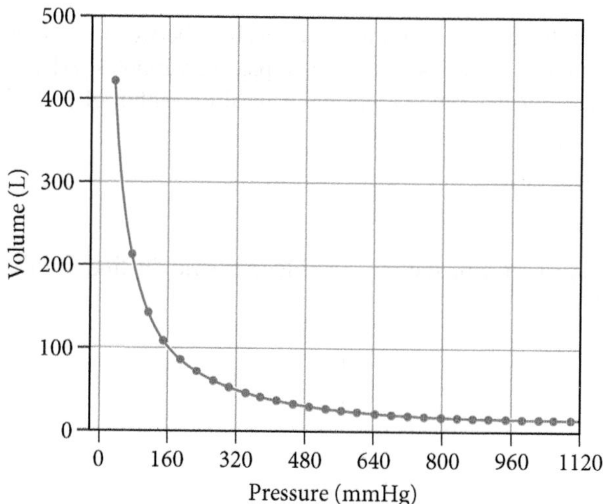

Volume Versus Pressure A plot of the volume of a gas sample—as measured in a J-tube—versus pressure. The plot shows that volume and pressure are inversely related.

The horizontal axis is the x-axis and is normally used to show the independent variable. The vertical axis is the y-axis and is normally used to show how the other variable (called the dependent variable) varies with a change in the independent variable. In this case, the graph shows that as the pressure of a gas sample increases, its volume decreases.

Many relationships in chemistry are *linear*, which means that if you change one variable by a factor of n the other variable will also change by a factor of n. For example, the volume of a gas is linearly related to the number of moles of gas. When two quantities are linearly related, a graph of one versus the other produces a straight line. For example, the graph below shows how the volume of an ideal gas sample depends on the number of moles of gas in the sample:

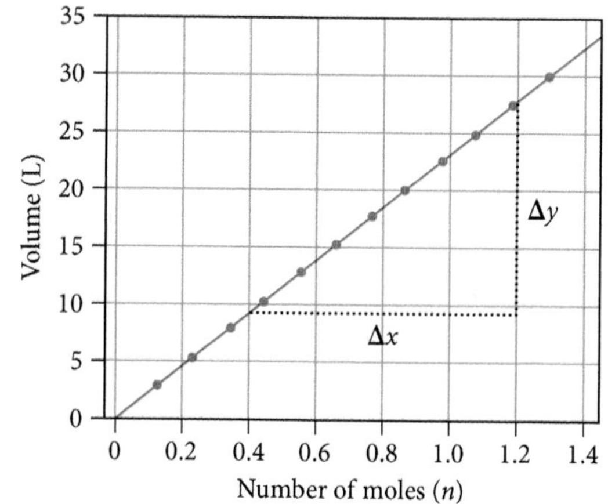

Volume Versus Number of Moles The volume of a gas sample increases linearly with the number of moles of gas in the sample.

A linear relationship between any two variables, x and y, can be expressed by the following equation:

$$y = mx + b$$

where m is the slope of the line and b is the y-intercept. The slope is the change in y divided by the change in x.

$$m = \frac{\Delta y}{\Delta x}$$

For the preceding graph, we can estimate the slope by simply estimating the changes in y and x for a given interval. For example, between $x = 0.4$ mol and 1.2 mol, $\Delta x = 0.80$ mol and we can estimate that $\Delta y = 18$ L. Therefore the slope is

$$m = \frac{\Delta y}{\Delta x} = \frac{18\ \text{L}}{0.80\ \text{mol}} = 23\ \text{L mol}^{-1}$$

In several places in this text, logarithmic relationships between variables can be plotted in order to obtain a linear relationship. For example, the variables $[A]_t$ and t in the following equation are not linearly related, but the natural logarithm of $[A]_t$ and t are linearly related.

$$\ln[A]_t = -kt + \ln[A]_0$$
$$y = mx + b$$

A plot of $\ln[A]_t$ versus t will therefore produce a straight line with slope $= -k$ and y-intercept $= \ln[A]_0$.

Appendix II:
Useful Data

A. Atomic Colours

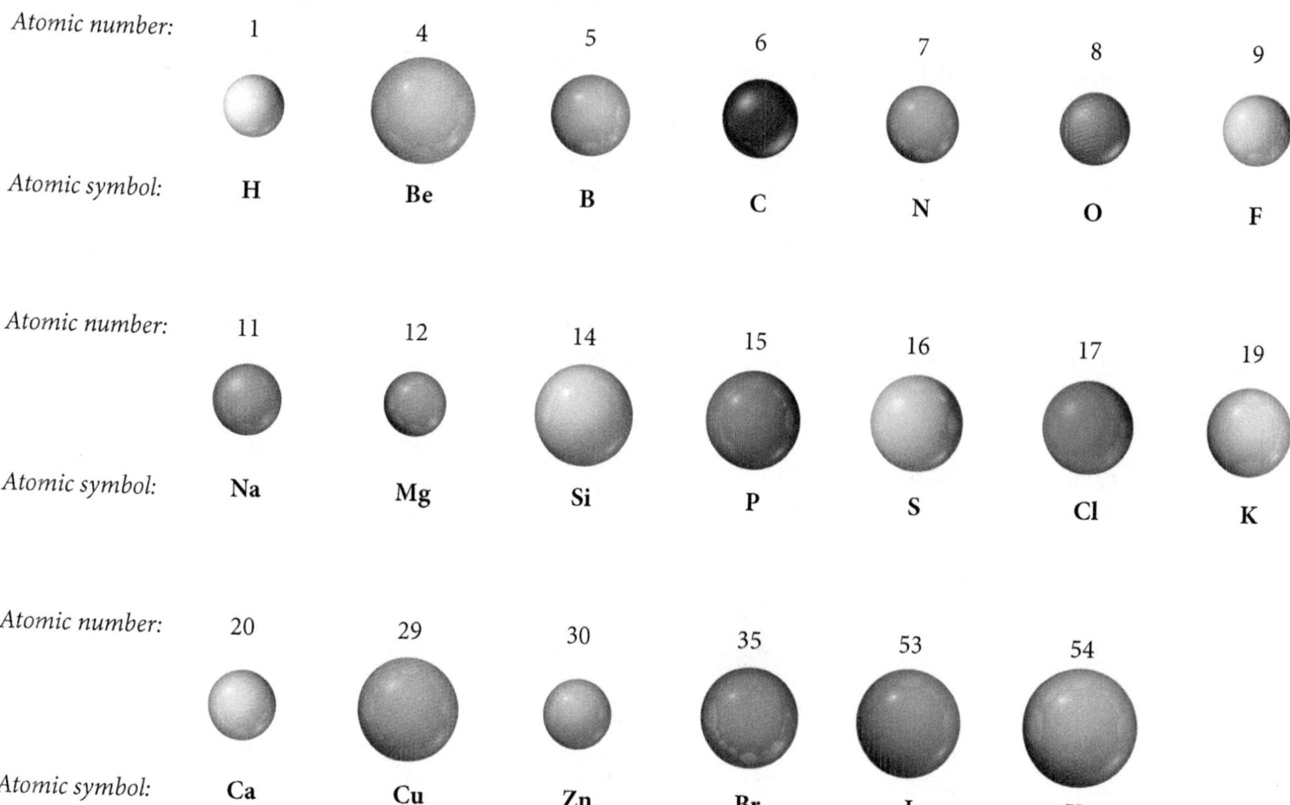

B. Standard Thermodynamic Quantities for Selected Substances at 25 °C

Substance	$\Delta_f H^\circ$(kJ mol^{-1})	$\Delta_f G^\circ$(kJ mol^{-1})	S°(J K^{-1} mol^{-1})
Aluminum			
Al(*s*)	0	0	28.32
Al(*g*)	330.0	289.4	164.6
Al^{3+}(*aq*)	−538.4	−483	−325
$AlCl_3$(*s*)	−704.2	−628.8	109.3
Al_2O_3(*s*)	−1675.7	−1582.3	50.9
Barium			
Ba(*s*)	0	0	62.5
Ba(*g*)	180.0	146.0	170.2
Ba^{2+}(*aq*)	−537.6	−560.8	9.6
$BaCO_3$(*s*)	−1213.0	−1134.4	112.1
$BaCl_2$(*s*)	−855.0	−806.7	123.7
BaO(*s*)	−548.0	−520.3	72.1
$Ba(OH)_2$(*s*)	−944.7		
$BaSO_4$(*s*)	−1473.2	−1362.2	132.2
Beryllium			
Be(*s*)	0	0	9.5
BeO(*s*)	−609.4	−580.1	13.8
$Be(OH)_2$(*s*)	−902.5	−815.0	45.5
Bismuth			
Bi(*s*)	0	0	56.7
$BiCl_3$(*s*)	−379.1	−315.0	177.[illegible]
Bi_2O_3(*s*)	−573.9	−493.7	15[illegible]
Bi_2S_3(*s*)	−143.1	−140.6	[illegible]
Boron			
B(*s*)	0	0	
B(*g*)	565.0	521.0	
BCl_3(*g*)	−403.8	−388.7	
BF_3(*g*)	−1136.0	−1119.[illegible]	

page)

Substance	$\Delta_f H°$(kJ mol^{-1})	$\Delta_f G°$(kJ mol^{-1})	$S°$(J K^{-1} mol^{-1})
$B_2H_6(g)$	36.4	87.6	232.1
$B_2O_3(s)$	−1273.5	−1194.3	54.0
$H_3BO_3(s)$	−1094.3	−968.9	90.0
Bromine			
$Br(g)$	111.9	82.4	175.0
$Br_2(l)$	0	0	152.2
$Br_2(g)$	30.9	3.1	245.5
$Br^-(aq)$	−121.4	−102.8	80.71
$HBr(g)$	−36.3	−53.4	198.7
Cadmium			
$Cd(s)$	0	0	51.8
$Cd(g)$	111.8	77.3	167.7
$Cd^{2+}(aq)$	−75.9	−77.6	−73.2
$CdCl_2(s)$	−391.5	−343.9	115.3
$CdO(s)$	−258.4	−228.7	54.8
$CdS(s)$	−161.9	−156.5	64.9
$CdSO_4(s)$	−933.3	−822.7	123.0
Calcium			
$Ca(s)$	0	0	41.6
$Ca(g)$	177.8	144.0	154.9
$Ca^{2+}(aq)$	−542.8	−553.6	−53.1
$CaC_2(s)$	−59.8	−64.9	70.0
$CaCO_3(s)$	−1207.6	−1129.1	91.7
$CaCl_2(s)$	−795.4	−748.8	108.4
$CaF_2(s)$	−1228.0	−1175.6	68.5
$CaH_2(s)$	−181.5	−142.5	41.4
$Ca(NO_3)_2(s)$	−938.2	−742.8	193.2
$CaO(s)$	−634.9	−603.3	38.1
$Ca(OH)_2(s)$	−985.2	−897.5	83.4
$CaSO_4(s)$	−1434.5	−1322.0	106.5
$Ca_3(PO_4)_2(s)$	−4120.8	−3884.7	236.0
Carbon			
C(*s*, graphite)	0	0	5.7
C(*s*, diamond)	1.88	2.9	2.4
$C(g)$	716.7	671.3	158.1
$CH_4(g)$	−74.6	−50.5	186.3
[illegible]$Cl(g)$	−81.9	−60.2	234.6
[illegible](g)	−95.4		270.2
[illegible]	−124.2	−63.2	177.8
[illegible]	−134.1	−73.7	201.7
[illegible]	−95.7	−62.3	309.7
(*l*, [illegible]	−128.2	−66.4	216.4
CH_3[illegible]	108.6	−102.5	218.8
(*g*, me[illegible]			
CH_3OH([illegible]	0	−361.4	129.0
$CH_3OH(g)$		32.7	242.9
$C_2H_2(g)$		−166.6	126.8
$C_2H_4(g)$		−162.3	239.9
$C_2H_6(g)$		209.9	200.9
[illegible]		68.4	219.3
[illegible]		−32.0	229.2
$C_2H_5OH(l)$	−277.6	−174.8	160.7
$C_2H_5OH(g)$	−234.8	−167.9	281.6
C_2H_3Cl (*g*, chloroethene)	37.2	53.6	264.0
$C_2H_4Cl_2$ (*l*, dichloroethane)	−166.8	−79.6	208.5
C_2H_4O (*g*, ethanal)	−166.2	−133.0	263.8
$C_2H_4O_2$ (*l*, acetic acid)	−484.3	−389.9	159.8
$C_3H_8(g)$	−103.85	−23.4	270.3
C_3H_6O (*l*, acetone)	−248.4	−155.6	199.8
C_3H_7OH (*l*, propan-2-ol)	−318.1		181.1
$C_4H_{10}(l)$	−147.3	−15.0	231.0
$C_4H_{10}(g)$	−125.7	−15.71	310.0
$C_6H_6(l)$	49.1	124.5	173.4
$C_6H_5NH_2$ (*l*, aniline)	31.6	149.2	191.9
C_6H_5OH (*s*, phenol)	−165.1	−50.4	144.0
$C_6H_{12}O_6$ (*s*, glucose)	−1273.3	−910.4	212.1
$C_{10}H_8$ (*s*, naphthalene)	78.5	201.6	167.4
$C_{12}H_{22}O_{11}$ (*s*, sucrose)	−2226.1	−1544.3	360.24
$CO(g)$	−110.5	−137.2	197.7
$CO_2(g)$	−393.5	−394.4	213.8
$CO_2(aq)$	−413.8	−386.0	117.6
$CO_3^{2-}(aq)$	−677.1	−527.8	−56.9
$HCO_3^-(aq)$	−692.0	−586.8	91.2
$H_2CO_3(aq)$	−699.7	−623.2	187.4
$CN^-(aq)$	151	166	118
$HCN(l)$	108.9	125.0	112.8
$HCN(g)$	135.1	124.7	201.8
$CS_2(l)$	89.0	64.6	151.3
$CS_2(g)$	116.7	67.1	237.8
$COCl_2(g)$	−219.1	−204.9	283.5
$C_{60}(s)$	2327.0	2302.0	426.0
Cesium			
$Cs(s)$	0	0	85.2
$Cs(g)$	76.5	49.6	175.6
$Cs^+(aq)$	−258.0	−292.0	132.1
$CsBr(s)$	−400	−387	117
$CsCl(s)$	−438	−414	101.2
$CsF(s)$	−553.5	−525.5	92.8
$CsI(s)$	−342	−337	127
Chlorine			
$Cl(g)$	121.3	105.3	165.2
$Cl_2(g)$	0	0	223.1
$Cl^-(aq)$	−167.1	−131.2	56.6
$HCl(g)$	−92.3	−95.3	186.9
$HCl(aq)$	−167.2	−131.2	56.5

Substance	$\Delta_f H°$(kJ mol^{-1})	$\Delta_f G°$(kJ mol^{-1})	$S°$(J K^{-1} mol^{-1})
$ClO_2(g)$	102.5	120.5	256.8
$Cl_2O(g)$	80.3	97.9	266.2
Chromium			
$Cr(s)$	0	0	23.8
$Cr(g)$	396.6	351.8	174.5
$Cr^{3+}(aq)$	−1971		
$CrO_4^{2-}(aq)$	−872.2	−717.1	44
$Cr_2O_3(s)$	−1139.7	−1058.1	81.2
$Cr_2O_7^{2-}(aq)$	−1476	−1279	238
Cobalt			
$Co(s)$	0	0	30.0
$Co(g)$	424.7	380.3	179.5
$CoO(s)$	−237.9	−214.2	53.0
$Co(OH)_2(s)$	−539.7	−454.3	79.0
Copper			
$Cu(s)$	0	0	33.2
$Cu(g)$	337.4	297.7	166.4
$Cu^{+}(aq)$	51.9	50.2	−26
$Cu^{2+}(aq)$	64.9	65.5	−98
$CuCl(s)$	−137.2	−119.9	86.2
$CuCl_2(s)$	−220.1	−175.7	108.1
$CuO(s)$	−157.3	−129.7	42.6
$CuS(s)$	−53.1	−53.6	66.5
$CuSO_4(s)$	−771.4	−662.2	109.2
$Cu_2O(s)$	−168.6	−146.0	93.1
$Cu_2S(s)$	−79.5	−86.2	120.9
Fluorine			
$F(g)$	79.38	62.3	158.75
$F_2(g)$	0	0	202.79
$F^{-}(aq)$	−335.35	−278.8	−13.8
$HF(g)$	−273.3	−275.4	173.8
Gold			
$Au(s)$	0	0	47.4
$Au(g)$	366.1	326.3	180.5
Helium			
$He(g)$	0	0	126.2
Hydrogen			
$H(g)$	218.0	203.3	114.7
$H^{+}(aq)$	0	0	0
$H^{+}(g)$	1536.3	1517.1	108.9
$H_2(g)$	0	0	130.7
Iodine			
$I(g)$	106.76	70.2	180.79
$I_2(s)$	0	0	116.14
$I_2(g)$	62.42	19.3	260.69
$I^{-}(aq)$	−56.78	−51.57	106.45
$HI(g)$	26.5	1.7	206.6
Iron			
$Fe(s)$	0	0	27.3
$Fe(g)$	416.3	370.7	180.5
$Fe^{2+}(aq)$	−87.9	−84.94	−113.4
$Fe^{3+}(aq)$	−47.69	−10.54	−293.3
$FeCO_3(s)$	−740.6	−666.7	92.9
$FeCl_2(s)$	−341.8	−302.3	118.0
$FeCl_3(s)$	−399.5	−334.0	142.3
$FeO(s)$	−272.0	−255.2	60.75
$Fe(OH)_3(s)$	−823.0	−696.5	106.7
$FeS_2(s)$	−178.2	−166.9	52.9
$Fe_2O_3(s)$	−824.2	−742.2	87.4
$Fe_3O_4(s)$	−1118.4	−1015.4	146.4
Lead			
$Pb(s)$	0	0	64.8
$Pb(g)$	195.2	162.2	175.4
$Pb^{2+}(aq)$	0.92	−24.4	18.5
$PbBr_2(s)$	−278.7	−261.9	161.5
$PbCO_3(s)$	−699.1	−625.5	131.0
$PbCl_2(s)$	−359.4	−314.1	136.0
$PbI_2(s)$	−175.5	−173.6	174.9
$Pb(NO_3)_2(s)$	−451.9		
$PbO(s)$	−217.3	−187.9	68.7
$PbO_2(s)$	−277.4	−217.3	68.6
$PbS(s)$	−100.4	−98.7	91.2
$PbSO_4(s)$	−920.0	−813.0	148.5
Lithium			
$Li(s)$	0	0	29.1
$Li(g)$	159.3	126.6	138.8
$Li^{+}(aq)$	−278.47	−293.3	12.24
$LiBr(s)$	−351.2	−342.0	74.3
$LiCl(s)$	−408.6	−384.4	59.3
$LiF(s)$	−616.0	−587.7	35.7
$LiI(s)$	−270.4	−270.3	86.8
$LiNO_3(s)$	−483.1	−381.1	90.0
$LiOH(s)$	−487.5	−441.5	42.8
$Li_2O(s)$	−597.9	−561.2	37.6
Magnesium			
$Mg(s)$	0	0	32.7
$Mg(g)$	147.1	112.5	148.6
$Mg^{2+}(aq)$	−467.0	−455.4	−137
$MgCl_2(s)$	−641.3	−591.8	89.6
$MgCO_3(s)$	−1095.8	−1012.1	65.7
$MgF_2(s)$	−1124.2	−1071.1	57.2
$MgO(s)$	−601.6	−569.3	27[illegible]
$Mg(OH)_2(s)$	−924.5	−833.5	[illegible]
$MgSO_4(s)$	−1284.9	−1170.6	[illegible]
$Mg_3N_2(s)$	−461	−401	[illegible]
Manganese			
$Mn(s)$	0	0	[illegible]
$Mn(g)$	280.7	238.5	[illegible]
$Mn^{2+}(aq)$	−219.4	−225.6	[illegible]
$MnO(s)$	−385.2	−362[illegible]	[illegible]

[illegible] page)

Substance	$\Delta_f H°$(kJ mol^{-1})	$\Delta_f G°$(kJ mol^{-1})	$S°$(J K^{-1} mol^{-1})
$MnO_2(s)$	−520.0	−465.1	53.1
$MnO_4^-(aq)$	−529.9	−436.2	190.6
Mercury			
$Hg(l)$	0	0	75.9
$Hg(g)$	61.4	31.8	175.0
$Hg^{2+}(aq)$	170.21	164.4	−36.19
$Hg_2^{2+}(aq)$	166.87	153.5	65.74
$HgCl_2(s)$	−224.3	−178.6	146.0
$HgO(s)$	−90.8	−58.5	70.3
$HgS(s)$	−58.2	−50.6	82.4
$Hg_2Cl_2(s)$	−265.4	−210.7	191.6
Nickel			
$Ni(s)$	0	0	29.9
$Ni(g)$	429.7	384.5	182.2
$NiCl_2(s)$	−305.3	−259.0	97.7
$NiO(s)$	−239.7	−211.7	37.99
$NiS(s)$	−82.0	−79.5	53.0
Nitrogen			
$N(g)$	472.7	455.5	153.3
$N_2(g)$	0	0	191.6
$NF_3(g)$	−132.1	−90.6	260.8
$NH_3(g)$	−45.9	−16.4	192.8
$NH_3(aq)$	−80.29	−26.50	111.3
$NH_4^+(aq)$	−133.26	−79.31	111.17
$NH_4Br(s)$	−270.8	−175.2	113.0
$NH_4Cl(s)$	−314.4	−202.9	94.6
$NH_4CN(s)$	0.4		
$NH_4F(s)$	−464.0	−348.7	72.0
$NH_4HCO_3(s)$	−849.4	−665.9	120.9
$NH_4I(s)$	−201.4	−112.5	117.0
$NH_4NO_3(s)$	−365.6	−183.9	151.1
$NH_4NO_3(aq)$	−339.9	−190.6	259.8
$HNO_3(g)$	−133.9	−73.5	266.9
$HNO_3(aq)$	−207	−110.9	146
$NO(g)$	91.3	87.6	210.8
$NO_2(g)$	33.2	51.3	240.1
[illegible]$_3^-(aq)$	−206.85	−110.2	146.70
[illegible]r(g)	82.2	82.4	273.7
[illegible]	51.7	66.1	261.7
[illegible]	50.6	149.3	121.2
[illegible]	95.4	159.4	238.5
N[illegible]	81.6	103.7	220.0
N_2[illegible]	−19.5	97.5	209.2
[illegible]	9.16	99.8	304.4
[illegible]	[illegible]3.1	113.9	178.2
[illegible]	[illegible]	117.1	355.7
Oxygen			
$O(g)$	[illegible]	231.7	161.1
$O_2(g)$	[illegible]	0	205.2
$O_3(g)$	[illegible]	163.2	238.9
$OH^-(aq)$	[illegible]	−157.3	−10.90

Substance	$\Delta_f H°$(kJ mol^{-1})	$\Delta_f G°$(kJ mol^{-1})	$S°$(J K^{-1} mol^{-1})
$H_2O(l)$	−285.8	−237.1	70.0
$H_2O(g)$	−241.8	−228.6	188.8
$H_2O_2(l)$	−187.8	−120.4	109.6
$H_2O_2(g)$	−136.3	−105.6	232.7
Phosphorus			
P_4(s, white)	0	0	41.1
P_4(s, red)	−17.6	−12.1	22.8
$P(g)$	316.5	280.1	163.2
$P_2(g)$	144.0	103.5	218.1
$P_4(g)$	58.9	24.4	280.0
$PCl_3(l)$	−319.7	−272.3	217.1
$PCl_3(g)$	−287.0	−267.8	311.8
$PCl_5(s)$	−443.5		
$PCl_5(g)$	−374.9	−305.0	364.6
$PF_5(g)$	−1594.4	−1520.7	300.8
$PH_3(g)$	5.4	13.5	210.2
$POCl_3(l)$	−597.1	−520.8	222.5
$POCl_3(g)$	−558.5	−512.9	325.5
$PO_4^{3-}(aq)$	−1277.4	−1018.7	−220.5
$HPO_4^{2-}(aq)$	−1292.1	−1089.2	−33.5
$H_2PO_4^-(aq)$	−1296.3	−1130.2	90.4
$H_3PO_4(s)$	−1284.4	−1124.3	110.5
$H_3PO_4(aq)$	−1288.3	−1142.6	158.2
$P_4O_6(s)$	−1640.1		
$P_4O_{10}(s)$	−2984	−2698	228.9
Platinum			
$Pt(s)$	0	0	41.6
$Pt(g)$	565.3	520.5	192.4
Potassium			
$K(s)$	0	0	64.7
$K(g)$	89.0	60.5	160.3
$K^+(aq)$	−252.14	−283.3	101.2
$KBr(s)$	−393.8	−380.7	95.9
$KCN(s)$	−113.0	−101.9	128.5
$KCl(s)$	−436.5	−408.5	82.6
$KClO_3(s)$	−397.7	−296.3	143.1
$KClO_4(s)$	−432.8	−303.1	151.0
$KF(s)$	−567.3	−537.8	66.6
$KI(s)$	−327.9	−324.9	106.3
$KNO_3(s)$	−494.6	−394.9	133.1
$KOH(s)$	−424.6	−379.4	81.2
$KOH(aq)$	−482.4	−440.5	91.6
$KO_2(s)$	−284.9	−239.4	116.7
$K_2CO_3(s)$	−1151.0	−1063.5	155.5
$K_2O(s)$	−361.5	−322.1	94.14
$K_2O_2(s)$	−494.1	−425.1	102.1
$K_2SO_4(s)$	−1437.8	−1321.4	175.6
Rubidium			
$Rb(s)$	0	0	76.8
$Rb(g)$	80.9	53.1	170.1
$Rb^+(aq)$	−251.12	−283.1	121.75

Substance	$\Delta_f H°$(kJ mol^{-1})	$\Delta_f G°$(kJ mol^{-1})	$S°$(J K^{-1} mol^{-1})
$RbBr(s)$	−394.6	−381.8	110.0
$RbCl(s)$	−435.4	−407.8	95.9
$RbClO_3(s)$	−392.4	−292.0	152
$RbF(s)$	−557.7		
$RbI(s)$	−333.8	−328.9	118.4
Scandium			
$Sc(s)$	0	0	34.6
$Sc(g)$	377.8	336.0	174.8
Selenium			
$Se(s$, gray$)$	0	0	42.4
$Se(g)$	227.1	187.0	176.7
$H_2Se(g)$	29.7	15.9	219.0
Silicon			
$Si(s)$	0	0	18.8
$Si(g)$	450.0	405.5	168.0
$SiCl_4(l)$	−687.0	−619.8	239.7
$SiF_4(g)$	−1615.0	−1572.8	282.8
$SiH_4(g)$	34.3	56.9	204.6
$SiO_2(s$, quartz$)$	−910.7	−856.3	41.5
$Si_2H_6(g)$	80.3	127.3	272.7
Silver			
$Ag(s)$	0	0	42.6
$Ag(g)$	284.9	246.0	173.0
$Ag^+(aq)$	105.79	77.11	73.45
$AgBr(s)$	−100.4	−96.9	107.1
$AgCl(s)$	−127.0	−109.8	96.3
$AgF(s)$	−204.6	−185	84
$AgI(s)$	−61.8	−66.2	115.5
$AgNO_3(s)$	−124.4	−33.4	140.9
$Ag_2O(s)$	−31.1	−11.2	121.3
$Ag_2S(s)$	−32.6	−40.7	144.0
$Ag_2SO_4(s)$	−715.9	−618.4	200.4
Sodium			
$Na(s)$	0	0	51.3
$Na(g)$	107.5	77.0	153.7
$Na^+(aq)$	−240.34	−261.9	58.45
$NaBr(s)$	−361.1	−349.0	86.8
$NaCl(s)$	−411.2	−384.1	72.1
$NaCl(aq)$	−407.2	−393.1	115.5
$NaClO_3(s)$	−365.8	−262.3	123.4
$NaF(s)$	−576.6	−546.3	51.1
$NaHCO_3(s)$	−950.8	−851.0	101.7
$NaHSO_4(s)$	−1125.5	−992.8	113.0
$NaI(s)$	−287.8	−286.1	98.5
$NaNO_3(s)$	−467.9	−367.0	116.5
$NaNO_3(aq)$	−447.5	−373.2	205.4
$NaOH(s)$	−425.8	−379.7	64.4
$NaOH(aq)$	−470.1	−419.2	48.2
$NaO_2(s)$	−260.2	−218.4	115.9
$Na_2CO_3(s)$	−1130.7	−1044.4	135.0
$Na_2O(s)$	−414.2	−375.5	75.1
$Na_2O_2(s)$	−510.9	−447.7	95.0
$Na_2SO_4(s)$	−1387.1	−1270.2	149.6
$Na_3PO_4(s)$	−1917	−1789	173.8
Strontium			
$Sr(s)$	0	0	55.0
$Sr(g)$	164.4	130.9	164.6
$Sr^{2+}(aq)$	−545.51	−557.3	−39
$SrCl_2(s)$	−828.9	−781.1	114.9
$SrCO_3(s)$	−1220.1	−1140.1	97.1
$SrO(s)$	−592.0	−561.9	54.4
$SrSO_4(s)$	−1453.1	−1340.9	117.0
Sulfur			
$S_8(s$, rhombic$)$	0	0	32.1
$S_8(s$, monoclinic$)$	0.3	0.096	32.6
$S(g)$	277.2	236.7	167.8
$S_2(g)$	128.6	79.7	228.2
$S_8(g)$	102.3	49.7	430.9
$S^{2-}(aq)$	41.8	83.7	22
$SF_6(g)$	−1220.5	−1116.5	291.5
$HS^-(aq)$	−17.7	12.4	62.0
$H_2S(g)$	−20.6	−33.4	205.8
$H_2S(aq)$	−39.4	−27.7	122
$SOCl_2(l)$	−245.6		
$SO_2(g)$	−296.8	−300.1	248.2
$SO_3(g)$	−395.7	−371.1	256.8
$SO_4^{2-}(aq)$	−909.3	−744.6	18.5
$HSO_4^-(aq)$	−886.5	−754.4	129.5
$H_2SO_4(l)$	−814.0	−690.0	156.9
$H_2SO_4(aq)$	−909.3	−744.6	18.5
$S_2O_3^{2-}(aq)$	−648.5	−522.5	67
Tin			
$Sn(s$, white$)$	0	0	51.2
$Sn(s$, gray$)$	−2.1	0.1	44.1
$Sn(g)$	301.2	266.2	168.5
$SnCl_4(l)$	−511.3	−440.1	258.6
$SnCl_4(g)$	−471.5	−432.2	365.8
$SnO(s)$	−280.7	−251.9	57.2
$SnO_2(s)$	−577.6	−515.8	49.0
Titanium			
$Ti(s)$	0	0	30.7
$Ti(g)$	473.0	428.4	180.3
$TiCl_4(l)$	−804.2	−737.2	252.[illegible]
$TiCl_4(g)$	−763.2	−726.3	35[illegible]
$TiO_2(s)$	−944.0	−888.8	[illegible]
Tungsten			
$W(s)$	0	0	[illegible]
$W(g)$	849.4	807.1	[illegible]
$WO_3(s)$	−842.9	−764.0	[illegible]

(co[illegible]

Substance	$\Delta_f H°$(kJ mol^{-1})	$\Delta_f G°$(kJ mol^{-1})	$S°$(J K^{-1} mol^{-1})
Uranium			
$U(s)$	0	0	50.2
$U(g)$	533.0	488.4	199.8
$UF_6(s)$	−2197.0	−2068.5	227.6
$UF_6(g)$	−2147.4	−2063.7	377.9
$UO_2(s)$	−1085.0	−1031.8	77.0
Vanadium			
$V(s)$	0	0	28.9
$V(g)$	514.2	754.4	182.3

Substance	$\Delta_f H°$(kJ mol^{-1})	$\Delta_f G°$(kJ mol^{-1})	$S°$(J K^{-1} mol^{-1})
Zinc			
$Zn(s)$	0	0	41.6
$Zn(g)$	130.4	94.8	161.0
$Zn^{2+}(aq)$	−153.39	−147.1	−109.8
$ZnCl_2(s)$	−415.1	−369.4	111.5
$ZnO(s)$	−350.5	−320.5	43.7
ZnS (s, zinc blende)	−206.0	−201.3	57.7
$ZnSO_4(s)$	−982.8	−871.5	110.5

C. Aqueous Equilibrium Constants

1. Dissociation Constants for Acids at 25 °C

Name	Formula	K_{a_1}	K_{a_2}	K_{a_3}
Acetic	CH_3COOH	1.8×10^{-5}		
Acetylsalicylic	$HC_9H_7O_4$	3.3×10^{-4}		
Adipic	$H_2C_6H_8O_4$	3.9×10^{-5}	3.9×10^{-6}	
Arsenic	H_3AsO_4	5.5×10^{-3}	1.7×10^{-7}	5.1×10^{-12}
Arsenous	H_3AsO_3	5.1×10^{-10}		
Ascorbic	$H_2C_6H_6O_6$	8.0×10^{-5}	1.6×10^{-12}	
Benzoic	C_6H_5COOH	6.3×10^{-5}		
Boric	H_3BO_3	5.4×10^{-10}		
Butanoic	C_3H_7COOH	1.5×10^{-5}		
Carbonic	H_2CO_3	4.3×10^{-7}	5.6×10^{-11}	
Chloroacetic	$CH_2ClCOOH$	1.4×10^{-3}		
Chlorous	$HClO_2$	1.1×10^{-2}		
Citric	$H_3C_6H_5O_7$	7.4×10^{-4}	1.7×10^{-5}	4.0×10^{-7}
Cyanic	$HCNO$	2×10^{-4}		
Formic	$HCOOH$	1.8×10^{-4}		
Hydrazoic	HN_3	2.5×10^{-5}		
Hydrocyanic	HCN	6.2×10^{-10}		
Hydrofluoric	HF	6.3×10^{-4}		
Hydrogen chromate ion	$HCrO_4^-$	3.0×10^{-7}		
Hydrogen peroxide	H_2O_2	2.4×10^{-12}		
ydrogen nate ion	$HSeO_4^-$	2.2×10^{-2}		
ulfuric	H_2S	8.9×10^{-8}	1×10^{-19}	
luric	H_2Te	2.3×10^{-3}	1.6×10^{-11}	

Name	Formula	K_{a_1}	K_{a_2}	K_{a_3}
Hypobromous	$HBrO$	2.8×10^{-9}		
Hypochlorous	$HClO$	4.0×10^{-8}		
Hypoiodous	HIO	2.3×10^{-11}		
Iodic	HIO_3	1.7×10^{-1}		
Lactic	$HC_3H_5O_3$	1.4×10^{-4}		
Maleic	$H_2C_4H_2O_4$	1.2×10^{-2}	5.9×10^{-7}	
Malonic	$H_2C_3H_2O_4$	1.5×10^{-3}	2.0×10^{-6}	
Nitrous	HNO_2	5.6×10^{-4}		
Oxalic	$H_2C_2O_4$	6.0×10^{-2}	6.1×10^{-5}	
Paraperiodic	H_5IO_6	2.8×10^{-2}	5.3×10^{-9}	
Phenol	C_6H_5OH	1.3×10^{-10}		
Phosphoric	H_3PO_4	7.5×10^{-3}	6.2×10^{-8}	4.2×10^{-13}
Phosphorous	H_3PO_3	5×10^{-2}	2.0×10^{-7}	
Propanoic	C_2H_5COOH	1.3×10^{-5}		
Pyruvic	$HC_3H_3O_3$	4.1×10^{-3}		
Pyrophosphoric	$H_4P_2O_7$	1.2×10^{-1}	7.9×10^{-3}	2.0×10^{-7}
Selenous	H_2SeO_3	2.4×10^{-3}	4.8×10^{-9}	
Succinic	$H_2C_4H_4O_4$	6.2×10^{-5}	2.3×10^{-6}	
Sulfuric	H_2SO_4	Strong acid	1.2×10^{-2}	
Sulfurous	H_2SO_3	1.6×10^{-2}	6.4×10^{-8}	
Tartaric	$H_2C_4H_4O_6$	1.0×10^{-3}	4.6×10^{-5}	
Trichloroacetic acid	CCl_3COOH	2.2×10^{-1}		
Trifluoroacetic acid	CF_3COOH	3.0×10^{-1}		

tion Constants for Hydrated Metal Ions at 25 °C

Cation	Hydrated Ion	K_a
Al	$Al(H_2O)_6{}^{3+}$	1.4×10^{-5}
Be^{2}	$(H_2O)_6{}^{2+}$	3×10^{-7}
Co^{2+}	$O)_6{}^{2+}$	1.3×10^{-9}
Cr^{3+}	$)_6{}^{3+}$	1.6×10^{-4}
Cu^{2+}	$^{2+}$	3×10^{-8}
Fe^{2+}		3.2×10^{-10}

Cation	Hydrated Ion	K_a
Fe^{3+}	$Fe(H_2O)_6{}^{3+}$	6.3×10^{-3}
Ni^{2+}	$Ni(H_2O)_6{}^{2+}$	2.5×10^{-11}
Pb^{2+}	$Pb(H_2O)_6{}^{2+}$	3×10^{-8}
Sn^{2+}	$Sn(H_2O)_6{}^{2+}$	4×10^{-4}
Zn^{2+}	$Zn(H_2O)_6{}^{2+}$	2.5×10^{-10}

3. Dissociation Constants for Bases at 25 °C

Name	Formula	K_b
Ammonia	NH_3	1.76×10^{-5}
Aniline	$C_6H_5NH_2$	7.5×10^{-10}
Bicarbonate ion	HCO_3^-	2.3×10^{-8}
Carbonate ion	CO_3^{2-}	1.8×10^{-4}
Codeine	$C_{18}H_{21}NO_3$	1.6×10^{-6}
Diethylamine	$(C_2H_5)_2NH$	6.9×10^{-4}
Dimethylamine	$(CH_3)_2NH$	5.4×10^{-4}
Ethylamine	$C_2H_5NH_2$	4.5×10^{-4}
Ethylenediamine	$C_2H_8N_2$	8.3×10^{-5}
Hydrazine	H_2NNH_2	1.3×10^{-6}
Hydroxylamine	$HONH_2$	1.1×10^{-8}

Name	Formula	K_b
Ketamine	$C_{13}H_{16}ClNO$	3×10^{-7}
Methylamine	CH_3NH_2	4.4×10^{-4}
Morphine	$C_{17}H_{19}NO_3$	1.6×10^{-6}
Nicotine	$C_{10}H_{14}N_2$	1.0×10^{-6}
Piperidine	$C_5H_{10}NH$	1.33×10^{-3}
Propylamine	$C_3H_7NH_2$	3.5×10^{-4}
Pyridine	C_5H_5N	1.7×10^{-9}
Strychnine	$C_{21}H_{22}N_2O_2$	1.8×10^{-6}
Triethylamine	$(C_2H_5)_3N$	5.6×10^{-4}
Trimethylamine	$(CH_3)_3N$	6.4×10^{-5}

4. Solubility Product Constants for Compounds at 25 °C

Compound	Formula	K_{sp}
Aluminum hydroxide	$Al(OH)_3$	1.3×10^{-33}
Aluminum phosphate	$AlPO_4$	9.84×10^{-21}
Barium carbonate	$BaCO_3$	2.58×10^{-9}
Barium chromate	$BaCrO_4$	1.17×10^{-10}
Barium fluoride	BaF_2	2.45×10^{-5}
Barium hydroxide	$Ba(OH)_2$	5.0×10^{-3}
Barium oxalate	BaC_2O_4	1.6×10^{-6}
Barium phosphate	$Ba_3(PO_4)_2$	6×10^{-39}
Barium sulfate	$BaSO_4$	1.07×10^{-10}
Cadmium carbonate	$CdCO_3$	1.0×10^{-12}
Cadmium hydroxide	$Cd(OH)_2$	7.2×10^{-15}
Cadmium sulfide	CdS	8×10^{-28}
Calcium carbonate	$CaCO_3$	4.96×10^{-9}
Calcium chromate	$CaCrO_4$	7.1×10^{-4}
Calcium fluoride	CaF_2	1.46×10^{-10}
Calcium hydroxide	$Ca(OH)_2$	4.68×10^{-6}
Calcium hydrogen phosphate	$CaHPO_4$	1×10^{-7}
Calcium oxalate	CaC_2O_4	2.32×10^{-9}
Calcium phosphate	$Ca_3(PO_4)_2$	2.07×10^{-33}
Calcium sulfate	$CaSO_4$	7.10×10^{-5}
Chromium(III) hydroxide	$Cr(OH)_3$	6.3×10^{-31}
Cobalt(II) carbonate	$CoCO_3$	1.0×10^{-10}
Cobalt(II) hydroxide	$Co(OH)_2$	5.92×10^{-15}
Cobalt(II) sulfide	CoS	5×10^{-22}
Copper(I) bromide	$CuBr$	6.27×10^{-9}
Copper(I) chloride	$CuCl$	1.72×10^{-7}
Copper(I) cyanide	$CuCN$	3.47×10^{-20}
Copper(II) carbonate	$CuCO_3$	2.4×10^{-10}
Copper(II) hydroxide	$Cu(OH)_2$	2.2×10^{-20}
Copper(II) phosphate	$Cu_3(PO_4)_2$	1.40×10^{-37}
Copper(II) sulfide	CuS	1.27×10^{-36}
Dimercury(2+) bromide	Hg_2Br_2	6.40×10^{-23}
Dimercury(2+) carbonate	Hg_2CO_3	3.6×10^{-17}
Dimercury(2+) chloride	Hg_2Cl_2	1.43×10^{-18}

Compound	Formula	K_{sp}
Dimercury(2+) chromate	Hg_2CrO_4	2×10^{-9}
Dimercury(2+) cyanide	$Hg_2(CN)_2$	5×10^{-40}
Dimercury(2+) iodide	Hg_2I_2	5.2×10^{-29}
Iron(II) carbonate	$FeCO_3$	3.07×10^{-11}
Iron(II) hydroxide	$Fe(OH)_2$	4.87×10^{-17}
Iron(II) sulfide	FeS	3.72×10^{-19}
Iron(III) hydroxide	$Fe(OH)_3$	2.79×10^{-39}
Lanthanum fluoride	LaF_3	2×10^{-19}
Lanthanum iodate	$La(IO_3)_3$	7.50×10^{-12}
Lead(II) bromide	$PbBr_2$	4.67×10^{-6}
Lead(II) carbonate	$PbCO_3$	7.40×10^{-14}
Lead(II) chloride	$PbCl_2$	1.17×10^{-5}
Lead(II) chromate	$PbCrO_4$	2.8×10^{-13}
Lead(II) fluoride	PbF_2	3.3×10^{-8}
Lead(II) hydroxide	$Pb(OH)_2$	1.43×10^{-20}
Lead(II) iodide	PbI_2	9.8×10^{-9}
Lead(II) phosphate	$Pb_3(PO_4)_2$	1×10^{-54}
Lead(II) sulfate	$PbSO_4$	1.82×10^{-8}
Lead(II) sulfide	PbS	9.04×10^{-29}
Magnesium carbonate	$MgCO_3$	6.82×10^{-6}
Magnesium fluoride	MgF_2	5.16×10^{-11}
Magnesium hydroxide	$Mg(OH)_2$	2.06×10^{-13}
Magnesium oxalate	MgC_2O_4	4.83×10^{-6}
Manganese(II) carbonate	$MnCO_3$	2.24 × 10
Manganese(II) hydroxide	$Mn(OH)_2$	1.6 × 10
Manganese(II) sulfide	MnS	2.3 ×
Mercury(II) hydroxide	$Hg(OH)_2$	3.1
Mercury(II) sulfide	HgS	1.
Nickel(II) carbonate	$NiCO_3$	
Nickel(II) hydroxide	$Ni(OH)_2$	13
Nickel(II) sulfide	NiS	0^{-12}
Silver bromate	$AgBrO_3$	
Silver bromide	$AgBr$	
Silver carbonate	Ag_2C	

xt page)

Compound	Formula	K_{sp}
Silver chloride	$AgCl$	1.77×10^{-10}
Silver chromate	Ag_2CrO_4	1.12×10^{-12}
Silver cyanide	$AgCN$	5.97×10^{-17}
Silver iodide	AgI	8.51×10^{-17}
Silver phosphate	Ag_3PO_4	8.89×10^{-17}
Silver sulfate	Ag_2SO_4	1.20×10^{-5}
Silver sulfide	Ag_2S	6×10^{-51}
Strontium carbonate	$SrCO_3$	5.60×10^{-10}
Strontium chromate	$SrCrO_4$	3.6×10^{-5}
Strontium phosphate	$Sr_3(PO_4)_2$	1×10^{-31}
Strontium sulfate	$SrSO_4$	3.44×10^{-7}
Tin(II) hydroxide	$Sn(OH)_2$	5.45×10^{-27}
Tin(II) sulfide	SnS	1×10^{-26}
Zinc carbonate	$ZnCO_3$	1.46×10^{-10}
Zinc hydroxide	$Zn(OH)_2$	3×10^{-17}
Zinc oxalate	ZnC_2O_4	2.7×10^{-8}
Zinc sulfide	ZnS	2×10^{-25}

5. Complex Ion Formation Constants in Water at 25 °C

Complex Ion	K_f
$[Ag(CN)_2]^-$	1×10^{21}
$[Ag(EDTA)]^{3-}$	2.1×10^{7}
$[Ag(en)_2]^+$	5.0×10^{7}
$[Ag(NH_3)_2]^+$	1.7×10^{7}
$[Ag(SCN)_4]^{3-}$	1.2×10^{10}
$[Ag(S_2O_3)_2]^-$	2.8×10^{13}
$[Al(EDTA)]^-$	1.3×10^{16}
$[AlF_6]^{3-}$	7×10^{19}
$[Al(OH)_4]^-$	3×10^{33}
$[Al(ox)_3]^{3-}$	2×10^{16}
$[CdBr_4]^{2-}$	5.5×10^{3}
$[Cd(CN)_4]^{2-}$	3×10^{18}
$[CdCl_4]^{2-}$	6.3×10^{2}
$[Cd(en)_3]^{2+}$	1.2×10^{12}
$[CdI_4]^{2-}$	2×10^{6}
$[Co(EDTA)]^{2-}$	2.0×10^{16}
$[Co(EDTA)]^-$	1×10^{36}
$[Co(en)_3]^{2+}$	8.7×10^{13}
$[Co(en)_3]^{3+}$	4.9×10^{48}
$[Co(NH_3)_6]^{2+}$	1.3×10^{5}
$[Co(NH_3)_6]^{3+}$	2.3×10^{33}
$[Co(OH)_4]^{2-}$	5×10^{9}
$[Co(ox)_3]^{4-}$	5×10^{9}
$[Co(ox)_3]^{3-}$	1×10^{20}
[illegible]$(SCN)_4]^{2-}$	1×10^{3}
[illegible]$DTA)]^-$	1×10^{23}
[illegible]$]^-$	8.0×10^{29}
[illegible]	5×10^{5}
[illegible]	1.0×10^{25}
[[illegible]	5×10^{18}
[Cu [illegible]	1×10^{20}
[Fe(C [illegible]	1.7×10^{13}
[illegible]	3×10^{8}
[illegible]	1.5×10^{35}
$[Fe(CN)_6]^{3-}$	2×10^{43}
$[Fe(EDTA)]^{2-}$	2.1×10^{14}
$[Fe(EDTA)]^-$	1.7×10^{24}
$[Fe(en)_3]^{2+}$	5.0×10^{9}
$[Fe(ox)_3]^{4-}$	1.7×10^{5}
$[Fe(ox)_3]^{3-}$	2×10^{20}
$[Fe(SCN)]^{2+}$	8.9×10^{2}
$[Hg(CN)_4]^{2-}$	1.8×10^{41}
$[HgCl_4]^{2-}$	1.1×10^{16}
$[Hg(EDTA)]^{2-}$	6.3×10^{21}
$[Hg(en)_2]^{2+}$	2×10^{23}
$[HgI_4]^{2-}$	2×10^{30}
$[Hg(ox)_2]^{2-}$	9.5×10^{6}
$[Ni(CN)_4]^{2-}$	2×10^{31}
$[Ni(EDTA)]^{2-}$	3.6×10^{18}
$[Ni(en)_3]^{2+}$	2.1×10^{18}
$[Ni(NH_3)_6]^{2+}$	2.0×10^{8}
$[Ni(ox)_3]^{4-}$	3×10^{8}
$[PbCl_3]^-$	2.4×10^{1}
$[Pb(EDTA)]^{2-}$	2×10^{18}
$[PbI_4]^{2-}$	3.0×10^{4}
$[Pb(OH)_3]^-$	8×10^{13}
$[Pb(ox)_2]^{2-}$	3.5×10^{6}
$[Pb(S_2O_3)_3]^{4-}$	2.2×10^{6}
$[PtCl_4]^{2-}$	1×10^{16}
$[Pt(NH_3)_6]^{2+}$	2×10^{35}
$[Sn(OH)_3]^-$	3×10^{25}
$[Zn(CN)_4]^{2-}$	2.1×10^{19}
$[Zn(EDTA)]^{2-}$	3×10^{16}
$[Zn(en)_3]^{2+}$	1.3×10^{14}
$[Zn(NH_3)_4]^{2+}$	2.8×10^{9}
$[Zn(OH)_4]^{2-}$	2×10^{15}
$[Zn(ox)_3]^{4-}$	1.4×10^{8}

D. Standard Electrode Potentials at 25 °C

Half-Reaction	$E°$ (V)
$F_2(g) + 2\,e^- \longrightarrow 2\,F^-(aq)$	2.87
$O_3(g) + 2\,H^+(aq) + 2\,e^- \longrightarrow O_2(g) + H_2O(l)$	2.08
$Ag^{2+}(aq) + e^- \longrightarrow Ag^+(aq)$	1.98
$Co^{3+}(aq) + e^- \longrightarrow Co^{2+}(aq)$	1.82
$H_2O_2(aq) + 2\,H^+(aq) + 2\,e^- \longrightarrow 2\,H_2O(l)$	1.78
$PbO_2(s) + 4\,H^+(aq) + SO_4^{2-}(aq) + 2\,e^- \longrightarrow PbSO_4(s) + 2\,H_2O(l)$	1.69
$MnO_4^-(aq) + 4\,H^+(aq) + 3\,e^- \longrightarrow MnO_2(s) + 2\,H_2O(l)$	1.68
$2\,HClO(aq) + 2\,H^+(aq) + 2\,e^- \longrightarrow Cl_2(g) + 2\,H_2O(l)$	1.61
$MnO_4^-(aq) + 8\,H^+(aq) + 5\,e^- \longrightarrow Mn^{2+}(aq) + 4\,H_2O(l)$	1.51
$Au^{3+}(aq) + 3\,e^- \longrightarrow Au(s)$	1.50
$2\,BrO_3^-(aq) + 12\,H^+(aq) + 10\,e^- \longrightarrow Br_2(l) + 6\,H_2O(l)$	1.48
$PbO_2(s) + 4\,H^+(aq) + 2\,e^- \longrightarrow Pb^{2+}(aq) + 2\,H_2O(l)$	1.46
$Cl_2(g) + 2\,e^- \longrightarrow 2\,Cl^-(aq)$	1.36
$Cr_2O_7^{2-}(aq) + 14\,H^+(aq) + 6\,e^- \longrightarrow 2\,Cr^{3+}(aq) + 7\,H_2O(l)$	1.33
$O_2(g) + 4\,H^+(aq) + 4\,e^- \longrightarrow 2\,H_2O(l)$	1.23
$MnO_2(s) + 4\,H^+(aq) + 2\,e^- \longrightarrow Mn^{2+}(aq) + 2\,H_2O(l)$	1.21
$IO_3^-(aq) + 6\,H^+(aq) + 5\,e^- \longrightarrow \frac{1}{2}\,I_2(aq) + 3\,H_2O(l)$	1.20
$Br_2(l) + 2\,e^- \longrightarrow 2\,Br^-(aq)$	1.09
$AuCl_4^-(aq) + 3\,e^- \longrightarrow Au(s) + 4\,Cl^-(aq)$	1.00
$VO_2^+(aq) + 2\,H^+(aq) + e^- \longrightarrow VO^{2+}(aq) + H_2O(l)$	1.00
$HNO_2(aq) + H^+(aq) + e^- \longrightarrow NO(g) + 2\,H_2O(l)$	0.98
$NO_3^-(aq) + 4\,H^+(aq) + 3\,e^- \longrightarrow NO(g) + 2\,H_2O(l)$	0.96
$ClO_2(g) + e^- \longrightarrow ClO_2^-(aq)$	0.95
$2\,Hg^{2+}(aq) + 2\,e^- \longrightarrow 2\,Hg_2^{2+}(aq)$	0.92
$Ag^+(aq) + e^- \longrightarrow Ag(s)$	0.80
$Hg_2^{2+}(aq) + 2\,e^- \longrightarrow 2\,Hg(l)$	0.80
$Fe^{3+}(aq) + e^- \longrightarrow Fe^{2+}(aq)$	0.77
$PtCl_4^{2-}(aq) + 2\,e^- \longrightarrow Pt(s) + 4\,Cl^-(aq)$	0.76
$O_2(g) + 2\,H^+(aq) + 2\,e^- \longrightarrow H_2O_2(aq)$	0.70
$MnO_4^-(aq) + e^- \longrightarrow MnO_4^{2-}(aq)$	0.56
$I_2(s) + 2\,e^- \longrightarrow 2\,I^-(aq)$	0.54
$Cu^+(aq) + e^- \longrightarrow Cu(s)$	0.52
$O_2(g) + 2\,H_2O(l) + 4\,e^- \longrightarrow 4\,OH^-(aq)$	0.40
$Cu^{2+}(aq) + 2\,e^- \longrightarrow Cu(s)$	0.34

Half-Reaction	$E°$ (V)
$BiO^+(aq) + 2\,H^+(aq) + 3\,e^- \longrightarrow Bi(s) + H_2O(l)$	0.32
$Hg_2Cl_2(s) + 2\,e^- \longrightarrow 2\,Hg(l) + 2\,Cl^-(aq)$	0.27
$AgCl(s) + e^- \longrightarrow Ag(s) + Cl^-(aq)$	0.22
$SO_4^{2-}(aq) + 4\,H^+(aq) + 2\,e^- \longrightarrow H_2SO_3(aq) + H_2O(l)$	0.20
$Cu^{2+}(aq) + e^- \longrightarrow Cu^+(aq)$	0.16
$Sn^{4+}(aq) + 2\,e^- \longrightarrow Sn^{2+}(aq)$	0.15
$S(s) + 2\,H^+(aq) + 2\,e^- \longrightarrow H_2S(g)$	0.14
$AgBr(s) + e^- \longrightarrow Ag(s) + Br^-(aq)$	0.071
$2\,H^+(aq) + 2\,e^- \longrightarrow H_2(g)$	0.00
$Fe^{3+}(aq) + 3\,e^- \longrightarrow Fe(s)$	−0.036
$Pb^{2+}(aq) + 2\,e^- \longrightarrow Pb(s)$	−0.13
$Sn^{2+}(aq) + 2\,e^- \longrightarrow Sn(s)$	−0.14
$AgI(s) + e^- \longrightarrow Ag(s) + I^-(aq)$	−0.15
$N_2(g) + 5\,H^+(aq) + 4\,e^- \longrightarrow N_2H_5^+(aq)$	−0.23
$Ni^{2+}(aq) + 2\,e^- \longrightarrow Ni(s)$	−0.23
$Co^{2+}(aq) + 2\,e^- \longrightarrow Co(s)$	−0.28
$PbSO_4(s) + 2\,e^- \longrightarrow Pb(s) + SO_4^{2-}(aq)$	−0.36
$Cd^{2+}(aq) + 2\,e^- \longrightarrow Cd(s)$	−0.40
$Fe^{2+}(aq) + 2\,e^- \longrightarrow Fe(s)$	−0.45
$2\,CO_2(g) + 2\,H^+(aq) + 2\,e^- \longrightarrow H_2C_2O_4(aq)$	−0.49
$Cr^{3+}(aq) + e^- \longrightarrow Cr^{2+}(aq)$	−0.50
$Cr^{3+}(aq) + 3\,e^- \longrightarrow Cr(s)$	−0.73
$Zn^{2+}(aq) + 2\,e^- \longrightarrow Zn(s)$	−0.76
$2\,H_2O(l) + 2\,e^- \longrightarrow H_2(g) + 2\,OH^-(aq)$	−0.83
$Mn^{2+}(aq) + 2\,e^- \longrightarrow Mn(s)$	−1.18
$Al^{3+}(aq) + 3\,e^- \longrightarrow Al(s)$	−1.66
$H_2(g) + 2\,e^- \longrightarrow 2\,H^-(aq)$	−2.23
$Mg^{2+}(aq) + 2\,e^- \longrightarrow Mg(s)$	−2.37
$La^{3+}(aq) + 3\,e^- \longrightarrow La(s)$	−2.38
$Na^+(aq) + e^- \longrightarrow Na(s)$	−2.71
$Ca^{2+}(aq) + 2\,e^- \longrightarrow Ca(s)$	−2.76
$Ba^{2+}(aq) + 2\,e^- \longrightarrow Ba(s)$	−2.90
$K^+(aq) + e^- \longrightarrow K(s)$	−2.92
$Li^+(aq) + e^- \longrightarrow Li(s)$	−3.04

E. Vapour Pressure of Water at Various Temperatures

T (°C)	P (Torr)	T (°C)	P (Torr)	T (°C)	P (Torr)	T (°C)	P (Torr)
0	4.58	21	18.65	35	42.2	92	567[illegible]
5	6.54	22	19.83	40	55.3	94	6[illegible]
10	9.21	23	21.07	45	71.9	96	[illegible]
12	10.52	24	22.38	50	92.5	98	[illegible]
14	11.99	25	23.76	55	118.0	100	[illegible]
16	13.63	26	25.21	60	149.4	102	[illegible]
17	14.53	27	26.74	65	187.5	104	[illegible]
18	15.48	28	28.35	70	233.7	106	[illegible]
19	16.48	29	30.04	80	355.1	10[illegible]	[illegible]
20	17.54	30	31.82	90	525.8	[illegible]	[illegible]

Appendix III:

Answers to Selected Exercises

Chapter 1

21. **a.** chemical **b.** physical **c.** physical **d.** chemical

23. **a.** chemical **b.** physical **c.** chemical **d.** chemical

25. **a.** physical **b.** chemical **c.** physical

27. **a.** 273.15 K **b.** −196 °C **c.** 310.2 K

29. 195.7 K

31. **a.** 1.2 nm **b.** 22 fs **c.** 1.5 Gg **d.** 3.5 ML

33. **a.** 4.5×10^{-9} s **b.** 1.8×10^{-14} s **c.** 1.28×10^{-10} m **d.** 3.5×10^{-5} m

35. **a.** 1245 kg 1.245×10^6 g 1.245×10^9 mg
b. 515 km 5.15×10^6 dm 5.15×10^7 cm
c. 122.355 s 1.22355×10^5 ms 0.122355 ks
d. 3.345 kJ 3.345×10^3 J 3.345×10^6 mJ

37. **a.** 2.54998×10^2 km **b.** 2.54998×10^{-1} Mm **c.** 2.54998×10^8 mm **d.** 2.54998×10^7 cm

39. 10 000 1 cm squares

41. The density of the penny is 7.70 g cm^{-3}. The density of pure copper is 8.96 g cm^{-3} (Table 1.4), therefore the penny cannot be pure copper.

43. 1.26 g cm^{-3}

45. **a.** 463 g **b.** 3.7 L

47. 1.97×10^2 kg

49. **a.** 73.5 mL **b.** 88.2 °C **c.** 645 mL

51. **a.** 1050501 **b.** 0.0020 **c.** 0.000000000000002 **d.** 0.001090

53. **a.** 3 **b.** ambiguous, without more information assume 3 significant figures **c.** 3 **d.** 5 **e.** ambiguous, without more information assume 1 significant figure

55. **a.** 3 **b.** unlimited number of significant figures **c.** 6 **d.** 2

57. **a.** 156.9 **b.** 156.8 **c.** 156.8 **d.** 156.9

59. **a.** 1.84 **b.** 0.033 **c.** 0.500 **d.** 34

61. **a.** 41.4 **b.** 133.5 **c.** 73.0 **d.** 0.42

63. 1 kg m^2 s^{-2} = 1 J

65. **a.** 391.3 **b.** 1.1×10^4 **c.** 5.96 **d.** 5.93×10^4

67. **a.** 3.25×10^3 g **b.** 2.50×10^{-4} s **c.** 345 cm^3 **d.** 0.0257 km

69. 48 min

71. **a.** 1.95×10^{-4} km^2 **b.** 1.95×10^4 dm^2 **c.** 1.95×10^6 cm^2

73. 2.5×10^{10} m^2 = 2.5×10^4 km^2

75. 0.98 mL

77. 3.1557×10^7 s/solar year

79. **a.** extensive **b.** intensive **c.** intensive **d.** intensive **e.** extensive

81. **a.** 2.2×10^{-6} **b.** 0.0159 **c.** 6.9×10^4

83. 6.4×10^3 cm^3 (or 6.4 L)

85. 0.78 L

87. 7.6 g cm^3

89. 1.85×10^5 kg

91. 390 km (3.9×10^2 km)

93. 6.8×10^{-15}

95. H_2 molecules: 1.28×10^{11} km; ping pong balls: 2.4×10^{19} km

97. 488 g

99. 0.492

101. 18.5 bar

103. 1 J = 1 kg m^2 s^{-2}
m = kg, v^2 = (m s^{-1})^2: $\frac{1}{2} mv^2$ = kg m^2 s^{-2}
P = N m^{-2} = (kg m s^{-2})(m^{-2}) = kg m^{-1} s^{-2}, V = m^3:
$\frac{3}{2}$ PV = (= kg m^{-1} s^{-2})(m^3) = kg m^2 s^{-2}

105. **a.** 1.6×10^4 nm^3 (or 1.6×10^{-20} L) **b.** 1.3×10^{-18} g **c.** 170 g **d.** 1.3×10^{20} nanocontainers **e.** 2.0 L (probably a lot of nanocontainers compared to the 5 L of blood in the human body)

107. No. Since the container is sealed the atoms and molecules can move around, but they cannot leave. If no atoms or molecules can leave, the mass must be constant.

109. 343 1 cm cubes

111. **a.** the dark block **b.** the light-coloured blo **c.** cannot tell

Chapter 2

27. 13.4 g

29. These results are not consistent with the l at a proportions because sample 1 is comp pro- Cl to 1 part C and sample 2 is compo to 1 part C. The law of definite pro given compound always contain portion of elements by mass.

31. 23.8 g

33. For the law of multiple proportions to hold, the ratio of the masses of O combining with 1 g of O's in the compound should be a small whole number. $0.3369/0.168 = 2.00$

35. Sample 1: 1.00 g O_2/1.00 g S; sample 2: 1.50 g O_2/1.00 g S
Sample 2/sample 1 = 1.50/1.00 = 1.50
3 O atoms/2 O atoms = 1.5

37. -2.3×10^{-19} C

39. 9.4×10^{13} excess electrons, 8.5×10^{-17} kg

41. 1836 e^-

43. a. $^{63}_{29}Cu$ **b.** $^{65}_{29}Cu$ **c.** $^{40}_{19}K$ **d.** $^{40}_{18}Ar$

45. a. 7 ^1_1p and 7 ^0_1n **b.** 11 ^1_1p and 12 ^0_1n **c.** 86 ^1_1p and 136 ^0_1n **d.** 82 ^1_1p and 126 ^0_1n

47. 6 ^1_1p and 8 ^1_0n, $^{14}_6C$

49. a. 28 ^1_1p and 26 e^- **b.** 16 ^1_1p and 18 e^- **c.** 35 ^1_1p and 36 e^- **d.** 24 ^1_1p and 21 e^-

51.

Symbol	Ion Formed	Number of Electrons in Ion	Number of Protons in Ion
Ca	Ca^{2+}	18	20
Be	Be^{2+}	2	4
Se	Se^{2-}	36	34
In	In^{3+}	46	49

53. The atomic mass of gallium is 69.723 u.

55. The fluorine-19 isotope must have a large percent abundance, which would make fluorine produce a large peak at this mass. Chlorine has two isotopes (Cl-35 and Cl-37). The atomic mass is simply the weighted average of these two, which means that there is no chlorine isotope with a mass of 35.45 u.

57. 121.8 u, Sb

59. Br-79 78.92 u 50.69%

61. 2.3×10^{24} atoms

63. a. 0.295 mol Ar **b.** 0.0543 mol Zn **c.** 0.144 mol Ta **d.** 0.0304 mol Li

65. 2.11×10^{22} atoms

67. a. 1.01×10^{23} atoms **b.** 6.78×10^{21} atoms **c.** 5.39×10^{21} atoms **d.** 5.6×10^{20} atoms

69. a. 36 g **b.** 0.187 g **c.** 62 g **d.** 3.1 g

1. 2.6×10^{21} atoms
3.239×10^{-22} g

. potassium, metal **b.** barium, metal
iodine, nonmetal **d.** oxygen, nonmetal
ntimony, metalloid
um and potassium
8 metal **b.** halogen
earth metal **d.** alkaline earth metal

c.

83. a. use they are in the same group or fam-
c. 3 the same group or family have similar

85. 1.50 g

87. C_2O_3 **b.** 1+

89. 4.82245 × **d.** 1+

91. ^{237}Pa, ^{238}U, ^{239}Np, ^{240}Pu, ^{235}Ac, ^{234}Ra, ^{241}Am, ^{244}Cf etc.

93.

Symbol	Z	A	#p	#e^-	#n	Charge
O^{2-}	8	16	8	10	8	2−
Ca^{2+}	20	40	20	18	20	2+
Mg^{2+}	12	25	12	10	13	2+
N^{3-}	7	14	7	10	7	3−

95. $V_n = 8.2 \times 10^{-8}\ pm^3$, $V_a = 1.4 \times 10^6\ pm^3$, 5.9×10^{-12} %

97. 15.985 u

99. 2.90×10^{23} atoms

101. Li-6 = 7.494%, Li-7 = 92.506%

103. 75.0% gold, 25.0% Pd

105. 106.91 u

107. 0.422

109. 63.67 g mol^{-1}

111. 25.06 g mol^{-1}

113. If the u and mole were not based on the same isotope, the numerical values obtained for an atom of material and a mole of material would not be the same. If, for example, the mole was based on the number of particles in C-12 but the u was changed to a fraction of the mass of an atom of Ne-20, the number of particles and the number of u that make up one mole of material would no longer be the same. We would no longer have the relationship where the mass of an atom in u is numerically equal to the mass of a mole of those atoms in grams.

115. The different isotopes of the same element have the same number of protons and electrons, so the attractive forces between the nucleus and the electrons is constant and there is no difference in the radii of the isotopes. Ions, on the other hand, have a different number of electrons than the parent atom from which they are derived. Cations have fewer electrons than the parent atom. The attractive forces are greater because there is a larger positive charge in the nucleus than the negative charge in the electron cloud. So, cations are smaller than the atom they are derived from. Anions have more electrons than the parent. The electron cloud has a greater negative charge than the nucleus, so the anions have larger radii than the parent.

Chapter 3

23. a. 3 Mg, 2 P, 8 O **b.** 1 Ba, 2 Cl **c.** 1 Fe, 2 N, 4 O **d.** 1 Ca, 2 O, 2 H

25. a. NH_3 **b.** C_2H_6 **c.** SO_3

27. a. atomic **b.** molecular **c.** atomic **d.** molecular

29. a. molecular **b.** ionic **c.** ionic **d.** molecular

31. a. molecular element **b.** molecular compound **c.** atomic element

33. a. CaO **b.** ZnS **c.** RbBr **d.** Al_2O_3

35. a. $Ca(OH)_2$ **b.** $CaCrO_4$ **c.** $Ca_3(PO_4)_2$ **d.** $Ca(CN)_2$

37. **a.** magnesium nitride **b.** potassium fluoride
c. sodium oxide **d.** lithium sulfide
e. cesium fluoride **f.** potassium iodide
g. strontium chloride **h.** barium chloride

39. **a.** tin(II) oxide **b.** chromium(III) sulfide
c. rubidium iodide **d.** barium bromide

41. **a.** copper(I) nitrite **b.** magnesium acetate
c. barium nitrate **d.** lead(II) acetate
e. potassium chlorate **f.** lead(II) sulfate

43. **a.** $NaHSO_3$ **b.** $Ca(MnO_4)_2$
c. $AgNO_3$ **d.** K_2SO_4
e. $RbHSO_4$ **f.** $KHCO_3$

45. **a.** cobalt(II) sulfate heptahydrate
b. $IrBr_3 \cdot 4\, H_2O$
c. magnesium bromate hexahydrate
d. $K_2CO_3 \cdot 2\, H_2O$

47. **a.** carbon monoxide **b.** nitrogen triiodide
c. silicon tetrachloride **d.** tetranitrogen tetraselenide
e. diiodine pentoxide

49. **a.** PCl_3 **b.** ClO **c.** S_2F_4
d. PF_5 **e.** P_2S_5

51. **a.** hydroiodic acid **b.** nitric acid
c. carbonic acid **d.** phosphoric acid

53. **a.** HF **b.** HBr **c.** H_2SO_3

55. **a.** inorganic **b.** organic
c. organic **d.** inorganic

57. **a.** alkene **b.** alkane
c. alkyne **d.** alkane

59. **a.** $CH_3CH_2CH_2CH_3$ **b.** propane
c. $CH_3CH_2CH_2CH_2CH_2CH_2CH_2CH_3$
d. pentane

61. **a.** functionalized hydrocarbon, alcohol
b. hydrocarbon
c. functionalized hydrocarbon, ketone
d. functionalized hydrocarbon, amine

63. **a.** pentane
b. 2-methylbutane
c. 2-methyl-4-(1-methylethyl)heptane
d. 4-ethyl-2-methylhexane

65. **a.**
```
            CH3
            |
            CH2
            |
CH3—CH2—CH—CH2—CH2—CH3
```
b.
```
            CH3
            |
            CH2
            |
CH3—CH2—C—CH2—CH3
            |
            CH3
```
c.
```
      CH3  CH3
      |    |
CH3—CH—CH—CH3
```
d.
```
                    CH3                    CH3
                    |                      |
        CH3         CH2                    CH2
        |           |                      |
CH3—C—CH2—CH—CH2—CH2—CH—CH2—CH3
        |
        CH3
```

67. **a.** but-1-ene
b. 3,4-dimethylpent-2-ene
c. 3-(1-methylethyl)hex-1-yne
d. 3,6-dimethylnon-4-yne

69.
a. $CH_3—CH_2—CH_2—C{\equiv}C—CH_2—CH_2—CH_3$
b. $CH_3—CH_2—CH{=}CH—CH_2—CH_2—CH_2—CH_2—CH_3$
c.
```
          CH3
          |
HC≡C—C—CH2—CH3
          |
          CH3
```
d.
```
                          CH3
                          |
            CH3           CH2  CH3
            |             |    |
CH3—CH=C—CH2—CH—CH—CH3
```

71. **a.** methylbenzene
b. bromobenzene
c. chlorobenzene

73. **a.** 1,4-dibromobenzene
b. 1,3-diethylbenzene
c. 1-chloro-2-fluorobenzene

75. **a.** CH3 / CH3, C, H2 **b.** Br / Br **c.** Cl / CH3

77. **a.** propan-1-ol
b. 4-methylhexan-2-ol
c. 2,6-dimethylheptan-4-ol
d. 3-methylpentan-3-ol

79. **a.** methyl butanoate
b. propanoic acid
c. 5-methylhexanoic acid
d. ethyl pentanoate

81. **a.** ethoxypropane, or ethyl propyl ether
b. ethoxypentane, or ethyl pentyl ether
c. propoxypropane, or dipropylether
d. ethoxybutane, or butyl ethyl ether

83. **a.** diethylamine
b. methylpropylamine
c. butylmethylpropylamine

85. **a.** 46.01 u **b.** 58.12 u
c. 180.16 u **d.** 238.03

87. **a.** 0.554 mol **b.** 28.4 mol
c. 0.378 mol **d.** 1093 mol

89. **a.** 2.2×10^{23} molecules
b. 7.06×10^{23} molecules
c. 4.16×10^{23} molecules
d. 1.09×10^{23} molecules

91. **a.** 0.0790 g **b.** 0.84 g
c. 2.992×10^{-22} g

93. 0.10 mg

95. **a.** 74.87% C **b.** 79.88% C
c. 92.24% C **d.** 37.23% C

97. NH_3: 82.25% N
$CO(NH_2)_2$: 46.65% N
NH_4NO_3: 35.00% N
$(NH_4)_2SO_4$: 21.20% N
NH_3 has the highest N content

99. 20.8 g F

101. 196 μg KI

103. **a.** 2:1 **b.** 4:1 **c.** 6:2:1

105. **a.** 0.885 mol H **b.** 5.2 mol H
c. 29 mol H **d.** 33.7 mol H

107. **a.** 3.3 g Na **b.** 3.6 g Na
c. 1.4 g Na **d.** 1.7 g Na

109. **a.** Ag_2O **b.** $Co_3As_2O_8$
c. $SeBr_4$

111. **a.** C_5H_7N **b.** $C_4H_5N_2O$

113. $C_{13}H_{18}O_2$

115. NCl_3

117. **a.** $C_{12}H_{14}N_2$ **b.** $C_6H_3Cl_3$
c. $C_{10}H_{20}N_2S_4$

119. CH_2

121. C_2H_4O

123. **a.** alkene; 2,3,4-trimethylpent-2-ene
b. alkane; 2,2,4-trimethylhexane
c. carboxylic acid; 3-methylpentanoic acid
d. amine; butyl(1-methylethyl)amine
e. alcohol; 2,4-dimethylhexan-1-ol

125. 1.50×10^{24} molecules EtOH

127. **a.** K_2CrO_4, 40.27% K, 26.78% Cr, 32.95% O
b. $Pb_3(PO_4)_2$, 76.60% Pb, 7.63% P, 15.77% O
c. H_2SO_3, 2.46% H, 39.07% S, 58.47% O
d. $CoBr_2$, 26.94% Co, 73.06% Br

[illegible] 1.80×10^2 g Cl/yr

[illegible] = Fe

[illegible]adiol = $C_{18}H_{24}O_2$

[illegible]O_2

14[illegible]

145. [illegible] atoms

147. 4[illegible]

149. 0.2[illegible]

151. 22.0[illegible]

153. 7.8 × [illegible]

155. $C_5H_{10}S$[illegible]

157. X_3Y_2

159. The sphere in the molecular models represents the electron cloud of the atom. On this scale, the nucleus would be too small to see.

161. The statement is incorrect because a chemical formula is based on the ratio of atoms combined not the ratio of grams combined. The statement should read: "The chemical formula for ammonia (NH_3) indicates that ammonia contains three hydrogen atoms to each nitrogen atom."

163. O, S, H

Chapter 4

25. $2\,SO_2(g) + O_2(g) + 2\,H_2O(l) \longrightarrow 2\,H_2SO_4(aq)$

27. $2\,Na(s) + 2\,H_2O(l) \longrightarrow H_2(g) + 2\,NaOH(aq)$

29. $C_{12}H_{22}O_{11}(aq) + H_2O(l) \longrightarrow 4\,C_2H_5OH(aq) + 4\,CO_2(g)$

31. **a.** $PbS(s) + 2\,HBr(aq) \longrightarrow PbBr_2(s) + H_2S(g)$
b. $CO(g) + 3\,H_2(g) \longrightarrow CH_4(g) + H_2O(l)$
c. $4\,HCl(aq) + MnO_2(s) \longrightarrow MnCl_2(aq) + 2\,H_2O(l) + Cl_2(g)$
d. $C_5H_{12}(l) + 8\,O_2(g) \longrightarrow 5\,CO_2(g) + 6\,H_2O(g)$

33. **a.** $2\,CO_2(g) + CaSiO_3(s) + H_2O(l) \longrightarrow SiO_2(s) + Ca(HCO_3)_2(aq)$
b. $2\,Co(NO_3)_3(aq) + 3\,(NH_4)_2S(aq) \longrightarrow Co_2S_3(s) + 6\,NH_4NO_3(aq)$
c. $Cu_2O(s) + C(s) \longrightarrow 2\,Cu(s) + CO(g)$
d. $H_2(g) + Cl_2(g) \longrightarrow 2\,HCl(g)$

35. **a.** yes **b.** no
c. yes **d.** no

37. **a.** soluble Ag^+, NO_3^- **b.** soluble Pb^{2+}, $C_2H_3O_2^-$
c. soluble K^+, NO_3^- **d.** soluble NH_4^+, S^{2-}

39. **a.** NO REACTION **b.** NO REACTION
c. $CrBr_2(aq) + Na_2CO_3(aq) \longrightarrow CrCO_3(s) + 2\,NaBr(aq)$
d. $3\,NaOH(aq) + FeCl_3(aq) \longrightarrow Fe(OH)_3(s) + 3\,NaCl(aq)$

41. **a.** $K_2CO_3(aq) + Pb(NO_3)_2(aq) \longrightarrow PbCO_3(s) + 2\,KNO_3(aq)$
b. $Li_2SO_4(aq) + Pb(C_2H_3O_2)_2(aq) \longrightarrow PbSO_4(s) + 2\,LiC_2H_3O_2(aq)$
c. $Cu(NO_3)_2(aq) + MgS(aq) \longrightarrow CuS(s) + Mg(NO_3)_2(aq)$
d. NO REACTION

43. **a.** Complete:
$H^+(aq) + Cl^-(aq) + Li^+(aq) + OH^-(aq) \longrightarrow H_2O(l) + Li^+(aq) + Cl^-(aq)$
Net: $H^+(aq) + OH^-(aq) \longrightarrow H_2O(l)$
b. Complete:
$Mg^{2+}(aq) + S^{2-}(aq) + Cu^{2+}(aq) + 2\,Cl^-(aq) \longrightarrow CuS(s) + Mg^{2+}(aq) + 2\,Cl^-(aq)$
Net: $Cu^{2+}(aq) + S^{2-}(aq) \longrightarrow CuS(s)$
c. Complete:
$Na^+(aq) + OH^-(aq) + H^+(aq) + NO_3^-(aq) \longrightarrow H_2O(l) + Na^+(aq) + NO_3^-(aq)$
Net: $H^+(aq) + OH^-(aq) \longrightarrow H_2O(l)$
d. Complete:
$6\,Na^+(aq) + 2\,PO_4^{3-}(aq) + 3\,Ni^{2+}(aq) + 6\,Cl^-(aq) \longrightarrow Ni_3(PO_4)_2(s) + 6\,Na^+(aq) + 6\,Cl^-(aq)$
Net: $3\,Ni^{2+}(aq) + 2\,PO_4^{3-}(aq) \longrightarrow Ni_3(PO_4)_2(s)$

45. Complete:
$Hg_2^{2+}(aq) + 2\,NO_3^-(aq) + 2\,Na^+(aq) + 2\,Cl^-(aq) \longrightarrow Hg_2Cl_2(s) + 2\,Na^+(aq) + 2\,NO_3^-(aq)$
Net: $Hg_2^{2+}(aq) + 2\,Cl^-(aq) \longrightarrow Hg_2Cl_2(s)$

47. Molecular: $HBr(aq) + KOH(aq) \longrightarrow H_2O(l) + KBr(aq)$
Net ionic: $H^+(aq) + OH^-(aq) \longrightarrow H_2O(l)$

49. **a.** $H_2SO_4(aq) + Ca(OH)_2(aq) \longrightarrow 2\,H_2O(l) + CaSO_4(s)$
b. $HClO_4(aq) + KOH(aq) \longrightarrow H_2O(l) + KClO_4(aq)$
c. $H_2SO_4(aq) + 2\,NaOH(aq) \longrightarrow 2\,H_2O(l) + Na_2SO_4(aq)$

51. **a.** $2\,HBr(aq) + NiS(s) \longrightarrow H_2S(g) + NiBr_2(aq)$
b. $NH_4I(aq) + NaOH(aq) \longrightarrow H_2O(l) + NH_3(g) + NaI(aq)$
c. $2\,HBr(aq) + Na_2S(aq) \longrightarrow H_2S(g) + 2\,NaBr(aq)$
d. $2\,HClO_4(aq) + Li_2CO_3(aq) \longrightarrow H_2O(l) + CO_2(g) + 2\,LiClO_4(aq)$

53. **a.** Ag: 0 **b.** Ag: +1
c. Ca: +2, F: −1 **d.** H: +1, S: −2
e. C: +4, O: −2 **f.** Cr: +6, O: −2

55. **a.** +2 **b.** +6 **c.** +3

57. **a.** redox reaction, oxidizing agent: O_2, reducing agent: Li
b. redox reaction, oxidizing agent: Fe^{2+}, reducing agent: Mg
c. not a redox reaction **d.** not a redox reaction

59. **a.** $S(s) + O_2(g) \longrightarrow SO_2(g)$
b. $2\,C_3H_6(g) + 9\,O_2(g) \longrightarrow 6\,CO_2(g) + 6\,H_2O(g)$
c. $2\,Ca(s) + O_2(g) \longrightarrow 2\,CaO(g)$
d. $C_5H_{12}S(l) + 9\,O_2(g) \longrightarrow 5\,CO_2(g) + SO_2(g) + 6\,H_2O(g)$

61. **a.** $3\,K(s) + Cr^{3+}(aq) \longrightarrow Cr(s) + 3\,K^+(aq)$
b. $2\,Al(s) + 3\,Fe^{2+}(aq) \longrightarrow 2\,Al^{3+}(aq) + 3\,Fe(s)$
c. $2\,BrO_3^-(aq) + 3\,N_2H_4(g) \longrightarrow 2\,Br^-(aq) + 3\,N_2(g) + 6\,H_2O(l)$

63. **a.** $PbO_2(s) + 2\,I^-(aq) + 4\,H^+(aq) \longrightarrow Pb^{2+}(aq) + I_2(s) + 2\,H_2O(l)$
b. $5\,SO_3^{2-}(aq) + 2\,MnO_4^-(aq) + 6\,H^+(aq) \longrightarrow 5\,SO_4^{2-}(aq) + 2\,Mn^{2+}(aq) + 3\,H_2O(l)$
c. $S_2O_3^{2-}(aq) + 4\,Cl_2(g) + 5\,H_2O(l) \longrightarrow 2\,SO_4^{2-}(aq) + 8\,Cl^-(aq) + 10\,H^+(aq)$

65. **a.** $H_2O_2(aq) + 2\,ClO_2(aq) + 2\,OH^-(aq) \longrightarrow O_2(g) + 2\,ClO_2^-(aq) + 2\,H_2O(l)$
b. $Al(s) + MnO_4^-(aq) + 2\,H_2O(l) \longrightarrow Al(OH)_4^-(aq) + MnO_2(s)$
c. $3\,Cl_2(g) + 6\,OH^-(aq) \longrightarrow 5\,Cl^-(aq) + ClO_3^-(aq) + 3\,H_2O(l)$

67. **a.** $3\,Cl^-(aq) \longrightarrow 2\,Cl(aq) + ClO_3^-(aq)$
b. $Cu_2O(aq) + 2\,H^+(aq) \longrightarrow Cu(s) + Cu^{2+}(aq) + H_2O(l)$

69. $2\,C_6H_{14}(g) + 19\,O_2(g) \longrightarrow 12\,CO_2(g) + 14\,H_2O(g)$, 68 mol O_2

71. **a.** 5.0 mol NO_2 **b.** 14 mol NO_2
c. 0.281 mol NO_2 **d.** 53.1 mol NO_2

73.

mol SiO_2	*mol C*	*mol SiC*	*mol CO*
3	9	3	6
2	6	2	4
5	15	5	10
2.8	8.4	2.8	5.6
0.517	1.55	0.517	1.03

75. 9.3 g HBr, 0.12 g H_2

77. **a.** 5.56 g $BaCl_2$ **b.** 6.55 g $CaCO_3$
c. 6.09 g MgO **d.** 6.93 g Al_2O_3

79. **a.** 4.42 g HCl **b.** 8.25 g HNO_3
c. 4.24 g H_2SO_4

81. **a.** Na **b.** Na
c. Br_2 **d.** Na

83. 3 molecules Cl_2

85. **a.** 2 mol **b.** 7 mol
c. 9.40 mol

87. 0.5 mol O_2

89. **a.** 2.5 g **b.** 31.1 g **c.** 1.16 g

91. 2.91 grams CO remaining

93. limiting reactant: Pb^{2+}, theoretical yield: 34.5 g $PbCl_2$, percent yield: 85.2%

95. limiting reactant: NH_3, theoretical yield: 240.5 kg CH_4N_2O, percent yield: 70.02%

97. **a.** 1.17 mol L^{-1} LiCl **b.** 0.123 mol L^{-1} $C_6H_{12}O_6$
c. 0.00453 mol L^{-1} NaCl

99. **a.** 1.3 mol **b.** 1.5 mol
c. 0.211 mol

101. 37 g

103. 0.27 mol L^{-1}

105. 6.0 L

107. 37.1 mL

109. 2.1 L

111. 3.32 mol L^{-1}

113. 1.1 g

115. 3.1 kg

117. limiting reactant: $C_7H_6O_3$, theoretical yield: 1.63 g $C_9H_8O_4$, percent yield: 74.8%

119. b.

121. **a.** $2\,HCl(aq) + Hg_2(NO_3)_2(aq) \longrightarrow Hg_2Cl_2(s) + 2\,HNO_3(aq)$
b. $KHSO_3(aq) + HNO_3(aq) \longrightarrow H_2O(l) + SO_2(g) + KNO_3(aq)$
c. $2\,NH_4Cl(aq) + Pb(NO_3)_2(aq) \longrightarrow PbCl_2(s) + 2\,NH_4NO_3(aq)$
d. $2\,NH_4Cl(aq) + Ca(OH)_2(aq) \longrightarrow 2\,NH_3(g) + 2\,H_2O(g) + CaCl_2($

123. 22 g

125. 6.9 g

127. $NaNO_3$ is more economical

129. BrF_3 is the oxidizing agent, Au is the redu
38.8 g $KAuF_4$

131. Ca^{2+} and Cu^{2+} present in the original so
Net ionic for first precipitate:
$Ca^{2+}(aq) + SO_4^{2-}(aq) \longrightarrow CaSO$
Net ionic for second precipitate:
$Cu^{2+}(aq) + CO_3^{2-}(aq) \longrightarrow C$

133. 0.333 g PH_3
135. 30.8 kg CO_2
137. 1.6 g C_2H_2
139. 11.8 g AgI
141. 5.6% by mass
143. 14 g KO_2. In designing the unit you would need to consider the theoretical yield and % yield of the reaction, how changing the limiting reactant would affect the reaction, the stoichiometry between KO_2 and O_2 to determine the mass of KO_2 required to produce enough O_2 for 10 minutes. You might also consider the speed of the reaction and whether or not the reaction produced heat. Additionally, because your body does not use 100% of the oxygen taken in with each breath, the apparatus would only need to replenish the oxygen used. The percentage of oxygen in air is about 20% and the percentage in exhaled air is about 16%, so we will assume that 4% of the air would need to be replenished with oxygen.
145. 37.9 g B_5H_9
147. **d.** A quick mental calculation shows that there are less than 0.040 moles of K and more than 0.01 moles of O_2. Since K and O_2 react 4 to 1 and the ratio of K to O_2 in the mixture is less than this, K is the limiting reactant.
149. **a.** add 0.50 mol solute (4 particles)
b. add 1.0 L of solvent
c. add 0.33 L of solvent

Chapter 5

25. **a.** 0.864 atm **b.** 12.7 psi
c. 87500 Pa **d.** 656 Torr
e. 0.875 bar
27. **a.** 1.064 atm **b.** 808.5 Torr
c. 107.8 kPa **d.** 1078 mbar
e. 1.078 bar
29. **a.** 832 mmHg **b.** 718 mmHg
31. 4.4×10^2 mmHg
33. 58.9 mL
35. 4.22 L
37. 3.1 L The volume would not be different if the gas was argon.
1.17 bar
2.1 mol
s, the final gauge pressure is 43.5 psi which exceeds naximum rating.

10^2 bar, 17.7 bottles purged
51. re more moles of gas in (b), therefore, the
53. is greater.
55. 9.
57. 44. rr
59. 5.33
61. P_{total} =
$mass_{He}$ = 0.437 g, $mass_{O_2}$ = 0.237 g,
63. 1.86 bar
65. $\chi_{N_2} = 0.627$, $\chi_{O_2} = 0.373$, $P_{N_2} = 0.696$ bar, $P_{O_2} = 0.415$ bar
67. $P_{H_2} = 0.933$ bar, $mass_{H_2} = 0.0539$ g
69. 7.42×10^{-2} g
71. 39 L
73. $V_{H_2} = 48.2$ L, $V_{CO} = 24.1$ L
75. 22.5 g NaN_3
77. 59.7%
79. **a.** yes **b.** no
c. No. Even though the argon atoms are more massive than the helium atoms, both have the same kinetic energy at a given temperature. The argon atoms therefore move more slowly, and so exert the same pressure as the helium atoms.
d. He
81. F_2: $u_{rms} = 442$ m s^{-1}, $KE_{avg} = 3.72 \times 10^3$ J mol^{-1};
Cl_2: $u_{rms} = 324$ m s^{-1}, $KE_{avg} = 3.72 \times 10^3$ J mol^{-1};
Br_2: $u_{rms} = 216$ m s^{-1}, $KE_{avg} = 3.72 \times 10^3$ J mol^{-1};
rankings: u_{rms}: $Br_2 < Cl_2 < F_2$; KE_{avg}: $Br_2 = Cl_2 = F_2$;
rate of effusion: $Br_2 < Cl_2 < F_2$
83. rate $^{238}UF_6$/rate $^{235}UF_6$ = 0.99574
85. krypton
87. A has the higher molar mass, B has the higher rate of effusion.
89. 0.469 mol O_2
91. That the volume of gas particles is small compared to the space between them breaks down under conditions of high pressure. At high pressure the particles themselves occupy a significant portion of the total gas volume.
93. 0.05903 L (ideal); 0.0716 L (V.D.W.); Difference because of high pressure, at which Ne no longer acts ideally.
95. 97.8%
97. 27.8 g mol^{-1}
99. C_4H_{10}
101. 4.70 L
103. $2\,HCl(aq) + K_2S(s) \longrightarrow H_2S(g) + 2\,KCl(aq)$, 0.191 g $K_2S(s)$
105. 11.8 L
107. $mass_{air} = 8.57$ g, $mass_{He} = 1.20$ g, mass difference = 7.37 g
109. 4.76 L/s
111. total force = 2.73×10^4 N; no, the can cannot withstand this force
113. 5.8×10^3 balloons
115. 4.0 cm
117. 77.7%
119. 0.3 g
121. 311 K
123. 5.0 g
125. C_3H_8
127. 0.37 g Ar
129. 98.6 mbar
131. **a.** C_3H_5
b. molar mass = 82.1 g mol^{-1}, C_6H_{10}
133. 30% N_2H_4
135. 25%

137. $P_{CH_4} = 7.3 \times 10^{-2}$ bar, $P_{O_2} = 4.2 \times 10^{-1}$ bar, $P_{NO} = 2.8 \times 10^{-3}$ bar, $P_{CO_2} = 5.0 \times 10^{-3}$ bar, $P_{H_2O} = 5.0 \times 10^{-3}$ bar, $P_{NO_2} = 2.5 \times 10^{-2}$ bar, $P_{OH} = 1.0 \times 10^{-3}$ bar, $P_{total} = 0.532$ bar
139. 0.42
141. Because helium is less dense than air, the balloon moves in a direction opposite the direction the air inside the car is moving due to the acceleration and deceleration of the car.
143. −29%
145. **a.** is not true because the kinetic energy of the molecules is the same because they are at the same temperature.
b. is not true because if the gases are present in equal amounts, they have the same partial pressure.
c. is not true because if the kinetic energies are the same for both, then the heavier molecule (b) has a lesser average velocity.

Chapter 6

33. **a.** 1.92×10^9 J **b.** 51.4 Cal **c.** 2.37×10^6 J **d.** 681 cal
35. **a.** 9.987×10^6 J **b.** 9.987×10^3 kJ **c.** 2.77 kWh
37. d.
39. **a.** heat, + **b.** work, − **c.** heat, +
41. -7.27×10^2 kJ
43. 311 J
45. The drinks that went into cooler B had more thermal energy than the refrigerated drinks that went into cooler A. The temperature difference between the drinks in cooler B and the ice was greater than the difference between the drinks and the ice in cooler A. More thermal energy was exchanged between the drinks and the ice in cooler B, which resulted in more melting.
47. 4.7×10^5 J
49. **a.** 7.6×10^2 °C **b.** 4.3×10^2 °C **c.** 1.3×10^2 °C **d.** 49 °C
51. -2.8×10^2 J
53. 490 J
55. -1238 J mol^{-1} for $H_2O_2(l) \longrightarrow \frac{1}{2}O_2(g) + H_2O(l)$
57. $\Delta U = -3463$ kJ, $\Delta H = -3452$ kJ
59. **a.** exothermic, − **b.** endothermic, + **c.** exothermic, −
61. -4.30×10^3 kJ
63. 9.5×10^2 g CO_2
65. 77 g
67. Final temperature 28.4 °C
69. Specific heat capacity of substance A 1.10 J g^{-1} °C^{-1}
71. Measurement B corresponds to conditions of constant pressure. Measurement A corresponds to conditions of constant volume. When a fuel is burned under constant pressure some of the energy released does work on the atmosphere by expanding against it. Less energy is manifest as heat due to this work. When a fuel is burned under constant volume, all of the energy released by the combustion reaction is evolved as heat.
73. $\Delta_r U = -6322$ kJ mol^{-1}, $\Delta_r H = -6328$ kJ mol^{-1}
75. -1.6×10^5 J mol^{-1}
77. **a.** $-\Delta H_1$ **b.** $2\ \Delta H_1$ **c.** $-\frac{1}{2}\Delta H_1$
79. -23.9 kJ mol^{-1}
81. 87.8 kJ mol^{-1}
83. **a.** $\frac{1}{2}N_2(g) + \frac{3}{2}H_2(g) \longrightarrow NH_3(g)$, $\Delta_f H° = -45.9$ kJ mol^{-1}
b. $C(s, \text{graphite}) + O_2(g) \longrightarrow CO_2(g)$, $\Delta_f H° = -393.5$ kJ mol^{-1}
c. $2\ Fe(s) + \frac{3}{2}O_2(g) \longrightarrow Fe_2O_3(s)$, $\Delta_f H° = -824.2$ kJ mol^{-1}
d. $C(s, \text{graphite}) + 2\ H_2(g) \longrightarrow CH_4(g)$, $\Delta_f H° = -74.6$ kJ mol^{-1}
85. -380.2 kJ mol^{-1}
87. **a.** -137.1 kJ mol^{-1} **b.** -41.2 kJ mol^{-1} **c.** -137 kJ mol^{-1} **d.** 290.7 kJ mol^{-1}
89. $6\ CO_2(g) + 6\ H_2O(l) \longrightarrow C_6H_{12}O_6(s) + 6\ O_2(g)$, $\Delta_r H° = 2803$ kJ mol^{-1}
91. -113.0 kJ mol^{-1}
93. **a.** 5.49 g CO_2 **b.** 5.96 g CO_2 **c.** 6.94 g CO_2
Natural gas, $CH_4(g)$, contributes the least to the increase by producing the least $CO_2(g)$ per kJ of heat produced.
95. 2×10^{13} kg yr^{-1}
9000 years to double the amount of carbon dioxide
97. $\Delta U = -1.7$ J, $q = -0.5$ J, $w = -1.2$ J
99. 78 g
101. $\Delta_r H = 6.0$ kJ mol^{-1}, 1.1×10^2 g
103. 26.1 °C
105. palmitic acid: 9.9368 Cal g^{-1}, sucrose: 3.938 Cal g^{-1}, fat contains more Cal g^{-1} than sugar
107. $\Delta H = \Delta U + nR\Delta T$
109. 5.7 Cal g^{-1}
111. $\Delta U = 0$, $\Delta H = 0$, $q = -w = 3.0 \times 10^3$ J
113. -294 kJ mol^{-1}
115. 94.1 kJ emitted
117. 23.9 °C
119. 22 L
121. 230 g NH_4NO_3
123. 240 g CO_2
125. 2.1 L C_7H_{16}
127. 67.6 g ice minimum
129. $C_v = \frac{3}{2}R$, $C_p = \frac{5}{2}R$
131. $q = 1030$ kJ, $\Delta H = 1030$ kJ, $\Delta U = 950$ kJ, $w =$ [illegible]
133. -1292 kJ mol^{-1}
135. **d.**
137. **a.** At constant pressure, heat can be ad[illegible] eat can be done on the system. $\Delta U =$ [illegible] $q = \Delta U - w$.
139. The aluminum is cooler because [illegible] capacity (specific heat).

141. $q = -2418 \text{ J mol}^{-1}$, $w = -5 \text{ J mol}^{-1}$, $\Delta_r H = -2418 \text{ J mol}^{-1}$, $\Delta_r U = -2423 \text{ J mol}^{-1}$

143. **b.** $\Delta H > \Delta U$

Chapter 7

49. 499 s

51. **(i)** d, c, b, a
(ii) a, b, c, d

53. **a.** 4.74×10^{14} Hz **b.** 5.96×10^{14} Hz
c. 5.8×10^{18} Hz

55. **a.** 3.14×10^{-19} J **b.** 3.95×10^{-19} J
c. 3.8×10^{-15} J

57. 1.03×10^{16} photons

59. **a.** 79.8 kJ mol^{-1} **b.** 239 kJ mol^{-1}
c. 798 kJ mol^{-1}

61. 4.64×10^5 m s^{-1}

63. $n = 1$

65. **a.** 122 nm, UV **b.** 103 nm, UV
c. 486 nm, visible **d.** 434 nm, visible

67. $n = 2$

69.

71. 3.6×10^6 m s^{-1}

73. 5.39 nm

75. 1.1×10^{-34} m. The wavelength of a baseball is negligible with respect to its size.

77. $\Delta v = 1.05 \times 10^5$ m s^{-1}

79. 2s

81. **a.** $l = 0$ **b.** $l = 0, 1$
c. $l = 0, 1, 2$ **d.** $l = 0, 1, 2, 3$

83. **c.**

85. See Figures 7.25 and 7.26. The 2s and 3p orbitals would, on average, be farther from the nucleus and have more nodes than the 1s and 2p orbitals.

87. **a.** $1s^22s^22p^63s^23p^2$

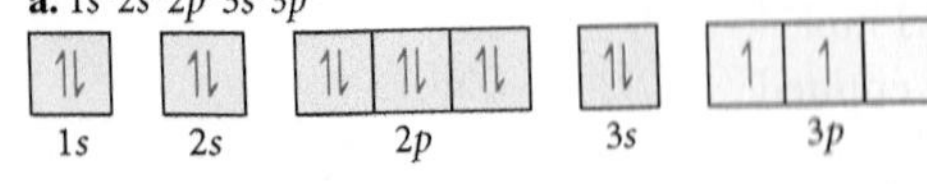

b. $1s^22s^22p^4$

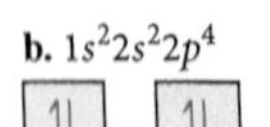
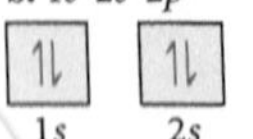
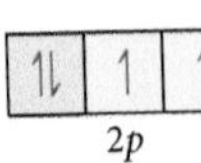

$^22s^22p^63s^23p^24s^1$

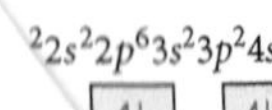
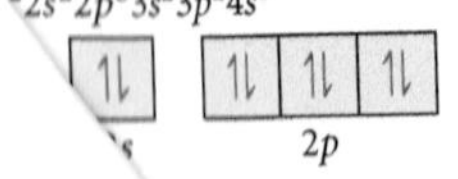

e.
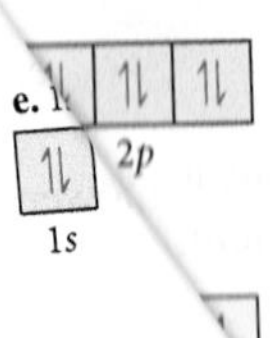

89. **a.** $[\text{He}]2s^22p^3$

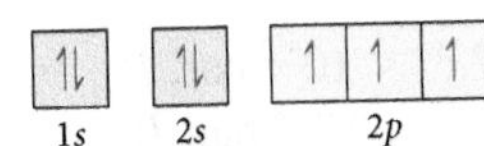

b. $[\text{Ar}]\,4s^23d^{10}4p^3$

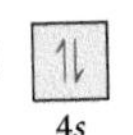
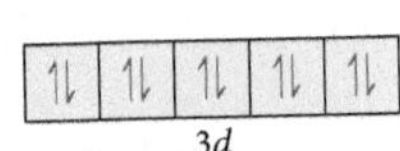

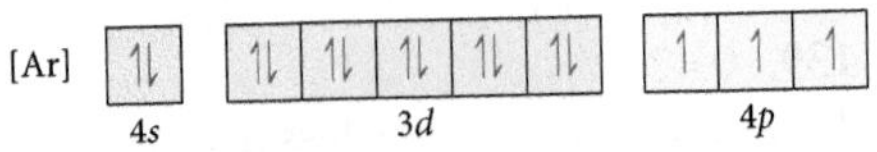

c. $[\text{Ar}]\,4s^23d^{10}$

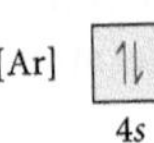
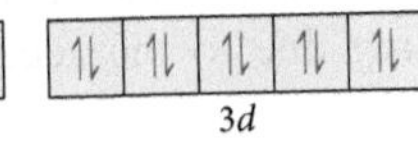

d. $[\text{Kr}]\,4d^{10}$

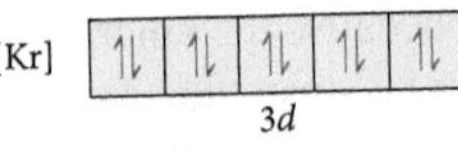

91. **a.** [Ne] **b.** [Kr] **c.** [Kr] **d.** [Ar] $3d^6$ **e.** [Ar] $3d^9$

93. **a.** [Ar] $4s^23d^8$, [Ar] $3d^8$
b. [Ar] $4s^23d^5$, [Ar] $3d^3$
c. [Kr] $5s^24d^1$, [Kr]
d. [Xe] $6s^24f^{14}5d^3$, [Xe] $4f^{14}$

95. **a.** [Ne] $3s^23p^6$, diamagnetic
b. [Ar] $3d^3$, paramagnetic
c. [Ar] $3d^8$, paramagnetic
d. [Ar] $3d^5$, paramagnetic

97. 344 nm

99. 6.4×10^{17} photons s^{-1}

101. 2.18×10^{-18} J; 0.0545 nm

103. 91.2 nm

105. **a.** 4 **b.** 9 **c.** 16

107. $n = 4 \longrightarrow n = 3$, $n = 5 \longrightarrow n = 3$, $n = 6 \longrightarrow n = 3$, respectively

109. 4.84×10^{14} s^{-1}

111. 11 m

113. 6.78×10^{-3} J

115. 632 nm

117. Vanadium has three unpaired electrons in the 3d orbitals and is therefore paramagnetic. V^{3+} has two unpaired electrons in the 3d orbitals and is also paramagnetic.

119. **a.** [Ar] $4s^13d^5$, [Ar] $3d^5$, [Ar] $3d^4$, [Ar] $3d^3$
b. [Ar] $4s^13d^{10}$, [Ar] $3d^{10}$, [Ar] $3d^9$

121. **a.** $E_1 = 2.51 \times 10^{-18}$ J, $E_2 = 1.00 \times 10^{-17}$ J, $E_3 = 2.26 \times 10^{-17}$ J
b. 26.5 nm, UV; 15.8 nm, UV

123.

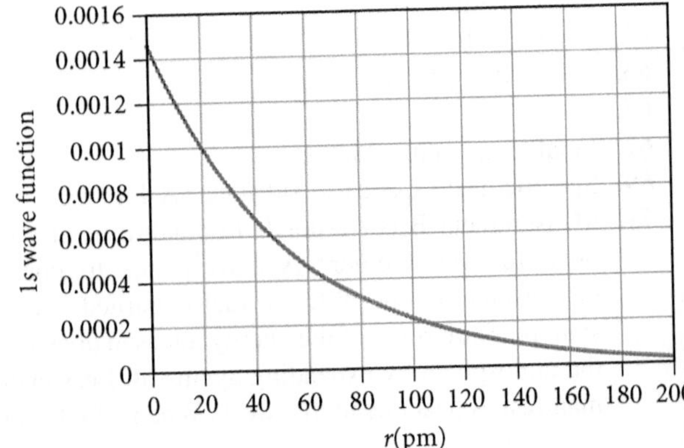

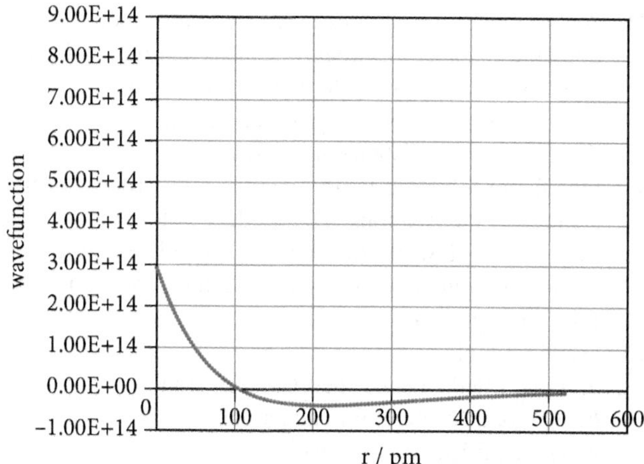

The plot for the 2*s* wave function extends below the *x*-axis. The *x*-intercept represents the radial node of the orbital.

125. $7.39 \times 10^5\ \mathrm{m\ s^{-1}}$

127. $\Delta E = 1.1 \times 10^{-20}\ \mathrm{J},\ 7.5 \times 10^2\ \mathrm{nm}$

129. 11 m

131. $1.390 \times 10^3\ \mathrm{kJ\ mol^{-1}},\ 86.1\ \mathrm{nm}$

133. **a.** yes **b.** no **c.** yes **d.** no

135. $2p \longrightarrow 1s$

Chapter 8

31. **a.** [Ne] $3s^2 3p^3$ **b.** [Ar] $4s^2 3d^{10} 4p^2$ **c.** [Kr] $5s^2 4d^2$ **d.** [Kr] $5s^2 4d^{10} 5p^5$

33. **a.** 1 **b.** 10 **c.** 5 **d.** 2

35. **a.** V, As **b.** Se **c.** V **d.** Kr

37. **a.** 2 **b.** 1 **c.** 10 **d.** 6

39. reactive metal: **a.**; reactive nonmetal: **c.**

41. The valence electrons of nitrogen will experience a greater effective nuclear charge. The valence electrons of both atoms are screened by two core electrons but N has a greater number of protons and therefore a greater net nuclear charge.

43. **a.** 1+ **b.** 2+ **c.** 6+ **d.** 4+

45. K: 2.2, Ca: 2.85, Sc: 3.00, Ti: 3.15, V: 3.30, Cr: 2.95, Mn: 3.6, Fe: 3.75, Co: 3.9, Ni: 4.05, Cu: 3.7, Zn: 4.35, Ga: 5, Ge: 5.65, As: 6.3, Se: 6.95, Br: 7.6, Kr: 8.25
The effective nuclear charge felt by the outer electrons increases going left to right and this results in the general observation that the elements' radii decrease over the same series.

47. **a.** In **b.** Si **c.** Pb **d.** C

49. F, S, Si, Ge, Ca, Rb

51. **a.** Li **b.** I^- **c.** Cr **d.** O^{2-}

53. O^{2-}, F^-, Ne, Na^+, Mg^{2+}

55. O^{2-}: $Z_{eff} = 3.85$, O: $Z_{eff} = 4.55$. Z_{eff} for O is larger, therefore it has a smaller radius.

57. Ga^{3+}: $Z_{eff} = 15.05$, Ga: $Z_{eff} = 5$. Z_{eff} for Ga is smaller, therefore it has a larger radius

59. **a.** Br **b.** Na
c. cannot tell based on periodic trends
d. P

61. In, Si, N, F

63. **a.** second and third **b.** fifth and sixth **c.** sixth and seventh **d.** first and second

65. The Z_{eff} value for Mg, Mg^+ and Mg^{2+} will increase over the series and therefore the successive ionization energies will also increase.

67. **a.** Na **b.** S **c.** C **d.** F

69. **a.** Sr
b. Bi
c. cannot tell based on periodic trends
d. As

71. S, Se, Sb, In, Ba, Fr

73. $Sr(s) + I_2(g) \longrightarrow SrI_2(s)$

75. $2\ Li(s) + 2\ H_2O(l) \longrightarrow 2\ Li^+(aq) + 2\ OH^-(aq) + H_2(g)$

77. $H_2(g) + Br_2(g) \longrightarrow 2\ HBr(g)$

79. Br: $1s^2 2s^2 2p^6 3s^2 3p^6 4s^2 3d^{10} 4p^5$
Kr: $1s^2 2s^2 2p^6 3s^2 3p^6 4s^2 3d^{10} 4p^6$
Krypton's 4s and 4p subshells in its valence shell are completely full, giving it chemical stability. Bromine is missing an electron from its 4*p* subshell and subsequently has a high electron affinity. Bromine tends to be easily reduced by gaining an electron, giving the bromide ion stability due to the filled 4*p* subshell which corresponds to krypton's chemically stable electron configuration.

81. A substitute for K^+ would need to exhibit a 1+ electric charge and have similar mass and atomic radius. Na^+ and Rb^+ would not be good substitutes because their radii are significantly smaller and larger, respectively. Based on mass, Ca^+ and Ar^+ are the closest to K^+. Because the first ionization energy of Ca^+ is closest to that of K^+, Ca^+ is the best choice for a substitute. The difficulty lies in Ca's low second ionization energy, making it easily oxidized.

83. Si, Ge

85. **a.** N: [He] $2s^2 2p^3$, Mg: [Ne] $3s^2$, O: [He] $2s^2 2p^4$, F: [He] $2s^2 2p^5$, Al: [Ne] $3s^2 3p^1$
b. Mg, Al, N, O, F
c. Al, Mg, O, N, F
d. Aluminum's first ionization energy is lower than Mg because its 3*p* electron is shielded by the 3*s* orbital. Oxygen's first ionization energy is lower than that of N because its fourth 2*p* electron experiences electron–electron repulsion by the other electron in its orbital.

87. For main-group elements, atomic radii decrease across a period because the addition of a proton in the nucle and an electron in the outermost energy level incre Z_{eff}. This does not happen in the transition met cause the electrons are added to the $n_{highest-1}$ or the Z_{eff} stays roughly the same.

89. Noble gases are exceptionally unreactive d bility of their completely filled outer and their high ionization energies. The gies of Kr, Xe, and Rn are low eno compounds.

91. 16: ns^2np^4, 17: ns^2np^5. Group 17 one electron to achieve a noble group 16 elements require t for one electron is less ne will merely give them an

93. 85

95. a. One If By Land (O, Ne, I, F, B, Y, La, Nd)
b. Atoms are Fun (N, U, Fe, Ra, S, Mo, Ta backwards)

97. a. $d_{Ar} \approx 2\ g\ L^{-1}$, $d_{Xe} \approx 6.5\ g\ L^{-1}$
b. $d_{118} \approx 13\ g\ L^{-1}$
c. mass $= 3.35 \times 10^{-23}$ g/Ne atom, density of Ne atom $= 2.3 \times 10^4\ g\ L^{-1}$. The separation of Ne atoms relative to their size is immense.
d. Kr: 2.69×10^{22} atoms/L, Ne: 2.69×10^{22} atoms/L. It seems Ar will also have 2.69×10^{22} atoms/L. $d_{Ar} = 1.78\ g\ L^{-1}$. This corresponds to accepted values.

99. Density increases to the right, because, though electrons are added successively across the period, they are added to the 3*d* subshell which is not a part of the outermost principal energy level. As a result, the atomic radius does not increase significantly across the period while mass does.

101. 168, noble gas

103. A relatively high effective nuclear charge is found in gallium with its completed 3*d* subshell and in thallium with its completed 4*f* subshell, accounting for the relatively high first ionization energies of these elements.

105. The second electron affinity requires the addition of an electron to something that is already negatively charged. The monoanions of both of these elements have relatively high electron density in a relatively small volume. As we shall see in Chapter 9, the dianions of these elements do exist in many compounds because they are stabilized by chemical bonding.

107. 120, 170

109. Fr, [Rn] $7s^1$, >265, <376, >1.879, <29
a. $Fr^+(aq)$, $OH^-(aq)$, $H_2(g)$ **b.** $Fr_2O(s)$ **c.** $FrCl(s)$

111. Li: 1.3, Na: 2.2, K: 2.2, Rb: 2.2. Clearly the simple Slater's rules cannot be used to compare properties of elements in a particular group, only elements in a period.

113. a. any group 16 element **b.** any group 15 element
c. any group 1 element

115. Since Ca has valence electrons of $4s^2$, it has a relatively low ionization energy to lose 2 electrons. Whereas, F has a highly exothermic electron affinity when gaining 1 electron, but not a second electron because of its $^2 2p^5$ valence electrons. Therefore, calcium and fluo- combine in a 2:1 ratio.

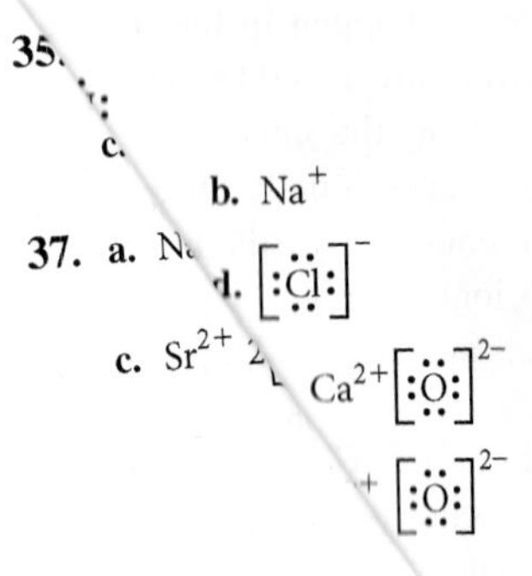

39. a. SrSe **b.** $BaCl_2$
c. Na_2S **d.** Al_2O_3

41. As the size of the alkaline earth metal ions increases, so does the distance between the metal cations and oxygen anions. Therefore, the magnitude of the lattice energy decreases accordingly because the potential energy decreases as the distance increases.

43. One factor affecting lattice energy is the product of the charges of the two ions. The product of the ion charges for CsF is −1 while that for BaO is −4. Because this product is four times greater, the lattice energy is also four times greater.

45. $-708\ kJ\ mol^{-1}$

47. a. H:H, filled valence shell for each atom
b. :C̤̈l:C̤̈l:, filled octet for each atom
c. Ö=Ö, filled octet for each atom
d. :N≡N:, filled octet for each atom

49. a. H—P̈—H with H below P **b.** :S̈—C̤̈l: with :C̤̈l: below S
c. H—Ï: **d.** H—C—H with H above and below C

51. a. :F̤̈—S̤̈—F̤̈: **b.** H—Si—H with H above and below Si
c. :Ö=C—Ö: with H above C and H below O **d.** H—C—S̤̈—H with H above and below C

53. a. pure covalent **b.** polar covalent
c. pure covalent **d.** ionic bond

55. :C≡O:, 25% (dipole arrow over the bond)

57. a. :Ï: above and below C, :Ï—C—Ï: **b.** :N≡N—Ö:
c. H—Si—H with H above and below Si **d.** :C̤̈l—C—C̤̈l: with :O: double-bonded above C

59. a. H—N̈=N̈—H **b.** H—N̈—N̈—H with H below each N
c. H—C≡C—H **d.** H—C=C—H with H below each C

61. a.  :Ö—Se=Ö: ⟷ :Ö=Se—Ö: (formal charges −1, +1, 0 ⟷ 0, +1, −1)

b. 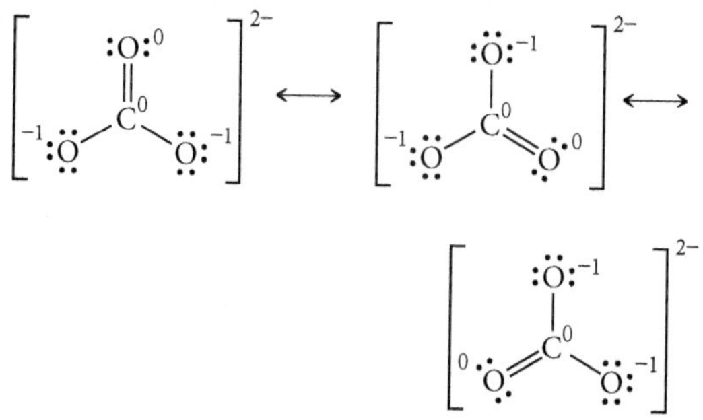 $[CO_3]^{2-}$ resonance structures: C(=O)(–O)(–O) with formal charges O 0, C 0, O −1, O −1 ⟷ ⟷

c. $[:\ddot{Cl}—\ddot{O}:]^-$ (0, −1)

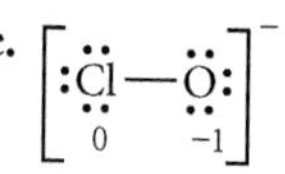

d.  $[:\ddot{O}=\ddot{N}—\ddot{O}:]^-$ (0, 0, −1) ⟷ $[:\ddot{O}—\ddot{N}=\ddot{O}:]^-$ (−1, 0, 0)

63. 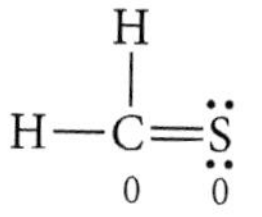 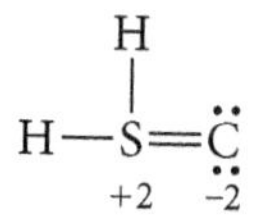 H—C(H)=S (0, 0)   H—S(H)=C (+2, −2) H_2CS is the better structure.

65. :O≡C—Ö: There is a positive charge on one oxygen (which is electronegative) and a negative charge on the other. A combination of unnecessary charge separation and the positive charge on an electronegative atom means this Lewis structure does not contribute significantly to the resonance hybrid.

67. a. 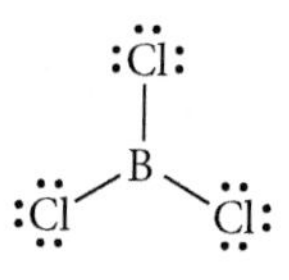 BCl_3 (B bonded to three :Cl:)   b. Ö=N—Ö: ⟷ :Ö—N=Ö:

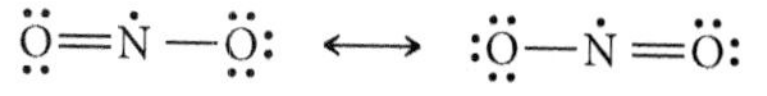

c. 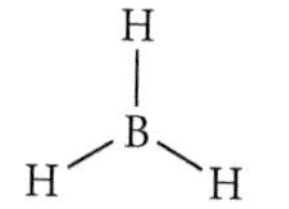 BH_3 (B bonded to three H)

69. a. 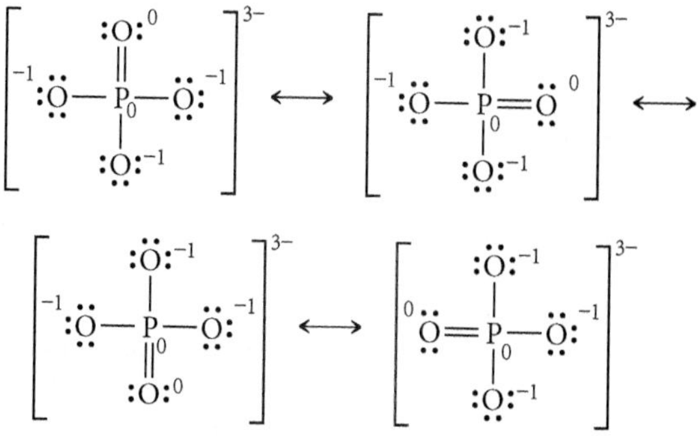 $[PO_4]^{3-}$ resonance structures: P(0) with one P=O (0) and three P—O (−1) ⟷ ⟷ ⟷

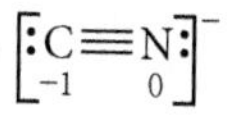

b. $[:C≡N:]^-$ (−1, 0)

c. $[SO_3]^{2-}$ resonance structures: S(0) with one S=O (0) and two S—O (−1) ⟷ ⟷

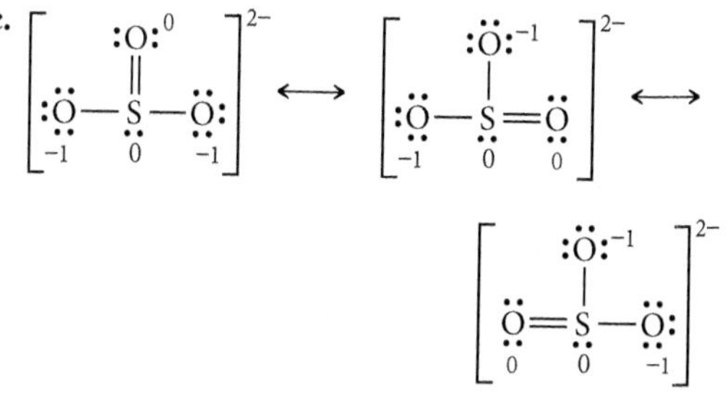

d. 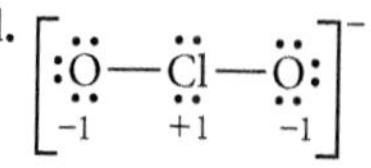 $[:\ddot{O}—\ddot{Cl}—\ddot{O}:]^-$ (−1, +1, −1)

71. a. 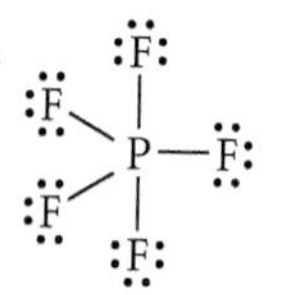 PF_5 b. 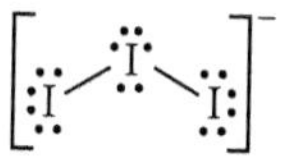 $[I_3]^-$ c. 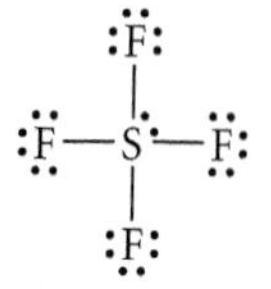 SF_4 d. 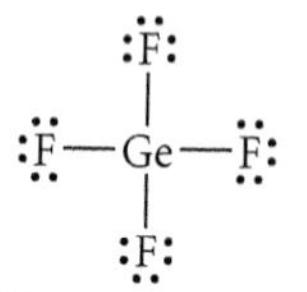 GeF_4

73. H_3CCH_3, H_2CCH_2, HCCH

75. -128 kJ mol^{-1}

77. -614 kJ mol^{-1}

79. The higher wavenumber value absorption belongs to the C=N stretch and the lower one belongs to the C—N stretch. The single bond requires less energy to stretch so it absorbs at lower energy.

81. a. 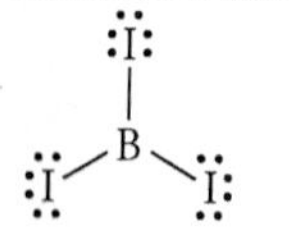 BI_3 b. 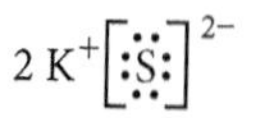 $2\ K^+[:\ddot{S}:]^{2-}$

c. 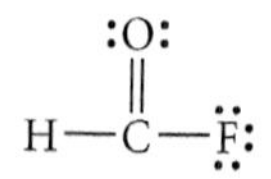 H—C(=O)—F   d. 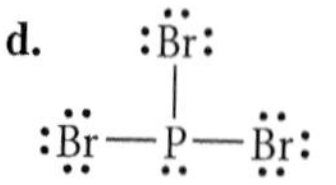 PBr_3

83. a. 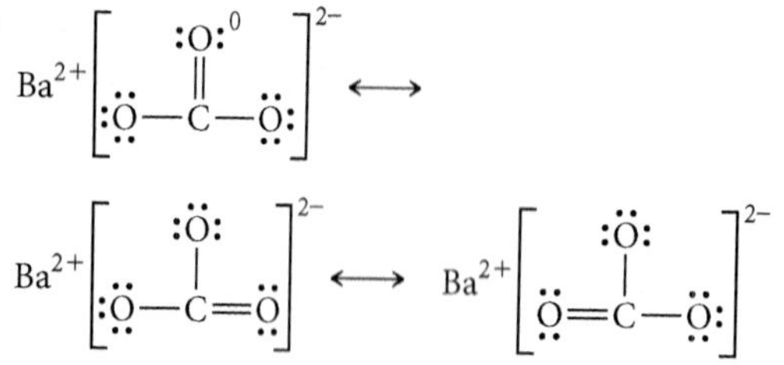 $Ba^{2+}[CO_3]^{2-}$ (C(=O)(–O)(–O), formal charges shown) ⟷ $Ba^{2+}[CO_3]^{2-}$ ⟷ $Ba^{2+}[CO_3]^{2-}$

b. $Ca^{2+}\ 2[:\ddot{O}—H]^-$

c. $K^+[NO_3]^-$ ⟷ $K^+[NO_3]^-$ ⟷ $K^+[$…

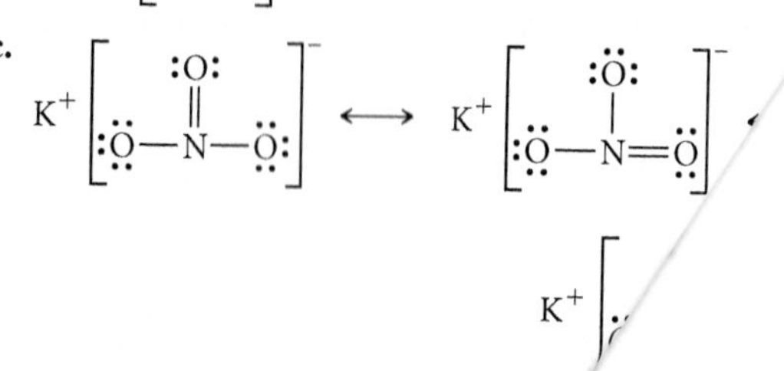

d. 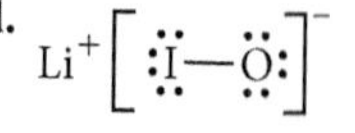 $Li^+[:\ddot{I}—\ddot{O}:]^-$

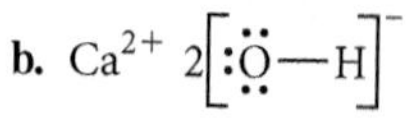

85. a. H—C(H)—C(H)—H / H—C(H)—C(H)—H (four-membered ring: C_4H_8)

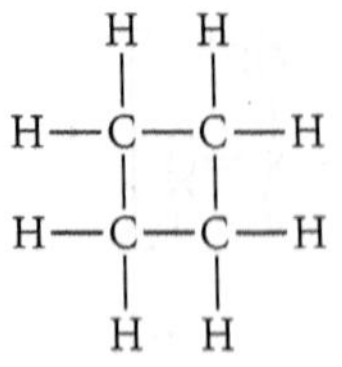

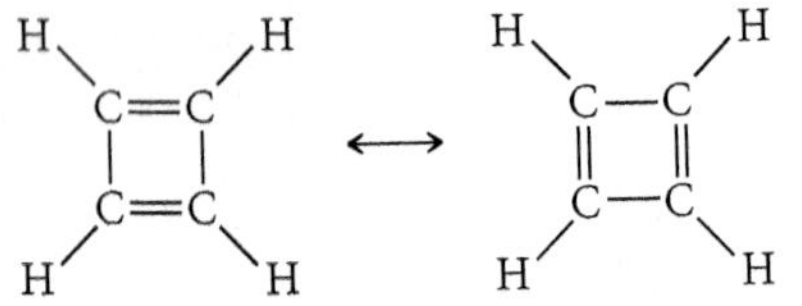

b. H—C=C—H / H—C=C—H ⟷ H—C—C—H / H—C=C—H (cyclobutadiene resonance structures)

c. cyclohexane: six CH_2 groups in a ring (H—C—H at each carbon)

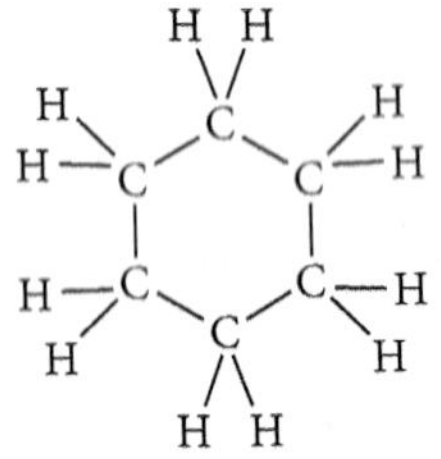

d. benzene resonance structures: C_6H_6 ring with alternating double bonds ⟷ ring with double bonds shifted

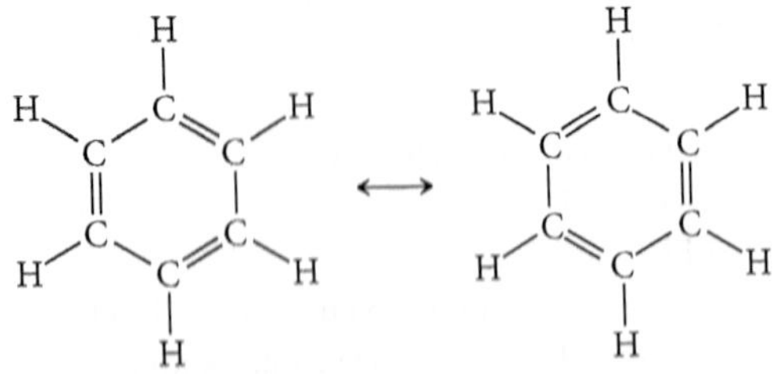

87. CH_2O_2, H—C(=O:)—Ö—H

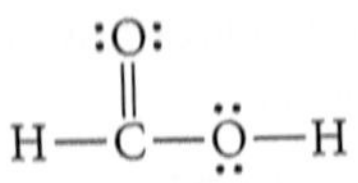

89. The reaction is exothermic due to the energy released when the Al_2O_3 lattice forms.

91. H—Ö—N(=O:)—Ö: ⟷ H—Ö—N(—Ö:)=Ö ⟷ H—Ö=N(—Ö:)—Ö:

Formal charges: (H 0, O 0, N +1, O −1, O 0) ⟷ (H 0, O 0, N +1, O 0, O −1) ⟷ (H 0, O +1, N +1, O 0, O −1)

Most important: the first two structures

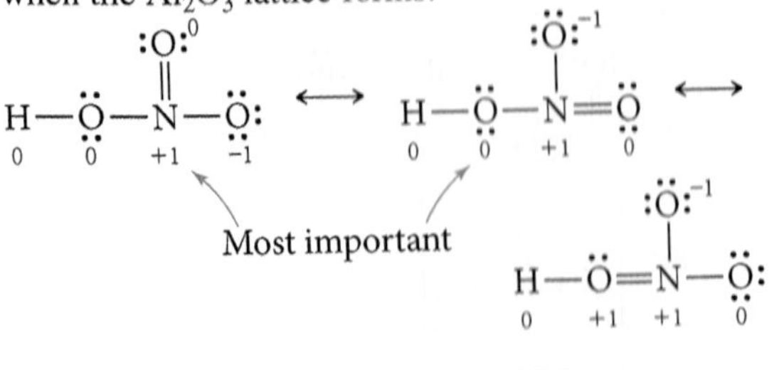

93. $[\ddot{C}{=}N{=}\ddot{O}]^-$ (formal charges −2, +1, 0) ⟷ $[{:}C{\equiv}N{-}\ddot{O}{:}]^-$ (formal charges −1, +1, −1)

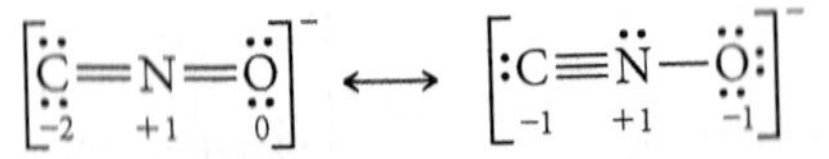

The fulminate ion is less stable because nitrogen is more [illegible]ectronegative than carbon and should therefore be ter[illegible]al to accomodate the negative formal charge.

97. :S: = C—N(H)—H; bonds labeled [illegible]ar, Polar, Polar

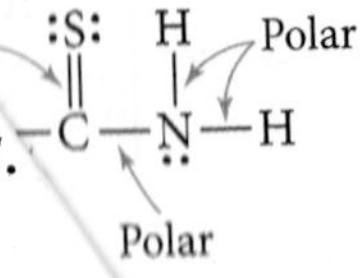

b. $[{:}\ddot{O}{:}]^-$

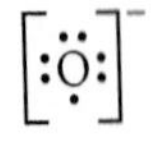

c. :Ö—[illegible]

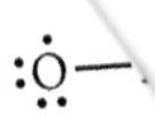

d. H—C(H)(—)—Ö—Ö·

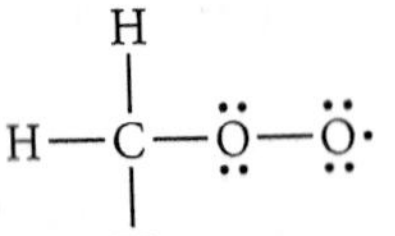

99. $\Delta_r H_{(H_2)} = -243\ \text{kJ mol}^{-1} = -121\ \text{kJ g}^{-1}$

$\Delta_r H_{(CH_4)} = -802\ \text{kJ mol}^{-1} = -50.0\ \text{kJ g}^{-1}$

CH_4 yields more energy per mole while H_2 yields more energy per gram.

101. a. Ö=Cl(=O:)(=O:)—Ö—Cl(=O:)(=O:)=Ö

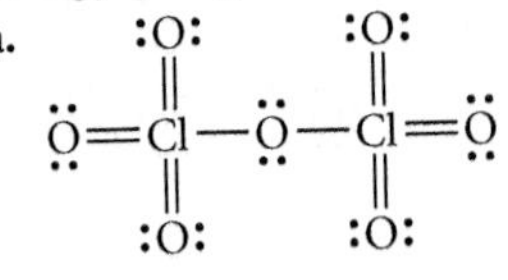

b. H—P(=O:)(—Ö—H)—Ö—H

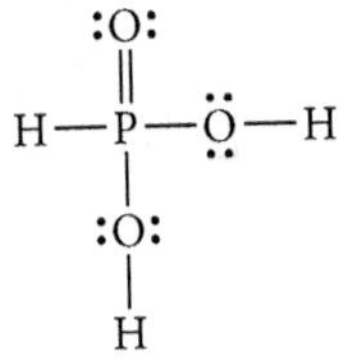

c. H—Ö—As(=O:)(—Ö—H)—Ö—H

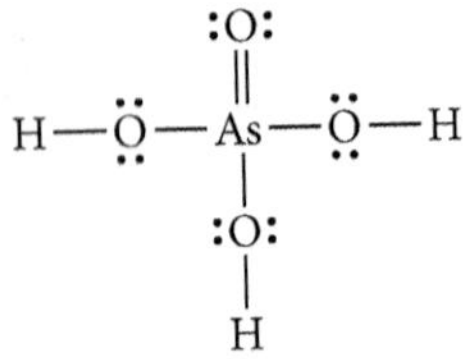

103. Na^+F^-, Na^+O^{2-}, $Mg^{2+}F^-$, $Mg^{2+}O^{2-}$, $Al^{3+}O^{2-}$

105. 333 kJ mol^{-1}

107. H—C≡C—H

109. Ö=S̈=Ö + :Ö—H ⟶ H—Ö—S(=O:)—Ö:

H—Ö—S(=O:)—Ö: + Ö=Ö ⟶ :Ö—S(=O:)—Ö: + H—Ö—Ö·

:Ö—S(=O:)—Ö: + H—Ö—H ⟶ H—O—S(=O)(=Ö)—O—H

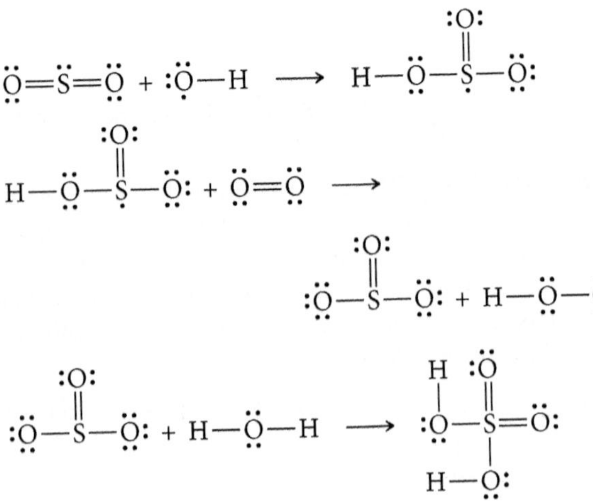

$\Delta_r H = -174\ \text{kJ mol}^{-1}$

111. $r_{HCl} = 113$ pm

$r_{HF} = 84$ pm

These values are close to the accepted values.

113. P_4 tetrahedron: each P bonded to the other three, with one lone pair on each P

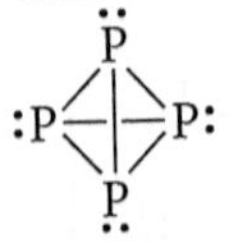

115. 126 kJ mol^{-1}

117. The oxidation number of the S atoms bonded directly to hydrogen atoms is −1. The oxidation number of interior S atoms is 0.

119. 536 kJ mol^{-1}

121. The compounds are energy rich because a great deal of energy is released when these compounds undergo a reaction that breaks weak bonds and forms strong ones.

123. The theory is successful because it allows us to predict and account for many chemical observations. The theory is limited because electrons cannot be treated as localized "dots."

Chapter 10

35. 4

37. a. 4 e^- groups, 4 bonding groups, 0 lone pairs
b. 5 e^- groups, 3 bonding groups, 2 lone pairs
c. 6 e^- groups, 5 bonding groups, 1 lone pair

39. a. e^- geometry: tetrahedral
molecular geometry: trigonal pyramidal
idealized bond angle: 109.5°, deviation
b. e^- geometry: tetrahedral
molecular geometry: bent
idealized bond angle: 109.5°, deviation
c. e^- geometry: tetrahedral
molecular geometry: tetrahedral
idealized bond angle: 109.5°, deviation (due to large size of Cl compared to H)
d. e^- geometry: linear
molecular geometry: linear
idealized bond angle: 180°

41. H_2O has a smaller bond angle due to lone pair–lone pair repulsions, the strongest electron group repulsion.

43. a. seesaw, SF_4 (S bonded to four F)
b. T-shape, ClF_3 (Cl bonded to three F)
c. linear, $[F{-}I{-}F]^-$
d. square planar, $[IBr_4]^-$ (I bonded to four Br)

45. a. linear, $H{-}C{\equiv}C{-}H$
b. trigonal planar, $H_2C{=}CH_2$
c. tetrahedral, $H_3C{-}CH_3$

47. a. The lone pair will cause lone pair–bonding pair repulsions, pushing the three bonding pairs out of the same plane. The correct molecular geometry is trigonal pyramidal.
b. The lone pair should take an equatorial position to minimize 90° bonding pair interactions. The correct molecular geometry is seesaw.
c. The lone pairs should take positions on opposite sides of the central atom to reduce lone pair–lone pair interactions. The correct molecular geometry is square planar.

49. a. C: tetrahedral
O: bent
($H_3C{-}O{-}H$)
b. C's: tetrahedral
O: bent
($H_3C{-}O{-}CH_3$)
c. O's: bent
($H{-}O{-}O{-}H$)

51. The vectors of the polar bonds in both CO_2 and CCl_4 oppose each other with equal magnitude and sum to 0.

53. PF_3, polar
SBr_2, polar
$CHCl_3$, polar
CS_2, nonpolar

55. a. polar **b.** polar
c. polar **d.** nonpolar

57. a. 0 **b.** 3 **c.** 1

59. P:
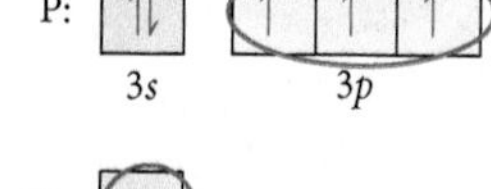

H_1:
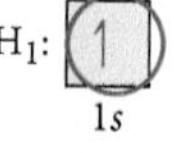

H_2:
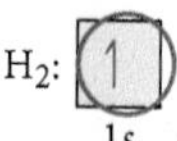

H_3:
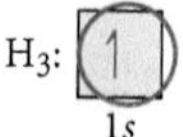

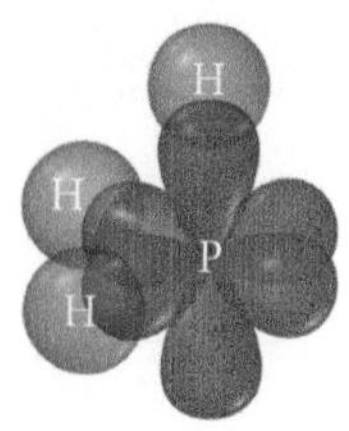

Expected bond angle = 90°
Valence bond theory is compatible with experimentally determined bond angle of 93.3° without hybrid orbitals.

61.
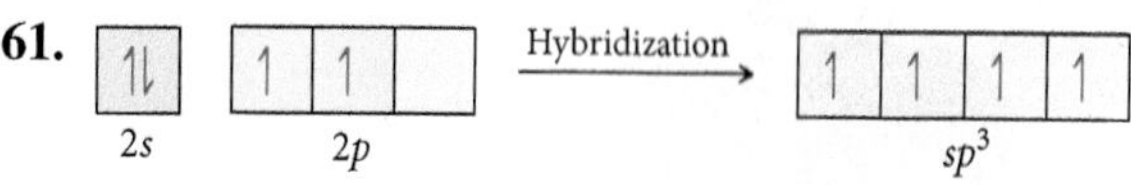

63. sp^2

65. a. sp^3

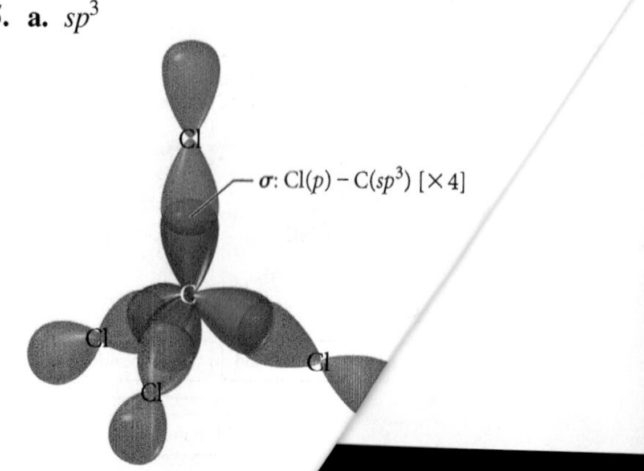

b. *sp*^{3}

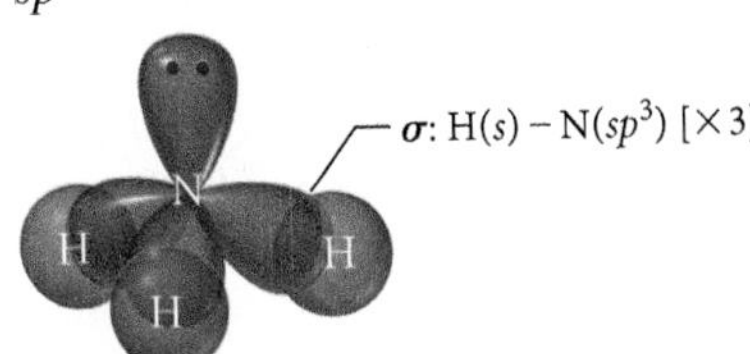

c. *sp*^{3}

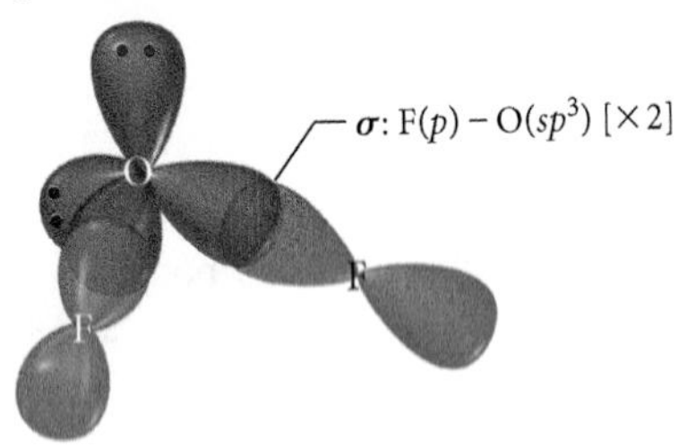

d. *sp*

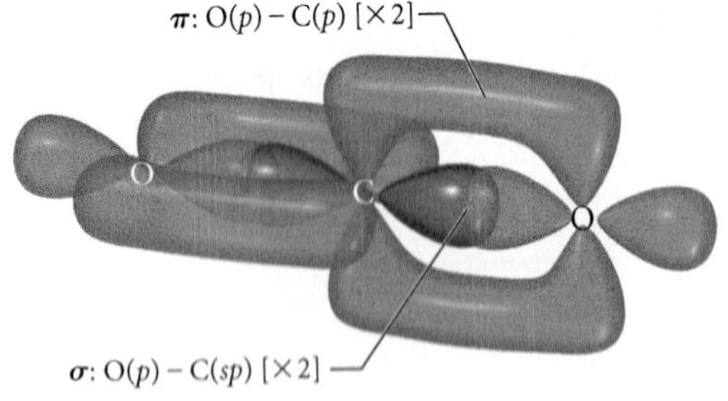

67. a. *sp*^{2}

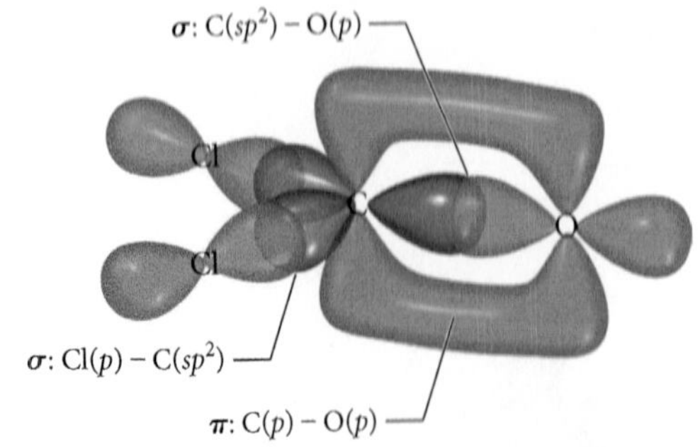

b. *sp*^{3}

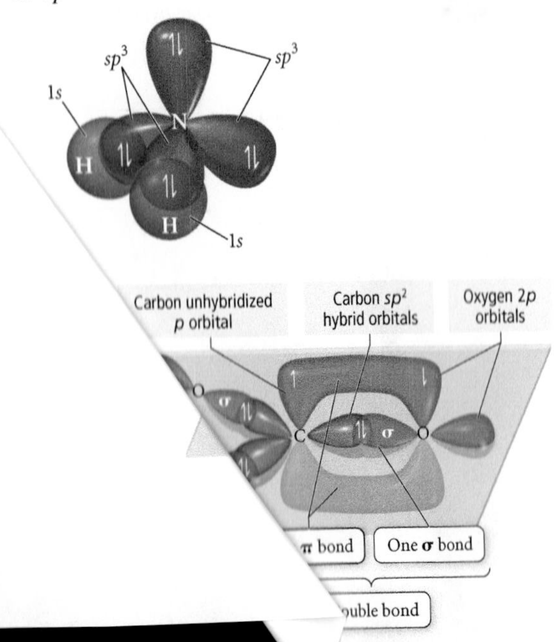

69. a. N's: *sp*^{2}

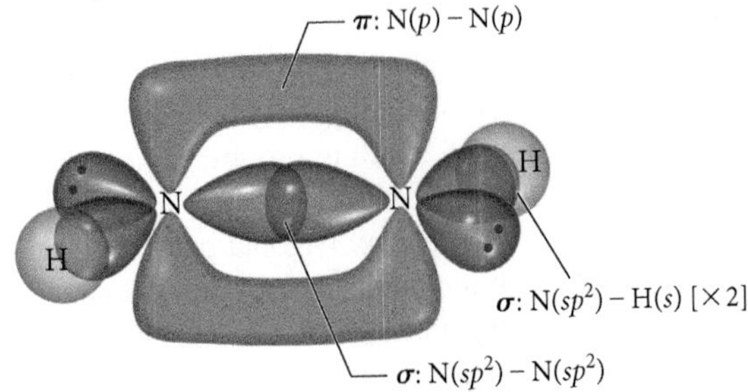

b. N's: *sp*^{3}

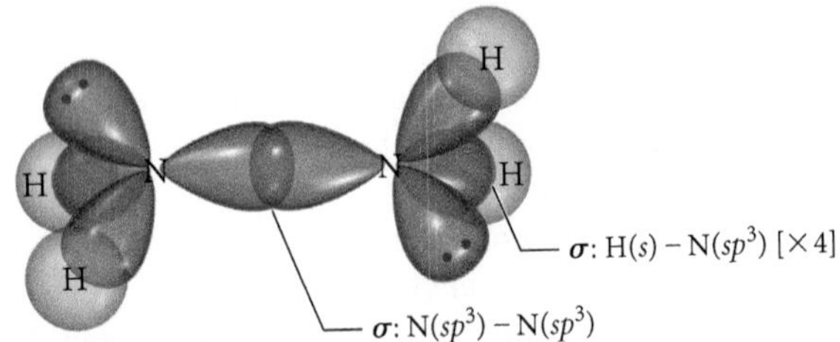

c. C: *sp*^{3}
N: *sp*^{3}

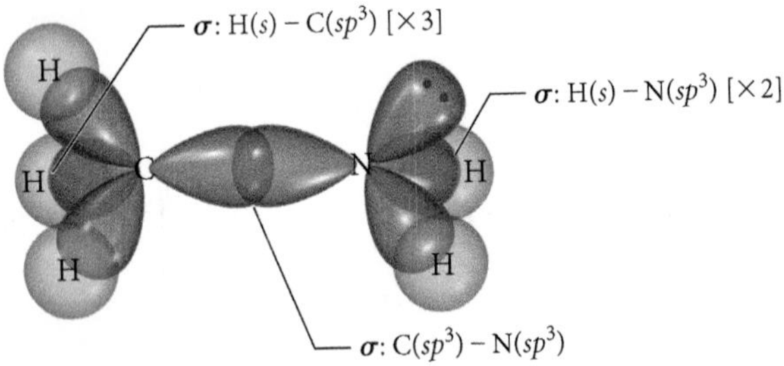

71. H–C(H)(H)–C(H)(NH$_2$)–C(=O)–O–H

sp^3 (the CH$_3$ carbon, the CH carbon, and N); *sp*^{2} (the C=O carbon); *sp*^{3} (the O of OH)

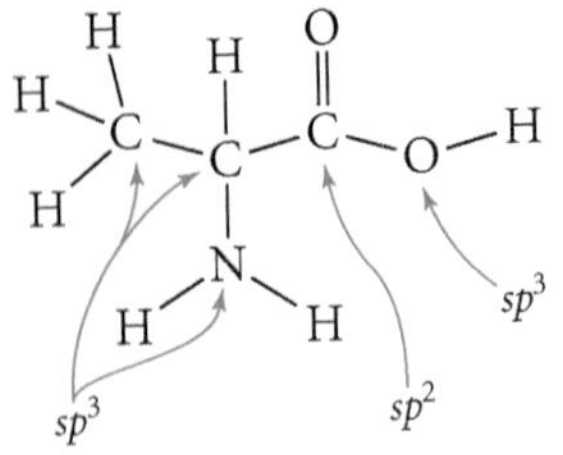

73.

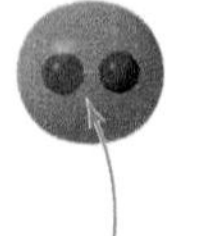

Constructive interference

75. Be_2^{+}

$\uparrow$ σ^*_{2s}

$\uparrow\downarrow$ σ_{2s}

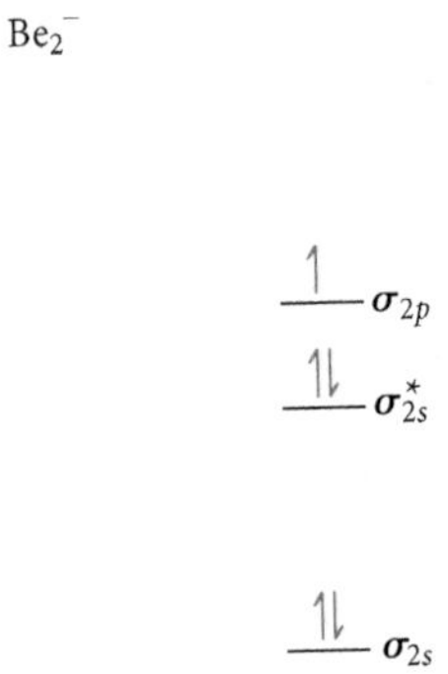

Be_2^{-}

$\uparrow$ σ_{2p}

$\uparrow\downarrow$ σ^*_{2s}

$\uparrow\downarrow$ σ_{2s}

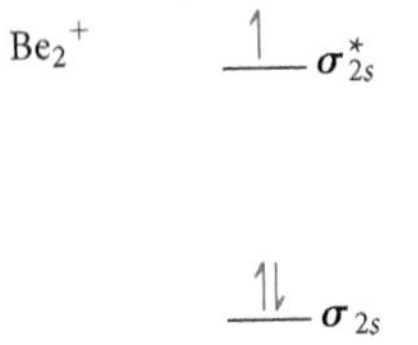

bond order $Be_2^{+} = 1/2$
bond order $Be_2^{-} = 1/2$
Both will exist in gas phase.

77. Bonding Antibonding

 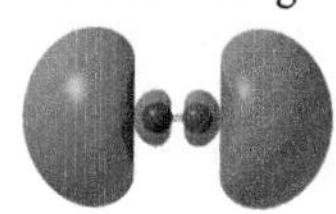

79. a.

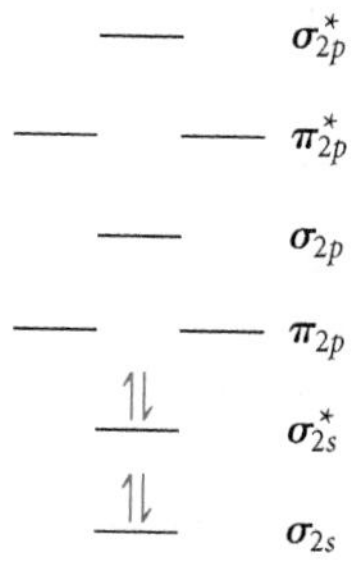

— σ^*_{2p}
— — π^*_{2p}
— σ_{2p}
— — π_{2p}
↑↓ σ^*_{2s}
↑↓ σ_{2s}

bond order = 0
diamagnetic

b.

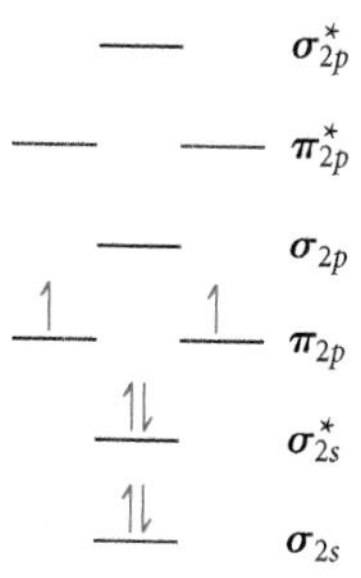

— σ^*_{2p}
— — π^*_{2p}
— σ_{2p}
↑ ↑ π_{2p}
↑↓ σ^*_{2s}
↑↓ σ_{2s}

bond order = 1
paramagnetic

c.

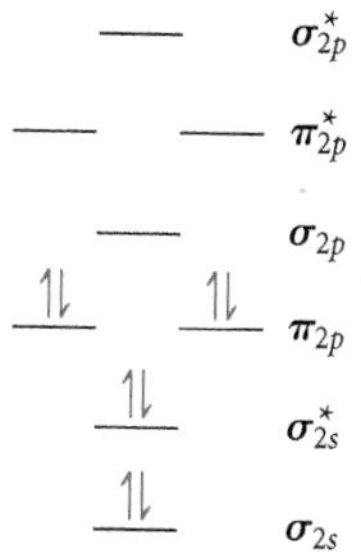

— σ^*_{2p}
— — π^*_{2p}
— σ_{2p}
↑↓ ↑↓ π_{2p}
↑↓ σ^*_{2s}
↑↓ σ_{2s}

bond order = 2
diamagnetic

d.

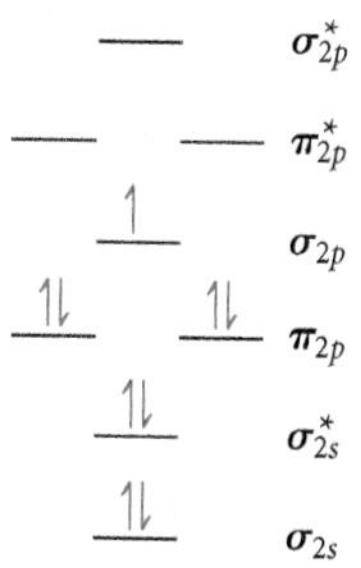

— σ^*_{2p}
— — π^*_{2p}
↑ σ_{2p}
↑↓ ↑↓ π_{2p}
↑↓ σ^*_{2s}
↑↓ σ_{2s}

bond order = 2.5
paramagnetic

81. a. not stable **b.** not stable
c. stable **d.** not stable

83. C_2^- has the highest bond order, the highest bond energy, and the shortest bond length.

85.

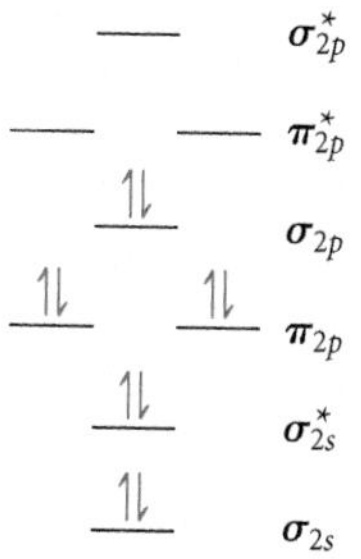

— σ^*_{2p}
— — π^*_{2p}
↑↓ σ_{2p}
↑↓ ↑↓ π_{2p}
↑↓ σ^*_{2s}
↑↓ σ_{2s}

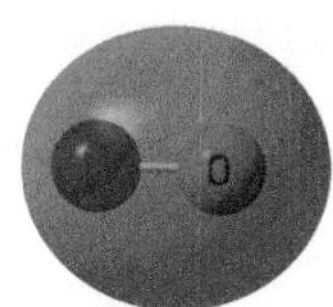

bond order = 3

87. a.

89. a. p-type **b.** n-type

91. Eleven each bonding and antibonding molecular orbitals. There are 22 electron is the bonding MOs.

93. a.

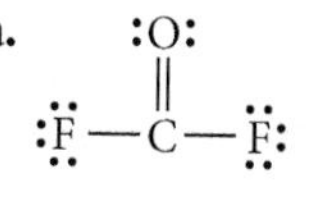

:O:
‖
:F̤—C—F̤:

trigonal planar
polar
C: sp^2

b.

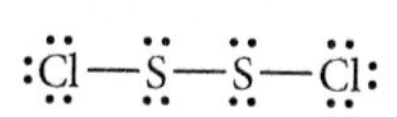

:C̤l—S̤—S̤—C̤l:

bent
polar
S's: sp^3

95. a.

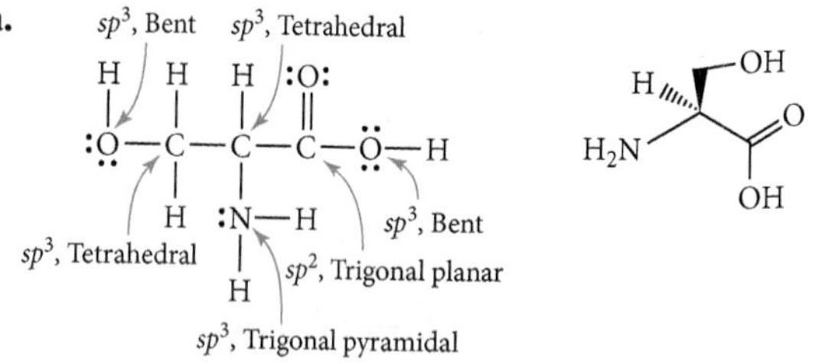

H H H :O:
| | | ‖
:Ö—C—C—C—Ö—H
| |
H :N—H
|
H

sp^3, Bent; sp^3, Tetrahedral; sp^3, Bent; sp^3, Tetrahedral; sp^2, Trigonal planar; sp^3, Trigonal pyramidal

H₂N, OH, O, OH (skeletal structure)

b.

H :O: H H :O:
| ‖ | | ‖
:N—C—C—C—C—Ö—H
| | |
H H :N—H
|
H

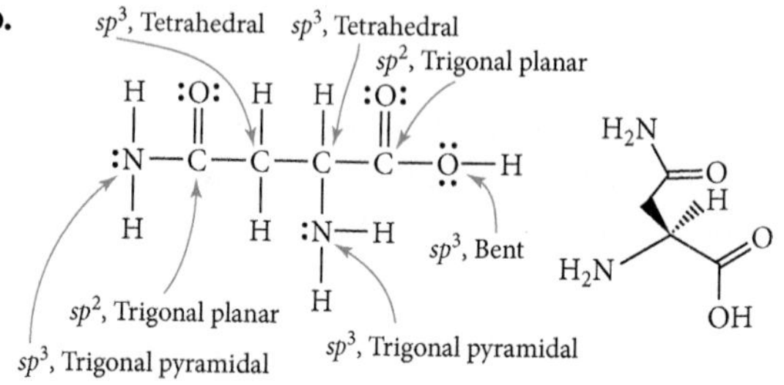

sp^3, Tetrahedral; sp^3, Tetrahedral; sp^2, Trigonal planar; sp^3, Bent; sp^2, Trigonal planar; sp^3, Trigonal pyramidal; sp^3, Trigonal pyramidal

H_2N, O, H, H_2N, O, OH (skeletal structure)

c.

H H H :O:
| | | ‖
:S̤—C—C—C—Ö—H
| |
H :N—H
|
H

sp^3, Bent; sp^3, Tetrahedral; sp^3, Bent; sp^3, Tetrahedral; sp^2, Trigonal planar; sp^3, Trigonal planar

SH, H, N, H, H, O, OH (skeletal structure)

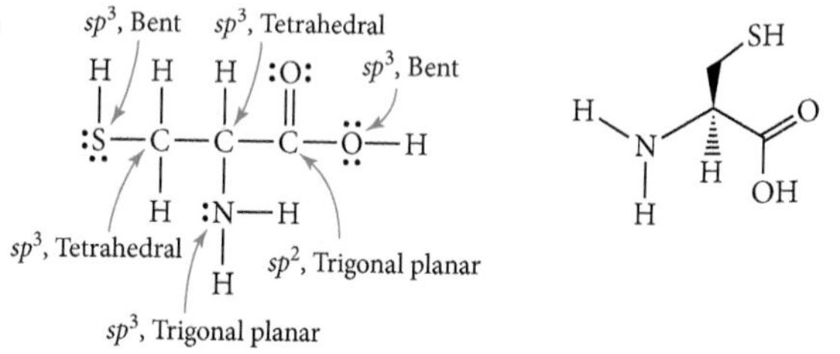

97. σ bonds: 25
π bonds: 4
lone pairs: on O's and N
N's (with methyl group): sp^3 orbitals
N (without methyl group): sp^2
O's: p orbitals

99. a. water soluble **b.** fat soluble
c. water soluble **d.** fat soluble

101.

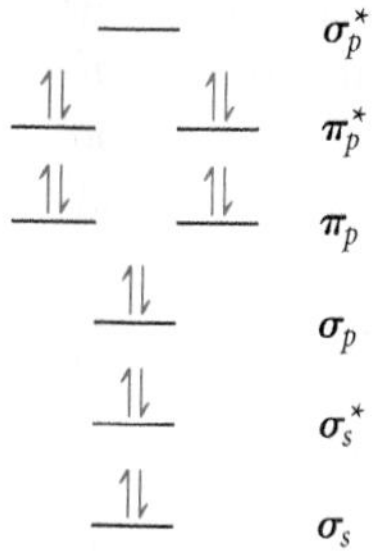

— σ^*_p
↑↓ ↑↓ π^*_p
↑↓ ↑↓ π_p
↑↓ σ_p
↑↓ σ^*_s
↑↓ σ_s

bond order = 1

103. BrF, unhybridized, linear

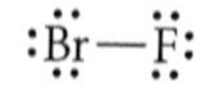

:B̤r—F̤:

BrF_2^- has two bonds and three lone pairs on the [cut off] tral atom. The electron geometry is trigonal bipyr[cut off] with the three lone pairs equatorial. The mole[cut off] ometry is linear.

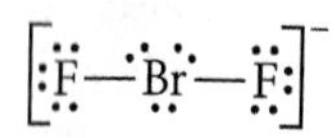

$[:\ddot{F}—\ddot{B}r—\ddot{F}:]^-$ [cut off]al [cut off]idal

BrF_3 has three bonds and two lone p[cut off] geom- atom. The electron geometry is t[cut off] with the two lone pairs equatorial [cut off] etry is T-shaped.

[:F̤—B

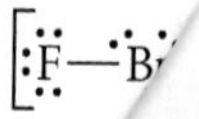

BrF_4^- has four bonds and two lone pairs on the central atom. The electron geometry is octahedral with the two lone pairs on the same axis. The molecular geometry is square planar.

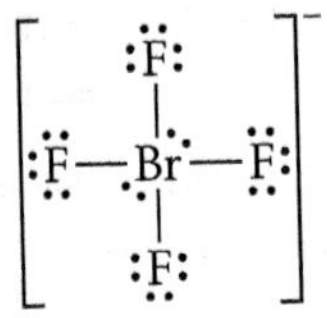

$[F-Br(F)(F)-F]^-$

BrF_5 has five bonds and one lone pair on the central atom. The electron geometry is octahedral. The molecular geometry is square pyramidal.

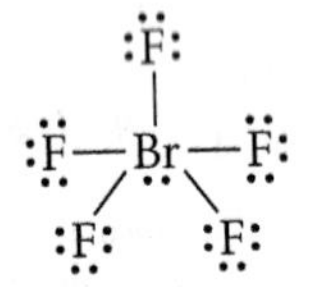

BrF_5: F—Br—F with F above and two F below

105. The moments of the two Cl's cancel.

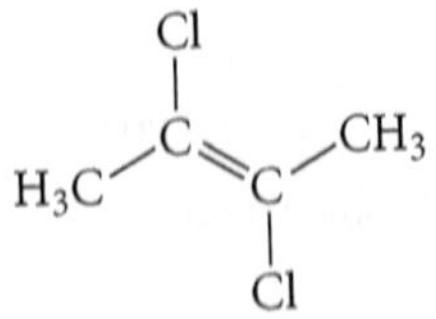

$H_3C-C(Cl)=C(Cl)-CH_3$

107. a. 10 **b.** 14 **c.** 2

109. According to valence bond theory, CH_4, NH_3, and H_2O are all sp^3 hybridized. This hybridization results in a tetrahedral electron group configuration with a 109.5° bond angle. NH_3 and H_2O deviate from this idealized bond angle because their lone electron pairs exist in their own sp^3 orbitals. The presence of lone pairs lowers the tendency for the central atom's orbitals to hybridize. As a result, as lone pairs are added, the bond angle moves further from the 109.5° hybrid angle and closer to the 90° unhybridized angle.

111. NH_3 is stable due to its bond order of 3.

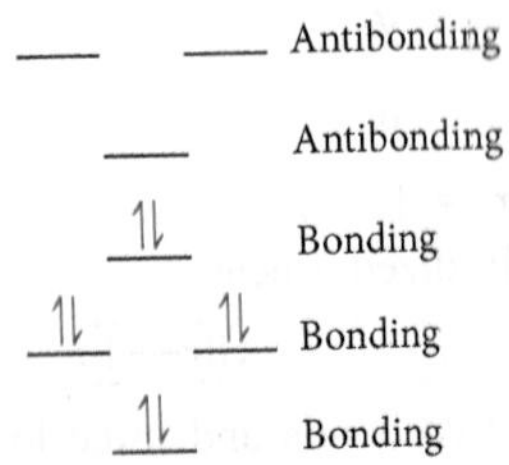

__ __ Antibonding

__ Antibonding

⇅ Bonding

⇅ ⇅ Bonding

⇅ Bonding

... the central N has two electron groups, so the ... is sp and the ONO angle is 180°. In NO_2^- ... as three electron groups, two bonds and one ... al hybridization is sp^2 but the ONO bond ... down a bit because of the lone pair. A ... 15° is a good guess. In NO_2 there are ... but one group is a single electron. ... tion would be sp^2, but since one ... uch smaller than a lone pair or ... ct that the ONO bond angle will spread and be greater than 120°. As a guess the angle is probably significantly greater than 120°.

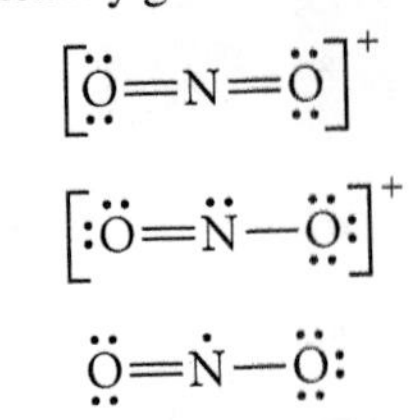

$[O=N=O]^+$

$[:O=N-O:]^+$

$O=N-O:$

115. This observation may be because the $5d$ orbitals are very close in energy to the $6s$ orbitals on the Ba. Thus, these may contribute to the bonding scheme rather than the $6p$ orbitals.

117. A molecule with four bonding groups and one lone pair would need five equivalent positions around the central atom. In two dimensions, this could be accommodated with a pentagon shape around the central atom. The idealized bond angles would be 72°; however, because of the lone pair occupying one of the positions, the bond angles would be less than 72°.

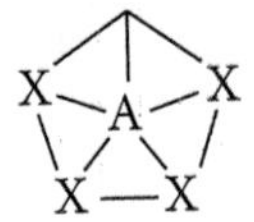

AX_4 (pentagonal arrangement: X—A—X, X—X)

Chapter 11

47. a. dispersion
b. dispersion, dipole–dipole, hydrogen bonding
c. dispersion, dipole–dipole
d. dispersion

49. a. dispersion, dipole–dipole
b. dispersion, dipole–dipole, hydrogen bonding
c. dispersion
d. dispersion

51. Boiling point increases with increasing intermolecular forces. The molecules increase in their intermolecular forces as follows: **a,** dispersion forces; **b,** stronger dispersion forces (broader electron cloud); **c,** dispersion forces and dipole–dipole interactions; **d,** dispersion forces, dipole–dipole interactions, and hydrogen bonding.

53. a. CH_3OH, hydrogen bonding
b. CH_3CH_2OH, hydrogen bonding
c. CH_3CH_3, more electrons, broader electron cloud causes greater dispersion forces

55. a. Br_2, smaller mass results in weaker dispersion forces
b. H_2S, lacks hydrogen bonding
c. PH_3, lacks hydrogen bonding

57. a. not homogeneous
b. homogeneous; dispersion, dipole–dipole, hydrogen bonding, ion–dipole
c. homogeneous; dispersion
d. homogeneous; dispersion, dipole–dipole, hydrogen bonding

59. Water. Surface tension increases with increasing intermolecular forces, and water can hydrogen bond while acetone cannot.

61. Compound A

63. When the tube is clean, water experiences adhesive forces with glass that are stronger than its cohesive forces, causing it to climb the surface of a glass tube. Water does not experience strong intermolecular forces with oil, so if the tube is coated in oil, the water's cohesive forces will be greater and it will not be attracted to the surface of the tube.

65. The water in the 12 cm dish will evaporate more quickly. The vapour pressure does not change but the surface area does. The water in the dish evaporates more quickly because the greater surface area allows for more molecules to obtain enough energy at the surface and break free.

67. Water is more volatile than vegetable oil. When the water evaporates, the endothermic process results in cooling.

69. 0.405 L

71. 91 °C

73. 24.7 kJ mol^{-1}; normal boiling point is 240 K

75. 42 Torr or 55 mbar

77. 22.0 kJ

79. −2.7 °C

81. 30.5 kJ

83. **a.** solid **b.** liquid
c. gas **d.** supercritical fluid
e. solid/liquid **f.** liquid/gas
g. solid/liquid/gas

85. N_2 has a stable liquid phase at 1 atm.

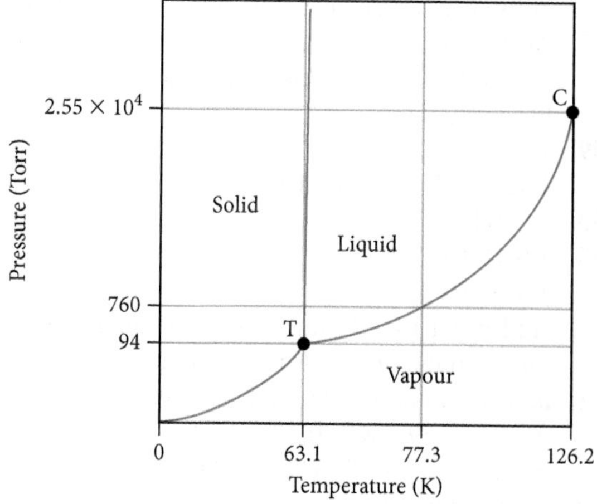

87. **a.** below 0.036 mbar **b.** rhombic

89. Water has strong intermolecular forces. It is polar and experiences hydrogen bonding.

91. Water's exceptionally high specific heat capacity has a moderating effect on Earth's climate. Also, its high $\Delta_{vap}H°$ causes water evaporation and condensation to have a strong effect on temperature.

93. 162 pm

95. **a.** 1 **b.** 2 **c.** 4

97. $l = 393$ pm, $d = 21.3$ g cm^{-3}

99. 134.5 pm

101. 6.0×10^{23} atoms mol^{-1}

103. **a.** atomic **b.** molecular
c. ionic **d.** atomic

105. LiCl(*s*). The other three solids are held together by intermolecular forces while LiCl is held together by stronger coulombic interactions between the cations and anions of the crystal lattice.

107. **a.** HOOH, there are more ways to make hydrogen bonds in HOOH than in CH_3OH.
b. $SiCl_4(s)$, larger, stronger dispersion forces
c. Xe(*s*), larger, stronger dispersion forces
d. CaO(*s*), ions have greater charge, and therefore stronger coulombic forces

109. TiO_2

111. Cs: 1(1) = 1
Cl: 8(1/8) = 1
1:1
CsCl
Ba: 8(1/8) + 6(1/2) = 4
Cl: 8(1) = 8
4:8 = 1:2
$BaCl_2$

113. The general trend is that melting point increases with increasing numbers of electrons. This is due to the fact that the electrons of the larger molecules are held more loosely and a stronger dipole moment can be induced more easily. HF is the exception to the rule. It has a relatively high melting point due to hydrogen bonding.

115. **a.** i < iii < ii
b. iv < i < iii < ii

117. **a.** All molecules shown in the plot partake in hydrogen bonding, but water is able to form a network of hydrogen bonds. The boiling point for water, therefore, does not follow an "expected" trend.
b. The boiling points of the alcohols increase as the alkyl chain gets larger because they have more electrons and are more polarizable.

119. yes, 1.22 g

121. gas ⟶ liquid ⟶ solid

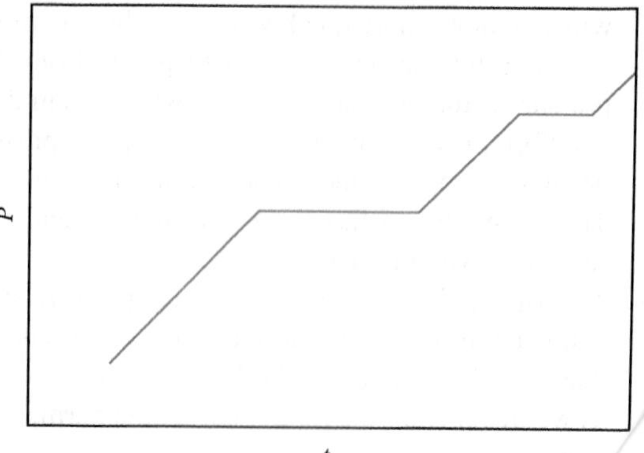

123. The ideal gas law assumes that there are n… between the molecules. At these high pressur… nia molecules are closer to one another, s… gen bonds between ammonia molecules a… ar- effect and will pull on one another stro… sper- the volume. This is different than for … n will gon, where even at these high pressu… ures. sion forces have little effect on th… better obey the ideal gas law, ev…

125. 26 °C

127. 3.4×10^3 g H_2O

129. CsCl has a higher melting point than AgI because of its higher coordination number. In CsCl, one anion bonds to eight cations (and vice versa) while in AgI, one anion bonds only to four cations.

131. a. $4r$

b. $c^2 = a^2 + b^2 \quad c = 4r,\ a = l, b = l$
$(4r)^2 = l^2 + l^2$
$16r^2 = 2l^2$
$8r^2 = l^2$
$l = \sqrt[3]{8r^2}$
$l = 2\sqrt{2}r$

133. 8 atoms/unit

135. a. $CO_2(s) \longrightarrow CO_2(g)$ at 195 K

b. $CO_2(s) \longrightarrow$ triple point at 216 K $\longrightarrow CO_2(g)$ just above 216 K

c. $CO_2(s) \longrightarrow CO_2(l)$ at somewhat above 216 K $\longrightarrow CO_2(g)$ at around 250 K

d. $CO_2(s) \longrightarrow CO_2(g) \longrightarrow$ supercritical fluid

137. 55.843 g mol^{-1}

139. 2.00 g cm^{-3}

141. Decreasing the pressure will decrease the temperature of liquid nitrogen. Because the nitrogen is boiling, its temperature must be constant at a given pressure. As the pressure decreases, the boiling point decreases, and therefore so does the temperature. If the pressure drops below the pressure of the triple point, the phase change will shift from vapourization to sublimation and the liquid nitrogen will become solid.

143. body diagonal = $\sqrt{6}r$, radius = $(\sqrt{3} - \sqrt{2})r/\sqrt{2} = 0.2247r$

145. 70.7 L

147. 0.48 atm

149. The water within a container with a larger surface area will evaporate more quickly because there is more surface area for the molecules to evaporate from. Vapour pressure is the pressure of the gas when it is in dynamic equilibrium with the liquid. The vapour pressure is dependent only on the substance and the temperature. The larger the surface area, the more quickly it will reach the dynamic state.

The triple point will be at a lower temperature since the
usion equilibrium line has a positive slope. This means
t we will be increasing both temperature and pressure
travel from the triple point to the normal melting

155. id segment will have the least steep slope
akes the most kJ mol^{-1} to raise the tempera-
li ase.
tantial intermolecular attractions in the
ly none in the gas.

Chapter 1

29. a. hexan
b. water, n
bonding
Cl4; dispersion forces
c. hexane, tol
ion, dipole–dipole, hydrogen
spersion forces

d. water, acetone, methanol, ethanol; dispersion, ion–dipole

31. $HOCH_2CH_2CH_2OH$

33. a. water; dispersion, dipole–dipole, hydrogen bonding

b. hexane; dispersion

c. water; dispersion, dipole–dipole

d. water; dispersion, dipole–dipole, hydrogen bonding

35. a. endothermic

b. The lattice energy is greater in magnitude than the heat of hydration.

c.

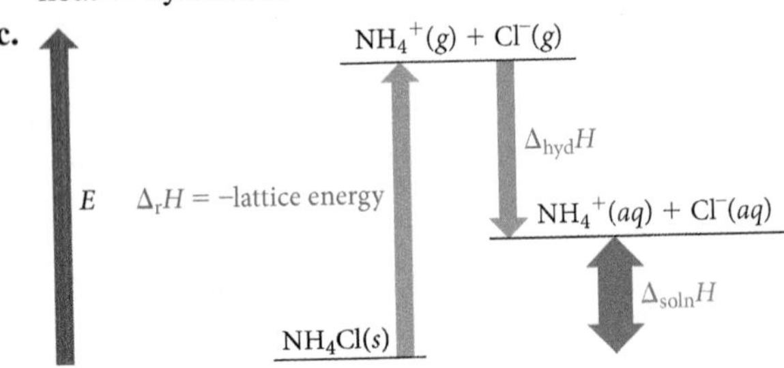

d. The solution forms because chemical systems tend toward greater entropy.

37. −797 kJ mol^{-1}

39. $\Delta_{soln}H = -6.3 \times 10^1$ kJ mol^{-1}, 7 kJ of energy evolved

41. unsaturated

43. About 31 g will precipitate.

45. Boiling water releases any O_2 dissolved in it. The solubility of gases decreases with increasing temperature.

47. As pressure increases, nitrogen will more easily dissolve in blood. To reverse this process, divers should ascend to lower pressures.

49. 1.1 g

51. 1.92 mol L^{-1}, 2.0 m, 10.4%

53. 0.340 L

55. 1.6×10^2 g Ag

57. 1.4×10^4 g

59. Add water to 7.31 mL of concentrated solution until a total volume of 1.15 L is acquired.

61. a. Add water to 3.73 g KCl to a volume of 100 mL.

b. Add 3.59 g KCl to 96.41 g H_2O.

c. Add 5.0 g KCl to 95 g H_2O.

63. a. 0.417 mol L^{-1}

b. 0.444 mol kg^{-1}

c. 7.41% by mass

d. 0.00794

e. 0.794% by mole

65. 0.89 mol L^{-1}

67. 15 m, 0.22

69. The level has decreased more in the beaker filled with pure water. The dissolved salt in the seawater decreases the vapour pressure and subsequently lowers the rate of vaporization.

71. 30.7 Torr

73. a. $P_{hep} = 24.4$ Torr, $P_{oct} = 5.09$ Torr

b. 29.5 Torr

c. 80.8% heptane by mass, 19.2% octane by mass

d. The vapour is richer in the more volatile component.

75. $P_{chl} = 51.9$ Torr, $P_{ace} = 274$ Torr, $P_{tot} = 326$ Torr. The solution is not ideal. The chloroform–acetone interactions are stronger than the chloroform–chloroform and acetone–acetone interactions.

77. freezing point (fp) $= -1.27\ °C$, bp $= 100.349\ °C$

79. $1.8 \times 10^2\ g\ mol^{-1}$

81. 26.5 bar

83. $6.36 \times 10^3\ g\ mol^{-1}$

85. **a.** fp $= -0.558\ °C$, bp $= 100.154\ °C$
b. fp $= -1.98\ °C$, bp $= 100.546\ °C$
c. fp $= -2.5\ °C$, bp $= 100.70\ °C$

87. **a.** $-0.632\ °C$ **b.** 5.5 bar **c.** $100.18\ °C$

89. 3.4

91. 23.0 Torr

93. Chloroform is polar and has stronger solute–solvent interactions than nonpolar carbon tetrachloride.

95. The main intermolecular interactions keeping both methanol and water in the liquid phase at room temperatures are hydrogen bonds. Therefore, disrupting the methanol–methanol and water–water hydrogen bonds to form similar methanol–water hydrogen bonds is roughly thermoneutral.

To dissolve pentanol, however, the dispersion forces between the alkyl chain in pentanol are disrupted, as are the hydrogen bonds in water. The interactions between water and the alkyl chain that would be formed upon dissolving pentanol would not give back the same amount of energy as those disrupted, so the dissolution would be energetically unfeasible. Note that there would be hydrogen bonds between the O—H group of pentanol and water, but that is not enough to dissolve the pentanol in water. Instead, a film on the surface of the water would be formed.

97. $\Delta_{soln}H = 51\ kJ\ mol^{-1}$, $-8.7\ °C$

99. $2.2 \times 10^{-3}\ mol\ L^{-1}\ bar^{-1}$

101. $1.3 \times 10^4\ L$

103. 0.24 g

105. $-24\ °C$

107. **a.** 1.1% by mass/V **b.** 1.6% by mass/V
c. 5.3% by mass/V

109. 2.479

111. 0.224 bar

113. χ_{CHCl_3}(original) $= 0.657$, P_{CHCl_3}(condensed) $= 0.346$ atm

115. $1.74\ mol\ L^{-1}$

117. $C_6H_{14}O_2$

119. 12 g NaCl

121. Molar mass $= 125.4\ g\ mol^{-1}$
Molecular formula: P_4

123. $6.4 \times 10^{-3}\ L$

125. 20.8% glucose by mass, 79.2% sucrose by mass

127. $P_{iso} = 0.131$ bar, $P_{pro} = 0.068$ bar. The major intermolecular attractions are between the OH groups. The OH group at the end of the chain in propyl alcohol is more accessible than the one in the middle of the chain in isopropyl alcohol. In addition, the molecular shape of propyl alcohol is a straight chain of carbon atoms, while that of isopropyl alcohol is a branched chain and is more like a ball. The contact area between two ball-like objects is smaller than that of two chain-like objects. The smaller contact area in isopropyl alcohol means the molecules don't attract each other as strongly as do those of propyl alcohol. As a result of both of these factors, the vapour pressure of isopropyl alcohol is higher.

129. 0.0097 m

131. Na_2CO_3 0.058 mol L^{-1}, $NaHCO_3$ 0.065 mol L^{-1}

133. The water should not be immediately cycled back into the river. As the water was warmed, dissolved oxygen would have been released, since the amount of a gas able to be dissolved into a liquid decreases as the temperature of the liquid increases. As such, the water returned to the river would lack dissolved oxygen if it was still hot. To preserve the dissolved oxygen necessary for the survival of fish and other aquatic life, the water must first be cooled.

135. **b.** NaCl

137. NaCl molality $= 0.02\ m$, the boiling point will be $100.02\ °C$. Adding salt to boiling water is for biochemical reasons (taste), not to decrease the cooking time by increasing the boiling point.

Chapter 13

25. **a.** Rate $= -\frac{1}{2}\frac{\Delta[HBr]}{\Delta t} = \frac{\Delta[H_2]}{\Delta t} = \frac{\Delta[Br_2]}{\Delta t}$
b. $1.8 \times 10^{-3}\ mol\ L^{-1}\ s^{-1}$
c. 0.040 mol Br_2

27. **a.** Rate $= -\frac{1}{2}\frac{\Delta[A]}{\Delta t} = -\frac{\Delta[B]}{\Delta t} = \frac{1}{3}\frac{\Delta[C]}{\Delta t}$
b. $\frac{\Delta[B]}{\Delta t} = -0.0500\ mol\ L^{-1}\ s^{-1}$,
$\frac{\Delta[C]}{\Delta t} = 0.150\ mol\ L^{-1}\ s^{-1}$

29.

$\Delta[Cl_2]/\Delta t$	$\Delta[F_2]/\Delta t$	$\Delta[ClF_3]/\Delta t$	Rate
-0.012 mol $L^{-1}\ s^{-1}$	-0.036 mol $L^{-1}\ s^{-1}$	0.024 mol $L^{-1}\ s^{-1}$	0.012 mol $L^{-1}\ s^{-1}$

31. **a.** $0 \longrightarrow 10$ s: Rate $= 8.7 \times 10^{-3}\ mol\ L^{-1}\ s^{-1}$
$40 \longrightarrow 50$ s: Rate $= 6.0 \times 10^{-3}\ mol\ L^{-1}\ s^{-1}$
b. $1.4 \times 10^{-2}\ mol\ L^{-1}\ s^{-1}$

33. **a.** (i) $1.0 \times 10^{-2}\ mol\ L^{-1}\ s^{-1}$
(ii) $8.5 \times 10^{-3}\ mol\ L^{-1}\ s^{-1}$
(iii) $0.013\ mol\ L^{-1}\ s^{-1}$
b.

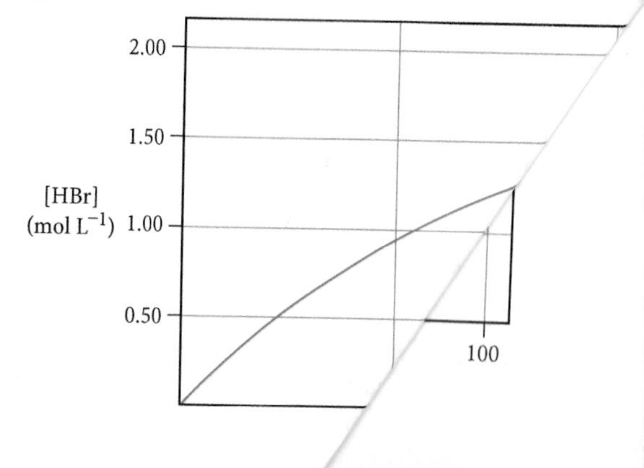

35. a. first order

b.

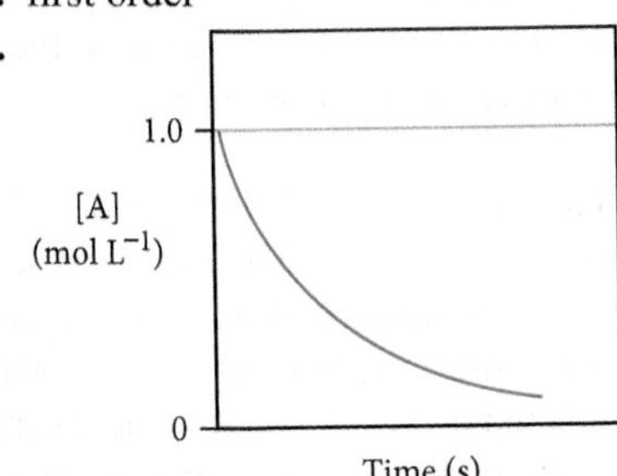

c. Rate $= k[\text{A}]^1, k = 0.010\ \text{s}^{-1}$

37. a. s^{-1} **b.** $\text{L mol}^{-1}\ \text{s}^{-1}$ **c.** $\text{mol L}^{-1}\ \text{s}^{-1}$

39. a. Rate $= k[\text{A}][\text{B}]^2$ **b.** third order
c. 2 **d.** 4
e. 1 **f.** 8

41. second order, Rate $= 5.25\ \text{L mol}^{-1}\ \text{s}^{-1}[\text{A}]^2$

43. Rate $= k[\text{NO}_2][\text{F}_2], k = 2.57\ \text{L mol}^{-1}\ \text{s}^{-1}$, second order.

45. a. zero order **b.** first order **c.** second order

47. second order, $k = 2.25 \times 10^{-2}\ \text{L mol}^{-1}\ \text{s}^{-1}$, [AB] at 25 s $= 0.619\ \text{mol L}^{-1}$

49. first order, $k = 1.12 \times 10^{-2}\ \text{s}^{-1}$, Rate $= 2.8 \times 10^{-3}\ \text{mol L}^{-1}\ \text{s}^{-1}$

51. a. $4.5 \times 10^{-3}\ \text{s}^{-1}$ **b.** Rate $= 4.5 \times 10^{-3}\ \text{s}^{-1}[\text{A}]$
c. 1.5×10^2 s **d.** 2.2×10^2 s
e. $[\text{A}] = 0.0908\ \text{mol L}^{-1}$

53. a. 4.88×10^3 s **b.** 8.5×10^3 s
c. 1.7×10^3 s **d.** $0.146\ \text{mol L}^{-1}$ at 200 s, $0.140\ \text{mol L}^{-1}$ at 500 s

55. 6.8×10^8 yrs; 8.4×10^{17} atoms

57.

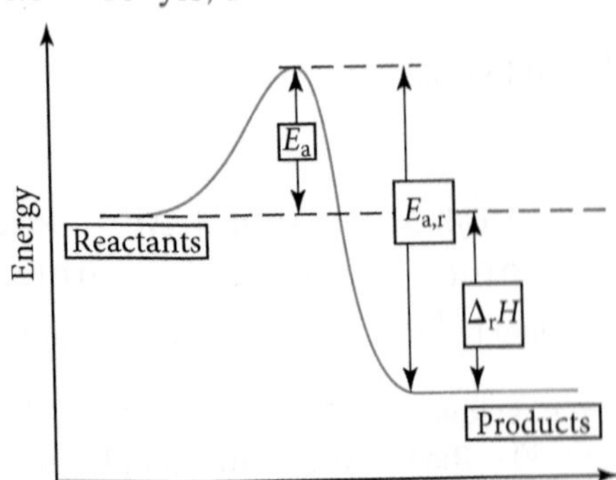

. $17\ \text{s}^{-1}$
$61.90\ \text{kJ mol}^{-1}$
$= 251\ \text{kJ mol}^{-1}, A = 7.93 \times 10^{11}\ \text{s}^{-1}$
$= 23.0\ \text{kJ mol}^{-1}, A = 8.05 \times 10^{10}\ \text{L mol}^{-1}\ \text{s}^{-1}$
2 kJ mol^{-1} **b.** $0.101\ \text{s}^{-1}$
J mol^{-1}
75.

ism is valid.
b.) $\rightleftharpoons 2\ \text{NO}_2(g) + \text{Cl}_2(g)$

77. Heter $k_2 k_1 [\text{NO}_2\text{Cl}]^2$
because $_2] + k_2[\text{NO}_2\text{Cl}]$
greater su sts require a large surface area
substrate to nly happen at the surface. A
s greater opportunity for the
lts in a faster reaction.

79. 2×10^{12}

81. a. first order, $k = 0.0462\ \text{h}^{-1}$ **b.** 15.0 h
c. 49.8 h

83. $0.0531\ \text{mol L}^{-1}\ \text{s}^{-1}$

85. Rate $= kP_{\text{CH}_3\text{CHO}^2}, k = 4.5 \times 10^{-4}\ \text{bar}^{-1}\ \text{s}^{-1}$, 370 mbar

87. 219 Torr

89. 1×10^{-7} s

91. 1.6×10^2 s

93. a. 2

b.

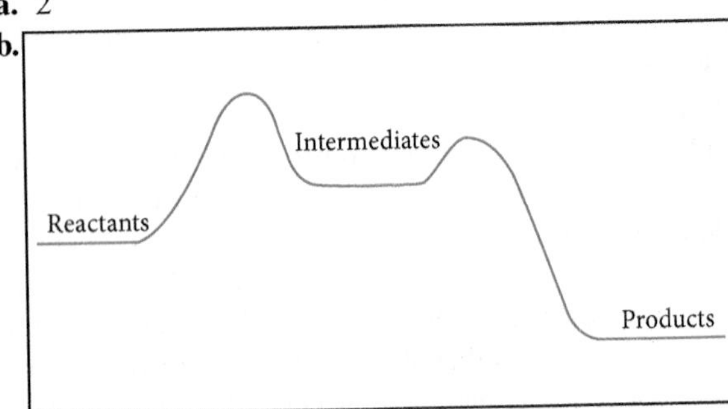

c. first step **d.** exothermic

95. a. 5.41 s **b.** 2.2 s for 25%, 5.4 s for 50%
c. 0.28 at 10 s, 0.077 at 20 s

97. a. From the Arrhenius plot, $E_a = 89.5\ \text{kJ mol}^{-1}$, $A = 4.29 \times 10^{11}\ \text{L mol}^{-1}\ \text{s}^{-1}$
b. $2.5 \times 10^{-5}\ \text{L mol}^{-1}\ \text{s}^{-1}$
c. $6.1 \times 10^{-4}\ \text{mol L}^{-1}\ \text{s}^{-1}$

99. a. No
b. No bond is broken and the two radicals attract each other.
c. Formation of diatomic gases from atomic gases.

101. 1.35×10^4 years

103. a. Rate $= k_1[\text{H}_2][\text{I}_2]$: first order in both H_2 and I_2; therefore, the mechanism is valid.
b. The rate law predicted by proposed mechanism II is:

$$\text{Rate} = \frac{k_1 k_2 [\text{H}_2][\text{I}_2]}{k_{-1} + k_2[\text{H}_2]}$$

Under low H_2 pressures, the rate law becomes:

Rate $= \dfrac{k_1 k_2}{k_{-1}}[\text{H}_2][\text{I}_2]$ which predicts a reaction that is first order in both H_2 and I_2; therefore, the mechanism is valid.

c. Under high pressures of H_2, the rate law becomes: Rate $= k_1[\text{I}_2]$ which is first order overall and zero order in H_2.

105. a. $$\text{Rate} = \frac{k_1 k_2 [\text{NO}]^2[\text{Br}_2]}{k_{-1} + k_2[\text{NO}]}$$

b. Rate $= k_1[\text{NO}][\text{Br}_2]$; second order

c. Rate $= \dfrac{k_1 k_2}{k_{-1}}[\text{NO}]^2[\text{Br}_2]$; third order

107. a. 0% **b.** 25% **c.** 33%

109. 174 kJ

111. a. 0.754 bar
b. 3.246 bar

113. a. $1.00 \times 10^{-5}\ \text{s}^{-1}$
b. 4.5 hours

115. a. second order

b. $CH_3NC + CH_3NC \underset{k_2}{\overset{k_1}{\rightleftharpoons}} CH_3NC^* + CH_3NC$(fast)

$CH_3NC^* \xrightarrow{k_3} CH_3CN$ (slow)

$\text{Rate} = k_3[CH_3NC^*]$

$k_1[CH_3NC]^2 = k_2[CH_3NC^*][CH_3NC]$

$$[CH_3NC^*] = \frac{k_1}{k_2}[CH_3NC]$$

$$\text{Rate} = k_3 \times \frac{k_1}{k_2}[CH_3NC]$$

$\text{Rate} = k[CH_3NC]$

117. $\text{Rate} = k[A]^2$

$$\text{Rate} = -\frac{d[A]}{dt}$$

$$\frac{d[A]}{dt} = -k[A]^2$$

$$-\frac{d[A]}{[A]^2} = k\,dt$$

$$\int_{[A]_0}^{[A]} -\frac{1}{[A]^2}d[A] = \int_0^t k\,dt$$

$$\left[\frac{1}{[A]}\right]_{[A]_0}^{[A]} = k\,[t]_0^t$$

$$\frac{1}{[A]} - \frac{1}{[A]_0} = kt$$

$$\frac{1}{[A]} = kt + \frac{1}{[A]_0}$$

119. $\text{Rate} = k[CO][Cl_2]^{\frac{3}{2}}$

121. $[Cl_2] = 0.0084\ \text{mol L}^{-1}$, $[NO] = 0.017\ \text{mol L}^{-1}$

123. a. $$\text{Rate} = \frac{k_2[E]_0[S]}{[S] + K_M}$$

$$\frac{1}{2}\,k_2[E]_0 = \frac{k_2[E]_0[S]}{[S] + K_M}$$

$$\frac{1}{2}([S] + K_M) = [S]$$

$K_M = [S]$: The Michaelis constant is the concentration of substrate that yields a rate of 1/2 V_{max}.

b.

[S] (mmol L^{-1})	Rate ($\text{mmol L}^{-1}\text{ s}^{-1}$)
0.1	0.0109
1.0	0.104
10	0.707
100	1.68
1000	1.94

125. $$\text{Rate} = \frac{k_1k_2k_3[E][A][B]}{k_{-1}k_{-2}[C]}$$

127. B is first order and A is second order.
B will be linear if you plot ln[B] vs. time, A will be linear if you plot 1/[A] vs. time.

129.

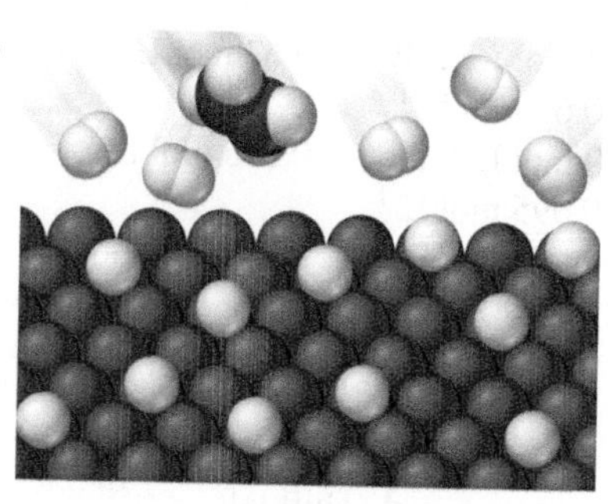

Chapter 14

21. a. $K_P = \dfrac{(P_{H_2})^2(P_{S_2})}{(P_{H_2S})^2}$ **b.** $K_c = \dfrac{[Cu^{2+}]}{[Ag^+]^2}$

c. $K = P_{H_2}^2[OH^-]^2[Li^+]$

23. The concentration of the reactants will be greater. No, this is not dependent on initial concentrations; it is dependent on the value of K.

25. a. Figure v

b. The change in the decrease of reactants and increase of products would be faster.

c. No, catalysts affect kinetics, not equilibrium.

27. a. 1.1×10^{-7} (reactants favoured)

b. 3.0×10^3 (products favoured)

c. 1.2×10^{-14} (reactants favoured)

29. 1.3×10^{-29}

31. a. $2.53 \times 10^{-23}\ \text{mol L}^{-1}$ **b.** $1.3 \times 10^{22}\ \text{mol L}^{-2}$

c. 81.9

33. a. $K_c = \dfrac{[HCO_3^-][OH^-]}{[CO_3^{2-}]}$ **b.** $K_P = P_{O_2}^3$

c. $K_c = \dfrac{[H_3O^+][F^-]}{[HF]}$ **d.** $K_c = \dfrac{[NH_4^+][OH^-]}{[NH_3]}$

35. 136

37.

T(K)	P_{N_2}	P_{H_2}	P_{NH_3}	K
350	0.121	0.105	0.565	2.28×10^3
415	0.110	0.224	0.128	13.2
515	0.120	0.140	4.11×10^{-3}	0.0512

39. 2.20×10^2 mbar

41. 3.9×10^3

43. 120

45. More solid NH_4HS will form.

47. Additional solid Ag_2SO_4 will not dissolve.

49. a. $[A] = 0.20\ \text{mol L}^{-1}$, $[B] = 0.80\ \text{mol L}^{-1}$

b. $[A] = 0.33\ \text{mol L}^{-1}$, $[B] = 0.67\ \text{mol L}^{-1}$

c. $[A] = 0.38\ \text{mol L}^{-1}$, $[B] = 1.2\ \text{mol L}^{-1}$

51. $[N_2O_4] = 0.0363\ \text{mol L}^{-1}$, $[NO_2] = 0.0274\ \text{mol L}^{-1}$

53. $P_{CO_2} = 2.25$ bar, $P_{CO} = 0.03$ bar

55. $1.9 \times 10^{-3}\ \text{mol L}^{-1}$

57. $P_{Cl_2} = P_{F_2} = 6.61 \times 10^{-4}$ bar, $P_{ClF} = 0.499$ bar

59. a. [A] = 0.38 mol L^{-1}, [B] = 0.62 mol L^{-1}, [C] = 0.62 mol L^{-1}
b. [A] = 0.90 mol L^{-1}, [B] = 0.095 mol L^{-1}, [C] = 0.095 mol L^{-1}
c. [A] = 1.0 mol L^{-1}, [B] = 3.2×10^{-3} mol L^{-1}, [C] = 3.2×10^{-3} mol L^{-1}

61. a. shift left **b.** shift right **c.** shift right

63. a. shift right **b.** unchanged **c.** unchanged **d.** shift left

65. a. shift right **b.** shift left **c.** no effect

67. Increase temperature $\longrightarrow$ shift right, decrease temperature $\longrightarrow$ shift left. Increasing the temperature will increase the equilibrium constant.

69. **b.** and **d.**

71. a. 1.7×10^2

b. $\frac{[HbCO]}{[HbO_2]} = 0.85$ or 17/20

CO is highly toxic, as it blocks O_2 uptake by hemoglobin. CO at a level of 0.1% will replace nearly half of the O_2 in blood.

73. a. 1.95 bar **b.** 1.42 bar

75. 0.40 g

77. b, c, and d.

79. 1.12 bar

81. 3.2×10^2 g, 21% yield

83. 0.12 bar

85. 0.72 bar

87. 0.017 g

89. 0.193

91. a. 38.6 **b.** 169 mbar

93. $P_{NO} = P_{Cl_2} = 4.6 \times 10^2$ mbar

95. 1.27×10^{-2}

97. a. $[Ag^+] = [Cl^-] = 1.3 \times 10^{-5}$ mol L^{-1}
b. 4.8×10^{-3} mol L^{-1}

99. d.

101. $Q = 1$, which is greater than K_P. The reaction will proceed to the left.

Chapter 15

33. a. acid, $HNO_3(aq) \longrightarrow H^+(aq) + NO_3^-(aq)$
b. acid, $NH_4^+(aq) \rightleftharpoons H^+(aq) + NH_3(aq)$
c. base, $KOH(aq) \longrightarrow K^+(aq) + OH^-(aq)$
d. acid, $HC_2H_3O_2(aq) \rightleftharpoons H^+(aq) + C_2H_3O_2^-(aq)$

35. a. $H_2CO_3(aq)$ (acid) + $H_2O(l)$ (base) $\rightleftharpoons$ $H_3O^+(aq)$ (conj. acid) + $HCO_3^-(aq)$ (conj. base)
b. $NH_3(aq)$ (base) + $H_2O(l)$ (acid) $\rightleftharpoons$ $NH_4^+(aq)$ (conj. acid) + $OH^-(aq)$ (conj. base)
c. $HNO_3(aq)$ (acid) + $H_2O(l)$ (base) $\longrightarrow$ $H_3O^+(aq)$ (conj. acid) + $NO_3^-(aq)$ (conj. base)
d. $C_5H_5N(aq)$ (base) + $H_2O(l)$ (acid) $\rightleftharpoons$ $C_5H_5NH^+(aq)$ (conj. acid) + $OH^-(aq)$ (conj. base)

37. a. Cl^- **b.** HSO_3^- **c.** CHO_2^- **d.** F^-

39. $H_2PO_4^-(aq) + H_2O(l) \rightleftharpoons HPO_4^{2-}(aq) + H_3O^+(aq)$
$H_2PO_4^-(aq) + H_2O(l) \rightleftharpoons H_3PO_4(aq) + OH^-(aq)$

41. a. strong **b.** strong **c.** strong **d.** weak, $K_a = \frac{[H_3O^+][HSO_3^-]}{[H_2SO_3]}$

43. a, b, c

45. a. F^- **b.** NO_2^- **c.** ClO^-

47. a. 8.3×10^{-7} mol L^{-1}, basic
b. 1.2×10^{-10} mol L^{-1}, acidic
c. 2.9×10^{-13} mol L^{-1}, acidic

49. a. pH = 7.77, pOH = 6.23
b. pH = 7.00, pOH = 7.00
c. pH = 5.66, pOH = 8.34

51.

$[H_3O^+]$	$[OH^-]$	pH	Acidic or Basic
7.1×10^{-4}	1.4×10^{-11}	3.15	Acidic
3.7×10^{-9}	2.7×10^{-6}	8.43	Basic
8×10^{-12}	1×10^{-3}	11.1	Basic
6.3×10^{-4}	1.6×10^{-11}	3.20	Acidic

53. $[H_3O^+] = 1.5 \times 10^{-7}$ mol L^{-1}, pH = 6.81

55. a. $[H_3O^+] = 0.25$ mol L^{-1}, $[OH^-] = 4.0 \times 10^{-14}$ mol L^{-1}, pH = 0.60
b. $[H_3O^+] = 0.015$ mol L^{-1}, $[OH^-] = 6.7 \times 10^{-13}$ mol L^{-1}, pH = 1.82
c. $[H_3O^+] = 0.072$ mol L^{-1}, $[OH^-] = 1.4 \times 10^{-13}$ mol L^{-1}, pH = 1.14
d. $[H_3O^+] = 0.105$ mol L^{-1}, $[OH^-] = 9.5 \times 10^{-14}$ mol L^{-1}, pH = 0.979

57. a. 1.8 g **b.** 0.57 g **c.** 0.045 g

59. 2.21

61. $[H_3O^+] = 2.5 \times 10^{-3}$ mol L^{-1}, pH = 2.60

63. a. 1.78 (approximation valid)
b. 2.13 (approximation breaks down)
c. 2.68 (approximation breaks down)

65. 2.75

67. 6.8×10^{-6}

69. 0.0070%

71. a. 0.42% **b.** 0.60% **c.** 1.3% **d.** 1.9%

73. 3.61×10^{-5}

75. a. pH = 1.90, percent ionization = 5.0%
b. pH = 2.12, percent ionization = 7.6%
c. pH = 2.28, percent ionization = 11.0%

77. a. 0.939 **b.** 1.07 **c.** 2.19 **d.** 3.02

79. a. $[OH^-] = 0.15$ mol L^{-1}, $[H_3O^+] = 6.7 \times 10^{-14}$ mol L^{-1}, pH = 13.17, pOH = 0.83
b. $[OH^-] = 0.003$ mol L^{-1}, $[H_3O^+] = 3.3 \times 10^{-12}$ mol L^{-1}, pH = 11.48, pOH = 2.52
c. $[OH^-] = 9.6 \times 10^{-4}$ mol L^{-1}, $[H_3O^+] = 1.0 \times 10^{-11}$ mol L^{-1}, pH = 10.98, pOH = 3.02
d. $[OH^-] = 8.7 \times 10^{-5}$ mol L^{-1}, $[H_3O^+] = 1.1 \times 10^{-10}$ mol L^{-1}, pH = 9.94, pOH = 4.06

81. 13.841

83. 0.104 L

85. a. $NH_3(aq) + H_2O(l) \rightleftharpoons NH_4^+(aq) + OH^-(aq)$, $K_b = \frac{[NH_4^+][OH^-]}{[NH_3]}$
b. $HCO_3^-(aq) + H_2O(l) \rightleftharpoons H_2CO_3(aq) + OH^-(aq)$, $K_b = \frac{[H_2CO_3][OH^-]}{[HCO_3^-]}$
c. $CH_3NH_2(aq) + H_2O(l) \rightleftharpoons CH_3NH_3^+(aq) + OH^-(aq)$, $K_b = \frac{[CH_3NH_3^+][OH^-]}{[CH_3NH_2]}$
87. $[OH^-] = 1.6 \times 10^{-3}$ mol L^{-1}, pH = 11.21, pOH = 2.79
89. 7.5
91. 7×10^{-7}
93. a. neutral
b. basic, $ClO^-(aq) + H_2O(l) \rightleftharpoons HClO(aq) + OH^-(aq)$
c. basic, $CN^-(aq) + H_2O(l) \rightleftharpoons HCN(aq) + OH^-(aq)$
d. neutral
95. $[OH^-] = 2.0 \times 10^{-6}$ mol L^{-1}, pH = 8.30
97. a. acidic, $NH_4^+(aq) + H_2O(l) \rightleftharpoons NH_3(aq) + H_3O^+(aq)$
b. neutral
c. acidic, $Co(H_2O)_6^{3+}(aq) + H_2O(l) \rightleftharpoons Co(H_2O)_5(OH)^{2+}(aq) + H_3O^+(aq)$
d. acidic, $CH_2NH_3^+(aq) + H_2O(l) \rightleftharpoons CH_2NH_2(aq) + H_3O^+(aq)$
99. a. acidic **b.** basic
c. acidic **d.** acidic
101. NaOH, $NaHCO_3$, NaCl, NH_4ClO_2, NH_4Cl
103. a. 5.13 **b.** 8.87 **c.** 7.0
105. $[K^+] = 0.15$ mol L^{-1}
$[F^-] = 0.15$ mol L^{-1}
$[HF] = 1.6 \times 10^{-6}$ mol L^{-1}
$[OH^-] = 1.6 \times 10^{-6}$ mol L^{-1}
$[H_3O^+] = 6.3 \times 10^{-9}$ mol L^{-1}
107. $H_3PO_4(aq) + H_2O(l) \rightleftharpoons H_2PO_4^-(aq) + H_3O^+(aq)$, $K_{a_1} = \frac{[H_3O^+][H_2PO_4^-]}{[H_3PO_4]}$
$H_2PO_4^-(aq) + H_2O(l) \rightleftharpoons HPO_4^{2-}(aq) + H_3O^+(aq)$, $K_{a_2} = \frac{[H_3O^+][HPO_4^{2-}]}{[H_2PO_4^{2-}]}$
$HPO_4^{2-}(aq) + H_2O(l) \rightleftharpoons PO_4^{3-}(aq) + H_3O^+(aq)$, $K_{a_3} = \frac{[H_3O^+][PO_4^{3-}]}{[HPO_4^{2-}]}$
109. a. $[H_3O^+] = 0.048$ mol L^{-1}, pH = 1.32
b. $[H_3O^+] = 0.12$ mol L^{-1}, pH = 0.92
111. $[H_2SO_3] = 0.418$ mol L^{-1}
$[HSO_3^-] = 0.082$ mol L^{-1}
$[SO_3^{2-}] = 6.4 \times 10^{-8}$ mol L^{-1}
$[H_3O^+] = 0.082$ mol L^{-1}
113. a. $[H_3O^+] = 0.51$ mol L^{-1}, pH = 0.29
b. $[H_3O^+] = 0.11$ mol L^{-1}, pH = 0.96 (*x is small* approximation breaks down)
c. $[H_3O^+] = 0.059$ mol L^{-1}, pH = 1.23
115. a. HCl, weaker bond **b.** HF, electron affinity
c. H_2Se, weaker bond
117. a. H_2SO_4, more oxygen atoms bonded to S
b. $HClO_2$, more oxygen atoms bonded to Cl
c. HClO, Cl has higher electronegativity
d. CCl_3COOH, Cl has higher electronegativity
119. S^{2-}, its conjugate acid (H_2S) is a weaker acid than H_2Se
121. ii because the methyl group is electron "donating"
123. a. Lewis acid **b.** Lewis acid
c. Lewis base **d.** Lewis base
125. a. acid: Fe^{3+}, base H_2O **b.** acid: Zn^{2+}, base: NH_3
c. acid: BF_3, base: $(CH_3)_3N$
127. a. weak **b.** strong **c.** weak **d.** strong
129. If blood became acidic, the H^+ concentration would increase. According to Le Châtelier's principle, equilibrium would be shifted to the left and the concentration of oxygenated Hb would decrease.
131. 274 mL of HCl solution can be neutralized; all the acid will be neutralized.
133. $[H_3O^+]$(Great Lakes) = 3×10^{-5} mol L^{-1}, $[H_3O^+]$(West Coast) = 4×10^{-6} mol L^{-1}. The rain over the Great Lakes is about 8 times more concentrated.
135. 2.7
137. a. 2.000 **b.** 1.52 **c.** 12.95
d. 11.07 **e.** 5.03
139. a. 1.260 **b.** 8.08 **c.** 0.824
d. 8.57 **e.** 1.171
141. a. $CN^-(aq) + H^+(aq) \rightleftharpoons HCN(aq)$
b. $NH_4^+(aq) + OH^-(aq) \rightleftharpoons NH_3(aq) + H_2O(l)$
c. $CN^-(aq) + NH_4^+(aq) \rightleftharpoons HCN(aq) + NH_3(aq)$
d. $HSO_4^-(aq) + C_2H_3O_2^-(aq) \rightleftharpoons SO_4^{2-}(aq) + HC_2H_3O_2(aq)$
e. no reaction between the major species
143. 0.794
145. $K_a = 8.3 \times 10^{-4}$
147. 1.41
149. 6.79, the autoionization of water cannot be ignored at such low concentration of acid.
151. 2.14
153. $[A^-] = 4.14 \times 10^{-5}$ mol L^{-1}
$[H^+] = 2.4 \times 10^{-4}$ mol L^{-1}
$[HA_2^-] = 2.0 \times 10^{-4}$ mol L^{-1}
155. 11.30
157. 50.4 g $NaHCO_3$
159. b.
161. $CH_3COOH < CH_2ClCOOH < CHCl_2COOH < CCl_3COOH$

Chapter 16

29. d.
31. a. 3.62 **b.** 9.11
33. in pure water: 2.0%, in $NaC_7H_5O_2$: 0.063%. The percent ionization in the sodium benzoate solution is much smaller because the presence of the benzoate ion shifts the equilibrium to the left.
35. a. 1.86 **b.** 8.84 **c.** 3.20
37. $HCl + CH_3COONa \longrightarrow CH_3COOH + NaCl$
$NaOH + CH_3COOH \longrightarrow CH_3COONa + H_2O$

39. **a.** 3.62 **b.** 9.11

41. **a.** 7.46 **b.** 11.08 **c.** 4.61

43. **a.** 3.86 **b.** 8.95

45. 6.3

47. 3.6 g

49. **a.** 4.74 **b.** 4.68 **c.** 4.81

51. **a.** initial 7.00 final 1.70 **b.** initial 4.70 final 4.56 **c.** initial 10.78 final 10.66

53. 1.5 g; 3.6 g

55. **a.** yes **b.** no **c.** yes **d.** no **e.** no

57. **a.** 7.4 **b.** 0.3 g **c.** 0.14 g

59. **d.** KClO/HClO = 1.09

61. **a.** does not exceed capacity
b. does not exceed capacity
c. does not exceed capacity
d. does not exceed capacity

63. **a.** 8.10 **b.** 7.96

65. **a.** (i) pH = 8, (ii) pH = 7
b. (i) weak acid, (ii) strong acid

67. **a.** 40.0 mL HI for both
b. KOH: neutral, CH3NH2: acidic
c. CH3NH2
d. Titration of KOH with HI:

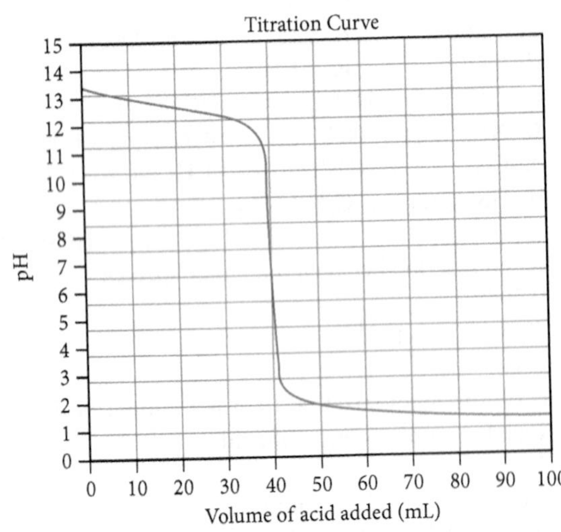

Titration of CH_3NH_2 with HI:

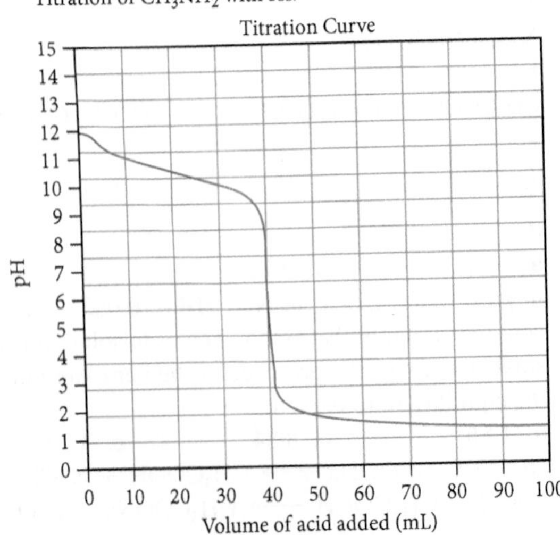

69. **a.** pH = 9, added base = 30 mL
b. 0 mL **c.** 15 mL
d. 30 mL **e.** 30 mL

71. **a.** 0.757 **b.** 30.6 mL **c.** 1.038
d. 7 **e.** 12.15

73. **a.** 13.06 **b.** 28.8 mL **c.** 12.90
d. 7 **e.** 2.07

75. **a.** 2.86 **b.** 16.8 mL **c.** 4.37
d. 4.74 **e.** 8.75 **f.** 12.17

77. **a.** 11.94 **b.** 29.2 mL **c.** 11.33
d. 10.64 **e.** 5.87 **f.** 1.90

79. **a.** (i) **b.** (ii)

81. pK_a = 3, 82 g mol^{-1}

83. First equivalence: 22.7 mL
Second equivalence: 45.4 mL

85. The solution will appear red. The pH range is 4 to 6.

87. **a.** phenol red, *m*-nitrophenol
b. alizarin, bromothymol blue, phenol red
c. alizarin yellow R

89. **a.** $BaSO_4(s) \rightleftharpoons Ba^{2+}(aq) + SO_4^{2-}(aq)$, $K_{sp} = [Ba^{2+}][SO_4^{2-}]$
b. $PbBr_2(s) \rightleftharpoons Pb^{2+}(aq) + 2\,Br^-(aq)$, $K_{sp} = [Pb^{2+}][Br^-]^2$
c. $Ag_2CrO_4(s) \rightleftharpoons 2\,Ag^+(aq) + CrO_4^{2-}(aq)$, $K_{sp} = [Ag^+]^2[CrO_4^{2-}]$

91. **a.** 7.31×10^{-7} mol L^{-1} **b.** 3.72×10^{-5} mol L^{-1}
c. 3.32×10^{-4} mol L^{-1}

93. **a.** 1.07×10^{-21} **b.** 7.14×10^{-7}
c. 7.44×10^{-11}

95. AX_2

97. 2.07×10^{-5} g/100 mL

99. (iii) $Be(OH)_2$

101. **a.** 0.0183 mol L^{-1} **b.** 0.00755 mol L^{-1}
c. 0.00109 mol L^{-1}

103. **a.** 5×10^{14} mol L^{-1} **b.** 5×10^{8} mol L^{-1}
c. 5×10^{4} mol L^{-1}

105. **a.** more soluble, CO_3^{2-} is basic
b. more soluble, S^{2-} is basic
c. not, neutral
d. not, neutral

107. precipitate will form, CaF_2

109. precipitate will form, $Mg(OH)_2$

111. **a.** 0.018 mol L^{-1} **b.** 1.4×10^{-7} mol L^{-1}
c. 1.1×10^{-5} mol L^{-1}

113. **a.** $BaSO_4$, 1.1×10^{-8} mol L^{-1}
b. 3.0×10^{-8} mol L^{-1}

115. 8.7×10^{-10} mol L^{-1}

117. 5.6×10^{16}

119. $S = 6.3 \times 10^{-12}$ mol L^{-1}

121. 4.05

123. 3.57

125. HCl, 4.7 g

127. **a.** $NaOH(aq) + KHC_8H_4O_4(aq) \longrightarrow Na^+(aq) + K^+(aq) + C_8H_4O_4^{2-}(aq) + H_2O(l)$
b. 0.1046 mol L^{-1}

129. 4.72

131. 176 g mol^{-1}; 1.0×10^{-4}

133. 14.2 L

135. 1.6×10^{-7} mol L^{-1}

137. 8.0×10^{-8} mol L^{-1}
139. 6.29
141. 0.172 mol L^{-1}
143. The ratio by mass of dimethyl ammonium chloride to dimethyl amine needed is 3.6.
145. 0.20 mol L^{-1} benzoic acid, 0.45 mol L^{-1} sodium benzoate
147. $K_{sp} = 8.5 \times 10^{-15}$
149. 51.6 g
151. 1.8×10^{-11} (based on this data)
153. **a.** 5.5×10^{-25} mol L^{-1}
b. 5.5×10^{-4} mol L^{-1}
155. 1.4 L
157. 12.97
159. **a.** $pH < pK_a$ **b.** $pH > pK_a$
c. $pH = pK_a$ **d.** $pH > pK_a$
161. **b.**
163. **a.** no difference **b.** less soluble **c.** more soluble

Chapter 17

23. **a.** and **c.**
25. System A has only two ways of distributing its 20 J of energy (microstates). System B is significantly more complex—it has more modes in which to place energy and, therefore, more potential microstates.
27. **a.** $\Delta S_{sys} > 0$ **b.** $\Delta S_{sys} < 0$
c. $\Delta S_{sys} < 0$ **d.** $\Delta S_{sys} < 0$
29. **a.** $\Delta S_{sys} > 0, \Delta S_{surr} > 0$, spontaneous at all temperatures
b. $\Delta S_{sys} < 0, \Delta S_{surr} < 0$, nonspontaneous at all temperatures
c. $\Delta S_{sys} < 0, \Delta S_{surr} < 0$, nonspontaneous at all temperatures
d. $\Delta S_{sys} > 0, \Delta S_{surr} > 0$, spontaneous at all temperatures
31. **a.** 1.29×10^3 J mol^{-1} K^{-1}
b. 5.00×10^3 J mol^{-1} K^{-1}
c. -3.83×10^2 J mol^{-1} K^{-1}
d. -1.48×10^3 J mol^{-1} K^{-1}
33. **a.** -649 J mol^{-1} K^{-1}, nonspontaneous
b. 649 J mol^{-1} K^{-1}, spontaneous
c. 123 J mol^{-1} K^{-1}, spontaneous
d. -76 J mol^{-1} K^{-1}, nonspontaneous
35. 108.9 J mol^{-1} K^{-1}
37. **a.** 1.93×10^5 J mol^{-1}, nonspontaneous
b. -1.93×10^5 J mol^{-1}, spontaneous
c. -3.7×10^4 J mol^{-1}, spontaneous
d. 4.7×10^4 J mol^{-1}, nonspontaneous
39. -2.247×10^6 J mol^{-1}, spontaneous
41.

$\Delta_r H$	$\Delta_r S$	$\Delta_r G$	*Low Temperature*	*High Temperature*
−	+	−	Spontaneous	Spontaneous
−	−	Temperature dependent	Spontaneous	Nonspontaneous
+	+	Temperature dependent	Nonspontaneous	Spontaneous
+	−	+	Nonspontaneous	Nonspontaneous

43. It increases.
45. **a.** $CO_2(g)$, greater molar mass and complexity
b. $CH_3OH(g)$, gas phase
c. $CO_2(g)$, greater molar mass and complexity
d. $SiH_4(g)$, greater molar mass
e. $CH_3CH_2CH_3(g)$, greater molar mass and complexity
f. NaBr(*aq*), aqueous
47. **a.** He, Ne, SO_2, NH_3, CH_3CH_2OH. From He to Ne there is an increase in molar mass, beyond that, the molecules increases in complexity.
b. $H_2O(s)$, $H_2O(l)$, $H_2O(g)$; increase in entropy in going from solid to liquid to gas phase.
c. CH_4, CF_4, CCl_4; increasing entropy with increasing molar mass.
49. **a.** -120.8 J mol^{-1} K^{-1}, decrease in moles of gas
b. 133.9 J mol^{-1} K^{-1}, increase in moles of gas
c. -42.0 J mol^{-1} K^{-1}, small change because moles of gas stay constant
d. -390.8 J mol^{-1} K^{-1}, decrease in moles of gas
51. -89.3 J mol^{-1} K^{-1}, decrease in moles of gas
53. $\Delta_r H° = -1277$ kJ mol^{-1},
$\Delta_r S° = 313.6$ J mol^{-1} K^{-1},
$\Delta_r G° = -1.370 \times 10^3$ kJ mol^{-1}; yes
55. **a.** $\Delta_r H° = 57.2$ kJ mol^{-1},
$\Delta_r S° = 175.8$ J mol^{-1} K^{-1},
$\Delta_r G° = 4.8$ kJ mol^{-1}; nonspontaneous, becomes spontaneous at high temperatures
b. $\Delta_r H° = 176.2$ kJ mol^{-1},
$\Delta_r S° = 285.1$ J mol^{-1} K^{-1},
$\Delta_r G° = 91.2$ kJ mol^{-1}; nonspontaneous, becomes spontaneous at high temperatures
c. $\Delta_r H° = -33.2$ kJ mol^{-1}, $\Delta_r S° = -214.9$ J mol^{-1} K^{-1}, $\Delta_r G° = 30.8$ kJ mol^{-1}; nonspontaneous, becomes spontaneous at high temperatures
d. $\Delta_r H° = -91.8$ kJ mol^{-1},
$\Delta_r S° = -198.1$ J mol^{-1} K^{-1},
$\Delta_r G° = -32.8$ kJ mol^{-1}; spontaneous
57. **a.** 2.8 kJ mol^{-1} **b.** 91.2 kJ mol^{-1}
c. 30.9 kJ mol^{-1} **d.** -32.8 kJ mol^{-1}
Values are comparable. The method using $\Delta_r H°$ and $\Delta_r S°$ can be used to determine how $\Delta_r G°$ changes with temperature.
59. **a.** -72.5 kJ mol^{-1}, spontaneous
b. -11.4 kJ mol^{-1}, spontaneous
c. 9.1 kJ mol^{-1}, nonspontaneous
61. -29.4 kJ mol^{-1}
63. **a.** 19.3 kJ mol^{-1}
b. (i) 2.2 kJ mol^{-1} (ii) -3.5 kJ mol^{-1}
c. The partial pressure of iodine is very low.
65. 20.9 kJ mol^{-1}
67. **a.** 1.48×10^{90} **b.** 2.09×10^{-26}
69. **a.** -33.8 kJ mol^{-1} **b.** 0 kJ mol^{-1} **c.** -16.6 kJ mol^{-1}
71. **a.** 1.90×10^{47} **b.** 1.51×10^{-13}
73. $\Delta_r H° = -9.36$ kJ mol^{-1}; $\Delta_r S° = 22.1$ J mol^{-1} K^{-1}
75. 4.8
77. **a.** + **b.** − **c.** −
79. **a.** $\Delta_r G° = 175.2$ kJ mol^{-1}, $K = 1.95 \times 10^{-31}$, nonspontaneous
b. 133 kJ mol^{-1}, yes

81. Cl_2: $\Delta_r H^\circ = -182.1 \text{ kJ mol}^{-1}$,
$\Delta_r S^\circ = -134.4 \text{ J mol}^{-1} \text{ K}^{-1}$,
$\Delta_r G^\circ = -142.0 \text{ kJ mol}^{-1}$ $K = 7.94 \times 10^{24}$
Br_2: $\Delta_r H^\circ = -45.0 \text{ kJ mol}^{-1}$,
$\Delta_r S^\circ = -134.2 \text{ J mol}^{-1} \text{ K}^{-1}$,
$\Delta_r G^\circ = -5.0 \text{ kJ mol}^{-1}$ $K = 7.5$
I_2: $\Delta_r H^\circ = -48.3 \text{ kJ mol}^{-1}$,
$\Delta_r S^\circ = -132.2 \text{ J mol}^{-1} \text{ K}^{-1}$,
$\Delta_r G^\circ = -8.9 \text{ kJ mol}^{-1}$ $K = 37$
Cl_2 is the most spontaneous, Br_2 is the least. Spontaneity is determined by the standard enthalpy of formation of the dihalogenated ethane. Higher temperatures make the reactions less spontaneous.

83. **a.** 107.8 kJ mol^{-1} **b.** 5.0×10^{-7} bar
c. spontaneous at higher temperatures, $T = 923.4$ K

85. **a.** 2.22×10^5 **b.** 94.4 mol

87. **a.** $\Delta_r G^\circ = -689.6 \text{ kJ mol}^{-1}$, $\Delta_r G^\circ$ becomes less negative
b. $\Delta_r G^\circ = -665.2 \text{ kJ mol}^{-1}$, $\Delta_r G^\circ$ becomes less negative
c. $\Delta_r G^\circ = -632.4 \text{ kJ mol}^{-1}$, $\Delta_r G^\circ$ becomes less negative
d. $\Delta_r G^\circ = -549.3 \text{ kJ mol}^{-1}$, $\Delta_r G^\circ$ becomes less negative

89. With one exception, the formation of any oxide of nitrogen at 298 K requires more moles of gas as reactants than are formed as products. For example, 1 mol of N_2O requires 0.5 mol of O_2 and 1 mol of N_2, 1 mol of N_2O_3 requires 1 mol of N_2 and 1.5 mol of O_2, and so on. The exception is NO, where 1 mol of NO requires 0.5 mol of O_2 and 0.5 mol of N_2:

$$\frac{1}{2}N_2(g) + \frac{1}{2}O_2(g) \longrightarrow NO(g)$$

This reaction has a positive $\Delta_r S^\circ$ because what is essentially mixing of the N and O has taken place in the product.

91. 15.0 kJ mol^{-1}

93. **a.** Positive, the process is spontaneous. It is slow unless spark is applied.
b. Positive, although the change in the system is not spontaneous; the overall change, which includes such processes as combustion or water flow to generate electricity, is spontaneous.
c. Positive, the acorn/oak tree system is becoming more ordered, so the processes associated with growth are not spontaneous. But they are driven by spontaneous processes such as the generation of heat by the sun and the reactions that produce energy in the cell.

95. At 18.3 mbar $\Delta_r G = 0$,
At 1 bar $\Delta_r G^\circ = 59.5 \text{ kJ mol}^{-1}$

97. 372.78 K or 99.62 °C

99. **a.** 3.24×10^{-3}
b. $NH_3 + ATP + H_2O \longrightarrow NH_3{-}P_i + ADP$

$$NH_3{-}P_i + C_5H_8O_4N^- \longrightarrow C_5H_{10}O_3N_2 + P_i + H_2O$$

$$\overline{NH_3 + C_5H_8O_4N^- + ATP \longrightarrow C_5H_{10}O_3N_2 + ADP + P_i}$$

$$\Delta_r G^\circ = -16.3 \text{ kJ mol}^{-1}, K = 7.20 \times 10^2$$

101. **a.** $-95.3 \text{ kJ mol}^{-1}$. Since the number of moles of reactants and products are the same, the decrease in volume affects the entropy of both equally, so there is no change in $\Delta_f G^\circ$.
b. $102.8 \text{ kJ mol}^{-1}$. The entropy of the reactants (1.5 mol) is decreased more than the entropy of the product (1 mol). Since the product is relatively more favoured at lower volume, $\Delta_r G^\circ$ is less positive.
c. $204.2 \text{ kJ mol}^{-1}$. The entropy of the product (1 mol) is decreased more than the entropy of the reactant (0.5 mol). Since the product is relatively less favoured, $\Delta_r G^\circ$ is more positive.

103. $\Delta_r H^\circ = -93 \text{ kJ mol}^{-1}$, $\Delta_r S^\circ = -2.0 \times 10^2 \text{ J mol}^{-1} \text{ K}^{-1}$

105. $\Delta_{vap}S$ diethyl ether $= 86.1 \text{ J mol}^{-1} \text{ K}^{-1}$,
$\Delta_{vap}S$ acetone $= 88.4 \text{ J mol}^{-1}, \text{K}^{-1}$,
$\Delta_{vap}S$ benzene $= 87.3 \text{ J mol}^{-1} \text{ K}^{-1}$,
$\Delta_{vap}S$ chloroform $= 88.0 \text{ J mol}^{-1} \text{ K}^{-1}$
Because water and ethanol hydrogen bond they are more ordered in the liquid and we expect $\Delta_{vap}S$ to be more positive.
ethanol $38600/351.0 = 110 \text{ J mol}^{-1}\text{K}^{-1}$,
$H_2O = 40700/373.2 = 109 \text{ J mol}^{-1}\text{K}^{-1}$

107. -9 kJ mol^{-1}; K = 39; solubility = 6 mol L^{-1}

109. c.

111. c.

113. **a.** and **b.** are both ture

Chapter 18

37. **a.**

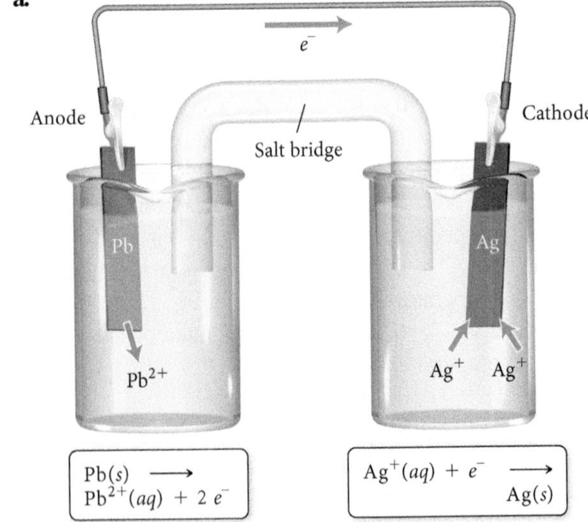

b.

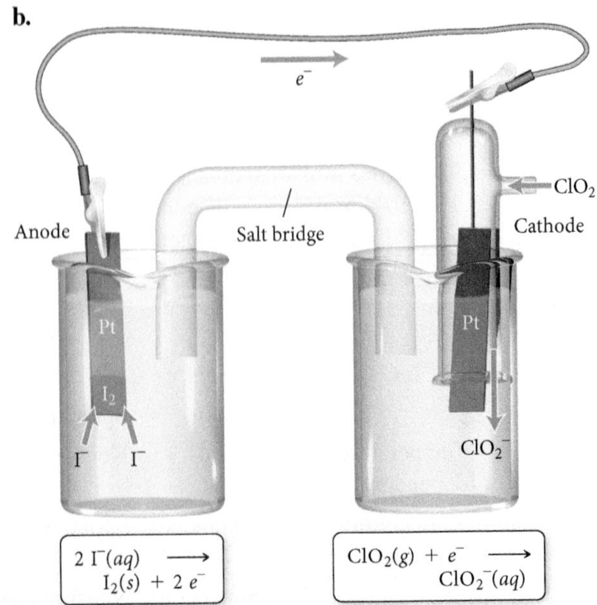

c.

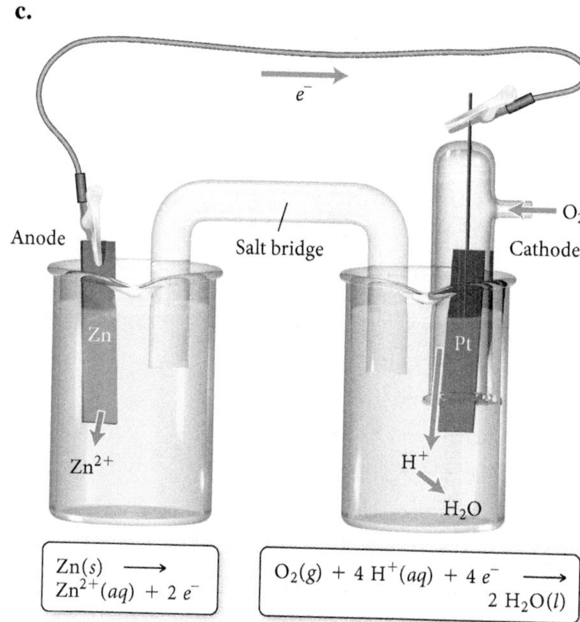

39. **a.** 0.93 V **b.** 0.41 V **c.** 1.99 V

41. a, c, d.

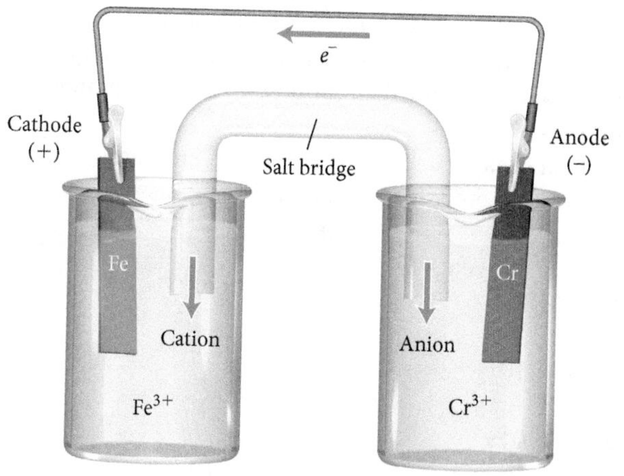

b. $Cr(s) + Fe^{3+}(aq) \longrightarrow Cr^{3+}(aq) + Fe(s), E^\circ_{cell} = 0.69\ V$

43. **a.** $Pb(s)\,|\,Pb^{2+}(aq)\,||\,Ag^{+}(aq)\,|\,Ag(s)$

b. $Pt(s), |\,I^{-}(aq)\,|\,I_2(s)\,||\,ClO_2(g)\,|\,ClO_2^{-}(aq)\,|\,Pt(s)$

c. $Zn(s)\,|\,Zn^{2+}(aq)\,||\,O_2(g)\,|\,H^{+}(aq), HO_2(l)\,|\,Pt(s)$

45.

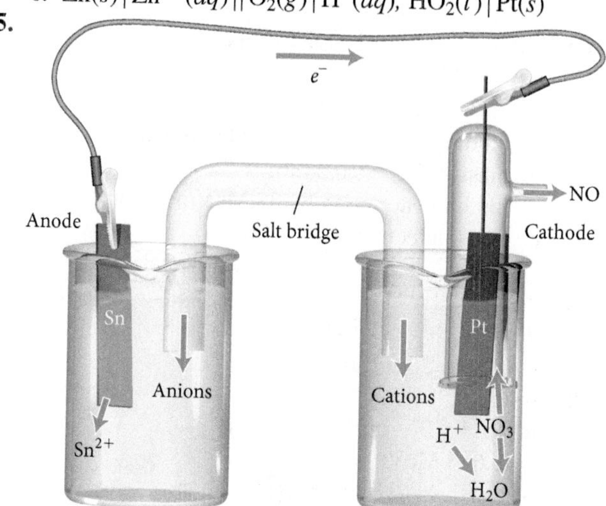

$$3\ Sn(s) + 2\ NO_3^{-}(aq) + 8\ H^{+}(aq) \longrightarrow 3\ Sn^{2+}(aq) + 2\ NO(g) + 4\ H_2O(l), E^\circ_{cell} = 1.10\ V$$

47. b. and c.

49. aluminum

51. **a.** yes, $2\ Al(s) + 6\,H^{+}(aq) \longrightarrow 2\,Al^{3+}(aq) + 3\,H_2(g)$

b. no

c. yes, $Pb(s) + 2\ H^{+}(aq) \longrightarrow Pb^{2+}(aq) + H_2(g)$

53. **a.** yes, $3\ Cu(s) + 2\ NO_3^{-}(aq) + 8\ H^{+}(aq) \longrightarrow 3\ Cu^{2+}(aq) + 2\ NO(g) + 4\ H_2O(l)$

b. no

55. **a.** −1.70 V, nonspontaneous **b.** 1.97 V, spontaneous

c. −1.51 V, nonspontaneous

57. **a.**

59. **a.** $-432\ kJ\ mol^{-1}$ **b.** $52\ kJ\ mol^{-1}$

c. $-1.7 \times 10^{2}\ kJ\ mol^{-1}$

61. **a.** 5.31×10^{75} **b.** 7.7×10^{-10} **c.** 6.3×10^{29}

63. 5.6×10^{5}

65. $\Delta_r G^\circ = -7.\underline{9}7\ kJ\ mol^{-1}, E^\circ_{cell} = 0.041 V$

67. **a.** 1.04 V **b.** 0.97 V **c.** 1.11 V

69. 1.87 V

71. **a.** 0.56 V **b.** 0.52 V

c. $[Ni^{2+}] = 0.003\ mol\ L^{-1}, [Zn^{2+}] = 1.60\ mol\ L^{-1}$

73. $[Cd^{2+}{}_{(aq)}]/[Fe^{2+}{}_{(aq)}] = 0.0204$

75.

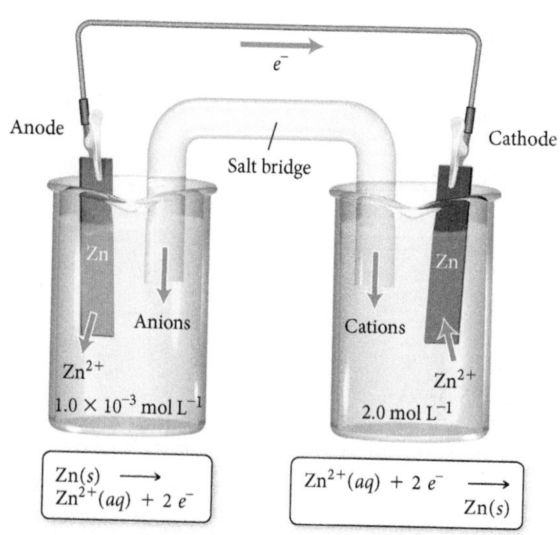

77. $\dfrac{[Sn^{2+}](ox)}{[Sn^{2+}](red)} = 4.2 \times 10^{-4}$

79. 0.3762

81. 1.038 V

83. a. and c.

85. minimum voltage = 0.17 V

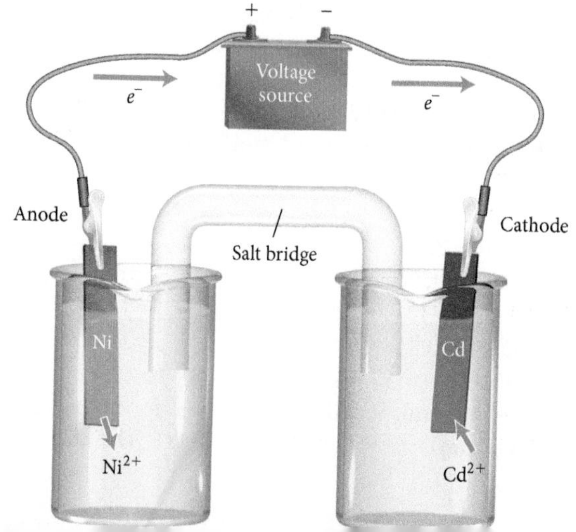

87. oxidation: $2\ Br^-(l) \longrightarrow Br_2(g) + 2\ e^-$
reduction: $K^+(l) + e^- \longrightarrow K(l)$

89. oxidation: $2\ Br^-(l) \longrightarrow Br_2(g) + 2\ e^-$
reduction: $K^+(l) + e^- \longrightarrow K(l)$

91. **a.** anode: $2\ H_2O(l) + \longrightarrow O_2(g) + 4\ H^+(aq) + 4\ e^-$
cathode: $2\ H_2O(l) + 2\ e^- \longrightarrow H_2(g) + 2\ OH^-(aq)$
b. anode: $2\ I^-(aq) \longrightarrow I_2(s) + 2\ e^-$
cathode: $Pb^{2+}(aq) + 2\ e^- \longrightarrow Pb(s)$
c. anode: $2\ H_2O(l) \longrightarrow O_2(g) + 4\ H^+(aq) + 4\ e^-$
cathode: $2\ H_2O(l) + 2\ e^- \longrightarrow H_2(g) + 2\ OH^-(aq)$

93.

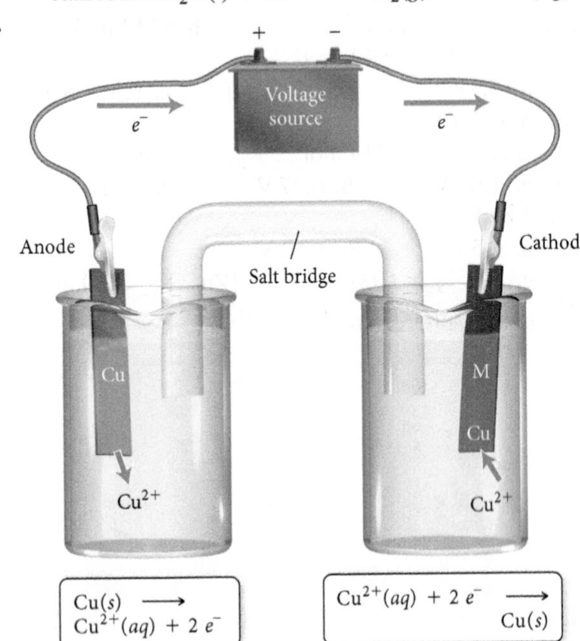

95. 1.8×10^2 s

97. 1.2×10^3 A

99. $2\ MnO_4^-(aq) + 5\ Zn(s) + 16\ H^+(aq) \longrightarrow 2\ Mn^{2+}(aq) + 5\ Zn^{2+}(aq) + 8\ H_2O(l)$
34.9 mL

101. The drawing should show that several Al atoms dissolve into solutions as Al^{3+} ions and that several Cu^{2+} ions are deposited on the Al surface as solid Cu.

103. **a.** 68.3 mL **b.** cannot be dissolved
c. cannot be dissolved

105. 0.3

107. There are no paired reactions that produce more than about 5 or 6 V.

109. **a.** 2.83 V **b.** 2.71 V **c.** 16 h

111. 176 h

113. 0.71 V

115. **a.** $\Delta_r G^\circ = 461$ kJ mol^{-1}, $K = 1.4 \times 10^{-81}$
b. $\Delta_r G^\circ = 2.7 \times 10^2$ kJ mol^{-1}, $K = 2.0 \times 10^{-48}$

117. MCl_4

119. 51.3%

121. pH = 0.85

123. 0.86 mol L^{-1}

125. 4.1×10^5 L

127. 435 s

129. 8.46% U

131. The overall cell reaction for both cells is $2\ Cu^+(aq) \longrightarrow Cu^{2+}(aq) + Cu(s)$. The difference in E° is because $n = 1$ for the first cell and $n = 2$ for the second cell. For both cells, $\Delta_r G^\circ = -35.1$ kJ mol^{-1}.

133. **a.**

Chapter 19

31. **a.** ${}^{234}_{92}U \longrightarrow {}^{4}_{2}He + {}^{230}_{90}Th$
b. ${}^{230}_{90}Th \longrightarrow {}^{4}_{2}He + {}^{226}_{88}Ra$
c. ${}^{214}_{82}Pb \longrightarrow {}^{0}_{-1}e + {}^{214}_{83}Bi$
d. ${}^{13}_{7}N \longrightarrow {}^{0}_{+1}e + {}^{13}_{6}C$
e. ${}^{51}_{24}Cr + {}^{0}_{-1}e \longrightarrow {}^{51}_{23}V$

33. ${}^{232}_{90}Th \longrightarrow {}^{4}_{2}He + {}^{228}_{88}Ra$
${}^{228}_{88}Ra \longrightarrow {}^{0}_{-1}e + {}^{228}_{89}Ac$
${}^{228}_{89}Ac \longrightarrow {}^{0}_{-1}e + {}^{228}_{90}Th$
${}^{228}_{90}Th \longrightarrow {}^{4}_{2}He + {}^{224}_{88}Ra$

35. **a.** ${}^{221}_{87}Fr$ **b.** ${}^{0}_{-1}e$ **c.** ${}^{0}_{+1}e$ **d.** ${}^{0}_{-1}e$

37. **a.** stable, N/Z ratio is close to 1, acceptable for low Z atoms
b. not stable, N/Z ratio much too high for low Z atom
c. not stable, N/Z ratio is less than 1, much too low
d. stable, N/Z ratio is acceptable for this Z

39. Sc, V, and Mn each have odd numbers of protons. Atoms with an odd number of protons typically have less stable isotopes than those with an even number of protons.

41. **a.** beta decay **b.** positron emission
c. positron emission **d.** positron emission

43. **a.** Cs-125 **b.** Fe-62

45. 2.34×10^9 years

47. 0.57 MBq

49. 10.8 h

51. 2.66×10^3 y

53. 2.40×10^4 y

55. 2.7×10^9 y

57. ${}^{235}_{92}U + {}^{1}_{0}n \longrightarrow {}^{144}_{54}Xe + {}^{90}_{38}Sr + 2\ {}^{1}_{0}n$

59. ${}^{2}_{1}H + {}^{2}_{1}H \longrightarrow {}^{3}_{2}He + {}^{1}_{0}n$

61. ${}^{238}_{92}U + {}^{1}_{0}n \longrightarrow {}^{239}_{92}U$
${}^{239}_{92}U \longrightarrow {}^{239}_{93}Np + {}^{0}_{-1}e$
${}^{239}_{93}Np \longrightarrow {}^{239}_{94}Pu + {}^{0}_{-1}e$

63. ${}^{249}_{98}Cf + {}^{12}_{6}C \longrightarrow {}^{257}_{104}Rf + 4\ {}^{1}_{0}n$

65. 9.0×10^{13} J

67. **a.** mass defect = 0.13701 u
binding energy = 7.976 MeV/nucleon
b. mass defect = 0.54369 u
binding energy = 8.732 MeV/nucleon
c. mass defect = 1.16754 u
binding energy = 8.431 MeV/nucleon

69. 7.228×10^{10} J g^{-1} U-235

71. 7.84×10^{10} J g^{-1} H-2

73. radiation: 25.5 J; fall: 370 J

75. 68 km

77. **a.** ${}^{1}_{1}p + {}^{9}_{4}Be \longrightarrow {}^{6}_{3}Li + {}^{4}_{2}He$
1.615 MeV
b. ${}^{209}_{83}Bi + {}^{64}_{28}Ni \longrightarrow {}^{272}_{111}Rg + {}^{1}_{0}n$
236.4 MeV

c. ${}^{179}_{74}\text{W} + {}^{0}_{-1}e \longrightarrow {}^{179}_{73}\text{Ta}$
1.573 MeV

79. a. ${}^{114}_{44}\text{Ru} \longrightarrow {}^{0}_{-1}e + {}^{114}_{45}\text{Rh}$
b. ${}^{216}_{88}\text{Ra} \longrightarrow {}^{0}_{+1}e + {}^{216}_{87}\text{Fr}$
c. ${}^{58}_{30}\text{Zn} \longrightarrow {}^{0}_{+1}e + {}^{58}_{29}\text{Cu}$
d. ${}^{31}_{10}\text{Ne} \longrightarrow {}^{0}_{-1}e + {}^{31}_{11}\text{Na}$

81. 2.9×10^{18} beta emissions, 37 Gy
83. 1.6×10^{-5} L
85. 1.022 MeV
87. 7.72 MeV
89. ${}^{14}\text{N}$
91. 0.15%
93. 1.24×10^{21} particles
95. 2.42×10^{-12} m
97. −0.7 MeV, there is no coulombic barrier for collision with a neutron.
99. a. 1.164×10^{10} kJ **b.** 0.1299 g
101. U-235 forms Pb-207 in seven α-decays and four β-decays and Th-232 forms Pb-208 in six α-decays and four β-decays.
103. 3.0×10^{2} K
105. ${}^{21}_{9}\text{F} \longrightarrow {}^{21}_{10}\text{Ne} + {}^{0}_{-1}e$
107. Nuclide A is more dangerous because the half-life is shorter (18.5 days) and so it decays faster.

Chapter 20

35. a. alkane **b.** alkene **c.** alkyne **d.** alkene

37. a. $CH_3-C\equiv C-CH_3$ (sp^3, sp, sp, sp^3)

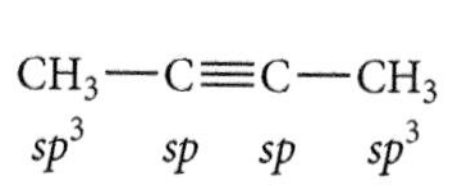

b. cyclopentene ring: CH_2 sp^3; HC sp^2; CH sp^2; HC sp^2; CH sp^2

c. $CH_3-CH(CH_3)-CH=CH_2$ (CH_3 substituent sp^3; sp^3, sp^3, sp^2, sp^2)

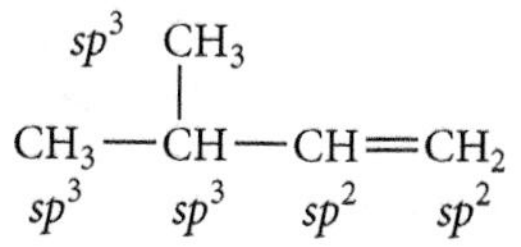

d. $CH_3-CH=CH_2$ (sp^3, sp^2, sp^2)

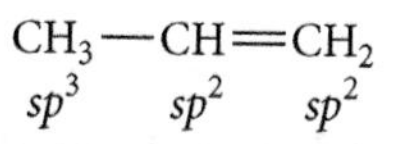

39. a. [resonance structures of anthracene] $\longleftrightarrow$

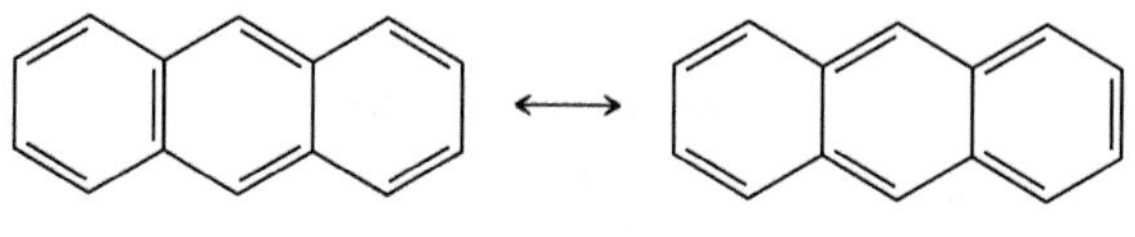

b. [resonance structures of pyrene] $\longleftrightarrow$

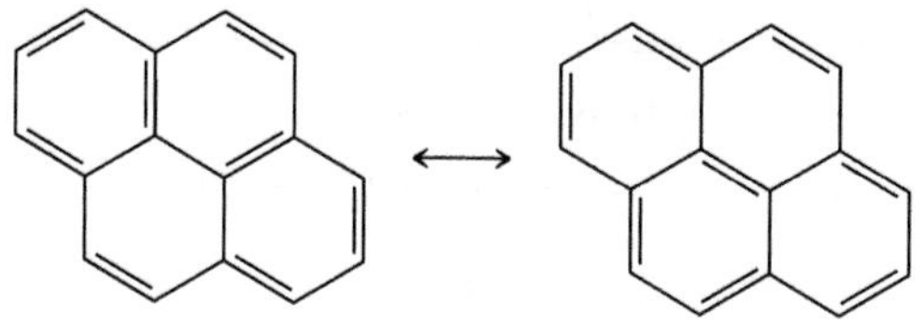

41. a. NH_2-CH_3 (sp^3, sp^3)

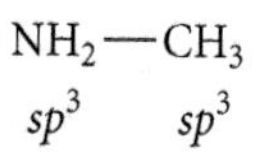

b. $CH_3-C(=O)-O-CH_2-CH_3$ (O sp^2; CH_3 sp^3; C sp^2; O sp^3; CH_2 sp^3; CH_3 sp^3)

c. $CH_3-C(=O)-CH_3$ (O sp^2; sp^3, sp^2, sp^3)

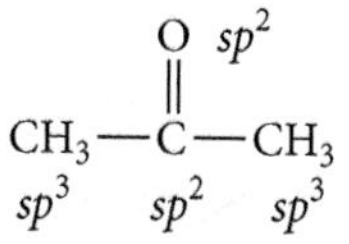

d. $CH_3-CH_2-C(=O)-Cl$ (O sp^2; sp^3, sp^3, sp^2; Cl sp^3)

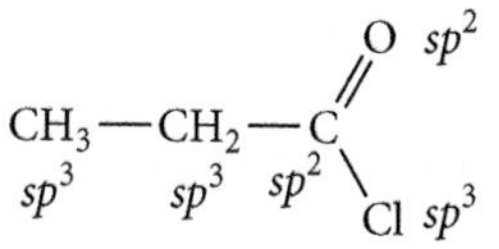

43. a. NH_2-CH_3 (dipole arrow toward NH_2)

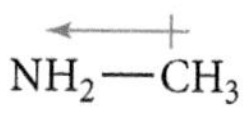

b. $CH_3-C(=O)-O-CH_2-CH_3$ (dipole arrows toward both O atoms)

c. $CH_3-C(=O)-CH_3$ (dipole arrow toward O)

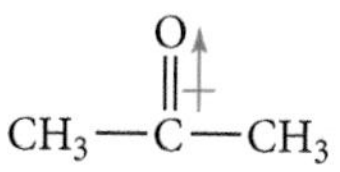

d. $CH_3-CH_2-C(=O)-Cl$ (dipole arrows toward O and Cl)

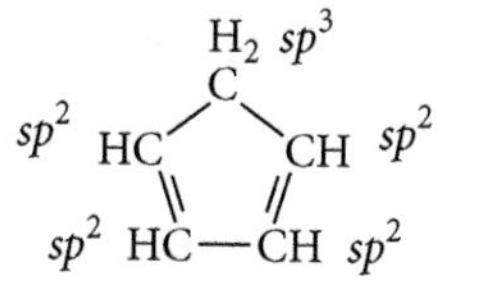

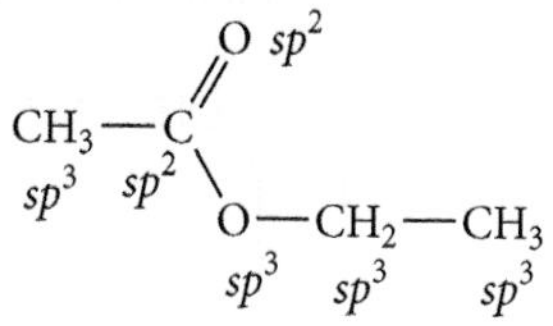

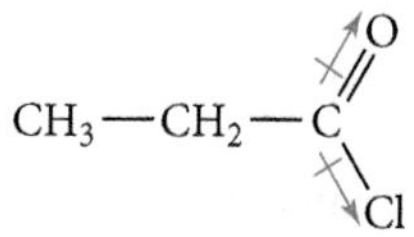

45. $CH_3CH_2CH_3 < CH_3COCH_3 < CH_3CHOHCH_3$

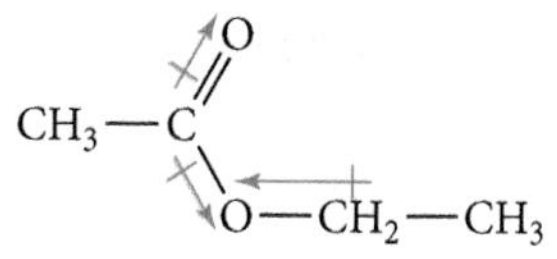

47. $CH_2=CH-CH_2-CH_2-CH_2-CH3$
$CH_3-CH=CH-CH_2-CH_2-CH_3$
$CH_3-CH_2-CH=CH-CH_2-CH_3$

49. $CH_3-CH_2-CH_2-CH_2-CH_2-CH_2-CH_3$

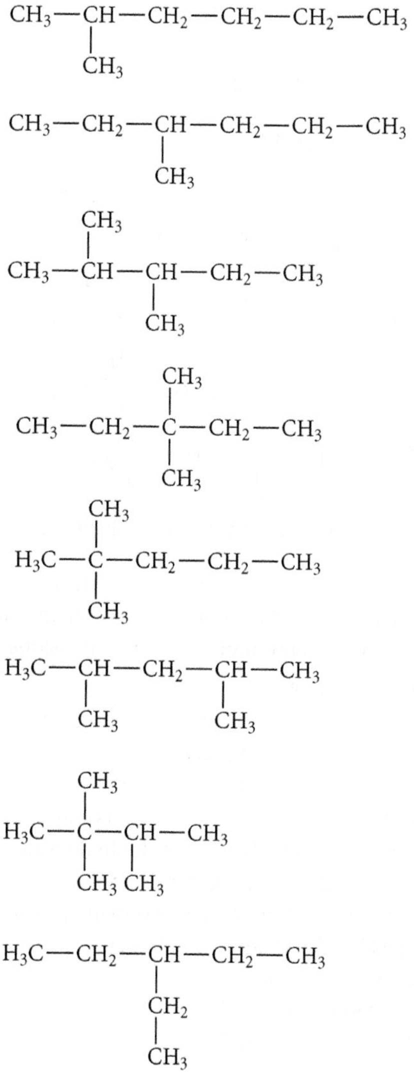

$CH_3-CH(CH_3)-CH_2-CH_2-CH_2-CH_3$

$CH_3-CH_2-CH(CH_3)-CH_2-CH_2-CH_3$

$CH_3-CH(CH_3)-CH(CH_3)-CH_2-CH_3$

$CH_3-CH_2-C(CH_3)_2-CH_2-CH_3$

$H_3C-C(CH_3)_2-CH_2-CH_2-CH_3$

$H_3C-CH(CH_3)-CH_2-CH(CH_3)-CH_3$

$H_3C-C(CH_3)_2-CH(CH_3)-CH_3$

$H_3C-CH_2-CH(CH_2CH_3)-CH_2-CH_3$

51. a. not constitutional isomers
b. constitutional isomers
c. constitutional isomers

53. For example,

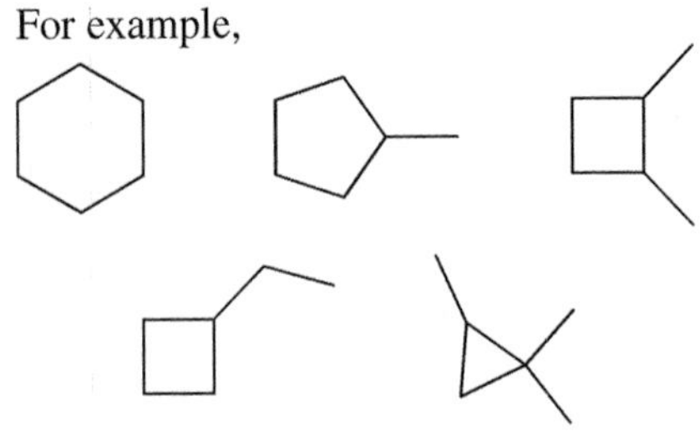

55. For example,

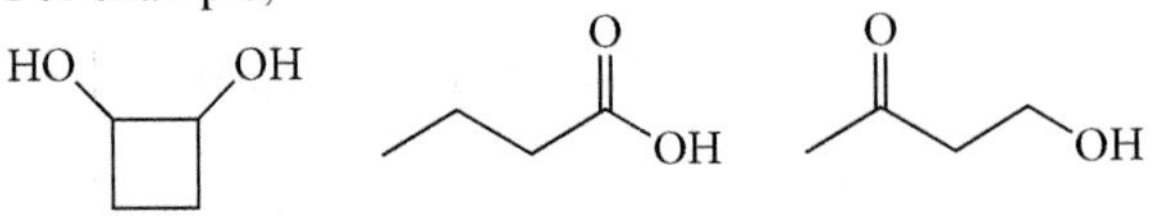

57.

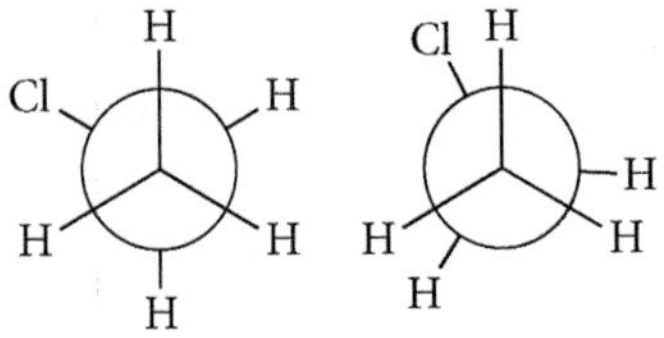

Staggered   Eclipsed

59.

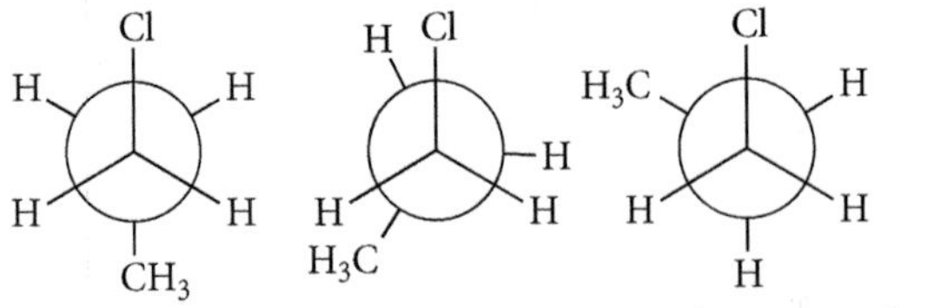

Antistaggered   Eclipsed   Gauche-staggered

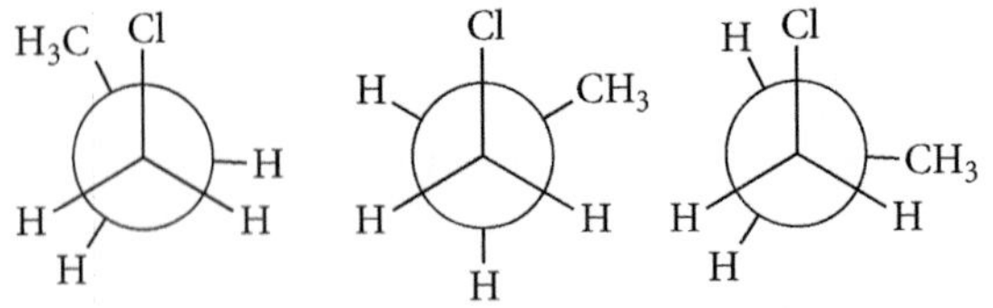

Eclipsed   Gauche-staggered   Eclipsed

61. a. *Z* **b.** *E* **c.** *Z* **d.** *E*

63. a. enantiomers **b.** same **c.** enantiomers

65. a. same **b.** enantiomers **c.** same

67. a. achiral **b.** *S*; *R* **c.** *S*

69. a. *S* **b.** *R* **c.** *S* **d.** *R*

71. a. IHD = 3 **b.** IHD = 3

c. IHD = 4 **d.** IHD = 6

73. a. IHD = 1; a carboxylic acid or ester could be present, or a combination of a ketone or aldehyde group along with an alcohol or ether group.

b. IHD = 0; an alcohol or ether group must be present.

75. a. N—H; 3100–3500 cm^{-1} (medium)

b. C=O, 1630–1800 cm^{-1};

C—O, 1050–1250 cm^{-1};

O—H, 3200–3500 cm^{-1}

77. a. 3 **b.** 6

79. a. $H_2C{=}CH{-}C({=}O){-}NH_2$ (sp^2 sp^2 sp^2 sp^3) ⟷ $H_2\overset{+}{C}{-}CH{=}C(O^-){-}NH_2$ (sp^2 sp^2 sp^2 sp^3) ⟷ $H_2C{=}CH{-}C(O^-){=}\overset{+}{N}H_2$ (sp^2 sp^2 sp^2 sp^2)

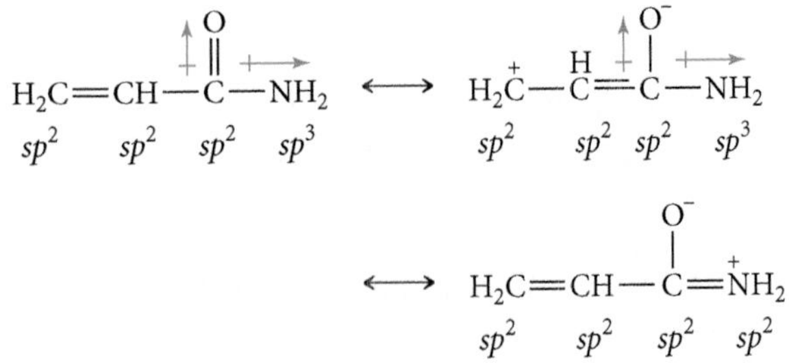

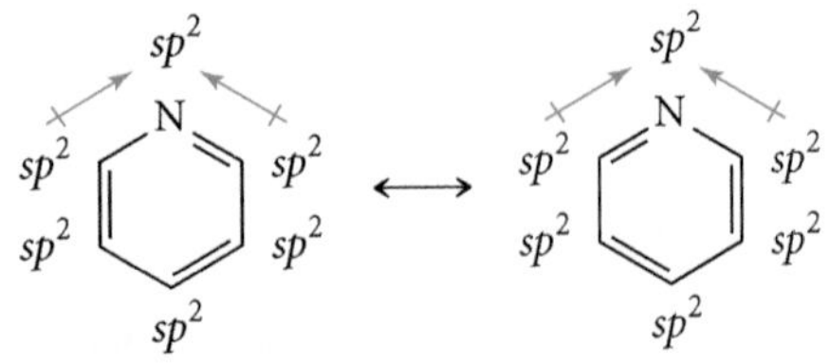

b. (pyridine resonance structures; all atoms sp^2)

c. H, Cl, H, H; sp^2 sp^2

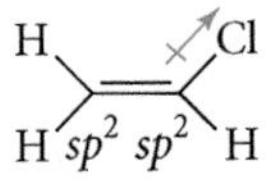

81. a. Examples: $CH_3CH_2CH_2{-}C({=}O)NH_2$; H_2N…OH

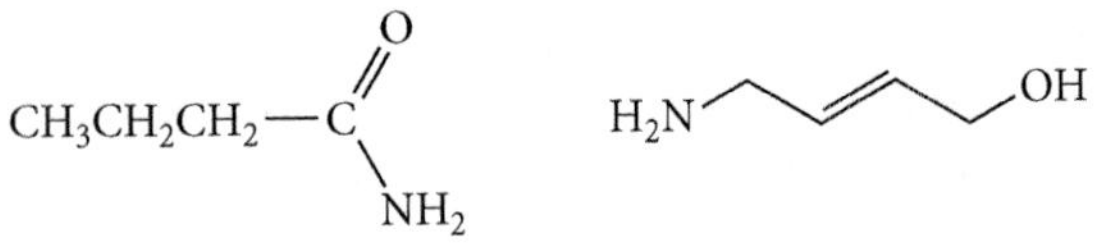

b. Examples:

c. Examples:

83. a. $CH_3{-}CH_2{-}CH(CH_3){-}CH{=}CH_2$

Can exist as a stereoisomer.

b. $CH_3{-}CH{=}C(CH_3){-}CH_2{-}CH(CH_3){-}CH_3$

Can exist as a stereoisomer.

c. $H_3C{-}CH{=}C(CH_2CH_2CH_3){-}CH_2{-}CH_2{-}CH_3$

Cannot exist as a stereoisomer.

85.

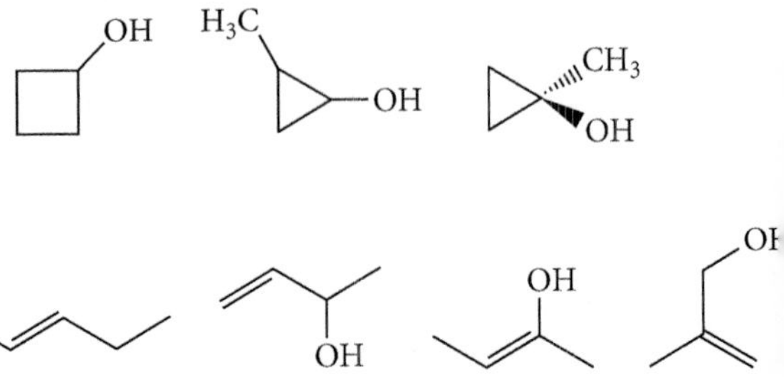

87. a. IHD = 1

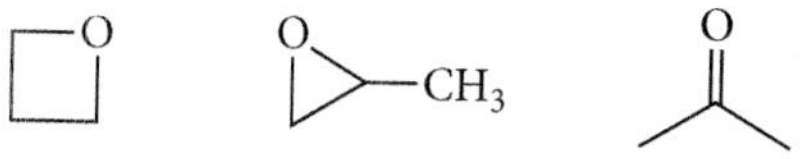

b. IHD = 1

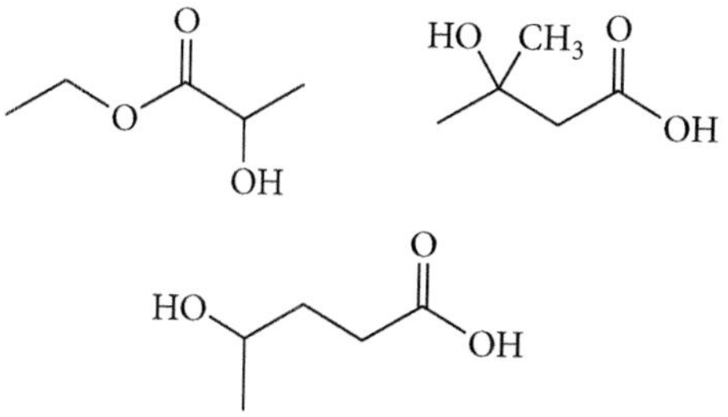

c. IHD = 4

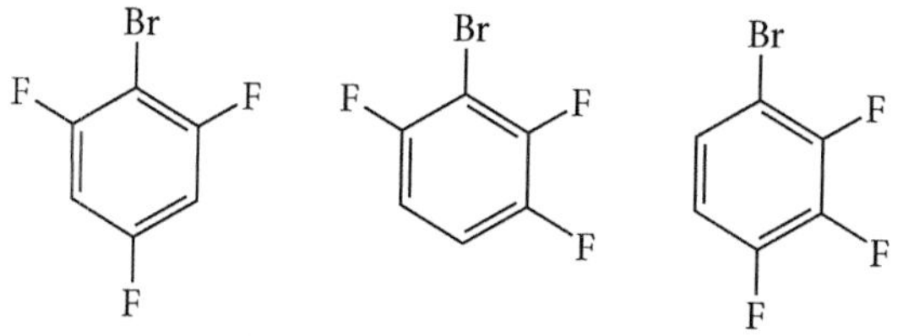

89. a. IR: C—O, 1050–1250 cm^{-1}; O—H, 3200–3500 cm^{-1}; C—H, 2850–3300 cm^{-1}; ^{13}C—NMR: 6 peaks
b. IR: C=O, 1630–1800 cm^{-1}; C—H, 2850–3300 cm^{-1} ^{13}C—NMR: 3 peaks

91. a.

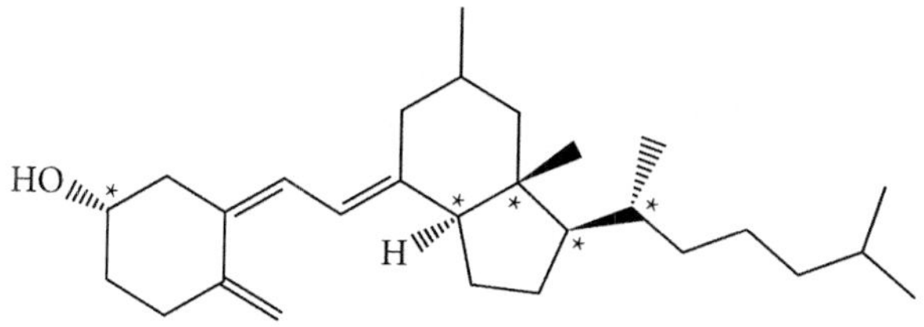

b.

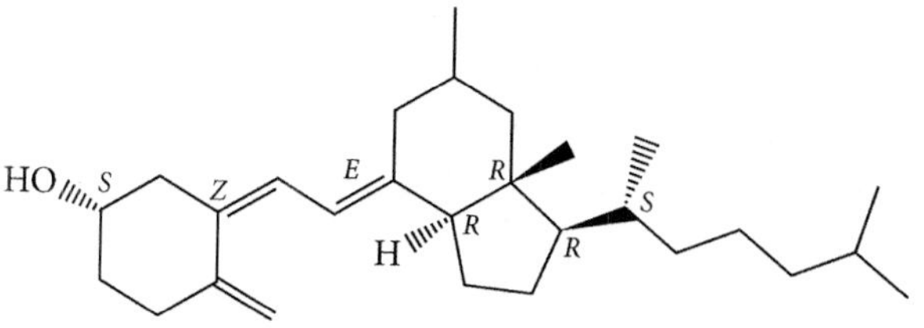

93. 8
95. propan-1-ol
97. diethyl ether
99.

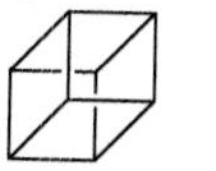

(hydrogen atoms not shown)

101. (**b**) and (**d**) are chiral.
103. 4 unique carbon atoms

Chapter 21

31. a.

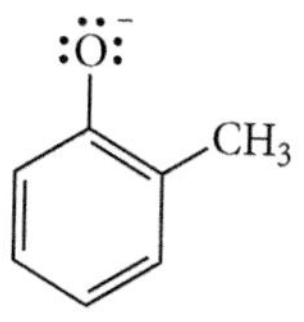

b.

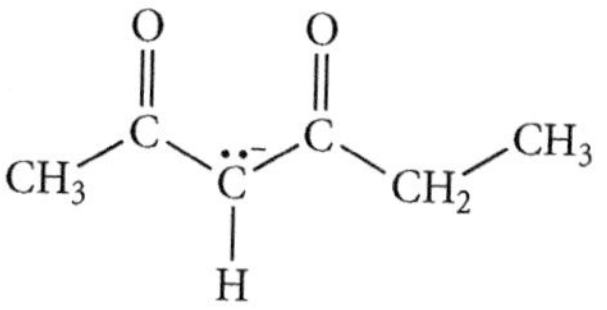

c. $CH_3CH_2NH_2$

d. $CH_3CH_2CO_2^-$

33.

a. $CH_3—\ddot{O}—H + H—SO_4H \longrightarrow CH_3—\overset{+}{O}H_2 + HSO_4^-$

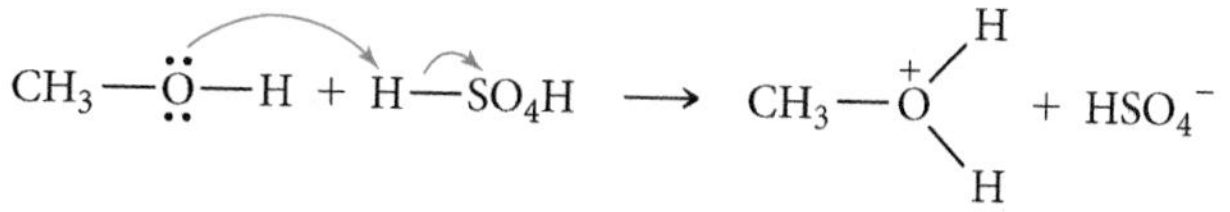

b. $CH_3CH_2\ddot{N}H_2 + H—SO_4H \longrightarrow CH_3CH_2NH_3^+ + HSO_4^-$

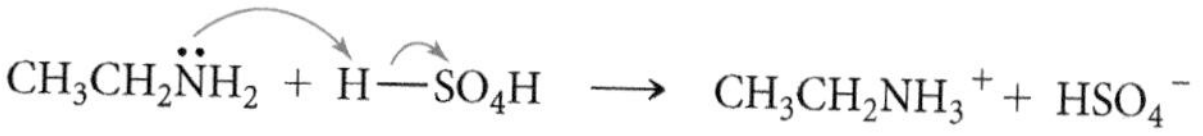

c. $HO—C(=O)—O^- + H—SO_4H \longrightarrow HO—C(=O)—OH + HSO_4^-$

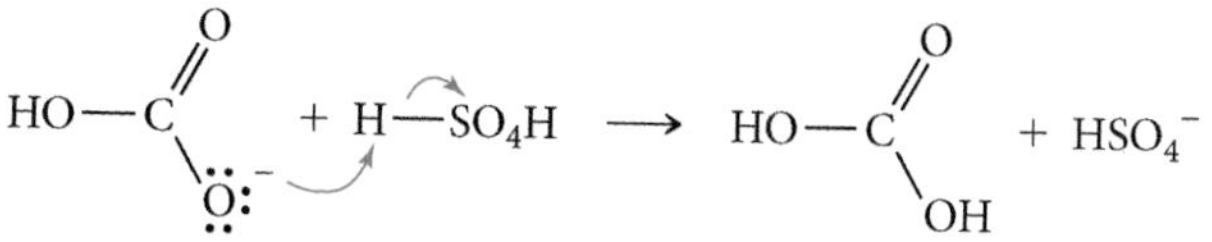

d. $CH_3—\ddot{O}^- + H—SO_4H \longrightarrow CH_3—OH + HSO_4^-$

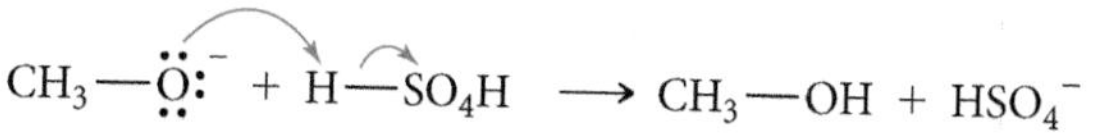

35. a. $NaNH_2$ **b.** NH_3 **c.** HCl

37.

a.

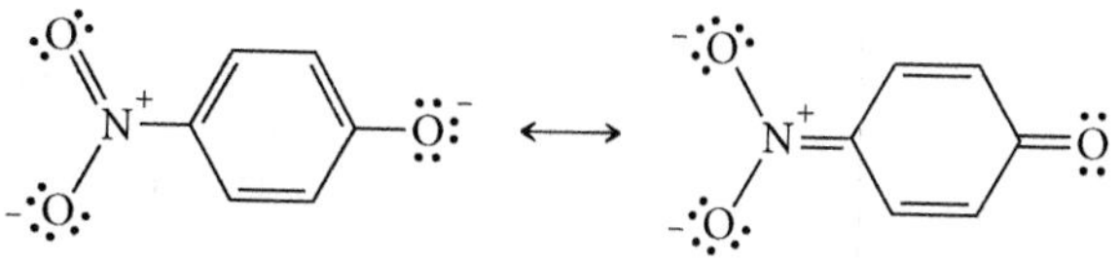

b.

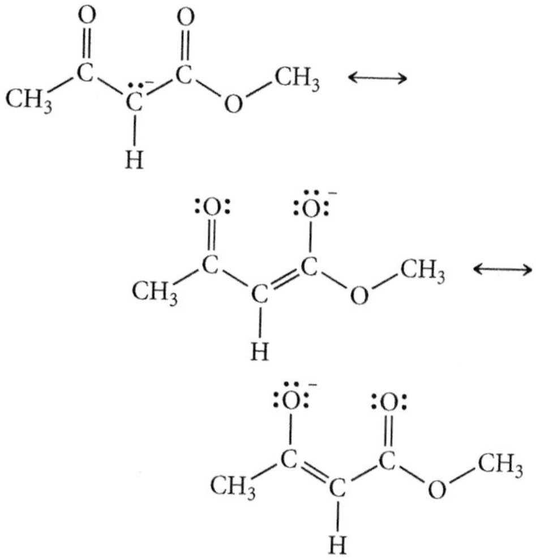

39. a. $\overset{-3}{CH_3}-\overset{+1}{C}(=O)H$ **b.** $\overset{-3}{CH_3}-\overset{0}{C}\equiv\overset{0}{C}-\overset{-3}{CH_3}$

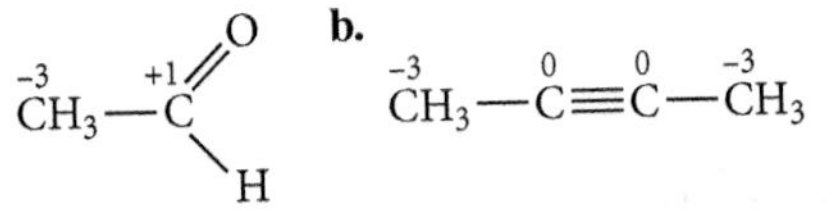

c. $Cl(H)\overset{0}{C}=\overset{0}{C}(H)Cl$

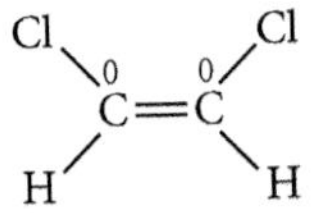

41. a. $CH_3CH_2CH_3 + 5\,O_2 \longrightarrow 3\,CO_2 + 4\,H_2O$
b. $CH_3CH_2CH{=}CH_2 + 6\,O_2 \longrightarrow 4\,CO_2 + 4\,H_2O$
c. $2\,CH{\equiv}CH + 5\,O_2 \longrightarrow 4\,CO_2 + 2\,H_2O$

43. a. $CH_3-C(=O)-CH_2CH_3$ **b.** $CH_3CH_2CH_2CH_2CH_3$

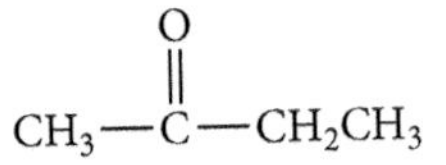

c. cyclohexyl–OH **d.** $CH_3CH_2CH_2NO_2$

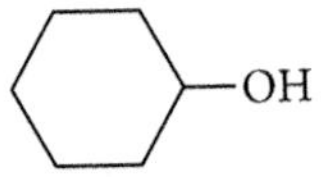

45. a. $K_2Cr_2O_7$, H_2SO_4 **b.** H_2, Pd/C

47. a. cyclopentyl–Cl + NaCN $\longrightarrow$ cyclopentyl–CN + NaCl

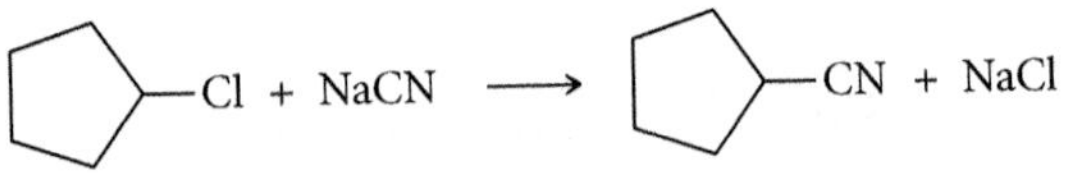

b. $CH_3CH_2CH(Br)CH_3 + NaI \longrightarrow CH_3CH_2CH(I)CH_3 + NaBr$

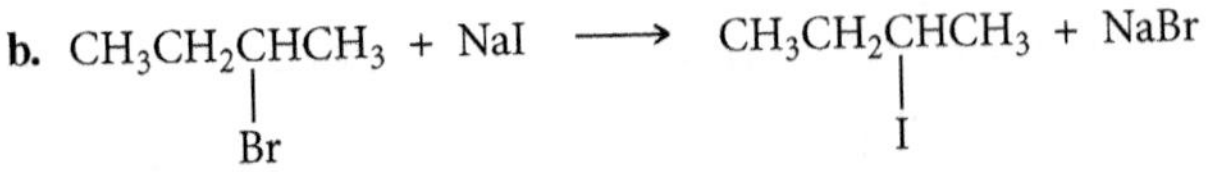

c. $(CH_3CH_2)_2NH + ClCH_2CH_2OH \xrightarrow{NaOH}$
$(CH_3CH_2)_2N-CH_2CH_2OH + H_2O + NaCl$

49. a. S_N1 **b.** S_N2

51. a. $(CH_3)_3C-Br \rightleftharpoons (CH_3)_3C^+ + Br^-$

$(CH_3)_3C^+ + CH_3CH_2\ddot{O}H \longrightarrow (CH_3)_3C-\overset{+}{O}(H)-CH_2CH_3$

$(CH_3)_3C-\overset{+}{O}(H)-CH_2CH_3 + H_2\ddot{O}: \longrightarrow$
$(CH_3)_3COCH_2CH_3 + H_3O^+$

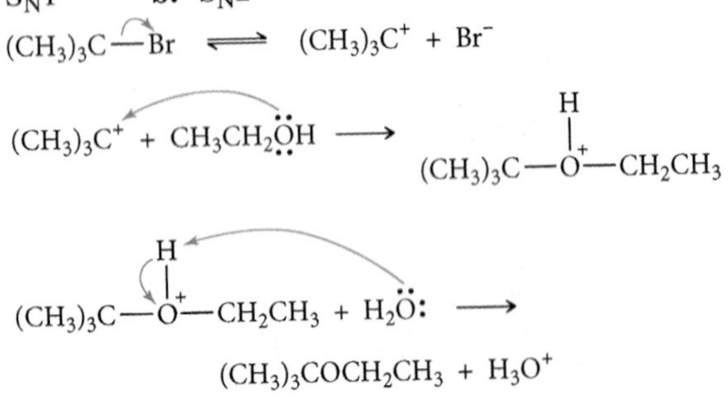

b. $CH_3CH_2CH_2-Cl + :NH_3 \longrightarrow [CH_3CH_2CH_2NH_3^+]\,Cl^-$

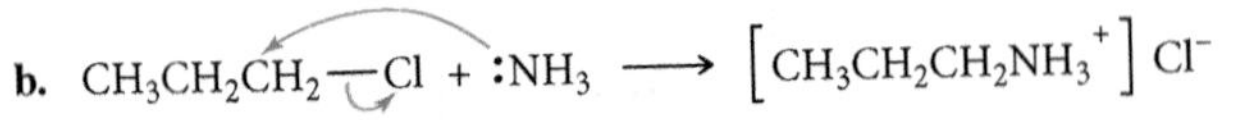

53. a. $H_3C-C(H)(CH_2CH_3)(Br) + I^- \longrightarrow$

$I-C(H)(CH_2CH_3)(CH_3) + Br^-$ inversion

b. 2-methylcyclopentyl–Cl (CH_3, Cl) + $CN^- \longrightarrow$ 2-methylcyclopentyl–CN (CH_3) + Cl^- inversion

c. 3-methylcyclopentyl bromide (H_3C, Br) + $H_2O \longrightarrow$

3-methylcyclopentanol (H_3C, OH) + 3-methylcyclopentanol (H_3C, OH) + HBr

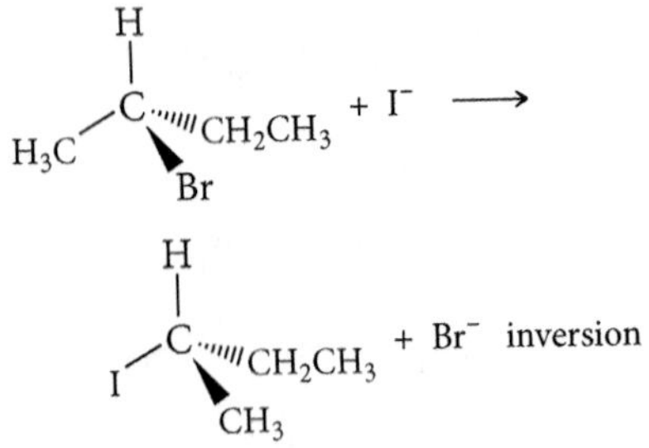

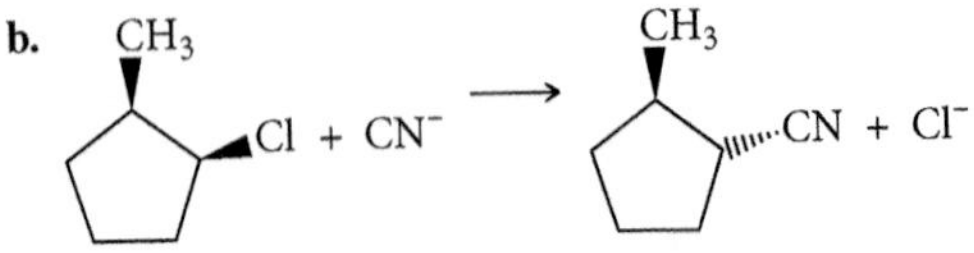

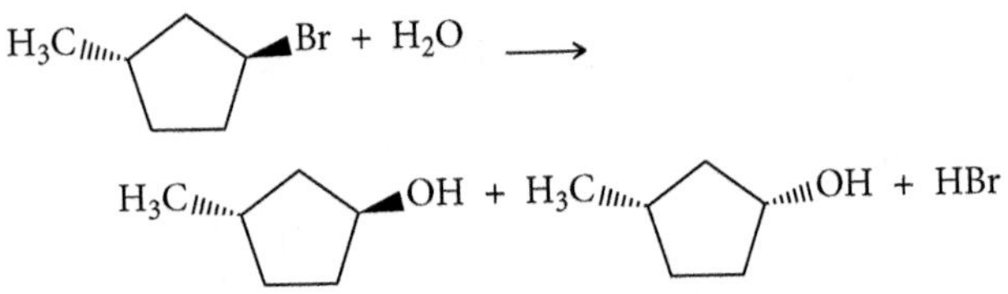

racemization

55.

a. $CH_3CH_2CH_2CH_2CH_2OH \xrightarrow[\text{Heat}]{H_2SO_4}$

$CH_3CH_2CH_2CH{=}CH_2 + H_2O$

b. $CH_3CH_2CH(Cl)CH_2CH_3 + CH_3CH_2O^-Na^+ \xrightarrow[\text{Heat}]{CH_3CH_2OH}$

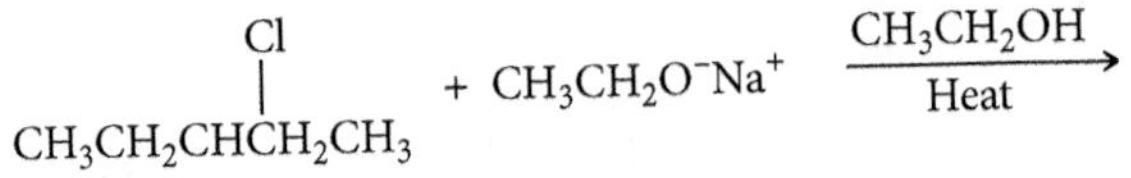

$CH_3CH{=}CHCH_2CH_3 + CH_3CH_2OH + NaCl$

c. cyclopentyl–Br + $CH_3CH_2O^-Na^+ \xrightarrow[\text{Heat}]{CH_3CH_2OH}$

cyclopentene + CH_3CH_2OH + NaBr

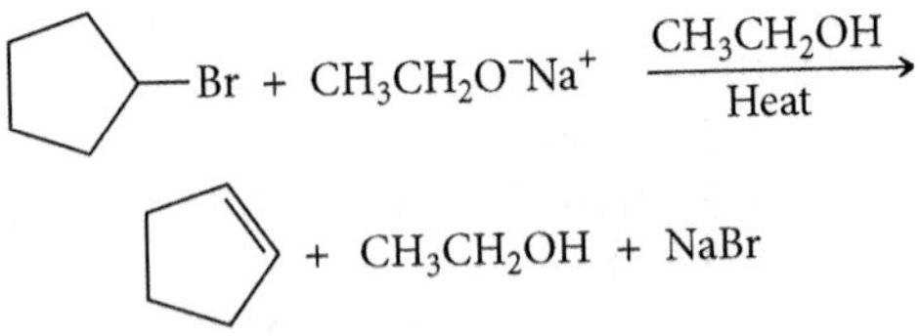

d. $CH_3CH_2C(OH)(CH_3)CH(CH_3)_2 \xrightarrow[\text{Heat}]{H_2SO_4} CH_3CH{=}C(CH_3)-CH(CH_3)_2$ (minor) +

$CH_3CH_2C(CH_3){=}C(CH_3)_2$ (major) + H_2O

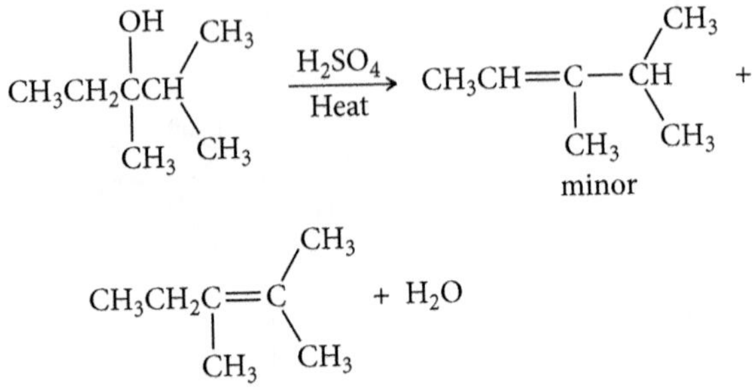

57. a. 2-methyl-2-butene (major) + 3-methyl-1-butene (minor)

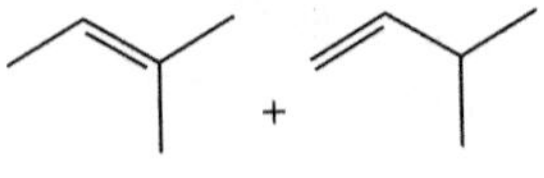

b. cyclopentylidene=$CHCH_2CH_3$ (major) + cyclopentyl–$CH{=}CH(CH_3)$ (minor)

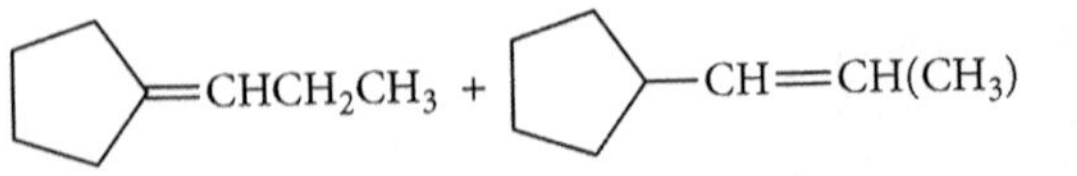

c. 1-methylcyclopentene (major) + 3-methylcyclopentene (minor)

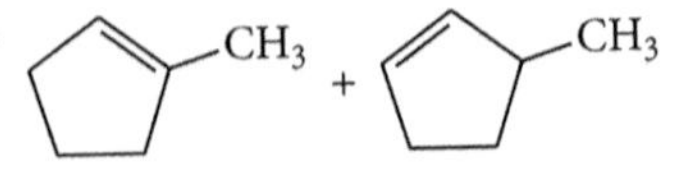

59. a. E2 **b.** E1

61.

a. $Na^+ \; H_3C{-}\ddot{\underset{..}{O}}{:}^-$ + $H_3C{-}CH(H){-}CH(I){-}CH_2{-}CH_3 \longrightarrow$

[pent-2-ene, skeletal structure] $+ \; CH_3OH + NaI$

b. [2-chloro-2-methylbutane] $\rightleftharpoons$ [2-methylbut-2-yl cation] $+ \; Cl^-$

[2-methylbut-2-yl cation] $+ \; H\ddot{O}CH_3 \longrightarrow$ [2-methylbut-2-ene] $+ \; H_2O^+CH_3$

$H_2O^+CH_3 + Cl^- \longrightarrow HOCH_3 + HCl$

63.

a. $CH_3{-}CH(H){-}CH(Cl){-}CH_3$

b. $CH_3{-}CH(CH_3){-}CH(Br){-}CH(H){-}CH_3 + CH_3{-}CH(CH_3){-}CH(H){-}CH(Br){-}CH_3$

c. $CH_3{-}CH_2{-}CH(Br){-}CH(Br){-}CH_3$

d. $CH_3{-}CH(CH_3){-}CH(H){-}C(CH_3)(Cl){-}CH_3$

65. a. $CH_3{-}CH(CH_3){-}CH{=}CH_2 + H_2 \xrightarrow{Pd/C}$

$CH_3{-}CH(CH_3){-}CH_2{-}CH_3$

b. $CH_2{=}CH{-}CH_3 + H_2 \xrightarrow{Pd/C} CH_3{-}CH_2{-}CH_3$

67. a. $CH_3{-}CH(CH_3){-}CH(OH){-}CH_3$

b. [cyclohexene oxide: cyclohexane ring fused to an epoxide O]

c. $CH_3{-}C(CH_3)(CH_3){-}CH(OH){-}CH_2(OH)$ (printed: CH3 and OH above C and CH; OH above CH_2; CH3 below C)

69. a. H^+, H_2O **b.** HCl
c. H_2, Pd/C **d.** Br_2

71. a. $CH_3{-}CH_2{-}CH_2{-}C(=O){-}H + CH_3CH_2OH \overset{H^+}{\rightleftharpoons}$

$CH_3{-}CH_2{-}CH_2{-}C(OH)(OCH_2CH_3){-}H$

b. $CH_3{-}CH_2{-}C(=O){-}CH_3 + CH_3{-}CH(OH){-}CH_3 \overset{H^+}{\rightleftharpoons}$

$CH_3{-}CH_2{-}C(OH)(O{-}CH(CH_3)_2){-}CH_3$

c. [cyclopentyl]${-}C(=O){-}H + CH_3OH \overset{H^+}{\rightleftharpoons}$ [cyclopentyl]${-}C(OH)(OCH_3){-}H$

73. a. [phenyl]${-}MgBr + CH_3CHO \xrightarrow[2)\ H_3O^+]{1)\ \text{Diethyl ether}}$

[phenyl]${-}CH(OH){-}CH_3$

b. $CH_3{-}CH(CH_3){-}MgBr + H{-}C(=O){-}H \xrightarrow[2)\ H_3O^+]{1)\ \text{Diethyl ether}}$

$CH_3{-}CH(CH_3){-}CH_2OH$

c. $CH_3MgI + CH_3CH_2C(=O)CH_2CH_3 \xrightarrow[2)\ H_3O^+]{1)\ \text{Diethyl ether}}$

$CH_3CH_2C(OH)(CH_3)CH_2CH_3$

75. a. [phenyl]${-}MgBr$ **b.** [cyclohexyl]${-}MgBr$

77. a. $CH_3{-}CH_2{-}CH_2{-}CH_2{-}C(=O){-}OCH_2CH_3 + H_2O$

b. [phenyl]${-}C(=O){-}OCH_3 + H_2O$

79.

a. $CH_3-CH_2-CH_2-CH_2-CH_2-C(=O)OH$ + $ClC(=O)-C(=O)Cl$

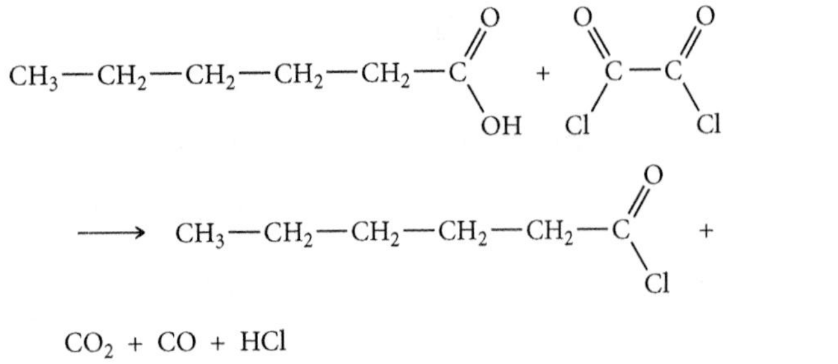

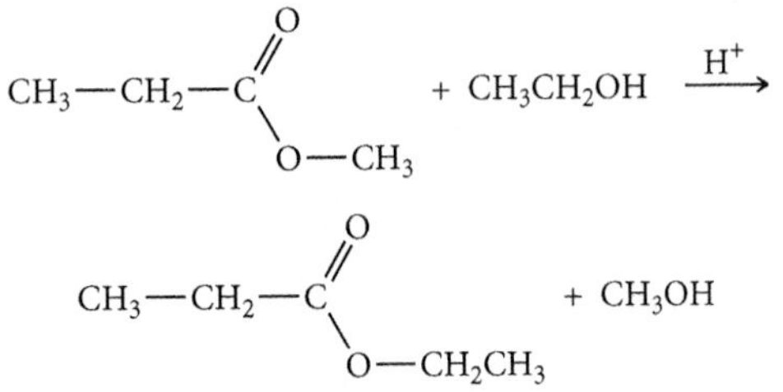

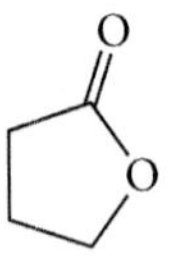

⟶ $CH_3-CH_2-CH_2-CH_2-CH_2-C(=O)Cl$ + CO_2 + CO + HCl

b. $CH_3-CH_2-C(=O)-O-CH_3$ + CH_3CH_2OH $\xrightarrow{H^+}$ $CH_3-CH_2-C(=O)-O-CH_2CH_3$ + CH_3OH

c. $CH_3-C(=O)-O-CH_3$ + NH_3 ⟶ $CH_3-C(=O)-NH_2$ + CH_3OH

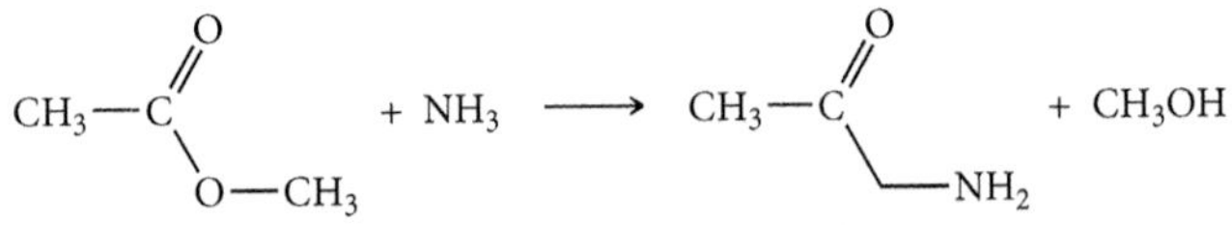

d. cyclohexyl–$C(=O)-O-CH_3$ $\xrightarrow{H_2O,\ H^+}$ cyclohexyl–$C(=O)OH$ + CH_3OH

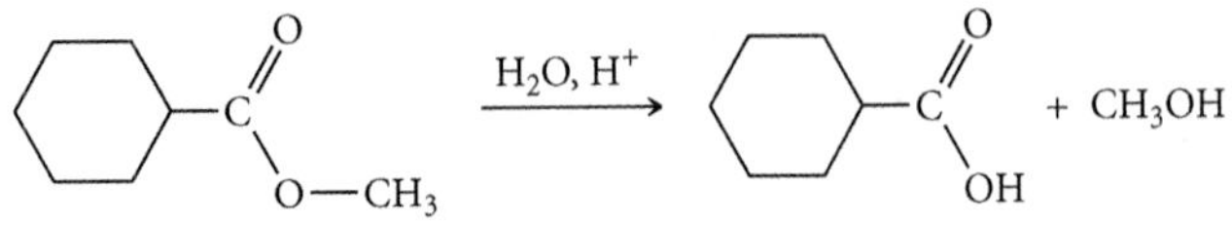

81. a. (five-membered cyclic ester, lactone) **b.** (six-membered cyclic anhydride)

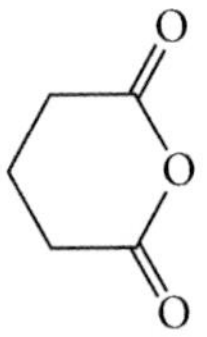

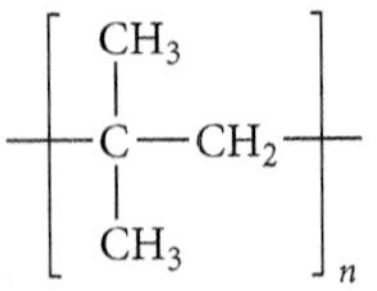

83. a. NaO_2CCH_3 **b.** 1) $(COCl)_2$; 2) two equivalents $NH(CH_3)_2$

85.
a. benzene–Cl
b. benzene–$C(=O)CH_3$
c. benzene–$C(CH_3)_3$

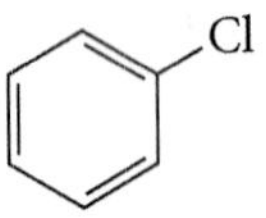

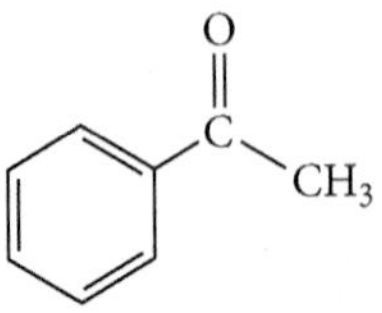

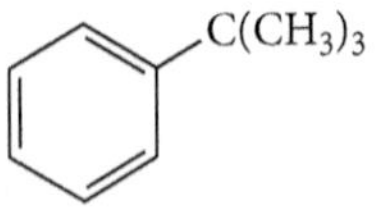

87. a. $AlCl_3$, benzene–$C(=O)Cl$

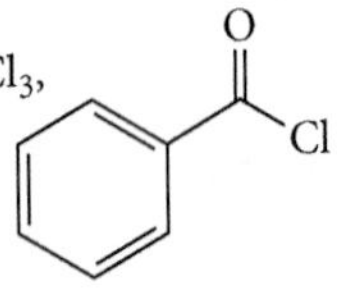

b. $AlCl_3$, butyl chloride (Cl)

c. Cl_2, $FeCl_3$

89. … $-CF_2-CF_2-CF_2-CF_2-CF_2-CF_2-$ …

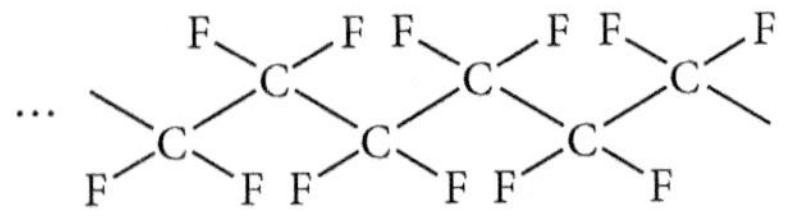

91. $HO-C(=O)-C_6H_4-C(=O)-O-CH_2-CH_2-OH$ (ester group circled)

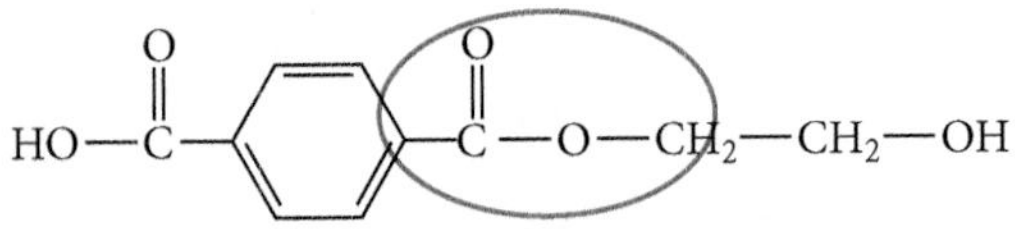

93. a. $\left[-C(CH_3)_2-CH_2-\right]_n$ **b.** $\left[-CH(CN)-CH_2-\right]_n$

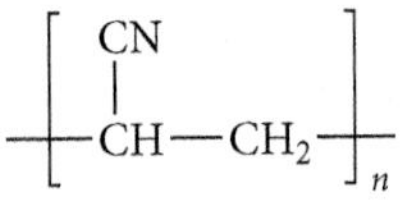

95. a. acid–base **b.** nucleophilic substitution
c. nucleophilic addition **d.** nucleophilic substitution

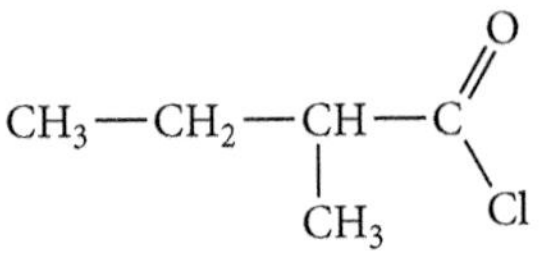

97. a. Ph–C(OH)(CH_2CH_3)(CH_3) + Ph–C(CH_2CH_3)(CH_3)(OH)

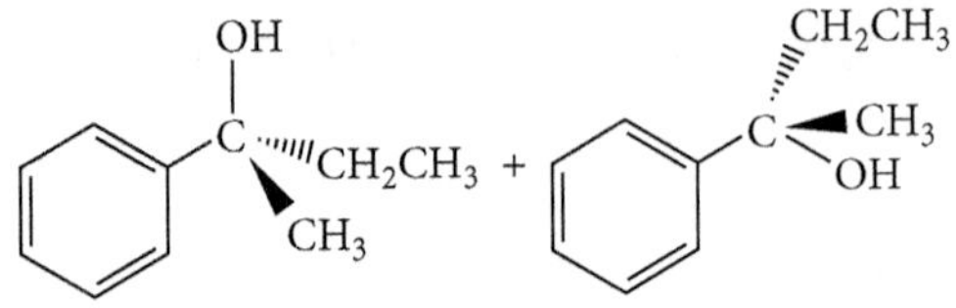

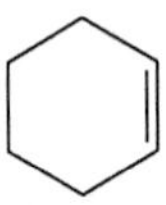

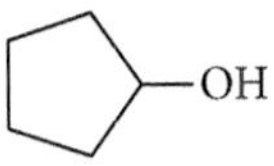

racemic mixture

b. $CH_3-CH_2-C(H)(CN)(CH_3)$

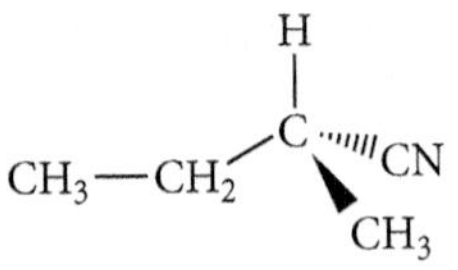

R enantiomer

99.
a. $CH_3-CH_2-CH(CH_3)-C(=O)Cl$
b. (cyclohexene)
c. cyclopentyl–OH
d. $:\!\overset{-}{C}H_2-C(=O)-O-CH_2CH_3$

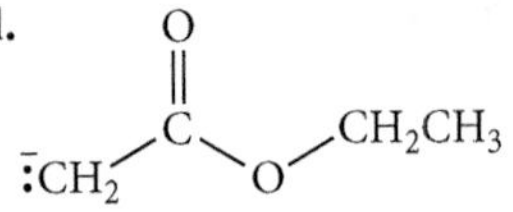

101.
a. Ph–CH(OH)–CH_2CH_3 ; Ph–CH=CH–CH_3

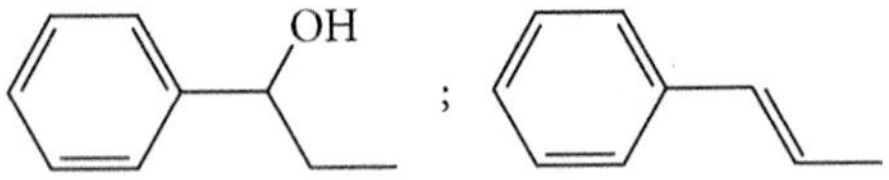

b. $CH_3-CH_2-C(=O)ONa$; $CH_3-CH_2-C(=O)-O-C(=O)-CH_3$

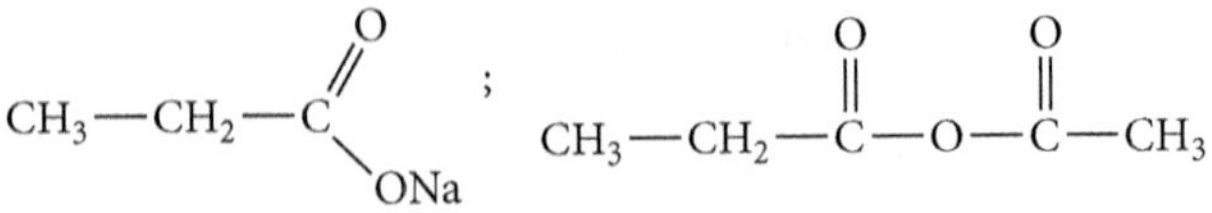

103. 558 g

105. a. 0.92 kg
b. $SOCl_2$ reaction by-products: 0.56 kg HCl, 0.98 kg SO_2
$(COCl)_2$ reaction by-products: 0.56 kg HCl, 0.67 kg CO_2, 0.43 kg CO

107.

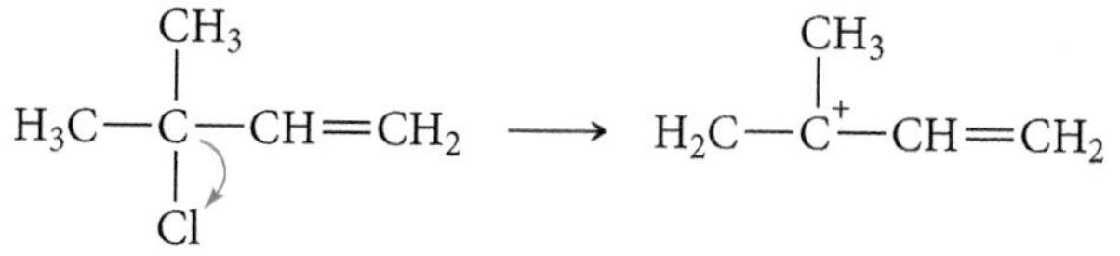

$$H_3C{-}C(CH_3)(Cl){-}CH{=}CH_2 \longrightarrow H_2C{-}\overset{+}{C}(CH_3){-}CH{=}CH_2$$

Carbocation resonance structures:

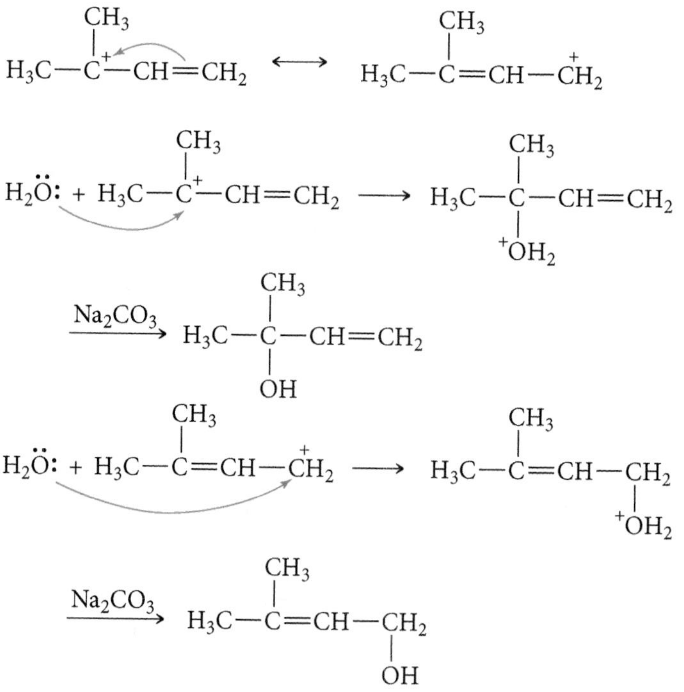

$$H_3C{-}\overset{+}{C}(CH_3){-}CH{=}CH_2 \longleftrightarrow H_3C{-}C(CH_3){=}CH{-}\overset{+}{C}H_2$$

$$H_2\ddot{O}\!: + H_3C{-}\overset{+}{C}(CH_3){-}CH{=}CH_2 \longrightarrow H_3C{-}C(CH_3)(\overset{+}{O}H_2){-}CH{=}CH_2$$

$$\xrightarrow{Na_2CO_3} H_3C{-}C(CH_3)(OH){-}CH{=}CH_2$$

$$H_2\ddot{O}\!: + H_3C{-}C(CH_3){=}CH{-}\overset{+}{C}H_2 \longrightarrow H_3C{-}C(CH_3){=}CH{-}CH_2{-}\overset{+}{O}H_2$$

$$\xrightarrow{Na_2CO_3} H_3C{-}C(CH_3){=}CH{-}CH_2{-}OH$$

109. **a.** $K_2Cr_2O_7$, H_2SO_4

b. 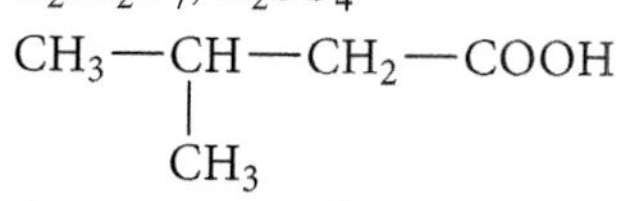 $CH_3{-}CH(CH_3){-}CH_2{-}COOH$

c. CH_3CH_2OH, H^+

111.

a.

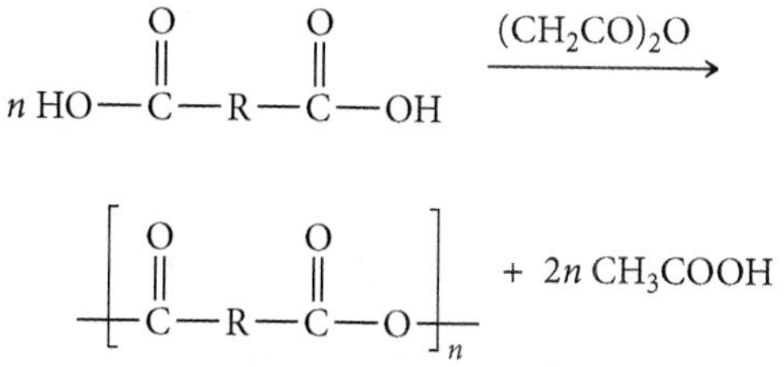

$$n\ HO{-}\overset{O}{\overset{\|}{C}}{-}R{-}\overset{O}{\overset{\|}{C}}{-}OH \xrightarrow{(CH_2CO)_2O} \left[{-}\overset{O}{\overset{\|}{C}}{-}R{-}\overset{O}{\overset{\|}{C}}{-}O{-}\right]_n + 2n\ CH_3COOH$$

b.

$$n\ HO{-}\overset{O}{\overset{\|}{C}}{-}R{-}\overset{O}{\overset{\|}{C}}{-}OH + n\ Cl{-}\overset{O}{\overset{\|}{C}}{-}R'{-}\overset{O}{\overset{\|}{C}}{-}Cl$$

$$\xrightarrow{Base} \left[{-}\overset{O}{\overset{\|}{C}}{-}R{-}\overset{O}{\overset{\|}{C}}{-}O{-}\overset{O}{\overset{\|}{C}}{-}R'{-}\overset{O}{\overset{\|}{C}}{-}O{-}\right]_n + 2n\ HCl$$

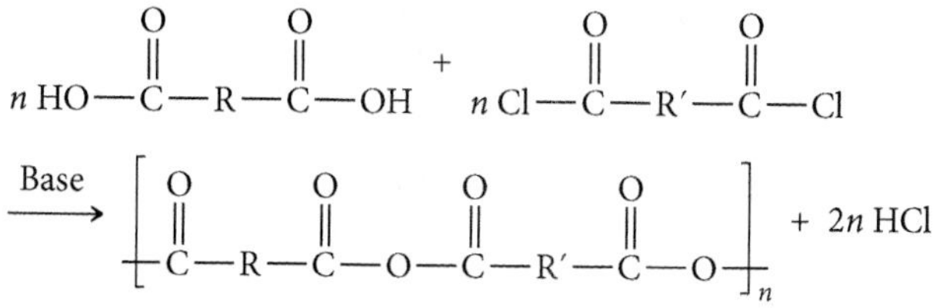

113. Excess NH_3 reacts with the HCl by-product.

115. Reduction

Chapter 22

31. **a.** not a fatty acid **b.** not a fatty acid **c.** saturated fatty acid **d.** steroid

33. **a.** saturated fatty acid **b.** not a fatty acid **c.** not a fatty acid **d.** monounsaturated fatty acid

35.

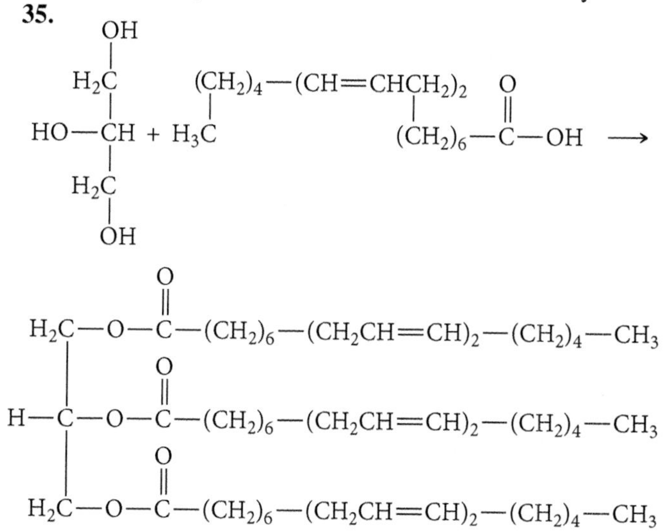

$$HOCH_2{-}CH(OH){-}CH_2OH + H_3C{-}(CH_2)_4{-}(CH{=}CHCH_2)_2{-}(CH_2)_6{-}\overset{O}{\overset{\|}{C}}{-}OH \longrightarrow$$

$$H_2C{-}O{-}\overset{O}{\overset{\|}{C}}{-}(CH_2)_6{-}(CH_2CH{=}CH)_2{-}(CH_2)_4{-}CH_3$$

$$H{-}C{-}O{-}\overset{O}{\overset{\|}{C}}{-}(CH_2)_6{-}(CH_2CH{=}CH)_2{-}(CH_2)_4{-}CH_3$$

$$H_2C{-}O{-}\overset{O}{\overset{\|}{C}}{-}(CH_2)_6{-}(CH_2CH{=}CH)_2{-}(CH_2)_4{-}CH_3$$

Triglyceride is expected to be an oil.

37. **a.** monosaccharide **b.** not a carbohydrate **c.** disaccharide **d.** not a carbohydrate

39. **a.** aldose, hexose **b.** aldose, pentose **c.** ketose, tetrose **d.** aldose, tetrose

41.

a. Five-membered ring (furanose) structure: $HO{-}CH_2$ on ring carbon [R]; ring O; ring carbon with H and OH [S]; ring carbons $HC(OH)$ [R], $C(H)(OH)$ [S], $C(OH)(H)$ [R].

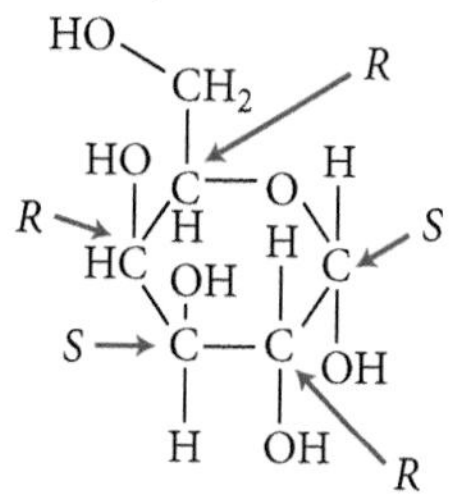

b. $HC(=O)$ at top; H—C[R]—OH; H—C[R]—OH; H—C[R]—OH; $H_2C{-}OH$

c. $HO{-}CH_2{-}\overset{O}{\overset{\|}{C}}$; H—C[R]—OH; $HO{-}CH_2$

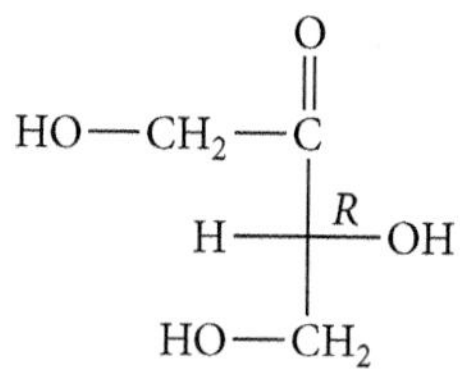

d. Five-membered ring: ring O; $C(H)(OH)$; $C(H)$ [S]; HC [S]; $C(H)(OH)$ [R]; substituents H, OH, H, OH as drawn.

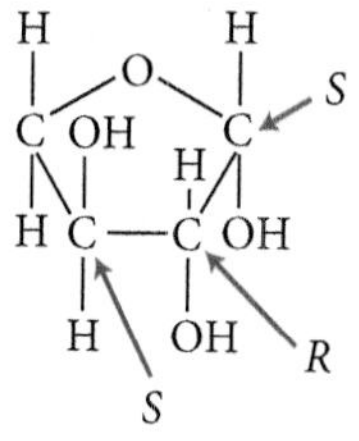

43.

$$\overset{O}{\overset{\|}{C}}H{-}[H{-}C{-}OH]{-}[HO{-}C{-}H]{-}[H{-}C{-}OH]{-}[H{-}C{-}OH]{-}H_2C{-}OH$$

Haworth projection: six-membered ring with ring O; $H_2C{-}OH$ on C5; substituents H, H, H, OH, HO, OH, H, H, OH as drawn.

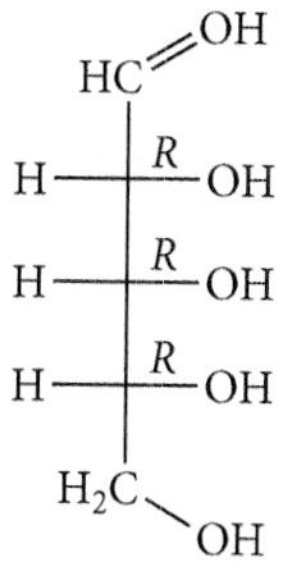

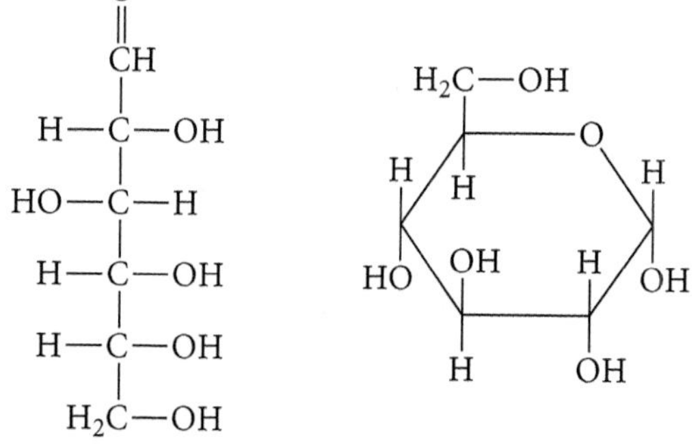

45. H_2C—OH HO H H H H OH OH OH O; H_2C—OH H H H HO OH H OH H OH O

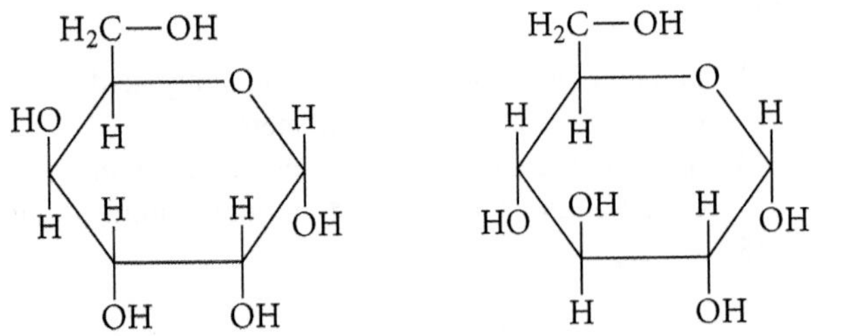

47. 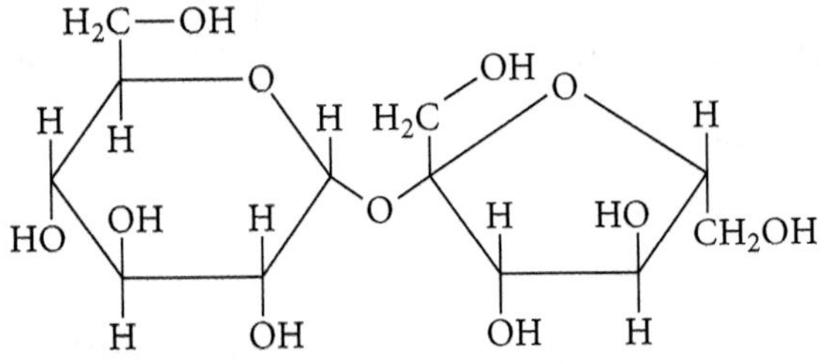 Glucose — Fructose

49. a. H_3N^+—CH—C(=O)—O^-, HO—CH, CH_3

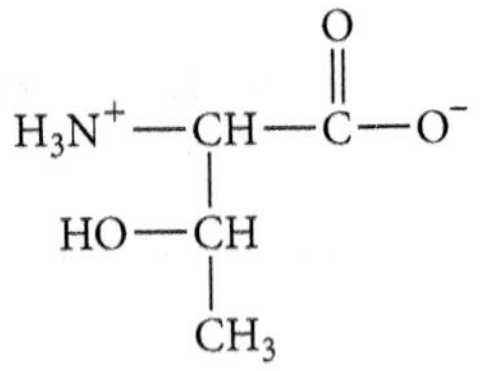

b. H_3N^+—CH—C(=O)—O^-, CH_3

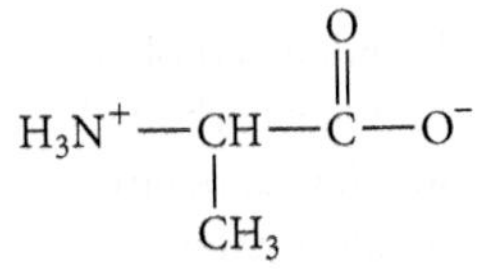

c. H_3N^+—CH—C(=O)—O^-, CH_2, H_3C—CH, CH_3

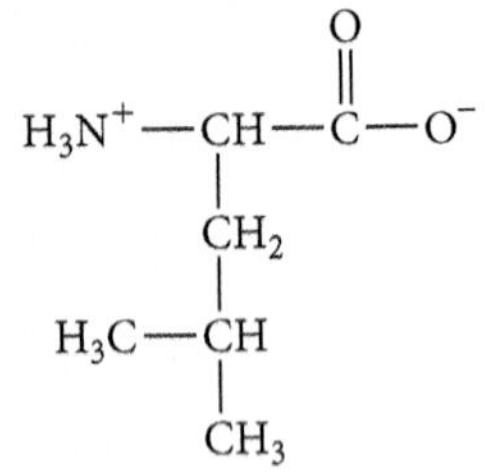

d. H_3N^+—CH—C(=O)—O^-, CH_2, CH_2, CH_2, CH_2, NH_2

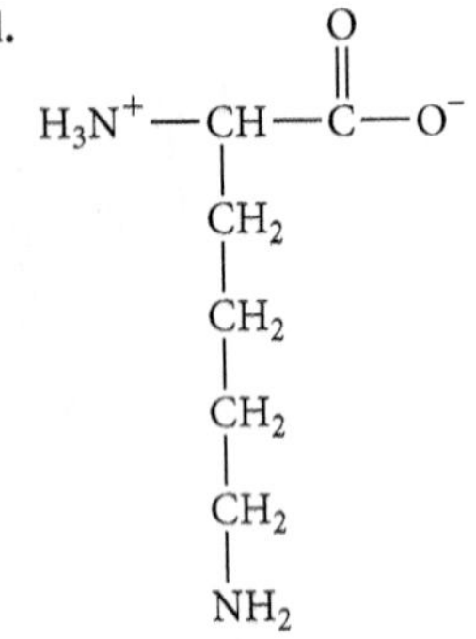

51. H_2N—C(H)(H_3C)—C(=O)—OH; H_3C—C(H)(H_2N)—C(=O)—OH

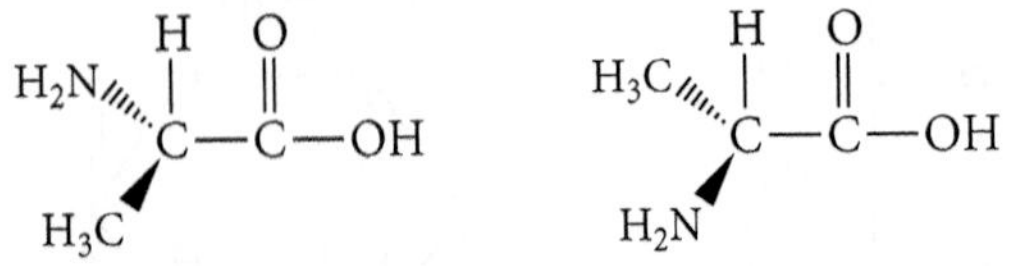

53. 6: Ser-Gly-Cys, Ser-Cys-Gly, Gly-Ser-Cys, Gly-Cys-Ser, Cys-Ser-Gly, Cys-Gly-Ser

55. H_2N—CH(CH_2OH)—C(=O)—OH + H_2N—CH($CH_2C_6H_4OH$)—C(=O)—OH →
H_2N—CH(CH_2OH)—C(=O)—NH—CH($CH_2C_6H_4OH$)—C(=O)—OH + H_2O

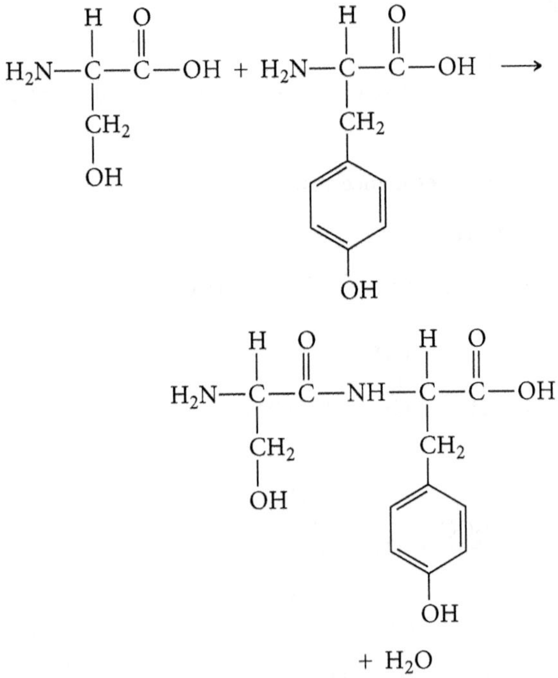

57. a. H_2N—CH($CH_2CH_2C(=O)NH_2$)—C(=O)—NH—CH($CH_2CH_2SCH_3$)—C(=O)—NH—CH(CH_2SH)—C(=O)—OH

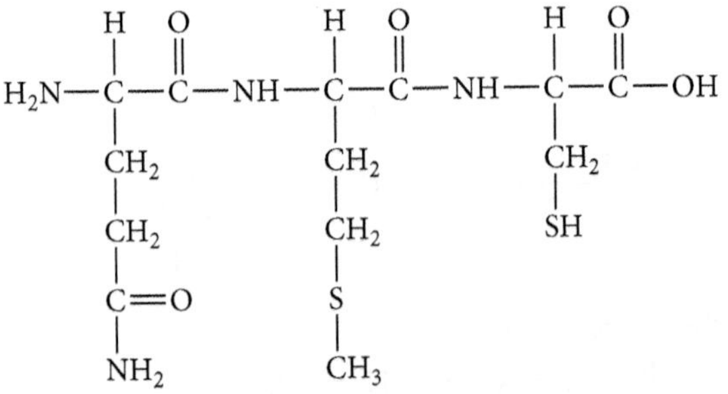

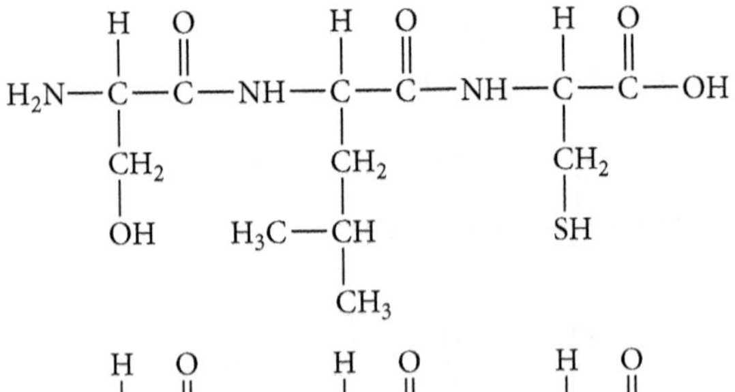

b. H_2N—CH(CH_2OH)—C(=O)—NH—CH($CH_2CH(CH_3)$)—C(=O)—NH—CH(CH_2SH)—C(=O)—OH

c. H_2N—CH(CH_2SH)—C(=O)—NH—CH($CH_2CH(CH_3)$)—C(=O)—NH—CH(CH_2OH)—C(=O)—OH

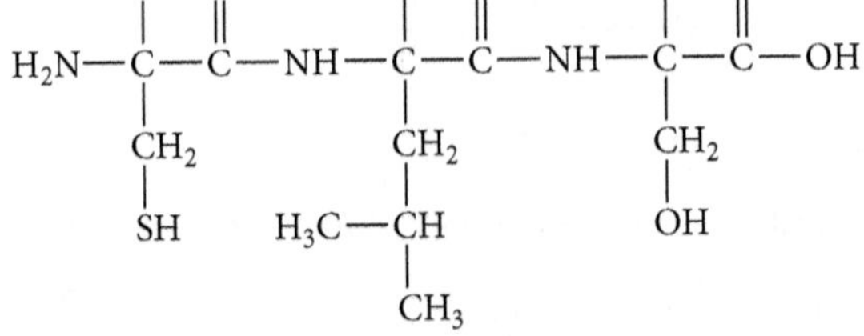

59. tertiary

61. primary

63. a. A b. not a nucleotide
c. T d. not a nucleotide

65. NH_2 N C N HC CH N C N H; O C N C NH HC N C N C NH_2 H

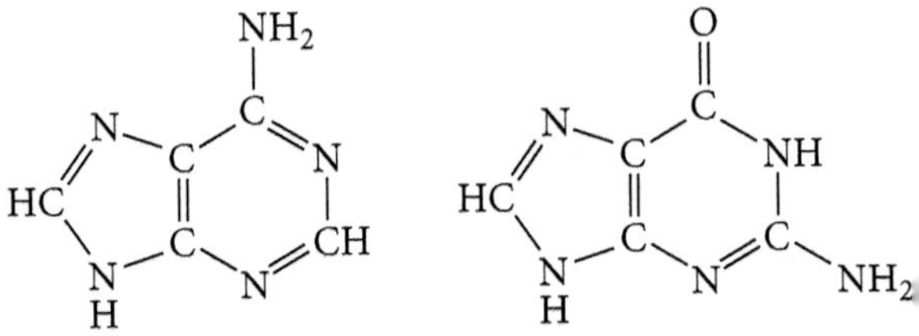

67. A C A T G C G
69. 154 codons, 462 nucleotides
71. **a.** protein **b.** carbohydrate **c.** lipid
73. A codon is composed of three nucleotides. A codon codes for a specific amino acid while a gene codes for an entire protein.
75.

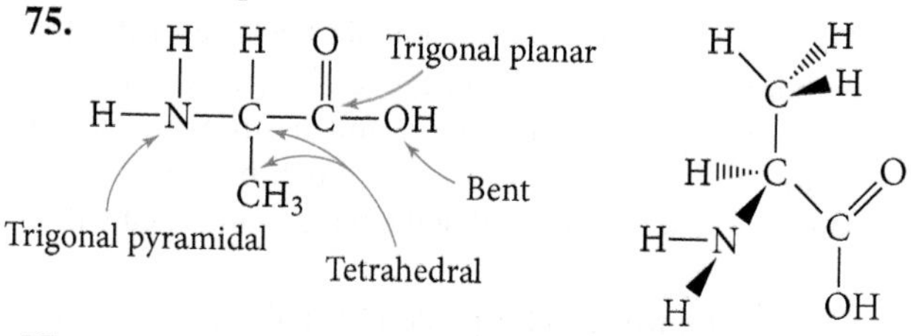

Trigonal planar
Bent
Trigonal pyramidal
Tetrahedral

77. valine, leucine, isoleucine, phenylalanine
79. Gly-Arg-Ala-Leu-Phe-Gly-Asn-Lys-Trp-Glu-Cys
81. **a.** β

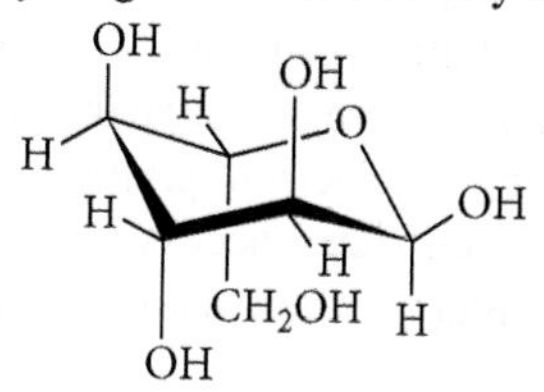

b. α

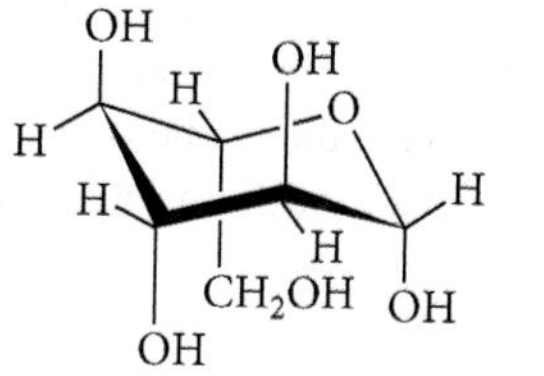

83. As the temperature increases, the favourable entropy for uncoiling a chain becomes dominant. On cooling, the favourable enthalpy of forming hydrogen bonds between paired bases is dominant.
85.
a. L-alanine
b. L-cysteine
c. L-serine
d. L-aspartic acid

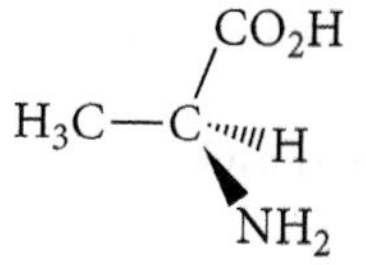

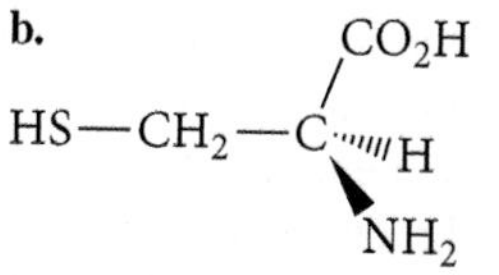

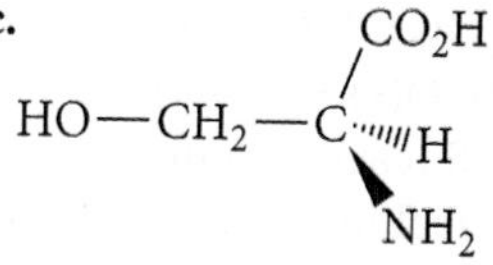

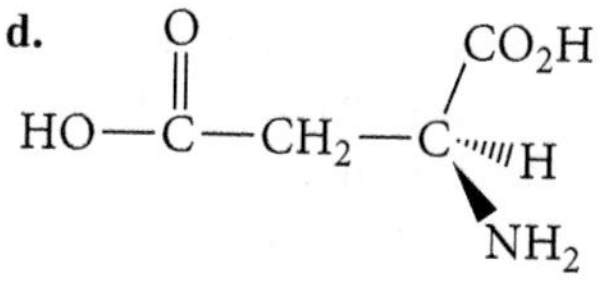

87. When the fake thymine nucleotide is added to the replicating DNA, the chain cannot continue to form because the $-N{=}N^+{=}NH$ group on the sugar prevents future phosphate linkages.
89. $V_{max} = 47.6, K_t = 1.68$
91. $H_3N^+{-}CH_2COO^- + H^+ \rightleftharpoons (H_3N^+{-}CH_2COOH\ [HA]/[A^-] = 2,$
$H_3N^+{-}CH_2COO^- \rightleftharpoons H_2NCH_2COO^- + H^+\ [HA]/[A^-] = 0.4, pH = 6.0$
93. A three-base codon codes for a single amino acid. If there are only three bases, there could be 27 different three-base codon arrangements. Therefore, you could theoretically code for the 20 different amino acids needed.

Chapter 23

17. **a.** +4 **b.** +4 **c.** +4
19. $Ca_3Al_2(SiO_4)_3$
21. 4
23. tetrahedrons stand alone, orthosilicates
25. amphibole or double-chain structure; $Ca^{2+}, Mg^{2+}, Fe^{2+}, Al^{3+}$
27. 950 g
29. NCl_3 has a lone pair that BCl_3 lacks, giving it a trigonal pyramidal shape, as opposed to BCl_3's trigonal planar shape.
31. **a.** 6 vertices, 8 faces **b.** 12 vertices, 20 faces
33. *closo*-Boranes have the formula $B_nH_n^{2-}$ and form fully closed polyhedra, *nido*-boranes have the formula B_nH_{n+4} and consist of a cage missing a corner, and *arachno*-boranes have the formula B_nH_{n+6} and consist of a cage missing two or three corners.
35. Graphite consists of covalently bonded sheets that are held to each other by weak interactions, allowing them to slip past each other. Diamond is not a good lubricant because it is an extremely strong network covalent solid, where all of the carbon atoms are covalently bonded.
37. Activated charcoal consists of fine particles, rather than a lump of charcoal, and subsequently has a much higher surface area.
39. Ionic carbides are composed of carbon, generally in the form of the carbide ion, C_2^{2-}, and low-electronegativity metals, such as the alkali and alkaline earth metals. Covalent carbides are composed of carbon and low-electronegativity nonmetals or metalloids, such as silicon.
41. **a.** solid $\longrightarrow$ gas
b. gas $\longrightarrow$ liquid $\longrightarrow$ solid
c. solid $\longrightarrow$ gas
43. **a.** $CO(g) + CuO(s) \longrightarrow CO_2(g) + Cu(s)$
b. $SiO_2(s) + 3\ C(s) \longrightarrow SiC(s) + 2\ CO(g)$
c. $S(s) + CO(g) \longrightarrow COS(g)$
45. **a.** +2 **b.** +4 **c.** +4/3
47. Fixing nitrogen refers to converting N_2 to a nitrogen-containing compound.
49. White phosphorus consists of P_4 molecules in a tetrahedral shape with the atoms at the corners of the tetrahedron. This allotrope is unstable because of the strain from the bond angles. Red phosphorus is much more stable because one bond of the tetrahedron is broken, allowing the phosphorus atoms to make chains with bond angles that are less strained.
51. saltpeter: 13.86% N by mass
Chile saltpeter: 16.48% N by mass
53. HN_3 has a positive $\Delta_f G°$, meaning that it spontaneously decomposes into H_2 and N_2 at room temperature. There are no temperatures at which HN_3 will be stable. $\Delta_f H$ is positive and $\Delta_f S$ is negative, so $\Delta_f G$ will always be negative.
55. **a.** $NH_4NO_3(aq) + \text{heat} \longrightarrow N_2O(g) + 2\ H_2O(l)$
b. $3\ NO_2(g) + H_2O(l) \longrightarrow 2\ HNO_3(l) + NO(g)$
c. $2\ PCl_3(l) + O_2(g) \longrightarrow 2\ POCl_3(l)$
57. $NO_3^-, NO_2^-, N_3^-, N_2H_5^+, NH_4^+$

59. :C̈l—P̈—C̈l: with :C̈l: above P; and PCl_5 (P with five :C̈l: atoms)

Trigonal pyramidal Trigonal bipyramidal

61. $CO(NH_2)_2 + 2\,H_2O \longrightarrow (NH_4)_2CO_3$
14 g

63. P_4O_6 forms if there is only a limited amount of oxygen available, while P_4O_{10} will form with greater amounts of oxygen.

65. The major source of oxygen is the fractionation of air by which air is cooled and liquefied and oxygen is separated from the other components.

67. a. superoxide **b.** oxide **c.** peroxide

69. Initially, liquid sulfur becomes less viscous when heated because the S_8 rings have greater thermal energy which overcomes intermolecular forces. Above 150 °C the rings break and the broken rings entangle one another, causing greater viscosity.

71. a. 4.3×10^{-22} g **b.** 4×10^{-19} g

73. $2\,FeS_2(s) \xrightarrow{heat} 2\,FeS(s) + S_2(g)$
5.2×102 L

75. $CS_2 + 3\,Cl_2 \longrightarrow CCl_4 + S_2Cl_2$; Cl reduced, S oxidized

77. 8 kg from lignite, 39 kg from bituminous coal

79. Chlorine is much more electronegative than iodine, allowing it to withdraw an electron and ionize in solution much more easily.

81. a. $rate_{HCl}/rate_{Cl_2} = 1.394$
b. $rate_{HCl}/rate_{HF} = 0.7408$
c. $rate_{HCl}/rate_{HI} = 1.873$

83. $4\,Na_2O_2 + 3\,Fe \longrightarrow 4\,Na_2O + Fe_3O_4$

85. The bond length of the O_2 species increases as electrons are added because they are added to the π^* antibonding orbital. O_2^{2-} is diamagnetic.

87. 2.0 mol of C—C bonds, 714.8 kJ mol^{-1}, 6.9×10^2 kJ mol^{-1}. This value, calculated from the bond energy, is too low because it doesn't include van der Waals attractions between C atoms not directly bonded to each other.

89. -50 kJ mol^{-1}

91. a. -13.6 kJ mol^{-1} **b.** -11.0 kJ mol^{-1}
c. -24.8 kJ mol^{-1}
Fe_2O_3 is the most exothermic because it has the highest oxidation state and is therefore able to oxidize the most CO per mol Fe.

93. a. Ö=C=C=C=Ö **b.** *sp*
c. -92 kJ mol^{-1}

95. a. 7.6×10^{-22} **b.** 1.2×10^{-8}
c. $[N_2H_4] = 0.009$ mol L^{-1}, $[N_2H_5^+] = 0.0025$ mol L^{-1}, $[N_2H_6^{2+}] = 7.0 \times 10^{-13}$ mol L^{-1}

97. The acid is HO—N̈=N—OH and the base is $H_2N—N^+(=O)—O^-$

The acid is weaker than nitrous acid because of electron donation by resonance in contributing structures such as

HO—N̈⁻—N=ÖH⁺ (with $\ominus$ on N and $\oplus$ on OH).

The base is weaker than ammonia because of electron withdrawal by the electronegative nitrogen group.

99. The triple bond in nitrogen is much stronger than the double bond in oxygen, so it is much harder to break. This makes it less likely that the bond in nitrogen will be broken.

101. Sodium dinitrogen phosphate (NaH_2PO_4) can act as a weak base or a weak acid. A buffer can be made by mixing it with either Na_2HPO_4 or with Na_3PO_4, depending on the desired pH of the buffer solution.

103. F is extremely small and so there is a huge driving force to fill the octet by adding an electron, giving a -1 oxidation state. Other halogens have access to *d* orbitals, which allows for more hybridization and oxidation state options.

105. SO_3 cannot be a reducing agent because the oxidation state of S is +6, the highest possible oxidation state for S. Reducing agents need to be able to be oxidized. SO_2 can be a reducing agent or an oxidizing agent because the oxidation state of S is +4.

Chapter 24

15. Typically, metals are opaque, are good conductors of heat and electricity, and are ductile and malleable, meaning they can be drawn into wires and flattened into sheets.

17. aluminum, iron, calcium, magnesium, sodium, potassium

19. Fe: hematite (Fe_2O_3), magnetite (Fe_3O_4)
Hg: cinnabar (HgS)
V: vanadinite [$Pb_5(VO_4)Cl$], carnotite [$K_2(UO_2)_2(VO_4)_2 \cdot 3\,H_2O$]
Nb: columbite [$Fe(NbO_3)2$]

21. $MgCO_3(s) + heat \longrightarrow MgO(s) + CO_2(g)$
$Mg(OH)_2(s) + heat \longrightarrow MgO(s) + H_2O(g)$

23. The flux is a material that will react with the gangue to form a substance with a low melting point. MgO is the flux.

25. Hydrometallurgy is used to separate metals from ores by selectively dissolving the metal in a solution, filtering out impurities, and then reducing the metal to its elemental form.

27. The Bayer process is a hydrometallurgical process by which Al_2O_3 is selectively dissolved, leaving other oxides as solids. The soluble form of aluminum is $Al(OH)_4^-$.

29. Sponge powdered iron contains many small holes in the iron particles due to the escaping of the oxygen when the iron is reduced. Water-atomized powdered iron has much more smooth and dense particles as the powder is formed from molten iron.

31. **a.** 50% Cr, 50% V by moles; 50.5% Cr, 49.5% V by mass
b. 25% Fe, 75% V by moles; 26.8% Fe, 73.2% V by mass
c. 25% Cr, 25% Fe, 50% V by moles; 24.8% Cr, 26.6% Fe, 48.6% V by mass

33. Cr and Fe are very close to each other in mass, so their respective atomic radii are probably close enough to form an alloy. Also, they both form body-centred cubic structures.

35. A: solid, 20% Cr, 80% Fe
B: liquid, 50% Cr, 50% Fe

37. A: solid, 20% Co and 80% Cu overall. Two phases; one is the Cu structure with 4% Co, and the other is the Co structure with 7% Cu. There will be more of the Cu structure.
B: solid Co structure, 90% Co, 10% Cu

39. C would fill interstitial holes; Mn and Si would substitute for Fe.

41. **a.** Mo_2N **b.** CrH_2

43. **a.** zinc **b.** copper **c.** manganese

45. $-19.4\ \text{kJ mol}^{-1}$

47. When Cr is added to steel it reacts with oxygen to form a thin and highly adherent oxide layer on the surface which acts as an effective barrier against corrosion. A Cr–steel alloy would be used in any situation where the steel might be easily oxidized, such as when it comes in contact with water.

49. rutile: 33.3% Ti by moles, 59.9% Ti by mass
ilmenite: 20.0% Ti by moles, 31.6% Ti by mass

51. Titanium must be arc-melted in an inert atmosphere because the high temperature and flow of electrons would cause the metal to oxidize in a normal atmosphere.

53. TiO_2 is the most important industrial product of titanium and it is often used as a pigment in white paint.

55. The Bayer process is a hydrometallurgical process used to separate Al_2O_3 from other oxides. The Al_2O_3 is selectively dissolved by hot, concentrated NaOH. The other oxides are removed as solids and the Al_2O_3 precipitates out of solution when the solution is neutralized.

57. cobalt and tungsten

59. 3.3 kg Fe, 2.0 kg Ti

61. Four atoms surround a tetrahedral hole and six atoms surround an octahedral hole. The octahedral hole is larger because it is surrounded by a greater number of atoms.

63. Mn has one more valence electron than does Cr, which allows it to attain higher positive oxidation states.

65. Ferromagnetic atoms, like paramagnetic ones, have unpaired electrons. However, in ferromagnetic atoms, these electrons align with their spin oriented in the same direction, resulting in a permanent magnetic field.

67. The nuclear charge of the last three is relatively high because of the lanthanide series in which the 4*f* subshell falls between them and the other six metals of the group.

69. **a.** 16.0 cm **b.** 4.95 cm **c.** 14%

71. 92%

73. 5.4×10^7

75. First, roast to form the oxide.
$$4\ CoAsS(s) + 9\ O_2(g) \longrightarrow 4\ CoO(s) + 4\ SO_2(g) + As_4O_6(s)$$
Then reduce the oxide with coke.
$$CoO(s) + C(s) \longrightarrow Co(s) + CO(g)$$
The oxides of arsenic are relatively volatile and can be separated, but they are poisonous.

77. Au and Ag are found in elemental form because of their low reactivity. Na and Ca are group 1 and group 2 metals, respectively, and are highly reactive as they readily lose their valence electrons to obtain noble gas configurations.

Chapter 25

15. **a.** $[Ar]\ 4s^23d^8$, $[Ar]\ 3d^8$
b. $[Ar]\ 4s^23d^5$, $[Ar]\ 3d^3$
c. $[Kr]\ 5s^24d^1$, $[Kr]\ 5s^14d^1$
d. $[Xe]\ 6s^24f^{14}5d^3$, $[Xe]\ 4f^{14}5d^3$

17. **a.** +5 **b.** +7 **c.** +4

19. **a.** +3, 6 **b.** +2, 6
c. +2, 4 **d.** +1, 2

21. **a.** hexaaquachromium(III)
b. tetracyanocuprate(II)
c. pentaaminebromoiron(III) sulfate
d. aminetetraaquahydroxycobalt(III) chloride

23. **a.** $[Cr(NH_3)_6]^{3+}$ **b.** $K_3[Fe(CN)_6]$
c. $[Cu(en)(SCN)_2]$ **d.** $[Pt(H_2O)_4][PtCl_6]$

25. **a.** $[Co(NH_3)_3(CN)_3]$, triaminetricyanocobalt(III)
b. $[Cr(en)_3]^{3+}$, tris(ethylenediamine)chromium(III)

27. (structures: Mn bonded to four H_3N/NH_3 ligands and a fifth NH_3, with the sixth position bonded through N of NO_2 (O, O on N) in one isomer, and through O of O—N—O in the other)

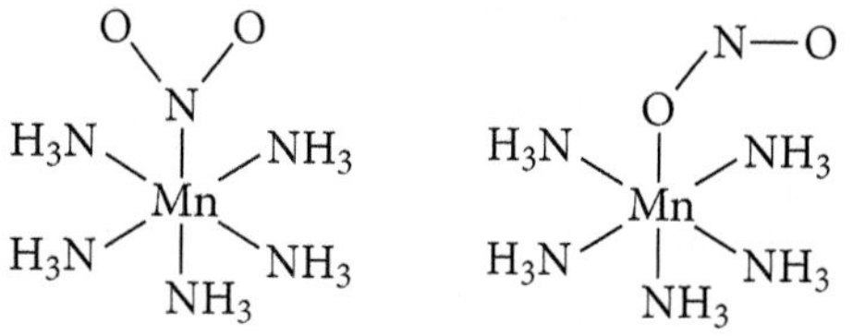

29. $[Fe(H_2O)_5Cl]Cl \cdot H_2O$, pentaaquachloroiron(II) chloride monohydrate
$[Fe(H_2O)_4Cl_2] \cdot 2\ H_2O$, tetraaquadichloroiron(II) dihydrate

31. b, c, e.

33. **a.** 3 **b.** 2 (enantiomers)

35. **a.** (structures of octahedral Cr with three NH_3 and three CO ligands)
Fac *Mer*

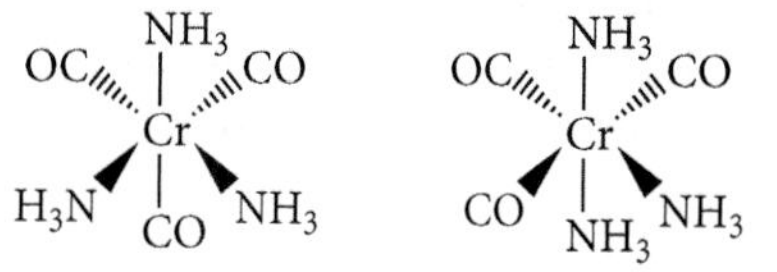

b. (structures of square planar Pd with two H_2O... ligands: H_2O, CO, Cl, CO)
Cis *Trans*

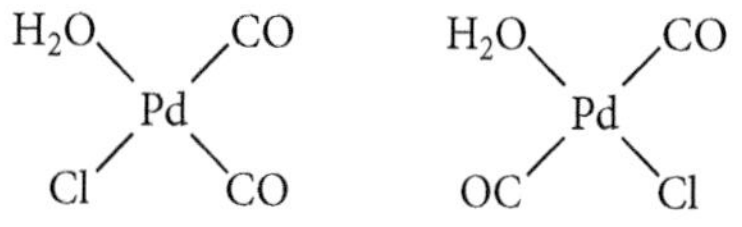

37. *cis* isomer is optically active

39. a. 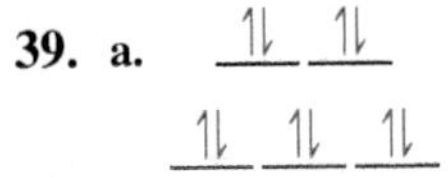

b.

c.

d.

41. 163 kJ mol^{-1}
43. $[Co(CN)_6]^{3-} \longrightarrow$ 290 nm, colourless
$[Co(NH_3)_6]^{3+} \longrightarrow$ 440 nm, yellow
$[CoF_6]^{3-} \longrightarrow$ 770 nm, green
45. weak
47. a. 4 b. 3 c. 1
49. 3
51. porphyrin
53. Water is a weak-field ligand that forms a high-spin complex with hemoglobin. Because deoxyhemoglobin is weak-field it absorbs large wavelength light and appears blue. Oxyhemoglobin is a low-spin complex and absorbs small wavelength light, so O_2 must be a strong-field ligand.
55. a. [Ar] $4s^1 3d^5$, [Ar] $3d^5$, [Ar] $3d^4$, [Ar] $3d^3$
b. [Ar] $4s^1 3d^{10}$, [Ar] $3d^{10}$, [Ar] $3d^9$
57. a. H—N—H (with H below N) b. [S=C=N]⁻ c. H–O–H
59. $[MA_2B_2C_2]$ all *cis*; A *trans* and B and C *cis*; B *trans* and A and C *cis*; C *trans* and A and B *cis*; all *trans*.
$[MA_2B_3C]$ will have *fac–mer* isomers.
$[MAB_2C_3]$ will have *fac–mer* isomers.
$[MAB_3C_2]$ will have *fac–mer* isomers.
$[MA_3B_2C]$ will have *fac–mer* isomers.
$[MA_2BC_3]$ will have *fac–mer* isomers.
$[MA_3BC_2]$ will have *fac–mer* isomers.
$[MAB_4C]$ will have AC *cis–trans* isomers.
$[MA_4BC]$ will have BC *cis–trans* isomers.
$[MABC_4]$ will have AB *cis–trans* isomers.

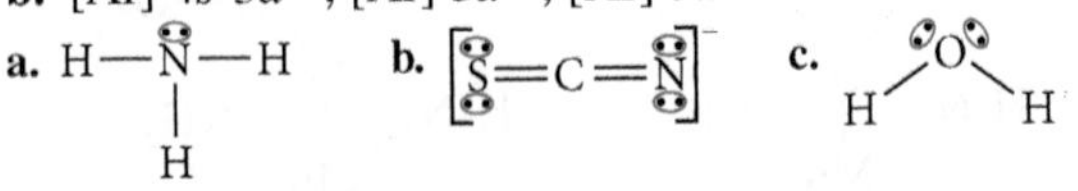

61. $[Fe(ox)_3]^{3+}$, optical isomers

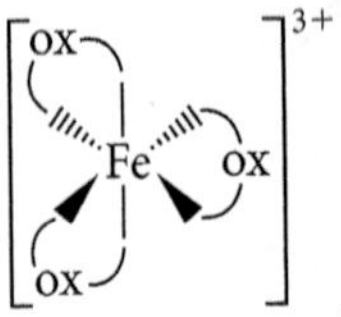

63. paramagnetic

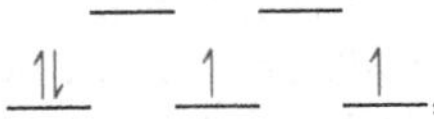

65. 1.–5. $[Ru(H_2O)_2(NH_3)_2Cl_2]^+$ isomers

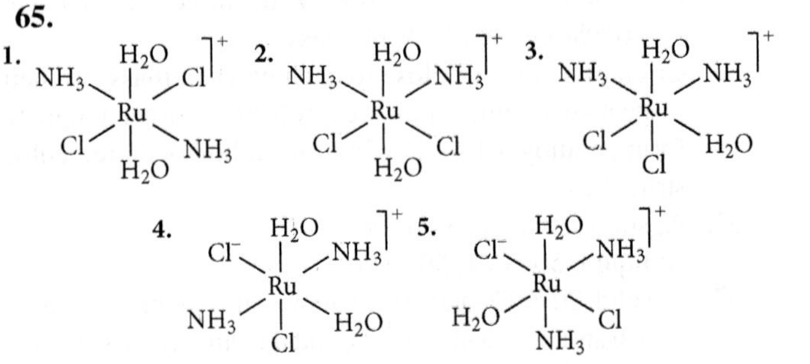

Only structure 3 is chiral. This is its mirror image.

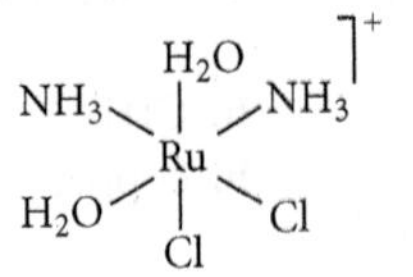

67. 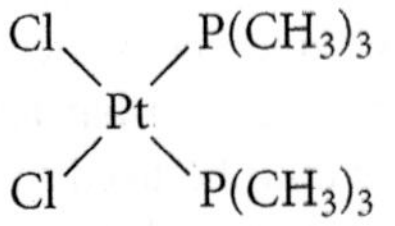 *cis*-dichlorobis (trimethylphosphine) platinum(II)

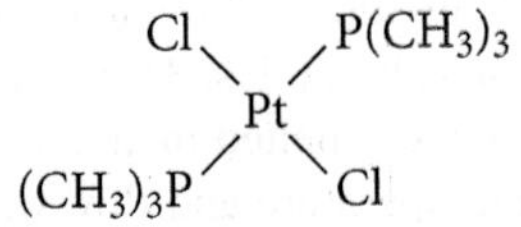

trans-dichlorobis (trimethylphosphine) platinum(II)

69. d_{z^2}
$d_{x^2-y^2}$ and d_{xy}
d_{xz} and d_{yz}
71. a. 2×10^{-8} mol L^{-1}
b. 6.6×10^{-3} mol L^{-1}
c. NiS will dissolve more easily in the ammonia solution because the formation of the complex ion is favourable, removing Ni^{2+} ions from the solution and allowing more NiS to dissolve.
73. Prepare a solution that contains both $[MCl_6]^{3-}$ and $[MBr_6]^{3-}$ and see if any complex ions that contain both Cl and Br form. If they do it would demonstrate that these complexes are labile.
75. pH = 10.1
77. Ligand B results in the larger Δ.

Appendix IV:

Answers to In-Chapter Practice Problems

Chapter 1

1.1. Conceptual Connection
View (**a**) best represents the water after vaporization. Vaporization is a physical change, so the molecules must remain the same before and after the change.

1.1. **a.** 29.9 °C

1.2. 0.1704 nm, 170.4 pm

1.2. For More Practice
73 times

1.3. 2.3×10^{-28} kg fm^{-3} or 2.3×10^{14} g cm^{-3}

1.3. For More Practice
density = 4.50 g cm^{-3}, titanium

1.2. Conceptual Connection
(**c**) The sample expands. However, because its mass remains constant while its volume increases, its density decreases.

1.4. The thermometer shown has markings every 1 °C; thus, the first digit of uncertainty is 0.1. The answer is 103.4 °C.

1.5. **a.** Each figure in this number is significant by rule 1: three significant figures.

b. This is a defined quantity that has an unlimited number of significant figures.

c. Both 1's are significant (rule 1) and the interior zero is significant as well (rule 2): three significant figures.

d. Only the two 9's are significant, the leading zeroes are not (rule 3): two significant figures.

e. There are five significant figures because the 1, 4, and 5 are nonzero (rule 1) and the trailing zeroes are after a decimal point so they are significant as well (rule 4).

f. The number of significant figures is ambiguous because the trailing zeroes occur before an implied decimal point (rule 4). Assume two significant figures.

g. Three significant figures.

1.6. **a.** 0.381

b. 121.0

c. 1.174

d. 2.497

e. 5.2×10^{10}

1.7. 0.855 cm

1.8. 2.70 g cm^{-3} (could be aluminum)

Chapter 2

2.1. Conceptual Connection
Most of the matter that composed the log underwent a chemical change by reacting with oxygen molecules in the air. The products of the reaction (mostly carbon dioxide and water) were released as gases into the air.

2.1. For the first sample:

$$\frac{\text{mass of oxygen}}{\text{mass of carbon}} = \frac{17.2\text{ g O}}{12.9\text{ g C}} = 1.33 \text{ or } 1.33{:}1$$

For the second sample:

$$\frac{\text{mass of oxygen}}{\text{mass of carbon}} = \frac{10.5\text{ g O}}{7.88\text{ g C}} = 1.33 \text{ or } 1.33{:}1$$

The ratios of oxygen to carbon are the same in the two samples of carbon monoxide, so these results are consistent with the law of definite proportions.

2.2. **a.** $Z = 6, A = 13, {}^{13}_{6}C$
b. 19 protons, 20 neutrons

2.2. Conceptual Connection
(b) The number of neutrons in the nucleus of an atom does not affect the atom's size because the nucleus is miniscule compared to the atom itself. The number of neutrons, however, does affect the mass of the isotope; more neutrons means more mass.

2.3. 47.87 u

2.4. 1.3×10^{22} C atoms

2.4. For More Practice
6.87 g W

2.3. Conceptual Connection
(b) The carbon sample contains more atoms than the copper sample because carbon has a lower molar mass than copper. Carbon atoms are lighter than copper atoms, so a 1 g sample of carbon contains more atoms than a 1 g sample of copper. The carbon sample also contains more atoms than the uranium sample because, even though the uranium sample has 10 times the mass of the carbon sample, a uranium atom is more than 10 times as massive (238 g mol^{-1} for U versus 12 g mol^{-1} for carbon).

Chapter 3

3.1. **a.** molecular element
b. molecular compound
c. atomic element
d. ionic compound
e. ionic compound

3.2. K_2S

3.3. AlN

3.1. Conceptual Connection
"Mercury(I)" could be interpreted to mean Hg^+ instead of $Hg_2{}^{2+}$. Oxidation state could be misinterpreted as the charge. The name "dimercury(2+)" is unambiguous because there is no question as to composition or charge.

3.4. **a.** iron(II) sulfide
b. tin(II) chlorate

3.4. For More Practice
a. RuO_2
b. $Co_3(PO_4)_2$

3.5. dinitrogen pentoxide

3.5. For More Practice
PBr_3

3.2. Conceptual Connection
$AlCl_3$ can be considered to be an ionic compound made up of Al^{3+} and Cl^- ions, and the formula can be inferred from the ionic charges. NCl_3 is a molecular compound.

3.6. 3-methylhexane

3.7. 3,5-dimethylheptane

3.8. **a.** 4,4-dimethylpent-2-yne
b. 3-ethyl-4,6-dimethylhept-1-ene

3.3. Conceptual Connection
cyclohexa-1,3,5-triene; yes, the systematic name gives the structure

3.9. **a.** 2-chloropropanoic acid
b. penta-2,4-dione

3.9. For More Practice
a. propanal
b. 1,2-dibromo-3-methylbenzene

3.10. 164.10 u

3.11. 9.696×10^{-4} mol

3.11. For More Practice
1.06 g H_2O

3.12. 53.29%

3.12. For More Practice
74.19% Na

3.13. 4.0 g O

3.13. For More Practice
3.60 g C

3.14. CH_2O

3.15. $C_{13}H_{18}O_2$

3.16. C_6H_6

3.16. For More Practice
$C_2H_8N_2$

3.4. Conceptual Connection
$C > O > H$

3.17. C_2H_5

3.18. C_2H_4O

Chapter 4

4.1. $SiO_2(s) + \mathbf{3}\, C(s) \longrightarrow SiC(s) + \mathbf{2}\, CO(g)$

4.2. $\mathbf{2}\, C_2H_6(g) + \mathbf{7}\, O_2(g) \longrightarrow \mathbf{4}\, CO_2(g) + \mathbf{6}\, H_2O(g)$

4.1. Conceptual Connection
Both **(a)** and **(d)** are correct. When the number of atoms of each type is balanced, the sum of the masses of the substances involved will be the same on both sides of the equation. Since molecules change during a chemical reaction, their number is not the same on both sides, nor is the number of moles necessarily the same.

4.3. **a.** Insoluble.
b. Insoluble.
c. Soluble.
d. Soluble.

4.4. For this reaction, according to the solubility rules, no precipitation should occur. Therefore, there is no net reaction since all of the ions remain soluble.

4.4. For More Practice
For this reaction, the copper(II) hydroxide product will be insoluble, but the sodium bromide will be completely soluble. Therefore, the net ionic equation is:
$Cu^{2+}(aq) + 2\, OH^-(aq) \longrightarrow Cu(OH)_2(s)$

4.5. $H_2SO_4(aq) + 2\, LiOH(aq) \longrightarrow 2\, H_2O(l) + Li_2SO_4(aq)$
$H^+(aq) + OH^-(aq) \longrightarrow H_2O(aq)$

4.6. $2\, HBr(aq) + K_2SO_3(aq) \longrightarrow H_2O(l) + SO_2(g) + 2\, KBr(aq)$

4.6. For More Practice
$2\, H^+(aq) + S^{2-}(aq) \longrightarrow H_2S(g)$

4.7. **a.** Cr = 0.
b. $Cr^{3+} = +3$.
c. $Cl^- = -1, C = +4$.
d. $Br = -1, Sr = +2$.
e. $O = -2, S = +6$.
f. $O = -2, N = +5$.

4.8. **a.** This is a redox reaction in which Li is the reducing agent (it is oxidized) and Cl_2 is the oxidizing agent (it is reduced).
b. This is a redox reaction in which Al is the reducing agent and Sn^{2+} is the oxidizing agent.
c. This is not a redox reaction because no oxidation states change.
d. This is a redox reaction in which carbon is the reducing agent and oxygen is the oxidizing agent.

4.2. Conceptual Connection
(d) Since oxidation and reduction must occur together, an increase in the oxidation state of a reactant will always be accompanied by a decrease in the oxidation state of a reactant.

4.9. $Cr(s) + 2\, H^+(aq) \longrightarrow 2\, Cr^{2+}(aq) + H_2(g)$

4.9. For More Practice
$Cu(s) + 4\,H^{+}(aq) + 2\,NO_3^{-}(aq) \longrightarrow Cu^{2+}(aq) + 2\,NO_2(g) + 2\,H_2O(l)$

4.10. $3\,ClO^{-}(aq) + 2\,Cr(OH)_4^{-}(aq) + 2\,OH^{-}(aq) \longrightarrow 3\,Cl^{-}(aq) + 2\,CrO_4^{2-}(aq) + 5\,H_2O(l)$

4.11. $2\,ClO_2 + H_2O \rightarrow ClO_2^{-} + ClO_3 + 2\,H^{+}$

4.12. 4.08 g HCl

4.12. For More Practice
22 kg HNO_3

4.3. Conceptual Connection
(c) Since each O_2 molecule reacts with 4 Na atoms, 12 Na atoms are required to react with 3 O_2 molecules.

4.4. Conceptual Connection
(c) Nitrogen is the limiting reactant, and there is enough nitrogen to make 4 NH_3 molecules. Hydrogen is in excess, and two hydrogen molecules remain after the reactants have reacted as completely as possible.

4.13. H_2 is the limiting reactant, since it produces the least amount of NH_3. Therefore, 29.4 kg NH_3 is the theoretical yield.

4.14. CO is the limiting reactant, since it only produces 114 g Fe. Therefore, 114 g Fe is the theoretical yield; percentage yield = 63.4% yield

4.5. Conceptual Connection
The limiting reactant is the 1 mol H_2O, which is completely consumed. The 1 mol of H_2O requires 3 mol of NO_2 to completely react; therefore, 2 mol NO_2 remain after the reaction is complete.

4.15. 0.214 mol L^{-1} $NaNO_3$

4.15. For More Practice
44.6 g KBr

4.16. 402 g $C_{12}H_{22}O_{11}$

4.16. For More Practice
221 mL of KCl solution

4.6. Conceptual Connection
(b) The mass of a solution is equal to the mass of the solute plus the mass of the solvent. Although the solute seems to disappear, it really does not, and its mass becomes part of the mass of the solution, in accordance with the law of mass conservation.

4.17. 667 mL

4.17. For More Practice
0.105 L

4.18. 51.4 mL HNO_3 solution

4.18. For More Practice
0.170 g CO_2

Chapter 5

5.1. 1.005 bar, 753.8 Torr

5.1. For More Practice
1.3×10^{-2} mbar

5.2. 2.1 bar at a depth of approximately 11 m.

5.3. 123 mL

5.4. 11.3 L

5.5. 1.65 bar, 23.9 psi

5.6. 16.0 L

5.6. For More Practice
1.30×10^{3} mbar

5.1. Conceptual Connection
(a) Since 1 g of H_2 contains the greatest number of moles (due to H_2 having the lowest molar mass of the listed gases), and since one mole of *any* ideal gas occupies the same volume, the H_2 will occupy the greatest volume.

5.7. $d = 4.91\ g\ L^{-1}$

5.7. For More Practice
44.6 g mol^{-1}

5.8. 70.8 g mol^{-1}
5.9. 6.10×10^{-2} mol
5.10. 4.2 bar
5.11. 12.0 mg H_2
5.12. 82.3 g Ag_2O
5.12. For More Practice
7.10 g
5.13. 6.61 L O_2
5.2. Conceptual Connection
(b) Since the total number of gas molecules decreases, the total pressure—the sum of all the partial pressures—must also decrease.
5.14. $u_{rms} = 238 \text{ m s}^{-1}$
5.3. Conceptual Connection
(c) Since the temperature and the volume are both constant, the ideal gas law tells us that the pressure depends solely on the number of particles. Sample (c) has the greatest number of particles per unit volume, and therefore has the greatest pressure. The pressures of (a) and (b) at a given temperature are identical. Even though the particles in (b) are more massive than those in (a), they have the same average kinetic energy at a given temperature. The particles in (b) move more slowly than those in (a), and so exert the same pressure as the particles in (a).
5.15. $\frac{\text{rate}_{H_2}}{\text{rate}_{Kr}} = 6.44$
5.4. Conceptual Connection
The temperature of the samples must follow the order of A < B < C. Curve A is the lowest temperature curve because it deviates the most from ideality. The tendency for the intermolecular forces in carbon dioxide to lower the pressure (relative to that of an ideal gas) is greatest at low temperature (because the molecules are moving more slowly and are therefore less able to overcome the intermolecular forces). As a result, the curve that dips the lowest must correspond to the lowest temperature, and this is used to differentiate between curves B and C as well.

Chapter 6

6.1. Conceptual Connection
The correct answer is **(a)**. When ΔU_{sys} is negative, energy flows out of the system and into the surroundings. The energy increase in the surroundings must exactly match the decrease in the system.
6.2. Conceptual Connection
(a) heat, sign is positive **(b)** work, sign is positive **(c)** heat, sign is negative
6.1. $\Delta U = 71$ J
6.2. $C_s = 0.38 \frac{\text{J}}{\text{g} \cdot {}^\circ\text{C}}$
The specific heat capacity of gold is 0.128 J/g · °C; therefore the rock cannot be pure gold.
6.2. For More Practice
$T_f = 42.1$ °C
6.3. Conceptual Connection
Bring the water; it has the higher heat capacity and will therefore release more heat as it cools.
6.3. 37.9 g Cu
6.4. Conceptual Connection
(c) The specific heat capacity of substance B is twice that of A, but since the mass of B is half that of A, the quantity $m \times C_s$ will be identical for both substances so that the final temperature is exactly midway between the two initial temperatures.
6.4. For Practice
$\Delta U = -997$ J
6.5. 39.6 kJ mol^{-1}

6.6. $\Delta_r U = -3.91 \times 10^3$ kJ/mol C_6H_{14}

6.6. For More Practice

$C_{cal} = 4.55$ kJ °C^{-1}

6.5. Conceptual Connection

$\Delta_r H$ represents only the heat exchanged; therefore $\Delta_r H = -2658$ kJ mol^{-1}. $\Delta_r U$ represents the heat *and work* exchanged; therefore $\Delta_r U = -2661$ kJ mol^{-1}. The signs of both are negative because heat and work are flowing out of the system and into the surroundings. Notice that the values of $\Delta_r H$ and $\Delta_r U$ are similar in magnitude, as is the case for many chemical reactions.

6.7. $\Delta_r U = \Delta_r H = -2348$ kJ mol^{-1} (amount of gases on both sides of the reaction are the same)

6.6. Conceptual Connection

An endothermic reaction feels cold to the touch because the reaction absorbs heat from the surroundings. When you touch the vessel in which the reaction occurs, you lose heat to the system (the reaction), which makes you feel cold. The heat absorbed by the reaction (from your body, in this case) does not go to increasing its temperature, but rather becomes potential energy stored in chemical bonds.

6.8. -2.06×10^3 kJ

6.8. For More Practice

33 g C_4H_{10}

99 g CO_2

6.9. $\Delta_r H = -68$ kJ mol^{-1}

6.7. Conceptual Connection

The value of q_r with the greater magnitude (−12.5 kJ) must have come from the bomb calorimeter. Recall that $\Delta_r U = q_r + w_r$. In a bomb calorimeter, the energy change that occurs in the course of the reaction all takes the form of heat (q). In a coffee-cup calorimeter, the amount of energy released as heat may be smaller because some of the energy may be used to do work (w).

6.10. $N_2O(g) + NO_2(g) \longrightarrow 3\ NO(g)$, $\Delta_r H = 157.6$ kJ mol^{-1}

6.10. For More Practice

$3\ H_2(g) + O_3(g) \longrightarrow 3\ H_2O(g)$, $\Delta_r H = -868.1$ kJ mol^{-1}

6.11. a. $Na(s) + \frac{1}{2}Cl_2(g) \longrightarrow NaCl(s)$, $\Delta_f H^\circ = -411.2$ kJ mol^{-1}

b. $Pb(s) + N_2(g) + 3\ O_2(g) \longrightarrow Pb(NO_3)_2(s)$, $\Delta_f H^\circ = -451.9$ kJ mol^{-1}

6.12. $\Delta_r H^\circ = -851.5$ kJ mol^{-1}

6.13. $\Delta_r H^\circ = -1648.4$ kJ mol^{-1}

111 kJ emitted (−111 kJ)

6.14. 1.3×10^2 kg

Chapter 7

7.1. 5.83×10^{14} s^{-1}

7.2. 2.64×10^{20} photons

7.2. For More Practice

435 nm

7.1. Conceptual Connection

(i) microwaves, visible light, X-rays

(ii) X-rays, visible light, microwaves

(iii) X-rays, visible light, microwaves

7.3. Photoelectrons are emitted with KE $= 6.0 \times 10^{-20}$ J

7.2. Conceptual Connection

Observation A corresponds to 632 nm; observation B corresponds to 325 nm; and observation C corresponds to 455 nm. The shortest wavelength of light (highest energy per photon) must correspond to the photoelectrons with the greatest kinetic energy. The longest wavelength of light (lowest energy per photon) must correspond to the instance where no photoelectrons were observed.

7.4. 397 nm

7.4. For More Practice

$n = 1$

7.3. Conceptual Connection
(c) The energy difference between $n = 3$ and $n = 2$ is greatest because the energy differences get closer together with increasing n. The greater energy difference results in an emitted photon of greater energy and therefore shorter wavelength.

7.4. Conceptual Connection
Because of the baseball's large mass, its de Broglie wavelength is minuscule. (For a 150 g baseball, it is on the order of 10^{-34} m.) This minuscule wavelength is insignificant compared to the size of the baseball itself, and therefore its effects are not observable.

7.5. For the 5d orbitals:

$n = 5$

$l = 2$

$m_l = -2, -1, 0, 1, 2$

The 5 integer values for m_l signify that there are five 5d orbitals.

7.6. **a.** l cannot equal 3 if $n = 3$. $l = 2$.
b. m_l cannot equal -2 if $l = 1$. Possible values for $m_l = -1, 0,$ or 1
c. l cannot equal 1 if $n = 1$. $l = 0$

7.5. Conceptual Connection
Atoms are usually drawn as spheres because most atoms contain many electrons occupying a number of different orbitals. Therefore, the shape of an atom is obtained by superimposing all of its orbitals. If we superimpose the s, p, and d orbitals we get a spherical shape, as shown in Figure 7.29.

7.6. Conceptual Connection
(d) is a smaller orbital; it falls off at ~700 pm rather than ~1200 pm like the others represented in (a), (b), and (c). (d), therefore is the 2s orbital. (a) has two nodes; therefore, it is the 3s orbital. For similar reasons, (c) and (b) are the 3p orbital (one node) and 3d orbital (zero nodes), respectively.

7.7. Conceptual Connection
(c) Penetration results in less shielding from nuclear charge and therefore lower energy.

7.7. **a.** Cl $1s^2 2s^2 2p^6 3s^2 3p^5$ or [Ne] $3s^2 3p^5$
b. Si $1s^2 2s^2 2p^6 3s^2 3p^2$ or [Ne] $3s^2 3p^2$
c. Sr $1s^2 2s^2 2p^6 3s^2 3p^6 4s^2 3d^{10} 4p^6 5s^2$ or [Kr] $5s^2$
d. O $1s^2 2s^2 2p^4$ or [He] $2s^2 2p^4$

7.8. There are no unpaired electrons

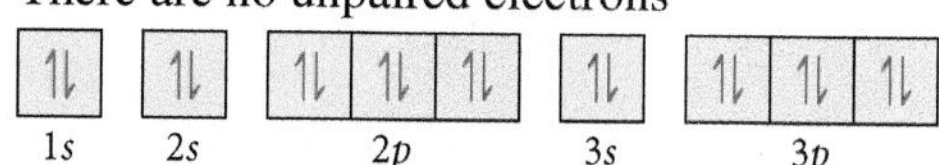

7.8. Conceptual Connection

$$n = 4,\ l = 0,\ m_l = 0,\ m_s = +\frac{1}{2};\ n = 4,\ l = 0,\ m_l = 0,\ m_s = -\frac{1}{2}$$

7.9. [Xe] $6s^2 4f^{14} 5d^6$

7.10. [Kr] $5s^1 4d^5$ (half-filled d sublevel)

7.11. **a.** [Ar] $3d^7$. Co^{2+} is paramagnetic.

Co^{2+} [Ar] [⇅][⇅][↑][↑][↑]
3d

b. [He] $2s^2 2p^6$. N^{3-} is diamagnetic.

N^{3-} [He] [⇅] [⇅][⇅][⇅]
2s 2p

c. [Ne] $3s^2 3p^6$. Ca^{2+} is diamagnetic.

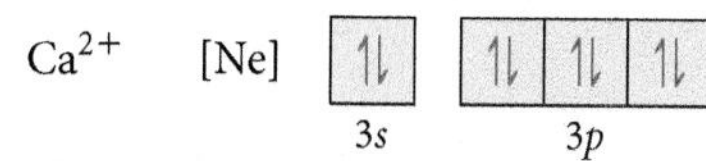

d. In^{3-} [Kr] $4d^{10}$

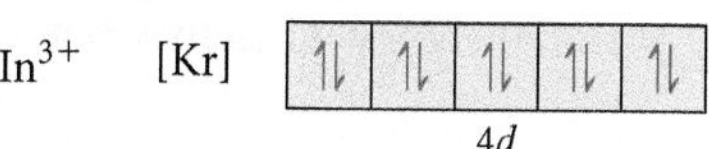

Chapter 8

8.1. $1s^2\,2s^2\,2p^6\,3s^2\,3p^3$ or [Ne] $3s^2\,3p^3$. The five electrons in the $3s^2\,3p^3$ orbitals are the valence electrons, while the 10 electrons in the $1s^2\,2s^2\,2p^6$ orbitals belong to the core.

8.2. Bi [Xe] $6s^2\,4f^{14}\,5d^{10}\,6p^3$

8.2. For More Practice

I [Kr] $5s^2\,4d^{10}\,5p^5$

8.3. **a.** $S = 3.80$; $Z_{eff} = 5.20$ **b.** $S = 11.25$; $Z_{eff} = 6.75$ **c.** $S = 34.80$; $Z_{eff} = 2.20$

8.1. Conceptual Connection

The element W has the larger radius because it is in the third transition row and Fe is in the first. Atomic radii increase from the first to the second transition row and stay roughly constant from the second to the third.

8.4. **a.** Sn

b. cannot predict

c. W

d. Se

8.4. For More Practice

Rb > Ca > Si > S > F

8.5. **a.** K

b. F^-

c. Cl^-

8.5. For More Practice

$Cl^- > Ar > Ca^{2+}$

8.2. Conceptual Connection

The isotopes of an element all have the same radii for two reasons: (1) neutrons are found entirely within the nucleus and are negligibly small compared to the size of an atom, and therefore extra neutrons do not increase atomic size; and (2) neutrons have no charge and therefore do not attract electrons in the way that protons do.

8.6. **a.** I

b. Ca

c. cannot predict

d. F

8.6. For More Practice

F > S > Si > Ca > Rb

8.3. Conceptual Connection

As you can see from the successive ionization energies of any element, valence electrons are held most loosely and can therefore be transferred or shared most easily. Core electrons, on the other hand, are held tightly and are not easily transferred or shared. Consequently, valence electrons are most important to chemical bonding.

8.7. **a.** $2\,Al(s) + 3\,Cl_2(g) \longrightarrow 2\,AlCl_3(s)$

b. $2\,Li(s) + 2\,H_2O(l) \longrightarrow 2\,Li^+(aq) + 2\,OH^-(aq) + H_2(g)$

c. $H_2(g) + Br_2(l) \longrightarrow 2\,HBr(g)$

Chapter 9

9.1. :C≡O:

9.2.

```
   O
   ‖
   C
 ╱   ╲
H     H
```

9.1. Conceptual Connection

The reasons that atoms form bonds are complex. One contributing factor is the lowering of their potential energy. The octet rule is just a handy way to predict the combinations of atoms that will have a lower potential energy when they bond together.

9.3. $\left[\begin{array}{c} \text{H} \\ | \\ \text{H—N—H} \\ | \\ \text{H} \end{array}\right]^+$

9.4. KI < LiBr < CaO

9.4. For More Practice

$MgCl_2$

9.2. Conceptual Connection

We would expect MgO to have the higher melting point because, in our bonding model, the magnesium and oxygen ions are held together in a crystalline lattice by charges of 2+ for magnesium and 2− for oxygen. In contrast, the NaCl lattice is held together by charges of 1+ for sodium and 1− for chlorine. The experimentally measured melting points of these compounds are 801 °C for NaCl and 2852 °C for MgO, in accordance with our model.

9.3. Conceptual Connection

(**b**) In a highly exothermic reaction, the energy needed to break bonds is less than the energy released when the new bonds form, resulting in a net release of energy.

9.5. $CH_3OH(g) + \frac{3}{2}O_2(g) \longrightarrow CO_2(g) + 2\,H_2O(g)$

$\Delta_r H = -641\text{ kJ mol}^{-1}$

9.5. For More Practice

$\Delta_r H = -8.0 \times 10^1\text{ kJ mol}^{-1}$

9.6. **a.** pure covalent

b. ionic

c. polar covalent

9.4. Conceptual Connection

(**b**) We are given that the dipole moment of the HCl bond is about 1 D and that the bond length is 127 pm. Previously, we calculated the dipole moment for a 130 pm bond that is 100% ionic to be about 6.2 D. We can therefore estimate the bond's ionic character as 1/6 × 100%, which is closest to 15%.

9.7. $[:\ddot{O}{=}\ddot{N}{-}\ddot{O}:]^- \longleftrightarrow [:\ddot{O}{-}\ddot{N}{=}\ddot{O}:]^-$

9.8.

Structure	(a)			(b)			(c)		
	:N̈=N=Ö:			:N≡N—Ö:			:N̈—N≡O:		
number of valence e^-	5	5	6	5	5	6	5	5	6
number of nonbonding e^-	−4	−0	−4	−2	−0	−6	−6	−0	−2
1/2 (number of bonding e^-)	−2	−4	−2	−3	−4	−1	−1	−4	−3
Formal charge	**−1**	**+1**	**0**	**0**	**+1**	**−1**	**−2**	**+1**	**+1**

Structure (b) contributes the most to the correct overall structure of N_2O.

9.8. For More Practice

The nitrogen is +1, the singly bonded oxygen atoms are −1, and the double-bonded oxygen atom has no formal charge.

9.9. XeF_4 (four :F̈: atoms bonded to Xe, Xe with two lone pairs) ⟷ XeF_4 with formal charges: Xe +2, two F atoms −1 each (not bonded to Xe)

9.10.

H—Ö—P(=O:)(—Ö—H)—Ö—H (P double bonded to :O:, single bonded to :Ö—H below) ⟷ H—Ö—P^{+1}(—:Ö:$^{-1}$)(—:Ö:—H)—Ö—H

Chapter 10

10.1. Conceptual Connection
The geometry of a molecule is determined by how the **terminal atoms** are arranged around the central atom, which is in turn determined by how the electron groups are arranged around the *central* atom. The electron groups on the terminal atoms do not affect this arrangement.

10.1. Electron and molecular geometries are both tetrahedral.

10.2. Conceptual Connection
(d) All electron groups on the central atom (or interior atoms, if there is more than one) determine the shape of a molecule according to VSEPR theory.

10.2. bent, ClNO bond angle <109.5°

10.3. linear, III bond angle = 180°

10.4.

Atom	Number of Electron Groups	Number of Lone Paris	Molecular Geometry
Carbon (left)	4	0	Tetrahedral
Carbon (right)	3	0	Trigonal planar
Oxygen	4	2	Bent

:O:
H C H
H C O
H

10.5. The molecule is nonpolar.

10.3. Conceptual Connection
(a) In Lewis theory, a covalent chemical bond is the sharing of electrons (represented by dots). **(b)** In valence bond theory, a covalent chemical bond is the overlap of half-filled atomic orbitals. **(c)** The answers are different because Lewis theory and valence bond theory are different *models* for chemical bonding. They both make useful and often similar predictions, but the assumptions of each model are different, and so are their respective descriptions of a chemical bond.

10.4. Conceptual Connection
Applying valence bond theory, we see that a double bond is actually composed of two different kinds of bonds, one σ and one π. The orbital overlap in the *p* bond is side-to-side between two *p* orbitals and, consequently, not as efficient as the end-to-end overlap in an *s* bond. Since the strength of the bond depends in part on the degree of overlap between the orbitals and the π bond is weaker than an *s* bond, the bond energy of a double bond is less than twice the bond energy of a single σ bond.

10.6.

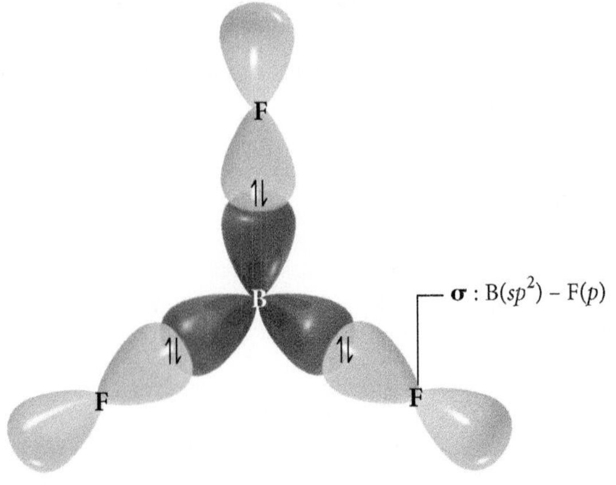

10.7. Since there are only two electron groups around the central atom (C), the electron geometry is linear. According to Table 10.3, the corresponding hybridization on the carbon atom is *sp*.

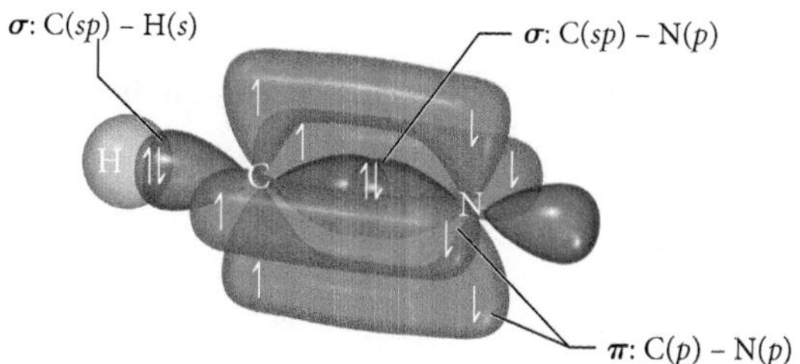

10.8. Since there are only two electron groups about the central atom (C), the electron geometry is linear. The hybridization on C is *sp*.

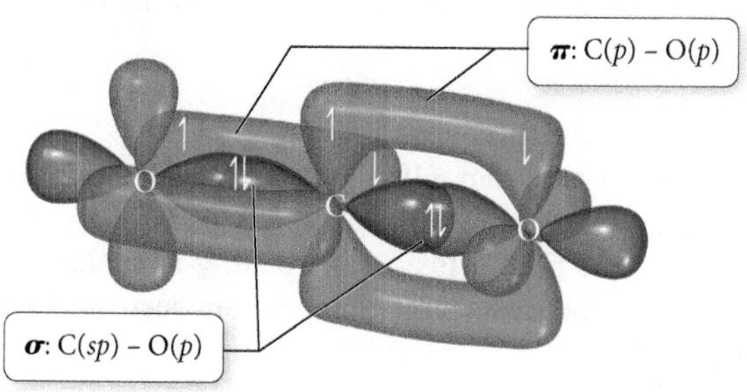

10.8. For More Practice
The carbon atom is sp^2 hybridized.

10.9. H_2^+ bond order $= +\frac{1}{2}$
Since the bond order is positive, the H_2^+ ion should be stable; however, the bond order of H_2^+ is lower than the bond order of H_2 (bond order = 1). Therefore, the bond in H_2^+ is weaker than in H_2.

10.10. The bond order of N_2^+ is 2.5, which is lower than that of the N_2 molecule (bond order = 3), therefore the bond is weaker. The MO diagram shows that the N_2^+ ion has one unpaired electron and is therefore paramagnetic.

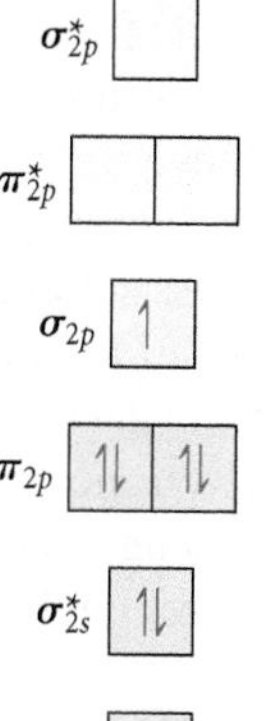

10.10. For More Practice
The bond order of Ne_2 is 0, which indicates that dineon does not exist.

10.11. NO^+ has the same energy level ordering and number of valence electrons (i.e., 10) as N_2. Therefore, the bonding description is the same as in N_2: The bond order of NO^+ is 3. NO^+ is diamagnetic.

10.5. Conceptual Connection
In MO theory, atoms will join together (or bond) when the electrons in the atoms can lower their energy by occupying the molecular orbitals of the resultant molecule. Unlike Lewis theory or valence bond theory, the chemical "bonds" in MO theory are not localized between atoms, but spread throughout the entire molecule.

Chapter 11

11.1. Conceptual Connection
(**a**) When water boils, it simply changes state from liquid to gas. Water molecules do not decompose during boiling.

11.1. (**b**) and (**c**)

11.2. HF has a higher boiling point than HCl because, unlike HCl, HF is able to form hydrogen bonds.

11.3. 5.83×10^3 kJ

11.3. For More Practice
47 °C

11.2. Conceptual Connection
(**b**) Although the *rate of vaporization* increases with increasing surface area, the *vapour pressure* of a liquid is independent of surface area. An increase in surface increases both the rate of vaporization and the rate of condensation—the effects of surface area exactly cancel and the vapour pressure does not change.

11.4. 33.8 kJ mol^{-1}

11.5. 9.35 bar

11.3. Conceptual Connection
The warming of the ice from −10°C to 0 °C absorbs only 20.9 J/g of ice. The melting of the ice, however, absorbs about 334 J/g of ice. (You can obtain this value by dividing the heat of fusion of water by its molar mass.) Therefore, the melting of the ice produces a larger temperature decrease in the water than does the warming of the ice.

11.4. Conceptual Connection
(**b**) The solid will sublime into a gas. Since the pressure is below the triple point, the liquid state is not stable.

11.6. 7.18 g cm^{-3}

Chapter 12

12.1.
a. not soluble
b. soluble
c. not soluble
d. not soluble

12.1. Conceptual Connection
The first alcohol on the list is methanol, which is highly polar and forms hydrogen bonds with water. It is miscible in water and has only limited solubility in hexane, which is nonpolar. However, as the carbon chain gets longer in the series of alcohols, the OH group becomes less important relative to the growing nonpolar carbon chain. Therefore the alcohols become progressively less soluble in water and more soluble in hexane. This table demonstrates the rule of thumb *like dissolves like.* Methanol is like water and therefore dissolves in water. It is unlike hexane and therefore has limited solubility in hexane. As you move down the list, the alcohols become increasingly like hexane and increasingly unlike water and therefore become increasingly soluble in hexane and increasingly insoluble in water.

12.2. Conceptual Connection
(**b**) Some potassium bromide precipitates out of solution. The solubility of most solids decreases with decreasing temperature. However, the solubility of gases increases with decreasing temperature. Therefore, the nitrogen becomes more soluble and will not bubble out of solution.

12.3. Conceptual Connection
Ammonia is the only compound on the list that is polar, so we would expect its solubility in water to be greater than those of the other gases (which are all nonpolar).

12.2. 2.7×10^{-4} mol L^{-1}

12.3. 42.5 g $C_{12}H_{22}O_{11}$

12.3. For More Practice

3.3×10^4 L

12.4. **a.** $M = 0.415$ mol L^{-1}

b. $m = 0.443\ m$

c. % by mass = 13.2%

d. $\chi = 0.00793$

e. mol % = 0.793%

12.5. 0.600 mol L^{-1}

12.5. For More Practice

0.651 m

12.6. 22.5 Torr

12.6. For More Practice

0.144

12.4. Conceptual Connection

The solute–solvent interactions must be stronger than the solute–solute and solvent–solvent interactions. The stronger interactions lower the vapour pressure from the expected ideal value of 150 mmHg.

12.7. **a.** $P_{benzene} = 26.6$ Torr

$P_{toluene} = 20.4$ Torr

b. 47.0 Torr

c. 52.5% benzene; 47.5% toluene

The vapour will be richer in the more volatile component, which in this case is benzene.

12.8. $T_f = -4.8$ °C

12.9. 101.84 °C

12.10. 12 bar

12.5. Conceptual Connection

(c) The 0.50 mol L^{-1} $MgCl_2$ solution will have the highest boiling point because it has the highest concentration of particles. We expect 1 mol of $MgCl_2$ to form 3 mol of particles in solution because it is an ionic compound that dissociates to Mg^{2+} and 2 Cl^- in aqueous solution (although it effectively forms slightly fewer).

12.11. −0.63 °C

12.12. 0.014 mol NaCl

Chapter 13

13.1. $\dfrac{\Delta[H_2O_2]}{\Delta t} = -4.40 \times 10^{-3}\ \text{mol L}^{-1}\ \text{s}^{-1}$

$\dfrac{\Delta[I_3^-]}{\Delta t} = 4.40 \times 10^{-3}\ \text{mol L}^{-1}\ \text{s}^{-1}$

13.2. **a.** Rate $= k[CHCl_3][Cl_2]^{1/2}$. (Fractional-order reactions are not common but are occasionally observed.)

b. $3.5\ \text{mol}^{-1/2}\ \text{L}^{1/2}\ \text{s}^{-1}$

13.1. Conceptual Connection

(c) All three mixtures have the same total number of molecules, but mixture (c) has the greatest number of NO molecules. Since the reaction is second order in NO and only first order in O_2, mixture (c) has the fastest initial rate.

13.3. 5.78×10^{-2} mol L^{-1}

13.4. 0.0277 mol L^{-1}

13.5. 1.64×10^{-3} mol L^{-1}

13.6. 87.7 s

13.2. Conceptual Connection

(c) The reaction is most likely second order because its rate depends on the concentration (therefore it cannot be zero order), and its half-life depends on the initial concentration (therefore it cannot be first order). For a second-order reaction, a doubling of the initial concentration results in the quadrupling of the rate.

13.7. $2.09 \times 10^{-5}\ \text{L mol}^{-1}\ \text{s}^{-1}$

13.8. $6.13 \times 10^{-4}\ \text{L mol}^{-1}\ \text{s}^{-1}$

13.3. Conceptual Connection

(c) Since the reactants in part (a) are atoms, the orientation factor should be about one. The reactants in parts (b) and (c) are both molecules, so we expect orientation factors of less than one. Since the reactants in (b) are symmetrical, we would not expect the collision to have as specific an orientation requirement as in (c), where the reactants are asymmetrical and must therefore collide in such way that a hydrogen atom is in close proximity to another hydrogen atom. Therefore, we expect (c) to have the smallest orientation factor.

13.9. Overall reaction: $2\ NO + Cl_2 \longrightarrow 2\ NOCl$

$$\text{Rate} = \frac{k_2k_1[NO]^2[Cl_2]}{k_{-1} + k_2[NO]}$$

The rate law could be further simplified if more information about the mechanism was available. For example, if it was known that step 2 was rate-determining, then the rate law would become:

$$\text{Rate} = \frac{k_2k_1}{k_{-1}}[NO]^2[Cl_2]$$

Chapter 14

14.1. $K_c = 10.9\ \text{mol}^{-2}\ \text{L}^2;\ K_P = 4.39 \times 10^{-3}\ \text{bar}^{-2}$

14.2. $K_P = \dfrac{P_{Cl_2}^{\ 2}}{P_{HCl}^{\ 4}P_{O_2}},\ K = K_P \times (P°)^3$

14.2. For More Practice

$K = \dfrac{[Fe^{2+}]P_{H_2}}{[H^+]^2} \times \dfrac{c°}{P°}$. The last term is required to make the equilibrium constant unitless. While one can write an expression for K_c, the numerical value will not equal the thermodynamic equilibrium constant. The most important concept here is that all solutes are in terms of concentration, and all gases are in terms of partial pressure in the equilibrium constant.

14.1. Conceptual Connection

(b) Since Δn for gaseous reactants and products is zero, K_p equals K_c.

14.2. Conceptual Connection

(b) The reaction mixture will contain 1 mol of A and 10 mol of B so that $[B] > [A] = 10$.

14.3. 2.1×10^{-13}

14.3. For More Practice

1.4×10^2

14.4. $K = 0.0141$

14.5. $K = 4.8$

14.6. $Q = 0.49, Q > K$, therefore the reaction will proceed left toward reactants.

14.3. Conceptual Connection

(c) Since N_2O_4 and NO_2 are both in their standard states, they each have a partial pressure of 1.0 bar. Consequently, $Q_P = 1$. Since $K_P = 0.15, Q_P > K_P$, and the reaction proceeds to the left.

14.7. $P_I = 0.077$ bar

14.8. $P_{N_2} = 0.092$ bar, $P_{O_2} = 0.092$ bar, $P_{NO} = 0.066$ bar

14.9. $P_{NO_2} = 0.150$ bar, $P_{N_2O_4} = 0.125$ bar

14.10. $[Fe^{3+}] = 0.106\ \text{mol L}^{-1}$, $[SCN^-] = 0.006\ \text{mol L}^{-1}$, and $[Fe(SCN)^{2+}] = 0.569\ \text{mol L}^{-1}$

14.11. $P_{H_2S} = 1.00$ bar, $P_{H_2} = 1.00$ bar, $P_{S_2} = 5.13 \times 10^{-6}$ bar

14.12. Using the *x is small* approximation, $P_{H_2S} = 1.00 \times 10^{-3}$ bar, $P_{H_2} = 7.58 \times 10^{-6}$ bar, $P_{S_2} = 0.100$ bar

14.4. Conceptual Connection

(a) The *x is small* approximation is most likely to apply to a reaction with a small equilibrium constant and an initial concentration of reactant that is not too small. The bigger the equilibrium constant and the smaller the initial concentration of reactant, the less likely that the *x is small* approximation will apply.

14.13. Adding Br_2 increases the concentration of Br_2, causing a shift to the left (away from the Br_2). Adding BrNO increases the concentration of BrNO, causing a shift to the right.

14.14. Decreasing the volume causes the reaction to shift right. Increasing the volume causes the reaction to shift left.

14.15. If we increase the temperature, the reaction shifts to the left. If we decrease the temperature, the reaction shifts to the right.

Chapter 15

15.1. **a.** H_2O donates a proton to C_5H_5N, making it the acid. The conjugate base is therefore OH^-. Since C_5H_5N accepts the proton, it is the base and becomes the conjugate acid $C_5H_5NH^+$.

b. Since HNO_3 donates a proton to H_2O, it is the acid, making NO_3^- the conjugate base. Since H_2O is the proton acceptor, it is the base and becomes the conjugate acid, H_3O^+

15.1. Conceptual Connection

(b) H_2SO_4 and H_2SO_3 are two different acids, not a conjugate acid–base pair.

15.2. Conceptual Connection

ClO^-, because the weaker the acid, the stronger the conjugate base.

15.2. **a.** $[H_3O^+] = 6.7 \times 10^{-13}$ mol L^{-1}

Since $[H_3O^+] < [OH^-]$, the solution is basic.

b. $[H_3O^+] = 1.0 \times 10^{-7}$ mol L^{-1}

Neutral solution

c. $[H_3O^+] = 1.2 \times 10^{-5}$ mol L^{-1}

Since $[H_3O^+] > [OH^-]$, the solution is acidic.

15.3. **a.** 8.02 (basic)

b. 11.85 (basic)

15.4. 4.3×10^{-9} mol L^{-1}

15.5. 1.8×10^{-2} mol L^{-1}

15.6. 3.28

15.7. 2.72

15.8. 1.8×10^{-6}

15.3. Conceptual Connection

(c) The validity of the *x is small* approximation depends on both the value of the equilibrium constant and the initial concentration—the closer that these are to one another, the less likely the approximation will be valid.

15.9. 0.85%

15.4. Conceptual Connection

Solution **(c)** has the greatest percent ionization because percent ionization increases with decreasing weak acid concentration. Solution **(b)** has the lowest pH because the equilibrium H_3O^+ concentration increases with increasing weak acid concentration.

15.10. 2.7×10^{-7} mol L^{-1}

15.5. Conceptual Connection

(a) A weak acid solution will usually be less than 5% dissociated. Therefore, since HCl is the only strong acid, the 1.0 mol L^{-1} solution is much more acidic than either a weak acid that is twice as concentrated or a combination of two weak acids with the same concentrations.

15.11. $[OH^-] = 0.020$ mol L^{-1}

pH = 12.30

15.12. $[OH^-] = 1.2 \times 10^{-2}$ mol L^{-1}

pH = 12.08

15.13. **a.** weak base

b. pH-neutral

15.14. 9.07

15.15. **a.** pH-neutral

b. weak acid

c. weak acid

15.16. **a.** basic
b. acidic
c. pH-neutral
d. acidic

15.17. 3.83

15.18. $[SO_4^{2-}] = 0.00386 \text{ mol L}^{-1}$
pH = 1.945

15.19. $5.6 \times 10^{-11} \text{ mol L}^{-1}$

15.6. Conceptual Connection
(a) Since the carbon atom in (a) is bonded to another oxygen atom which draws electron density away from the C—H bond (weakening and polarizing it), and the carbon atom in (b) is bonded only to other hydrogen atoms, the proton in structure (a) is more acidic.

15.7. Conceptual Connection
The most basic nitrogen is (d) because it is attached to an electron-donating methyl group. The least basic nitrogen is (b) because it is attached to a highly electronegative fluorine atom. Since nitrogen (c) is in close proximity to the electron-donating methyl group, it is more basic than (a), which is close to the electron withdrawing fluorine. d > c > a > b

Chapter 16

16.1. pH = 4.44

16.1. For More Practice
pH = 3.44

16.2. 9.04

16.1. Conceptual Connection
(a) Since the pH of the buffer is less than the pK_a of the acid, the buffer must contain more acid than base ($[HA] > [A^-]$). In order to raise the pH of the buffer from 4.25 to 4.72, you must add more of the weak base (adding a base will make the buffer solution more basic).

16.3. 4.87

16.3. For More Practice
4.65

16.2. Conceptual Connection
(b) Since acid is added to the buffer, the pH will become slightly lower (slightly more acidic). Answer (a) reflects too large a change in pH for a buffer, and answers (c) and (d) are in the wrong direction.

16.4. 9.68

16.4. For More Practice
9.56

16.5. hypochlorous acid (HClO); 2.4 g NaClO

16.3. Conceptual Connection
(a) Adding 0.050 mol of HCl will destroy the buffer because it will react with all of the NaF, leaving no conjugate base in the buffer mixture.

16.6. 1.74

16.7. 8.04

16.4. Conceptual Connection
(c) Since the volumes and concentrations of all three acids are the same, the volume of NaOH required to reach the first equivalence point (and the only equivalence point for titrations i and iii) is the same for all three titrations.

16.8. $2.30 \times 10^{-6} \text{ mol L}^{-1}$

16.9. 5.3×10^{-13}

16.10. $1.21 \times 10^{-5} \text{ mol L}^{-1}$

16.11. $FeCO_3$ will be more soluble in an acidic solution than $PbBr_2$ because the CO_3^{2-} ion is a basic anion, whereas Br^- is the conjugate base of a strong acid (HBr) and is therefore pH-neutral.

16.12. $Q > K_{sp}$; therefore, a precipitate forms.

16.13. $2.9 \times 10^{-6} \text{ mol L}^{-1}$

16.14. **a.** AgCl precipitates first; $[NaCl] = 7.1 \times 10^{-9} \text{ mol L}^{-1}$

b. $[Ag^+]$ is 1.5×10^{-8} mol L^{-1} when $PbCl_2$ begins to precipitate, and $[Pb^{2+}]$ is 0.085 mol L^{-1}.

16.15. 9.6×10^{-6} mol L^{-1}

16.5. Conceptual Connection

(c) Only NaCN contains an anion (CN^-) that forms a complex ion with Cu2$^+$ [from Table 16.3 we can see that $K_f = 1.0 \times 10^{25}$ for $[Cu(CN)_4{}^{2-}]$. Therefore, the presence of CN^- will drive the dissolution reaction of CuS.

Chapter 17

17.1. a. positive
b. negative
c. positive

17.2. a. -548 J K^{-1} mol^{-1}
b. ΔS_{sys} is negative.
c. ΔS_{univ} is negative, and the reaction is not spontaneous.

17.2. For More Practice

375 K

17.1 Conceptual Connection

Biological systems do not violate the second law of thermodynamics. The key to understanding this concept is realizing that entropy changes in the system can be negative as long as the entropy change of the universe is positive. Biological systems can decrease their own entropy, but only at the expense of creating more entropy in the surroundings (which they do primarily by emitting the heat they generate by their metabolic processes). Thus, for any biological process, ΔS_{univ} is positive.

17.3. $\Delta G = -101.6 \times 10^3$ J mol^{-1}

Therefore, the reaction is spontaneous. Since both $\Delta_r H$ and $\Delta_r S$ are negative, as the temperature increases, $\Delta_r G$ will become more positive.

17.2 Conceptual Connection

(a) Sublimation is endothermic (it requires energy to overcome the intermolecular forces that hold solid carbon dioxide together), so $\Delta_r H$ is positive. The number of moles of gas increases when the solid turns into a gas, so the entropy of the carbon dioxide increases and $\Delta_r S$ is positive. Since $\Delta_r G = \Delta_r H - T\Delta_r S$, $\Delta_r G$ is positive at low temperature and negative at high temperature.

17.4. -153.2 J K^{-1} mol^{-1}

17.5. $\Delta_r G^\circ = -36.3$ kJ mol^{-1}

Since $\Delta_r G^\circ$ is negative, the reaction is spontaneous at this temperature.

17.6. $\Delta_r G^\circ = -42.1$ kJ mol^{-1}

Since the value of $\Delta_r G^\circ$ at the lowered temperature is more negative (or less positive) (which is -36.3 kJ mol^{-1}), the reaction is more spontaneous.

17.7. $\Delta_r G^\circ = -689.6$ kJ mol^{-1}

Since $\Delta_r G^\circ$ is negative, the reaction is spontaneous at this temperature.

17.7. For More Practice

$\Delta_r G^\circ = -689.7$ kJ mol^{-1} (at 25 °C)

The value calculated for $\Delta_r G^\circ$ from the tabulated values (-689.6 kJ mol^{-1}) is the same, to within 1 in the least significant digit, as the value calculated using the equation for $\Delta_r G^\circ$.

$\Delta_r G^\circ = -649.7$ kJ mol^{-1} (at 500.0 K)

You could not calculate $\Delta_r G^\circ$ at 500.0 K using tabulated $\Delta_f G^\circ$ values because the tabulated values of free energy are calculated at a standard temperature of 298 K, much lower than 500 K.

17.8. $+107.1$ kJ mol^{-1}

17.9. $\Delta_r G = -129$ kJ mol^{-1}

The reaction is more spontaneous under these conditions than under standard conditions because $\Delta_r G$ is more negative than $\Delta_r G^\circ$.

17.3 Conceptual Connection

(a) A high concentration of reactants relative to products will lead to making the term $RT \ln Q$ in Equation 17.14 negative. $\Delta_r G$ will be more negative than $\Delta_r G^\circ$ and the reaction will be more spontaneous.

17.10. $\Delta_r G = -20.3\ \text{kJ mol}^{-1}$, more $PbCl_2$ could dissolve

17.10. For More Practice
$T = 331\ \text{K}$

17.11. $-33.0\ \text{kJ mol}^{-1}$

17.12. $\Delta_r H^\circ = -60.4\ \text{kJ mol}^{-1}$; $\Delta_r S^\circ = -68.4\ \text{J K}^{-1}\text{mol}^{-1}$

17.13. $P_{CO_2} > 0.011\ \text{bar}$

Chapter 18

18.1. 0.31 V

18.2. $E^\circ_{cell} = 0.36\ \text{V}$

18.3. (**a**) The reaction *will* be spontaneous under standard conditions.
(**b**) The reaction *will not* be spontaneous under standard conditions.

18.1. Conceptual Connection
(**d**) The reduction of HNO_3 is listed below the reduction of Br_2 and above the reduction of I_2 in Table 18.1. Since any reduction half-reaction is spontaneous when paired with the reverse of a half-reaction below it in the table, the reduction of HNO_3 is spontaneous when paired with the oxidation ofI^-, but is not spontaneous when paired with the oxidation of Br^-.

18.2. Conceptual Connection
(**c**) Ag falls *above* the half-reaction for the reduction of H^+ but *below* the half-reaction for the reduction of NO_3^- in Table 18.1.

18.4. $\Delta_r G^\circ = 1.1 \times 10^2\ \text{kJ mol}^{-1}$
Since $\Delta_r G^\circ$ is positive, the reaction is not spontaneous.

18.3. Conceptual Connection
(**a**) Br is more electronegative than I. If the two atoms were in competition for the electron, the electron would go to the more electronegative atom (Br). Therefore, I_2 does not spontaneously gain electrons from Br^-.

18.5. 4.5×10^3

18.6. $K = 4.2 \times 10^{45}$

18.4. Conceptual Connection
(**a**) Since $K < 1$, E°_{cell} is negative (under standard conditions, the reaction is not spontaneous). Since $Q < K, E_{cell}$ is positive (the reaction is spontaneous under the nonstandard conditions of the cell).

18.7. $K_{sp} = 2.8 \times 10^{-39}$

18.8. Anode: $2\ H_2O(l) \longrightarrow O_2(g) + 4\ H^+(aq) + 4\ e^-$
Cathode: $2\ H_2O(l) + 2\ e^- \longrightarrow H_2(g) + 2\ OH^-(aq)$

18.9. 6.0×10^1 min

18.5. Conceptual Connection
Cu is the only metal in the list that does not act as a sacrificial anode. This is because Cu is a weaker reducing agent than Fe. Mn, Mg, and Zn are all stronger reducing agents than Fe and thus can serve as sacrificial anodes.

Chapter 19

19.1. ${}^{216}_{84}\text{Po} \longrightarrow {}^{212}_{82}\text{Pb} + {}^{4}_{2}\text{He}$

19.2. **a.** ${}^{235}_{92}\text{U} \longrightarrow {}^{231}_{90}\text{Th} + {}^{4}_{2}\text{He}$
${}^{231}_{90}\text{Th} \longrightarrow {}^{231}_{91}\text{Pa} + {}^{0}_{-1}e$
${}^{231}_{91}\text{Pa} \longrightarrow {}^{227}_{89}\text{Ac} + {}^{4}_{2}\text{He}$
b. ${}^{22}_{11}\text{Na} \longrightarrow {}^{22}_{10}\text{Ne} + {}^{0}_{-1}e$
c. ${}^{76}_{36}\text{Kr} + {}^{0}_{-1}e \longrightarrow {}^{76}_{35}\text{Br}$

19.2. For More Practice
Positron emission (${}^{40}_{19}\text{K} \longrightarrow {}^{40}_{18}\text{Ar} + {}^{0}_{+1}e$) or electron capture (${}^{40}_{19}\text{K} + {}^{0}_{+1}e \longrightarrow {}^{40}_{18}\text{Ar}$)

19.1. Conceptual Connection
(**c**) The arrow labelled x represents a decrease of 2 neutrons and 2 protons, indicative of alpha decay. The arrow labelled y represents a decrease of 1 neutron and an increase of 1 proton, indicative of beta decay.

19.3. **a.** positron emission
b. beta decay
c. positron emission

19.2. Conceptual Connection
(b) The half-life is the time it takes for the number of nuclei to decay to one-half of their original number.

19.4. 10.7 y

19.5. $t = 964$ y
No, the C-14 content suggests that the scroll is from about C.E. 1000, not 500 B.C.E.

19.6. 1.0×10^9 y

19.3. Conceptual Connection

$$2.7593 \times 10^{-11} \frac{\text{J}}{\text{U-235 }\cancel{\text{atom}}} \times \frac{6.0221 \times 10^{23}\text{ U-235 }\cancel{\text{atoms}}}{1\text{ mol U-235}}$$

$$= 1.6617 \times 10^{13}\text{ J/mol U-235}$$

The fission of 1 mol of U-235 produces about 17 billion kJ. This is 17 million times more energetic than a chemical reaction that produces 1000 kJ mol^{-1}.

19.7. Mass defect = 1.934 u
Nuclear binding energy = 7.569 MeV/nucleon

19.4. Conceptual Connection
Lawrencium-256

19.5. Conceptual Connection
Nuclide A. Because nuclide A has a shorter half-life, more of the nuclides will decay, and therefore produce radiation, before they exit the body.

Chapter 20

20.1.

a.

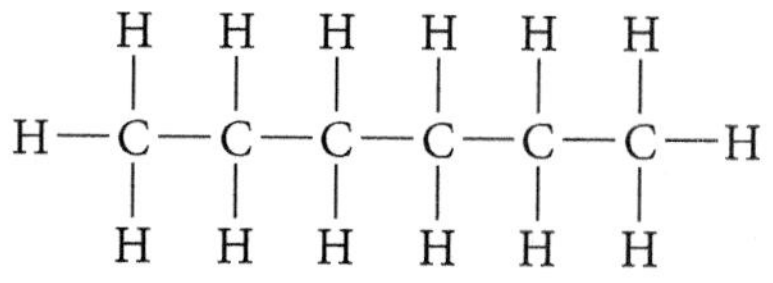

```
    H   H   H   H   H   H
    |   |   |   |   |   |
H — C — C — C — C — C — C — H
    |   |   |   |   |   |
    H   H   H   H   H   H
```

$CH_3—CH_2—CH_2—CH_2—CH_2—CH_3$

b.

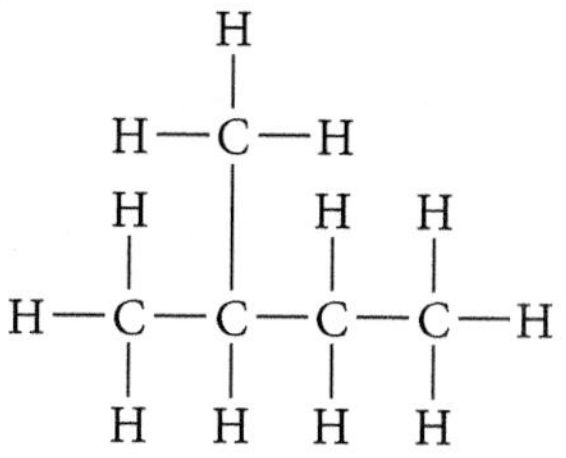

```
        H
        |
    H — C — H
    H   |   H   H
    |   |   |   |
H — C — C — C — C — H
    |   |   |   |
    H   H   H   H
```

$CH_3—CH(CH_3)—CH_2—CH_3$

c.

```
        H  H
         \/
   H      C      H
    \   /   \   /
H — C         C — H
     \       /
H —   C — C   — H
      |    \
      H     H
```

```
        H2
        C
      /   \
   CH2     CH2
     \     /
    H2C — CH2
```

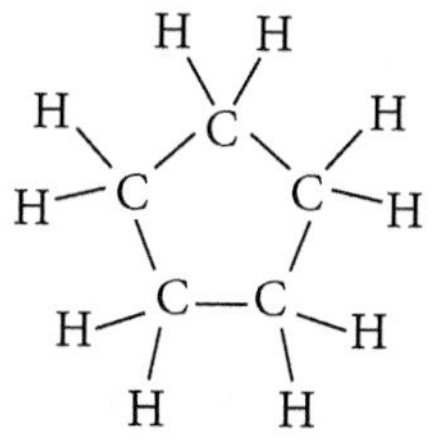

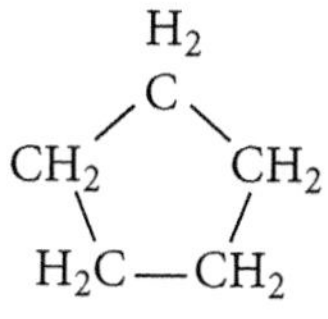

20.1. Conceptual Connection
(c) and **(d)**, which also have the molecular formula C_6H_{12}

20.2. Conceptual Connection
gauche-staggered

20.2. **a.** *Z*
b. *E*
c. *E*

20.3. Conceptual Connection

(b) This structure is the only one that contains a carbon atom (the one on the left) with four different substituent groups attached (a Br atom, a Cl atom, an H atom, and a CH_3 group).

20.3. **a.** *S*
b. *S*
c. *R*

20.4. **a.** IHD = 2; Possible combinations are two rings, one ring and a double bond, two double bonds, or one triple bond.
b. IHD = 2; Possible combinations are two rings, one ring and a double bond, two double bonds, or one triple bond.

20.4. For More Practice

a. IHD = 3
b. IHD = 4

20.5. propanone (or acetone)

Chapter 21

21.1. $H\ddot{\underset{\cdot\cdot}{O}}{:}^- \;+\; H{-}\overset{+}{O}(H){-}H \longrightarrow HO{-}H + H{-}O{-}H$

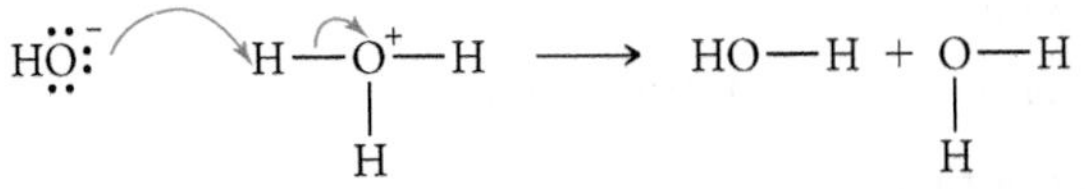

21.2. OH^-

21.3. **a.** $\overset{-3}{C}H_3{-}\overset{+3}{C}{\equiv}N$ **b.** $\overset{-2}{C}H_3Cl$

c.

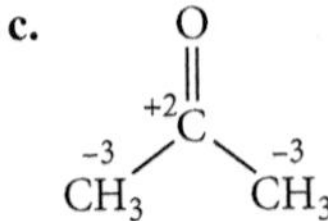

21.4. $LiAlH_4$ or H_2, Pd/C

21.1. Conceptual Connection

This can be confirmed by determining the oxidation states for carbon or nitrogen atoms in the functional group. All reactions involve a change in oxidation state.

21.2. Conceptual Connection

From Table 21.1, the pK_a values of the conjugate acids are in the increasing order: $HI < HBr < HCl < HF < CH_3COOH < H_2O < CH_3OH < NH_3$. This means that good leaving groups are the conjugate bases of strong acids. That is, good leaving groups are weak bases.

21.5. S_N1 (weak nucleophile, secondary alkyl halide). Product is a racemic mixture:

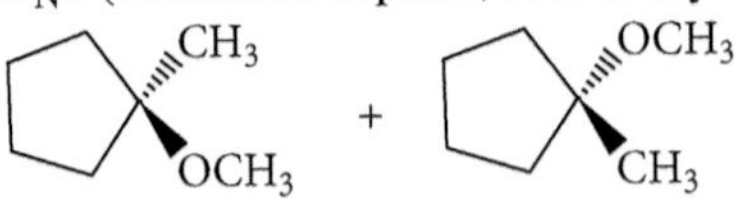

CH$_3$ / OCH$_3$ + OCH$_3$ / CH$_3$

21.3. Conceptual Connection

$H_2O + H_2SO_4 \longrightarrow H_3O^+ + HSO_4^-$; In fact, HSO_4^- is the only conjugate base in this reaction mixture. Given that HSO_4^- (which is also an acid), is reacting as a base towards a carbocation, a carbocation must be extremely acidic ($pK_a << -5.2$).

21.4. Conceptual Connection

$\overleftrightarrow{H{-}X}$

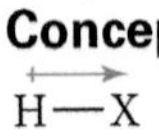

The hydrogen atom in HX is very electropositive, and it is electrophilic.

21.5. Conceptual Connection

$>C{=}C< \quad H^+ \longrightarrow -\overset{+}{C}{-}\overset{H}{C}-$

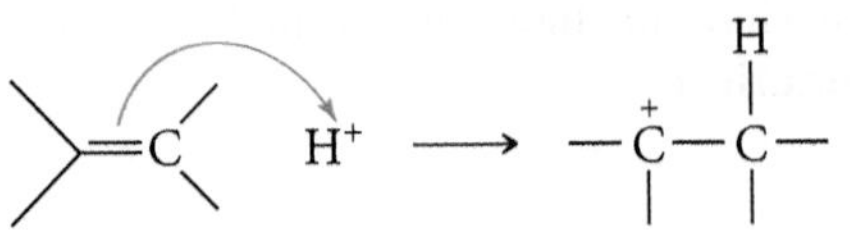

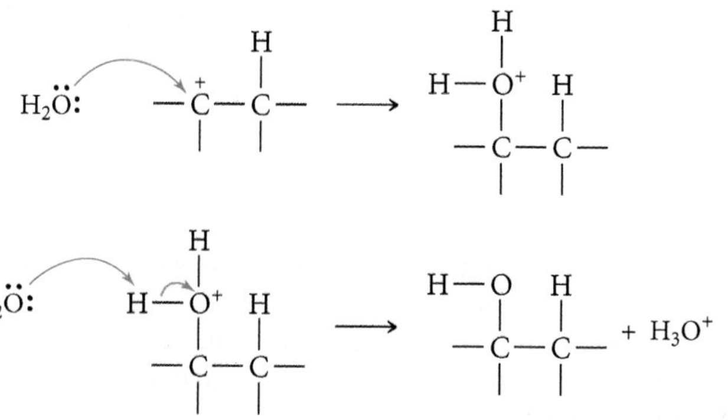

$$H_2\ddot{O}: \quad -\overset{+}{C}-\overset{H}{C}- \longrightarrow -\overset{H-O^+}{C}-\overset{H}{C}-$$

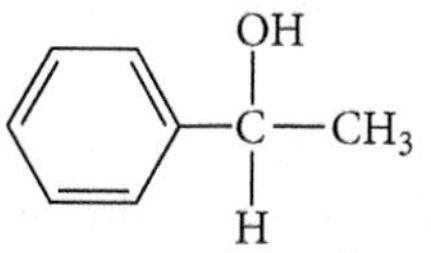

$$H_2\ddot{O}: \quad -\overset{H-O^+}{C}-\overset{H}{C}- \longrightarrow -\overset{H-O}{C}-\overset{H}{C}- + H_3O^+$$

21.6. a. $C_6H_5-C(OH)(H)-CH_3$ b. 1-methylcyclohexanol (cyclohexane ring bearing OH and CH_3)

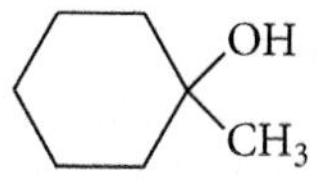

21.7. $(CH_3CO)_2O$

21.6. Conceptual Connection

$RCOCl + NH_3 \longrightarrow RC(O)NH_2 + HCl$; The extra mole of NH_3 reacts with the HCl to form NH_4Cl.

21.7. Conceptual Connection

E H (resonance structures of the arenium ion: + charge on the ring carbons ortho, para, ortho) $\longleftrightarrow$ $\longleftrightarrow$

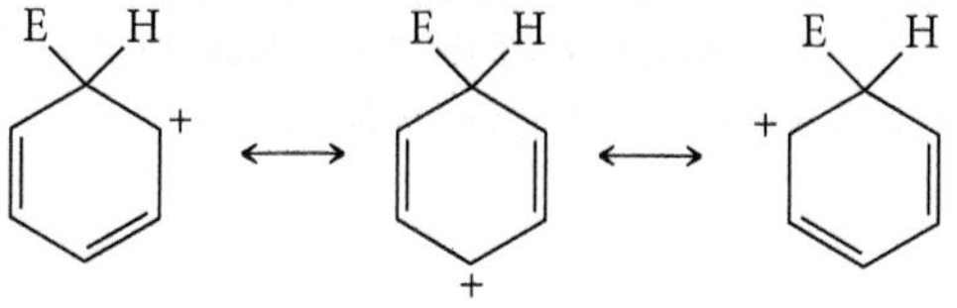

Chapter 22

22.1. C3, *S*; C4, *R*; C5, *R*

22.2.

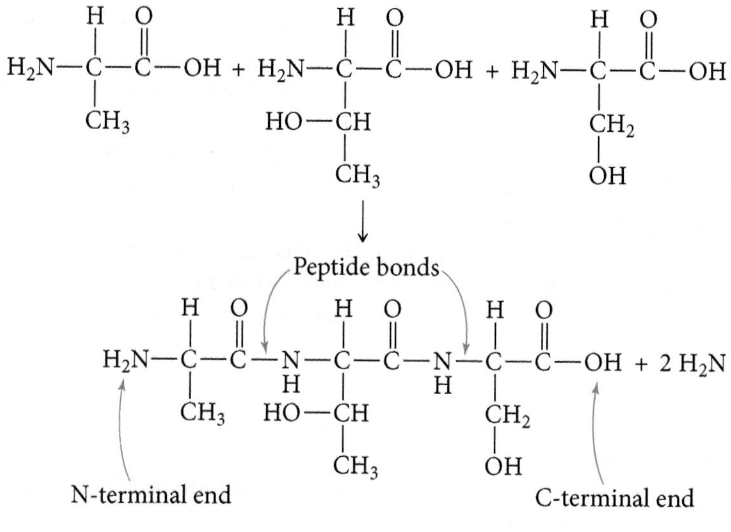

$$H_2N-\underset{CH_3}{\overset{H}{C}}-\overset{O}{\overset{\|}{C}}-OH + H_2N-\underset{HO-CH-CH_3}{\overset{H}{C}}-\overset{O}{\overset{\|}{C}}-OH + H_2N-\underset{CH_2-OH}{\overset{H}{C}}-\overset{O}{\overset{\|}{C}}-OH$$

$$\downarrow$$

Peptide bonds

$$H_2N-\underset{CH_3}{\overset{H}{C}}-\overset{O}{\overset{\|}{C}}-\underset{H}{N}-\underset{HO-CH-CH_3}{\overset{H}{C}}-\overset{O}{\overset{\|}{C}}-\underset{H}{N}-\underset{CH_2-OH}{\overset{H}{C}}-\overset{O}{\overset{\|}{C}}-OH + 2\,H_2N$$

N-terminal end C-terminal end

22.1. Conceptual Connection

Six possible tripeptides can form from the three amino acids. They are (1) Ser-Gly-Ala; (2) Gly-Ala-Ser; (3) Ala-Ser-Gly; (4) Ala-Gly-Ser; (5) Ser-Ala-Gly; (6) Gly-Ser-Ala. Notice that bonding the amino acids in reverse order results in a different molecule because the N-terminal and the C-terminal ends reside on different amino acids. For example, in Ser-Gly-Ala, the N-terminal amino acid is Ser (conventionally drawn on the left) and the C-terminal side is Ala. In Ala-Gly-Ser, in contrast, the N-terminal amino acid is Ala and the C-terminal one is Ser.

22.2. Conceptual Connection

The number of unique two-base sequences of four bases is $4^2 = 16$. The number of unique three-base sequences of four bases is $4^3 = 64$. Thus, a two-base system could code for 16 amino acids, and a three-base system could code for 64 amino acids.

Chapter 23

23.1. $KAlSi_3O_8$

23.2. $x = 2$

23.3. Orthosilicate (or neosilicate): Each of the two Be ions has a charge of 2+ for a total of 4+, and the SiO_4 unit has a charge of 4−.

23.4. Inosilicate (or pyroxene): Ca and Mg each have a charge of 2+ for a total of 4+, and the Si_2O_6 unit has a charge of 4− (two SiO_3^{2-} units).

23.1. Conceptual Connection
An increase in pressure favours the denser phase; in this case, diamond.

23.2. Conceptual Connection
(a) Since the carbonate ion is basic, adding acid to the solution drives the dissolution reaction to the right because the acid reacts with the carbonate ion. (Recall from Section 16.5 that the solubility of an ionic compound with a basic anion increases with increasing acidity.)

23.5. $2\ H_2S(g) + 3\,O_2(g) \longrightarrow 2\ H_2O(g) + 2\ SO_2(g)$
S changes from the −2 to +4 oxidation state.

23.6. The oxidation state for Cl is +7 in ClO_4^- and −1 in Cl^-.

23.7. The oxidation number changes from −1 to 0 for the oxidation of the Cl in HCl to Cl_2 and from +5 to +4 for the reduction of the Cl in $NaClO_3$ to ClO_2. The oxidizing agent is $NaClO_3$ and the reducing agent is HCl.

Chapter 24

24.1. At 50 mol % Ni and 1000 °C, this is a solid phase with half of the atoms each Ni and Cu.

24.2. At 50 mol % Ni and 1400 °C, this is a liquid phase with half of the atoms each Ni and Cu.

24.3. At 900 °C and 60 mol % Cr, this is a two-phase region with more Ni-rich face-centred cubic crystals than Cr-rich body-centred cubic crystals. The Ni-rich phase is about 42 mol % Cr and 58 mol % Ni. The Cr-rich phase is about 94 mol % Cr and 6 mol % Ni.

24.4. At 900 °C and 98 mol % Cr, this is a single-phase region with 100 mol % of the Cr-rich body-centred cubic crystals, which contains 2% Ni.

24.1. Conceptual Connection
M_4X. Since there are twice as many tetrahedral holes as metal atoms in a closest packed structure, and since one-eighth of them are occupied by nonmetal atoms, there must be one quarter as many nonmetal atoms as metal atoms.

Chapter 25

25.1. pentaamminecarbonylmanganese(II) sulfate

25.2. sodium tetrachloroplatinate(II)

25.3. The complex ion $[Cr(H_2O)_3Cl_3]^+$ fits the general formula MA_3B_3, which results in *fac* and *mer* isomers.

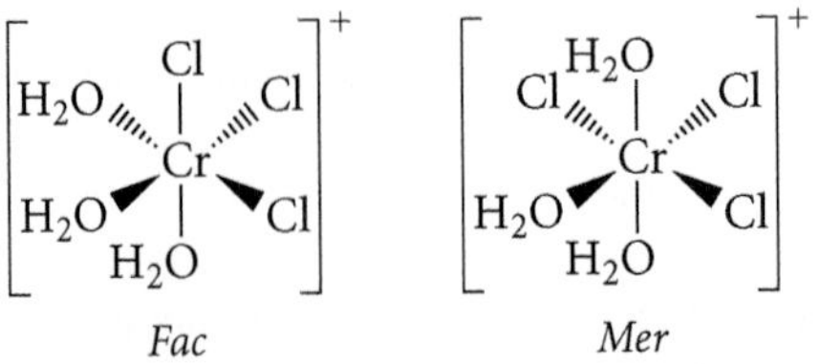

Fac

Mer

25.4. The oxalate ligand is a small bidentate ligand so it will have to occupy two adjacent (*cis*) positions of the octahedron. There are three ways to arrange the two NH_3 and two Cl^- ligands in the four remaining positions. One has both NH_3 and both Cl^- in *cis* positions (*cis* isomer). Another has the NH_3 ligands in a *trans* arrangement with both Cl^- in *cis* positions (*trans*-ammine isomer). The third has both NH_3 ligands *cis* and the Cl^- ligands *trans* (*trans*-chloro isomer).

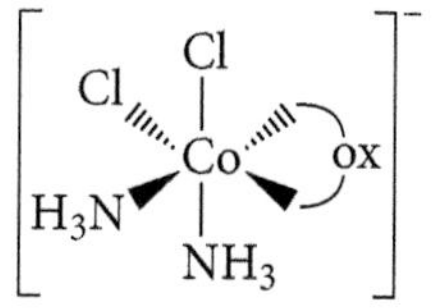

Cis isomer

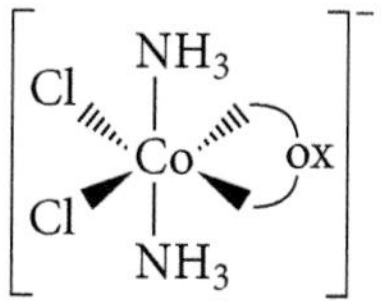

Trans (in NH_3)

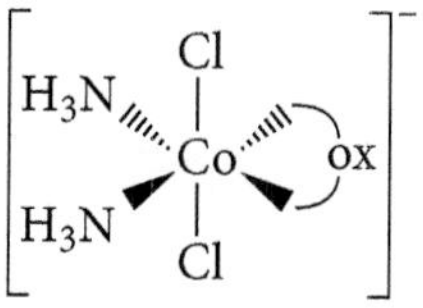

Trans (in Cl^-)

25.5. Both the *fac* and *mer* isomers are superimposable (by rotating 180°) on their mirror images, so neither one is optically active.

25.6. 288 kJ mol^{-1}

25.1. Conceptual Connection

Ligand B forms a yellow solution, which means that the complex absorbs in the violet region. Ligand A forms a red solution, which means that the complex absorbs in the green region. Since the violet region of the electromagnetic spectrum is of shorter wavelength (higher energy) than the green region, ligand B produces a higher Δ.

25.7. 5 unpaired electrons

25.8. 1 unpaired electron

Glossary

absolute configuration The exact three-dimensional spatial arrangement of atoms at a chirality centre. (20.7)

absorbed dose The amount of radiation energy absorbed by body tissue. (19.11)

accuracy A term that refers to how close a measured value is to the actual value. (1.4)

acid A molecular compound that is able to donate an H^+ ion (proton). In water, this increases the concentration of H^+. (3.4)

acid ionization constant (K_a) The equilibrium constant for the ionization reaction of a weak acid; used to compare the relative strengths of weak acids. (15.4)

acid–base reaction A reaction in which an acid reacts with a base and the two neutralize each other, producing water. (4.5)

acid–base titration A laboratory procedure in which a basic (or acidic) solution of unknown concentration is reacted with an acidic (or basic) solution of known concentration, in order to determine the concentration of the unknown. (16.4)

acidic solution A solution containing an acid that creates additional H_3O^+ ions, causing $[H_3O^+]$ to increase. (15.6)

actinoid An element with similar properties to actinium. (2.7)

activated carbon Very fine carbon particles with high surface area. (23.5)

activated complex (transition state) A high-energy intermediate state between reactant and product. (13.5)

activation energy (E_a) An energy barrier in a chemical reaction that must be overcome for the reactants to be converted into products. (13.5)

active site The specific area of an enzyme at which catalysis occurs. (13.7)

activity A measure of deviation from the standard state. (14.3)

actual yield The amount of product actually produced by a chemical reaction. (4.9)

acyl group A functional group with the group RCO, in which the carbon atom is also bonded to a polar group. (20.4)

addition polymer A polymer that is formed by the simple addition of monomers, without the elimination of atoms. (21.10)

alcohol A member of the family of organic compounds that contain a hydroxyl functional group (—OH). (3.5)

aldehyde A functional group with the formula RCHO, in which the R group may also be a hydrogen atom. (20.4)

aldose A sugar that is an aldehyde. (22.3)

alkali metals Highly reactive metals in group 1 of the periodic table. (2.7)

alkaline battery A dry-cell battery that employs slightly different half-reactions in a basic medium. (18.6)

alkaline earth metals Fairly reactive metals in group 2 of the periodic table. (2.7)

alkaloid Organic bases found in plants; they are often poisonous. (15.2)

alkane A hydrocarbon containing only single bonds. (3.5, 20.3)

alkene A hydrocarbon containing one or more carbon–carbon double bonds. (3.5, 20.3)

alkyne A hydrocarbon containing one or more carbon–carbon triple bonds. (3.5, 20.3)

alloy A metallic material that contains more than one element. (24.4)

alpha (α) decay The form of radioactive decay that occurs when an unstable nucleus emits a particle composed of two protons and two neutrons. (19.3)

alpha (α) particle A low-energy particle released during alpha decay; equivalent to a He-4 nucleus. (19.3)

α-helix A pattern in the secondary structure of a protein that occurs when the amino acid chain is wrapped tightly in a coil with the side chains extending outward. (22.5)

aluminosilicates Members of a family of compounds in which aluminum atoms substitute for silicon atoms in some of the silicon lattice sites of the silica structure. (23.3)

amino acid Organic compound that contains a carbon atom, called the α-carbon, bonded to four different groups: an amine group, an R group, a carboxylic acid group, and a hydrogen atom. (22.4)

ammonia NH_3, the strong smelling compound in which nitrogen displays its lowest oxidation state (–3). (23.6)

amorphous solid A solid in which atoms or molecules do not have any long-range order. (11.2)

ampere (A) The SI unit for electrical current; $1\ A = 1\ C\ s^{-1}$. (18.2)

amphiboles Minerals with double silicate chains. (23.3)

amphoteric Able to act as either an acid or a base. (15.3)

amplitude The vertical height of a crest (or depth of a trough) of a wave; a measure of wave intensity. (7.2)

angle strain In cyclic hydrocarbons, the difference between the actual bond angles in the ring and the ideal 109.5°. (20.6)

angular momentum quantum number (l) An integer that determines the shape of an orbital. (7.5)

angular node A plane or surface where there is zero probability of finding an electron. (7.6)

anhydrous Not containing any associated water molecules. (3.4)

anion A negatively charged ion. (2.4)

anode The electrode in an electrochemical cell where oxidation occurs; electrons flow away from the anode. (18.2)

antibonding orbital A molecular orbital that is higher in energy than any of the atomic orbitals from which it was formed. (10.8)

antistaggered conformation The rotational conformation about a C–C bond in which the bulky groups are located 180° from each other. (20.6)

aqueous solution A solution in which water acts as the solvent. (4.3, 12.2)

***arachno*-boranes** Boranes with the formula B_nH_{n+6}, consisting of a cage of boron atoms that is missing two or three corners. (23.4)

arc-melting A method in which the solid metal is melted with an arc from a high-voltage electric source in a controlled atmosphere to prevent oxidation. (24.5)

aromatic hydrocarbon A class of organic molecules that contain rings with alternating single and double C–C bonds. (20.3)

Arrhenius definitions (of acids and bases) The definitions of an acid as a substance that produces H^+ ions in aqueous solution and a base as a substance that produces OH^- ions in aqueous solution. (4.5, 15.3)

Arrhenius equation An equation which relates the rate constant of a reaction to the temperature, the activation energy, and the frequency factor; $k = Ae^{\frac{-E_a}{RT}}$. (13.5)

Arrhenius plot A plot of the natural log of the rate constant (ln k) versus the inverse of the temperature in kelvins ($1/T$) that yields a straight line with a slope of $-E_a/R$ and a y-intercept of ln A. (13.5)

atmosphere (atm) A unit of pressure based on the average pressure of air at sea level; 1 atm = 101 325 Pa. (5.2)

atomic element Those elements that exist in nature with single atoms as their basic units. (3.3)

atomic mass The average mass in u of the atoms of a particular element based on the relative abundance of the various isotopes; it is numerically equivalent to the mass in grams of one mole of the element. (2.5)

atomic number (Z) The number of protons in an atom; the atomic number defines the element. (2.4)

atomic radius Average bonding radius for a given element, determined from large numbers of compounds. (8.5)

atomic solids Solids whose composite units are atoms; they include nonbonding atomic solids, metallic atomic solids, and network covalent solids. (11.12)

atomic theory The theory that each element is composed of tiny indestructible particles called atoms, that all atoms of a given element have the same mass and other properties, and that atoms combine in simple, whole-number ratios to form compounds. (2.3)

aufbau principle The principle that indicates the pattern of orbital filling in an atom. (7.7)

autoionization The process by which water acts as an acid and a base with itself. (15.6)

Avogadro's law The law that states that the volume of a gas is directly proportional to its amount in moles ($V \propto n$). (5.3)

Avogadro's number The number of ^{12}C atoms in exactly 12 g of ^{12}C; equal to 6.0221421×10^{23}. (2.6)

axial bond In the chair conformation of cyclohexane, the bonds that are pointed vertically above and below the ring. (20.6)

balanced chemical equation A chemical equation in which the numbers of each type of atom on either side are equal. (4.2)

ball-and-stick model A representation of the arrangement of atoms in a molecule that shows how the atoms are bonded to each other and the overall shape of the molecule. (3.3)

band gap An energy gap that exists between the valence band and conduction band of semiconductors and insulators. (10.8)

bar A unit of measure that is equal to 100 000 Pa. (5.2)

barometer An instrument used to measure atmospheric pressure. (5.2)

base ionization constant (K_b) The equilibrium constant for the ionization reaction of a weak base; used to compare the relative strengths of weak bases. (16.5)

base name The part of an element's name that is used in the name of its monoatomic anion. (3.4)

basic solution A solution containing a base that creates additional OH^- ions, causing the $[OH^-]$ to increase. (15.6)

becquerel (Bq) The SI unit of radioactivity that is equal to one decay event per second. (19.5)

bent geometry A local molecular geometry where the bond angle is less than 180°. (10.3)

benzene A hydrocarbon with the formula C_6H_6 that consists of a planar, six-carbon ring. (3.5)

beta (β) decay The form of radioactive decay that occurs when an unstable nucleus emits an electron. (19.3)

beta (β) particle A medium-energy particle released during beta decay; equivalent to an electron. (19.3)

β-pleated sheet A pattern in the secondary structure of a protein that occurs when the amino acid chain is extended and forms a zigzag pattern. (22.5)

bidentate Describes ligands that donate two electron pairs to the central metal. (25.3)

bimolecular An elementary step in a reaction that involves two particles, either the same species or different, that collide and go on to form products. (13.6)

binary acid An acid composed of hydrogen and a nonmetal. (3.4)

binary molecular compound A compound that contains only two different elements. (3.4)

biochemistry The study of the chemistry occurring in living organisms. (22.1)

black phosphorus An allotrope of phosphorus with a structure similar to that of graphite; the most thermodynamically stable form. (23.6)

body-centred cubic A unit cell that consists of a cube with one atom at each corner and one atom at the centre of the cube. (11.11)

boiling point The temperature at which the vapour pressure of a liquid equals the external pressure. (11.5)

boiling point elevation The effect of a solute that causes a solution to have a higher boiling point than the pure solvent. (12.6)

bomb calorimeter A piece of equipment designed to measure $\Delta_r U$ for combustion reactions at constant volume. (6.5)

bond energy The energy required to break 1 mol of the bond in the gas phase. (9.6)

bond length The average length of a bond between two particular atoms in a variety of compounds. (9.6)

bond order For a molecule, the number of electrons in bonding orbitals minus the number of electrons in nonbonding orbitals divided by two; a positive bond order implies that the molecule is stable. (10.8)

bond stretching vibration A molecular motion in which a bond stretches and then contracts. (9.6)

bonding atomic radius For nonmetals, one-half the distance between the two atoms bonded together. For metals, one-half the distance between two of the atoms next to each other in a crystal of the metal. (8.5)

bonding orbital A molecular orbital that is lower in energy than any of the atomic orbitals from which it was formed. (10.8)

bonding pair A pair of electrons shared between two atoms. (9.4)

boranes Compounds composed of boron and hydrogen. (23.4)

Born–Haber cycle A hypothetical series of steps based on Hess's law that represents the formation of an ionic compound from its constituent elements. (9.5)

Boyle's law The law that states that volume of a gas is inversely proportional to its pressure $\left(V \propto \frac{1}{P}\right)$. (5.3)

brass A widely used alloy that contains copper and zinc. (24.5)

Brønsted–Lowry definitions (of acids and bases) The definitions of an acid as a proton (H^+ ion) donor and a base as a proton acceptor. (15.3)

bronze An alloy of copper and tin that has been used for thousands of years. (24.5)

buffer A solution containing significant amounts of both a weak acid and its conjugate base (or a weak base and its conjugate acid) that resists pH change by neutralizing added acid or added base. (16.2)

buffer capacity The amount of acid or base that can be added to a buffer without destroying its effectiveness. (16.3)

buffering action The way a buffer solution reacts with small amounts of acid or base to maintain a fairly constant pH. (16.2)

calcination The heating of an ore in order to decompose it and drive off a volatile product, such as CO_2. (24.3)

calorie (cal) A unit of energy defined as the amount of energy required to raise one gram of water 1 °C; equal to 4.184 J. (6.2)

Calorie (Cal) Shorthand notation for the kilocalorie (kcal), or 1000 calories; also called the nutritional calorie, the unit of energy used on nutritional labels. (6.2)

calorimetry The experimental procedure used to measure the heat evolved in a chemical reaction. (6.5)

capillary action The ability of a liquid to flow against gravity up a narrow tube due to adhesive and cohesive forces. (11.4)

carbanion A chemical species that contains a carbon atom with a formal negative charge. (20.2)

carbides Binary compounds composed of carbon combined with a less electronegative element. (23.5)

carbocation A chemical species that contains a carbon atom with a formal positive charge. (21.4)

carbohydrate A biomolecule having the general formula $(CH_2O)_n$. (22.3)

carbon black A fine powdered form of carbon. (23.5)

carbonyl group A functional group consisting of a carbon atom double-bonded to an oxygen atom (C=O). (20.4)

carboxylic acid An organic acid containing the functional group —COOH. (15.2)

catalyst A substance that is not consumed in a chemical reaction, but increases the rate of the reaction by providing an alternate mechanism in which the rate-determining step has a smaller activation energy. (13.7)

catenation The bonding of an element to itself. (20.2)

cathode The electrode in an electrochemical cell where reduction occurs; electrons flow toward the cathode. (18.2)

cathode ray A stream of electrons produced when a high electrical voltage is applied between two electrodes within a partially evacuated tube. (2.4)

cathode ray tube An evacuated glass tube with electrodes inside, one on each end. When a high voltage is applied to the electrodes, a beam of electrons passes between the electrodes. (2.4)

cation A positively charged ion. (2.4)

cell potential (cell emf) (E_{cell}) The potential difference between the cathode and the anode in an electrochemical cell. (18.2)

cellulose A polysaccharide that consists of glucose units bonded together by β-glycosidic linkages; the main structural component of plants, and the most abundant organic substance on earth. (22.3)

Celsius (°C) scale The temperature scale most often used by scientists (and by most countries other than the United States), on which pure water freezes at 0 °C and boils at 100 °C (at atmospheric pressure). (1.3)

chain reaction A series of reactions in which previous reactions cause future ones; in a fission bomb, neutrons produced by the fission of one uranium nucleus induce fission in other uranium nuclei. (19.7)

chair conformation The most stable conformation of cyclohexane. (20.6)

charcoal A fuel similar to coal made by heating wood in the absence of air. (23.5)

Charles's law The law that states that the volume of a gas is directly proportional to its temperature ($V \propto T$). (5.3)

chelate A complex ion that contains either a bi- or polydentate ligand. (25.3)

chelating agent The coordinating ligand of a chelate. (25.3)

chemical bond The sharing or transfer of electrons to attain stable electron configurations for the bonding atoms. (9.3)

chemical change A change that alters the molecular composition of a substance; see also *chemical reaction.* (1.1)

chemical energy The energy associated with the relative positions of electrons and nuclei in atoms and molecules. (6.2)

chemical equation A one-line expression that shows the reactants and products in a chemical reaction. (4.2)

chemical equivalence A term used to describe the situation of atoms that have the same molecular structure surrounding them, which results in the atoms having identical chemical shifts. (20.8)

chemical formula A symbolic representation of a compound which indicates the elements present in the compound and the relative number of atoms of each. (3.3)

chemical property A property that a substance displays only by changing its composition via a chemical change. (1.1)

chemical reaction A process in which one or more substances are converted into one or more different ones. (4.2)

chemical shift In NMR spectroscopy, the difference in absorption frequency of a particular nucleus from the absorption frequency of a reference nucleus. (20.8)

chemical symbol A one- or two-letter abbreviation for an element that is listed directly below its atomic number on the periodic table. (2.6)

chirality The type of isomerism in which molecules are non-superimposable mirror images. (20.7)

chirality centre A carbon atom with four different substituents in a tetrahedral arrangement. (20.7)

chromosome The DNA-containing structures that occur in the nuclei of living cells. (22.6)

***cis–trans* isomerism** *cis*-isomers have the same functional group on the same side of a bond and *trans*-isomers have the same functional group on opposite sides of a bond. (20.7)

Claus process An industrial process for obtaining sulfur through the oxidation of hydrogen sulfide. (23.8)

Clausius–Clapeyron equation An equation that displays the exponential relationship between vapour pressure and temperature;

$$\ln (P_{vap}) = \frac{-\Delta_{vap}H}{R}\left(\frac{1}{T}\right) + \ln \beta \text{ (11.5)}$$

***closo*-boranes** Boranes that have the formula $B_nH_n^{2-}$ and form the full ico-sahedral shape. (23.4)

coal A solid, black fuel with high carbon content, the product of the decomposition of ancient plant material. (23.5)

codon A sequence of three bases in a nucleic acid that codes for one amino acid. (22.6)

coffee-cup calorimeter A piece of equipment designed to measure Δ_rH for reactions at constant pressure. (6.7)

coke A solid formed by heating coal in the absence of air that consists primarily of carbon and ash. (23.5)

colligative property A property that depends on the amount of a solute but not on the type. (12.6)

collision frequency The number of collisions that occur per unit time. (13.5)

collision model A model of chemical reactions in which a reaction occurs after a sufficiently energetic collision between two reactant molecules. (13.5)

colloidal dispersion (colloid) A mixture in which a dispersed substance is finely divided but not truly dissolved in a dispersing medium. (12.8)

combustion analysis A method of obtaining empirical formulas for unknown compounds, especially those containing carbon and hydrogen, by burning a sample of the compound in pure oxygen and analyzing the products of the combustion reaction. (3.8)

combustion reaction A type of chemical reaction in which a substance combines with oxygen to form one or more oxygen-containing compounds. (4.2)

common ion effect The tendency for a common ion to decrease the solubility of an ionic compound or to decrease the ionization of a weak acid or weak base. (16.2)

common name A traditional name of a compound that gives little or no information about its chemical structure; for example, the common name of $NaHCO_3$ is "baking soda." (3.4)

complementary Capable of precise pairing; in particular, the bases of nucleic acids. (22.6)

complementary properties Those properties that exclude one another, i.e., the more you know about one, the less you know about the other. For example, the wave nature and particle nature of the electron are complementary. (7.4)

complete ionic equation An equation which lists individually all of the ions present as either reactants or products in a chemical reaction. (4.4)

complex carbohydrate Another term for a polysaccharide based on the fact that it is made up of many simple sugars. (22.3)

complex ion An ion that contains a central metal ion bound to one or more ligands. (16.8, 25.3)

concentrated solution A solution that contains a large amount of solute relative to the amount of solvent. (4.9, 12.5)

condensation The phase transition from gas to liquid. (11.5)

condensation (step-growth) polymerization The process by which a polymer is formed by elimination of an atom or small group of atoms (usually water) between pairs of monomers. (21.10)

conduction band In solids, a higher energy set of normally empty molecular orbitals that are involved in electrical conduction. (10.8)

configurational isomerism A type of stereoisomerism in which atoms or functional groups are connected in the same sequence, but there is a difference in the spatial locations of atoms or groups. (20.6)

conformational isomerism A type of stereoisomerism that is the result of bond rotations. (20.6)

conformer A conformational isomer. (20.6)

conjugate acid Any base to which a proton has been added. (15.3)

conjugate acid–base pair Two substances related to each other by the transfer of a proton. (15.3)

conjugate base Any acid from which a proton has been removed. (15.3)

conjugation A sequence of alternating single and double bonds that results in delocalized π bonding. (20.3)

constitutional isomer A molecule that has the same molecular formula, but atoms are connected in a different sequence. (20.5)

constructive interference The interaction of waves from two sources that align with overlapping crests, resulting in a wave of greater amplitude. (7.2)

contact process An industrial method for the production of sulfuric acid. (23.8)

conversion factor A factor used to convert between two different units; a conversion factor can be constructed from any two quantities known to be equivalent. (1.3)

coordinate covalent bond (dative bond) The bond formed when a ligand donates electrons to an empty orbital of a metal in a complex ion. (25.3)

coordination compound A neutral compound made when a complex ion combines with one or more counterions. (25.3)

coordination isomers Isomers of complex ions that occur when a coordinated ligand exchanges places with the uncoordinated counterion. (25.4)

coordination number (coordination compounds) The number of molecules or ions directly bound to the metal atom in a complex ion. (25.3)

coordination number (unit cells) The number of atoms with which each atom in a crystal lattice is in direct contact. (11.11)

core electrons Electrons in complete principal energy levels, and complete *d* and *f* sublevels, not including the valence electrons. (8.3)

corrosion The gradual, nearly always undesired oxidation of metals that occurs when they are exposed to oxidizing agents in the environment. (18.8)

Coulomb's law The equation that describes the potential energy between two charged particles. (7.7)

covalent bond A chemical bond in which two atoms share electrons that interact with the nuclei of both atoms, lowering the potential energy of each through electrostatic interactions. (3.2, 9.2)

covalent carbides Binary compounds composed of carbon combined with low-electronegativity nonmetals or metalloids. (23.5)

covalent radius (bonding atomic radius) Defined in nonmetals as one-half the distance between two atoms bonded together, and in metals as one-half the distance between two adjacent atoms in a crystal of the metal. (8.5)

critical mass The necessary amount of a radioactive isotope required to produce a self-sustaining fission reaction. (19.7)

critical point The temperature and pressure above which a supercritical fluid exists. (11.8)

critical pressure (P_c) The pressure required to bring about a transition to a liquid at the critical temperature. (11.5)

critical temperature (T_c) The temperature above which a liquid cannot exist, regardless of pressure. (11.5)

crystalline lattice The regular arrangement of atoms in a crystalline solid. (11.11)

crystalline solid A solid in which atoms, molecules, or ions are arranged in patterns with long-range, repeating order. (11.2)

cubic closest packing A closest-packed arrangement in which the third layer of atoms is offset from the first; the same structure as the face-centred cubic. (11.11)

cyclic hydrocarbons Carbon atoms that are arranged to form one or more ring structures. (20.3)

cycloalkane An alkane that has a cyclic molecular structure. (3.5)

cycloalkene An alkene that has a cyclic molecular structure. (3.5)

cyclotron A particle accelerator in which a charged particle is accelerated in an evacuated ring-shaped tube by an alternating voltage applied to each semi-circular half of the ring. (19.10)

Dalton's law of partial pressures The law stating that the sum of the partial pressures of the components in a gas mixture must equal the total pressure. (5.6)

de Broglie relation The observation that the wavelength of a particle is inversely proportional to its momentum, $\lambda = \frac{h}{mv}$ (7.4)

degenerate A term describing two or more electron orbitals with the same value of *n* that have the same energy. (7.7)

dehydration The elimination of water from an alcohol to yield an alkene. (21.5)

dehydrohalogenation The elimination of HX from an alkyl halide to yield an alkene. (21.5)

density (*d*) The ratio of an object's mass to its volume. (1.3)

deposition The phase transition from gas to solid. (11.6)

derived unit A unit that is a combination of other base units. For example, the SI unit for speed is metres per second ($m\ s^{-1}$), a derived unit. (1.3)

destructive interference The interaction of waves from two sources aligned so that the crest of one overlaps the trough of the other, resulting in cancellation. (7.2)

deterministic A characteristic of the classical laws of motion, which imply that present circumstances determine future events. (7.4)

dextrorotatory isomer An enantiomer that rotates plane-polarized light clockwise. (20.7)

diacid An organic molecule that contains two carboxylic acid groups that functions as a monomer in step-growth polymerization. (21.10)

diamagnetic The state of an atom or ion that contains only paired electrons and is, therefore, slightly repelled by an external magnetic field. (7.7)

diamond An elemental form of carbon with a crystal structure that consists of carbon atoms connected to four other carbon atoms at the corners of a tetrahedron, creating a strong network covalent solid. (23.5)

diastereomers Configurational isomers that are not mirror images. (20.7)

diffraction The phenomena by which a wave emerging from an aperture spreads out to form a new wave front. (7.2)

diffusion The process by which a gas spreads through a space occupied by another gas. (5.9)

difunctional monomer A monomer that has two functional groups, used in step-growth polymerization reactions. (21.10)

dilute solution A solution that contains a very small amount of solute relative to the amount of solvent. (4.9, 12.5)

dimensional analysis The use of units as a guide to solving problems. (1.3)

dimer The product that forms from the reaction of two monomers. (20.14)

diode A device that allows the flow of electrical current in only one direction. (10.8)

diol An organic molecule that contains two alcohol groups that functions as a monomer in step-growth polymerization. (21.10)

dipeptide Two amino acids linked together. (22.4)

dipole moment (μ) A measure of the separation of positive and negative charge in a molecule. (9.7)

dipole–dipole force An intermolecular force exhibited by polar molecules that results from the uneven charge distribution. (11.3)

dipole-induced dipole force An intermolecular force between molecules that have a permanent dipole and an atom or molecule that is nonpolar. (11.3)

diprotic acid An acid that contains two ionizable protons. (4.5, 15.4)

disaccharide A carbohydrate composed of two monosaccharides. (22.3)

dispersion force An intermolecular force exhibited by all atoms and molecules that results from fluctuations in the electron distribution. (11.3)

disproportionation reaction A reaction in which a reactant is both oxidized and reduced. (4.6)

double bond The bond that forms when two pairs of electrons are shared between two atoms. (9.4)

dry-cell battery A battery that does not contain a large amount of liquid water, often using the oxidation of zinc and the reduction of MnO_2 to provide the electrical current. (18.6)

dynamic equilibrium The point at which the rate of the reverse reaction or process equals the rate of the forward reaction or process. (11.5, 12.4, 14.2)

***E, Z* system** The protocol for assigning stereochemical configuration of an alkene with three or more different groups. (20.7)

eclipsed conformation The rotational conformation about a C–C bond in which the groups are located 0° from each other. (20.6)

effective nuclear charge The actual nuclear charge experienced by an electron, defined as the charge of the nucleus plus the charge of the shielding electrons. (7.7)

effusion The process by which a gas escapes from a container into a vacuum through a small hole. (5.9)

electrical charge A fundamental property of certain particles that causes them to experience a force in the presence of electric fields. (2.4)

electrical current The flow of electric charge. (18.2)

electrochemical cell A device in which a chemical reaction either produces or is carried out by an electrical current. (18.2)

electrode A conductive surface through which electrons can enter or leave a half-cell. (18.2)

electrolysis The process by which electrical current is used to drive an otherwise nonspontaneous redox reaction. (18.7)

electrolyte A substance that dissolves in water to form solutions that conduct electricity. (4.3)

electrolytic cell An electrochemical cell which uses electrical current to drive a nonspontaneous chemical reaction. (18.2)

electromagnetic radiation A form of energy embodied in oscillating electric and magnetic fields. (7.2)

electromagnetic spectrum The range of the wavelengths of all possible electromagnetic radiation. (7.2)

electrometallurgy The use of electrolysis to produce metals from their compounds. (24.3)

electromotive force (emf) The force that results in the motion of electrons due to a difference in potential. (18.2)

electron A negatively charged, low-mass particle found outside the nucleus of all atoms that occupies most of the atom's volume but contributes almost none of its mass. (2.4)

electron affinity (EA) The energy released when an electron is added to a neutral atom in the gas phase. (8.8)

electron capture The form of radioactive decay that occurs when a nucleus assimilates an electron from an inner orbital. (19.3)

electron configuration A notation that shows the particular orbitals that are occupied by electrons in an atom. (7.7)

electron geometry The geometrical arrangement of electron groups in a molecule. (10.3)

electron groups A general term for lone pairs, single bonds, multiple bonds, or lone electrons in a molecule. (10.2)

electron spin A fundamental property of electrons; spin can have a value of $\pm \frac{1}{2}$. (7.7)

electronegativity The ability of an atom to attract electrons to itself in a covalent bond. (9.7)

electrophile A molecule that contains an atom with positive charge which can accept electrons from another molecule, such as a nucleophile. (21.4)

electrophilic addition An addition reaction between some electrophiles and a carbon–carbon double bond. (21.6)

elementary step An individual step in a reaction mechanism. (13.6)

emission spectrum The range of wavelengths emitted by a particular element; used to identify the element. (7.3)

empirical formula A chemical formula that shows the simplest whole number ratio of atoms in the compound. (3.3)

empirical formula molar mass The sum of the masses of all the atoms in an empirical formula. (3.8)

enantiomers Two molecules that are nonsuperimposable mirror images of one another. (20.7, 25.4)

endothermic reaction A chemical reaction that absorbs heat from its surroundings; for an endothermic reaction, $\Delta H > 0$. (6.6)

endpoint The point of pH change where an indicator changes colour. (16.4)

energy The capacity to do work. (6.2)

enthalpy (*H*) The sum of the internal energy of a system and the product of its pressure and volume; the energy associated with the breaking and forming of bonds in a chemical reaction. (6.6)

enthalpy of reaction The enthalpy change for a chemical reaction.

enthalpy of solution The overall enthalpy change upon solution formation (12.3):

$$\Delta_{\text{soln}}H = \Delta_{\text{solute}}H + \Delta_{\text{solvent}}H + \Delta_{\text{mix}}H$$

entropy A thermodynamic function that is proportional to the number of energetically equivalent ways to arrange the components of a system to achieve a particular state; a measure of the energy randomization or energy dispersal in a system. (12.2, 17.2)

enzyme A biochemical catalyst made of protein that increases the rates of biochemical reactions. (13.7, 22.4)

equatorial bond In the chair conformation of cyclohexane, the bonds that are pointed outward, to the sides of the ring. (20.6)

equilibrium constant (K_c) The ratio, at equilibrium, of the activities of the products of a reaction raised to their stoichiometric coefficients to the activities of the reactants raised to their stoichiometric coefficients. (14.3)

equivalence point The point in a titration at which the added solute completely reacts with the solute present in the solution; for acid–base titrations, the point at which the amount of acid is stoichiometrically equal to the amount of base in solution. (16.4)

equivalent dose The absorbed dose multiplied by a dimensionless radiation weighting factor (W_R) for different types of radiation. (19.11)

ester linkage The bonds that form between a carboxylic acid and an alcohol to form an ester, such as those in triglycerides. (22.2)

exact numbers Numbers that have no uncertainty and thus do not limit the number of significant figures in any calculation. (1.4)

exoergic Adjective for a nuclear or chemical reaction for which the standard Gibbs energy change is negative. (19.8)

exothermic reaction A chemical reaction that releases heat to its surroundings; for an exothermic reaction, $\Delta H < 0$. (6.6)

exponential factor A number between 0 and 1 that represents the fraction of molecules that have enough energy to make it over the activation barrier on a given approach. (13.5)

extensive property A property that depends on the amount of a given substance, such as mass. (1.3)

extractive metallurgy The process by which an elemental metal must be extracted from the compounds in which it is found. (24.3)

face-centred cubic A crystal structure whose unit cell consists of a cube with one atom at each corner and one atom in the centre of every face. (11.11)

family A group of organic compounds with the same functional group. (3.5, 20.4)

family (group) Columns within the main group elements in the periodic table that contain elements that exhibit similar chemical properties. (2.7)

Faraday's constant (*F*) The charge in coulombs of 1 mol of electrons: $F = 96\,485\ \text{C mol}^{-1}$. (18.4)

fatty acid A carboxylic acid with a long hydrocarbon tail. (22.2)

ferromagnetic The state of an atom or ion that is very strongly attracted by an external magnetic field. (24.5)

fibrous protein A protein with a relatively linear structure; fibrous proteins tend to be insoluble in aqueous solutions. (22.5)

film-badge dosimeter A device for monitoring exposure to radiation consisting of photographic film held in a small case that is pinned to clothing. (19.5)

first law of thermodynamics The law stating that the total energy of the universe is constant. (6.3)

Fischer esterification The reaction between a carboxylic acid and an alcohol, catalyzed by acid, that yields an ester. (21.8)

Fischer projection A way to represent the absolute configurations of molecules, usually monosaccharides. (22.3)

flux In pyrometallurgy, material that will react with the gangue to form a substance with a low melting point. (24.3)

formal charge The charge that an atom in a Lewis structure would have if all the bonding electrons were shared equally between the bonded atoms. (9.8)

formation constant (K_f) The equilibrium constant associated with reactions for the formation of complex ions. (16.8)

formula mass The average mass of a molecule of a compound in u. (3.6)

formula unit The smallest, electrically neutral collection of ions in an ionic compound. (3.3)

free radical A molecule or ion with an odd number of electrons in its Lewis structure. (9.9)

freezing The phase transition from liquid to solid. (11.6)

freezing point depression The effect of a solute that causes a solution to have a lower melting point than the pure solvent. (12.6)

frequency (ν) For waves, the number of cycles (or complete wavelengths) that pass through a stationary point in one second. (7.2)

frequency factor The number of times that reactants approach the activation energy per unit time. (13.5)

fuel cell A voltaic cell that uses the oxidation of hydrogen and the reduction of oxygen, forming water, to provide electrical current. (18.6)

fullerenes Carbon clusters bonded in roughly spherical shapes containing from 36 to over 100 carbon atoms. (23.5)

functional group A characteristic atom or group of atoms that imparts certain chemical properties to an organic compound. (3.5, 20.4)

GABA (γ-aminobutanoic acid) receptor A receptor protein that inhibits neurotransmission. (20.7)

gamma (γ) ray The form of electromagnetic radiation with the shortest wavelength and highest energy. (7.2, 19.3)

gamma (γ) ray emission The form of radioactive decay that occurs when an unstable nucleus emits extremely high frequency electromagnetic radiation. (19.3)

gangue The undesirable minerals that are separated from specific ores. (24.3)

gas-evolution reaction A reaction in which two aqueous solutions are mixed and a gas forms, resulting in bubbling. (4.5)

gauche-staggered conformation The rotational conformation about a C–C bond in which the bulky groups are located 60° from each other. (20.6)

Geiger-Müller counter A device used to detect radioactivity that uses argon atoms that become ionized in the presence of energetic particles to produce an electrical signal. (19.5)

gene A sequence of codons within a DNA molecule that codes for a single protein. (22.6)

Gibbs energy (G) A thermodynamic state function related to enthalpy and entropy by the equation $G = H - TS$: chemical systems tend towards lower Gibbs energy, also called the *chemical potential.* (17.5)

Gibbs energy of formation ($\Delta_f G°$) The change in free energy when 1 mol of a compound forms from its constituent elements in their standard states. (17.7)

globular protein A protein that folds into a roughly spherical shape so that its polar side chains are oriented outward and its nonpolar side chains toward the interior; globular proteins tend to be soluble in water. (22.5)

glycogen A highly branched form of starch. (22.3)

glycolipid A triglyceride composed of a fatty acid, a hydrocarbon chain, and a sugar molecule as the polar section. (22.2)

glycosidic linkage A bond between carbohydrates that results from a dehydration reaction. (22.3)

Graham's law of effusion The expression of the ratio of rates of effusion of two different gases. (5.9)

graphite An elemental form of carbon consisting of flat sheets of carbon atoms, bonded together as interconnected hexagonal rings held together by intermolecular forces, that can easily slide past each other. (22.6)

gray (Gy) SI unit of absorbed dose that corresponds to 1 J of radiation energy absorbed per kilogram of body tissue. (19.11)

Grignard reaction The reaction between a carbon-centred nucleophile, RMgX, and an aldehyde or ketone, to yield an alcohol. (21.7)

ground state The lowest energy state. (7.7)

Haber–Bosch process The industrial process for producing ammonia from nitrogen gas and hydrogen gas. (23.6)

half-cell One half of an electrochemical cell where either oxidation or reduction occurs. (18.2)

half-life ($t_{1/2}$) The time required for the concentration of a reactant or the amount of a radioactive isotope to fall to one-half of its initial value. (13.4)

halogens Highly reactive nonmetals in group 17 of the periodic table. (2.7)

heat (q) The flow of energy caused by a temperature difference. (6.2)

heat capacity (C) The quantity of heat required to change a system's temperature by 1 °C. (6.4)

heat of fusion ($\Delta_{fus}H°$) The amount of heat required to melt 1 mole of a solid. (11.6)

heat of hydration ($\Delta_{hyd}H$) The enthalpy change that occurs when 1 mol of gaseous solute ions are dissolved in water. (12.3)

heat of reaction The enthalpy change for a chemical reaction. (6.6)

heat of vaporization ($\Delta_{vap}H°$) The amount of heat required to vaporize one mole of a liquid to a gas. (11.5)

Heisenberg's uncertainty principle The principle stating that due to the wave–particle duality, it is fundamentally impossible to precisely determine both the position and velocity of a particle at a given moment in time. (7.4)

hemiacetal A molecule in which a carbon atom is bonded to –OH, –OR, –H, and –R groups. (21.7)

hemiketal A molecule in which a carbon atom is bonded to –OH, –OR, and two –R groups. (21.7)

Henderson–Hasselbalch equation An equation used to easily calculate the pH of a buffer solution from the initial concentrations of the buffer components, assuming that the *x is small* approximation is [base] valid: $\text{pH} = \text{p}K_a + \log\frac{[\text{base}]}{[\text{acid}]}$ (16.2)

Henry's law An equation that expresses the relationship between solubility of a gas and pressure: $S_{gas} = k_H P_{gas}$ (12.4)

Hess's law The law stating that if a chemical equation can be expressed as the sum of a series of steps, then $\Delta_r H$ for the overall equation is the sum of the enthalpies of reactions for each step. (6.8)

heteroatom In organic molecules, an atom other than carbon or hydrogen. (20.8)

heterogeneous catalysis Catalysis in which the catalyst and the reactants exist in different phases. (13.7)

hexagonal closest packing A closest-packed arrangement in which the atoms of the third layer align exactly over those in the first layer. (11.11)

hexose A six-carbon sugar. (22.3)

highest occupied molecular orbital (HOMO) The highest energy molecular orbital that is occupied by electrons in the ground state. (10.8)

high-spin complex A complex ion with weak field ligands that have the same number of unpaired electrons as the free metal ion. (25.5)

homogeneous catalysis Catalysis in which the catalyst exists in the same phase as the reactants. (13.7)

HOMO-LUMO gap The energy difference between highest occupied and lowest unoccupied molecular orbitals. (10.8)

Hund's rule The principle stating that when electrons fill degenerate orbitals they first fill them singly with parallel spins. (7.7)

hybrid atomic orbitals (hybrid orbitals) Orbitals formed from the combination of standard atomic orbitals that correspond more closely to the actual distribution of electrons in a chemically bonded atom. (10.7)

hybridization A mathematical procedure in which standard atomic orbitals are combined to form new, hybrid orbitals. (10.7)

hydrate An ionic compound that contains a specific number of water molecules associated with each formula unit. (3.4)

hydrazine N_2H_4, a nitrogen and hydrogen compound in which nitrogen has a negative oxidation state (–2). (23.6)

hydrocarbon An organic compound that contains only carbon and hydrogen. (3.5)

hydrogen azide HN_3, a nitrogen and hydrogen compound with a higher hydrogen-to-nitrogen ratio than ammonia or hydrazine. (23.6)

hydrogen bond A strong dipole–dipole attractive force between a hydrogen bonded to O, N, or F and one of these electronegative atoms on a neighbouring molecule. (11.3)

hydrogen bonding A strong type of intermolecular bonding that occurs between polar molecules that contain hydrogen atoms bonded directly to small electronegative atoms. (11.3)

hydrogenation The catalyzed addition of hydrogen to alkene double bonds to make single bonds. (13.7, 21.3)

hydrolysis The splitting of a chemical bond with water, resulting in the addition of H and OH to the products. (22.3)

hydrometallurgy The use of an aqueous solution to extract metals from their ores. (24.3)

hydronium ion H_3O^+, the ion formed from the association of a water molecule with an H^+ ion donated by an acid. (4.5, 15.3)

hypercoordination The phenomenon of main group elements being bonded to more than four other atoms or appear to have more than four pairs of electrons (an octet) around the central atom. (9.10)

ideal gas A gas that exactly follows the ideal gas law. (5.4)

ideal gas constant The proportionality constant of the ideal gas law, *R*, equal to 8.314 J mol^{-1} K^{-1} or 0.08314 bar L mol^{-1} K^{-1}. (5.4)

ideal gas law The law that combines the relationships of Boyle's, Charles's, and Avogadro's laws into one comprehensive equation of state with the proportionality constant *R* in the form $PV = nRT$. (5.4)

ideal solution A solution that follows Raoult's law at all concentrations for both solute and solvent. (12.6)

Imperial system A measurement system. (1.3)

indeterminacy The principle that present circumstances do not necessarily determine future events in the quantum-mechanical realm. (7.4)

index of hydrogen deficiency (IHD) The number of pi bonds and rings in a molecule, calculated from the molecular formula. (20.8)

indicator A dye whose colour depends on the pH of the solution it is dissolved in; often used to detect the endpoint of a titration. (16.4)

induction agent A drug that induces sleep, used in anesthesia. (20.7)

inductive effect The through-bond donation or withdrawal of electron density. (20.4, 21.2)

infrared (IR) absorption spectroscopy The measurement of molecular absorption of infrared frequency radiation to give information about molecular structure. (9.6, 20.8)

infrared (IR) radiation Electromagnetic radiation emitted from warm objects, with wavelengths slightly larger than those of visible light. (7.2)

insoluble Incapable of dissolving in water or extremely difficult to form a solution. (4.3)

integrated rate law A relationship between the concentrations of the reactants in a chemical reaction and time. (13.4)

intensive property A property such as density that is independent of the amount of a given substance. (1.3)

interconversion Functional group transformation, for example among alcohols, aldehydes, or ketones, and carboxylic acids. (21.3)

interference The superposition of two or more waves overlapping in space, resulting in either an increase in amplitude (constructive interference) or a decrease in amplitude (destructive interference). (7.2)

internal energy (*U*) The sum of the kinetic and potential energies of all of the particles that compose a system. (6.3)

International System of Units (SI) The standard unit system used by scientists, based on the metric system (1.3)

interstitial alloy An alloy in which small, usually nonmetallic atoms fit between the metallic atoms of a crystal. (24.4)

inversion The change in absolute configuration at a chirality centre during a reaction. (21.4)

ion An atom or molecule with a net charge caused by the loss or gain of electrons. (2.4)

ion product constant for water (K_w) The equilibrium constant for the autoionization of water. (15.6)

ion–dipole force An intermolecular force between an ion and the oppositely charged end of a polar molecule. (11.3)

ion-induced dipole force An intermolecular force between ions and a nonpolar molecule. (11.3)

ionic bond A chemical bond formed between two oppositely charged ions, generally a metallic cation and a nonmetallic anion, that are attracted to one another by electrostatic forces. (3.2, 9.2)

ionic carbides Binary compounds composed of carbon combined with low-electronegativity metals. (23.5)

ionic compound A compound composed of cations and anions bound together by electrostatic attraction. (3.3)

ionic resonance structure For hypercoordinate compounds, a resonance structure that has one or more ionic bond, and all atoms or ions have octets. (9.10)

ionic solids Solids whose composite units are ions; they generally have high melting points. (11.12)

ionization energy (IE) The energy required to remove an electron from an atom or ion in its gaseous state. (8.7)

ionizing power The ability of radiation to ionize other molecules and atoms. (19.3)

isotopes Atoms of the same element with the same number of protons but different numbers of neutrons and consequently different masses. (2.4)

joule (J) The SI unit for energy: equal to 1 kg m^2 s^{-2}. (6.2)

kelvin (K) The SI standard unit of temperature. (1.3)

Kelvin scale The temperature scale that assigns 0 K (−273 °C) to the coldest temperature possible, absolute zero, the temperature at which molecular motion virtually stops. 1 K = 1 °C. (1.3)

ketone A functional group in which a carbon atom is double-bonded to an oxygen atom, and two R groups. (20.4)

ketose A sugar that is a ketone. (22.3)

kilogram (kg) The SI standard unit of mass defined as the mass of a block of metal kept at the International Bureau of Weights and Measures at Sèvres, France. (1.3)

kilowatt-hour (kWh) An energy unit used primarily to express large amounts of energy produced by the flow of electricity; equal to 3.60×10^6 J. (6.2)

kinetic energy The energy associated with motion of an object. (1.2, 6.2)

kinetic molecular theory A model of an ideal gas as a collection of point particles in constant motion undergoing completely elastic collisions. (5.8)

lanthanoid contraction The trend toward levelling off in size of the atoms in the third and fourth transition rows due to the ineffective shielding of the *f* sublevel electrons. (25.2)

lanthanoid An element with similar properties to lanthanum. (2.7)

lattice energy The energy associated with forming a crystalline lattice from gaseous ions. (9.5)

law See *scientific law.*

law of conservation of energy A law stating that energy can neither be created nor destroyed, only converted from one form to another. (1.2, 6.2)

law of conservation of mass The physical law that matter is neither created nor destroyed in a chemical reaction. (2.3)

law of definite proportions A law stating that all samples of a given compound have the same proportions of their constituent elements. (2.3)

law of mass action The relationship between the balanced chemical equation and the expression of the equilibrium constant. (14.3)

law of multiple proportions A law stating that when two elements (A and B) form two different compounds, the masses of element B that combine with one gram of element A can be expressed as a ratio of small whole numbers. (2.3)

Le Châtelier's principle The principle stating that when a chemical system at equilibrium is disturbed, the system shifts in a direction that minimizes the disturbance. (14.8)

leaching The process by which a metal is separated out of a mixture by selectively dissolving it into solution. (24.3)

lead–acid storage battery A battery that uses the oxidation of lead and the reduction of lead(IV) oxide in sulfuric acid to provide electrical current. (18.6)

leaving group The group that is removed from the substrate in a substitution reaction. (21.4)

lever rule The rule that states that in a two-phase region, whichever phase is closest to the composition of the alloy is the more abundant phase. (24.4)

levorotatory Capable of rotating the polarization of light counterclockwise. (20.7)

Lewis acid An atom, ion, or molecule that is an electron pair acceptor. (15.10)

Lewis base An atom, ion, or molecule that is an electron pair donor. (15.10)

Lewis electron-dot structures (Lewis structures) A drawing that represents chemical bonds between atoms as shared or transferred electrons; the valence electrons of atoms are represented as dots. (9.1)

Lewis theory A simple model of chemical bonding using diagrams that represent bonds between atoms as lines or pairs of dots. In this theory, atoms bond together to obtain stable octets (eight valence electrons). (9.1)

lifetime (τ) The time for a reactant to decrease to $1/e$ of the original concentration. (13.4)

ligand A neutral molecule or an ion that acts as a Lewis base with the central metal ion in a complex ion. (16.8, 25.3)

ligand field theory The theory of bonding in coordination compounds that explains the colours of transition metal complexes. (25.1)

limiting reactant The reactant that has the smallest stoichiometric amount in a reactant mixture and consequently limits the amount of product in a chemical reaction. (4.8)

linear accelerator A particle accelerator in which a charged particle is accelerated in an evacuated tube by a potential difference between the ends of the tube or by alternating charges in sections of the tube. (19.10)

linear geometry The molecular geometry of three atoms with a 180° bond angle due to the repulsion of two electron groups. (10.2)

linkage isomers Isomers of complex ions that occur when some ligands coordinate to the metal in different ways. (25.4)

lipid A member of the class of biochemical compounds that are insoluble in water but soluble in nonpolar solvents; include fatty acids, triglycerides, and steroids. (22.2)

lipid bilayer The double-layered structure of lipid molecules that makes up cell membranes. (22.2)

lithium–ion battery A battery that produces electrical current throughout the motion of lithium ions from the anode to the cathode. (18.6)

litre (L) A unit of volume equal to 1000 cm^3 or 1.057 qt. (1.3)

locant In the names of organic molecules, a number that indicates the location of a substituent or group. (3.5)

lone pair A pair of electrons associated with only one atom. (9.4)

lowest unoccupied molecular orbital (LUMO) The lowest energy molecular orbital that is not occupied by electrons in the ground state. (10.8)

low-spin complex A complex ion with strong field ligands that have fewer unpaired electrons than the free metal ion. (25.5)

magic numbers Certain numbers of nucleons N or $Z = 2, 8, 20, 28, 50, 82$, and $N = 126$) that confer unique stability. (19.4)

magnetic quantum number (m_l) An integer that specifies the orientation of an orbital. (7.5)

main-group elements Those elements found in the *s* or *p* blocks of the periodic table, whose properties tend to be predictable based on their position in the table. (2.7, 23.2)

manometer An instrument used to determine the pressure of a gaseous sample, consisting of a liquid-filled U-shaped tube with one end exposed to the ambient pressure and the other end connected to the sample. (5.2)

Markovnikov's rule When alkenes undergo electrophilic addition, the hydrogen atom adds to the double bond in such a way as to generate the most stable carbocation, which then reacts to form a C–X bond. (21.6)

mass A measure of the quantity of matter making up an object. (1.3)

mass defect The difference in mass between the nucleus of an atom and the sum of the separated particles that make up that nucleus. (19.8)

mass number (A) The sum of the number of protons and neutrons in an atom. (2.4)

mass percent composition (mass percent) An element's percentage of the total mass of a compound containing the element. (3.7)

mass spectrometry An experimental method of determining the precise mass and relative abundance of isotopes in a given sample using an instrument called a *mass spectrometer*. (2.5)

mean free path The average distance that a molecule in a gas travels between collisions. (5.9)

melting (fusion) The phase transition from solid to liquid. (11.6)

melting point The temperature at which the molecules of a solid have enough thermal energy to overcome intermolecular forces and become a liquid. (11.6)

metallic atomic solids Atomic solids held together by metallic bonds; they have variable melting points. (11.12)

metallic bonding The type of bonding that occurs in metal crystals, in which metal atoms donate their electrons to an electron sea, delocalized over the entire crystal lattice. (9.2)

metallic carbides Binary compounds composed of carbon combined with metals that have a metallic lattice with holes small enough to fit carbon atoms. (23.5)

metalloid A category of elements found on the boundary between the metals and nonmetals on the periodic table, with properties intermediate between those of both groups; also called *semimetals*. (2.7)

metallurgy The part of chemistry that includes all the processes associated with mining, separating, and refining metals and the subsequent production of pure metals and mixtures of metals called *alloys*. (24.1)

metal A large class of elements that are generally good conductors of heat and electricity, malleable, ductile, lustrous, and tend to lose electrons during chemical changes. (2.7)

metre (m) The SI standard unit of length. (1.3)

metric system The system of measurements used in most countries in which the metre is the unit of length, the kilogram is the unit of mass, and the second is the unit of time. (1.3)

microwaves Electromagnetic radiation with wavelengths slightly longer than those of infrared radiation; used for radar and in microwave ovens. (7.2)

millibar (mbar) A unit of pressure equal to 10^{-3} bar or 100 Pa. (5.2)

millilitre (mL) A unit of volume equal to 10^{-3} L or 1 cm^3. (1.3)

millimetre of mercury (mmHg) A common unit of pressure referring to the air pressure required to push a column of mercury to a height of 1 mm in a barometer; 760 mmHg = 1 atm. (5.2)

minerals Homogenous, naturally occurring, crystalline inorganic solids. (24.2)

miscibility The ability to mix without separating into two phases. (11.3)

miscible The ability of two or more substances to be soluble in each other in all proportions. (12.2)

molality (*m*) A means of expressing solution concentration as the number of moles of solute per kilogram of solvent. (12.5)

molar heat capacity The amount of heat required to raise the temperature of one mole of a substance by 1 °C. (6.4)

molar mass The mass in grams of one mole of atoms of an element; numerically equivalent to the atomic mass of the element in u. (2.6)

molar solubility The solubility of a compound in units of moles per litre. (16.5)

molar volume The volume occupied by one mole of a substance. (5.5)

molarity (*M*) A means of expressing solution concentration as the number of moles of solute per litre of solution. (4.9, 12.5)

mole (mol) A unit defined as the amount of material containing 6.0221421×10^{23} (Avogadro's number) particles. (2.6)

mole fraction (χ_A) The number of moles of a component in a mixture divided by the total number of moles in the mixture. (5.6)

mole fraction (χ_{solute}) A means of expressing solution concentration as the number of moles of solute per moles of solution. (12.5)

mole percent A means of expressing solution concentration as the mole fraction multiplied by 100%. (12.5)

molecular compound Compounds composed of two or more covalently bonded nonmetals. (3.3)

molecular element Those elements that exist in nature with diatomic or polyatomic molecules as their basic unit. (3.3)

molecular equation An equation showing the complete neutral formula for each compound in a reaction. (4.4)

molecular formula A chemical formula that shows the actual number of atoms of each element in a molecule of a compound. (3.3)

molecular geometry The geometrical arrangement of atoms in a molecule. (10.3)

molecular orbital theory An advanced model of chemical bonding in which electrons reside in molecular orbitals delocalized over the entire molecule. In the simplest version, the molecular orbitals are simply linear combinations of atomic orbitals. (10.8)

molecular solids Solids whose composite units are molecules; they generally have low melting points. (11.12)

molecularity The number of reactant particles involved in an elementary step. (13.6)

monodentate Describes ligands that donate only one electron pair to the central metal. (25.3)

monomer The individual unit repeated in a chain to form a polymer. (21.10)

monoprotic acid An acid that contains only one ionizable proton. (15.4)

monosaccharide A simple carbohydrate containing 3 to 8 carbon atoms, with only one aldhehyde or ketone group. (22.3)

nanotubes Long, tubular structures consisting of interconnected C_6 rings. (23.5)

natural abundance The relative percentage of a particular isotope in a naturally occurring sample with respect to other isotopes of the same element. (2.4)

Nernst equation The equation relating the cell potential of an electrochemical cell to the standard cell potential and the reaction quotient $E_{cell} = E^{\circ}_{cell} - \frac{0.0257\ V}{n} \log Q$. (18.5)

net ionic equation An equation that shows only the species that actually change during the reaction. (4.4)

network covalent atomic solids Atomic solids held together by covalent bonds; they have high melting points. (11.12)

neutral The state of a solution where the concentrations of H_3O^+ and OH^- are equal. (15.6)

neutralization reaction The reaction between an acid and a base. (4.5)

neutron An electrically neutral subatomic particle found in the nucleus of an atom, with a mass almost equal to that of a proton. (2.4)

Newman projection formula A representation of a molecular conformation in which one looks down the C—C bond of interest. (20.6)

nickel–cadmium (NiCad) battery A battery that consists of an anode composed of solid cadmium and a cathode composed of NiO(OH)(*s*) in a KOH solution. (18.6)

nickel–metal hydride (NiMH) battery A battery that uses the same cathode reaction as the NiCad battery but a different anode reaction, the oxidation of hydrogens in a metal alloy. (18.6)

***nido*-boranes** Boranes that have the formula B_nH_{n+4} and consist of a cage of boron atoms missing one corner. (23.4)

nitration An electrophilic aromatic substitution reaction in which a hydrogen is replaced by an NO_2 group. (21.9)

noble gases The group 18 elements, which are largely unreactive (inert) due to their stable filled *p* orbitals. (2.7)

node A point where the wave function (ψ), and therefore the probability density (ψ^2) and radial distribution function, all go through zero. (7.6)

nonbonding atomic radius The radius of an atom determined from the distance between atomic centres in an atomic solid. (8.5)

nonbonding atomic solids Atomic solids held together by dispersion forces; they have low melting points. (11.12)

nonbonding electrons Lone-pair electrons. (9.4)

nonbonding orbital An orbital whose electrons remain localized on an atom. (10.8)

nonelectrolyte A compound that does not dissociate into ions when dissolved in water. (4.3)

nonmetal A class of elements that tend to be poor conductors of heat and electricity and usually gain electrons during chemical reactions. (2.7)

nonvolatile Not easily vaporized. (11.5)

normal boiling point The temperature at which the vapour pressure of a liquid equals 1 atm or 760 Torr. (11.5)

n-type semiconductor A semiconductor that employs negatively charged electrons in the conduction band as the charge carriers. (10.8)

nuclear binding energy The amount of energy that would be required to break apart the nucleus into its component nucleons. (19.8)

nuclear equation An equation that represents nuclear processes such as radioactivity. (19.3)

nuclear fission The splitting of the nucleus of an atom, resulting in a tremendous release of energy. (19.7)

nuclear fusion The combination of two light nuclei to form a heavier one. (19.9)

nuclear magnetic resonance (NMR) spectroscopy A type of spectroscopy that measures the difference in energy between nuclear spin states under an external magnetic field. (20.8)

nuclear theory The theory that most of the atom's mass and all of its positive charge is contained in a small, dense nucleus. (2.4)

nucleophile A chemical species that can donate electrons to an electrophilic site on another molecule, leading to bond formation. (21.4)

nucleophilic addition The addition reaction between a nucleophile and an aldehyde or ketone. (21.7)

nucleophilicity A measure of the effectiveness, or strength, of a nucleophile. (21.4)

nucleotide The individual unit composing nucleic acids; each consists of a phosphate group, a sugar, and a nitrogenous base. (22.6)

nucleus The very small, dense core of the atom that contains most of the atom's mass and all of its positive charge; it is composed of protons and neutrons. (2.4)

nuclide A particular isotope of an atom. (19.3)

octahedral geometry The molecular geometry of seven atoms with 90° bond angles. (10.2)

octahedral hole A space that exists in the middle of six atoms on two adjacent close-packed sheets of atoms in a crystal lattice. (24.4)

octet Eight electrons in the valence shell of an atom. (9.3)

octet rule The tendency for most bonded atoms to possess or share eight electrons in their outer shell to obtain stable electron configurations and lower their potential energy. (9.3)

1,2 elimination The loss of atoms or groups, bonded to adjacent carbon atoms in an alkane, yielding an alkene. (21.5)

optical activity The ability of chiral compounds to rotate the plane of plane-polarized light. (20.7)

orbital A probability distribution map, based on the quantum-mechanical model of the atom, used to describe the likely position of an electron in an atom; also an allowed energy state for an electron. (7.5)

orbital diagram A diagram which gives information similar to an electron configuration, but symbolizes an electron as an arrow in a box representing an orbital, with the arrow's direction denoting the electron's spin. (7.7)

ore A rock that contains a high concentration of a specific mineral. (24.2)

organic chemistry The study of carbon-based compounds. (20.1)

organic compound A molecular compound composed of carbon, hydrogen, and possibly nitrogen, oxygen, sulfur, or a halogen. (3.5)

organic molecule A molecule containing carbon combined with several other elements including hydrogen, nitrogen, oxygen, or sulfur. (20.1)

orientation factor In the collision model, the fraction of sufficiently energetic collisions in which the reactants are in the correct orientation to react. (13.5)

orthosilicates Silicates in which tetrahedral SO_4^{4-} ions stand alone. (23.3)

osmosis The flow of solvent from a solution of lower solute concentration to one of higher solute concentration. (12.6)

osmotic pressure The pressure required to stop osmotic flow. (12.6)

Ostwald process An industrial process used for commercial preparation of nitric acid. (23.6)

overall order The sum of the orders of all reactants in a chemical reaction. (13.3)

overpotential Additional voltage that must be applied in order to make some nonspontaneous electrolysis reactions occur. (18.7)

oxalyl chloride $(COCl)_2$, a reagent used to convert a carboxylic acid to the corresponding acyl chloride. (21.8)

oxidation The loss of one or more electrons; also the gaining of oxygen or the loss of hydrogen. (4.6)

oxidation state A positive or negative whole number that represents the "charge" an atom in a compound would have if all shared electrons were assigned to the atom with a greater attraction for those electrons. (4.6)

oxidation–reduction (redox) reaction Reactions in which electrons are transferred from one reactant to another and the oxidation states of certain atoms are changed. (4.6)

oxidizing agent A substance that causes the oxidation of another substance; an oxidizing agent gains electrons and is reduced. (4.6)

oxonium ion A chemical species in which an oxygen atom carries a formal positive charge. (21.5)

oxyacid An acid composed of hydrogen and an oxyanion. (3.4)

oxyanion A polyatomic anion containing a nonmetal covalently bonded to one or more oxygen atoms. (3.4)

ozone O_3, an allotrope of oxygen that is a toxic, blue, diamagnetic gas with a strong odour. (23.7)

packing efficiency The percentage of volume of a unit cell occupied by the atoms, assumed to be spherical. (11.11)

paramagnetic The state of an atom or ion that contains unpaired electrons and is, therefore, attracted by an external magnetic field. (7.7)

parent formula The formula of the aliphatic alkane that has the same number of carbon atoms in a given organic compound. (20.8)

partial pressure (P_n) The pressure due to any individual component in a gas mixture. (5.6)

parts by mass A unit for expressing solution concentration as the mass of the solute divided by the mass of the solution, multiplied by a multiplication factor. (12.5)

parts by volume A unit for expressing solution concentration as the volume of the solute divided by the volume of the solution, multiplied by a multiplication factor. (12.5)

parts per billion (ppb) A unit for expressing solution concentration in parts by mass where the multiplication factor is 10^9. (12.5)

parts per million (ppm) A unit for expressing solution concentration in parts by mass where the multiplication factor is 10^6. (12.5)

pascal (Pa) The SI unit of pressure, defined as $1\ N\ m^{-2}$. (5.2)

Pauli exclusion principle The principle that no two electrons in an atom can have the same four quantum numbers. (7.7)

penetrating power The ability of radiation to penetrate matter. (19.3)

penetration The phenomenon of some higher-level atomic orbitals having significant amounts of probability within the space occupied by orbitals of lower energy level. For example, the 2*s* orbital penetrates into the 1*s* orbital. (7.7)

peptide bond The amide group that joins two amino acids. (22.4)

percent by mass A unit for expressing solution concentration in parts by mass with a multiplication factor of 100%. (12.5)

percent ionic character The ratio of a bond's actual dipole moment to the dipole moment it would have if the electron were transferred completely from one atom to the other, multiplied by 100%. (9.7)

percent ionization The concentration of ionized acid in a solution divided by the initial concentration of acid, multiplied by 100%. (15.7)

percent yield The percentage of the theoretical yield of a chemical reaction that is actually produced; the ratio of the actual yield to the theoretical yield, multiplied by 100%. (4.8)

period A row in the periodic table. (2.7)

periodic law A law based on the observation that when the elements are arranged in order of increasing mass, certain sets of properties recur periodically. (2.7)

periodic property A property of an element that is predictable based on an element's position in the periodic table. (8.1)

permanent dipole A permanent separation of charge; a molecule with a permanent dipole always has a slightly negative charge at one end and a slightly positive charge at the other. (11.3)

pH The negative log of the concentration of H_3O^+ in a solution; the pH scale is a compact way to specify the acidity of a solution. (15.6)

phase The sign of the amplitude of a wave; can be positive or negative. (7.6)

phase diagram A map of the phase of a substance as a function of pressure and temperature. (11.8)

phenyl group A benzene ring as a substituent in an organic molecule. (3.5)

phosphine PH_3, a colourless, poisonous gas that smells like decaying fish and has an oxidation state of -3 for phosphorus. (23.6)

phospholipid Compound similar in structure to a triglyceride but with one fatty acid replaced by a phosphate group. (22.2)

phosphorescence The long-lived emission of light that sometimes follows the absorption of light by certain atoms and molecules. (19.2)

photoelectric effect The observation that many metals emit electrons when light falls upon them. (7.2)

photon (quantum) The smallest possible packet of electromagnetic radiation with an energy equal to $h\nu$. (7.2)

phyllosilicates Minerals having sheets of silica tetrahedra. (23.3)

physical change A change that alters only the state or appearance of a substance but not its chemical composition. (1.1)

physical property A property that a substance displays without changing its chemical composition. (1.1)

pi (π) bond The bond that forms between two *p* orbitals that overlap side to side. (10.7)

p–n junctions Tiny areas in electronic circuits that have p-type semiconductors on one side and n-type on the other. (10.8)

polar covalent bond A covalent bond between two atoms with significantly different electronegativities, resulting in an uneven distribution of electron density. (9.7)

polyamide A step growth polymer in which monomers are connected by amide groups. (21.10)

polyatomic ion An ion composed of two or more atoms. (3.3)

polydentate Describes ligands that donate more than one electron pair to the central metal. (25.3)

polyester A step growth polymer in which monomers are connected by ester groups. (21.10)

polyethylene An addition polymer made from the monomer ethene (ethylene). (21.10)

poly (ethylene terephthalate) (PET) A step-growth polymer composed of the monomers dimethyl terephthalate and ethan-1,2-diol. (21.10)

polymer A long, chain-like molecule composed of repeating units called monomers. (21.10)

polypeptide A chain of amino acids joined together by peptide bonds. (22.4)

polyprotic acid An acid that contains more than one ionizable proton and releases them sequentially. (4.5, 15.9)

polysaccharide A long, chain-like molecule composed of many monosaccharide units bonded together. (22.3)

poly (vinyl chloride) (PVC) An addition polymer made from the monomer chloroethene. (21.10)

positron The particle released in positron emission; equal in mass to an electron but opposite in charge. (19.3)

positron emission The form of radioactive decay that occurs when an unstable nucleus emits a positron. (19.3)

positron emission tomography (PET) A specialized imaging technique that employs positron-emitting nuclides, such as fluorine-18, as a radiotracer. (19.12)

potential difference A measure of the difference in potential energy (usually in joules) per unit of charge (coulombs). (18.2)

potential energy The energy associated with the position or composition of an object. (1.2, 6.2)

powder metallurgy A process by which metallic components are made from powdered metal. (24.3)

precipitate A solid, insoluble ionic compound that forms in, and separates from, a solution. (4.4)

precipitation reaction A reaction in which a solid, insoluble product forms upon mixing two solutions. (4.4)

precision A term that refers to how close a series of measurements are to one another or how reproducible they are. (1.4)

prefix multipliers Multipliers that change the value of the unit by powers of 10. (1.3)

pressure A measure of force exerted per unit area; in chemistry, most commonly the force exerted by gas molecules as they strike the surfaces around them. (5.1)

pressure–volume work The work that occurs when a volume change takes place against an external pressure. (6.4)

primary structure The sequence of amino acids in a protein chain. (22.5)

primary valence The oxidation state on the central metal atom in a complex ion. (25.3)

principal group The highest priority functional group in an organic molecule, which determines the suffix in the name. (3.5)

principal level (shell) The group of orbitals with the same value of *n*. (7.5)

principal quantum number (*n*) An integer that specifies the overall size and energy of an orbital. The higher the quantum number, *n*, the greater the average distance between the electron and the nucleus and the higher its energy. (7.5)

probability density The probability (per unit volume) of finding the electron at a point in space as expressed by a three-dimensional plot of the wave function squared (ψ^2). (7.6)

products The substances produced in a chemical reaction; they appear on the right-hand side of a chemical equation. (4.2)

proton A positively charged subatomic particle found in the nucleus of an atom. (2.5)

p-type semiconductor A semiconductor that employs positively charged "holes" in the valence band as the charge carriers. (10.8)

pyrometallurgy A technique of extractive metallurgy in which heat is used to extract a metal from its mineral. (24.3)

pyrosilicates Silicates in which two SO_4^{4-} tetrahedral ions share a corner. (23.3)

pyroxenes Silicates in which SO_4^{4-} tetrahedral ions bond together to form chains. (23.3)

qualitative analysis A systematic way to determine the ions present in an unknown solution. (16.7)

quantitative analysis A systematic way to determine the amounts of substances in a solution or mixture. (16.7)

quantum number One of four interrelated numbers that determine the shape and energy of orbitals, as specified by a solution of the Schrödinger equation. (7.5)

quantum-mechanical model A model that explains how electrons exist in atoms. (7.1)

quartz A silicate crystal which has a formula unit of SiO_2. (23.3)

quaternary structure The way that subunits fit together in a multimeric protein. (22.5)

R group General representation of an alkyl group in an organic compound. (20.4)

***R, S* system** The protocol for assigning stereochemical configuration of a chirality centre. (20.7)

racemic mixture An equimolar mixture of two enantiomers that does not rotate the plane of polarization of light at all. (20.7)

racemization The loss of stereochemical purity in a chemical reaction, such as in S_N1 substitutions. (21.4)

radial distribution function A function that represents the total probability of finding an electron within a thin spherical shell at a distance *r* from the nucleus. (7.6)

radial node A spherical region in which there is zero probability of finding an electron. (7.6)

radiation weighting factor (W_R) The factor that the absorbed dose is multiplied by to give the equivalent dose. (19.11)

radio waves The form of electromagnetic radiation with the longest wavelengths and smallest energy. (7.2)

radioactive The state of those unstable atoms that emit subatomic particles or high-energy electromagnetic radiation. (19.1)

radioactivity The emission of subatomic particles or high-energy electromagnetic radiation by the unstable nuclei of certain atoms. (2.4, 19.1)

radiocarbon dating A form of radiometric dating based on the C-14 isotope. (19.6)

radiometric dating A technique used to estimate the age of rocks, fossils, or artifacts that depends on the presence of radioactive isotopes and their predictable decay with time. (19.6)

radiotracer A radioactive nuclide that has been attached to a compound or introduced into a mixture in order to track the movement of the compound or mixture within the body. (19.12)

random coil Section of a protein's secondary structure that has a less regular pattern than α-helixes or β-pleated sheets. (22.5)

random error Error that has equal probability of being too high or too low. (1.4)

Raoult's law An equation used to determine the vapour pressure of a solution; $P_{soln} = X_{solv}P°_{solv}$. (12.6)

rate constant (*k*) A constant of proportionality in the rate law. (13.3)

rate law A relationship between the rate of a reaction and the concentration of the reactants. (13.3)

rate-determining step The step in a reaction mechanism that occurs much more slowly than any of the other steps. (13.6)

reactants Substances that are consumed in a chemical reaction. (4.2)

reaction intermediates Species that are formed in one step of a reaction mechanism and consumed in another. (13.6)

reaction mechanism A series of individual chemical steps by which an overall chemical reaction occurs. (13.6)

reaction order A value in the rate law that determines how the rate depends on the concentration of the reactants. (13.3)

reaction quotient (*Q*) The ratio, at any point in the reaction, of the concentrations or partial pressures of the products of a reaction raised to their stoichiometric coefficients to the concentrations or partial pressures of the reactants raised to their stoichiometric coefficients. (14.6)

real gas A gas that does not obey the assumptions that define an ideal gas. (5.10)

recrystallization A technique used to purify solids in which the solid is put into hot solvent until the solution is saturated; when the solution cools, the purified solute comes out of solution. (12.4)

red phosphorus An allotrope of phosphorus similar in structure to white phosphorus but with one of the bonds between two phosphorus atoms in the tetrahedron broken; red phosphorus is more stable than white. (23.6)

redox reaction A chemical reaction in which electrons are transferred from one reactant to another. (4.6)

reducing agent A substance that causes the reduction of another substance; a reducing agent loses electrons and is oxidized. (4.6)

reduction The gaining of one or more electrons; also the gaining of hydrogen or the loss of oxygen. (4.6)

refining A process in which the crude material is purified. (24.3)

resonance effect The stabilization of a chemical species through π delocalization. (21.2)

resonance hybrid The actual structure of a molecule that is intermediate between two or more resonance structures. (9.8)

resonance structures Two or more valid Lewis structures that are shown with double-headed arrows between them to indicate that the actual structure of the molecule is intermediate between them. (9.8)

reversible As applied to a reaction, the ability to proceed in either the forward or the reverse direction. (14.2)

reversible process A reaction that achieves the theoretical limit with respect to free energy. (17.4)

reversible reaction A reaction that achieves the theoretical limit with respect to free energy and will change direction upon an infinitesimally small change in a variable (such as temperature or pressure) related to the reaction. (17.7)

roasting Heating that causes a chemical reaction between a furnace atmosphere and a mineral in order to process ores. (24.3)

rotamer A conformational isomer. (20.6)

sacrificial anode An anode used to prevent corrosion that consists of a metal that is more easily oxidized than the metal object to be protected. (18.8)

salt An ionic compound formed in a neutralization reaction by the replacement of an H^+ ion from the acid with a cation from the base. (4.5)

salt bridge An inverted, U-shaped tube containing a strong electrolyte such as KNO_3 that connects the two half-cells, allowing a flow of ions that neutralizes the charge buildup. (18.2)

saturated fat A triglyceride with no double bonds in the hydrocarbon chain; saturated fats tend to be solid at room temperature. (22.2)

saturated hydrocarbon A hydrocarbon containing no double bonds in the carbon chain. (20.3)

saturated solution A solution in which the dissolved solute is in dynamic equilibrium with any undissolved solute; any added solute will not dissolve. (12.4)

scintillation counter A device for the detection of radioactivity using a material that emits ultraviolet or visible light in response to excitation by energetic particles. (19.5)

second (s) The SI standard unit of time, defined as the duration of 9 192 631 770 periods of the radiation emitted from a certain transition in a cesium-133 atom. (1.3)

second law of thermodynamics A law stating that for any spontaneous process, the entropy of the universe increases ($\Delta S_{univ} > 0$). (17.2)

secondary structure The regular periodic or repeating patterns in the arrangement of protein chains. (22.5)

secondary valence The number of molecules or ions directly bound to the metal atom in a complex ion; also called the *coordination number.* (25.3)

seesaw geometry The molecular geometry of a molecule with trigonal bipyramidal electron geometry and one lone pair in an axial position. (10.3)

selective precipitation A process involving the addition of a reagent to a solution that forms a precipitate with one of the dissolved ions but not the others. (16.6)

semiconductor A material with intermediate electrical conductivity that can be changed and controlled. (2.7)

semipermeable membrane A membrane that selectively allows some substances to pass through but not others. (12.6)

shielding The effect on an electron of repulsion by electrons in lower energy orbitals that screen it from the full effects of nuclear charge. (7.7)

sievert (Sv) The SI unit for equivalent dose. (19.11)

sigma (σ) bond The resulting bond that forms between a combination of any two *s, p,* or hybridized orbitals that overlap end to end. (10.7)

significant figures (significant digits) In any reported measurement, the nonplaceholding digits that indicate the precision of the measured quantity. (1.4)

silica A silicate crystal which has a formula unit of SiO_2, also called *quartz.* (23.3)

silicates Covalent atomic solids that contain silicon, oxygen, and various metal atoms. (23.3)

simple cubic A unit cell that consists of a cube with one atom at each corner. (11.11)

slag In pyrometallurgy, the waste liquid solution that is formed between the flux and gangue; usually a silicate material. (24.3)

Slater's rules Empirical rules for estimating the shielding constant and the effective nuclear charge experienced by each valence electron. (8.5)

smelting A form of roasting in which the product is liquefied, which aids in the separation. (24.3)

solubility The amount of a substance that will dissolve in a given amount of solvent. (12.2)

solubility product constant (K_{sp}) The equilibrium expression for a chemical equation representing the dissolution of a slightly to moderately soluble ionic compound. (16.5)

soluble The ability to dissolve to a significant extent, usually in water. (4.3)

solute The minority component of a solution. (4.3, 12.1)

solution A homogenous mixture of two substances. (4.3, 12.1)

solvent The majority component of a solution. (4.3, 12.1)

soot An amorphous form of carbon that forms during the incomplete combustion of hydrocarbons. (23.5)

space-filling model A representation of a molecule that shows how the atoms fill the space between them. (3.3)

specific heat capacity (C_s) The amount of heat required to raise the temperature of 1 g of a substance by 1 °C. (6.4)

spectator ion Ions in a complete ionic equation that do not participate in the reaction and therefore remain in solution. (4.4)

spherical node See *radial node*. (7.6)

spin quantum number (m_s) The fourth quantum number, which denotes the electron's spin as either ½ (up arrow) or −½ (down arrow). (7.7)

spontaneous process A process that occurs without ongoing outside intervention. Gibbs energy is released in a spontaneous process. (17.1)

square planar geometry The molecular geometry of a molecule with octahedral electron geometry and two lone pairs. (10.3)

square pyramidal geometry The molecular geometry of a molecule with octahedral electron geometry and one lone pair. (10.3)

staggered conformation The rotational conformation about a C–C bond in which the groups are located 60° from each other. (20.6)

standard boiling point The temperature at which the vapour pressure of a liquid equals 1 bar. (11.5)

standard cell potential (standard emf) ($E°_{cell}$) The cell potential for a system in standard states (solute concentration of 1 mol L^{-1} and gaseous reactant partial pressure of 1 atm). (18.2)

standard change in free energy The change in free energy for a process when all reactants and products are in their standard states. (17.7)

standard change in Gibbs energy ($\Delta_r G°$) The criterion for reaction spontaneity, calculated either from the standard changes in enthalpy and entropy, or from tabulated values of Gibbs energies of formation. (17.7)

standard electrode potential The potential of an electrode in a half-cell. (18.3)

standard enthalpy change ($\Delta H°$) The change in enthalpy for a process when all reactants and products are in their standard states. (6.9)

standard enthalpy of formation ($\Delta_f H°$) The change in enthalpy when 1 mol of a compound forms from its constituent elements in their standard states. (6.9)

standard entropy change for a reaction ($\Delta_r S°$) The change in entropy for a process in which all reactants and products are in their standard states. (17.6)

standard heat of formation ($\Delta_f H°$) See *standard enthalpy of formation.* (6.9)

standard hydrogen electrode (SHE) The half-cell consisting of an inert platinum electrode immersed in 1 mol L^{-1} HCl with hydrogen gas at 1 atm bubbling through the solution; used as the standard of a cell potential of zero. (18.3)

standard molar entropy ($S°$) A measure of the energy dispersed into one mole of a substance at a particular temperature. (17.6)

standard pressure 100 000 Pa, or 1 bar. (5.2)

standard state For a gas the standard state is the pure gas at a pressure of exactly 1 bar; for a liquid or solid the standard state is the pure substance in its most stable form at a pressure of 1 bar and the temperature of interest (often taken to be 25 °C); for a substance in solution the standard state is a concentration of exactly 1 mol L^{-1}. (6.9)

standard temperature and pressure (STP) The conditions of $T = 0$ °C (273.15 K) and $P = 1$ bar; used primarily in reference to a gas, also known as *standard conditions*. (5.5)

starch A polysaccharide that consists of glucose units bonded together by α-glycosidic linkages; the main energy storage medium for plants. (22.3)

state function A function whose value depends only on the state of the system, not on how the system got to that state. (6.3)

steady-state approximation The assumption that the rate of formation of an intermediate is equal to its rate of consumption. (13.6)

step-growth polymerization See *condensation (step-growth) polymerization*. (21.10)

stereoisomers Molecules in which the atoms are bonded in the same order, but have a different spatial arrangement. (25.4)

steric strain The repulsive interaction between groups bonded to adjacent carbon atoms that hinders bond rotation. (20.6)

steroid A lipid with a four-ring structure. (22.2)

stock solution A highly concentrated form of a solution used in laboratories to make less concentrated solutions via dilution. (4.9)

stoichiometry The numerical relationships between amounts of reactants and products in a balanced chemical equation. (4.7)

stretching vibration A molecular motion in which a bond stretches and then contracts. (9.6)

strong acid An acid that completely ionizes in solution. (4.3, 15.4)

strong base A base that completely dissociates in solution. (15.5)

strong electrolyte A substance that completely dissociates into ions when dissolved in water. (4.3)

strong force Of the four fundamental forces of physics, the one that is the strongest but acts over the shortest distance; the strong force is responsible for holding the protons and neutrons together in the nucleus of an atom. (19.4)

strong-field complex A complex ion in which the crystal field splitting is large. (25.5)

structural formula A molecular formula that shows how the atoms in a molecule are connected or bonded to each other. (3.3, 20.3)

structural isomers Molecules with the same molecular formula but different structures. (20.3, 25.4)

sublevel (subshell) Those orbitals in the same principal level with the same value of n and l. (7.5)

sublimation The phase transition from solid to gas. (11.6)

substituent An atom or group of atoms that has been substituted for a hydrogen atom in an organic compound. (3.5)

substitutional alloy An alloy in which one metal atom substitutes for another in the crystal structure. (24.4)

substrate The reactant molecule of a biochemical reaction that binds to an enzyme at the active site. (13.7)

supersaturated solution An unstable solution in which more than the equilibrium amount of solute is dissolved. (12.4)

surface tension The energy required to increase the surface area of a liquid by a unit amount; responsible for the tendency of liquids to minimize their surface area, giving rise to a membrane-like surface. (11.4)

surroundings In thermodynamics, everything in the universe which exists outside the system under investigation. (6.2)

synthesis The process of making compounds in one or more steps. (21.1)

system In thermodynamics, the portion of the universe which is singled out for investigation. (6.2)

systematic error Error that tends towards being consistently either too high or too low. (1.4)

systematic name An official name for a compound, based on well-established rules, that can be determined by examining its chemical structure. (3.4)

temperature A measure of the average kinetic energy of the atoms or molecules that compose a sample of matter. (1.3)

termolecular An elementary step of a reaction in which three particles collide and go on to form products. (13.6)

tertiary structure The large-scale bends and folds produced by interactions between the R groups of amino acids that are separated by large distances in the linear sequence of a protein chain. (22.5)

tetrahedral geometry The molecular geometry of five atoms with 109.5° bond angles. (10.2)

tetrahedral hole A space that exists directly above the centre point of three closest packed metal atoms in one plane, and a fourth metal located directly above the centre point in the adjacent plane in a crystal lattice. (24.4)

theoretical yield The greatest possible amount of product that can be made in a chemical reaction based on the amount of limiting reactant. (4.8)

thermal energy A type of kinetic energy associated with the temperature of an object, arising from the motion of individual atoms or molecules in the object; see also *heat*. (1.2, 6.2)

thermal equilibrium The point at which there is no additional net transfer of heat between a system and its surroundings. (6.4)

thermochemistry The study of the relationship between chemistry and energy. (6.1)

thermodynamics The general study of energy and its interconversions. (6.3)

thionyl chloride $SOCl_2$, a reagent used to convert a carboxylic acid to the corresponding acyl chloride. (21.8)

third law of thermodynamics The law stating that the entropy of a perfect crystal at absolute zero (0 K) is zero. (17.6)

three-dimensional formula A representation of a molecular shape in three dimensions, showing some bonds as solid and hashed wedges. (20.6)

torr The unit equal to one millimetre of mercury and 133.3 Pa. (5.2)

torsional strain The difference in potential energy of staggered and eclipsed conformations. (20.6)

transesterification The conversion of one ester to another, by the reaction between an ester and an alcohol in the presence of acid. (21.8)

transition elements (transition metals) Those elements found in the *d* block of the periodic table whose properties tend to be less predictable based simply on their position in the table. (2.7)

transmutation The transformation of one element into another as a result of nuclear reactions. (19.10)

triglyceride Triesters composed of glycerol with three fatty acids attached. (22.2)

trigonal bipyramidal geometry The molecular geometry of six atoms with 120° bond angles between the three equatorial electron groups and 90° bond angles between the two axial electron groups and the trigonal plane. (10.2)

trigonal planar geometry The molecular geometry of four atoms with 120° bond angles in a plane. (10.2)

trigonal pyramidal geometry The molecular geometry of a molecule with tetrahedral electron geometry and one lone pair. (10.3)

triple bond The bond that forms when three electron pairs are shared between two atoms. (9.4)

triple point The unique set of conditions at which all three phases of a substance are equally stable and in equilibrium. (11.8)

triprotic acid An acid that contains three ionizable protons. (15.4)

T-shaped geometry The molecular geometry of a molecule with trigonal bipyramidal electron geometry and two lone pairs in axial positions. (10.3)

two-phase region The region between the two phases in a metal alloy phase diagram, where the amount of each phase depends upon the composition of the alloy. (24.4)

Tyndall effect The scattering of light by a colloidal dispersion. (12.8)

ultraviolet (UV) radiation Electromagnetic radiation with slightly smaller wavelengths than visible light. (7.2)

unified atomic mass unit (u) A unit used to express the masses of atoms and subatomic particles, defined as 1/12th the mass of a carbon atom containing six protons and six neutrons. (2.4)

unimolecular Describes a reaction that involves only one particle that goes on to form products. (13.6)

unit cell The smallest divisible unit of a crystal that, when repeated in three dimensions, reproduces the entire crystal lattice. (11.11)

units Standard quantities used to specify measurements. (1.3)

unsaturated fat A triglyceride with one or more double bonds in the hydrocarbon chain; unsaturated fats tend to be liquid at room temperature. (22.2)

unsaturated hydrocarbon A hydrocarbon that includes one or more double or triple bonds. (20.3)

unsaturated solution A solution containing less than the equilibrium amount of solute; any added solute will dissolve until equilibrium is reached. (12.4)

valence band In solids, a lower energy set of filled molecular orbitals. (10.8)

valence bond theory An advanced model of chemical bonding in which electrons reside in quantum-mechanical orbitals localized on individual atoms that are a hybridized blend of standard atomic orbitals; chemical bonds result from an overlap of these orbitals. (10.6)

valence electrons The electrons important in chemical bonding. For main-group elements, these electrons are in the outermost principal energy level. (7.7, 8.3)

valence shell electron pair repulsion (VSEPR) theory A theory that allows prediction of the shapes of molecules based on the idea that electrons—either as lone pairs or as bonding pairs—repel one another. (10.2)

van der Waals equation The extrapolation of the ideal gas law that considers the effects of intermolecular forces and particle volume in a nonideal gas: $P + a\left(\frac{n}{V}\right)^2 \times (V - nb) = nRT$ (5.10)

van der Waals radius (nonbonding atomic radius) Defined as one-half the distance between the centres of adjacent, nonbonding atoms in a crystal. (8.5)

van't Hoff factor (*i*) The ratio of moles of particles in a solution to moles of formula units dissolved. (12.7)

vaporization The phase transition from liquid to gas. (11.5)

vapour pressure The partial pressure of a vapour in dynamic equilibrium with its liquid. (5.6, 11.5)

vapour pressure lowering (ΔP) The difference in vapour pressure between a pure solvent and a solution of the solvent $\Delta P = P^{\circ}_{\text{solvent}} - P_{\text{solvent}}$. (12.6)

viscosity A measure of the resistance of a liquid to flow. (11.4)

visible light Those frequencies of electromagnetic radiation that can be detected by the human eye. (7.2)

volatile Tending to vaporize easily. (11.5)

volt (V) The SI unit of potential difference. (18.2)

voltaic (galvanic) cell An electrochemical cell which produces electrical current from a spontaneous chemical reaction. (18.2)

volume (*V*) A measure of space. Any unit of length, when cubed (raised to the third power), becomes a unit of volume. (1.3)

washing soda The hydrated crystal of sodium carbonate, $Na_2CO_3 \cdot 10\,H_2O$. (23.5)

wave function (ψ) A mathematical function that describes the wave-like nature of the electron. (7.5)

wavelength (λ) The distance between adjacent crests of a wave. (7.2)

wavenumber The reciprocal of wavelength. (9.6)

weak acid An acid that does not completely ionize in water. (4.3, 15.4)

weak base A base that only partially ionizes in water. (15.5)

weak electrolyte A substance that does not completely ionize in water and only weakly conducts electricity in solution. (4.3)

weak-field complex A complex ion in which the crystal field splitting is small. (25.5)

white phosphorus An unstable allotrope of phosphorus consisting of P_4 molecules in a tetrahedral shape, with the phosphorus atoms at the corners of the tetrahedron. (23.6)

work (*w*) The result of a force acting through a distance. (6.2)

X-ray diffraction A powerful laboratory technique that allows for the determination of the arrangement of atoms in a crystal and the measuring of the distance between them. (11.10)

X-rays Electromagnetic radiation with wavelengths slightly longer than those of gamma rays; used to image bones and internal organs. (7.2)

Zaitsev's rule When isomeric alkenes are produced in an elimination reaction, the major product is usually the most substituted alkene. (21.5)

zero-point energy The tiny amount of energy that substances have at 0 K that is due to the uncertainty principle. (17.6)

zwitterion A molecule that has positive and negative formal charges on different atoms, but has no net charge. (22.4)

Photo Credits

Chapter 1 Page 2, center right: Siede Preis/Photodisc/Getty Images; center left: Michael Dalton/Fundamental Photographs. Page 4, center left: Winnipeg Free Press/Wayne Glowacki/The Canadian Press. Page 5, Pressmaster/Fotolia. Page 11, bottom right: Vesna Njagulj/Dreamstime; bottom left: IBM Research/Zurich. Page 13, top left: Richard Megna/Fundamental Photographs; top center: Richard Megna/Fundamental Photographs; center right: Stacey Stambaugh/Pearson Education; center right: Richard Megna/ Fundamental Photographs. Page 24, bottom left: Roman Sigaev/Fotolia; center left: Richard Megna/Fundamental Photographs; center right: Richard Megna/Fundamental Photographs. Page 25, center right: Stacey Stambaugh/Pearson Education; center Stacey Stambaugh/Pearson Education; bottom left: Stacey Stambaugh/Pearson Education; center left: Stacey Stambaugh/Pearson Education; bottom center: Warren Rosenberg/ Fundamental Photographs; bottom right: Warren Rosenberg/Fundamental Photographs. Page 27, bottom left: NASA. **Chapter 2** Page 31, top left: Veeco Instruments; top center: IBM Research Division. Page 32, center left: Charles D. Winters/Science Source; center: "Charles D. Winters/Science Source"; center right: Joseph Calev/Shutterstock. Page 35, top center: Richard Megna/Fundamental Photographs. Page 37, center right: Rutherford Museum/McGill University; bottom right: Smithsonian Institution. Page 38, center left: Richard Megna/Fundamental Photographs. Page 41, bottom right: NASA. Page 47, bottom left: Dmitri Mendeleev; center right: Gary J. Shulfer/Lang C Marvin. Page 48, top center: Clive Streeter/DK Images; top center: Tom Bochsler/Pearson Education; top right: Mirek Hejnicki/Fotolia; top center: Steffen Foerster/Shutterstock; top right: Enricoros; top right: Gary Ombler/DK Images; top left: Matthias Zepper; top right: Harry Taylor/DK Images; top left: Charles D. Winters/Science Source; top right: Charles D. Winters/Science Source; center right: Perennou Nuridsany/Science Source. Page 49, center right: Richard Megna/Fundamental Photographs; bottom right: Martyn F. Chillmaid/ Science Source. Page 50, top left: Charles D. Winters/Science Source; center left: Charles D. Winters/Science Source. Page 54, bottom right: Almaden Research Center/IBM Research. **Chapter 3** Page 58, bottom right: Malerapaso/Getty Images. Page 59, bottom left: Richard Megna/Fundamental Photographs; bottom center: Charles Falco/ Science Source; bottom right: "Charles D. Winters/Science Source". Page 61, top right: 1999 Richard Megna/Fundamental Photographs; top right: 1999 Richard Megna/ Fundamental Photographs. Page 62, center left: "Charles D. Winters/Science Source." Page 63 top right: Charles Falco/Science Source. Page 64, bottom right: Basement Stock/ Alamy; bottom center: Sidney Moulds/Science Source. Page 67, center right: 2011 Richard Megna/Fundamental Photographs; center right: 2011 Richard Megna/Fundamental Photographs. Page 69, bottom center: Richard Megna/Fundamental Photographs; center right: Shutterstock. Page 70, bottom left: lightpoet/Fotolia. Page 83, top right: Jay Herman/ Goddard Space Flight Center/NASA. Page 86, center right: Lawton Shaw. **Chapter 4** Page 101, top left: Kitty/Shutterstock; center Eva Blanda/Shutterstock; top right: Stephen Rees/Shutterstock; top right: Fredredhat/Shutterstock. Page 102, center left: Travis D. Fridgen; top left: Teresa Kasprzycka/Shutterstock. Page 107, bottom right: Richard Megna/Fundamental Photographs; top left: Richard Megna/Fundamental Photographs; top center: Richard Megna/Fundamental Photographs; top right: Richard Megna/ Fundamental Photographs. Page 109, top right: Martyn F.Chillmaid/Science Source. Page 110, center DK Images. Page 112, bottom left: Eric Schrader/Pearson Science; top left: Eric Schrader/Pearson Science. Page 113, center left: "Richard Megna/Fundamental Photographs." Page 115 bottom left: Tom Bochsler/PH College/Pearson Education; bottom right: Charles D. Winters/Science Source. Page 116, top left: Richard Megna/Fundamental Photographs; top right: Richard Megna/Fundamental Photographs. Page 120, bottom right: Olga Sapegina/Fotolia. **Chapter 5** Page 153, center right: Patrick Watson/Pearson Education. Page 157, bottom right: Carlos Caetano/Shutterstock. Page 158, top left: Andy Crawford/DK Images. Page 161, top right: Renn Sminkey/CDV, LLC/Pearson Science. Page 167, center right: NASA. Page 186, center right: Hubble Heritage Team/NASA. Page 194, center left: Tom Bochsler/Pearson Education/PH College. **Chapter 6** Page 198, center left: Canadian Curling Association/Courtesy of TSN; top left: Canadian Curling Association/Courtesy of TSN; bottom left: Canadian Curling Association/Courtesy of TSN. Page 199, top right: Jodie Johnson/Fotolia. Page 201, top right: From the Historical and Interpretive Collections of The Franklin Institute, Philadelphia, PA. Page 202, top right: Stephen Barnes/Energy/Alamy; top left: Gl Archive/Alamy; top center: NASA. Page 206, top left: B Calkins/Shutterstock. Page 217, center right: Stan Fellerman/Corbis; center left: Tom Bochsler/Pearson Education. Page 227, center right: Richard Megna/ Fundamental Photographs. Page 237, bottom right: Manfredxy/Fotolia. Page 238, top right: Md8speed/Shutterstock. Page 239, center right: Shutterstock. **Chapter 7** Page center left: Juefraphoto/Fotolia. Page 214, center right: NASA. Page 241, center right: NASA; center right: Mark Yeg; center Multichill; center right: NASA; center Travis D. Fridgen. Page 243, center ExcellentPhoto/Getty Images. Page 245, top left: Richard Griffin/Fotolia. Page 246, center Poznyakov/Shutterstock; bottom left: Sierra Pacific Innovations. Page 247, top right: Pearson Education.; center right: Fermilab/Reidar Hahn; bottom right: Bonita R. Cheshier/Shutterstock. Page 253, bottom right: Karin Hildebrand Lau/Shutterstock. Page 254, top left: Tom Bochsler/Pearson Education; bottom American National Standards Institute/Pearson Science; center right: Sherri Camp/Fotolia; bottom American National Standards Institute/Pearson Science. Page 258, center left: Jerry Mason/Science Source; bottom American National Standards Institute/Pearson Science; bottom American National Standards Institute/Pearson Science; center Andrew Lambert Photography/Science Source; center Andrew Lambert Photography/Science Source; center right: Andrew Lambert Photography/Science Source. Page 262, center left: Segre Collection/AIP/Science Source. Page 263, center: Icon Sportswire/AP Images. Page 264, top center: Andy Martin Jr/Alamy. **Chapter 8** Page 296, center left: The State Tretyakov Gallery, Moscow.; top center: Richard Megna/Fundamental Photographs; top left: Charles D. Winters/Science Source; bottom left: Science Source. Page 318, center left: Kerstin Waurick/Getty Images; center right: Steve Gorton/DK Images; center Enricoros; center left: DennisS.K/Creative Commons; top right: Harry Taylor/DK Images; top right: DK Images; center Charles D. Winters/Science Source; center left: Richard Megna/Fundamental Photographs; center right: Manamana/Shutterstock; center right: "Charles D. Winters/ Science Source"; top right: Charles D.Winters/Science Source; center right: Ted Kinsman/ Science Source. Page 319, bottom right: Andrew Lambert Photography/Science Source. Page 320, top center: Richard Megna/Fundamental Photographs; top right: Richard Megna/Fundamental Photographs; top left: Richard Megna/Fundamental Photographs. Page 321, top right: 1994 Richard Megna/Fundamental Photographs; center right: Richard Megna/Fundamental Photographs. Page 323, bottom right: Glenn Grant/National Science Foundation; top right: Jeffrey Daly/Fotolia. **Chapter 9** Page 331, center right: Science Source. Page 332, center Tim Ridley/DK Images; top right: John A. Rizzo/Photodisc/ Getty Images; top left: Madlen/Shutterstock. Page 343, bottom left: Richard Megna/ Fundamental Photographs; bottom right: Richard Megna/Fundamental Photographs. Page 361, bottom right: Dean bertoncelj/Shutterstock; top left: FrontPage/Shutterstock. **Chapter 10** Page 376, top right: CDV, LLC/Pearson Science; top center: CDV, LLC/ Pearson Science; bottom center: CDV, LLC/Pearson Science. Page 377, top right: CDV, LLC/Pearson Science; bottom right: CDV, LLC/Pearson Science. Page 388, bottom right: Kip Peticolas/Fundamental Photographs; bottom center: Richard Megna/Fundamental Photographs. Page 389, top right: Soare Cecilia/Fotolia. Page 410, bottom center: Richard Megna/Fundamental Photographs. **Chapter 11** Page 428, top left: Andrew Syred/Science Source. Page 431, bottom right: Svetlana Larina/Shutterstock. Page 442, bottom left: Douglas Allen/Getty Images. Page 443, bottom right: Johnson Space Center/NASA; center right: Andrei Kuzmik/Shutterstock. Page 444, bottom right: Renn Sminkey/Pearson Science. Page 445, top right: Photos of StatSpin products provided by StatSpin Inc; center right: Sinclair Stammers/Science Source; top right: Ken Kay/Fundamental Photograph. Page 447, top right: Jason Stitt/Fotolia. Page 451, top left: Michael Dalton/Fundamental Photographs. Page 455, top left: Dr. P.A. Hamley; top center: Dr. P.A. Hamley; top center: Dr. P.A. Hamley; top right: Dr. P.A. Hamley. Page 456, center left: Charles D. Winters/ Science Source; top left: Michaelhansen/Fotolia. Page 457, bottom left: CDV, LLC/ Pearson Science; bottom right: Can Balcioglu/Shutterstock; bottom center: Gregory Johnston/Fotolia. Page 462, top left: Jet Propulsion Laboratory/NASA. Page 463, top right: CDV, LLC/Pearson Science; bottom left: Amit Dave/Reuters. Page 464, center left: Ted Kinsman/Science Source; top left: Karl J. Blessing/Shutterstock. Page 465, bottom right: Science Source. Page 472, center Mark J. Winter; center left: Andrew Syred/Science Source; center right: Atu Studio/Shutterstock; center right: Mirka Moksha/Shutterstock; top left: Robinheal/Fotolia. Page 474, bottom center: Charles D. Winters/Science Source; bottom right: Astrid & Hans-Frieder Michler/Science Photo Library/Science Source. Page 475, top center: Daniel Schwen, used under a Creative Commons license; http:// creativecommons.org/licenses/by-sa/2.5/deed.en.; top left: Tim Parmenter/The Natural History Museum, London/DK Images. Page 479, top center: Harry Taylor/DK Images; bottom left: Nivaldo Jose Tro; top left: Daniel Täger/Fotolia. **Chapter 12** Page 486, top center: Mana Photo/Shutterstock. Page 487, center right: Charles D. Winters/Science Source. Page 492, top right: Chuck/Fotolia. Page 496, bottom left: Richard Megna/ Fundamental Photographs; bottom right: Richard Megna/Fundamental Photographs; bottom center: Richard Megna/Fundamental Photographs. Page 497, bottom right: Richard Megna/Fundamental Photographs; center right: Richard Megna/Fundamental Photographs. Page 500, bottom left: Nyos degassing system conceived, designed, and manufactured by a French company, Data Environment, and the University of Savoie, France Courtesy J. C. Sabroux.; center left: Thierry Orban/Sygma/Corbis. Page 504, bottom left: Travis D. Fridgen. Page 507, top right: Gerry Broome/AP Images. Page 514, top left: Clark Brennan/Alamy. Page 516, center right: Masonjar/Shutterstock. Page 521, center Dtimiraos/Getty Images; top left: Sam Singer; center left: RubberBall/Alamy; bottom right: Richard Megna/Fundamental Photographs; top center: Sam Singer; top right: Sam Singer. Page 522, top right: BG Smith/Fotolia; top left: Eric Gevaert/Shutterstock; center right: Heros1973/Fotolia; bottom right: Okea/Fotolia; bottom right: Alexander Hoffmann/Fotolia. Page 523, center right: Image created using the LightWorks rendering engine. Copyright LightWork Design www.lightworkdesign.com; t Kip Peticolas/ Fundamental Photographs. **Chapter 13** Page 533, t 100ker/Shutterstock. Page 565, bottom right: Mark R Schoeberi/NASA. Page 566, bottom right: The Ozone Hole, Inc. Page 570 bottom left: Pearson Education. **Chapter 14** Page 585, top right: Ken Eward. Page 595, center left: Center for Disease Control. Page 617 top left: Richard Megna/ Fundamental Photographs; top left: Richard Megna/Fundamental Photographs. **Chapter 15** Page 630, center left: Clive Streeter/DK Images. Page 631, top left: Patryk Kosmider/ Shutterstock; center right: Eric Schrader/Pearson; top center: Shima-Risu/Fotolia. Page 643, bottom left: CNRI/Science Source. Page 655, center right: Eric Schrader/Pearson. Page 672, bottom left: British Antarctic Survey/Science Source. Page 673, bottom right: BlueOrange Studio/Fotolia. Page 681, top left: Eco Images/Universal Images Group/ Getty Images. **Chapter 16** Page 686, center left: Richard Megna/Fundamental Photographs; center right: Richard Megna/Fundamental Photographs; center Richard Megna/ Fundamental Photographs. Page 697, bottom right: Steve Dunwell/The Image Bank/ Getty Images. Page 699, center right: Richard Megna/Fundamental Photographs; center left: Richard Megna/Fundamental Photographs; center Richard Megna/Fundamental Photographs. Page 711, top right: Tom Bochsler/Pearson Education; bottom right: Tom Bochsler/Pearson Education. Page 714, center right: Astrid & Hanns-Frieder Michler/Science Source; bottom left: Bernhard Edmaier/Science Source. Page 717, bottom right: Douglas Knight/Shutterstock. Page 718, bottom left: Richard Megna/Fundamental Photographs. Page 719, top center: Charles D. Winters/Science Source; top right: Charles D. Winters/Science Source. Page 723, center right: Charles D. Winters/Science Source. Page 724, top center: Jerry Mason/Science Source; top right: Charles D. Winters/Science Source. Page 727, center left: Richard Megna/Fundamental Photographs; top left: Richard Megna/Fundamental Photographs. **Chapter 17** Page 739, bottom right: Henrik Winther Ander/Fotolia; center right: Dave King/DK Images. Page 740, center right: Daniel Schwen; Igor Kali/Fotolia. Page 741, bottom left: Richard Megna/Fundamental Photographs; center left: Look Die Bildagentur der Fotografen GmbH/Alamy; t Evgenyb/Fotolia. Page 742, top left: Johan Kocur. Page 747, top left: Jan Will/Fotolia. Page 768, Stephen Finn/Fotolia. **Chapter 18** Page 786, top left: Carla Browning/University of Alaska Fairbanks.; center left: Marcel Sloover. Page 787, top left: Richard Megna/Fundamental Photographs; top center: Richard Megna/Fundamental Photographs. Page 788, top left: Alejandro Díaz Díez/AGE Fotostock. Page 798, center left: Richard Megna/Fundamental Photographs. Page 810, top left: DK Images. Page 811, top right: CDV, LLC/Pearson Science. Page 813, top right: Tony Avelar/Bloomberg/Getty Images; center right: Ruaridh Stewart/Zumapress/Newscom; top right: Maksym Yemelyanov/Fotolia. Page 817, top right: Charles D. Winters/Science Source. Page 821, bottom right: Lusoimages/Shutterstock. Page 822, top left: Donovan Reese/Riser/Getty Images; center left: stokkete/See portfolio/Fotolia; bottom Jovan Nikolic/Fotolia. Page 823, top center: Pearson Education. **Chapter 19** Page 833, top right: PadraicRyan; center right: Alberto Fanelli/Getty Images; bottom left: SPL/Science Source. Page 834, top left: AFP/Getty Images; bottom left: Klaus Guldbrandsen/Science Source. Page 842, bottom right: Hank Morgan/Science Source; top left: Tyler Fridgen. Page 846, bottom left: Rudolf Friederich/Fotolia; top left: Baz Ratner/Reuters. Page 849, bottom right: Otto Hahn, A Scientific Autobiography," Charles Scribner's Sons, new York, 1966, courtesy AIP Emilio Segre Visual Archives. Page 850, center left: US Navy. Page 851, Marlee/Fotolia. Page 852, top right: STR/AFP/Getty Images; center left: STR/AP Images. Page 856, bottom left: Fox Photos/Hulton Archive/Getty Images; top right: General Atomics MS 15-124. Page 857, top right: David Parker/Science Source; center right: Fermilab Visual Media Services. Page 860, center left: Zuma Press/Alamy. Page 861, top right: D. Silbersweig/Science Source; center right: CentreOscar Lambret/Science Source; bottom center: Cordelia Molloy/Science Source. **Chapter 20** Page 869, top right: CDV LLC/Pearson Science. Page 870, bottom right: Smithsonian Institution. Page 875, bottom right: Bogdan Vasilescu/Fotolia. Page 878, bottom left: Didden/See portfolio/Fotolia. Page 879, bottom right: David R. Frazier/Danita Delimont Photography/Newscom; center right: Ivan_Sabo/Shutterstock. Page 882 top left: Perfectpre/Fotolia. Page 895 top right: Uwimages/Fotolia. **Chapter 21** Page 910, top center: Travis D. Fridgen; center Chip East/Reuters; center right: Travis D. Fridgen. Page 921, center right: Design Pics Inc/Alamy. Page 925, center right: Robert Hoetink/Shutterstock. Page 941, bottom right: picsfive/Fotolia. Page 942, top right: Second Chance Armor. Page 943, center left: Roman Milert/Fotolia. **Chapter 22** Page 957, top right: Library and Archives Canada. Page 960, top left: Maxwellartandphoto.com/Pearson Science; center David Murray/DK Images. Page 961, center left: Lawton Shaw. Page 973, top center: Steve Moss/Alamy. Page 974, top left: Janice Haney Carr/Center for Disease Control. Page 979, top left: Adrian T. Sumner/Getty Images. Page 980, top left: National Cancer Institute. Page 994, bottom left: Chip Clark/Fundamental Photographs; bottom left: USGS. **Chapter 23** Page 1000, bottom left: Pepmiba/Fotolia. Page 1001, top center: Lijuan Guo/Fotolia. Page 1002, top left: Y. Shirai/Rice University Office of News and Media Relations. Page 1003, top right: From Metals Handbook, 9th Edition, Volume 9: Metallography and Microstructures, American Society for Metals, Metals Park, Ohio, 1985. Page 1004 top left: Blue Lemon Photo/Fotolia. Page 1007, top right: DaimlerChrysler AG/Insurance Institute for Highway Safety. Page 1011, center right: NOAA. Page 1013, bottom left: Richard Megna/Fundamental Photographs. Page 1014, center left: Westphalia/Getty Images; top left: Richard Megna/Fundamental Photographs. Page 1016, top left: Martyn F. Chillmaid/Science Source. **Chapter 24** Page 1025, top right: http://images-of-elements.com/vanadium.php. Page 1026, top center: Harry Taylor/DK Images; center left: Robert Harding Picture Library Ltd/Alamy. Page 1030, center left: Photo courtesy of Metal Powder Industries Federation. Page 1037 center right: Richard Megna/Fundamental Photographs. Page 1038, top left: Joseph P. Sinnot/Fundamental Photographs. Page 1039, center right: Balendran Bala/Fotolia; bottom right: Dirk Hoffmann/Fotolia; bottom right: Igor/Fotolia; top right: Leungchopan/Shutterstock. Page 1040, bottom left: Heatbath Corporation. **Chapter 25** Page 1046, bottom right: Asya Babushkina/Shutterstock; center left: Tim Parmenter/DK Images; bottom left: Harry Taylor/DK Images; top left: Tim Parmenter/DK Images; bottom center: Harry Taylor/DK Images. Page 1054, center Richard Megna/Fundamental Photographs; center right: Richard Megna/Fundamental Photographs. Page 1058, bottom left: Richard Megna/Fundamental Photographs; bottom left: Richard Megna/Fundamental Photographs. Page 1059, center left: Richard Megna/Fundamental Photographs. Page 1062, bottom left: Richard Megna/Fundamental Photographs Page Uluc Ceylani/Shutterstock

Index

Note: Page numbers followed by *f* indicate material in figures; page numbers followed by *t* indicate material in tables.

F

N

S

U

V

W

Conversion Factors and Relationships

Length
SI unit: meter (m)

$1\ \text{Å} = 10^{-10}\ \text{m}$

Temperature
SI unit: kelvin (K)

$0\ \text{K} = -273.15\ °\text{C}$

$$\frac{T}{K} = \frac{T_C}{°C} + 273.15$$

Energy (derived)
SI unit: joule (J)

$1\ \text{J} = 1\ \text{kg m}^2\ \text{s}^{-2}$

$= 0.23901\ \text{cal}$

$= 1\ \text{C V}$

$1\ \text{cal} = 4.184\ \text{J}$

$1\ \text{eV} = 1.6022 \times 10^{-19}\ \text{J}$

Pressure (derived)
SI unit: pascal (Pa)

$1\ \text{Pa} = 1\ \text{N m}^{-2}$

$= 1\ \text{kg m}^{-1}\ \text{s}^{-2}$

$1\ \text{atm} = 101\ 325\ \text{Pa}$

$= 760\ \text{Torr}$

$1\ \text{bar} = 10^5\ \text{Pa}$

$= 750.1\ \text{Torr}$

$1\ \text{Torr} = 1\ \text{mmHg}$

Volume (derived)
SI unit: cubic meter (m^3)

$1\ \text{L} = 10^{-3}\ \text{m}^3$

$= 1\ \text{dm}^3$

$= 10^3\ \text{cm}^3$

$1\ \text{cm}^3 = 1\ \text{mL}$

Mass
SI unit: kilogram (kg)

$1\ \text{u} = 1.66053873 \times 10^{-27}\ \text{kg}$

$1\ \text{metric ton} = 1000\ \text{kg}$

Geometric Relationships

$\pi = 3.14159 \cdots$

Circumference of a circle $= 2\pi r$

Area of a circle $= \pi r^2$

Surface area of a sphere $= 4\pi r^2$

Volume of a sphere $= \frac{4}{3}\pi r^3$

Volume of a cylinder $= \pi r^2 h$

Fundamental Constants

Atomic mass unit	1 u 1 g	$= 1.66053873 \times 10^{-27}$ kg $= 6.02214199 \times 10^{23}$ amu
Avogadro's number	N_A	$= 6.02214179 \times 10^{23}\ \text{mol}^{-1}$
Bohr radius	a_0	$= 5.29177211 \times 10^{-11}$ m
Boltzmann's constant	k	$= 1.38065052 \times 10^{-23}\ \text{J K}^{-1}$
Electron charge	e	$= 1.60217653 \times 10^{-19}$ C
Faraday's constant	F	$= 9.64853383 \times 10^{4}\ \text{C mol}^{-1}$
Gas constant	R	$= 0.0831447215\ \text{L bar mol}^{-1}\ \text{K}^{-1}$ $= 8.31447215\ \text{J mol}^{-1}\ \text{K}^{-1}$
Mass of an electron	m_e	$= 5.48579909 \times 10^{-4}$ amu $= 9.10938262 \times 10^{-31}$ kg
Mass of a neutron	m_n	$= 1.00866492$ amu $= 1.67492728 \times 10^{-27}$ kg
Mass of a proton	m_p	$= 1.00727647$ amu $= 1.67262171 \times 10^{-27}$ kg
Planck's constant	h	$= 6.62606931 \times 10^{-34}$ J s
Speed of light in vacuum	c	$= 2.99792458 \times 10^{8}\ \text{m s}^{-1}$ (exactly)

SI Unit Prefixes

a	f	p	n	μ	m	c	d	k	M	G	T	P	E
atto	femto	pico	nano	micro	milli	centi	deci	kilo	mega	giga	tera	peta	exa
10^{-18}	10^{-15}	10^{-12}	10^{-9}	10^{-6}	10^{-3}	10^{-2}	10^{-1}	10^{3}	10^{6}	10^{9}	10^{12}	10^{15}	10^{18}